SPANISH GARDENS

SPANISH GARDENS

Marquesa de Casa Valdés

ANTIQUE
COLLECTORS'
CLUB

Dustjacket: *Campo del Moro, Fountain of the Shells*
Patio of the Sisters, Seville

Frontispiece: *Patio, Don Gome Estate*

I.S.B.N.-84-85-86103-5

First published in Spain 1973.
English edition first published 1987 for the Antique Collectors' Club by the Antique Collectors' Club Ltd.
Translation by Edward Tanner.
Printed in Spain by Gráficas Morvedre S.A., El Puig, Valencia.

To Juan and to my daughters, without whose help and support this book would never have been written.

ACKNOWLEDGEMENTS

In these pages I wish to record my deepest gratitude to all those who have given me their assistance so that this book should see the light of day.

Above all to the Marqués de Lozoya who guided me from the very outset with his wise counsel and vast learning, and to Doña Maria Luisa Caturla whose friendship and great knowledge of art and history were most valuable.

To the memory of my late sister Pepita, who accompanied me to so many of the places described in the book, lending her aid and shrewd judgment at every turn.

I am also indebted to my daughter and son-in-law Beatriz and Ignacio, and to their daughter Beatriz, for their valuable help in correcting the text.

To my good friends in Barcelona, in particular, the Marqués de Marianao and Doña Catalina Martorell, who co-operated so lovingly, accompanying me to the beautiful buildings of Barcelona and Tarragona.

To the Duke and Duchess of Medinaceli and their son the Duke of Segorbe, who with their usual kindness, allowed me to reproduce the plan of the gardens of Oca.

To the Marqués de Santo Domingo who permitted me to photograph his garden at Avila and gave me access to valuable books. The Marqués de Ferrera assisted with the material which he possesses in his magnificent library at Avilés.

I am indebted to Princess Pío for the photograph of the Montaña del Príncipe Pío, which she sent from her Palace of Mombello in Italy.

The Director of the Archivo General de Palacio, Don Conrado Monterero, helped in every possible way, during the long hours of work spent at the archives, and Don Teófilo Bombín was always on hand for consultation.

Doña Matilde Serrano welcomed me warmly at the Palace Library, and Doña Paulina Junquera, who is in charge of the Tesoro Artistico del Patrimonio Nacional, gave me interesting information about the books concerning my work.

Don Dalmiro de la Valgoma, the permanent secretary of the Academia de la Historia, obtained useful references for me about the history of gardens.

The Curator of the Archaeological Museum in Madrid, Don Martín Almagro, put the Museum library at my disposal and made it possible for me to photograph the Roman mosaics, as did Señorita Isabel Ceballos Escalera, who so capably assisted me.

Doctor Helmut Schlunk, the Director of the German Archaeological Institute, kindly lent me certain books which were invaluable for the chapter on Roman gardens.

The Librarian of the Instituto Valencia de Don Juan, the late Don Pedro Longás, gave me his help, as did Don José Simón Díaz at the Instituto de Estudios Madrilenos.

El Comandante Don Ignacio Hernando Cardoso kindly and very skilfully drew various plans used in this book.

Don José Filgueira Valverde, the Curator of the Museum at Pontevedra, placed photographs and information about the *pazos* of Galicia at my disposal.

Don Francisco Bellot, the Director of the Botanical Gardens of Madrid, gave invaluable help and co-operation in illustrating and classifying plants.

I am grateful to Don Juan Pañella, the Principal of the School of Horticulture of Montjuich in Barcelona, and also to Don Luis Riudor, the Head Architect of the Parks and Gardens of Barcelona.

In Granada I had the good fortune to meet a man who has since been my very good friend for many years, Don Francisco Prieto Moreno, the architect and curator of the Alhambra, and he very kindly acompanied me around the Arab remains and showed me the latest excavations and restorations. Don Luis Seco de Lucena, the renowned Arabist and Professor at the University of Granada, and Doña Joaquina Eguaras both gave valuable assistance in revising the chapters on Arab gardens.

The extensive knowledge of Don Rafael Manzano, Curator of the Alcázar of Seville, was a great help to me in studying the Alcázar gardens.

I am grateful to the daughters of the sculptor Juan Cristóbal for their information about the Palacio de Cadalso de los Vidrios.

I have very appreciative memories of Don Rafael Castejón, the famous Arabist of Córdoba, to whom I owe considerable information about the cities of Córdoba and Medina Azahara.

Don Gerardo Afán de Ribera produced documents for me from his archives about his illustrious ancestors and the Houses of Pilate and las Dueñas in Seville, as did Don Joaquín González Moreno, secretary to the Duke and Duchess of Medinaceli.

Doña Carmen Aguirre welcomed me at her Cigarral de la Cadena in Toledo and made documents and the reproduction of a picture available to me.

Don Vicente Oliva, the owner of the *Bosque* at Béjar, provided me with documents and his genealogy.

I thank Don Francisco Fernández Navarrete, Marqués de Legard for the information on his Palace of Abalos (Rioja).

Rear-Admiral Don Jorge Guillén kindly showed me the various routes of the botanical expeditions to the New World.

I thank the Conde de España and Don Gabriel Alomar for their interesting information about the Balearic Islands.

Don Javier Carvajal provided me with reproductions of the plans of his two gardens in Somosaguas.

Don Emilio García Gómez kindly revised the Arab chapters; Doña Marita Martínez del Río de Redo assisted me with documents on and photographs of Mexican flora, and the review *Artes de Mexico* kindly supplied information and photographs.

Don Francisco Carreras de Catalayud and his wife offered me a most pleasant stay in Valencia and a visit to the garden of Montforte and the Botanic Garden.

In Paris the Viscount de Noailles gave me valuable help concerning various French gardens.

Monsieur Jean Adhémar at the Cabinet d'Estampes de la Bibliothèque Nationale de Paris greatly facilitated my studies there by providing documents and plans from the time of Philip V.

To them all I express through these pages my lasting and profound gratitude, not forgetting Miss Jessie Gibson who responded with her unfailing kindness and unselfishness to every emergency as it arose, thus easing my task.

PHOTOGRAPHS WERE TAKEN BY THE FOLLOWING PHOTOGRAPHERS:

Domínguez. Archaeological Museum. Madrid.
Magallón. National Library. Madrid.
Villanueva. Patrimonio Nacional. Madrid.
Oronoz. Madrid.
Santiago Saavedra. Madrid.
Archivo de *Blanco y Negro.* Madrid.
Archivo de *Semana.* Madrid.
Author. Madrid.
Más. Barcelona.
Sálmer. Barcelona.
Marino Alonso. Valencia.
Alberto Paláu. Seville.
Ferrazo. Villagarcía de Arosa. Pontevedra.
British Museum. London.
Peter Coats Esq. London.
Bibliothèque Nationale. Cabinet d'Estampes. Paris.
Artes de México. Mexico.
Biblioteca Laurentina. Florence.

THE AUTHOR WISHES TO THANK THE OWNERS OF PRIVATE GARDENS WHO SO KINDLY HELPED HER AND ALLOWED HER TO TAKE PHOTOGRAPHS:

MADRID

Somosaguas. Don Alfonso Valdecasas.
Somosaguas. Don Javier Carvajal.
Cadalso de los Vidrios. The daughters of Juan Cristóbal.

CASTILE

Lupiana. Doña Sol Barzanallana de la Cuesta.
San Segundo. Avila. Marqués de Santo Domingo.
La Granjilla. Doña Esperanza Borrell. Viuda de Aguirre.
Abalos. Haro. Marqués de Legarda.

TOLEDO

Buenavista. Duquesa Vda. de Pastrana.
Cigarral de Marañón. Marañón Family.
Palacio de Galiana. Doña Carmen Marañón.
Cigarral de la Cadena. Doña Carmen de Aguirre.

BEJAR

El Bosque. Béjar. Don Vicente Oliva.

GALICIA

Pazo de Oca. Duques de Medinaceli & Duque de Segorbe.
Santa Cruz de Rivadulla. Marqueses de Santa Cruz de Rivadulla.
San Lorenzo. Santiago. Duquesa de Soma.
Pazo de Conde. Corunna. Condes de Torre Penela.
La Pastora. Vigo. Doña Fabiola Larios de Ozores.
Casa de Jaz. Corunna. Condesa de Maceda & her sisters.
Casa de Rubianes. Marquesa Vda. de Aranda Villagarcia.
El Faramello. Santiago. Sra. de Ribero de Aguilar.

MALAGA

El Retiro. Malaga. Duques de Aveyro and family.

CORDOBA

Rejas de Don Gome. Marqueses de Viana.
Moratalla. Hornachuelos. Marqueses de Viana.

GRANADA

Palacio de Cuzco. Víznar. Esperanza Damas de Fernández Figares.
Jardín Narváez. Loja. Doña Julia Díaz Berbel.
Carmen de los Cipreses. Don Nicolás María López.
Carmen de la Purificación. Don Manuel Torres Molina.
Carmen de San Agustín. Sres. de Rodríguez Acosta.

SEVILLE

Jardín de la Casa de Pilatos. Duques de Medinaceli.
Jardín de las Dueñas. Duquesa de Alba.
Casa de Nerviıon. Marquesa Vda. de Nerviıon.
Hacienda de Doña María Dos Hermanas. Srta. Concha Ibarra.

CATALONIA

Santa Clotilde. Costa Brava. Marqués de Roviralta.
Cap Roig. Costa Brava. Sres. de Woedvosky.
Parque Sama. Tarragona. Marqués de Marianao.

MALLORCA

Son Canet. Mrs. Roffey.
Son Berga. Sres. de Quint-Zaforteza.
Son Forteza. Don. Rafael Villalonga.
Son Torrella. Hon. Mrs. Hilgarth.
Defla. Condes de España.
S'Avall. Sres. de Don Juan March.
Cala Ratjada. Sres. de Don Bartolomé March.
Son Julía. Channing Hare.

CANARY ISLANDS

Lanzarote. Don César Manrique.

FOREWORD

These lines are merely a prelude to a book which has come to fill a great gap in the ever-increasing Spanish bibliography of Art. The Gardens of Spain *is the product of many years of travel and study by a person eminently qualified for this most difficult task. Teresa Ozores y Saavedra, Marquesa de Casa Valdés, was born in a family and an atmosphere intimately linked with the* pazos *— the ancestral mansions — of Galicia, secluded enclosures where water flowing in fountains or lying in pools combines with stone and clipped boxwood to produce gentle, melancholy poetry. But Teresa Ozores is also an 'international Spaniard' — deeply sensitive to the beauty of her native land, yet attuned to the course of art throughout the world through her extended stays abroad each year. And indeed, no one who spends an entire lifetime within the confines of his native city, town or village will ever understand Spain. Spain is the great junction of eastern and western cultures, a 'province' for most of its history, receiving artistic influences from Rome, Paris, Damascus or Baghdad; thus only by following these international currents to their source can one understand the rich cultural fusion Spain embodies today.*

Gardens of Spain! Some of the most beautiful, those situated on the slopes of the Alhambra plateau, bear the name of a song — and of a woman: Carmen. Spain, one of the loveliest lands on God's great earth, is unsurpassed in the majesty, variety and beauty of her countryside. Her architectural and artistic heritage is priceless; here, all the great trends of European culture blend with oriental styles of building and of decoration. And yet, above all Spain's ancient buildings, landscapes and museums, I take my greatest delight in its ancient villages and in its gardens. In old walled towns scattered throughout the Peninsula, from the Pyrenees to the Straits, I find supreme pleasure in exploring narrow streets and peaceful squares among churches, convents and palaces, in search of new and unexpected sights. In gardens I seek a place of repose where I can enjoy the company of the best of all friends, a book. But sometimes, especially during the magic of a Spanish sunset, even a book is superfluous. One's thoughts, or better still, one's dreams suffice.

Gardens of Spain! Andrea Navagero, Venetian ambassador during the reign of Charles V, wrote that nowhere, throughout the entire Peninsula, had he found so pleasant a spot as the gardens of the Alcázar of Seville. And indeed, on a sunny moring in May, the Moorish charm of secluded corners with tiled benches surrounding fountains bedecked by flower pots, the fragrance of roses entwining the trunks of cypress and of date-palms and orange blossoms, the sound of water and the song of nightingales all combine to make the gardens of Alcázar a place of great solace from the anguish of our times.

In their gardens Spaniards find a setting conducive to their spirituality — always obsessed by questions of Time and Eternity — a place in which to distinguish the ephemeral and transitory from the eternal and unchanging. The water in their fountains and irrigation channels flows like time, like life itself:

'Our lives are the rivers
That flow into the sea
Which is death...'

In the garden, permanence is represented by marble and in a way by the flowers that die only to be reborn each spring with renewed vigour and splendour. The garden tells us nothing is eternal, not even the stars; only God, the Great Artist, and his spirit, which moves man to create beauty.

I once wrote that the garden could not have originated in the forests of the north, where the sun's rays can scarcely penetrate the foliage, nor in pleasant tropical groves where everything flourishes without effort in the hot and humid atmosphere. Perhaps the garden originated in the deserts of the Near East where flower and fruit gardens can be created by springs as retreats from the dryness of a hostile environment, a delightful refuge to be carefully and faithfully tended. The Bible places our first parents in a garden, and the Koran promises one as a reward for the faithful. There were wonderful gardens in the parched land of Chaldea, and gardens are mentioned in the ancient and detailed accounts of life in Egypt.

Through its delightful and scholarly prose and lavish illustrations, the Marquesa's book traces the many European and Oriental styles brought to Spain. In the remnants of Roman gardens discovered in houses excavated in Merida we can discern elements of the traditional Mediterranean cloister-garden: an enclosure, hidden from the outside, where family life could unfold without unwelcome intrusions; a rectangle surrounded by porticos, with a pool in its centre forming a mirror for the flowers in beds and pots. The mosaics that adorned these secluded gardens are the most enduring remnant of Roman life, and all that remains of the villas and urban dwellings of Roman civilisation in the Peninsula. The flowers withered, the water ceased to flow, and the porticos crumbled away centuries ago, but the mosaics remain with their portrayal of pagan mythology, their floral designs and geometric patterns.

Except for a reference in San Isidoro's Etymologies, *we have no records of Visigothic gardens. Orchards rather than gardens probably surrounded the dwellings of the chieftain-kings of Asturias and León. From the eleventh century onwards, after the 'thousand-year terror' had ended, there spread throughout Europe a triumphant optimism which, in the words of the monk Raúl Glauber, caused Europe to blossom with the white mantle of new churches. Migrations had ceased, great monarchies were being formed and the Church was rich and powerful as never before. The Roman Empire, ever to be remembered, was being supplanted by a spiritual Empire: Christianity, within which new nations were taking shelter. The new imperial art was Romanesque, its vaults reminiscent of the buildings of Rome. The Church preserved the use of*

Mediterranean cloister-gardens just as it retained Latin in its liturgy and ancient music in the Gregorian chant. Hence, the wonder of the cloister-gardens, where stone capitals bloom more vigorously than flowers. Gardens conducive to silence and peace in Ripoll and in San Cugat, in Tarragona, in Silos and in Santa María la Real de Nieva! The cloister-garden tradition continued during the Gothic period with the added innovation of intricate lacery on the arches. Laymen, too, now sought secluded places for their recreation. Both in war and in hunting man had to cope with nature. Their refuge was to be the garden room that figures in medieval manuscripts, on tapestries and primitive panels: enclosed areas around fountains encircled by flowers. The Alcázar in Seville, despite its Renaissance and Baroque alterations, may represent the last trace of this type of garden, found among the secluded corners, so perfect for lovers' colloquies and the music of strolling players and minstrels.

As the Muslim invaders consolidated their positions in the Orient, Africa and Spain, they became passionately fond of gardening, and highly skilled in it. Throughout these conquered territories they developed a technique learned from the Persians and Byzantines, for the nomadic Bedouins of the desert knew little themselves of flowers, irrigation channels and fountains; but through their intense receptivity they gathered the fruit of ancient oriental cultures and by way of Byzantium — Greek and Roman cultures. It is in Spain that the oldest and most beautiful Islamic gardens have survived. In the Alhambra one can still see a typical Mediterranean garden-patio: the Patio de los Leones. This patio also displays an innovation borrowed from Persia of the Sassanides, whose designs are found on many Persian carpets: the Ryad, a rectangular garden with a long water channel flowing through its axis and pavilions at both ends. The Patio of the Alberca, also in the Alhambra, and the main garden of the Generalife are other examples; Teresa de Casa Valdés provides a detailed description of both.

During the Renaissance, open expanses and broad vistas were preferred; porticos and steps were decorated with statues, all to form the background for courtly festivities. It was the triumph of stone over nature, architect over gardener, with hedges of boxwood and myrtle fashioned as stone. In such gardens, as Eugenio d'Ors puts it, one could dispense with flowers. With flowers perhaps, but not with water, which spurted from monumental fountains peopled with marble and bronze figures, or lay in pools reflecting the porticos and balustrades.

This 'monarchical' concept of the garden reached its perfection in the Baroque style, which swept through Europe from St. Petersburg to Caserta. Gardens became 'theatres' in which gods and demigods of stone and metal enacted Ovid's Metamorphoses, *with characters brought to life by water leaping up in high fountain jets or spilling over in cascades to form liquid palaces. Water tricks and fireworks were the festive hallmark of baroque gardens.*

To Spain, always somewhat provincial, came the Renaissance garden of Italy and the courtly garden of France; but, always rebellious, she stamped such international models with her own spirit. Arab influence was too deeply imprinted on the Spanish soul to be erased by the new fashions from Florence or Versailles. The architect Fernando Chueca Goitia speaks of Spain's persistent love, even in the eighteenth century, for the secluded and intimate, and its limited appreciation of vast panoramas. The interior of a central-European cathedral can be seen at a glance, while a Spanish cathedral is divided by the great central choir, and one must discover its outstanding features one by one. The architects who planned the vast site of the Escorial divided it into seventeen patios. In neither Aranjuez nor San Ildefonso do we find distant views as at Versailles, Shoenbrun or Caserta; instead, we find a series of enclosures that, in a very different spirit, continue the tradition of the medieval garden. This explains why the Duke of Saint-Simon, accustomed to an uninterrupted view of the grande pelouse and the pièce d'eau, was displeased by Aranjuez, where he felt confined by lattice work and hedges in all directions, unnecessary details, trop de colifichets! Spain aspires to be European but not in all things.

This foreword is but a brief indication of what you will find in this book. Teresa Ozores has studied Spanish gardens at length and in depth, providing a wealth of new material, a most valuable contribution to the history of Spanish gardening. She has read widely in the literature of gardening — by both historical chroniclers and modern researchers. An indefatigable traveller, she has journeyed over the entire Peninsula from north to south, and east to west, stopping wherever she heard of an ancestral house with garden and pool or a beflowered Andalusian or Canarian orchard. She has managed to capture the poetry of the botanic gardens of Madrid, Valencia and la Orotava. She understands fountains, flower-beds and statues and, with an enthusiast's fervour and a gardener's experience, is knowledgeable in the cultivation of each species of flower.

We would hope that this book might revive a love for gardens in Spain, where they are at present in grave danger. While it is true that the policy of state and municipal authorities is to make new parks, other policies are destroying private gardens, which have added such beautiful surroundings to the older city quarters and prevented excessive urban crowding. The cities of Spain are becoming solid blocks where it is impossible to breathe. Local councils impose taxes for gardens as if they were building properties, encouraging the conversion of open areas — which with their trees and flowers, provide breathing space and a note of poetry — into multi-office sky-scrapers, attracting hundreds of cars. Such policies have made the capital of Spain the densest and most polluted city in Europe.

A 'Society of the Friends of Gardens', based in Madrid with branches in the provinces, could help to reverse this troubling trend. The Marquesa de Casa Valdés would be our President; and her book our point of reference, our spiritual guide.

page xviii

El Marqués de Lozoya

PREFACE TO THE ENGLISH EDITION

A whisper, a melody, a verse, a fragrance, a caress, a smile, a tear. . .the garden is all these things, but most of all it is a dream. A creative passion that grows in the mind, that matures, that must be perfected, resulting in an idea; and then comes the most difficult part, putting it down on paper and then executing the design. All this will be impossible if we do not possess a wide-ranging knowledge — about plants, shapes, colours, light, climate, history; in short, about how to create a garden.

This is the story of the fantasies which once arose in the mind of a king or a gardener; it is the history of Spanish gardens. They are the realisations of dreams; over the centuries, the daily work of watering, nurturing, pruning and sowing has given us these historic gardens. My grandmother, with love and devotion, studied and wrote about all of them. It was the first stage in confirming Spain as a country of great gardens, on a par with other European countries.

This book is now republished in translation, but otherwise in its original form. It has simply not been possible to include the restorations carried out recently in several historic gardens, such as the Royal Botanic Garden of Madrid, nor add new gardens created since 1973.

There is a great deal to learn, and a sensibility to be developed, in order to plant trees, dig rivers, move mountains, or merely sow a few bulbs, just for the pleasure of experiencing a dawn or a sunset in our garden. Colleges for training gardeners have been established in different parts of Spain; my grandmother worked very hard to achieve this, although she never saw them. ("Without good gardeners, there will never be good gardens.") Landscape architects and garden designers are essential if we want to create good gardens. We have adopted the right approach, but we have only taken the first step of a very long journey.

This March the daffodils are flowering, and there is snow on the ground. Every March it will be the same with the spring flowers bursting into bloom; and it is the duty of gardeners and landscape artists to turn this simple beauty into a magnificent one, and thus create their own memorial.

"To build, to plant, whatever you intend,
to rear the column, or the Arch to bend,
to swell the Terras or to sink the grott;
In all let nature never be forgot.
Consult the genius of the Place in all,
That tells the water or to rise or fall. . ." (Pope)

This beautiful history of gardens is a book in which one can see how other gardeners, in different times and with different ideas, solved practical problems concerning terrain, water and winds, as well as questions of aesthetics. It tells us how they consulted the *genius loci,* how he whispered to them the secrets of each corner, dell and shady place, and how they afterwards created the splendid gardens which appear in this book. We should gaze at many of these magic gardens as the quiet accomplices of musicians, painters and poets. Who has not listened to the Concierto de Aranjuez, read the verses of Pope or looked at a Monet painting without feeling moved? We should treat these silent contributors to such works with loving care and admiration.

It is a long journey that we are engaged upon. There is always a new step to be taken, always a new solution to be sought in order to avoid the routine application of inappropriate foreign styles. Spain must develop its own style, in accordance with its light, landscape and nature, and this book may be of some help. We must make use of our local materials and numerous native plants such as cistus, rosemary, ericas and lavenders, which will give our gardens fragrance and provide harmonious colours and shapes well adapted to the environment. As time goes by we shall certainly find our way in the world of gardening. We shall listen to the *genius loci* and, guided by his whispers, we shall forge our own style.

Javier Mariátegui Valdés
Landscape architect

CONTENTS

DEDICATION VII
ACKNOWLEDGEMENTS VIII
FOREWORD XIII
INTRODUCTION 1
Chapter 1. Roman Gardens in Spain 3
Chapter 2. The Arrival of the Arabs 19
Chapter 3. Granada and its Gardens 33
Chapter 4. The Gardens of Seville 57
Chapter 5. Medieval and Cloister Gardens 75
Chapter 6. The Gardens of the Renaissance 89
Chapter 7. The Gardens during the Austrian Dynasty. Philip II to Philip IV 103
Chapter 8. The Gardens of Aranjuez. Philip II to Philip IV. El Buen Retiro. La Quinta del Duque del Arco 119
Chapter 9. Aranjuez in the time of the Bourbons in the Eighteenth Century 141
Chapter 10. The Gardens of La Granja 153
Chapter 11. History of Spanish Botanical Gardens and the Botanical Expeditions to the New World during the Eighteenth Century 167
Chapter 12. Galician "Pazos". The "Sones" of Mallorca. The "Cigarrales" of Toledo 197
Chapter 13. The Neoclassical Style. Charles III and Charles IV. Aranjuez during the Nineteenth Century. The Gardens of the Campo del Moro 223
Chapter 14. Nineteenth and Twentieth Centuries. The Romantic Garden. Gaudí. Forestier and Neo Arabism. Modern Gardens. The Palm Groves of Elche 245
Chapter 15. Present-day Gardens in Spain 269
GENERAL BIBLIOGRAPHY 281
INDEX OF PERSONS 285
INDEX OF PLACES 292

The creation of beauty has always been the supreme aspiration of every human being.

One of the purposes in publishing this book is the desire to describe as completely as possible the gardens that exist today in Spain and relate their history and the history of those that have disappeared.

In England, France, Italy and many other European countries, there is an extensive bibliography, both general and specialised, on this art; in Spain, the subject has barely been studied, or at least, has almost always been partially described in the rare books that have been published to date.

Since our Civil War of 1936-1939, many of the gardens described in these books have vanished, victims of neglect and the destruction of war. On the other hand, other new gardens have emerged in this modern era of urban developments and coastal resorts of all colours, and artistic monuments possess gardens that decorate and beautify them.

The higher standard of living and the intensive tourism that takes place today in Spain have reawakened the art of gardening.

The accelerated pace of modern life requires fresh air and a garden as a place for relaxation; sports, such as golf, swimming and tennis have made sun and outdoor living attractive.

All of this has led to a greater attraction toward nature and a longing to find peace and rest amidst it.

Let us then look at the gardens of Spain: what they were, what they are today, and what they could be tomorrow, with the description of the plants and the periods in which they appeared.

We hope that with this overview we can orientate the lovers of flowers, gardens and forests who feel the desire to travel across this Peninsula, where the variety of countryside and climate, combined with its fascinating history, have produced the most beautiful and oldest gardens in the world.

1 ROMAN GARDENS IN SPAIN

The first gardens in Spain designed solely for the adornment of dwellings and the pleasure of their inhabitants were legacies of Greece, by way of Rome.

In ancient Greece, gardens were associated with religious rites. Sacred groves, grottoes and temples were dedicated to the deities, and in particular to Priapus, the god of fertility. From the earliest times the Greek countryside was inhabited by tombs and sanctuaries, a practice later imitated by the topiarius or Roman gardener.

Love of nature was integral to Greek philosophy. Plato installed his academy near Athens in a gymnasium planted with trees. His favourite pupil, Aristotle, founded his school of philosophy in a Lyceum surrounded by plane-trees, where he taught while strolling; hence the term "peripatetics", applied to his followers. In the academy of the Platonists, the Lyceum of the Peripatetics, the Portico of the Stoics and the Garden of the Epicureans, all interspersed with trees and statues, philosophers lectured and expounded along pleasant, spacious avenues, which, depending on the hour, were dedicated to the exercise of either body or mind.

"The genius of the founders still lived in those venerable seats."[1]

The plane-tree, planted in the Agora in Athens, was the Greeks' favourite.[2] The Romans, who imitated them in everything, introduced this tree to Italy to adorn their squares and to line their parks and avenues.

The Romans, centuries later, were not originally inclined to either philosophy or physical exercise, but in the second century B.C. the Hellenistic influence began to penetrate their society. In designing their palaces the Romans adopted such Greek terms as palaestra, gymnasium, exedra, peristyle, etc., although altering their use and original function. The gymnasium, used by athletes in Greek times, and the exedras, from which the games were watched, survived in Roman constructions in the form of covered walks, reception areas and meeting places.

CONIMBRIGA. *Photo Author.*

PLAN, HOUSE OF THE EXEDRA. *A. García y Bellido.*

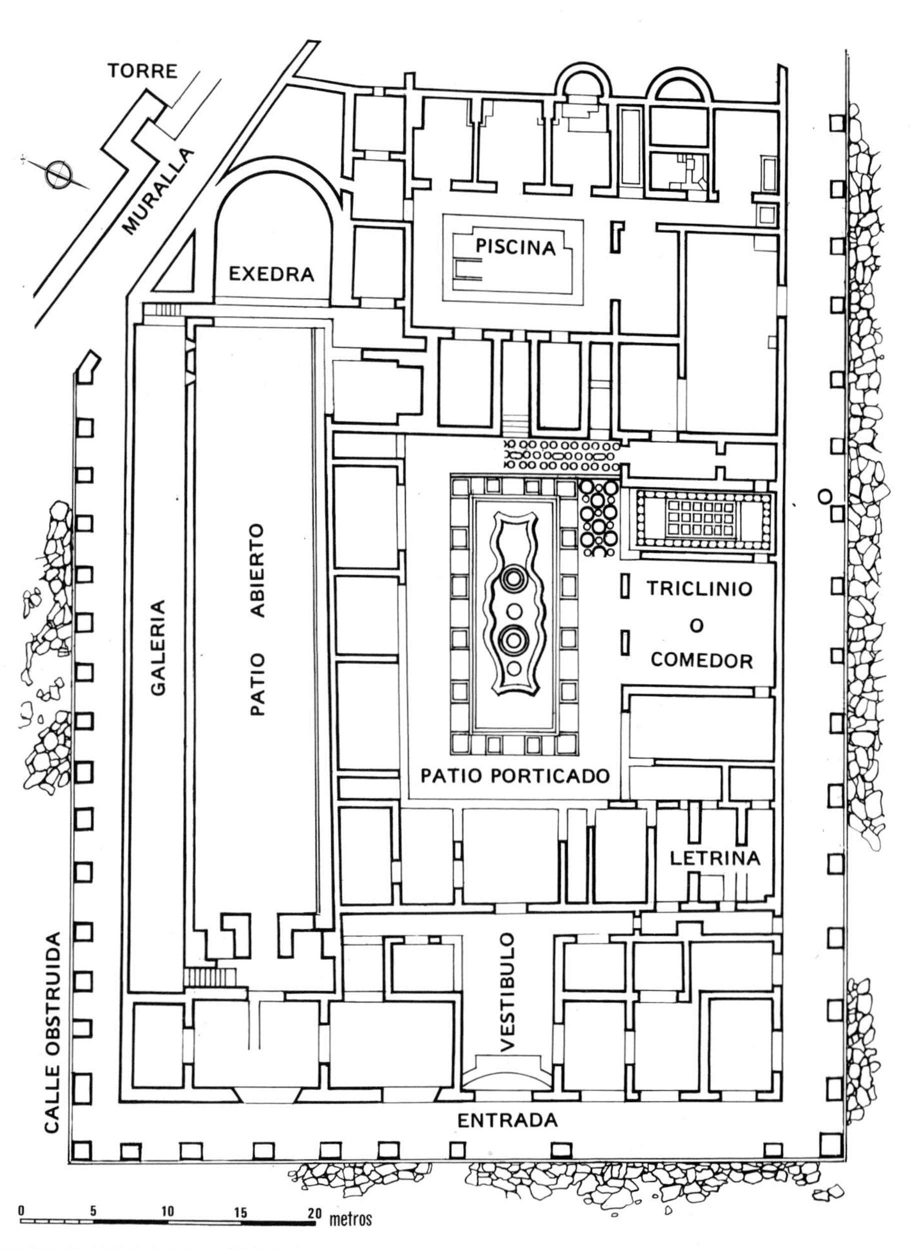

The xystus was originally a portico or terrace planted with trees, or a covered garden, where in Greek times athletes would exercise during the winter. The essential element of these exercise areas was a portico with annexes opening onto a shady promenade. During the Roman period, the term xystus referred to "any form of terrace planted as a garden, but apparently, always in connection with a portico."[3] Water was never lacking in Roman gardens. Distributed in some places by an elaborate canal system, it was often brought at great expense by means of aqueducts, a few of which still survive in Spain.

Rome was a city of water, with its countless conduits and fountains, and the Romans were precursors to the Arabs in their skill at contriving such systems. Water was a real necessity during the dry, parched summers of the Mediterranean region and no pleasure could be derived from a garden without it.

The Graeco-Roman ideal was, thus, to be surrounded by gardens and covered walks, which they always included in their designs, both civic and domestic, merging their buildings with vegetation, light and sun by means of peristyles and porticos connecting house and garden. As P. Grimal tells us: "The most significant and seminal Hellenistic contribution to the Italic house was the introduction of columns and porticos. The use of columns is the fundamental Italic characteristic. They came into popularity during the early fourth century B.C., not so much to support the vault as to provide a transition between the room and the outside."

Porticos gave the Roman streets their characteristic appearance and were also to be found in the Roman-built cities of Spain, such as Italica and Mérida.

In the Iberian Peninsula, excavation has revealed porticos and peristyles dating back to the time of Hadrian and the Antonines. This design concept has survived throughout Spain in the form of Andalusian patios, convent cloisters and other derivatives of the Latin *Hortus Conclusus.*

In his writings on Italica, a town near Seville, A. García Bellido tells us that "the known dwellings of this new town, built by Hadrian in the second century A.D., were of the *Domus* type, that is to say each house was the residence of one family rather than groups of neighbours, as in the large urban concentrations. In this respect, Italica resembled cities of leisure and recreation, such as Pompeii, rather than trading, industrial and commercial cities, such as the port of Ostia, whose population was mainly proletarian."[4]

We know that the Emperor Hadrian, a native of Italica, never set foot there again after his early years, but resided for a time, while Emperor, in Tarragona. During this time he endowed Italica with a new town and the title of Roman Colony, the first to exist in Spain. A great Hellenist, Hadrian surrounded himself with Greek scholars and poets and his style of life is clearly revealed by the sumptuous villa he built at Tivoli, near Rome.

The design of a typical Italica house includes all the classic Graeco-Roman features: the open courtyard, the cryptoporticus and the exedra, suggesting that the architects who built this town were familiar with Vitruvian principles. Its two most important characteristics were the fusion of house and garden by means of courtyards, where daily family life unfolded, and the use of a central axis, generally the principal room, around which the house was constructed and from which the garden could be viewed through the peristyle. This is the oldest known design in which a garden is arranged symmetrically in relation to the centre of a house.

La Casa de los Pájaros (House of Birds) was probably the home of a prominent family. As can be observed, the design is axial with the peristyle centred upon the vestibule — probably covered — a relic of the atrium found in early Roman houses. At the entrance, a short concave wall probably served as a screen or partition to hide the interior courtyard. Several of these exist in Italica.

Interestingly, such partitions, in the form of wooden trellises, are still used in Sevillan patios today, probably for the same purpose.

Beyond the vestibule of the House of Birds lay a colonnaded courtyard whose large central cistern, with wells at either end, indicates that it was probably a garden.[5] At the back of the

HADRIAN. Prado Museum, Madrid. *Photo Mas.*

ITALICA. PLAN, HOUSE OF BIRDS. *A. García y Bellido.*

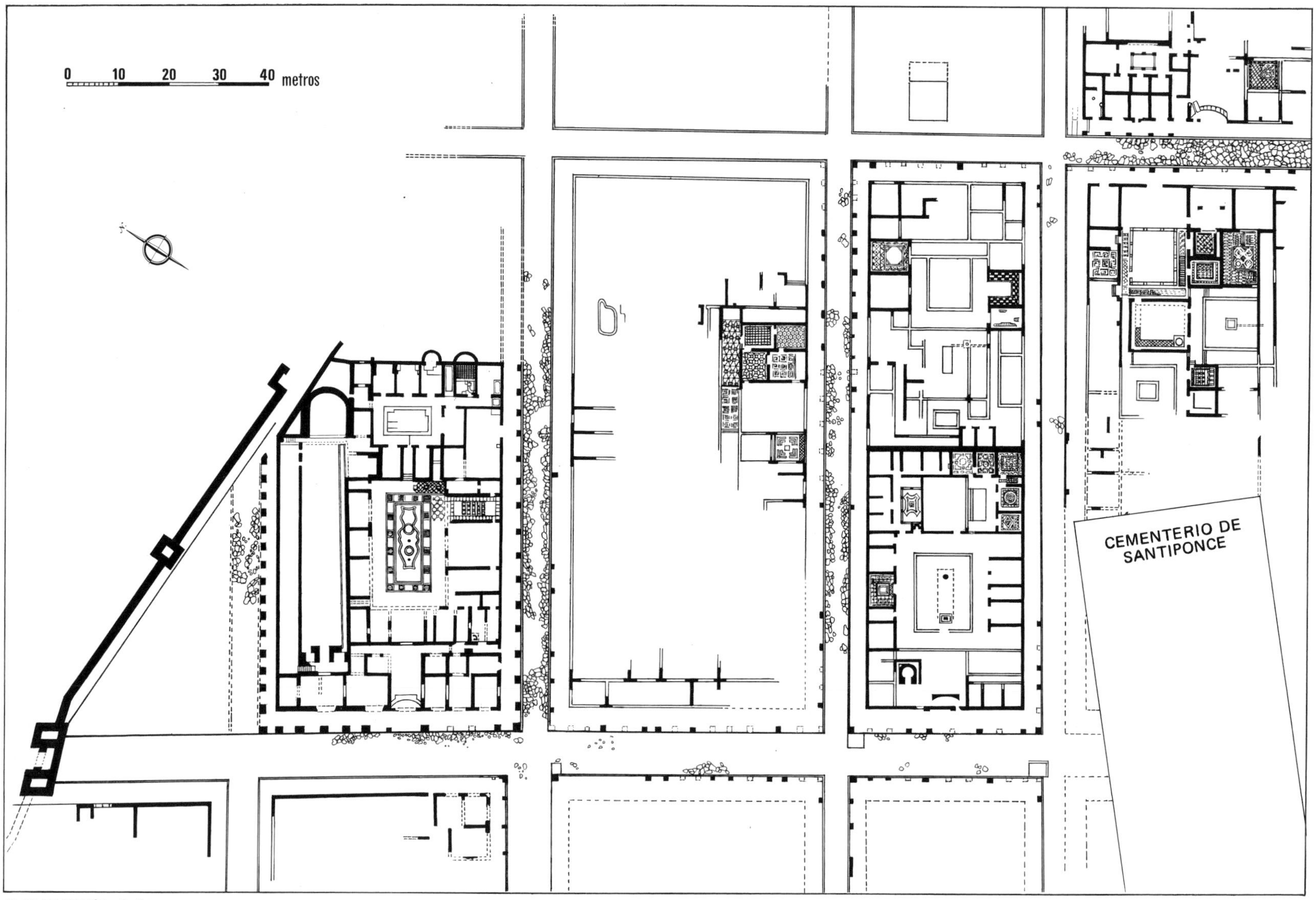

0 10 20 30 40 metros

CEMENTERIO DE SANTIPONCE

PLAN OF ITALICA. *Author.*

ITALICA. PERISTYLE. *A. García y Bellido.*

courtyard lay a large, square room — probably the triclinium, or dining room — and on either side, two smaller open courtyards. The courtyard on the right contained a swimming pool with steps; the courtyard on the left was adorned with a fountain of intricate design, which in modern times would be termed baroque, surrounded by columns. The house derives its name from a many-coloured mosaic still preserved in one of its rooms, with each small tile depicting a different bird. It shows us the knowledge the artists of Italica possessed of birds, both wild and domestic.

Symmetry is clearly fundamental to the houses of Italica, whose spacious and harmonious design reflects prosperity and elegance.

They all contain open courtyards and peristyles, once gardens with fountains and bathing pools. Some of the pools were decorated with mosaics depicting fish, suggesting they might have been constructed for the purpose of raising them. Pergolas covered with vines or ivy provided shade and cool protection from the scorching Sevillan summers. Judging from their large size and numerous outbuildings, these must have been houses of great luxury with eminent inhabitants.

Conímbriga, situated on one of the Peninsula's major Roman roads, the so-called Antonius' Way, was a way station between Olísipo (Lisbon) and Brácara Augusta (Braga),[6] but we know nothing of this city's size.

Judging from the map reprinted here, showing buildings all of which appear to be luxurious villas, we may presume that Conímbriga was a residential city inhabited by wealthy patricians and designed for their leisure and recreation, in the style of modern resorts. The city appears to have reached its zenith during the era of the Flavians and the Antonines.

A gardened peristyle can be clearly observed in one of the houses, with its central canal looping to form a double cross, displaying a highly developed sense of perspective and the decorative value of water and vegetation.

The map shows another house whose peristyle and canal display the same design, in the form of a cross, also undoubtedly used as a garden.

Several Roman houses have recently been discovered in Mérida with the same decoration in their central pond. The design used in the ponds of the Conímbriga and Mérida houses, alternating semicircles and rectangles, "is a classic motif of Roman art, found in a garden plan derived from a painting of Herculaneum. It appears to possess the characteristics of a *pulpitum* or theatre platform. The front of the Roman theatre at Mérida, dating from the time of Hadrian, also has this shape. The pond at Conímbriga may have been inspired by the garden court of the Villa dei Setti Bassi, on the Via Latina, which displayed the same festooned design. This decorative style could have been inspired by the architectural forms of these theatre decorations and probably also used those formed by the

ITALICA. HOUSE OF EXEDRA. *A. García y Bellido.*

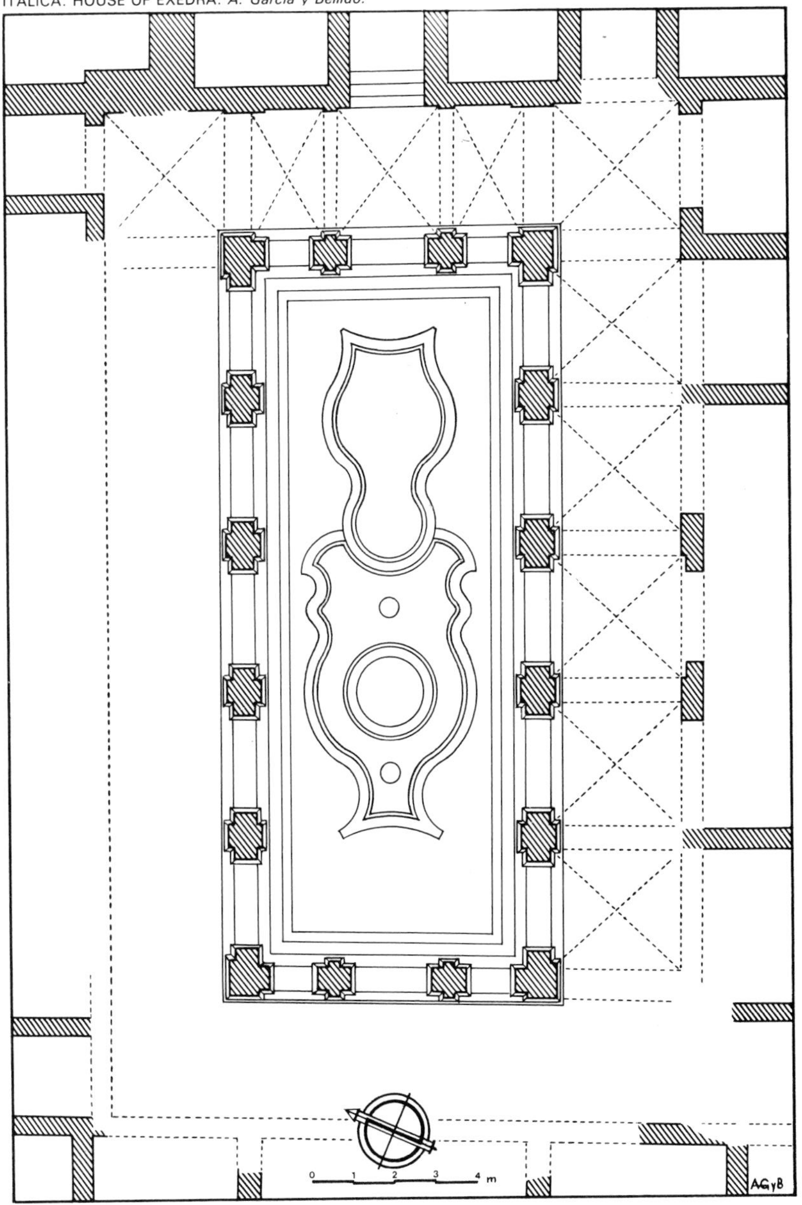

MAP OF CONIMBRIGA. Coimbra. Portugal.

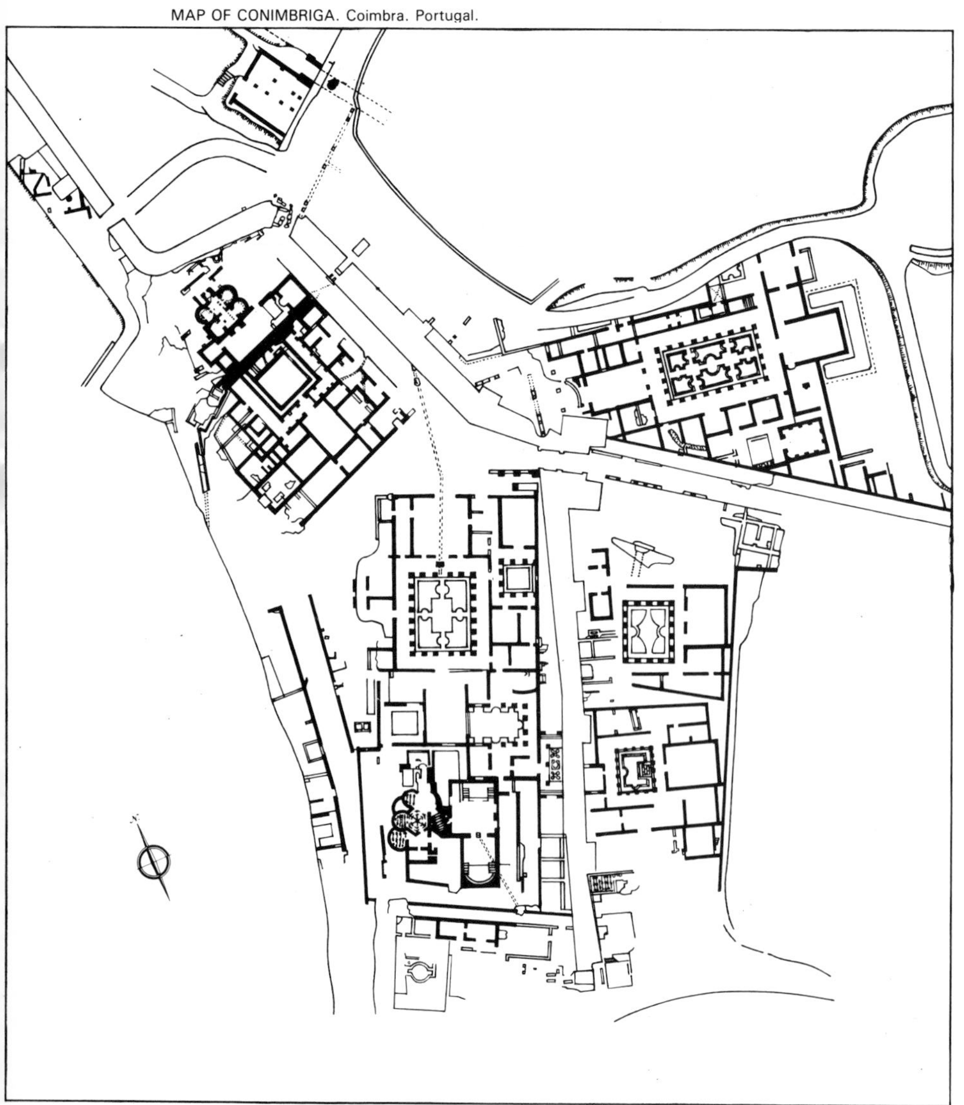

gardens, converted into purely ornamental motifs."[7]

While ruins and mosaics are all that remain of Spain's Roman houses, which we can now only imagine, in Italy, the cities of Herculaneum and Pompeii have been preserved intact, with their frescos and statues as they appeared in ancient times. Buried by the eruption of Mount Vesuvius in 79 A.D., they escaped the ravages of barbarian invasion.

Excavation has revealed their courtyards and peristyles and the paintings that decorated their walls, depicting countrysides in order to extend the perspective of the garden.

"The hollow spaces formed by the buried plants have also permitted identification of their species, which are similar to current species."[8] We also know that plants were arranged in the Pompeiian parterres in groups to form low, compact shrubs.

The layout and design principles of a Graeco-Roman villa are explained by Vitruvius: "First comes a peristyle and afterwards, an atrium, surrounded by paved porticos with a view of the palaestra and the walks."[9]

In the Exedra house in Italica there is a long open walk or palaestra paralleled by a covered walk, the cryptoporticus, orientated toward an exedra in the same form as that once provided in Greece for spectators of athletic games and which in Roman times were used as places for conversation and leisure.

Vitruvius tells us that "these exedras were spacious with seating arranged for the repose of philosophers, rectors and other men of letters who met in them to discuss their learning."[10]

In his Villa Laurentia, on the seacoast near Ostia (this city is today located some distance inland), Pliny the Younger possessed a cryptoporticus or gallery with windows on both sides, "heated by the sun's rays and perfumed by the violets planted on its terrace."[11]

The orientation of the villas was clearly very important in Rome, and Vitruvius tells us that they had to be constructed facing either toward or away from the sun, depending on the region. "In northern countries, they will be built with few openings, placed on the warmest side, and in the warmer southern countries, they will have large windows facing north. This orientation is also advisable for dining rooms, affording a view of the garden through central doors when one is reclining on the triclinium."[12] No greater refinement or sense of beauty can be conceived.

In the plan of the Exedra house in Italica,[13] the triclinium faces north, suggesting that the architects who constructed the new Italica were familiar with Vitruvian principles, and while they were perhaps less extensive than those of Italy, these villas all possessed their gardens and green areas. We know nothing of the inhabitants of the houses of Italica, Clunia,

Conímbriga and so many other Roman cities in Spain, as yet unexcavated, but those that have been unearthed clearly show us that their way of life was similar to that of Rome and that gardens and walks existed in spite of the Iberian climate, which was often cold and arid.

Vitruvius attached great importance to houses destined for prominent persons. To receive guests, they should have "magnificent vestibules, great reception rooms and spacious peristyles, gardens with long tree-lined avenues, and everything in them should be beautiful and majestic."[14]

Palaces of this description unquestionably existed in Spain. Perhaps the Clunia palace in Burgos was one of them.

Varro tells us of the great land-holders established by the Roman conquest in the western Mediterranean, who lived on large African, Spanish and Gallic estates, and gave the provinces their Roman character. "In some cases they survived the fall of the Empire. They left in Spain not only the vestiges of their wealth, but also the elegance of their way of life and the beauty of their gardens, particularly in places where the essence of Roman civilisation was embodied and symbolised."[15]

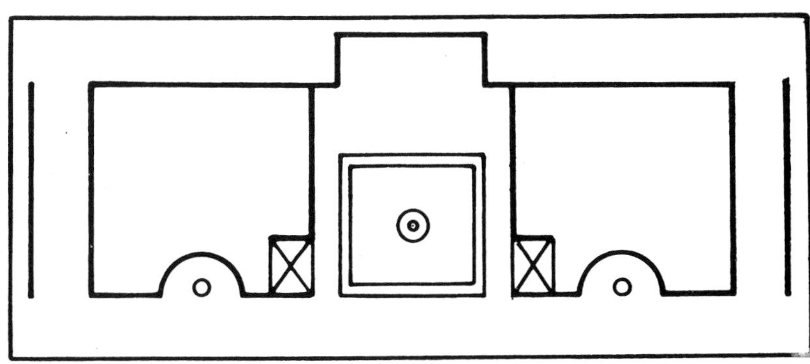

GARDEN PLAN. Auditorium Mecene. *P. Grimal.*

GARDEN PLAN. Herculaneum. *P. Grimal.*

CONIMBRIGA, ROMAN GARDEN. *Photo Author.*

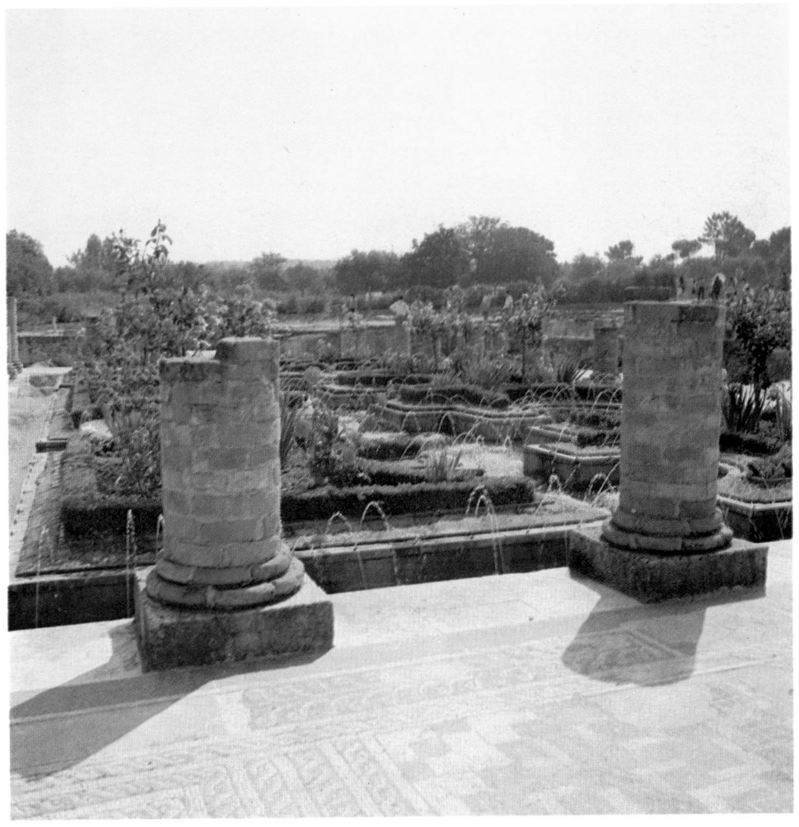

PERISTYLE, ROMAN HOME.

Spain was one of the richest and most prosperous of the Roman provinces, so often mentioned in the writings of Mela, Strabo, Columella, Varro and Pliny the Elder. In agricultural terms, the Peninsula was extremely important for its enormous quantities of oil, wine and grain, which it exported to Rome.

With the spread of Roman civilisation through conquest came the knowledge of new varieties of trees and plants from Italy and the other Roman colonies, often brought by the Emperors from their conquests in the Orient. Their flowers were almost identical to those we know in our gardens today. Columella, a native of Gades (Cadiz), described the care of a garden, naming marigolds, narcissus, snapdragons, lilies, white and blue hyacinths, violets, pansies, roses, poppies and many vegetables and aromatic plants. He makes special mention of lettuces, which he says grew "in his native country — that of the Tartessians — his beloved Gades; their leaves were pale and curled and their stems white."[16]

The most commonly used shrubs in Roman gardens were laurel, myrtle and acanthus, together with trees of all species, particularly the oak, the plane — beloved of the Greeks — the cypress and fruit trees, such as the peach, which came from Persia, and the cherry, which was introduced by Lucullus from Ponto at the time of his conquests.

MERIDA. PERISTYLE. *Photo Author.*

One of the principal elements of Roman decoration consisted of garlands where fruit, flowers and foliage intermingled. In his praise of flowers Pliny the Elder refers explicitly to the variety of colours and shapes of the wreaths and garlands, which he says "could not be reproduced in painting."[17]

This fragment of a mosaic depicting a garland is housed in the Archaeological Museum in Madrid. It was brought from Naples by Charles III from the excavations at Pompeii or Herculaneum and once decorated the Royal Library in Madrid. "It undoubtedly formed part of an artistic frieze in a Roman chamber, but of such exquisite workmanship and harmony in colour and composition, the oak leaves and acorns in particular, that it can well be considered a masterpiece of ancient art."[18]

These garlands were used to decorate their porticos and gardens, and others of ivy hung between the plane-trees near the hippodrome of Pliny the Younger, according to his beautiful description of his Tuscan villa: "Facing these pleasing buildings lies a spacious hippodrome, entirely open in its centre, allowing the whole to be viewed with one glance upon entering. It is surrounded on every side with plane-trees covered with ivy, so that while above they are adorned with their own foliage, below, their bodies enjoyed a borrowed verdure, the ivy twining around the trunks and branches from tree to tree, connecting them. Between each plane-tree boxwood has been planted, and behind these, bay trees which blend their shade with that of the planes."[19]

This shows us that Pliny was an artist and a gardener and possessed a sense of perspective.

The Romans were truly fond of creeping plants, such as grapevines, ivy, volubilis and all that might serve to decorate pergolas and porticos.[20]

They also knew the art of sculpting shrubbery; the *toparius,* or Roman gardener, used myrtle, laurel, rosemary and boxwood, which he shaped in fanciful forms or as hedges. They were practised in grafting, layering, the cultivation of nearly all plants and the performance of most agricultural tasks.

Strabo describes the forests of green oak and olive trees that existed in Spain and relates "Hercules' legendary quest for the golden apple of the Hesperides, a garden situated in the middle of the ocean between Spain and Morocco. The name Hesperus signifies evening and, by extension, sunset and the west. Hesperus' daughters, the Hesperides, lived in a beautiful garden which bore fruit of gold."[21] This fruit is presumed to be the orange, which probably originated in eastern Asia, in India and China, from which it gradually spread to all southern countries. It is not known for certain if it existed in Spain during the Roman era, or if it was brought by the Arabs. Pierre Grimal speaks of the orange tree among the trees existing in Rome during the reign of Augustus, growing amongst palm, pine and cypress trees.[22] It is therefore probable that it also grew in Spain.

Strabo speaks of a tree in Gades "whose leaves, a forearm in length and four fingers in width, have a sword-like shape." Although differing in some of its characteristics, this might have been the *draecena draco,*[23] a famous and very ancient tree native to the Canary Islands, whose red sap it is said, was used by the Guanches (who then inhabited the islands) to preserve their mummies.

Pliny the Elder, who lived in Spain for a few years, frequently alludes in his *Natural History* to the vegetation and flora of Spain, which we include in this chapter for the glimpse it provides of the plants that existed in the various regions of Spain in Roman times, before the arrival of the Arabs.

Nearly all of the flowers, herbs and fruit that grow in our European gardens were imported. The apple, however, was native to Italy, and when the Romans tasted the more exotic flavour of apricots, pomegranates, lemons and oranges they referred to all of these new fruits by the same name of apple or *malus,* distinguishing between each by adding the name of its country of origin; hence, *malus persica* to designate the apricot.[24]

Pliny describes the Spanish *quermes,* an insect resembling the cochineal, which was used to dye the cloaks worn by generals. It lived in the kermes oak, a short stocky tree similar to the evergreen oak found in very high quality in Spain.[25]

Pliny the Elder also spoke of honey, describing a variety "deriving from esparto fields and bearing their flavour. Great quantities of wax and honey were exported, mainly from the Betica (Andalusia). The esparto region lay for the most part inland from New Carthage (Cartagena)."[26] Great fields of esparto still exist in the mountains around Alcalá de Henares and in Alcarria, in the province of Guadalajara near Madrid — a honey-laden region — where until recently women could be seen in the villages seated in the doorways to their houses weaving strands of esparto, with the reeds in their mouths, making patches eventually to be sown together to form mats.

In the days of Pliny the Elder, it was common in Spain to add resin to wine (as is still done in Greece), and great quantities were exported. Wines from the Barcelona region, Valencia and the Balearic Islands were comparable to Italy's best.[27]

GARLAND MOSAIC. Arch. Museum. Madrid. *Photo Dominguez.*

PLINY DEDICATES HIS "NATURAL HISTORY" TO TITUS. FLORENCE. *Bibl. Laurenziana.*

Oil was another of the great export products, and as early as the first century A.D., Pomponius Mela speaks of a forest called Oleastrum, or "of oil" that lay near the port of Gades.[28]

There are numerous descriptions of plants native to Spain in Pliny's *Natural History.* He describes the castor oil plant, whose small whitish berries are used to produce the purgative oil.

They cultivated fruit trees, such as the apple and plum, which they knew how to graft, and pear trees, those from Numancia (province of Soria) in particular, and also figs from Sagunto (near Valencia) that were dried (as now) and kept in boxes, — those from Ibiza were famous for their size and quality.[29]

In his book XV, Pliny the Elder tells us that "a graft was recently made in Betica from a plum tree onto an apple tree, yielding a product known as *malina.* The plum was also grafted onto the almond, yielding the *amygdalina*; the stone contains a real almond; no fruit has been more ingeniously contrived."[30]

The pomegranate was given the name *punica granatum* by Linnaeus, who kept the name given it by the Romans when they brought it from Carthage to Italy at the time of the Punic Wars.[31]

Pliny relates that the pistachio, a tree bearing a highly prized green almond, once grew in Spain. They no longer do today.

"In the time of Strabo," he says, "the acorn was the main source of nourishment for the Peninsula's northern and northwestern populations; the flour produced from acorns was used to make bread which could be stored for long periods."[32]

The Romans were an agricultural people par excellence and had a great appreciation for wheat, barley and other Spanish cereals. The Peninsula was therefore one of the Empire's principal granaries.

"These cereals were used to brew beer and *caelia,* which" Orosius tells us "had a bitter taste and an intoxicating warmth." He adds that the people of Numancia got drunk on this beverage before leaving the city on their last battle.

To store their grain the Romans used silos, many of which have been found on the Iberian Peninsula in the form of cavities hollowed out of rock, such as the Castro of Coaña (Asturias).[33]

"The flax of Saétabis (Jativa, in Valencia) was very well known and considered the best in Europe. In Tarragona, as well, there was flax of very fine texture and extraordinary whiteness which was highly esteemed. Zoelia, between Asturias and Galicia, was also famous for its flax."[34]

"Alfalfa was one of the mainstays of ancient agriculture. According to Pliny the Elder it came to Italy from Greece, where it had been brought from Asia during the Persian wars, and so derived its Greek and Roman name: *"Medica"*. As Cato does not mention it among the other crops, it is probable that the Romans did not as yet grow it in Cato's day. But by the time of Varro (116 to 27 B.C.), and Virgil, it was well established in Italy. In Columella's day, it was produced in Andalusia, and the Moors, who loved plants, kept it alive there as if a vestal fire, while in Italy it was lost during the dark ages. From Spain it spread again all over Southern Europe and in America it was commonly exchanged for tobacco during the sixteenth century."[35]

The native shrubs of Spain known to Pliny were numerous, among them the yew (*taxus baccata*) which grows abundantly in the sierras and mountains. "The male fruit is poisonous", he writes, "and its pods, especially in Hispania, contain a lethal poison." (In the female berries the seed is poisonous but not the red, fleshy pulp that covers it.) "It seems it was used by the fierce races of the north-west of Spain to commit suicide rather than fall into the hands of the Romans during the Cantabrian wars."[36]

Boxwood and juniper grew as they do today in the forests of the Peninsula.

Pliny describes other shrubs, such as the genista or fragrant broom, aloe, and above all, roses (which he says bloomed in Carthage in early winter).[37] The wild rose, which he refers to as *cynorrhodon,* must have been the dog rose with single-petalled flowers, as the Greek prefix *cyno* means dog.

Spain was always very famous for its great variety of aromatic and medicinal herbs — such as camomile, mint, thyme, oregano and many more — which even today are more numerous than in other countries.

Pliny the Elder tells us that the cantabric herb, classified later by Linnaeus as *convulvulus cantabrica,* was discovered in Hispania in the time of Augustus. He also says that "a drink composed of a hundred herbs to which honeyed wine is added is served at festive gatherings." This is the sole known reference to this herb cocktail.[38]

Among the innumerable references to Iberian plants of Roman times, vegetables, such as cabbages, onions and artichokes were particularly famous.

"Spices and opium were also used; the latter, which was extracted from poppies, could, in Pliny's words, cause death."[39]

We have now broadly covered the Roman account of flora found in Spain during the occupation; it undoubtedly included the same plants, flowers and trees, with a few exceptions and variations due to climate, found in imperial Rome, and they were no doubt used for the same decorative purposes.

In his epigrams written during the last years of Nero's reign, Martial, a native of Bilbilis, a Roman city on the imperial Saragossa-Mérida road, condemns the luxury of Roman gardens as vain and artificial. He possessed a garden devoted to philosophy in Nomentum, near Rome. Perhaps the harsh and dry climate of his native land contributed to his austere morality; nature in its primitive state, as it must have appeared in his own region, held more attraction for him.

His thirty-five years amidst the refinement of Rome in no way reduced his preference for rusticity. He eventually returned to his village, which he describes in these words: "Seek the heights of Spanish Tarraco... and see Bilbilis and the River Jalon."[40]

Although he grew old in Rome, Martial longed for the "gold-bearing" Tagus and his native river near Bilbilis. His desire was to own a fruit-growing country house in those wild, uncultivated parts. "This land is dear to me, wherein small means make me rich and a slender store is luxury. In Rome,

CASTRO DE COANA. ROMAN SILO. *Photo Author.*

four togas or more become threadbare in a summer; there (in Bilbilis) during four autumns, one covers me."[41]

His protectress, Marcella, also from Bilbilis, gave him a small farm, which he says gave him no cause to envy those of Rome. He describes its fruit, its vined arches, and shaded walks, its clear water, and meadows, its rose bushes which, flowering twice a year, rivalled those of Paestum; the herb-pots, green in January, defying frost, the tame eel and the dove-cot as white as doves themselves. "These are my lady's gifts to me returned after seven lustres; Marcella has given me this house and tiny realm. If Nausicaa were to yield me her sire's gardens, I could say to Alcinous, I prefer my own."[42]

Marcella's rustic property fulfilled Martial's greatest aspiration.[43]. But he did not live long to enjoy it. He died four years after his return to Spain. "The ideal of Martial, a petit bourgeois who never adapted to either Rome or his native

MOSAIC OF FLOWERS. Arch. Museum. Madrid. *Photo Palacios.*

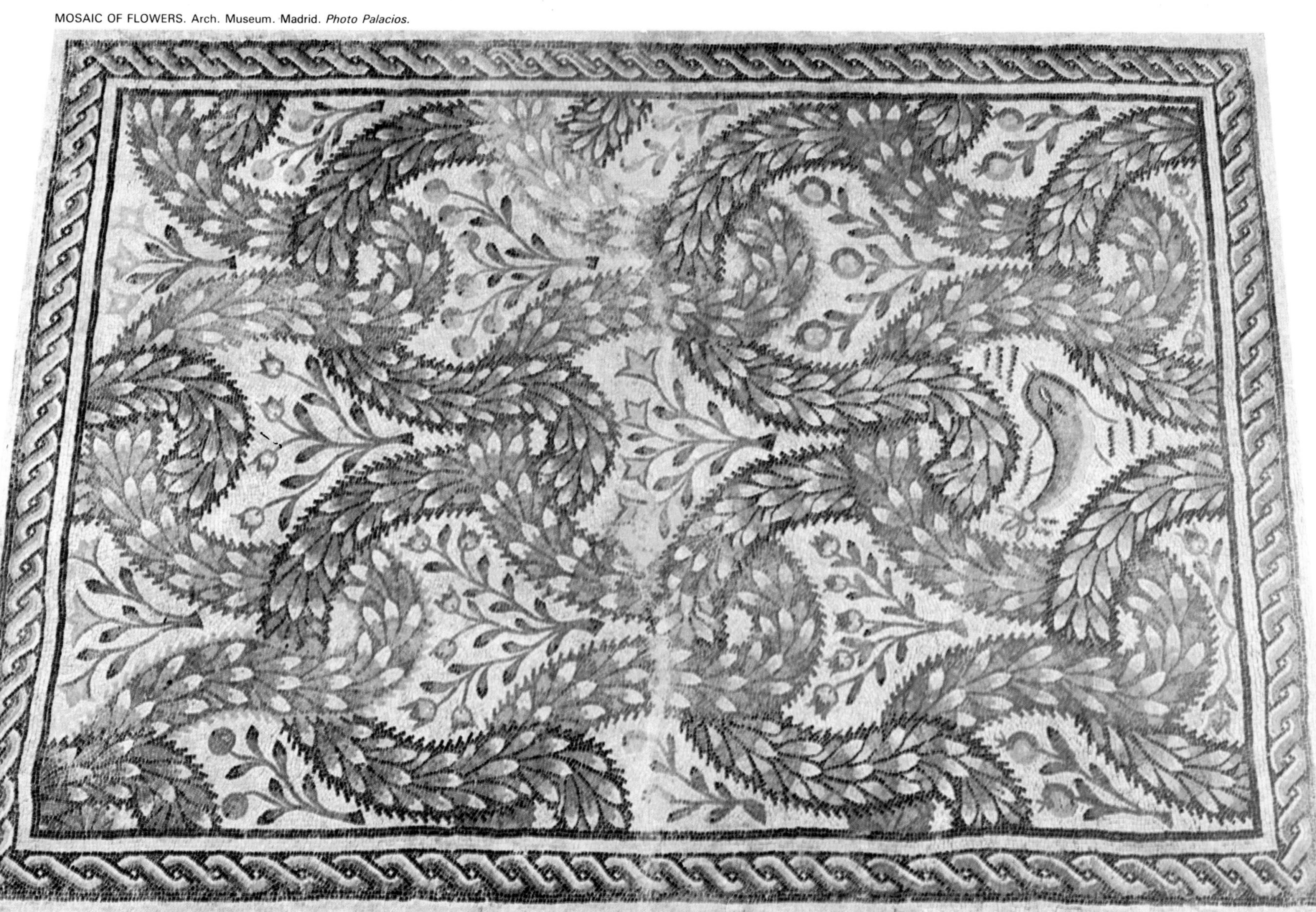

country, typifies the Latin conception of a garden, semi-urban and semi-rustic."[44]

Martial also describes "a famous house that stands in the land of Tartesius, where rich Córdoba woos tranquil Betis. Where fleeces are yellow-pale with native ore, and living gold o'er-lays the western flock. In the middle of the house, shadowing all the abode, stands with dense leafage Caesar's plane which an unconquered guest's propitious hand planted and which, then but a shoot, began from that hand to grow. 'He seems to feel who was its creator and lord; so green is it that with its boughs it climbs high to heaven.' "[45]

For Martial, the characteristic plants for pleasure gardens were myrtle, boxwood and laurel, which he may well have possessed on his country estate. Martial shows us the special appreciation shared by all Romans for the country and vegetation, even in the harsh climate of the Iberian plateau.

In an epigram Martial speaks of "Betis, with thy hair wreathed with the olive crown."[46]

At the end of the Empire, in the fourth century, the mosaic floors of Roman villas in Spain were extremely decorative and must have been executed by highly accomplished artists.

In the Archaeological Museum in Madrid there is a beautiful mosaic floor which was found in the Soto del Ramalete (Tudela) in 1946 by Don Blas Taracena; it belonged to a Roman villa with hypocausts and mosaics which appear to date from the fourth century A.D. The design is complex and ornate, though somewhat crude. The garlands appear to consist of laurel or other lanceolate leaves. They are most artfully and gracefully intertwined, and in the spaces between them, pomegranates appear in the lower portion, and in the centre and upper portions, madonna lilies. The flowers depicted in the other sections could be tulips or similar flowers, perhaps wild, but they are not mentioned in any Roman treatise of the period. The lower central space is decorated with a very primitive and amusing dolphin. Plaited cords form the classic Greek outer border.

In Mérida, a fragment of a mosaic representing grape and wine harvest motifs has also been preserved.

Thus, Spain, with a climate in its Mediterranean region similar to that of Italy, brought the greatest riches to the Empire. Rome, in turn, left the deep imprint of its civilisation on the Peninsula, constructing aqueducts, bridges, temples and villas and leaving behind the earliest examples of the art of gardening. This art was destined to perish under the barbarian invasions; it was the product of a style of life and a culture now buried forever in the ruins of Roman palaces and gardens.

These buildings would gradually fall into obscurity and neglect, "invaded by yellow mustard weeds" to quote Rodrigo Caro, until, with the arrival of the Arabs in the south, gardens of oriental inspiration appeared distinguishing Spain from the rest of Europe.

MERIDA. VENDIMIA MOSAIC. *Photo Author.*

CONIMBRIGA. *Photo Author.*

[1] GIBBON, E.: *Decline and Fall of the Roman Empire,* Pelican Book, Chatto & Windus, 1960, page 571.
[2] GRIMAL, P .: *Les Jardins Romains,* Paris, P.U.F., 1969, page 69.
[3] GRIMAL, P.: *Op. cit.,* page 249.
[4] GARCÍA Y BELLIDO, A.: *Colonia Aelia Augusta, Itálica,* Instituto Español de Arqueología, Madrid, 1960, page 81.
[5] GARCÍA Y BELLIDO, A.: *Op. cit.,* page 83.
[6] GRIMAL, P.: *Op. cit.,* pages 268, 269 and 271.
[7] "RUINAS DE CONÍMBRIGA", *Boletin da Direçao dos Edificios y Monumentos Nacionaes,* numbers 52-53, June-September, 1948.
[8] MASSON, Georgina: *Italian Gardens,* Thames & Hudson, London, 1966, page 16.
[9] VITRUVIUS: *Les dix livres de l'Architecture,* translated by Claude Perrault, 1673, Libraires Associés, Paris, 1965, page 182.
[10] VITRUVIUS: *Op. cit.,* page 160.
[11] PLINY: *Letter to Gallius,* vol. I, book II, Loeb Classical Library, London, 1961, page 159.
[12] VITRUVIUS: *Op. cit.,* pages 170-179.
[13] GARCÍA Y BELLIDO, A.: *Op. cit.,* page 93.
[14] VITRUVIUS: *Op. cit.,* page 181.
[15] GRIMAL, P.: *Op. cit.,* page 367.
[16] COLUMELA: *De Re Rustica,* Book X, Loeb Classical Library, William Heinemann, 1960, page 23.
[17] PLINY: *Natural History,* Loeb Classical Library, book XXI.
[18] DE LA RADA Y DELGADO, Juan de Dios: *Museo Español de Antigüedades,* vol. III, 1874, page 23.
[19] PLINY.: *Epistles. "To Domitius Apollinaris",* Loeb Classical Library, book V, vol. I, page 389.
[20] GRIMAL, P.: *Op. cit.,* page 286.
[21] GARCÍA Y BELLIDO, A.: *España y los españoles hace dos milaños,* Espasa-Calpe, Col. Austral, Madrid, 1968, pages 104 & 105.
[22] GRIMAL, P.: *Op. cit.,* page 430.
[23] GARCIA Y BELLIDO, A.: *Op. cit.,* page 203.
[24] GIBBON, E.: *Op. cit.,* page 27.
[25] GARCÍA Y BELLIDO, A.: *La España del siglo I de nuestra era,* Espasa-Calpe, Col. Austral, Madrid, 1947, page 265 (commentaries).
[26] GARCÍA Y BELLIDO, A.: *Op. cit.,* book XI, page 265 (commentaries).
[27] GARCÍA Y BELLIDO, A.: *Op. cit.,* page 166, and commentaries, page 266.
[28] GARCÍA Y BELLIDO, A.: *Op. cit.,* pages 34 & 53.
[29] GARCÍA Y BELLIDO, A.: *Op. cit.,* page 170.
[30] GARCÍA Y BELLIDO, A.: *Op. cit.,* page 168.
[31] HERRERA, ALONSO DE: *Agricultura general,* Madrid, Imprenta Real, 1818, Addition to vol. II, page 239.
[32] GARCÍA Y BELLIDO, A.: *Op. cit.,* pages 170 & 268.
[33] GARCÍA Y BELLIDO, A.: *Op. cit.,* page 268.
[34] GARCÍA Y BELLIDO, A.: *Op. cit.,* pages 232, 241 & 269 (commentary).
[35] VARRO: *De Re Rustica* (Fairfax Harrison), III, XVI, 12-15, Loeb Classical Library, W. Heinemann, London, 1967, page 506.
[36] GARCÍA Y BELLIDO, A.: *Op. cit.,* page 171, & commentary, page 268.
[37] GARCÍA Y BELLIDO, A.: *Op. cit.,* page 181, & commentaries, page 271.
[38] GARCÍA Y BELLIDO, A.: *Op. cit.,* pages 182 & 272.
[39] GARCÍA Y BELLIDO, A.: *Op. cit.,* page 178.
[40] MARTIAL: *Epigrams,* vol. II, book X, CIV, Loeb Classical Library, William Heinemann, London, 1961, page 233.
[41] MARTIAL: *Op. cit., vol. II, book X, page 229.*
[42] MARTIAL: *Op. cit.,* vol. II, book XII, page 341.
[43] RIBER, LORENZO: *Marco Valerio Marcial,* Espasa-Calpe, Madrid, 1941, page 229.
[44] GRIMAL, P.: *Op. cit.,* page 419.
[45] MARTIAL: *Op. cit.,* vol. II, book IX, page 119.
[46] MARTIAL: *Op. cit.,* vol. II, book XII, page 387.

2 THE ARRIVAL OF THE ARABS

We have no knowledge of gardens during the Visigothic period after the barbarian invasion of Spain had laid waste to Roman temples and palaces with their ponds and peristyles.

During the Caliphate of Córdoba in the tenth century, two centuries after the Arabs first came, Spain was divided roughly into two parts by an imaginary line starting on the Levantine coast in the region of Valencia and crossing the Peninsula obliquely through Salamanca, ending between Oporto and Lisbon.

When the Arabs occupied Spain, the Christians, who were descendants of the Goths, retired to the mountains of Asturias under the leadership of Pelayo, and formed the Asturian monarchy. Judging by the sites they selected for their palaces, the Kings of Asturia appear to have had a sense of beauty; for instance, Santa María de Naranco, built by Ramiro around 847, is situated high above the town of Oviedo; later on, King Silo held his court in Santianes de Pravia, on the river Nalón, a place of great natural beauty.

Christian art at this time was crude and rudimentary, drawing its inspiration, though imperfectly, from Córdoba, no doubt passed on by the monks and nobles who fled from the capital of the Caliphate and took refuge deep in the mountains of the north. These places, which even today are difficult to find, include San Baudelio de Berlanga in Soria, San Miguel de Escalada in León, Santa María de Lebeña in Santander, San Millán de la Cogolla (Suso) in the Rioja and many more, all built by the Mozarabs, or Moorish-influenced Christians. They formed their independent kingdoms, such as Navarre, León, Castille and León, Navarre-Aragon and Barcelona, between the ninth and tenth centuries. During these dark ages in the north of Spain, the Christians clung to their rough and primitive customs; their art was poor, their buildings mean and small, and their agriculture backward.

Meanwhile, Arab domination in the south was producing the most brilliant period of Islamic art. Their civilisation was shaped by philosophers bearing the legacies of Greek culture, such as Averroes of Córdoba, who translated Aristotle; by poets and doctors versed in botany and the exact sciences; and by

SCULPTURES ON STONE AT MEDINA AL-ZAHRA. *Photo S. Saavedra.*

agriculturists who wrote numerous treatises, one of the most important being *The Book of Agriculture* by Abu Zacaria Amed Ibn al-Awwan, a Sevillian.[1] Abu Zacaria lived in the twelfth century, shortly before the conquest of Seville by Saint Ferdinand (1246). His treatise was inspired by Kutsami, the author of *Agriculture in Nabathea* (a province in Arabia between the Euphrates and the Red Sea).

It is not surprising, therefore, that Castillians like the chieftain El Cid and King Peter I, sought contact with Muslims and adopted their art and customs, which were superior to their own. King Peter employed Arab craftsmen to build palaces and gardens; their style and techniques remained alive well after the Renaissance, and survive still.

The Muslims who invaded the Peninsula in the eighth century were desert nomads, a pastoral people who lived in tents and had relatively little culture of their own. Before invading Spain they had conquered the Far East, Persia, Egypt, Syria, and even India, imitating the art of these conquered regions, especially that of the Sassanians[2], Persia and Byzantium, which they developed to a particularly high level in Spain.

As Professor Hugh Trevor-Roper tells us: "The Arabs themselves, in spite of the splendid civilisation they built up, had little of their own to offer. They were merely carriers. But as carriers, their services to Europe were enormous. For when the Arabs had conquered Asia and Africa, where the Greeks had founded cities, they lived amidst the remembrance of the schools of Alexandria, Ephesus and Carthage. They had absorbed what Arab writer after Arab writer would afterwards devoutly call 'The science of the Greeks'."[3]

SAINT MARTIN TOWER (thirteenth century) Teruel. *Photo Author.*

In penetrating the Peninsula the Arabs found themselves in contact with the ancient Roman and Visigothic civilisations, from which they adopted the elements most useful to their way of life.

Their first concern was to organise their places of worship, or mosques, displacing the Christian churches. Christian churches only survived in remote parts of Asturias where the Arabs never, or only briefly penetrated. They used the capitals and columns of Roman ruins to support the wooden beams of their own new buildings. For the *muezzin,* or call to prayer, they built minarets (*manar-faro* or *alminar*), taking the remains of the Lighthouse of Alexandria as their model. Some archaeologists believe these minarets were built according to a square design used in part of their dominions, like the Giralda in Seville and, later, the beautiful Saint Martin's Tower in Teruel, made of brickwork with polychrome ceramics, and the countless mudejar towers built throughout Spain by the Moriscos in the thirteenth century, especially in Aragón.

They constructed domes, a form apparently used centuries earlier in Persia, and, for the first time in Spain, arches in the shape of horseshoes. According to María Luisa Caturla this shape was inspired by designs etched in the rock of Visigothic funeral monuments in Asturias — the first examples of this arch, which is indigenous to Spain. There are sarcophagi from this period in the portico of the Mozarab temple of Suso (San Millán de la Cogolla), hidden in the Sierra de la Demanda (Rioja). The Arabs never built the horseshoe arch until their invasion of Spain; afterwards they introduced it into Africa.

The polychrome ceramic friezes they employed were an art form originating in the Tigris-Euphrates valley. Their vivid colours added a note of joy and freshness to patios and rooms. Mosaics with a lace-work pattern (*lacerias*) were a common decorative motif.

Arab ceramics encrusted with copper or gold reflectors, once crafted in the towns of Rakka in Mesopotamia and Rhages in Persia (destroyed by Gengis Khan about 1226)[4], were perfected in Spain, thus creating the Hispano-Arab ceramics of which Manises, near Valencia, was one of the most important factories. The formula used to obtain the copper lustre has never been rediscovered. Tiles with metallic reflections were probably invented in Baghdad around the year 800. The Koran forbade the use of precious vessels of silver and gold, so the Mohammedans took to using vases with a metallic glaze. In Samaria they were already in fashion, and from there they spread to all the Arab countries.

The mosaics of the *mihrab* (sacred niche) in the Mosque at Córdoba are the admirable work of Byzantine craftsmen brought by Alhaquen II and have inspired the potter's art ever since.

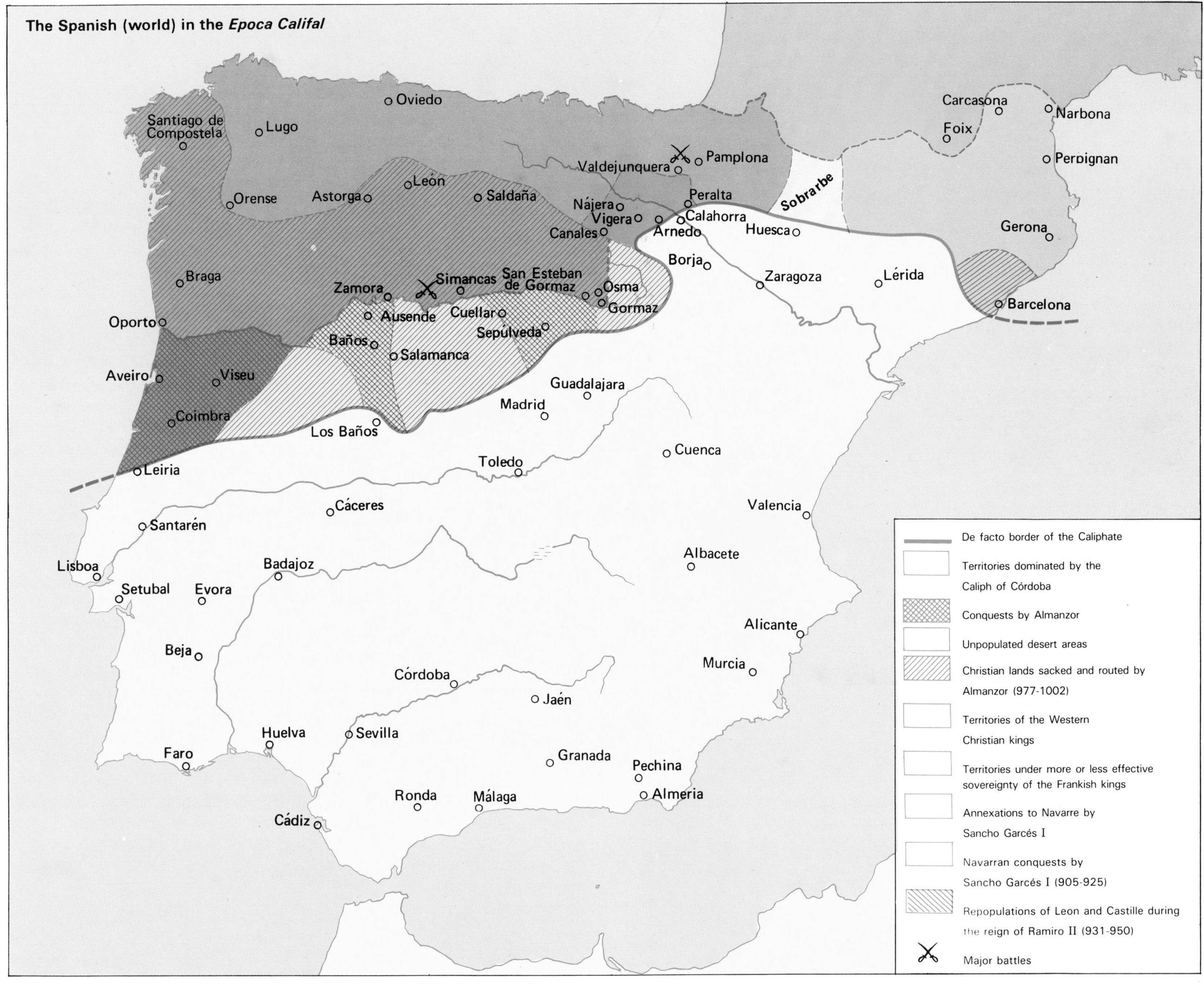

Polychrome tiles are especially suited to hot countries and their bright colours and lustre add particular splendour to southern dwellings. On summer evenings, in the Patio of the Arrayanes in the Alhambra at Granada, they look like jewels set in the frieze, bathed by the golden light of the setting sun. They require warmth and sunshine, however, to bring them to life. In northern countries, cold and dampness make them dull, diminishing their beauty and brilliance.

The Arabs perfected the ancient industries of Syria and Persia and spread their products from one end of their dominions to the other, a significant contribution to civilisation in the Middle Ages.

Like all nomads they lived in close contact with nature, which figured in all their later decorations in the form of stylised flowers and plants carved or moulded in their wood and plaster work. For these wandering shepherds, fountains and gardens represented dream-like havens beyond the burning sands.[5] They loved trees, especially palm trees, plants and flowers, and, as noted earlier, they cultivated their lands according to the principles of Nabathean agriculture.

The chronicles of the aforementioned Abu Zacaria tell of the numerous plants and trees they introduced into Spain. He

TILES IN THE PATIO COMARES. *Photo Dominguez.*

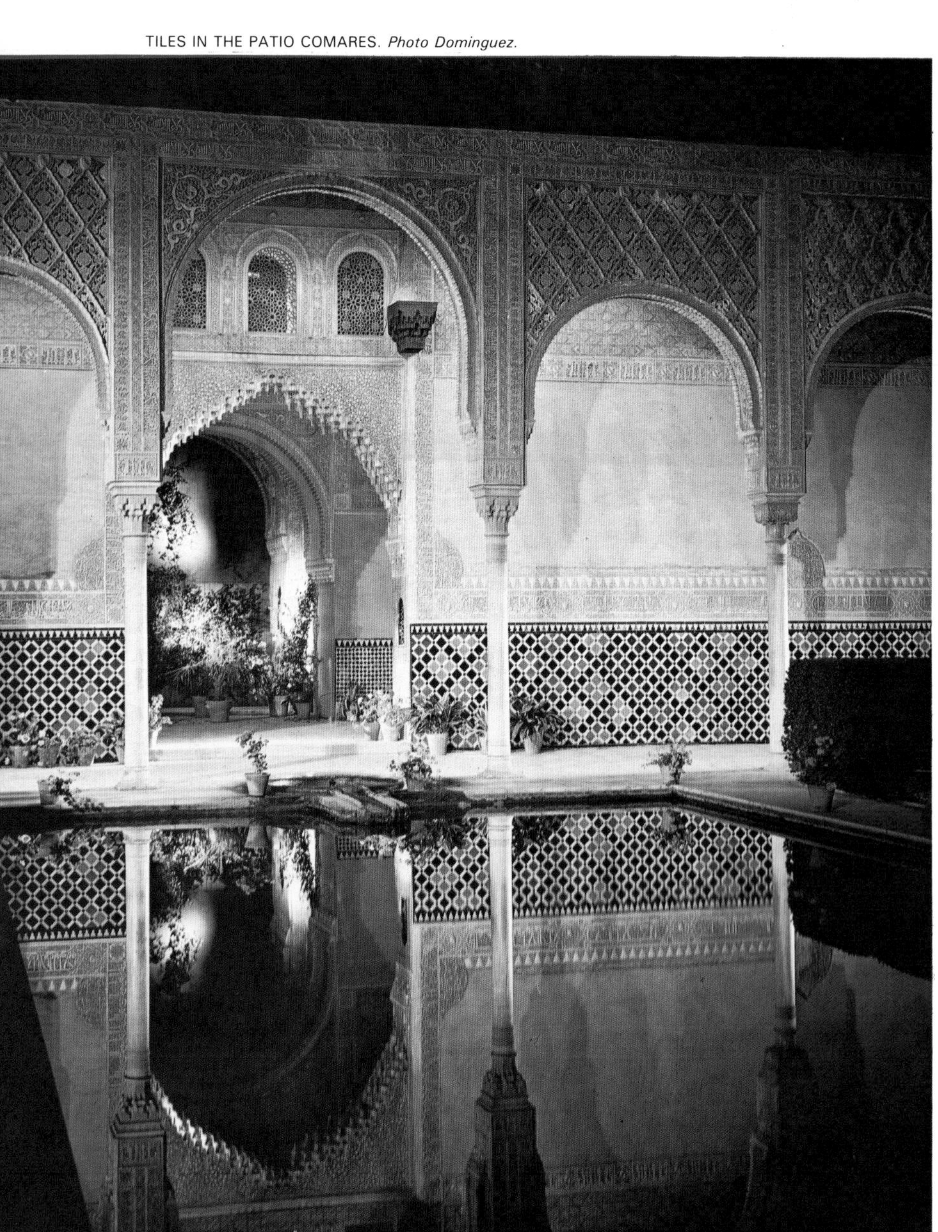

describes the cultivation of one of them, sugar-cane, at length. Before its introduction into Spain food was sweetened with honey, a custom which persists today for the preparation of such Spanish sweets as *turron* and other confectionery of the Levantine region. These sweets are similar to those prepared in Arab countries. In some Andalusian villages, *alfajores,* cakes made with honey and almonds, are still baked today. The marzipan of Toledo has the same origin.

Rice came originally from India and South East Asia, where it had been known for more than five thousand years. But while Asian rice grew in swampy regions, Abu Zacaria tells of rice cultivated by the Arabs in dry ground.[6] It was unknown in the Middle East and Mediterranean regions until many centuries later. The earliest reference to rice in Egypt is that of Theophrastus in the year 375 B.C., and the Greeks learned of it through Alexander's great expedition to India. During the Roman Empire, rice was imported from the East and was not cultivated in the Mediterranean countries until the Arabs introduced it into the Nile delta. The Muslims brought it to Spain, and the Spaniards, in turn, took it to northern Italy in the fifteenth century, where it is mentioned for the first time in a letter written by the Duke of Milan in 1475.[7]

The Arabs cultivated rice in the swampy wastes of the Albufera near Valencia, and today it is still one of this region's principal sources of income. Its highest degree of perfection was reached in the days of the Arabs.[8]

The lands of Gandia in Valencia and all those bordering the Mediterranean as far as Gibraltar were devoted to the cultivation of sugar-cane and cotton, still observed today near Motril and Salobreña on the southern coast. Most of the Andalusian lands were planted with olive trees, while those of Jerez, Granada and Málaga were covered with vineyards.[9]

In Játiva (Valencia) the Arabs were the first to make paper from flax. They also took up cultivation of the silkworm. By the twelfth century there were many prospering factories in Granada, Toledo, Seville and Valencia, although apparently, long before the Arab period, silk was known to the Romans, who cultivated the mulberry tree and produced beautiful fabrics in Spain. "The Muslims greatly expanded this industry, and their *alcaicerias* (market places for raw silk) were a source of great wealth."[10] Under the Caliphate, the suburb now known as San Andrés in Córdoba was the district of the *tiraceros,* or embroiderers from Tiraz. In the time of Almanzor, the tenth century, more than five thousand workers, both men and women, were employed in this trade.

They were skilled in the cultivation of all species of fruit tree and practised the art of grafting, layering, and other methods of plant propagation and cultivation. In Elche (Alicante), they planted forests of date-palms (*phoenix datiliferus*), which they may have brought to Spain (although another version attributes this to the Phoenicians). They also grafted the damascene apricot tree onto the almond tree, as the Romans had done, to produce a sweet kernel.

They cultivated orange, citron and lemon trees, then considered exotic; these trees originally came from India and China but had been adapted to temperate climates. The lemon tree is believed to have originated in Asia and to have been brought from the Island of Citrea, hence its name. The citron apparently came from India and Japan,[11] and the orange, according to Kutsami, is mentioned by Abu Zacaria as coming from India.[12] This proves that this tree was already very ancient when the Arabs invaded Spain.

They introduced cotton, probably from Egypt, sesame (*ajonjolí*), capers (*alcaparra*), gillyflower (*alelí*), all Arab names, and many other vegetables, trees and flowers previously unknown in the Peninsula.

Many of their flowers, such as irises, narcissi and madonna lilies mentioned in their treatises on agriculture, came originally from Persia, Syria and the Far East and had been known in the time of the Romans, for Columella refers to them in the verses at the beginning of Book X of his *De Re Rustica*. It is probable that jasmine came to Europe by way of Spain.

The practice of planting cypresses in cemeteries came to Spain from Persia; they are the symbol of death, just as the almond tree in flower is the symbol of life and hope.

"Spices had much greater economic significance in the ancient world than today, as they were used to preserve food. Cloves, pepper, nutmeg and cinnamon, imported from Spain, were widely used for this purpose."[13] The capacity of cloves to preserve food can be demonstrated by preparing a pomander, a dried orange popularly used in England in the fifteenth century to give fragrance. It is made by pricking holes over the entire orange and inserting cloves. This process allows the orange to dry without rotting, retaining the scent of the spice.

The Arabs knew the healing properties of plants, and their doctors in Córdoba were widely famed. Abderraman III and Almanzor taught and fostered the study of botany and medicine. From the most ancient and skilful agriculturalists in the world, those of Egypt and Babylon, they learned the art of channelling water for irrigation and storing it by means of reservoirs and cisterns. As mentioned earlier, this technology already existed during the Roman era and has been discovered in the excavations of Italica, Clunia, Mérida and many other Roman cities. Water was brought from the mountains by means of aqueducts and sluices, since the plants and crops could not survive without it. An Arab cistern still exists today in the cellar of the House of the Weathercocks in Cáceres, larger than both the cistern in Constantinople and that in Montánchez (Cáceres), which date from a slightly later period.

By these processes they collected water from the hills and mountains to irrigate the orchards and fertile valleys of Murcia, Valencia, Granada and Almería. They constructed complex devices to carry water to high altitudes, where they created orchards and gardens, such as the Cerro del Sol above the Generalife in Granada, of which traces still remain.

They invented an instrument called *marhifal,* to level the ground. In Valencia levelled ditches and conduits have remained intact, and even more remarkably, the order and method established by the Arabs for irrigation is still observed. The farmer of this region knows even today the hour when water will reach his fields and the time allowed for watering them. He never fails to open the sluice-gates that serve as a barrier for the water. These regulations are controlled by

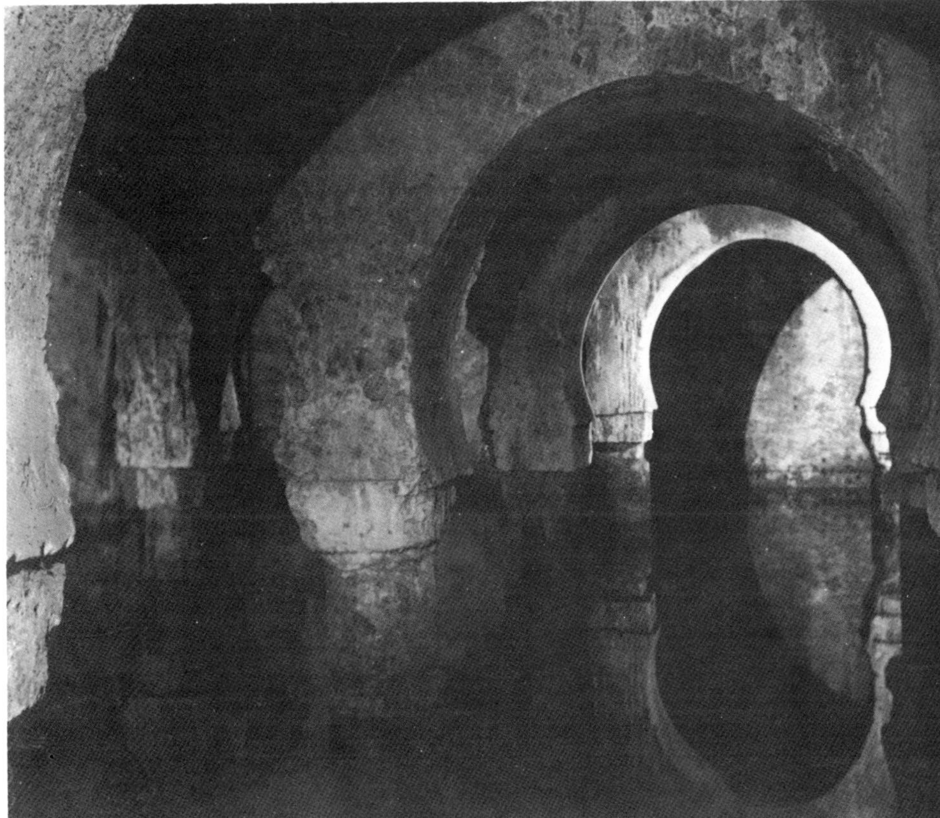

ARAB CISTERN. Veletas Palace. Ciaceres. *Photo Mias.*

TRIBUNAL DE LAS AGUAS. Valencia.

village worthies who assemble periodically in council before the Gothic porch of the Cathedral in Valencia. This is the famous Tribunal de las Aguas.

Hispanic-Muslim farmers had attained such a high standard of perfection, according to Abu Zacaria's chronicle, that accounts by historians of the fertility of the land and the opulence of the cities should not be doubted. For example, San Fernando reported in 1253 that millions of olive, fig and other fruit trees had been planted in the province of Seville.

"The plain of Granada, watered by five rivers dividing into a thousand rivulets, formed a garden nearly thirty leagues long, planted with orange trees, pomegranates, vines and fruit trees. What a beautiful sight it must have been in the time of the kings of Granada, when more than thirty working mills, an infinite number of crenellated towers and over three hundred leisure houses could be seen.

"In Arab times there were more than twelve thousand hamlets or tiny villages on the shores of the Guadalquivir and its banks could be compared with the garden of Arruzafa in Córdoba, or that of the Generalife at Granada, both for the variety of its fruits and the beauty of its flowers."[14]

With the expulsion of the Arabs from Spain, the canals and waterways, whose upkeep required constant care, were neglected and clogged. The whole country, in spite of its rich soil, suffered as a result and its wealth declined.[15] This did not prevent the Arab influence in Spain from leaving a lasting impression on gardens and art throughout the centuries. By the law not of the strong but of the wisest, Arab influence has endured throughout the Renaissance up to modern times. While the style may differ the elements and spirit of Arabic design still survive.

Arabic art has been so solidly and deeply implanted in Spain for so many centuries that Gothic art and, later, the Renaissance never succeeded in uprooting orientalism as the popular art; all these other movements intermingled with it. Its influence, however, spread only slightly to the rest of Europe.

Art, for the Arabs, was inseparable from nature and from gardening, a skill they gained from Persia and Syria, as mentioned earlier. These were dry and barren countries, where — as in Spain — a garden was a most treasured jewel, precisely because of the difficulty in attaining it. The Arabs designed their gardens according to their particular way of life: women and children lived apart in the harem,[16] while the master spent his life peacefully within the walls of his dwelling, savouring the beauty of his secluded garden. He desired nothing more from his home than rest and silence, and above all, the enjoyment of a deliciously cool and shady setting.

Water was essential to such an environment. It flowed through the rooms, sang in the marble fountains and trickled through patios and gardens in small marble or ceramic channels.

According to the chronicles, Medina al-Zahra and Córdoba were the sites of fabulous gardens watered by the Guadalquivir. Traces of gardens dating from this period have also been found in Castilleja, near Murcia, and in the palaces of Almería and Malaga, which have now been restored.

MEDINA AL-ZAHRA. Pavilion. *Photo Oronoz.*

The Arabs usually built their estates on the banks of rivers. An example is the Palace of Galiana situated in the valley of Toledo on the banks of the Tagus, where remnants of the device used by the Moors to draw water from the river still stand, now restored.

Mohamed al-Edrisi, a geographer who lived in the twelfth century, tells us in his *Description of Spain:* "The gardens surrounding Toledo are irrigated by canals over which water-wheels have been erected to carry water to the vegetable gardens. These produce remarkable quantities of unusually beautiful and delicious fruit. On all sides lovely estates and castles can be admired."[17] In the chronicle of Al-Maqqari, Ibn Badrun relates that "King Al-Mamun (Yahya) of Toledo ordered the construction of a lake, in whose centre stood a crystal pavilion; water was lifted to its roof, and from there it ran down to all sides, like artificial rain, into the water below. The pavilion was thus enclosed in a mantle of limpid water which, being constantly renewed, was also fresh, and Al-Mamun could sit inside without being touched by the water. He could also light wax candles within if he wished."[18]

This last detail may have been invented, as the smoke from candles would probably have made the atmosphere intolerably stuffy. At any rate, the description brings to mind the triclinium of the Canopus of Hadrian, at Tivoli, over whose dome water trickled in the same way.

Andrea Navagero, the ambassador sent from Venice in 1526, confirms these descriptions of the Palace of Galiana: "The Tagus rises in Aragón, not far from Calatayud, where it is said Bilbilis, the birthplace of Martial, once stood. Before it reaches Toledo the river flows through a plain called *Huerta del Rey* (King's Orchard) which is watered by *norias,* wheels invented

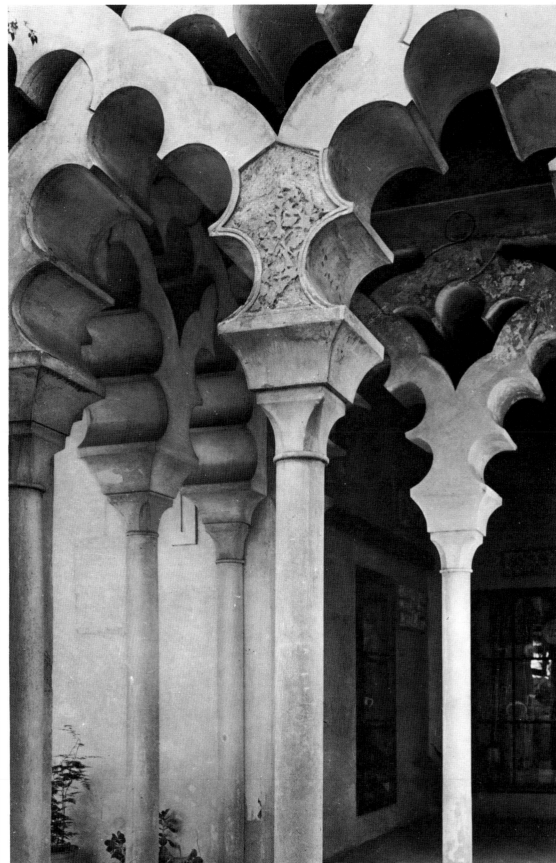

FORTRESS OF MALAGA. *Photo Más.*

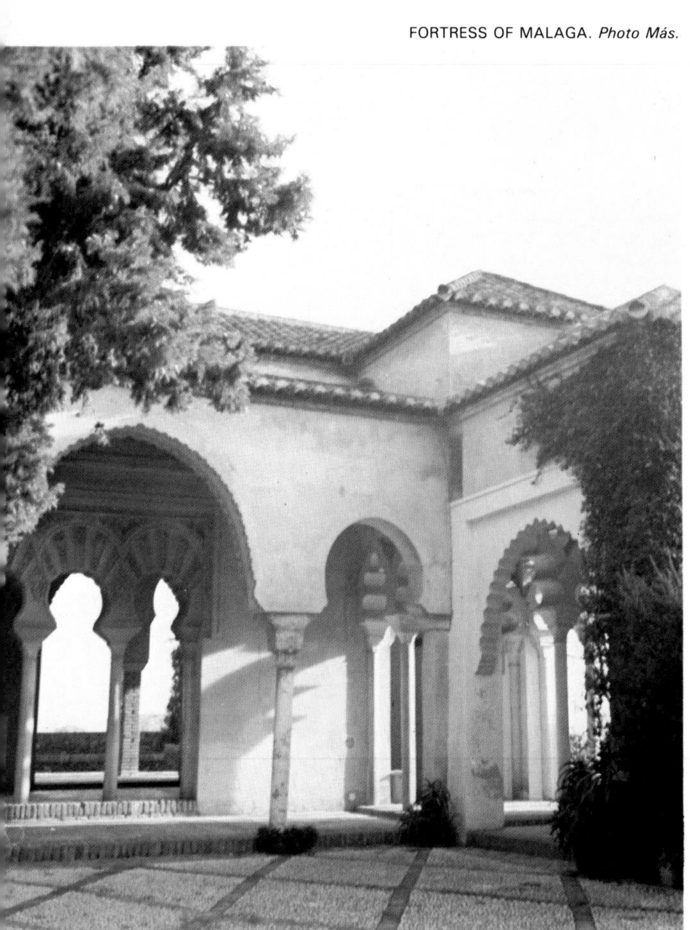

by the Arabs to draw water from the river. Because of this, the plain is covered by trees and bears much fruit, and the whole of it is cultivated and divided into orchards. They supply the town with vegetables, especially cardoons, carrots and egg-plant, which are much in demand here. In this plain there is an old ruined palace called Galiana. Galiana was the daughter of a Moorish king, of whom many tales are told — true or invented — of events that supposedly occurred in the time of the French knights. Be this as it may, the ruins show the palace to have been very fair and its site most peaceful."[19]

As an indication of Muslim skill in matters of agriculture, Jerónimo Münzer, an important nobleman who travelled through Spain in the years 1494 and 1495, when a great many Muslims still remained in Aragón, tells us: "Among all the kingdoms of Spain, Aragón is without doubt the one that has the greatest number of Moors, who are expert farmers. They pay a very high tax comprising the fourth part of their fruit, not counting other levies, and this is why the Spanish proverb says, 'He who owns no Moors has no gold.' In Aragón many towns are inhabited solely by Arabs and it is a remarkable thing that in some districts and territories where scarcely fifteen Christians could scrape a living, about sixty Moors live with ease; they have wonderful skill in the management of water and in the cultivation of the land, and as they eat very meagrely they accumulate considerable riches."[20]

The façades of Arab dwellings were bare, betraying nothing of the luxury within. All were pervaded by intimacy and secrecy; access was gained by a twisting passage so that the splendour of the patio should not be seen until after the second turning. The buildings were simple in the extreme, made of poor quality brick or whitewashed rubblework, but the patios inside, and their secret gardens, undoubtedly contained a profusion of fruit trees and flowers. This is the origin of the popular song:

"Mine is the same condition
As the house of the Moorish king:
Outside the plaster is rotting
But treasure lies hidden within."

The hot, dry climate was an important reason for creating these gardens. Mrs. Villiers Stuart tells us that: "This love of plants and flowers was characteristic of Muslims, particularly the Shiah Muslims of Persia, to such an extent that, owing partly to the conditions of the country and partly to the religious restrictions of the Koran forbidding distinctions between human beings — dwelling as they did on the delights of the eight-fold Paradise — the garden became the paramount influence throughout Muslim art."[21] Their art was imbued with Islamic symbolism, the promise, for the faithful, of a paradise in the form of a garden of delights, divided into eight parts and traversed by a river, an image replicated in the Patio of the Riad in the Generalife at Granada.

The Patio of Orange Trees in the Mosque of Córdoba is perhaps the most ancient walled garden in the world. It was begun by Abd al-Rahman II about the year 776. Almanzor "the Victorious" enlarged the mosque c.987-990, adding eight naves to its eastern side, so that the pond no longer lay at its centre. The Mosque's floor plan shows that the Patio of Orange Trees was designed and planted in conjunction with this final addition.

PALACE OF GALIANA. Toledo. *Photo S. Saavedra.*

PATIO OF THE ORANGE TREES. Mosque at Córdoba. *Photo S. Saavedra.*

According to Mrs. Villiers Stuart, each row of orange trees was aligned with the pillars inside the mosque and with the nineteen arches that once opened onto the garden in the Arab fashion. One can imagine moments of prayer in the mosque; the light filtering through the rows of orange trees must have formed an impressive image of seclusion and poetry. The arches have since been filled in to permit the construction of chapels, and the rows of orange trees are no longer aligned with the pillars inside the mosque. Perhaps Mrs. Stuart's description was but a legend; if so, it was a very beautiful one. According to the chronicles of Córdoba, orange trees were unknown there until the time of Alfonso X "the Wise", (twelfth and thirteenth centuries). In the time of Abderraman III, the patio was planted with olive trees, palms and laurels.

The Moroccan ambassador sent by Muley Ismael to Charles II (1690-1691) describes the mosque in Córdoba as it appeared at the time: "This mosque has a great patio with a pond in its centre. All around this patio a hundred and seventeen orange trees are planted."[22]

An anonymous author, M***, on a journey to Spain around the year 1700, describes the Patio of Orange Trees as "a square garden of nearly three acres, planted with very fine large orange trees forming beautiful avenues, just as our elms do in France. This was the work of the Moors, and that country is still richly endowed with their legacy."[23] This description seems to agree with that of Mrs. Villiers Stuart, assuming the rows of orange trees were indeed aligned with the mosque's columns.

One curious feature of this patio is its underground cistern, undoubtedly intended to supply the fountains.

At the beginning of the last century, Count Alexander Laborde wrote his *Picturesque and Historical Journey through Spain*, an account which, without any doubt, is the most detailed of its kind ever published; and while his historical information and style are somewhat outdated, his descriptions and observations on Spanish monuments are of considerable interest. Here is what he says about the garden of the mosque at Córdoba: "It is a sort of raised garden over a vast cistern: the four or five feet of earth that cover its vaults suffice to support and feed these lovely trees, among which there are orange trees thirty-five to forty feet high and palm trees about sixty feet high. In the centre of this vegetation above the front of the building which forms the fourth façade of the enclosure, rises a square windowed tower crowned with a rotunda that serves as a belfry."[24]

The patio has since fallen into neglect. The cistern has apparently been used as an ossuary and access to it is difficult. The hundred-year old orange trees described by Laborde at the beginning of the nineteenth century can no longer be seen, and those that remain lack symmetry.

Larch wood, *thuya articulata,* was used to build the panelled ceilings and, when taken down, was as sound as when placed there nearly eleven centuries before; the planks were much sought after by guitar-makers. This tree grew plentifully near Gumiel as it still does in the Berber mountains near Tetuan, from whence it was brought to Spain.[25]

The Alcázar was situated opposite the mosque where the Bishop's Palace stands today; it possessed beautiful gardens watered by the Guadalquivir. The palace now has a garden at the rear, probably the remains of much more extensive gardens in the time of the Kings. It still contains a fountain probably dating from the eighteenth century, with a pavilion and raised baroque ponds. These ponds probably provided water for the garden and were a replica of an earlier pond or reservoir existing in Arab times. Important archaeological excavations have recently been conducted here.

The building, known as the Alcázar of the Christian Kings, appears to date from the era of the Catholic Monarchs. It is here that Mrs. Villiers Stuart believed the word *glorieta* (bower) originated; Arab gardens, she explains, were usually divided into eight sections, and in the Alcázar gardens she found traces of what appeared to be eight fountains surmounted by eight pavilions. These, she contended, symbolised the eight pearl pavilions of the Islamic paradise. Today, the gardens of the Christian Kings only contain two square ponds, which were enclosed in the seventeenth century with iron railings, for it was into one of these ponds that the poet Gongora's rebellious sister Marica pushed the Bishop's page.

A few steps below there is a seventeenth century fountain in a small garden of sculpted boxwood. Today, modern gardens with rectangular pools have replaced the original gardens.

Chroniclers have left numerous descriptions of the gardens and fountains that once existed in the palace and town of Medina al-Zahra. Recent excavations have confirmed these accounts, which had earlier seemed fanciful.

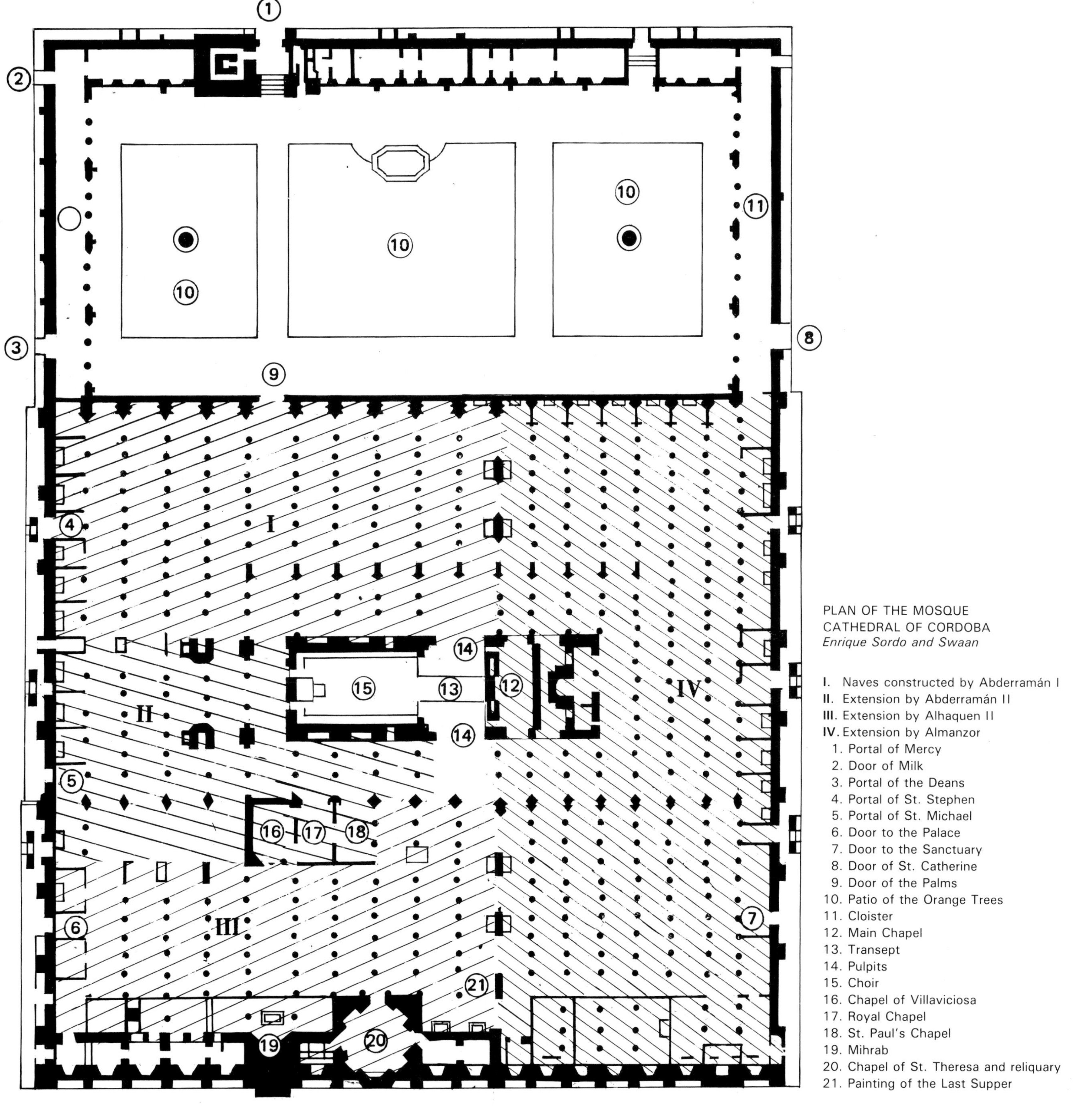

PLAN OF THE MOSQUE
CATHEDRAL OF CORDOBA
Enrique Sordo and Swaan

I. Naves constructed by Abderramán I
II. Extension by Abderramán II
III. Extension by Alhaquen II
IV. Extension by Almanzor

1. Portal of Mercy
2. Door of Milk
3. Portal of the Deans
4. Portal of St. Stephen
5. Portal of St. Michael
6. Door to the Palace
7. Door to the Sanctuary
8. Door of St. Catherine
9. Door of the Palms
10. Patio of the Orange Trees
11. Cloister
12. Main Chapel
13. Transept
14. Pulpits
15. Choir
16. Chapel of Villaviciosa
17. Royal Chapel
18. St. Paul's Chapel
19. Mihrab
20. Chapel of St. Theresa and reliquary
21. Painting of the Last Supper

In front of the Arab palace which has now been rebuilt and restored, there is a wide pool nearly as large as the building.

In line with the building there is a small pavilion with another, slightly smaller pool behind it, and one on either side. These four ponds are bordered by broad stone walks paralleled by small canals which still show traces of their original red paint. This design, surrounding the palace with water and gardens, so striking in its refinement, is the only such example of the eighteenth century surviving in Europe today.

Ibn Hayyan[26] relates that, among its marvels, there were two fountains whose basins were of such an extraordinary form and so priceless for their exquisite workmanship that, in his opinion, they constituted the principal ornament of the palace.

Another of the marvels of Medina al-Zahra was the Hall of the Caliphs, whose ceiling was of gold (probably golden mosaics) and transparent marbles. In the centre of the room, according to Ibn Backuwal, was a pond of porphyry filled with mercury, while from the ceiling hung a single pearl, a gift from the Emperor of Constantinople. When the rays of the sun penetrated this apartment the glitter of its walls was dazzling, and when Al-Nasir wished to inspire fear in any of his visitors, he signalled to one of his slaves to set the mercury in motion. Lightning bolts appeared to flash through the room and the company would tremble at the room's apparent motion. The abundance of mercury in Spain, which apparently came from Los Pedroches near Córdoba, must have given the Caliph this idea.[27]

One can well imagine the astonishment of the rough northern chieftains Sancho of León and García of Navarre when they were made to walk the length of this series of salons, at the end of which, scarcely visible, waited the Caliph, as impassive and mysterious as a deity.[28]

In the gardens of the Alcázar at Córdoba, according to Al Maqqari, was a water jet of surprising strength, attaining a height never before seen in east or west.[29] The Arabs were the first to construct such vertical water spouts.

Ibn Said also describes the houses and gardens built by sultans and Cordoban caliphs, and those of rich landowners. The palace of the Rusafa (Arruzafa) was built by Abd al-Rahman. Passionately fond of flowers and plants, he created his garden with all the rare and exotic species that came to him from Syria and other distant countries. The safari pomegranate, considered the best of its species, was apparently cultivated here for the first time.[30]

This author goes on to describe the many palaces and pleasure gardens on the outskirts of Córdoba, in particular, the magnificent Almanzor on the banks of the Guadalquivir. Then known as Al-Zahra,[31] it possessed a large lake covered with water lilies. At Abd al-Rahman's death the palace was raised to the ground.

Recent reconstruction of the hall of Medina al-Zahra has revealed the great differences between its art and that of Granada. Its origins are Byzantine and of a purer style. The art of the caliphs represented the golden age of Islam in Spain, while the more baroque art of Granada, two centuries later, showed signs of decadence.

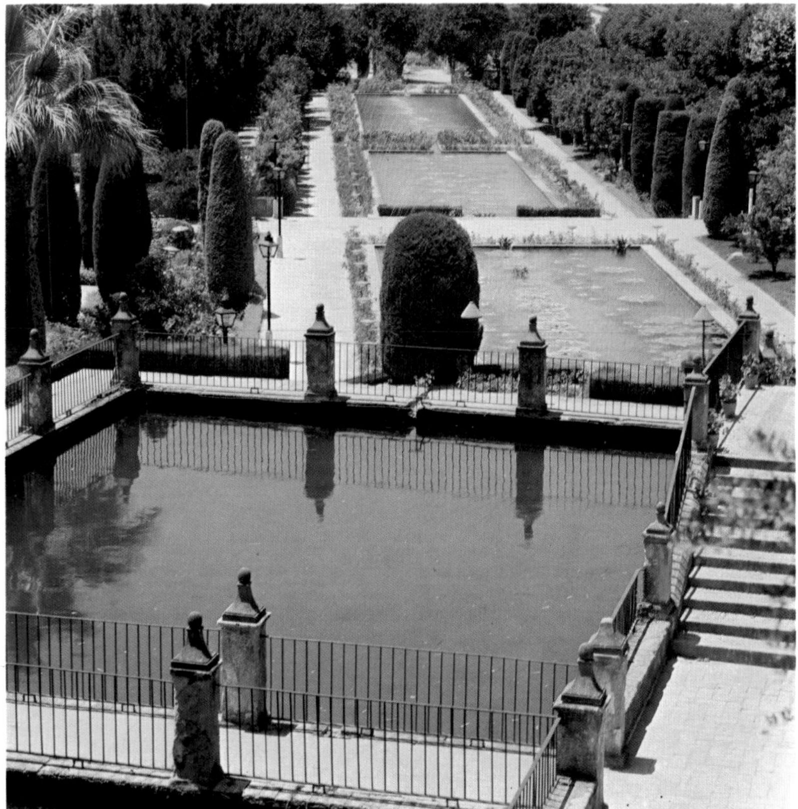

POND AT THE ALCÁZAR OF THE CHRISTIAN KINGS. Córdoba. *Photo S. Saavedra.*

1 ABU ZACARIA AMED IBN AL-AWWAN, SEVILLANO: *Libro de la Agricultura,* translated by José Banquieri, Madrid, 1878.
2 LOZOYA, MMarqués de: *Historia del arte hispánico,* Ed. Salvat, Barcelona, 1931, vol. I, page 204.
3 TREVOR ROPER, H.: *The Rise and Fall of Christian Europe,* Thames & Hudson, London, 1965, pages 141-142.
4 LOZOYA, Marqués de: *Op. cit.,* vol. I, page 270.
5 VILLIERS STUART, Mrs.: *Spanish Gardens,* Batsford, London, 1929, page 4.
6 ABU ZACARIA: *Op. cit.,* vol. I, chap. XX, page 346.
7 ANGEL, Rosemary: "Sugar, Spices and Potatoes", *Journal of the Royal Horticultural Society,* November 1968, vol. XCIII.
8 LABORDE, A.: "Voyage en Espagne", *Revue Hispanique,* Paris, 1925, Ed. Fouché-Delbosc, page 460.
9 LABORDE, A.: *Op. cit.,* page 461.
10 PICATOSTE, F.: *Compendio de la Historia de España,* Sucesores de Hernando, Madrid, 1914, page 79.
11 HERRERA, Alonso de: *Agricultura general,* edicion de la Real Sociedad Matritense, Madrid, 1818, vol. II, page 305.
12 ABU ZACARIA: *Op. cit.,* vol. I, page 196.
13 ANGEL, Rosemary, *Op. cit.,* page 473.
14 LABORDE, A.: *Op. cit.,* page 460.
15 VILLIERS STUART, Mrs.: *Op. cit.,* page 6.
16 GROMORT, Georges: *Jardins d'Espagne,* A. Vincent, Paris, 1926, vol. I.
17 AL-EDRISI: *Viajes de extranjeros por España y Portugal,* compiled by J. García Mercadal. Ed. Aguilar, Madrid, 1952, vol. I, page 192.
18 AL-MAQQARI: *History of the Mohammedan Dynasties,* translated by Pascual Gayangos, London, 1840-1843, vol. II, book VII, chapter V, page 263.
19 NAVAGERO: "Viaje por España", in *Viajes de extranjeros por España y Portugal, Op. cit.,* vol. I, page 845.
20 MÜNZER, Jerónimo: "Relacion de viaje". *Op. cit.,* Ed. Aguilar, Madrid, 1952, vol. I, page 415.
21 VILLIARS STUART, Mrs.: *Op. cit.,* page 4.
22 A MOROCCAN AMBASSADOR: "Viaje a España". *Op. cit.,* Ed. Aguilar, vol. II, page 1227.
23 M***: "Viajes". *Op. cit.,* Ed. Aguilar, vol. III, page 97.
24 LABORDE, A.: *Op. cit.,* page 491.
25 FORD, Richard: *Handbook for Travellers in Spain,* 3rd edition, Murrays Guide Books, London, 1855, vol. I, page 228.
26 AL-MAQQARI: *Op. cit.,* Vol. I, book III, chap. III, page 236.
27 AL-MAQQARI: *Op. cit.,* page 237, note 19, page 503.
28 LOZOYA, Marqués de: *Op. cit.,* vol. I, page 223.
29 AL-MAQQARI: *Op. cit.,* vol. I, page 208.
30 AL-MAQQARI: *Op. cit.,* vol. II, book VI, chap. II, page 86;
31 AL-MAQQARI: *Op. cit.,* vol. I, page 243.

ALCÁZAR OF THE CHRISTIAN KINGS. Cordoba. *Photo Más.*

3 GRANADA AND ITS GARDENS

Of all the gardens created by the Arabs in Toledo, Córdoba, Almería and other provinces during their time of power in Spain, there remains only the memory of their legends and the chronicles of their historians. But the gardens of the Alhambra and the Generalife live on, the oldest in Europe and the only gardens that remain from the thirteenth and fourteenth centuries, perhaps because they were royal residences.

Granada and its gardens form, without question, one of the world's most beautiful sites because of their spectacular setting, their Arab mystique and the water that nourished Granada's red mountain soil. Luxuriant with verdure, crowned by the perpetual snows of the Sierra Nevada and bathed by the Mediterranean with its nearby coasts of Motril, Almuñécar and Salobreña, Granada possesses a mixture of mountain and tropical climate unique in Europe.

The enchantment of Granada was praised by all who passed its way: Mohamed al-Edrisis, who toured the whole of Spain in the twelfth century to provide news and a description of its land to his master, the Christian King Roger II of Sicily; Abd al-Basit, the Egyptian traveller who described Granada in glowing terms during the last years of Arab domination (1465 to 1466);[1] Jerónimo Münzer a few years after the fall of Granada; and many others up to the time of the romantics, including Washington Irving, who fell under its spell and wrote his best pages there. George Ticknor wrote in his *Memoirs* at the beginning of the nineteenth century of his enthusiasm for Spain. And, much against his will, the sceptical Richard Ford is not prevented by his own severe criticisms from dedicating his *Handbook for Travellers* "to his well-beloved Spain in remembrance of pleasant years spent there."[2] Ford dwells at length on the state of the Alhambra in the nineteenth century, destroyed and ransacked after the advance of the French invasion, and later abandoned during the reign of Isabella II (1845-1870).

FOUNTAIN OF THE LIONS. ALHAMBRA. *Photo S. Saavedra.*

FLOWER BEDECKED BALCONIES. *Photo Author.*

VIEW OF THE ALHAMBRA. Granada. *Photo Palacios.*

As discussed earlier, the Arabs designed their gardens for their sedentary and contemplative life; a complex and refined art very far removed from our modern life and mentality, where beauty was created to be contemplated at leisure, with no sense of the passing of time.

"The gardens of Spain have preserved their essential style of garden-patio, so typical of southern Spanish life. These patios, through the centuries, are the result of perfect adaptation to climate and atmosphere."[3]

In the words of Prieto Moreno, "during the heat of summer, people seek coolness within the walls of their dwellings, and it is in Spain where the patio, common to all Mediterranean cultures, has maintained its tradition more than in any other country, symbolizing as it does the daily life of those who dwell there."

The Granada garden is not a purely architectural creation, for vegetation and landscape play as important a part as the construction surrounding them.

Today, even in the humblest dwellings, family life revolves around the patio, whether large or small, always filled with flower pots, rose bushes and climbing jasmine. There is usually a fountain or well in the middle of the patio, and most well-to-do people reserve certain portions of the house for use in summer or winter, according to the position of the house.

The garden itself is composed of a series of enclosures, much like patios, but formed by hedges and greenery instead of walls. "The Generalife," Prieto Moreno tells us, "is a continuous series of them."

"In Granada a few patios of Arab and Morisco houses still survive, where the square pool, the trellised vine, the sunken earthenware jar, the portico and pavements represent perfect models, on a small scale, of the classic Arab garden."[4]

Access to these dwellings, even the most imposing of them, is generally gained along a narrow passage shut in by high white-washed walls and devoid of all ornament. The little vestibule is entered by a simple rustic door. This ante-chamber is placed at an angle to block visibility from the outside. Entering the patio with its central fountain one can finally see inside the house, so hidden from curious eyes. Just as in Roman villas, this patio communicates with the principal rooms of the house, where family life unfolds. Behind the house lie the flower and vegetable gardens.

In all Andalusian cities, "the patio", writes Prieto Moreno, "is the centre or meeting place of the house and its source of light, which penetrates to all the rooms. It provides greenery by means of potted plants, such as geraniums, carnations and lilies and provides seclusion without interrupting contact with nature".

"The shapes and proportions of these garden-patios are quite varied: they may be square or rectangular and enclosed on one or two sides by a wall or clipped hedge."

"The Granadan's garden is thus an integral part of his home, providing everything necessary for leisurely and continuous enjoyment of beauty and landscape: mild climate, the colour and fragrance of flowers, fruit, luxuriant growth and the murmur of water. Granada's special setting has engendered a unique cultural climate as well, a love for music and dancing heard in popular songs accompanied by the guitar; these are never lacking to complete the poetry of a Granada garden."

"In these gardens each tree, each pot of flowers has a distinct personality, though interspersed with fruits and vegetables in the Arab fashion. Direct and personal care by their owners is essential to these gardens, and without it, they would certainly disappear. So, too, would the walls, steps and balustrades, as they are composed of the poorest materials."[5]

Only the pavements are of rich stonework following the tradition of Roman mosaics. They often display intricate patterns representing plants or geometric shapes in the art and technique typical of the local artisan, still very skilful today. These pavements are made of black and white pebbles gathered in the rivers Darro and Genil.

Prieto Moreno continues:

"Water is a vital element of all gardens but in Granada it is their very essence. The water systems introduced and built by the Moslems are still used today, and indeed, no others exist. Nothing would have been possible without their skill in bringing water from the foot of the Sierra to their gardens; without their ingenuity in designing channels that followed the natural terraces of the hillsides, the profusion of fountains and jets at the Generalife and the Alhambra, would have never been."

PATIO MACHUCA. *Photo Prieto Moreno.*

DETAIL OF PEBBLEWORK. *Drawing by Prieto Moreno.*

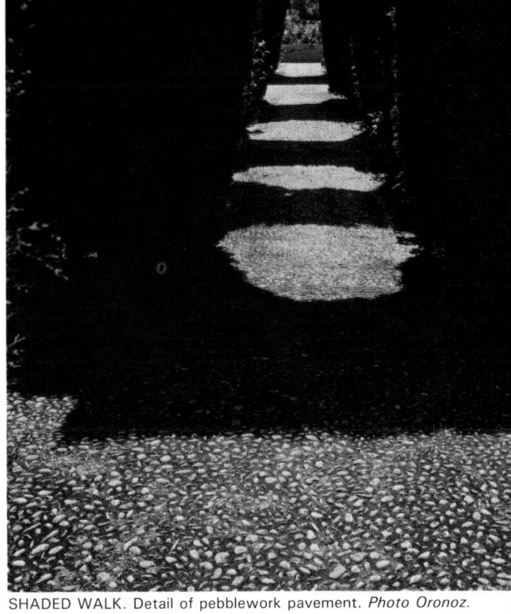

SHADED WALK. Detail of pebblework pavement. *Photo Oronoz.*

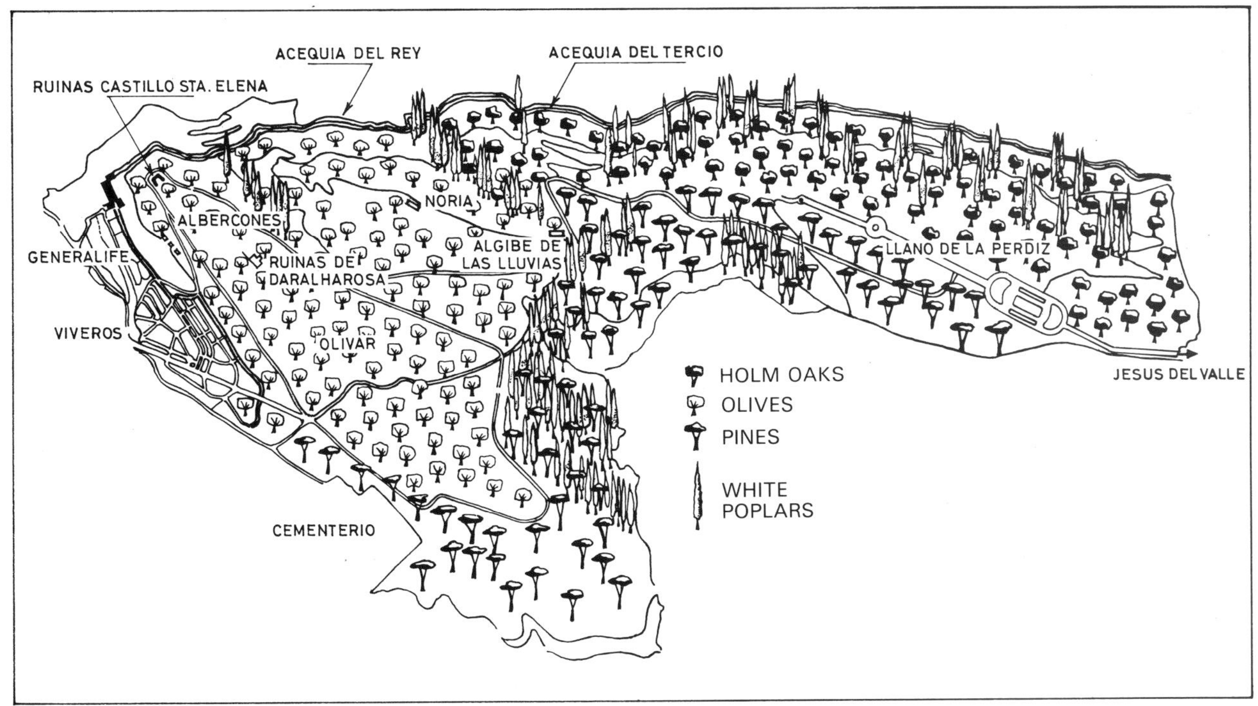

THE COURSE OF THE DARRO. *Drawing by Prieto Moreno.*

The Arab palaces of Granada can in effect be ranked according to the size of their pools, from the Throne Room in the Tower of Comares, with its great pond, to the Court of the Lions, an intimate area whose fountain is its most important feature.

"These gardens are situated, with even greater effect, in the majestic landscape of Granada, surrounded by olive-clad hills rising above the red earth, amidst the gypsy caves of Sacromonte, whitewashed and framed by prickly pears, and the irregular, varied Sierra set against the serene plain."[6]

* * *

"The Alhambra was built as a fortress, a defensive stronghold above the valley of Granada. The Court lived within its walled enclosure seeking military protection against the constant threat of internal armed conflict that shook the kingdom."[7]

"The first sovereign who, in the thirteenth century, established his residence on the ridge of the Asabica, or Red Mountain was Mohamed Ben Alahmar (1238-1272), founder of the dynasty."[8] For a year after entering Granada he lived in the Alcazaba on the Albaicín, a slope facing the Alhambra. But the following year, he climbed to the top of the hill where the Alhambra now stands, and choosing a site for his future apartments, traced the castle's foundations.

The two adjoining palaces that contain the three patios of interest to us were constructed a century later by two great builders: Yusuf I (1333-1354), only a few of whose towers from the royal residence, its walls and the Royal Bath remain, and his son Mohamed V (1353-1391). Mohamed V built nearly all the rest of the Palace of the Lions, and it was during his reign that Granada attained its greatest prosperity.

According to Arab chroniclers, Mohamed Ben Alahmar, the dynasty's founder, ordered the creation of a royal canal, which took its waters from the river Darro, about a league from Granada, and carried them through the hills towards the Generalife, passing through the patio of the Riad, to finally empty into the pools of the Alhambra. Before he did so, the slopes of these two mountains must have been bare red earth. It is to these waters, which have flowed through the same canal ever since, that we owe the gardens of the Alhambra and the Generalife. This humble stream gave rise to dream palaces, gardens, orchards and shady woods, with buildings, vegetation and water fusing as one."[9]

The construction of Comares can be attributed almost entirely to Yusuf I, while the Court of the Lions was the work of Mohamed V. These are the two principal patios of the Alhambra, each a palace unto itself.

The site of the Alhambra bears a certain resemblance to that

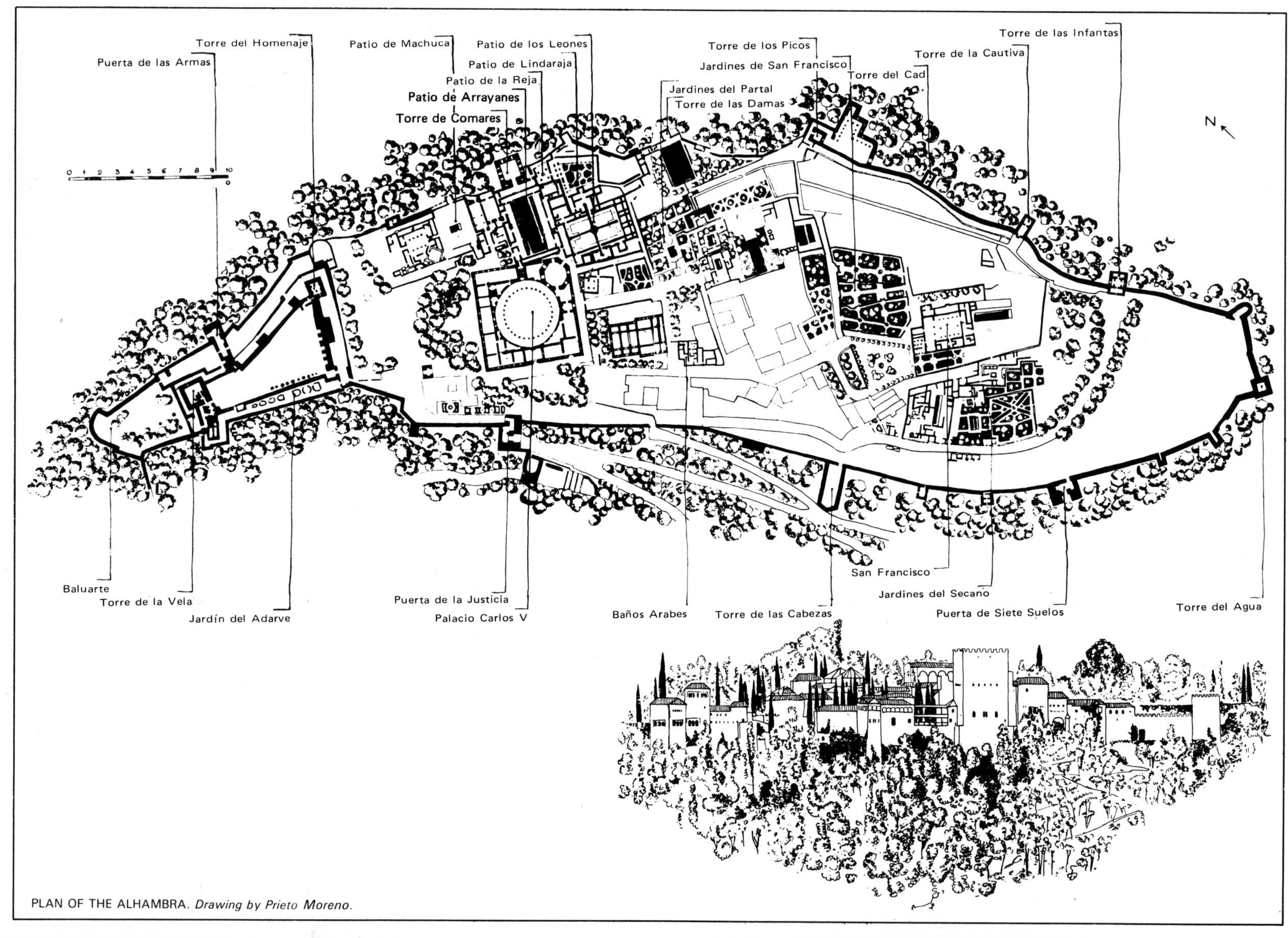

PLAN OF THE ALHAMBRA. *Drawing by Prieto Moreno.*

of the Alcázar in Segovia in that it is shaped like a ship with its prow facing the setting sun.

Walking south and passing by the Alcazaba, one comes upon the Garden of the Adarves, the work of the Marqués of Mondéjar, Governor of the Alhambra in the sixteenth century. This garden with its fountains and shrubbery is commonly known as the Garden of the Painters, and is completely detached from the other gardens of the Alhambra. It consists of a narrow strip of land enclosed by the walls of the Alcazaba, and forms a kind of bastion or balcony overlooking the wonderful landscape with the watch-tower rising above. This garden has a pronounced Italian flavour.

The entrance to the Alcázar reveals the first garden-patio, containing a fountain and decorated with tiles, and provides our first impression of gardened space bounded on the north by a wall of cypresses. At the bases of these trees are clusters of fresh silver centaurea (*centaurea candidissima*).

"The Patio of Machuca today forms the entrance to the principal rooms of the Alhambra and, with its fountain, is a prelude to the Patio of the Alberca (pool), which leads in its turn to the Patio of the Mexuar. It was in this patio that on Monday and Thursday mornings the King of Granada held audiences for his subjects, accompanied by the leading members of his family and other worthies, and where he listened to the petitions and grievances of his people."[10]

This patio has beautiful brightly coloured tiles and a low bubbling fountain, giving the impression of a spring rising from the marble floor.

"The Patio of the Alberca, named Patio of Comares in the sixteenth century is the largest in the Alhambra. According to the cursive inscriptions on the ceramic frieze over its northern portico, it was apparently decorated in part during the autumn of 1369, when Mohamed V wrote to Mecca giving an account of the conquest of Algeciras."[11]

Here one can appreciate the concept of the rectangular garden-patio, and since the Tower of Comares was the Throne Room, one can imagine the pomp with which the Caliphs of Granada were surrounded in true oriental fashion.

The Caliph of Granada sat on his throne, like the Caliph of Córdoba mentioned in the previous chapter, at the end of a long suite of rooms to inspire fear and reverence.

The Throne Room lay within the massive structure of the Tower of Comares, reflected in the green waters of its pool. According to Prieto Moreno, the most significant elements of Granada garden-craft are strongly represented here. These are his words:

"Within his salon, the monarch enjoys the firmament of its rich polychrome ceiling, representing the seven Islamic heavens; all around him, he contemplates the Granada landscape, whose poetry is enhanced when seen through the slatted side and rear windows that decorate this vast square room. Before his feet the still waters of the pool spread like a carpet. The naturalist motif is completed by geometric depictions of plants. In this setting we can sense the spirit of nomadic ancestors dwelling within his heart, the memory of which he preserves through his extreme, sedentary refinement.

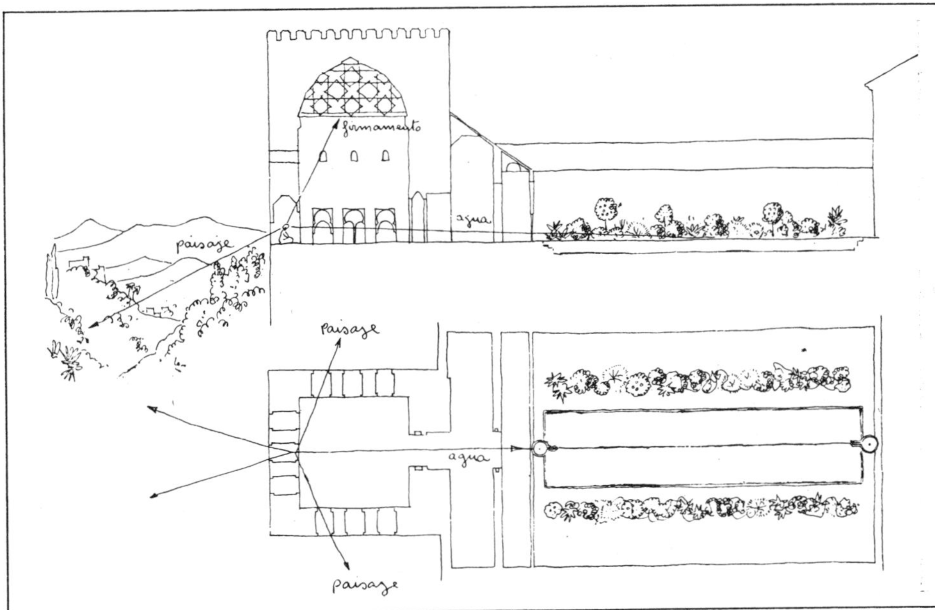

SKETCH OF THE COMARES PATIO. *Drawing by Prieto Moreno.*

VIEW OF THE GENERALIFE. *Photo S. Saavedra.*

This is the focus, where, in the oriental style, the principal compositional elements converge."

The garden and its vegetation are all arranged in relation to this figure: the monarch seated on his throne,"[12] thus creating the most pleasing harmony between the reflection of the white marble, the dark myrtle hedges and the bright green aromatic foliage of the orange trees."[13]

In the two fountains at either end of the pool the water spouts are low, probably to convey the impression of a natural spring bringing freshness and life."[14]

In Arab times this pool was apparently "surrounded by a Moorish balustrade, which was pulled down and sold during the reign of Charles IV by the Governor Luis Bacerelli, whose daughters gradually sold all they could wrench from the walls of the Alhambra."[15]

Here one can observe how the great oblique mass of Charles V's palace interrupts the view that the Arab alcazar must have had in the Muslim period.

VIEW OF THE COMARES PATIO towards the Machuca Palace. *Photo Más.*

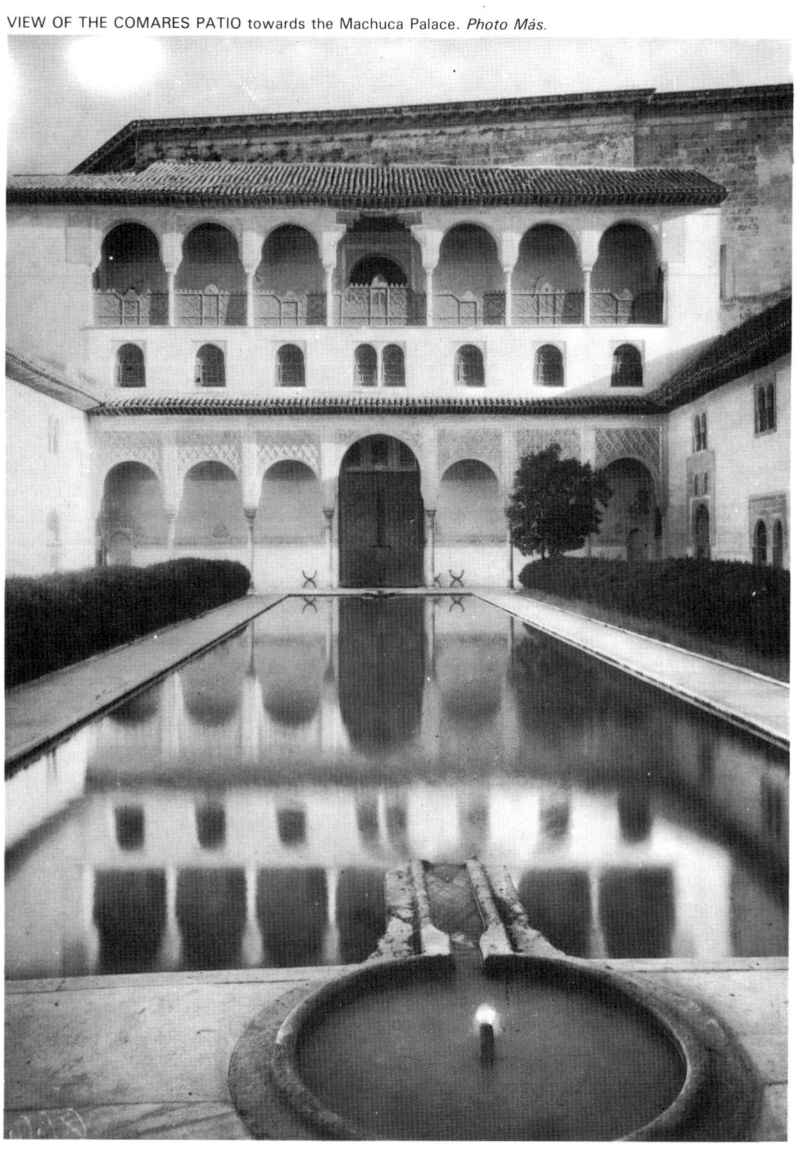

This palace, built by Machuca, is a Renaissance masterpiece. It is wedged between the Arab palaces and the southern slopes of the Alhambra hill. It obviously required a much larger site and gardens that would set off the splendid façade.

In the time of Yusuf I the Court of Comares must have had a portico or hall of the same name towards the south, since destroyed by this building.[16]

Moving from this patio through a narrow passage and a small side door (which were not there in the Arab period), and entering the Court of Lions, one perceives a complete change of atmosphere. This court appears more intimate, though more ornate and complex, because of its fountain. Today it contains only great sandy areas, but in Arab times it was a luxuriant garden. Antonio de Lalaing (a nobleman in the retinue of Philip the Fair) who visited the Alhambra on 20 September 1502, saw in this patio six orange trees affording pleasant shade to all below. "Beneath them it is always cool."[17] They must have been quite old to provide such shelter. Here again the garden played an integral part in daily royal life.

For a certain time, near the end of Muslim rule in Granada, this palace must have been completely separate from that of Comares. Hernando de Baeza, the secretary of Boabdil, the last Nazarite monarch, tells how Boabdil's father, Muley Hasán, when he took the "Romía" — Doña Isabel del Solís — as his mistress: "From then on made his life with her and never again spoke to or saw his wife, the queen; and she, with her children, kept her house and court and followers in the Court of the Lions, while the king kept to the Tower of Comares with his other queen."[18] His first queen was the faithful Fátima, Boabdil's mother. (Appendix I).

There is a family atmosphere to the Court of the Lions, the scene of intimate royal life. Its structure is so delicate that its survival through the Alhambra's ensuing years and vicissitudes is astonishing.

Professor G. Marcais says in his study on Granada: "Its proportions are so harmonious and the decoration so graceful that one seems to enter an atmosphere of nobility and poetry." The Court of the Lions was undoubtedly one of the Alhambra's gardens, filled with plants and centred on its fountain. The water that runs through narrow channels to the spouts inside adjoining rooms must once have watered these plants. In the sixteenth century the entire patio was paved with white marble. Antonio Gallego Burín: "In 1585 it was newly paved with blue and white tiles, planted as a garden once more from 1808 to 1846, when the garden was again removed on account of the dampness it caused."[19]

Nowadays, in spite of its bareness, one has the impression of standing beneath a tent supported by its slender columns.

On summer evenings this patio is bathed in a golden light in which the stone glows red as fire. On one occasion the notes of Andrés Segovia's guitar created an unforgettable atmosphere of solemnity and poetry.

Small fountains are placed on each side of the patio, fed by four narrow channels, like silver ribbons, traversing the adjacent rooms, forming a cross under the central fountain, and completing an image of delicious coolness. The basin of the Fountain of the Lions has a lovely Arabic inscription in praise of the garden that then existed here: "Water, overflowing, resembles diamonds, pearls and liquid silver." Both this inscription and the patio itself seem like a page out of *The Arabian Nights.*

The patios of the Reja and the Lindaraxa, two small Renaissance gardens, date from a remodelling period when apartments were built at the Alhambra for Charles V. The Arab basin, brought in 1626 from the Patio of the Mexuar to the Lindaraxa, was mounted on a sixteenth century column, and its rim still bears a beautiful Arab poem. This garden retains its solemn and austere atmosphere. In 1829, Washington Irving lived in the apartments Philip V and his wife Isabella Farnese had occupied, overlooking this patio.

DARAXA PATIO. *Photo Más.*

COURT OF LIONS. *Photo Palacios.*

DETAIL OF LION. *Photo S. Saavedra.*

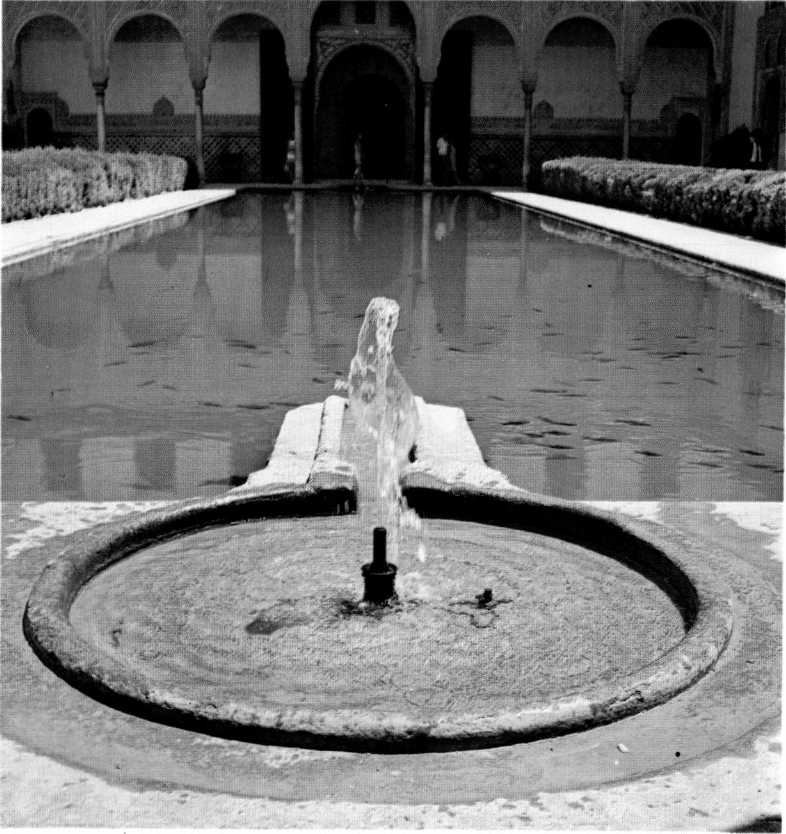

DETAIL OF COMARES FOUNTAIN. *Photo S. Saavedra.*

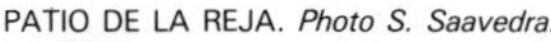

PATIO DE LA REJA. *Photo S. Saavedra.*

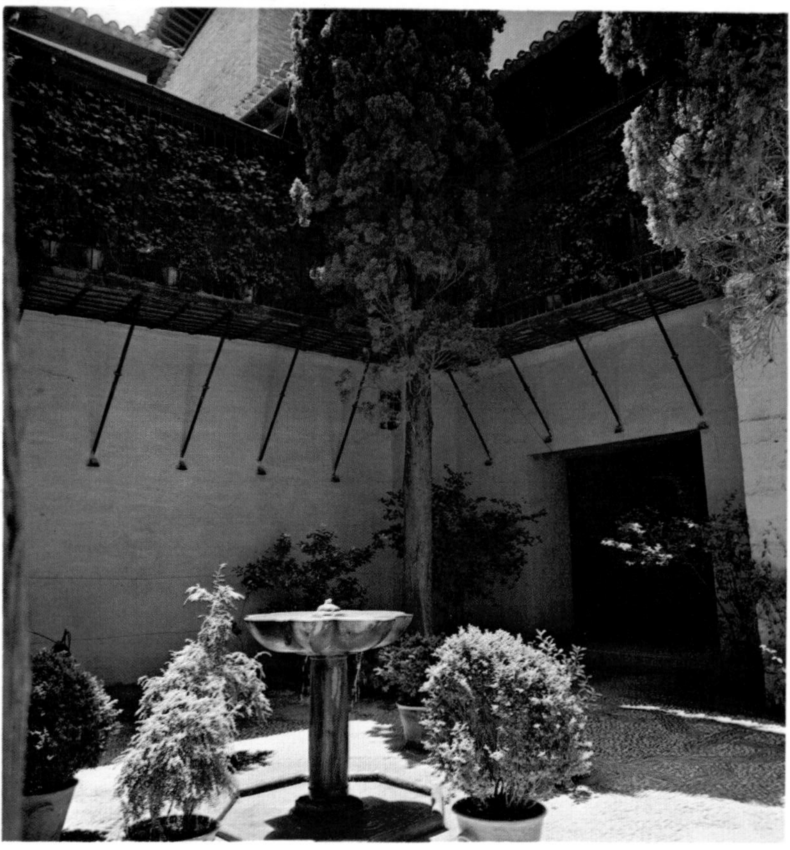

The Patio de la Reja, with its splendid views over the nearby slope of the Albaicín, is like the ante-room of the Garden of Daraxa and has the distinctive and sober style of the Toledo patios with their typically Castilian galleries of columns and lintels.

Modern gardens have been planted in the Partal (Arabic for portico) on the site of the old outbuildings of the palace; and patios and pools have been reconstructed and serve to frame the view of the Alhambra's defensive towers.

The Pool of the Partal is wider and shorter than that of Comares, and its still waters reflect two marble lions of the same style as those of the Patio of the Lions, but of better workmanship. They came from the Maristán, a lunatic asylum built by the Arabs between 1365 and 1367 and pulled down in the nineteenth century, when the lions were brought here.[20] This patio has a charming pavilion, which to judge by its decoration appears to have been built between the thirteenth and fourteenth centuries. It was designed as a place from which to view both the surrounding landscape and the palace grounds, accommodating the oriental preference for viewing scenery from a sheltered vantage point. The original square brick columns have since been replaced by slender white marble pillars that add a light and graceful air to this truly oriental pavilion.

The Generalife is undoubtedly the crowning wonder of Arab garden art and embodies all its precepts. The rulers of Granada built it as a country retreat where they could relax and meditate in close communion with nature. There were other palaces, of which traces remain, higher up the hill known as the Cerro del Sol, but when the water-wheels and other devices used to irrigate them stopped functioning, they were abandoned, and the hill has been barren and deserted since the fifteenth century.

Between the Alhambra and the Huerta Real lies a ravine, plunging steeply towards the river Darro. The monarchs must have crossed it from the Torre de los Picos. Across the ravine is a brick archway which was used until about a century ago as the entrance for climbing up to the Genralife, reached by a narrow passage.[21] From the entranceway, steps led up to the southern Pavilion of the Riad. Today the original entrance through a side door has been restored.

The Generalife is the first garden watered by the Royal Canal as it flows down the red hillside through the centre of the Patio of the Riad, and it is marvellous to consider that this rivulet alone was used to water the entire hill of the Alhambra, thanks to the art and skill of the Arabs.

The buildings consisted merely of two simple pavilions facing each other across the canal in the principal patio. The patio's charm lay in its typical Arab garden. Today the fruit trees, vegetables and aromatic herbs have disappeared, but it still retains its oriental atmosphere, distinguishing it from other fourteenth century European gardens.

The Koran describes the Islamic paradise as a "dark green luxuriant garden with a river running through it, planted with fruit trees, pomegranates and palms. The blessed can be found here, resting on cushions of green — the colour of the believers —

dressed in silk and brocade, inside their magnificently carpeted pavilions, among *houris* (nymphs) and heavenly youths."[22] This passage seems to describe the Generalife itself, which must have been built according to the symbolism of Islamic religious beliefs.

"Garden without equal," says the old ballad of Abenamar, and the Visar Ibn al-Jatib praises the site for the "luxuriance of its trees with their abundant shade, and its salutary atmosphere, constantly refreshed by brooks of clear running water. This place was divided from the royal residence by a high strong high wall, defended by a deep moat."[23]

Nearly all the authors agree that the word *Generalife* means *most noble garden.* The Arabs reached it by way of a now hidden passage.

Unlike the Alhambra, where vegetation is confined by its marble courts, the Generalife derives its charm from simplicity. Resembling a simple country house, it is composed of two small pavilions almost hidden by the greenery, which in Arab times consisted of a simple garden.

From the Generalife, towards the west, the imposing view of the Alhambra's towers can be seen silhouetted against the fertile valley of Granada fading into the distance; to the northwest stand the lofty snow-capped peaks of the Sierra Nevada, the highest in Spain, bright against the blue sky; they impart a feeling of both shelter and space.

The Institute of Arab Studies at Granada still preserves a treatise on agriculture and gardening by a thirteenth century poet from Almería, Ibn Luyun, containing a prescription for the ideal Andalusian country house. The description is close to that of the Generalife, which is understandable, because as mentioned earlier, the Koran depicts paradise as *a garden of delights traversed by a river.*

"Choose the dominant position," he says, "to build a house and garden, to better keep watch and defend it.

"It should face the midday sun, the door placed laterally, and the well or pool should be slightly raised, or better still, instead of the well there should be a canal running under the shade of trees and plants.

"Near at hand, beds will be planted with evergreens of all varieties that will brighten the view, and further on, flowers of many kinds and evergreen trees.

"The property will be surrounded with vines and in the central part it will be shaded by trellises covering the walks and flanking the paths that run along the borders on one side. In the centre an open pavilion will be installed for the hours of rest, framed by climbing rose trees, myrtle and all manner of beautiful garden flowers.

"It will be longer than it is broad so that the eye will not tire in its contemplation.

"A Pavilion will be set aside in the lower part for guests who come to bear company to its master. It will have its own door and pool which, hidden by a clump of trees, will not be seen from afar.

VIEW OF ALHAMBRA. *Photo Prieto Moreno.*

POND IN THE PARTAL GARDENS. *Photo S. Saavedra.*

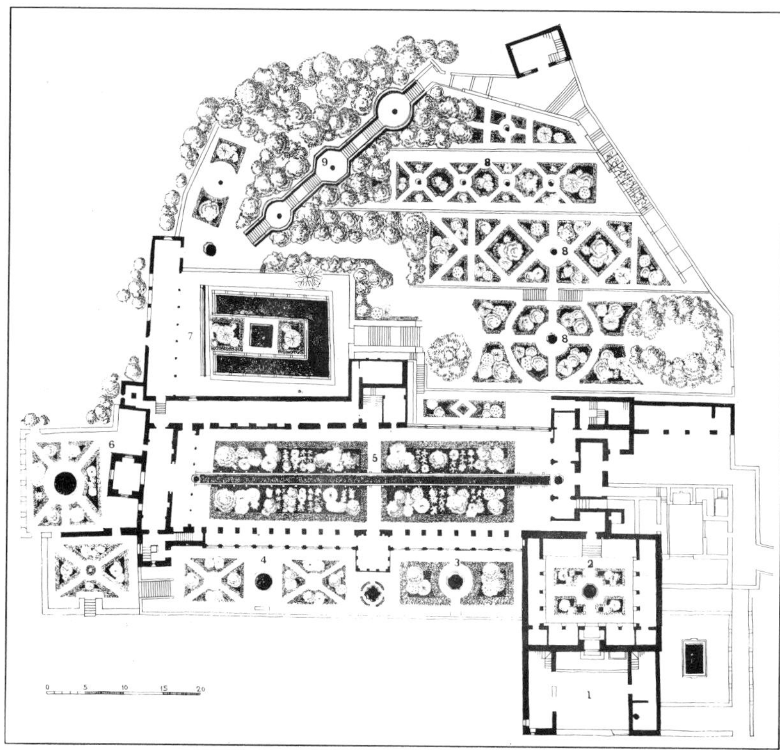
PLAN OF THE GENERALIFE. *Photo Prieto Moreno.*

ARCHES, NORTHERN PAVILION. *Photo Más.*

It will be fitting also to built a dove-cot and a habitable tower."[24]

This Arab manuscript has now been completely translated by Doña Joaquina Eguaras, formerly Director of the Archaeological Museum of Granada.

In spite of additions made in later periods, especially by its Italian owners in the seventeenth century, the Court of the Acequia or Riad has retained its thoroughly Arabic atmosphere. "Within its gardens the ideal of serenity and seclusion is achieved, and yet one can enjoy a panoramic view of Granada"[25] and the gypsy quarter of the Albaicín from the shelter of its north gallery running the length of the garden. A relatively recent addition is the double row of arches, which allow light to penetrate into the Riad, filtering through the windows without destroying the atmosphere of seclusion and mystery. In the Arab period the gallery was composed of slightly higher arches, but around 1671 a new row of arches was added, giving the building a heavier appearance.

In the centre of this gallery stands a small square pavilion, richly decorated with Arab stuccos. It protrudes from the gallery to command a better view, and in a small garden below there is a pretty fountain.

"From this northern pavilion of the Patio of the Riad one can enjoy Arab gardening at the height of its development. The two fountains on either side of the canal symbolize the lotus flower floating on the water. The same design or type of fountain can be found in the Taj Mahal in India, in the Shalimar gardens of Kashmir, and in Lahore, all originating from the gardens of Persia."[26]

The waters of the Darro coming down from the mountains are diverted into the Royal Canal and rush through this garden. In Arab times, as now, this canal was used for irrigation, and the patio was filled with small creeping plants, probably of wild origin, arranged so as not to hide the porches and columns of the handsome façade.

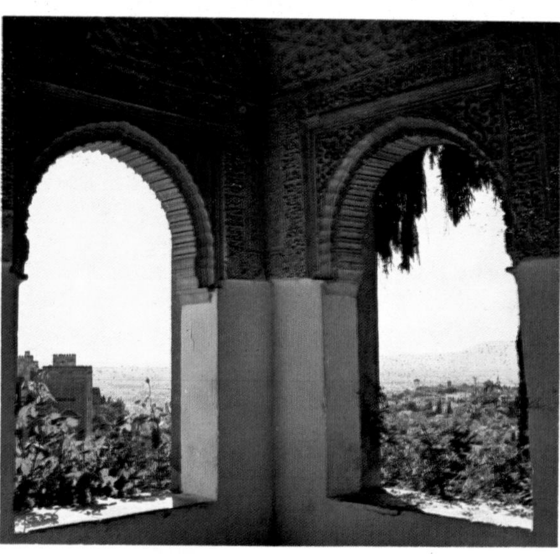
INTERIOR OF THE PAVILION. *Photo S. Saavedra.*

At the end of the Riad are the five richly decorated arches of its northern pavilion. The Arab text inscribed on them tells us that they were restored by the care and diligence of King Ismail, presumably the first of this name (1314 to 1325), in the year of "victory, religion and triumph." Probably this refers to the victory won by the Nazarites in 1319 in the valley of Granada, which cost the lives of the Castilian infantes Don Juan and Don Pedro. "The Generalife was probably built in the thirteenth or early fourteenth century."[27] During the reign of the Catholic Monarchs two more storeys were added to the northern pavilion, destroying the delicacy of the building, which originally blended intimately with the landscape.

"This Patio of the Riad is perhaps the best example of an accumulation of expressive elements along an axis: the portico, the fountain, the canal, the jets of water, the flowers and the distant landscape seen from the balcony all combine to produce an exquisite harmony, revealing the ecstasy of the Islamic soul."[28]

The water jets that criss-cross all along the canal and the row of cypresses planted on its banks, were added at a later date, somewhat spoiling its simple, rustic appearance.

Some years ago, while repairing the damage caused in 1958 by a fire in the section between the Patio of the Riad and the higher Patio of the Cypress of the Sultana, the archaeologist Jesús Bermúdez Pareja discovered "evidence of a garden similar to that described by Ibn Luyun, which can be identified as being of the Persian type predominating in both east and west during the later Middle Ages until it was superseded by Italian Renaissance gardens."[29]

This was the Generalife's original garden, found beneath the earth and rubble. The old pavement was in the form of a cross, and in its centre a summer-house must have stood on a bridge over the canal. In the words of Ibn Luyun: "Let a gazebo be built from which views in all directions may be enjoyed."

"Beneath the rubble of nearly five centuries — seventy centimetres thick — the ancient flower borders were found, and in the paths alongside the canal, there are holes through which the garden was watered."[30] The existence of a garden at this level was confirmed by the presence of dark, organic loam. The soil of the original garden was about forty-five centimetres. Underneath, the ground is hard, compact and stony, unsuitable for cultivation. This was probably the natural earth of the mountain side. The original garden was found to contain small cavities for the planting of trees, possibly cypresses and orange trees, all on a dwarfed scale in accordance with the oriental custom. The growth of other plants was restricted by the shallowness of good soil. They were probably similar to those cultivated in pots, and the whole effect must have resembled a lawn planted with small, well-tended trees such as can be seen not only in Persian tapestries of gardens, but also in oriental miniatures, in the background of early Flemish pictures and tapestries and in European paintings of the fifteenth and sixteenth centuries."[31]

The plants of the original garden of the Patio of the Acequia

RIAD GARDEN. *Photo Oronoz.*

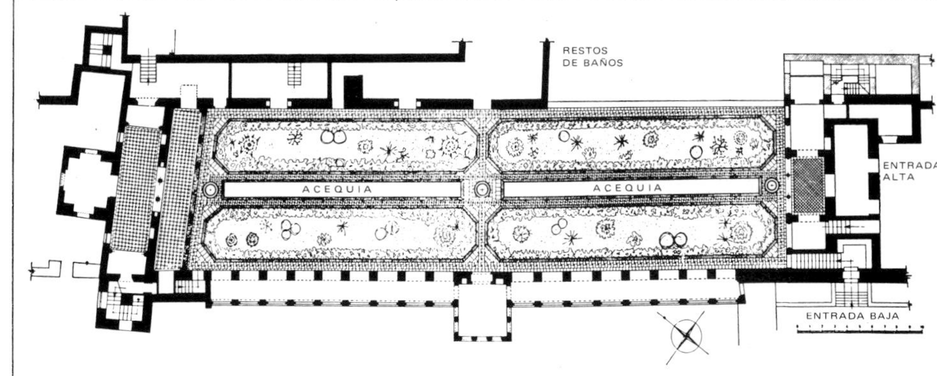

PLAN OF THE RIAD GARDEN. "Cuadernos de la Alhambra"

probably did not hide the view of the porch and pavilions as they do today.

Except for its plants, this patio has now been restored to its original level and design, with its central fountain. The four flower borders that fringe the canal have rounded corners of the original brick.

According to James Dickie: "In the Arab treatise of Al-Himyari the names of twenty common flowers can be counted: myrtle (from the Arab *rayhan*); white jasmin, which in Arab times covered plain walls; wild yellow jasmin, narcissus variegated white, yellow and green (the poet's narcissus, rival to the rose in poetry); violets (Almanzor's favourite flower, growing in profusion in the gardens of the *Amiriyya* in Córdoba); red and yellow gillyflowers, scented jonquils, trumpet-shaped narcissus, red roses, *lillium candidum,* blue iris; water lilies, almond blossoms, daisies (which also means camomile); poppies (sometimes red); bean flowers; ivy flowers; and the flowers of cultivated and wild pomegranate."[32]

Among Al-Himyari's omissions, Peres mentions six plants that appear in other Arab texts. These are: sweet basil, *alhucema* (lavender), orange blossom, carnation, sweet marjoram and oleander. "But," continues Dickie, "to this account could be added at least twenty-four other plants and trees, namely: thyme, mint, saffron (all these were used in Arab cookery), lupin, lemon trees, laurel, vine, palm, cherry trees, pear trees, plum trees, blackberries, carob trees, banana trees, cypress, willows, medlar trees, quince, apple, colocynth, fig trees, mandrake (the satanic plant *par excellence* as its etymology shows: *apple of the genie),* acanthus and, probably, *alcolaz* — colocasia or Egyptian bean (*arum colocasia*).

"This account is not limited to garden flowers as such, but includes wild flowers and even certain vegetables, because the Arab garden was orchard, fruit garden and kitchen garden all in one."[33]

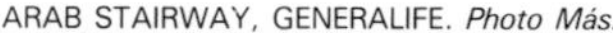

ARAB STAIRWAY, GENERALIFE. *Photo Más.*

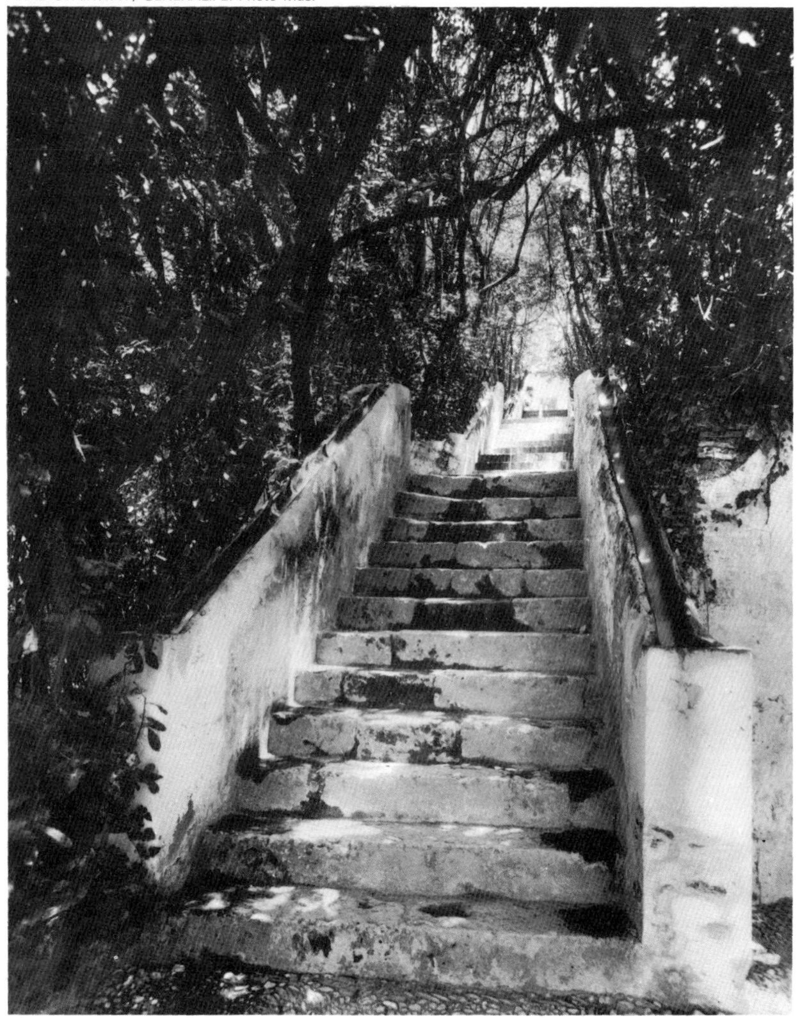

The porticos of the Generalife had alcoves at the side where the inhabitants probably slept on cushions or couches.

Their life was very simple and took place in the galleries of their pavilions, forerunners to the modern living room. They had neither kitchens nor outbuildings, and their food was probably cooked over wood fires in any of the rooms, or perhaps out of doors, presaging the modern barbecue.

Through a small door at the back of the northern portico, a few steps lead up to the Patio of the Sultana's Cypress. Many legends surround the old cypress which is said to date from the late fifteenth century.

There is a profound stillness about this garden, with its U-shaped pool and the central fountain, added in a later period. Its water jets produce a beautiful symphony in green and silver. Nothing is known about the date of its construction, although according to the descriptions of Andrea Navagero, a Venetian ambassador who travelled through Spain around 1526, there already existed in Arab times "a green patio like a field planted with a few very handsome trees; the water flows in such a way that, when certain canals are closed, one can see the water rise under one's feet, moistening everything about one, and then gently disappear again without seeing another soul." He also describes the numerous patios and fountains of the Generalife and its canal of running water, planted with myrtle and orange trees. He mentions, too, the running water that flows through the inside of the palace and its apartments, adding that, "in many of them it is pleasant to pass a summer siesta."[34]

This patio is enclosed by plain walls. A broad staircase, built in the last century and quite out of keeping with the atmosphere, leads to the upper gardens.

The upper gardens have terraces that are much more modern, in the Italian style. They were probably designed by their owners, the Grimaldi Palavicinis, a Genoese family who inherited the Generalife through the Marqués of Campotejar. This family descended from the Moor Ibn-Hud, a converted Muslim who, taking part in the resistance and acting as go-between during the siege of Granada, assumed the name of Granada-Benegas. For his faithful services he was rewarded by the Catholic monarchs with the gift of this property.

Previously Don Pedro Bammigas, or Benegas, son of the Mayor of Luque, who had married a Granada princess, became a renegade and lived in this city as a Muslim. He suggested to Don Alvaro de Luna that he should set his own brother-in-law Yusuf in opposition to the ungrateful Mohamed IX *el Izquierdo*. Don Alvaro accepted the challenge and this led to the battle of La Higueruela (10 July 1431).[35] (See Appendix II).

The last owner of the Generalife was Dona Matilde Giustiniani y Giustiniani upon whom King Alfonso XIII bestowed the title of Marquesa del Generalife after she had been engaged for many years in a law suit with the Spanish State regarding the possession of this property. She probably inherited it from her husband Giacomo Durazzo Palavicino. She died in Genoa in the spring of 1970.

In 1921 King Alfonso XIII restored the Generalife to Spain as a national heritage.

At the extreme eastern end of these three terraced gardens there are three flights of steps with circular landings, and on each of these, at floor level, a tiny fountain. Their parapets consist of whitewashed walls hollowed out on top, and decorated with glazed Arab tiles. The stairway is covered by a thick canopy of laurels and hazel trees, and water rushes down the tiles on top of the walls.

The pavement of the three landings, with its black and white cobblestones, is typical of Granada. The steps are of stone, and in Arab times water flowed down them. This is the most authentic part of the Generalife, having undergone little or no change since the time of the Arabs, before the fall of Granada.

Andrea Navagero observed that "in a garden located at the highest part of these grounds, there is a broad stairway leading to a plateau. All the water that runs through the palace flows from a crag there, controlled by means of locks, which allow the water to be released at will in the desired quantities. The stairway is artfully designed, with steps hollowed to retain water; the tops of the parapets are shaped to form a channel that runs from top to bottom, and as the locks that control each part work independently of each other, water can be made to flow down either the parapets or the steps, or both at the same time if so desired so that the whole stairway is flooded, soaking anyone who might be ascending it and thus providing a source of fun and practical jokes."[36]

Don Francisco Prieto Moreno, former curator of the Alhambra, has created some fine gardens on the site of those once kept before the entrance to the Generalife. An open air theatre has also been added where musical performances are sometimes held. This park is strictly in keeping with the history of Arab gardens, and is arranged in the form of a Moslem dwelling. Its walls consist of cypress hedges, and it is traversed by a canal.

* * *

Words are inadequate to describe the enchantment of Granada with its cool shady gardens, the water that spouts from fountain

SULTANA CYPRESS PATIO. *Photo Oronoz.*

COMMON OF THE CYPRESSES. *Photo S. Saavedra.*

ENGRAVING OF THE ALHAMBRA. *"Delices de l'Espagne".*

to fountain, and the fragrance of its flowers. The experience, for those who visit, is unforgettable.

The Arabs seem to have lavished on Granada all their gardening knowledge and art, and their influence has lingered on in Spain through the centuries.

In his treatise on agriculture, published by the Cardinal Cisneros in Alcalá de Henares in 1513, Alonso de Herrera refers to "the myrtle that is ever green and joyful, and thus perfect for monastery cloisters and pleasure gardens; it can be clipped in cupped shapes, flat as a table, and the branches can be arched or bent when young to form chairs and other fanciful shapes such as those found in the Royal Palace at Granada and in the mansion of the Generalife, a practice the Greeks and Romans called topiary."[37] Herrera must surely be referring to the *topiarius,* the name given to the gardener of ancient Rome. This term was adopted in England in the eighteenth century to describe the art of clipping shrubs, which came to England through the Dutch influence introduced by the Stuarts. Herrera's reference is very interesting as it shows that the Arab influence on gardening still continued in Spain and that this method of clipping bushes was already in use. It is not known whether their techniques then spread to Italy[38] or whether the Italians had themselves preserved them as remnants of the Graeco-Roman tradition, since they were mentioned by Latin authors.

The way up to the Alhambra, with its fountain dating from the reign of Charles V, passes through magnificent elm trees, said to have been planted by Sebastiani, one of Napoleon's generals. They convert this place into a shady, enchanting garden where the murmur of water and the song of the nightingale never cease. Until the seventeenth century this hill was almost bare.

THE CARMENES OF GRANADA

The *carmenes* of Granada are small country houses on the outskirts of Granada. Like the *cigarreles* of Toledo, they always face the city with a view of the valley and the Alhambra. Their Arab name, *yanna,* means orchard or rustic property.[39]

There is evidence in old Arab documents that around 1448 the slope of the Albaicín was covered with these farms.

Those still standing today date from the seventeenth and eighteenth centuries. The most typical are those on the slope of the Albaicín, looking out on to the magnificent panorama. Because of the slope, the houses and gardens had to be carefully planned. They generally have rooms in the basement to provide cool retreat from the summer heat, as is still the practice in the old houses of Seville. In the gardens of the *carmenes* flowers and aromatic plants such as rosemary, lavender (which in Andalusia takes the Arab name of *alhucema*) and cotton-lavender usually mingle with vegetables in picturesque confusion, due perhaps to the Arab tradition of combining both kitchen and flower gardens. *Carmenes* also usually possess small auxiliary structures such as summer-houses, covered galleries, and small turrets, enabling the inhabitants to contemplate the view sheltered from curious gazers, according to the oriental custom.

To reach the *carmenes* one must climb the steep, paved alleys of the Albaicín (the slope facing the Alhambra) between high walls and convents, with belfries that once were the minarets of the old mosques.

The traffic and bustle of Granada's centre are left behind, for cars cannot go here. Only an occasional drove of mules can be seen trudging slowly, laden with sand and building materials.

The Carmen of the Cypresses is entered through a narrow archway which leads directly into the house. In the centre is a small patio leading to the garden. This property belongs to the heirs of Nicolás María López, a well-known writer who at the beginning of the century used to gather his circle of friends, among them Angel Ganivet and other Granada intellectuals, in a charming pergola at the foot of the cypress arbour. The drawing room in the basement, adjoining the patio, preserves its romantic atmosphere, with furniture of the nineteenth century period. This was the setting for many a peaceful summer evening.

The garden is divided into steep terraces with narrow paths edged by boxwood or myrtle. It has a large rectangular pond and various fountains of different sizes, including the classic *pilar* or Granada fountain attached to the wall. A walk covered by a vine trellis gives shelter from the sun.

According to Prieto Moreno, this is the most important carmen on the Albaicín. The dark silhouette of the cypresses stands out against the Granada sky, and in autumn the diospiros shed their leaves, leaving their orange-coloured fruit bare in striking contrast against their dark trunks. The light is admirable, and, the terraced garden is first and foremost a place for viewing the Alhambra.

The Carmen of the Purification, perched on the southeastern slope of the Albaicín, is reached via vine-covered walks that surround the wall and the entrance to the house. The garden is extremely varied with beautiful fountains, and on one of the walls stands a classic old *pilar* with typical black and white stonework in front. In the corner to the left of the estate there are three low fountains in the Arab style forming the background of the garden. Here again, vegetables and fruit trees mingle, affording a view of the Alhambra from the successive terraces. It belongs to the well-known photographer Manuel Torres Molina.

The Carmen of Our Lady of Sorrows, also situated on the southern slopes of the Albaicín, is built against the highest portion of the slope. Its garden is squarer than those previously described. To the left of the entrance at the foot of the wall, is a rectangular reservoir. It belongs today to Don Santiago Navarro.

On the two lower terraces there are a number of circular fountains of various sizes, irregularly placed. From this spot the Alhambra can be seen with the Tower of la Vela (The Watch Tower) on the horizon. The light which changes constantly throughout the day, attains its greatest splendour in the evening with the last rays of the setting sun.

Descending again through the narrow streets we arrive at the Plaza Nueva in the centre of the city. The change of atmosphere, only minutes away, is startling: from the Albaicín reminiscent of the Arab market place and dark gypsy children playing in the streets, to the nearby town, so European and cosmopolitan.

Taking the Darro road towards the hill of the Chapiz, we come to an Arab house, which Emilio García Gómez describes as follows:

CARMEN OF THE PURIFICATION. *Photo Author.*

CHARLES V PILAR. *Photo Más.*

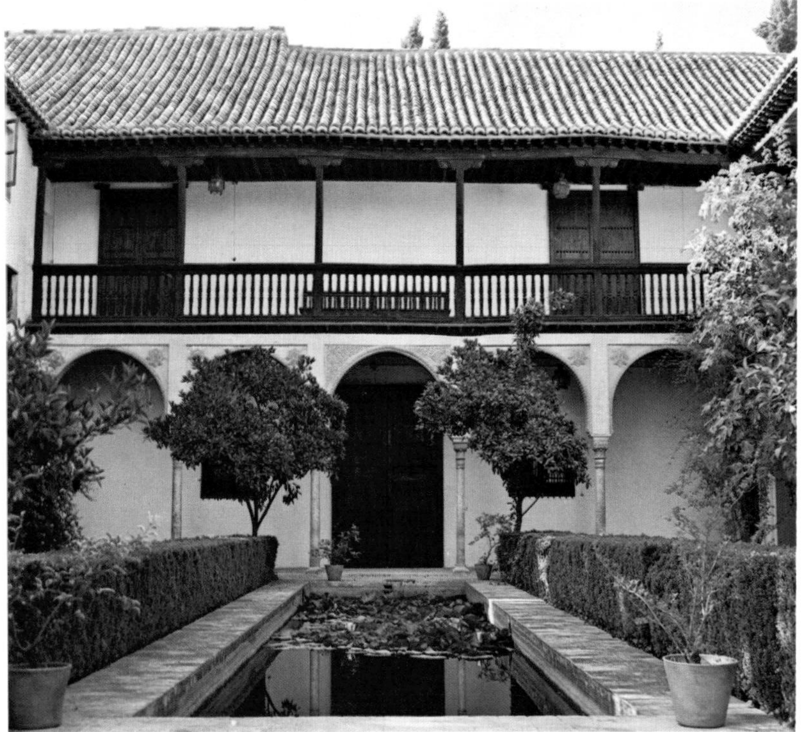

CASA DEL CHAPIZ. *Photo S. Saavedra.*

STATUE OF FERNANDO VI AND GARDEN OF THE MARTYRS. *Photo Oronoz.*

"A high latticed wall divides it from the gypsy caves on the slopes of the Sacromonte (the hillside opposite the Generalife). The house has an elegant façade, and there are Arab arches with stars between the *albanegas,* or stuccoed patterns, fine marble columns and a high gallery with a wooden railing. It was once the palace of a Morisco called the *Chapiz* and today houses the School of Arab Studies of Granada.[40]

The pool that lies at its foot belongs to the Morisco period, forming an axis around which lies a pretty garden of trim hedges stretching away to the left side of the house. In the top gallery we can observe the wooden posts with their carved supports, typical of the Granada style of the sixteenth century.

Following the hill of the Chapiz and turning to the right through an intricate maze of narrow streets, we arrive at the Carmen of St. Augustine, situated in the Plaza del Abad, just below the Church of El Salvador. It belongs to Don José Rodriguez Acosta and was recently reconstructed in the modern style by the Granada architect García de Paredes. Because of its elongated shape, it none the less harmonises with the older houses on the hill. Its site is a fortunate one: on the heights of the Albaicín bordering on the Sacromonte. Built on two levels, the carmen is of beautiful proportions and is the most outstanding of the modern *carmenes* of Granada.

The entrance, as usual, is at the back at the highest point. Here a rustic garden is planted, composed of rosemary, lavender-cotton and other wild shrubs, with fine trees of all species. There is a remarkable variety of plants, and a large pool occupies the lower level of the garden constructed by the Catalan gardener Beltrán in 1964. All the details are of fine quality, as is the old *pilar* set against the patio wall. The house is cheerful and full of light.*

Passing to the opposite side of the Alhambra, on a small hill near the Alhambra Palace Hotel, there is a great white stone cross, erected in 1901 to commemorate the martyrs captured there and put to death in the fourteenth century. Its wide terrace, commonly called the "Balcony of Paradise", leads to the grand entrance of the Garden of the Martyrs, which today has been turned into a public park by the Granada Municipality. According to Gallego Burín, these lands were acquired in 1845 by a private owner, and later by General Don Carlos Calderón, who constructed a pleasure house, with an orchard and gardens. Later they became the property of the Belgian, Hubert Meersmans, who later sold them to the Duke del Infantado.

The most striking feature of these gardens is the abundance of water which flows through the highest portion in a wide stream and forms a lake in a leafy wood. Crossing this wood towards the north, in the direction of the Alhambra, we come to a wrought-iron gate; on its left stands a red house. A marble slab on the wall explains that the Count of Tendilla built a convent here for the Carmelites, of which St. John of the Cross was Prior from 1582 to 1588. In the garden there is a large cedar tree which tradition says he planted himself. He alludes to this tree, and the battlements of the Alhambra as seen in the distance in his poem, "La Noche Oscura."[41]

CARMEN SAN AUGUSTIN. *Photo S. Saavedra.*

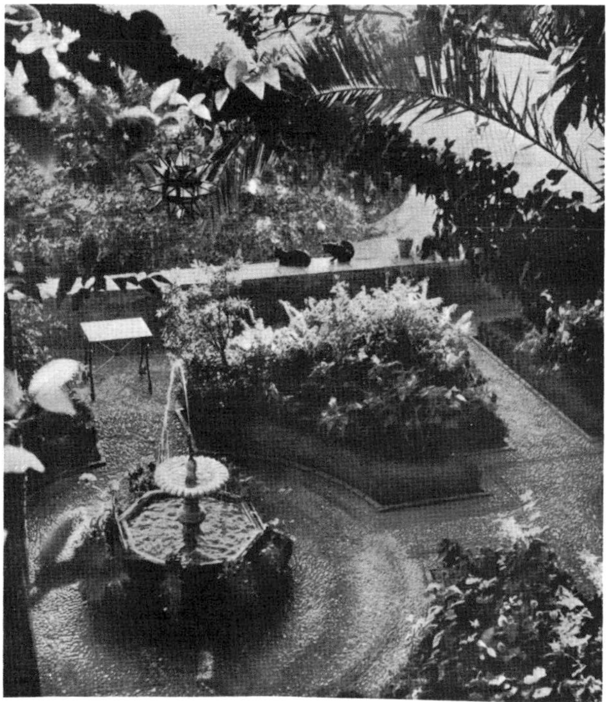

CARMEN "MANUEL DE FALLA". *Photo Prieto Moreno-Charbonnier.*

This garden is larger and more monumental than any in Granada and, like them all, is built in terraces. On the highest level there is a fine circular pool set among trees, and on a lower level but parallel to this garden, there is another pool surrounded by hedges of clipped boxwood. Against the wall a fountain falls in cascades.

On the terrace that forms the entrance to the house stand two terracotta statues, pained in white, representing King Ferdinand VI and his stepbrother Charles III. In life they did not particularly care for one another, but here they are destined to preside together over the garden.

Retracing our steps towards the Alhambra Palace Hotel and descending a steep street on the left, we arrive at the suburb of Antequeruela Alta, so named because of the Arab refugees who fled here after the conquest of Antequera in 1410. This leads us to the Carmen of Manuel de Falla, with its terraced garden and eighteenth century fountain in the centre. (This fountain has now been removed). The view of the valley and town is superb. Here the celebrated master lived and composed his music. The Duchess of Lécera later occupied it for many years and she made this carmen a hospitable centre where prominent visitors to Granada met in the mornings for pleasant social gatherings.

Retracing our steps and crossing the broad square that serves as entrance to the Alhambra Palace, we continue by the alley on the opposite side called *Callejon de la Sierra.* This leads to a carmen built in 1920 by the painter Rodríguez Acosta and housing many of his pictures. He left this building as a foundation to encourage the arts and sciences, with residential quarters for artists.

During his extensive travels he collected classical sculptures, which he placed in the terraced garden carved out

GARDEN OF THE MARTYRS. *Photo Oronoz.*

GARDEN OF PRIETO MORENO. *Photo S. Saavedra.*

of the steep hillside. This is the only feature of this garden that is consistent with Granada style. Its overall effect is somewhat cold, but undoubtedly in good taste. No gay flower pots are to be seen, nor the warm polychrome glazed tiles. Stone, marble, cypresses, boxwood and myrtle hedges are all it contains. Despite its undoubted merit, this garden is somewhat out of its element — it could just as easily be situated in Rome, Florence or Hadrian's Villa. It seems a pity that with such a wealth of traditional Granada elements at hand, the owner should have turned for inspiration to Italy, where gardens of this kind are very common.

Nevertheless, the solid proportions of these green enclosures forming a background for the exedras and porticos, as they did in ancient Rome, are much to be admired.

"Water," Mrs. Byne tells us, "does not run and ripple as in other Granada gardens, but lies in quiet pools, and the only colour they reflect, aside from white and green, is the deep blue of the southern sky."[42]

Within the walls of the Alhambra, adjoining the Parador of

PLAN OF VIZNAR PALACE GARDEN. *Photo Prieto Moreno.*

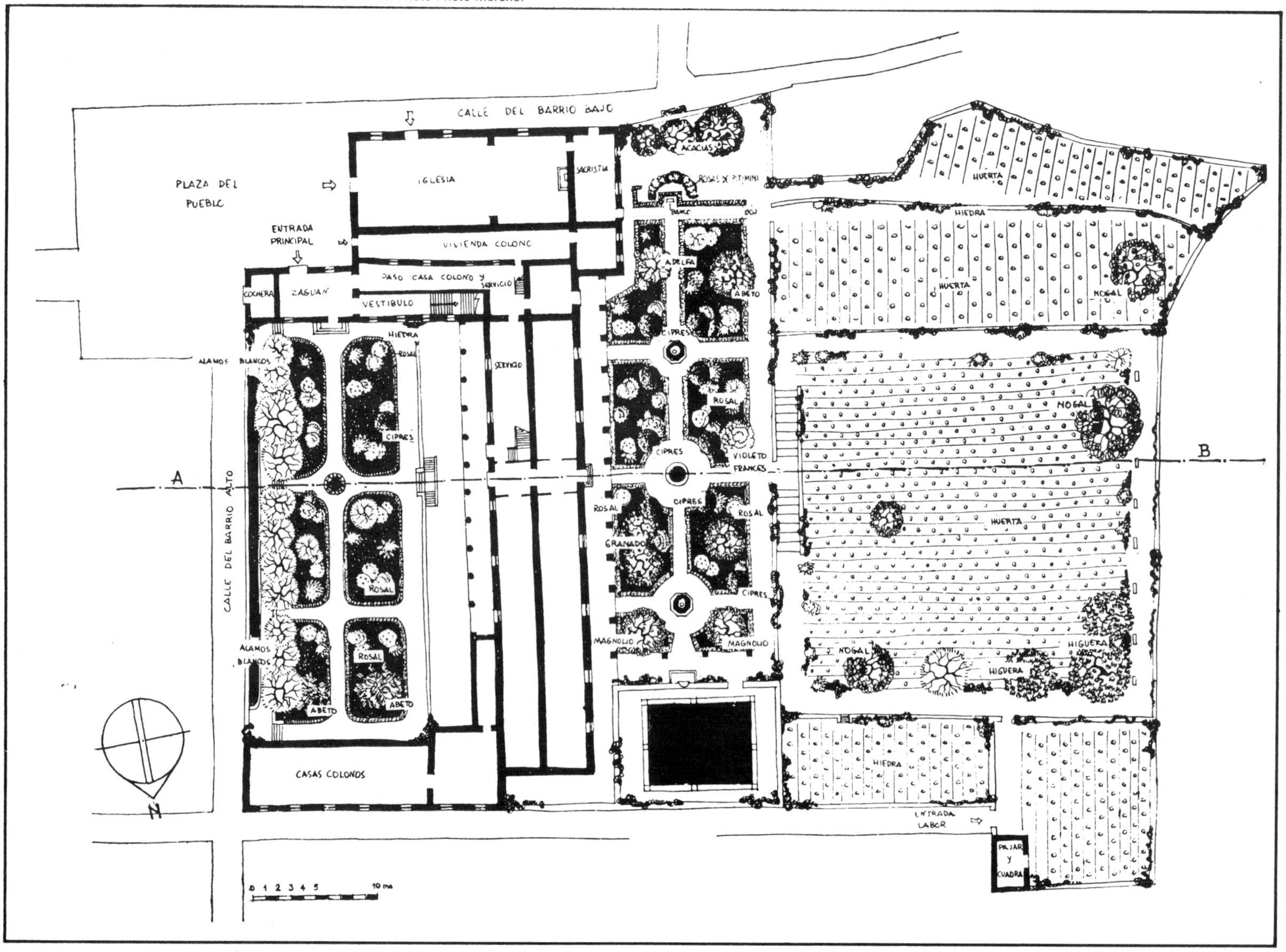

St. Francis, the curator of the fortress, Don Francisco Prieto Moreno has built his home facing north, like the Torre de las Damas, towards the Albaicín.

This garden looks like a theatre box from which to observe the lively and dynamic world of the Albaicín suburb, its distant murmur crossing the valley of the Darro to reach this peaceful garden. Seclusion blends here with joy and good spirits. A pretty fountain adorns the centre and, as at the Carmen of St. Augustine, modern architecture has been successfully adapted to the landscape.

La Zubia

Five kilometres from Granada, along a narrow road that ends in the village of Trevenque down in the valley, we travel across flat and fertile land towards a historic site: La Zubia, the summer palace of the Archbishop of Granada in the eighteenth century and now a children's home. In 1492 the Catholic Queen Isabel hid in a laurel grove here to avoid being taken prisoner by the Arabs during the siege of Granada. All that remains to recall this episode is an ivy tunnel with a column in its centre supporting a bust of Queen Isabel. There are also two kneeling statues and a balcony overlooking the valley.

The adjoining chapel has a brick façade with the coats of arms of the Catholic Monarchs; but the interior decoration dates from the eighteenth century.

Palace of Cuzco. Víznar

The Palace of Cuzco is situated in the mountain village of Víznar about eleven kilometres from Granada. It was here that the poet Federico García Lorca met his tragic death during the Civil War of 1936-1939.

This unexpected eighteenth century palace bears little resemblance to the Granada carmens, but some of their features can none the less be found — not in the structure of the palace, but in the spirit of the Arab garden: the water reserve that runs through the highest part of the garden to feed its fountains, the building interposed between the horizon and the lower terrace where, through its broad central hall, the axis crosses between the upper and lower gardens, and finally, the spacious terrace situated, as in the carmens of Granada, to command a pleasant view of the valley. This terrace runs the length of the big house and is adorned with classic designs in clipped boxwood hedges. Where they cross there are "three fountains with the same character and arrangement as in the three higher terraced gardens of the Generalife."[43]

This palace and garden, with such Italian classicism, are completely out of place in the Granada landscape. Here Arab concepts, eighteenth century Italian influence and perhaps the traditional axis of French gardens all merge. None the less, its luminosity, its seclusion and perspective make this property one of the most beautiful in the environs of Granada.

The entrance to the palace is from the village square through a door in the centre of the façade, which gives access to a wide hall. Here are situated both a monumental stairway

POND OF THE RODRIGUEZ ACOSTA FOUNDATION.

GARDEN OF THE RODRIGUEZ ACOSTA FOUNDATION.

CUZCO PALACE. ACCESS THROUGH THE HOUSE. *Photo Author.*

FOUNTAIN IN THE UPPER GARDÈN. *Photo S. Saavedra.*

leading to the palace, and a small side door which opens on to the upper garden, in the true Arab tradition. At the far side of this hall three steps lead down to the garden with its six rectangular plots edged with boxwood. In the centre there is a beautiful stone fountain with circular ledges protruding from the basin's edge, probably for supporting flower pots or sculptures. This fountain is aligned with the principal fountain in the lower garden along an axis running through the house.

The northern façade of the palace has a double porticoed gallery. The interior walls of the upper gallery are decorated with frescoes in the form of medallions representing scenes from *Don Quixote.* In its architecture and elaborate decoration it resembles Italian palaces of the same period.

In the garden below the southern façade there are two beautiful specimens of *magnolia grandiflora,* probably as old as the palace itself, and many fruit trees. The special charm of this site is its combination of lush verdure, reminiscent of northern gardens, with the clear light of the Andalusian skies and the magnificent view of the Sierra Elvira. In the silence of this garden the only sound is the murmur of its fountains.

In the palace entrance, on the wall opposite the door, is a marble slab that reads: "His Illustrious Excellency Don Juan Manuel de Moscoso y Peralta, of H.M. Council, Bishop of the Holy Churches of Arequipa (his birthplace), Córdoba in Tucuman, Cuzco in the Kingdom of Peru, and at present Archbishop of Granada, an office entrusted to him for having reconquered those provinces in the general uprising of 1700, for which particular services his Majesty the King bestowed upon him the Great Cross of the Royal and Distinguished Spanish Order of Charles III. He also defrayed the cost of the Palace of Víznar, completed in 1795."

Madoz tells us that "this archbishop was descended from an illlustrious and very powerful South American family and was Bishop of Tucuman and Cuzco. The Spanish government, suspecting him of promoting insurrection in Peru, in which the Inca chief Tupac Amaro figured, brought the bishop to Spain and, in order to keep him away from South America, gave him the See of Granada. Others contend that these suspicions were unfounded and that he contributed with his considerable income and prestige to the defeat of the rebels."[44] Be this as it may, Moscoso y Peralta was a refined man of exquisite taste. According to Madoz he spent most of the year in his delightful retreat of Víznar, where his retinue and servants rivalled those of a king. He died in 1811.

"His ashes," continues Madoz, "were placed in a cinerary urn in St. Michael's Chapel in the Cathedral of Granada, at his own expense. The bas-relief of St. Michael in this chapel was executed by Juan Adán, a sculptor who contributed several statues to Aranjuez. This chapel, dating from 1804-1811, was the last to be built on this side of the cathedral."

Loja. Gardens of Narváez

At a distance of 57 kilometres from Granada, across the valley towards Málaga, the town of Loja stands on a plateau. Its square is dominated by the statue of General Narváez, Duke of Valencia and leader of the moderate party of Queen Isabella II. Called the *Espadón de Loja* (Broadsword of Loja), he was one of the most staunch defenders of the Crown and his loyalty never wavered. At his death in 1868 the monarchy collapsed. He had been married to Alexandrina María Tascher de la Pagerie, a relative of Josephine de Beauharnais.

Beyond the village of Loja runs the road to Iznájar, and near this river lie the house and property that once belonged to General Narváez. The garden, dating from the reign of Isabel, is difficult to classify. Its style is romantic, that is to say without axis or terraces; it is composed of asymmetrical patterns, yet executed with classical features, such as the use of clipped boxwood hedges. We learned from the present owner, Doña Julia Díaz Berbel, widow of Díaz Jiménez, that it was planned by gardeners from La Granja. This might well be true due to the importance and prestige of the illustrious general, in which case the use of clipped hedges is understandable. Perhaps one of the last of the Bouteloues, a family of royal gardeners, may have designed it.

Romantic gardens were laid out in this period with winding paths between lawns and flower beds, and that is why this garden

MURALS IN CUZCO PALACE. *Photo S. Saavedra.*

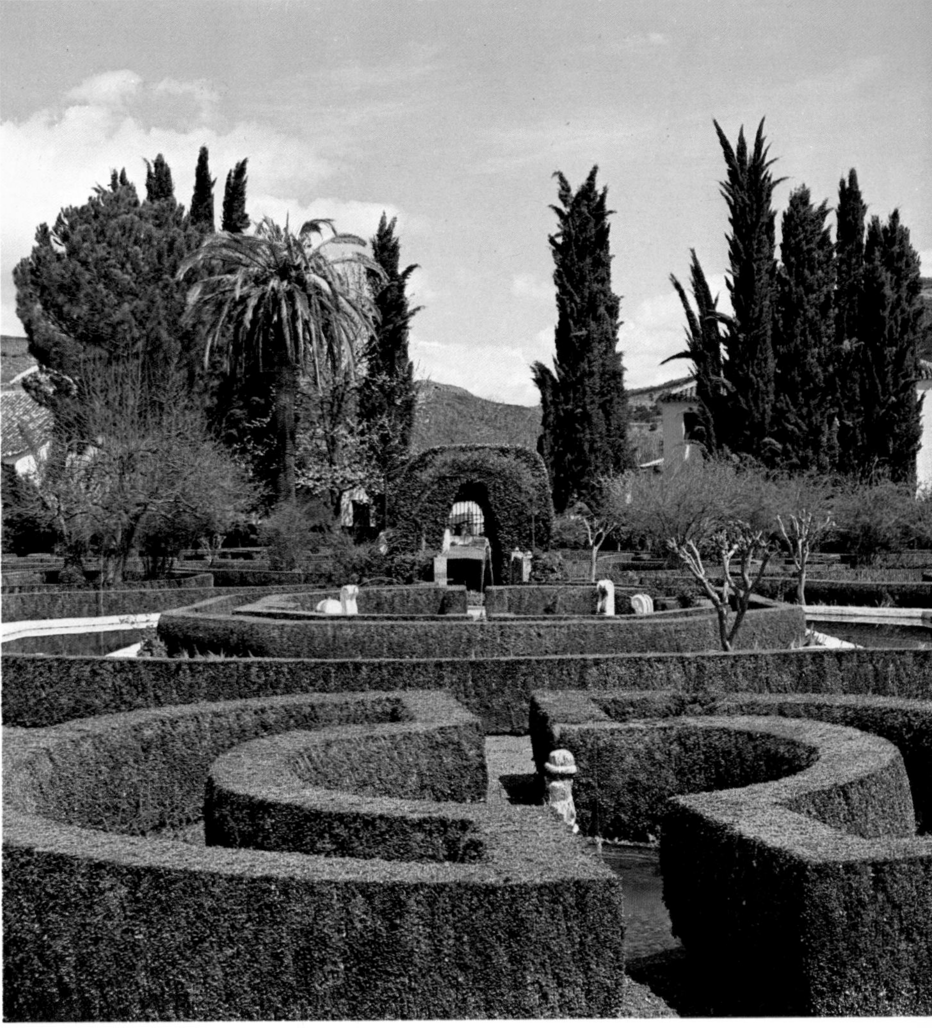

LOJA. NARVAEZ GARDEN. *Photo S. Saavedra.*

is unique. On either side are broad covered walks planted with bay laurels — a slow-growing tree — which developed here to large proportions because of the abundance of water. A pool is incorporated into this setting by means of a central vista with a large fountain encircled by an octagonal canal, a solution which does not interrupt the garden's natural rhythm. At the back stands a delightful summer-house covered with thick and dense foliage, with benches and a table, providing a cool respite from the summer heat.

Alongside the laurel walk nearest to the entrance runs the classic Arab *acequia,* or waterway.

There are other circular fountains in the garden, including a large cascade set into the wall of the southern façade.

The trees, limes, elms and conifers are magnificent and well cared for by the old gardeners, whose grandfathers knew General Narváez when he came to this peaceful retreat to rest from his many and arduous tasks.

The house is small, and, at one time had an oil mill among its buildings. There is still a dignified drawing room dominated by a large oil painting of Queen Isabel II at some thirty years of age, by Sáenz Santa María. Many souvenirs and objects still remain in the house, and the present owners have saved the property from ruin by their care and devotion. Near the house the tomb of General Narváez stands in lonely splendour.

LAUREL TUNNEL. NARVÁEZ GARDEN. *Photo S. Saavedra.*

APPENDIX I

The Arabs applied the name *Romia,* to Christians who became Muslims; the word was used almost as a surname to signify a person who was subject to Roman domination.

The Arabs originally applied this name to Greeks of the Eastern (Byzantine) Empire, and afterwards to all Christians, and in particular Dona Isabel de Solis, who later took the name of Zorayya, "Morning Star", on account of her great beauty. Hernando de Baeza relates how this young girl — according to some the daughter of the Governor of Martos[1], and according to others, of Commander Sancho Ximenes de Solís[2] — was captured by the Moors of Granada during a raid on Aguilar, a town about seven leagues from Granada; when she went to the well to draw water for her animals some youths seized her in order to sell her, and the Sultan gave her to his son.

Old but still amorous, the Sultan soon took the girl to his bed-chamber, as was his custom with palace maidens, and kept her as his Queen, giving her raiment and jewels befitting royalty and unequalled by any other Queen of Granada.

[1] FORD, Richard: *Handbook for Travellers in Spain,* 3rd. ed. Murrays Guide Books, London, 1855, page 292.

[2] IRVING, Washington: *Chronicle of the Conquest of Granada,* Baudry, Paris, 1842, page 27.

His infatuation led to a debilitating split in the Kingdom, which eased the task of the Catholic Monarchs and eventually brought about the fall of Granada. The Arabs were divided into two camps. On one side were the Venegas who supported Fátima, the wife of Abu Hassan, and her son Boabdil. Lowered by his mother on a rope from the window of the Tower of Comares in the dead of night, Boabdil fled to Guadix and rallied his supporters to march against his father, overthrowing him in 1482. On the other side were the Abencerrajes, who supported Zorayya. According to tradition, they were assassinated by Boabdil in the room which bears their name. Zorayya later retired with her children to the Court of the Catholic Monarchs, embracing once more the Catholic faith.

APPENDIX II

In the spring of 1431 Don Alvaro de Luna made a preliminary raid on the Granada valley, in preparation for the campaign Don Juan II was to undertake that summer. At the battle of La Higueruela, in the Granada valley, the Moors of Granada suffered an overwhelming defeat, but Don Juan failed to take advantage of this defeat and decided against attacking Granada. According to some accounts he lacked sufficient forces; others contend that the Monarch of Granada paid a large sum of gold to the King's counsellers to advise him against assaulting the city.

Before the battle of La Higueruela, the Prince of Granada, Aber Yusuf Aben, transferred his allegiance to the Castilian Monarchs. (This information was kindly made available by Don Luis Seco de Lucena. Granada).

[1] "Descripción de España" by Mohamed al-Edrisi, and "El Reino de Granada en 1465-66" by Abd al-Basit. *Viajes de extranjeros por España y Portugal,* compiled by J. Garcia Mercadal. Ed. Aguilar, Madrid, 1952, vol. I, pages 200 & 255.

[2] FORD, Richard: *Handbook for Travellers in Spain.* 3rd. ed., Murrays Guide Books, London, 1855. Dedication. Vol. I.

[3] FORESTIER, J.N.: "Jardins Mediterranéens". *Carnet de Plans et Dessins.* Emile Paul, Editeurs, Paris, 1920.

[4] PRIETO MORENO, Francisco: *Los jardines de Granada.* Ed. Cigüeña, Madrid, 1952, page 14.

[5] PRIETO MORENO, F.: *Op. cit.,* pages 16 & 17.

[6] PRIETO MORENO, F.: *Op. cit.,* pages 16 & 17.

[7] PRIETO MORENO, F.: *Op. cit.,* page 19.

[8] GROMORT, Georges: *Jardins d'Espagne,* A. Vincent, Paris, 1925, vol. I.

[9] TORRES BALBÁS, L.: *La Alhambra y el Generalife de Granada,* Ed. Plus Ultra, Madrid, page 14.

[10] TORRES BALBÁS, L.: *Op. cit.,* page 53.

[11] GASPAR REMIRO, Mariano: *Correspondencia diplomática entre Granada y Fez, siglo XIV,* Granada, 1916, pages 261-270.

[12] PRIETO MORENO, F.: *Op. cit.,* page 21.

[13] TORRES BALBÁS, L.: *Op. cit.,* page 67.

[14] PRIETO MORENO, F.: *Op. cit.,* page 21.

[15] FORD, Richard: *Op. cit.,* vol. I, page 299.

[16] TORRES BALBÁS, L.: *Op. cit.,* page 74.

[17] LALAING, Antonio de: "Primer viaje de Felipe el Hermoso", *Viajes de extranjeros por España y Portugal, Op. cit.,* vol. I, page 475.

[18] BAEZA, Hernando de: "Las cosas que pasaron entre los Reyes de Granada", *Relaciones de algunos sucesos de los últimos tiempos del Reino de Granada,* published by the Sociedad de Bibliófilos Españoles, Madrid, 1868, pages 7 & 8.

[19] GALLEGO BURÍN, Antonio: *Granada.* "Rodriguez Acosta" Foundation, Madrid, 1961, page 145.

[20] TORRES BALBÁS, L.: *Op. cit.,* page 119.

[21] TORRES BALBÁS, L.: *Op. cit.,* page 140.

[22] Koran, sura 55, verse 76. Petite Bibliothèque Payot, Paris, 1958, page 272.

[23] AL-MAQQARI: *History of the Mohammedan Dynasties,* translated by Pascual Gayangos, London, 1843, vol. II, book VIII, page 360.

[24] TORRES BALBÁS, L.: *Al Andalus,* vol. IV, 1936-1939, page 439. The Arab text was published in *La Crestomatía Arábigo-Española* by Lerchundi y Simonet (Granada, 1881), pages 136-137. It was translated into French — and our quotation is from this version — by E. Levi-Pronenàl in his work, *L'Espagne Musulmane au Xème siècle,* Paris, 1932, pages 174-175.

[25] PRIETO MORENO, F.: *Op. cit.,* page 84.

[26] VILLIERS STUART, Mrs.: *Spanish Gardens,* Batsford, London, 1929, page 28.

[27] TORRES BALBÁS, L.: *Op. cit.,* page 147.

[28] PRIETO MORENO, F.; *Op. cit.,* page 85.

[29] BERMÚDEZ PAREJA, Jesús: *Cuadernos de la Alhambra,* Granada, 1965, no. 1, page 28.

[30] DICKIE, James: "Notas sobre la jardinería árabe en la España musulmana". *Miscelánea de estudios árabes y hebraicos,* University of Granada, 1966, page 82.

[31] BERMÚDEZ PAREJA, J.: *Op. cit., Op. cit.,* page 28.

[32] DICKIE, J.: *Op. cit.,* pages 85 & 86.

[33] DICKIE, J.: *Op. cit.,* page 87.

[34] NAVAGERO, A.: "Viaje por España", *Viajes de extranjeros por España y Portugal, Op. cit.,* vol. I, page 855.

[35] LOZOYA, Marqués de: *Historia de España,* Ed. Salvat, Madrid, 1967, vol. II, page 360.

[36] NAVAGERO, A.: *Op. cit.,* vol. I, page 855.

[37] HERRERA, Alonso de: *Agricultura general,* Ed. Antonio Sancha, Madrid 1777, book III, page 118.

[38] TORRES BALBÁS: *Op. cit.,* page 155.

[39] We owe this information to Don Luis Seco de Lucena, an eminent Arabist and Professor of the University of Granada.

[40] GARCÍA GÓMEZ: *Silla del Moro y neuvas escenas andaluzas,* Espasa-Calpe, Col. Austral, Madrid, 1954, page 93.

[41] GALLEGO BURÍN: *Op. cit.,* page 229.

[42] BYNE, Arthur, and STAPLEY, Mildred: *Spanish Gardens and Patios,* New York, 1924, page 178.

[43] PRIETO MORENO, F.: *Op. cit.,* page 188.

[44] MADOZ: *Diccionario geográfico-estadístico-histórico de España,* Madrid, 1847, vol. VIII, page 517.

4 THE GARDENS OF SEVILLE

EL ALCÁZAR

"The largest Moorish garden left in Spain, that of the Alcázar at Seville, was planted a hundred years after the Christian conquest by St. Ferdinand in 1248; it owes its style to the Moorish craftsmen who, in 1350, during the reign of Pedro the Cruel, remained in Seville, unmolested. It was they who designed this palace for the King of Castile on the ruins of the former citadel."[1] Artisans from Granada and Toledo apparently also took part in its construction which therefore conformed to Moorish style and traditions. Its construction was contemporary with that of the Alhambra in Granada, but on Christian territory.

"Glory to our Lord the Sultan Don Pedro. . . May Allah help and protect him." says the Gothic inscription that frames the ornamental lintel over the doorway, where in Muslim script in cobalt blue and white tiles, the heraldic motto of the Alhamares, repeated eight times, can still be read: "There is no conqueror but Allah."[2] They must have felt confident that neither the King nor his Father Confessor could read Arabic![3]

"How much of King Pedro's construction remains is impossible to say with any certainty, but the Moorish stamp given to the design has never been lost. What we admire today is an example of Mudejar art, added to and restored by successive kings of Spain who fell under its spell." The ghost of King Pedro, very oriental in his outlook, lingers still in the Alcázar gardens. He was given to wandering the town in search of adventures, one of which gave rise to the famous legend of the *candilejo* or small oil lamp, later used by the nineteenth century poet Duque de Rivas in one of his best historical romances. The story relates how the King came to order his own effigy to be erected at the corner of a street still called *Cabeza del Rey Don Pedro.* According to the legend, the monarch, on one of his nocturnal outings, fought and killed a man beneath the window of an old woman. Hearing the clash of swords, the old woman looked out by the light of an oil lamp. All that she saw were two figures, one of whom fell to the ground, but as the other withdrew, she heard the creaking of his knee joints. The sound filled her with terror for it was well

POND WITH STATUE OF MERCURY. *Photo S. Saavedra. By permission of the National Heritage.*

known that King Pedro suffered from this affliction. Dropping her lamp, which rolled until it came to stop at the feet of the corpse, she closed her window and disappeared.

When the crime was discovered the following day, King Pedro, who was known for his sense of justice as well as his penchant for cruelty, commanded the Mayor to hang the culprit's head at the scene of the crime without delay, or answer with his own.

Mayor: "Lamps have no tongues.
King: But they who own them do.
Let cords of torture loose their lips."

The officers were not long in discovering the owner of the lamp, and she was tortured until she confessed that the King himself was responsible for the crime. King Pedro then emerged from behind a pillar and threw a purse of money to the old woman, saying,

"'Twas I who killed the man,
But I am judged by none save God alone."[4]

And so it was that the following day he had his effigy erected. A replica of it, dating from the eighteenth century, still remains; the original effigy is kept in a niche in the patio at the entrance to the Casa de Pilatos, home of the Dukes of Medinaceli.

Entering the Alcázar of Seville through the long passage that leads from the Patio de Banderas (Flag Court) we come to a large square planted with shrubs. Beneath it lies the Garden of the Crucero, a Gothic reconstruction of an old Almohad garden known as the Baths of María Padilla. Rodrigo Caro writes: "It was named *crucero* because its shape is that of a cross, and though you enter it at the same level, a subterranean garden of orange trees divided into four squares lies beneath it, so far below that the shoots of the trees can scarcely reach the top. This crucero is built on strong brick and stone arches with parapets on all sides, to contain a great pool of water."[5]

A VIEW OF POND WITH FOUNTAIN. *Photo S. Saavedra.* By permission of the National Heritage.

DETAIL OF THE ALMOHAD GARDEN. (12th century). *Photo Author.* By permission of the National Heritage.

This garden was filled in during the eighteenth century after the Lisbon earthquake. Excavators are now exploring its northern wall — covered by uninteresting masonry — and have already revealed the arches that supported the high garden paths, supported five metres above the lower level.

Crucero gardens are not exclusive to Seville; the Generalife and the Court of the Lions had the same form. They appear to originate from the Abbasides of Iraq, though their more remote origin may have been in Persia. These gardens were introduced into Spain by the Almohads in the twelfth century.

There is also an earlier example in a palace of this period, excavated near the Kutubiya in Marrakesh.

In the same Alcázar and on the site previously occupied by the *Casa de Contratacion* (Exchange for Trade with America), a garden of the same style has now been unearthed. It is divided into four squares, with two canals that meet in a central pool and paths raised on low walls decorated with pointed brick arches. The corner arches are horseshoe shaped. It is all encrusted with well-preserved stucco work dating from the twelfth century.

In this garden we have a perfect western reflection of the Persian paradise.

The entrance to the gardens of the Alcázar is decorated with a square pool surrounded by an iron railing with gilt balls placed

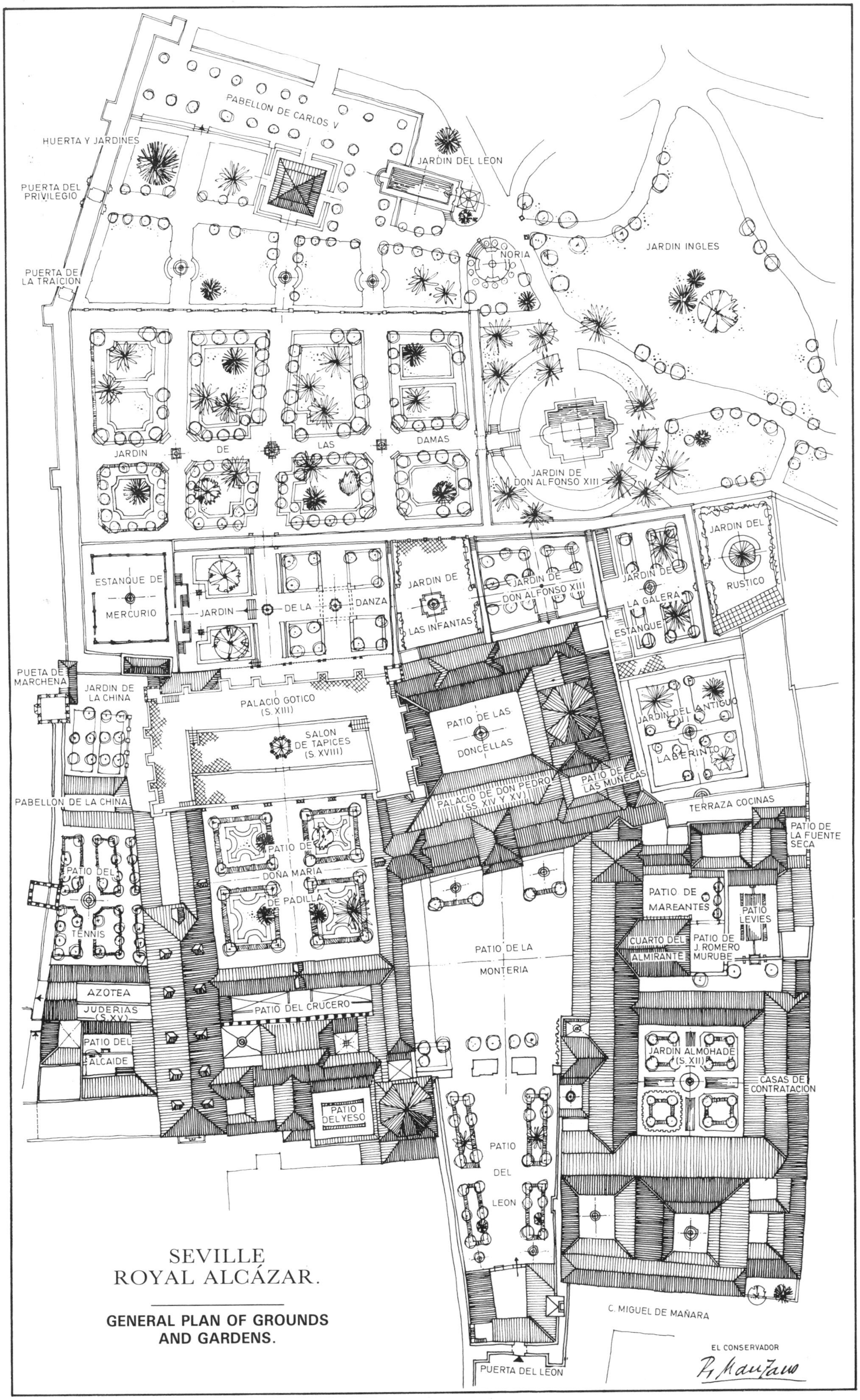

PABELLON DE CARLOS V
HUERTA Y JARDINES
JARDIN DEL LEON
PUERTA DEL PRIVILEGIO
NORIA
JARDIN INGLES
PUERTA DE LA TRAICION
JARDIN DE LAS DAMAS
JARDIN DE DON ALFONSO XIII
JARDIN DEL RUSTICO
ESTANQUE DE MERCURIO
JARDIN DE LA DANZA
JARDIN DE LAS INFANTAS
JARDIN DE DON ALFONSO XIII
JARDIN DE LA GALERA
ESTANQUE
PUETA DE MARCHENA
JARDIN DE LA CHINA
PALACIO GOTICO (S. XIII)
SALON DE TAPICES (S. XVIII)
PATIO DE LAS DONCELLAS
JARDIN DEL ANTIGUO LABERINTO
PATIO DE LAS MUÑECAS
PALACIO DE DON PEDRO (SS. XIV Y XV)
PABELLON DE LA CHINA
TERRAZA COCINAS
PATIO DE LA FUENTE SECA
PATIO DEL TENNIS
PATIO DE DOÑA MARIA DE PADILLA
PATIO DE MAREANTES
PATIO LEVIES
CUARTO DEL ALMIRANTE
PATIO DE J. ROMERO MURUBE
PATIO DE LA MONTERIA
AZOTEA
JUDERIAS (S. XV)
PATIO DEL CRUCERO
PATIO DEL ALCAIDE
JARDIN ALMOHADE (S. XII)
CASAS DE CONTRATACION
PATIO DEL YESO
PATIO DEL LEON
C. MIGUEL DE MAÑARA
PUERTA DEL LEON

SEVILLE
ROYAL ALCÁZAR.

GENERAL PLAN OF GROUNDS AND GARDENS.

EL CONSERVADOR

R. Manzano

DETAIL OF LION. *Photo S. Saavedra.*
By permission of the National Heritage.

at intervals along the top. In accordance with the Italian taste of the seventeenth century, a pretty bronze fountain, once gilt, stands in the centre of this pool. It has ten water spouts and is crowned by a statue of Mercury, the work of Diego Pesquera. It was cast by Bartolomé Morel at the end of the sixteenth century in the style of Cellini and John of Bologna. The railing and the lions, which still show traces of the old gilding, were also cast by Morel and bear the date 1576.

The Giraldillo, or statue of Faith, that crowns the Tower of the Giralda was also the work of Bartolomé Morel and was cast in 1568.

In the days of Rodrigo Caro the fountain was still gilded and there were flamingos and swans on the lake. In the Arab tradition, the lake served as a reservoir to collect water for the irrigation of the lower gardens. This fountain stands at the foot of a high arcade built in the time of the Almohads and decorated in the sevententh century with grotesques and later with frescoes representing mythological scenes. The stream of water that still pours from the roof of the gallery into this pond flows from the Roman conduit of the Caños de Carmona.

The overall effect, writes Mrs. Villiers-Stuart, is marred by the fact that the Arab living quarters and the gardens are now separated.[6] The rooms lack brightness and life, as they are deprived of their patios, gardens and fountains. Arab palaces, or Alcázares, were based on a blending of house with garden-court, as in Granada. Now the only access to the palace rooms is through the Patio de Banderas; the rooms are closed on the garden side, and the garden has thus lost its purpose of ornament and complement to Arab architecture. The charm of a series of courts or halls — some closed, some half-open, and some in the open air — is now lost.

POOL, GALERAS GARDENS. *Photo Paláu.* By permission of the National Heritage.

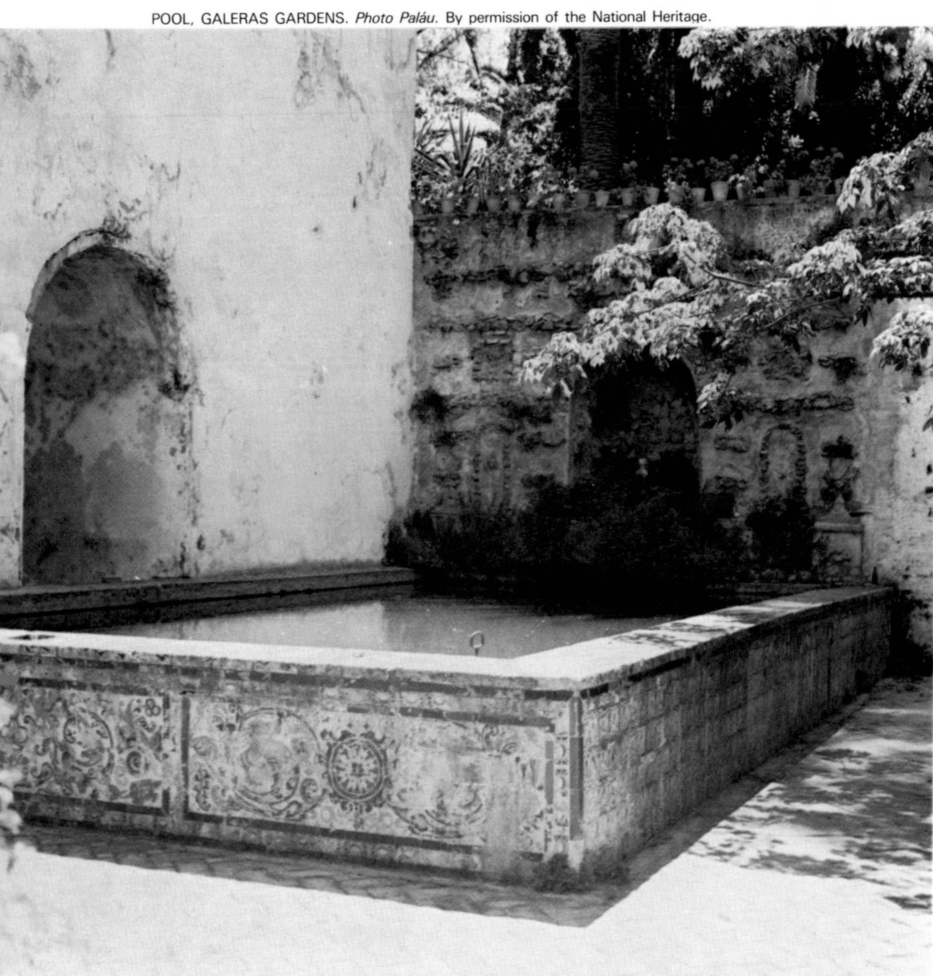

"This garden, designed on a flat site that in Moorish days stretched down to the Guadalquivir, included in its confines the Palace de Santelmo and the Torre del Oro. It is now an enclosure of over sixteen acres whose chief defect is its lack of vista, compared with the dynamic landscape of the Alhambra at Granada.[7]

On the northern side, Don Pedro's fortified walk runs along the walls, from which the city and the Guadalquivir can be seen. These terraces were altered during the reign of Philip V, and others were built at different levels, giving the garden new outlooks.

Rodrigo Caro observes: "On this wall there is a covered corridor formed by columns of jasper, and above it, an uncovered walk with a balustrade, providing a view of much of the city and outlying fields as well as these gardens."

As one descends from the terrace of the Baños de María Padilla the atmosphere of the garden changes. The central fountain can be glimpsed through the glistening foliage of the two immense magnolias that enclose it, and we find ourselves in the oriental world.[8] Rodrigo Caro continues: "We go down to these gardens by an uncovered stairway lavishly decorated with tiles so exquisitely and daintily worked that I doubt whether its equal could be found elsewhere. Beyond this we enter a garden called the Garden of Las Damas where clipped myrtle figures of nymphs, oreads and napeas stand on myrtle tables with satyrs and sileni, guiding them as though they were dancing in a ring."[9]

These gardens, until fairly recently (Madoz did not see them in 1845) contained strange figures of warriors and ladies cut in myrtle. At the foot of the stairs, today made of stone, two tall marble columns stand on either side as pedestals for a pair of sculptures representing The Dance, giving this court its name. Today only the columns and a simple rectangular garden divided into four flower beds remain.

Lady Holland, in her Spanish diary writtten in 1811, describes them thus: "The gardens of the Alcázar are preserved in the Moorish style; one part is precisely as at the Conquest with hedges of myrtle clipped into various shapes. Another part was laid out by King Pedro: rows of myrtle warriors, giants and ladies with wooden heads and arms, carrying in their hands swords, clubs, musical instruments, etc. Further on is the garden of Charles V with a pavilion for refreshments, a delightful spot. The whole garden is filled with *jets d'eau,* cascades, fountains and aquatic tricks and devices. I was as pleased with these hanging gardens as Charles V or any child could be."[10]

Elsewhere Rodrigo Caro says: "From these gardens one passes to the new gardens through a door with a wrought iron grille, to find two giants formed of small-leaved myrtle,

THE ALCAZAR AS SEEN FROM THE WALLS. *Photo Paláu.* By permission of the the National Heritage.

representing the fight between Hercules and Anteo.

"The whole garden is filled with jets, cascades, fountains and water tricks designed to soak the unwary."[11]

The poet Angel Saavedra, Duque de Rivas, also speaks of passing through:

> "... those gardens
> Where, flanking the entrance, giants of myrtle stand,
> Varied in posture but equal in their gaze,
> as warily each scans the other's form."[12]

The topiary figures which at that time still grew in this part of the Alcázar, appear to have been created around the time of Charles V of Philip II. This assumption is supported by the fact that the English adopted the Dutch garden style in 1688, with the arrival of William of Orange. Their gardens were small and intimate, planted with hedges to form green enclosures. This was the style of the ancient Roman topiarius, with a multitude of fantastic figures of birds and people cut out of boxwood or yew, many of which still survive in English gardens. It seems probable that Philip II's gardens at Aranjuez, a century earlier, underwent this same influence, as Dutch gardeners were employed there. The gardens of the Alcázar may also have dated from this period, because as noted, Rodrigo Caro describes clipped myrtle figures there as early as 1634.

Continuing our way and going down a few steps, we find ourselves on a path paved in brick and tile, with a hexagonal marble fountain surrounded by a profusion of silver centaurea. The tiled benches provide a particularly colourful effect.

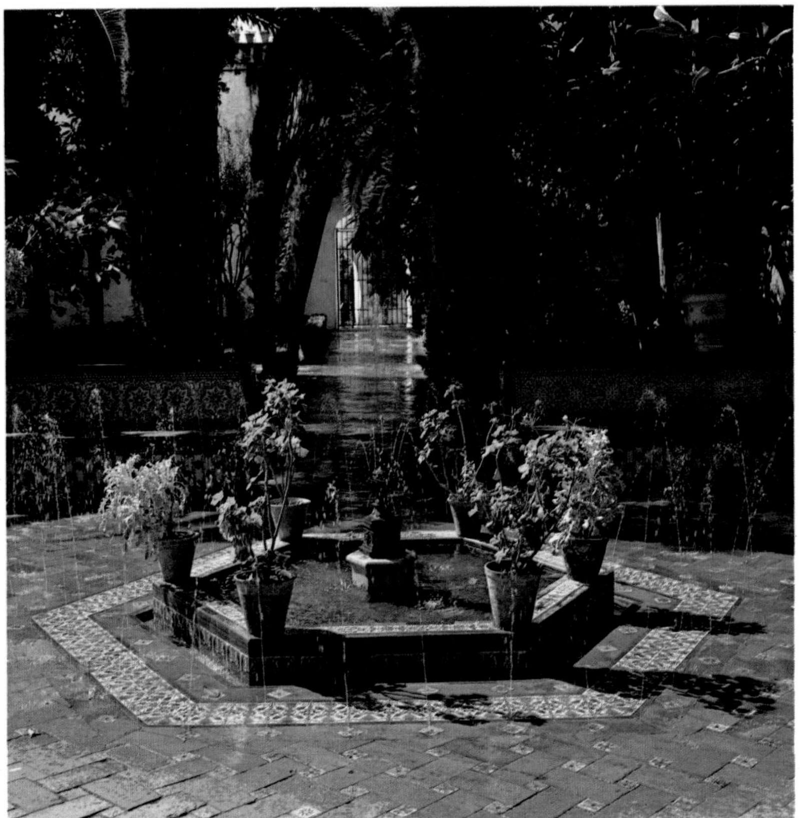

HEXAGONAL FOUNTAIN, PATIO OF THE INFANTAS. *Photo S. Saavedra.* By permission of the National Heritage.

Gromort, the French architect, writes: "It is surprising to find oneself in a royal park with such simple and human elements which could belong to any bourgeois property. No view lies before us, but as we go down a few steps another simple door gives us a glimpse of a second peaceful patio containing a pretty fountain."[13]

The oldest gardens are, undoubtedly, these small patios surrounding the palace: the Patio of the Dance, that of the Galleys, that of King Alfonso XIII (so named on account of the stairs which he had built to give access to this court), and lastly, at an angle, the Patio of the Prince. The large tiled reservoir or *alberca* still remains in the Patio of the Galleys, where two ships were at one time placed, with their cannons used to shoot jets of water at each other.

NEPTUNE FOUNTAIN. *Photo Paláu.* By permission of the National Heritage.

STATUE OF NEPTUNE. *Photo Paláu.* By permission of the National Heritage.

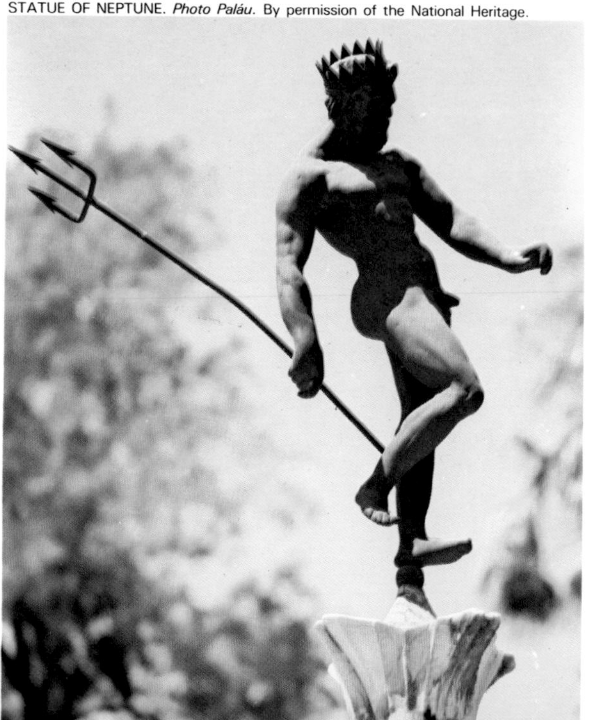

Prince Don Juan, son of "the Catholic King", was born in 1478 in the room overlooking the Garden of the Prince. His premature death altered the course of Spanish history. Looking today from these patios towards the façade of the Alcázar, with its several steep stairways leading to the rooms, we are reminded that the old Moorish chambers must have been on the same level as the gardens, forming part of them, like the Baths of María Padilla and the buried Garden of the Crucero.

Coming down from the large square pool, and crossing the Garden of the Dance through the arch that leads to the Ladies' Garden, we see a beautiful Carrara marble Renaissance fountain — the loveliest in Seville — crowned by a statue of Neptune, also the work of Bartolomé Morel.

The parterre into which we have entered through the iron gates is of stately proportions. It is irregular in shape, measuring about forty-five metres by seventy-five. Tiled paths divide this area into eight sections containing arabesques cut out of myrtle and boxwood, handsome trees and lush foliage. The garden is adorned with three fountains placed at the crossings of these paths. In Rodrigo Caro's words: "It is divided into eight squares marked out by garden walks and paths paved with bricks and tiles, and where they cross there are fountains. These beds are planted with fine-leaved myrtle and various designs worked out in thyme, lavender and sweet marjoram. The royal arms, castles, lions, eagles and other figures are so skilfully and beautifully represented in these plants that they look like paintings, and occasionally, even like the real things themselves. There are also clumps of evergreen orange trees. Today into these paths are set many water jets that soak the unwary who pause to admire the garden and the grottoes, much to the amusement of onlookers."[14]

"The walks are always slightly raised so that the beds can be flooded and the feet of passers-by kept dry. This system of irrigation, called *riego en manta,* or blanket watering, is used throughout Spain, but has been lost in India, Turkey and Kashmir where it originated. The water conduits are hidden beneath the paths."[15]

In the old days this central part of the garden, surrounded by pillars and grilles, was called the Ladies' Garden (de las Damas), remade over the original gardens upon the wedding of Charles V and Isabel of Portugal. The portrait of the Emperor can still be seen over the door in the background.[16] The walls are decorated with grotesques, probably from the seventeenth century, which are a continuation of those of the great pool or *alberca.* A large Baroque fountain dominates this garden; at one time it was equipped with a hydraulic system, and in the paths there are still tiny water spouts for playing pranks on the visitors.

If we follow an avenue paved in brick and tile we come to the Charles V pavilion, built in 1540 by Juan Hernández.

Rodrigo Caro tells us: "From this garden we proceed to the *Huerta de la Alcoba* (Orchard of the Alcove) which also belongs to the royal house. Aside from trees and vegetable patches, it contains a dense wood of citrus, lime, lemon and orange trees, and in their midst, a resting place formerly called the *Alcoba,* which has given its name to the orchard. The *Alcoba* is built in an interesting and costly manner, with marble columns all around, and in its centre, a room covered inside and out by attractive tile work. The pavement is surrounded and crossed by open white marble channels of flowing water, making this a pleasant retreat for siestas during the summer heat."[17]

This building of exquisite proportions is raised upon a rectangular terrace two steps high. It consists simply of a square porch with arches and columns surrounding a small room. The smooth walls of this edifice are lined with tiles of an incredible richness, so that the white columns stand out in contrast against the multi-coloured walls. The inner walls of the room are entirely covered from ceiling to floor with ceramics.

Here one can compare "the four processes once used to manufacture *majolica* decoration in Spain. The earliest form is that of tile work or *alicatado,* where the *majolica* is cut out in separate colours and inlaid on the background. This art was brought from the east by the Arabs. The second, called *cuerda seca,* (dry line) was used in the Alhambra at Granada. It is so called because of the raised line of grease and manganese which divides the wet colours and prevents them from running together. It is a way of imitating the *alicatados* with less work. *Cuenca y arista* (basin and arris) was the name given to the third process, where the design is imprinted or hollowed out, leaving ridges to separate the colours. In the early sixteenth century, Nicolaso Pisano from Pisa introduced a fourth process, the direct method of painting on faience as practised in Florence by the Della Robbias. Tiles decorated in this way were thus called pisanos.[18] The tiles form the principal colour motif of these gardens, and are of more importance than the flowers."[19]

The hall is covered by a circular dome of finely carved cedar.

On the floor of the pavilion a round marble fountain with narrow channels adds life and coolness to the room, in the best Arab tradition. After the gardens of María Padilla, this pavilion is the most interesting sight in the grounds. Charles V, charmed by the oriental spirit of the Alcázar, wanted to add a gem of oriental tile work to the royal garden.

Inside the pavilion, a ceramic slab provides a plan of the labyrinth that once existed in the gardens of the Alcázar, but which was destroyed at the beginning of the century and reconstructed at another site with a different design.

CHARLES V PAVILION. *Photo Oronoz.* By permission of the National Heritage.

SLAB WITH ANCIENT LABYRINTH.
Photo Paláu. By permission of the National Heritage.

INTERIOR, CHARLES V PAVILION.
Photo S. Saavedra. By permission of the National Heritage.

The Alcázar casts a subtle spell which grows with every return to its gardens. The luxuriance and exuberance of the vegetation defy belief, both in the spring with the fragrance of orange blossoms and jasmin, and in the autumn when the daturas in cascades of white trumpets exhale a delicate perfume.

There is an old orange tree in the lower garden near the pavilion that tradition attributes to Pedro the Cruel's time.

"These marvellous gardens have been replanted several times, but throughout the centuries they have always preserved their Arab character and atmosphere."[20]

At the end, on the right and in line with Charles V's pavilion, another slightly raised pool has been preserved bearing the unfortunate name "Bath of Juana la Loca" (the Mad). It has a lovely Renaissance basin with four spouts, each issuing from a mask. A lion or chimera presides over this fountain, and the pavilion shows a marked Italian baroque influence.

Raised on a small platform adjoining the pavilion is an old Arab irrigation wheel, or *noria.*

Two gardens were planted in these grounds during this century. The first, created by the Marqués de la Vega Inclán during the reign of Alfonso XIII, offers paved walks, benches and the low-tiled fountains that were so much in vogue in the time of Forestier and the Ibero-American Exhibition. There is also an arbour or *glorieta* with a summer-house built over another ancient *noria.* The second garden is the work of the late Sevillian poet Romero Murube, who was Curator of the Alcázar for many years.

DATURA, ALCAZAR. *Photo author.* By permission of the National Heritage.

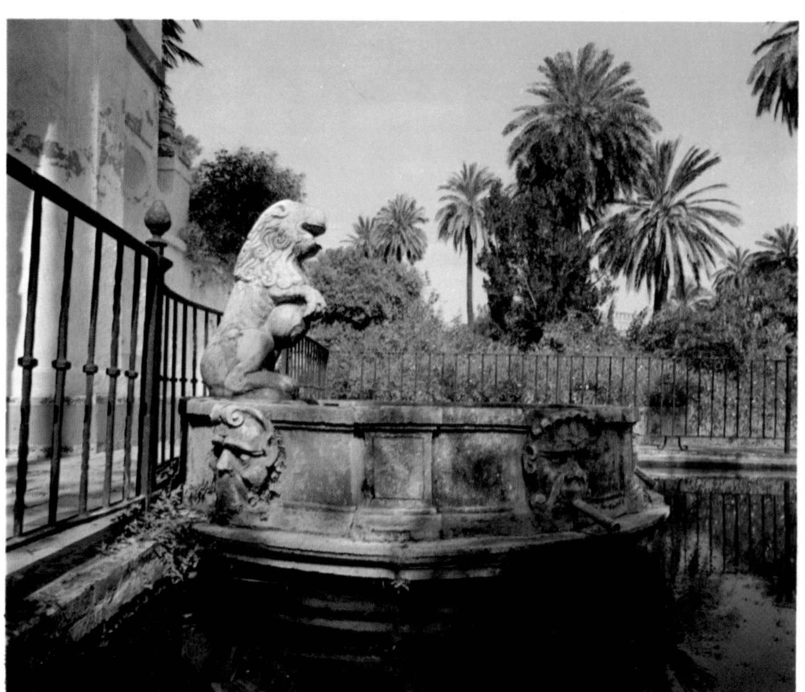

LION BATH, JUANA LA LOCA. *Photo S. Saavedra.* By permission of the National Heritage.

PEDRO THE CRUEL'S ORANGE TREE. *Photo S. Saavedra.* By permission of the National Heritage.

Called the Poet's Garden, it comprises two rectangles, each containing a pool surrounded by hedges of thuya. In the centre there is a stone fountain which came from a convent in Sanlucar. This garden, with its two columns and its semi-circle in the background, recalls those by Forestier who exerted such an influence in Seville.

To properly appreciate the garden it is essential to walk along the ramparts, from which a general view can be gained.

It is with a sense of nostalgia that we leave these gardens, which, in the words of poet Angel Saavedra:

"Form a rich enchanted whole,
Never forgotten in my mind—
And as I record it
My soul and heart seem to throb."[21]

ANDALUSIAN PATIOS

As explained in a previous chapter, Andalusian patios symbolize their inhabitants' way of life. Mrs. Villiers Stuart observes that: "the three principal cities of Andalusia — Seville, Granada and Córdoba — each evolved a style of domestic architecture all its own. This is best seen in the patio. The Moorish use of a plain exterior combined with a richly decorated interior is common to all buildings in the south of Spain. In each case the building material is the same, a whitewashed mixture of brick and rubblework, but the results obtained differ considerably."

VEGA INCLAN GARDEN. *Photo S. Saavedra.* By permission of the National Heritage.

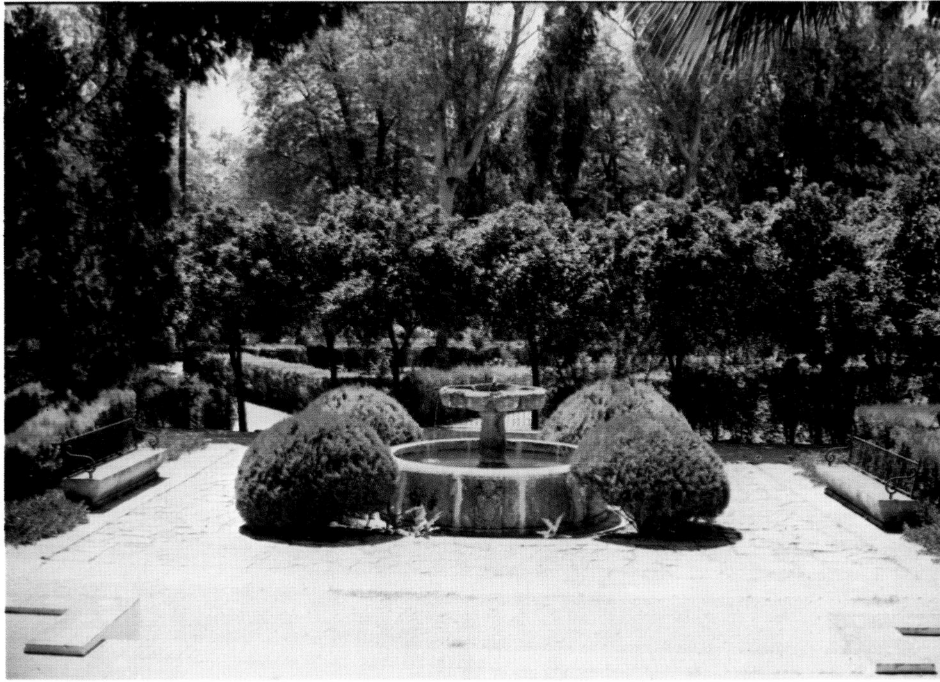

FOUNTAIN, POET'S GARDEN. *Photo S. Saavedra.* By permission of the National Heritage.

POET'S GARDEN. *Photo S. Saavedra.* By permission of the National Heritage.

TYPICAL GRANADA PATIO. *Photo Author.*

HOUSE OF PILATE. *Photo S. Saavedra.*

SEVILLIAN PATIO. *Photo Author.*

The most typical Granada patios are generally found in the old houses in the flat part of the town.

"The galleries of these patios are generally supported by columns or wooden posts, as in the Casa del Chapiz, the Patio de la Reja in the Alhambra, and the Casa del Carbón, where the brackets at the entrance are covered with Arab ornaments.

"As the richest city of the south, Seville naturally boasts the most elaborate architectural patios. Their height, fine marble pavements and pillars, profusion of tile work and magnificent *rejas* (iron grates), give an impression of sumptuousness and grandeur more akin to the great Italian palaces of the Renaissance than to their modest neighbours of the Guadalquivir valley. Beautiful as these Seville patios are, they lack the special appeal and intimate charm of the Cordoba interiors and other humbler Andalusian towns."[22]

The palace of the Duke and Duchess of Medinaceli has, through the centuries, combined the Mudejar and Renaissance styles.

This palace, known as *Casa de Pilatos* (House of Pilate), was built by Don Fadrique Enríquez de Rivera, first Marqués de Tarifa, who travelled to the Holy Land between 1518 and 1520 accompanied by other noblemen of Seville. He brought back precious jewels and relics which are still kept in the palace today.

Returning from his pilgrimage, described by the Poet Juan del Encina, Don Fadrique founded the Way of the Cross in Seville. It is believed that he measured the distance from the floor of Pilate's house in Jerusalem — which was all that remained of that building — to Golgotha, and using these measurements he established a "Way of the Cross" from his house in Seville to the small chapel called the Cruz del Campo in Carmona on the outskirts of the town. Every Friday in Lent this "Way of the Cross" or pilgrimage, began in the palace or "first station", with the theme: "Jesus is condemned in the House of Pilate."

Throughout his travels in Italy he made notes and sketches, especially in Bologna where it seems a palace of similar proportions exists. All around the palace of this extraordinary individual, the cornice depicts the story of his pilgrimages.

His nephew, Don Per Afán de Ribera, was named Duque de Alcalá de los Gazules by Philip II, and from 1559 to 1572, the Viceroy of Naples. During that time he brought back a splendid collection of marble and antique statues from Italy, among them two statues of Pallas Athene, of the period of Phidias, that once adorned Pius V's forum of Ulpianus. Today they grace the corners of the palace's great patio, in whose centre stands a handsome fountain by Antonio Aprile de Carona, also brought from Napes and dated 1533.

It was Don Fernando, third Duke of Alcalá de los Gazules and nephew to Don Per Afán de Ribera, who, during the reign of Philip IV, contributed most to the brilliance of this palace.

This illustrious personage, born in Seville in 1583, pursued careers in arms and letters. Viceroy of Naples and Sicily and later Ambassador to Rome in 1624, he returned to Spain laden with the honours bestowed on him by Pope Urban VIII, which included the Grand Jubilee of the Way of the Cross of the Cruz del Campo. To commemorate this special favour he erected an altar of coloured marble which can be seen today at the door of the palace. Documentary evidence indicates that this building was then popularly known as *Casa de Pilatos* because it was the first "Station of the Cross" in the Way established by Don Per Afán in the previous century.[23]

This Duke of Alcalá was a great patron of artists and men of letters, many of whom came to his famous library. Here, Spanish painters of the time, such as Pablo de Céspedes, Herrera the Old, Pacheco, and the poets Rioja and Cervantes, would meet among the antiques collected by Don Per Afán. "Cervantes," says Mrs. Villiers Stuart "was at that time Commoissioner of Taxes for Seville, and very bored the great man seems to have been with this prosaic work, after his strenuous life of adventures by land and sea."

In a reference to the "nine houses of grandees of Spain and eleven of titled noblemen that adorn this great city," Rodrigo Caro makes special mention of that of the Dukes of Alcalá, because, in addition to its exceptional architecture, its owners have collected marble statues of princes and great figures of two great colossi of Pallas, the goddess of wisdom, and many other treasures of antiquity; His Excellency the Duke Don Fernando Afán de Ribera, the present owner of the house, has collected a great library containing many volumes of science and literature, manuscripts and ancient medals that rival the world's most renowned collections."[24]

In the great hall, on either side of the entrance to the chapel, are two kneeling marble statues of Doña Fernanda and Doña Maria de Ribera.

The small chapel is entirely lined with mavellous tiles, and in its centre stands a replica of the column to which Jesus was

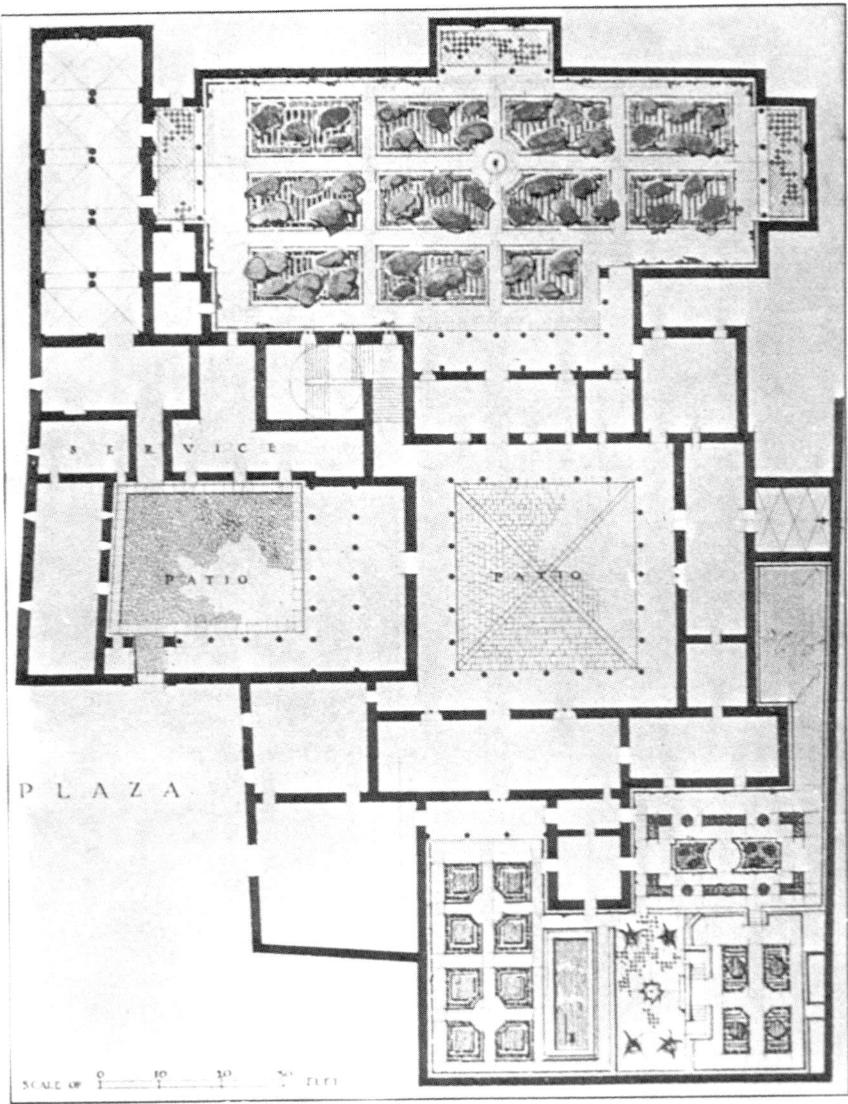

PLAN, HOUSE OF PILATE. Byne.

GRAND PATIO, HOUSE OF PILATE. *Photo S. Saavedra.*

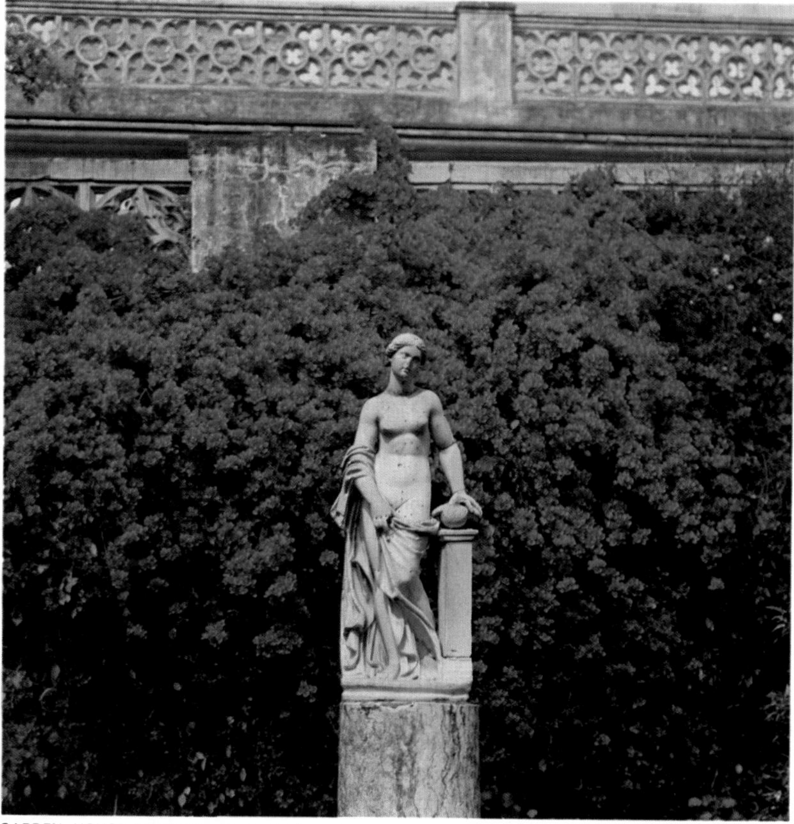

GARDEN, HOUSE OF PILATE. *Photo S. Saavedra.*

PLAN, HOUSE OF THE SISTERS. Byne.

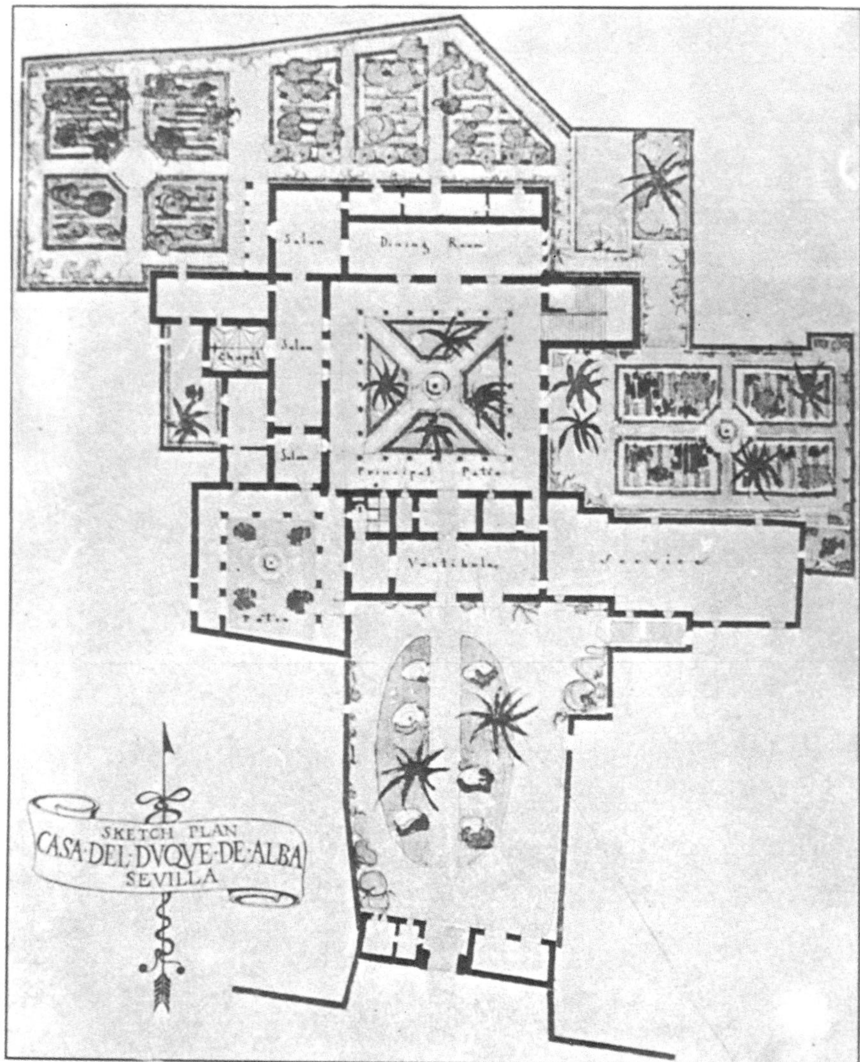

bound. Relics brought by Cardinal Mendoza housed in the sacristy, include fragments of the true column and of the cross.

The Casa de Pilatos has two gardens, one on either side of the great central court. Crossing the patio and entering the garden on the left, we find a rectangular area, at either end of which an Italian architect has constructed upper and lower loggias, or galleries. It was here that the Roman and Greek statues brought from Rome, Capua and Naples were placed.

It was between these Renaissance loggias that the palace's first garden was laid out. All that remains from this distant past are a few orange trees, a gigantic magnolia, the tallest in Seville, and a lemon tree.

As we walked through the garden one afternoon, the Palace Curator Don Joaquin González Moreno described its history. "Early in the seventeenth century," he explained, "it was observed that the plants growing here were deprived of sun by the high walls of the palace. The first arrangement of plants was somewhat haphazard. But in 1640, when a beautiful fountain of Carrara marble in the Italian style was placed in the centre, the garden began to acquire pleasing proportions and harmony.

"In 1850 the space was laid out a new, in the style of a romantic garden, divided into eleven equal squares, with the fountain still in its centre. Four marble benches were placed beneath an iron belvedere, covered with an imperial jasmine which is very rare in these latitudes. The old lemon and orange trees were spared."

At the time of my visit these trees were laden with fruit and we were able to observe how bravely these trees grow in the shady patios of Seville, despite the lack of sunshine.

Returning once more across the grand central patio of the Casa de Pilatos, we come to the "modern" or "small" garden to the right of the entrance. It was planted at the beginning of this century when the buildings that once stood here were pulled down. It has upper and lower levels divided by a long, narrow pool. On either side of the pool stand two slender columns, one crowned by the Venus of the Fish, the other by the Venus of the Dove, both nineteenth century. The capitol of the column on the right is Roman, of composite design and dating from one of the finer periods of Roman art.

In 1875, on one of her journeys to Spain the Empress Eugenie brought a rambler rose tree of a variety not well known here at that time, with pale pink flowers. She planted it here herself in one of the eight rose beds of the lower garden, and it still blooms every year.

Another fine example of Andalusian gardens can be seen in the Mudejar palace of the Duchess of Alba. Its cheerful entrance, with its long, sunny garden, can be seen from the street through the grilled door, which is unusual for an Andalusian house; generally there is an entrance hall and then a patio to be crossed before the garden is reached.

This palace once belonged to the illustrious Pineda family who were obliged to sell it in order "to redeem from his captivity the good knight, great in all things, Pedro de Pineda, taken prisoner by the Moors, with many other noblemen of Seville, in the disaster of the Ajarquia of Málaga in 1483."[25] It was bought by Doña Catalina de Ribera, who founded the Hospital de la Sangre in the suburb of La Macarena. It is known as "Palacio de las Dueñas" (palace of the ladies) because of the adjoining convent of nuns in whose church it had a gallery.[26] Its history is closely connected with that of the Casa de Pilatos, for the second Duke of Alcalá once lived in *las Dueñas,* and the third Duke, who was to bring such glory to the Ribera family, was born here.

Completed at the end of the fifteenth century, this Mudejar palace is of a purer style than *Pilatos,* as no additions were made in later centuries.

Across a spacious hall lies the central patio with its columns, Moorish arches and a ceramic covered fountain, whose large marble basin probably dates from the Renaissance.

Through the centre of the right hand side of this patio we pass on to a garden that surrounds the entire house.

We come first to a rectangular section designed as a *crucero* garden (in the form of a cross), with walks bordered by tall hedges of ancient boxwood and slender cypress forming pillars. In the centre lies a low octagonal fountain, decorated with tile work of ancient design, and to one side, a charming pergola with a marble table. Situated here too is an *alberca,* or reservoir, indispensable for the watering of all Spanish gardens.

ENTRANCE, GARDEN OF THE SISTERS. *Photo "Semana".*

MARBLE TABLE, GARDEN OF THE SISTERS. *Photo S. Saavedra.*

PATIO OF THE SISTERS. *Photo S. Saavedra.*

Continuing our walk around the house which is surrounded by vegetation, we come to another garden patio, with its central fountain, near the approach to the house. In this beautiful place, orange and lemon trees, and flowers of all species mingle in a gay symphony.

Such Sevillian patios are not limited to the wealthy; throughout the city, there are many modest houses each with small patios tended lovingly by their owners. Moreover a number of mansions once inhabited by nobility now serve to house many families, who keep the patios as filled with flowers as in their heyday.

LATTICE WINDOW OF TOWER. *Photo Author.*

HACIENDA DONA MARIA, OLD SAPIDILLA TREE. *Photo Author.*

ARAB PAVILION DONA MARIA. *Photo S. Saavedra.*

Hacienda of the Tower of Doña Maria

On the outskirts of Seville there are numerous charming properties with *cortijos* (farmhouses), and country houses.

In Dos Hermanas, a town near Seville, we find the Hacienda (Estate) of the Tower of Doña María, owned by Señorita Concha Ibarra. The lovely house of this important olive growing estate has a large, cheerful, sun-drenched patio with its well, surrounded by orange trees. The tower that gave its name to the property is said to have belonged to Doña María Padilla, the mistress of Pedro I. The tower, which has been preserved in good condition, has two floors, the top floor being reached by a steep staircase probably as old as the tower itself. At the base of the stairs, inserted in the wall, is an original square stone in the form of an open worked rosette, which serves to let light into the room and to decorate the tower façade. According to legend, a long tunnel runs from the tower's cellar to the Alcázar.

The outer garden is reached through the broad portico of the patio. Here stands a venerable sapote (*achras sapota*), the national tree of Brazil which, judging by its huge gnarled trunk and roots, is probably about two hundred years old.

Continuing to the left, on slightly raised ground, we find a garden of clipped hedges and cypress arches with a central path leading to a Moorish pavilion. This was built at the time of the Hispano-American Exhibition of 1929 by a Moroccan architect who brought in the decorative materials, such as the door nails and the Arab door knocker.

In the last century this property was a shooting lodge belonging to the Duke and Duchess of Montpensier.

Mrs. Villiers Stuart describes the Cordoba type of patio as "the simplest and most homely. Stone pillars are often replaced by masonry piers; tiles are used sparingly. The pavement is a pebble mosaic, and the colour decoration consists, as a rule, of bands of blue, yellow or red Kalsomine wash, a simple means, in strong sunlight, of producing a very charming and telling effect."[27]

Most of the Palace of Las Rejas de Don Gome, owned by the Marquis of Viana, in Córdoba, dates from the sixteenth century, but some parts date back further.

This palace used to belong to the Marquis of Villaseca, who in 1818, as a young man, was visited by Geoge Ticknor, author of the *History of Spanish Literature.* Ticknor attended his evening *tertulias* (social and literary gatherings), and wrote in his Memoirs, "this is the most pleasant house in Cordoba."[28] It was here that Ticknor met the Duke of Rivas and his brother, the poet Angel de Saavedra (later to succeed him in the title), then youths, who accompanied him on horseback on an expedition to the Sierra de Córdoba.

The garden of this house was successfully restored at the beginning of this century. It has three patios divided in the Arab manner by high walls, which are probably original. It is "reminiscent of the patios leading from Pedro the Cruel's Alcázar. The irregularity of the plan suggests that period rather than the great days of Arab Córdoba."[29] Entrance is gained through a spacious patio with a handsome specimen of the palm tree *phoenix canariensis* in its centre.

To reach the interior garden on the southern side of the house, one must pass through a sequence of reception rooms, one of whose walls are painted with frescoes depicting the story of Tobias. The garden consists of first a patio planted with orange trees — five arranged in a circle and many others climbing up the walls intermingled with tangerine and lemon trees — forming a veritable jungle of greenery.

Passing through a side door we enter a second patio, where sturdy Roman pillars support pots of *centaurea candidissima,* a classic decorative plant much used in Andalusia. This patio has three wide grilled windows corresponding to the three doorways in the façade of the house, providing a view of the street.

Finally, the oldest part of the garden has a bower of cypresses, arched and clipped to form an eight-arched belvedere. In the centre stands a white marble statue of a lady, popularly known as *La Madama;* she holds a vase, which like a fountain, pours its water into the pool at her feet.

This patio leads to the large garden, a forest of palm and orange trees with classic designs in clipped boxwood and myrtle, filled with a poetic charm.

This palace today possesses sixteen patios, each with its fountain, one of the loveliest being that adjoining the chapel. The walls are arranged to provide shade at all times of the day. Access from one patio to another is through small side doors that lend mystery and enchantment to the garden, softening the severity of its high walls. The beauty and indescribable atmosphere of the Garden of Las Rejas de Don Gome are a perfect expression of their "closed, oriental patio, where all elements converge in a central motif designed for meditation, the contemplation of beauty and the refreshment of cool shade in the Islamic tradition."[30]

In more recent years, the Marquesa de Viana devoted herself entirely, and with exquisite taste, to the restoration and decoration of this old palace. She succeeded in making it one of the loveliest private residences in Spain.

There are still private houses in Córdoba, like that of Don Antonio Herruzo and that of Don Richardo Lopez, with delightful gardens which complement the old Moorish palaces of Córdoba; another beautiful garden is that of Don Rafael Castejón, where two eighteenth century fountains of grey marble stand against a wall.

ENTRANCE PATIO, DON GOME. Córdoba. *Photo S. Saavedra.*

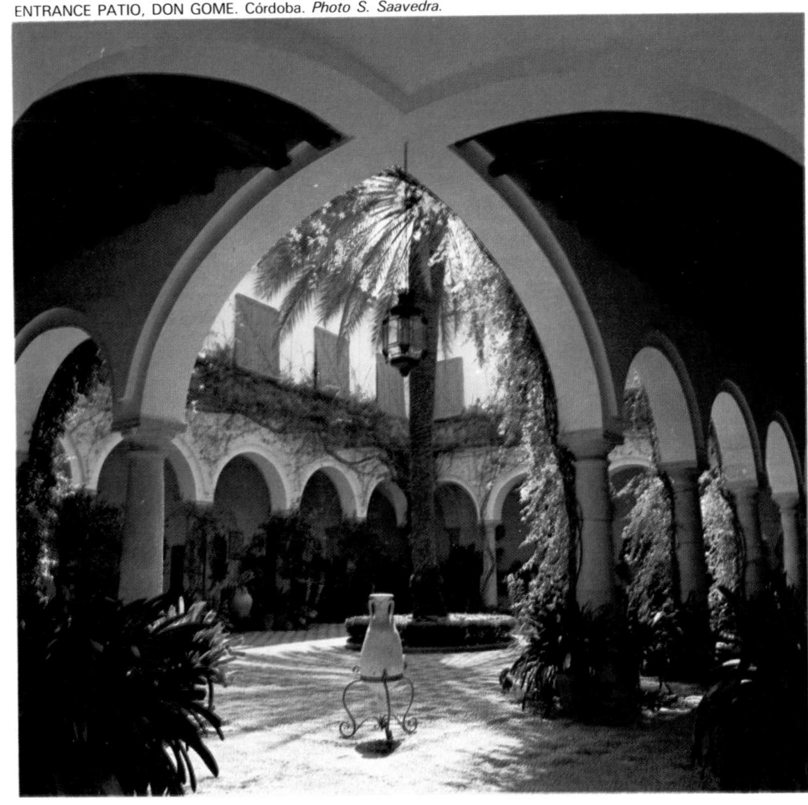

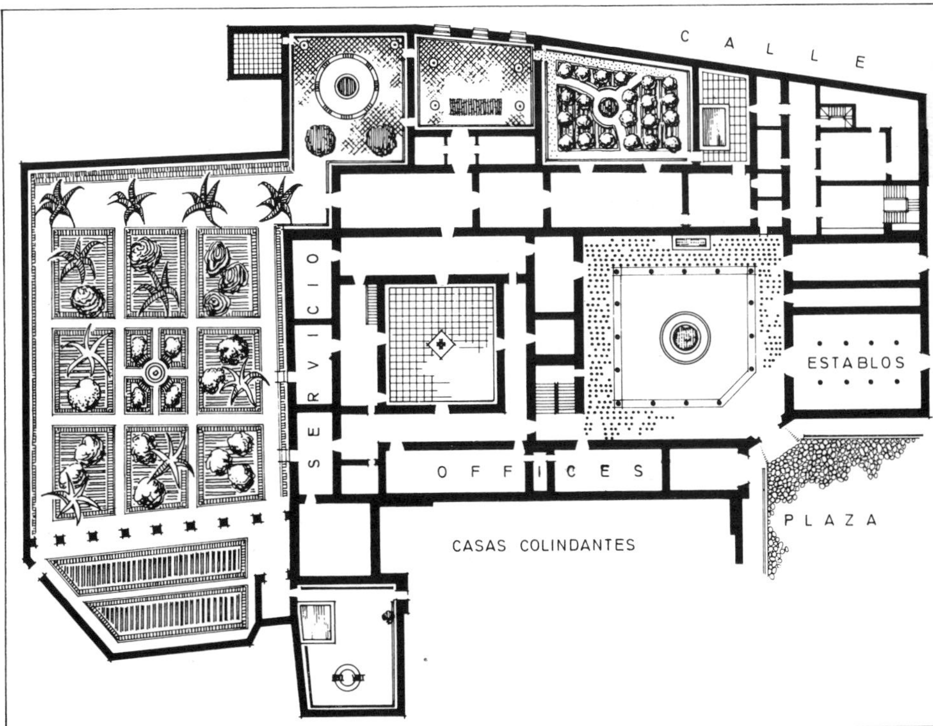

PLAN OF DON GOME ESTATE. Byne.

PATIO, DON GOME ESTATE. *Photo S. Saavedra.*

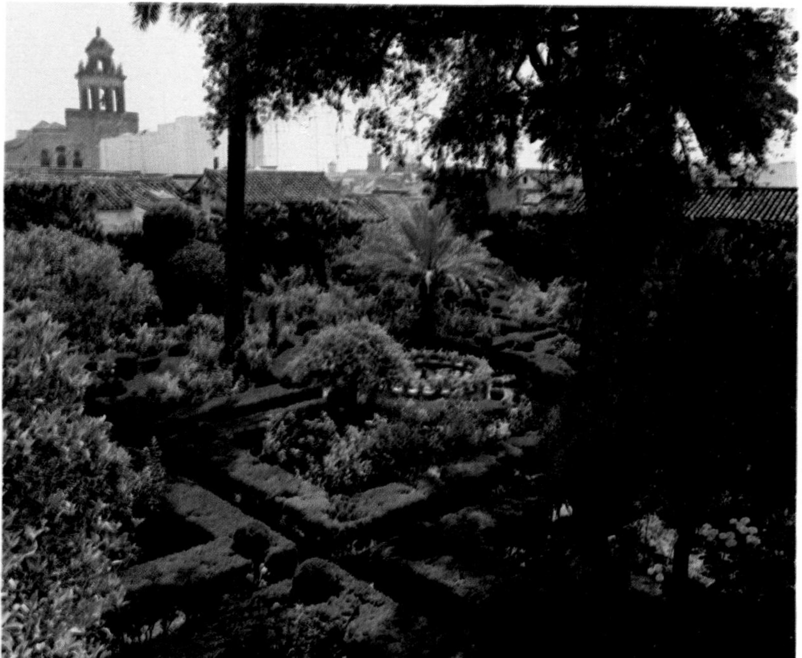
MAIN GARDEN, DON GOME ESTATE. *Photo S. Saavedra.*

PATIO OF THE MADAMA. DON GOME ESTATE. *Photo S. Saavedra.*

DETAIL MADAMA. *Photo S. Saavedra.*

[1] VILLIERS STUART, Mrs.: *Spanish Gardens,* Batsford, London, 1929, page 44.
[2] MONTOTO, Santiago: *El Alcázar de Sevilla,* Ed. Plus Ultra, Madrid, 1948, page 134.
[3] VILLIERS STUART, Mrs.: *Op. cit.,* page 44.
[4] RIVAS, Duque de: "Una antigualla de Sevilla", romance III, *Obras completas,* Seville, 1854, vol. III, page 6.
[5] CARO, Rodrigo: *Antigüedades de Sevilla,* printed by Andrés Grande, Seville, 1634, page 56.
[6] VILLIERS STUART, Mrs.: *Op. cit.,* page 47.
[7] VILLIERS STUART, Mrs.: *Op. cit.,* page 47.
[8] GROMORT, Georges: *Jardins d'Espagne,* A. Vincent, Paris, 1926, vol. I.
[9] CARO Rodrigo: *Op. cit.,* page 56.
[10] HOLLAND, Lady Elisabeth: *Spanish Journal,* ed. by the Earl of Chichester, London, 1910, page 58.
[11] CARO, Rodrigo: *Op. cit.,* page 57.
[12] RIVAS, Duque de: "El Alcázar de Sevilla". *Op. cit.,* romance I, page 16.
[13] GROMORT, Georges: *Op. cit.,* vol. I.
[14] CARO, Rodrigo: *Op. cit.,* page 57.
[15] VILLIERS STUART, Mrs.: *Op. cit.,* page 52.
[16] ROMERO MURUBE, Joaquín: *Alcázar de Sevilla,* Patrimonio Nacional, Madrid, 1968, page 109.
[17] CARO, Rodrigo: *Op. cit.,* page 57.
[18] VILLIERS STUART, Mrs.: *Op. cit.,* page 49.
[19] VILLIERS STUART, Mrs.: *Op. cit.,* page 51.
[20] VILLIERS STUART, Mrs.: *Op. cit.,* page 53.
[21] RIVAS, Duque de: "El Alcázar de Sevilla" *Op. cit.,* romance I, page 17.
[22] VILLIERS STUART, Mrs.: *Op. cit.,* pages 56 & 57.
[23] GONZÁLEZ MORENO, Joaquín: *Don Fernando Enríquez de Rivera, tercer Duque de Alcalá de los Gazules,* Seville, 1969, page 147.
[24] CARO, Rodrigo, *Op. cit.,* page 63.
[25] ARCHIVO de don Luis Gerardo Afan de Ribera, Seville.
[26] GONZÁLEZ MORENO, J.: *Op. cit.,* page 36.
[27] VILLIERS STUART, Mrs.: *Op. cit.,* page 57.
[28] TICKNOR, George: *Life, Letters and Journals,* Boston, 1876, page 227.
[29] VILLIERS STUART, Mrs.: *Op. cit.,* page 63.
[30] GROMORT, Georges: *Op. cit.,* vol. I.

HOUSE OF DON RICARDO LOPEZ. Córdoba. *Photo S. Saavedra.*

PLAZA ROMERO DE TORRES. *Photo S. Saavedra.*

5 MEDIEVAL AND CLOISTER GARDENS

We have already seen how *alcázares* with their gardens, patios and mosques were built during the tenth to fifteenth centuries in the south of Spain, then occupied by the Arabs, and how they attained unsurpassed refinement and perfection.

By contrast, in the north of Spain, where the nobles and monks had sought refuge from the Arab invasion and established the Christian Court, architecture and sculpture were crude and primitive, though influenced by oriental art, as can be appreciated in the pre-Romanesque churches that still stand in Asturias and León.

The *Mozarabes,* Christians who had lived with the Arabs and learned their techniques of tile-making, plaster-work, bronzes and wood-carving, brought their art to the north and applied it to Christian buildings. The brickwork in the convent of Santa Clara in Tordesillas near Valladolid reminds us of the decoration of the tower of the Giralda in Seville.

San Miguel de Escalada in the province of León was built by the Abbot Alfonso and his monks, who had fled persecution by the Arab chiefs in Córdoba in the year 913. The use of horseshoe arches in the beautiful porch, where ancient columns were employed, shows the Cordoban influence.

Living conditions during the Middle Ages were not conducive to gardening. There was neither time nor space for gardens in the walled enclosures of castles, perched as they usually were on rocky promontories so as to command the best view. Life was a continuous struggle to resist invasion and, in most cases, there was only one meagre well to supply the needs of the inhabitants. "During those turbulent days monasteries alone afforded the tranquillity necessary for gardens and the other arts of peace";[2] monks cultivated orchards and gardens to produce fruit and vegetables for their sustenance.

The Marqués de Lozoya writes in his interesting study on Spanish gardens: "There also prevailed among Christian people in the Middle Ages the concept of the cloister-garden, small and secluded, where men sought refuge from the adversity of nature, with which they had to contend in their pursuits of war and hunting. In the borders of illuminated

"LE ROMAN DE LA ROSE" (fifteenth century). *British Museum. London.*

SANTA CLARA DE TORDESILLAS. *Photo Más.*

OLITE CASTLE. *Photo Más.*

manuscripts and on Gothic tapestries, lovers' colloquies and the games of jugglers are depicted in secluded gardens with fountains bordered by tiny flowers. In Spain the gardens of the Castle of Olite were particularly famous, founded at the beginning of the fifteenth century by Charles III (the Noble), King of Navarre (1387-1425).

These gardens, like the rest of the Alcázar, were probably a synthesis of European styles at the twilight of the age of chivalry. Charles brought French architects and sculptors, Flemish glass-makers and plumbers, and Andalusian stucco-workers, potters and tile-makers. There were raised gardens surrounded by galleries as well as lower gardens merging into orchards and woodland."[3]

Yarnoz, who restored the Castle of Olite, tells us: "Charles III of Navarre paid special attention to the gardens of the royal mansion and endeavoured to introduce and acclimatise various plants there. One of these gardens, that adjoining the Queen's chamber, was literally suspended in air, by the very skilful use of Gothic arches. Stone slabs were laid over arches and covered with two metres of soil. This garden, intended no doubt for the Queen's pleasure, was surrounded by a Gothic gallery, and the buttress of one of these arches still stands. This hanging garden might easily have been the one called "de los Toronjales (grapefruit) because of its position, sheltered against the north winds which are always harmful to grapefruit trees."[4]

Some historians say that the first orange trees known in France arrived about 1550, when five were presented by the last of the Queens of Navarre, Doña Catalina, to the Queen of France. "One of these orange trees, which can well be called historic, was said to have been planted in the Palace of Pamplona by Queen Eleanor, wife of Charles the Noble. After it was sent to France the tree was at first kept at Fontainebleau but during the reign of Louis XIV it was brought to the magnificent conservatory at Versailles, where it survived until the beginning of the twentieth century, known by the names of "Grand Connétable" or "Grand Bourbon". It is almost certain that this venerable orange tree originated in the gardens of Olite. There is a tradition in Versailles that it had come from Pamplona, but the climate of Olite was much more favourable for these trees than that of Pamplona, so it is more probable that it came from there."[5] At the Palace of Olite there was an aviary with a water tank for singing birds, swans and peacocks. Canals watered the gardens, and exotic species, including pomegranates, lemon and orange trees, flourished. There was a tiny garden for bathing, and the Belvedere Garden with its fountain.

In the gardens of Tafalla and the tower at Pamplona the King kept bird and lion cages. He reared deer and ostriches and enjoyed exhibiting wild animals, as did Alfonso V of Aragón in the Real of Valencia, and Henry IV of Castille in his palaces of Segovia and Balsaín.[6]

During his travels in the sixteenth century, Philip II's archer, Enrique Cock, described the gardens of El Real in Valencia with their clipped myrtle figures representing various animals and a tournament of knights, calling it "work of the Moors." "Between the arches on the sides of the bridge there was an abundance of myrtle and other greenery among which oranges and lemons hung, the whole so skilfully arranged that one seemed to be passing through a well-cultivated orchard.

"In addition, there were newly-planted orange trees, a joy to behold, with their roots spreading out in all directions. Between them, the river Guadalaviar could be seen as from a window."[7] Here one can appreciate the Arab sense of perspective, akin to contemplating a view through a building.

"El Real, which once belonged to the Moors, is a very lovely building with beautiful gardens; in one of them, jousting knights and various animals are clipped in the greenery."[8]

Filipe de Guana later records that he saw these gardens on the occasion of Philip III's wedding to Margaret of Austria in 1599, and that the Huerta del Patriarca "was beautifully decorated with benches of coloured tiles and trellises of orange and lemon trees bearing their yellow fruit; its walls were planted with myrtle; channels of clear water crossed the orchard, and one could see the apparatus for distributing it to other waterways."

He speaks of the fountain, and gardens divided into squares (probably sown by throwing mixed flower-seeds in the Arab manner), "in some of the squares tiny herbs abounded with their flowers of different colours, and in others there were various native species of fruit and other trees that the Patriarch had ordered for his orchard." He also describes "the high walls interwoven with green orange trees, which with their oranges resembled tapestries of green and yellow satin and afforded great pleasure."[10] He also mentions the animals: wild boar, fallow deer, ostriches, white swans and wild beasts in cages.

This Valencian garden has a pronounced medieval Arab flavour. The arch over the bridge of El Real has remained as it was when Cock saw it in the time of Philip II, "its windows decorated in the Roman style with myrtle (which the Arabs called *arrayn*), orange and lemon trees" so that crossing the bridge was like traversing a long, broad platform in some pleasant royal orchard, in the daytime bright with sunshine, and at night glittering with lights."[11] The Arab tradition, which lived on relatively unchanged, is evident in these gardens. They were created and tended by the Moriscos (Moors who remained in Spain after the banishment of the Muslims, adopting or pretending to adopt the Catholic faith).

Enrique Cock also visited the palace of the Duke of Infantado in Guadalajara, which possessed gardens, fountains in its rooms in the Arab style, and a pool with swans.

Describing the house of the Duke of Infantado, Antonio Lalaing tells us: "In a small chamber on the lower floor a fountain provides water for the entire house. This water was channelled into the great drawing room where another similar small fountain stands, and both run from the garden to a large fishpond, very deep and full of trout and other fish."[12]

Each of these fountains probably stood in the centre of its respective room connected by a small channel with the fountain in the garden. This palace and garden, with their obvious Moorish influence, were certainly constructed long before Lalaing's

SAN MIGUEL DE ESCALADA. León. *Photo Author.*

CLARISAS CLOISTER. Pedralbes. *Photo Más.*

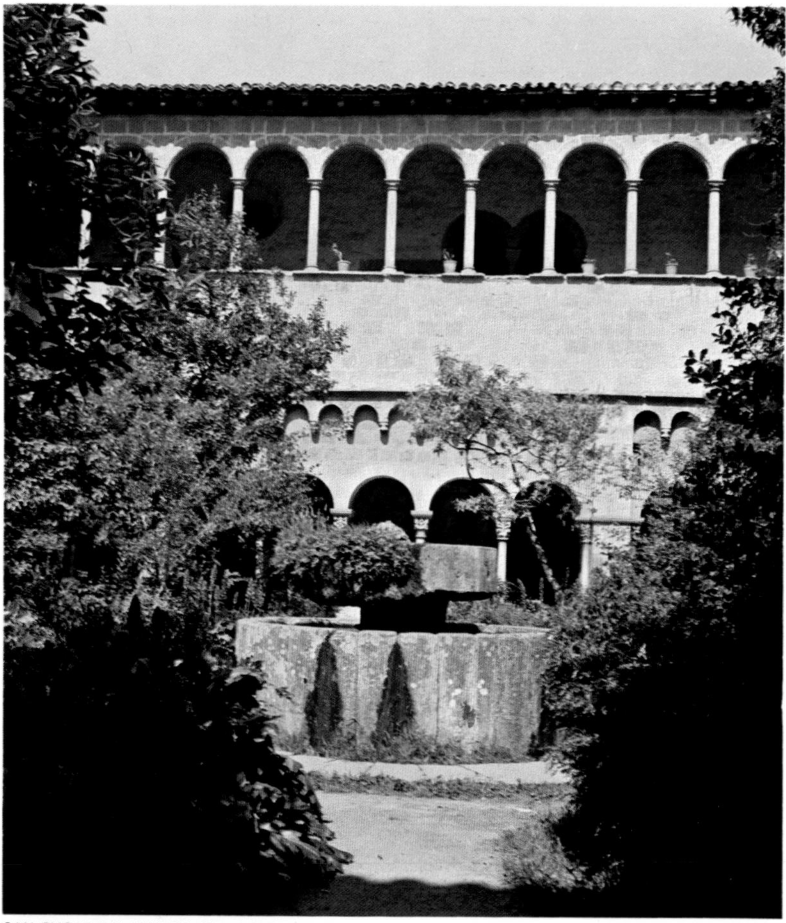

SAN CUGAT DEL VALLES. *Photo Author.*

SAN PABLO DEL CAMPO. Barcelona. *Photo Más.*

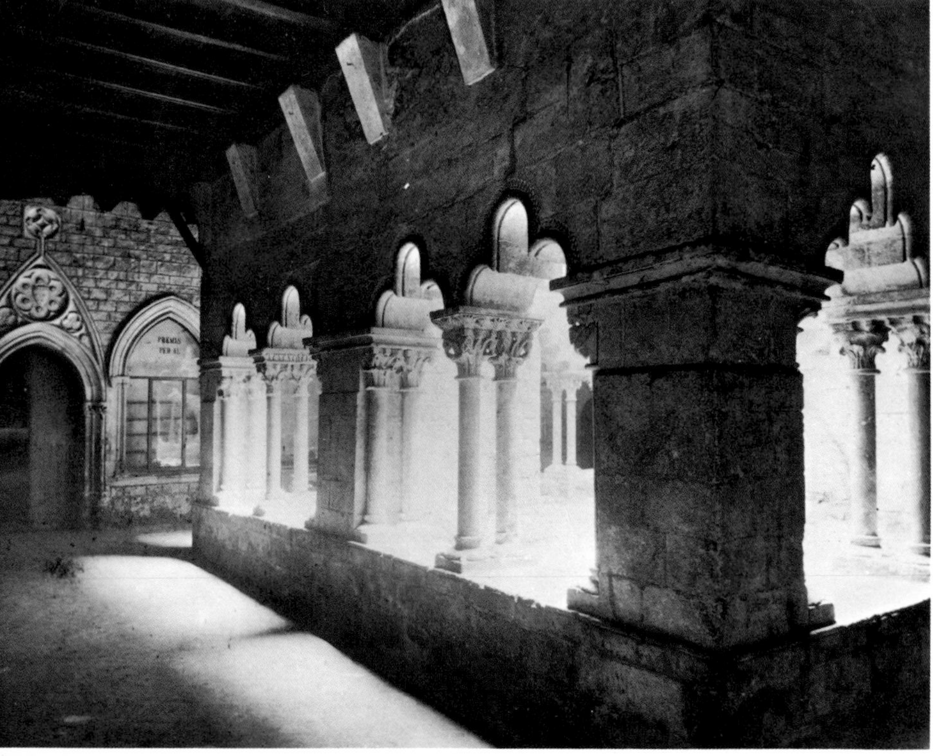

visit, since the lower rooms of the house would have been stables and servants' quarters in a medieval castle.

Let us now turn our attention from these palace gardens to Spain's cloisters.

The Benedictines, established during the tenth and eleventh centuries, were among the first orders in Spain.

Most of the abbeys devoted a plot in their orchards to the cultivation of medicinal herbs, many of which the monks succeeded in acclimatising. Inspired by the Roman gardens, they also grew flowers such as roses and madonna lilies to decorate their altars.

The Rule of St. Benedict, the basis of all subsequent rules, is distinguished by its genuine Roman character. Not only does the Benedictine monastery's design around a rectangular colonnaded court recall a Roman villa with its *impluvium,* but the coarse monastic garment or habit worn by the Benedictines is nothing more than a slight adaptation — in a rough fabric, naturally — of the elegant vestments of the Roman *cives.*[13]

This Roman influence is not surprising when we consider that "hermits often established themselves in the ruins of Roman villas in Italy, and it was from a grotto by the ruins of Nero's villa at Subiaco that the most famous of them emerged at the end of the fifth century to lay down the rule of the first monastic order in western Europe.

Both at Subiaco where he planted a rose garden, and later at Cassino, St. Benedict established himself and his monks among the ruins of Roman villas, and there can be little doubt that the monastery cloister evolved from the colonnaded peristyle of the Roman country house, and that, without its shelter, classical culture and gardening would never have survived the Early Middle Ages."[14]

Christian cloisters can generally be distinguished from patios by the low wall or parapet, sometimes adorned with fretwork that surrounds them and serves as a base for columns. In Graeco-Roman and Arab patios, the columns stand on the floor.

The cloisters of Spanish monasteries contain gardens of many periods and styles because of the convergence of Graeco-Roman and Arab traditions. Religious communities obviously required peace, silence, and above all, seclusion, as did the Arabs for different reasons. It was therefore natural for them to place their gardens, as the Arabs had, within colonnaded enclosures.

San Cugat del Vallés, built near Barcelona during the Reconquest in the eleventh century, contains one of the most beautiful Benedictine cloisters. In the centre of this cloister is a fountain with two basins, one above the other, surrounded by orange and laurel trees. The cloister reminds us of early Roman courtyards, such as those in the Santi Cuattro Coronati and San Paolo Fuora Muri. The central fountain at San Cugat appears to belong to the Roman period, like that in Santi Cuattro Coronati, but the basins of the latter are circular instead of octagonal. This type of fountain is frequently found in old Catalonian cloisters, and is also to be seen in the cloister of Barcelona Cathedral, in the chapel dedicated to Saint George, and in the Convent of the Poor Clares at Pedralbese, to mention but a few.

The cloister of the Convent of the Poor Clares is one of the most beautiful in Spain. Founded in 1325 by Queen Elisenda de Moncada, it possesses a triple gallery, the lower two dating from the fourteenth century, with pointed arches mounted on slender monolithic columns.[15] In a corner of the cloister stands a beautiful fountain with upper and lower basins, crowned by a white marble angel in an attitude of prayer.

The parish of San Pablo del Campo, founded by Wifredo II in 914, is the oldest in Barcelona. It has a tiny secluded cloister with trilobate arches that is very intimate and primitive.

The Gothic quarter of Barcelona gives us a feeling of what medieval Mediterranean cities must have been like. Some of the houses are of Catalan-Gothic style, with fine columns of a type also found in Majorca.

In the beautiful Palacio de la Diputación (Provincial Council) is a patio, strangely situated on the upper storey, planted with orange trees; it contains a fine fountain supporting a statuette of St. George.

The cloister in Barcelona Cathedral dates from the fifteenth century. At its northern corner stands a Gothic fountain-pavilion with a picture of St. George on the ceiling of the dome. In the centre is a double-basined fountain similar to that found in other Catalan cloisters, but octagonal in this case and carved in the Gothic period. Beside this fountain-pavilion is a square pond called the Fountain of the Geese.

In a narrow street opposite the main façade of the Cathedral stands a typical medieval dwelling. It is the house of the Archdeacon, whose courtyard, in spite of its tiny proportions, has all the characteristics of the classic Catalonian patio with its exterior stairway and central wall. Such features make Catalonian patios unlike any others in Spain.

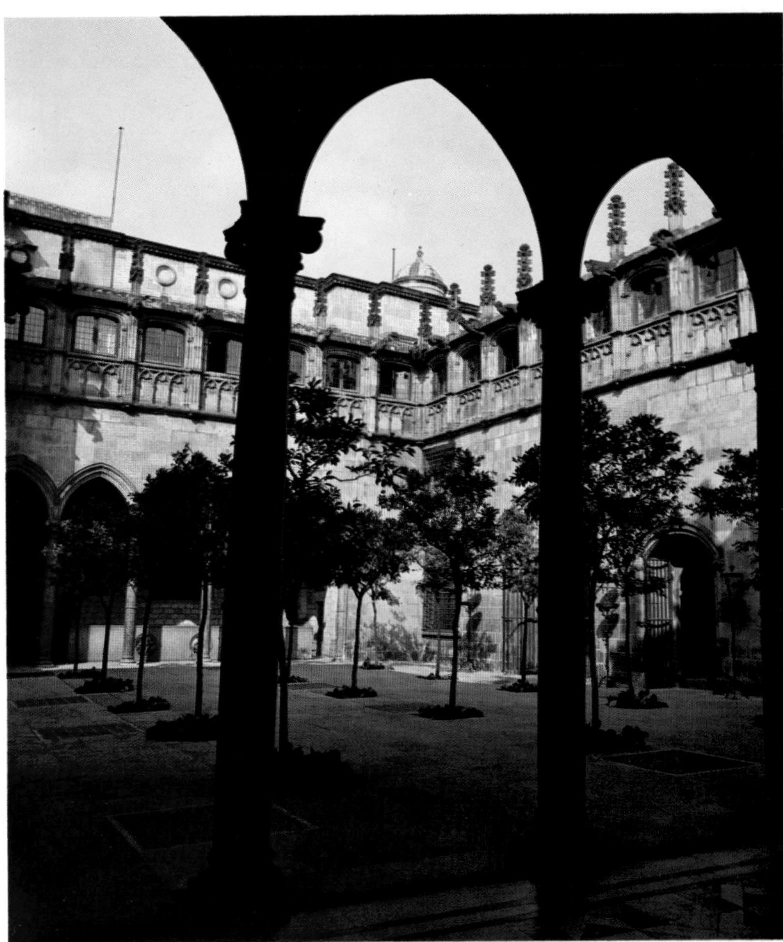

PATIO OF THE ORANGE TREES. Diputación. Barcelona. *Photo S. Saavedra.*

HOUSE OF THE ARCHDEACON. Barcelona. *Photo Author.*

GOTHIC FOUNTAIN. CATHEDRAL OF BARCELONA. *Photo Más.*

PAVILION, POBLET. *Photo Más.*

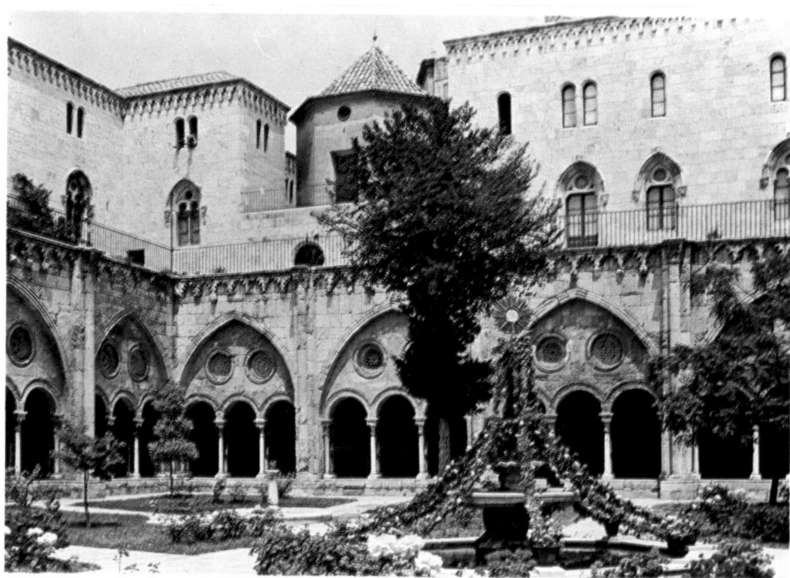

CLOISTER, TARRAGONA CATHEDRAL.

SILOS MONASTERY. Burgos. *Photo Más.*

As mentioned earlier, Benedictine monks were among the first to arrive in Spain. Their duties included reading and manual labour, and in the monastery of Santo Domingo de Silos (Burgos) they attached great importance to the Gregorian chant. The cloister of this monastery is one of the finest examples of Spanish Romanesque. A tall cypress, which inspired a poem by Friar Just Pérez del Urbel, grows in the northern corner. This cloister is a haven of peace and golden Castilian light, in which, according to Lozoya, "the shadow of the solitary tree points the hours like the hand of a sundial, on the capitals in the gallery."

This cypress is not as old as it looks. It was planted by a French monk who came from the Benedictine Abbey of Ligugé, (Vienne) France in 1880; it owes its extraordinary development to the shelter of the cloister.

The garden that has recently been laid out in the centre of the cloister is not in keeping with the medieval setting. The paths are paved with rough, irregularly shaped stones, where square slabs would have been more appropriate. In the garden's centre is an old basin of blackened stone, probably a baptismal font, now used as a fountain. The round pond is encircled with the same inappropriate pavement. Originally there must have been a well and a small kitchen garden for the monastery's use.

The great gardeners among the early religious orders, says Mrs. Villiers Stuart, were the Cistercians, who came to Spain in the twelfth century.

The accumulation of riches in the Order of Cluny and its great influence in court circles had weakened the spirit of St. Benedict and the first Benedictine monks. "In order to restore the purity of this spirit a great reformer, St. Bernard, retired to the desert of Citeaux, near Dijon, France and founded the Cistercian Order, becoming the first Abbot of Clairvaux. From this base, white monks set forth to travel throughout Europe as the black monks of Cluny had done in days of old."[16]

The monks of Citeaux cultivated vineyards and produced the renowned *Clos Vougeot* and *Romanée* in Burgundy, among many others.

SANTAS CREUS. CLOISTER OF ABAD. *Photo Más.*

They encouraged agriculture and horticulture, and their monasteries were generally built beside rivers to permit irrigation. It was they who moved the well from its traditional spot in the centre of the cloister to the corner nearest to the refectory door, for greater convenience in washing work-soiled hands before meals.[17]

"The most important Cistercian edifice in the Peninsula is the monastery of Poblet, founded in the twelfth century soon after the Reconquest. Here Martin the Humane lived. Here too the arcades serve as a covering to the terraces of the Royal Palace. The charm of the cloister, which has such great Romanesque importance, lies especially in the belvedere beside the northern gallery and its lovely fountain."[18]

This monastery was founded by the Cistercians who came from Toulouse in 1159. The great cloister was built between 1303 and 1341 in the Gothic style. Against the southern corner, near the refectory — as is customary in Cistercian monasteries — stands a Romanesque pavilion of earlier construction than the cloister, with a wide-basined fountain of the same primitive style as Poblet's original construction and probably dating from the same time. It has the charm typical of abandoned gardens.

"From this main cloister," Federico Carlos Sainz de Robles writes, "through a vaulted passage that was once the parlour, one penetrates into the ancient twelfth century cloister, one of the most beautiful remaining from the Romanesque period, with its old bay laurels and hazel trees, a most lovely garden, full of poetry."[19] In the centre of this garden, almost hidden by hedges and tall cypresses, is a small fountain. The Royal Palace also has a patio with an ancient central well. Behind the monastery there are some marvellous specimens of cypress *cupressus sempervirens* such as can be seen only on the Mediterranean coast.

The cloisters of Santas Creus have not, up to now, been remodelled, like that of Tarragona, and therefore still keep their old monastic atmosphere.

"In the unequalled series of cloister-gardens of Spain," says Lozoya, "none can compare with the great cloister of Tarragona

SANTAS CREUS. PAVILION. *Photo Author.*

SANTAS CREUS. CLOISTER. *Photo Más.*

Cathedral. In every respect it is the building which bears most clearly the Cistercian imprint."[20] This garden has recently been remodelled, and rose-beds have been planted, with writing formed in cotton lavender around them. This destroys the monastic atmosphere of the beautiful cloister, giving it the appearance of a public park. In one corner, however, there is a marvellous and truly unique orange tree, clipped to form several platforms. Apparently, this cloister was originally planted entirely with orange trees, and grilles had to be inserted in all the arches to prevent people from stealing the fruit.

On the island of Majorca stands one of the most beautiful cloisters of the southern Gothic style: that of San Francisco de Palma. It was built in 1286 with pointed arches, slender columns and a single-storied gallery. Its central well dates from the seventeenth century. The church contains the tomb of the mystic monk Ramon Lull, an extraordinary figure of the Middle Ages, born in 1235.

The Carthusian monks, who followed the rule of St. Benedict, built several admirable monasteries in Spain. One of them, the Cartuja de Miraflores near Burgos, is famous for the cultivation of roses, and its friars still make rosaries with rose petals.

The Order of St. Jerome arrived in Spain in the fourteenth century, adopting the rule of St. Augustine. Their first and most important monastery was the magnificent St. Bartholomew of Lupiana in the Alcarria, (Guadalajara), built in about 1373 and now partially destroyed. Although the Hieronymites were also established in Italy, this Order is essentially Spanish and became very powerful. The cloister of Lupiana is one of the finest of the Renaissance cloisters in Castille. It was built in the first part of the sixteenth century for Don Alfonso Carrillo de Albornoz, Archbishop of Toledo, and is the masterpiece of the architect Alonso de Covarrubias (1488-1570). The golden light of the Alcarria filters through the open-work balustrades, gilding the limestone of its lovely columns.

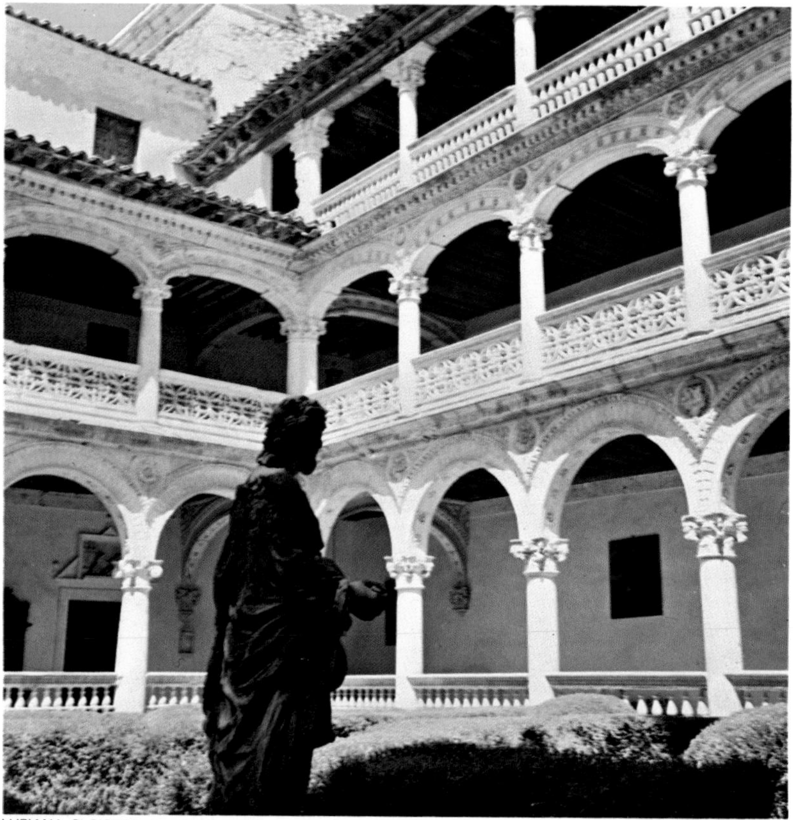

LUPIANA CLOISTER. Guadalajara. *Photo Author.*

SAN FRANCISCO CLOISTER. Palma de Majorca. *Photo Author.*

SAN MILLAN COGOLLA. Suso. *Photo Más.*

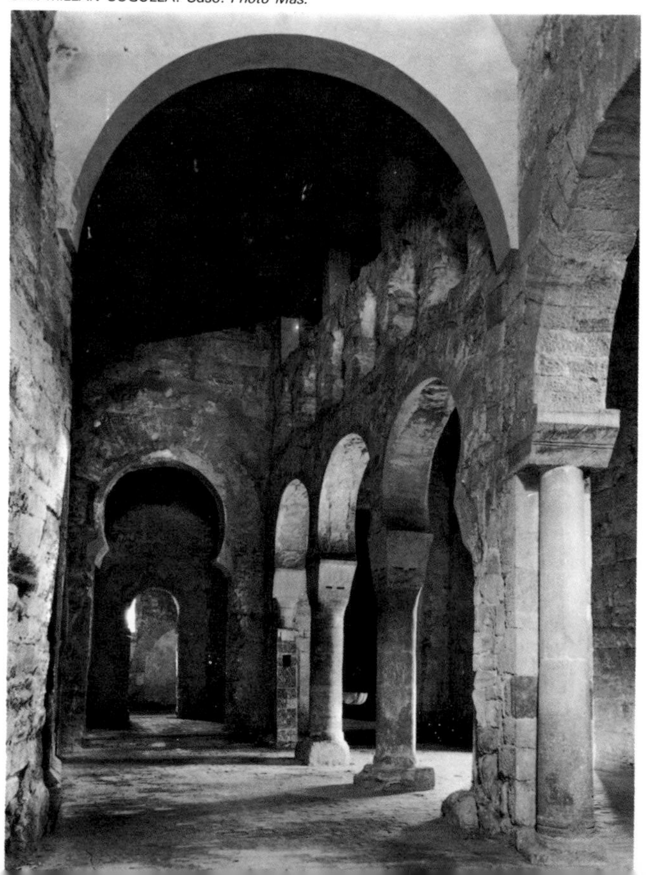

The Order of St. Jerome was the favourite of the early members of the Royal House of Austria. It was under the protection of the Hieronymites in Yuste that Charles V wished to die; and Philip II chose them to rule the monastery of Escorial. Hidden amid the sierras they built their famous monastery of Guadalupe after the discovery of the image of Our Lady, which inspired great devotion. They occupied it from 1389 onwards. "The most characteristic part of Guadalupe," Lozoya tells us, "is the great cloister in which Almohade forms are adapted with singular and beautiful effect to the monastic arrangement. In the north-west corner, as in most Cistercian cloisters, is a small fountain-pavilion for ablutions, with an inlaid tile pavement. The most interesting feature is the central pavilion, built about 1405. In this pavilion the monks tried to reproduce, in whitewashed brickwork, a stone Gothic construction. The *Mudejar* influence appears in the Moorish interlaced lines and the intricate network of blue and green ceramic tiles. This influence is even more evident today as the bricks have been exposed in the entire upper section."[21]

In a secluded corner of the Rioja region, hidden among the foothills of the Sierra de la Demanda, lie the two monasteries of San Millán de la Cogolla. The lower of the two, called "de Yuso", is an enormous neoclassic construction which has been called the "Escorial of the Rioja." In the diary of Jovellanos we read that at the end of the eighteenth century the Yuso monastery, which had belonged to the Benedictine Order, still had "a large apothecary's shop well-stocked with many fine jars of earthenware and glass of all shapes and sizes. The botanic garden offered many herbs and plants, and a few trees: two acacias, a Babylon willow, Lombardy and Caroline poplars, a fine birch tree and three kinds of laurel — the common or bay, the imperial, and another medical variety, a Persian species. There was a pond for leeches, with a thick grille over the inlet, and running water, a small conservatory for delicate and exotic plants, and a good herb garden, well-stocked."

The strangest item was the viper's nest: "Against a wall in a southern position there is a small enclosure, about a yard and a half deep, with very smooth inside walls. In the bottom of this enclosure are stones, rubble and weeds. Here live the vipers, here they breed, to be sold for consumption and replaced every year." This extraordinary trade may have been based on a therapeutic practice, in which the body of this poisonous reptile was used to make a nourishing broth.

None of all this remains at Yuso. It is assumed that the monastery was abandoned upon the disendowment of Church property in 1835. The orchard and the botanic garden have disappeared, but the apothecary's room is still there, in ruins, with the shelves that once contained flasks and bottles. A stream of running water can also be seen in a corner of the courtyard at the entrance to the monastery; it must have fed the leeches' pool mentioned by Jovellanos.

Scarcely a kilometre away, on the summit of the mountain, stands the higher of the two monasteries, Suso, a small Mozarab *cenobium* or monastery built about the tenth century. It was the boyhood home of medieval poet Ganzalo de Berceo and contains the tombs of the legendary Infantes de Lara. No more poetic place can be seen in Spain.

ORANGE TREE. TARRAGONA CATHEDRAL.

GUADALUPE CLOISTER. *Photo Oronoz.*

SAN LORENZO CLOISTER. Compostela. *Photo S. Saavedra.*

FONSECA CLOISTER. Compostela. *Photo Author.*

The monasteries of Galicia have a special charm and mystery, due to the misty light and the colour of their ancient stones.

The monastery of Poyo — occupied today by the Order of Our Lady of Mercy — is on the outskirts of Pontevedra, situated on a summit overlooking the Bay of Marín. In the cloister there is a monumental eighteenth century fountain which is more ornamental than utilitarian, which is rare in monastic cloisters.

The Fonseca cloister, today the School of Pharmacy of Santiago de Compostela, is one of the most beautiful of the Spanish Renaissance, with its harmonious proportions, delicate columns, gargoyles and marvellous stone cresting along the edge of the roof.

The radiance of this cloister, whose stone is of the sombre hue of northern cities, is spectacular in the spring when its four great pale pink azaleas bloom and bring life to this ancient site.

On the outskirts of Compostela stands the Monastery of San Lorenzo, which previously belonged to the Franciscans and is now the property of the Duchess of Soma. It was acquired by her parents, the Duke and Duchess of Terranova, following the disendowment of Church property.

The cloister contains a dense network of boxwood hedges clipped in patterns which can only be appreciated from the upper windows. Don José Filgueira Valverde, Curator of the Museum of Pontevedra, says that the design is similar to that of old iron grills once used to bake a Galician pastry called *flores* (flowers). This garden is reputed to be about four hundred years old. In the centre of the western side a few steps lead down to a fountain or natural spring which is surmounted by a statue of the Virgin.

The chapel of this ancient monastery has a magnificent sixteenth century marble altarpiece, reputed to be the work of Aprile di Carona, who was also responsible for the central fountain in the Casa de Pilatos in Seville. This altarpiece was brought to Santiago by the Duchess of Terranova in the last century. It came from the Convent of San Francisco in Seville, together with the white marble kneeling statues on the side walls of the church.

The Cloister of the Evangelists in the Monastery of El Escorial is a beautiful example of vegetation blended with architecture in which ponds bordered with boxwood harmonise with the severe Renaissance structure. The elegance of its fountain-pavilion and the originality of its design make it a model of the cloister-garden in Spain. It now shows an eighteenth century influence stemming from its restoration in 1717, when the great parterres were added on the northern and southern sides of the monastery. They are called The Friars' Gardens, and their construction in the French style may have been ordered by Philip V.

According to the chronicler Father Sigüenza, these gardens were planted during the time of Philip II, in the Arab manner, by simply scattering seeds of a great variety of flowers. Father Sigüenza tells us that "in these two squares twelve fountains are distributed; around each of them there are four square flower beds, forming gay and artistic sections. Wide paths are seen on either side, and sown in the beds are flowers of various colours — white, blue, red, yellow, crimson and other pleasing mixtures; they are so well placed that, from the windows above, the effect is of rich carpets brought from Turkey, Cairo or Damascus.

In the centre of each pond there is a granite pineapple from

POYO CLOISTER. Pontevedra. *Photo S. Saavedra.*

CLOISTER OF THE EVANGELISTS. Escorial.

which water gushes like a crystal spray. On the walls, from the grilles downwards, there are wooden trellises of rose bushes, *ligustrum* (privet), musk roses, jasmine, honeysuckle and — amazingly — oranges and lemons, whose flowers and fruit we enjoy in spite of the cold westerly and northerly winds from the sierra."[23]

These masses of delicate flowers could not have blended so well as the classic boxwood hedges that adorn the severe façade of the monastery today, though the original garden must have produced a much gayer effect.

The engraving "Les Délices de l'Espagne" shows the original design of the Friars' Garden before it was altered in the time of Philip V. It shows the square plots sown with flowers at the foot of the southern façade, and the avenues of trees, since removed.

This garden was created by Friar Marcos de Cardona who had also designed the garden at Yuste for the Emperor Charles V. Today, although the fountains of the Escorial garden no longer play, the ingenious design of terraced spaces remains.

It would be impossible to mention all the monastic gardens created over the centuries in Spain; they were surely more numerous and survived for a longer time, through the Renaissance and Baroque periods, than those in the rest of Europe. Cloisters in Spanish monasteries have always been built to meet the needs of the communities living in them and to provide shelter from the harsh climate.

"There are cloisters all over Europe," says Lozoya, "but only those of Spain retain the Moorish flavour of Mediterranean gardens."

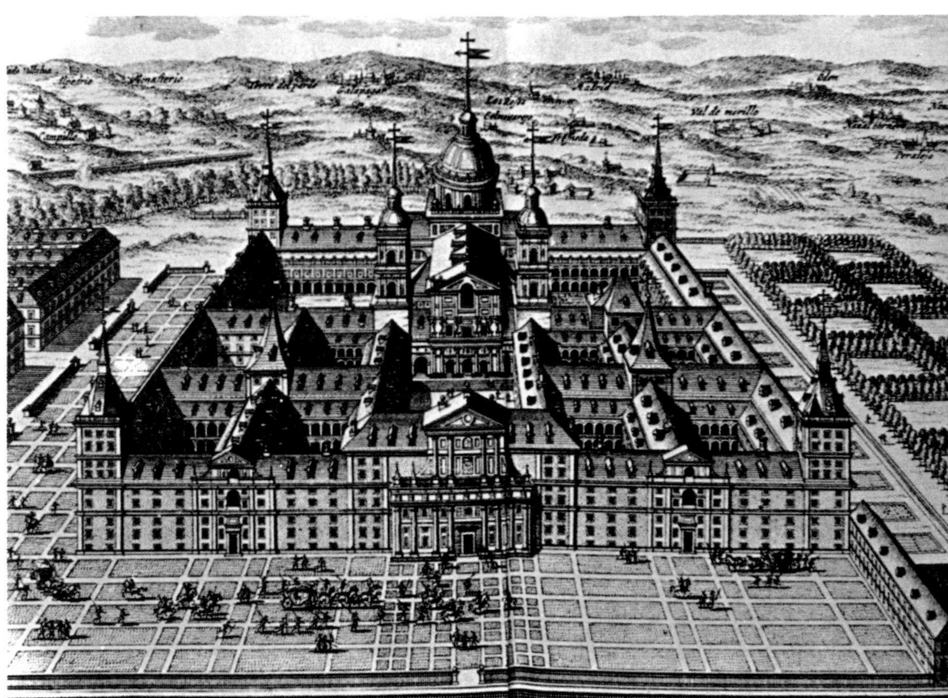

VIEW OF ESCORIAL MONASTERY. *"Les Délices de l'Espagne".*

HOUSE OF THE CONVALESCENTS. Escorial. *Photo Author.*

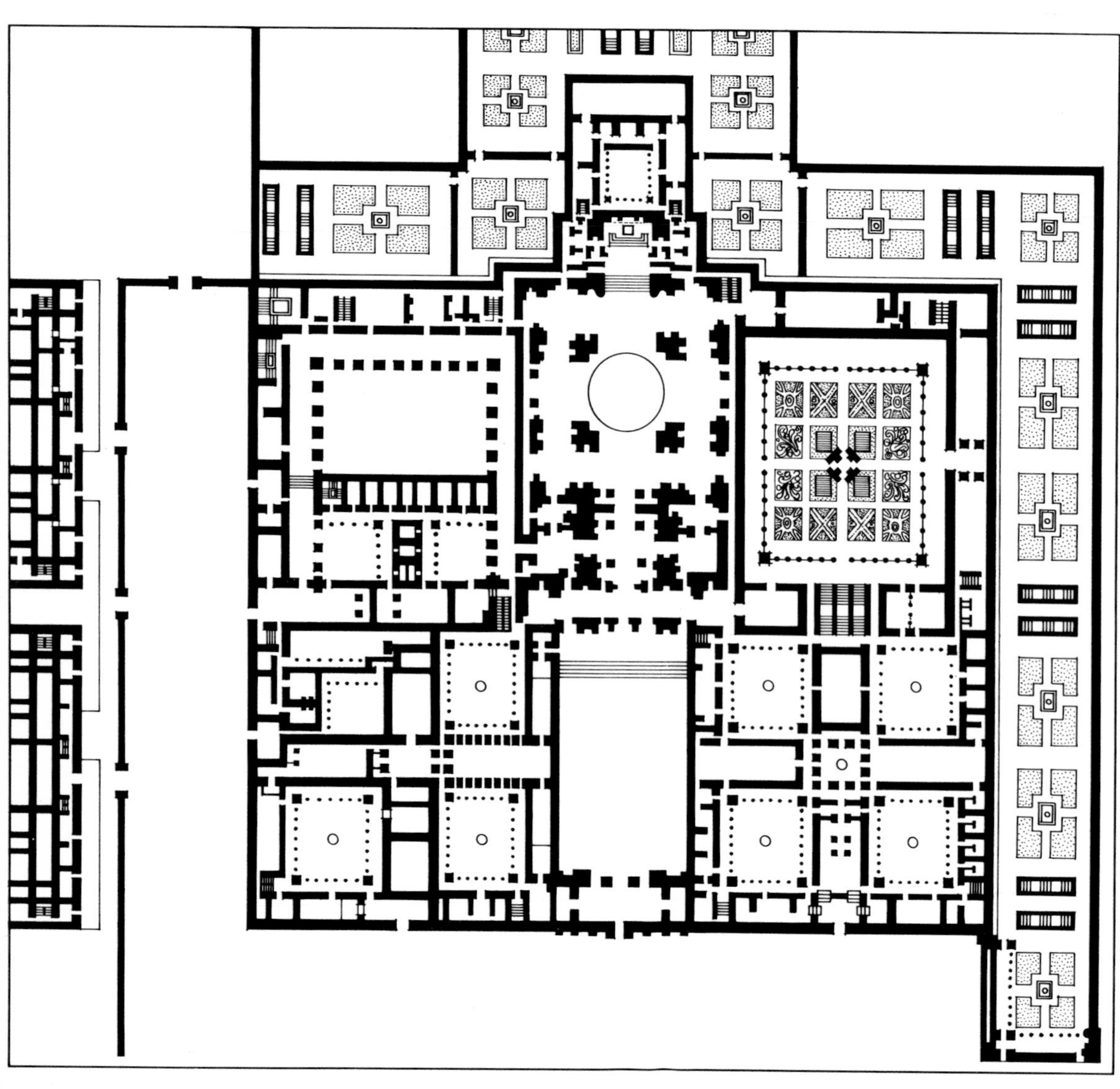

PLAN OF THE ESCORIAL MONASTERY.

[1] LOZOYA, Marqués de: *Historia del arte hispánico,* Ed. Salvat, Barcelona, 1931, vol. I, page 297.

[2] VILLIERS STUART, Mrs.: *Spanish Gardens,* Batsford, London, 1929, page 71.

[3] LOZOYA, Marqués de: *Los jardines españoles,* Ed. Ciguena, Madrid, 1951, page 19.

[4] *Palacio Real de Olite. Restauración de los Cuatro Vientos,* Pamplona, "Príncipe de Viana" Institution, no. 11, pages 11 and 13.

[5] ITURRALDE Y SUIT J.: *El Palacio Real de Olite,* Pamplona, 1922, page 25.

[6] LOZOYA, Marqués de: *Op. cit.,* page 22.

[7] COCK, Enrique: *Viaje de Felipe II en 1585 a Zaragoza, Barcelona y Valencia.* Published by Morel Fatio, 1876, page 233.

[8] COCK, Enrique: *Op. cit.,* page 245.

[9] The Patriarch was the Blessed Juan de Ribera, natural son of Don Per Afán de Ribera, Duque de Alcalá de los Gazules, owner of the House of Pilate in Seville. He was Patriarch of Antioch and Archbishop of Valencia in 1532.

[10] GAUNA, Felipe de: *Relación de las fiestas celebradas en Valencia con motivo del casamiento de Felipe III, 1599.* Acción Valeciana, 1926, page 262.

[11] GAUNA, Felipe de: *Op. cit.,* page 165.

[12] LALAING, Antonio: "Primer viaje de Felipe el Hermoso", *Viajes de extranjeros por España y Portugal,* compiled by J. Garcia Mercadal, Ed. Aguilar, Madrid, 1952, vol. I, page 487.

[13] LUIS, Carlos María de: *Los monasterios asturianos,* Oviedo, 1966, page 138.

[14] MASSON, Georgina: *Italian Gardens,* Thames & Hudson, London, 1966, page 46.

[15] LOZOYA, Marqués de: *Historia del arte hispánico,* Ed. Salvat, Barcelona, 1931, vol. II, page 154.

[16] LOZOYA, Marqués de: *Op. cit.,* vol. II, page 5.

[17] VILLIERS STUART, Mrs.: *Op cit.,* page 76.

[18] LOZOYA, Marqués de: *Op. cit.,* vol. II, pages 18-20.

[19] SAINZ DE ROBLES: *Monasterios de España.* Ed. Aguilar, Madrid, 1953, page 277.

[20] LOZOYA, Marqués de: *Op. cit.,* vol. II, page 27.

[21] LOZOYA, Marqués de: *Op. cit.,* vol. II, page 482.

[22] *Diario de Jovellanos (años 1795-1796),* Institute of Asturian Studies, Oviedo, 1954, vol. II, page 84.

[23] SIGÜENZA, Fray José de: *La fundación del Monasterio de El Escorial,* Ed. Aguilar, Madrid, 1963, page 397.

6 THE GARDENS OF THE RENAISSANCE

Following the conquest of Granada by Ferdinand and Isabella, the art of gardening does not appear to have changed significantly: Mudejar art had already been established throughout Spain, and the gardens planted by the Moors survived, as traditions were handed down. Irrigation by means of pools and small channels — whose construction was the first step in creating any garden — the use of bricks and tiles, plaster-work and carved ceilings all continued, although through Italian influence the Moorish basins were now raised on graceful columns. Thus, when Charles V ordered the construction of the Patios of the Reja and the Lindaraxa in the Alhambra he had the beautiful fountain (familiar through Sargent's watercolours) moved from the Mexuar patio to the Lindaraxa where it was mounted on a Renaissance pedestal.[1] These fountains would no longer be contemplated from a sitting position on the floor as in the time of the Arabs.

It is well known that the Catholic Monarchs loved and cared for the Alhambra and the Generalife (though the latter passed to other hands), altering them and making additions which were not always fortunate in order to convert them into royal seats. They chose Granada for their last resting place, erecting the sumptuous chapel for this purpose.

Their grandson, Charles V, who must have been naturally artistic, appreciated the atmosphere and beauty of Granada to such an extent that he and Isabella of Portugal honeymooned there in 1526. Later, he built the magnificent Palace of Machuca (never completed) perhaps in a desire to make the Alhambra a dwelling worthy of his splendour, or perhaps because he could not adapt his life and that of his court to the austere rooms of the Muslims. Their sedentary and contemplative way of life bore no resemblance to that of this restless and enterprising Flemish monarch. There is a tradition that Charles V liked to spend the winter in Castile because he had better facilities there for his warmth and shelter, and in the summer — like all northerners — he loved the sun and warmth of the south. After his wedding, he spent the hot summer months in the Alhambra, prolonging his stay from June to December, which was probably the happiest period of his hectic life.

DOORWAY, PALACIO DEL VISO. *Photo S. Saavedra.*

FOUNTAIN OF THE UPPER TERRACE. Yuste. *Photo S. Saavedra.*

FAÇADE OF THE EMPEROR'S HOUSE. Yuste. *Photo S. Saavedra.*

He perpetuated his memory in the Alcázar of Seville with the pavilion he built in its gardens, a model of art and beauty and a continuation of Arab art in all its forms. Neither the channel nor the water jet playing in its chamber were omitted.

At the end of his life he sought a place for retirement which would be hidden and secluded and yet dominate a beautiful view, just as an Arab might have conceived it. The Emperor wished above all for this retreat to adjoin a Hieronymite monastery; these conditions he found in the Province of Caceres, at Yuste, where his palace was built at the close of the Gothic period. The Emperor's house was designed to be small and simple, similar to his birthplace in Ghent. The work was begun in 1554 by Fray Antonio de Villacastín, a monk from the Sisla at Toledo who was later to be appointed supervisor of the work performed on the Escorial in 1563.

Charles V arrived at Yuste in November 1556, and died there on 21 September 1558.

There is nothing oriental about the austerity of Yuste, but the simple terrace and the gardens with their pond and semi-tropical vegetation of the Tiétar valley attest to the Emperor's desire to perpetuate Moslem art, whose subtle charm had been rooted in Spain for centuries.

Antonio Ponz tells us that "Charles V was accompanied by the celebrated artist Juanelo Turriano, who probably entertained him at times with his clocks and machinery,"[3] At the Emperor's death Turriano left Yuste for Toledo where he designed the wheel that lifted water from the river Tagus to the Alcázar.[4]

A high wall in the garden separates the monastery and the palace. After crossing the threshold of the wide porch that leads to the Emperor's private enclosure, we find a wide paved ramp supported by brick arches, built so that the Emperor could go up to the palace on horseback, but as he was so ill and physically exhausted he rarely used it.

Here stands the spacious portico with two rows of Tuscan granite columns supported by brick pilasters, facing the ramp. This porch is the finest architectural feature of the austere palace; it is vaguely reminiscent of the Renaissance Italian *loggia* but also suggests an Andalusian influence, open as it is on the south-west façade to the view of the beautiful landscape.

In the left-hand corner of this terrace the Emperor ordered the erection of a stone fountain made of marble-like granite from a nearby quarry in Plasencia. This fountain is octagonal outside and circular inside and is hewn out of a single block of stone. Rising from the centre is a column with a capital carved to represent the folds of drapery. The column supports a basin with four masks emitting fine streams of water. "The water [at Yuste] is very famous for its health-giving properties; and the Emperor drank no other."[5] The rest of the basin is finely chiselled in the form of minute scales, the work of a local artist.

According to Señor Martín, "this terrace was probably covered with flower pots, and immediately around the fountain, a profusion of orange trees and flowers. A similar arrangement existed on the lower floor."[6]

In the southern corner of the terrace, at the right-hand side of the entrance ramp and at the same height as the balustrade of this terrace, is a sundial carved by Juanelo in stone. It is today unfortunately almost hidden by the branches of a thick fig tree.

There is a mounting stone at the foot of the central pillar, facing west, which the Emperor used only once.[7]

The facade of the palace opens to the south and consists of two blocks, each with a balcony, separated by a sun gallery with a simple wooden balustrade; below lies the large square pond in which tradition says the Emperor fished for trout and tench from this balcony. Today the pond has receded further from the building than in Charles V's time. The basement has no access to the garden on this side.

We shall not linger to describe the gloomy apartments; passing through the house from the terrace entrance we find a corridor that ends at a door aligned with the entrance and opening onto another wide terrace that faces east forming an angle with the open cloister of the monastery, recently restored. From here we see a square garden formed of classic designs in cypress, *arizonica glauca.* Rather more a tree than a shrub, this plant is not appropriate for its use here, and we fear that the design will soon be obscured as they spread outwards. This could have been prevented if the garden had been planted with boxwood or some other slow-growing shrub.

In hot weather the Emperor moved his quarters to the ground

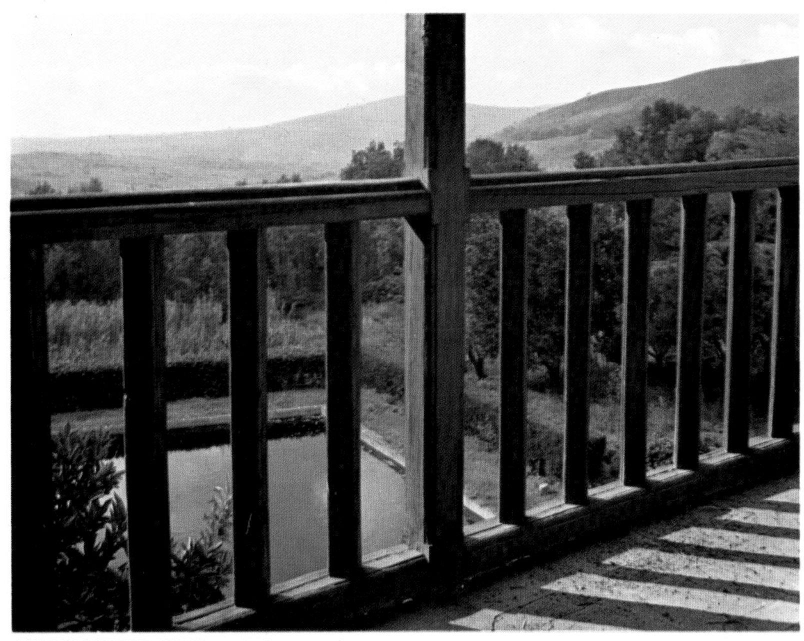

VIEW FROM TERRACE. *Photo Author.*

THE EMPEROR. *Private collection.*

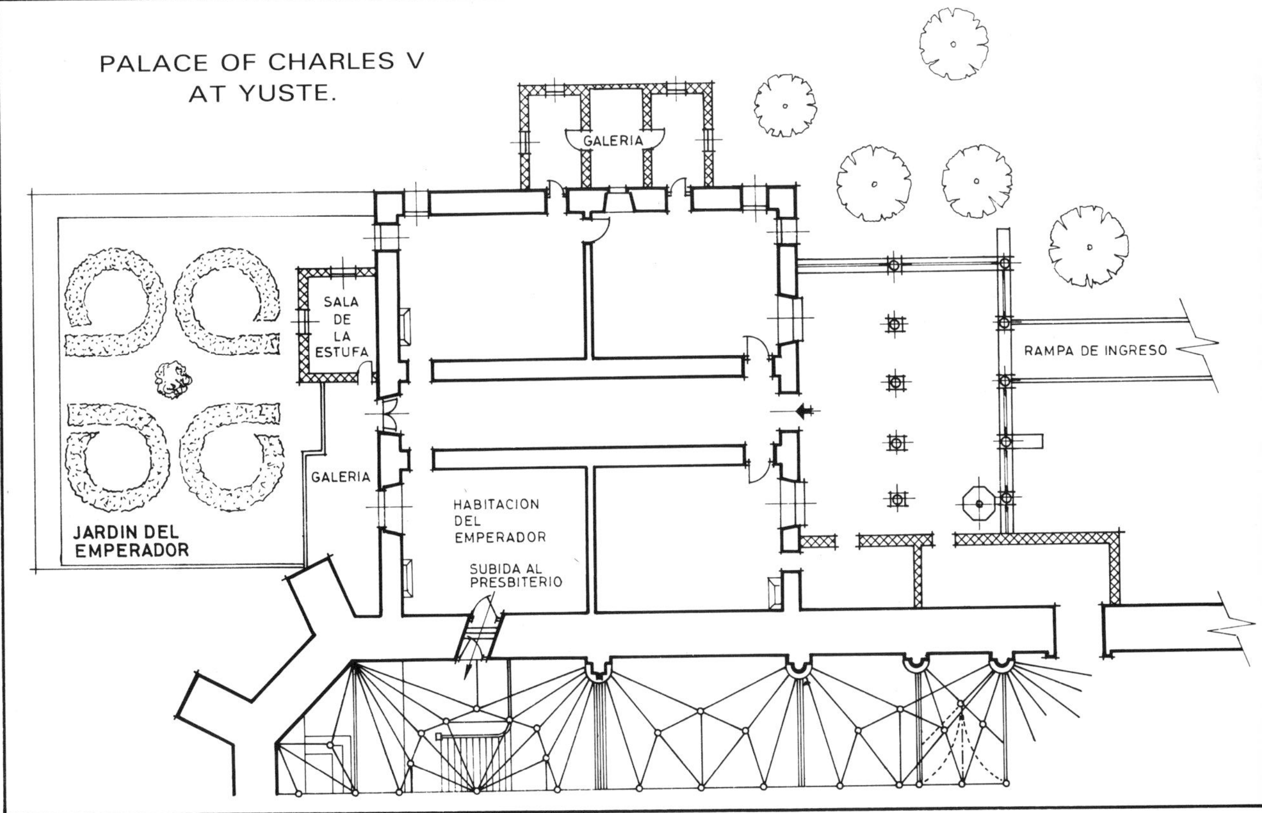

PLATERESQUE CLOISTER. *Photo S. Saavedra.*

THE EMPEROR'S GARDEN. *Photo Author.*
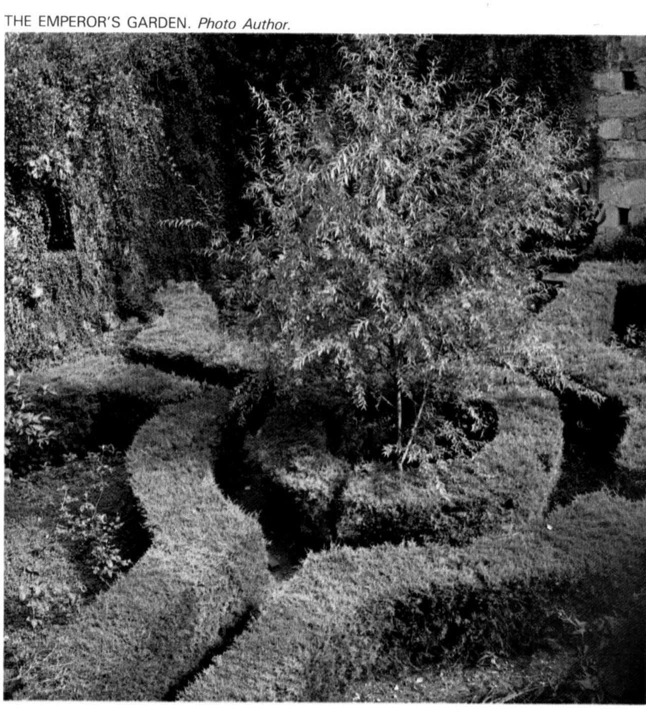

floor of the palace facing this garden, perhaps following Andalusian custom, and he spent the last two summers of his life there. A porch with slender columns gives access to this garden patio, the coolest place in the palace, planted in his time with many varied flowers and containing a central fountain, since removed. The sunlight, the murmur of the fountain, the cool shade and the scent of orange trees must have been a delight to the senses, showing how much Charles V had been influenced by his periods of residence in the Alhambra and the Alcázar of Seville.

Father Sigüenza tells us that Fray Marcos de Cardona, a Hieronymite monk from La Murta in Barcelona and a remarkable arboriculturist and gardener for the Emperor and for Philip II, took vegetables, plants and orange trees to the Escorial from the Vera de Plasencia.[8]

"The Emperor, upon his arrival at Yuste, expressed his desire to enliven the site with plants. On the eastern side a garden sprang up full of flowers and herbs and shaded by aromatic trees (lemon, citrus and orange), while water murmured in the fountain."[9]

The Emperor, who had always been a lover of nature, birds and flowers, devoted many hours to his garden and he is said to have ordered from Tunis not only the best of his laurels, but the pretty flower known as Indian pink (*tagetes erecta*), sent from the African shore to his gardens in Spain whence, in time, it won its way into every cottage garden in Europe."[10]

Stirling relates how in the spring preceding the Emperor's death, "a lily in his garden, growing beneath his windows, bore two buds, one of which flowered and in due course withered; the other remained a bud through the summer and autumn, to the great astonishment of the gardeners and the friars. But on the night of the twentieth of September (the night before the Emperor's death), it burst into full bloom, as an emblem," he says, "of the whiteness of the parting spirit, and of the sure and certain hope of its reception into the mansions of bliss."[11] This lily was placed on Charles V's coffin.

Two central fountains are to be seen today in the two beautiful cloisters of the monastery. In the cloister called the "Plateresque" there is a simple curb-stone and a central column, carved with leaves, that does not seem to be of the same period as the cloister; one of these fountains might have adorned the Emperor's garden.

The monastery was burned down by French troops in 1809 and remained in ruins for many years. Recently it was given over to the State by its owners, the Marqueses de Mirabel, Dukes of Montellano, and has been very efficiently restored by the *Dirección General de Bellas Artes.*

PRIVATE GARDENS IN THE SIXTEENTH CENTURY

Private gardens of the Renaissance in Spain have unfortunately not been preserved; we must settle for the descriptions of poets and chroniclers and a few pictures and engravings.

One of the loveliest and least known Castilian palaces,

Saldañuela, about nine kilometres from Burgos, must surely have possessed a fine Renaissance garden. Travelling from Madrid toward France, one reaches Saldañuela by turning right in the village of Sarracín on the road to Soria and driving about one kilometre. The façade that faces the road is very beautiful.

Lampérez tells us: "The palace, with its defensive tower and the capitals of the *loggia,* is one of the most beautiful examples of Spanish Plateresque. Its style belongs to the Italian-Spanish Renaissance. In the interior patio a fountain is built into the wall — unusual for Spain — in a vaulted niche framed by two male figures on inverted pyramid bases. The bowl, supported upon the shoulders of a statue of Atlas, receives water from the breasts of three nude female statuettes (the Three Graces). On each side of this fountain are two large windows decorated in severe classical style, which contrasts strongly with the Plateresque fantasy of the rest of the building."[12] It differs from the Palace of Cadalso de los Vidrios (discussed later) in its use of limestone of a warm and luminous colour as opposed to the grey granite of Cadalso.

Lampérez adds that "the palace was built in the second quarter of the sixteenth century and belonged to Ana Isabel Osorio, Señora of Sarracín from about 1520 to 1530; she is buried in the village church. The coat of arms that adorns the colonnaded façade appears to be hers and must have appeared on the tower at one time. In 1768 the owner of Saldañuela was Don Juan Felipe de Borja, Marqués de Cañizares."

After years of neglect Saldañuela belongs today to the Burgos Savings Bank, which has carried out extensive repairs in the interior of the building and added an annexe to adapt it to the needs of a boys' school, without spoiling the main façade.

The young Bartolomé de Villalba, who chronicled his travels through Spain in 1577, describes the marvels of gardens such as the Huerta de Bargas on the banks of the river Tagus, "a garden full of amusements, myrtle hedges and countless garden innovations" and he refers to the Huerta del Mosul, apparently near Talavera, as "very fertile and delightful, and on its slopes camomile, clover, rosemary, thyme, marjoram and lavender were being gathered, and everything was in full bloom."[13]

He also mentioned the garden of Don Fabián de Monroy in the Vera de Plasencia on an island formed by the river Xerete which, he tells us, had its house on the river's edge. It had a summer-house with coloured tiles and a pond, where a marble nymph spouted water in all directions, and another female figure with a serpent, a cupid and a viper. He found a circle paved with Talavera tiles, another fountain where a figure of a kneeling queen shed water, and an arbour by the river, "there being much gardening at this site."

About twenty-five kilometres along the road from Béjar to Plasencia lies the village of Aldeanueva del Camino, and four kilometres from there, towards the right, there stands the ancient palace of the Dukes of Alba on the banks of the river Ambroz.

Let us listen again to the young Bartolomé de Villalba, now describing the travels of a fictional pilgrim: "After this our Pilgrim passed on to the enclosure named La Abadía on the land of the Duke of Alba and was welcomed by a Flemish gardener, who acted as his guide.

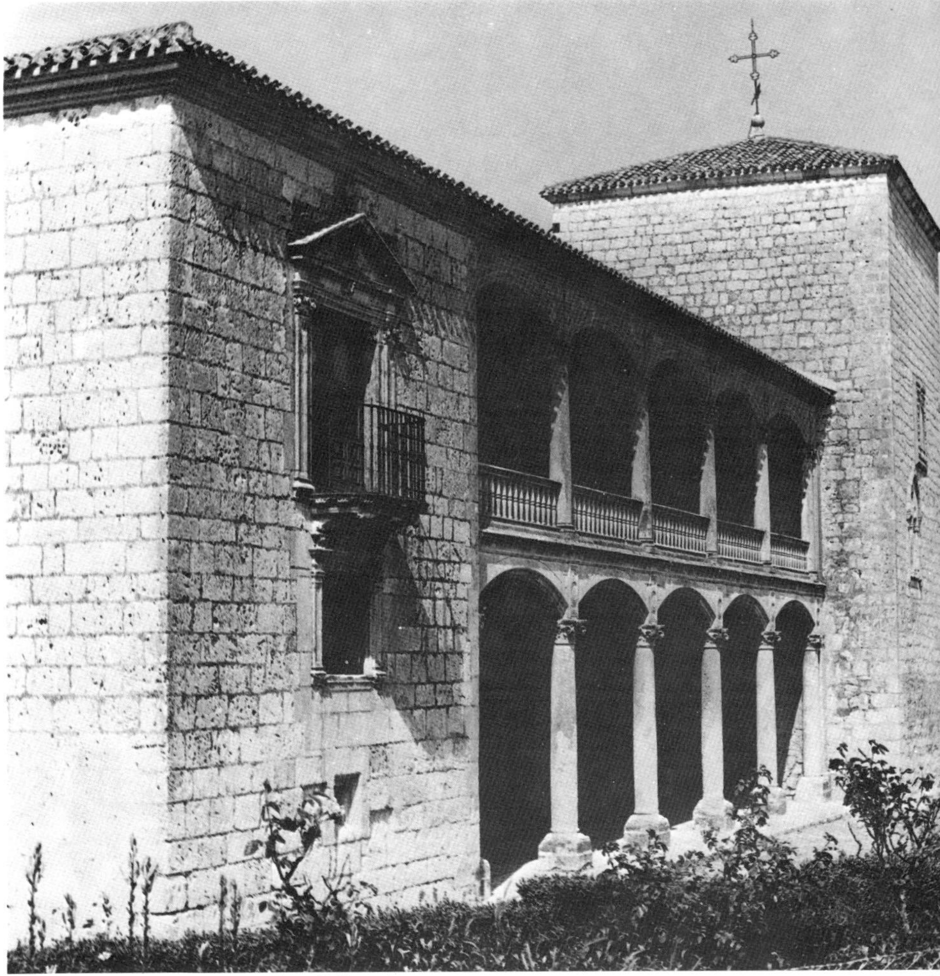

PALACE OF SALDANUELA. Burgos. *Photo S. Saavedra.*

INTERIOR PATIO. *Photo S. Saavedra.*

GARDENS OF LA ABADIA. *Photo Más.*

"The Pilgrim saw the paths of myrtle, the tables cut out of orange trees and figures representing animals, birds and legendary figures. But what he most admired was the tall fountain with four basins, the seven planets and twenty-five figures sculptured in full, and the portraits of the Duke and Duchess of Alba (probably Don Fernando Alvarez de Toledo with his wife, Doña María de Guzman Enríquez). He was astonished at the water patterns produced by all these figures, and the sound they made." The principal sculptor of this fountain was the Italian Francesco Camiliani, in 1555.

Amongst all these marvels he noted "a lake or pool in which there were about ten giants measuring more than twenty spans in height, with muscular limbs and powerful shoulders."

He relates many other things about the sculptures in this garden until he arrives at a large quadrangle, "its walls adorned by orange leaves, jasmine and other plants with their flowers and foliage", and he observes twenty-four Roman busts, remarking that meals must have been taken here because of the number of chairs.

From there he proceeded along paths covered with citrus and lemon trees, through the plantations of the orchard, admiring the plots with their variety of plants brought from Flanders and Germany and the remote ends of the earth, among which was southernwood (*artemisia abrotanus*) with its scented yellow flowers.

He also saw strawberries for the first time, which he named *fraules* (their Valencian name). He noted that they had the scent and colour of the strawberry tree (*arbutus unedo*). Once he had seen the garden, the pilgrim lay down for a siesta under the whisper of the orange trees, "the murmur of the water and the sweet scent of orange blossom and roses."[14]

All these descriptions were recorded with varying degrees of imagination in about 1578, when this garden must have been at the height of its splendour, because the pilgrim "observed that everything was tidy and well-cared for."[15]

In his speech to the Royal Academy of History in Madrid in 1919, the Duke of Alba related that his ancestor, the Duke Don Fernando had brought the artist Benvenuto from Italy to direct the work on his palaces; Benvenuto was later to be engaged to build the Hospital de la Sangre of Seville in 1570.[16]

The glory of this garden must soon have faded. Don Fernando died in 1582 and his son, Don Fadrique, in 1585. The poet Lope de Vega dedicated a brief poem to a *"Description of La Abadía, Garden of the Duke of Alba"* in his *Rimas,* and it is well known that this poet acted as secretary to the young duke, the grandson of the Grand Duke Don Fernando; he must certainly have visited the Abadía gardens for he describes them in detail at the end of the sixteenth century, and at that time they must still have been in good condition. When did neglect set in? Probably in the late eighteenth or early nineteenth century, when, like so much of Spain's art, it fell prey to the French invasion.

Very few Spanish families have continued and maintained the gardens created by their ancestors, whereas in England knowledge and love of flowers and gardens have been handed down from father to son like a sacred trust, and nearly all the beautiful gardens that still exist are the work of several generations.

At any rate, two hundred years after Abadía's creation, Don Antonio Ponz (author of a well-known book on travels through Spain in the eighteenth century) observed the garden's decay; although he still saw the statues and fountains in their original places, most of them were "in ruins" and the fountains were no longer operating. The upper garden was completely neglected, and the steps leading down to the second had crumbled.

Ponz nonetheless gives a detailed description of the fountain, which he declares to be "one of the most beautiful I have seen in Spain." It must have been very complicated, judging by the marble figures and the four basins that composed it; he compares it to "the lovely one in the Casa de Campo" in Madrid, and the most recent one in the gardens of Aranjuez, called the Fountain of the Tritons, which Velázquez painted and of which we will speak later. Ponz continues that Abadía's fountain "offers more sculptures, is grander, and contains a greater volume of water. . . On the pedestal of one of the statues I found engraved the name of the sculptor and the year in which the fountain was built: Francisco Camiliani of Florence. Opus 1555."[18]

We shall not linger further over the description of these late Renaissance gardens, of which practically nothing remains. Consider, by comparison, how many gardens of this period have been preserved in Italy, cherished with such zeal, and now regarded as part of the national artistic heritage. The Boboli gardens in Florence, rich in statues and fountains still in all their glory, and the Villa Gamberaia in Settignano, a privately owned monumental Baroque garden, whose owner keeps it in admirable condition, are but two examples.

In 1920 the Abadía gardens were again described, with a plan and photographs, by the late architect Winthuysen.[19] He saw only "the good statue of Andromeda" still standing on its niche as described by Ponz; not a trace remained of the fountain, nor anything else.

Following the Civil War of 1936 to 1939, Don Tomás Martín Gil visited these gardens and sent a detailed article to the Review of the Society of the Friends of Art. Nothing at all remained, not even the old cypress that Winthuysen had seen some years earlier.

Not far from the Abadía gardens, on the outskirts of the town of Béjar (Salamanca), the Duke of Béjar had a country seat called El Bosque (The Woods). This property, which is still preserved, is situated on the northern slope of the Sierra de la Candelaria from where its abundant supply of water springs. The great pond that is to be seen today must originally have been a natural lake.

Beneath the lintel of the entrance door is engraved the date 1567, when Don Francisco de Zúñiga y Sotomayor, Duke of Béjar, probably constructed the Palace of El Bosque and its gardens. The pond and the leafy grove of popular trees in what is now called "The Old Forest Way" also dates from this period.

The house is of irregular design with the lintels over the balconies formed by heavy stone coats of arms of the Zuñiga Sotomayor family.

Beneath it lies the great pool, the most prominent feature of

STATUE OF ANDROMEDA. Abadía. *Photo Mias.*

EL BOSQUE. SUMMER-HOUSE. Béjar. *Photo Author.*

the garden used as a reservoir with water flowing into a lower pool. A small island has probably graced this pond since its creation. The island's wrought-iron summer-house, on the other hand, was probably added in the last century, of which it is so typical. In this century of speed, with outboard motors and water-skiing, a ride in a row-boat on a small pond may seem slow and dull, but in former times this was one of the chief ways of spending afternoons on royal estates and in private gardens. This pond measures about 68 by 77 metres, an impressive achievement for that time. Opposite the house, on the other side of the lake, there is a stone fountain with an octagonal basin mounted on a graceful column.

A short semicircular wall with a stone bench all along it, forms the background. In the centre of the masonry are two crests: the arms of Zúñiga and Sotomayor on the left, and the initials F.G., presumably standing for Francisco and Guiomar, on the right; both are surmounted by sixteenth century ducal crowns. This fountain is known as the Eight Water Spouts.

At the eastern end of the pond, almost hidden by ancient elm and plane trees, is another monumental fountain with a strong, solid appearance in the Baroque style. The escutcheon here is more ornate than that in the first fountain and also bears the arms of Zúñiga and Sotomayor. Water gushes from two masks on the sides of the fountain and falls into a wide pool of the same Baroque design. It is known as the Fountain of la Sábana (or sheet). These are the principal features of the garden of El Bosque.

The lower garden is divided from the large pool by a broad poplar avenue and is placed on a much lower level. It is reached by steep granite steps; half-way down the steps is a platform with a small summer-house covered with creepers, which appears to date from the last century. Originally this lower garden must have been used as an orchard and kitchen garden, watered from the lake by means of a broad conduit still intact.

This lower garden is laid out in the "picturesque" nineteenth century style with twisting paths bordered by great boxwood hedges. At one end of the garden is a fountain with a lead figure of a boy holding a goose. Another fountain on the opposite side has a double basin and several water jets but is quite plain. The oldest of the fountains, apparently dating back to the park's creation, is attached to a low wall and surmounted by a great shield bearing the arms of Don Francisco de Zúñiga under a thick canopy of greenery. It has several water jets called *burlas,* or jokes, that spring up from the floor at the turn of a handle and drench unwary visitors. In this part of the garden there are a number of Wellingtonias (*sequoiadendron gigantea*) of enormous proportions. (We shall see many of them later on.) They cannot be older than the late nineteenth century when they were introduced to Spain from North America.

Don Mariano Téllez Girón y Beaufort, Duke of Osuna, inherited the dukedom of Béjar from his brother, Don Pedro de Alcántara, in 1844. His life of adventure and extravagance among the courts of Europe led to his ruin compelling him to sell the property in 1869 to Don Cipriano Rodríguez Arias, whose descendants have taken good care of it.

EL BOSQUE. FOUNTAIN AND HOUSE IN THE BACKGROUND. *Photo Author.*

PALACE OF CADALSO DE LOS VIDRIOS. *Photo S. Saavedra.*

The lower garden was probably created at the beginning of the nineteenth century when the estate was still in the hands of the Duke of Béjar, Don Pedro de Alcántara.

It was to the grandson of the founder of El Bosque, Don Alonso, that Cervantes dedicated the first part of his immortal novel, *Don Quixote.*

(I am indebted to Don Vicente Oliva, the present owner of this historic garden, for all these details.)

In the village of Cadalso de los Vidrios, near San Martin de Valdeiglesias in the province of Madrid, stands the palace that once belonged to the Marqués de Villena. The turrets on the corners of the façade show that it was originally a fortress. Legend has it that a previous owner, Don Alvaro de Luna, Señor de Escalona, was told by an astrologer that "he would die in Cadalso" (meaning, on the scaffold). Believing this prophecy, he never again set foot in Cadalso de los Vidrios.

Lampérez records that the palace was built in 1534, a date corresponding to the "Spanish Renaissance" style of Charles V. For a time it was the property of the Figueroa-Acuña family, but in the eighteenth century it reverted back to its first owners, the Marqueses de Villena. This can be seen in a plan drawn by the architect Ventura Rodriguez in 1777 at the command of the Infante Don Luis de Borbón, a brother of Charles III.[20] We know that in 1740, the Italian architect Santiago Bonavía, addressed a letter concerning the construction of a small theatre in the garden of Aranjuez[21] to the Marqués de Villena. The Marqués must have taken a personal interest in his gardens for those of Cadalso de los Vidrios had horse-chestnut trees, which were rare in Spain at that time, and he had them marked for transplanting to Aranjuez.[22] His signature appears on many documents of the period.

According to Lampérez, the Palace of Cadalso de los Vidrios had an open gallery on the main floor along the whole of the side facing the garden, which was square and enclosed by walls. On the lower floor of this façade was an openwork porch and a *mirador,* or balcony, projecting from its centre, composed entirely of Ionic columns, brackets and lintels, of a very Spanish style. "The garden is typical of the sixteenth century and has a strong architectural component. It was not very spacious but had great beauty. Rectangular in shape, it is framed by the façade of the palace and a wide encircling wall with an open arcade on one side, benches in the spaces, and above, a walk running its entire length, decorated by benches, pergolas and balconies. The garden was planted in the classic style, and in its centre stood an octagonal pavilion with columns. The overall style is Plateresque, rather coarse because of the quality of the stone used. Not far away there was a pool. In the nineteenth century the palace passed to another owner. There was a fire in 1917, but the exterior and the monumental part were spared."[23]

It was probably abandoned for a number of years, during which time stone motifs and ornaments were sold. The Count of Romanones acquired many of these, as will be seen later, for his country house, Buenavista, at Toledo.

Around the year 1930 the sculptor Juan Cristóbal bought the

EL BOSQUE. SABANA FOUNTAIN. Béjar. *Photo Author.*

CADALSO DE LOS VIDRIOS. WALKWAY ON SURROUNDING WALL. *Photo S. Saavedra.*

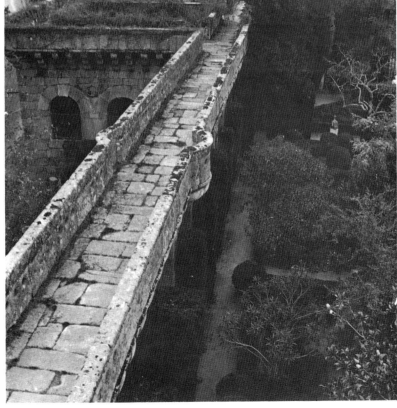

VISÓ DEL MARQUES. PATIO. *Photo Author.*

palace. He restored the building, which had completely collapsed, and replanted the garden with paths bordered by tall boxwood hedges. In the centre stands one of his most famous sculptures, representing the torso of a woman.

His widow and daughters have collected part of his work, including the statues of Cervantes and Manuel de Falla in stone, and his marvellous self-portrait in polychrome wood.

Lampérez tells us: "The gardens of Spanish palaces of the sixteenth century correspond to two different types: one of them, probably of Italian descent, is distinguished by its monumental arrangement, fountains with statues and fantastic plant-sculptures; the other is of Hispano-Arab tradition and therefore essentially national, displaying the characteristics of natural vegetation and large reservoirs made of tiles or marble, with water jets."[24]

Another remnant from the time of the House of Austria is a large mansion in the village of Viso del Marqués, nineteen kilometres from Santa Cruz de Mudela in the province of Ciudad Real. It was once the palace of Don Alvaro de Bazán, Marqués de Santa Cruz y del Viso, who defeated the Turks in the Battle of Lepanto. There is nothing outstanding about the outside of the building, but the interior patio is very beautiful.

Its walls are covered with frescoes representing Don Alvaro's naval victories. Lampérez tells us: "It was begun in 1564

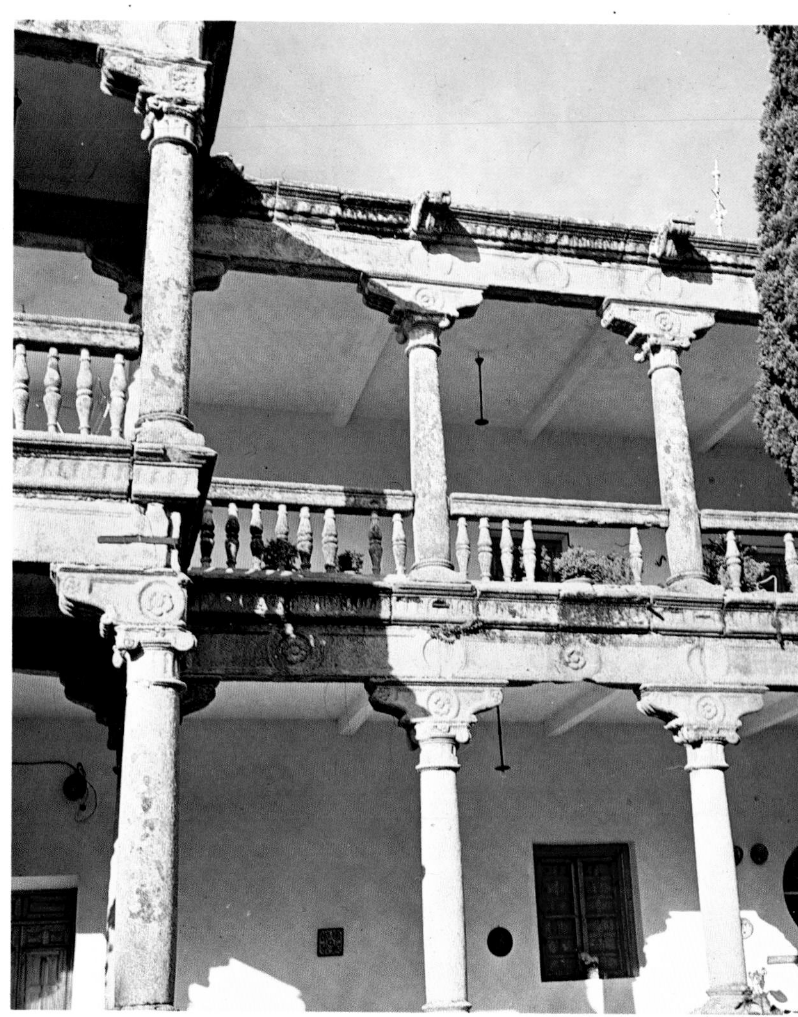

CADALSO DE LOS VIDRIOS. DETAIL OF GALLERY. *Photo Author.*

according to the designs of Juan Bautista Castello, *el Bergamasco*. From 1571, it is believed that the supervisor of the work was a certain Maese Domingo from Genoa, and the master carpenter his fellow-countryman, Maese Alberto."[25]

Another of their compatriots, Juan B. Prioli, appears in 1585. The painters were César Arbasia and, later, the brothers Pérola (Juan and Esteban), and Castello's sons, Nicolás and Fabrizio.[26]

"These painters," says Cavestany, "came from Italy in the sixteenth century in the service of Don Alvaro de Bazán. They painted the frescoes in the rooms of his palace of el Viso very tastefully, decorating them with allegories, flowers, fruit, war trophies, etc. that form a frame for historic events — battles, by land and sea associated with the victorious name of the Marqués de Santa Cruz. They worked there for twenty years, marrying in Almagro." The Pérola brothers assisted Antonio Mohedano, who is mentioned for his paintings of fruit and flowers, in Córdoba Cathedral, and did other work in Villanueva de los Infantes.[27]

The entire palace is in the Italian style, both in its structure and decoration.[28]

Across a fine reception room and down a few steps, lies a small garden of modern design with a fountain in its centre. On either side of the doorway is a kneeling statue of white marble on a grey marble background, representing Don Alonso de Bazán, Don Alvaro's brother, and his wife Doña María Figueroa. They are dated 1564, the year the palace was begun. These statues came from the chapel of the adjoining convent which they founded, and which was destroyed during the Civil War of 1936. The tomb of Don Alvaro de Bazán is in the parish church of Viso del Marqués.

In a small courtyard in the garden a curious figure-head of a vessel can be seen, representing a semi-clad woman.

The palace belongs to the Marqueses de Santa Cruz, and the archives of the Naval Ministry are now kept there. Part of the house is reserved for the owners.

VISO DEL MARQUES. GARDEN. *Photo S. Saavedra.*

VISO DEL MARQUES. GARDEN BENCH. *Photo S. Saavedra.*

[1] VILLIERS-STUART, Mrs.: *Spanish Gardens,* Batsford, London, 1929, page 22.

[2] MÉLIDA, Juan Ramón: *Catálogo monumental de España,* Cáceres, vol. II.

[3] PONZ, Antonio: *Viaje de España,* Ed. Aguilar, Madrid, 1947, vol. VII, letter VI, page 632.

[4] STIRLING, William: *Cloister Life of the Emperor Charles the Fifth,* London, 1853, page 268.

[5] ALARCÓN, Pedro de: *Viajes por España.* Ediciones Fax, Madrid, 1968, page 1121.

[6] MARTÍN, Juan José: *El Palacio de Carlos V en Yuste,* Archivo Español de Arte, Madrid, 1950, page 34.

[7] MARTÍN, Juan José: *Op. cit.,* page 37.

[8] SIGÜENZA, Fray José de: *La fundación del Monasterio de El Escorial,* Ed. Aguilar, Madrid, 1963, pages 23 and 24.

[9] MARTÍN, Juan José: *Op. cit.,* page 46.

[10] STIRLING, William: *Op. cit.,* page 130.

[11] STIRLING, William: *Op. cit.,* page 243.

[12] LAMPÉREZ Y ROMEA, V: *Boletín de la Sociedad Española de Excursiones,* Madrid, December 1915, year XXIII, 4th quarter.

[13] VILLALBA, Bartolomé de: *El Pelegrino Curioso, Doncel de Xérica,* Sociedad de Bibliófilos Españoles, Madrid, 1866, vol. I, pages 200, 224 and 225.

[14] *El Pelegrino Curioso:* pages 262-269.

[15] *El Pelegrino Curioso:* page 262.

[16] Installation Address by the Duke of Berwick and of Alba at the Royal Academy of History, Madrid, 1919.

[17] MARTÍN GIL, Tomás: "Una visita a los jardines de Abadía o Sotofermoso, de la Casa Ducal de Alba", *Arte Español,* Revista de la Sociedad Español de Amigos del Arte, Madrid, 1945, 2nd semester, page 66.

[18] PONZ, Antonio: *Op. cit.,* vol. III, letter I, page 676.

[19] WINTHUYSEN, Javier: *Jardines clásicos de España,* Madrid, 1930, page 33.

[20] LAMPÉREZ Y ROMEA, Vicente: *Arquitectura civil española,* Ed. Saturdino Calleja, Madrid, 1922, vol. I, pages 481-483.

[21] Archivo General de Palacio, Madrid: *Aranjuez,* file 11.

[22] Archivo General de Palacio, Madrid: *Aranjuez,* file 14, 14th October, 1744.

[23] LAMPÉREZ Y ROMEA, V.: *Op. cit.,* page 416.

[24] LAMPÉREZ Y ROMEA, V.: *Op. cit.,* page 419.

[25] GUILLÉN TATO, Julio: *El Palacio del Viso del Marqués,* Ciudad Real, 1963, page 12.

[26] LAMPÉREZ Y ROMEA, V.: *Op. cit.,* page 485.

[27] CAVESTANY, Julio: *Flores y bodegones en la pintura española,* Palacio de la Biblioteco National, Madrid, 1936 and 1940.

[28] Palomino tells us "that the whole interior, from the entrance hall onwards, is painted with excellent decorations, architecture, fables and stories of the Greeks and Romans, Carthaginians and Goths, with splendid copies of statues, serpents, tritons and satyrs; this is all executed in the style of Michelangelo; and the adornment of flutes, little snakes and reptiles in that of el Bergamesco and Becerra".

GARDENS DURING THE AUSTRIAN DYNASTY PHILIP II TO PHILIP IV

Of the gardens and palaces owned by members of the House of Austria, very few vestiges remain from Philip II's time; in due course we shall describe private properties — some of which still remain — owned by grandees in the time of Philip IV and later under the Bourbons.

We shall begin with the Casa de Campo, one of the last of the vanished royal properties.

The "Pilgrim" describes the Casa de Campo as follows: "It stands a stone's throw from the Royal Palace, in a fertile valley with a river and a pleasant meadow containing many sculptures, sprays of water, nymphs, gardens and a great number of small herbs, clipped in a thousand ways."[1]

The Casa de Campo was more important for its gardens, orchards, groves and fountains, than for its buildings. It dates from the year 1562 when the land was bought from the heirs of Don Fadrique de Vargas. "In Madrid the King owns a pleasure resort on the other side of the river Manzanares, called the Casa de Campo, in which he has a small house, offices, gardens, fountains, ponds, and a place where rabbits are caught; all can be seen from the Alcázar."[2] Mora writes: "The house was small; the architects Juan Bautista, Juan de Herrera and Luis de Vega seem to have taken part."[3]

Judging by the picture painted by an anonymous hand, it must have been very lovely with its cluster of roofs and its loggia, and the gardeners who laid out the garden must have been extremely competent; it seems to be a mingling of the Italian and Flemish styles, for Philip II is known to have employed Flemish gardeners.

Juan F. Peyron, a diplomat who travelled through Spain from 1772 to 1773, tells us that "at the entrance to the garden there is an equestrian statue of Philip III in bronze on a marble pedestal. It was begun by John of Bologna, the Douai-born sculptor and architect, and finished by his disciple Pedro Tacca." This statue was modelled from a portrait by Pantoja de la Cruz in 1613 and remained in the Casa de Campo until 1848 when it was moved to the centre of the Plaza Mayor. Its beauty can be compared with that of the

EL RETIRO. CASCADE. Malaga. *Photo S. Saavedra.*

statue of Henry IV on the Pont Neuf in Paris before it was destroyed during the French Revolution. (The statue that stands on this bridge today dates from 1818.)

Ponz also provides a description of the Casa de Campo that conforms with the anonymous pictures: "In the corners of a square flower-bed in the area where the equestrian statue stands, are four life-sized marble statues pouring water from urns, symbolising rivers; they are skilfully and magnificently sculpted according to the old Florentine School." These statues, which are no longer there, must certainly have come from Italy.

"A little further down the path from the equestrian statue", continues Ponz, "rises a beautiful marble fountain with four basins, one above the other. The largest and lowest basin is octagonal and stands at the top of four steps; at each corner is the head of a lion, whose paw is visible below. In the intermediate spaces, two-headed eagles and masks alternate, while the Golden Fleece forms festoons which hang from the lions' heads, the masks and the eagles. The mouldings on this basin contain various figures of shells, dolphins, foliage, etc. Supporting the second basin are three Tritons grouped around a column, also skilfully and magnificently carved; the underside of the basin is decorated with dolphins, shells and other ornaments. The third basin is supported by three more figures, smaller than the last, that is less than life-size; they do not represent any particular characters, but are male nudes of good workmanship. They stand out in almost complete relief, and lean against the column supporting this basin, from which three masks pour water. The fourth basin is supported by three children entirely in relief, and a small central column. The hands and arms of all these figures are linked together in various contrasting attitudes. Above the uppermost basin is a two-headed eagle, indicating that this fountain was built in the time of Charles V." Perhaps it was not set up then or was placed elsewhere and brought here later by Philip III. Iñíguez points out that "this fountain appears to be old and is called 'of the Eagle', though it may not be of the Emperor's time."[5] It is almost certainly Italian.

This fountain has undergone many changes. It was first removed from the Casa de Campo in the time of Isabella II (the middle of the nineteenth century), already somewhat dilapidated, and was to be placed in the Campo del Moro alongside that of the Tritons, which originally had been in Aranjuez, and that of las Conchas (the Shells) which will be described later, but there is no evidence that it was ever set up. When Queen Christina (the widow of Alfonso XII) founded the Augustine University in the Escorial at the end of the nineteenth century, the fountain was taken to its cloister, where it stands now. Its crowning eagle and large lower basin, however, are missing; according to the description by Juan F. Peyron, they must have been very beautiful. It now stands in the centre of a simple stone-bordered pool, mounted on a circular base of granite blocks. This Renaissance fountain was designed to play in a garden where the background of trees and foliage would set off its beautiful sculptures, so sensual and pagan; enclosed in this severe cloister by Herrera, like a caged bird, it presents a somewhat sad picture today.

GARDEN, CASA DE CAMPO. Painting by Felix Castello, 1637. Municipal Museum. Madrid. *Photo Oronoz.*

GARDENS AND PALACE, EL PARDO. Anonymous Madrilenian painting, first half 17th century. Arch. Museum. Burgos. *Photo Oronoz.*

Towards the end of the eighteenth century Antonio Ponz saw two other fountains in the Casa de Campo of different designs. "One consists simply of a round basin on a column, with a small figure above it representing Temperance, and a lower basin decorated with dolphins; the column supporting the upper basin displays the royal arms, with masks spurting water.

"Following the shrubberies adjoining this garden we find five large ponds, built for fish breeding (a practice also adopted at Yuste, La Fresneda and the Escorial). His Majesty breeds pheasants nearby, and other birds rare for our climate."[6] Nothing remains of this splendour today.

Describing the Palace of El Pardo in his study of the gardens of Philip II, Francisco Iñíguez wrote that "there was once a garden in the palace moat, mentioned by Argote de Molina."[7]

"The palace itself, built by Philip III, is square in shape; at its corners are four towers with very fine windows, each topped by turrets and spires. The palace is surrounded by a broad moat with many flower-beds, vases and pots of medicinal herbs and rare flowers brought with care from many regions; the walls of the moat are adorned with jasmine, ivy and roses, and in each corner stands a fountain with water flowing from stone masks. The house is entered through two stone bridges over the moat; beneath them are two enclosures caged by wire netting, where a multitude of birds singing in sweet harmony make this a very pleasant place."[8] The idea of converting the moat, which dated from the time of Enrique III (sixteenth century) into such a delightful spot with birds, fountains and rare and fragrant plants, "is one of the most ingenious that can be imagined," adds Iñíguez.

The oil painting of the garden of El Pardo in the museum at

CASA DE CAMPO. STATUE OF PHILIP III AND AGUILA FOUNTAIN. Municipal Museum. Madrid. *Photo Oronoz.*

THE ESCORIAL. AGUILA FOUNTAIN. *Photo S. Saavedra.*

PALACE OF EL PARDO. *"Délices de l'Espagne."*

LA GRANJILLA. DOORWAY BY HERRANO. *Photo Author.*

Burgos shows sumptuous gardens in the style of the time, with covered walks formed by clipped trees, geometrical designs, and fountains gushing from statues. These gardens do not look as though they were planted in a moat, but we must allow for the artist's imagination. The palace with its turrets and spires can clearly be distinguished.

The most important feature of El Pardo was the famous forest with a perimeter of nearly a hundred kilometres. Iñíguez wrote: "It is the most important ilex forest in Castilla la Nueva, immortalised by Velázquez in the backgrounds of his pictures, and a sad reminder of what once must have covered the now bare wastes of the plateau. Game was always, and still is, very plentiful."[9]

Today, the Palace of El Pardo has a beautiful and well-kept garden once again. This building, empty for so many years, was brought back to life when it was used as Franco's residence.

The only garden that still remains as in the time of Philip II, having preserved most of its original design, is La Granjilla (The Little Grange), once known as La Granja de la Fresneda (The Grange of the Ash Grove). The Friars' Garden in the Monastery of the Escorial, which was designed at the time of the foundation of the monastery, was recreated here by Philip V in 1717, with classic hedges of clipped boxwood.

In the valley called the Escorial de Abajo, or Lower Escorial, which lies before the ascent to the monastery as one approaches by the road from Madrid, stands a church built by Francisco de Mora. Nearby is an entrance marked "La Granjilla."

This is the famous Fresneda described by Father Sigüenza and

LA GRANJILLA. CLOISTER. *Photo Author.*

Don Antonio Ponz; it was once a resting house for the monks of the monastery who withdrew there twice a year to rest, in accordance with the Order's custom.

A long avenue leads to the house between two high stone walls; once we are clear of the walls, we see a world apart, filled with gardens, lawns and meadows, thanks to the abundance of water.

In reality there are two houses built here, almost certainly by Herrera. That on the left, on lower ground, was the convent where the monks stayed. Sigüenza says that "the cloister is very elegant, with Tuscan columns, though the architraves are of wood."

At one time this cloister was closed by an iron grille on its southern side, and the garden was "very pretty with musk-roses, jasmine and honeysuckle intertwined on the railings", a sweet-smelling wall. Today all this has disappeared and the patio remains open on this side. Across the house a stairway descends to the northern façade and the main entrance to the building, a severe construction of hewn granite featuring a double outside staircase with a stone handrail; over the lintel is a crest containing the gridiron of Saint Lawrence, the emblem of the Escorial. According to Sigüenza, this was the rest house for the friars, with its twenty cells facing north.

On the same side as the cloisters, towards the south and on slightly higher ground, is another house that served as "a resting place and apartment for royalty when they wish to withdraw for a while to be refreshed in this cool spot."[10]

The part of this second house that overlooks the cloister is modern, but the south side is of admirable proportions and has a fine doorway in the style of Herrera; the chains on the doorway indicate that it has been inhabited by royal guests. The garden that adorns this façade must once have had fountains in the centre of "three flower-beds with fine compartments and knots", that is to say, forming designs in the contemporary style, either in clipped boxwood or other aromatic plants. The terrace overlooking the valley was decorated with pots of sweet basil and a thousand different kinds of plants"[11] and was divided by water channels into the form of a cross with a central fountain. Here we can see the Arab influence once again.

The hedges, with their compartments and fountains, have since disappeared, but there is a cool lawn where the owners can place chairs and tables and enjoy this lovely terrace. On either side stand two ancient yews, perhaps from the time of the foundation, and a magnificent giant cedar of Lebanon; the latter is presumably of more recent planting for this tree did not grow in Spain at that time as did the yew. A little towards the west is a beautiful fountain of the period.

Near this terrace and in other parts of the estate several stone tables with benches used by the friars still remain. Everything on this property seems to have been arranged to provide a pleasant country retreat.

There must have been many gardens in La Fresneda, as Father Sigüenza goes on to describe: "Towards the north, surrounded by a stone wall, many aromatic plants are grown in their different beds and there are various compartments and mazes." Here there was also a fountain covered by a wooden and slate structure, surrounded by trellis-work." This garden must have been at the main entrance to the convent. The gardener was named Juan Angles, and was probably Flemish.[12]

The most important part of this property consisted of four great ponds where, as Father Sigüenza continues, "much water and many fish are collected." In the one nearest the house there was a fountain in the middle of a large fish pond, overhung and adorned with trees, and in another pond, divided from the first by a high wall, stood a fountain in the form of a large figure of Neptune reclining on dolphins, complete with his trident and crown as King of the Waters." These water devices must have been very complicated, according to Sigüenza's description. Trees and plants also surrounded these ponds, but none remain today.

In the third and lower pond he speaks of "an island, a hundred feet square, with its balustrade and finely carved stone seats. In the centre of the island stands a summer-house, roofed with timber and slate, and its trellised walls entwined with pomegranates, hazelnuts, vines, jasmine and honeysuckle."[13] Apparently a maze encircled the summer-house.

This square island still exists and is reached by a solid stone bridge, once equipped with a stone balustrade which Ponz saw as late as the end of the eighteenth century, but which has now disappeared. In the centre, the four stone pilasters that must once have supported the roof of the summer-house still remain, and in the middle of them stands a low stone pillar that must have been the pedestal of a table.

LA GRANJILLA. POND WITH ISLAND (THE ESCORIAL IN THE BACKGROUND). *Photo Author.*

ZARZUELA PALACE. WALL AND STAIRWAYS.

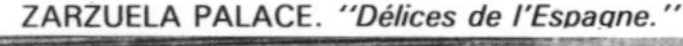

ZARZUELA PALACE. *"Délices de l'Espagne."*

Below lies the fourth pond, into which water descends from pond to pond, as in a series of dams. This water flows from the river Aulencia with its source in the nearby sierras. Ash trees, some of them obviously very old, form the greater part of the woods; hence the name of La Fresneda, changed later to La Granjilla.

At a short distance from the Escorial are other buildings also once used as farms, such as La Granja del Quexigal, near Robledo de Chavela, used by the friars to store wine and oil. The large house there was built by Herrera in the same period as the Escorial.

Father Sigüenza tells us that "Philip was not willing for any animal or beast of burden to live within or be attached to the monastery walls — only men, capable of reason and compelled by the faith they professed." This made it necessary to build houses apart from the main building for the various offices.[14] For this reason there are a number of small buildings in the Escorial, such as the Cachicanía — the house of the *cachican,* or gardener, found in a corner of the garden, and now rather dilapidated; it was designed and built by Francisco de Mora, a pupil of Herrera.[15] This small building and others outside the monastery enclosure, such as the Herrería — the Forge — (now the site of a golf course), and La Fresneda mentioned above, all bear the Herrera stamp, both in their severe classical design and for the use of the hard grey granite favoured by this architect and not used in Castile since the time of the Romans.[16]

It was Philip II who also introduced from Flanders the use of slates, so typical of that period, in classical domes and spires. The king did not like Arab pantiles such as had been in use up until then, but spires were not suitable for the climate of the sierra.[17] Domes and spires were designed for snow and stillness, and the strong winds and storms of Castile tended to bend them.[18]

* * *

We have described the Habsburg palaces from the time of Charles V and Philip II in previous chapters, and have seen accounts of the gardens of El Real and of the Patriarca at Valencia, and their decoration for the royal wedding of Philip III, as described by Felipe de Gauna; they had apparently remained unchanged since Arab times.

Our information about the baroque gardens of the seventeenth century, on the other hand, is very sparse.

Jacinto Polo Medina has left us a beautifully poetic description of the Literary Academies that were held in the garden of Espinardo, near Murcia, a property belonging to Don Juan Fajardo.

It is described as a most lovely orchard, producing the "fruit of silk" and many other types of fruit; its trees and clipped marble tables were watered by rivulets flowing from the *acequias* or canals. Flowers were plentiful and Jacinto Polo Medina dedicates a number of sonnets to them, very much in the style of Gongora of whom he was noted as an imitator. He also describes the "shaven orange trees", the various summer-houses that adorned the garden paths, and the marble statues.

The Palace of La Zarzuela was built on the outskirts of Madrid in 1636, to the west of El Pardo, for the Infante Don Fernando, brother of Philip IV and Governor of Flanders.

"The building, situated in the highest part of its surrounding Italian gardens with their two terraces, was rectangular in design and had only one principal, but rather lofty storey."[19]

As it appears in Alvarez Colmenar's engraving, the high terrace was supported by strong vaulted arches; descending from the terrace was a double stairway with iron railings, which still exists today.

The following description is found in the archives of the Royal Palace in Madrid: "In the garden there are three fountains with their basins interspersed with trees; on top is a small basin which receives the water and releases it through four pipes in the bottom.

"The garden has about three acres of rather poor earth; it is divided into twenty-six squares and has two sets of paths, one set of five from east to west, and another of nine from south to north. Twenty of the squares are decorated with designs in boxwood; the rest with rose bushes. Seven of them are planted with strawberries.

"Along the entire southern side, which borders on the orchard, is an iron railing composed of thirty sections and twenty-nine stone pilasters. At either side of the centre, where it forms a terrace with three arches and four pilasters on the front and another arch and pilaster on each side, there is a stairway down to the orchard."[20]

The Infante Don Fernando, according to Ponz, held magnificent festivals here for the King and other members of the Royal Family.[21]

At one time the palace had a theatre where recitals and musical shows were staged and came to be called *zarzuelas* on account of the site; this name has persisted to the present day to denote this type of light musical play. Among the first that were staged there were: *The Garden of Falerina* (1628), *The Laurel of Apollo* (1657)[22], and *The Scarlet of the Rose* (1659) by Calderón de la Barca. Years later, when this palace belonged to Philip IV, it served as the residence of Don Juan José of Austria, his natural son by the actress La Calderona.

Today the palace has been entirely reconstructed as the residence of King Juan Carlos and Queen Sophía. The gardens have recovered, if not their old design, a cared for and pleasant appearance. Like other royal properties they contain a single, enormous Wellingtonia, the last of those planted by Amadeo around 1871.

* * *

Of the private properties that existed near Madrid in the time of the House of Austria, one of the most famous for its gardens was the Orchard of La Florida and Montaña of the Prince Pío.

It dates from the sixteenth century, and passed through the hands of several proprietors until it became the property of the Marqués de Castel Rodrigo in 1647. He made a series of genuine improvements and created its magnificent gardens by acquiring the adjoining properties.

The house must have been very large, judging by a picture that once belonged to Princess Pío and which now hangs in the Palace of Mombello (Como) in Italy. Ezquerra de Bayo tells us: "Count Buenaventura de Harrach, who was born in Prague, toured Spain in the years 1673 and 1674 — during the reign of Philip IV — and described two visits to the Marqués de Castel

ZARZUELA PALACE. AS IT APPEARS TODAY.

MOUNTAIN PRINCIPE PÍO. Municipal Museum. *Photo Oronoz.*

AGREDA. NICHE. *Photo Author.*

AGREDA. PILON. *Photo S. Saavedra.*

CÓRDOBA. PILON.
CASA DON RAFAEL CASTEJÓN.
Photo S. Saavedra.

Rodrigo in his Palace of La Florida, which he had embellished, adorning the gardens with fountains, grottoes, steps and marble statues." He related that "the garden is at present divided into two parts; in front of the house there is a quadrangular parterre with a great variety of flowers surrounded by lattices and trellises, against which tiny pear trees and dwarf trees bearing good fruit, mixed with various orange trees are trained. At the end of this parterre is a superb grotto representing Mount Parnassus, filled with cascades and jets of water. On this wall, and also on the double ramp that leads to the other garden, there are marble statues like those made in Massa, near Genoa. This garden too is quadrangular and, instead of flowers, has a great stock of vegetables. A large part of the mountain also belongs to the Marqués; he has had a grotto of rocks constructed there and intends to have a considerable section of the mountain levelled."[23] All very much — as will be observed — in the Italian *grotesco* taste of the seventeenth century.

Madame d'Aulnoy (1679-1681) was known to be somewhat fanciful, but she writes in her *Mémoires* that: "La Florida is a very pleasant house, and the gardens greatly admired. There are a great number of Italian statues by the most famous masters. The waters murmur softly, and the perfume of flowers is delightful, as care has been taken to collect the rarest and most strongly scented. From there one descends to the Prado Nuevo where there are water jets and the trees are extremely tall. This path, though not flat, is nonetheless pleasant as the slope is so gentle as to be scarcely noticeable."[24]

The last owner, Doña Isabel María Pío de Saboya y Spínola de la Cerda, sold this property to Charles IV in 1792, as this monarch wished to add it to other estates he had acquired, among them the Moncloa Palace; he named it the Real Florida and used it as a means of reaching El Pardo through his own lands.

In the time of Fernando VII this property was transferred to his brother, Don Francisco de Paula, but little would have remained after the French invasion. In 1869 Queen Isabella II gave the Real Florida, together with the Park of the Retiro, to the State. Later the barracks of La Montaña were built there, the site of an attack in which many soldiers perished just prior to the Civil War.

The gardens of La Florida must have been situated more or less where the Northern Railway Station stands today, in terraces down the slope of the "Montaña", which still exists, forming part of the Parque del Oeste. Recently the Temple of Debod from Egypt has been erected on the top of this hill, where it is hoped its sandstone will survive Madrid's harsh, cold winters.

Also of this period — the end of the seventeenth century — are the few vestiges of the garden that the Marqueses de Paredes once owned in Agreda (province of Soria), with its fountain of two basins, today broken and incomplete. In this remote place at the foot of the Sierra del Moncayo, the home of the nun Sor María de Agreda, whose counsel Philip IV followed on all matters, there once were Baroque gardens like this one which must have been very beautiful. It was built above the river Queiles in the form of a square enclosed by a high wall with niches containing statues, two of which are still standing, and on both sides, windows with iron grilles looking out over the river. There is also a wide baroque doorway similar to those at La Abadía and Cáceres, that served as an entrance to the garden. Here there remain, against the wall on each side of the stairway, two large stone fountains with deep basins that, according to tradition, were used as baths, one for men, the other for women. This arrangement of the two fountains against a wall is found also in the house of Don Rafael Castejón in Córdoba.

Access to the garden of Agreda from the Palace of Paredes was by a stairway that started from an upper floor of the house and crossed over a narrow street. The present owner, Señor Jiménez Tudela, tends the remains of statues and stonework with loving care, and devotes the rest of the garden to vegetables. He has fashioned a centrepiece for the garden with the remains of a column and the basin of a fountain, inverted to serve as a pedestal.

AGREDA. REMNANTS OF FOUNTAIN. *Photo Author.*

THE GARDENS OF EL RETIRO, CHURRIANA (MÁLAGA)

The Count of Villalcázar de Sirga was a patron of the arts and literature. He owned an enormous house which still stands, with its great classical doorway, a last vestige of eighteenth century Málaga. This house probably contained the valuable collection of pictures and books to which Ponz refers. He also describes the pictures and sculptures that the count had collected in his country house of Churriana, and his antiques, including an Egyptian alabaster canopic vase, with its hieroglyphics, and four funeral urns of the same material that are still preserved by the family of the Duke of Aveyro.

The house and gardens of the Retiro, about nine kilometres from Málaga, were founded by Fr. Alonso de Santo Tomás, a Dominican and Bishop of that city from 1664 to 1692. He is believed to have been a natural son of King Philip IV, and the writer Deleito Piñuela confirms this when, speaking of the many royal bastards of this monarch, he says: "Among the other illegitimate sons, most of whom entered the religious life, was Don Alonso who became a Dominican friar and Bishop of Málaga."[25]

He retired to live there, hence its name: El Retiro, the Retreat. At his death he bequeathed the property to his convent of Santo Domingo of Málaga.

In the eighteenth century it passed into the possession of the Count of Villalcázar de Sirga, "a special patron of mine," Ponz tells us, "a person of exquisite taste, a great lover of the noble arts, and a resident of Málaga."[26]

Málaga archaeologist Juan Tembury and architect Fernando Chueca Goitia made an important study of the works of José Martín de Aldehuela[27], an architect from Cuenca who came to Málaga in 1778 and took part in nearly all the building that was carried out there between 1778 and 1802. The study claims that the most important work executed by Villalcázar and Aldehuela during this period was the Retiro in which an old fortress was renovated, enlarged and surrounded with gardens.

"The palace", they tell us, "is in the shape of a 'T'. This design was apparently intended to provide a variety of viewpoints overlooking the parkland and beautiful valley, where the river

BALCONY. RETIRO. Málaga. *Photo S. Saavedra.*

SIRENA FOUNTAIN. RETIRO. Málaga. *Photo S. Saavedra.*

SUNDIAL. RETIRO. Málaga. *Photo S. Saavedra.*

Guadalhorce glides by to the left of the garden; a long balcony of great beauty stands out from the left wing. The layout of the park is vast and complex with three main parts: the orchard, the patio and the pleasure garden."

All that remains from the time of Fr. Alonso de Santo Tomás in the seventeenth century is the section to the right of the eastern façade of the house. It consists of a covered walk called the vine-trellis, forming a cross, in the centre of which there is a tiled octagonal fountain with two sunken steps. According to Chueca and Tembury, this fountain is similar to that in the patio of the Hospital de Venerables of Seville. In line with the covered walk, this orchard-garden has a higher garden which is reached by a double staircase with a grotto and a fountain with a dolphin; these steps lead up to a square pond containing a small island in its centre, planted with oleanders. In the highest part of the estate there are avenues, a terraced vegetable garden, fruit trees, a maze now restored, and an unusual chapel with a dome, called the Bishop's Tomb, where apparently Don Alonso was once buried.

All of this section is very dark today and thickly overgrown with trees and shrubs, giving it a gloomy appearance.

The garden's finest ornament was a curious sundial of white marble with three hundred quadrants indicating the hour in countries known in the seventeenth century; Ponz describes it as follows: "On a marble piece in the garden there are three hundred quadrants or sundials, each angled slightly differently so as to face the sun throughout the day, from the time when it rises until it sets."[28] We were told that the position of this clock has been changed several times, probably to find the sun's rays through the growing trees, and it is now placed on a walk opposite the canal.

These higher gardens were probably the only ones on this estate when it became the property of the Count of Villalcázar. We shall now study the gardens Villalcázar created at the end of the eighteenth century, no doubt according to Aldehuela's design. Their development was probably contemporary with similar work performed at La Cónsula, another property in Churriana.

The dates that we have been able to find suggest that these gardens were built in two stages: first, the square garden with the Fountain of the Siren, in front of the main entrance to the house, built in 1780, and later that of the Cascade, built between 1790 and 1795.

Ponz, who went to Málaga in 1767, does not mention the existence of these gardens.

The square garden in front of the house seems to have been finished by 1782, and on his second visit to Málaga in 1791, Don Antonio Ponz found that the baroque garden with the cascade had already been finished.

The garden in front of the house, in the French style with its central axis, forms a large rectangle at the same level as the wide terrace.

In the centre stands the Fountain of the Siren, constructed with white marble carved in Italy, and consisting of a Triton and a sea-nymph riding a pair of dolphins.

To the left and joined to the balcony there is a low wall

looking on to the valley, with the foothills of the sierras in the background.

It is difficult today to make out the design of this garden because of the tremendous growth and variety of the trees; these trees are not original as this was a classical parterre in the style of those at La Granja. This problem arises in all gardens of this style that were filled with trees in the romantic period. The garden is laid out in octagonal form, with the broad boxwood hedge acting as a background to the series of busts and statues that adorn it. They are mythological figures, some of them very humorous with a certain air of caricature: a harlequin, a satyr, and Mercury wearing a straw hat and with a roguish look about him.

The busts have more personality than the statues, and are all the work of Italian sculptors.

Andalusian influence is evident only in the whitewashed benches and the multitude of flowerpots, inseparable from gardens in Málaga.

Once he had completed his garden, the Count must have felt a desire to enlarge it, and evidently took pleasure in doing so, perhaps encouraged by Aldehuela and inspired by the Italian baroque gardens of the time, which are so numerous and worthy of imitation.

MERCURY. *Photo Author.*

PLAN OF RETIRO GARDENS. Málaga. *From "Arte Espanol." Madrid. 1949.*

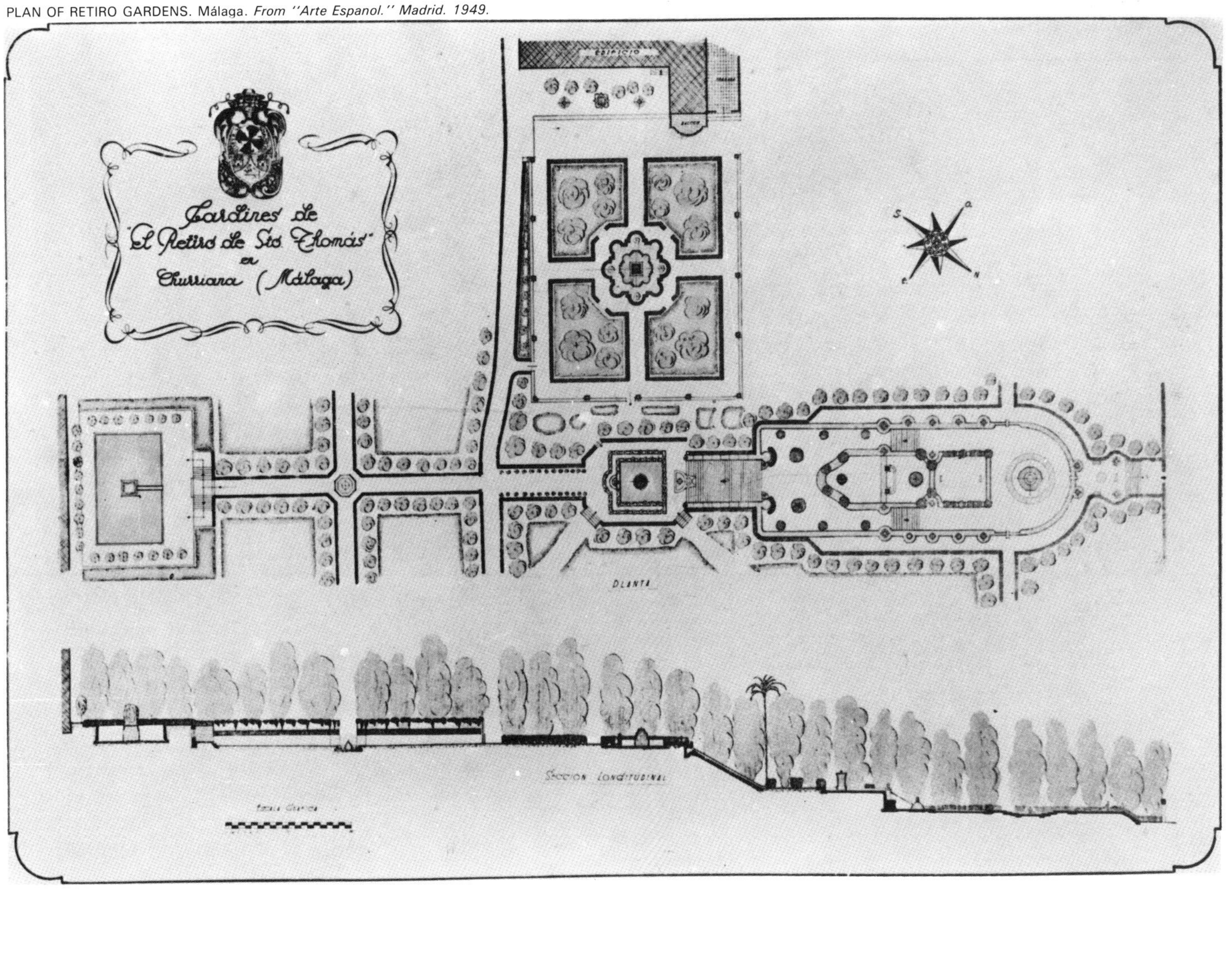

The conditions on the estate were favourable, as water was plentiful and the soil undoubtedly fertile.

At the end of the eighteenth century the gardens of La Granja were at the height of their glory. A few metres away from the first classical garden, a new one was laid out in the Baroque style. It crosses the central avenue of the first, and its cascade and waters supply a large canal, edged with cypresses and old walnut trees, that serves as a reservoir for the numerous water devices; this is the prettiest and most important feature of the garden, reminiscent of the *Riad* of the Arabs.

The cascade is divided into three terraces on a rather steep slope. Its design is no doubt influenced by French gardens, though the decoration could be Italian grotesque. A similar cascade, with its water falling at the sides, in the Quinta del Duque del Arco in El Pardo, near Madrid, will be mentioned later.

This Garden of the Cascade is composed of a square reservoir at its highest point, with a small island in the centre forming a water jet that rises from the rocks. At this level stands a broad central stairway made of stone and bordered by rivulets that flow down the steps in the same way as the water on the steps at the Generalife. Here it pours from two vases at the top of the steps.

On the second terrace there are two jets in the shape of palm trees, with a square central pool. At its edge are two seated, bearded terracotta figures, symbolising rivers and shedding their waters from two casks to a pool below. They were modelled by the sculptor Cháez.

Let us listen to Ponz, who after a second visit to his friend and patron Villalcázar around 1791, sees the garden already finished and writes: "Seeing the garden now, with the fountains, enlarged plantations and other improvements that the estate of Santo Tomás had undergone since I first saw it, it is difficult to recall how it used to look.

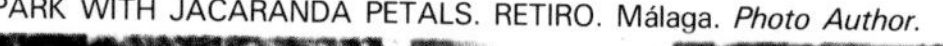
PARK WITH JACARANDA PETALS. RETIRO. Málaga. *Photo Author.*

"Among other innovations, a waterfall or cascade has been added on one side of the lovely flower garden, with various fanciful water devices; the result is an agreeable display much admired by natives and foreigners alike. These works were directed personally by the Count. There are some fountains with terracotta figures, almost life-size, made by the very inventive Cháez whom you knew before leaving for that court.

"The variety of flowers that adorn this beautiful garden in their different seasons is incredible. I had never seen before a particular striped lily from America and other rare flowers grown in this garden."[29]

On a crag in the centre of the last terrace there is an amusing figure of a shepherd playing his flute with his dogs beside him. A little further down there is a large circular tiled fountain with many water jets. The background of this garden is designed as a semicircle, probably to focus attention on the cascade and so that it may be contemplated from this point.

Let us turn now to the gardens of the Retiro in Málaga, which on the whole are rather too profusely decorated with shells and stalactites in the Italian fashion. The effect is overwhelming in such a small area and the number of water devices could have done with more space and a wider outlook. But it must be remembered that these gardens, like those of the Quinta del Duque del Arco and many others, were created in places limited to a single source of water, that is to say, an oasis in the midst of dry and barren wastes; they could therefore not be enlarged. Furthermore, Arab tradition still lingered in Spain and this required that gardens should be secluded and sheltered. Thus, the gardens of the Retiro are in reality three, superimposed over one another: the garden of Fr. Tomás from the time of the House of Austria, somewhat severe and recalling the Alcázar of Seville and its reservoir; the classical parterre in front of the house, of French tradition, belonging to the mid-eighteenth century; and in the last garden, the explosion of Italian baroque, somewhat decadent and intricate, which does not blend easily with the landscape of Málaga.

Today, time and vegetation have effaced its design and given it a rather wistful, neglected air; its fountains only play on rare occasions.

On the other hand, on the left bank of the canal there are green enclosures formed by tall cypresses, and at the end of June the wonderful jacaranda trees shed their blue petals, forming a thick carpet on the avenues in contrast to the dark green of the trees.

This estate now belongs to the Duke of Aveyro's family, which strives to keep it in perfect condition.

According to Antonio Ponz, "this fertile valley behind El Retiro, near the Guadalhorce river, was called La Hoya (The Hollow)." He describes the farm of Don Pedro Ortega Monroy, named San Isidro, which had a great avenue of Canadian poplars "like those in the gardens at Aranjuez", and two large orchards planted with lemon and orange trees.[30]

A short distance from the Retiro lies the property of La Cónsula, so named because its gardens were created by the Prussian Consul, Don Juan Roz.

The house is more elaborate in appearance than that of the Retiro, which retains many traces of its years as a convent and is devoid of ornamentation; La Cónsula can be classed as a small palace, with its double row of columns in front of the four façades, built at the end of the eighteenth century. The square garden is much smaller than that of the Retiro, and therefore lacks its atmosphere and perspective.

There are few traces nowadays of the garden designed by Aldehuela, facing north in front of the main entrance of the house. This position makes the gardens very shady, and perhaps the intention was to provide cool in the summer and protection from the strong Málaga sunshine.

Garden of Abalos, Haro (Rioja)

This garden is situated in the impressive countryside of the Rioja. It was built at the end of the seventeenth century, during the reign of Charles II, to complement the works carried out on the southern façade of the house. This construction consisted chiefly of two large towers and three galleries between them, one above the other, each with five stone arches.

These galleries, like the garden, show an Italian influence due to the lengthy visits to Italy by their owner at that time, Don Antonio Ramírez de la Piscina. The garden is reached through the house with its beautiful seventeenth century furniture and decoration.

With the passing years the design of the garden was gradually obliterated but, fortunately, the original plans used when the garden was created have been found in the archives; at the beginning of the twentieth century, it was replanted with boxwood from the nearby hills. Don Francisco Fernández Navarrete, Marqués de Legarda, the present owner, tends it most carefully and lovingly. This property has an extraordinary atmosphere, as though time were standing still. All the furniture and pictures in the house are of the seventeenth and eighteenth centuries. In the garden a few yew trees, as well as the classical design, give proof of the antiquity of the place.

The name 'Piscina' was adopted by an ancestor of the former owner, who took part in one of the first Crusades and discovered the sacrificial pool of Bethsaida in Jerusalem.[31] It lay near the Temple and was used to purify animals destined to be sacrificed.

It was an enormous reservoir, fifty metres long and thirteen metres deep, partly built of stone and lime and partly hollowed out of the rock. Though considered by some to have been a spring of medicinal water, it seems rather to have been intended to collect rain water in the winter in order to supply water to the Temple by an underground channel.

He brought back from his travels a piece of the Lignum Crucis, and for its veneration he built a Romanesque sanctuary in the village of Pecina, near Abalos, in the Rioja. This national monument, in ruins today, is called Santa María de la Piscina.

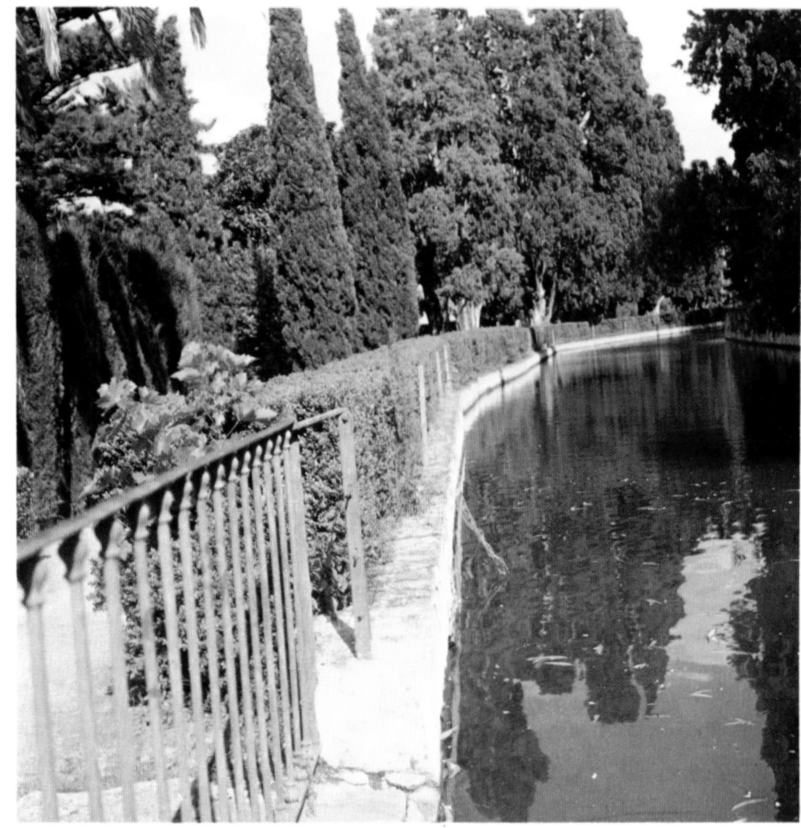

RIA. RETIRO. Málaga. *Photo Author.*

FACADE. CASA ABALOS. Rioja. *Photo S. Saavedra.*

PECINA SANCTUARY. *Photo Author.*

ABALOS GARDEN. *Photo Author.*

[1] VILLALBA, Bartolomé de: *El Pelegrino Curioso, Doncel de Xérica,* Sociedad de Bibliófilos Españoles, Madrid, 1886, vol. I, page 158.

[2] IÑÍGUEZ, Francisco: *Casas reales y jardines de Felipe II,* Consejo Superior de Investigaciones Científicas, Delegación de Roma, 1952, page 101.

[3] IÑÍGUEZ, F.: *Op. cit.,* pages 101 and 102.

[4] PEYRÓN, Juan Francisco: "Nuevo viaje en España en 1772-1773", *Viajes de extranjeros por España y Portugal,* compiled by J. García Mercadal, Ed. Aguilar, 1962, vol. III, page 859.

[5] IÑÍGUEZ, F.: *Op. cit.,* page 137.

[6] PONZ, Antonio: *Viaje de España,* Ed. Aguilar, Madrid, 1947, vol. VI, page 559.

[7] IÑÍGUEZ, F.: *Op. cit.,* page 135.

[8] ARGOTE DE MOLINA: *Libro de la montería del Rey Alfonso XI,* Seville, 1582.

[9] IÑÍGUEZ, F.: *Op. cit.,* page 136.

[10] SIGÜENZA, Fray José de: *La fundación del Monasterio de El Escorial,* Ed. Aguilar, Madrid, 1963, page 406.

[11] SIGÜENZA, Fray José de: *Op. cit.,* page 406.

[12] Detail kindly made available by Don Gabriel Sabau Bergamín, chronicler of the Real Sitio de El Escorial.

[13] SIGÜENZA, Fray José de: *Op. cit.,* page 407.

[14] SIGÜENZA, Fray José de: *Op. cit.,* page 400.

[15] CERVERA VERA, Luis: *Archivo Español de Arte,* Madrid, 1949, no. 87, page 215.

[16] IÑÍGUEZ, F.: *Op. cit.,* page 61.

[17] IÑÍGUEZ, F.: *Op. cit.,* page 61.

[18] CATURLA, María Luisa: *Pinturas, frondas y fuentes del Buen Retiro,* Revista de Occidente, Madrid, 1947, page 26.

[19] EZQUERRA DEL BAYO, Joaquín: *Catálogo de la Exposición del Antiguo Madrid,* 1926, page 74.

[20] Archivo General de Palacio, Madrid: *Inventarios Casa.* Administrative Section, year 1840, pages 171 and 172.

[21] PONZ, Antonio: *Op. cit.,* page 561.

[22] EZQUERRA DEL BAYO, J: *Op. cit.,* page 75.

[23] EZQUERRA DEL BAYO, Joaquín: "Casa de Campo y Heredamiento de La Florida y Montaña del Príncipe Pío", *Revista de la Biblioteca de Archivos y Museos del Ayuntamiento de Madrid,* no. X, pages 184 and 188.

[24] AULNOY, Madame d': "Relación del viaje de España", *Viajes de extranjeros por España y Portugal,* compiled by J. García Mercadal, Ed. Aguilar, 1959, vol. II, page 1033.

[25] DELEITO PIÑUELA, José: *El Rey se divierte,* Espasa-Calpe, Madrid, 1964, page 85.

[26] PONZ, A.: *Op. cit.,* vol. XI, letter VI, page 998.

[27] TEMBURY, Juan, y Chueca, Fernando: "José Martín de Aldehuela y sus obras en Málaga", *Arte Español,* Madrid, 1949, 1st quarter, III: "Palacios y jardines", page 10.

[28] PONZ, A.: *Op. cit.,* vol. XVIII, letter V, page 1646.

[29] PONZ, A.: *Op. cit.,* vol. XVIII, letter V, page 1646.

[30] PONZ, A.: *Op. cit.,* vol. XVIII, letter V, page 1647.

[31] ALVAREZ, O.F.M., Fray Arturo: "Jerusalén, 1969", *ABC,* 9th September 1969.

8 THE GARDENS OF ARANJUEZ. PHILIP II TO PHILIP IV. EL BUEN RETIRO. LA QUINTA DEL DUQUE DE ARCO.

ARANJUEZ. JARDINES DE LA ISLA. BRIDGE OF HERCULES.
Photo Oronoz. By permission of the National Heritage.

There are a few privileged spots in the world where situation, climate and fertile soil make their conversion into gardens inevitable. One such spot can be found near Madrid: Aranjuez, whose two rivers and mild climate make it the rarest of Castilian cities. The truly privileged garden spots are almost always surrounded by water or very near it, and such is the case in Aranjuez, where the Jardines de la Isla (Island Gardens) lie on the banks of the Tagus. This pleasant valley has had special significance since the fourteenth century, when Don Lorenzo Suárez de Figueroa, Grand Master of Santiago — a Military Order, based in nearby Ocaña — chose this site for the Central House and built a palace about 1387. In the sixteenth century it passed to the Catholic Monarchs, Isabella and Ferdinand.

According to Llaguno, "it had four facades, a colonnaded patio of white stone, and galleries on the second floor. There were entrances on the east and west."

"The Catholic Monarchs decorated the palace and added their coat of arms."[1] Queen Isabella apparently liked to stay here from time to time, and the name Catholic Monarchs was given posthumously to the avenue that leads directly from the garden entrance to the river. Destroyed by fire, the palace was rebuilt by Juan de Herrera between 1581 and 1584.

A wooden bridge led to the garden of La Isla, an island formed by the river.

"To judge by the size of some of the trees," says Ponz, "they must have been planted in the time of the Master of Santiago."[2]

Charles V enlarged the gardens and Philip II continued to buy land to complete the grove; he also had an irrigation system built. Luis de Vega designed avenues and bridges, and Juan Bautista de Toledo began the construction of the chapel in 1565.[3]

Although construction of the Palace, as designed by Juan de Herrera, was begun in 1581, it was not completed during Philip II's lifetime. The work was interrupted by his death in 1598, and was not resumed until 1715, during the reign of Philip V, based on plans by the architects Caro Idrogo, Marchand, Bachelieu and Bonavia. The palace was completed during Ferdinand VI's reign, and the stone bridge that leads to the Island Garden dates from that time.[4]

It is now almost impossible to discern the building originally conceived by Philip II; the efforts of the ensuing years have not been very successful. Only the private gardens of the King and Queen remain, encircled at the eastern facade, by a high path along the top of the wall.

Herrera's enclosing wall still stands in the Queen's garden, with its niches and busts, along with the walk over the arches, though this may not be just as Herrera planned it.

The statues have deteriorated badly and the central fountain dates only from the eighteenth century. The figures are of lead painted white.

Some sort of gardens probably existed in Charles V's time, as "in 1548 the wedding of his daughter María with Maximilian, King of Bohemia, and the son of his brother Ferdinand, was celebrated with great festivities in the admirable Island Garden, where in accordance with the Italian tastes of the Emperor, an Ariosto comedy was performed in the Roman style."[5]

The special charm of Aranjuez lies in its magnificent groves of old trees, like an oasis in the heart of Castile.

The inquisitive "Pilgrim" walked amid these wonders: "Our Pilgrim began to notice the height of the trees, so pleasing to our King, with willows, poplars and elms harmonising with the many lemon, citrus and orange trees. Where could you wish to find such unusual walks, such long avenues bordered by rivers, so many ponds, lakes and fountains? Who can explain such a multitude of sights, so many deer, such skilful gardening and such a variety of scented flowers — rose, jasmine, pinks, lilies, violets and countless others — all in such profusion that our Pilgrim believed that His Majesty had tried to recreate in Aranjuez what our parents had lost in the garden of Eden . . . So musing, he strolled through part of the small house. The church is also small, but very pretty."[6]

Philip II's Flemish background gave him a love for gardens. He sent his gardener Jerónimo Algora to visit gardens in France, England and Flanders, and probably Italy as well. Just before this gardener died in 1567, the architect Juan de Herrera wrote to Philip: "The books by Serlio* that you mention will not be needed, as we have plenty. There is one purported to be on Italian gardens which might be useful, though I believe it in reality to be about France and England, written when I sent him there."[7] "He rarely even mentioned Italy, as he had no faith in that country. It is very noticeable from a study of his documents that he always turns to the north and rarely to Italy, though he nevertheless had it very much in mind.[8]

Philip II must have possessed ample literature on Italian Renaissance gardens, but the gardeners he employed in Aranjuez

PALACIO ARANJUEZ. OLD PAINTING. Archaeological Museum. Madrid. By permission of the National Heritage.

were Dutch or Flemish; their style was more in harmony with his severe disposition. This can be seen in the gardens of La Isla where the only Italian features are the statues of mythological heroes, some of them placed there after Philip II's time by his Habsburg descendants and the Bourbons who succeeded them. This style was not at all to his liking, as he preferred Dutch gardens divided into small compartments with clipped hedges and laid out on flat ground, as in Holland. His reserved temperament was in keeping with these divisions and trellises, which were also reminiscent of the Arabs.

A great number of Flemish gardeners were certainly at work in the royal gardens during this period.

Lamberto Wyts, who acted as escort to Anne of Austria, Philip II's fourth wife, wrote an account of a journey made in 1570-1571, in which he says: "Two Flemish brothers named Hollebecke acted as guides at Aranjuez; one of them was in charge of the gardens and work, and the other distilled all manner of herbs. The palace was surrounded with rich pastures; the King had a farmer there, a native of Tournay called Curuble, who made butter. At that time the new palace at Aranjuez was being built; the foreman of the masonry was Flemish, from Audenarde."[9]

Iñíguez adds: "Many Flemings, such as Reugel and Hollebecke referred to above, were mentioned by name. There are also references to "the Dutchman" and "the Fleming" without mention of their names. Beginning in 1561, an Englishman and some Frenchmen worked at Aranjuez for several years. This does not include such royal architects as Juan Bautista de Toledo, Juan de Herrera and Gaspar de la Vega, who also plan gardens."[10]

Philip II's prime concern was the construction of an enormous reservoir in the Lake of Ontígola, in spite of the two rivers that irrigated the fields and gardens of Aranjuez. No doubt the King had in mind the Arabs' wise storage of water in Granada, which always preceded the construction of a garden. The Lake of Ontígola also fed the ponds for the breeding of fish.

The gardens were filled with a profusion of fountains, some built against walls, probably of Italian origin, and others monumental and ornate, as will be described later.

In 1566 the King sent for a number of willows, reeds and acacias. Great quantities of plants had already come from Flanders in 1565; lime trees were probably among them, and raspberries and hazel trees are also mentioned. In 1567 the King ordered walnut and bead trees to be planted in La Fresneda, and fruit trees in the Casa de Campo.[11]

Navagero mentions cypresses, laurels and orange trees; Ponz and other authors describe the old ash trees, chestnuts, pear trees and sour cherries; Texeira indicates the position of quince trees in the Casa de Campo on his map, and Philip II, in his letters to his daughters, speaks of the lemon trees of Aranjuez. Walsh explains that the idea of planting elms in Aranjuez is English, the result of the King's marriage to Mary Tudor.[12]

The King, in his methodical way, had the varieties of seeds

ARANJUEZ. QUEEN'S GARDEN. WALL BY HERRERO. *Photo Author.* By permission of the National Heritage.

sent from Flanders for Valencia and Aranjuez kept separate, and he ordered that each species should be planted separately in beds or pots, and not mixed.

He had an extraordinary craving for flowers, and it was essential that "the garden plots should be filled with them, and interspersed with strawberries and other plants." The flowers must have been sown by broadcasting mixed seed as in the garden of the Escorial, or in separate varieties. The King was very fond of roses, especially "the musk with evergreen leaves," which he also kept separate. They must have bloomed profusely, for in 1582 he distributed among the royal apothecary stores, hospitals and convents in Madrid about two tons of roses gathered in his various gardens. Gaspar de la Vega was asked to supply shears for the gardener "to trim the rose bushes at Aranjuez, or make them level so that they could be used as hedges." The varieties of roses included Alexandrine, Castilian, damask and musk.

The travellers also mention madonna lilies, violets and pinks.

In his letters to his daughters from Lisbon the King spoke of the jonquil with its yellow flower (similar to the daffodil), and sent them roses and orange blossoms, "so that you can see what they are like here." (Walsh.)

Clover was used for the lawns which required expert attention and, at the King's request, myrtle trees were also planted.

Game and birds abounded in the royal parks, and the King kept a lion-house at the Casa de Campo.[13]

Aranjuez was the most famous of Philip II's gardens; the palace, which was never finished, was in reality built for the garden and was originally quite small.

Philip II took a personal interest in its reconstruction

ARANJUEZ. APOLLO FOUNTAIN. *Photo Author. By permission of the National Heritage.*

because, although the artificial canal that worked some old mills in his father's time was already there, it was he who truly created the Island Garden; the plans were drawn up by Juan Bautista de Toledo, and the garden was called the *cuarto real* (royal square).

"The Flemish gardener saw this artist's plans for the Island Garden in 1561. He did not approve of rectangular plots; he preferred them square, but Juan Bautista would not agree to the alteration; his plan conformed to the shape of the land which was long and narrow. The plots should be similarly proportioned if the whole was to have unity."[14]

It was therefore laid out about 1562 in squares and rectangles, no doubt inspired by Flemish gardens, according to the royal instructions. The King was constantly pressing for the work to be speeded up. "In March of that year, on the occasion of the visit of the Empress Doña María, Philip II's sister, the fountains were already playing."[15] There is no trace today of this old design.

The fountains of the garden itself were of two types throughout. Some were low and placed in the middle of squares, as the King advised for Balsaín (near Segovia), and as could be seen at the Casa de Campo; others were tall with basins mounted one above the other. None remain today, at least in their original form.

Some of the low fountains found here today may be original, but they are so simple and ordinary that it is impossible to say with certainty.[16]

Queen Isabel de Valois, so beloved of Philip II, seems to have taken a personal interest in the gardens and in 1560 she asked her mother, Catherine de Medici, to send her a gardener. She wrote that the Garden of La Isla "n'est point encore en état, attendant votre jardinier"; adding, a few lines further on, "vous pouvant assurer, Madame, que c'est un fort beau lieu."[17] In these letters she describes Aranjuez with great enthusiasm.

Successive monarchs went on improving the work of their ancestors. In 1660, the architect Sebastián Herrera Barnuevo, on Philip IV's orders, transformed the gardens completely, giving them more or less their present appearance. The only major difference was that the squares and benches were enclosed with wooden lattices, probably to provide shade and shelter, as the large trees that now cast their shadows over the garden had not grown sufficiently. Today these trees tend to obliterate the perspective and design of the garden.

The moment one descends into this garden the immediate impression, despite the fountains and statues of a later period, is that of the secluded and restricted Renaissance garden with its rigid, austere design. It lacks both the exuberance of the Italian Renaissance gardens, always dependent on architecture, and the luxuriant vegetation and clipped hedges of northern gardens. It may be considered a Castilian version of a sixteenth-century garden, before Versailles had created parterres and canals, opening the view across the countryside. The Marquise de Villars, wife of the French Ambassador to the Court of Charles II in 1680, tells us: "Aranjuez is regarded here as one of the world's marvels. Its position is one of the loveliest because of its waters; if Monsieur Le Nôtre were to find something similar, what he would accomplish there would be breathtaking."[18]

The famous Saint Simon, while Ambassador in Spain (1721-1722) during the reign of Philip of Anjou, the first Bourbon, writes in his Memoirs: "The whole garden is in the old Flemish style. Accustomed as we are now to refined taste in our gardens, as introduced by Le Nôtre, who has been widely acclaimed and whose creations have become models, we cannot help finding Aranjuez mean and insignificant."[19]

Both the Marquise de Villars and Saint Simon were greatly mistaken. Despite the genius of Le Nôtre, his style could never have been adopted in Spain; opening up long perspectives would merely have revealed the barren wastes and bare mountain sides that encircle Aranjuez. Its narrow avenues were not intended for the dazzling court displays of Louis XIV. Everything at Aranjuez had necessarily to be intimate and on a small scale.

Philip IV, whose pale countenance is so familiar through the pictures of Velázquez, held his masked balls and beloved comedies in these gardens. Two fires broke out at the palace during his time, probably attributable to these festivities, for which quantities of wax candles were required. The first fire occurred in 1660 and the other five years later.[20]

Martin Hume relates that: "In the spring of 1622 there was a great series of festivals at Aranjuez to celebrate Philip IV's seventeenth birthday. One of the attractions was the presentation of a comedy in verse by the Count of Villamediana, dedicated to the Queen, and staged in a temporary and beautifully adorned canvas theatre erected amidst the trees on the "Island Garden." The comedy was called *La Gloria de Niquea*, and Isabella herself was to perform the role of the goddess of beauty. It was night, and the flimsy structure of silk and canvas was brilliantly lit with wax lights. The young King and his two brothers and sister were seated in front of the stage, and the Queen in the retiring-room behind the scenes. After applauding the prologue the audience was awaiting the Queen's entrance when a piercing shriek arose from the back; a moment later, a sheet of flame enveloped the drapery, and the stage and pavilion were ablaze. Panic seized the elegant spectators, and there was a rush to escape. The King made his way through the terror-struck audience to the back of the stage in search of his wife. At last he found her, half-swooning in the arms of Villamediana. The rumours soon spread that the Count had purposely set fire to the theatre so that he might gain credit for saving the Queen and enjoy the satisfaction of having clasped her in his arms, if but for a moment."[21] The end of this gallant and dashing courtier is well known: four months after this event Villamediana, whose boast was "*son mis amores reales*" (my loves are Royal), was murdered in the streets of Madrid, a murder rumoured to have been arranged by the King himself.

At any rate, Philip IV continued to hold splendid festivities and dramatic presentations, of which he and the Queen were very fond, at the royal palaces.

* * *

ARANJUEZ. FOUNTAIN OF THE HOURS. *Photo Author.* By permission of the National Heritage.

ARANJUEZ. JARDIN ISLA. *Engraving of a plan by Winthuysen.*

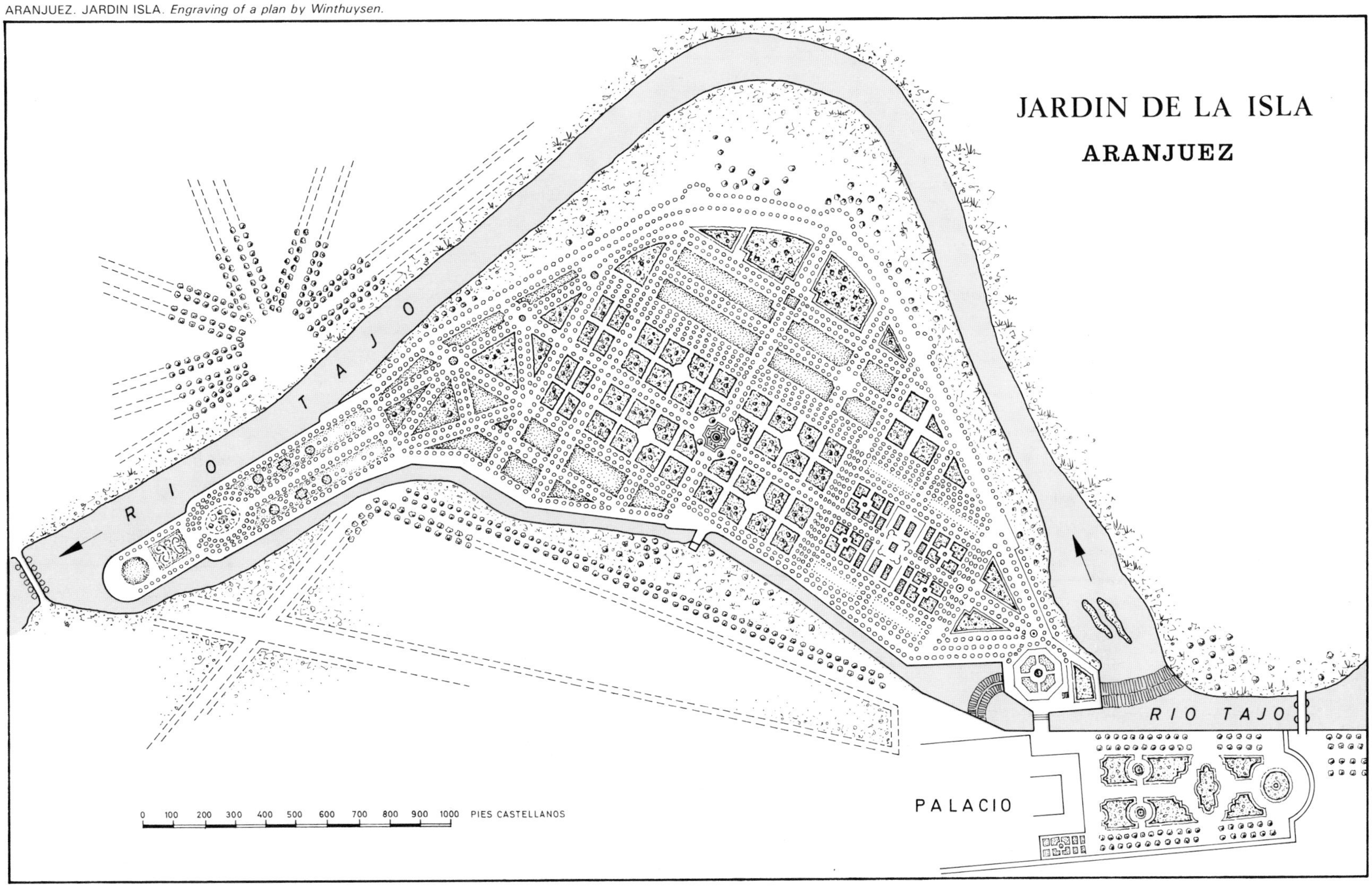

JARDIN DE LA ISLA

ARANJUEZ

RIO TAJO

RIO TAJO

PALACIO

0 100 200 300 400 500 600 700 800 900 1000 PIES CASTELLANOS

ARANJUEZ. JARDIN ISLA. *Engraving, "Délices de l'Espagne."*

ARANJUEZ. JARDIN ISLA. FOUNTAIN OF THE HARPIES. *Engraving, "Délices de l'Espagne."*

We shall now study the Jardín de la Isla as it appears today, after the changes of the seventeenth and eighteenth centuries.

In 1744 a bridge was built across the canal with marble steps and wrought iron balustrades. Here there is an enormous fountain with a statue of Hercules wrestling with the hydra. It is octagonal in shape and was built in 1661. A pond encircles it, and there are stone statues at the entrance to the four bridges that cross this pond. Ponz tells us: "Near them there is a large fountain with many marble figures around its basin, and on the central basin, a statue of Hercules struggling with the hydra. None of them has sufficient merit to justify an individual description; suffice it to say that this is the largest fountain of them all."[22]

Behind this fountain, and a little to the right, stands the fountain of Apollo. According to the concise Ponz: "There is a statue crowning the basin, and I am not sure whether, as I was told, it represents Apollo." (It looks more like Vertumnus who was usually portrayed with garlands of flowers and fruit.)

"The best things about this fountain are, in my modest opinion, some bas-reliefs of Neopolitan origin carved on the sides of the basin, representing the Labours of Hercules and alternating with the royal arms."[23]

Paulina Junquera, head of the historical department in the Royal Palace in Madrid, also points out "the important Neapolitan bas-reliefs on the sides of the basin,"[24] which already show Baroque characteristics.

Following the Avenue of the Fountains we come to the Fountain of the Hours which is not mentioned by Ponz. It is on ground level and is one of the simplest in the garden, and therefore scarcely noticed. According to old documents the shadow of the vertical jet of this fountain served to show the hours of the day on the pool's rim. (They are still marked there today.)

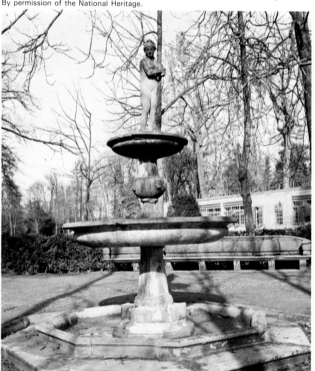

ARANJUEZ. JARDIN ISLA. JOHN OF AUSTRIA FOUNTAIN. *Photo Author.* ,
By permission of the National Heritage.

It thus made a very original sundial. Today, the shade of the old trees prevents the marking of the hours.

Continuing along the path we find ourselves surrounded on both sides by boxwood parterres. Many of the old designs, however, have disappeared, and the plan of the garden is somewhat blurred by the tall trees that did not exist when the garden was created.

The central axis of the garden is still visible with its bowers and fountains all in a line. The small squares were designed for seclusion, and to avoid the monotony of repeated features.

Along the central pathway we arrive at the so-called arbour of the Harpies, the work of the Toledo artists Juan Fernández and Pedro Taray (1615-1617). It was at one time surrounded by wooden lattices and today still has its finely carved stone benches, but the four pergolas have disappeared. In its centre stands a square fountain, the most attractive and classical of all. Four pilasters support slender columns with Corinthian capitals. Above them four busts of harpies or furies spurt water to the central fountain in which, seated on a pedestal, is the bronze figure of a child taking a thorn from his foot; this is a seventeenth century replica of the superb ancient statue in Rome.

Continuing along the axis of the fountains, we come to another arbour adorned with stone benches and a fountain named after Don Juan of Austria. According to tradition, the marble from which the basin was carved was brought by Don Juan from the Gulf of Lepanto, but this seems highly improbable. Above this basin is a smaller one with a bronze seventeenth-century female figure, probably Venus. Ponz tells us that the statue "is made of bronze and has no particular merit; some children on the pedestal are of better workmanship."[25] (They are no longer there.)

ARANJUEZ. FOUNTAIN OF JOHN OF AUSTRIA. *Engraving, "Délices de l'Espagne."*

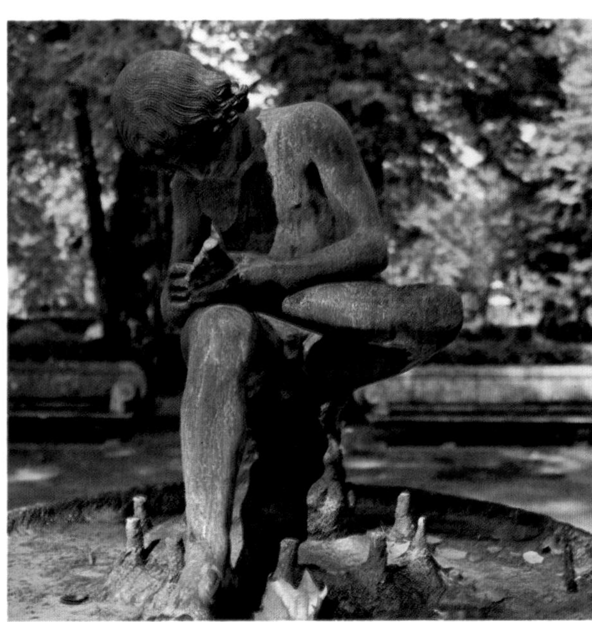

ARANJUEZ. DETAIL OF BOY WITH THORN. *Photo S. Saavedra.* By permission of the National Heritage.

ARANJUEZ. FOUNTAIN OF BOY WITH THORN. *Photo S. Saavedra.* By permission of the National Heritage.

ARANJUEZ. BACCHUS FOUNTAIN. *Photo S. Saavedra. By permission of the National Heritage.*

ARANJUEZ. BACCHUS FOUNTAIN. *Engraving, "Délices de l'Espagne."*

According to the engravings of *Les Délices de l'Espagne,* all these fountains were surrounded by hedges, and there were trellises at the corners of the squares. These protected the garden both from the rays of the sun and from indiscreet visitors and provided the seclusion and intimacy so typical of the period.

Last in this line of fountains is that of Bacchus. Ponz writes that "this fountain has a bronze statue of Bacchus quite different from his portrayals in antiquity as young and gallant. Here he appears monstrously fat, riding astride a barrel."[26] Lozoya contends nevertheless, that this figure represents Silenus, who is usually symbolized by these characteristics.

The basin of this fountain is of baroque design, and thus appears to date from the time of Philip IV, or later.

At this point, the axis of the fountains turns toward the left where we find the last remaining fountain, that of Neptune, the best in the Island Garden.

The inscription around the pedestal supporting the basin bears the date 1621, in the reign of Philip III; it must have been placed there early in that year, as the King died in March. Nowadays there are four stone pedestals around the basin, two of which support bronze groups by Algardi representing the goddess Cybele or Ceres in duplicate. The fountain is crowned by another of Neptune. Yves Bottineau tells us that this fountain was a gift to Philip IV from the Duke of Terranova[27], but the dates do not seem to agree.

In Ponz's time (the eighteenth century): "The Fountain of Neptune has seven bronze groups of medium size, with pedestals of the same material. They are placed around the basin with one on top representing Neptune, mounted on a shell-shaped chariot, armed with his trident and led by tritons. This group is repeated on one of the six surrounding pedestals. The figures of Ceres on her chariot drawn by lions and of Juno in the act of casting thunderbolts at the giants also appear in duplicate, so these six groups are in reality only three in duplicate. The seventh, depicting Jupiter casting thunderbolts at the giants, is unique, but is duplicated in a piece at the Buen Retiro, where there is also a duplicate of the group of Hercules wrestling with the hydra. All these sculptures are by the famous Italian sculptor Alejandro Algardi."[28]

Algardi decorated the Villa Doria Pamphili in Rome and, according to Ponz the bas-reliefs of St. Leon capturing Atila, in the Vatican are his work. If Algardi died in 1654, as Ponz says, and the fountain at Aranjuez dates from 1621, then the sculptures of Algardi could not have been part of the original fountain. According to tradition, these bronze groups were models of larger ones lost in a shipwreck on the way to Spain after the artist's death, and these had probably been sent earlier as samples.

The Fountain of the Tritons was once aligned with Algardi's fountain along this same walk at the extreme end of the island, which is called the Islet. Ponz saw it in place at the end of the eighteenth century: "It is named after three tritons on a step in the lower basin. Each triton carries on his shoulder a basket worked in different ways, and has a shield with a coat of arms in his hand. In the centre of the fountain, mounted on a pedestal, stands a column surrounded by three female figures about five palms in height, who seem to represent prettily dressed nymphs; between them are masks and other ornaments."[29] It bears the inscription "Philip IV, 1657", but it is of Genoese origin and much older. Madoz, in his description of the gardens of the Royal Palace in Madrid, says: "This beautiful fountain of Berruguete's time and style was in Aranjuez from 1657, but on its removal to the position it now occupies (in the Campo del Moro in Madrid) a new basin, which matches neither the form nor the material of the lovely fountain in its centre, had to be added."

There is a picture of this fountain painted in Aranjuez by Velázquez in the Prado Gallery; at one time it had been attributed to Del Mazo — more on this later.

THE GARDENS OF THE BUEN RETIRO, MADRID

The gardens of the Buen Retiro were the last to be created by the Habsburgs. They were originally a country estate belonging to the Conde-Duque de Olivares, the favourite minister of Philip IV. Conde-Duque de Olivares presented them to the King, who continued to enlarge the park with adjoining orchards. In Philip II's time there had been only the Royal Chamber (el Cuarto Real) of San Jerónimo on this site, near the monastery where Royalty used to retire during mourning, Lent, or penance; for this reason it was named El Retiro (The Retreat).

The Palace of El Buen Retiro was begun in late 1631. Today only a wing remains, housing the Army Museum. The Casón, now a Museum of Contemporary Art, has also been preserved; it is a square building, formerly called El Salón or The Ballroom, facing a parterre in the Retiro Park once known as the Flower Garden.

The garden was created by the Florentine Cosimo Lotti, who had helped to creat the Boboli Gardens in Florence and arrived in Madrid in 1628 to carry out Philip IV's plans.

"The favourite minister made the place into a park, and the palace was inaugurated in October of 1632 before it was completely finished. There were great celebrations, the first of many that would be held in this new abode of pleasure. Lope de Vega sang their praises and dedicated a poem. In one of the festivities the favourite performed equestrian exercises with reed spears (*correr las canas*) at the King's side — as was his habit — emulating the splendour of the King's attire."[30]

"The Conde-Duque de Olivares saw to the most insignificant details and enlarged the park by adding parcels of land. As a result, the gardens have always lacked unity and perspective. The great square pond was out of line and could not be seen from the palace. The small octagonal pond, which at that time had a turret in the centre, and the covered avenues and other ornaments were also out of alignment."[31]

The octagonal pond looks much larger and more important in the engraving than it does today, scarcely distinguishable amidst

BUEN RETIRO. OCHAVADO POND. *Engraving, "Délices de l'Espagne".*

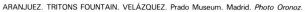

ARANJUEZ. TRITONS FOUNTAIN. VELÁZQUEZ. Prado Museum. Madrid. *Photo Oronoz.*

CAMINO DE ALCALA
Camino de Ambros
Camino de Vicaluaro
PVERTA DE ALCALA
PRADO DE LOS RECOLETOS
CALLE DE ALCALA
PRADO DE S. GERONIMO
PRADO ALTO
CANPO GRANDE
PRADO DE ATOCHA
CALLE DE ATOCHA
CANPO DE SAN BLAS
CAMINO DE VALLECAS
Pitipie de Quinientas Varas Castellanas
Pitipie de Quinientos Pacos de A dos Pies y Medio

the thick woods, lying, as it does, between the large pond and the parterre to the left of the Casón. There is now a rock formation in the middle, covered by a mass of vegetation; the pool is dry.

The large pond is also still there. It once had square pavilions at each corner. The King and Queen would fish here, and wonderful aquatic festivities were held on an oval island in the centre[32]. These festivities, held by Philip IV and successive monarchs up to Charles III, cost millions. They would become the target of caustic songs and satires among the people of Madrid.

Comedies were staged on the lake and in the Casón, where scenery was moved by costly machinery. *The Enchantments of Circe* was staged there on the eve of St. John in 1635 with scenery by Cosimo Lotti "according to plans drawn up by Don Pedro Calderón."[33] Literary Academies were held in 1637, attended by Lope de Vega and Quevedo. Calderón wrote "The Contest of Love and Jealousy" — *El Certamen del Amor y Celos* — by royal command, and it was performed on the great lake of the Buen Retiro; he also organised a poetry contest during the famous festivities of February 1637.[34]

A letter from the British Ambassador, Sir William Aston, reads as follows: "In the festival at the Buen Retiro in 1636, rare gardens and new water devices were inaugurated. The entertainment," he adds, "was the most original and brilliant I have ever attended, with three *scenarios,* each illuminated in the newest and most ingenious way — all due to the imagination of the Conde-Duque." In a further note he adds, "according to the architect Sebastián Herrera Barnuevo, the favourite had invented wind-resistant torches for these nocturnal celebrations."[35]

In 1640 a fire broke out at the Palace of Buen Retiro. This royal seat was unpopular in Madrid, where it was believed to be the palace of the Conde-Duque and a wasteful luxury.

The equestrian statue of Philip IV was placed in the entrance or garden-court surrounding the palace. It had been sculpted in Florence by Pedro Tacca, a pupil of John of Bologna, and was a gift to the Spanish King from Ferdinand, Grand Duke of Tuscany. (See Appendix III). The statue was apparently cast in bronze after sketches that Velázquez is believed to have made of Rubens' equestrian portrait of Philip IV, which was destroyed in the fire at the Alcázar in 1734. Juan F. Peyron saw the statue in the Retiro in 1772, and on another visit to Spain in 1772-1773 he gives one of the most detailed descriptions ever made.[36]

The statue is wonderfully balanced, with the entire weight of the horse resting on the hind legs and the tail, thanks, it is said, to calculations by Galileo. In 1844, during Queen Isabella II's childhood, when the area around the Royal Palace was being redesigned, this statue was moved from the Retiro to the Plaza de Oriente, opposite the Palace, where it still stands despite Madrid's many upheavals during the Civil War of 1936-1939.

The pedestal of this statue has some bas-reliefs representing the King offering the Cross of Santiago to Velázquez and protecting the arts and sciences.

Lady Elisabeth Holland travelled in Spain at the time of the Peninsular War, as she and her husband were very devoted to the Spanish cause and had many friends in Spain. She compares this statue to that of the ill-fated Charles I at Charing Cross in London, and says: "The statue is much admired, and deservedly so, as it is a fine specimen of workmanship; it has not, however, the spirit of the equestrian statue of Charles I of England at Charing Cross."[37]

There were at least seven hermitages around the Buen Retiro gardens at the time of Philip IV, occupied by hermits who were given an allowance; among others were the hermitages of San Isidro, San Bruno, the Magdalene, San Pablo and San Juan. That of San Antonio de los Portugueses was a present from the people of Portugal and had a festooned pool. In the eighteenth century the famous porcelain factory was established here[38], more or less where the statue of the Fallen Angel now stands.

María Luisa Caturla relates that "in order to tour the gardens and shorten the journey to the hermitages, Their Majesties used small carriages."[39] According to Derek Clifford, "the Hermitage of St. John the Baptist was occupied by no less a hermit than the Conde-Duque himself, devoting his time not to contemplation but to alchemy,"[40] but it seems unlikely that the King's

BUEN RETIRO. LARGE POND. *Engraving, "Délices de l'Espagne".*

BUEN RETIRO. PATIO WITH STATUE OF PHILIP IV. *Engraving, "Délices de l'Espagne."*

PLAN OF MADRID. Texeira 1656. Buen Retiro.

STATUE OF PHILIP IV. PRESENT LOCATION. *Photo Oronoz.*

BUEN RETIRO. ERMITA DE SAN PABLO. *Engraving, "Délices de l'Espagne."*

favourite would have used a consecrated place for this purpose. It was more probably a certain Don Vicencio Lupati, who claimed to turn base elements into silver and was lodged in the Retiro, probably in an outbuilding of the hermitage. He later made off with 2,000 ducats, taking advantage of the Conde-Duque.[41]

Derek Clifford also ascribes the origin of the hermitages that later flourished in the picturesque parks of England and France in the eighteenth and nineteenth centuries to those of the Buen Retiro[42], although he also mentions two much earlier hermitages in Italy. Lady Holland, who, in the autumn of 1804 stopped in Lerma (a town in Burgos on the road to France) at the Palace of the Duke of Lerma, Philip III's favourite, described a wood behind the palace where seven hermitages still stood, uninhabited. We do not know whether they were of Philip III's time or of a later date. All have now disappeared.

The outline of the hermitages in the Buen Retiro could be glimpsed through the foliage. One of the first and loveliest was Saint Paul's, in the Italian style, with its famous covered walks hung with creepers and a large fountain in its centre.[43]

Despite the lack of perspective, these gardens must have possessed great charm. "The spires of the tiny pavilions that housed the irrigation wheels, the jetties and their trellised enclosures could be seen around the large square pond. The hermitages with their secret gardens hidden among the trees or isolated on a large pond where they could only be reached by a single small bridge; the grottoes, the maze all must have had great appeal — all the more so for being private and intimate. . ."[44]

According to documents in the Royal Palace Archives in Madrid, the period between the death of Philip IV and the arrival of Philip V, that is to say the regency of Mariana of Austria (Philip IV's last wife) and later the reign of Charles II, must have been a time of decay and neglect in the royal gardens both at the Buen Retiro and in Aranjuez. All these documents record the abandoned state of the gardens and the interruption of building at the Palace of Aranjuez, which was not to be finished until well into the eighteenth century, no doubt also on account of the two fires that took place there. An attempt was made around 1712 to impose the French style upon the gardens of Buen Retiro, according to the precepts of Le Nôtre. Among the French artists and gardeners brought to Spain was René Carlier, later to become the chief designer of the gardens of La Granja in 1721.

The scheming Princesse des Ursins had gained a hold over the youthful Philip of Anjou and his wife, Marie Louise de Savoie. This clever woman took charge of the works at the Buen Retiro Palace, as well as its gardens, which she had remodelled. She corresponded with Louis XIV's great architect, Robert de Cotte (1656-1735), the brother-in-law of Jules Hardoin Mansart, and architect of the chapel at Versailles. Some of their very interesting correspondence has been preserved in the Bibliothèque Nationale in Paris.[45]

One subject of this correspondence was René Carlier, a pupil of Robert de Cotte who sent him to Spain to work for Jean Orry, the French administrator whom Louis XIV had sent as financial adviser to his grandson in an effort to support the troubled Spanish Treasury. M. de la Croix, who seems to have been an official of the Royal Library in Paris, also figures in the

a Madrid le 18 Xbre 1712.

Un voyage que j'ay fait aux eaux de Bagneres monsieur, et la deffense que les medecins font a ceux qui prennent des remedes de lire et d'ecrire m'ont empeché de vous marquer que j'avois receu vôtre derniere lettre. je serois bien fachée que vous pussiez croire que ce fut faute d'attention pour vous, vous estimant autant que je le fais. j'ay trouvé a mon retour a Madrid des plans de mr. Carlier pour faire les jardins du Retire ausquels leurs Mtez C. ont donné leur approbation. Elles seront cependant bien aises auparavant que de les faire mettre a execution que mr. le Duc d'Antin les fasse voir au Roy dont elles ont une grande opinion du gout. vous aurez la bonté s'il vous plaist monsieur de me mander vôtre sentiment. Le Roy et la Reyne vous en seront fort obligez. je vous la seray infiniment si vous estes aussy persuadé que je vous prie de l'estre du plaisir que j'aurois si vous voulez bien me faire la grace d'estre un peu de mes amis. la princesse des ursins

LETTER FROM THE PRINCESSE DES URSINS. Courtesy of the Bibliothèque Nationale. Paris.

correspondence. To both these people Robert de Cotte often sent letters.

The French artists who arrived in Spain were accustomed to gardens designed by Le Nôtre and his pupils, gardens with grand vistas, statues and fountains such as those surrounding the royal palaces of Versailles, Marly and Saint Cloud. These artists probably saw few possibilities in the Buen Retiro gardens, where the buildings were perched without plan or symmetry down the slope of the Prado de San Jerónimo, with the gardens at a higher level than the palace, lacking both unity and perspective.

Robert de Cotte, who never visited Spain, wrote to Carlier from Marly in January in 1713, stating that the gardens were "monotonous and lacking in perspective" and should be "lowered to the level of the Casón."[46] The present parterre at the Retiro, centred on the Casón, was probably dug out and levelled during this period.

Robert de Cotte painted some magnificent plans for this garden in watercolours, which are kept today in the Cabinet d'Estampes in the Bibliothèque Nationale in Paris. They show plans to "extend the gardens towards the river to give them vista and water; they were to be extended in three terraces of which the last could continue until it faded out of sight."[47] That is to say, they would have reached the spot where the Atocha Railway Station now stands. Robert de Cotte, who had never been to Madrid and had not seen the barren Castilian wastes that surround it, did not understand that such vast gardens could not be maintained without irrigation, an impossibility due to the scarcity of water. The Manzanares river was certainly inadequate.

The formation of an Orangery was also planned, probably

PLAN FOR BUEN RETIRO BY ROBERT DE COTTE. (Original state). Courtesy of the Bibliothèque Nationale. Paris.

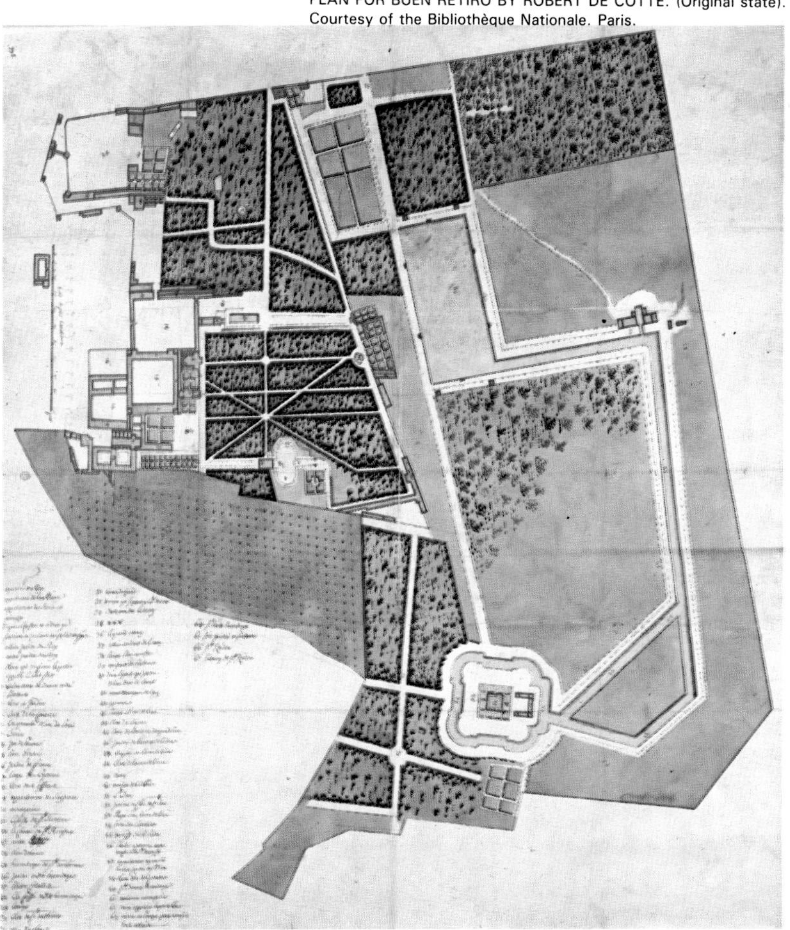

inspired by the one at Versailles. In December of 1712 the Princesse des Ursins wrote to Robert de Cotte[48] that his "plans for the Buen Retiro Gardens have been approved by Their Majesties, but before beginning the work they would wish the Duc d'Antin (son of Madame de Montespan and Louis XIV) to show them to the King, whose good taste they hold in high esteem."

This quite impracticable plan came to nothing, and the Retiro remained as it had been (except for the new parterre facing the Casón). On 14 February the young Queen died at the age of twenty-six, and the Princesse des Ursins set about finding a new wife for Philip V. Her choice fell upon Isabella de Farnese, whose poverty and obscurity, she believed, would not overshadow her own prominence. But when the Princess went to the village of Jadraque in Guadalajara to meet her, Isabella, following the shrewd advice of Cardinal Alberoni, provoked a quarrel with her; as is well known, the Princess was instantly dismissed and sent to the frontier, still wearing her ceremonial dress despite the severe cold. Orders were given that no halt should be made other than to change horses, and no word spoken to her during the journey.

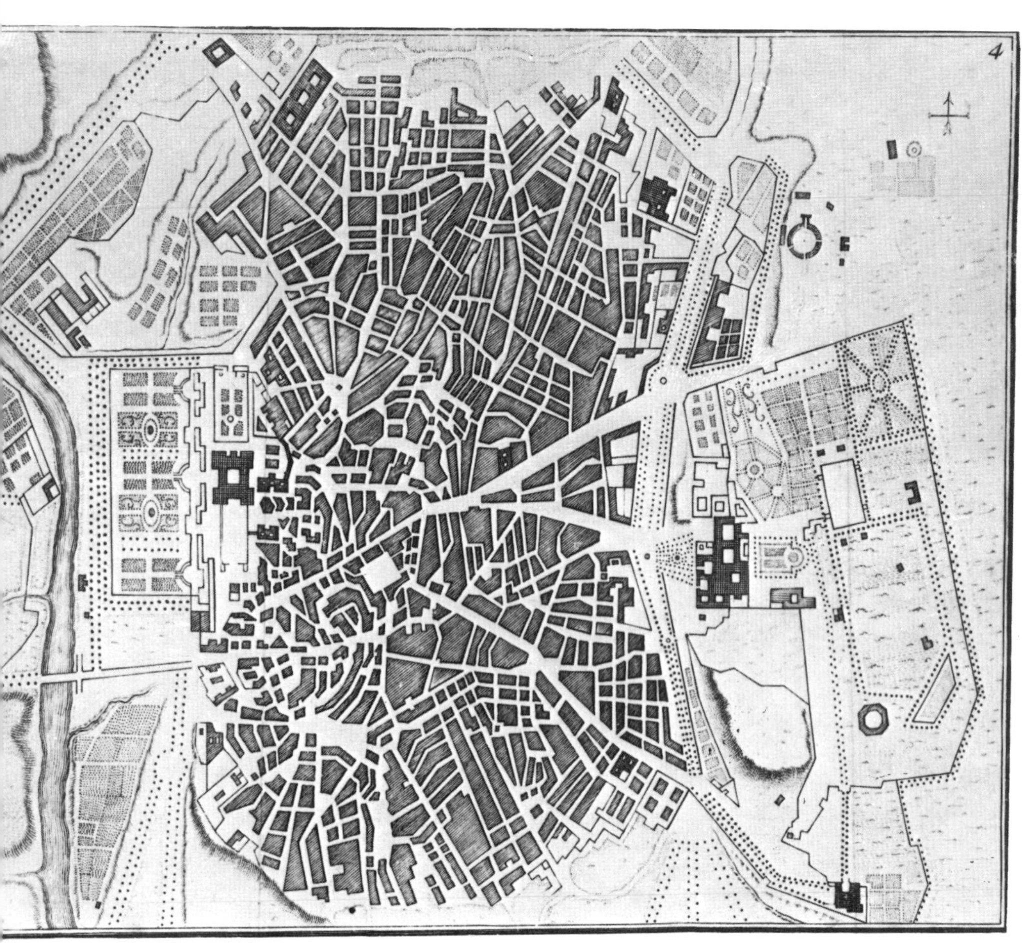

PLAN OF BUEN RETIRO. (Eighteenth century). *A. Ponz.*

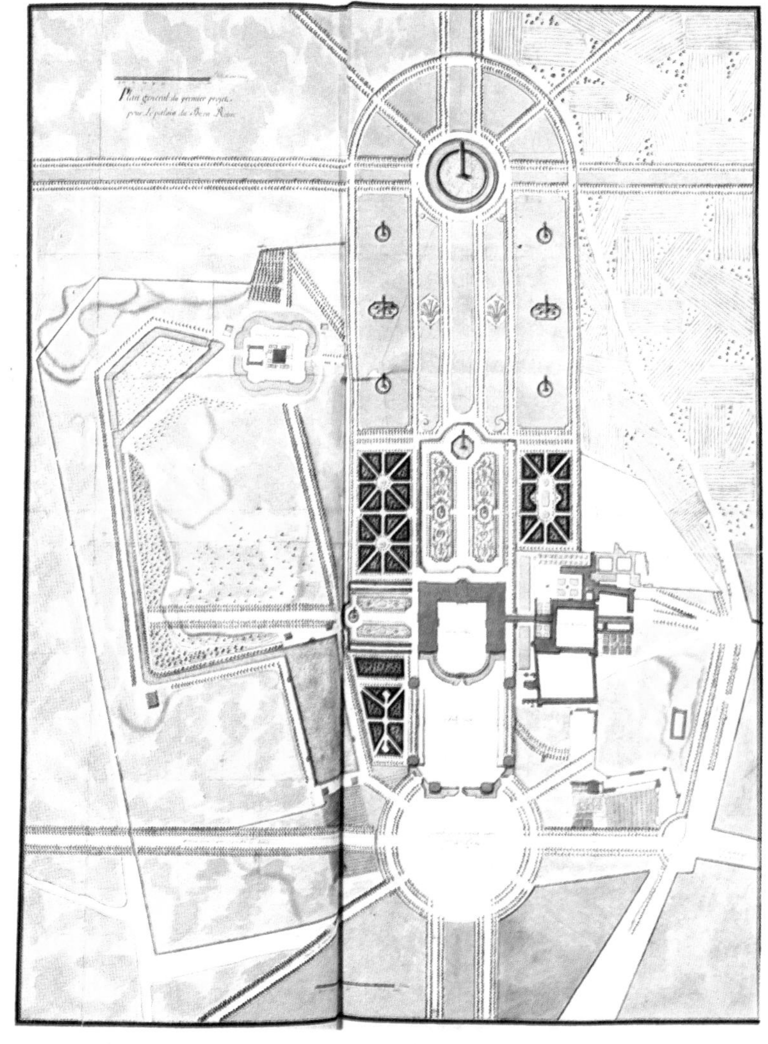
PLAN OF BUEN RETIRO WITH MODIFICATION PROPOSED BY ROBERT DE COTTE.
Courtesy of Bibliothèque Nationale. Paris.

All plans for the Retiro were thus laid aside. On 7 January 1715, M. Orry wrote to Robert de Cotte[49] from Madrid to inform him that "the changes that have taken place in this Court — (the arrest and banishment of the Princesse des Ursins) — are gradually bringing both payments and work to a standstill."*

M. D'Aubigny, the Princess's faithful companion, wrote to de Cotte that "payments have been held up by the Princess's arrest."[50] In February 1715, Orry returned, discredited, to France, followed in March by D'Aubigny.

Thus ended the plans for the Buen Retiro although, as indicated, the parterre in front of the Casón probably dates from this period. Its style is very French and formed part of what was called the *private gardens.* It does not figure in Texeira's map of 1656, but appears in one drawn by Antonio Ponz at the end of the eighteenth century. The only other trace of past glories is the small eight-sided pond, now forlorn and dried up. If Marie-Louise of Savoy had lived on Madrid might have had a miniature Versailles, facing south.

In Charles III's time, almost exactly where the Statue of the Fallen Angel now stands, and where the Hermitage of San Antonio de los Portugueses once stood, the famous porcelain factory was established. It was forbidden to visitors,[51] as its products were destined exclusively for the royal houses. Charles III opened it on his arrival in Madrid from Naples in 1759, when he brought with him the best workmen from Capodimonte,[52] which had been destroyed by fire. During the War of Independence the china factory of the Retiro became a French munitions foundry. In 1811 the French converted it into a fort, and when they retreated it was pillaged by the people. It is said that during the occupation of Madrid by Wellington's army it was deliberately burned down by General Hill, to eliminate a potential rival to British porcelain production. In the Royal Palace in Madrid there is a room entirely lined from top to bottom with porcelain made at the Retiro. It attained its greatest splendour during Charles III's reign. There is a similar room at Aranjuez.

The parterre had two handsome pools which appear to date from Charles III's time. The monumental gate that forms its entrance today from Calle Alfonso XII was constructed in 1922, incorporating the central part of an older gate that had been erected on the occasion of the arrival of Mariana de Newburgo in 1690 for her wedding as the second wife of the last of the Habsburgs, Charles II. This gate had originally been placed at the entrance to the Buen Retiro near the Church of San Jerónimo and was later placed in storage and forgotten for many years. The architect Luis Bellido used it as the centre of a semicircular composition, with two modern gates at the sides. The workmanship is beautiful; above the original gates are horns of plenty with clusters of fruit and the arms of Madrid and the House of Austria, wonderfully carved, with an inscription commemorating the wedding.[53] This gate was called "La Coronela."

PARTERRE. *Reproduction by Gromort.*

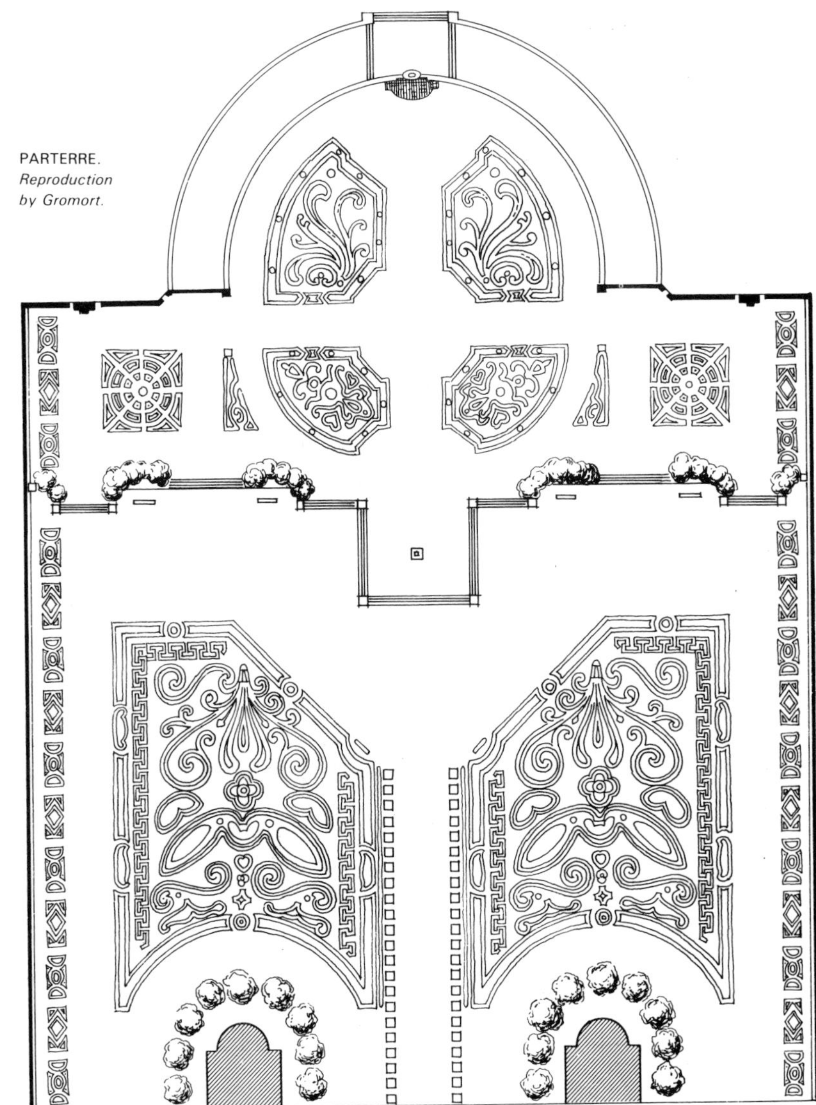

GATE TO RETIRO. LA CORONELA. *Photo S. Saavedra.*

CYPRESS CALVO. PARTERRE RETIRO. Madrid. *Photo Author.*

QUINTA DUQUE DEL ARCO. FOUNTAIN. *Photo Author.*

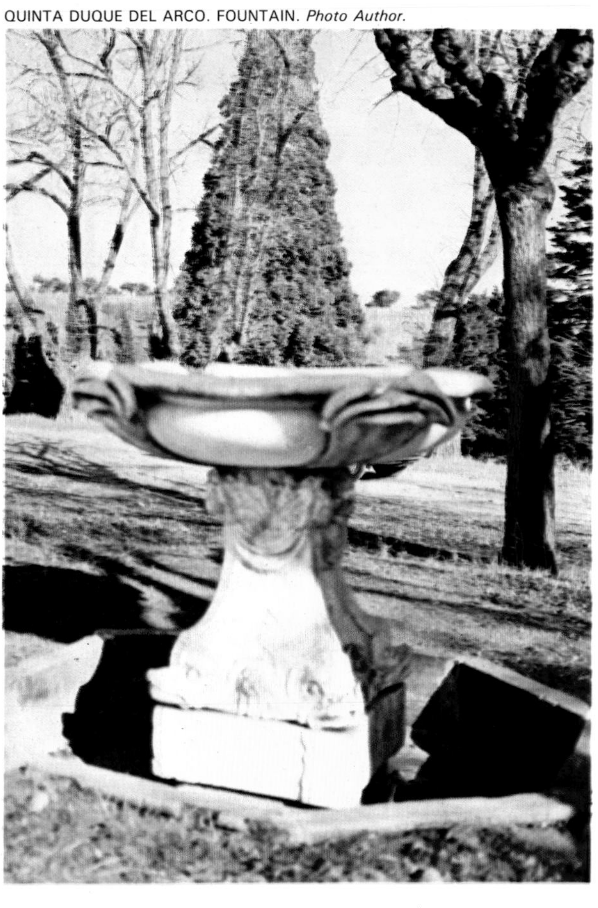

At one time the gardens reached as far as the Casón. On the left hand side of the parterre, entering from Calle Alfonso XII, is a wonderful specimen of the cypress (*taxodium distichium*), one of the finest we have ever seen, despite the dry soil conditions, which normally do not suit this tree. This parterre has recently been replanted as a rose garden, but it is a pity the old boxwood design was not restored.

In many parts of the Retiro the original *en manta* irrigating system still remains; this system consists of flooding the square beds, set at a lower level than the walks, through a network of water channels at the base of the trees, in the old Arab way.

QUINTA OF THE DUQUE DEL ARCO

The Quinta (estate) of the Duque del Arco is nestled in a fold of the mountains of El Pardo, facing east. It does not become visible until you are almost upon it.

To reach it turn right from the Pardo road, about five kilometres from Puerta de Hierro, where a signpost bears its name. There is a monumental gateway at the approach to the estate, apparently dating from the eighteenth century.

Alternatively, take the road to Fuencarral, entering Pardo by a gate in the upper part of the garden of La Quinta.

It is known to have been built by the Duque del Arco during the first part of Philip V's reign, probably in 1717. This is reflected in a carved marble fountain in front of the house, of the purest Louis XV style, but without the influence of the sculptors who worked at La Granja. It is therefore believed to be of earlier construction.

The house, of relatively little significance, appears to date from the late eighteenth century or to have been renovated at that time. It was given over to the Crown in the last years of Philip V's reign (1745) by the Countess de la Puebla del Maestre, Dowager Duchess del Arco. There used to be a beautiful garden on three different levels, adorned with fountains, statues, waterfalls and marble ornaments.[54]

It is rather surprising how disconnected the house appears from the garden. The obvious course would have been to build the house on high ground, affording a view of the terraced gardens. There is, in fact, a levelled site on the summit, as though this plan had once been entertained. Castilians, with their arid landscapes, are not accustomed to open vistas.

In 1785, Ponz recorded his visit to this country house, saying: "At one time there were many valuable pictures in the house, and there are still a great number depicting birds, hunting parties, fruit, flowers, landscapes, views, portraits, fables and other subjects. Among the portraits are six or eight original El Grecos, a number of the school of Carreños, copies of Velázquez, etc." According to Ezquerra de Bayo, Velázquez's magnificent portrait of the sculptor Alonso Cano once hung there. Another portrait, recorded in Charles III's estate, depicted a woman with a large beard: "Portrait measuring one yard and a quarter in height by three quarters in width, representing the portrait of the bearded woman Brígida del Río, aged fifty, from the hamlet of the Peñaranda seen in Madrid in 1590."[55]

The Habsburgs had always been fascinated by deformed creatures and freaks of nature; there were always a number of dwarfs, lunatics, etc. to be found in the palace, no doubt intended to provide distraction from the dull and monotonous existence so skilfully depicted by Velázquez. Another portrait of a bearded woman painted by Ribera still hangs today in the Hospital de Tavera in Toledo.

Madoz, another more recent traveller through Spain, did not see all of these pictures in the Quinta in 1847; he only mentions the "rich and elegant wallhangings, chairs and wallpapers" from the time of Ferdinand VII. They are still there, though in a dilapidated state; all the rest must have been moved to other royal sites.

Ponz continues: "Near the house there is a pretty garden, adorned with fountains, waterfalls and numerous, rather ordinary marble statues. Choice fruit is gathered in the orchard and the muscatel wine produced from the Quinta's vineyard is the most exquisite that can be found."[56]

It is remarkable how well the muscatel grape flourished in the sandy region of El Pardo.

QUINTA DUQUE DEL ARCO. GATE. *Photo S. Saavedra.*

This garden is an example of how a steep incline was used to create a classical terraced garden, which must have been very beautiful in its time. The cascade with its stepped sides seems to have been inspired by that in the park of Saint Cloud, near Paris, but on a much smaller scale.

The picturesque setting with natural running water and the sense of proportion in the design, attest to the skill of this garden's creator, influenced by French gardens while respecting the Spanish preference for seclusion.

In the Madrid Palace Archives there is an unpublished inventory dated 1840, containing the following description:

"Royal Quinta, First Garden of the Black Fountain, divided into four squares edged with semicircles of boxwood, rose bushes and other perennial plants. These four square beds are of very good design." (One can see that King Amadeo had not yet arrived with his Wellingtonias.)

"The Second Garden of the Cascade consists of three rectangles

QUINTA DUQUE DEL ARCO. *Plan by Winthuysen.*

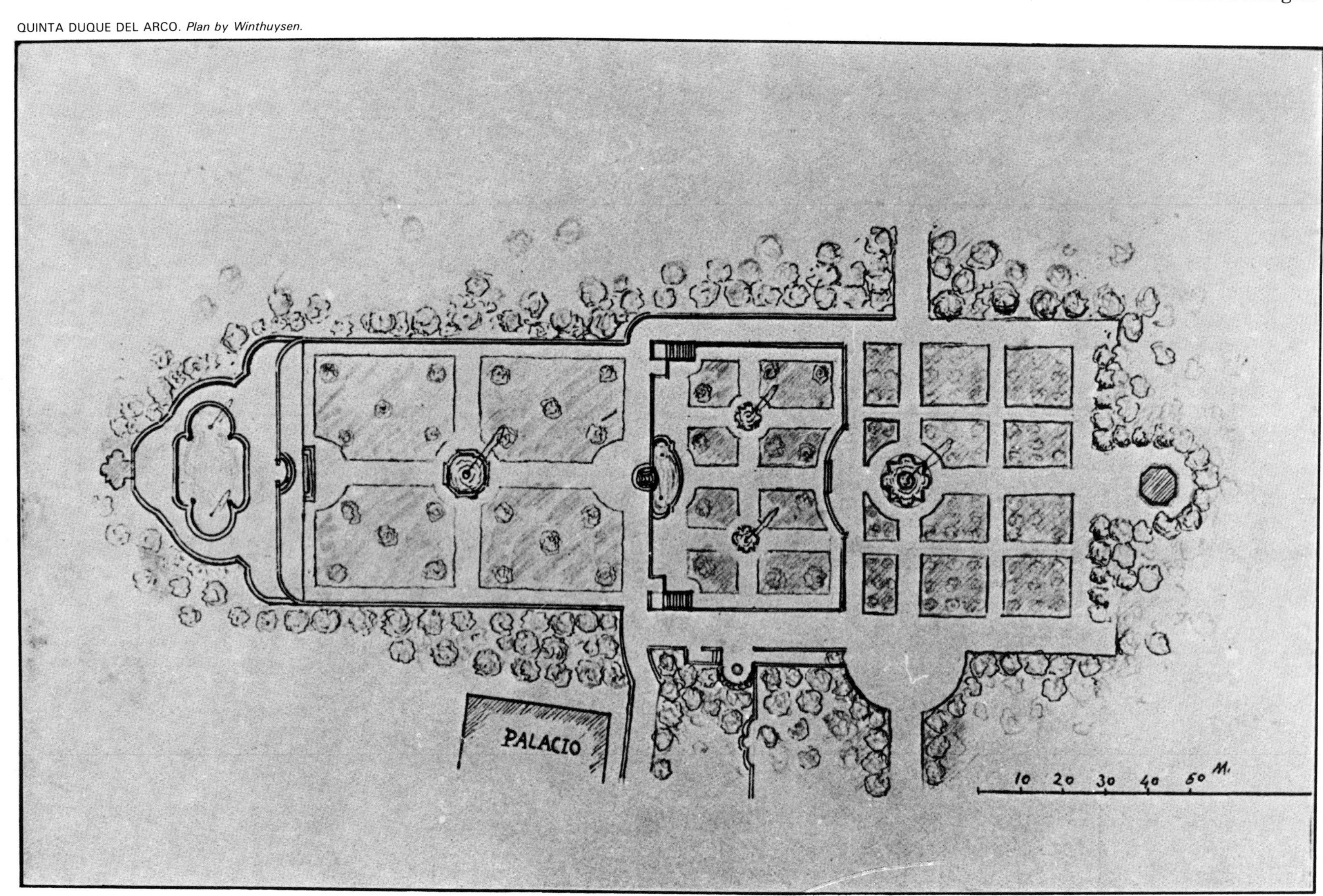

divided into eight plots forming a sort of labyrinth, the boxwood edgings, semicircles and ovals are planted with many and various rose bushes and other perennials. At each side of the garden are two small basins with water jets for practical jokes. The garden is surrounded by good trellised vines shaped in such a way that they echo the forms of the basins.

The Third Garden of the White Fountain, or Lower Garden, is divided into ten squares with edges and semicircles of boxwood and rose bushes. In the front of this garden is an octagonal summer-house, painted inside and out, with seats and a table of fine-grained stone and a crystal chandelier, all in good condition.

All of the aforementioned gardens are enclosed by iron railings with white stone pedestals at intervals, and good marble statues. Many of these railings have vines trained up them, enhancing their beauty.

There are two fine avenues from the sides of this garden; one leads to the upper pond and the other down to the Madrid gate.

A large pool in the highest part is used to water the gardens, with four water pipes bringing water from the Fuencarral side through conduits of brick and mortar. This water is sweet and good for drinking.

Fountains and ornaments

The Grotto: is adorned with a lead serpent, its tiny basin, wrought-iron doors, and six narrow outlets of water.

Black Fountain: with a pool and a pedestal with a jet that spurts water two yards high.

White Fountain: with a pedestal and a jet that spurts water four yards high. Its pool is large and all is in good condition.

Fountain of the Monkeys: this is decorated with two white stone monkeys, badly damaged, as is the basin.

In addition to these fountains there is a cascade fixed to the wall that divides these gardens; it is made of stone with bronze jets and pipes providing a regular flow of water through the wall. This water falls from the spouts down the cascade to a large pool, from which run pipes for the irrigation of most of this property.

There is also another pond with ten narrow outlets on what is called the upper path. All this water comes through underground pipes from the eastern side, uninterrupted all year-round. Most of the cultivated land is watered from this pond.

This country house has four gates named The Pardo Gate, the Madrid Gate, Fuencarral and Old Fuencarral. The boundary wall of this property is of stone with brick buttresses, and is somewhat dilapidated in parts."[57]

The concise author of this inventory, drawn up in 1840, found the garden and house in good condition, with all statues still in place and the fountains working. He was more or less a contemporary of Madoz. It is not known who lived in the house, enjoyed the lovely garden and spent their evenings in the octagonal summer-house.

In 1920, nearly a century later, this garden was described again by Xavier de Winthuysen, the architect who restored the terraced gardens of the Moncloa Palace. He found it in dilapidated condition, its statues gone.[58]

Today only the exedra can be distinguished, with its grotto and large baroque pool, dry and broken in the upper garden, the pilasters and vaulted niches are devoid of statues, and the cascade choked by weeds and brambles. Around 1871, some giant Wellingtonia conifers (*sequoiadendron gigantea*), much in vogue in Europe at that time, were planted in the lower garden, their shade and roots completely destroying the beautiful classical design described in 1840.

After the Civil War of 1936-1939 this country house was occupied by a girls' school. More recently attempts have been made by the National Heritage, with its usual thoroughness, to restore this garden, one of the most classical and complete of the early Bourbon era.

APPENDIX III

On 2 May 1634, the Conde-Duque de Olivares wrote from Aranjuez to the Ambassador-in-chief of Sorano, saying that he wanted a bronze equestrian statue like the portrait by Rubens, especially that of Philip III in the Casa de Campo, and that as the ancient tradition of those who specialised in this line was to be found in Florence, the best exponent of the art was to be commissioned there to sculpt the statue and an expert to value it.

By 1635 the work was in hand, having been entrusted to Tacca. It is almost certain that in the equestrian portrait by Rubens, destroyed in the fire of 1734, the horse was rearing up on its hind legs.

In March 1637 the mould was ready. It was to be Tacca's last work.

A portrait of the King was requested so that his features could be reproduced on the equestrian figure. One was sent in 1635 and another in 1640, depicting his face in detail. They must have been painted by Velázquez for only he was privileged to paint Philip IV. Cea Bermudez says that the second was a half-figure. Both portraits hung in the house of Pietro Tacca, where Baldinucci saw them after Tacca's death. In Florence they were believed to be the work of Rubens, but as Velázquez' style was not well known there the two were often confused.

There are two equestrian portraits of Philip IV in Florence today: one — a small one — in the Pitti Gallery; the other — life size — in the Uffizi.

It is almost certain that neither of these was the one sent to Pietro Tacca, for the position of the horse is different. The small one is a copy of the life-size portrait in the Prado and forms a pair with that of Queen Isabella of Bourbon. Justi believed they were a gift from the Monarchs to the Court of Florence.

The large equestrian portrait in the Uffizi is of a much later date and portrays Philip IV in his old age; only his head is painted from life and the rest is copied from Rubens' equestrian portrait, now lost.

The painter took this for his model; he would also have before his eyes Tacca's equestrian statue in the Buen Retiro. The allegorical figures in the Uffizi equestrian portrait seem to have been taken from Rubens' studio, though because of its late date, which the aged face confirms, the picture cannot be his.

In addition to the pictures, a bust of the King, larger than life-size, was also sent in 1636. Martínez Montañés was brought to Madrid especially for this sculpture, and Velázquez painted his portrait at that time. (Prado Museum.)

Miscellaneen aus drei Jahrhunderten Spanischen Kunstlebens die Reiterstatue Philipps IV von Pietro Tacca, vol. II, p. 254.

[1] IÑÍGUEZ, Francisco: *Casas reales y jardines de Felipe II,* Consejo Superior de Investigaciones Científicas, Delegación de Roma, 1952, page 114.

[2] PONZ, Antonio: *Viaje de España,* Ed. Aguilar, Madrid, 1947, vol. I, letter V, page 96.

[3] IÑÍGUEZ, F.: *Op. cit.,* page 114.

[4] IÑÍGUEZ, F.: *Op. cit.,* page 116.

[5] LE BRETON, Lucas: *Charles V,* Ed. Bayard, Paris, 1958, page 300.

[6] VILLALBA, Bartolomé de: *El Pelegrino Curioso, Doncel de Xérica,* Sociedad de Bibliófilos Españoles, Madrid, 1886, vol. I, pages 146 & 147.

* Serlio, an Italian architect and sculptor who wrote a famous treatise on architecture founded on the ancient systems. In 1541 Serlio was summoned to the Palace of Fontainebleau by François I of France.

[7] IÑÍGUEZ, F.: *Op. cit.,* page 124.

[8] IÑÍGUEZ, F.: *Op. cit.,* page 125.

[9] WYTS, Lamberto: "Viaje por España. 1570-1571', *Viajes de extranjeros por España y Portugal,* compiled by J. García Mercadal, Ed. Aguilar, 1952, vol. I, page 1175.

[10] IÑÍGUEZ, F.: *Op. cit.,* page 125.

[11] IÑÍGUEZ, F.: *Op. cit.,* page 128.

[12] IÑÍGUEZ, F.: *Op. cit.,* page 128.

[13] IÑÍGUEZ, F.: *Op. cit.,* page 132.

[14] IÑÍGUEZ, F.: *Op. cit.,* page 145.

[15] IÑÍGUEZ, F.: *Op. cit.,* page 148.

[16] IÑÍGUEZ, F,: *Op. cit.,* page 150.

[17] GONZÁLEZ DE AMEZÚA, Augustín: *Isabel de Valois,* Madrid, 1949, vol. III, page 111, April 1560.

[18] VILLARS, Marquesa de: "Cartas a la señora de Coulanges", *Viajes de extranjeros por España y Portugal,* compiled by J. García Mercadal, Ed. Aguilar, 1959, col. II, letter XVI, page 864.

[19] SAINT SIMON, Duque de: "Viaje a Espana", *Viajes de extranjeros por España y Portugal,* compiled by J. García Mercadal, Ed. Aguilar, 1962, vol. III, page 341.

[20] VILLIERS STUART, Mrs.: *Spanish Gardens,* Batsford, London, 1929, page 109.

[21] HUME, Martin: *The Court of Philip IV,* London, 1907, page 58.

[22] PONZ, A.: *Op. cit.,* vol. I, letter V, page 97.

[23] PONZ, A.: *Op. cit.,* vol. I, letter V, page 97.

[24] JUNQUERA, Paulina: *Guía ilustrada del Real Palacio de Aranjuez,* by Paulina Junquera and María Teresa Ruiz Alcón, Madrid, 1959, page 58.

[25] PONZ, A.: *Op. cit.,* vol. I, letter V, page 97.

[26] PONZ, A.: *Op. cit.,* vol. I, letter V, page 97.

[27] BOTTINEAU, Yves: *L'art de Cour dans l'Espagne de Phillipe V,* Féret et Fils, Bordeaux, 1960, page 217 (note 73).

[28] PONZ, A.: *Op. cit.,* vol. I, letter V, page 97.

[29] PONZ, A.: *Op. cit.,* vol. I, letter V, pages 97 & 98.

[30] MARAÑÓN, Gregorio: *El Conde-Duque de Olivares,* Espasa-Calpe, Madrid, 1952, page 83.

[31] CATURLA, María Luisa: *Pinturas, frondas y fuentes del Buen Retiro,* Revista de Occidente, Madrid, 1947, page 46.

[32] CATURLA, María Luisa: *Op. cit.,* page 44.

[33] CATURLA, María Luisa: *Op. cit.,* page 44.

[34] MARAÑÓN, G.: *Op. cit.,* page 151.

[35] MARAÑÓN, G.: *Op. cit.,* page 170.

[36] PEYRON, Juan Francisco: "Nuevo viaje en España en 1772-1773", *Viajes de extranjeros por España y Portugal,* compiled by J. García Mercadal, Ed. Aguilar, 1962, vol. III, page 842.

[37] *The Spanish Journal of Elisabeth Lady Holland,* London, 1910, page 109.

[38] CATURLA, María Luisa: *Op. cit.,* page 42.

[39] CATURLA, María Luisa: *Op. cit.,* page 43.

[40] CLIFFORD, Derek: *History of Garden Design,* London, 1833, page 56.

[41] MARAÑÓN, G.: *Op. cit.,* page 113.

[42] CLIFFORD, Derek: *Op. cit.,* page 56.

[43] CATURLA, María Luisa: *Op. cit.,* pages 38 & 39.

[44] CATURLA, María Luisa: *Op. cit.,* pages 44 & 47.

[45] Bibliothèque Nationale, Paris, Cabinet d'Estampes: *Inventaire des papiers manuscrits du carnet de Robert de Cotte,* by Pierre Marcel, Paris, Honoré Champion, 1906.

[46] Bibliothèque Nationale, Paris: *Op. cit.,* letter 706 (III), 1019.

[47] Bibliothèque Nationale, Paris: *Op. cit.,* page 199, no. 712, July 1713.

[48] Bibliothèque Nationale, Paris: *Op. cit.,* pages 197 & 198, no. 704 (III), 1019.

[49] Bibliothèque Nationale, Paris: *Op. cit.,* letter 723, 1019.

* A letter exists with a statement of the expenses of the King of Spain, which records the journey of Jules Robert de Cotte, the son of the architect, who travelled to Spain to present to the King the details of the various plans; his journey cost more than £4,000.

[50] Bibliothèque Nationale, Paris: *Op. cit.,* letter 730 (III), 1019.

[51] BOURGOING, Barón de: "Un paseo por España (1777-1795)", *Viajes de extranjeros por España y Portugal,* compiled by J. García Mercadal, Ed. Aguilar, 1962, vol. III, page 973.

[52] TAPIAS, Enrique: *Carlos III y su época,* Ed. Aguilar, Madrid, 1952, page 216.

[53] SAN JOSÉ, Diego: *La Esfera,* 27th October 1917.

[54] EZQUERRA DEL BAYO, Joaquín: *Catálogo de la Esposición del Antiquo Madrid,* 1926, page 75.

[55] Archivo General de Palacio, Madrid: *Testamentaría de Carlos III,* vol. II, page 576.

[56] PONZ, A.: *Op. cit.,* vol. VI, page 565.

[57] Archivo General de Palacio, Madrid: *Inventarios Casa,* Administrative Section, Real Quinta, year 1840, pages 165, 166 & 167. Signed: Santiago Montoro.

[58] WINTHUYSEN, Javier: *Jardines clásicos de España,* Madrid, 1930, page 80.

ARANJUEZ. BASE OF THE OLD SUMMER-HOUSE. *Photo S. Saavedra.*

9 ARANJUEZ IN THE TIME OF THE BOURBONS IN THE EIGHTEENTH CENTURY

The eighteenth century opened in Spain with the arrival in 1701 of the young Philip of Anjou, advised and guided in both politics and art by the powerful Louis XIV.

In his portrait by the French Court painter Rigaud we see Philip before he left France, a young man of seventeen, attired, as his distinguished grandfather had advised, in the sombre black costume and white collar of the Spanish style.

In Spain at that time true royal residences did not exist. The Alcázar in Madrid was a dismal, gloomy palace which would soon be destroyed by the fire of 1734 and later rebuilt in the Italian style throughout the course of the eighteenth century. San Lorenzo of the Escorial was more suitable as a monastery than as a Royal Court.

Philip therefore chose the Palace of the Buen Retiro as his residence, and in 1715 began to rebuild the Palace of Aranjuez, in ruins after the two fires in 1660 and 1665.

On Philip's orders the architect Teodore Ardemans inspected the work on the Palace of Aranjuez in 1716 and noted that the buildings had already reached the second floor and that the new orchard had been completed.[1]

Reconstruction of the palace was begun by a military architect, Pedro Caro Idrogo, and after his death in 1732, continued by Etienne Marchand and Leandro Bachelieu (we transcribe the signature as it is spelt in various documents in the Palace Archives of Madrid).[2]

As is well known, the gardens were always of chief importance at Aranjuez because of the site's natural beauty.

The name Boutelou, a long dynasty of gardeners of French origin, appears throughout the records at Aranjuez. The first, Don Esteban, held the post of gardener in the Queen's Potager (kitchen garden) in 1720, and was asked to "tend the orchards because he was a man of great intelligence."[3] The King commanded all plants grown by him in 1722 to be preserved; at

PHILIP V. By Rigaud. Louvre Museum.

that time he was probably already at work in La Granja, continuing the gardens started there by René Carlier who died that year.

The gardens' care and the importation of new plants were always matters of keen interest to the King and Queen; in 1728 Etienne Marchand asked the Queen's permission to obtain seeds from Italy, of which there exists a very detailed list.[4]

By this time work had already begun on the new French parterre which was to adorn the southern façade of the palace. It had been necessary to clear an enormous amount of earth as there were derelict buildings and the ground was uneven. Gunpowder was used to blast the stone mounds so that the garden could be begun.[5]

It is evident that the gardeners at Aranjuez, Leandro Bachelieu, E. Marchand and E. Boutelou — all Frenchmen — had the techniques and principles of Le Nôtre's French gardens at their fingertips, constantly using such French terms as *Boulingrin, Gazon* and *Glacis.*

Long avenues were planted in the French manner with lime trees from Holland (The Hague or Rotterdam), or from Paris, brought down the Seine to Le Havre and then shipped to Bilbao.[6]

Lime trees and hornbeam (*carpinus betulus*), used to form hedges, horse chestnuts and maples were all introduced into Spain for the first time. Orders for seeds, bulbs and plants multiplied and Don Esteban Boutelou travelled to and fro between Aranjuez and San Ildefonso to tend both gardens.

Around 1740, Santiago Bonavía, a painter and architect summoned to Spain from Piacenza in 1733, and destined to spend the rest of his life at Aranjuez, built a small theatre where plays were to be presented on the Feast of St. Philip in May 1741.[7] These garden festivals were common, and complicated stage machinery was erected for such scenes as Neptune's chariot and a serenade called *The Rivalry of the Gods.*[8]

After his father's death about this time the second Esteban Boutelou enters the scene as head gardener and arboriculturist.[9] A hot-tempered young man, he had studied horticulture in Paris and his principles and theories were unsuited to Aranjuez's hot climate and poor soil. He did not allow frequent watering, for instance, and this caused the loss of many trees.[10] In June 1744 he had a series of quarrels with the Governor of the estate.

Work on the palace and garden nevertheless continued. A letter signed by Hubert Demandre and Pierre Puthois (nearly all authors refer to the latter as Pierre Pitué, but his signature appears as above in a letter dated 30 March 1744),[11] mentions the lead nymphs cast in the workshops of Balsaín (a village near La Granja) for the ponds of the new parterre at Aranjuez. They wished to apply a few coats of paint to give them the appearance of bronze and have them ready for the royal visit.

These nymphs can still be seen in the two small round ponds of the parterre. They are seated on a rock, embracing a dragon, in the style of those adorning the fountains of La Granja. They were brought in a cart to Aranjuez from Balsaín by Hubert

Demandre, but they are thought to have been made by Santiago Bousseau and finished by Demandre. They were probably set in position in September or October 1744.

One of the great drawbacks of the Island Gardens was the frequent rising of the river Tagus, so strong protecting walls had to be built. These walls were adorned with stone pilasters and iron railings that surrounded the main island and the smaller adjoining one called the Islet.

The railings at the sides of the parterre had wooden trellises and, later, hornbeam hedges.

Exotic plants, such as pineapples, grown for some time at the Buen Retiro, now became fashionable.

At the death of Philip V in 1746, the work still going on in both the palace and the gardens was halted by instructions from his son, Ferdinand VI, to Bonavía.[12]

In 1747 Boutelou planned to build a conservatory for pineapples, "like the one built by the Dutch at the Buen Retiro, and a room for flowers."[13]

The Duke of Huéscar wrote at this time from Versailles to the Minister José Carvajal y Lancaster about the forwarding of plants, with a list of their names in French.[14] Hyacinths and tulips were also sent in great quantities from Holland. The second Esteban Boutelou designed a flower garden on La Isla.[15]

On 16 June 1748 a great fire broke out in the Palace of Aranjuez. Santiago Bonavía sent estimates for the repair of the royal apartments, and in particular the Queen's boudoir. He made sketches for two bridges that were to cross the Island

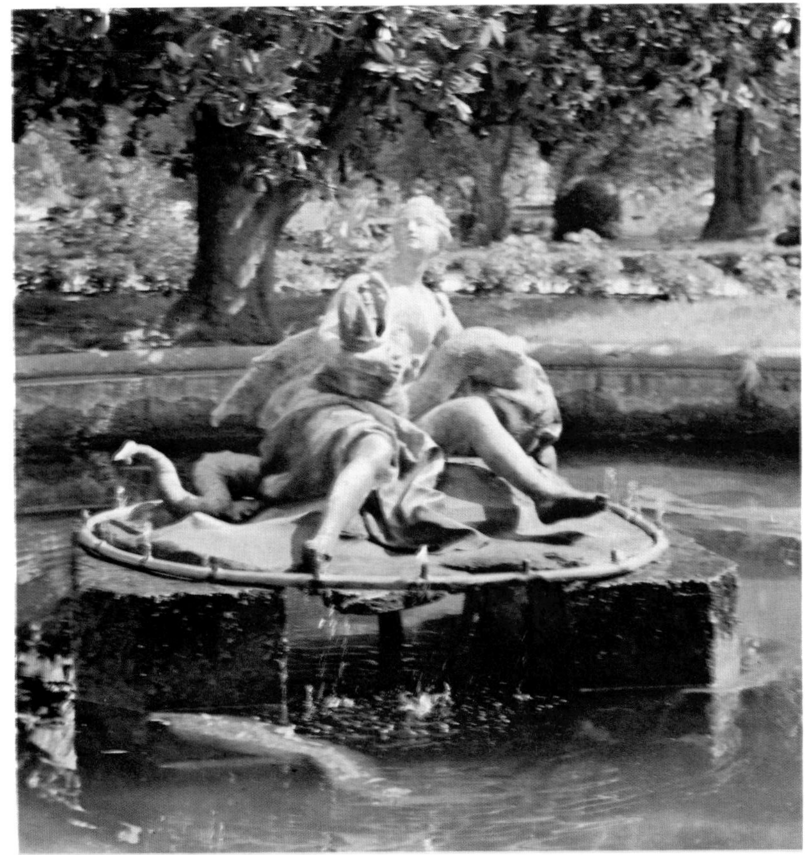

ARANJUEZ. NYMPH. POND. PARTERRE. *Photo Author.*

PLAN OF THE PARTERRE IN THE NEW GARDEN. Leandro Bachelieu. 1734. By permission of the National Heritage.

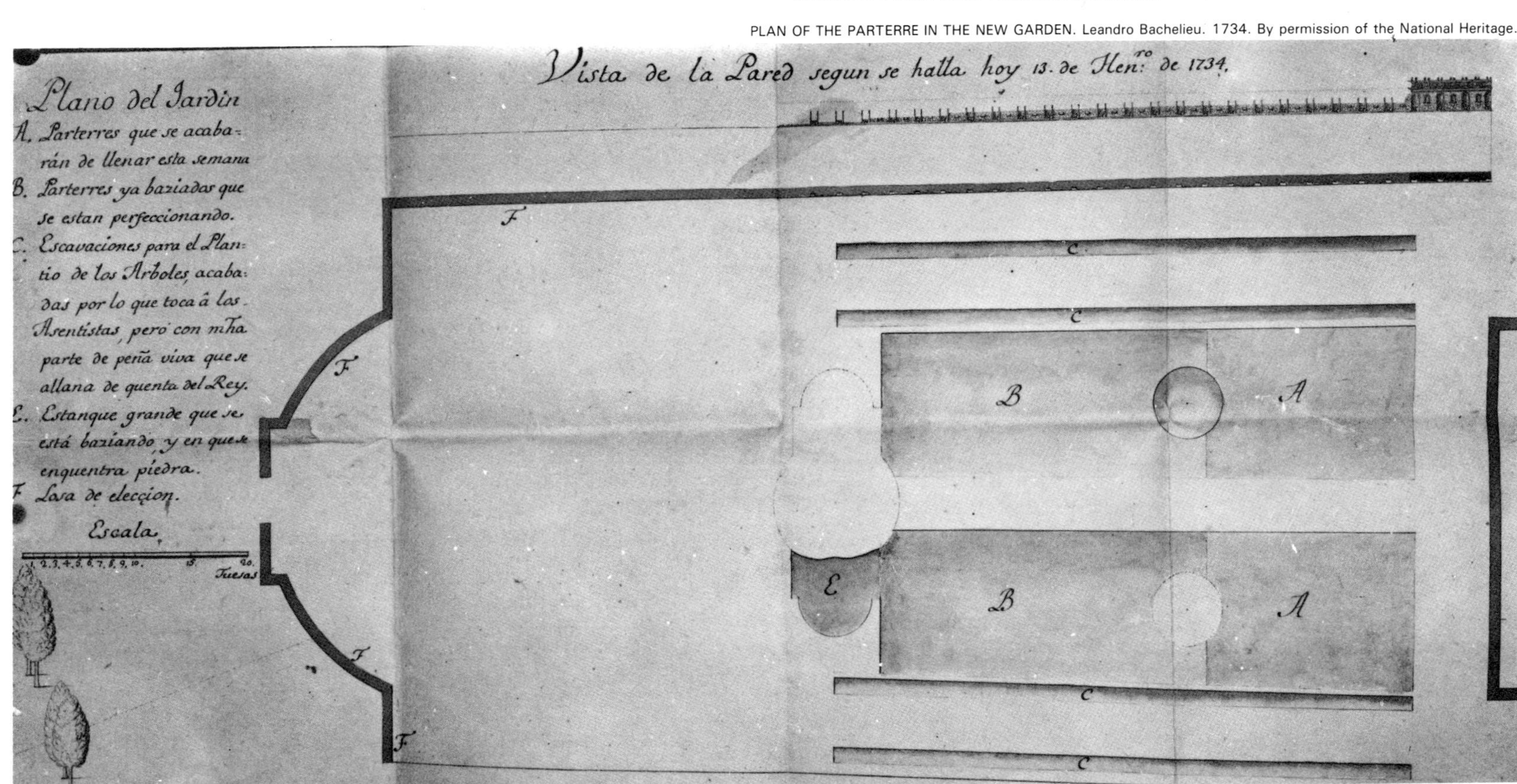

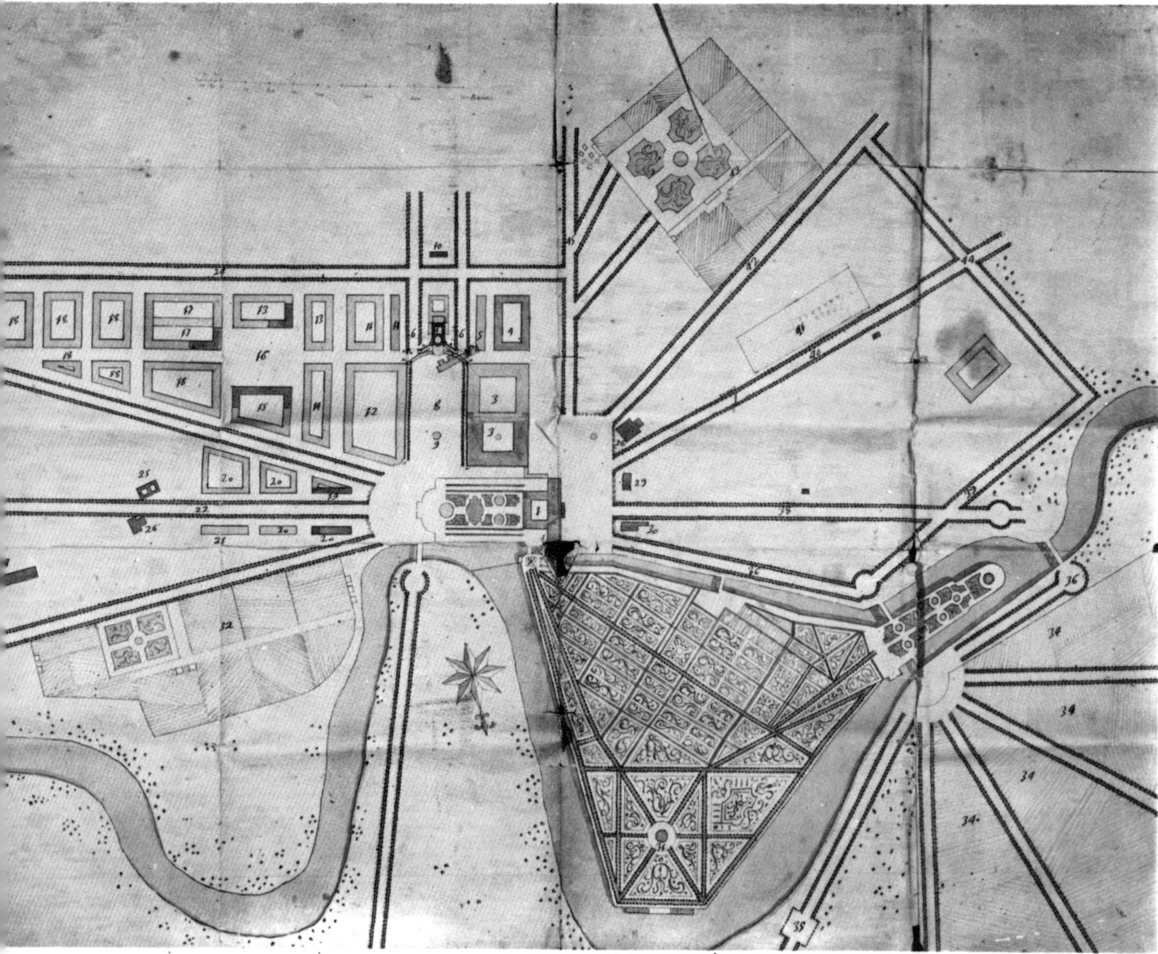

PLAN OF ARANJUEZ. Leandro Bachelieu, 1734. By permission of the National Heritage.

PROJECT FOR THE FLOWER GARDEN. Esteban Boutelou, 1748. By permission of the National Heritage.

Garden where it joins the Islet, to reach the Pico-Tagus orchards, more or less where the racecourse now stands.[16]

The great architect of the period, Ventura Rodríguez, designed a gateway for the entrance to the Island Garden.[17]

The King must have incurred great expense during that period, for the façade of the Royal Palace was being repaired after the ravages of the fire, and the Italian artist, Amigoni, was painting the ceilings.

Ferdinand decided to place stone statues of the three kings who had built the palace — Philip II who founded it, Philip V who rebuilt it, and Ferdinand VI who finished it so successfully — on the cornice of the pediment of the main façade. They were executed by Pedro Martinengho[18] and completed and paid for on 14 October 1750. The three statues were installed in 1752,[19] and are still in position today.

The planting and arrival of exotic trees, such as the *palo santo,* continued, together with numerous seeds and flowers.

Camels from Oran and buffaloes were used for these labours.

In 1750 Santiago Bonavía started his plans for the beautiful Chapel of San Antonio, which has been preserved intact to this day. In a letter to the Marqués de la Ensenada[20] he suggested a small house for three or four monks.

It was Bonavía who gave shape and harmony to this enclosed

square, unique in Spain, with its chapel, arches and finials reminiscent of the Place Stanislas in Nancy, France.

In 1751, the King ordered payment for stone (probably marble) brought from Genoa for the King's statue and the lions that were to be placed on the fountain in the Plaza at Aranjuez."[21]

By the end of that year work on the chapel was completed, and the fountain with its three lions was being erected in the square, where it still stands today.

King Ferdinand's statue, sculpted by Olivieri for the "new fountain", was set up on 8 April 1752, and Bonavía asked the Minister, the Marqués de la Ensenada, whether it should be placed facing the new chapel or the road and gardens, "which is more frequented and seems more natural."[22]

Its glory was of short duration, for in 1760, when the King was succeeded by his step-brother Charles III, the statue in the square was taken down[23] (the figure of a woman now stands in its place). The whereabouts of the statue are now unknown, although it may be the one behind the church of the Salesas Reales in Madrid, in the Plaza de Paris, where it is paired with that of his wife, Bárbara de Braganza.

The strong wall that had been built around the gardens as a protection against the frequent rising of the river, was adorned with pilasters of Colmenar stone (a village not far away), placed at intervals. They were topped by pretty flowerpots of glazed ceramic made in the Alcora factory (Valencia).[24] Bonavía ordered the construction of a summer-house in the upper garden near this palace on the banks of the river above the dam, and had the cascade decorated with fine Talavera flowerpots half a yard high."[25]

How much more beautiful the gardens must have looked then than they do today with the heavy cement vases that now crown the pilasters and railings throughout the gardens.

Bonavía was the guiding force in the reconstruction of Aranjuez, but towards 1755 the engineer Carlos de Witte entered

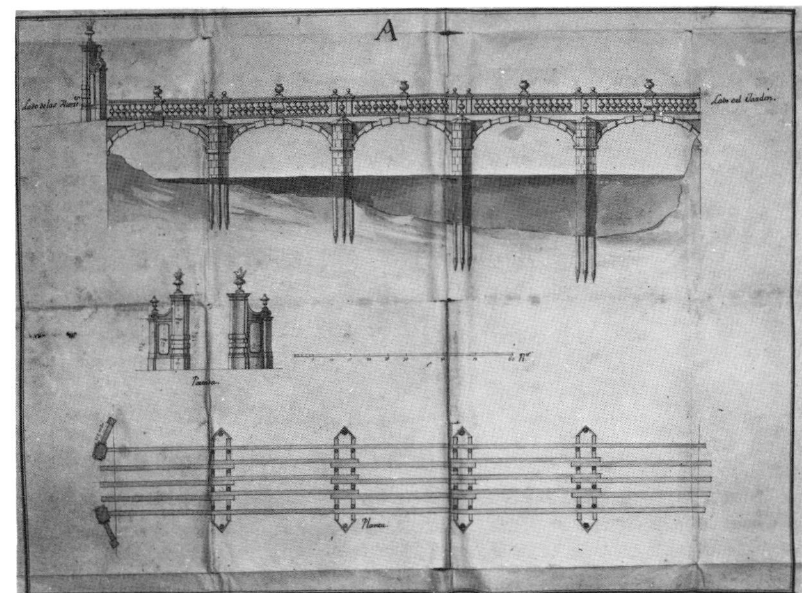

DESIGN OF BRIDGES FOR THE ISLAND. Santiago Bonavía, 1748. By permission of the National Heritage.

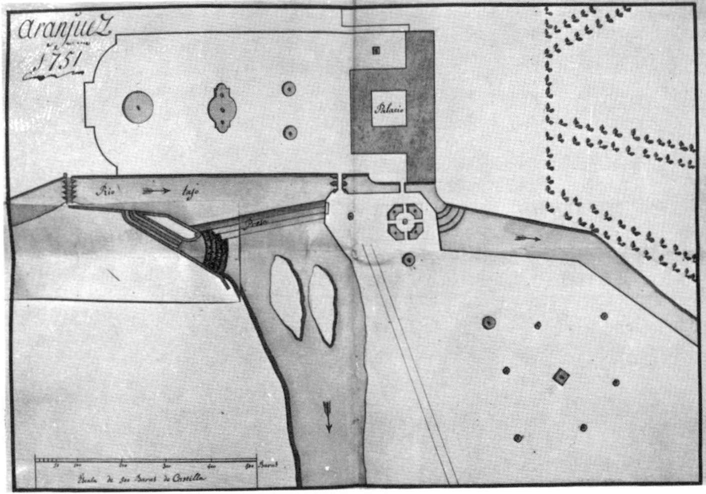

PLAN, ISLAND GARDEN. Santiago Bonavía, 1751. By permission of the National Heritage.

PLAN FOR THE GATE ON THE BRIDGE. GARDEN ON THE ISLAND. Ventura Rodríguez, 1749. By permission of the National Heritage.

the scene. He ordered the clearing of the "long avenue" and gave directions for two more avenues to be traced from the Queen's Walk to the pier of the Sotillo.[26]

Around 1755 a lovely summer-house was planned for the edge of the Island facing the canal in front of the palace. Bonavía designed it and construction appears to have been carried out by another French engineer, Jaime Marquet. Part of the work was done with seasoned wood (*"maderas secas"*[27]) on the site of an earlier summer-house.

The work was continually delayed and in January 1757 Bonavía wrote that "the summer-house was already being erected above the stone cascade so as to afford a view over the palace square. The wood has been carved and the slates are being put together for the roof."[28]

The basement and steps of this summer-house still remain by the iron balustrade on the side of the island facing the canal. Some documents refer to the "Chinese summer-house", but we do not know if it was the same one.

The influence of French gardens during this period is obvious. When talking of the semicircle at the entrance to the parterre, Bonavía mentions the "ha-ha" which can still be seen today. This consists of a wide, deep ditch that acts as a barrier, dividing the garden from the rest of the land without obstructing the view, as a wall would do.

This method of protection was invented by French gardeners for the Grand Trianon, whose gardens are cut off in this way

SKETCH OF SUMMER-HOUSE. Santiago Bonavía, 1755. By permission of the National Heritage.

STATUE OF FERDINAND VI. *Photo Oronoz.*

from the rest of the Park of Versailles; it was from here that this fashion must have spread to Spain. The British eighteenth-century landscape gardeners, such as Capability Brown, Repton, Kent, etc., used it frequently; and indeed the lovely English landscape is singularly adapted to this procedure, which divides while allowing the garden to merge into the surrounding countryside.

Hubert and Antoine Demandre, the sculptors of La Granja, requested permission to lodge in their own studio in Madrid in order to execute His Majesty's order for the fountains at Aranjuez.[30] They had the great cauldron for melting lead brought from Balsaín (by permission of Isabella Farnese, the Queen Mother), and they mention "the two ponds with nymphs opposite the room occupied by Their Majesties, and likewise the larger pool in front of the aforesaid room." But these nymphs had already been there since 1744 and the pond must have been the large one which was later modified by Isidro González Velázquez.

The Fountain of the Tritons once stood in the Island Gardens. "In view of the extreme narrowness of the basin of this fountain," said Santiago Bonavía, "it can only play for the short time Her Majesty is walking on the Islet, because the quantity of water and the small capacity of the basin cause it to overflow very rapidly, and the fountain cannot be operated at full strength, for, even as it is, the water splashes out."[31]

The King had the fountain moved a little further on to the Islet where it was to remain until 1845, when it was moved to the Campo del Moro in Madrid.

"Two seven-foot pedestals were placed in the parterre at either side of the ha-ha to support the sphinxes and make them visible from afar." This design was entrusted to Bernasconi.[32]

These sphinxes still adorn the parterre, but we do not know whether they are in their original position.

In the autumn of 1758, after the death that summer of his beloved Queen, Bárbara de Braganza, King Ferdinand conducted his affairs from the seclusion of the Castle of Villaviciosa, near Madrid. The King was to die the following year, completely insane.

Life at Aranjuez went on nevertheless, and Esteban Boutelou continued to cultivate Indian chestnuts, hornbeams and raspberries.

Four sentry boxes were built to adorn the entrance and exit of the Puente de Barcas (Bridge of Boats) and two were placed at the main gate of the parterre. The ditch "was crossed by a bridge and two white stone sentry boxes were crowned by statues of two children adorned with war trophies." The ditch was being dug to replace the wall that once skirted the east side of the garden.[33]

The children were sculpted by Juan Martínez Reyna and the sentry boxes were inspired by those by Gabriel, in the Place de la Concorde in Paris, with their *oeil-de-boeuf* windows crowned with garlands. No doubt humiliated at not being entrusted with this work, the French sculptor A. Demandre "asked leave to retire to France as he could be of no further use to His Majesty."

With the arrival of Charles III new work was begun on the other side of the Puente de Barcas; Esteban Boutelou made his Spring Garden there and began the Prince's Garden, both alongside the Queen's Walk.[34]

The Head Gardener wrote from Paris where he was studying the cultivation of pineapple plants, and requested that his two sons

SPHINX IN THE PARTERRE AT ARANJUEZ. *Photo Author.*

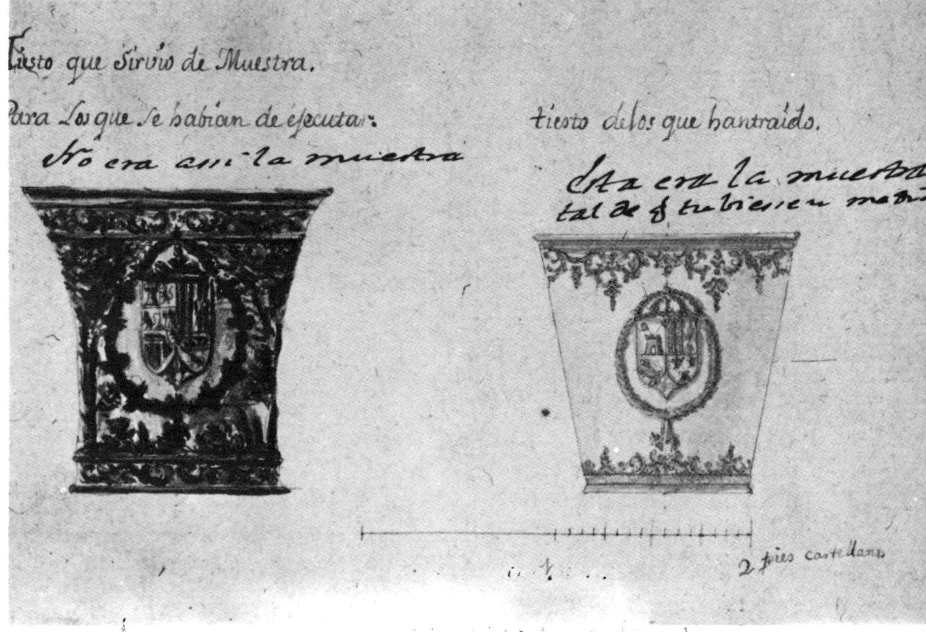

DRAWINGS FOR FLOWERPOTS, TALAVERA, 1752. By permission of the National Heritage.

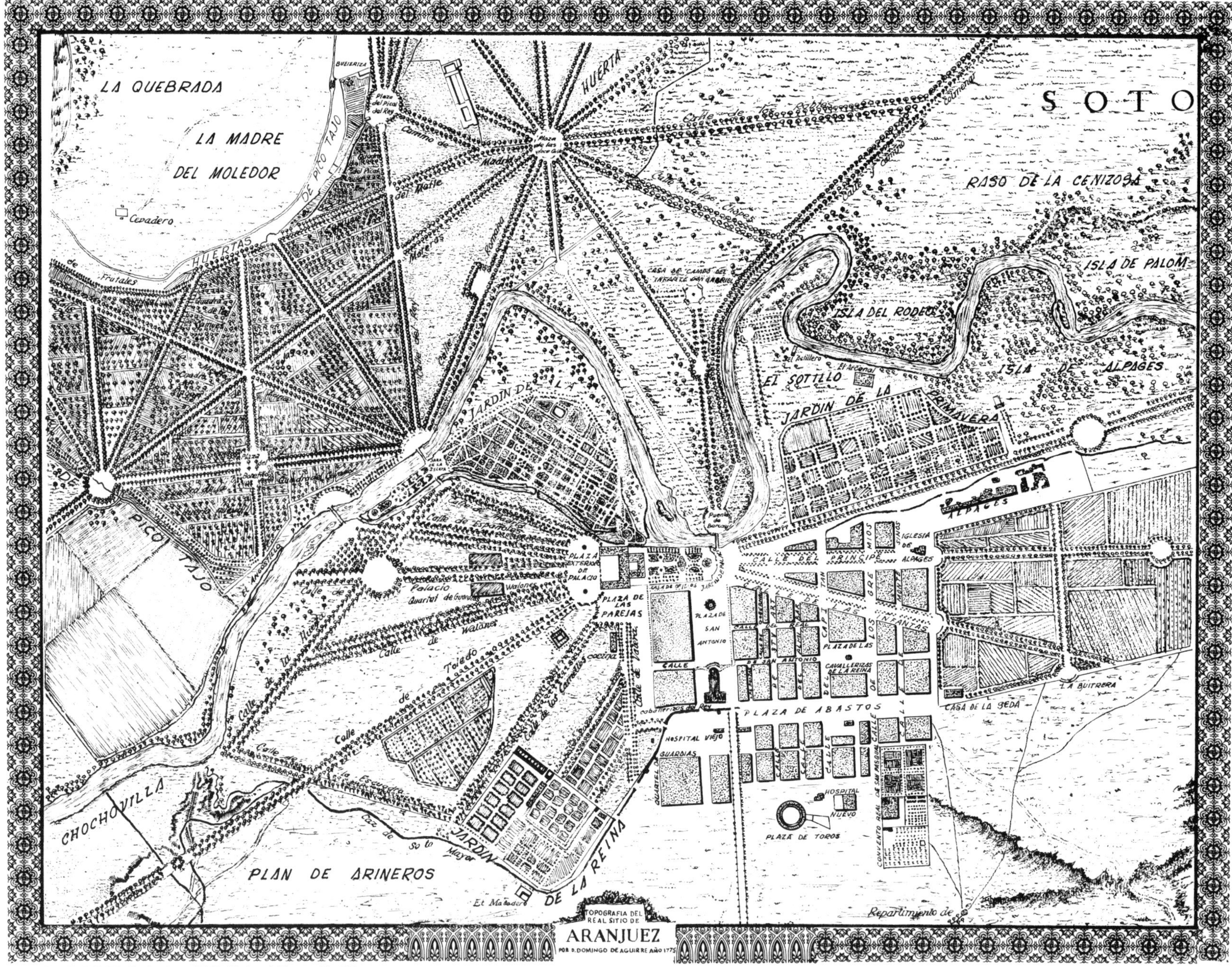

PLAN OF ARANJUEZ. D. Aguirre, 1775. National Library. Madrid.

Paul and Peter be sent to France to be trained as gardeners.[35] Jaime Marquet then held the post of architect and chief director.

Working in the Spring Garden and the Prince's Garden, Boutelou asked for cloches to protect his lettuces, asparagus, "and other rare produce for the royal table" from the frost.[36] His son Paul was sent to learn gardening in The Hague, and later in London, where he was to present himself to the Prince of Masserano. His expenses were defrayed by the Palace Treasury.[37] The previous year he had been working at Choisy-le-Roy.

A number of people ordered plants and fruit trees from Aranjuez. The Infante Don Louis, Charles III's brother, "wished to have greengage trees in his orchard of Boadilla", and plants and trees were sent from Aranjuez to the Botanic Garden of Migas Calientes. Exotic tropical plants were the order of the day. They first arrived in two large boxes sent by the Governor of New Orleans to the Marqués de Grimaldi.[38]

Almendrones (Jamaica trees) were sent from High Orinoco; "the taste of their nuts is a mixture of almond and hazel nuts, and huge trees grow from a nut half an inch long."[39]

Seeds also arrived from Choisy-le-Roy, despatched to Aranjuez from Bayonne — a long list of carnations, *giroflées, oeillets de poète* (Sweet William) and so on.[40] In the Valencian Orchard on the heights of Mira-el-Rey, mulberries were being grown in 1775 for the cultivation of the silkworm.

A topographic map of the gardens by Don Domingo de Aguirre in July 1773 has been preserved in the Fine Arts section of the National Library.

The upkeep of these gardens was very costly. We read that "in the Chinese summer-house the slate roof needs repairing, as there are many leaks and the sky shows through, for it is very dilapidated."[41] The benches, trellises and bridges (which were mostly wooden) were constantly in need of repair.

Thanks to Charles III, considerably more interest was being taken in botany and gardening.

The King and the architect Sabatini asked Esteban Boutelou to come to Madrid to plant trees to embellish the Hill of San Vicente and the road to El Pardo. Boutelou's son Paul was learning botany and gardening in the Trianon at Versailles with Louis XV's famous gardener Richard, who later made the Hameau in the Petit Trianon for Marie Antoinette.

Richard was also asked to send "a hundred broad-leaved plane-trees, half of them of the oriental, and half of the western varieties", which were to be sent from Paris by Francisco Ventura Llovera to the Count of Floridablanca.[42] (Llovera acted as Treasurer to the Court in Paris).

The English picturesque garden had now become fashionable, with its winding paths leading to belvederes, grottoes, bridges and rustic houses. Boutelou's son was told to bring "books and illustrations of gardens in the English style ordered by Don Esteban so that he could copy them at Aranjuez."[43]

By now the famous Don Esteban required the help of his son Paul who would later succeed him as head gardener of Aranjuez, and who at the time was managing the Prince's Garden. Members of the Court continued to receive fruit trees; we read of the Countess de Benavente sending a list of fruit trees for her orchard of the Alameda, and the Dowager Duchess of Arcos sending a list of fruit trees to provide shade and blossom, "to plant in the orchard that she has bought in La Florida, by the side of the road to El Pardo."[44] It later became the Palace of the Duchess Cayetana Alba, the rival of the Condesa-Duquesa de Benavente, and is known today as La Moncloa Palace.

The benches by the Fountains of the Boy with the Thorn and Bacchus in the Island Garden at Aranjuez today, date from this period. A sketch of them must have existed, because the architect Don Manuel Serrano and the sculptor Reyna gave instructions about them to Don Esteban Boutelou.

According to engravings of the time there used to be niches in the angles formed by the trellis work "and any trees that might be in the way were to be replaced by plane-trees as Boutelou had been instructed."[45] The bases and columns supporting these niches were of marble from Macael in Almería.[46]

Trees imported from the Indies still aroused great interest, and in 1786 a supply of "seeds grown in Chapultepac, near Mexico, called *ahuehuetes,* was received to sow in the garden of the Infante Don Antonio;"[47] along with "a tree called *argan* from Africa for Don Esteban Boutelou to plant in the Prince's Garden."

SENTRY BOX. ENTRANCE TO THE PARTERRE, 1760. *Photo S. Saavedra.*

A botanical garden had been established at Cartagena, and vines were brought to Aranjuez from Romanée in Burgundy, Syllery in Champagne, and from Ay. Plants were also sent from Caracas.[48]

One of the gardens was called "The Little Garden of Delights", and all these new gardens were probably designed according to the style of English landscape gardening. Don Esteban Boutelou must have been old and feeble by this time, judging from his signature, which became steadily less distinct. His two sons, Paul and Peter, were assisting him.

The architect Sabatini continued to request trees to plant in Madrid on the Hill of San Vicente.[49] The Duke of Alcudia, Don Manuel Godoy — the Queen's favourite — held the post, among many others, of Governor of the Royal Estate, and therefore all letters and requests at this time are addressed to him. We have seen his signature, in a fine and even hand, suggesting a cultured, probably vain man.

Many people addressed to him their requests for trees and plants from the Aranjuez nurseries, probably with distaste as the favourite was not popular. The Dowager Duchess of Infantado for her palace at Las Vistillas (Madrid), the Countess of Montijo (mother of the Empress Eugenie) and Count Cabarrus all made such requests.

Don Juan de Villanueva had been appointed Head Architect to His Majesty for the Royal Seats on 26 February 1789, and under his direction the "Bouteloues" (the popular name given to Esteban and his two sons) made the Prince's Garden and others for the Infantes Don Pedro and Don Antonio. Because of the French Revolution this was a time when the presence of Frenchmen was not popular and all those at Aranjuez were ordered to leave Spain.[50] The work continued nevertheless and there was a new project for some sculptures to be executed by Don Joaquín Arali, which would represent — as always in imitation of Versailles — the rivers Jarama and Tagus, "and two children that are to be made for a fountain to be placed in Aranjuez in the Prince's Garden, which requires 100 hundredweight of lead",[51] apart from other material. This magnificent fountain was sculpted by Juan Adán.

"Stone" was shipped for this purpose from Málaga to Cartagena for easier transportation to Madrid.[52]

But the Royal Family's days for enjoying these gardens were already numbered. Their royal relations in France had perished, and the end of their happy times in Aranjuez and La Granja was rapidly approaching.

BENCH IN THE ISLAND GARDEN. Aranjuez. *Photo Author.*

[1] Archivo General de Palacio, Madrid: *Aranjuez,* file 4.
[2] Idem, file 9.
[3] Idem, file 5.
[4] Idem, file 7.
[5] Idem, file 8, 28th. June 1732. Letter from Samaniego to Patiño.
[6] Idem, file 9, "Relación de plantas de don Fernando Triviño, Paris, 10th January 1735.
[7] Idem, file 11.
[8] Idem, file 11.
[9] Idem, file 14.
[10] Idem, file 14.
[11] Idem, file 15.
[12] Idem, file 17, 14th. February 1746.
[13] Idem, file 20, August 1747.
[14] Idem, file 20, April 1747.
[15] Idem, file 23, 8th. June 1748.
[16] Idem, file 21, 14th. August 1748. Signed: Bonavía.
[17] Idem, file 26, 7th. December 1749. Signed: Ventura Bonavía.
[18] Idem, file 26, 14th. October.
[19] Idem, file 28.
[20] Idem, file 25, 13th. September 1750.
[21] Idem, file 27, 21st. March 1751.
[22] Idem, file 28, Don Santiago Bonavía to the Marqués de la Ensenada.
[23] Idem, file 36, February 1760. Manuel Francisco Pinel to Richard Wall.
[24] Idem, file 29, 1753.
[25] Idem, file 27, 1751. Signed: Santiago Bonavía.
[26] Idem, file 31, January 1755.
[27] Idem, file 32, 25th. February 1756. Manuel Francisco Pinel to Richard Wall.
[28] Idem, file 33, 17th. January 1757. Letter from Bonavía.
[29] Idem, file 32, 9th. July 1756.
[30] Idem, file 33, 13th. August 1757.
[31] Idem, file 33, 4th. June 1757. To Manuel Francisco Pinel.
[32] Idem, file 33, 13th. August 1757. Santiago Bonavía to Richard Wall.
[33] Idem, file 36, 12th. December 1760. Juan Manuel Retortillo to Richard Wall.
[34] Idem, file 36, 23rd. January 1761.
[35] Idem, file 36, Paris, 25th. August 1760. Esteban Boutelou to Richard Wall.
[36] Idem, file 36, 23rd. January 1761. Jaime Marquet to Richard Wall.
[37] Idem, file 33, 22nd. July 1766. Marqués de Puentefuerte to the Marqués de Grimaldi.
[38] Idem, file 38, 20th. November 1766. To Don Esteban Boutelou.
[39] Idem, file 38, 5th. January 1775. Don Francisco Bonanza.
[40] Idem, file 40, 2nd. January 1775. Don Ventura Llovera to the Marqués de Grimaldi.
[41] Idem, file 40, year 1778.
[42] Idem, file 40, Paris, 7th. December 1778.
[43] Idem, file 41, Aranjuez, 5th. June 1780. To Don Francisco Llovera.
[44] Idem, file 41, Madrid, 10th. January 1781. To Don Esteban Escudero.
[45] Idem, file 41, El Pardo, 10th. February 1781.
[46] Idem, file 41, 29th. October 1783. To Don Francisco Sabatini.
[47] Idem, file 42, 1786. To Don Miguel Trejo.
[48] Idem, file 43, 25th. March 1788. Don Antonio Porlier to the Conde de Floridablanca.
[49] Idem, file 44, 8th. December 1791.
[50] Idem, file 49, 12th. February 1795.
[51] Idem, file 49, 7th. July 1795.
[52] Idem, file 51, 21st. September 1796. Signed: Francisco Sabatini.

10 THE GARDENS OF LA GRANJA

The gardens of La Granja are the masterpiece of Philip V and Isabella (Elizabeth) Farnese.

French gardening had already made a somewhat tentative appearance in Spain in the plans to remodel the Buen Retiro gardens in 1712 and later, simultaneous with the creation of La Granja, the planting of the parterre at Aranjuez with its long, radiating avenues.

But it was to be at San Ildefonso de La Granja that a new phase in Spanish gardening would begin, as the disciples of Le Nôtre crossed the Pyrenees. A multitude of artists, sculptors, gardeners and plumbers appeared on the scene, all well-acquainted with the parks of Versailles, Marly and Saint Cloud, the royal seats of the "Sun King" Louis XIV.

Louis XIV had died in 1715, and so could no longer advise his grandson, as he had in the case of the Buen Retiro. The gardens of La Granja are contemporary with Louis XV, and the statues and fountains are in the purest rococo style.

These gardens exemplify, above all, the use of vegetation as a background for the complicated fountains, which produce a more brilliant effect at La Granja than in any other European park.

Louis XIV's two great failures are said to have been the war with Holland and the water supply at Versailles. As for Versailles, the Monarch was obliged to channel still waters and to bring water from the river Seine by means of the costly hydraulic works at Marly-la-Machine. This could never produce the same effect as the pure, crystalline torrents rushing down to La Granja from the melting snows of the Peñalara.

The detailed studies of the gardens of La Granja made by Mlle. J. Digaud,[1] Yves Bottineau[2] and various Spanish authors are, above all, a description of the statues and fountains with an account of the mythological themes they represent and the sculptors who created them.

Our intention is different. We shall relate how these gardens came into being and follow their development step by step.

This site was selected as a royal seat for its beautiful wooded country which Philip found so attractive. At one time the

PLAZA OF THE EIGHT AVENUES. *Watercolour by Brambilla.*

Hieronymite monks of the Monastery del Parral in Segovia owned a modest hospice or farm here, and earlier, there had been a hunting lodge, built about 1450 by Henry IV, the brother of Isabella, the Catholic, who later gave it to the monks.

When Philip V built his palace he wanted the patio and fountain of the old hospice to be preserved, and the patio does, in fact, still remain. This greatly restricted the choice of the site, which could have been much higher.

The summer heat of Madrid was very unpleasant for King Philip, who had spent his youth among the cool arbours of Versailles, but the cold, austere monastery of the Escorial with the tombs of the Habsburgs, displeased him even more. He therefore used to cross the Sierra de Guadarrama and make hunting expeditions through the pleasant pine forests of Balsaín, where streams rushed down the valley. The ruins of Philip II's palace, destroyed by fire in Charles II's time, can still be seen. According to tradition, during one of his hunting parties, King Philip V discovered the friars' hospice at the foot of the sierra, hidden among dense vegetation which reminded him of the beloved Versailles of his youth, and he decided to build himself a similar palace in that place.

His naturally gloomy, melancholy disposition had been aggravated by the twenty years of worries and trouble during

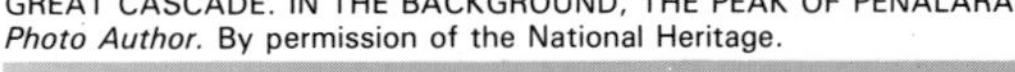

GREAT CASCADE. IN THE BACKGROUND, THE PEAK OF PENALARA.
Photo Author. By permission of the National Heritage.

which he had reigned, and his only wish was to retire and spend the rest of his days in some pleasant peaceful spot.

Once the land of San Ildefonso had been acquired in 1719, the building of the palace was entrusted to the architect Teodoro Ardemans. Most of it was built between 1721 and 1723.

The eastern façade facing the garden was not finished until 1739 by Sacchelti, a pupil of the Italian Juvara who has left many buildings in Turin. From 1723 onwards the work was speeded up under the King's personal supervision, as he and the Queen were constantly visiting the site. They wished above all to see the chapel and their private apartments completed before 1724, the year in which the King had decided to abdicate in favour of his son Luis.[3] But the schemes of man so often fail: Luis reigned for only eight months, dying in August of that same year, and Philip had to resume the government of Spain for twenty more years, until his death in 1746.

As is customary in the construction of extensive palace gardens, the garden at La Granja was laid out at the same time as the palace building, under the supervision of the architect René Carlier, a pupil of Robert de Cotte. De Cotte's plans for the Buen Retiro were mentioned in a previous chapter. Carlier had remained in the King's service since 1712 and continued until his death. Little is known about his life, and even his age is unknown. Breñosa and Castellarnau tell us in their Guide Book that they "do not know whether the gardens of La Granja were designed by him".[4] We do learn that in 1720 Carlier asked the King's permission to take the waters in France. On his return the King decided to lodge him at the Escorial so that he could recuperate from the malady from which he suffered.[5] At that time Carlier figured as head architect of the Retiro. He was probably no longer young when he started on the gardens of La Granja.

In a letter dated April 1721, Antonio Cázeres reported to the Marqués de Grimaldi on progress in constructing the palace: "The favourable weather is enabling Monsieur Carlier and the foreman to make good progress with the work; Carlier is having the land cleared and levelled for the aforesaid gardens while, at the same time, Monsieur Esteban (Boutelou) and Monsieur Solís are preparing the orchard."[6] It is known that Carlier died in the Escorial in 1722, a year after the work began.

At his death, direction of the work on the gardens passed to Don Esteban Boutelou, a Frenchman who had been head gardener at Aranjuez since 1712, and to Esteban Marchand, a military engineer, also French, assisted by Enrique Joly, a gardener employed at the Buen Retiro. When Boutelou was sent to La Granja, Joly moved to Aranjuez to take over his post, and is mentioned as working in the Queen's Garden in 1724.[7] Also employed as gardeners during this period were Solís, Basani and Salvador Lemmi, a Florentine and the first of a long line of gardeners recorded as working at La Granja, serving for ninety-six years up to 1820, and contemporary with the famous Boutelou family who were in charge of the gardens of Aranjuez, the Buen Retiro and the Alcázar at Seville for approximately one hundred and fourteen years until the exile of Queen Isabella II in 1868.

Antonio Ponz writes: "For the formation of the gardens and avenues the King employed an engineer named Marchand who planted and arranged everything as it stands today. A number of troops and many peasants were working that year on the levelling of the Gardens. The specialised aspects of the gardening were assigned to Solís and Don Esteban Boutelou, father of the famous Don Esteban Boutelou II, head gardener at Aranjuez; the fountains, statues and other sculptures were entrusted to the masters Frémin and Thierry who were held in high esteem in Paris; Frémin had studied in Rome."[8]

FACADE OF THE PARTERRE. *Photo Author.* By permission of the National Heritage.

The first sculptors to arrive in Spain in 1721 were Frémin and Thierry who established their workshops in the neighbourhood of Balsaín. The first task to be completed was apparently the great cascade aligned with the main façade of the palace, with steps of marble and coloured jasper. Carlier had his part in this before his death, because in February 1722 he gives an acount of the "work, entirely to my satisfaction, on the pond in the grove where the waters of the cascade are to flow"[9] and mentions "the plumber who has been laying the pipes for the principal fountain at the head of the cascade".[10]

Parallel to the cascade itself and in line with the palace, a river apparently once flowed down the hill and had to be diverted to another course. Otherwise it would have been inconceivable to have two parallel motifs with fountains descending vertically towards the palace, the second starting the Andromeda's fountain at a much higher level.

White marble was brought from Granada for the pool and cascade; marble was also brought from Genoa for the sculptures, executed from models in plaster of Paris and baked clay.[11]

When Carlier died in August 1722, René Frémin took over direction of the sculpture workshops. We owe nearly all the sculptures at La Granja to this artist and to Thierry. When Thierry returned to France in 1728, Frémin asked for his place to be taken by Santiago Bousseau, who worked there until his death in 1740. (With the exception of Carlier, who was a pupil of Robert de

PARTERRE DE LA FAMA. *Photo Author.* By permission of the National Heritage.

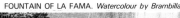

FOUNTAIN OF LA FAMA. *Watercolour by Brambilla.*

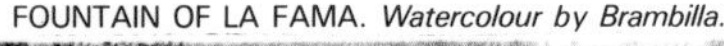

Cotte, all of the sculptors at La Granja were pupils of the great French sculptors of the Louis XV era: Girardon, Coysevox and the Coustou brothers.)

The second generation of sculptors — that is, after the death of Bousseau — consisted of Hubert Dumandré who succeeded him as director and whose name always appears as Demandre in documents signed by him, his brother Antoine, and Pierre Pitué who signed his name as Puthois in all the documents in the Archives at the Royal Palace. These sculptors made their careers in Spain and executed the later sculptures of Philip V's reign.

Their modelled figures are not as outstanding as those of the first teams at Balsaín, but their influence in Spain was greater. They executed the last two fountains, namely La Fama (Fame) and the Baths of Diana (the latter according to Bousseau's plans), and completed the statues that Carlier, Frémin, Thierry and Bousseau had left unfinished.[12]

Meanwhile, the avenues were being cut and levelled, lime-trees were being planted and the Orangery was being built. By 1724 all the trees were in place, plants and seeds were arriving from France, and Esteban Marchand was constructing the maze.[13]

The French gardeners made use of shrubs such as hornbeam *(carpinus betelus)* and yew, which had never been used in Spain before, for the formation of hedges, spheres and pyramids because they were easy to trim to any shape.[14] Boxwood, which was used for the edges and designs in the parterre *à la française* came from the Alcarria (Guadalajara) and the sierras of Cuenca.

Lime-trees were also introduced to form avenues. The first came to La Granja and Aranjuez from Holland in 1723, and horse-chestnuts arrived from France about the same time.[15] Plants were also imported from Italy by way of Alicante.

Esteban Boutelou must have been held in high esteem for the King gave orders that he was not to be hindered in his work. Even so, it took some twenty years to complete the garden.

Philip V would have liked his sculptures to be of marble or bronze like those at Versailles. Marble was possible, thanks to the quarries in El Paular near at hand, the pink marble from Alicante, and the white marble presumably from Macael (Almeria). (In 1759 Hubert Dumandré bought from Bernasconi red marble with white and yellow veins from the quarry at Cabra in Andalusia for the altarpiece of the chapel at Riofrio.)[16]

But the bronze figures desired by the monarch had to be cast in lead. Although a bronze-smith named Rey arrived from Rome, he did not come to an understanding with the French sculptors, so a procedure had to be adopted for varnishing the lead to give it the appearance of bronze.[17] In some cases it was painted gold or white to make it look like marble. The system of painting lead in gold or bronze had already been employed at Versailles, so bottles of varnish and red bronze powder to mix with it were sent from Paris.[17] Today, the sculptures are mostly painted a silvery-grey colour which bears little resemblance to bronze.

In exploring the gardens today the most important thing is to grasp the spirit that inspired the gardens of both Versailles and La Granja. The Versailles gardens were created as the living symbol of the pomp and power of the Sun King. His palace is

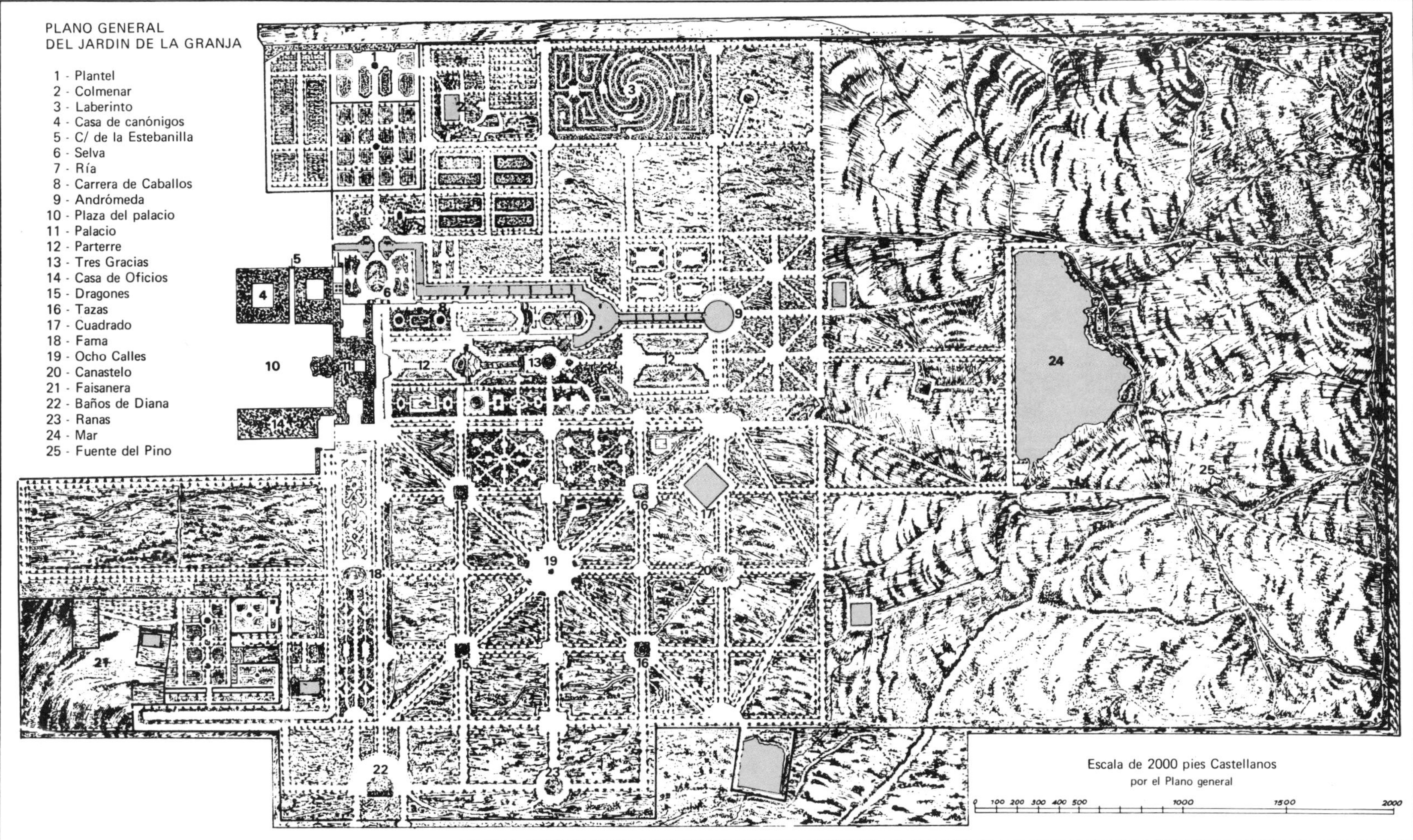

PLAN OF LA GRANJA. *X. Winthuysen.*

situated so as to overlook and dominate the parterres, pools and long extensions that merge with the silvery landscape of L'Ile de France. These features were essential for celebrations and pageantry, for balls and magnificent recepitons. Le Nôtre was their creator.

Although the gardens of La Granja were completely French in their inspiration, and to the taste of Philip V, they were really the refuge of a king in search of solitude, where the mountainous countryside made it impossible to apply Le Nôtre's principles without massive clearing, levelling and terracing as at Versailles. For this reason the gardens and fountains made at La Granja by French artists never possessed the unity and perspective of the parks of Louis XIV. The profusion of sculptures and fountains on the slopes of the mountain, and so near to the palace, are oppressive and overwhelming. On the other hand the King would not have been pleased with open perspectives over the barren Castilian plateau, which he found so unattractive.

Lady Holland, who was in Spain at the beginning of the nineteenth century, wrote in her diary: "The gardens are reckoned among the finest in Europe; they are in the old French style of high clipped hedges, *salons de verdure,* alleys, etc.; that is the style I prefer far beyond any other, yet these gardens are *sombre,* and striking only for the number of their fountains, which stand unrivalled. I was surprised at seeing channels to convey water to the roots of trees as employed at Aranjuez and Madrid. In those cities there is no moisture or coolness, but here the proximity of the mountains causes frequent thunder and rain storms."[19] As can be observed, the irrigation channels established by the Arabs, which had survived in Spain, did not escape Lady Holland's notice.

* * *

Our favourite itinerary when visiting the gardens is that suggested by Breñosa and Castellarnau in their *Guide to San Ildefonso.* Turning to the right after entering the great iron gates, we descend to the Parterre of La Fama (Fame), which is opposite the southern façade of the palace.

This is the gayest portion of the garden, the most successful, and that which bears most resemblance to French gardens. It is a large rectangle forming a *boulingrin** with vases and statues, bordered by a wide hedge of boxwood and clipped yew. At the far end is the Fountain of La Fama, by Dumandré and Pitué. Its very high vertical jet rises to a height of forty-seven metres and is said to be visible from the town of Segovia, ten kilometres away.

FOUNTAIN OF LATONA. GARDENS AT VERSAILLES.

Following the walk at the back of the parterre, and turning left we reach the Fountain of the Baths of Diana, also the work of Dumandré and Pitué according to plans by Santiago Bousseau.

This fountain, the last to be executed on the King's orders, was designed about 1737; a letter exists from René Frémin (who left La Granja for Paris in 1738) relating how: "Santiago Bousseau arrived from Paris on 18 January and they are instructing him about the model for the Baths of Diana, which Their Majesties wish to see completed by their next visit to San Ildefonso."[20] Polished marble was brought for this purpose according to measurements specified by Bousseau.[21]

This fountain seems to have been inspired by the Buffet d'eau de Mansart which stands in a shady alley in the gardens of the Grand Trianon at Versailles, although the one at La Granja is much more intricate and imposing, and in the style of Louis XV. The expressionless faces of the nymphs who lie in the waters and the other characters, their hair dressed in the style of the period, resemble the ladies painted by Nattier. Work on this fountain was to continue throughout the last years of Philip V's reign. Although it was already in position in 1742, according to a letter signed by Juan de Berrueta in February of 1743, the drains had not yet been laid.[22] The pool in front of the fountain was altered and enlarged and surrounded by a border of veined marble from El Paular.[23]

This fountain was very costly because of the amount of intricate workmanship entailed and the lead required for its

FOUNTAIN BY MANSART. GARDENS OF THE GRAND TRIANON. Versailles.

FOUNTAIN OF THE FROGS. La Granja. *Watercolour by Brambilla.*

conduits. It was the last that the King saw playing, shortly before his death, and it is said that he exclaimed on seeing it, "you have entertained me for three minutes, but you have cost me three million [reales]."[24]

Just as at Versailles the main mythological theme adopted was that of the god Apollo, the symbol adopted by the Sun King. Many sculptures at La Granja also represent Diana the huntress. Mademoiselle Digard tells us that this was "to please Philip V, with his love for nature".[25] On the other hand it may have been in honour of the domineering Isabella Farnese who always hunted at the side of her royal spouse. There is no doubt that the feminine themes of nymphs, naiads and nereids recur throughout.[26]

The cupids, rather plump cherubs, and the children who appear throughout the park at Versailles in accordance with Louis XIV's wish "to have childhood everywhere", are repeated at La Granja.

A semicircular area round the Fountain of the Baths of Diana was adorned with four vases and six statues, all the work of Dumandré and Pitué but of little interest.

Climbing a walk to the right of the Baths of Diana we reach the Fountain of the Frogs, by Frémin according to the model of the Fountain of Latona by Le Brun at Versailles. "The theme is the episode from Ovid's *Metamorphoses*."[27] It is the only pool at La Granja with a central group in marble.

A letter to the Marqués de Villarías states that "a marble group has been erected according to a drawing by Pedro de La Faye, and the lead statue of Latona removed."[28]

From the Fountain of the Frogs a path parallel to the Parterre of La Fama, called the Long Walk, takes us to the Square of the Eight Paths. This is a circular construction with arches of lead painted in bronze, now in bad condition, with a sculptured group in the centre. According to Breñosa and Castellarnau it represents Mercury and Psyche, although Ponz believes it depicts Apollo and Pandora. The workmanship is attributed to Frémin.

After this we follow a long avenue that crosses obliquely in front of the Fountain of Las Tazas (the Cups) mounting to the highest point in the gardens where the principal fountains are to be found; on the left they overlook the great cascade whose waters fall toward the centre of the palace façade. This first part of the garden was constructed in Carlier's time, and the influence of the cascade of Marly is evident.

Climbing up the Parterre of Andromeda we arrive at the fountain of the same name. This is the first of a series in a vertical line which form the pools of the Carrera de Caballos (the Horse Race). The diverted river mentioned earlier now flows here and carries its waters beyond the park.[29] According to Don Antonio Ponz the figures in the fountain are by Frémin and the vase by Thierry: both are cast in lead. This pool was already under construction in Carlier's time, as he tells us: "In the great pool that stores the water of the new river they are digging in a ditch for the wall that is to act as a dam for this river and retain its waters."[30] This refers to the channelling of the river to form the Carrera de Caballos; it comes out again lower down, near the palace.

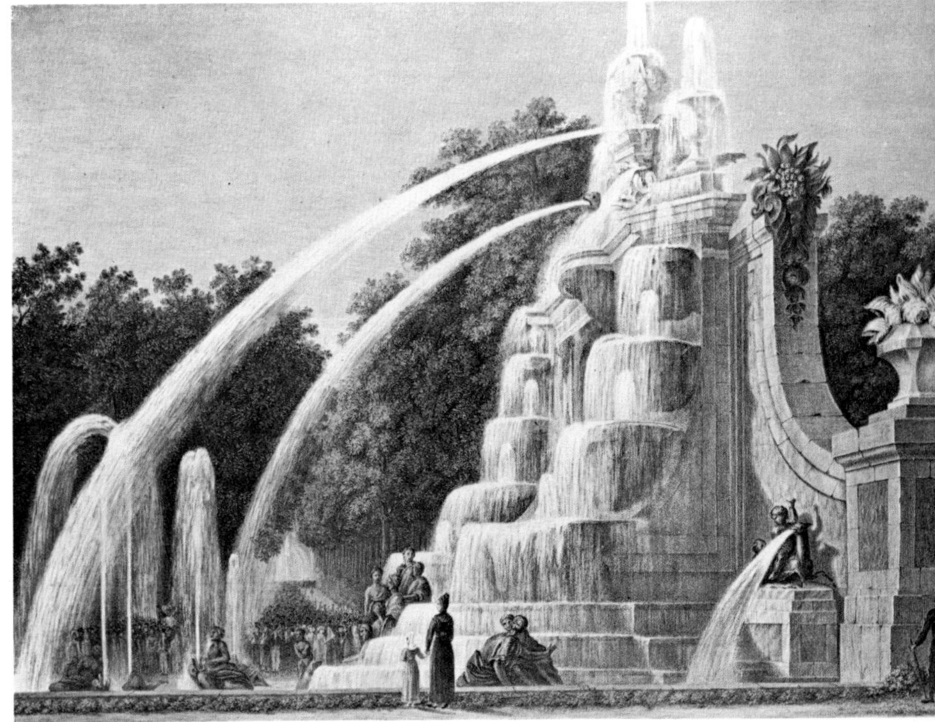

FOUNTAIN OF THE BATHS OF DIANA. *Watercolour by Brambilla.*

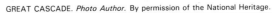

GREAT CASCADE. *Photo Author.* By permission of the National Heritage.

CENTRAL AVENUE. *Photo S. Saavedra.* By permission of the National Heritage.

PAVILION WITH FOUNTAIN OF THE THREE GRACES. *Photo Oronoz.* By permission of the National Heritage.

These complex fountains of the god Apollo, with his lyre on the upper step and Neptune's chariot on the lower one, remind us of the *Char Embourbé* which adorns the principal fountain of the Grand Canal at Versailles; they form the most spectacular group in the gardens, especially when the fountains are playing.

When we descend from the height of Andromeda's Fountain towards the palace, there is a parterre on our left; today it is neglected, but at one time it must have been similar to that of La Fama as it was also adorned with statues and vases. In Breñosa's day "the borders were filled with flowers and edged with boxwood, with spheres made of yew at regular intervals".[31] This must have been about 1884 when he wrote his Guide, and he describes with admiration "the magnificent cedar of Lebanon" which is still there in all its glory, and two Wellingtonias which at that time must have been of moderate height, about twelve years old at the most. Today, there are three giant wellingtonias, a cedar *atlantica glauca* and the huge cedar of Lebanon, all quite out of place in these classical eighteenth century gardens, as they deform and overshadow the parterre. Let us hope that it may be restored to the style of the Parterre of La Fama, open and cheerful, one of the best features of the gardens.

To reach the head of the main cascade from this point we must climb a small hill with a few steps, taking us to the rear of the French pavilion overlooking the cascade. It is a beautiful little pavilion of the French Regency style (the transition between Louis XIV and Louis XV), made of pink stone from Sepúlveda. According to Ponz: "The bas-reliefs depicting the four corners of the globe are important sculptures attributed to Thierry." This pavilion is one of the best proportioned and most elegant features in the garden.

Nearby stands the Fountain of the Three Graces, which unfortunately has been placed in front of the pavilion blocking its view and distracting from its classical lines.

This fountain appears to have been built by Thierry from 1721 to 1728. The theme of the Three Graces belongs to the Hellenistic era and was used in the Italian Renaissance. Frémin and Thierry probably derived it from Le Brun, who used it for his candelabra designs, combining this motif with that of the caryatids.[32]

The central avenue, with its beautiful statues alternating with vases, is particularly reminiscent of Versailles and the statues on either side of the *tapis vert* next to the Grand Canal.

From the summit of the Fountain of the Three Graces we behold the palace, so Italian, so Baroque, and like Saint Simon we think "that if it had been built on a higher level a terrace could have been added, to provide a view of the gardens."

The parterre, as it appears today at the foot of the cascade, is ablaze with colour, and the beautiful clusters of flowers are spectacular in their effect. My personal impression is that, although the park of La Granja is very beautiful, it does not serve the purpose intended for it, which was to provide a *jardin à la française;* the fountains are out of perspective because they have been placed in a rising slope, some of them, like the Baths of Diana, can be seen in a hollow from the palace, but nearly all of them are on different levels — even the two identical fountains of the Tazas and the Dragons. It seems strange that no attempt was made to raise the Fountain of Diana — the most important in the whole park — on some kind of base or pedestal so that it could be seen from the palace. From the map the park of La Granja seems well-designed and very French; but strolling through it, one discovers that the design is completely subordinate to the irregularities of the terrain.

The whole garden is somewhat overcrowded and heavy; the sculptures are typical of French rococo, far removed from the grandeur of the seventeenth century Versailles. The figures with their robes twisted and in disarray, their faces devoid of expression, do not faithfully convey the mythological themes they are intended to depict. All regard with placid and vacant serenity the events that befall them. Even Andromeda gazes with an impassive simper at the fierce attack of the Dragon which the artist has made as ferocious as possible...and indeed, the animals have been masterfully portrayed.

At the end of an avenue, near the Fountains of La Fama and the Baths of Diana, we find a small fountain recessed in a semicircular area beneath the path. This is the Queen's Fountain, and here our eyes rest happily on the two simple, classical pilasters of pink stone from Sepúlveda, belonging to the reign of Ferdinand VII.

CARRERAS DE CABALLOS. *Photo Author..* By permission of the National Heritage.

PALACE. EASTERN FAÇADE. *Photo S. Saavedra..* By permission of the National Heritage.

The water here is reputed to be the best and coolest at La Granja; it trickles from a gilt-bronze mask in the form of a sun. Sedeno, another La Granja historian, tells us that "it was executed in 1826 by the sculptor Telesforo Demandre."[33] The basin of coloured marble is shaped like a shell, and the pedestal of the same material, according to Breñosa, is probably antique and came from Rome together with the collection of statues that Philip V and Queen Isabella bought at the death of Queen Christine of Sweden.[34] This fountain is crowned by a charming figure of the nymph Arethusa, made in bronze that was once gilded. She is shown running, and the statue has considerably more movement and expression than most of the figures in the park. This is one of the most secluded and mysterious corners in the gardens.

FOUNTAIN OF ANDROMEDA. *Photo Oronoz.* By permission of the National Heritage.

If we cross in front of the palace, where the sphinxes are seated, opposite the entrance gates, a stairway with two flights and a handsome balustrade leads down to the lower garden. This is the *Selva,* or wilderness. In its centre there is a great oval pool divided in three levels, forming a cascade, and adorned with statues painted in bronze. Here the slope of the land has been used to advantage. It is surrounded by four statues on columns in the shape of inverted pyramids, of a much later date (late eighteenth or early nineteenth century). The lake is crossed by a charming bridge, adorned with four groups of children and animals, attributed to Frémin and Thierry.

We will conclude our tour by saying that these gardens owe their magnificence to their own beauty rather than to their resemblance to French gardens. We cannot believe that when they were completed these gardens could have reminded Philip V of his beloved Versailles. But he had left France at the age of seventeen, and his death was near when the Fountain of Diana was completed.

Despite its French origins, the Park of La Granja has a number of Arab features. First, access to the palace is not through a wide grilled gate opposite the main door as is the case in most European parks planned by Le Blond and other pupils of Le Nôtre; instead, entrance is by means of a side arch at an angle, before the main gateway is reached. Secondly, the use of irrigating channels which form a network of open conduits called *alcorques,*

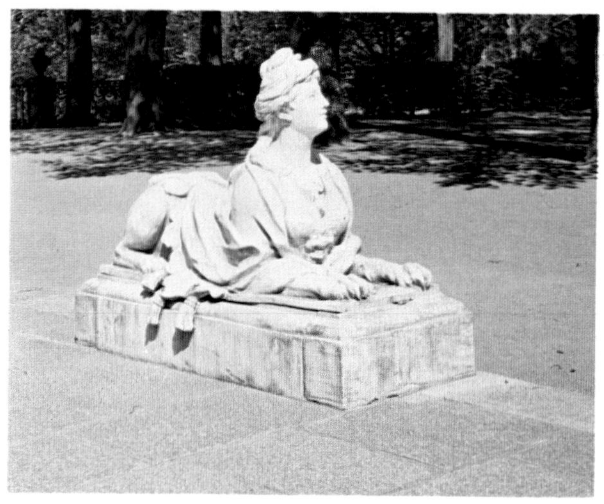

SPHINX, EASTERN FAÇADE.
Photo Author. By permission of the National Heritage.

is similar to those still to be seen at the Alcázar of Seville and in most Spanish gardens remaining from Arab times. Finally, on the mountainside, there is the lake or reservoir for the storage of water, similar to those at Granada and Aranjuez. Provision for water storage has always been the first step in planning gardens and orchards in Spain.

After Philip V's death his widow continued to live at La Granja for some thirteen years, partly because her royal spouse had bequeathed it to her for life, and partly because her stepson Ferdinand VI kept her confined there during his reign, because he feared the Italian Dowager Queen's intrigues. He himself lived mainly at Aranjuez and Villaviciosa. His only work at San Ildefonso was to construct his father's mausoleum in the chapel, completing it in 1756.

The Queen Mother maintained the palace and gardens, replaced many trees and took an interest in the crystal factory which had been founded in 1728. Ponz records: "Its origin lay in the fact that Don Juan Goyeneche abandoned the glass factory he had installed in the Nuevo Baztán (province of Madrid), where his palace was built by Churriguera, the famous eighteenth century architect, and his best workmen went to the Royal Seat, under the patronage of Isabella Farnese. In time they produced the best glass crystal in the world."[35] In La Granja the process of applying gold decoration in crystal by means of heat was discovered in the time of Charles IV.

During her widowhood Queen Isabella Farnese wanted to possess a palace of her own, so she had an enormous residence built at Riofrío, on a plain near Segovia. The architect was Don Virgilio Rabaglio who in 1752 also drew up a plan for the gardens that was never implemented.[36]

Construction on the Palace of Riofrío continued until the death of Ferdinand VI in 1759, but as he was succeeded by the Queen's own son Charles III, the palace was never inhabited, for she came to live permanently at the Court.

Inspired by the gardens of La Granja, King Charles III ordered gardens for his palace at Caserta during his reign in Naples from 1752 to 1756; he commissioned Sabatini's father-in-law Vanvitelli, who had worked with Juvara at the Albani Palace in Urbano.[37]

When Charles III came to the throne of Spain he took great interest in restoring the gardens of San Ildefonso, which soon recovered their former splendour. He also increased the size of the park by buying additional woodland.

This royal estate witnessed several historic events, among them the insurrection of the sergeants in the time of Maria Christina (widow of Ferdinand VII). In 1918, during the reign of Alfonso XIII, a fire broke out destroying part of the church quarters and a wing of the palace. Many art treasures perished. The Court used to spend the summer season there, as at that time they did not own the Palace of La Magdalena in Santander.

Although the Royal Family had gone north for the summer ever since the time of Queen Christina, the Infanta Isabel chose to spend all the summers of her life at La Granja. To commemorate her famous *coterie* a statue by Coullaut Valera was erected in 1928 on the spot in the park where she used to sit.

JARDIN DE LA SELVA. *Watercolour by Brambilla.*

QUEEN'S FOUNTAIN. *Photo Oronoz.* By permission of the National Heritage.

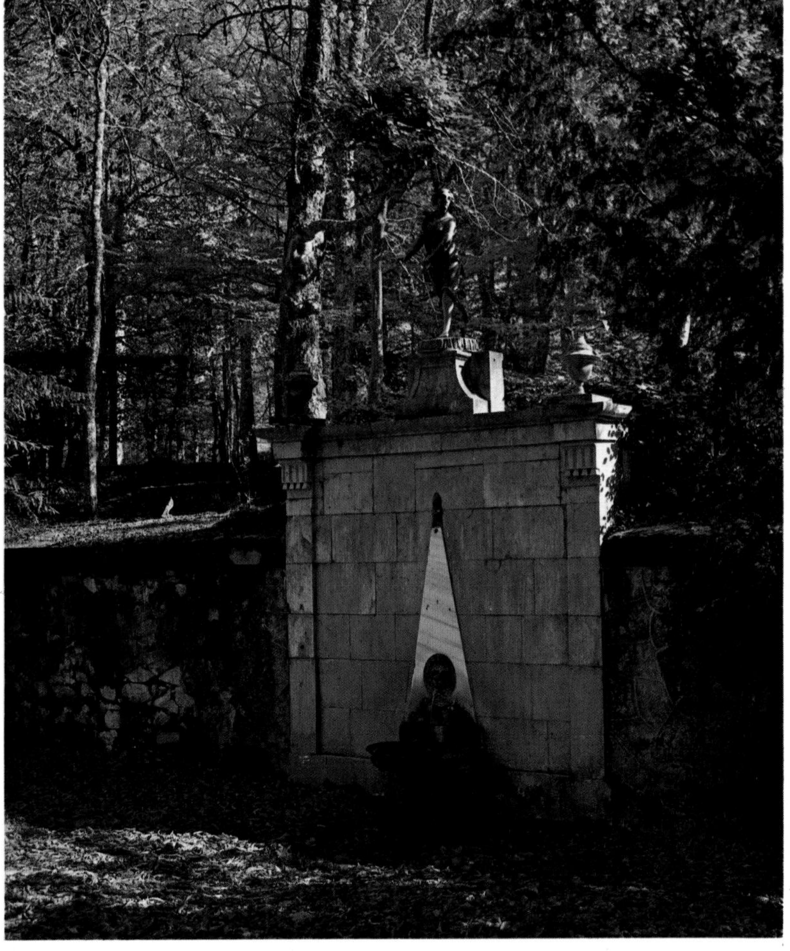

STATUE OF PRINCESS ISABEL.
Photo Oronoz. By permission of the National Heritage.

SCULPTURES. BRIDGE OF LA SELVA.
Photo S. Saavedra. By permission of the National Heritage.

[1] DIGARD,: J.: *Les Jardins de La Granja et leurs sculptures décoratives,* Ernest Leroux, Paris, 1934.
[2] BOTTINEAU, Yves: *L'art de Cour dans l'Espagne de Phillipe V,* Féret et Fils, Bordeaux, 1960.
[3] GROMORT, Georges: *Jardins d' Espagne,* Editions A. Vincent, Paris, 1926, vol. II.
[4] BREÑOSA, R., and CASTELLARNAU, J.M.: *Guía del Real Sitio de San Ildefonso de La Granja,* Madrid, 1884, page 158.
[5] Archivo General de Palacio, Madrid: *San Ildefonso,* file 3, 6 August 1722. Letter from Joseph Rodrigo to the Marqués de Villena.
[6] Idem, file 3.
[7] Archivo General de Palacio, Madrid: *Expedientes personales,* Enrique Joly.
[8] PONZ, Antonio: *Viaje de Espana,* Ed. Aguilar, Madrid, 1947, vol. X, page 886.
[9] Archivo General de Palacio, Madrid: *San Ildefonso,* file 3, February 1722.
[10] Idem, file 3, 8 October 1721.
[11] Idem, file 3, Balsaín, 1722. Letter from Antonio Cázeres to the Marqués de Grimaldi.
[12] DIGARD, J.: *Op. cit.,* pages 70, 245 & 246.
[13] Archivo General de Palacio, Madrid: *San Ildefonso,* file 4, 7 January 1725.
[14] GROMORT, G.: *Op. cit.,* vol. II.
[15] BREÑOSA, R. and CASTELLARNAU, J.M.: *Op. cit.,* page 155.
[16] Archivo General de Palacio, Madrid: *San Ildefonso,* file 25.
[17] DIGARD, J.: *Op. cit.,* page 176.
[18] Archivo General de Palacio, Madrid: *San Ildefonso,* file 13, 2 July 1743. Letter from Versailles to the Príncipe de Campoflorido.
[19] HOLLAND, Lady Elisabeth: *Spanish Journal,* edited by the Earl of Chichester, London 1910, page 77.
* A corruption of the English word "bowling green", a square court with a slightly rounded surface, and turfed; the term was used in French gardens.
[20] Archivo General de Palacio, Madrid: *San Ildefonso,* file 8, Palsaín, 22 January 1737. Letter to Don Esteban de la Cuadra.
[21] Idem, file 8.
[22] Idem, file 11.
[23] Idem, file 12, 5 January 1745.
[24] BREÑOSA, R., and CASTELLARNAU, J.M.: *Op. cit.,* page 180.
[25] DIGARD, J.: *Op. cit.,* page 83.
[26] DIGARD, J.: *Op. cit.,* page 83.
[27] DIGARD, J.: *Op. cit.,* page 85.
[28] Archivo General de Palacio, Madrid: *San Ildefonso,* file 11, 13 May 1744. Letter from the Marqués de Galiano to Villarías.
[29] BREÑOSA, R., and CASTELLARNAU, J.M.: *Op. cit.,* page 197.
[30] Archivo General de Palacio, Madrid: *San Ildefonso,* file 3, 23 April 1722. Letter from René Carlier to the Marqués de Grimaldi.
[31] BREÑOSA, R., and CASTELLARNAU, J.M.: *Op. cit.,* page 200.
[32] DIGARD, J.: *Op. cit.,* page 79.
[33] SEDEÑO, Santos Martín: *Descripción de San Ildefonso,* Segovia, 1867, page 123.
[34] BREÑOSA, R., and CASTELLARNAU, J.M.: *Op. cit.,* page 193.
[35] PONZ, A.: *Op. cit.,* vol. X, letter VII, page 905.
[36] Archivo General de Palacio, Madrid: *San Ildefonso,* file 21.
[37] INGERSOLL SMOUSE, Florence: "Les Jardins de Caserte", *La Révue de l'Art,* no. XXXV, Paris, 1914.

CHARLES III, AS A CHILD STUDYING BOTANY, by Ranc. Prado Museum. Madrid. *Photo Oronoz.*

11 HISTORY OF SPANISH BOTANICAL GARDENS AND THE BOTANICAL EXPEDITIONS TO THE NEW WORLD DURING THE EIGHTEENTH CENTURY

Knowledge and descriptions of Spanish flora have been studied and classified since the remotest times. Works left to us by the Romans were mentioned in an earlier chapter. The Arabs wrote scientific and botanical treatise, and translated the Greek Dioscorides's important book on plants and agriculture.

Unfortunately, very few Arab books have survived, for during the conquest of Granada in 1492, Cardinal Cisneros ordered a bonfire in the Bibarrambla in which most of these marvellous manuscripts were destroyed. We can only speculate on what treasures of science and wisdom they must have contained.

It is said that there was a botanical garden in Spain in Moorish times, namely that of King Naser in Gaudix (Granada), next to his palace, where medicinal herbs were no doubt grown. It was under the direction of an Arab from Corella (Navarre), Mohamed Ben Alí Ben Pharah, who was called Alschaphra. The Moors also brought many of the useful plants they discovered in the east, and naturalised them in the Peninsula by cultivating them in their gardens in Córdoba.

After the discovery of the New World, Spain contributed more than any other country to botanical knowledge in Europe. One of the purposes of the voyages of Christopher Columbus was to discover the shortest route to the Indies, where he hoped to meet the Grand Khan, described by Marco Polo as Emperor of the Tartars, and to obtain the precious spices so essential to medicine in that era. The importance of spices in the economy of the ancient world from time immemorial is well-known. Pepper, cloves, nutmeg, etc. were disguising the taste of tainted food so prevalent in the days before refrigeration. Spice prices were exorbitant and supplies inadequate to stock the apothecary shops of Europe.

Thus, when Columbus reached the Caribbean shores he began the search for cinnamon, cloves, nutmeg and rhubarb, which he mentions continually in his writings, lamenting that his ignorance of botany prevented him from identifying the wealth of plant life he found in the New World.

Martín Alonso Pinzón, his second-in-command, showed the Admiral two pieces of cinnamon, saying that a Portuguese member of the crew had seen a native carrying large bunches of it and "some large red nut-like fruit". Columbus thought he had discovered spices and nutmeg "in a field planted with all kinds of trees, all laden with fruit".

Columbus wrote in Lisbon on 4 March 1493 of finds of mastic (the gum of the *Pistacia lentiscus*), cotton, rhubarb and cinnamon.

"On the fourth voyage I discovered cocoa, whose beans are used by the Indians as currency for their transactions." Columbus's descriptions during his four voyages, guided solely by his keen gift of observation, has furnished invaluable information

Illuſtrado por el Doct.Lag. 105

MEDICA MALA. AVRANTIA MALA.

de todos eſtos fructos Perſianos. Porque ſi alguna malignidad en ſi tenia el Durazno, ſe corrigio mucho con la mezcla y conuerſacion del Membrillo: el qual es baſtante aun à corregir la venenoſidad de la eſcamonea. Comidas las flores del Priſco, purgan por arriba y por abaxo, con grãde violentia. Engañanſe los que pienſan, que todas eſtas Perſicas plantas, eran primero venenoſas en Perſia, y deſpues lleuadas à Egypto, y alli plantadas, ſe boluieron muy benignas y cordiales: y la cauſa de aqueſte error, es que las confunden con otra muy differente planta, llamada Perſea, de la qual à la fin d'eſte primero libro refiere lo meſmo Dioſcorides.

Debaxo de las Mançanas llamadas Medicas, porque nacen muy excellentes en la region de Media, ſe comprehenden las Cidras, los Limones, las Limas, las Toronjas, y las Naranjas: aun que Dioſcorides no conocio ſino tan ſolamẽte las cidras: el arbol de las quales ſe llama en Latin Citria malus. Llamò Perſico tambien à eſte fructo Dioſcorides, anſi como Aſſyrio, Plinio: porque en la vna region, y en la otra, multiplica en grande abundantia. La Naranja ſe dize en Latin Aurantia, porque quando es perfectamente madura, tiene color de oro. Para ſignificar el Limon, la Lima, y la Toronja, no tenemos nombre Griego, ni Latino, que proprio ſea, ſino les hazemos parte de malo Citrio, que nos ſignifica propriamente la Cidra. Los Valentianos llaman à la Narantia Toronja, ſiendo la Toronja otra eſpecie diuerſa, y no poco ſemejante à la Cidra. Veeſe el arbol que la produze, en vn jardin del Illuſtriſſimo y Reuerendiſſimo Señor Don Bartholome de la Cueua, Cardenal Ampliſſimo de la Sancta Ygleſia de Roma, y muy reſplandeciente eſpejo y dechado, de verdadera ſanctimonia y piedad, acompañada de valor, mageſtad, y grandeza. Todos aqueſtos fructos, aun que en forma y grandeza differan, toda via ſon dotados quaſi de la meſma virtud, y poſſeen las meſmas partes: y anſi las plantas que los produzen, tienen entre ſi grandiſſima ſemejança: en las hojas de las quales ſolamente ay eſta differentia, que las del Naranjo hazen junto al peçon cierto coraçoncillo diſtincto: y las otras ſon ſeguidas & iguales, como las del Laurel, ſin tener diuiſion alguna. Anſi en Inuierno, como en Verano, todas eſtan ſiempre verdes, y horadadas de ſubtiliſſimos agujeros. No ſe veen jamas biudas de fructo eſtas plãtas, porq̃ ſiẽpre el vno ſuccede al otro. Produzẽ vnas flores ſuauiſſimas, ordinariamẽte dos vezes al año: cõuiene à ſaber al entrar del Inuierno, y deſpues en la prima vera: las quales cõficionadas con miel,

Don Bartholome de la Cueua Cardenal.

O ò açucar,

ILLUSTRATION FROM DIOSCORIDES'S TREATISE ON BOTANY. National Library. Madrid.

to botanists making their classifications in subsequent centuries.[2]

In 1526, during the reign of Charles V, Gonzalo Fernández de Oviedo wrote a *Summary of the Natural and General History of the Indies,* in which he described the plants that came from America, la Isla Espanola (Spanish Island), Cuba and "Tierra Firme", mentioning maize and other products.

Hernán Cortés sent letters to the Emperor from the city of Temixitán (Mexico), describing cocoa, tomatoes and other vegetables.[3] A second report to Charles V in 1520 admiringly describes the marvellous gardens of the Aztec kings.

It is well-known that cocoa was a bitter product used by the Aztecs, who called it *chocolatl.* They prepared these beans by grinding them as today, but without using sugar, and very rarely honey or spices. They mixed the cocoa with maize-flour scented with American pepper. Apparently, nuns first thought of adding sugar, vanilla and cinnamon in the sixteenth century, producing chocolate as we know it. In Spain it became an exotic luxury, and cups of chocolate made with water were a favourite beverage of the well-to-do.

Queen Maria Theresa of Austria, the wife of Louis XIV of France, introduced the fashion of drinking chocolate at the French Court, but it seems that her husband, the Sun King, found it too expensive!

Philip II inherited a love of trees and plants from his father. In the National Library in Madrid there is a copy of the *Botanical Treatise* by the Greek physician Dioscorides, translated directly into Spanish by Dr. Andrés Laguna. This book had not been republished since the time of the Arabs.

This famous doctor (1494-1560) dedicated the book to Philip II in 1555 while he was still Crown Prince of Spain, and he coloured the plates of this copy himself.

In his introduction he asks the Prince to encourage the development of medicine through the study of herbs, "...extremely necessary for the public good; the Italian Princes and Universities pride themselves on their many excellent gardens stocked with every plant in the universe, and it is right and fitting that Your Majesty should provide at least one in Spain, supported from Royal funds. In so doing Your Majesty will serve his own health, so important to the world, and encourage Spain's many distinguished experts in the science of herbs."[4] Laguna, a physician and humanist from Segovia, was one of the most famous men of his time and exercised great influence on the development of botany in Spain. He studied medicine, Greek and botany in Paris, and later practised in Alcalá de Henares, which at that time was one of the cultural centres of the world. In 1539 he was summoned to Toledo by Charles V to attend to the Empress at her confinement, but in spite of all his efforts, she died shortly thereafter.

As a mark of esteem, and to show that he did not hold Laguna responsible for the misfortune, the Emperor included him in his retinue on his voyage to Ghent. Laguna lived for many years in the north of France, practising as a physician until, in 1549, he went to Rome; there, Pope Julius III

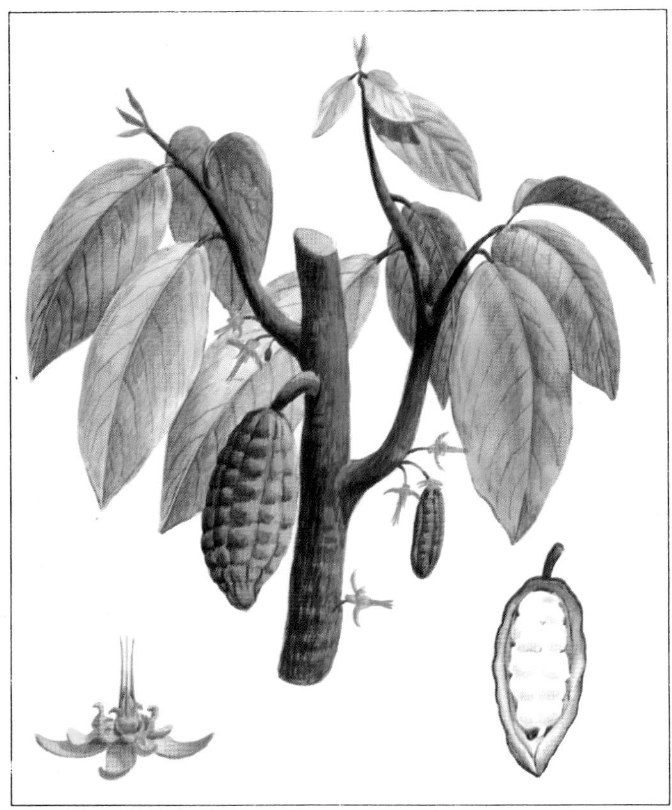

CACAO PLANT (*THEOBROMA CACAO*).

VEGETABLE GARDEN IN PADUA. Italy. *Photo Author.*

appointed him his personal physician. In this Renaissance court Laguna must have witnessed the construction of the famous villa of Pope Julius near the Via Flaminia in 1550, "attributed to the great architects of the time: Michaelangelo, Vasari, Ammanati and Vignola, who also created the wonderful gardens that stretched down to the banks of the Tiber,"[5] reflecting the refinement of this Pontiff.

Pope Julius loved pomp and splendour and hosted sumptuous banquets at his new palace. Doctor Laguna probably remained in this somewhat pagan atmosphere of art and culture until the Pope's death in 1555. During his stay in Italy he was an assiduous visitor of gardens, and must certainly have been familiar with the Botanical Gardens of Pisa and Padua which were Europe's first. The Padua Gardens are still in existence today, virtually unaltered.

It was Laguna's influence and learning that led Philip II to found the Botanical Garden of Aranjuez, the first in Spain since the time of the Arabs, but no longer in existence today. It is thought to have been near the orchards of the Picotajo, on the right bank of the river Jarama, and to have contained medicinal plants.

In this way King Philip began to take an interest in botany and to collect rare species of plants.

About this time a doctor from Seville, Nicholás Monardes, wrote a book called *Medicinal History of Items brought from our West Indies.*[6] Based on information given by the navigators who sailed there, this book mentioned tobacco, sassafras and twenty-five medicinal species. This was the first book to bring news of the New World's flora and it was translated into many languages; the English version was entitled *Joyfull Newes out of the Newefounde Worlde.*[7]

In 1570, Philip II commissioned a study of the "natural, ancient, and political history of New Spain." For this task he selected the palace physician Francisco Hernández (1514-1587) and sent him off to America in the capacity of *protomedico* or "medical examiner". Hernández was there for seven years, from 1571 to 1577 on this first scientific expedition to the New World. He described his efforts and his long and difficult journeys in sixteen volumes, with numerous drawings and sketches, naming many plants in the Mexican language and revealing valuable information on medicinal traditions and botanical gardening that were a part of the Aztec culture.[8] This important, richly-bound work, with its colour illustrations of plants and animals, was placed in the library of the Escorial, but remained unpublished. In the September of 1577, Dr. Hernández returned to Spain having left behind a copy of his manuscripts and rough sketches in Mexico. He was exhausted by his labours and gave up the prospect of a similar undertaking in Peru. He died in 1587.[9]

Cabrera de Córdoba, Philip II's historian and chronicler, tells us of the four hundred samples sent from America by Dr. Hernández: "Philip II sent physicians and herbalists, among them the licenciate Hernán, a learned and curious man, with painters to make sketches and paintings of every kind of herb, vegetable and mountain tree... He took Vicente Forte and other foreign experts to distil the quintessences, as he called subtle and humid basic and primary substances."[10]

It appeared for a time that Hernández's admirable and patient writings would pass into oblivion, perhaps for reasons of personal intrigue or a shift in ministerial fortunes. But fortunately Philip II came to the rescue by ordering the *protomedico* of Naples, Dr. Nardo Antonio Reccho, a distiller in Aranjuez, to prepare a compendium of Hernández's findings. An unpublished letter form this period in Juan de Herrera's handwriting, addressed to the King's secretary, Mateo Váquez (see Appendix IV), clearly shows Philip II's intention to publish the work; there are also two samples of the engravings that it was to contain, one in black and white, the other in colour.[11] But in the end Reccho did not publish his summary either. "Fortunately Friar Francisco Ximénez saw the need to furnish a medical guide for the haciendas and towns of Mexico that had neither physician nor pharmacist, and in 1615, in Mexico City, he published the first edition of Hernández's work. He based it, however, upon the incomplete summary by Reccho."[12]

In 1671 a fire broke out in the Escorial. Many manuscripts perished, among them nearly all of Hernández's writings. Meanwhile, however, the official Spanish historian Juan Bautista Muñoz, had rescued a hitherto unknown copy of the original manuscript, but without the drawings, "from the cockroaches and termites" of the Jesuit Colegio Máximo in Madrid (today the Instituto de San Isidro). From this new source Casimiro Gómez Ortega, director of the Botanical Garden, by order of Charles III in 1784, finally published the three first volumes in 1790. Even this work was incomplete, for it omitted the sections on animals and minerals.

GATE TO THE ROYAL BOTANICAL GARDEN. Madrid. *Photo S. Saavedra.*

A magnificent edition has now been published by the National University of Mexico of all Hernández's remaining works (*Complete Works,* 3 volumes, 1959-1960). There are no illustrations, but the text contains the names of all the plants he found.

This first natural history expedition led by Hernández to the New World revealed a wealth of botanical lore — most of it from the Aztecs — that would otherwise have perished forever.

* * *

In the Archives of the Royal Palace in Madrid there is an unpublished letter dated 1598, concerning the Prioress's Orchard near the Royal Alcázar, where herbs were cultivated to supply the royal apothecary shops as planned by Honorato Pomar, Philip III's doctor.[13] This medicinal herb garden did not survive long. The letter (see Appendix V) states that "the Valencian herbalist-physician who had been summoned was looking for a suitable place to grow the medicinal herbs for which he was responsible, and he decided that the best place was the Prioress's Orchard, as it was the easiest for physicians and apothecaries to reach. This had already proved to be the case in the time of Diego de Burgos and Dr. Nardo Antonio Reccho, who did not like the Casa de Campo. As the Valencian was old and a stranger to those parts, he was afraid of losing his health or even his life, and he believed that physicians and apothecaries would visit the Prioress's Orchard more often and would encourage those with a leaning towards the profession. Madrid, 20 May 1598." In 1581 Cardinal de Granvela visited the alembics of Vicente Forte, a distiller from Naples in the employ of Nardo Antonio, and said he thought they would be most useful for the herb garden — probably meaning the one at Aranjuez.[14] It all smacked of alchemy for they were following the precepts of Ramon Lull who was believed, perhaps wrongly, to have tendencies in this direction.

The Sevilian physician Simón Tovar, who died in 1596, owned a garden of medicinal and other exotic plants in Seville. He corresponded with several famous foreign botanists to whom he sent plants, among them the tuberose *(polianthes tuberosa),* a previously unknown Mexican plant. Tovar was the first man in Europe to edit annual catalogues of the plants he cultivated.

Father Sigüenza, the Hieronymite monk who wrote the *History of the Foundation of the Escorial* in beautiful Castilian prose, gives us the following lovely description of the Friars' Garden at Escorial: "Observe here an infinite variety of plants, shrubs and herbs which bloom profusely and of which an infinite number of beautiful fresh bunches can be arranged both in summer and winter without fail (no doubt they adorned the altars), and with a minimum of trouble for those who cultivated them (if they were sown in the *boleo* manner the mixed seeds were simply tossed in the air). Many pinks and carnations survive the severest winters, not only the varieties sent from our Indies, but also the Spanish wild and cultivated varieties. This does not occur even at Aranjuez and other well-cared-for gardens."[15]

During Philip III's reign, interest in botanical gardens suffered a decline; and those founded by royal command in Madrid and Aranjuez and by Simón Tovar in Seville were abandoned.

Towards the end of the seventeenth century Jaime Salvador, the friend and companion of Tournefort, owned a remarkable garden in San Juan Despí, on the banks of the river Llobregat near Barcelona. A large collection of strange plants were grown there, of which a considerble number still survived in 1783 (according to Abbot Pourret who took seeds of some varieties unknown to him to the Botanical Garden in Paris).[16]

The first collection of plants in Madrid was established in Philip V's time in some small gardens in Migas Calientes on the road to the Pardo along the river Manzanares. This garden had been created by Riqueur, the Kings apothecary, who made another in San Ildefonso. These gardens contained all the medicinal herbs essential for the exercise of his profession.

In 1755, during the reign of Ferdinand VI, the first true botanical garden in Madrid was formed. Ferdinand ordered it to be established in the garden at Migas Calientes, which had been bequeathed to him by Riqueur, including the plants belonging to Quer (the first director of the Botanical Garden). The garden at Migas Calientes was truly designed for scientific purposes; Quer and Minuart began to teach botany there in 1757 according to Tournefort's principles. In 1764, Quer died and was succeeded by Barnades. He had been educated at Montpellier and was already familiar with Linnaeus's doctrine. He, in his turn, was followed by the famous Gómez Ortega in 1771, with Palau as his assistant.[17]

One of the plants that came to Spain for this garden was the "tree of the cochineal or red dye", the coccus cactus, "which came from Oaxaca (Mexico) by way of Veracruz to Europe and was reputed to be the most precious fruit produced in America."[18]

In 1778 the plants were taken to Madrid's new Botanical Garden, which under the protection of Charles III was to become one of the most famous gardens of Europe. It opened in 1781.

Don Antonio Ponz saw the work in operation and described the Prado fountains in detail around 1771. Ten years later courses were being held there by Gómez Ortega, Palau and, especially, by José Cabanilles. He became director in 1801. Iriarte placed an elegant inscription over the entrance gate to the Paseo del Prado, and Villanueva left the mark of his neoclassical taste.[19]

At almost the same time Joseph I of Portugal founded two botanical gardens, one in Coimbra which still exists and has an important botanical library and fine specimens of *Eucalyptus citriodora* (lemon-scented), with aromatic leaves; and the other a very interesting garden in Lisbon.

Aside from imparting scientific knowledge to their students, botanical gardens in Spain were formed mainly for the exotic plants brought from the overseas colonies. Extra gardens were established for this purpose in Cádiz, Puerto de Santa María, Valencia, Cartagena and, above all, the Garden of Orotava in Tenerife. These were intended for the acclimatisation of tropical specimens to be planted, perhaps with an excess of optimism, in the parks of Aranjuez, la Granja and the Buen Retiro. All of them slowly succumbed to the severe Spanish climate and poor soil, even those growing in hothouses. In the Prince's Garden, the so-called "American Islands", considered the pearls of Aranjuez on account of their many exotic trees and shrubs, were still surviving by 1844, but were gradually withering.[20] They eventually all died, unable to withstand the Castilian climate and altitude.

COCHINEAL TREE. Unpublished watercolour from the General Archives of the Indies. Seville.

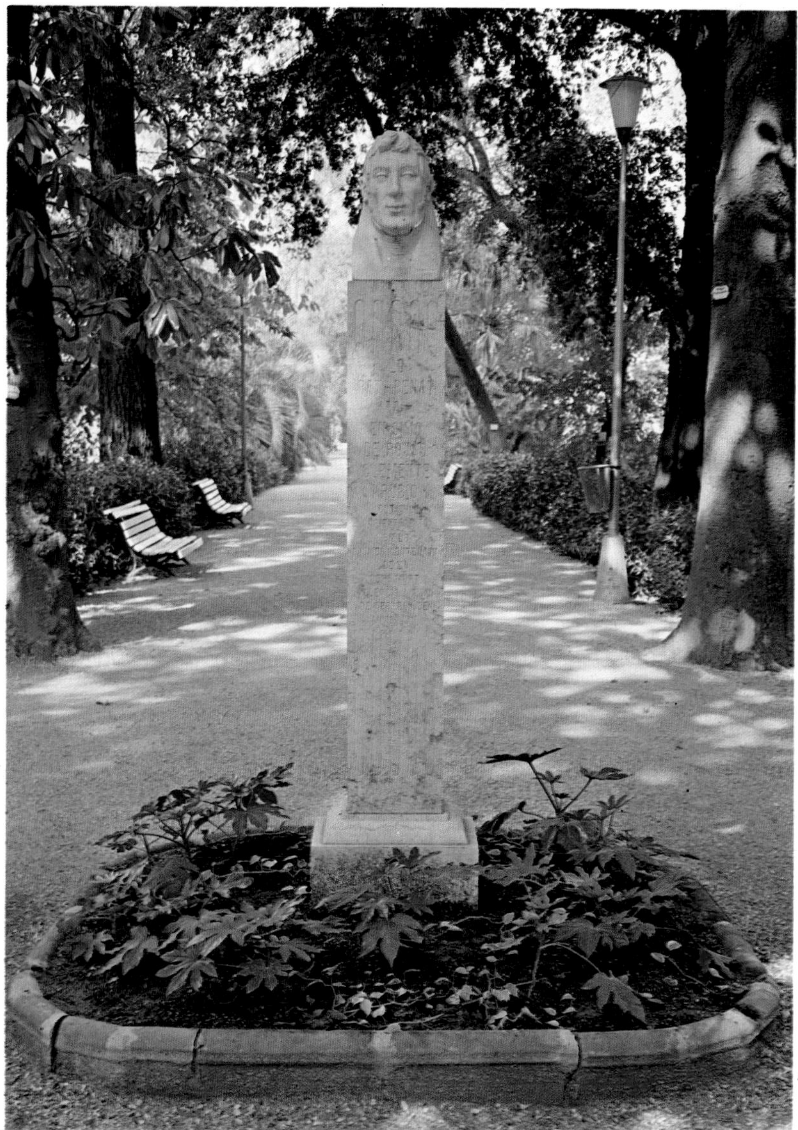
BOTANICAL GARDEN OF VALENCIA. BUST OF SIMONE DE ROJAS. 1827. *Photo M. Alonso.*

At Tenerife, on the other hand, plants from America and Asia flourished. In 1788 Charles III commanded the Marqués de Villanueva del Prado to establish plots of land for these exotic plants and seeds as the winter was too cold for them in the gardens of Madrid and Aranjuez. In this way the acclimatisation garden of Orotava was formed. Here tropical plants brought by explorers and scientists on their frequent expeditions to the New World still thrive,[21] providing one of the most interesting botanical gardens in Europe.

In the early years of the nineteenth century the "Principe de la Paz" (Prince of Peace), Manuel Godoy, created another botanical garden in Sanlúcar de Barrameda in the province of Cadiz, unfortunately destroyed in 1808 during the War of Independence.

Around 1632, the famous medical doctor Don Melchor Villena taught botany in Valencia and a botanical garden was established in the grounds of the hospital of San Lázaro. This garden was moved to the Plantío walk at the end of the last century, and finally all the plants and trees were carefully transferred to the ground it now occupies opposite the convent of San Sebastian. It extends for nearly ten acres and is laid out in squares with pretty paths. There are two sections: the botanical school and the acclimatisation garden. More than six thousand plants are cultivated, not counting the different varieties, many of them exotic and very rare. The climate of Valencia was such that it could be used, like so many others on the Mediterranean coast, to naturalize the plants that were brought from the Indies for Charles III. Botanical gardens, like cemeteries, are good places for peaceful meditation. Strolling through this perfectly kept garden, with its correctly classified labels and notices, one may admire fine specimens of the tropical tree *Sterculea platanifolia* or *Firmiana simplex* (the Chinese parasol of Linnaeus); a giant *Gleditschia triacanthos* from North America; the *Nolina recurvata* from Mexico; the *N. stricta,* a liliaceae from Southern Mexico and the *Cordelina indivisa atropurpurea,* a liliaceae from New Zealand, among many others. This is unquestionably the finest botanical garden in Spain today.

A botanical garden was formed in Santiago de Compostela in Galicia in 1845, on a plot of ground adjoining the University of Fonseca. It was half an acre in size, including its winter conservatory. A garden had been established there at the beginning of the nineteenth century on land belonging to the famous French Abbé Pourret. The explorers Ruiz and Pavón dedicated to him the genus *Pourretia,* Wil.

In 1858, more than a thousand species of plants were represented here, particularly those belonging to the Galician flora. Today this garden no longer exists, but a botanical garden is planned for the cultivation of medicinal plants in the Faculty of Pharmacy of Santiago, near the University Hall of Residence.

BOTANICAL EXPEDITIONS TO THE NEW WORLD DURING THE EIGHTEENTH CENTURY

The eighteenth century was a period of great botanical expeditions to the New World. None had been financed by the Crown since Dr. Hernández's expedition to New Spain (Mexico) during the reign of Philip II.

At the beginning of Philip V's reign, two Naval officers, Jorge Juan (1713-1773) and Antonio Ulloa (1716-1795), accompanied the illustrious scientists La Condamine, Pierre Bouguer and Louis Godin, the first explorers of French extraction to penetrate into equatorial America with the authority of the King of Spain.

Though not a botanist by profession Condamine gave Europe its first information about the tree *Hevea brasiliensis* of the *Euphorbia* family, whose sap is used to produce rubber. On a hazardous trip down the Amazon he discovered barbasco which contains the alkaloid rotetone, now used as an ingredient in insecticides. Finally he produced the first botanical data on the source of the drug later to be known as quinine.[22]

La Condamine described rubber, quinine, the famous poison curare, the *guayacan* (lignum vitae tree), and *ipecacuanha* (a medicinal root obtained from the *cephaelis epecacuanha*), more to express his wonder than to provide a truly scientific description. At that time it was believed that quinine only grew south of the equator.[23]

Ferdinand VI was the first Spanish monarch to take an interest in forming a botanical garden. His Minister, José Caravajal, asked Linnaeus (1707-1778) to send an expert to study the Spanish flora. Linnaeus sent his chosen pupil, Peter Löfling (1729-1756), who, to his surprise, found in Madrid a group of botanists already at work, among them Quer, Minuart, José Ortega, Vélez and Miguel Barnades. Löfling spent two years collecting plants, especially in the region of Madrid, and discovered 1,400 varieties.

But the Spanish Government had another mission in store for Löfling. An expedition had been organised to the Orinoco with the aim of preventing Dutch invasions, and scientists and botanists were sent together under the direction of José Iturriaga to gather useful information. They arrived in Venezuela in April 1754, but the tropical climate and constant fevers undermined Löfling's constitution. "In the end he brought back about six hundred plants, including thirty new genera and two hundred and fifty species not mentioned before by Linnaeus; but Löfling died a few months later in America. His collaborators were dispersed, and the illustrators brought back the drawings to Spain."[24]

It was during the reign of Charles III that the arts and sciences reached their peak. The King was extremely interested in building and town planning. During his reign great improvements were made in public buildings. Nearly all the great buildings of Madrid date from this period: the Royal Palace, the monumental arches in the Plaza de la Independencia and Puerta de Hierro, the Academy of Fine Arts of San Fernando, and the Natural History Museum (today the Prado Art Gallery), which was built by Villanueva to accommodate the large collections that were constantly arriving from the New World and to complement the Botanical Garden situated nearby. The architects Sabatini, Ventura Rodríguez and Villanueva worked indefatigably. Charles III was also fond of botany which he had studied from his childhood. The flora of our Peninsula was classified by Linnaeus and many of the genera still bear the names he gave them of botanists and prominent eighteenth century Spanish figures. The King fostered and encouraged this interest. Towards the middle of the eighteenth century began the great expeditions that were to explore South America and introduce large numbers of new plants. Because of the variety of climatic conditions in Spain's vast overseas territories, these plants would form the most valuable collection in the world. "The quinine tree, a great treasure of the King's American dominions, is the best remedy against tertian fevers. Charles III sent quantities of this product to the prelates of his dioceses to be distributed to the parish priests, and through them to the sick who were most in need."[25] "No other European country spent more in order to spread the knowledge of plants."[26]

The three great expeditions financed by Charles III and Charles IV to enlarge the plant collections in the Madrid Botanical Garden and in the royal gardens, and promote their study and classification are worth examining in some detail. One expedition was sent to the Kingdoms of Peru and Chile, the second to the New Kingdom of Granada (Colombia), and the third explored the Kingdom of New Spain (Mexico).

The first expedition took place because the French, and in particular Louis XVI's Minister Turgot, wished to send a scientific expedition to Peru to try to recover the manuscripts of Joseph de Jussieu who had explored that country in 1739, finding quinine and coca, but whose writings had been lost. The French proposed to send the French botanist Dombey, in the hope of procuring economic profit for France, just as Charles III had benefited enormously from quinine.

Turgot's proposal made a favourable impression in Spain — the King of Spain was, after all, Louis XVI's uncle — but the Minister for the Indies, José Gálvez, was not sympathetic

JARDIN ACLIMATACION. BUST OF MARQUÉS DE VILLANUEVA DEL PRADO. Orotava.

MAP OF THE BOTANICAL EXPEDITION OF H. RUIZ AND J. PAVON IN THE ANDES.
From "Flowers for the King" by A.R. Steele.

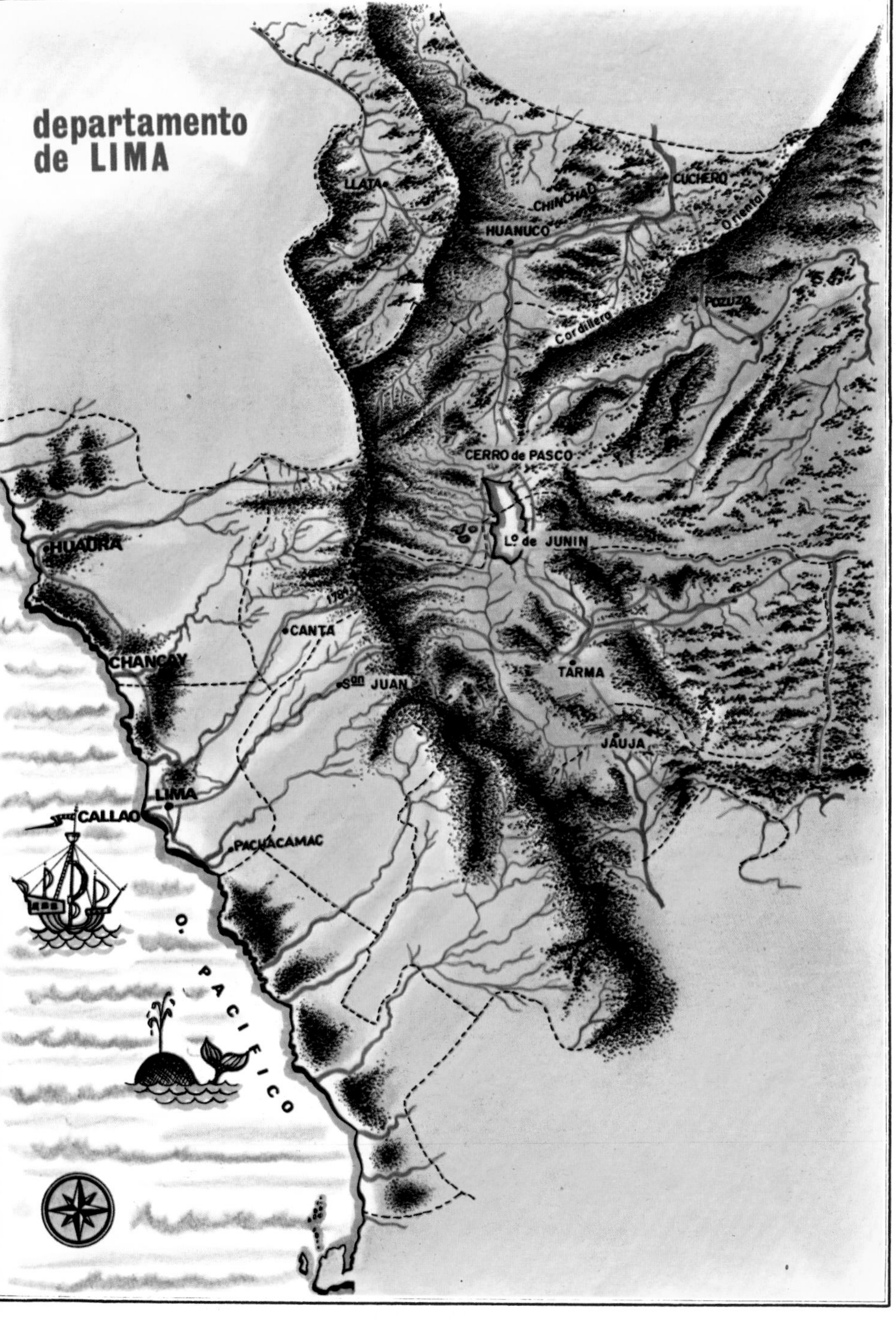

towards the French and insisted that "two Spanish professors" must accompany Dombey during the voyage. He so advised the French Government in 1776.[27]

The celebrated director of the Botanical Garden at that time, Casimiro Gómez Ortega (1740-1818), was responsible for finding suitable young men to go; he selected Hipólito Ruiz López (1754-1816) and José Antonio Pavón (1754-1838), both aged twenty-two when they were appointed to take part in the expedition. Although not very well versed in botany, they possessed practical knowledge of pharmacy.[28] Ortega decided it was essential that two painters should be included in the expedition in order to reproduce the flora and to copy it accurately without imaginative touches.[29] José Brunete and Isidro Galvez were chosen. The Frenchman Dombey, a Doctor of Medicine from Montpellier and friend of Antoine Jussieu, from the Botanical Gardens in Paris (Le Jardin des Plantes), was the oldest and most experienced member of the expedition. But in spite of Dombey's obvious superiority, both in years and in knowledge, and his poor opinon of Spanish botanists, Hipólito Ruiz was appointed leader of the expedition and chief botanist. These men were to spend four years together in Peru. The unfortunate Dombey set off in a position of inferiority to the Spaniards. His government paid him a salary which was less than half of the Spaniards, and he was required to "leave in Spain a duplicate of all his finds," as Steele relates.

After a voyage of five months aboard the *Peruano,* they at last reached Lima on 8 June 1778. They spent the first year conducting botanical research in the surrounding country, much to the consternation of the natives, who called them "herb-brewing sorcerers".[30]

One of the tasks entrusted to Dombey was the search for Jussieu's lost manuscripts, but he does not appear to have succeeded. The study of American cinnamon was another of his commissions. For over two centuries Spain had clung to the hope that the trees found in 1540 by Gonzalo Pizarro in Quito would relieve them of dependence on Ceylon for this valuable spice. Pedro de Maldonado, the enlightened Governor of Esmeraldas in the province of Quito, had sent samples for examination to Gómez Ortega in Madrid, but after examining the tree in South America, Dombey pronounced it to be completely different: Linnaeus's *Laurus indica* and not the Dutch *Cinnamomum Zeylanicum.*[31]

In the spring of 1779 the Spanish botanists set out on their journey to the Andes. Penetrating into virgin forests and risking their lives over dangerous mountain passes, they finally reached the town of Tarma, some 120 miles from Lima. They followed the ancient Inca pathways and all along the way collected plants which were completely new to them.[32] Among the many that they described were the scarlet trumpet flower *(Datura sanguinea)* — "the natives told them that some people had lost their reason simply by lying down to sleep beneath the shade of these trees. They are striking for their abundance of great red flowers that hang like bells."[33] Other discoveries included the marvellous *Tillandsias* many of which live without soil suspended in the air absorbing moisture from the atmosphere, and countless other plants that we see today in European conservatories and gardens.

Our botanists settled in Tarma, a town with a garrison of soldiers to protect it against the hostile Chunco Indians.

They also discovered the *Arbutus multiflora* which the Indians called *machamacha* ("drunk-drunk"), because its fruit produces this effect if taken in excess. The European strawberry tree *(Arbutus unedo)* possesses the same properties.[34]

The botanists remained in the province of Tarma for eleven months, making frequent excursions and expeditions. Among the deep ravines and mountain ranges they discovered a great number of trees, shrubs and herb specimens, which they sketched and dried. Nearly all were well known to the Indians as remedies for their ailments. "Among the vegetation that abounded most was the orchid family. Their rhizomes lying on the surface of the ground formed a kind of pavement over the dryest, stoniest soil, and the varied shades of their rare and precious flowers coloured that strange natural pavement."[35]

After many vicissitudes the botanists returned to Lima in January 1780, where they remained until April. During this time they obtained permission to spend another year in the Huánuco mountians, to the north of Lima, in order to explore the flora. Again they set off following the old Inca route from Cuzco to Quito and after many perilous adventures in the Andes, they arrived at last on the plain. Ruiz tells us: "There are five leagues of flat road from Ambo to Huánoco, through pleasant and interesting country with many farmhouses, orchards and plantations all along the way. A particularly sweet fragrance is noticeable along this road, given off constantly by the scented custard apples, guavas and other fruit-trees native to the country and the lime, lemon, grapefruit, citron and orange trees, that grow plentifully in these rich lands."[36] When they arrived at Huánaco and began to explore, they were spellbound by the flora. Among a thousand other plants they found the heliotrope, which Jussieu had seen on his expedition, innumerable scented flowers and creepers, and the spectacular jacaranda tree which Jussieu had also discovered. In July they left Huánaco, accompanied by their painters, for the mountains in the province of the Pantahuas. Between the villages of Acomayo and Chinchao, Ruez found purple quinine *(Cinchona purpurea),* which he was the first to examine.[37]

Ruiz recounts that: "in the year 1776 near the village of Cuchero, in the Province of the Pantahuas, Don Francisco Renquifo observed trees of fine Peruvian quinine, which he had seen and known previously in the Loja mountains, today a province of Equador."[38] La Condamine studied the origin of quinine on his way to Lima in 1737 and was the first to furnish data on this drug, to be known a century later as quinine.

Quinine had been known in Europe since 1652 but its origin was still undiscovered at this time, for the trees grew in Loja, the remote region of the Audiencia of Quito on the Peruvian border.[39]

Tradition has it that in 1638 the wife of the Viceroy of Peru, the Count of Chinchón, (the "Saintly Vicereine" of José María Pemán's play), was suffering form tertiary fevers and was cured, thanks to the powdered bark of the quinine tree discovered by the Indians and sent from Loja to the Viceroy in Lima.

CHINCHONA PURPUREA. *Drawing by I. Gálvez. Photo Oronoz.*

"The Countess of Chinchón was the first known user of this most useful medicinal remedy in Europe."[40]

The Jesuits, who were established in Peru years later, introduced it in Rome under the name the "Countess's powders" or "Jesuit powders."[41] The term "quinine" was not used until 1820, when this product was isolated as one of the two alkaloids that exist in the bark of the cinchona tree and found to be the best treatment for malaria. Linnaeus named it *Cinchona officialis* in honour of the Countess. In 1944 two American chemists developed synthetic quinine and today other products exist as a cure for malaria, among them atebrine.[42] The importance of quinine has consequently declined.

Ruiz and Pavón returned in July 1780 to the quinine country in the region of Huánuco, camping in the tiny mountain village of Cuchero. Here Ruiz discovered the *Cinchona nitida,* or true Peruvian quinine: "This species is one of the best and most effective", and the *Cinchona magnifolia,* or "orange flower", which, according to Dr. Mutis' classification, is the red quinine of Santa Fe; "this was the tallest and leafiest of all the varieties of quinine trees."[43]

The admirable account of the expedition written by Ruiz, which is so methodical and engaging, gives the impression that the French botanist Dombey got on better with Pavón than with Ruiz. One incident suggests that Dombey and Pavón may have lacked Ruiz's courage. While they were in Cuchero there was a false alert that they were encircled by more than three thousand Chuncho Indians. Dombey and Pavón fled in the middle of the night, but Ruiz remained in the village to face the assault bravely.[44]

In the Andes region of Chinchoa on their way back they observed the Indian practice of chewing coca leaves, much like modern chewing-gum; they soon appreciated its medicinal and bracing properties, which were indispensable at those altitudes. "Jussieu, during his expedition into the forested *yungas* of present-day Bolivia, had been the first botanist to study the coca plant in its native habitat."[45] "Coca leaves are laurel-like in form and come from the *Erythroxylon coca,* a shrub native in its wild state to the Peruvian jungle."[46]

Another curiosity observed during their travels was the glow-worm. Ruiz tells us: "We spent the night at Chavanilles (on the road to Huánuco) and nearby we found great numbers of glow-worms with such a bright clear light that two of them in a paper cone allowed me to read at night for a fortnight; no other artificial light was necessary."[47]

After returning to Lima the botanists set out along the Peruvian coast as far as Chancay, stopping at night in the *haciendas* of large landholders, who cultivated sugar-cane. At one of them they saw Linnaeus's *Parkingsonia aculeata* (a tree with handsome foliage, which has now been acclimatised in Barcelona and in the Balearic and Canary Islands). They also saw the *Xuarezia biflora* (Peruvian tea) while exploring in the Chancay province.[48]

Having heard of the wealth of flora in Chile, they asked the King's permission to visit that country. They were probably relieved to leave Peru for at that time the country was in a state of turmoil caused by the revolt of the Túpac Amaro brothers, pretenders to the crown of their Inca ancestors. This insurrection was cruelly and violently repressed.

In December 1781 the five members of the expedition left Lima to embark at the port of Callao for Chile, where they arrived in January 1782 at the port of Talcahuano, near Concepción. Here they were welcomed by Ambrose O'Higgins, Field Marshal in that city.

Their botanical expeditions through "those fertile lands"[49] began in February. Crossing the Bío-Bío river they explored the region of Fuerte Arauco, where they found, among many other plants, the *Alstromeria Ligtu,* from whose roots the Indians made a pure white starch which was palatable and nutritious for children and invalids.

These plants are cultivated today in Europe, especially in England, where they adorn many gardens. A description of the Concepción country's many trees and plants unknown to them would be lengthy. Ruiz alludes to it as "a charming and delightful country in all respects — 'an earthly paradise' ".[50]

Ruiz was the most enthusiastic botanist on the expedition, exploring fields and mountains alone and finding most of the

ERYTHROXYLON COCA.

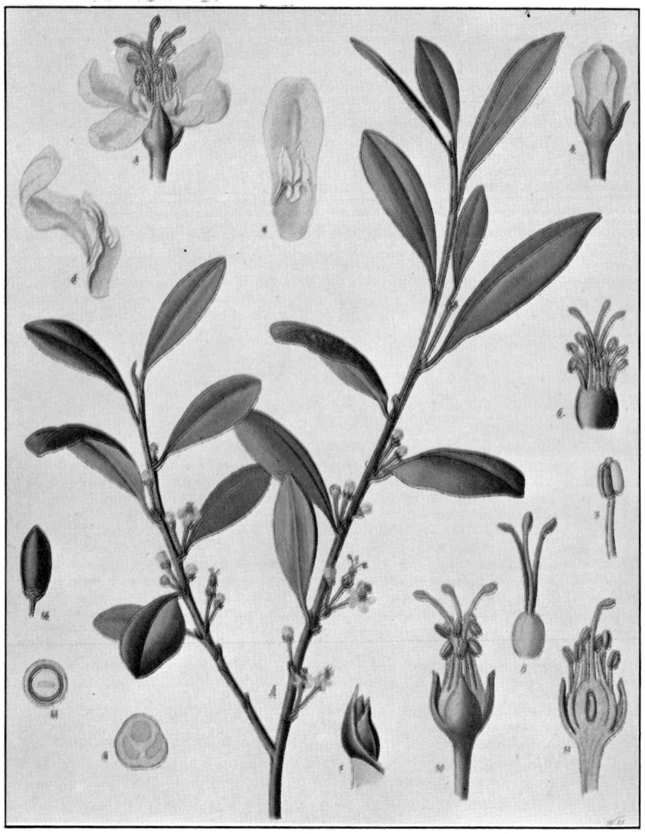

ALSTROMERIA O BOMAREA PULCHERRIMA.
Signed Mutis. Botanical Garden. Madrid. *Photo Oronoz.*

new plants. Dombey and Pavón explored together.

In Unabra, near the port of Talcahuano, the explorers made the most important discovery of the whole trip: the Chilean pine, or *Araucaria Araucana.* Don Antonio Vácaro and Ambrose O'Higgins had found these pines in the Andes range in 1781, when searching for wood to repair the vessel *San Pedro de Alcántara,* whose masts had been destroyed by lightning. "As these pine forests were on the mountain ridges of the Andes and Nahuelbuta, the timber was floated down the Bío-Bío river, as was done for the ruined Cathedral of Concepción. The pines grew in the land of the Pehuenche Indians, spreading as far as Valdivia, the most westerly part of Chile."[51]

Our botanists remained for more than a year in the town of Concepción and there, twenty leagues from Santa Juana, they found about seventy Chilean pines at the foot of the mountains. On account of its peculiar structure, this tree could not be classified with the known conifers and kept the name Araucana given by Jussieu in honour of the Araucan Indians. He apparently believed that these trees grew in Arauco, which lies on the coast, and not in the mountains forty or fifty leagues inland. According to native information these pine forests spread for two hundred leagues; that is, from thirty-six degrees to the Straits of Magellan.[52] Large pink and white flowers, called *copihues — Lapageria rosea,* of five varieties grew on these Araucarias and on other trees in southern Chile. These were parasitic creepers in their wild state living on the trees in the jungle and covering them with their bright flowers. They are the national flower of Chile.*

In homage to the Chilean trees, and to perpetuate their names and that of their former teacher Gómez Ortega, the botanists chose three varieties:

Gomortega nitida: "This is the tallest, leafiest and most attractive tree, after the Chilean pine, growing in this realm, and it can be distinguished from other trees at a considerable distance by the green and handsome lustre of its foliage."

Ruizia fragans, or boldo, known today as *Peumus fragans* (Ruiz and Pavón), a small visually striking tree with aromatic wood.

Pavonia sempervirens (Chilean laurel), known today as *Laurus sempervirens* of Ruiz and Pavón. "This is a tall, leafy, striking evergreen; its wood is soft and white with undulating veins in the centre, and a fragrance like sassafras wood."[53]

In Mexico in 1796 the name of *Tigridia Pavonia* was given to a very showy bulb with three-petalled flowers in all colours. There is also a shrub originating from Bourbon Island, called *Ruizia.*

At the end of March 1783 the explorers left Concepción to travel north by land. After stopping in Talca they arrived in Santiago de Chile on 15 April. Along the way Ruiz collected a number of plants of little importance, as he did on the road from Santiago to Valparaíso at the beginning of October.

At the end of their four year mission in the New World, the botanists received orders from the Superintendent of Peru to return to Lima and begin the journey home to Spain.

ARAUCARIA ARAUCANA O IMBRICATA.
"Flore des Serres".
British Museum. London

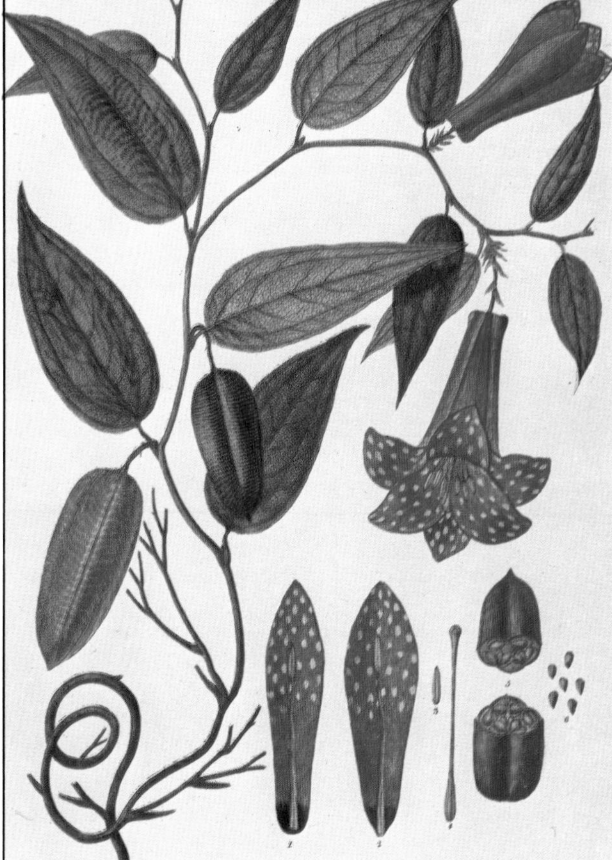

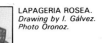

LAPAGERIA ROSEA.
Drawing by I. Gálvez.
Photo Oronoz.

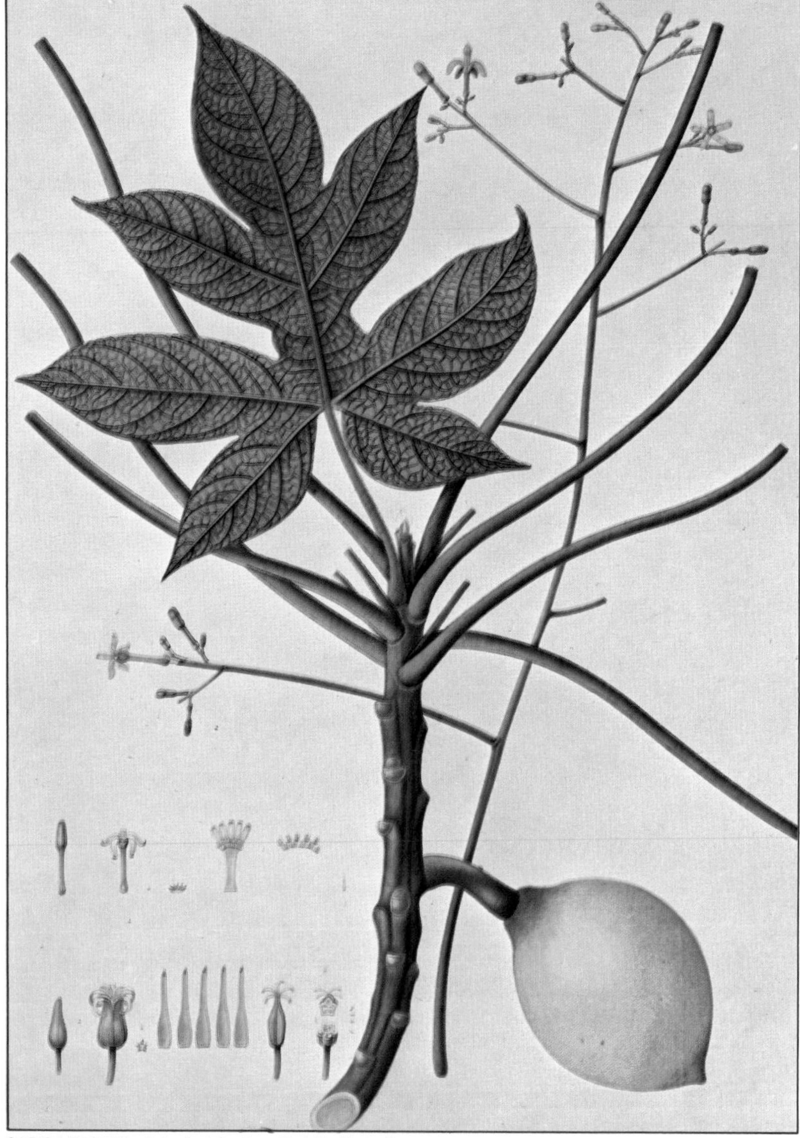

CARICA PAPAYA. Botanical Garden. Madrid. *Photo Oronoz.*

On 14 October 1783, the five companions boarded the vessel *Our Lady of Mercy* bound for Callao, with their chests of plants and their manuscripts. They arrived on 3 November.

"Dombey was nearing the end of his usefulness to the expedition. He complained of deafness and dimming eyesight; scurvy had sapped his strength; his gums were bleeding and he could eat very little. Dombey understandably turned his thoughts toward home; he would never again practice botany on Spanish soil."[54]

Taking with him his collections of stones, plants, shells and fossils, Dombey reached Cádiz in February 1785, went on to France and disappeared without trace.

Meanwhile Ruiz and Pavón, who were also preparing to return to Spain, received a new command from the King to "continue their commission in Peru through the mountains of Tarma, Huánuco and Cuchero. They were thus obliged to replace the utensils they had sold for a song a few days previously."[55] They had already shipped fifty chests filled with their collections and 1,013 drawings of plants on the ill-fated vessel *San Pedro de Alcántara* which sank with all their material off the coast of Portugal.

Having collected the most essential equipment for the journey to Huánuco, Ruiz and Pavón left Lima once more in May 1784, setting off through land which must have been dry and barren — for they describe a number of succulent plants and cacti — before ascending into the snow covered peaks of the Andes.

After crossing the hills of Pasco and enduring many hardships they once again reached Huánuco, a town they knew well, and from there headed towards the mountains of Pozuzo, "having heard of the fertility of this area which borders on that of the Carapacho Indians. From Portachuelo, a half-circle of the ridges of the Andes can be seen, covered in perpetual snow, and vast traces of tree-clad hills and mountains in similar formation extending as far as the Pampa del Sacramento, the whole presenting a most delightful and admirable view."[56]

The remote village of Pozuzo, the region's last Spanish outpost, consisted of one missionary and fourteen other persons. Tramping for days through the magnificent jungle that surrounded it "torn by brambles and branches, thirsty and exhausted in the smothering heat, they encountered a wealth of beautiful and unknown flora.

"One morning they noticed a multitude of small flowering trees that clothed the foot of the Pozuzo hills on the opposite side of the river, facing the village. The hills were so laden with flowers that they looked as though covered with snow. The explorers crossed over to examine them and found them to be *Bignonia alba,* entirely devoid of leaves and covered with large white flowers; two days later, they had already become soft fruit, and only one or two flowers remained. This small tree is one of the few in these mountains to shed its leaves."[58]

It would be impossible to describe all of their discoveries in these brief pages. Among the many plants they saw were the tallow tree *(Myristica longifolia),* used by the Indians to make torches; the papaya *(Carica septembolata)* with melon-like fruit and the *Aristolochia fragans*. Ruiz says that in Pozuzo he did not see "the flower of this unreliable plant until some fresh roots were taken to the garden of les Padres Agonizantes in Lima, where they bloomed profusely."[59]

In September they returned to Huánuco where they stayed for some time to dry their plants and to make drawings of them. This journey into the Peruvian jungle seems to have been the most successful of all. In May 1785 they left Huánuco again for the last important expedition they were to make, to the mountains of Chinchao and Cuchero, also in the Andes. They found a great number of trees and plants on this journey but also suffered a terrible setback. They had settled in at the *hacienda* of Macora when a fire broke out and in a short time destroyed all their plants and writings, the entire product of their great toil and trouble. Greatly discouraged, Ruiz wrote in March 1786: "Suffering as I am from repeated illnesses, I find that the cares of the expedition entrusted to me are too arduous and an ever-increasing burden, and as I have not the strength to go on I ask leave of the Minister for the Indies to return to Spain."[60] This permission was granted.

The botanists remained for some time in Huánuco, making their last few excursions into the mountains of Muña in August 1786. There they found the *Cinchona augustifolia* and the *Embothrium monospermum,* a shrub that is cultivated today in the temperate zones of Europe.

Returning once more to Pillao and its mountains, to the north-east of Huánuco, they looked upon the mountains of Peru for the last time. They embarked for Spain in March 1788 and arrived in Cádiz on 9 September, ending their American adventure.

The first work produced by this expedition was the *Quinologia* or *Study of the Cinchona,* published in Madrid in 1792, in which Ruiz classified the cinchona into seven varieties.[61] In 1794 his *Flora Peruviana y Chilensis Prodromus (Preliminary Flora of Peru and Chile)* was published under the names of Ruiz and Pavón. This last work ran into several editions; three volumes were finished, and the fourth remained in manuscript with one hundred engravings. The fifth and subsequent volumes, with their many engravings, were never published. They are in safe keeping at the Botanical Garden in Madrid, with manuscripts and drawings.[62]

Ruiz was the most active and intelligent member of the expedition to Peru and Chile. His keen mind and competent leadership led to the discovery of hundreds of new plants.[63] He was methodical in his writings, orderly and industrious. His *Relación,* the diary of that adventurous journey, is delightfully entertaining and often poetic. Pavón added virtually nothing of importance to the work of Ruiz.

The expedition of Ruiz and Pavón was unquestionably the most enterprising and extensive of its time and perhaps that which brought the greatest variety of plants to Europe from Peru and Chile.

* * *

The work of Celestino Mutis, another great Spanish botanical explorer in the New World, was more scientific because he combined the skills of physician, astronomer and botanist. On the other hand, his sphere of action may have been more restricted. He had already lived in Bogota for many years when his expedition through Colombia began, almost at the same time as that of Ruiz and Pavón in Peru and Chile.

Celestino Mutis (1732-1808), a native of Cádiz, was not only an important naturalist, but a resourceful doctor and distinguished mathematician and astronomer. In 1760, eager to study the flora and fauna of America, he sailed there as personal physician to Don Pedro Messía de la Cerda, Marqués de la Vega de Armijo, who had been appointed Viceroy of New Granada (Colombia). During his time in Colombia, Mutis was ordained priest. His passion for plants increased when he saw the rich vegetation of Equador, described enthusiastically in his letters to Linnaeus, with whom he corresponded frequently. In 1764 he sent samples of the quinine trees to Linnaeus, who used them to perform the first revision of La Condamine's incomplete findings. Eight years later Mutis discovered another species of cinchona tree near Bogota.

In an unpublished letter to the Marqués del Villar, the Viceroy Don Pedro Messia de la Cerda wrote: "The quina tree is found in many parts of the great mountain range, running

PORTRAIT OF CELESTINO MUTIS. Botanical Garden. Madrid. *Photo Oronoz.*

1
2
3
4
5
6
7

8

SELECTED PLANTS FROM THE RUIZ AND PAVÓN EXPEDITION. PERUVIAN AND CHILEAN FLORA. Botanical Garden. Madrid. *Photos Oronoz.*

1 FUCHSIA SIMPLICICAULIS. *Illustration by I. Gálvez.*
2 COFFEA SUBSESSILIS. *Illustration by I. Gálvez.*
3 SOLANUM GRANDIFLORUM. *Illustration by I. Gálvez and F. Pulgar.*
4 NARCISUS ASMANCAES. *Illustration by I. Gálvez and J. Brunete.*
5 PLUMERIA BICOLOR. *Illustration by I. Gálvez.*
6 TILLANDSIA JUNCEA. *Illustration by I. Gálvez.*
7 DATURA ARBOREA. *Illustration by I. Gálvez.*
8 GARDENIA LONGIFLORA. *Illustration by I. Gálvez and J. Brunete.*
9 CERBERA THEOCHA. *Illustration by F. Pulgar and J. Brunete.*
10 EMBOTHRIUM EMARGINATUM. *Illustration by I. Gálvez.*
11 RHEXI ROSMARINIFOLIA. *Illustration by I. Gálvez.*
12 XUAREZIA ENFLORA. *Illustration by I. Gálvez.*
13 TILLANDSIA RECURVATA. *Illustration by I. Gálvez.*

9

10

11

12

13

the length of South America from south to north, not only in the mountains of Cafanuma, but also in such places as Ayabaca and Guanacamba near Loja, and along the tracks from Quito to Santa Fe, where according to La Condamine, the soil is similar."[64]

The discovery in 1772 of a cinchona tree of a different variety in the mountains of Tena, near Bogota, opened up trade and communications with Spain by way of Cartagena de Indias and the Caribbean instead of the long voyage down the Pacific coast and around Cape Horn. But Mutis's repeated requests for a botanical expedition in New Granada remained unheeded by the Spanish Government. Eventually Charles III approved the undertaking with the encouragement and support of the Archbishop-Viceroy Don Antonio Caballero y Góngora, who was the inspiration behind the expedition. Mutis was appointed chief botanist and astronomer, and departed for Mariquita where he could examine the quinine trees growing in that area. In a letter he wrote from Mariquita on 18 May 1778, he observed that the Santa Fe quinine was greatly inferior to that of Peru, and that red quinine was preferable.[65]

There was much controversy about the relative quality of the quinines of New Granada and those of Peru, which Ruiz and Pavón had discovered.

Celestino Mutis wrote a letter to the Bailío (Knight Commander of the Order of Malta) and minister for the Indies, Fr. Don Antonio Valdés, telling him that "he found the selected red and yellow quinine from Loja somewhat better than that of Santa Fe, although there was relatively little difference between them."[66]

The expedition began work in the Mesa de Juan Díaz and then went on to Mariquita, ending some years later in Santa Fe.

Celestino Mutis had travelled around the country for over twenty years and knew it thoroughly, so he stayed in Mariquita where he devoted himself to the classification of the several local species of quinine, and his draughtsmen made their marvellous coloured plates. Very few people are familiar with the data that Mutis was preparing for *The Flora of Santa Fe de Bogota or New Granada,* which remained unpublished at his death in 1808, although they have been kept at the Madrid Botanical Garden since 1817. They consist of many loose manuscripts, diaries, descriptions, notes and unclassified observations, a considerable herbarium with other accessory collections, and 6,849 plant drawings. One of them, the *Cinchona lanceifolia* (Santa Fe Orange quinine), was engraved in La Gasca's time. "These drawings represent the flora of New Granada and are mostly in colour, though some are in black and white. They are the work of many different hands for, according to his pupil Zea, Mutis ended up with eighteen draughtsmen. The degree of perfection therefore varies. All the artists seem to have been Latin American. Antonio Garcia was the first to be appointed by the Government as official draughtsman of the expedition, but the most outstanding was Salvador Rizo who worked from 1784 and was head draughtsman, in charge of the others."[67] "In Mesa they gathered a huge collection of plants and the work took place at night by candlelight. Some of the plates were begun at five in the afternoon and not finished until nine the following morning. Work continued all through the night lest the flowers should wither."[68]

They made two copies of each plate, one in black ink and the other in colour. The remarkable thing is that the colours were extracted from natural American substances discovered by Mutis.[69] Today five volumes of these plates have been published jointly by the Institute of Hispanic Culture in Madrid and the Colombian Institute of Spanish Culture in Bogota.

Quinine was one of the main export trades of Colombia — of greater importance than coffee. It declined, however, when the Dutch and the English took advantage of Spain's failure to carry on the work of Mutis and the Viceroy Caballero, and established quinine plantations with our seeds in Java, India and Indo-China.[70]

Mutis also made important discoveries of plants other than quinine. He wrote to Don José Gálvez from Santa Fe, relating the discovery of tea in Bogota[71], found to be of good quality by the Professor of the Madrid Botanical Garden, Don Casimiro Gómez Ortega. Samples of coffee, cinnamon and tea grown in Santa Fe, Muxo and Gixon were sent out from Santa Fe.

Coffee had been brought to America by the Dutch, who took it to Surinam after planting it on the island of Java.[72] "They also brought cinnamon trees *(Cinnamomum zeylandica)* from Canton, nutmeg trees, shrubs bearing the tea *cha,* fruit of Paradise from Iolo, and three small Chinese varnish trees *Rhus*

ANTONIO VALDES. COMMANDER OF MALTA. MINISTER OF THE INDIES. *Photo Oronoz.*

CINCHONA LANCEIFOLIA. *Photo Oronoz.*

1

2

SELECTED UNPUBLISHED PLATES BY MUTIS.
Botanical Garden. Madrid. *Photos Oronoz.*

1 BAUHINIA (AMARIA) PETIOLATA. Signed Martinez.
2 DRIMYS GRANADENSIS. Signed Barrionuevo.
3 MELIA AZEDARACH. Signed Cortés.
4 AETANTHUS MUTISII (H.B.K.). Engler.
5 LLERASIA LINDENII TRIANA.
6 BIGNONIACEAE.
7 ARACEAE.
8 SWARTZIA RAMIFLORA. Signed F. Villarroel.
9 TRADESCANTIA. Signed Mutis.
10 BROWNEA SP. Signed Mutis.
11 HELIOCONIA SP.
12 INGA SP.
13 BOMAREA. Signed Mutis.
14 GYNANDROPSIS SPECIOSA (H.B.K.). Signed Mutis.
15 TILLANDSIA PASTENSIS, ANDRE.

3

4

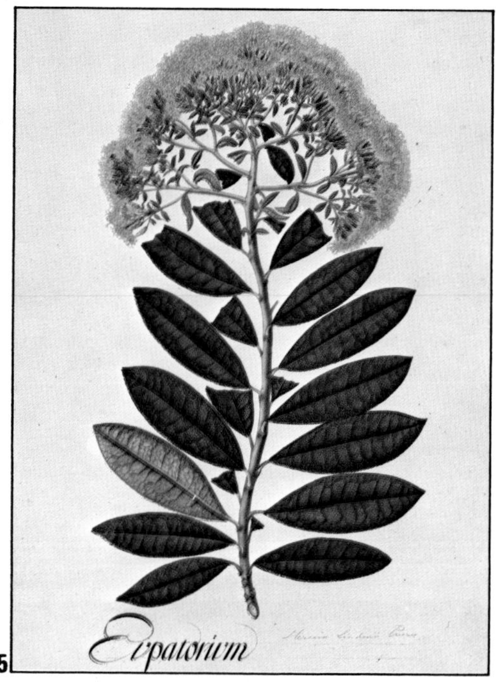

5

6

7

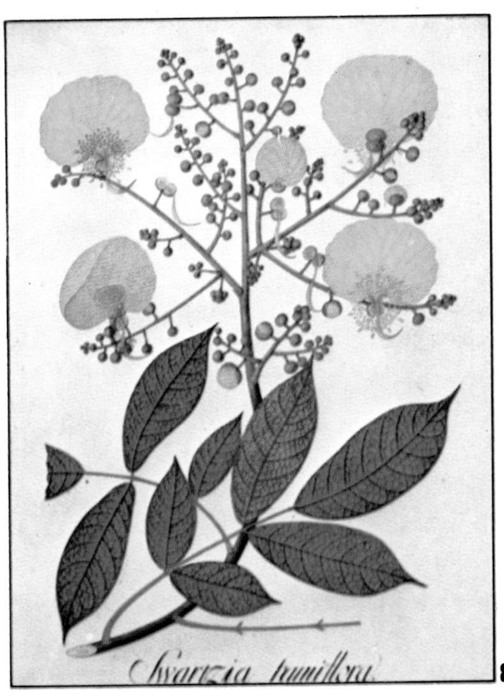

8

9

10

11

12

13

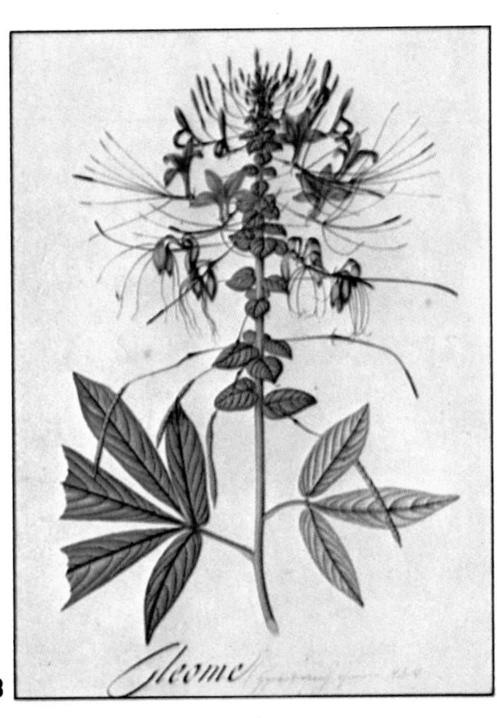

14

15

16

17

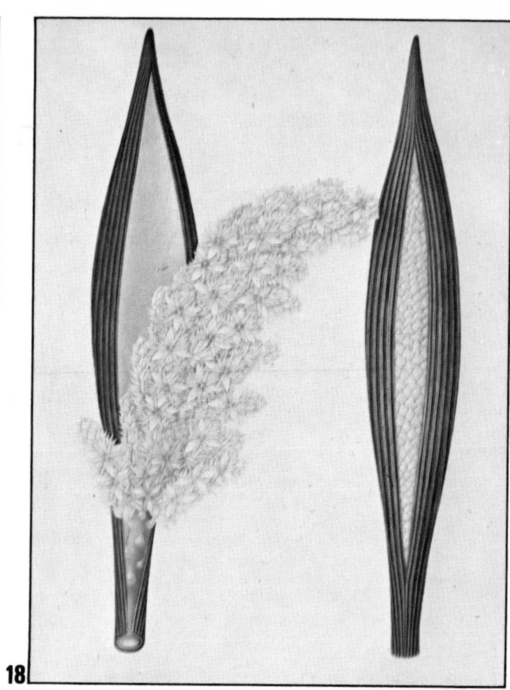

18

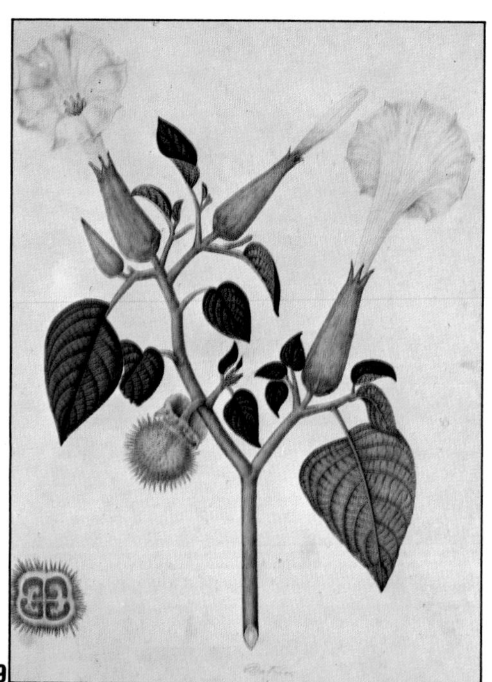

19

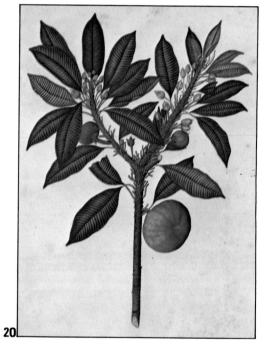

16 CATLEYA.
17 POURRETIA (PUYA NITIDA MEZ). Signed Martinez.
18 MAXIMILIANA PALMATUM. Signed F. Villarroel.
19 DATURA STRAMONIUM. Signed Turbaco.
20 ACHRAS SAPOTA.
21 CISSAMPELOS SP.
22 BOMAREA.

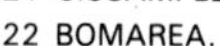

20

21

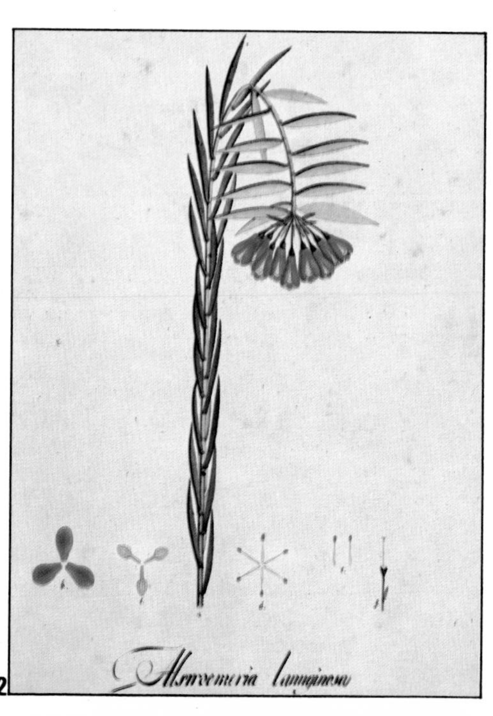

22

vernifer), and *Uxtica albea,* used to weave fine cloth exported from China. The best quality of cinnamon was that from the trees and seeds brought from Ceylon."[73]

The camphor tree (*Laurus camphora,* Linn.) is plentiful in the west of Japan and other neighbouring islands. The Chinese sell it in its crude state to the Dutch who bring it to Europe for purification in laboratories. A missionary wrote from Peking in 1736 explaining the method used in China to extract camphor from the tree called *Tchang.*[74] "*Laurus cassia* and *Laurus cinnamomum* also grow in the Philippine Islands."

In the sixteenth century, the explorer Gonzalo Pizarro, conqueror of Peru, found a tree which he claimed to be cinnamon in the eastern part of Quito, in the Quixos province. There were immense forests of such trees, resembling olive trees, and the natives used their flowers and fruit, which had the same substance and taste as cinnamon but were not true cinnamon.

It is recorded that these flowers, fruit and bark were sent to Spain, but the expected flavour was not found, either because of faulty selection, or damage in transit.[75]

The aim was to produce real cinnamon exactly like that of Ceylon — from which it originated — Java and Malabar.[76]

By 1800 the Frenchman Louis de Rieux wrote that in Santa Fe de Bogota Spain already possessed spices that could compete with those of Ceylon and replace such Dutch products as nutmeg (originating from the Molucca Islands), cinnamon, cloves and cayenne pepper. These four spices constituted the richest branch of trade in Asia.[77]

Celestino Mutis was the discoverer of the arboreal passion flower in 1785 of the *Mutisia clematis,* of the family Compositae, a climbing plant so named by Linnaeus.

Don Celestino spent the last years of his life in Bogota. Early 1801 the great scientists Humboldt and Bompland landed at the port of Cartagena de Indias, to visit him. They travelled up the river Magdalena as far as Honda and then completed the journey to Bogota on mules. Mutis gave the two learned men a warm welcome and presented them with a hundred of his best watercolours, which Humboldt took to the Science Institute in Paris.

After leaving Santa Fe they went on to Quito and then to Lima. From there they took the Loja road because they were anxious to visit this natural habitat of the cinchona. Afterwards they embarked in Callao for Mexico.[78]

Mutis died in Bogota on 11 September 1808 before he could realise his dream of publishing *Flora de Nueva Granada.* In 1817, after Mutis's death, Fernando VII ordered his collections sent to the Museum of Natural Sciences and the Royal Botanical Garden in Madrid. They filled one hundred and five chests. His manuscripts about the flora of New Granada and the study of quinine in Bogota were never published.[79] These works which had entailed so many years of toil, so much learning and such tremendous efforts, now lie forgotten on the dusty shelves among the archives of the Madrid Botanical Garden. Five volumes of plates by Mutis have now been published by the Institute of Hispanic Culture and the Colombian government.

The Ruiz and Pavón expedition had not yet returned to Spain in 1788 when Martín Sessé was sent out to New Spain (Mexico) on a similar mission. He was appointed in 1787, the last year of the reign of Charles III.

Accompanied by his pupil Mociño, a Mexican, he visited a large part of California, Mexico, Guatemala, and a few islands in the Atlantic.

Vicente Cervantes (1755-1829), an outstanding pupil of the Madrid Botanical garden, was appointed Professor of Botany in Mexico, and took up his new post in 1788 under Sessé's direction.[80] He was the first to teach botany in a public institution in America.

In 1790 Cervantes sent the first dahlia to the Madrid Botanical Garden, and also the starred violet, or *ipecacuanha,*

MUTISIA CLEMATIS. Signed Salvador Rizo.

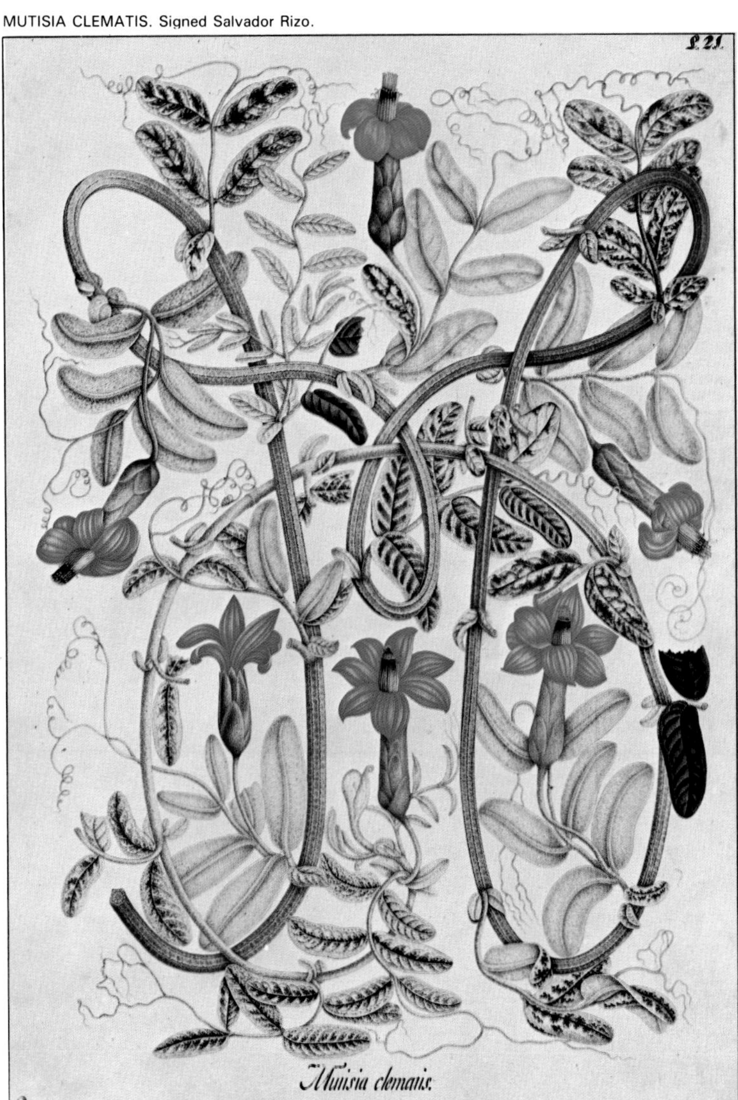

2

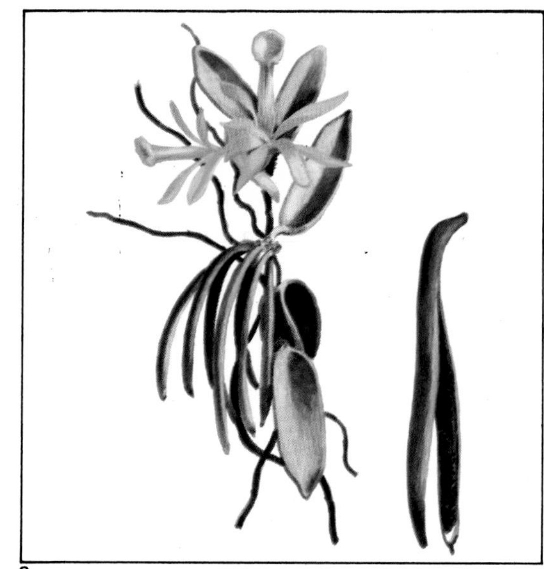

3

MAIN SPECIES

1 CLOVE (ZYZYGUM AROMATICUM, L.).
2 PEPPER (PIPER NIGRUM).
3 VANILLA (V. PLANIFOLIA, ANDRE).
4 GINGER (ZINGIBER OFFICINALE, ROSC.).
5 CINNAMON (CINNAMOMUM ZEYLANICUM).
6 NUTMEG (MYRISTICA FRAGANS).
7 CASSIA (CINNAMOMUM CASSIA BLUME).

4

5

6

7

which grows in the neighbourhood of Mexico City. The dahlia was originally of a single species and the genus *Cabanilles* was later formed. It is Mexico's national flower.

In all, three great expeditions were carried out in New Spain for scientific and historical purposes. The earliest, and probably most interesting, was that of Philip II's head physician, Francisco Hernández, both because of the effort in gathering the extraordinary amount of data and material, and because of the sixteen volumes that he wrote, with many maps and drawings. The most extensive, two centuries later, was Sessé's, from the coasts of Nicaragua to Canada. The most important, however, was Humboldt's because of its remarkable repercussions in the European scientific community, and the knowledge of Mexico it provided.[81]

Don Martín Sessé, in somewhat the same circumstances as Mutis, had already been in Mexico for some time and knew the language perfectly. It was his initiative that led to the expedition to Nueva Espana, through his correspondence with Casimiro Gómez Ortega. Ortega wanted Sessé to obtain new plants and seeds to enrich the Botanical Garden in Madrid and so, in 1787, he had him appointed by Royal Order to explore the territory of Mexico and to establish a botanical garden there. Don José Longinos and Don Juan del Castillo were also appointed as chemists, in addition to several draughtsmen.

Once the Botanical Garden and the School had been established in Mexico City, Sessé asked Don Celestino Mutis to send him tea, quinine and cinnamon from New Granada, and also a palm-tree that grew on the Maracaibo coasts, named *Cachipán* or *Tipirri,* the fruit of which was used by the Indians to make a nourishing bread.[83]

During these first excursions around the capital they reached Toluca in search of the "tree of little hands" (*Cheirostemon plantanoides* or *Chiranthodendron pentadactyla,* Larr.), which grew in the mountains about sixty miles from Mexico City. This tree was known and revered by the Aztecs, who appreciated its medicinal properties and regarded it as sacred. Its pink flowers look like little hands or claws. Dr. Hernández saw this tree in the ancient royal gardens in 1570 and 1572, and Fr. Bernardino de Sahagún gave the first written report of it in his *History of the Things of New Spain* (1565-1569). "The tree observed by Mociño and Sessé still grows, now about 210 years old, in Toluca in the modern allotments formed out of the Huitzila hill."[84]

Sessé, Cervantes and, a little later, Mociño were the principal botanical explorers of Mexico. "Over a period of eight years, from 1795 to 1804, they covered a distance of four thousand miles from Cape Arenas on the southern coast of Nicaragua to the mouth of the river Hiaqui in the Gulf of California.

They went on to explore the Prince William Gulf, the Bay of Bucarelli, the Islands of Queen Charlotte and Nutka, the Juan de Fuca Straits, the Californian Peninsula in the Pacific and the Islands of Cuba and Puerto Rico in the Atlantic."[85]

A considerable herbarium was collected on this journey and eventually found its way to the Botanical Garden in Madrid in 1820. Mociño kept part of the collection, which later disappeared. Copies by de Candolle, the Swiss botanist, ended up in Geneva.

DAHLIA. Sessé and Mocino Expedition. Mexico.

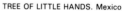

TREE OF LITTLE HANDS. Mexico.

In July 1789 the famous sailor Alessandro Malaspina, a native of Lombardy, undertook a journey around the world financed by King Charles IV. He was accompanied by the botanists Luis Nee, Pineda and Haenke. Malaspina's aim was to study the secrets and the works of nature in remote parts of the world.[86] Nee was a Frenchman, naturalized in Spain, and a well-known botanist. Before undertaking this voyage he had discovered many plants in the countryside of Gibraltar and Algeciras, among them the *Rhododendron ponticum,* var. Bética, a native of this region.

Nee began the study of botany in Montevideo, where he penetrated about ninety-six miles inland, and also in the Sacramento colony. He set sail again and visited the coasts of Patagonia in Argentina and the Falkland Islands. He then rounded Cape Horn and explored the Pacific coasts of Chile and Peru, crossing the country as far as the Mexican coast. On his numerous and extensive journeys, accompanied by Haenke, Nee collected more than ten thousand plants, brought back to Spain in 1794.[87]

On his return to the Peninsula, Malaspina was the victim of court intrigues of two of Queen Maria Louisa's ladies-in-waiting, La Matallano and La Pizarro, who tried to compromise him with the Queen in order to supplant the Prince of Peace (the favourite Godoy). As a result he was imprisoned in the barracks of the Guards, and later in the Castle of San Antón in Coruña. Afterwards he was forced to leave the Peninsula. He died soon afterwards in his native Lombardy.[88]

One of the last Spanish expeditions to American territory at the end of the eighteenth century was that of the Aragonese physician Baltasar Boldo, who studied the properties of plants in the Botanical Garden of Madrid. In 1796 the Government sent him with the Guantánamo Commission, which was to make plans for the Guinas Canal in Cuba, so that he could study the vegetation.

Boldo collected material on Cuban flora, and many of his handwritten descriptions and José Guió's drawings are preserved at the Botanical Garden in Madrid. His early death in 1799 prevented him from completing his work.[89]

At the end of the eighteenth century the botanist Juan Cuéllar was sent to the Philippines by the Philippines Company, to promote various kinds of cultivation and to study plants. He wrote several works before he died in Manila in 1793.[90]

By the beginning of the nineteenth century the activities of the Spanish botanists had come to an end. The armies of Napoleon were traversing Spain, destroying and burning what lay in their path. Gardens and parks were abandoned, and the exotic plants which had been naturalized with such care, perished.

One by one Spain lost its colonies, and a new generation of Europeans began to explore the Americas, the East and the Pacific.

About 1837 a botanist from Geneva, Edmond Boissier, crossed the Mediterranean countries to Persia, Mesopotamia, Palestine, etc. His main explorations in the Spanish peninsula were in the Andalusian sierras, and in Ronda he found the

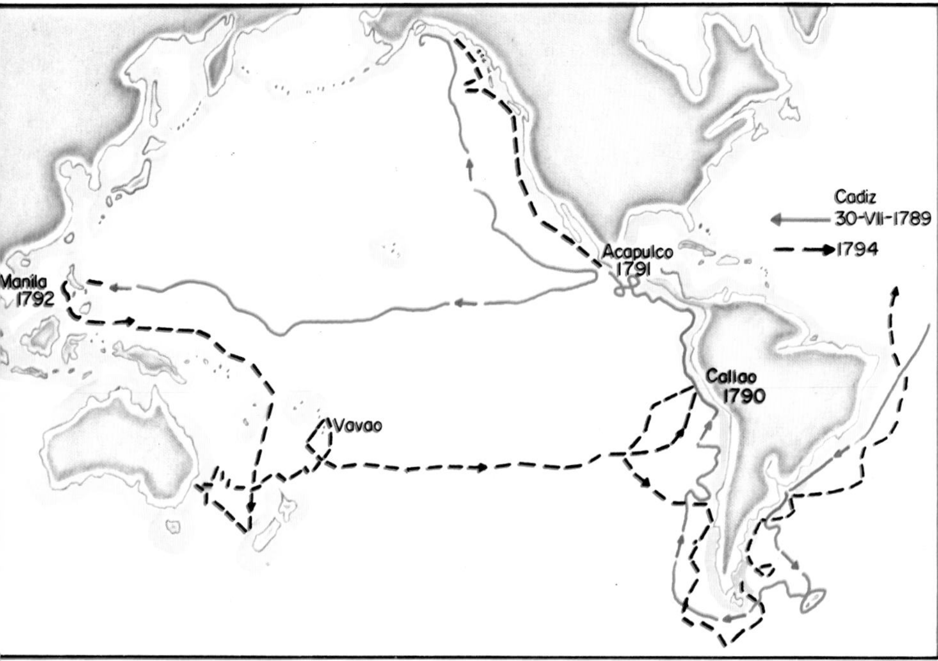

MAP OF THE ALESSANDRO MALASPINA EXPEDITION.

THE ALESSANDRO MALASPINA EXPEDITION. THE PENDULUM EXPERIMENT.

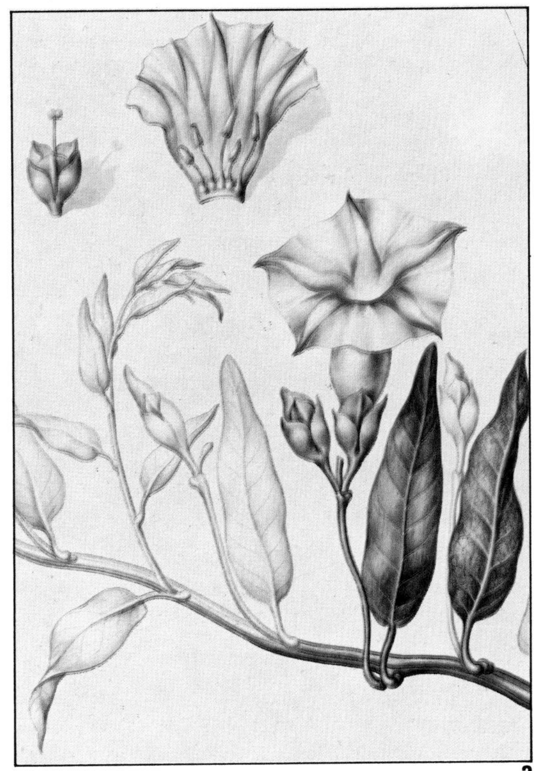

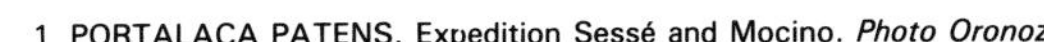

1 PORTALACA PATENS. Expedition Sessé and Mocino. *Photo Oronoz.*
2 CONVULVULUS QUERETARENSIS. Expedition Sessé and Mocino. *Photo Oronoz.*
3 SALVIA GLUTINOSA. Expedition Sessé and Mocino. Mexican flora. *Photo Oronoz.*
4 ACHRAS CAPIRI. Expedition Sessé and Mocino. Mexican flora. *Photo Oronoz.*

MAP OF THE SESSÉ, CERVANTES AND MOCINO EXPEDITION IN NEW SPAIN. Mexico.

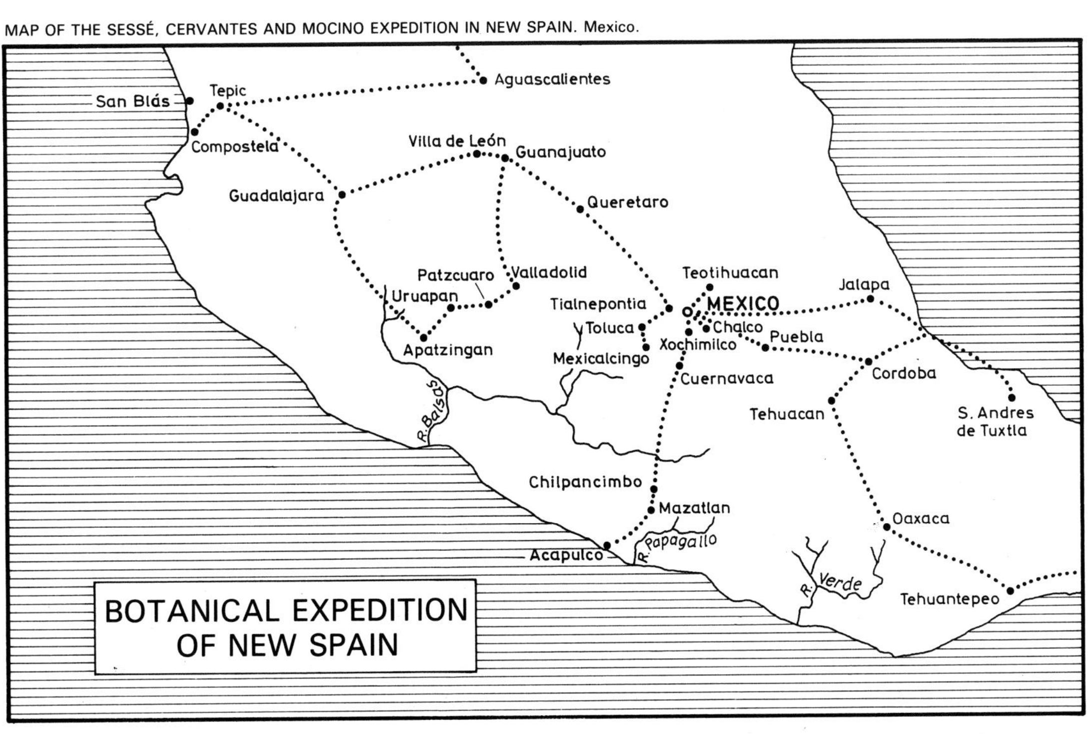

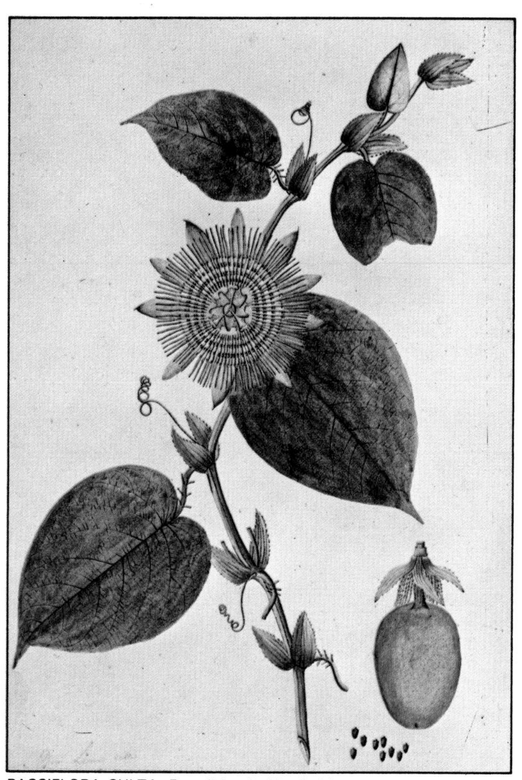

PASSIFLORA CULTA. Expedition L. Nee in Lima. Peru. Signed by José Guio.

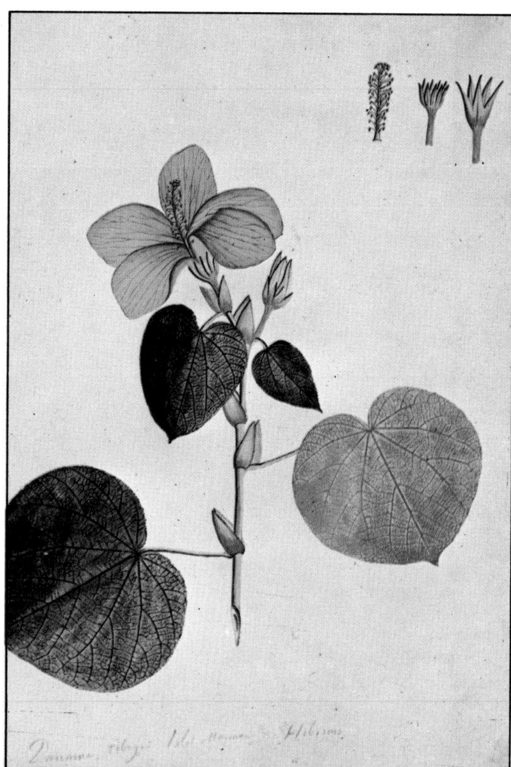

HIBISCUS TILIACEUS L. Expedition L. Nee. Panama. Island of Taboga.

LAPAGERIA SP. TALCAHUANO. Expediton L. Nee. Chile. Signed by José Guio.

CERBERA. THEVETIA. QUERETARO. Expedition L. Nee. Mexico.

BIGNONIA. Expedition L. Nee in Guamantango. (Peru). Obragillo. Huaro. Signed by F. Pulgar.

PASSIFLORA SP. Expedition L. Nee in Guamantango. (Peru). Signed by F. Pulgar.

Abies pinsapo, our only native conifer. Full of admiration he scaled the heights of the Sierra Nevada in Granada to classify its flora, and he collected a herbarium of more than a hundred thousand specimens during the year he spent in Spain.

His book *Voyage botanique dans le Midi de l'Espagne pendant l'année 1837,* is not only an admirable classification of Spanish flora, but is also amusing and well-written.

The German botanist Moritz Willkomm (1822-1897) was also famous for his study of the Spanish flora on which he spent thirty-two years, and which he described in his *Prodromus Florae Hispanicae.*

Thus the Spanish scientists of the eighteenth century, who risked their lives on the mountain ridges and crags of the New World to bring back the tuberoses, dahlias, orchids, heliotropes and so many other flowers that make our gardens fragrant and lovely today, lie forgotten forever. Their manuscripts and drawings, the fruit of so much labour and hardship, are lost and unpublished. Their discoveries were later to be attributed to explorers of other nationalities, who in all good faith were completely unaware that as early as the sixteenth century Mexican flora was represented in sixteen volumes, with marvellous sketches, on the library shelves of the Monastery of the Escorial, volumes which would never be published; and that the herbariums and writings of so many other Spanish botanists would only be published in incomplete form at the end of the nineteenth and early twentieth centuries. Most of them lie dusty and forgotten in the Archives of the Madrid Botanical Garden.

Today this old garden on the Paseo del Prado, surrounded by tall modern buildings and amidst the traffic and bustle of the capital, has an air of poetry. The exotic plants brought with such care and enthusiasm for Charles III from his dominions overseas, and comprising the most important collection in Europe, no longer flourish. The garden's greatest interest lies in its custody of the collections and herbariums brought by the Spanish pioneers, and the illustrations by Mutis, which are practically unknown.

A solitary camphor tree *(Cinnamomum camphor),* witness to past splendour, bravely withstands the hard winters and scorching summers of Madrid.

ABIES PINSAPO. Photo Author.

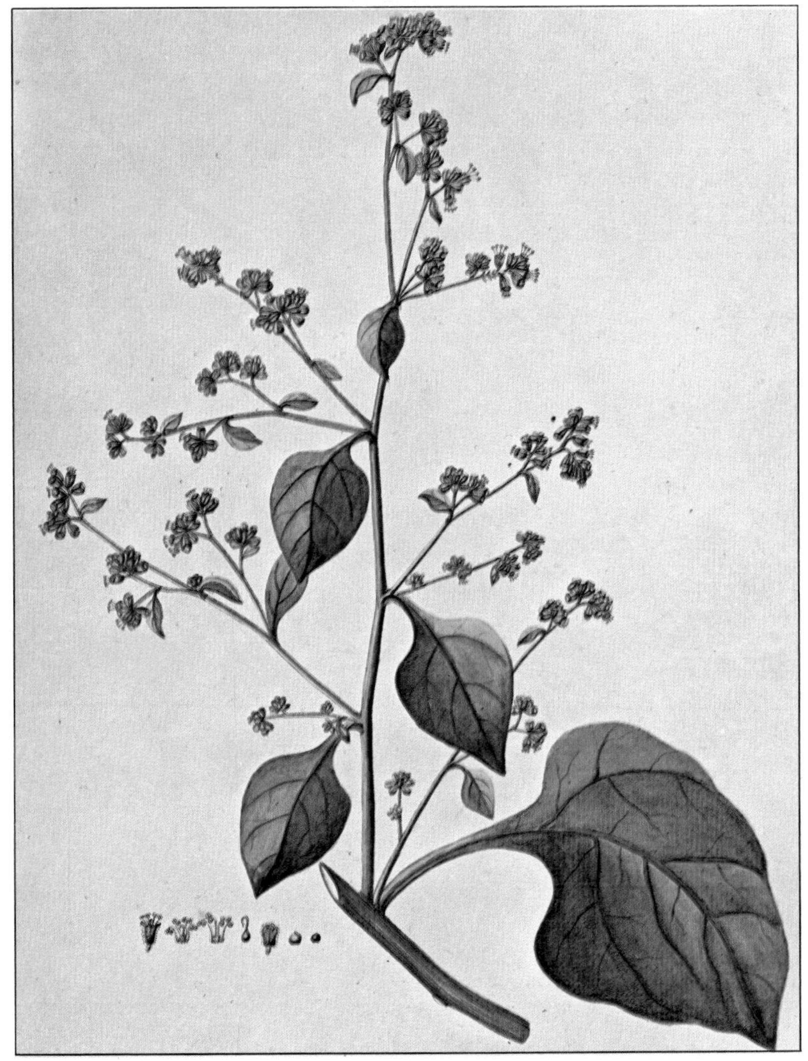

BOLDOA PURPURESCENS (H.R.M.) Royal Commission of Guantánamo. Cuba. Signed by José Guio.

APPENDIX IV

"After Doctor Nardo Antonio wrote to His Majesty that he had finished the book and compilation that His Majesty had ordered of the most useful herbs described in the books by Doctor Franciso Hernández, brought from New Spain, I attempted to engage illustrators here to engrave and make the prints of the simples and herbs in the same form and size as used in the books. I have had a sample made of one herb and am sending it today, one copy in colour and one merely printed. Both are of good quality and show that satisfactory illustrations can be provided if so desired. His Majesty would be performing a great service to the entire world by ordering the completion of this great work, which has been undertaken at so great a cost to himself and with so much work on the part of those who have been concerned in it. If it is not brought to a conclusion, all this will be lost and His Majesty's aim and intention unachieved; I therefore beg Your Worship to inform His Majesty that, as the matter is so well advanced, it is right that he should order these herbs to be engraved and the prints to be made. I understand that the cost of drawing new illustrations or reproducing those of other books, while leaving the books in their present clean condition (which is fitting as they are original copies) and of preparing the blocks and moulds will exceed 1,500 ducats.

Archive of the Valencia Institute of Don Juan.
Bundle 99. No. 101.
Madrid, 9 May 1582.
Juan de Herrera."

(Signed and sealed)

APPENDIX V

General Palace Archives
Administrative Section
File No. 335

"Sir,

I spoke to the herbalist doctor from Valencia whom Your Majesty summoned to reside here, recommending first that he should see the position and suitability of the Casa del Campo and other sites for the planting and care of medicinal herbs. He says that these herbs must be gathered in various places, and that some require water, others shelter, others cold and shade, and still others much sun, and that he cannot find a site suitable to these needs in the Casa del Campo. Furthermore he does not think one nursery should be separate from another, nor that the fountain should be placed in the sun; and that he finds no place so convenient as the Prioress's Orchard, where there is everything that is needed for the protection of all of these herbs, and that by putting them all together there, and with all the care and attention that he will give them, the greatest benefit that will result will be that the doctors and apothecaries will be familiar with them and will become proficient where they are not completely ignorant; that if the garden is in that position some curious people will come there who would not go the Casa del Campo, and also Your Majesty's personal physicians will be better satisfied as to its usefulness. He also says that it is appropriate for Your Majesty to command that the herbs be planted there, for it is known by experience from the time of Diego de Burgos and Doctor Nardo Antonio that the site is excellent. Moreover, he was himself probably frightened by the suggestion of residing at the Casa del Campo; as he is old and a stranger he is probably afraid of losing his life or health; it has seemed right to me to inform Your Majesty so that you can command what is to be done, and as the site of the Prioress's Orchard is suitable for this I do not find it unfitting that it should be used for this purpose, for many plants can be put in the shady parts, which are now unsightly and wild and will thus be beautified; it is also desirable that Your Majesty's doctors and apothecaries should see it from time to time, and that others should be attracted to this profession and embrace it.

Madrid. 26 March 1598."

(Signed and sealed)

"His Majesty deems it proper that this plantation should be within the precincts of the Prioress's Orchard in that part which Francisco de Mora will indicate, without any new horticulturist or gardener being appointed there, and that the Valencian doctor should be informed of this so that he and Mora can agree about the hours when he can come, and the plots where he is to put his plants.

Your Majesty says he understands that Juan Gomez, who lives in the *guarda del Sol,* cannot work there since he is in poor health, so may I be informed of where they are to be moved, and may I know from Mora who is to take his place."

(Signed and sealed)

CAMPHOR TREE. CINNAMOMUN CAMPHORA. Botanical Garden of Madrid. *Photo Author.*

[1] COLMEIRO, Miguel: *Bosquejo histórico y estadístico del Jardín Botánico de Madrid,* Madrid, 1875, page 2

[2] GUTIÉRREZ COLOMER, Dr. Leonardo: "El descubrimiento de América y los fármacos", *A B C,* 10th October 1969.

[3] COLMEIRO, MIGUEL: *La Botánica y los botánicos,* Madrid, 1858, page 26.

[4] Epístola Nuncupat: *Pedacio Dioscórides acerca de la materia medicinal y de los venenos mortíferos,* translated from Greek into vulgar Castilian by Dr. Andrés Laguna, in the house of Juan Latio, 1555.

[5] MASSON, GEORGINA: *Italian Gardens,* Thames & Hudson, London, 1966, pages 147 & 148.

[6] COLMEIRO, M.: *Op. cit.,* page 151.

[7] STEELE, Arthur Robert: *Flowers for the King,* Duke University Press, U.S.A, 1964, page 5.

[8] STEELE, Arthur Robert: *Op. cit.,* page 6.

[9] STEELE, Arthur Robert: *Op. cit.,* page 6.

[10] CABRERA DE CÓRDOBA, Luis: *Vida de Felipe II,* Madrid, 1876, vol. II, page 393.

[11] Archivo del Instituto Valencia de Don Juan, Madrid, envío 99, no. 101.

[12] STEELE, Arthur Robert: *Op. cit.,* page 6.

[13] Archivo General de Palacio, Madrid: *Casa y bosques,* file 335.

[14] Archivo del Instituto Valencia de Don Juan, Madrid, envío 99, no. 155.

[15] SIGÜENZA, Fray José de: *La Fundación del Monasterio de El Escorial,* Ed. Aguilar, Madrid, 1963, page 397.

[16] COLMEIRO, M.: *Op. cit.,* page 4.

[17] COLMEIRO, M.: *Op. cit.,* pages 5 & 6.

[18] Archivo General de Indias, Sevilla: *Indiferente,* file 1300. Cadiz, 20th February 1753. Letter from Nicolás Mace to Bartholomé de Valencia.

[19] TAPIAS, Enrique: *Carlos III y su época,* Ed. Aguilar, Madrid, 1962, page 362.

[20] Archivo General de Palacio, Madrid: *Aranjuez,* file 86. Aranjuez, 15th March 1844. Letter from the Count of Espelata to Isabel II.

[21] GARCÍA CABEZÓN: *Jardín de Aclimatación de La Orotava,* Tenerife, 1948.

[22] STEELE, Arthur Robert: *Op. cit.,* page 18.

[23] *Real Expedición Botánica del Nuevo Reino de Granada,* Ed. Cultura Hispánica, Madrid, 1954, vol. I, chap. XVIII, page 60.

[24] STEELE, Arthur Robert: *Op. cit.,* page 36.

[25] TAPIAS, Enrique: *Op. cit.,* page 373.

[26] HUMBOLDT, Alexander: *Essai politique sur le royaume de la nouvelle Espagne,* Paris, 1811. vol. III, chap. VII, page 120.

[27] STEELE, Arthur Robert: *Op. cit.,* page 51.

[28] STEELE, Arthur Robert: *Op. cit.,* page 51.

[29] STEELE, Arthur Robert: *Op. cit.,* page 54.

[30] JARAMILLO-ARANGO: *Relación histórica del viaje que hizo a los Reynos del Perú y Chile el botánico Hipólito Ruiz,* published by the Real Academia de Ciencias Exactas, Físicas y Naturales, Madrid, 1952, vol. I, page 3.

[31] STEELE, Arthur Robert: *Op. cit.,* pages 88, 89 & 90.

[32] JARAMILLO-ARANGO: *Op. cit.,* vol. I, page 74.

[33] JARAMILLO-ARANGO: *Op. cit.,* vol. I, page 95.

[34] JARAMILLO-ARANGO: *Op. cit.,* vol. I, page 97.

[35] JARAMILLO-ARANGO: *Op. cit.,* vol. I, page 114.

[36] JARAMILLO-ARANGO: *Op. cit.,* vol. I, page 127

[37] JARAMILLO-ARANGO: *Op. cit.,* vol. I, page 153.

[38] JARAMILLO-ARANGO: *Op. cit.,* vol. I, page 135.

[39] STEELE, Arthur Robert: *Op. cit.,* pages 18 & 19.

[40] Archivo General de Indias, Seville: *Indiferente,* file 1557, 1st November 1799. Letter from Rieux.

[41] MARCOY, Paul: *Viaje por los valles de la Quina,* Ed. Espasa-Calpe, Colección Austral, Madrid, 1968, page 173.

[42] STEELE, Arthur Robert: *Op. cit.,* appendix, page 335.

[43] JARAMILLO-ARANGO: *Op. cit.,* vol. I, page 164.

[44] JARAMILLO-ARANGO: *Op. cit.,* vol. I, pages 160 & 161.

[45] STEELE, Arthur Robert: *Op. cit.,* page 21.

[41] MARCOY, Paul: *Viaje por los valles de la Quina,* Ed. Espasa-Calpe, Colección Austral, Madrid, 1968, page 173.

[42] STEELE, Arthur Robert: *Op. cit.,* appendix, page 335.

[43] JARAMILLO-ARANGO: *Op. cit.,* vol. I, page 164.

[44] JARAMILLO-ARANGO: *Op. cit.,* vol. I, pages 160 & 161.

[45] STEELE, Arthur Robert: *Op. cit.,* page 21.

[46] CAMERON, Roderick: *Viceroyalties of the West,* London, 1968, page 254.

[47] JARAMILLO-ARANGO: *Op. cit.,* vol. I, page 184.

[48] JARAMILLO-ARANGO: *Op. cit.,* vol. I, page 199.

[49] JARAMILLO-ARANGO: *Op. cit.,* vol. I, page 208.

[50] JARAMILLO-ARANGO: *Op. cit.,* vol. I, page 229.

[51] Archivo General de Indias, Seville: *Indiferente,* files 1663-64-65, Lima, 5th June 1785. Unpublished letter addressed to the Baylio Frey Antonio Valdés, Ministro de Indias.

[52] JARAMILLO-ARANGO: *Op. cit.,* vol. I, page 247.

* Ruiz and Pavón gave it the name of Lapageria in honour of Josefina Tasher de Lapagerie, later Empress of the French.

[53] JARAMILLO-ARANGO: *Op. cit.,* vol. I, pages 234-238.

[54] STEELE, Arthur Robert: *Op. cit.,* page 131.

[55] JARAMILLO-ARANGO: *Op. cit.,* vol. I, page 283.

[56] JARAMILLO-ARANGO: *Op. cit.,* vol. I, page 287.

[57] JARAMILLO-ARANGO: *Op. cit.,* vol. I, page 291.

[58] JARAMILLO-ARANGO: *Op. cit.,* vol. I, page 300.

[59] JARAMILLO-ARANGO: *Op. cit.,* vol. I, page 303.

[60] JARAMILLO-ARANGO: *Op. cit.,* vol. I, page 318.

[61] COLMEIRO, M.: *Op. cit.,* page 180.

[62] COLMEIRO, M.: *Op. cit.,* page 180.

[63] COLMEIRO, M.: *Op. cit.,* page 181.

[64] Archivo General de Indias, Seville: *Indiferente,* file 1555, Santa Fe, June 1753.

[65] Idem, file 1555.

[66] Idem, file 1555, 23rd January 1789.

[67] COLMEIRO, M.: *Op. cit.,* page 42.

[68] *La Real Expedición Botánica del Nuevo Reino de Granada,* Ed. Cultura Hispánica, Madrid, 1954, vol. I, page 68.

[69] GREDILLA, Federico: *Biografía de José Celestino Mutis,* Madrid, 1911, page 340.

[70] *La Real Expedición Botánica del Nuevo Reino de Granada,* Ed. Cultura Hispánica, Madrid, 1954, vol. I, page 62.

[71] Archivo General de Indias, Seville: *Indiferente,* file 1545, Marquita, 19th November 1985.

[72] Idem, file 1545, Turbaco, 16th May 1787. To the Marqués de Sonora.

[73] Idem, file 1545, Philipines, 20th January 1789. Juan de Cuéllar.

[74] Idem, file 15, Manilla, 20th January 1790. Juan de Cuéllar.

[75] Idem, file 1300, Paris, 3rd March 1753. Altolaguirre.

[76] Idem, file 1300. Letter to the Marqués de la Ensenada.

[77] Idem, file 1557.

[78] GREDILLA, F.: *Op. cit.,* page 214.

[79] GREDILLA, F.: *Op. cit.,* page 382.

[80] GREDILLA, F.: *Op. cit.,* page 339.

[81] ARIAS DIVITO, Juan Carlos: *Las expediciones científicas españolas durante el siglo XVIII,* Ed. Cultura Hispánica, Madrid, 1968, page 47.

[82] ARIAS DIVITO, J.C.: *Op. cit.,* page 55.

[83] ARIAS DIVITO, J.C.: *Op. cit.,* page 90.

[84] *Artes de México,* no. 104, year XV, 1968, page 35.

[85] COLMEIRO, M.: *Op. cit.,* pages 184 & 185.

[86] GREDILLA, F.: *Op. cit.,* page 339.

[87] COLMEIRO, M.: *Op. cit.,* page 183.

[88] *Viaje político-cientfico alrededor del mundo por las corbetas "Descubierta" y "Atrevida", al mando de los capitanes don Alejandro Malaspina y don José Bustamante y Guerra,* 1789-1794. Published with an introduction by Don Pedro Novoa y Colson, Madrid, 1885. Historical introduction, page IX.

[89] COLMEIRO, M.: *Op. cit.,* page 186.

[90] COLMEIRO, M.: *Op. cit.,* page 182.

12 GALICIAN "PAZOS" THE "SONES " OF MALLORCA THE "CIGARRALES" OF TOLEDO

The gardens of Galicia, strange though it may seem, are winter gardens which should be visited in hazy and misty weather. It is then that they blossom in a veritable explosion of colour.

In February the acacias and camellias begin to flower. These trees, which are no more than shrubs in other less favoured countries, grow to great heights on this mild coast of north-eastern Spain. It is in winter that camellias of the purest and most dazzling white, camellias with the most vivid and gleaming red stripes and big double camellias *(reticulata flore pleno)* all light up the Galician gardens.

It is well worth the journey just to see them in the dream-like gardens that adorn the old mansions, the *pazos,* where even grey stone — covered with a velvet green blanket of lichen spreading over tables and benches — has been transformed into a kind of vegetation.

Later in the season the rhododendrons and azaleas follow, and the magnolia *Soulangiana* from Yunnan (China) are a mass of cupped blossoms of ivory or rose coloured mother-of-pearl.

These Galician gardens, like those in northern Portugal, are the product of several centuries of work — having grown and matured slowly over the years. In Portugal, one may see summer-houses and pergolas clipped and formed out of camellia trees, veritable flower studded mosaics. Inside there are often stone benches and small round fountains, as in the Casa dos Viscainhos in Braga, and the garden of Doña Virginia Machado in Vila Nova de Gaia (Oporto). In this same locality, on the Count of Campo Bello's property, there are two ancient camellia trees from Japan, that are said to be the first to have come to Europe in the sixteenth century. "The earliest camellias in Europe," writes Patricia Ledward, "were found in the garden of an ancient castle in Portugal, having been brought from Japan about 1556. According to tradition they were planted in the Campo Bello garden, although another version has it that they date only from 1670. The first living plants to come to Britain went to a Lord Petre in 1732, where, though coddled in his Essex hothouses, they soon died. Linnaeus named them in 1735 after Joseph Kamel (1661-1705), a botanist and Jesuit missionary from Moravia who travelled in Asia."[1]

The Galician *pazos* — a contraction of the word *palacio,* or

PAZO DE OCA. THE LAKES AND THE STONE BOAT. *Photo S. Saavedra.*

palace — cannot be spoken of without nostalgia, for the centuries have darkened their stones, wind and rain have beaten upon them, and the sun has so mellowed them that they have become a part of the crags and boulders of this region. Crenellated towers are glimpsed through the pine forests and woodlands of Galicia, mute witnesses to the battles and strife of the war-like Galician nobles. These nobles owned castles and strongholds, some of great antiquity. In the seventeenth and eighteenth centuries they added lateral and central buildings to provide more living space and planted baroque gardens as life became more comfortable and secure. Many of the gardens have now fallen into neglect, but their position is always spectacular, situated in some of the most beautiful landscapes of Europe: the Marinas de Betanzos (a bay and seaport near Coruña) and the Riás Bajas (inland bays near Vigo). These poetic and melancholy settings have inspired such literary works as the *Autumn Sonata* by Valle Inclán, *Los Pazos de Ulloa* by the Countess of Pardo Bazán and the poetry of Rosaliá de Castro.

PAZO SAN-THOMÉ. LA PASTORA. Vigo. GARDEN FAÇADE. *Photo Author.*

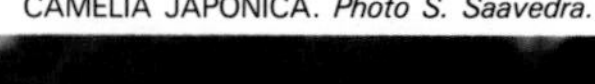

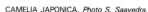

CAMELIA JAPONICA. *Photo S. Saavedra.*

CAMELIA JAPONICA. *Photo S. Saavedra.*

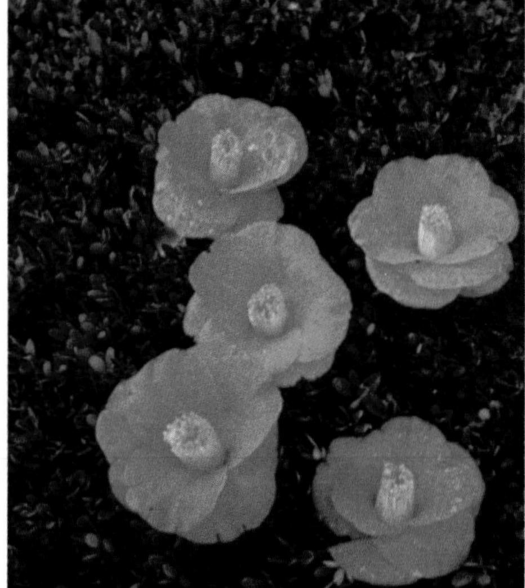

The mild, temperate climate that prevails here through the year has produced luxuriant subtropical vegetation so that little effort is required to create a garden; art is assisted by nature.

Throughout the eighteenth and nineteenth centuries there was a great love of gardening and plants in Galicia, as evidenced by the number of camellias, magnolias and eucalyptus trees that were planted. According to Lamperez, the art critic: "The regions of the north (Galicia, Asturias, Santander, Biscay and Guipúzcoa) became very important at this time on account of the industrious nature of their sons who had grown rich in New Spain (Mexico). The *hidalgos montaneses* (nobles from the mountains), formed a particularly wealthy and pretentious aristocracy in their native land, to which they were devoted, and they created a very noteworthy form of regional architecture."[2]

Gardens were adorned with statues, fountains and balustrades; knights and ladies of old would stroll among the flowers and fruit baskets and rest on the benches before the stone tables in the old summer houses, sheltered by the spreading oaks and chestnuts.

The grey stone of Galicia is very different from that in other parts of Spain. The hard, resistant, flinty granite, nearly white in colour, is used to make posts, walls and houses, and even today houses are built of hewn blocks and slabs of this stone, also found in the Guadarrama range near the village of La Cabrera in the province of Madrid. It is similar to the stone used by Philip II in the construction of the Escorial.

The expert stone cutters of this region may have brought their art from neighbouring Portugal. At any rate, they have filled Galicia with monumental fountains, stone crosses and the stone ornaments and figures that decorated palaces and gardens. Santiago de Compostela is a symphony in stone. There is a unity in the cathedral, the churches and the lordly mansions, where the greyish-green colour turns to gold in the light of the setting sun, as does the western façade of the Obradoiro of the great cathedral. In July — perhaps in honour of the Apostle on his feast day (25 July) — roofs and façades are covered in a profusion of *Trachelium coeruleum,* plants with feathery flowers of intense blue.

We shall not attempt to describe or mention all the *pazos* in

PAZO DE VALLE-INCLÁN. *Photo Ferrazo.*

two fifteenth century stone busts at the entrance gate to the park, one on either side of the arch, and a stone slab over the arch — also of this period — with the inscription: "This house was built by Don García de Caamaño, Year 1411."

The park was modified at the beginning of the century in the style of the English landscaped garden; it has several *araucarias excelsas,* camphor trees and other tropical plants, which owe their immense proportions to the rich peaty soil and their sheltered position at the foot of the mountain.

By climbing a short steep hill not far from Villagarcía we can see a stone belfry on our left, rising from the valley; this is San Pedro de Cea, a humble little village church surrounded by its tiny churchyard. Here there is a most extraordinary fountain of the late eighteenth century. Two stone archers stand on guard at either side; they are attired in long uniforms and tall helmets like those of the French soldiers of the time of the War of Independence, that is, of a later date than the fountain.

Water flows from two spouts, one representing a human face and the other, the opposite extremity of the human anatomy, suggesting the intention to mock the French soldiery against whom the Galicians were fighting at that time. The people of Villagarcía were, in 1808, the first in Galicia to rise against the invaders and proclaim their independence. They were heroic in their defence of the nearby pass of Siagoga.

Returning again towards the pleasant town of Villagarcía, we now take the road to Cambados; and having passed the village of Villajuán we follow the shores of Arosa bay. Near the hamlet of Caleiro we ascend the András road by the *pazo* which is said to have belonged to the famous author Don Ramon del Valle-Inclan (1869-1936). His family lived in this area, but the writer reputedly lived in the town of Puebla del Caramiñal on the other side of the bay.

What remains of this house reveals that it was once a stronghold with circular towers. It has two broad balconies, a small

STONE FIGURES. PAZO DE VALLE-INCLÁN. *Photo Ferrazo.*

PAZO SANTA CRUZ. OMBU, OR BELLA SOMBRA TREE. *Photo Author.*

PAZO SANTA CRUZ. ARBORESCENT FERN. *Photo Author.*

chapel and an outside stone stairway, all in a dilapidated condition. Soon there will be nothing left.

Evidence indicates that a garden existed here in the eighteenth century. This is confirmed by the presence of two tall pilasters surmounted by graceful, almost life-size stone figures. One is playing a guitar and the other holding a sword, but now they are almost completely hidden by a thick trellised vine.

We leave the Rías Bajas and continue our journey towards Santiago, stopping in the fertile valley of the river Ulla. Here we find the two *pazos* with the most famous gardens in Galicia: Oca and Santa Cruz de Rivadulla.

The *pazo* of Santa Cruz is eighteen kilometres from Santiago in the direction of Orense, near the river Ulla. The park was made by Don Juan Ibáñez de Mondragón, a Cardinal of the Roman *curia* or tribunal for ecclesiastical affairs; he was very influential in Rome, where he lived for many years. He made the original garden in the shape of a double cross in the upper part in front of the eastern façade. It was modelled on the garden of a Roman villa, and still retains its long avenues of olive trees, now old and gnarled.

At the entrance to the avenue there is an ancient tree called ombu or "bella sombra" (beautiful shade) (*Phytolaca dioica,* Linn.), which, judging by its old trunk and roots, must date from the same period. A native of the Argentine pampas, this tree is frequently mentioned in the popular songs of that country.

The rest of the large park is designed in the romantic landscape style of the last century, with its waterfall descending in dense shade. Further on in the same wood, is a little fountain opposite a stone table. Don Gaspar Melchor de Jovellanos, the celebrated writer and statesman who was a friend and kinsman

JOVELLANOS BENCH AND TABLE. *Photo S. Saavedra.*

of the owner of the house, used to work here and tradition says that in 1811 he signed his *Defence of the Central Party* at this table.

Jovellanos sought refuge from political persecution in this secluded and peaceful spot on two occasions, the second shortly before his death.[5]

The real creator of the lower garden which extends towards the south and west of the house, was Don Iván Armada y Fernández de Córdoba, Marqués de Santa Cruz de Rivadulla, the uncle of the present owner. From 1880 to 1899 he divided his time between this property and his house in Santiago. He was a great lover of botany and gardening and planted several exotic trees and a great collection of camellias which are still there, importing them mainly from Belgium and Portugal.

The large pool, the immense tulip-tree *(Liriodendron tulipifera)* behind it, and the stone sundial date from this period.

The wonderful thick plantation of tall boxwood trees is completely unique, due to the very sheltered situation. The rich soil and constant moisture in this *pazo* provide ideal conditions for a subtropical garden. Gardenias flower in the open, and tree-ferns flourish, such as the *Balantium antarticum,* native to this region.

Pazo de Oca

About eight kilometres from the *Pazo* of Santa Cruz, on the same road to Santiago, stands the palace of Oca, also in the Ulla valley. Its tower is of an earlier date than the main building, as was usual in these old Galician *pazos.* The owner hoped that his successors would continue the construction of the palace, adding another wing at the left end of the main façade overlooking the garden. The founder's wish that the building should be continued is expressed by means of a wide cuffed hand carved in the stone of the façade and the inscription "*Prosiga* (Continue), 1746."

PAZO SANTA CRUZ. SUNDIAL. *Photo Author.*

PAZO SANTA CRUZ. AVENUE OF OLIVE TREES. *Photo Author.*

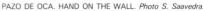

PAZO DE OCA. HAND ON THE WALL. *Photo S. Saavedra.*

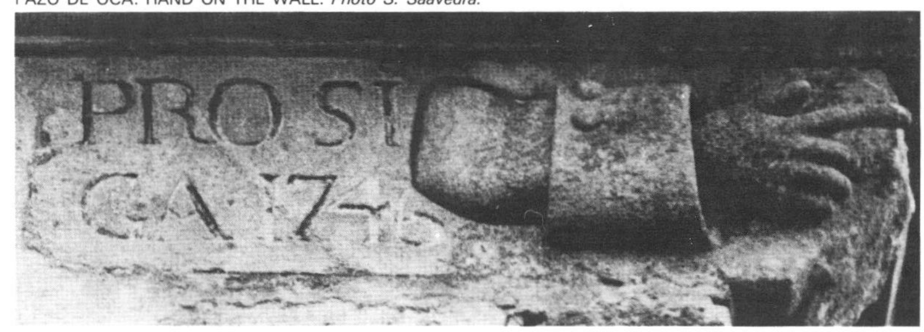

MAP OF OCA. *Dukes of Medinaceli.*

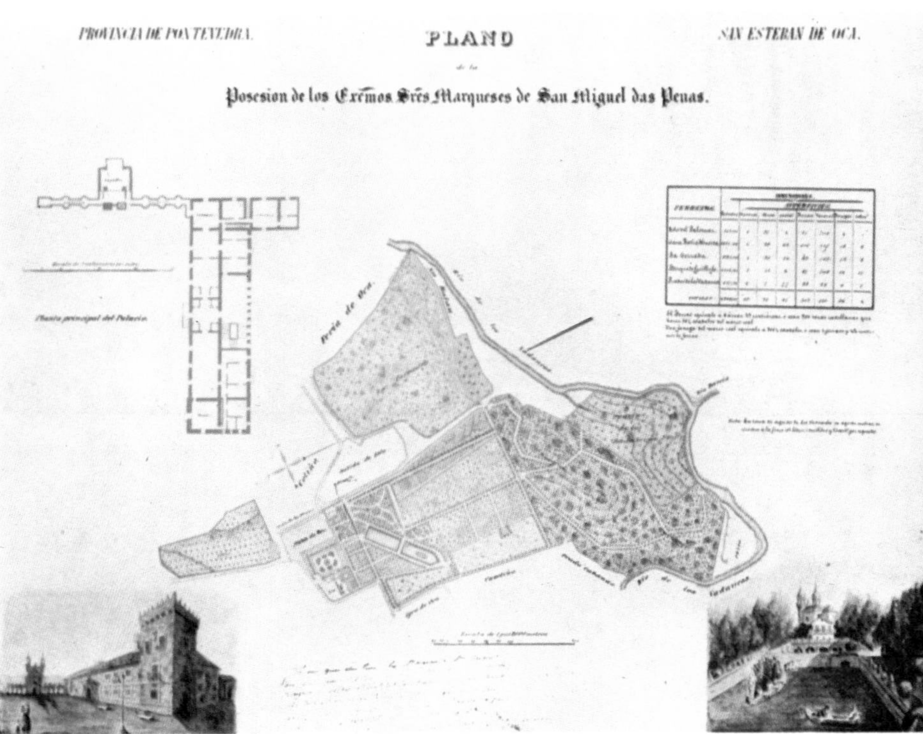

PAZO DE OCA. NORTH FAÇADE. *Photo Author.*

PAZO DE OCA. FOUNTAIN AND VIEW FROM THE SOUTHERN FAÇADE. *Photo Author.*

As in most Spanish houses, the gardens at Oca are reached through the house and across a broad entrance hall, leading to the southern façade, with its semicircular arches on the lower floor and a long gallery above. In front lies the square garden like a large patio. In the centre is a lovely eighteenth century stone fountain surrounded by clipped boxwood. The fountain, which has a curious three-lobed or clover-shaped pattern and a large central motif, was probably inspired by one in neighbouring Compostela. The view over the Ulla valley is arresting in its beauty.

An inner garden is reached through an archway under the lateral building, and beneath this arch a baroque fountain with two water spouts is built into the wall. The arch frames the view of the lower gardens with their ponds, which are formed by a stream diverted to run the length of the garden. There was once an old mill here. The atmosphere is dream-like; water flows throughout the garden, nourishing it. There are stone tables and benches in profusion, two facing each other on a slightly higher level, with a view over the countryside. They make a charming stop on the way to the lime avenue, where horse races were once held.

A broad stone bridge with balustrades separates the higher and the lower pond. The whole is inspired by the baroque style of Santiago. At both sides of this central bridge are continuous stone benches interspersed with pilasters, once crowned by ceramic urns, probably similar to those adorning a strange stone ship which lies in the centre of the lower pond. This vessel looks like a warship and is the principal motif in the garden. It is equipped with cannons, and two sailors stand in the prow and the stern. One of them is dressed in the long coat and three-cornered hat of an eighteenth century naval officer. At one time this mariner had a fishing rod and line from which hung a stone fish. The second sailor is wearing the usual apparel of a sailor or cabin-boy of the period, with stout boots. The pool itself is in the shape of a boat, pointed at the end.

The ponds are encircled by broad avenues overhung with ancient boxwood trees. At the end of a sidewalk there is a stone gateway, probably one of the entrances to the garden. It is surmounted by a stone semicircle, typical of this region, and which can also be seen on the façade of the nearby house of Guimarey (La Estrada) and the houses of Gimonde and Guimarans, all in the Ulla region.

These gardens were ordered by Don Fernando Gayoso de los Cobos, Marqués de Camarasa, towards the end of the eighteenth century,[6] but it is not known who the architects were. It is obvious that the owner found expression here for his ambition with considerable ingenuity and artistic taste, for the complete design, the river, the balustrades and stone motifs all form an architectural whole unique in Spain. Don Fernando must have been a very original personality for he created a beautiful and artistic abode to his own personal taste.

In 1873 an attempt was made to convert the garden by the upper pond into a landscaped garden, a fashion that destroyed so many of Europe's classical gardens. The last Marqués de Camarasa restored the gardens to their original design.

At the palace's northern façade, which contains the main entrance, stands the monumental chapel. This shows a marked baroque influence. It is joined at an angle to the main building by a passage with stone balustrades in the same style. The Galician historian Cousela Bouzás tells us: "The chapel of the Palace of Oca, in the parish of this name, is situated some four kilometres beyond Puente Ulla in the direction of Orense. It has thirty-five carved wooden figures, the work of the celebrated sculptor Gambino, on its three altars. On 11 June 1750, the owner of the property, Conde de Amarante, Marqués de Parga y de San Miguel das Penas, a resident of Santiago, signed a contract with Don Luis Parcero for the execution of the three altar pieces for the chapel dedicated to St. Anthony of Padua. The statues were ordered separately from Gambino. Once this work was completed and in place, it was inspected by Fray Manuel de los Mártires — the superintendent of works for the convent of Santo Domingo and the beautiful Gothic church in Santiago — and by another foreman appointed by the Count."[7] The side walls of the chapel contain two ancient stone tombs that belonged to the family and were brought from the Palace of La Junquera near La Puebla del Caramiñal on Arosa Bay, by the last Marqués de Camarasa. According to the inscription on one of them, this ancestor died of indigestion after eating cherries. This was verified, for when the tomb was opened it was found to be full of cherry stones!

GATE TO THE GARDEN. OCA. *Photo Author.*

BENCHES IN THE OCA GARDEN. *Photo Saavedra.*

STONE FIGURE ON THE BOAT. OCA. *Photo S. Saavedra.*

ENTRANCE TO THE GARDEN. OCA. *Photo S. Saavedra.*

PAZO DEL FARAMELLO. BRIDGE OVER THE RIVER. *Photo S. Saavedra.*

A feeling of sadness overwhelms us in this neglected garden, which was created with such care and enthusiasm. We sit on a moss-covered bench under a canopy of camellias and magnolias and listen to the slow dripping of the rain. The garden is shrouded in mist and we feel as though we are transported to an imaginary landscape. (More recent owners, the Duke and Duchess of Medinaceli, undertook the repair and embellishment of this beautiful house and garden.)

El Pazo del Faramello

We leave the Ulla valley to take the road to Santiago, where to our right before the *Pazo* de Rivadulla rises the Pico Sacro (the Holy Peak), the mountain behind which lies the city of the Apostle. But before entering the city, we will visit the *Pazo* del Faramello on the road between the town of Padrón and Santiago near the *humilladoiro,* a hill from which Compostela can be seen and where pilgrims would fall on their knees at the sight of the sacred city.

The Faramello is perched on the side of a deep valley with a brook running through the estate. The house faces a pine covered mountain across the valley. The slope has been ingeniously arranged in terraces. On one of these stands a beautiful stone *crucero,* or typical cross of the region, and a classical eighteenth century fountain with two basins, one above the other.

PAZO DE LOS CONDES DE TORRE-PENELA.
LA CORUNA FOUNTAIN. *Photo Author.*

OCA. BAROQUE CHURCH. *Photo S. Saavedra.*

A walk through this garden provides a sense of romance and mystery. Two rustic bridges cross the stream, and in the shady woods in front of the house there are chairs and tables from which to contemplate the waterfall and listen to the murmur of the water. It is a delightful spot.

The mountain opposite the Faramello was a *castro* (an ancient fortified camp, usually Celtic or Iberian) where, according to tradition, Queen Lupa lived. She was the owner and señora of all this territory in the time of the Celts. Legend has it that the Apostle St. James arrived to preach in this district between the years 15 and 25 of the Christian era, and had many followers there. He never forgot those years after he returned to Jerusalem, and he asked to be buried in Compostela. At his death his followers remembered his wish and placed his mutilated body in a boat and brought it to Spain. When they reached Padrón, on the banks of the river Ulla, they moored the boat to a *pedron* (a large stone), which is said to be the one displayed in a monument in the town and which has given the town its name. The sailors begged Queen Lupa to lend them a cart drawn by a pair of oxen to bear the holy corpse to Compostela, as they had to pass through her estates. But Doña Lupa hated the Apostle and instead of oxen sent wild bulls in the hope that they would drag the Apostle's body and tear it to pieces. Miraculously, the bulls knelt down at the sight of the corpse and then bore it gently to its final resting place. When Queen Lupa heard of this supernatural occurrence, she dissolved her armies, distributed her property, and became a Christian evangelist.

This *pazo* was built as a paper factory in 1710 for two Genoese, Don Bartolomé Piombino y Farcinetti and Jacobo Gambino (the father of the sculptor);[8] it later passed, through intermarriage, to the Rivero de Aguilar family.

* * *

Having paid our respects to the Apostle we shall leave Santiago for the region of Coruña, which is rich in memories of the past. The stately *Pazo* de Anceis, also known as the *Pazo* de Conde, is situated just outside the city. It is a beautiful well-preserved house, whose façade contains a fine eighteenth century escutcheon.

A stone fountain of the same period stands on the terrace at the east, or garden, side.

The small, romantic garden of San Carlos is in the town of Coruña. It is a square, walled enclosure with the tomb of Sir John Moore in the centre, guarded by four great poplars. Moore was a general in Wellington's army and a hero of the Peninsular War; he died in the battle of Elviña near Coruña on 16 January 1809. According to Richard Ford the body was removed later by the Marqués de La Romana.[9]

Behind this peaceful spot a large balcony commands a view over the city, and on either side, inscribed on white marble, there are two poems about Moore's death: an English poem by Charles Wolfe on the left and a poem by Rosalía de Castro in the Galician dialect on the right.

Among the loveliest *pazos* of the province is that of Mariñán, named after the nearby village, and also known as the *Pazo* de

PAZO TORRE PENELA. FAC DE WITH COAT OF ARMS. *Photo Author.*

EL FARAMELLO. BALCONY. *Photo S Saavedra.*

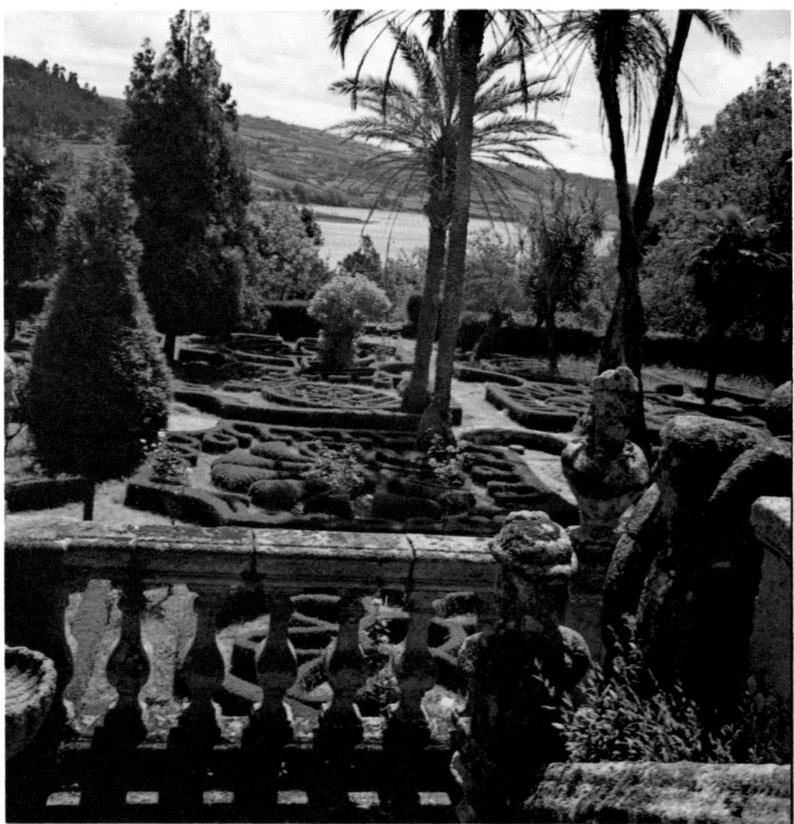

PAZO DE MARINAN. JARDIN LA CORUNA. *Photo Author.*

Bergondo. Its situation is unique in the Mariñas of Betanzos, near Sada, where long picturesque inlets penetrate inland. The terraced gardens go down to the shore.

The outstanding feature here is not the whitewashed building, which is more like the *casonas* (big houses) of Asturias than the Galician *pazos,* but the marvellous double stairway, adorned with busts, fountains and grey granite figures at the entrance to the house. Here two statues receive us: one of them holds a set of keys, the other stands, hand in pocket.

On the garden side more monumental steps lead to a wide terrace from where the beautiful gardens can be admired. They are formed of boxwood hedges in the French style, which of old was called "de broderie", and this influence is evident. The steps contain numerous baroque ornaments, coarsely sculpted but charming, all of them dating from the eighteenth century.

Javier Ozores tells us: "This *pazo* belonged to Gómez Pérez das Mariñas and later passed to Don Antonio Oca y Cadórniga who was married to Dona Violante de Ulloa, during whose ownership it attained its greatest splendour." Until recently it was the residence of the Bermúdez de Castro family, of the House of Láncara. The owner, Gerardo Láncara, was a well-known figure in Madrid society at the beginning of the century. The first eucalyptus trees to come to Galicia were planted in Bergondo.[10]

Today it belongs to the Diputación Provincial of Coruña, who use it as a holiday centre for boys, and the garden is carefully maintained.

PAZO DE MARINAN. FRONT ENTRANCE. *Photo S. Saavedra.*

In the garden of Señor and Señora de Tenreiro near the little fishing village of Puentedeume, also on the Bay of Betanzos, there is an amazing yew tree which, according to the old gardener, is six centuries old. We were rather dubious about this but it certainly is a venerable tree. The top is beautifully trimmed to form a double dome, and the lower branches are mushroom shaped and shelter a large circular verandah beneath them.

It is impossible to count the Galician *pazos* whose once fine gardens are slowly disappearing, sadly neglected and forgotten. They share the fate of all that is transitory and fades away with the passing of time.

The house of Jaz is an old property with its own chapel, though not strictly speaking a *pazo* and not as beautiful as those already mentioned. At the turn of the century it was turned into a gay and hospitable country house with wonderful views over the town and bay of Coruña.

Two enormous clipped yews guard the entrance. A garden of trim hedges, planted with blue agapanthus and red cannas, extends all around the house.

THE "SONES" OF ARAB ORIGIN IN MALLORCA

With very few exceptions, the gardens of Mallorca are built on land once occupied by the Arabs. Their skill in controlling water for irrigation is well known. The Arab occupation

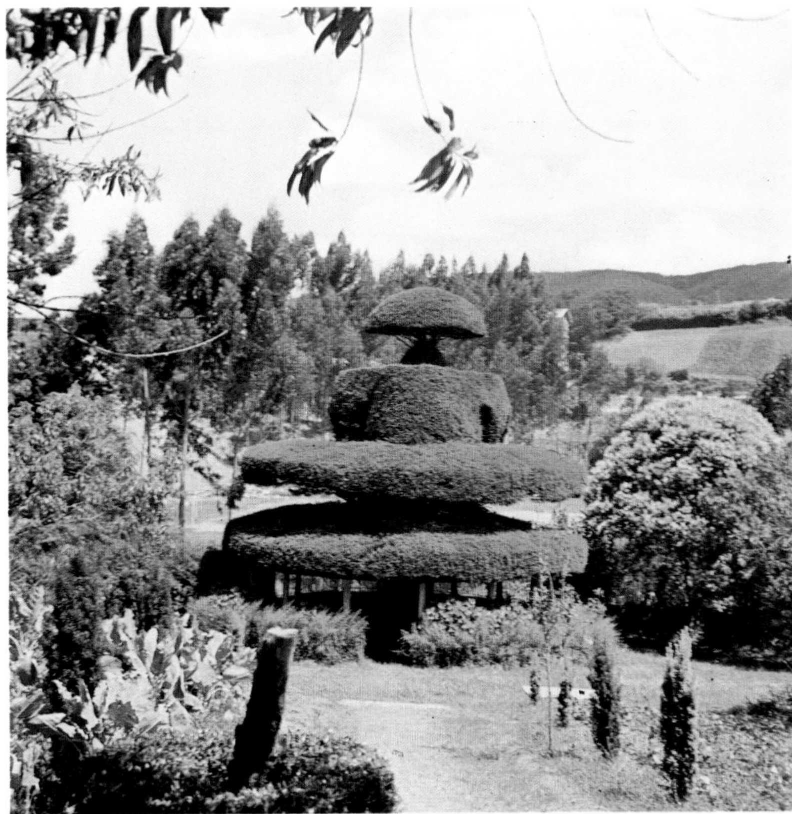

ANCIENT YEW. Puentedeume. *Photo Author.*

GARDEN OF THE CASA DE JAZ. La Coruna. *Photo Author.*

CASA DE JAZ. SOUTHERN FACADE. *Photo Author.*

MALLORCA. LA ALFABIA. COVERED WALK. *Photo S. Saavedra.*

LA ALFABIA. BAROQUE DOORWAY. *Photo S. Saavedra.*

occupation of Mallorca lasted four centuries, leaving behind the deep imprint of their civilisation and customs.

Jaime I conquered the island in 1229, and shared out the Arabs' palaces and properties among the knights who had fought with him. Some of these still remain in the ownership of the original families.

The *Sones* (a word which means "the house of") of Mallorca are nearly always built upon old Moorish foundations; and although they may have been completely transformed in the seventeenth and eighteenth centuries, the spirit in which the gardens are conceived shows Arab influence, in spite of their baroque ornamentation. These properties were normally situated on the foothills of a mountain, partly to benefit from the water flowing down the slopes, and partly to enjoy protection from the pirates who once plagued the coast. The Arabs loved views, and many of their properties overlooked the Bay of Palma.

The Arab Governor of Mallorca had his own country retreat at La Alfabia. Tradition says that his property was given to the Conde de Rosellón after the conquest of the island, and that later on, through various alliances over the centuries, it went to the Villalonga family. It was also the property of the Marqués of Vergel.

Today this garden is open to the public, which has deprived it of much of its charm. One approaches the house along an avenue of ancient plane trees leading up to a baroque porch, which acts as a kind of screen around a wide patio.

We cross the hall, on whose ceiling there is Mudejar panelling — the work of Moriscos in the thirteenth century. On the left-hand side is the shield of the Zaforteza family, with its five half-moons. The patio has a stone octagonal fontain with a much later bronze statue.

We enter the garden through a gateway which takes us to the outside of the house, where there is a stone stairway with water ducts running down its sides. This is certainly of Arab origin, as is the wide covered and paved gallery at right angles to the stairway. On the right, above the garden, is an ancient arched reservoir.

The long walk, covered with vines, wistaria and other climbing plants, is supported by octagonal stone columns with stone capitals at intervals. Fine jets of water shoot out of these, and cross each other, giving the feeling of coolness, which the Moors always sought to achieve. The effect is similar to the Patio of the Riad in the Generalife at Granada. The difference is that the Arabs of Mallorca did not have rivers to divert, such as the river Darro in Granada. They relied instead on rivulets flowing down the mountain sides. At the east end of this walk there is an old fountain of indeterminate age, with criss-crossing jets of water. While these decorations date from the eighteenth century the garden's layout is probably Arab.

On the same level as the house, there is another garden of ancient trees, probably laid out in the last century.

Inside the house, which is of traditional Mallorcan style, there is a fourteenth century Gothic wooden chair with carvings representing a lady and gentleman dressed in the style of the Middle Ages, playing chess under the shade of a tree, and on the front panel of the seat, two lions contest the capture of a rabbit.[11]

A short distance from the Alfabia on the road from Palma to Sóller, hidden in the fold of a mountain, stands the gateway to the Raxa estate, which in Moorish times was called Araxa and must have been an important agricultural property.

"When King Jaime divided the Moorish properties among his noblemen after the conquest of the Islands, he gave Raxa to the Conde de Ampurias as a reward for loyal service. From him it passed to Don Bernardo Guillén, the Sacristan of Gerona, and later to the noble families of San Martí and Zaforteza Tagament."[12] In 1670 it came into the possession of the Despuig family, one of whose descendants was Cardinal Antonio Despuig of Dameto. He restored it in the Italian style of the late eighteenth century as it appears today. The Cardinal was born in Palma in 1745, and was successively Bishop of Orihuela and Archbishop of Valencia and Seville. He must have spent many years in Italy, as after having bought the lands in Ariccia (an ancient Roman town in the Albano mountains) from the Scottish painter Hamilton,[13] he undertook a number of important excavations, and sent ships to Mallorca laden with the statues and inscriptions which for many years adorned his house at Raxa. One of these was the funeral urn of Claudius Marcellus which came from the Mausoleum of Augustus in Rome and which today is in Lonja de Palma. (Appendix VI).

He assembled a large collection of exotic plants in these Italianised gardens, and several naturalists from the Botanical Garden in Madrid, particularly Don Casimiro Ortega and Don Hipólito Ruiz, friends of the Cardinal, would send to Raxa for bulbs and plants imported from America.[14]

Despuig was a highly cultured eighteenth century man; he had a superb library, and was a patron of the arts in Mallorca.

In the garden of Raxa, it is probable that the stairway with the water ducts running down its side and the upper terraced garden were already there, along with the house that divided it from the lower garden. The pool, used as the garden's source of water, was also used for irrigation by the Moors. With all this in place the Cardinal could concentrate on ornamenting his monumental stairway, which consisted of seven miniature terraces. By the side of its balustrade two channels of water lead to grotesque faces spurting water into basins beside the house. Mrs. Villiers Stuart, saw in these terraces the eight symbolic terraces of the Islamic paradise, which were so often represented in Arab gardens. But since land was terraced throughout the island, simply to permit cultivation — perhaps by the very same Arabs — we must assume that the terraces were created for practical rather than symbolic reasons. On reaching the fifth terrace and turning left along the lateral path, we come to the large water tank ornamented by Cardinal Despuig with a semicircular belvedere with a stone table, obviously influenced by the *al fresco* meals served in Italian gardens in the eighteenth century, like those which Cardinal Gámbara liked so much at the Villa Lante. A more beautiful spot would be difficult to find.

At the top of the stairway is its crowning centrepiece: a

RAXA. POND. *Photo S. Saavedra.*

RAXA. STAIRWAY. *Photo S. Saavedra.*

RAXA. FOUNTAIN AND EXEDRA. FINAL STAIRWAY. *Photo S. Saavedra.*

RAXA. LOWER GARDEN. *Photo Author.*

semicircular portico with a fountain, whose gargoyle head spouts water into a shell-shaped basin. This Italianate structure is adorned by six Tuscan columns, and has a statue in the centre.

Descending the stairway again we pass through the house to reach the rooms which in years gone by housed the collections of statues. The house is classical Mallorcan, today more or less abandoned.

An American who once resided here tells an interesting story: as the house had no water or other conveniences, she undertook some extensive alterations, among other places, in the dining room. During this work she removed the furniture to a small room on the floor above, which could only be reached by a narrow staircase. One day she went upstairs and noticed that a priest's armchair, which had been placed on a table, was suspended in the air half a metre above it, against a wall. She called a friend, and between them they replaced the chair on the table, noticing a certain resistance as they did so, although there was nothing visible holding the chair up in the air. Later, she claims to have heard footsteps descending from the servants' quarters and stopping outside her door. On one occasion, thinking someone must be ill, she opened the door, but there was no one there. She says she never felt afraid because the beings seemed to be friendly.

Crossing the narrow patio and descending the stairway to the right we come to the lower garden. It is rectangular in shape, with a central pergola of arched cypresses sheltering a round fountain. The ancient trees lend it mystery and beauty. In the façade of the house overlooking this garden is the classical loggia of the Mallorcan house.

Returning along the avenue on our right, in a little square garden, is a handsome bust of a woman, perhaps one of the sculptures brought from Italy, which, after having been exhibited for many years in the Castle of Bellver, today are waiting to be taken elsewhere.

Cardinal Despuig's descendants, the Condes de Montenegro and Montoro, sold the property over the course of the years. When Chopin and Georges Sand stayed in Mallorca in 1839, the latter wrote in her memoirs[15] (in which Chopin refused to allow his name to appear), "that the Conde de Montenegro was at that time an octogenarian, whose palace in Palma they had visited, and who possessed a magnificent library collected by his uncle the Cardinal." It was in this library that, when they were being shown the map of the Mallorcan Valsequa — a manuscript dated 1439 which had belonged to Americo Vespuccio — someone upset an inkwell over it, to the consternation of Georges Sand and everyone else present.

On the outside of the gateway is the double-headed eagle of the Emperor Charles V. The Emperor's life was saved at the Battle of Augsburg by a Despuig to whom, and to whose descendants, the right was given to bear this image on their coat of arms.[16]

Turning to the left just after the ten kilometre mark on the road from Palma to Valdemosa, and continuing along the Esporlas road a short way, we find on the left an iron railing

RAXA. GATEWAY. *Photo S. Saavedra.*

RAXA. ANCIENT BUST. *Photo Author.*

supported by two columns from which rises a monumental stairway. This is the property of the Canet family. As can be seen from the plan the stairway is the most important part of the building as the house above is simply a large, square, whitewashed structure overlooking the valley. In the distribution of land after the Conquest this property was given to Ramón Canet, the Lord of Torellá. The present house was built in the first half of the eighteenth century upon Arab foundations. Today this monumental stairway, in the midst of the garden, has fallen into neglect. In 1932 the house was bought by the Gual Torrellá family, who built a landscaped garden below, containing a sizeable lily pond. The house is very large and has recently been converted into apartments, but the owners have preserved a drawing room of great character, its walls hung with numerous pictures of the time of the former owners.

From here one may easily reach the Cartuja de Valldemosa, an ancient Cistercian monastry. Tourists, attracted by the mystique of Chopin and Georges Sand, have ruined its atmosphere, but there are two houses with peaceful and charming gardens. Areas that once were the site of the monks' cells have been converted into small secluded plots with views over the valley, and in the background the white buildings of Palma can be seen.

This monastery has a wide square tower, as it was once the castle of King Sancho who built it in 1321. Bover tells us that for a long time "the King lived and kept his falconry there. In 1399 he gave it to King Martín of Aragon to found a Carthusian monastery, which it remained until 1835, when Mendizábal suppressed the religious orders."[17]

SON CANET. *Drawing by Arthur Byne.*

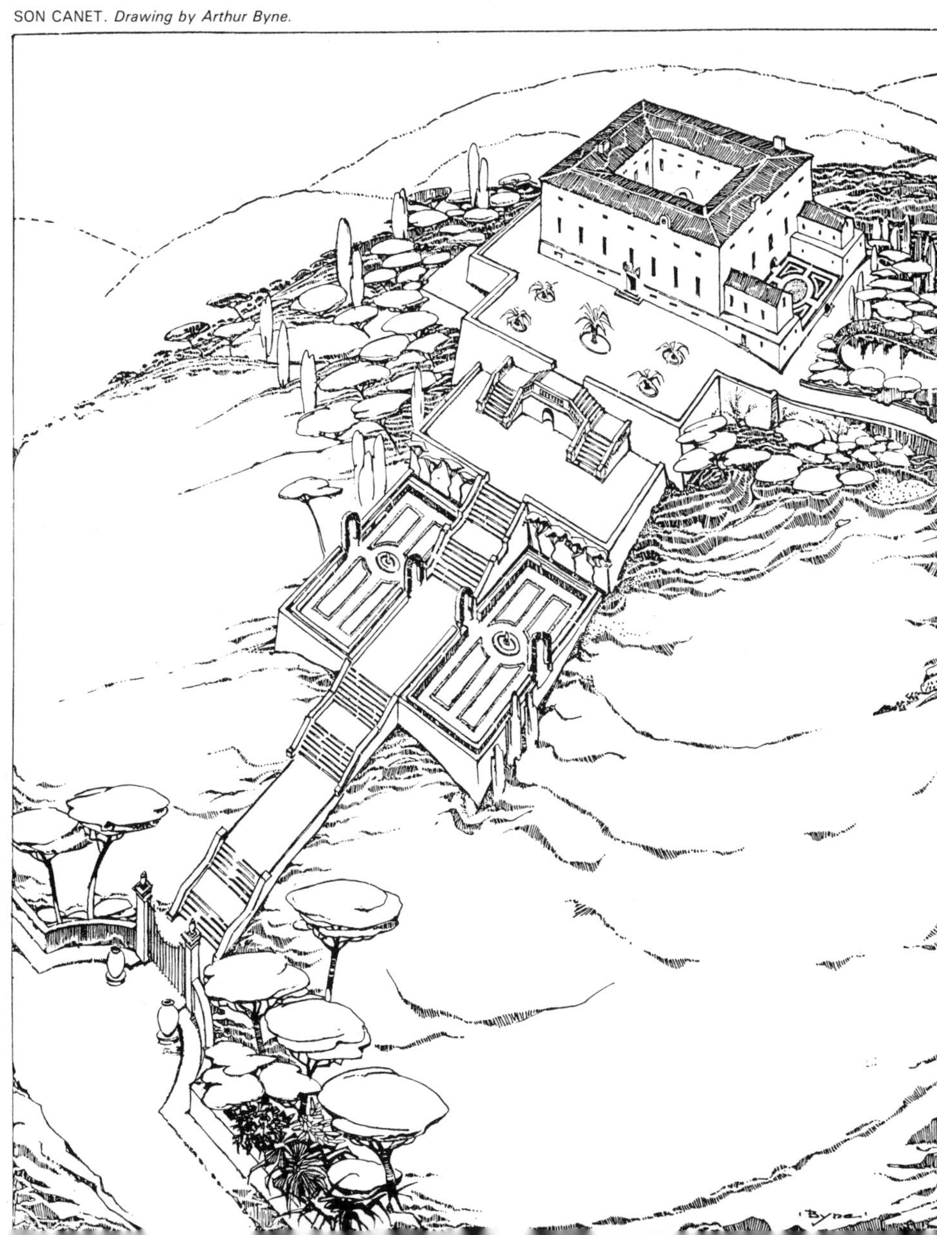

SON MARROIG. TEMPLE. *Photo S. Saavedra.*

MAP OF SON BERGA. *A. Byne.*

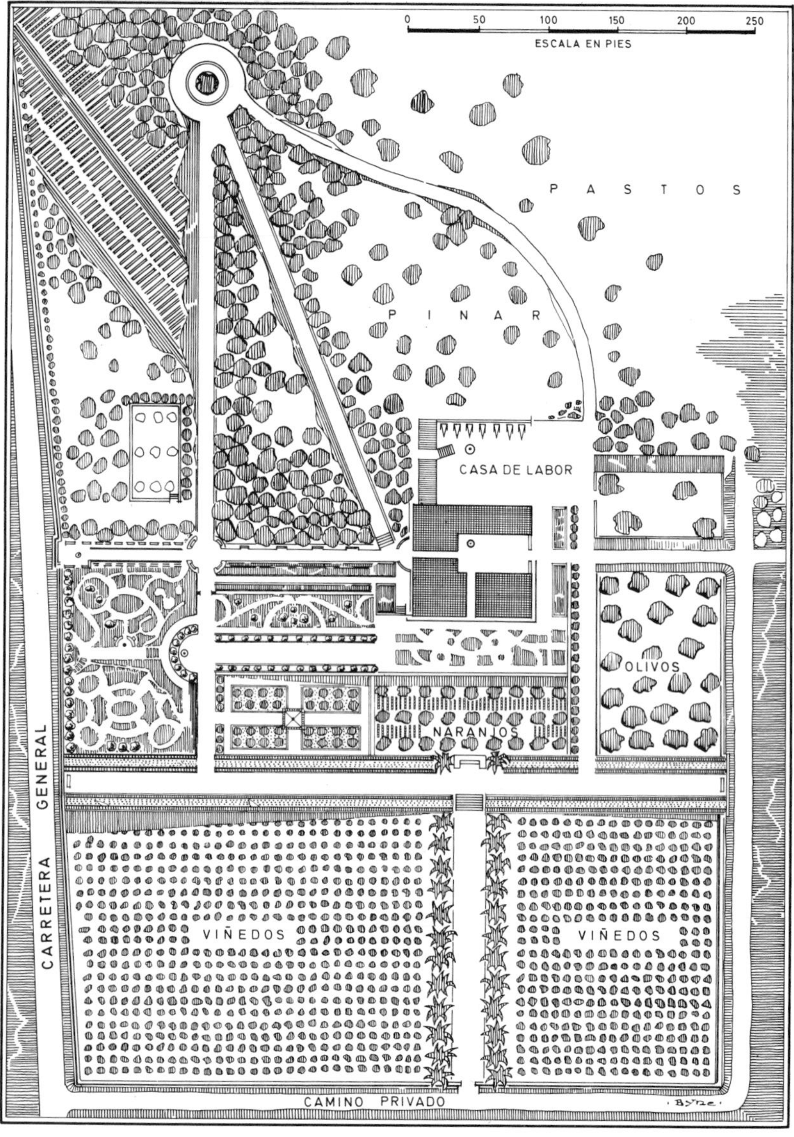

On leaving Valldemosa a handsome building with a typical Mallorcan loggia can be seen high up on the right. This is the San Moragues which has a beautiful baroque fountain in its patio.

This palace was the property of Leopold Salvador of Habsburg, Archduke of Austria. He lived on this coast for many years and had other palaces there, including San Marroig and Miramar. Opposite the north façade of San Moragues, on the hillside, there is a steeply sloping garden with balconies and stairways, and some very fine trees. Next to the house itself is a small garden with an oval pool. To the left is a curious white marble statue representing the Sacred Heart, signed by Monteverde in 1913, with a life-size female figure prostrate at its feet. Today this property is a Mallorcan museum.

Continuing our journey towards the steep and rocky western coast of the island we come to the Palace of Miramar, with the belvederes built by the Archduke of Austria on the sheer natural balconies overlooking the sea. After several bends we come to San Marroig, the ancient seat of the Marroig de Soles family. Here the Archduke built a temple of Carrera marble in imitation of the one on the flower-filled islet of the Pallavicini garden at Pegli near Genoa, with a marvellous view over the sea. He also built the road which goes down to the Na Foradada rock.

The house is filled with memorabilia from the Archduke's life and is open to the public. He left one wing unfinished when he died in 1915. The house belongs today to Doña Luisa Vives Ripoll.

This part of the coast is rich in Balearic flora, including those ancient olive trees which give the island so much character.

To visit the remaining old houses one must return to Palma and go out along the road to the small village of Establisments, site of the Son Berga, belonging to the Zaforteza family. This old country house, built in 1766, has a characteristic Mallorcan patio, with the bottom of a stone stairway beneath a striking and dignified arch.

The garden is in two parts: the lower older garden, to the east of the house at the foot of the façade, contains the loggia with its three arches. This is the charming Orange Garden, forming a small rectangle with an arbour in the centre covered in bougainvillea and supported by four Doric columns. The four long beds are each planted with two rows of orange trees. This same garden layout in the form of a cross was also once used at Roqueta, near the village of María de la Salud; it had the same type of arbour in the centre (now gone), but with square columns.

A long avenue of palm trees leads down to the road. It is a pity that its line is interrupted half-way down by a seat backed with tamarisks.

The upper garden, whose outside wall borders the main road, is a park which has been well laid out, obviously by a French gardener. The use of axis and perspective is clearly apparent, and the paths lead to a bench or architectural motif which is so typical of the French school, and seems like the work of a former century.

The garden has lost many of the motifs which were there when Mrs. Byne drew her plan, but it is still tidy and well kept. There is a view of Palma in the distance.

From Establisments we go to the charming little village of Puigpunyent, with its walls hanging with creeping geraniums of the species known as *Gitamilla* (Little Gipsy). Nearby, at the foot of a high mountain, we find the most romantic place in all Mallorca, Son Forteza de Puigpunyent, generally called "El Salt" after the waterfall at the foot of the nearby mountain. This is an old Mallorcan farmhouse with a wide terrace containing a fountain, probably eighteenth century, in the corner.

The terraced garden has two fine *Araucaria excelsa* trees on the side that faces towards Palma.

In the patio or "clastra" where the keepers of the property live (who are known as the "amo" (master) and the "madona" (madam), there is a large and ancient kitchen with a wide hearth and a masonry seat running around it. Here the country-people would gather for entertainment in the winter.

Down the road, about a quarter of a mile from the house, we come to a turning where there is a mysterious iron gate, permanently secured with a padlock. This is the least known and most beautiful part of the property. A long covered walk, reminiscent of the walk at La Alfabia, but longer, covered with hazel-trees and flanked by cypresses, leads to the foot of a rocky escarpment. Here the walk opens out into a small bower, with an iron frame around it covered with wistaria and vines, and beneath them an oval stone table looking down on a lake of waterlilies.

A waterfall rushes down the mountain side. This is El Salt. When it rains, water gushes into this lake, afterwards running in channels along the edge of the covered avenue. It is a place of indescribable beauty, and obviously of Arab origin.

Today this property belongs to Don Rafael Villalonga, who lives in Palma and spends the summer here.

To visit La Granja de Fortuny one has to return to Establisments. There is another road which crosses the mountain between Esporlas and Puigpunyent, but it is narrow and dangerous. It is best to take the road to Banalbufar, passing through Esporlas. At a distance of five kilometres, in a narrow valley, we come across the ancient Arab property called Alpich, which was said to possess water in abundance. After the Conquest of Mallorca it became a Cistercian monastery. Later it belonged to the Vida family, whose attractive *Son* is near Palma and has been converted into a hotel. In 1665 it passed into the hands of the Fortuny family, and today it is open to the public. It is one of the most outstanding *sones* of Mallorca from the architectural point of view, with its open colonnaded portico overlooking an old garden. In the centre of the garden there is a fountain with a jet of water that shoots up higher than the top of the house.[18] In one corner stands an ancient yew tree.

Mrs. Villiers Stuart says that when Sir John Carr dined here in 1809, he noted in his diary that "there were fountains whose waters played in every sort of fantastic shape".

The garden is in two parts, following the Arab tradition observed at Raxa and and Alfabia. There is the upper garden behind the house, on the mountainside, with fountains and arbours, and the lower garden below the fountain.

In almost all these *sones,* Palma can be seen in the distance from the loggia of the house, and we get the impression (as with

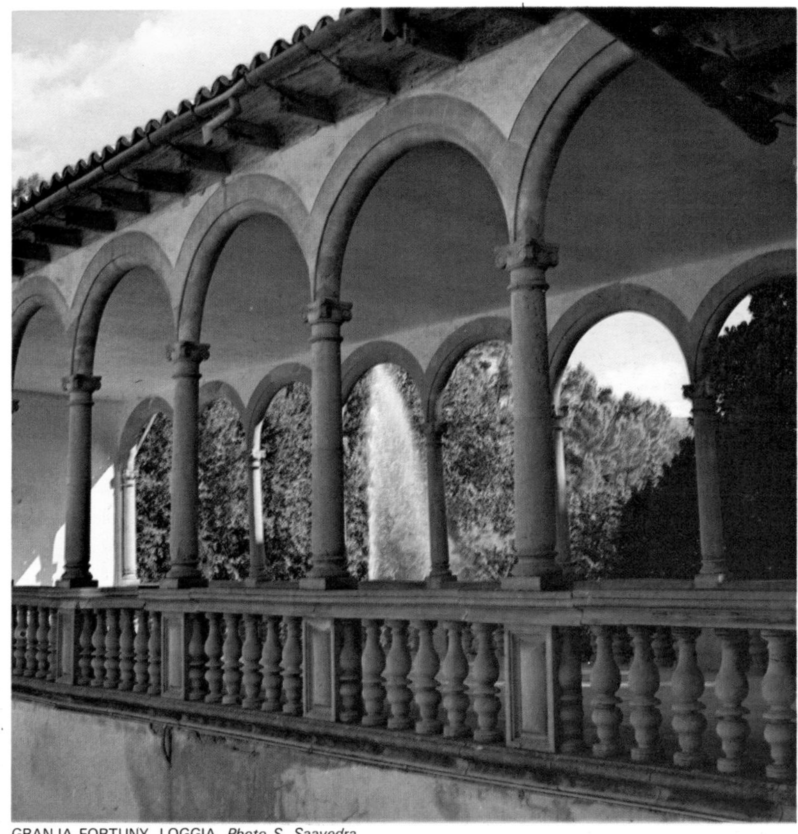

GRANJA FORTUNY. LOGGIA. *Photo S. Saavedra.*

SON FORTEZA. EL SALT: TERRACE FOUNTAIN. *Photo Author.*

GRANJA FORTUNY. FOUNTAIN. *Photo S. Saavedra.*

SON TORRELLA. PATIO. *Photo S. Saavedra.*

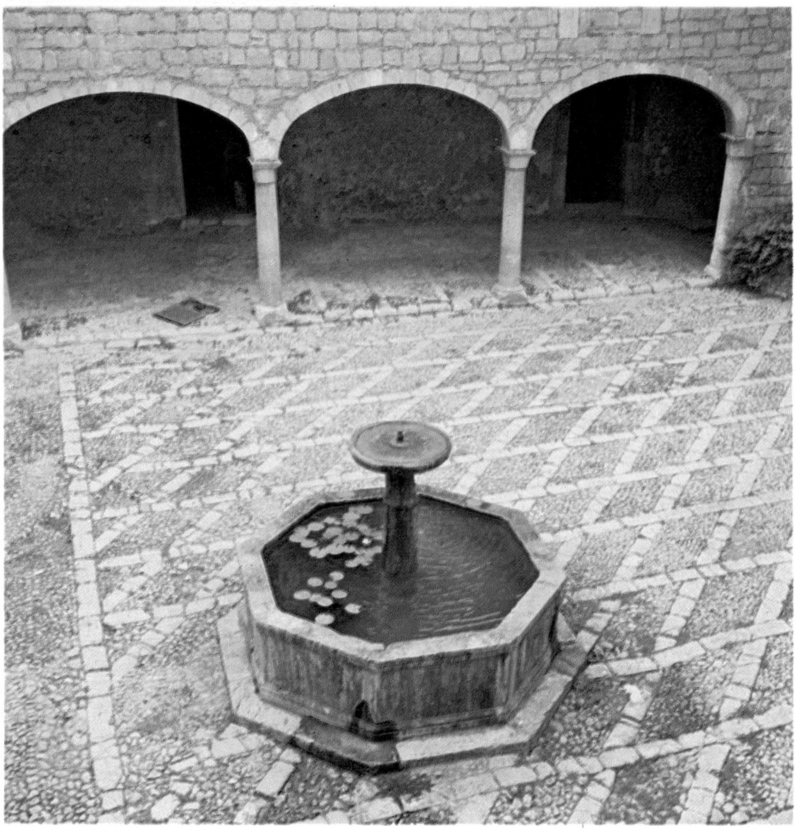

the Carmens of Granada and the Cigarrales of Toledo) that these old, and originally Arab, properties were designed to afford a view of the city.

We have still to come to Son Torrella, near the village of Santa Maria, on the road to Valldemosa. This is an elegant ancestral home distinguished by its possession of a two-storied patio surrounded with pillars and arches, and containing a fountain in the centre, which recalls the one on the terrace of Son Forteza at El Salt. Patios like this one are not usually found in Mallorca, for Mallorcan houses, both *sones* and town palaces, either lost their Arab patios, or never had them. In every Mallorcan town, patios follow the Catalan or Italian style with a stone stairway starting from the outer wall of the patio and giving it the appearance of an entrance hall.

As with Galicia, Mallorca's highest moment was in the eighteenth century, when the *sones* were transformed and decorated. Most of the gardens date from that period, probably because it was a time of prosperity and because of Italian influence.

Son Torrella had the good fortune to fall into loving hands and its original character has been restored and preserved. In the lower part of the property, where there was a small stream, lie a pretty garden and a swimming pool with a colonnaded loggia, in keeping with the house. An old cypress tree dominates the entrance.

The Castle of Defla, reached by the Sineu road over the plain, belongs to the Condes de España and is one of the few properties in Mallorca with a crenellated Arab tower. These defensive towers were always situated in the centre of the island, away from the pirate-infested coast. The house is next to the tower and has a patio with a central fountain and a chapel. There is also a beautiful terrace with eighteenth century balusters and clay figures.

THE CIGARRALES OF TOLEDO

The *cigarrales* of Toledo are small farms or countryhouses surrounding the imperial city, on the opposite bank of the river Tagus from Toledo. Most of them belonged to religious orders who used them for rest and retreat. "The original inhabitants and cultivators of the *cigarrales,*" Marañón tells us, "were the Arabs." The houses are generally small and the gardens compact; some of them were once convents, or smaller branches of the large monasteries in the city. Friars in poor health, or simply needing spiritual refreshment would come here for rest and retreat."[19]

Their position was always within sight of the city, in a landscape resembling Arabia or Africa, with its hedges of prickly pear and Agave around the houses, and its grey rocks against the red earth. The word *cigarral* stems from *cigarras* (crickets), heard here in great numbers in the heat of the summer. The gardens are naturally rugged and steep on account of their situation, and generally have narrow paths edged with scented shrubs, such as lavender and rosemary. On the high banks the irises, madonna lilies and roses grow almost spontaneously. In the autumn the Toledo hills are covered with a shrub whose leaves turn brilliant scarlet, the *Sumach (Rhus coriaria),* a name which reflects its place of origin. In spring the air is scented with lilac, wallflowers and roses, and vine-arbours provide shade.

The mountain sides are planted with ancient olive trees, mingled with almond and apricot trees. The latter were grafted by the Arabs onto the sweet almond and, according to Abu Zacaria in his book on agriculture,[20] were called *damasquinos,* for they were brought from Damascus. The fruit of this tree is smaller than that of the common apricot and is distinguished by tiny black spots on the skin. They grow more abundantly in La Puebla de Montalbán, but are slowly becoming extinct in the Toledo region, because the Arab skill for grafting has been lost. Those that still survive are old and cannot be replaced.

The almonds are used to make the famous marzipans of Toledo and the apricots go into exquisite crystallised fruits.

The cigarral of *La Cadena* is gay and cheerful. Situated on the top of the hill that overlooks Toledo on the western side, it has, in our opinion, the most beautiful view.

There are documents about this *cigarral* dating from 1600, the probable time of its construction. Father Mariana, the

SON TORRELLA. LOGGIA AND POND. *Photo S. Saavedra.*

DEFLA. FIGURE IN GARDEN. *Photo S. Saavedra.*

CASTLE OF DEFLA. *Photo S. Saavedra.*

CIGARRAL DE LA CADENA. DOORWAY. Toledo. *Photo Author.*

well-known Jesuit who wrote a history of Spain, is known to have lived here, probably during the last years of his life, for he died in 1623.

In 1667 the documents record "the Cigarral of La Cadena on the road to La Bastida, belonging to the Society of Jesus [The Jesuits], who used it as a school for spiritual exercises". These old documents describe it as "situated on the edge of the town, on the road to our Lady of La Bastida, entirely surrounded by thatched walls, mostly of mud but some of stone. It is planted with apricot, almond and other fruit trees, including olives, pears, apples and plums; there are also hawthorn bushes, blackberries, vines, roses and other flowers."[21]

In the lower part of this *cigarral* is a delightful corner consisting of a bower with a central fountain. The documents tell us that "a summerhouse stood nearby with a kitchen and a well", where the priests probably cooked their meals on hot summer days.

Whitewashed railings, so typical of the *cigarrales,* assist in the ascent to the house. The murmur of the Tagus as it glides through the valley is heard in the distance.

The *cigarral* of the late Doctor Maranon lies on the road to the mountains of Toledo, further south than the last one. The view of the city is superb, and the kindly spirit of the great Don Gregorio Maranon seems to linger in this place he loved so much.

CIGARRAL DE MARANON. STONE PLAQUE. *Photo Author.*

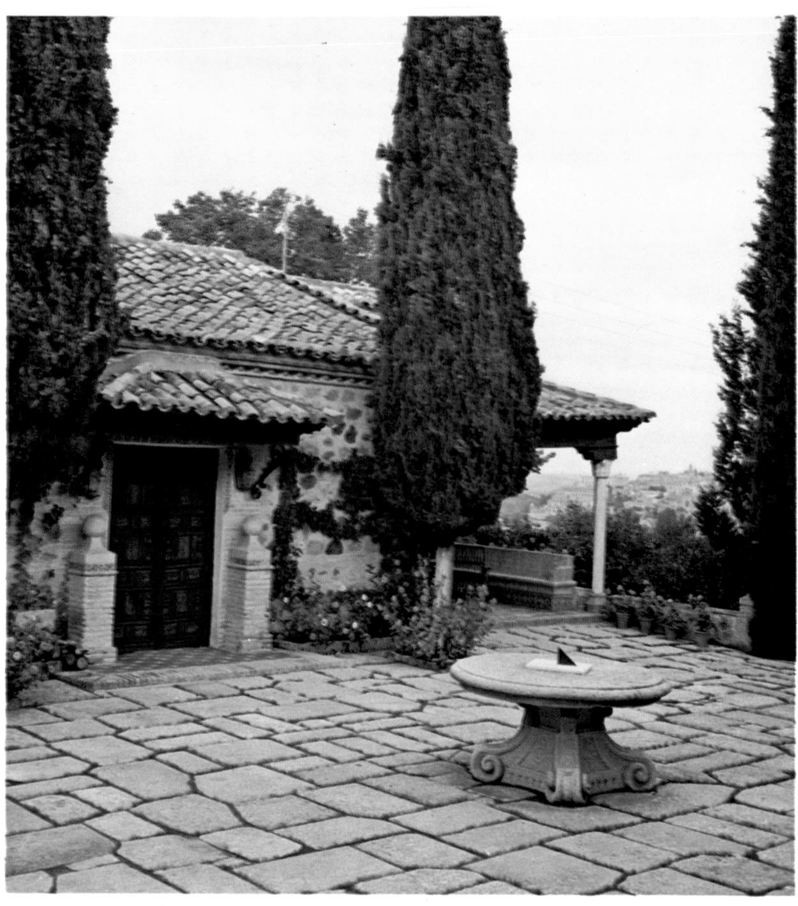

CIGARRAL DE MARANON. ENTRANCE. *Photo Author.*

We recall him seated on the terrace, contemplating the marvellous view of the city.

At the entrance lies a broad paved rectangle, in the centre of which stands a round marble table with sundial, a gift from the Count of Romanones. It came from Alvaro de Luna's palace in Cadalso de los Vidrios.

Two old cypresses stand guard at either side of the door, through which so many renowned figures have passed. Today the house conveys to us a sense of longing for a vanished presence. We descend a narrow path leading to the bench where the Doctor used to meditate or read. Going down a few steps we come to a small square with a tiny fountain on the wall. Over it a marble slab commemorates Maurice Barrés's stay in Toledo. It was here that he wrote *Le Gréco ou le sécret de Tolèdo,* and here also that his famous portrait was painted by Zuloaga, with the view of Toledo in the background.

It was known long ago as "de Menores" as it served as a place of retreat and rest for the *Clérigos Regulares Menores* (Lesser Regular Clergy), who were introduced in Spain in the sixteenth century during the lifetime of their founder, St. Francis Caracciolo. According to Ramón Parro, who wrote an excellent *History of Toledo,* "these regular priests never had a proper convent, but a modest hostelry in Toledo, on a small street called 'de Menores'."[22] "Their quarters in Toledo were established outside the town, in the *cigarral* founded in 1618."[23]

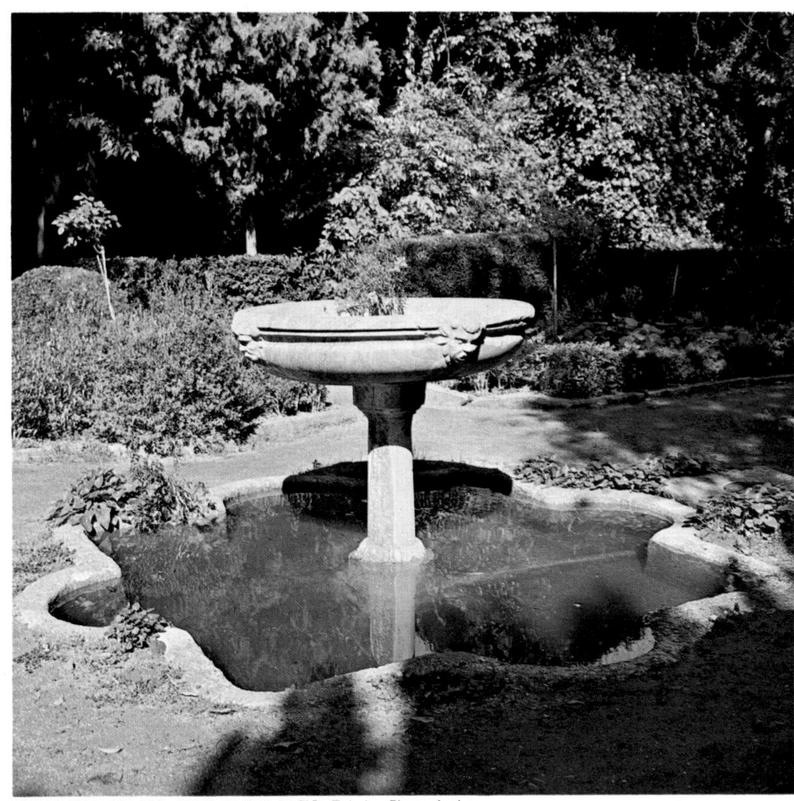

BUENAVISTA PALACE. POND IN THE PATIO. Toledo. *Photo Author.*

VIEW OF TOLEDO FROM LA CADENA. *Photo Author.*

The *cigarral* of Buenavista is situated in the valley on the banks of the river, quite some distance from town; it is the only *cigarral* on the outskirts of the city. The term *cigarral* is hardly appropriate because this is really a small palace. It was founded by Cardinal de Sandoval y Rojas in the sixteenth century and designed by Doménico Theotocópuli (El Greco). Tirso de Molina (the seventeenth century writer famous for his *Cigarrales de Toledo*) describes it as a "country seat or *cigarral,* so appropriately named Buenavista by its illustrious owner".[24]

Marañón tells us: "A literary Academy used to meet in the Palace of Buenavista. The praise of this princely mansion was fervently sung by the poet Medinilla, and it served as a pleasant retreat for the greatest men of letters of the time. The gardens were filled with cages of exotic birds and a profusion of pagan statues that the Cardinal had sent from Italy; his humanistic and somewhat pagan spirit is portrayed in a quaotation from Horace engraved on the lintel of the door: 'Ille terrarum mihi praeter omnes angulus ridet' (Ode IV, Book II). This is the corner of the earth that smiles at me more than any other."[25]

There are no longer any bird cages or pagan statues in the garden. The Count of Romanones, owner of Buenavista, adorned the wide terrace above the river with stone motifs from the Palace of Cadalso de los Vidrios, and the very old black elm trees may well be those that cast their shadow over the seventeenth century poets.

Inside the house there is a secluded patio in the centre of which stands a beautiful sixteenth century grey marble fountain, which belonged to the Cardinal. The Tagus flows gently past the property towards Talavera and the sea.

Towards sunset Toledo turns golden-pink and seems to vibrate with life as do so many other beautiful cities that face west, such as Segovia, Granada, Compostela.

BUENAVISTA. DOOR. *Photo Author.*

BUENAVISTA PALACE.

APPENDIX VI

We know that Despuig was sent to Rome with Cardinals Lorenzana and Muzquiz to help the unfortunate Pope Pius VI in 1797. The latter, a victim of the French Revolution, had come into conflict with Napoleon — at that time Pro-Consul of the Directory in Italy — who had conquered and plundered Italy in 1796. Pope Pius held Despuig in high esteem and made him Patriarch of Antioch a few months before he died in 1799, exiled by Napoleon to Valence.

After the Pope's death Despuig returned to Spain, but was again sent to Venice for the election of the new Pope, Pius VII. He was made a Cardinal in 1803. Pius VII's pontificate was an unlucky one. In order to re-establish Roman Catholicism in France he had to agree to crown Napoleon in Nôtre Dame (on 2 December 1804); but of course, Napoleon seized the crown from the Pope's hands and placed it on his own head. Rome was occupied by the French in 1807 and the Pope finally went into exile, but not before he had taken the courageous step (in 1809) of excommunicating Napoleon. The faithful Despuig accompanied the Pope and was never again to see his native land. He died in Lucca in 1813, ten years before the Pope.

[1] LEDWARD, Patricia: *Amateur Gardening,* 19th September 1970, page 30.

[2] LAMPÉREZ Y ROMEA, V.: *Arquitectura civil española,* Ed. Saturnino Calleja, Madrid, 1922, vol. I, page 624.

[3] *Los pazos gallegos.* Marqués de Quintanar, Javier Oxores and José Cao Moure, cuaderno IV, Vigo, 1929.

[4] *Los pazos gallegos.* Marqués de Quintanar, Javier Ozores and José Cao Moure, cuaderno VII, Vigo, 1932.

[5] ODRIOZOLA, Antonio: Centro Agronómico de Lourizán (Pontevedra).

[6] Archivo de Camarasa. Casa de Pilatos. Seville.

[7] COUSELO BOUZÁS, J.: *Galicia artística en el siglo XVIII y primera mitad del XIX,* Santiago, 1933, page 367.

[8] COUSELO BOUZÁS, J.: *Op. cit.,* page 695.

[9] FORD, Richard: *Handbook for travellers in Spain,* 3rd ed., Murrays Guide Books, London, 1855, part II, page 596.

[10] *Los pazos gallegos.* Marqués de Quintanar, Javier Ozores and José Cao Moure, cuaderno I, Vigo, 1928.

[11] PIFFERER Y CUADRADO: *Islas Baleares,* Barcelona, 1888, page 997.

[12] BOVER, Joaquín María: *Noticias históricas y topográficas de la isla de Mallorca,* Palma, 1864, page 220.

[13] BOVER, J.M.: *Op. cit.,* page 220.

[14] ALOMAR, Gabriel: *Anales de la Fundación Juan March,* "El Cardenal Despuig" (reprint), Madrid, 1964, page IX.

[15] SAND, Georges: *Un hiver à Mallorque,* Paris, 1839.

[16] BYNE, Arthur, and STAPLEY, Mildred: *Mallorcan Houses and Gardens,* page 14.

[17] BOVER, J.M.: *Op. cit.,* page 70.

[18] BYNE, Arthur, and STAPLEY, Mildred: *Op. cit.,* page 10.

[19] MARÑÓN, Gregorio: *Elogio y nostalgia de Toledo,* Espasa-Calpe, Madrid, 1941, pages 38 & 55.

[20] ABU ZACARIA AMED IBN AL-AWWÁN, SEVILLANO: *Libro de la Agricultura,* translated by José Banquieri in 1802, Seville, 1878, page 180.

[21] Archivo de doña Carmen Azañón de Aguirre, Toledo.

[22] PARRO, Ramón: *Toledo en la mano,* Toledo, 1857, vol. II, page 83.

[23] MARAÑÓN, G.: *Op. cit.,* page 52.

[24] TIRSO DE MOLINA: Los cigarrales de Toledo, Espasa-Calpe, Col. Austral, Madrid, 1968, page 49.

[25] MARAÑÓN, G.: *El Greco y toledo,* Espasa-Calpe, Madrid, 1956, page 99.

THE TAGUS VIEWED FROM BUENAVISTA. *Photo Author.*

13 THE NEOCLASSICAL STYLE

CHARLES III AND CHARLES IV

The Neoclassical style appeared in Spain towards the end of the reign of Charles III, in the late eighteenth century. It was to continue until after the War of Independence (1808—1814), well into the nineteenth century.

This style drew its inspiration from Graeco-Roman ruins, beginning with the discovery in 1748 of Herculaneum and later of Pompeii, which had been buried since the year 79 on the slopes of Vesuvius. King Charles III was the guiding force behind these excavations; they aroused the admiration of the German archaeologist Winckelmann, who expounded his theories in several treatises.

The neoclassical movement was inspired further by the marbles and bas-reliefs of the friezes in the Parthenon at Athens, transported by Lord Elgin from Greece to London at the beginning of the nineteenth century. By so doing he launched the vogue for classical art.

The rococo art of Louis XV, which inspired Philip V's La Granja, had been dominant through the eighteenth century. Now neoclassicism was to dominate in the design of gardens as well as architecture and decoration.

In France, straight lines were already beginning to come into favour in the time of Louis XVI, and Graeco-Roman motifs were being imitated. Temples, statues of mythological deities, and pillars were appearing in the gardens, all in the purest form of the style called "Pompeian". Cypress hedges were used to set off statues; parks were filled with grottoes, ruins and hermitages in the "picturesque" style; and paths were traced in winding patterns. It was a return to nature as described by Jean Jacques Rousseau in *La Nouvelle Héloïse*, and Milton in his *Paradise Lost.*

This movement was also inspired by the paintings of ruins by Claude Gellée (Le Lorrain) and Poussin. It began in England where the countryside was remarkably suitable for rustic imitation. Later it spread to France, where Marie Antoinette played at shepherdess in the hamlet she had had built by the architect Mique at the Petit Trianon in Versailles towards the end of the eighteenth century. Her village contained a mill, a dairy and a tower based on drawings by Hubert Robert, and

CAMPO DEL MORO. FOUNTAIN OF THE SHELLS.
Photo S. Saavedra. By permission of the National Heritage.

TEMPLE OF VILLANUEVA. Aranjuez. *Photo Author.* By permission of the National Heritage.

executed by the gardener A. Richard, who had to remove part of the botanical garden that her grandfather-in-law, Louis XV, had created.

It was not long before this naturalistic trend reached Spain. At Aranjuez the Royal Family built the Casa del Labrador, a little palace in the Pompeian style. Built somewhat earlier than 1803, the date indicated on the façade (several of the ceilings were painted in 1792),[1] it contains a collection of statues, most of which came from the excavations at Tivoli in Italy. While Charles IV was still Prince of Asturias he laid out the landscape garden known as the Prince's Garden, which is approached by the magnificent Queen's Avenue, three kilometres in length. There is an artificial lake decorated with the Temple of Venus, an exquisite work by Villanueva, which once had statues between its pillars. Their square bases still remain. No doubt they were inspired by the Temple of Love in the garden of the Petit Trianon at Versailles.

The so-called Swiss Mountain, crowned by a pavilion, and the Chinese Pagoda are typical of styles fashionable in England at that time. A fish-hatchery has now been set up in this lake. These gardens are quite sombre, for the trees have grown to enormous proportions. There are a number of fountains among their arbours, like the lovely Fountain of Narcissus, of the same period as the garden, and the rather complicated Fountain of Apollo.

By following a long avenue to the left, before we reach the Prince's Garden we find the remains of a castle in the background, on the banks of the Tagus. It has now been

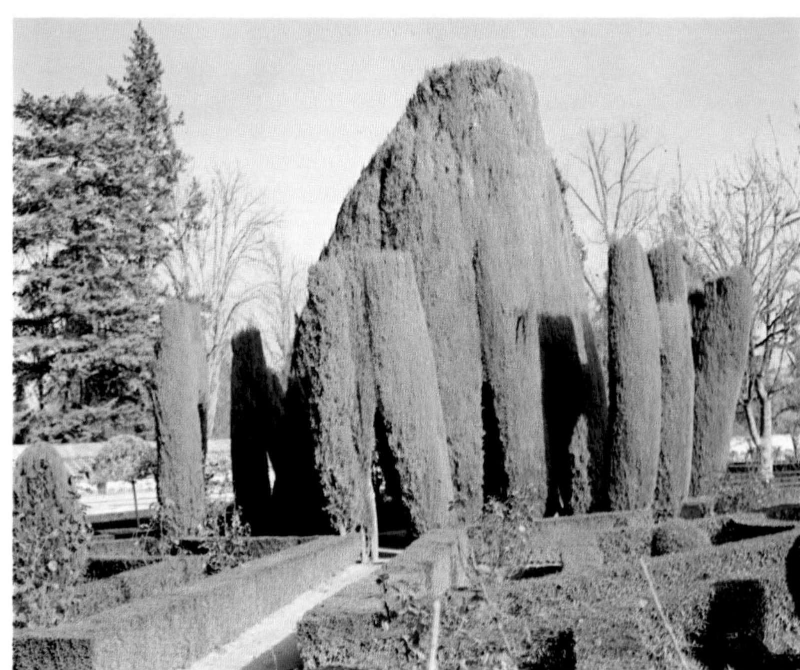

JARDIN DEL PRINCIPE. PERGOLA CYPRESSES. Aranjuez. *Photo Author.* By permission of the National Heritage.

CHINESE PAGODA. Aranjuez. *Photo Author.* By permission of the National Heritage.

converted into a restaurant. Further on is an enchanting little garden known as La Florera, very much in the English style. It was apparently designed by an Irish architect in the time of Charles III for the Prince; it lends a note of gaiety and colour to the park.[2] Four trellis-covered pavilions are arranged in a square, in whose centre stands a large pavilion decorated and furnished in the style of the period. Arches of roses encircle the outer edge of this little garden with its boxwood hedges, and opposite is the lovely cypress bower, which was painted by Rusiñol. There is a baroque pool of grey marble in the centre, now adorned with "the figure of Neptune, reclining and grouped with a seahorse", which, according to Madoz, "was placed in a secluded corner of the Prince's Garden, with its waters forming a little stream; it is one of the best statues there."[3]

This is a delightful, sunny garden. If we go down to the banks of the Tagus we shall find the Mariners' House, which has recently been restored. Here there are barges and other royal boats used for sailing on the river, and some very fine ones still remain. Some of these boats are portrayed in Amigoni's picture of the musician Farinelli in Ferdinand VI's time.

Today Aranjuez, rather like Versailles, lives only on memories, a witness to past glories. It evokes a nostalgia characteristic of royal sites that have become museums, sites that were once alive with the splendour of the Court.

Arriving from Madrid along several magnificent avenues, we

LA FLORERA PAVILION. Aranjuez. *Photo Author.* By permission of the National Heritage.

JARDIN DEL PRINCIPE. NARCISSUS FOUNTAIN. Aranjuez. *Photo Oronoz.* By permission of the National Heritage.

CASA DEL LABRADOR. Aranjuez. *Photo Oronoz.* By permission of the National Heritage.

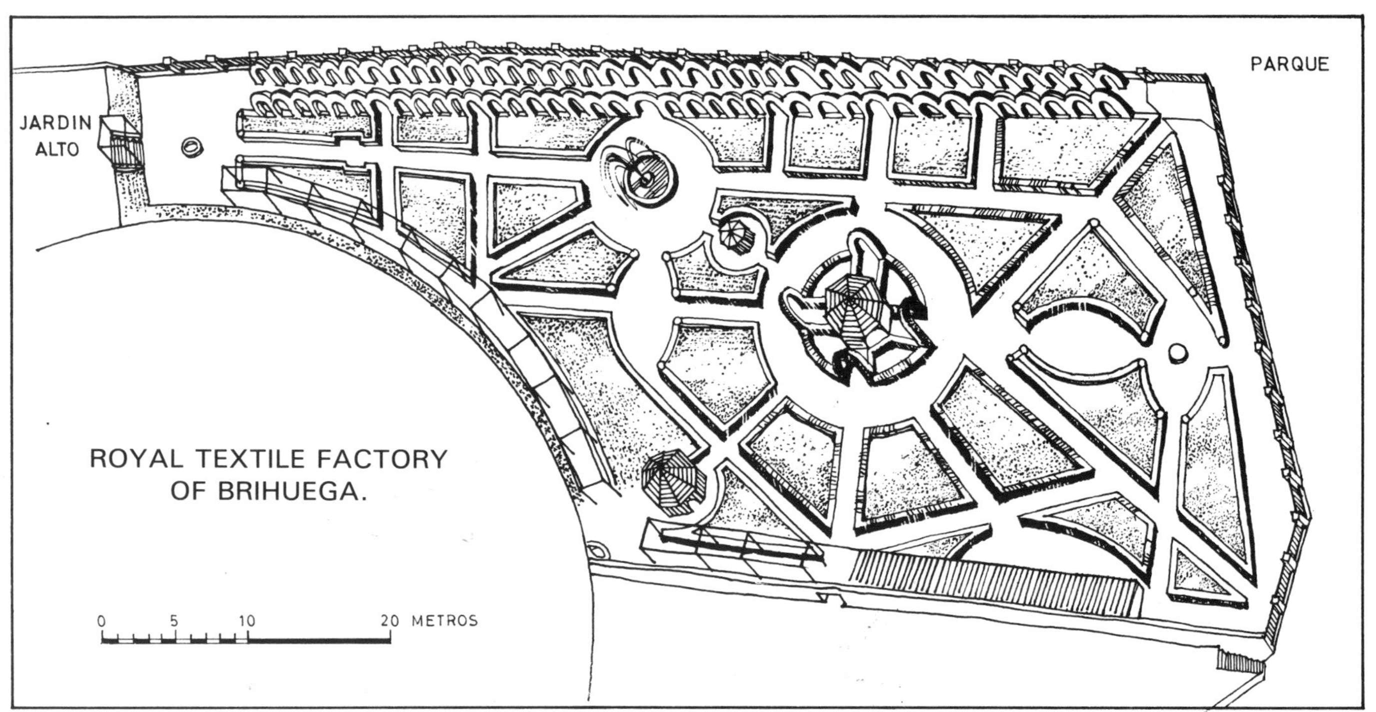

LA FLORERA. POND AND STATUE OF NEPTUNE. Aranjuez.
Photo Author. By permission of the National Heritage.

PIEDRAHÍTA PALACE. *Photo Author.*

encounter the ugliest feature of the approach to Aranjuez: the iron suspension bridge, which is so little in keeping with the entrance to the lovely gardens. Routing the Andalusian Highway through the arches of the Plaza de San Antonio, which are of such architectural beauty, is also regrettable for it has destroyed the peace and atmosphere. It is to be hoped that this road will be re-routed in order to restore to the square its eighteenth century character, and that the square will be ornamented with flowerbeds.

Boadilla del Monte

Boadilla del Monte was once the site of eighteenth century gardens, since destroyed. This palace was built by Ventura Rodríguez for the Infante Don Luis, the brother of Charles III. He was called the Cardinal-Prince, and was appointed Archbishop of Seville and later of Toledo. He renounced both his ecclesiastical offices, and his rank of Infante, in order to marry Doña Teresa Vallabriga, and was banished from the Court.[4] The gardens of clipped boxwood with their stairways, and the lower garden adorned with classical parterres, described by Winthuysen, survived until the war of 1936.

Piedrahíta

The Palace of Piedrahíta, in the province of Avila, deserves special mention. The Duke of Alba had it built by the French architect Jacques Marquet who was in charge of the work at Aranjuez in 1759. In 1764 Marquet built this château in the austere landscape of the foothills of the Sierra de Gredos, in the French eighteenth century style.[5] All the typical details of

VIEW FROM THE GARDENS. Brihuega. *Photo Author.*

iron gate, *cour d'honneur,* and two little round ponds, with figures of children adorning the entrance terrace were incorporated. In front of the façade facing the garden, Marquet planned a large circular pond in the background, and two side ponds, all according to the French tradition, but the material used — grey granite — makes them look severe and out of place. History relates that the Duchess of Alba, Doña Cayetana, spent her summers at Piedrahíta accompanied by Goya, who painted some of his tapestry cartoons here, such as *La Vendimia* (The Grape Harvest) which shows the Sierra de Gredos in the background. The palace was burned down by the French during the War of Independence, but was rebuilt in this century and is now a boys' school.

The Garden of the Cloth Factory, Brihuega

This very unusual little garden is situated on a hillock overlooking the town of Brihuega and the Tajuña valley. It surrounds an old cloth factory of the time of Charles III. The building is well-proportioned and has a broad entrance hall and a doorway bearing the date 1783.

The garden consists of a circular terrace planted in the taste of the period, with edges of trimmed boxwood. Arab influence can be seen in the irrigation channel which feeds two fountains. It once ran down to the lower terraced garden, since destroyed.

The garden's special charm lies in the skilful arrangement of the cypress arches so as to hide the limited size of the garden, giving it perspective, and yet at the same time providing an atmosphere of seclusion, in the Arab tradition.

It has a classical wrought-iron handrail of the same period, and a wide terrace affording a view through the cypress arches

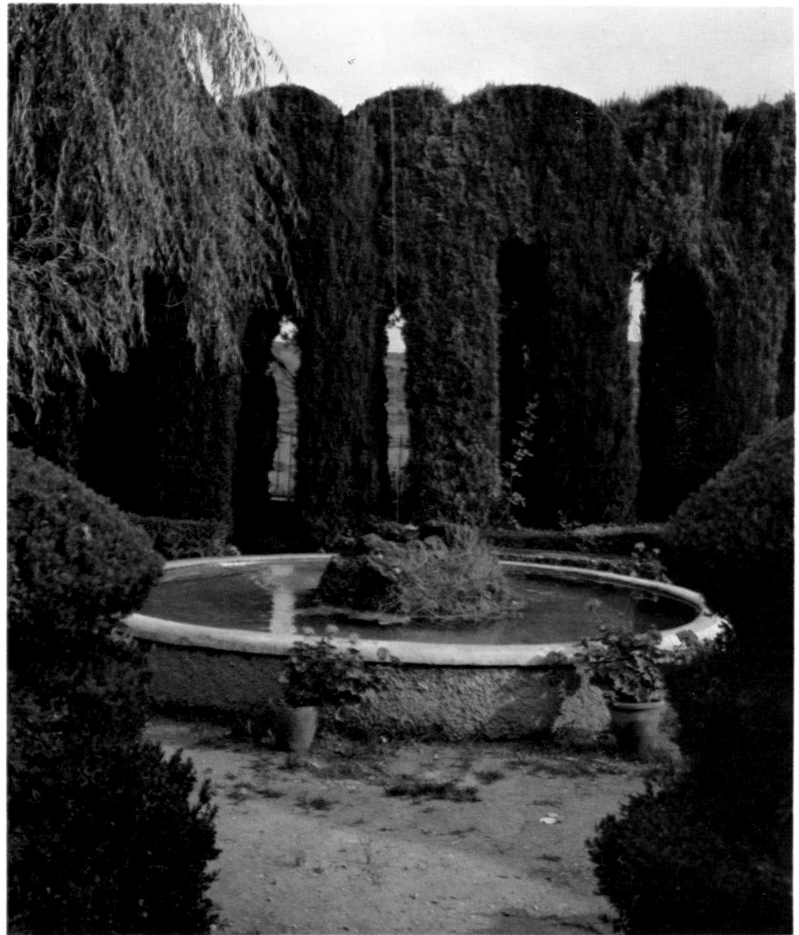

GARDENS. Brihuega. *Photo Author.*

GARDENS IN AUTUMN. Brihuega. *Photo Author.*

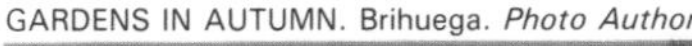

BENCHES. CASITA DE ARRIBA. El Escorial. *Photo Author.*

CASITA DE ARRIBA. El Escorial. *Photo Author.*

over the deep valley with its gleaming red soil. The position is as dramatic as the landscape surrounding the Generalife.

NEOCLASSICISM AT THE ESCORIAL

The House of the Crown Prince (*La Casita del Príncipe*, or *de Abajo*), is one of those charming and lavishly decorated pavilions, or follies, built during the reign of Charles III. It was the work of the architect Villanueva in 1772 for the future Charles IV, at that time Prince of Asturias, and is a miniature palace. The plan of the garden is in the classical style of the period, with Italian and French influence.

It is a pity that the inevitable Wellingtonias were planted in this tiny garden during the last century, for they have obscured its plan and added a gloomy note to the little palace.

The House of the Prince (*La Casita del Infante*, or *de Arriba*), dating from Charles III's time, is more graceful and unusual. The King had it built for his favourite son, Don Gabriel, a very scholarly and cultured prince, whose death a month before the King's own in 1788 caused the King great sorrow.

Its position on top of the mountain is more cheerful, and the garden has a very successful neoclassical layout, with two square fountains of severe granite that suit their surroundings well.

Behind the house, opposite the exit from the terrace, there is an octagonal stone table with matching benches; they do not look very comfortable but are pleasing in appearance. The semicircular terrace is well conceived and has two side gardens on a lower level, with their respective fountains. They must have been very lovely, but today, as at the Casita del Princípe, the effect of their layout has been obliterated by the enormous conifers planted in the last century, which are massive and shady.

Winthuysen says: "We know of no other small garden which, by its lightness and the order and charm of its contents, better represents the adaptation of neoclassicism to the Spanish taste, and which has not been spoilt by later works."[6]

Prince Don Juan Carlos of Bourbon spent some time in this little palace during the years 1960 and 1961.

EL RETIRO, MADRID

On entering the Retiro Park by the Coach Road that ends in Alcalá street, we see on our left an artificial mound with stones forming a rockery, which for a long time was the resort of all the cats of the neighbourhood. It also contains the ruins of a Romanesque hermitage placed there at the end of the nineteenth century, and the remains of a romantic garden dating from the time of Ferdinand VII. A nearby fisherman's cottage (*Casita del Pescador*) is reached by a small bridge across an irregularly shaped pond, with an iron railing completely surrounding it. The proportions and the elegance of this cottage make it a model of the architecture of the period, with its graceful pinnacle finished off with spheres and sharp points, which fit in so well with the Madrid environment.

THE LABYRINTH OF HORTA

A number of properties of the neoclassical period with charming pavilions and gardens built at the beginning of the nineteenth century, such as the Casa Gomis, once stood on the outskirts of Barcelona. But all this has been enveloped by the spread of the city and the only one that has survived is the Labyrinth of Horta which was the property of the Marqués de Alfarrás. The authorities in Barcelona have had the good taste and discernment to preserve it, rescuing it from the clutches of the builders and restoring and opening its park to the public; but the countryside overlooking Barcelona, once so beautiful and wooded, is now becoming more and more built up with utilitarian constructions.

The Labyrinth, situated, as we said, on a hill, is a garden of the purest neoclassical style, very lovely and quite extensive. The house is a mixture of neo-Gothic and pseudo-Arab, and does not blend there with the pavilions and the Italian style of the garden. The Italian Doménico Bagutti began its construction in 1794.

The main feature is the cypress maze. A marble bas-relief at its entrance portrays Ariadne, the daughter of the King of Crete, giving her lover Theseus the thread which she has spun to guide him out of the labyrinth after slaying the Minotaur. All these mythological themes are very typical of the period, but instead of

CASITA DEL PESCADOR. Retiro. Madrid. *Photo Author.*

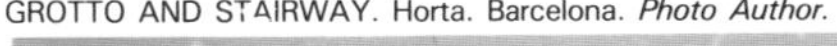

GROTTO AND STAIRWAY. Horta. Barcelona. *Photo Author.*

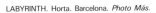

LABYRINTH. Horta. Barcelona. *Photo Más.*

POND AND PAVILION. Horta. Barcelona. *Photo Salmer.*

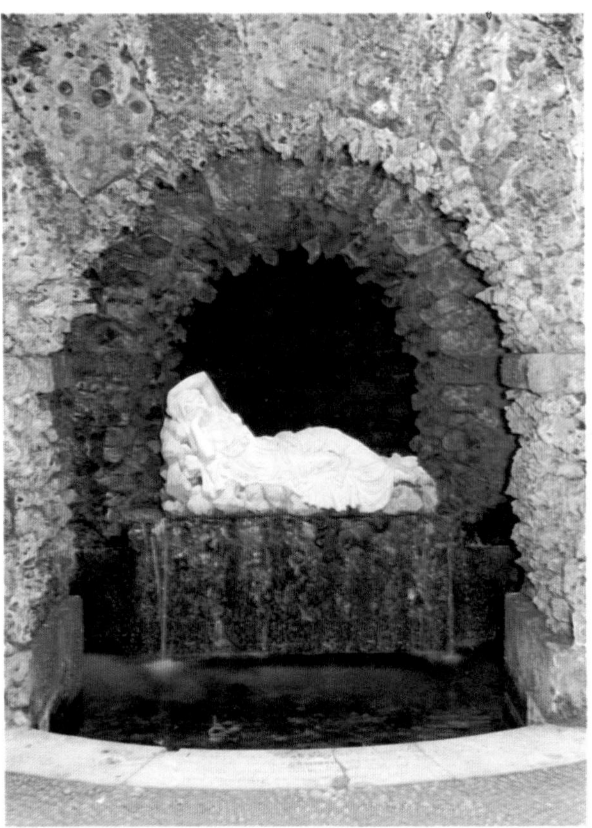

NYMPH OF THE GROTTO. Stourhead. England. *Photo Trans Globe.*

being confronted by the bull of Minos in the centre, we find the figure of Daphnis or Cupid.

This labyrinth, with its high cypress walls, resembles the gardens of Italian villas, from which the statues in the park must certainly have come.

We go up the avenue flanked by cypresses, and reach the great pool or reservoir which is surrounded by a wide balustrade.

Every detail is in harmony and in good taste, but the loveliest feature is a neoclassical pavilion perched on the edge of the pool, a veritable jewel which seems to transport us to an English garden with buildings of the Adam period. A tablet commemorates the visit of Charles IV with all his family in 1802.

It appears likely that either Doménico Bagutti or the Marqués de Alfarrás knew Stourhead Park in Wiltshire, which was designed by Henry Hoare towards the end of the eighteenth century. It is a model of landscape gardening. There is a grotto at the edge of the big lake, with a reclining nymph, reminding us of a similar grotto in the garden at Horta. It contains a female figure in the same posture as one found at Stourhead, by which it was probably inspired.

There is another grotto at the foot of the steps, on the same level as the maze. It also is made of stone-like lava, and a whitened plaster nymph stands erect in the background.

The whole garden slopes towards the labyrinth, with cascades, pools and stairways all centred upon it. The naturally sloping ground is therefore turned to the garden's advantage, as in Tivoli (Italy).

To the north of the house, a small garden of clipped boxwood is reached through a doorway decorated with beautiful bas-reliefs.

Two stone lions by this doorway commemorate the visit of Ferdinand VII in an inscription on the shields which they hold between their paws.

The Barcelona City Council has undertaken the restoration of these gardens, which are unique in Spain. They have recently been opened to the public.

The Alameda of Osuna

On the road from Madrid to Barcelona, in the district of Canillejas, is a neoclassical garden created towards the end of the eighteenth century by the Duke and Duchess of Osuna, Don Pedro Alcántara Téllez Girón and Doña Alonso Pimentel, the Condesa-Duquesa de Benavente. Now greatly ravaged by time and war, it was originally planted in 1783 on their estate "Mi Capricho" ("My Caprice"). Rural festivals were held there and Goya immortalised scenes from them in his tapestry cartoons. At that time the estate must have stretched as far as the edge of the Jarama, where the airport of Barajas is situated today; a few groups of solitary pines still remain as relics of those days.

The new owner planned the palace and garden according to the neoclassical style of the period, and among its foliage she built the rustic cottages of "el Ermitaño" ("The Hermit") and "La Vieja" ("The Old Woman"), under the direction of Angel María Tadey. "In 1808, on the instructions of the Duchess, who was already a widow, Antonio López Aguado built the ballroom, a rotunda like a circular pavilion."[7] The Duchess was very friendly with another noteworthy woman of her time: Elisabeth, Lady Holland, who lived in Madrid around 1803 and who mentions the Duchess frequently in her diary. "The garden is rather crowded with a profusion of different ornaments," she writes, "some in the German sentimental taste, others in a tawdry, citizen-like style. *La Casa de la Vieja* is very pretty. The mansion is excellent and well furnished."[8]

At that time those gardens of which we see traces today would not have existed. As Lozoya says: "Their magnificence and refinement of taste blend; they were made for the grandson of the founders, Don Pedro de Alcántara, between 1834 and 1844." At that time Martín López Aguado, the son of Ferdinand VI's famous architect, designed a dream garden enriched by a series of small and very fine monuments in the purest neoclassical style; Lady Holland never knew these. "The ballroom, with its circular colonnade, was in the centre of a pond and the guests came to it in gondolas across the water. On a small island shaded by great cypresses, there is a monument to the memory of the third Duke of Osuna, reminiscent of the tombs that are to be seen in romantic memorials."[9]

There are a great number of exquisite buildings here and there among the trees. A monument opposite the western façade of the palace, on the other side of a broad avenue, takes the form of a portico dominated by a bust which is now crumbling away, and which portrays the founding Duchess. On a nearby mound stands a circular pavilion with Corinthian columns, similar to

PALACE AND POND. Alameda de Osuna. *Photo Author.*

GROTTO. Horta. Barcelona. *Photo Author.*

PAVILION. Alameda de Osuna. *Photo Mas.*

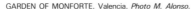

GARDEN OF MONFORTE. Valencia. *Photo M. Alonso.*

the one in the Prince's Garden at Aranjuez, but of white stone, and not far away is the "Abejero" (the Beehive), also neoclassical in form. It once housed a statue (now gone) of Venus, by Juan Adán.

The Alameda (The Poplar Grove) of Osuna was contemporary with La Moncloa Palace, which will be described presently, and with which we managed to become familiar before the Civil War of 1936-1939 when it was destroyed; it was the property of the Duchess Cayetana who was the rival of the Condesa-Duquesa de Benavente.

The Alameda also suffered the consequences of the war. For many years it was owned by los senores de Bauer, in whose hands it recovered some of its former splendour.

Today this little palace is hemmed in between Barajas airport and a viaduct; some of its pavilions and statues have disappeared, while urbanisation and the buildings of this densely populated district of Madrid have greatly disfigured its situation.

At the present time it is most sadly neglected, but the estate has recently been acquired by new owners who are planning to restore it; we trust that they will preserve the original spirit of the garden which is, moreover, a national monument.

The Garden of Monforte, Valencia

On the edge of the river Turia in Valencia, near the gardens which used to belong to El Real, is a garden in the neoclassical style, though created much later: the Garden of Monforte. It has recently been reduced in size by the building work which is gradually encroaching on it. As the ground is completely flat, the interest of the garden lies in the statues and urns of Carrara marble, brought from Italy, and in its graceful design.

It was the work of Juan Bautista Romero, Marqués de San Juan, who constructed it about 1848. Though small it is so complete in itself, so well-balanced and harmonious that — as Lozoya puts it — "it is not excelled by earlier gardens either in evocative power or in poetic atmosphere. Everything in it is intimate and secluded, as in the old gardens of Spain; the effect of its magnificent cypress screens forming a background for the arbours, of its flower-filled parterres and its little stairways crowned by statues, is truly delightful."[10]

Particularly charming is the statue of Ceres, standing alone on a pedestal surrounded by jets of water, like those at the entrance to the grotto near a romantic lake.

The only thing that betrays its later date is the little round pool by the entrance, encircled by an iron railing in the style typical of the period of Queen Isabel II. This garden was painted by Santiago Rusiñol, and it is hoped that it will not perish in the days to come, a victim of the enormous blocks of flats that surround it. The pavilion, of the same period, and exquisitely proportioned, stands at the entrance to the property and must be crossed in order to reach the garden.

In the Plaza de Alfonso el Magnánimo there is a garden called La Glorieta (The Arbour) which was laid out in 1817 and has a beautiful fountain of Italian marble with two tritons, the work of

Ponzanelli, a seventeenth century sculptor from Genoa. It was brought here from the villa of Canon Pontons.[11]

La Moncloa Palace

If we continue along the Pardo road, some distance from the site of Montaña del Príncipe Pío, we can see an elegant building that rises high up on the right. It has been erected since the Civil War on the very site of the famous La Moncloa Palace above the Casa de Campo.

According to Ezquerra del Bayo, the palace that stood here until the war was built by Don Gaspar de Haro y Guzmán, Marqués del Carpio (who succeeded as favourite of Philip IV when his uncle the Conde-Duque de Olivares fell from favour). The young Don Gaspar, a man of charm and substantial fortune, "erected the building which, in his time, was known as the painted house" because of the copies of oil paintings hanging on the walls of its rooms.

But the real creator of La Moncloa was Doña María Ana de Silva y Sarmiento, dowager Duchess of Arcos, who acquired the estate in 1781, at the end of the reign of Charles III, after it had passed through several ownerships. Doña María Ana, the daughter of the Marqués de Santa Cruz, was very cultured and

GARDEN OF MONFORTE. STATUE OF CERES. Valencia. *Photo M. Alonso.*

EXEDRA. Alameda de Osuna. *Photo Mas.*

of refined taste, and she completely reformed the palace in the neoclassical style that was then dominant. It was one of the best examples of the period, and was inspired by works recently excavated in Herculaneum and Pompeii by Charles III.

The Duchess of Arcos enjoyed her estate for only two years, for she died in 1784. It was inherited by her only daughter, the child of her first marriage with the Duke of Huéscar, the famous Cayetana, Duchess of Alba, who was to be immortalised by Goya. She maintained the estate for eighteen years and it was she who formed the terraced gardens. She also ordered the creation of an artificial cave, reached by a sloping path from the garden of the summer house, running almost underneath the palace, where a "buttery" or dairy had been installed, following the example of Marie Antoinette.

Not very far away, on the opposite bank of the Manzanares, Goya had his famous countryhouse, the Quinta del Sordo, where he lived for many years. Presumably he would attend the festivals given by the Duchess who owned the property of La Moncloa until her early death in 1802.

In 1792 King Charles IV had bought the palace, gardens and orchard of La Florida and Montaña del Príncipe Pío from the Marquesa de Castel Rodrigo. These were situated close to La Moncloa but nearer Madrid. In February 1795, the Royal Family acquired more property from Godoy between the Duchess of Alba's palace and La Florida. The estate called Orchard of La Moncloa was included in these properties. It was the King's plan to acquire all the land between the Pardo and his Madrid palace so that he could travel through his estates from one palace to another.

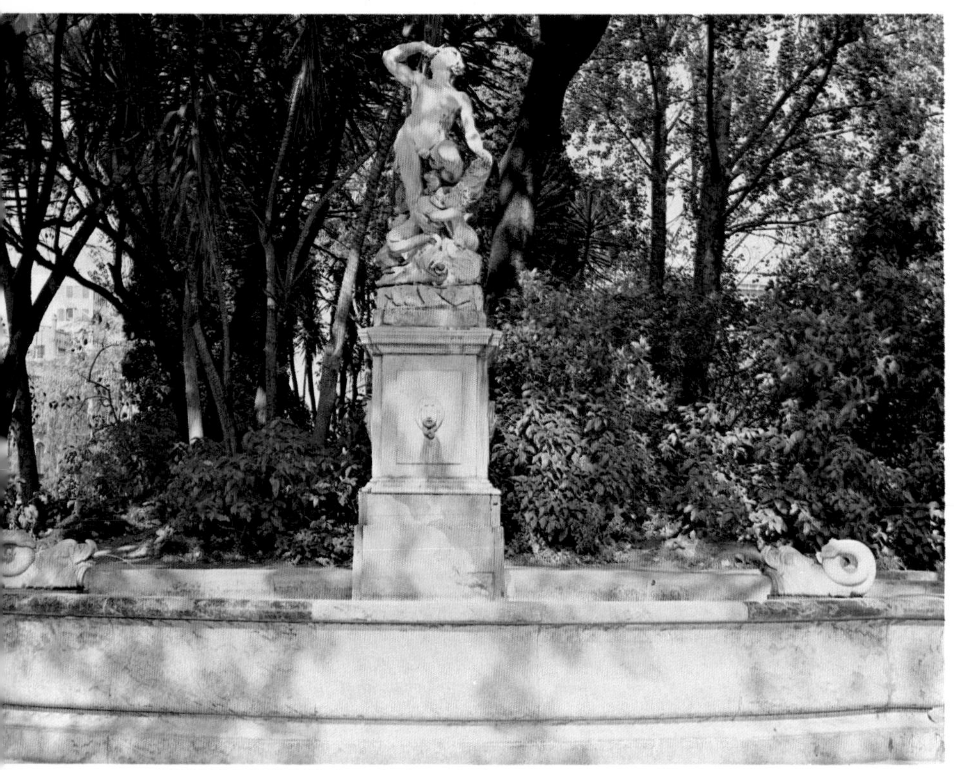

PONZANELLI FOUNTAIN. Valencia. *Photo M. Alonso.*

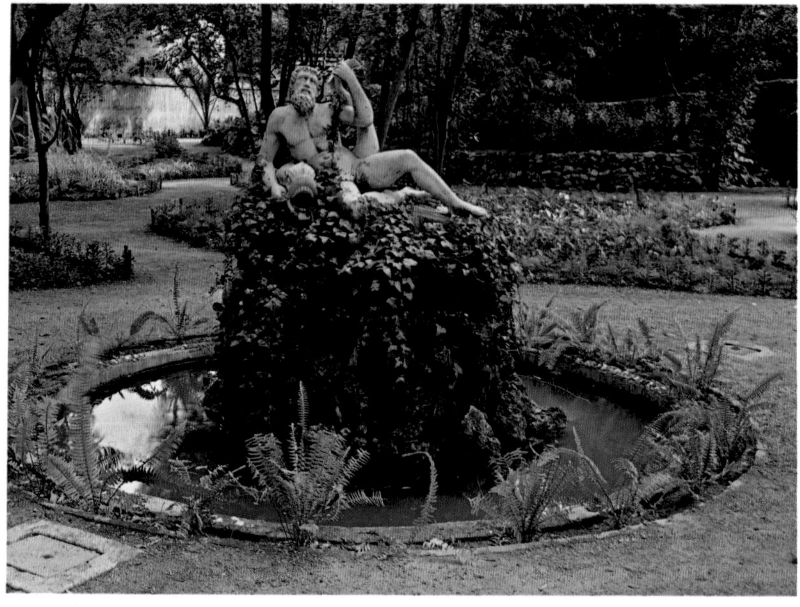

GARDEN OF MONFORTE. NEPTUNE POND. Valencia. *Photo M. Alonso.*

When Dona Cayetana died La Moncloa was acquired by the Royal Patrimony, and these estates as a whole were given the name of Real Florida.

The estate underwent the vicissitudes of the French occupation and the reigns of Joseph Bonaparte and Fernando VII until Queen Isabel II handed it over to the State, together with the Retiro Park.

In 1918 the Spanish Society of Friends of Art undertook the restoration of this building on the authority of the Ministry of Development, and it regained its original late eighteenth century appearance. Don Javier Winthuysen reconstructed the terraced garden in its original enchanting form with classical contours. Today its fountains and beautiful woodland have been replaced by a barren waste; all traces of the gardens have disappeared.

During the last war it was a battlefront and was destroyed beyond all hope of reconstruction. Another palace was built on the same site, in the same style, but in different form, with gardens limited to the immediate proximity of the house. It is today the residence of President Felipe Gonzalez.

ARANJUEZ DURING THE NINETEENTH CENTURY

When Charles IV began his reign, Madrid was opening up avenues and walks for which trees were ordered from the nurseries of Aranjuez.[13] Don Claudio Boutelou, the head gardener of the Royal Botanical Garden and the Buen Retiro, sent for them for the Paseo del Prado.[14]

Private individuals also gave their orders, and we read of the Count of Fernán Núñez asking for plants for his estate at Barajas in a letter addressed to Don Pablo Boutelou, the son and successor of Don Esteban as head gardener at Aranjuez.

Repairs to the fountains in the gardens on the Island were urgently needed, especially the restoration of the Fountain of Apollo with its statues "in the place known as Puerta del Sol", the work being entrusted to the sculptor Pedro Rurón.[15]

In spite of the Revolution, Charles IV sent to France for plants and seeds, and it is interesting to note that a letter was sent to him from Paris on 6 Fructidor of the year II (1803), announcing their dispatch. The letter was addressed to Don Pablo Boutelou from the firm of seed merchants, Vilmorin Andrieux.

The third Esteban Boutelou, who must have been the son of Pablo, appears on the scene in 1803; he was probably a youngster for he earned less than the other gardens.

Repairs continued to be necessary at Aranjuez and we read that in April 1805 "the King decided to regild the fountains in the Prince's Garden and the spring Garden, and he asked for Joaquín Demandre to go from San Ildefonso to perform this task with the help of two assistants."[17]

In February 1806 a hurricane broke over the royal site and "a tree fell on the Fountain of la Espina, in the Island Garden, knocking over the statue and shattering the basin."[18]

At that time the head gardeners were Don Pablo in the Prince's Garden, and the third Don Esteban Boutelou in the Spring Garden.

The outbreak of the War of Independence was imminent, and yet, in April 1808, the naïve Charles IV still looked on the cunning Napoleon as "his most intimate ally". The uprising of 2 May was drawing near.

In July the King and Queen left for Bayonne and exile, accompanied by Godoy. French troops encamped at Aranjuez under the command of Generals Dupont and Vedel.

Fernando VII reigned with a Central Council. Aranjuez suffered from the consequences of the invasion, with its gardens and statues destroyed and neglected.

Charles IV had left his pictures and furniture packed, ready to be sent to him, but the French took them away with other furniture from the palace, as is recorded in the inventories in the Archives.[19]

Forgetful of old enemies, by November 1816 Don Pablo Boutelou was once more sending to Vilmorin Andrieux for bulbs and seeds.[20]

The Countess of Chinchón, Charles IV's unfortunate cousin, and wife of the favourite, Godoy, was living in Boadilla and on 8 October 1817 she wrote in a firm, clear hand asking for fruit trees from the nurseries of Aranjuez; perhaps she wanted to forget her unhappy years at court. The Condesa-Duquesa de Benavente sent similar orders for her "beloved countryhouse", the Alameda of Osuna, which she called "My Caprice".

Fernando VII decided to bring the Fountain of Hercules and Antaeus created by Juan Adán in 1795[22] from Aranjuez to Madrid so that it could be restored by the leading sculptor José Ginés. For this work the sons of the late Juan Adán provided stone similar to that of the fountain. There was a plan to place it in the "garden of La Moncloa, opposite the palace. Their Majesties could not enjoy it as they were confined in Madrid"; it was nevertheless returned to Aranjuez after its restoration, and there it remains, in the parterre.

After the invasion, as the French had rented out the land at Aranjuez, in 1808 the King decided to keep for his own enjoyment only the Island Garden and those on the other side of the river, bounded by the Queen's Avenue from bridge to bridge and consisting of the Prince's Garden and the Spring Garden. These gardens surrounded the Casa del Labrador, built by Charles IV and María Luisa in imitation of Marie Antoinette's hamlet at Versailles; they required special care.

Don Casimiro Bonavia, possibly a descendant of the great architect, succeeded Pablo Boutelou as head gardener of the Prince's Garden and the Spring Garden at an annual salary of 500 ducats.[23] The gardens had lost their former splendour, money was scarce and payments were difficult to make.

There is a very interesting account from this period concerning an order to Fleurs et Compagnie of Lyon, with lists made out by Pablo Boutelou of plants and flowers. Many of them —

GARDEN OF MONFORTE. GROTTO WITH WATER "TRICKS". Valencia. *Photo M. Alonso.*

camellias, andromedas, azaleas and gardenias — are best suited to acid soil and heathland and must have had difficulty adapting to the lime soil of Aranjuez.[24] But such considerations did not seem to worry the gardeners of that time, for they cultivated tropical plants without any regard for frost or poor soil. At the Madrid Botanical Garden and the Buen Retiro they grew bananas and pineapples in conservatories at tremendous expense.

In 1822 the name Andrés Boutelou is mentioned for the first time as head gardener of Aranjuez. He was the grandson of Don Pablo.[25]

A vine arbour was made for the Prince's Garden in 1826, and on the nearby hill a summer house and a Chinese pagoda, similar to one destroyed in the War of Independence. The Hermitage was reroofed in the original rustic style, and 1,937 feet of fretwork were placed around the Florera.

Philip II's idea of channeling the river Tagus from Lisbon to Aranjuez was again brought up at this time. Now that the use of steam had been discovered, Fernando VII commanded that eight steamboats should navigate between Puente Verde and Portugal.[27] A suspension bridge was built to permit road transport to Andalusia; at that time the bridge had iron chains and not the arches we see today. At either end four enormous

LA MONCLOA PALACE.

statues from the Royal Palace in Madrid were placed, and preserved until recently.[28]

By now the Carlist War had broken out and nothing was done in the gardens, apart from removing the name of the Infante Don Carlos from the notices at Aranjuez in an attempt to blot out all memory of him; the house that had been built for him in the Island Garden became a school.

Fernando Boutelou who became Director General of the Gardens on 10 May 1843, restored the gardens and plantations[30] shortly before the coming-of-age of Isabel II that November.

The fashion for exotic plants continued: there were two sections in the Prince's Garden called "American Islands", considered the "Pearls of Aranjuez" for their many tropical trees and bushes.[31]

In 1847 the name of Don Fernando's brother Esteban Boutelou, appears as Inspector of Gardens and Woods. A park in the English style was planned for the Palace of La Zarzuela.

It was at this time that the idea for the Garden of the Campo del Moro was conceived and plans were made to beautify the immediate surroundings of the palace.

There is no doubt that the new generation of Boutelous were very eminent, and Esteban Boutelou's accounts of cultivation and of plants are veritable botanical treatises worthy of publication. By now Spain had become a world leader in the field of botany.[32]

In 1857 the gardens of Aranjuez were divided into:

The Prince's Garden and its departments
The Island Garden
The Garden of Prince Francisco
The Park of Miraflores
The Garden of the Vine Arbour.[33]

All the neighbouring gardens that once had belonged to the Royal Estate, including La Flamenca, were now rented out.

In 1868 Doña Cristina, the Queen-Regent, left Spain; shortly afterwards Isabel II followed her into exile, and the Provisional Government was set up.

Attention does not appear to have been lavished on the gardens during this period, and in fact between 1868 and 1870 furniture, trees and plants from the Royal Estate were sold.[34]

But a letter from the administrator of the Estate on the arrival of Amadeo of Savoy in 1871, expressed "the spontaneous and sincere loyalty of the staff to the person of Amadeo I".[35] They were known to prefer him to the Republic.

During his short reign Amadeo appears to have taken an interest in trying to improve the Royal Estate.

The gardens were cleared and the Casa de Infantes was returned to Prince Sebastian (13 September 1871). This house, given by Charles IV to his brother Antonio, was situated on the Island and must have had its separate garden, the remains of which still exist, with a circular pond and a bronze statue of Diana the huntress, behind the present conservatories.

Wellingtonias (*Sequoiadendron gigantea*) made their appearance in Amadeo's time, and the *Abies pinsapo*, a fir tree

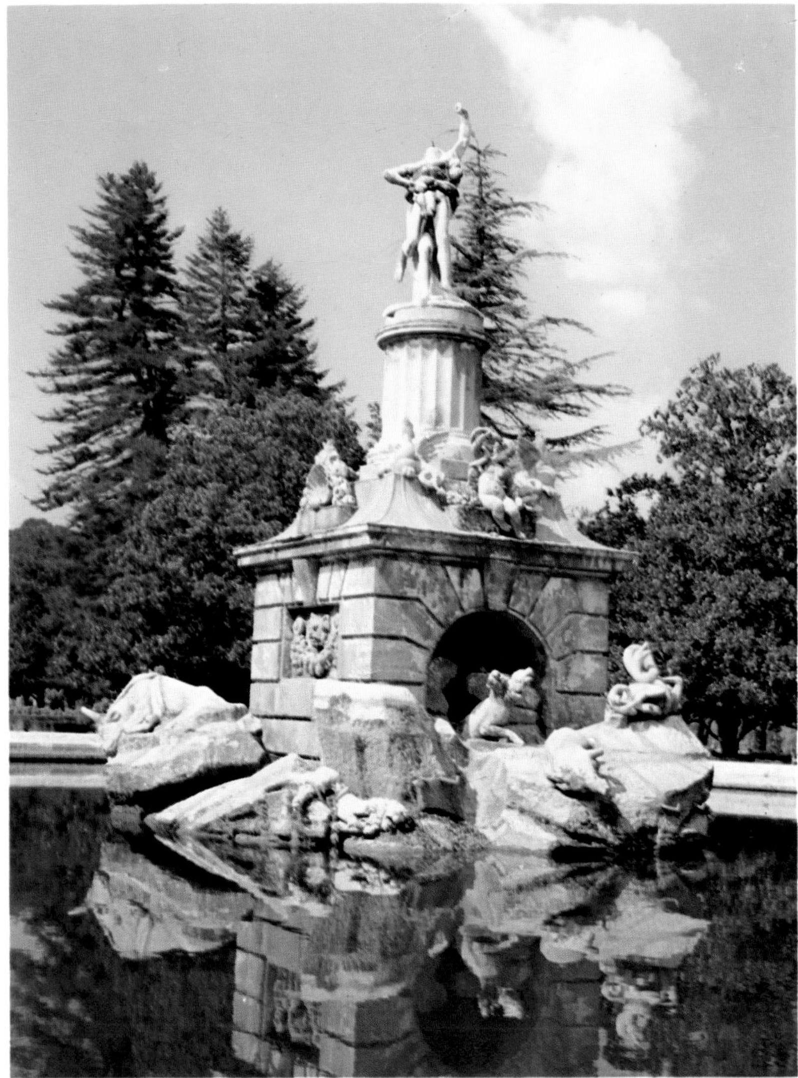

PARTERRE. STATUE OF HERCULES AND ANTEO. Aranjuez.
Photo Author. By permission of the National Heritage.

native to the Ronda mountains of Spain, but never before planted in gardens, came from the Quinta de la Esperanza.[36] These trees were planted in the parterre by the entrance and grew quite large.

During the reign of Alfonso XII this parterre was rebuilt, for it had been laid out a hundred and forty-three years earlier. The boxwood edges that had been preserved "as a marvel of the art of gardening" from the time of Fernando VI, were replaced by flowers, trees and lawns according to modern taste; the large pond had to be altered to store water, as the more abundant plants and lawns required much more irrigation than the old *en manta* system.

This parterre had been destroyed during the Revolution and consideration was given to sowing it with lawn seed in the English style; fortunately the chief architect, José Delgado de Lena,[37] did not agree.

The nurseries of Aranjuez had been famous since the time of Philip V, and successive monarchs had taken care to furnish them with the trees and plants continually being discovered both in Europe and America. As there were no commercial nurseries in Spain, those at Aranjuez offered a unique source of plants.

A list of trees ordered in 1876 for the nurseries included a large variety of conifers, then considered novel:

1,000 Abies excelsa (thorny)
500 Abies normaniana
500 Wellingtonias
500 Cedars of Lebanon
50 Magnolias grandiflora.[38]

A year later five hundred eucalyptus trees were received at Aranjuez from Australia; they included the following varieties:

50 eucalyptus Resinifera
50 eucalyptus Flooded gum
100 eucalyptus Colossea
100 eucalyptus Tereticornis
200 eucalyptus Globulus

These varieties were sent from Tarrasa, and some no longer exist.[39] Forty camellias for the hothouses and fifty hydrangeas were also requested. The fashion for indoor potted plants had arrived, and in 1882 gas was used to heat the greenhouses.

The head gardener was Don Pedro Testard, probably a Frenchman, and plants were sent from Aranjuez to Madrid for exhibitions. There are on record strange lists of rose-bushes in the nurseries.

Pyramid rose, Avanes, ramblers grafted on the dog rose, Bengal roses, Musk roses (an old variety from the time of Philip II), roses of Alexandria, of Villaviciosa, of Castellaus.[40]

Also on the list of 1889 were the *Araucaria imbricata* or Chilean pine, the *Chamerops* (half-hardy palm) and rhododendrons for Casa de Campo.

Towards the end of the century, during her widowhood, Queen Cristina wanted to have indoor plants cultivated at Aranjuez to decorate the Royal Palace in Madrid, and in 1887 a hothouse was installed on the Island for this purpose. Rose

ALCAZAR OF MADRID AND THE CAMPO DEL MORO. Engraving from "Delices de l'Espagne".

DIANA THE HUNTRESS (BRONZE). Aranjuez. *Photo S. Saavedra.*

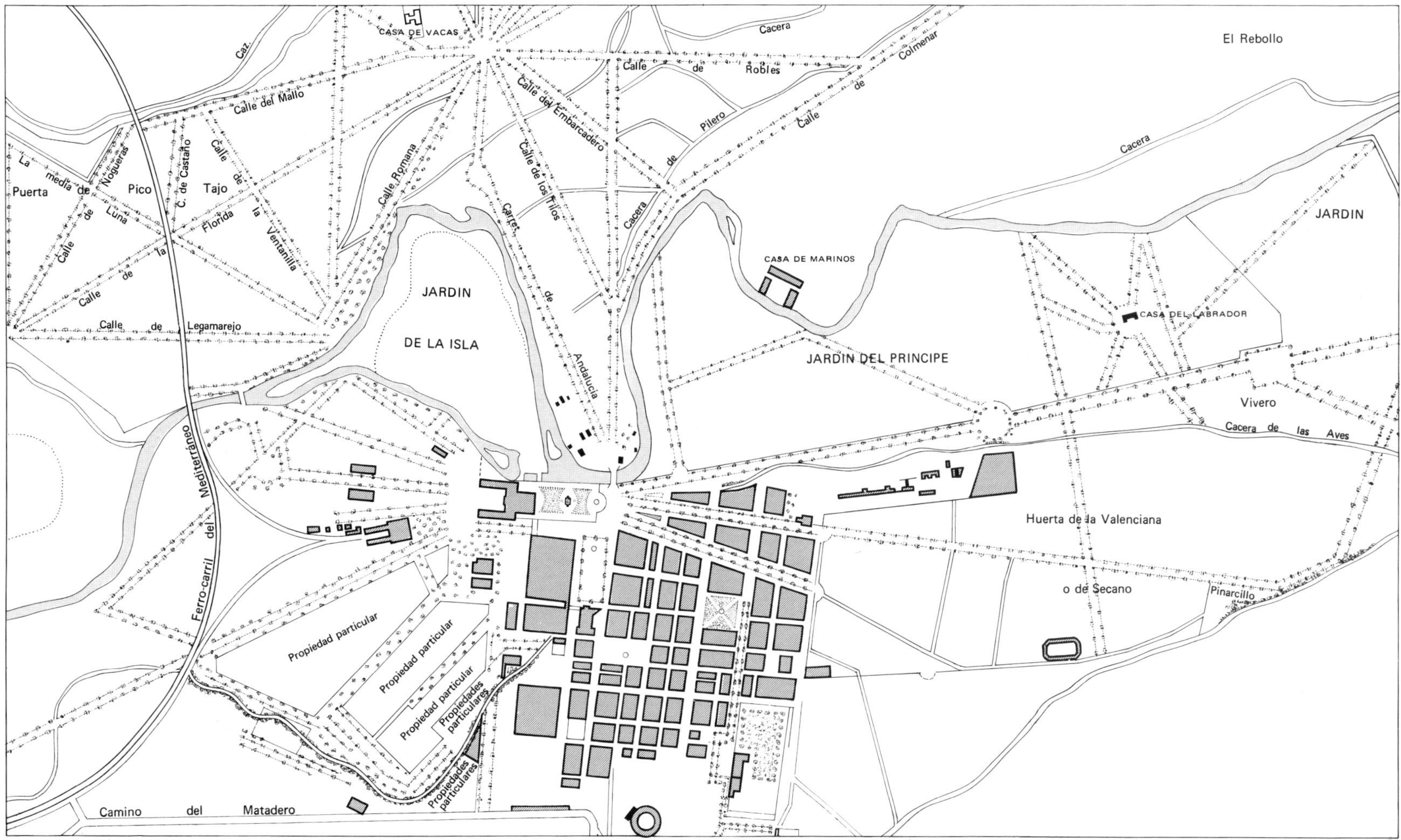

PLAN OF ARANJUEZ. 19th century. Madrid Palace archives.

bushes, bulbs and carnations were brought for the royal apartments in 1907.

After the reign of Isabel II the palace at Aranjuez was never again to be inhabited. With modern means of transport the members of the Royal Family would come for the day, and the palace and gardens would be open to the public, sharing the fate of the other royal residences in Europe.

During the reign of Alfonso XIII, horse-races were held in the spring beneath the shade of the ancient elms and plane trees. The old avenues were filled with modern motor cars in which people came to picnic in the shade, sheltered from the fierce heat of the sun.

THE GARDENS OF THE CAMPO DEL MORO

The ancient Alcazar of Madrid, which was burned down in December of 1734, was situated at the edge of a steep slope, and was apparently a strategic position in the time of the Moors. Some fortified walls can still be seen in this ravine. The garden consisted of a small enclosure, called "the King's Square", next to the palace on the site of the present Plaza de la Armeria. The rest was uncultivated land until well into the nineteenth century.

When the plans for the new palace were drawn up during the reign of Philip V, there was first a design by Sacchetti for gardens in the Campo del Moro, followed by other designs by the second Esteban Boutelou, head gardener of Aranjuez, and by the Parisian, Garnier d'Isle, Louis XV's architect; later in Charles III's time, plans were prepared by Ventura Rodríguez, Satatini and many others, but were never executed[41], no doubt because of the difficulties caused by the uneven territory. Philip V would not agree to the suggestion put forward by Abbot Juvara to build the palace on the heights of Leganitos near the present site of the church of the Buen Suceso.[42]

The Plaza de Oriente as we know it today was not constructed until the brief reign of Joseph Bonaparte, "the King of Little Squares", in 1811. It is only fair to say that he did his best to beautify ramshackle Madrid by adding dignity and perspective to the eastern facade of the palace. Its construction entailed the destruction of houses and gardens, including the Royal Library, the Pelota Court and the Prioress's Orchard next to the Convent of the Incarnation, which was the parish church of the palace.[43] On the opposite

PLAZA DE ORIENTE. STATUE OF PHILIP IV. *Photo Salmer.*

side near the parish church of Santiago, it was necessary to level ground. All this land was replenished with rich topsoil, and in 1847 the monumental fountain for the centre of the square was planned, with the equestrian statue of Philip IV, which is still there.

This mass of land, therefore, never contained gardens until 1840. The same year, the Director of the Royal House and Patrimony, Don Martín de los Heros, began work on the Campo del Moro on the western side of the palace. Isabel II was still a child of thirteen and under the guardianship of the Venerable Don Augustin Arguelles.

Documents in the Palace Archives reveal that in 1835 the gardens of the Retiro and other royal estates were completely neglected and suffered from a lack of water and gardeners.[44]

Work at the Campo del Moro continued. In 1844 the Fountain of the Tritons was taken there from Aranjuez, sadly in need of restoration.

Carrying out the necessary reforms at the Campo del Moro involved considerable movement of earth, a labour which took many years, for in 1864 they were still "planning to level the Campo del Moro further".[45] It was named the New Palace Park.

On the same axis as the Fountain of the Tritons, but on a lower level, situated in a circular space, there is another very beautiful fountain which was only just being placed in position in Madoz's time: it is called the Fountain of the Shells. It was designed by Ventura Rodríguez at the end of the eighteenth century to adorn the gardens of the Palace of Boadilla, the residence of Don Luis, Charles III's brother. It remained there for many years until the Duke and Duchess of San Fernando de Quiroga (she was a sister of the Countess of Chinchón, both of them daughters of Don Luis) presented it to Fernando VII. Fernando in turn gave it to his wife María Cristina, who had it taken to the Real Quinta de Vista Alegre, an estate which the Madrid City Council had bought for her in 1829 as a wedding gift. The Queen was very fond of this property with its beautiful gardens to which she added a lake. The King planned to build a great palace there, and when he died in 1833, three million reales had already been spent on it. It remained unfinished for many years until María Cristina asked for permission to give it to her two daughters and it became the property of Isabel II and Luis Fernando.[46] The inventory of this estate made in 1845 includes a "large fountain of white Granada marble composed of three sections"[47], which must have been the Fountain of the Shells; but there is no fountain in the inventory of 1849. It must therefore have been placed in the Campo del Moro about 1845, at the same time as the Fountain of the Tritons.

There was also talk at this time of taking "the damaged fountain from the Casa de Campo and placing it in the square to match the one brought from the royal property of Vista Alegre."[48]

This fountain must have been removed from the Casa de Campo at the same time as the equestrian statue of Philip III, which was taken to the Plaza Mayor about the year 1840 and remained in the Campo del Moro until the enclosure of the New Palace Park was prepared in 1867.[49] During the childhood of Alfonso XIII the Queen Regent, Doña Cristina, founded the University in the Escorial in 1885. It was run by the Augustinian fathers under the name of the Royal College of María Cristina. The fountain was taken there and placed in the centre of the cloisters, but very much altered, without the crowning eagle and without the lower basin.[50] (This fountain is described in the chapter on gardens of the Austrian Dynasty).

From 1841 onwards, during the youth of Isabel II, there was a strong desire to embellish the Court gardens. The Director of the Royal gardens and forests was Don Fernando Boutelou who had been appointed in 1839, and in whose family there was a long tradition of palace gardening. This gardener sent for plants not only from neighbouring France, but also from more distant countries in South America, such as Cuba and Mexico, with the ambitious aim of incorporating in the royal parks plants suited to heathlands, such as camellias, rhododendrons and gardenias, as well as plants and trees from tropical countries such as the *Araucaria brasiliana*.[51]

In 1844 the Queen Regent, living in exile in Paris, sent seeds to her daughters. Exhibitions of plants and flowers from the Buen Retiro, the Casino and the Real Florida were held in Madrid. Fernando Boutelou had completely restored the royal gardens and gave account of their good condition in spite of the scarcity of water at the Retiro. Meanwhile, the gardens of the Plaza de Oriente were being planted (1844-1845), including 100,000 boxwood plants from the Alcarria, in Guadalajara. The square was levelled and loam was brought from the neighbouring Montaña Príncipe Pío.[52]

In 1847 the School of Horticulture was founded in the park of the Royal Palace. The head gardener, under the orders of Boutelou, was François Viet who frequently journeyed to Paris to stock the royal gardens with plants.[53]

CAMPO DEL MORO. FOUNTAIN OF THE TRITONS.
Photo S. Saavedra. By permission of the National Heritage.

CAMPO DEL MORRO. FOUNTAIN OF THE SHELLS.
Photo S. Saavedra. By permission of the National Heritage.

STAIRWAY AND FACADE OF THE PALACE.
Alameda de Osuna. *Photo Author.*

[1] TORMO, Elías: *Aranjuez*, Madrid, 1930.

[2] NICHOLS, Rose: *Spanish Gardens*, London, 1924, page 179.

[3] MADOZ: *Diccionario geográfico-estadístico-histórico de España*, Madrid, 1847, vol. II, page 438.

[4] WINTHUYSEN, Javier: *Jardines clásicos de España*, Madrid, 1930, page 99.

[5] Archivo General de Palacio, Madrid: *Expedientes personales.* Jaime Marquet, case 622, record 33.

[6] WINTHUYSEN, Javier: *Op. cit.*, page 112.

[7] LOZOYA, Marqués de: *Los jardines españoles*, Ed. Cigüena, Madrid, 1951, page 38.

[8] HOLLAND, Lady Elisabeth: *Spanish Journal.* Edited by the Earl of Chichester, London, 1910, page 143.

[9] LOZOYA, Marqués de: *Op. cit.*, page 38.

[10] LOZOYA, Marqués de: *Op. cit.*, page 42.

[11] RAFOLS, J. F.: "Arquitectura del Renacimiento español", *Manual de Historia del Arte*, Barcelona, 1929.

[12] EZQUERRA DEL BAYO, Joaquín: *El Palacete de la Moncloa*, Sociedad Española de Amigos del Arte, Madrid, 1929, page 29.

[13] Archivo General de Palacio, Madrid, *Aranjuez*, file 52, 3 January 1801.

[14] Idem, file 52, 30 November 1803.

[15] Idem, file 52, 21 June 1802.

[16] Idem, file 52, 4 December 1803.

[17] Idem, file 53, 29 April 1805.

[18] Idem, file 53, 26 October 1805.

[19] Idem, file 58.

[20] Idem, file 59, 9 November 1816.

[21] Idem, file 60.

[22] Idem, file 50.

[23] Idem, file 62.

[24] Idem, file 63.

[25] Idem, file 64, 25 June 1822.

[26] Idem, file 66, 17 November 1826.

[27] Idem, file 67, 18 August 1828.

[28] Idem, file 69.

[29] Idem, file 83.

[30] Idem, file 85.

[31] Idem, file 86.

[32] Idem, file 92 & 93.

[33] Idem, file 102 (year 1857).

[34] Idem, file 119.

[35] Idem, file 120 (year 1871).

[36] Idem, file 120, 15 December 1871.

[37] Idem, file 127, January 1876.

[38] Idem, file 128, 15 December 1876.

[39] Idem, file 128, 11 October 1877.

[40] Idem, file 139 (year 1884).

[41] GARC/IA MERCADAL, Fernando: *Parques y jardines*, Afrodisio Aguado, 1949, page 222.

[42] BOTTINEAU, Yves: *L'art de Cour dans l'Espagne de Phillipe V*, Féret et Fils, Bordeaux, 1960, page 507.

[43] EZQUERRA DEL BAYO, J.: *Op. cit.*, page 64.

[44] Archivo General de Palacio, Madrid: *Casa y bosques*, file 335 (year 1839).

[45] Idem, file 335 (year 1864).

[46] When Fernando VII's private estate was wound up in 1857, Vista Alegre was awarded to the Duke and Duchess of Montpensier who sold it to Don Jose Salamanca in 1858; the latter celebrated magnificent festivals there, and died in the palace in 1883.

[47] Archivo General de Palacio, Madrid: *Inventarios casa*, Administrative Section, file 13.

[48] Archivo General de Palacio, Madrid: *Casa y bosques*, file 335 (year 1848).

[49] Idem, file 335.

[50] EZQUERRA DEL BAYO, J.: *Op. cit.*, page 146.

[51] Archivo General de Palacio, Madrid: *Casa y bosques*, file 335 (year 1845).

[52] Idem, file 335 (year 1847).

[53] Idem, file 335 (year 1849).

14

NINETEENTH AND TWENTIETH CENTURIES
THE ROMANTIC GARDEN. GAUDI.
FORESTIER AND NEOARABISM
MODERN GARDENS
THE PALM GROVES OF ELCHE

Following the late neoclassical period, which produced Horta in Barcelona, the Alameda of Osuna in Madrid and Monforte in Valencia, public gardens and parks began to reflect the influence of the nineteenth century romantic gardens, with their lakes, grottoes and artificial mountains. A typical example is La Florida in Vitoria, with its central bandstand, its lake and its mount, all reminiscent of a provincial French garden. Four statues of kings were brought here, which were made in the eighteenth century to decorate the cornice of the Royal Palace in Madrid, but were never used.

The use of irregular and winding paths continued nearly everywhere, and beautiful gardens were formed in semitropical regions such as Málaga. One garden, la Concepcíon, is an exotic park in the bottom of the valley. It contains one of the finest collections of palm-trees in Europe, thanks to the abundance of water and the protection offered by the mountains.

The garden has a long tunnel of climbing vines, and there are fountains, walks, grottoes and bridges, all created at the end of the nineteenth century. A lovely terrace overlooks the valley.

This period produced a particularly extraordinary garden of rare species and tropical plants in Arucas, on Grand Canary Island. The property of the Marquesa de Arucas, it is remarkable for its high wall entirely covered with *Monstera deliciosa* or philodendron, which bears edible fruit — a rare occurrence in Europe.

Famous specimens of *Dracena draco* — among the finest in existence — are found in the garden of the Seminary of La Laguna at Icod de los Vinos on Tenerife island. Their age is incalculable, for these trees date back to the time of the ancient Canary Islanders, the Guanches, who used the red sap to preserve their mummies.

By the end of the nineteenth century, the art of gardening in Spain had declined considerably. Parks were still laid out according to the precepts of English landscape gardening, but without considering the proportions and natural features of the site. Where beautiful terraced gardens would have been more

THE FAMOUS GREEN STAIRWAY OF SANTA CLOTILDE. *Photo S. Saavedra.*

appropriate, paths were traced over hills and slopes with no attempt to accentuate the site's natural topography. Such gardens were replicated throughout Europe with frequent monotony and an astonishing lack of imagination.

Hothouses and conservatories came into use in all important gardens in England during this period, which coincided with the reign of Queen Victoria. Their use was introduced in Kew Gardens at the end of the eighteenth century by William Chambers; it then spread to the private gardens of the English aristocracy. The enormous hothouses built by Joseph Paxton in the middle of the nineteenth century at Chatsworth, the home of the Duke of Devonshire, are a fine example.

These conservatories were used to collect and acclimatise the exotic plants brought back by botanical expeditions from South America. Most of these expeditions led by Kingston Ward, George Forrest and others, took place at the beginning of the twentieth century.

Hothouses produced the perfect conditions for acclimatisation in the damp, dismal English climate. Soon European magnates would have their own artificial gardens of orchids and other plants which previously had grown only in the jungles of Colombia, Peru, Chile and Brazil.

Conservatories and hothouses were used in Spain as well. One stood in the Rose Garden of the Retiro in Madrid until quite recently.

Rhododendrons, azaleas and camellias began to appear in such gardens as the park at Stourhead in Wiltshire, providing a vivid display of colour to gardens once decorated solely with pavilions surrounded by shady trees, and lakes edged with weeping willows.

The end of the century witnessed the appearance of

MOSAICULTURE. *Photo Author.*

FLOWER BASKET. *Photo Author.*

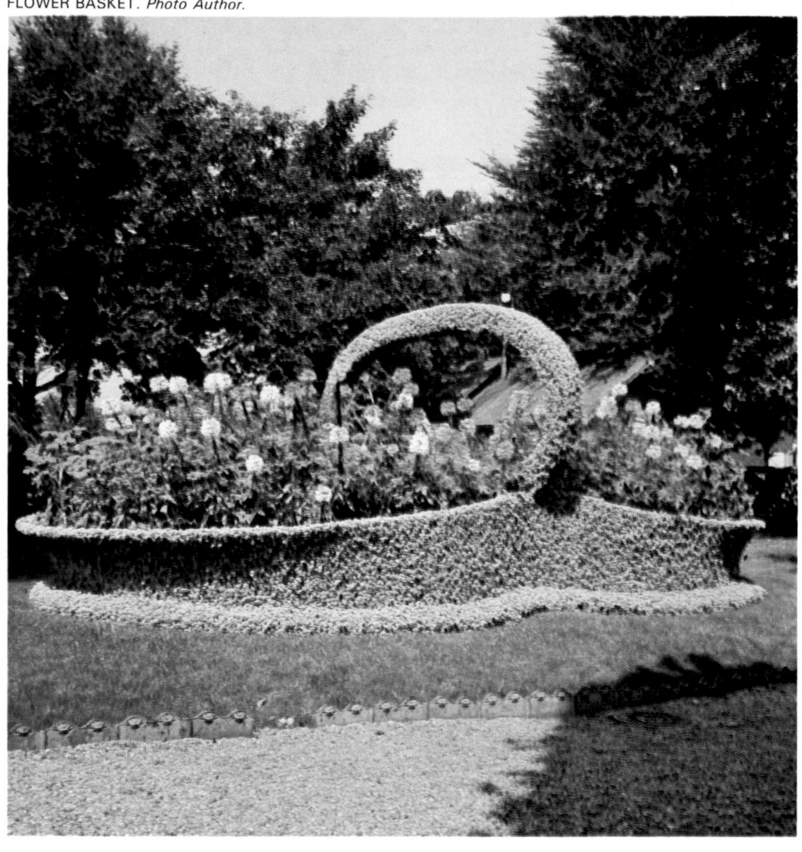

DRACENA DRACO. La Laguna Seminary. Tenerife. *Photo Author.*

mosaiculture, the art of filling flowerbeds in summer with plants from the conservatories, such as geraniums, begonias, petunias, etc., making patterns with the different shades of the foliage, and then replacing them with other plants when they have finished blooming. The purpose was to obtain colours for as long as possible. This form of decoration can still be seen in public parks, occasionally in the form of floral clocks and baskets (now somewhat outdated).

The Samá Park in Tarragona was built in 1881 by Don Salvador Samá, Marqués de Marianao, and the architect Fontseré y Mestres. It was a very extensive garden with several grottoes, waterfalls and an artificial lake. It was intended as a zoological garden and there is still a beautiful avenue of plane trees, rather unusually decorated with parrots which once stood on iron perches between every tree. Today its principal feature is its fine collection of palm trees.

Since the beginning of the twentieth century, near the Abroñigal Stream in Madrid, the Quinta de la Fuente del Berro (House of the Watercress Fountain) has been a model of this kind of gardening.

During the same period the hills in the Parque del Oeste were converted into landscape gardens with winding paths edged with rockery.

In the early twentieth century, Spanish gardening was dominated by Don Cecilio Rodríguez, whose memory has been perpetuated by a garden in the Retiro, where his skills, demonstrated by ponds and different levels of flat terrain, cannot be denied. It was completed after the Civil War of 1936-1939 by Ramón Ortiz Ferré who succeeded him as head gardener of the Madrid parks.

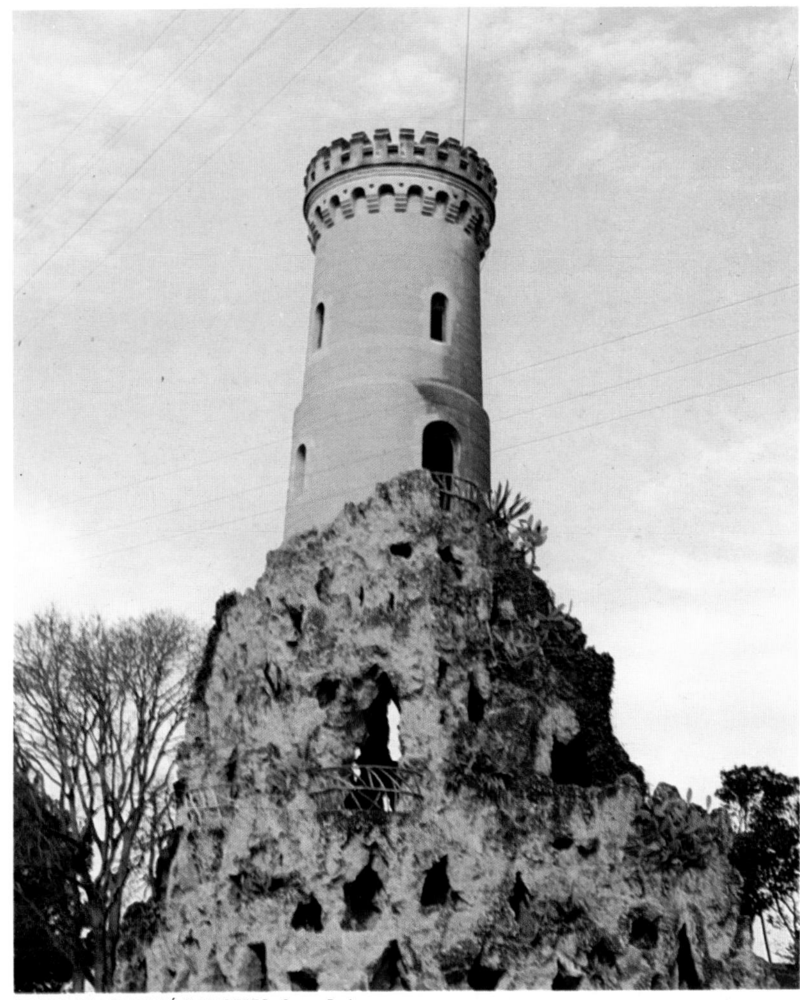

TOWER BY FONTSERÉ Y MESTRES. Sama Park.

CECILIO RODRIGUEZ GARDEN.
El Retiro. Madrid. *Photo Author.*

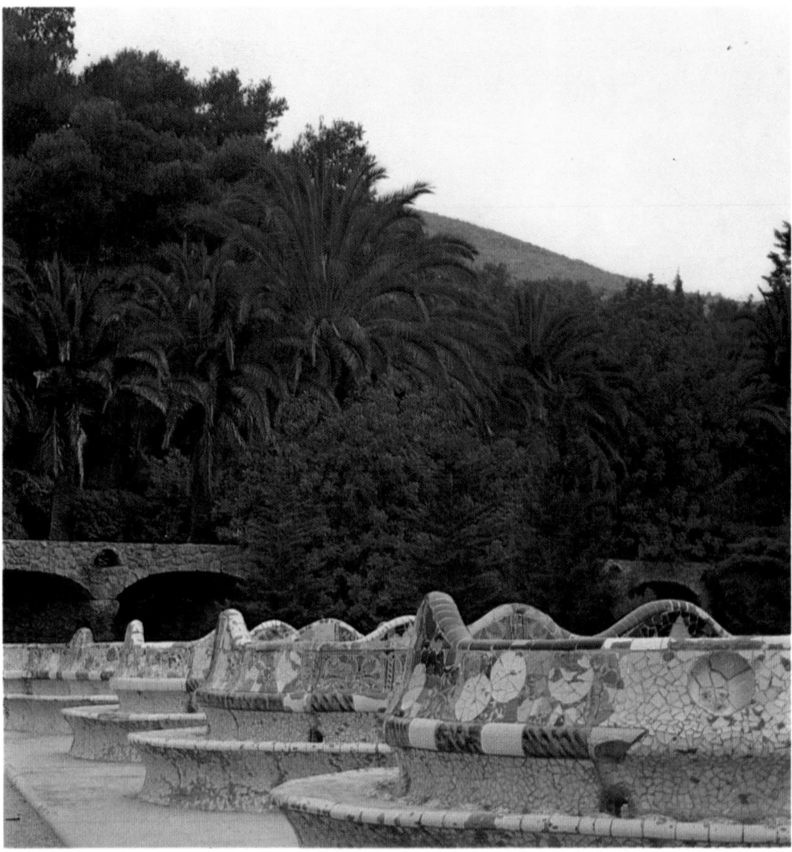

GUELL PARK. THE TERRACE. Gaudí. *Photo S. Saavedra.*

GUELL PARK. COLUMNS. Gaudí. *Photo S. Saavedra.*

At that time an architectural genius appeared in Barcelona, Antonio Gaudí (1852-1926), whose work is appreciated more and more with the passing of time. The architect of the extraordinary Sagrada Familia also produced a unique garden, commissioned by his friend Don Eusebio Güell as a project for a garden-city containing sixty houses. The boundary wall, the two entrance pavilions, the monumental stairway and the so-called Gothic temple were all built between 1900 and 1914.[1] The peculiarity of this garden is that it contains neither trees nor flowers, but simply glazed tiles and stone trees. It is a highly original work of art, typical of the epoch of the "modern style" at the beginning of the century.

In the late nineteenth century and early twentieth, Gaudí heavily influenced Catalan artists, particularly the young Picasso in his "blue" period.

Gaudí used the reddish local stone to build terraces and paths, supported by fantastic stone palm trees, by which an enormous esplanade is reached. Here he used Jujol's tile mosaics with amazing skill, creating a decorative border of benches to surround the vast area. The most original part of the design is the use of massive Doric columns to support the square, perhaps in imitation of a Greek temple or the Mosque in Córdoba, for the columns, slanting at unequal angles, are arranged in rows. The great double stairway is decorated with tiles of beautifully coloured squares. In the centre, at the foot of the two stairways, we are surprised by a dragon, also adorned with polychrome tiles.

There are only two houses in the park, one of which was Gaudí's home, now a museum. It was built by Franscisco Berenguer, and Gaudí lived there from 1906 until he died in a tram accident in 1926. He seems to have been inspired to some extent by the work of Fontseré y Mestres, who built the grottoes and the lake of the Samá Park in Tarragona, and for whom he worked as a designer. It is surprising to see that despite the scarcity of vegetation, his work lacks neither form nor colour.

THE ARRIVAL OF FORESTIER

Around 1918 the renowned French architect, J.N. Forestier (1861-1930), was brought to Spain by King Alfonso XIII. The King wanted Forestier to adapt part of the gardens of San Telmo (an ancient property of the Duke of Montpensier) and their immediate surroundings for the Hispanic-American Exhibition which was to take place in Seville.

Forestier drew plans for the Park of María Luisa, an extension of San Telmo. Inspired by the Arab gardens which had captivated him with their charm, he used local materials — bricks, lime and tiles — to retrace these gardens in the Arab style into a series of small compartments or enclosures like those in the Alhambra and the Generalife, but adapted to modern times.

CASTILLEJA DE GUZMÁN PALACE. J. N. Forestier. *Photo Saavedra.*

MOSAIC GARDEN. Güell Park. Gaudí. *Photo Saavedra.*

MAP OF MARÍA LUISA PARK. Seville. J. N. Forestier.

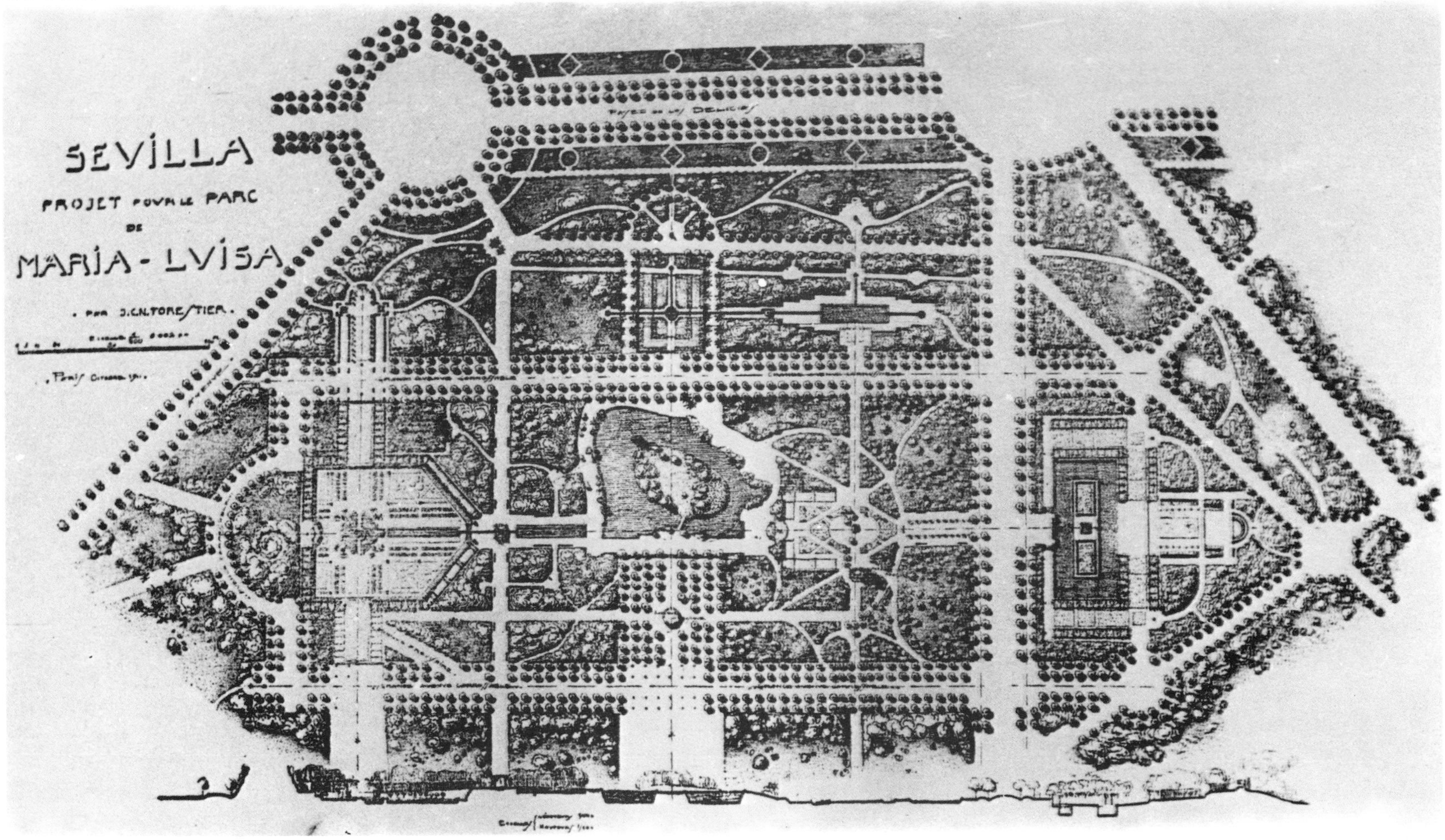

GARDEN OF CASTILLEJA DE GUZMÁN. J. N. Forestier. *Photo S. Saavedra.*

Turning such a vast expanse of land as the Park of María Luisa into Moorish gardens, divided by hedges into compartments, each one different with its fountain, benches and tiles, each imparting a sense of seclusion, was the work of a genius.

Forestier's talent as a landscape-architect, and his keen sense of perspective, were given full range in the estate of the Marqués de Castilleja de Guzmán on the outskirts of Seville. The land, raised slightly above the river's level, lends itself to an architectural garden with terrace and viewpoints surrounded by olive trees. Forestier's knowledge of plants was very evident.

The house is typical of the eighteenth century in Seville, with its colonnaded patio in the centre providing access to the garden.

The garden was laid out on classical lines, with a fine central avenue punctuated by a solid column, which breaks the perspective. It is surrounded by a small circular area with mosaics, which the poet Romero Murube described as "Horatian".

On the parapet overlooking the river is a summer house, also of simple, austere lines, which affords a wonderful view over the Guadalquivir. Beautiful stairways to the left of the garden lead down to an orchard with orange and other fruit trees and a covered walk like a pergola, so much in vogue at that time.

There was a great variety of shrubs, plants and trees when the garden was first made, but little trace of them remains today. Apparently some of the olive trees came from Italy.

Sadly this estate was never inhabited by its owner: reverses of fortune forced him to abandon the project.

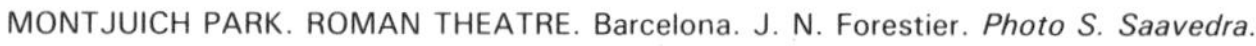

MONTJUICH PARK. ROMAN THEATRE. Barcelona. J. N. Forestier. *Photo S. Saavedra.*

MONTJUICH PARK. PERGOLA. J. N. Forestier. *Photo S. Saavedra.*

Forestier's masterpiece was undoubtedly the Park of Montjuich in Barcelona, which he constructed for the Iberian-American Exhibition. He was brought to this city by the painter José María Sert in 1915 to trace a garden on Montjuich hill, which up to then had been an uncultivated mountain with no means of access. By his skilful terracing Forestier transformed it into one of the finest parks in Spain and the principal adornment of the city. Work on it continued until 1929. He founded Spain's first School of Gardening there, where he himself taught botany in which he was intensely interested. A succession of his disciples have continued his work, among them Rubío, Riudor and Mirambell, and they have created some very lovely gardens.

The lily pond is typical of Forestier's gardens, for he had been greatly influenced by Claude Monet's paintings of waterlilies at Giverny, and also by Japanese gardens.

Forestier, through his learning and experience, clearly initiated a new phase of gardening in Spain. He introduced a large number of trees and plants and launched the neo-Arab style, with its use of tiles and ceramics in benches, bathrooms, terraces and flat roofs — all the rage in the 'twenties. The offices of the daily newspaper *ABC* in the Paseo de la Castellana in Madrid, the buildings designed by the architect Aníbal González for the Iberoian-American Exhibition in the Plaza de España in Seville and the Hotel Alfonso XIII — all typical of the period — still display this influence.

Numerous examples of Forestier's work survive in private gardens, such as the one he created for the Marqués de Viana on his estate of Moratalla, in Hornacheulos (Córdoba), which

MORATALLA. PARTERRE. J. N. Forestier. *Photo S. Saavedra.*

DESIGN FOR MONTJUICH. J. N. Forestier.

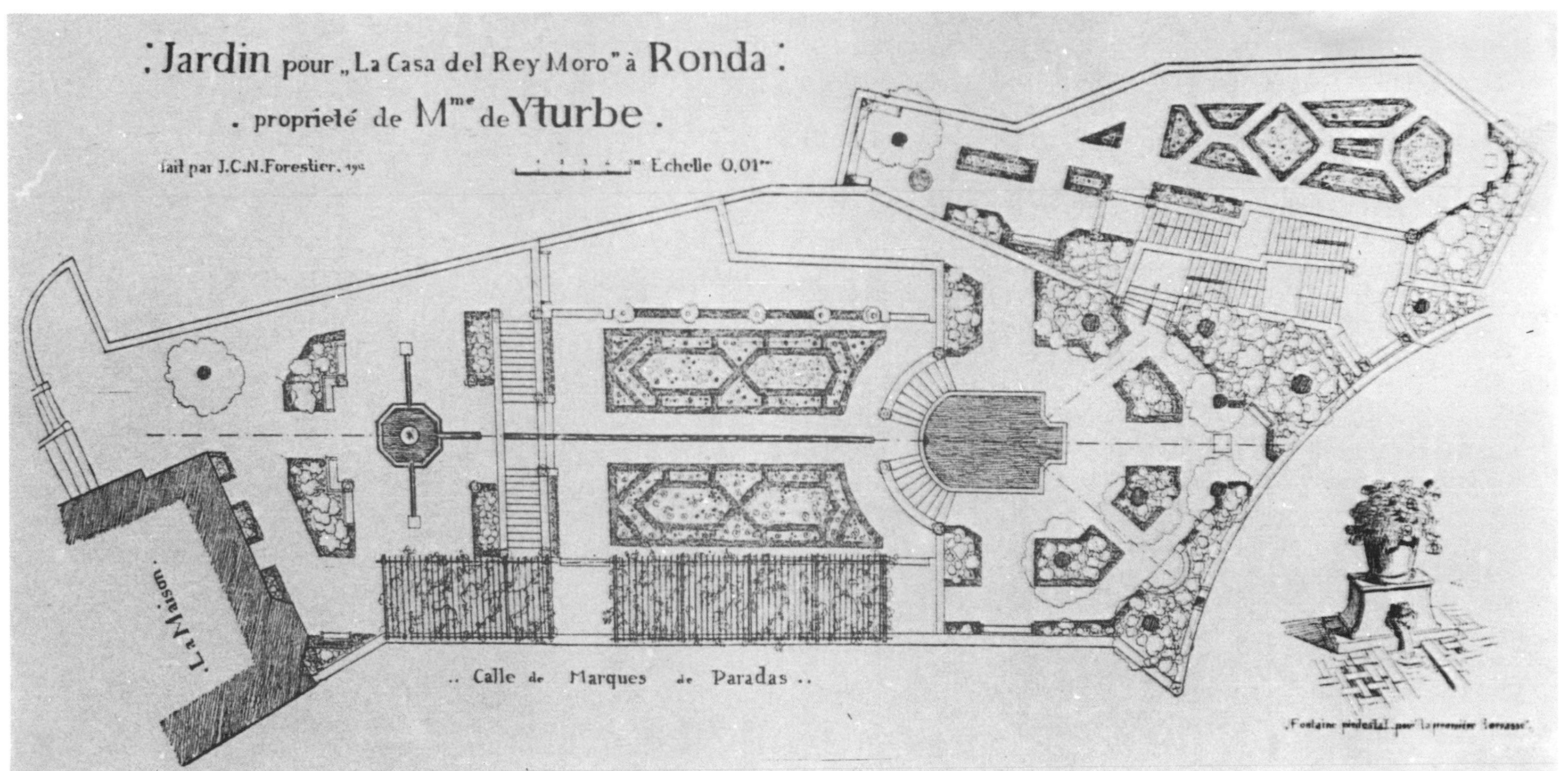

MAP OF THE GARDEN DEL REY MORO. J. N. Forestier.

MORATALLA. DEER. *Photo S. Saavedra.*

MORATALLA. FENCE AND GATEWAY. J. N. Forestier. *Photo S. Saavedra.*

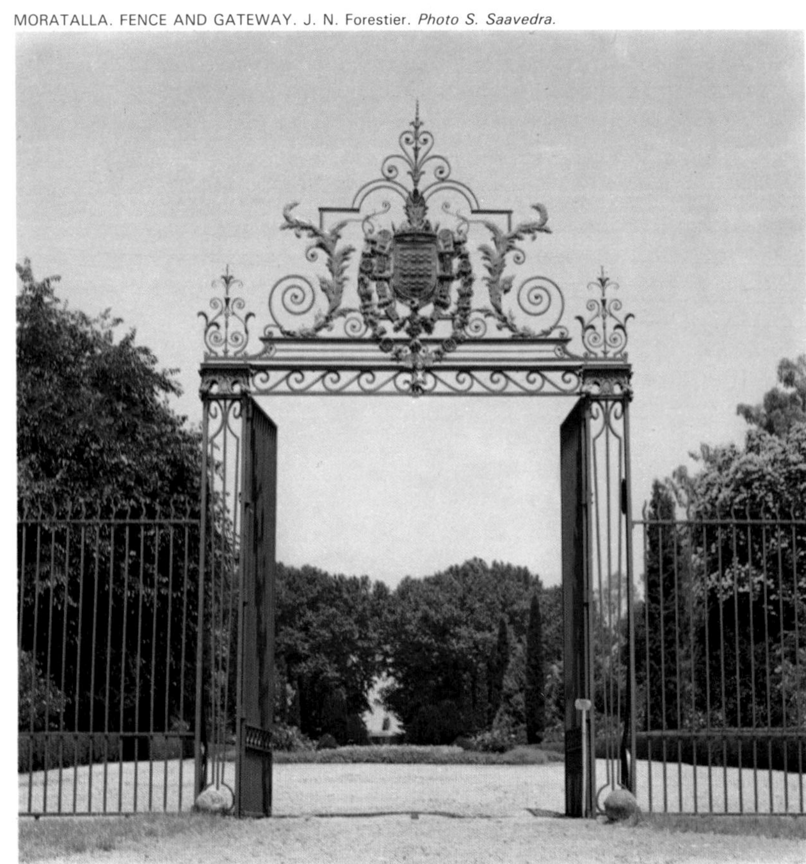

departs so radically from the traditional Andalusian style. With its great wrought-iron gate and its central avenue, reminiscent of the approach to the French château, it is unique in Spain.

At the northern façade of the Palacio de Liria in Madrid he laid out a beautiful parterre with arabesques formed of clipped boxwood, very much in keeping with the style of the palace.

The spectacular position of Ronda, with its deep ravine spanned by the ancient bridge over the river Guadalevín, renders it outstanding among the cities of Spain. It contains a number of stately homes, like those of Mondragón, and the Marquis and Marchioness of Salvatierra, whose garden is like a terrace above the river, looking out over the Sierra de las Nieves and containing a magnificent specimen of the Spanish fir *Abies pinsapo*; this conifer is native to these mountains.

La Casa del Rey Moro (House of the Moorish King) was acquired by the Duchess of Parcent about 1920. Its position next to the Salvatierra house, high above the Guadalevín, was ideal for the creation of an Arab garden. In Moorish times the residence of a king or governor probably stood here, for a gallery hewn out of the rock leads down to the river, providing a source of drinking water in case of siege.

Forestier's talent turned this narrow, irregularly-shaped strip of land to full advantage. The plan of the garden is admirable. It is divided into three terraces and retains throughout its typically French axis and perspective; and yet, he has managed so clearly to adapt it to the Arab features of tiles, water channels, hedges and cypresses. The small white marble fountain on the first terrace came from the Duchess of Parcent's home in Paris. Today, this garden is neglected and its design can be appreciated only from the original plan.

When he returned to France, after his appointment as Director of the Bois de Boulogne in Paris, Forestier created the rose garden of the Garden of Bagatelle. The French State acquired it through his mediation from the heirs of Sir Richard Wallace, thus ensuring its preservation. Here he created both the rose garden and another lovely garden whose high cypress borders convert it into a green room, with an open water-channel trickling down the steps and spreading out in the centre. This stream becomes a pool and contains a beautiful collection of Japanese irises (*Kaemphieri* and *Laevigata*). His commemorative plaque is here. The only discordant note is that of the marble fountain which dates from the beginning of the century.

When we look at Forestier's gardens today they may seem somewhat old-fashioned, with the angular and modernistic lines of their age. Even so, Forestier was without question one of the great figures of landscaping and architectural history. His sojourn in Spain left a mark that changed the general trend of modern gardening.

He spent his latter years in a house in the Bois de Boulogne, later to be occupied by the Duke and Duchess of Windsor, and created a delightful garden there in which he placed an Arab fountain in memory of Spain, of which he always spoke with enthusiasm.

BAGATELLE. FORESTIER'S GARDEN. Paris.

LIRIA PALACE. PARTERRE. J. N. Forestier.

SANTA MARÍA DE SISLA. CERAMIC CHAIR. *Photo Author.*

GARDEN OF THE MARQUÉS DE SANTO DOMINGO. Avila. *Photo S. Saavedra.*

ROYAL PALACE. SABATINI GARDENS. Madrid. *Photo S. Saavedra.*

He paid his last visit to Spain in 1929, a year before his death, to attend the Barcelona Exhibition. He had helped to position the illuminations in the great central avenue; they were the work of Bohigas and consisted of tall columns with indirect lighting, a fashion which was then at its height.

Forestier's influence is evident in the magnificent house built by the Contess of Arcentales in the Renaissance style at the Monastery of Santa María de Sisla, on a mountain overlooking Toledo. Following the fashion of the time a square garden was created with tiled chairs, probably from Talavera, bearing the date 1920. This was due to the influence of Forestier. There is also a pergola, now ruined, which contains benches of the same kind; they are very unusual, but rather inconvenient for social gatherings as the benches and seats are some distance from each other and separated by trees, not exactly conducive to the exchange of confidences.

A few years before the Civil War of 1936 the surroundings of the Royal Palace in Madrid were much improved by the formation of the gardens of Sabatini at the north façade, for which the unsightly old stables were demolished. The area is now an open green space, which is so necessary in this densely populated district. Its layout harmonises well with the classical style of the building. The garden was executed according to earlier plans by García Mercadal. Don Cecilio Rodríguez completed the planting between 1942 and 1943. The gardens of the Plaza de Oriente were also relaid at this time.

* * *

Around 1931, the Marques de Santo Domingo created some unusual gardens in Avila. Their position is spectacular because they are set within the framework of seven of the towers of the famous walls.

There is a magnificent view from the high parapet, and the style of the garden is very appropriate for the surroundings, with its old stone terraces and ponds, which are classical and severe. It contains a pergola that invites one to rest and meditate amid the profusion of roses that adorn it.

All Spanish gardens suffered during the disastrous years of our civil war. Many of them vanished completely: la Moncloa Palace, the Casa de Campo, which was a battlefront throughout the war, and the gardens of Boadilla del Monte, near Alcorcón (Madrid).

In 1940, when the war was over, the gardens gradually began to revive. Those of Cecilio Rodríguez in the Retiro, which were closed to the public, were completed, and many others were laid out to surround and set off the national monuments being restored by the Department for the Direction of Fine Arts and the National Heritage.

Restoration was also conducted on the ancient gardens of Moorish castles, such as the Alcazabas of Málaga and Almeria; public parks and approaches to towns were adorned with hedges and flowers. Today the entrances to Toledo, Avila, and other cities of artistic merit have been transformed, enhancing the beauty of the ancient buildings.

The Rose Garden of the Parque del Oeste in Madrid, the work of head gardener Ramón Ortiz Ferré, was opened in the spring of 1956. The International New Rose Congress is held there annually, enhancing the reputation of Spanish growers throughout the world and raising the national standard of production. The profusion of blooms and the blaze of colour astonish foreign visitors.

Much has been achieved in recent years with gardens in such places as housing-estates and holiday resorts, and in the gardens of universities, hospitals and other public buildings.

In Madrid, on the Cuesta de la Vega, descending towards the Manzanares, two gardens were constructed by Ramón Ortiz Ferré in 1955 in the form of successive terraces. The first, and more successful, is dedicated to the Italian musician Boccherini, who died in Madrid in 1802. His bust stands in the middle of the garden with two little round ponds on either side. It is simple and very lovely. Against the wall in the background, forming a kind of portico, is a fountain with a marble basin, and an inscription: "If God wanted to hear music He would choose Haydn; but if He wanted to hear man speak He would choose Boccherini. J. B. Cartier."

In the second garden, formed by a lower terrace, stands the bronze bust of that exquisite and sensitive Spanish writer, Azorín. We see him contemplating the valley, lost in thought and melancholy, amid the bustle of the great city, just as he contemplated it in his lifetime from the refuge of his spiritual life.

There is a shady park in the town of Soria which was probably laid out in the last century, for it contains an avenue of ancient elms, one of which curiously houses in its upper branches a circular terrace serving as a bandstand.

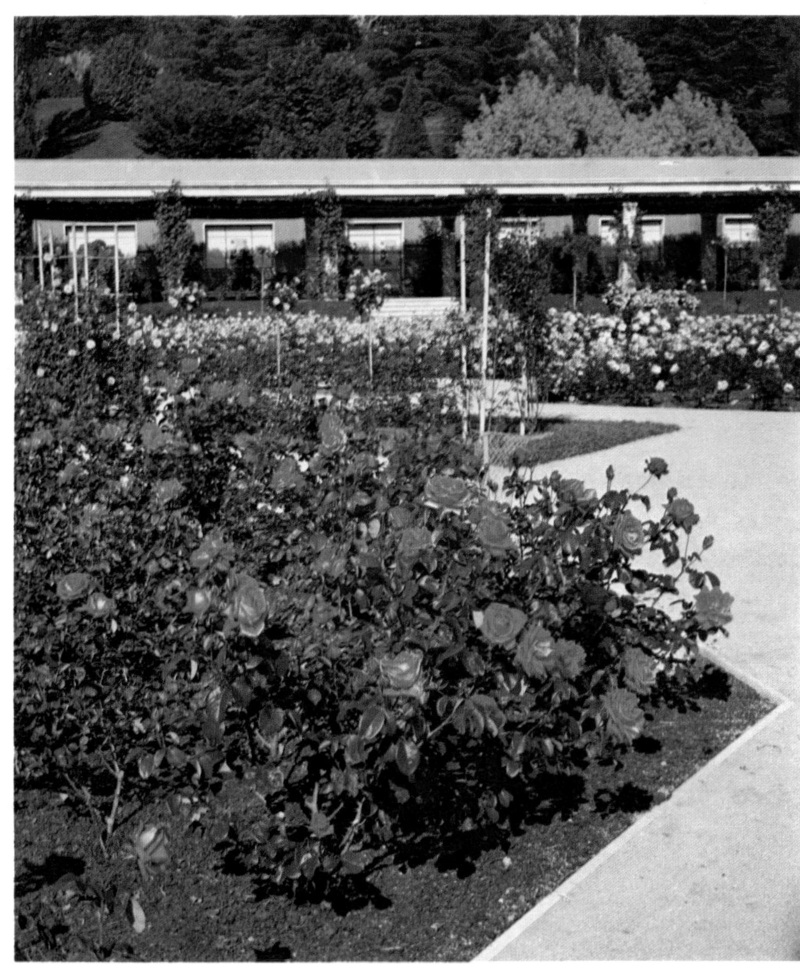

ROSE GARDEN IN THE PARQUE DEL OESTE. MARQUESA DE CASA VALDES ROSE. Pedro Dot. *Photo Author.*

CUESTA DE LA VEGA.
BUST OF AZORIN. *Photo Oronoz.*

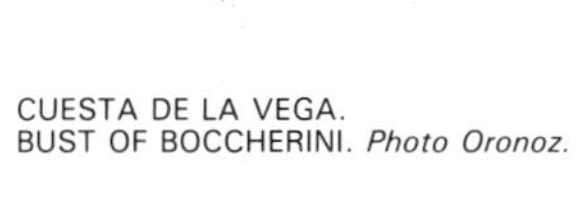

CUESTA DE LA VEGA.
BUST OF BOCCHERINI. *Photo Oronoz.*

BOTANICAL GARDEN. MARIMURTA. *Photo S. Saavedra.*

SANTA CLOTILDE. Costa Brava. *Photo S. Saavedra.*

MODERN GARDENS IN CATALONIA, MAJORCA AND THE CANARY ISLANDS

The gardens of the Costa Brava were created during the first decades of the twentieth century, long before this coast became so popular, by people of refinement and intelligence who could appreciate natural beauty. Most of the gardens are suspended on the bare rock of the cliffs, entailing twice the normal effort and labour, for soil had to be brought in and the rocky ground often had to be loosened with explosives.

Northward along the coast from Barcelona, in the town of Blanes, we find the Botanical Garden of Marimurta, founded by the German Carlos Faust. He bought the estate little by little to form extensive gardens overhanging the sea, and to cultivate Mediterranean plants, especially succulents. A flight of steps in the Italian style leads to the Temple of Linnaeus with its magnificent views.

Today it is a botanical institute with a library, a laboratory and a very fine garden.

From there we pass on to the Garden of Pinya de Rosa in Lloret de Mar, which belongs to Fernando Rivière and is devoted to exotic and succulent plants. There are two greenhouses and beautiful ponds.

Almost opposite, on a neighbouring height, Santa Clotilde is perched on the edge of the cliff. This is the wonderful Italian-style garden of the Marqués and Marquesa of Roviralta de Santa Clotilde. It was designed by Rubío, a disciple of Forestier, around 1920, when this coast must have been a haven of peace and solitude. Paul Roviralta's fine artistic sense has made this a garden of very beautiful classical lines.

Four enormous cypresses stand like sentinels in front of the house. They are unique specimens, for their branches have been allowed to grow until they touch the ground, and they spread out in a thick circular mass, forming a background to four eighteenth century statues.

The rest of the garden is formed of ramps and stairways down the hillside. They are cleverly planned to converge in small squares surrounded by Italian and Roman busts, all of fine quality. Contemplated from below, these stairs appear to be green, for the riser of each step is covered with horizontal shoots of ivy, producing a lovely effect.

The garden is tended and cared for very well and its owner lives there permanently.

Continuing up the coast we come to S'Agaró, where Señor Ensesa has been responsible for some truly artistic town-planning, all designed in the Renaissance style, with the houses built of stone and looking like Italian palaces. The hotel is also well designed.

From there we move on to Palafruguell and the Garden of Cap Roig. It was laid out on the mountainside in 1926 by Col. and Mrs Woevodsky and blends well with the countryside. All of its soil had to be brought in. There are twenty-six varieties of mimosa, and large collections of geraniums, lilies and perennial plants, most of them indigenous.

It is mainly a rock-garden, wonderfully suited to the uneven

PINYA DE ROSA. *Photo S. Saavedra.*

SANTA CLOTILDE. ROMAN BUST. *Photo S. Saavedra.*

conditions of the land. From its height the blue waters of the Mediterranean can be seen through the pine trees. A tiny beach lies below at the bottom of a deep cleft.

A castle has recently been built of old stones and furnished with valuable pieces. The estate has now been donated to Catalonia.

Catalans are particularly fond of trees and plants, and they have continued to embellish their gardens by applying their experience and learning. Despite the work achieved by Forestier at Montjuich in Barcelona, the greater part of the mountain was occupied by troops during the early decades of the twentieth century, especially on the side facing the port and the sea.

A few years ago, before Montjuich Castle had been handed over to the City Council, the landscape-architect of the Parks of Barcelona, Dun Luis Riudor, organised a general plan for this mountain, removing huts and other buildings that disfigured its slopes. At the top, with its beautiful view over the port, he created the Mirador del Alcalde, a garden of succulent plants, carpeted with exquisite *Ganzanias*. Tropical trees have recently been planted here: Parkingsonias, a leguminous tree with yellow flowers, the "wool tree" (*Chorisia speciosa*), the *Aeonium canariense*, and many others that flourish on this sheltered and sunny slope. This garden has mosaic floors in an abstract pattern, the work of Subirats.

CAP ROIG. WOEDOVSKY. *Photo S. Saavedra.*

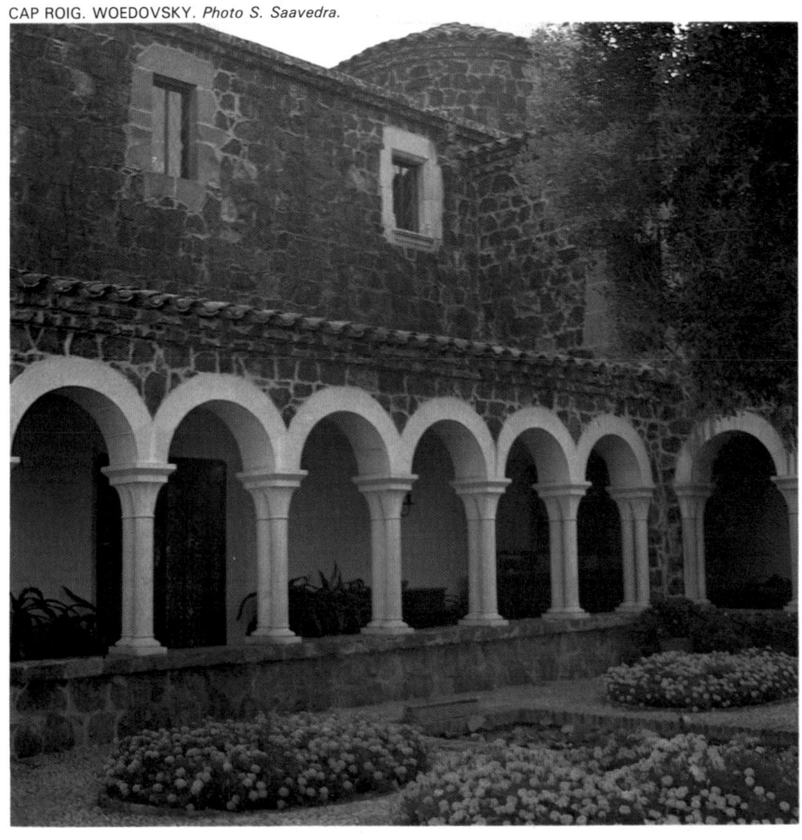

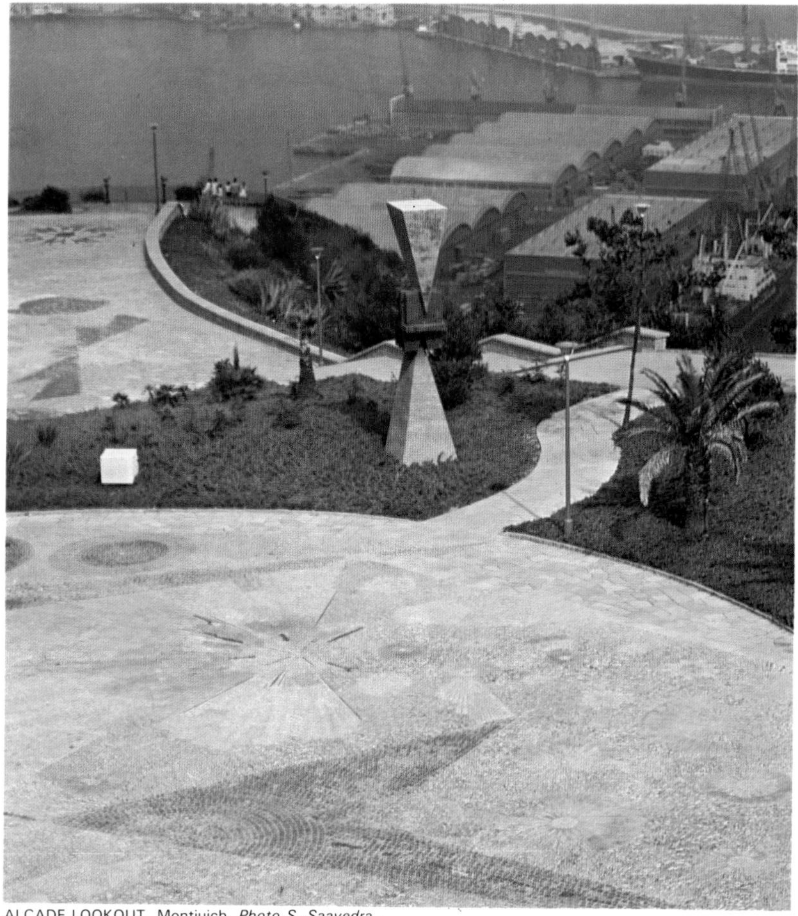

ALCADE LOOKOUT. Montjuich. *Photo S. Saavedra.*

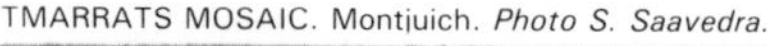

TMARRATS MOSAIC. Montjuich. *Photo S. Saavedra.*

In the spring of 1970 three gardens were dedicated to Catalan poets, under the technical direction of Don Joaquin Casamor, Don Miguel Crespo and Don Juan Pañella.

The first of these gardens is dedicated to Mosén Jacinto Verdaguer, and lies on the southern side of the mountain on the way up to the castle, planted with bulbs and rhizomes. It slopes gently up the hillside, providing a gay splash of colour. There is a pond surrounded by a rockery planted with appropriate flowers to produce a natural effect.

The second is a classical garden, dedicated to Joan Maragall, surrounding the Palacete de Albéniz on the northern side of Montjuich. This mansion was the royal pavilion at the time of the Exhibition. King Alfonso XIII and Queen Victoria Eugenia received illustrious visitors here, and important guests are still accommodated here today.

This garden, which is near the pueblo Español (Spanish Village), covers about seven and a half acres and overlooks the city. Opposite the palace, on the other side of the parterre, is a classical temple containing a very fine sculpture by Theóphile Barrau.

One of the most successful features is the skilful combination of valuable materials such as bronze, marble and Bañolas stone with its golden patina, so effectively used in the benches, the temple and columns. The garden is a model of mosaiculture, in which lovely modern varieties of flowers bloom briefly.

COSTA Y LLOBERA GARDEN. Montjuich. *Photo S. Saavedra.*

The last garden is dedicated to the Majorcan poet Mosén Costa i Llobera. It is below the Mirador del Alcade, on the southern slope of the mountain, overlooking the port in full sunlight. It is given over to cacti and other succulent plants, and in order to provide surroundings and conditions similar to those in their countries of origin, this garden has been constructed in the form of a rockery with big boulders, an art of which Don Juan Panella is a master.

It is about seven and a half acres in size, and with modern methods of transplantation, specimens several years old have been brought from Mexico, Peru and other places; more than eight hundred varieties have been collected.

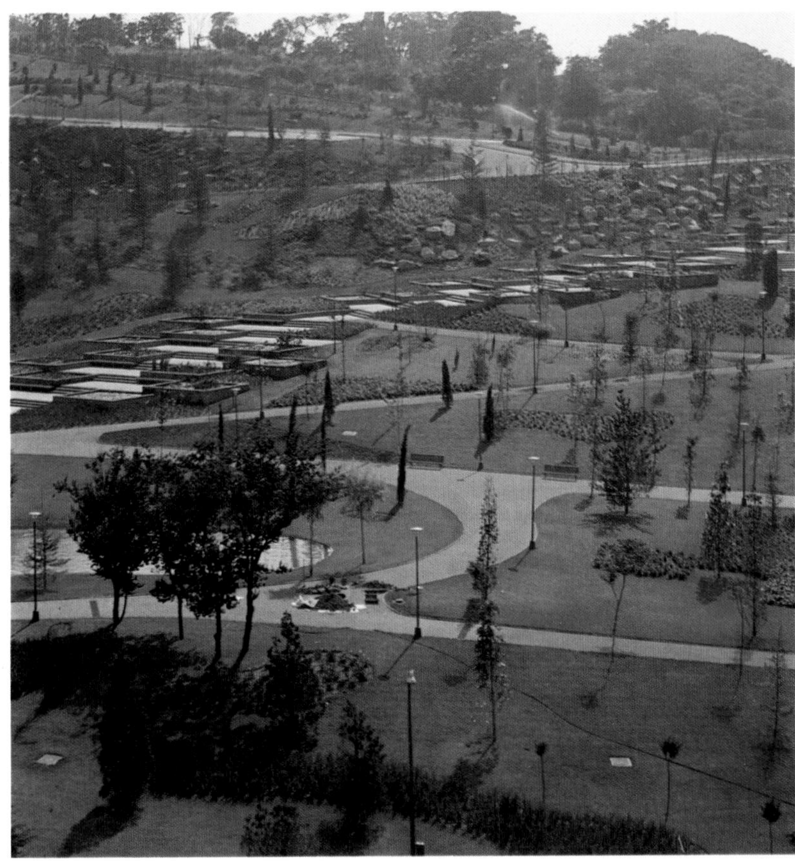

MOSÉN JACINTO VERDAGUER GARDEN. *Photo S. Saavedra.*

Modern Gardens in Majorca

Tourism, and the popularity of Majorca as a holiday resort and place to live, has raised the standard of gardens on the island. Beautiful, well cared-for gardens are kept at the hotels Formentor, and Es Moli at Deya, which are models of their kind. There are also housing estates where gardens have been skilfully laid out.

The garden of Don Juan March at S'Avall is a model of adaptation and acclimatisation of a class of xerophytic vegetation to a climate which suits it.

CASCADE IN THE MOSÉN JACINTO VERDAGUER GARDEN WITH PALM TREES. *Photo S. Saavedra.*

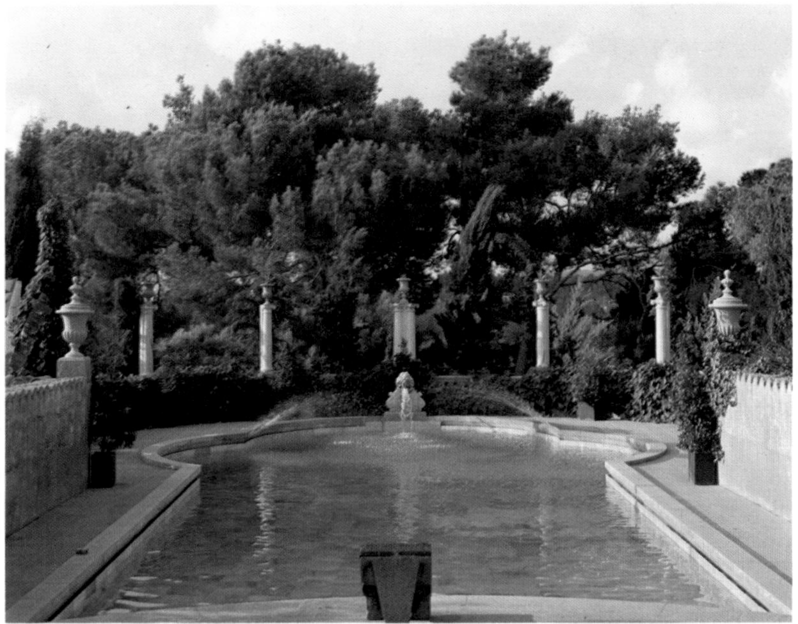

POOL, SON JULIA. Mallorca. *Photo S. Saavedra.*

SCULPTURE BY BERROCAL. Cala Ratjada. *Photo S. Saavedra.*

SCULPTURE BY HENRY MOORE. Cal Ratjada. *Photo S. Saavedra.*

CACTUS GARDEN. S'Avall. *Photo S. Saavedra.*

Don Juan Pañella, Director of the School of Gardening of Montjuich in Barcelona, has created a veritable masterpiece here. Cacti, agaves, aloes and other succulent plants from Mexico, Peru and all parts of the world grow in these gardens. They are an impressive sight, some like huge columns rearing up towards the sky, others like broad round balls, bristling with spines, nature's way of protecting them.

The garden's layout is as magnificent and varied as its collection of plants. Señor March's house was the *son* of the Marqués de Palmer. In front of it there is a classical garden with trimmed hedges, fine old fountains of great beauty, and paths covered with broken shells.

The house is reached by a long avenue planted with multicoloured oleanders, which are spectacular in June.

Not far from S'Avall, at Lluchmayor on the road to Palma by way of el Arenal, is the *Son* Julía, the house of the American painter Channing Hare. The house is newer than the other *sones* we have visited; an inscription over the door says it was built in 1810 by Don José Togores y Zanglada, Conde de Ayamans, and restored by his great-grandson in 1895.

The house does not possess great character, but in the garden opposite the front door is a round fountain of fine proportions. A stairway, undoubtedly designed by Mr. Hare, ascends to the main floor where a wide terrace divided by a loggia leads to an elegant, classical swimming pool.

The garden was also designed by its owner, and contains all the refinements of a connoisseur: a collection of shrubs, roses and carnations, a little river with a bridge, and — most original of all — an avenue of poplars planted to form an archway over the road, against which their white trunks stand out in sharp contrast.

Another splendid garden has been created by Don Bartolomé March on a pine-covered mountain. It has collections of hibiscus, bougainvilleas and many other plants requiring constant attention because the shade of the pine-trees is a great hindrance to the cultivation of flowers.

A long avenue leads to the house, with borders of vivid blue *Agapanthus Africanus.*

The garden was laid out by the English landscape-architect Russell Page. Its axis is centred upon the main house.

Modern statues by Henry Moore, Barbara Hepworth, Piche Roland, Brigitte Meier-Denninhoff, Berrocal, Corbero and Avalos adorn it.

The gardens are impeccably cared for by Don Camilo, the head gardener, and contain an infinite variety of plants. They descend towards the modern house overlooking the bay of Cala Ratjada. There are hothouses where interesting orchids and other exotic plants are grown.

* * *

The Canary Islands are of volcanic origin, and their lava-covered slopes are an impressive sight.

This is particularly true of Lanzarote, where the painter and

FOUNTAIN. Cala Ratjada. *Photo Author.*

HOME OF CESAR MANRIQUE. IN A SEA OF LAVA. Lanzarote. *Photo S. Saavedra.*

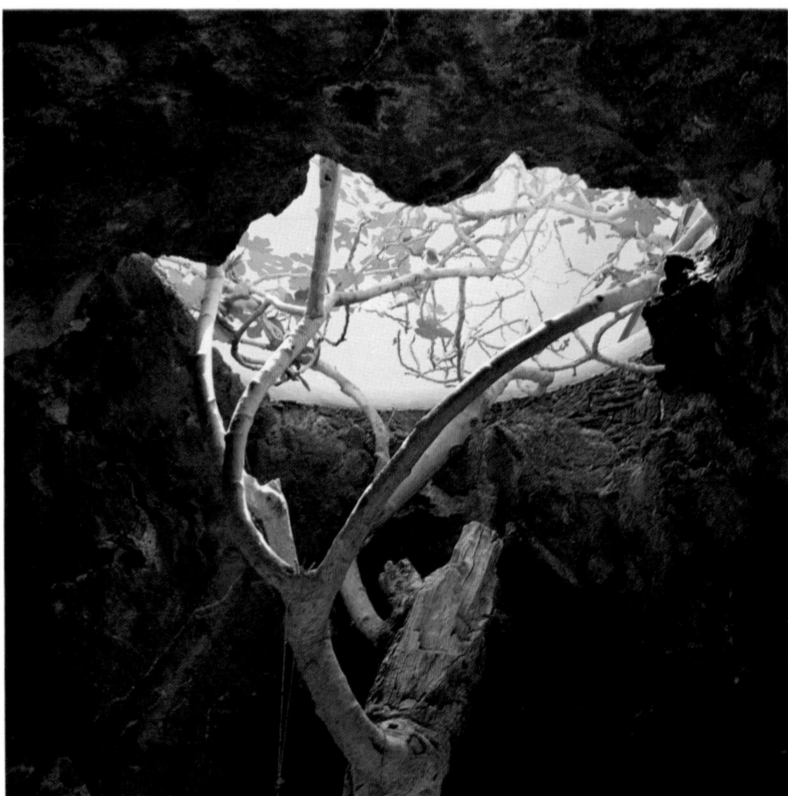

TREE IN A CAVITY. Lanzarote. *Photo S. Saavedra.*

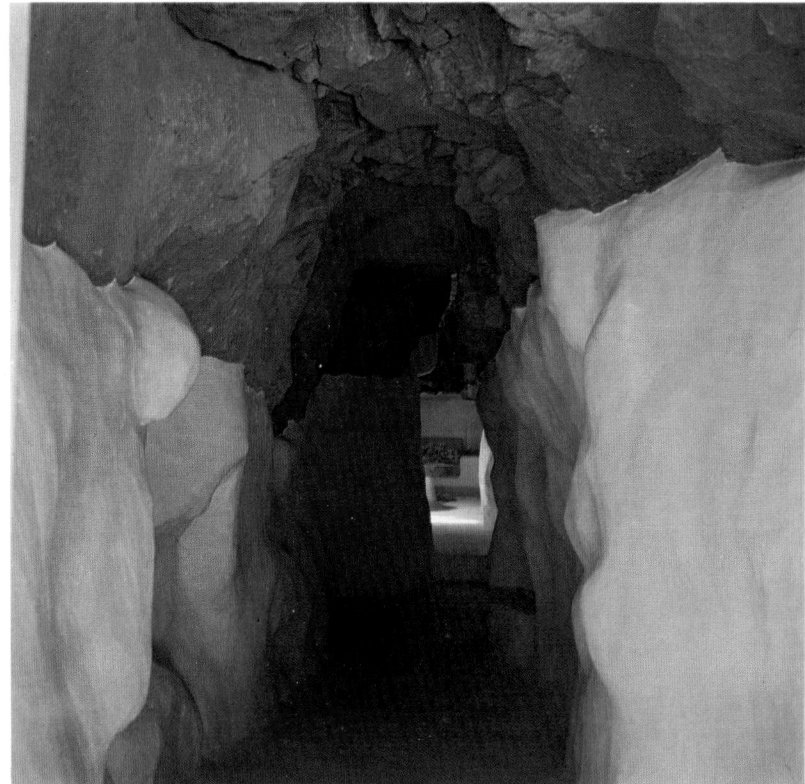

TUNNEL JOINING TWO CAVITIES. Lanzarote. *Photo S. Saavedra.*

JAMEOS DEL AGUA. Lanzarote. *Photo S. Saavedra.*

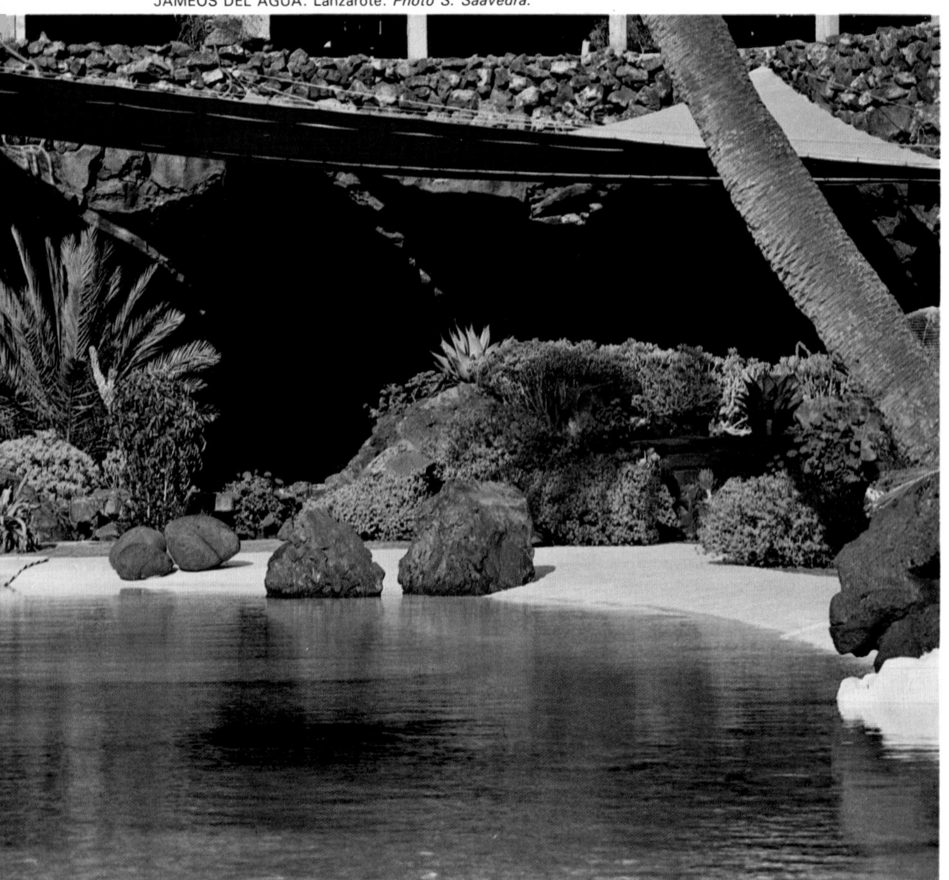

sculptor César Manrique has created a striking home. His house, positioned in a sea of lava, was constructed to conform with the "bubbles" or cavities formed in the ground when the lava erupted. Rooms have been constructed in these cavities and linked by passages dynamited through the rock.

In the rooms that open toward the sky (it never rains here) trees have been planted. The house is modern and cheery, with the fireplaces typical of the island.

Near Arrecife is the unusual Club de los Jameos del Agua, considered one of the best night clubs in Europe.

In the village of Tafira Alta, on the Island of Grand Canary, the Swede, E. R. Svenson Sventenius, has recently created a garden with a selection of plants native to the Canary Islands, arranged knowledgably and with exquisite taste to make a valuable modern collection. E. R. Svenson Sventenius is an eminent botanist and has written numerous books about the flora of the Canaries to which he has devoted his life. He is at present Director of this garden which is called de Viera y Clavijo.

THE PALM GROVES OF ELCHE

The Mediterranean regions of Spain, like those of Africa, are barren, calcareous, and flooded with clear, transparent light.

We cross massifs of dramatic high mountains that look as though they have been hewn with a knife. Some of the steep crags are crowned by castles, and it is impossible to imagine how they

ELCHE PALM GROVE. *Photo S. Saavedra.*

were built; such are the castles of Sax or of Villena, all are of the same mellow stone. Trees are nonexistent.

By taking the coast road from Alicante we come to the great bay of Santa Pola, near Elche. Here the countryside changes, for the whole of this area is a fertile plain watered by canals and other means of irrigation.

Just as in a desert oasis, tall palm-trees rise up, slender and flexible, swaying in the breeze.

The palm grove of Elche is very old, perhaps Phoenician; coins minted before the time of Christ show that palm groves stood here in ancient times. It is probably that when the Phoenicians made their colonising incursions along the Mediterranean they took dates with them from the Orient for food, and that the seed germinated in these favourable lands, giving rise to the enormous plantation that exists today. It is unique in Europe.

The largest plantation at Elche is that of the Priest, which covers 13,000 square metres and contains about a thousand date-palms of the variety *Phoenix datilifera*, native to Persia and spread throughout Africa. Its height ranges upward to thirty metres. It is a dioecious tree; the male produces a flower like a tuft from which the pollen fertilises the female in the spring. This fertilisation is effected artificially.

In the plantation there also grow cycads, lemons, pomegranates, oranges, bananas, and every kind of vegetation which is to be found in the Mediterranean region. It is not so much a garden as a model orchard cultivated with great care.

The age of the date-palms is reckoned by the marks of the

GARDEN IN THE CANARIES. Tafira. Grand Canary. *Photo Author.*

IMPERIAL PALM. Elche. *Photo Author.*

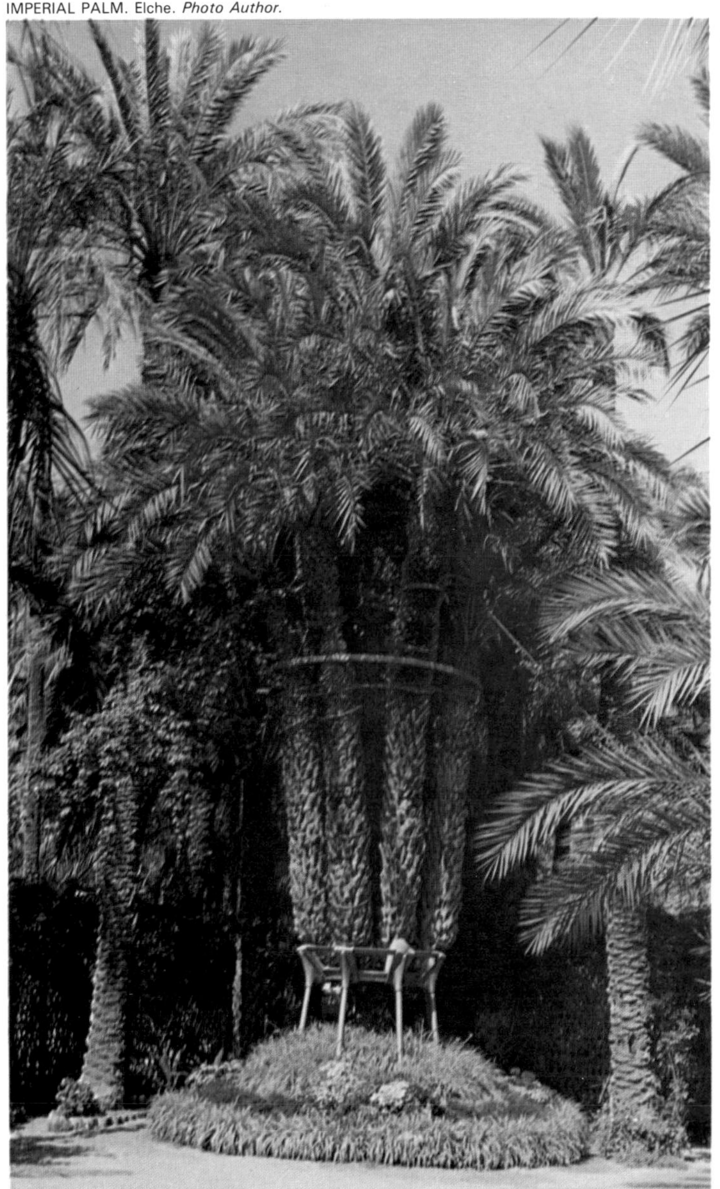

rings left by the initial cuts on the palms, each ring representing one year; how old they are can be judged by the smoothness of the trunk, for they grow smoother as the years go by. Some are as much as two hundred and fifty years old.

The most important tree in the plantation is the imperial date-palm, named after the Empress Elisabeth of Austria. This palm-tree is a botanical phenomenon, for after sixty-five or seventy years of life as a male, it began to blossom like a candelabra, with seven offshoot trunks, today supported by iron props. It is reckoned to be about a hundred and fifty years old. The priest Castaño first noticed this anomaly about 1880. This priest, after whom the orchard is named, was the descendant of horticulturists from whom he inherited both the estate and his love for the care of palm-trees.

At his death in 1918, the estate was bought by Don Juan Orts, the chronicler of Elche and an expert in the Fine Arts; he died in 1958. Today it is owned by his widow, Doña María Serrano, who lives there all the year round. The property has been declared a national artistic garden. It has changed somewhat in appearance since it has become a garden of cactacea and rock plants, which is not very appropriate in this area where the ground is so flat.

A short distance from this palm-grove is the Hort del Gat, which has a large pond and is arranged in squares with the palms growing along the sides of the irrigation channels in the classic manner.

The Municipal Park is also a very well-kept palm grove. The lower part is called Hort de Baix and lies on the edge of a deep ravine made by the river Vinalapó. An iron railing separates the Hort del Chololater which belongs today to the Savings Bank. It used to be the estate of Señor Asencio, a kind and friendly native of Elche who some years ago welcomed us to his house among the palm-trees, so that we could attend the moving thirteenth century drama — the Mystery Play which is performed in the church of Santa María in honour of the feast of the Assumption of the Virgin in August.

In this flat country, planted with orchards and palm-groves, we notice the small size of the houses of the landowners, with hardly any windows and with porches used for the date harvest and for relaxation.

We are once more reminded of the Arabs, who spent their

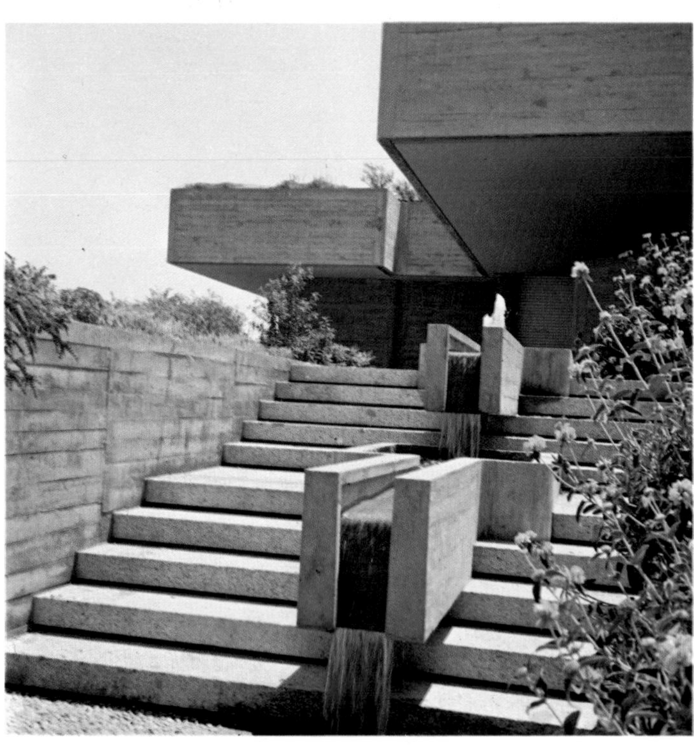

VALDECASAS GARDEN. Somosaguas. *Photo Author.*

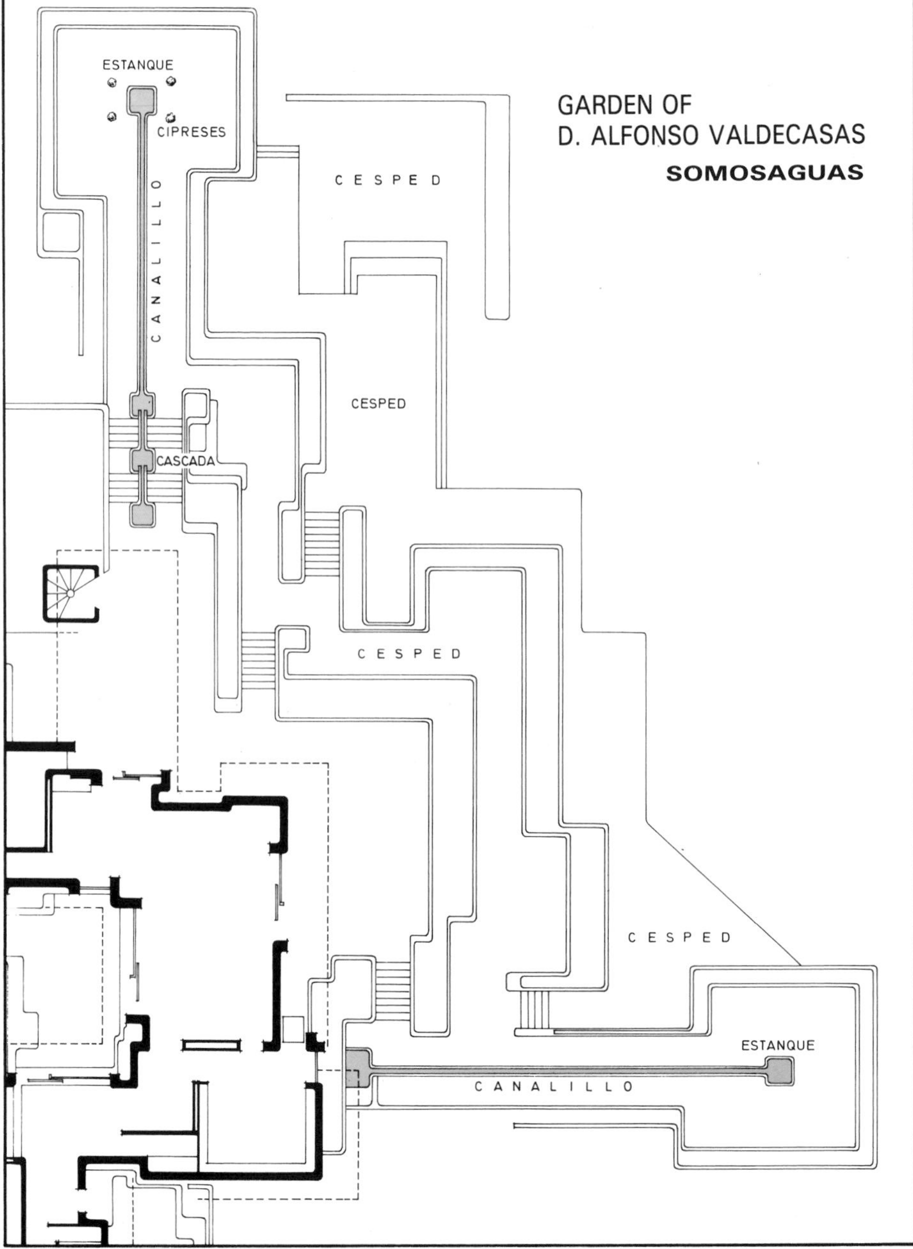

VALDECASAS GARDEN. Somosaguas. *Photo S. Saavedra.*

lives between orchard and garden. We would like to remain there forever, contemplating the palm-trees and the blue sky.

Arab traditions persist in modern Spanish architecture. In the housing estate of Somosaguas, near Madrid, architect Javier Carvajal has constructed two houses with gardens, completed in 1968. Here we see a modern interpretation of the Oriental riad, with a series of cascades leading to the lower garden. In the first garden, the property of the Valdecasas family, this riad is oriented toward the north, framed by two cypresses. The garden's most significant composition lies to the west; the pond with its vertical jet, whose channel descends several levels to a small round pool framed by four tall cypresses.

The house is also constructed on several levels, with a small, intimate patio and central fountain — a modern version of the Arab courtyard.

The second house, belonging to the architect, has an asymmetrical pond, also crossed by a canal running north.

GARDEN OF DON JAVIER CARVAJAL. Somosaguas. *Photo Author.*

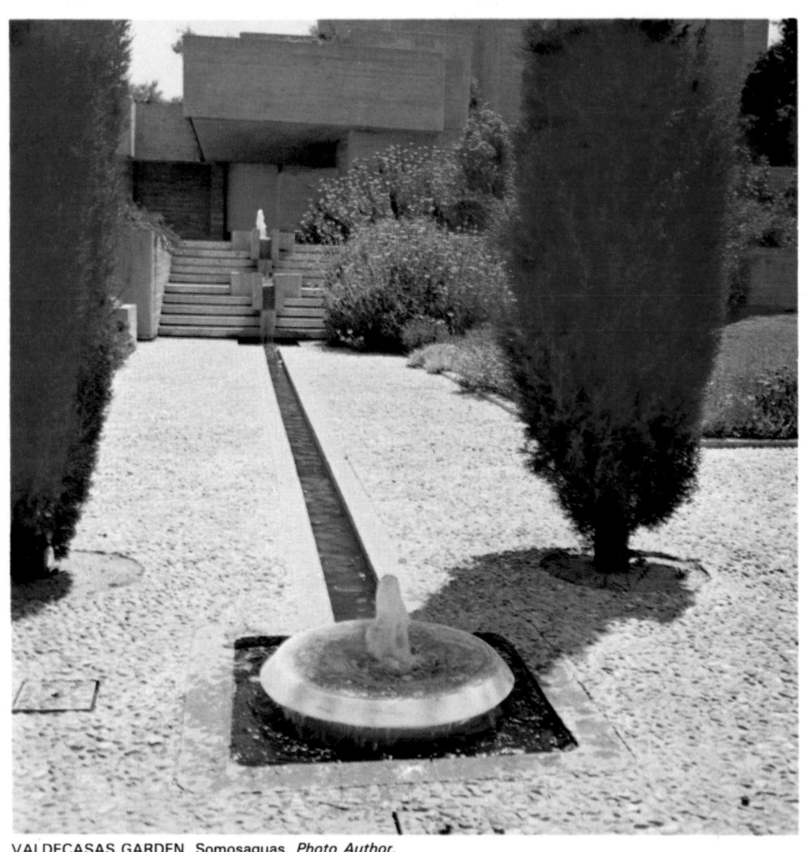

VALDECASAS GARDEN. Somosaguas. *Photo Author.*

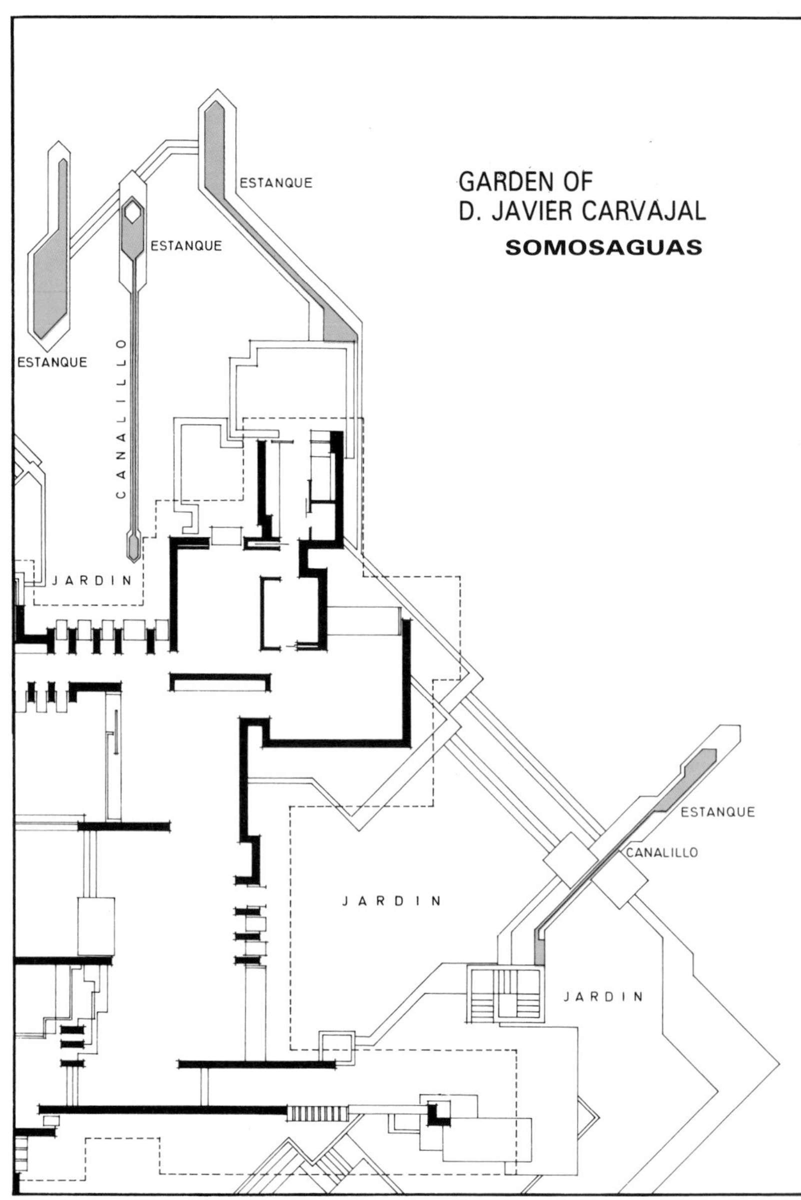

[1] BASSEGO DE NONNELL, Juan, and GARROT, José María: *Guía de Gaudí*, Ediciones Literarias y Científicas, Barcelona, 1970, page 56.

[2] GROMORT, Georges: *Jardins d'Espagne*, Editions A. Vincent, Paris, 1926, vol. II.

15 PRESENT-DAY GARDENS IN SPAIN

The geographical formation of the Iberian Peninsula has been compared to an inverted soup plate, because the central plateau can only be reached by climbing the mountain ranges that surround it. From any point on the Spanish coastline, after crossing a strip of low-lying land — naturally wider in some places than others — the only way to the highlands in the centre lies across massive mountains, sometimes through rugged passes.

This geography has produced the greatest variety of climate and soil anywhere in Europe. We pass from the subtropical Mediterranean zone, or from the mild and rainy regions of the north, to the central plateau with its harsh climate, torrid in summer and cold in winter, dry and severe at all times, almost always with a scarcity of water. Such conditions are hardly conducive to horticulture.

The land in the centre of the Peninsula is mainly calcareous frequently containing Tertiary fossils (of the Miocene). The regions of Murcia and Almería contain bleak sandstone and white gypsum. The Cantabrian and north-west coasts are covered with forests thousands of years old, offering a great variety of heathers and heaths, camellias, rhododendrons and other calcifugous plants.

The construction of reservoirs has helped considerably to overcome these conditions, yet even so, the terrain must be carefully considered when a garden is to be made, for soil characteristics determine water characteristics. More often than not, Spanish soil is calcareous and thus unsuitable for a great number of plants that cannot tolerate lime and that cannot extract the elements they need from this basic soil.

Therefore, the first step in planning a new garden is to have the soil analysed to find out whether it is acid or calcareous. This is easy today, for throughout Spain there are numerous centres, laboratories and manufacturers of fertilisers offering analyses free of charge.

Secondly, we must consider location.

If our garden is located on a plateau, our choice of plants will be much more limited, for we shall encounter severe frosts in

MEDITERRANEAN GARDEN. *Photo S. Saavedra.*

ROSE GARDEN. *Photo Author.*

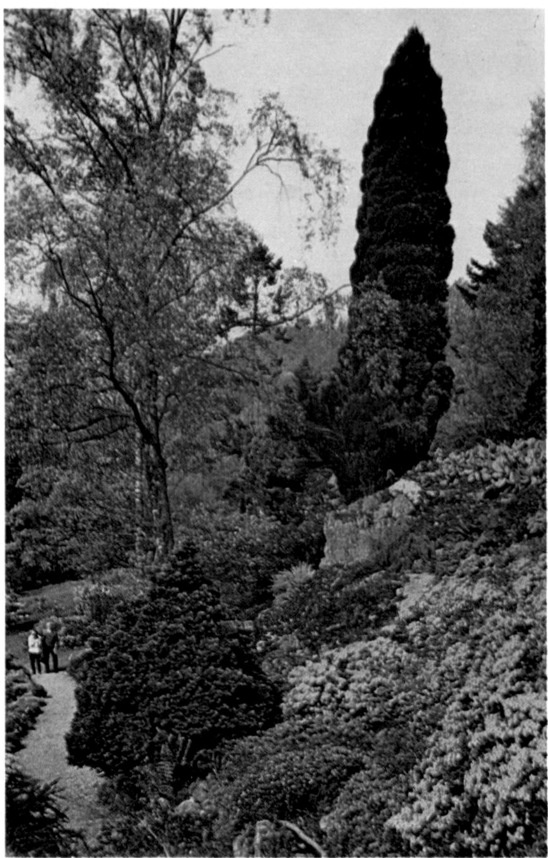

ROCK GARDEN.

winter and hot dry summers. Even so, much can be achieved — for example — with the cultivation of roses, for nowhere are roses bred so large, so pure, or so brightly coloured as on the Castilian plateau, for the light sandy soil of some of its districts suits them well if they are always properly fertilised and watered.

As noted earlier, this work began with the Arabs who knew well the Spanish soil conditions, and who stored water in cisterns and canals and were masters of this art, which is still practised on our soil.

Today the whole system of agriculture in Spain has changed, thanks to irrigation by spraying.

Let us decide, then, what kind of garden we wish to create, whether it is to be a classical, romantic or modern garden. Not all styles will be suitable for our particular type of house. Besides, much is influenced by the size of the plot available. Nowadays, a typical household garden measures between 500 and 1,000 square metres in extent, at the most a hectare (or two-and-a-half acres), especially if our house is located in an urban area, which is usual today. It is of utmost importance that the style of the house and the contours of the site adapt to the garden and vice versa.

It is important also, once a plot has been acquired, that the house, if possible, should be situated at the highest point as obviously a house placed in a hollow at the bottom of the garden will have no view or perspective, two important factors that contribute to the beauty of a residence. Orientation is also important, above all in cold and windy areas, where gardens must be sheltered.

A well-placed house, with its garden facing south, is assured of success, provided a level area is left around it to form a terrace.

We must study the most important factors and our personal requirements in each case.

A garden, even more than a house, is a personal creation — the work of an artist — a Maecenas, a dreamer who has planned it for his recreation and pleasure and centred on it all his loving care, hopes and illusions. This has been so throughout history, in royal parks as well as in private gardens. Hardly ever do we see a garden created by a corporation or a society, except perhaps in monasteries or botanical gardens established for the study and classification of plants and even then an individual will have been the guiding force.

Gardens have survived throughout history immortalising their creators who have left their mark upon them. Many gardens have perished through their owners' neglect, reminding us that existence is transitory. Plants cannot live without love, whether they grow in a vast English park, in a humble patio with potted plants, or in the window-boxes of a block of tenements.

For those who spend only short periods in their gardens, it is essential to determine when they would like the garden to reach its peak of glory so that the appropriate plants can be selected. Nothing is more discouraging than to learn that "the garden was marvellous a few weeks ago," as it is impossible for the flowers to go on blooming all year round.

Once the site for our garden has been chosen, the next step is

ALPINE PHLOX. *Photo Author.*

to adapt it to its natural surroundings. It will be successful only if it forms part of the adjoining countryside and blends with it. There is a garden for every landscape. In the rough crags and stony ground of the Sierre de Guadarrama, rockeries — so often abused elsewhere — are a natural form of decoration, needing only to be enriched with a collection of alpine plants. In the north, lawns, woodlands and waterfalls are more appropriate.

Rock-gardens bloom only in the spring, for in their natural state the plants used normally appear when the snows melt; they are accustomed to the high altitudes of mountain ranges and therefore spend long dormant periods in winter. A truly successful rock garden is much more difficult to create than one might suppose. It must be placed in a natural position, not built up against the wall of a house. Placement of the stones is an art in itself. It is often believed that simply spreading a large number of stones (even paving stones) over the surface of the ground and then adding a collection of plants (often unsuitable for the purpose) is sufficient to create a rock-garden. But the true rock-garden is a very different thing. The rocks — local stones if possible — should be buried to two-thirds of their depth in order to properly recreate natural conditions so that the plants are sheltered in the cavities of the stones. The real experts in Alpine gardens, the Swiss and the English, fill the spaces between the rocks alternatively with calcareous and acid heathland soil, so as to meet the requirements of each plant.

As far as possible, they also imitate the stratification or formation of the local rock so as to produce the most natural effect; they slant the stones inwards at an oblique angle in order to catch all the rain that falls, which in Spain is usually very little. Wild mountain plants growing locally will do best. There are numerous mountain plants and bulbs in Spain much sought after by the enthusiasts who comb our highlands in search of new treasures.

Classical gardens with their hedges, pools, fountains and statues, in either the Italian or French style, are best avoided,

DIAGRAM OF ROCK PLACEMENT.
COMPLETE BOOK OF GARDENING. KEW GARDENS.

GARDEN OF CLIPPED BOXWOOD. *Photo Author.*

WHITE GARDEN. Munstead, England.

BROAD BANDS OF VIVIDLY COLOURED PLANTS. Hascombe. Court. *Photo Peter Coats.*

CLASSICAL GARDEN. *Photo Author.*

"GAVA" CLIMBING ROSE. *Photo Author.*

unless one has an old house one wishes to reframe in its original setting, or already possesses the appropriate garden ornaments. In that case, trim borders and a layout of straight lines are essential, even in a small garden.

With modern houses a common mistake is to overdecorate, surrounding a tiny plot with privet or santolina, putting up arches with rambling roses, beds of annuals, statues and steps, so popular in the last century, and in general, occupying so much space that the garden begins to look like a public park. If ornaments are not of good quality, that is stone or marble and preferably antique, they do not serve their purpose. The use of cement or wrought iron is not usually very decorative, even though such ornaments may in themselves be charming.

Because of the lack of space and the cost of labour, present-day gardens are increasingly following the example of the English who have always taken the lead in the art of gardening because of the expert knowledge and love they devote to it.

English gardens usually consist of a lawn, a rose-garden, wide borders of perennials grouped according to variety and colour (called "herbaceous borders"), a water-garden (plants growing in water), a rock-garden with collections of alpines usually connected by a small stream; and a wild garden, composed of bushes and trees gradually merging into the woodland, where bulbs are planted and allowed to multiply without further cultivation. There is also a tendency in English gardens to specialize in collections of such plants as rhododendrons and camellias, in heath-gardens, rose gardens and gardens of a particular colour — greys, whites or blues.

Because of its southern position, Spain offers extensive areas in which subtropical plants can be cultivated, areas which have not as yet been sufficiently appreciated. Even so, the Mediterranean coasts are now adorned with gardens of bougainvillea, a flower unknown half a century ago, and a variety of other plants from the southern hemisphere. In the Canary and Balearic Islands, as described in the last chapter, there are a number of gardens with collections of cacti, hibiscus, etc.; other gardens are given over to tropical plants, such as the Acclimatisation Garden of La Oratava in Tenerife, and the Garden of Canary Island Plants at Tafira on Grand Canary, both of which have already been mentioned.

Spanish flora is among the most varied in Europe, and Cantabrian flora, like that of the Mediterranean and Balearic regions, is planted in gardens throughout the world.

In modern times the rose growers Pedro Dot and Camprubí Nadal from Barcelona have produced two bicoloured roses, the *Condesa de Sastago* and the *Marquesa de Urquijo*, which were among the first of this kind and made them famous in the world of roses; B. Munné, another Catalan rose grower, produced the climbing rose *Gavá* which is sensational for its shape, its pale pink shade with the yellow base to the petals, and a perfume rarely found in hybrid tea roses.

Another Catalan, Lorenzo Pahisa, developed a lovely rose, *Lorenzo Pahisa*, which we have seen in its full splendour in the rose garden of Bagatelle, a mass of great blooms like mother-of-pearl with glistening foliage. Pedro Dot also specialises in miniature rose bushes, of which he has produced numerous varieties.

If we had our choice of sites on which to build our summer residence, we should seek a gently sloping hillside, not too high up, in an open valley somewhere in the north, if possible near the sea. The house would be roomy and modern, and the ground floor windows would open like doors on a level with the garden. We would then look on to an extensive lawn with fine, well-cut grass. Near the house there would be broad beds of fragrant flowers: white petunias, *nicotianas*, pinks, and a wide variety of lilies: the *Lilium regale*, delicate and shell coloured, the *auratum*, the *speciosum* and some of the new hybrid varieties from the Far East, such as *Imperial Crimson* and *Imperial Gold* which bloom spectacularly and fragrantly in August.

The blue agapanthus, the *africanus* or the *umbellatus*, are very valuable plants for the summer garden. Their flowers last for a long time and they are hardy and decorative particularly when planted in large clusters, if space permits.

In the north the *Phlox decussata*, Japanese anemones, the white *Leucanthemos*, and brightly coloured annuals such as zinnias, *Cosmos*, marigolds, asters and many others all bloom in August and September and are indispensable for providing colour in the garden.

Delphiniums, though decorative and one of the few truly blue flowers, are less appropriate as they bloom in June and July — too early for most holidays.

AGAPANTHUS. *Photo Author.*

ROCK GARDEN OF PLANTS FROM THE CANARIES. *Photo Author.*

CRATAEGUS HEDGE. *Photo Author.*

The lower edges of the flower beds would be lined with clumps of heliotropes — so often overlooked in the choice of flowers — alternating with other scented flowers.

Fragrant climbing plants, such as honeysuckle, jasmine and *Mandevilla*, would cover the walls of the house. Shrubs would be planted next to the walls; they might include: *Datura suaveolens* like white trumpets, with its delightfully perfumed blossom, and the *Eupatorium micranthum*, whose feathery flowers have a smoky scent like incense and are at their best in the summer months.

On the more sheltered walls the wine red bougainvillea and the blue *Plumbago* mix well together.

On the lawn, we would plant a few ash-grey trees, such as the cedar *atlantica glauca*, or a *Magnolia grandiflora*, which is indispensable in northern gardens for the delightful scent of its flowers.

If our house is a weekend retreat near a big town on the Castilian plateau, it must be livable and pleasant in the winter and spring months, when escape from the capital is so important. Our garden here must be sheltered from the icy winds blowing off the surrounding sierras. Tall cypress hedges backed by slender poplars, which turn gold in autumn, are a perfect solution, seen throughout the Castilian countryside, and romanticised by poet Antonio Machado:

> "I have come back to see the gold poplars,
> Poplars by the roadside, on the banks
> of the Duero..."

Hardy rustic shrubs blend well with the austere landscape and provide colour in the autumn and spring; the *Crataegus pyracantha*

WALLS COVERED WITH BOUGAINVILLEA. *Photo Author.*

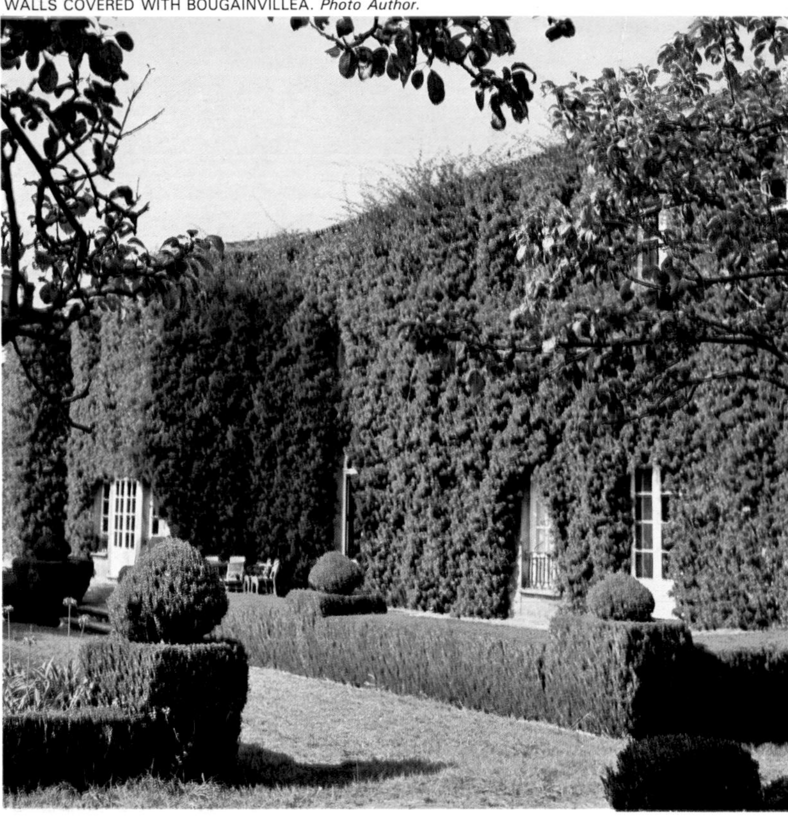

STERNBERGIA LUTEA. *Photo Author.*

BERBERIS. AUTUMNAL TONES. *Photo Author.*

comes in many varieties, all with red or yellow berries, and fragrant white flowers in the spring.

Berberis are also very suitable and some of them turn beautiful shades in the autumn.

Broad beds parallel to the house, one to three metres in width, would be filled with shrubs and perennials to provide colour from July to October, when the fierce sun parches everything and we abandon our garden.

On our return from holidays in September, beneath the shubs would be golden-coloured flowers, like goblets rising from the earth. They are *Sternbergia lutea* or *Oporanthus*, which thrive in Castile.

When the first frosts come, the barberries and the many varieties of *Cotoneasters* will begin to change colour, their gracefully drooping branches laden with red berries, and their foliage in some varieties turning purplish; when flowers are scarce, this produces a vivid and welcome contrast with the bushes of grey foliage, such as the *Teucrium fruticans*.

It is now possible to have collections of improved species of asters in different varieties and heights: the *novae-angliae*, the *novi-belgii*, the *Amellus*, big flowered varieties and dwarf varieties for alpine gardens; their colours range from delicate pink to red and violet. Modern and rustic varieties of Korean chrysanthemums are also available with many tiny flowers, some of them hanging in cascades. They bloom in November when there is little other colour in the garden and the winds descend from the sierras across the bare dry countryside.

Towards the end of December the Chinese deciduous shrub *Chimo- nanthus fragrans* gives colour and scent to the garden; it is covered with curious flowers like pale yellow stars with a scent of hyacinth.

BANKS OF THE DUERO IN SORIA. *Photo Author.*

TEUCRIUM, WITH GREY COLORATION. *Photo Author.*

BANKSIAE LUTEA ROSES. *Photo Author.*

PRUNUS "TAI-HAKU". *Photo Author.*

At the end of January and February a thousand varieties of small bulbs appear to brighten up the garden: crocuses, grape hyacinths, *Galanthus nivalis* (snowdrops), bergenias (or *Megasea*), and saxifrages (commonly called "bears' ears"), begin to flower in pink clusters, and their large gleaming perennial leaves are very decorative. They survive the frost and will flourish in the shade in the coldest places.

Among shrubs offering white flowers in winter, none can compare with the *Viburnum Tinus* (or Laurustinus); it is easy to trim and its dark green foliage is very decorative in the garden. The yellow-flowered jasmine *nudiflorum* and the *primulinum*, with its double flowers, also begin to blossom in February; both are useful for covering walls.

In March, if the weather has been mild, the *Forsythia* will begin to light up in the garden, its long trailing branches a mass of golden flowers; it is a spectacular shrub which gives the garden its first real burst of colour. Almost at the same time comes the *Mahonia*, a bush with shiny foliage which tends to trail, and with fragrant yellow flowers. Next come the violets and the very decorative "Judas-tree" (*Cercis Siliquastrum*). The latter is covered with flowers of a bright cyclamen pink before the leaves appear. (Care must be taken not to place it near the forsythias, for these ladies like to reign alone and the pink colour clashes with them. White *Cercis Siliquastrum* may be used but are rather insipid and difficult to obtain). Next, the Japanese quince trees (*Cydonia japonica* or *Chaenomeles lagenaria*) begin to come out, and they too are incompatible with the forsythia. This is also blossom time for the large family of almond trees, apple trees and Japanese cherries, among them the *Prunus* "Tai-haku", with its great white flowers, and the *Malus floribunda Eleyii*, whose deep pink blossom is among the most decorative in the garden.

Peonies bud in April and should be planted in groups. The wild variety in Spain, *Paeonia mollis*, has a singular old rose coloured bloom. It is of medium height and harmonises well in a rustic garden. It grows wild on the mountains among the holm oaks and in the pastures throughout nearly all of Castile.

Groups of *Kaufmanniana* tulips also bloom at this time. Their flowers, in bright shades of red, orange or yellow, open out like stars and are the only tulips that do not look pretentious in a rustic garden. A wide variety of flowers now appears: primulas, narcissi, hyacinths, irises, which will reach their full splendour by the end of April, and rosemary in the adjoining fields, spreading in great blue and grey patches.

By the end of April, the walls of the house are bright with the climbing rose *Banksiae lutea*, known as the saffron rose. Butter yellow, it gives off a pleasing tea-like perfume. Lilacs and philadelphus now begin to bloom with their scent of lemon, and the white spiraeas with an almond perfume.

The large blue flowers of the *Vinca variegata* add a silvery note to the shade beneath the trees.

The fragrant dark red, almost black, wallflowers will beautify any garden.

May! Where to begin? Roses, valerian, honeysuckle, wild flowers, oriental poppies, giant delphiniums, Madonna lilies, the *Lilium regale*, whose perfume is more delicate than that of the

Madonna lily, and countless other queens of the garden all put on glorious apparel to celebrate the arrival of good weather.

A word about roses: in country gardens the old varieties, that is those existing before the development of hybrid teas, are preferable. The hybrid tea rose has become very popular for its wonderful variety of form and colour, and because it blooms throughout the summer and often well into the winter. Cross-breeding, however, has robbed it of nearly all its perfume, and many of the modern colours, like the orange-red, strike a harsh note among the more delicate tones of other flowers.

Old roses, like great *prima donnas* in the theatre, reign for a short time, but nothing compares with their true rose scent, so rarely encountered today; the musk rose, the Gallic rose or Rose of Provence, and the *centifolia*, which in Madrid we used to call the rose of San Isidro because it bloomed during this festival, when whistles with big paper roses were sold on the eve of San Isidro; the Bourbon roses, grooved like camellias, are very charming; the *Honorine de Brabant*, which forms a bush, *Variegata di Bologna*, *Souvenir de la Malmaison*, the *Rosa mundi*, another variegated Gallic rose, are all examples; the damask rose was probably called the Rose of Alexandria in Philip II's time...

BROAD BED OF IRISES. *Photo Author.*

BOTANICAL TULIPS. *Photo Author.*

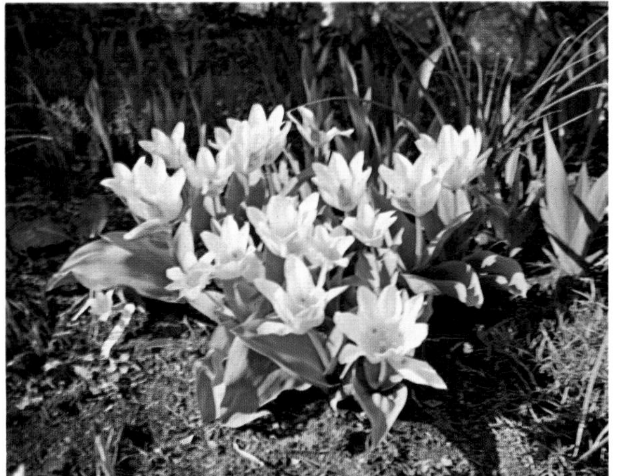

PINK CLOUD IRIS. *Photo Author.*

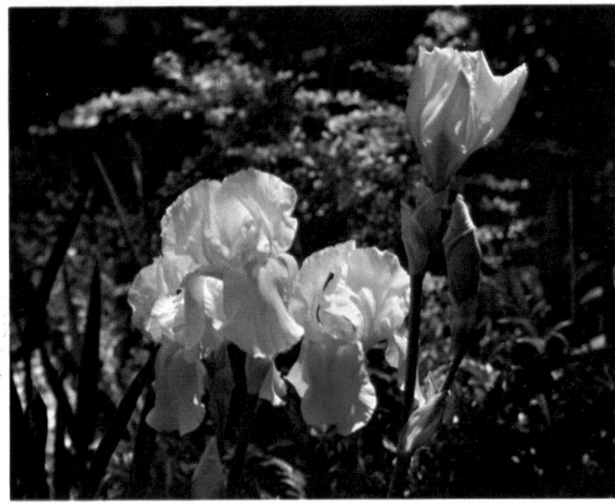

BED OF BRIGHTLY COLOURED PLANTS. *Photo Author.*

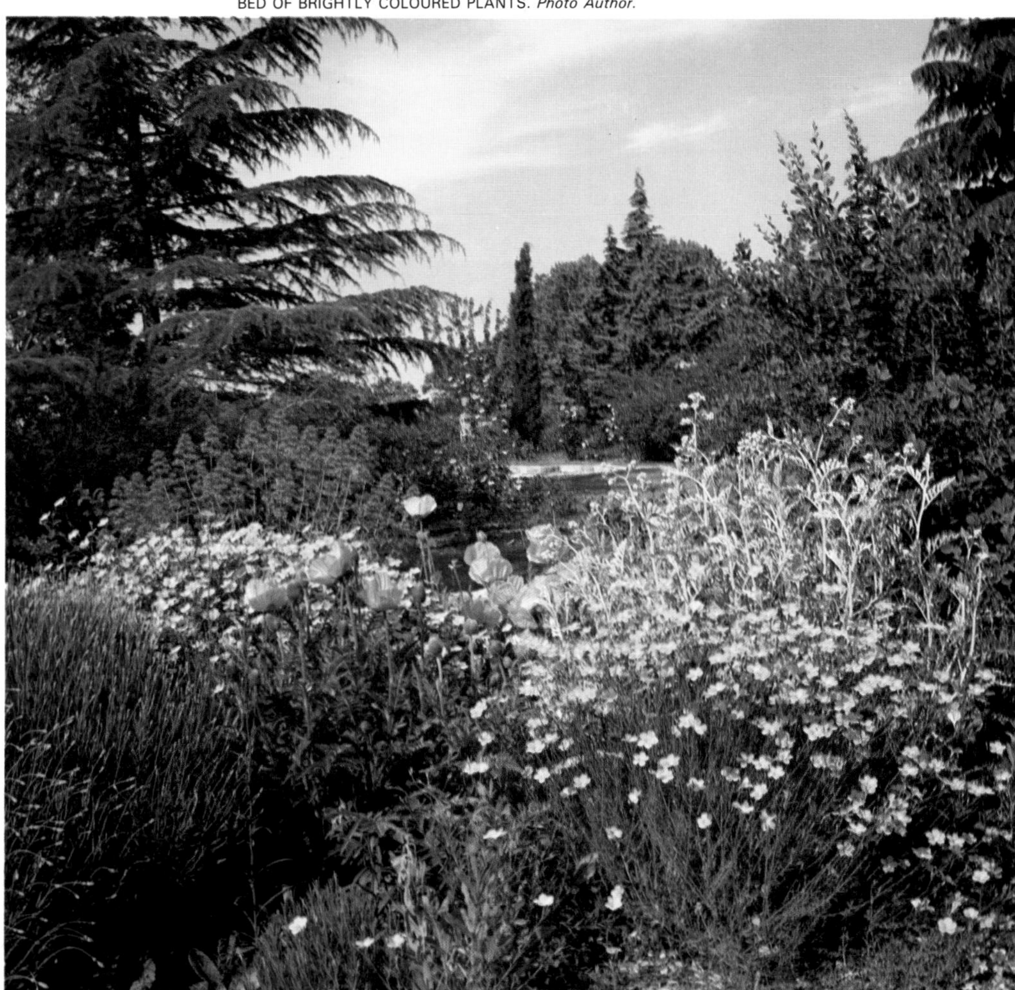

Older climbing roses include the *Noisettiana* variety, *Meréchal niel*, a salmon shade difficult to find today, and the Penelope rose, *moschata hybrida*, almost white and with an exquisite perfume. Many of these shrub roses still grow in the abandoned gardens of old cloisters and palaces.

In June the *Hypericum calycinum* blooms on shady slopes. It is a creeping plant with large yellow or orange flowers, which can be planted beneath trees where nothing else grows. The *Lamium maculatum aureum* of the nettle family quickly forms a thick carpet of variegated plants, also with yellow flowers.

At the edges of the garden, where the wild vegetation begins, the fragrant Spanish broom (*Genista hispanica*) would be introduced to form great golden patches in July, together with the salvia, *Sclarea turquestanica*, which has flowers of a delicate lilac shade that blend with the broom. One of the most decorative of the shrubs is the *Rhus Cotinus purpureus*, called the "wig tree" because of its striking feathery tufts; it does not require much attention. The "Tree of Paradise" (*Elaeagnus angustifolia*) is aromatic and its grey foliage adds a silvery note to the garden; it survives dry conditions well.

Trees that do well in countryside where the holm oak grows are the cypresses *Cupressus sempervirens*, of which hedges can be formed, for the *macrocarpa* have a much shorter lifespan. They can also be planted separately and lend distinction to the surroundings, particularly at either side of the entrance.

The Castilian landscape does not suit trees such as the *Magnolia grandiflora*, a northern, almost aquatic tree, requiring abundant moisture and a good depth of soil. It is sad to see these trees standing pale and dusty, in parks and avenues that do not provide the right conditions.

The Spanish Mediterranean coasts were once adorned with Roman gardens in the Tarragona region and Arab gardens in Alicante, Elche and Almeria. Today, however, the Costa Blanca and the Costa del Sol have lost their character and their countryside to modern housing development and skyscrapers, which are so unsuitable to this climate; and yet, people have come to live here from all over the world and housing must be provided for them. Vegetation flourishes here, and gardens are formed in a few years. Classical and romantic gardens are out of place here because of the grand and austere landscape that surrounds them. The most successful gardens in this region are those which follow the Arab custom of combining gardens with orchards. Orange trees, fig trees and almond trees grow in picturesque profusion, edged with aloes and prickly pears.

The garden proper should be near the house, containing mostly aromatic trees if possible: jasmines, honeysuckle and rambler roses on the walls of the house, not forgetting the wonderful *gitanilla*, a climbing or hanging geranium, unrivalled in colour and profusion in these lands. A fountain or pool will reflect the blue of the sky, and oleanders will swing in the evening breeze. The aim here is not an ordinary garden, but a flower and fruit orchard of cherished plants, such as the Arabs created in which to live and delight.

Such gardens are the mark of the true plant lover and as they do not have to conform to any particular plan they will harmonise all the better with the countryside. If the water supply permits, a lawn is most desirable, for in these parts it is like an oasis.

"VARIEGATA DI BOLOGNA". ROSE. *Photo Author.*

ROSA MUNDI. *Photo Author.*

MOSCHATA "PENELOPE" ROSE. *Photo Author.*

Palm trees have been vastly overused in the last century, and today one can virtually determine the age of a garden by the presence of *Chamaerops* and *Phoenix canariensis.* (The latter in particular takes up far too much space for smaller gardens.)

Anyone who has seen the palm groves of Elche and the *Phoenix canariensis* in Maspalomas, Grand Canary before the recent housing developments there, will understand that for their beauty to be fully effective these trees must be numerous and they must spread clear to the horizon; they have their own particular atmosphere, which is exotic and tropical. A single specimen in a garden especially among northern conifers from the mountains, is never particularly effective.

* * *

The study of Spanish gardens as they have evolved over the centuries leads us to one very basic conclusion: man is instinctively drawn toward nature as a source of refreshment, aesthetic pleasure and solace from the demands of his daily existence.

Today, with the stress of urban life, the garden has become more precious than ever, and it should not surprise us that the image of paradise has been sustained for so many centuries as a place where man, in communion with nature, is at one with God.

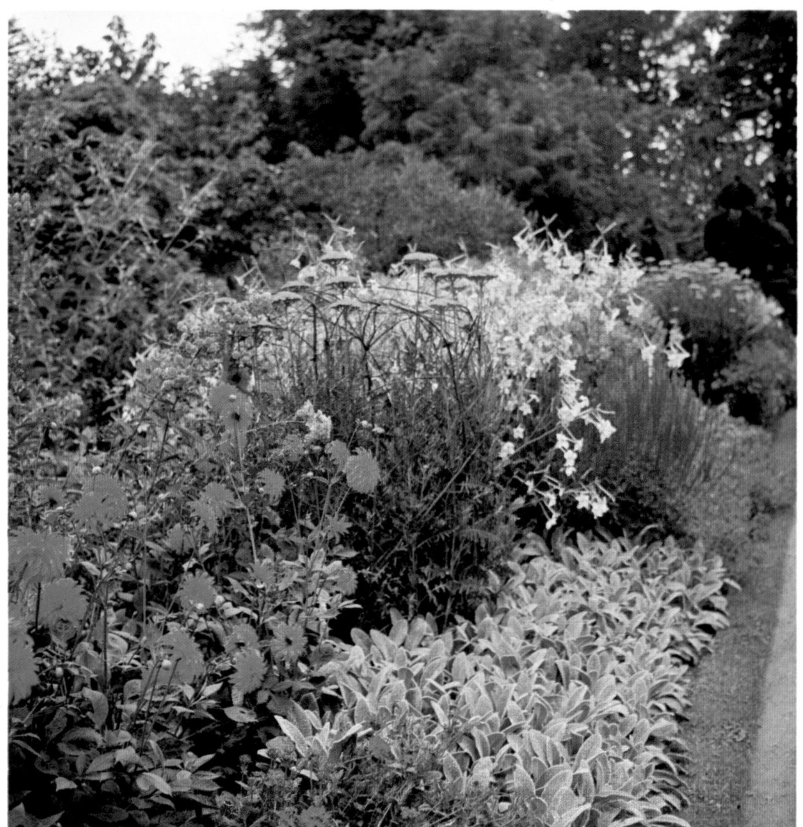

BED OF VIVIDLY COLOURED PLANTS. *Photo Author.*

GENERAL BIBLIOGRAPHY

ABU ZACARIA AMED IBN AL-AWWAN, SEVILLANO: *Libro de la Agricultura*, translated by José Banquieri in 1802, Seville, 1878.
ALARCÒN, Pedro A. de: *Viajes por España*, Ediciones Fax, Madrid, 1968.
AL-MAQQARI: *History of the Mohammedan Dynasties*, translated by Pascual Gayangos, London, 1840-1843.
ARIAS DIVITO, Juan Carlos: *Las expediciones científicas españolas durante el siglo XVIII*, Publ. Cultura Hispánica, Madrid, 1968.
ALVAREZ COLMENAR, J.: *Les Délices de l'Espagne et du Portugal*, Leyde, 1707.
ARGOTE DE MOLINA: *Libro de la montería del Rey Alfonso XI*, Seville, 1582.

BAEZA, Hernando de: *Relaciones de algunos sucesos de los últimos tiempos del Reino de Granada*, Sociedad de Bibliófilos Españoles, Madrid, 1868.
BOTTINEAU, Yves: *L'art de Cour dans l'Espagne de Phillipe V*, Féret et Fils, Bordeaux, 1960.
BOVER, Joaquín María: *Noticias históricas y topográficas de la isla de Mallorca*, Palma, 1864.
BYNE, Arthur, and STAPLEY, Mildred: *Spanish Gardens and Patios*, New York, 1924.
— *Mallorcan Houses and Gardens.*

CABRERA DE CÒRDOBA, Luis: *Vida de Felipe II*, Madrid, 1876.
CAMERON, Roderick: *Viceroyalties of the West*, London, 1968.
CARO, Rodrigo: *Antigüedades de Sevilla*, Imp. Andrés Grande, Seville, 1634.
CATURLA, María Luísa: *Pinturas, frondas y fuentes del Buen Retiro*, Revista de Occidente, Madrid, 1947.
COCK, Enrique: *Viaje de Felipe II en 1585 a Zaragoza, Barcelona y Valencia*, Pub. by Morel Fatio, 1876.
CLIFFORD, Derek: *History of Garden Design*, London, 1966.
COLMEIRO, Miguel: *Bosquejo histórico y estadístico del Jardín Botánico de Madrid*, Madrid, 1875.
— *La Botánica y los botánicos*, Madrid, 1858.
COLUMELA: *De Re Rustica*, book X, Loeb Classical Library, William Heinemann, 1960.
COUSELO BOUZÀS, José: *Galicia artística en el siglo XVIII y primera mitad del XIX*, Santiago, 1933.
Corán: Sura 55, verse 76, 2 vols. Petite Bibliothèque Payot, Paris, 1958.
CAVESTANY, Julio: *Flores y bodegones en la pintura española*, Palacio de la Biblioteca Nacional, Madrid, 1936 and 1940.

DE LA RADA Y DELGADO, Juan de Dios: *Museo Español de Antigüedades*, 1874.
DELEITO PIÑUELA, José: *El Rey se divierte*, Espasa-Calpe, Madrid, 1964.
Diario de Jovellanos (years 1795-1796), Institute of Asturian Studies, Oviedo, 1954.
DIGARD, J.: *Les Jardins de la Granja et leurs sculptures décoratives*, Ernest Leroux, Paris, 1934.

Epístola Nuncupat: *Pedacio Dioscórides acerca de la materia medicinal y de los venenos mortíferos.* Translated from Greek into vulgar Castilian by Dr. Andrés Laguna. Amberes, in the house of Juan Latio, 1555.

EZQUERRA DEL BAYO, Joaquín: *Catálogo de la Exposición del Antiguo Madrid*, 1926.
— *El Palacete de la Moncloa*, Sociedad Española de Amigos del Arte, Madrid, 1929.

FORD, Richard: *Handbook for Travellers in Spain*, 3rd. ed., 2 vols., Murrays Guide Books, London, 1855.
FORESTIER, J. N.: "Jardins Méditerranéens", *Carnet de Plans et Dessins*, Emile Paul Editeurs, Paris, 1920.
FRIERA, Joaquín: *Rosas de España*, Madrid, 1957.

GALLEGO BURÍN, Antonio: *Granada, Fundación "Rodríguez Acosta"*, Madrid, 1961.
GARCÍA GÓMEZ, Emilio: *Silla del Moro y nuevas escenas andaluzas*, Espasa-Calpe, Col. Austral, Madrid, 1954.
GARCÍA Y BELLIDO, A.: *Colonia Aelia Augusta, Itálica*, Instituto Español de Arqueología, Madrid, 1960.
— *España y los españoles hace dos mil años*, Espasa-Calpe, Col. Austral, Madrid, 1968.
— *La España del siglo I de nuestra era*, Espasa-Calpe, Col. Austral, Madrid, 1947.
GARCÍA MERCADAL, Fernando: *Parques y jardines*, Afrodisio Aguado, 1949.
— *Viajes de extranjeros por España y Portugal*, Publ. Aguilar, Madrid, 1952-1958-1962, 3 vols.
GASPAR REMIRO, Mariano: *Correspondencia diplomática entre Granada y Fez, siglo XIV*, Granada, 1916.
GAUNA, Felipe de: *Relación de las fiestas celebrades en Valencia con motive del casamiento de Felipe III, 1599*, Acción Bibliográfica Valenciana, 1926.
GIBBON, E.: *Decline and Fall of the Roman Empire*, Pelican Book, Chatto and Windus, 1960.
GONZÁLEZ AMEZÚA, Agustín: *Isabel de Valois*, Madrid, 1949.
GONZÁLEZ MORENO, Joaquín: *Don Fernando Enríquez de Rivera, tercer Duque de Alcalá de los Gazules*, Seville, 1969.
GREDILLA, Federico: *Biografía de José Celestino Mutis*, Madrid, 1911.
GRIMAL, P.: *Les Jardins Romains*, Paris, P.U.F., 1969.
GROMORT, Georges: *Jardins d'Espagne*, Editions A. Vincent, Paris, 1926, vols. I-II.

HERRERA, Alonso de: *Agricultura general*, Ed. Antonio de Sancha, Madrid, 1777, book III.
— *Agricultura general*, adición de la Real Sociedad Económica Matritense, Madrid, 1818, vol. II.
HOLLAND, Lady Elizabeth: *Spanish Journal*, edited by the Earl of Chichester, London, 1910.
HUMBOLDT, Alexander: *Essai politique sur le royaume de la nouvelle Espagne*, Paris, 1811.
HUME, Martin: *The Court of Philip IV*, London, 1907.

IÑÍGUEZ, Francisco: *Casas reales y jardines de Felipe II*, Consejo Superior de Investigaciones Científicas, Delegación de Roma, 1952.

JARAMILLO-ARÀNGO: *Relación histórica del viaje que hizo a los Reynos de Perú y Chile el botánico don Hipólito Ruiz*, published by the Real Academia de Ciencias Exactas, Físicas y Naturales, Madrid, 1952.

La Real Expedición Botánica del Nuevo Reino de Granada, Publ. Cultura Hispánica, Madrid, 1954.
LABORDE, A.: "Voyage en Espagne", *Revue Hispanique*, Paris, 1925, Ed. Foulché-Delbosc.
LAMPÉREZ Y ROMEA, Vicente: *Arquitectura civil española*, Publ. Saturnino Calleja, Madrid, 1922.
LE BRETON, Lucas: *Charles V*, Publ. Bayard, Paris, 1958.
Los pazos gallegos, Marqués de Quintenar, Javier Ozores y José Cao Moure, Vigo, 1929.
LOZOYA, Marqués de: *Historia del arte hispánico*, Publ. Salvat, Barcelona, 1931, 5 vols.
– *Historia de España*, Publ. Salvat, Madrid, 1967, 6 vols.
– *Los jardines españoles*, Publ. Cigüeña, Madrid, 1951.

MADOZ: *Diccionario geográfico-estadístico-histórico de España*, Madrid, 1847.
MARAÑÓN, Gregorio: *El-Conde-Duque de Olivares*, Espasa-Calpe, Madrid, 1952.
– *El Greco y Toledo*, Espasa-Calpe, Madrid, 1956.
– *Elogio y nostalgia de Toledo*, Espasa-Calpe, Madrid, 1941.
MARTIAL: *Epigrams*, Loeb Classical Library, W. Heinemann, London, 1961.
MARCOY, Paul: *Viaje por los valles de la Quina*, Publ. Espasa-Calpe, Colección Austral, Madrid, 1968.
MASSON, Georgina: *Italian Gardens*, Thames & Hudson, London, 1966.
MÉLIDA, José Ramón: *Catálogo monumental de España*, vol. II, Cáceres, 1914-1916, Madrid, 1924.

NICHOLS, Rose: *Spanish Gardens*, London, 1924.
NOVO Y COLSON: *Viaje político y científico alrededor del mundo al mando de don Alejandro Malaspina*, Madrid, 1885.

PARRO, Ramón: *Toledo en la mano*, Toledo, 1857.
PICATOSTE, F.: *Compendio de la Historia de España*, Sucesores de Hernando, Madrid, 1914.
PIFFERER Y CUADRADO: *Islas Baleares*, Barcelona, 1888.
PLINY: *Epistles*, Loeb Classical Library, London, 1961, 2 vols.
– *Natural History*, Loeb Classical Library, London, 21 vols.
PONZ, Antonio: *Viaje de España*, Publ. Aguilar, Madrid, 1947.
PRIETO MORENO, Francisco: *Los jardines de Granada*, Publ. Cigüeña, Madrid, 1952.

RAFOLS, J. F.: *Arquitectura del Renacimiento español*, Manual de Historia del Arte, Barcelona, 1929.
RIBER, Lorenzo: *Marco Valerio Marcial*, Espasa-Calpe, Madrid, 1941.
RIVAS, Duque de: *Obras Completas*, Seville, 1854.

SAINZ DE ROBLES: *Monasterios de España*, Publ. Aguilar, Madrid, 1953.
SAND, Georges: *Un hiver à Mallorque*, Paris, 1839.
SIGÜENZA, Fray José de: *La fundación del Monasterio de El Escorial,* Publ. Aguilar, Madrid, 1963.
STEELE, Arthur Robert: *Flowers for the King*, Duke University Press, U.S.A., 1964.
STIRLING, William: *Cloister Life of the Emperor Charles the Fifth*, London, 1853.
STUART THOMAS, Graham: *The Old Shrub Roses*, Phoenix House Ltd., London, 1955.

TAPIAS, Enrique: *Carlos III y su época*, Publ. Aguilar, Madrid, 1962.
TICKNOR, George: *Life, Letters and Journals*, Boston, 1876.
TIRSO DE MOLINA: *Los cigarrales de Toledo*, Espasa-Calpe, Col. Austral, Madrid, 1968.
TORRES BALBÁS, L.: *Al Andalus*, vol. IV, 1936-1939.
TREVOR ROPER, H.: *The Rise and Fall of Christian Europe*, Thames & Hudson, London, 1965.

VARRO: *De Re Rustica* (Fairfax Harrison), Loeb Classical Library, W. Heinemann, London, 1967.
VILLALBA, Bartolomé de: *El Pelegrino Curioso, Doncel de Xerica*, Sociedad de Bibliófilos Españoles, Madrid, 1886, vol. I.
VILLIERS STUART, Mrs.: *Spanish Gardens*, Batsford, London, 1929.
VITRUVIUS: *Les dix livres de l'Arquitecture*, translated by Claude Perrault, 1673, Libraires Associés, Paris, 1965.

WASHINGTON IRVING: *Chronicle of the Conquest of Granada*, Baudry, Paris, 1842.
WINTHUYSEN, Javier: *Jardines clásicos de España*, Madrid, 1930.

ARTICLES – PAMPHLETS – JOURNALS

ALVAREZ, O. F. M., Fray Arturo: "Jerusalén, 1969", *A B C,* 9 September 1969.
ANGEL, Rosemary: "Sugar, Spices and Potatoes", *Journal of the Royal Horticultural Society*, November 1968, vol. XCIII, part XI.
ALOMAR, Gabriel: Anales de la Fundación Juan March, "El Cardenal Despuig", (reprint), Madrid, 1964.
Artes de México, no. 104, year XV, 1968.

BASSEGO DE NONNEL, Juan, and GARROT, José María: *Guía de Gaudí*, Ediciones Literarias y Científicas, Barcelona, 1970.
BERMÚDEZ PAREJA, Jesús: *Cuadernos de la Alhambra*, Granada, 1965, no. 1.
BREÑOSA, R., and CASTEL ARNOA, J. M. de: *Guía y descripción del Real Sitio de San Ildefonso*, Madrid, 1884.

CAVESTANY, Julio: *Flores y bodegones en la pintura española*, Palacio de la Biblioteca Nacional, Madrid, 1936 and 1940.
CERVERA VERA, Luis: *Archivo Español de Arte*, Madrid, 1949, no. 87.

DICKIE, James: *Miscelánea de estudios árabes y hebraicos*, Universidad de Granada, 1966.
Discurso de ingreso del Duque de Berwick y de Alba en la Real Academia de la Historia, Madrid, 1919.

EZQUERRA DEL BAYO, Joaquiın: "Casa de Campo y Heredamiento de la Florida y Montaña del Príncipe Pío, *Revista de la Biblioteca de Archivos y Museos del Ayuntamiento de Madrid*, no. X.

GARCÍA CABEZÓN: *Jardín de Aclimatación de la Orotava*, Tenerife, 1948.
GUILLÉN TATO, Julio: *El Palacio del Viso del Marqués*, Ciudad Real, 1963.
GUTIÉRREZ COLOMER, Dr. Leonardo: "El descubrimiento de América y los fármacos", A B C, 10 October 1969.

INGERSOLL SMOUSE, Florence: "Les jardins de Caserte", *La Révue de l'Art*, no. XXXV, Paris, 1914.
ITURRALDE Y SUIT, J.: *El Palacio Real de Olite*, Pamplona, 1922.

JUNQUERA, Paulina: *Guía ilustrada del Real Palacio de Aranjuez*, by Paulina Junquera and María Teresa Ruiz Alcón, Madrid, 1959.

LAMPEREZ Y ROMEA, V.: *Boletín de la Sociedad Española de Excursiones*, Madrid, 1915, year XXIII, 4th quarter.
LEDWARD, Patricia: *Amateur Gardening*, 19 September 1970.
LUIS, Carlos María de: *Los monasterios asturianos*, Oviedo, 1966.

MARTÍN, Juan José: *El Palacio de Carlos V en Yuste*, Archivo Español de Arte, Madrid, 1950.
MARTÍN GIL, Tomás: "Una visita a los jardines de Abadía o Sotofermoso, de la Casa Ducal de Alba", *Arte Español*, Revista de la Sociedad de Amigos del Arte, Madrid, 1945, 2nd half-year.
MONTOTO, Santiago: *El Alcázar de Sevilla*, Publ. Plus Ultra, Madrid, 1948.

ODRIOZOLA, Antonio: Centro Agronómico de Lourizán (Pontevedra).

Palacio Real de Olite. Pamplona, Institución "Príncipe de Viana", no. 11.

ROMERO MURUBE, Joaquín: *El Alcázar de Sevilla*, Patrimonio Nacional, Madrid, 1968.
"Ruinas de Conímbriga". *Boletin da Direçao dos Edificios y Monumentos Nacionales*, nos. 52-53, June-September 1948.

SAN JOS/E, Diego: *La Esfera*, 27 October 1917.
SEDEÑO, Santos Martín: *Descripción de San Ildefonso*, Segovia, 1867.

TEMBURY, Juan, and CHUECA, Fernando: "José Martín de Aldehuela y sus obras en Málaga", *Arte Español*, "Palacios y Jardines", Madrid, 1947, 1st quarter.
TORMO, Elías: *Aranjuez*, Madrid, 1930.
TORRES BAB/AS, L.: *La Alhambra y el Generalife de Granada*, Publ. Plus Ultra, Madrid.

UNPUBLISHED DOCUMENTS

Archivo General de Palacio, Madrid: *Aranjuez*, files 4, 5, 7, 8, 9, 11, 14, 17, 20, 21, 25, 26, 27, 28, 29, 31, 32, 33, 36, 38, 40, 41, 42, 43, 44, 49, 51, 86.
Archivo General de Palacio, Madrid: *San Ildefonso*, files 3, 4, 8, 11, 12, 13, 21, 25.
Archivo General de Palacio, Madrid: *Casa y bosques:*, file 335.
Archivo General de Palacio, Madrid: *Expendientes personales.* Enrique Joly, box 597, expendiente 32; Jaime Marquet, box 622, expendiente 33.
Archivo General de Palacio, Madrid: *Inventarios casa*, Administrative Section, Real Quinta, year 1840, pages 165, 166 & 167.
Archivo General de Palacio, Madrid: *Testamentaria de Carlos III*, vol. II, page 576.
Archivo del Instituto Valencia de Don Juan, Madrid, envío 99, nos. 101, 155.
Archivo de Camarasa, Duques de Medinaceli, Seville.
Archivo General de Indias, Seville: *Indiferente*, files 15, 1300, 1545, 1555, 1557, 1663-64-65.
Archivo de don Luis Gerardo Afán de Ribera, Seville.
Bibliothèque Nationale, Paris, Cabinet d'Estampes: *Inventaire des papiers manuscrits de carnet de Robert de Cotte*, par Pierre Marcel, Paris, Honoré Champion, 1906. Letters: 704 (III), 1019; 706 (III), 1019; 712, 723 (1019).
Archivo de doña Carmen Azañón de Aguirre. Toledo.

INDEX OF PERSONS

Note: As the text of this book has been translated from the Spanish, some page endings may have altered slightly. Readers are therefore advised, if they cannot find a reference on the page number given, to refer to the previous or the following page.

ABD AL-BASIT, 33.
ABD AL-RAHMÁN II, 27, 30.
ABDERRAMÁN III, 23, 28.
ABENAMAR, 41.
ABU HASSAN, 54.
ABU ZACARIA AMED IBN AL-AWWAN, 20-22, 24, 217.
ACUÑA, Ana de, 97.
ADÁN, Juan, 52, 150, 232, 235.
ADRIAN, Emperor, 4, 7, 25.
AFÁN DE RIBERA, Fernando, 67.
AFÁN DE RIBERA, Per, 67, 68.
AGUIRRE, Domingo de, 149.
ALBA, Duke of, 93, 94, 226.
ALBA, Duchess Cayetana, 149, 227, 232, 234.
ALBERONI, Cardinal, 132.
ALCALÁ DE LOS GAZULES, Duke of, 67, 69.
ALCÁNTARA, Pedro de (*see* BÉJAR, Duke of).
ALCÁNTARA, TÉLLEZ GIRÓN, Pedro (*see* OSUNA, Duke of).
ALCINOO, 14.
ALCUDIA, Duke of (*see* GODOY, Manuel).
ALDEHUELA, José Martín de, 111-113.
AL-EDRISI, Mohamed, 25, 33.
ALEXANDER THE GREAT, 22.
ALFARRÁS, Marqués de, 229, 230.
ALFONSO, Abad, 75.
ALFONSO V OF ARAGON, 76.
ALFONSO X "THE WISE", 28.
ALFONSO XII, 238.
ALFONSO XIII, 35, 64, 163, 239, 241, 248, 258.
ALGARDI, Alejandro, 126.
ALGORA, Jerónimo, 120.
ALHAQUEM, II, 20.
AL-HIMYARI, 44.
AL-MA'MUN (Yahyá), 25.
ALMANZOR, 22, 23, 27, 30, 44.
AL-MAQQARI, 25, 30.
AL-NASIR, 30.
ALOMAR, Gabriel, 261.
ALONSO PIMENTEL, Josefa (*see* BENAVENTE, Countess of, and OSUNA, Duchess of).
ALVAREZ COLMENAR, 109.
ALVAREZ OF TOLEDO, Fernando, 94.
AMADEO OF SAVOY, 109, 136, 237.
AMARANTE, Conde de, 205.
AMIGONI, 144, 225.
AMMANATI, Bartolomé, 169.
AMPURIAS, Conde de, 211.
ANNE OF AUSTRIA, 121.
ANDRIEUX, Vilmorin, 235.
ANGLES, Juan, 107.
ANJOU, Philip of, 122, 130, 141.
ANTIN, Duke of, 132.
ANTONIUS, Emperor, 7.
APRILE DE CARONA, Antonio, 67, 84.
ARALI, Joaquín, 150.
ARBASIA, César, 99.
ARCENTALES, Countess of, 254.
ARCO, Duke of, 134.
ARCOS, Dowager Duchess of, 149, 233, 234.
ARDEMANS, Teodoro, 141, 155.
ARGOTE DE MOLINA, 105.
ARGUELLES, Augustín, 240.
ARIOSTO, Ludovico, 120.
ARISTOTLE, 3, 19.
ARMADA E IBÁÑEZ DE MONDRAGÓN, Juan, 202.
ARMADA Y FERNÁNDEZ DE CÓRDOBA, Iván, 203.
ARUCAS, Marquesa de, 245.
ASTON, William, 129.
AUBIGNY, M. D', 133.
AUGUSTO, César Octavio, 11, 13.
AULNOY, Madame d', 110.
AVALOS, Juan de, 261.
AVERROES DE CÓRDOBA, 19.
AVEYRO, Duke of, 111, 114.
AYAMANS, Conde de, 261.

BACHELIEU, Leandro, 120, 141, 142.
BAEZA, Hernando de, 38, 54.
BAGUTTI, Doménico, 229, 230.
BALDINUCCI, Felipe, 138.
BAMMIGAS, Pedro, 44.
BARNADES, Miguel, 171, 173.
BARRAU, Théophile, 258.
BARRÉS, Maurice, 219.
BASANI, 155.
BATISTA, Juan, de Toledo, 119.
BAUER, 232.
BAZÁN, Alonso de, 99.
BAZÁN, Alvaro de (*see* SANTA CRUZ Y DEL VISO, Marqués de).
BEAUHARNAIS, Josephine of, 53.
BÉJAR, Duke of, 95, 231.
BELTRÁN, 48.
BELLIDO, Luis, 133.
BEN ALAHMAR, Mohamed, 36.
BENAVENTE, Condesa-Duquesa de, 149, 231, 232, 235.
BENEGAS (*see* BAMMIGAS, Pedro).
BERCEO, Gonzalo de, 83.
BERENGUER, Francisco, 248.
BERMÚDEZ DE CASTRO, 208.
BERMÚDEZ PAREJA, Jesús, 43.
BERNASCONI, 147, 156.
BERROCAL, sculptor, 261.
BERRUETA, Juan de, 158.
BERRUGUETE, Pedro, 127.
BOABDIL, 38, 54.
BOHIGAS, 254.
BOISSIER, Edmond, 190.
BOLDO, Baltasar, 190.
BOLOGNA, John of, 60, 103, 129.
BOMPLAND, Aimé, 187.
BONAPARTE, Joseph, 234, 239.
BONAPARTE, Napoleón, 46, 190, 220.
BONAVÍA, Casimiro, 235.
BONAVÍA, Santiago, 97, 120, 142-147.
BOURBON, Infante don Luis de, 97.
BORJA, Juan Felipe de (*see* CAÑIZARES, Marqués de).
BOTTINEAU, Yves, 126, 153.
BOUGUER, Pierre, 173.
BOUSSEAU, Santiago, 142, 155, 156, 158.
BOUTELOU, Andrés, 236.
BOUTELOU, Claudio, 234.
BOUTELOU, Esteban, 141-143, 147, 149, 150, 155, 156, 235, 237, 239.
BOUTELOU, Fernando, 237, 241.
BOUTELOU, Pablo, 149, 150, 235, 236.
BOUTELOU, Pedro, 149, 150.
BOUZÁS, Cousela, 205.
BOVER, Joaquín María, 213.
BRAGANZA, Barbara of, 145, 147.
BREÑOSA Y TEJADA, Rafael, 155, 157, 159, 160, 162.

BRUCE, Thomas (*see* ELGIN, Lord).
BRUNETTE, José, 174.
BUCARELLI, Luis, 38.
BURGOS, Diego de, 170, 194.
BYNE, Arthur, 50, 213, 215.

CABALLERO Y GÓNGORA, Antonio, 182, 183.
CABANILLES, José, 171.
CABARRÚS, Count, 150.
CABRERA DE CÓRDOBA, Luis, 169.
CALDERÓN, Carlos, 48.
CALDERÓN, María (La Calderona), 109.
CALDERÓN DE LA BARCA, Pedro, 109, 129.
CAMARASA, Marqués de (*see* GAYOSO DE LOS COBOS, Fernando).
CAMILIANI, Francesco, 94, 95.
CAMPO BELLO, Condes de, 197.
CAMPOTEJAR, Marqués de, 44.
CAMPRUBÍ NADAL, 273.
CANDOLLE, Augustín Piramo de, 190.
CANET, Ramón, 213.
CAÑIZARES, Marqués de, 93.
CARDONA, Fr. Marcos de, 85, 92.
CARLIER, Renato, 130, 131, 142, 155, 156, 159.
CARO, Rodrigo, 15, 58, 60-63, 67.
CARO IDROGO, Pedro, 120, 141.
CARPIO, Marqués del, 233.
CARR, John, 215.
CARREÑO DE MIRANDA, Juan, 134.
CARRILLO DE ALBORNOZ, Alfonso, 82.
CARVAJAL, Javier, 265.
CARVAJAL Y LANCASTER, José, 143, 173.
CASAMOR, Joaquín, 258.
CASTAÑO, Chaplain, 264.
CASTEJÓN, Rafael, 71, 111.
CASTELLARNAU Y DE LLOPART, Joaquín María de, 155, 157.
CASTELLO, Fabrizio, 99.
CASTELLO, Juan Bautista, 99.
CASTELLO, Nicolás, 99.
CASTEL RODRIGO, Marqués de, 109, 110.
CASTEL RODRIGO, Marquésa de, 234.
CASTILLEJA DE GUZMÁN, Marqués de, 250.
CASTILLO, Juan del, 189.
CASTRO, Rosalía de, 198, 207.
CATALINA DE NAVARRA, (Catherine of Navarre), 76.
CATHOLIC KINGS, 28, 43, 44, 51, 54, 62, 89, 119.
CATÓN, 12.
CATURLA, María Luisa, 20, 129.
CAVESTANY, Julio, 98.
CÁZERES, Antonio, 155.
CEA BERMÚDEZ, Francisco, 138.
CELLINI, Benvenuto, 60, 94.
CERES (Cybele), 126.
CERVANTES, Vicente, 187, 189.
CERVANTES SAAVEDRA, Miguel de, 67, 97.
CÉSPEDES, Pablo de, 67.
CHÁEZ, (sculptor), 114.
CHAMBERS, William, 246.
CHARLES I, 129.
CHARLES II, 28, 115, 122, 130, 133, 155.
CHARLES III, 10, 76, 97, 129, 133, 135, 145, 147, 149, 163, 170-173, 182, 187, 193, 223, 225-228, 233, 234, 239, 240.
CHARLES IV, 38, 110, 163, 173, 190, 223, 224, 228, 230, 234, 235, 237.
CHARLES V, 38, 39, 61, 63, 82, 85, 89, 90-92, 97, 104, 108, 119, 120, 168, 212.
CHARLES THE NOBLE, 76.
CHINCHÓN, Count of, 175.
CHINCHÓN, Countess of, 175, 235, 240.
CHOPIN, Frédéric, 212-214.
CHRISTINA OF HABSBURG, 104, 238, 241.
CHRISTINA OF SWEDEN, Queen, 162.
CHUECA, Fernando, 111, 112.
CHURRIGUERA, José, 163.
CID, El, 20.
CISNEROS, Cardinal, 46, 167.
CLAUDIUS MARCELLUS, 211.
COCK, Enrique, 76, 77.
COLMEIRO, Miguel, 200.
COLUMBUS, Christopher, 167, 168.
COLUMELA, 10, 12, 23.
CORBERO, sculptor, 261.
CORTÉS, Hernán, 168.
COSTA Y LLOBERA, Mosén Miguel, 259.
COTTE, Robert de, 130-133, 155, 156.
COULLAUT VALERA, 163.
COUSELO BOUZÁS, José, 205.
COUSTOU brothers, 156.
COVARRUBIAS, Alonso de, 82.
COYSEVOX, Antonio, 156.
CRESPO, Miguel, 258.
CRISTÓBAL, Juan, sculptor, 97, 98.
CROIX, M. de la, 130.
CUÉLLAR, Juan, 190.

DE CANDOLLE (*see* CANDOLLE, Augustín Piramo de).
DELEITO PIÑUELA, José, 111.
DELGADO DE LENA, José, 238.
DEMANDRE, Joaquín, 235.
DEMANDRE, Telesforo, 162.
DESPUIG family, 211.
DESPUIG, Nicolás, 212.
DESPUIG Y DAMETO, Antonio, 211, 212, 220.
DEVONSHIRE, Duke of, 246.
DÍAZ BERBEL, Julia, 53.
DÍAZ, JIMÉNEZ, 53.
DICKIE, James, 44.
DIGARD, J., 153, 159.
DIOSCÓRIDES, 168.
DOMBEY, José, 173, 174, 176-178.
DON ANTONIO, Infante, 149, 150, 237.
DON CARLOS, Infante, 237.
DON FERNANDO, Infante, 108, 109.
DON JUAN, Infante, 43.
DON JUAN, Prince, 62.
DON LUIS, Infante, 149, 226, 240.
DON PEDRO, Infante, 43, 150.
DON SEBASTIÁN, Infante, 237.
DOT, Pedro, 273.
DUMANDRÉ, Antoine, 147, 156-159.
DUMANDRÉ, Hubert, 142, 147, 156-159.
DUPONT DE L'ÉTANG, Pedro Antonio, 235.
DURAZZO, PALAVICINO, Giacomo, 45.

ECHEVARRIETA family, 245.
EGUAROS, Joaquina, 42.
ELGIN, Lord, 223.
EL GRECO (Doménico THEOTOCÓPULI), 134, 220.
ELISENDA DE MONCADA, Queen, 79.
ENCINA, Juan del, 66.
ENRÍQUEZ DE RIVERA, Fadrique (*see* TARIFA, Marqués de).
ENSENADA, Marqués de la, 144, 145
ESCALONA, Duke of, 97.
ESPAÑA, Condes de, 216.
ESTRABO, 10-12.
EUGENIE, Empress, 68.
EZQUERRA DE BAYO, Joacquín, 109, 134, 233.

FAJARDO, Juan, 108.
FALLA, Manuel de, 49.
FARINELLI, 225.
FÁTIMA, 38, 54.
FAUST, Carlos, 256.
FERDINAND I OF GERMANY, 120.
FERDINAND IV, 120, 143, 144, 147, 163, 171, 173, 238.
FERDINAND VII, 110, 135, 161, 163, 187, 228, 231, 234-236, 240.

FERDINAND, Grand Duke of Tuscany, 129.
FERDINAND, PACHECO, Juan, 97.
FERDINAND, SAINT, 57.
FERNÁNDEZ DE OVIEDO, Gonzalo, 168.
FERNÁNDEZ, Juan, 125.
FERNÁNDEZ, NAVARRETTE, Francisco, (see LEGARDA, Marqués de).
FERNÁN NÚÑEZ, Count of, 235.
FIDIAS, 67.
FIGUEROA, María de, 99.
FILGUEIRA VALVERDE, José, 84.
FLORIDABLANCA, Count of, 149.
FONTSERE Y MESTRES, 247, 248.
FORD, Richard, 33, 207.
FORESTIER, J. N., 64, 65, 245, 248, 250, 251, 253, 254, 256, 257.
FORTE, Vicentio, 169, 170.
FORTUNY family, 215.
FORREST, George, 246.
FRÉMIN, Renato, 155, 156, 158-160, 162.

GABRIEL, Jacques-Ange, 147.
GALILEO, 129.
GALLEGO BURÍN, Antonio, 39, 48.
GÁLVEZ, Isidro, 174.
GÁLVEZ, José, 173, 183.
GÁMBARA, Cardinal, 211.
GAMBINO, Jacobo, 205, 207.
GANIVET, Angel, 47.
GARCÍA, Antonio, 182.
GARCÍA DE CAAMAÑO Y MENDOZA, Josepe, 200.
GARCÍA DE PAREDES, 48.,
GARCÍA OF NAVARRE, 30.
GARCÍA GÓMEZ, Emilio, 48.
GARCÍA LORCA, Federico, 51.
GARCÍA MERCADAL, 254.
GARCÍA Y BELLIDO, A., 4.
GARNIER, D'ISLE, 239.
GAUDÍ, Antonio, 245, 248.
GAUNA, Felipe de, 77, 108.
GAYOSA, Miguel, 200.
GAYOSA DE LOS COBOS, Fernando, 204, 205.
GELLÉE, Claude, 223.
GENERALIFE, Marquesa del, 45.
GHENGIS KHAN, 20.
GINÉS, José, 235.
GIRARDON, Francisco, 156.
GODIN, Louis, 173.
GODOY, Manuel, 150, 172, 190, 234, 235.
GÓMEZ, Juan, 194.
GÓMEZ DE FIGUEROA, Ruy, 97.
GÓMEZ ORTEGA, Casimiro, 170, 171, 174, 177, 183, 189, 211.
GÓMEZ PÉREZ DAS MARIÑAS, 208.
GÓNGORA Y ARGOTE, Luis de, 28.
GONZÁLEZ, Aníbal, 251.
GONZÁLEZ MORENO, Joaquín, 68.
GONZÁLEZ VELÁZQUEZ, Isidro, 147.
GOYA Y LUCIENTES, Francisco de, 227, 231, 234.
GOYENECHE, Juan, 163.
GRANADA-BENEGAS, 44.
GREAT KHAN, 167.
GRANVELA, Cardinal de, 170.
GRIMAL, Pierre, 4, 11.
GRIMALDI, Marqués de, 149, 155.
GROMORT, Georges, 61.
GUAL TORRELLÁ family, 213.
GÜELL, Eusebio, 248.
GUILLÉN, Bernardo, 211.
GUIÓ, José, 190.
GUISTINIANI Y GUISTINIANI, Matilde, 45.
GUZMÁN, Gaspar de (*see* OLIVARES, Conde-Duque de).
GUZMÁN ENRÍQUEZ, María de, 94.

HABSBURG, Leopoldo Salvador, 214.
HAENKE, Tadeo, 190.
HAMILTON, Gavin, 211.
HARDOIN MARSART, Jules, 130.
HARO Y GUZMÁN, Gaspar de (*see* CARPIO, Marqués del).
HARRACH, Count Buenaventura de, 109.
HENRY III, 105.
HENRY IV, 76, 104, 154.
HEPWORTH, Barbara, 261.
HERCULES, 11, 235.
HERNÁNDEZ, Francisco, 169, 170, 173, 189, 194.
HERNÁNDEZ, Juan, 63.
HEROS, Martín de los, 240.
HERRARA, Alonso de, 46.
HERRERA, Francisco de (*called* EL VIEJO), 67.
HERRERA, Juan de, 103, 107, 108, 119-121, 170, 194.
HERRERA BARNUEVO, Sebastián, 122, 129.
HERRUZO, Antonio, 71.
HILGARTH, Mrs., 216.
HILL, General, 133.
HOARE, Henry, 230.
HOLLEBECKE brothers, 121.
HOLLAND, Lady Elisabeth, 60, 129, 130, 157, 231.
HORACE, 220.
HUBERT ROBERT, painter, 223.
HUÉSCAR, Duke of, 143, 234.
HUMBOLDT, Alexander, 187, 189.
HUME, Martin, 122.

IBÁÑEZ MONDRAGÓN, Juan, 202.
IBARRA, Concha, 70.
IBN AL-JATIB, 41.
IBN BACKUWAL, 30.
IBN HAYYAN, 30.
IBN HUD, 44.
IBN LUYUN, 41, 43.
IBN SAID, 30.
INFANTADO, Duque del, 48.
INFANTADO, Dowager Duchess of, 150.
IÑÍGUEZ, Francisco, 104 a 106, 121.
IRIARTE, architect, 171.
IRVING, Washington, 33, 39.
ISABEL AMALIA EUGENIA, 264.
ISABEL DE SOLÍS, 38, 54.
ISABEL DE VALOIS, 122.
ISABEL FRANCISCA, Infanta (La Chata), 163.
ISABEL OF PORTUGAL, 63, 89.
ISABELLA FARNESE, 39, 132, 147, 153, 159, 162, 163.
ISABELLA OF BOURBON, Queen, 138.
ISABELLA II, 53, 54, 104, 110, 129, 155, 234, 237, 239-241.
ISABELLA THE CATHOLIC, 51, 119, 154.
ISMAIL, King, 43.
ITURRIAGA, José, 173.

JAIME I, 210.
JIMÉNEZ TUDELA, 111.
JOLY, Enrique, 155.
JORGE JUAN, 173.
JOSÉ I DE PORTUGAL, 171.
JOVELLANOS, Gaspar Melchor de, 83, 202.
JUAN II, 54.
JUAN CARLOS OF BOURBON, 109, 228.
JUAN CRISTÓBAL, sculptor, 97.
JUAN JOSÉ OF AUSTRIA, 109.
JULIUS III, Pope, 169.
JULIUS CAESAR, 15.
JUNQUERA, Paulina, 124.
JUSSIEU, Antoine, 174.
JUSSIEU, Joseph de, 173, 175-177.
JUSTI, 138.
JUVARA, Felipe, 155, 163, 239.

KAMEL, Joseph, 197.
KUT[illegible]AMI, 20, 23.

LABORDE, Alexandre de, 28.
LA CONDAMINE, Carlos de, 173, 175, 179, 182.

LA FAYE, Pedro de, 159.
LA GASCA, Mariano, 182.
LAGUNA, Andrés, 168, 169.
LALAING, Antonio de, 38, 77.
LAMPÉREZ Y ROMEA, Vicente, 93, 97, 98, 198.
LÁNCARA, Gerardo, 208.
LARA, Infantes de, 83.
LA ROMANA, Marqués de, 207.
LEBLOND, Alejandro Juan Bautista, 162.
LE BRUN, Charles, 159, 160.
LECERA, Duchess of, 49.
LEGARDA, Marqués de, 115.
LE LORRAIN, 223.
LEMMI, Salvador, 155.
LE NÔTRE, André, 122, 130, 131, 142, 153, 157, 162.
LINNAEUS, 12, 13, 171-176, 179, 187, 197, 256.
LLAGUNO Y AMÍROLA, Eugenio, 119, 112.
LLULL, Raimundo (*see* LULIO, Raimundo).
LÖFLING, Pedro, 173.
LONGINOS, José, 189.
LÓPEZ, Nicolás María, 47.
LÓPEZ, Ricardo, 71.
LÓPEZ AGUADO, Antonio, 231.
LÓPEZ AGUADO, Martín, 231.
LORCA, Federico García, 51.
LORENZANA, Cardinal, 220.
LORING family, 245.
LOTTI, Cosme, 127, 129.
LOUIS XIV, 76, 122, 130, 132, 141, 153, 157, 159.
LOUIS XV, 134, 149, 153, 156, 158, 223, 224, 239.
LOUIS XVI, 173, 223.
LOZOYA, Marqués de, 75, 80, 81, 83, 85, 126, 231.
LÚCULO DEL PONTO, 10.
LUISA FERNANDA, 240.
LULIO, Raimundo, 82, 170.
LUNA, Alvaro de, 45, 54, 97, 219.
LUPA, Queen, 207.
LUPATI, Vicencio, 130.

MACHADO, Antonio, 274.
MACHADO, Virginia, 197.
MACHUCA, Pedro, 38.
MADOZ, Pascual de, 52, 60, 127, 135, 137, 225, 240.
MAESE ALBERTO, 99.
MAESE DOMINGO, 99.
MALASPINA, Alejandro, 190.
MANRIQUE, César, 262.
MANSART, Julio, 158.
MARAGALL, Joan, 258.
MARAÑÓN, Gregorio, 216, 218-220.
MARCAIS, G., 39, 42.
MARCELA, 14.
MARCH, Bartolomé, 261.
MARCH, Juan, 259, 261.
MARCHAND, Etienne (*see* MARCHAND, Esteban).
MARCHAND, Esteban, 120, 141, 142, 155, 156.
MARGARET OF AUSTRIA, 77.
MARÍA, *Sister Marica,* 28.
MARIE ANTOINETTE, 149, 223, 234, 235.
MARÍA CRISTINA OF BOURBON, 163, 237, 240.
MARIE LOUISE OF SAVOY, 130, 133, 190, 235.
MARIANA, Juan de, 218.
MARIANA OF AUSTRIA, 130.
MARÍA TERESA OF AUSTRIA, Queen, 168.
MARIANAO, Marqués de, 247.
MARQUET, Jaime, 146, 149, 226, 227.
MARROIG DE SÓLLER, 214.
MARTIAL, 13-15, 25.
MARTÍN, Juan José, 90.
MARTÍN OF ARAGÓN, King, 213.
MARTIN THE HUMANE, 81.
MARTÍN GIL, Tomás, 95.
MARTINENGHO, Pedro, 144.
MARTÍNEZ DEL MAZO, Juan Bautista (*see* MAZO).
MARTÍNEZ MONTAÑÉS, Juan, 138.
MARTÍNEZ REYNA, Juan, 138.
MÁRTIRES, Fr. Manuel de los, 205.
MASSERANO, Prince of, 149.
MAXIMILIAN II, 120.
MAZO, Juan Bautista MARTÍNEZ DEL, 127.
MÉDICI, Catherine de, 122.
MEDINILLA, Baltasar Elisio, 220.
MEERSMANS, Huberto, 48.
MEIER DENNINHOFF, Brigitte, 261.
MELA, Pomponio, 10, 12.
MÉLIDA, Juan Ramón, 90.
MENDIZÁBAL, 213.
MENDOZA, Cardinal, 68.
MENGS, Rafael, 223.
MESSÍA DE LA CERDA, Pedro, 179.
MICHAEL ANGELO BUONARROTI, 169.
MILAN, Duke of, 22.
MILTON, John, 223.
MINUART, Juan, 171, 173.
MIQUE, architect, 223.
MIRABEL, Marqueses de, 92.
MIRAMBELL Y GIOL, Francisco, 251.
MOCIÑO, José Mariano, 187, 189, 190.
MOHAMED V, 36, 37.
MOHAMED IX, el Izquierdo, 45.
MOHAMED BEN ALÍ BEN PHARAH (*called* ALSCHAPHRA), 167.
MOHEDANO, Antonio, 99.
MONARDES, Nicolás, 169.
MONDÉJAR, Marqués de, 37.
MONET, Claude, 251.
MONROY, Fabián de, 93.
MONTELLANO, Dukes of, 92.
MONTENEGRO Y DE MONTORO, Condes de, 212.
MONTESPAN, Madame de, 132.
MONTEVERDE, Julio, 214.
MONTIJO, Countess of, 150.
MONTPENSIER, Dukes of, 70, 248.
MOORE, General, 207.
MOORE, Henry, 261.
MORA, Francisco de, 103, 106, 108, 194.
MOREL, Bartolomé, 60, 62.
MOSCOSO Y PERALTA, Juan Manuel de, 52.
MOS Y DE VALLADARES, Marqués de (*see* QUIÑONES DE LEÓN, Fernando).
MULEY HASÁN, 38.
MULEY ISMAEL, 28.
MUNNÉ, B., 273.
MÜNZER, Jerónimo, 27, 33.
MUÑOZ, Juan Bautista, 170.
MUTIS, José Celestino, 171, 175, 179, 182, 183, 187, 189, 193.
MUZQUIZ, Cardinal, 220.

NARVÁEZ, Ramón María de, 52, 54.
NATTIER, Juan Marcos, 158.
NAUSICAA, 14.
NAVAGERO, Galiana Andrea, 25, 44, 45, 121.
NAVARRO, Santiago, 47.
NEE, Luis, 190.
NERO, 13.
NEWBURGO, Mariana de, 133.

OCA Y CADÓRNIGA, Antonio, 208.
O'HIGGINS, Ambrose, 176, 177.
OLIVA, Vicente, 97.
OLIVARES, Conde-Duque de, 127, 129, 130, 138, 223.
OLIVIERI, Juan Domingo, 145.
OROSIO, Pablo, 12.

ORRY, Jean, 130, 133.
ORTEGA, José, 173.
ORTEGA MONROY, Pedro, 114.
ORTIZ FERRÉ, Ramón, 247, 255.
ORTS, Juan, 264.
OSORIO, Ana Isabel, 93.
OSUNA, Duke of, 96, 231.
OSUNA, Duchess of, 231.
OZORES, Javier, 199, 208.
OZORES, Ruy, 199.

PACHECO DEL RÍO, Francisco, 67.
PADILLA, María, 70.
PAGE, Russell, 261.
PAHISA, Lorenzo, 273.
PALAU Y VERDERA, Antonio, 171.
PALAVICINI, Grimaldi, 44.
PALMER, Marqués de, 261.
PANTOJA, Juan de la Cruz, 103.
PAÑELLA, Juan, 258, 259, 261.
PARCERO, Luis, 205.
PARDO BAZÁN, Countess of, 198.
PARCENT, Duchess of, 253.
PAREDES, Marqueses de, 110.
PARGA, Y SAN MIGUEL DAS PENAS, Marqués de, 205.
PARRO, Ramón, 219.
PAULA, Francisco de, 110.
PAVÓN, José Antonio, 172, 174-179, 182, 187.
PAXTON, Joseph, 246.
PEDRO I THE CRUEL, 20, 57, 58, 80, 64, 70.
PELAYO, 19.
PEMÁN, José María, 175.
PERÉS Y PERES, Ramón Domingo, 44.
PÉREZ DE URBEL, Fr. Justo, 80.
PÉROLA, Esteban, 99.
PÉROLA, Juan, 99.
PESQUERA, Diego de, 60.
PEYRON, Juan Francisco, 103, 104, 129.
PHILIP THE FAIR, 38.
PHILIP II, 61, 67, 76, 77, 82, 84, 92, 103, 105, 106, 108, 119-122, 127, 144, 154, 168-170, 173, 189, 198, 236, 238, 277.
PHILIP III, 77, 104, 105, 108, 126, 130, 138, 170.
PHILIP IV, 67, 103, 108-111, 122, 123, 127, 129, 130, 138, 233.
PHILIP V, 39, 60, 84, 85, 106, 120, 130, 132, 134, 141, 143, 144, 153, 154, 156-159, 162, 163, 171, 173, 223, 238, 239.
PICASSO, Pablo Ruiz, 248.
PINEDA, Antonio, 190.
PINEDA, Pedro de, 69.
PINZÓN, Martín Alonso, 168.
PÍO DE SABOYA Y SPÍNOLA DE LA CERDA, Doña Isabel María, 109, 110.
PIOMBINO Y FARCINETTI, Bartolomé, 207.
PISANO, Nicolaso, 63.
PITUÉ, Pierre, 142, 156-159.
PIUS VI, Pope, 220.
PIUS VII, Pope, 220.
PIZARRO, Gonzalo, 174, 187.
PLATO, 3.
PLINY THE YOUNGER, 8, 10.
PLINY THE ELDER, 10 a 13.
POLO, Marco, 167.
POLO MEDINA, Jacinto, 108.
POMAR, Honorato, 170.
PONTÓNS, Canon, 233.
PONZ, Antonio, 90, 95, 104, 105, 107, 109, 111, 112, 114, 119, 121, 124-126, 133-135, 155, 159, 160, 163, 171.
PONZANELLI, Jacobo Antonio, 233.
POURRET, Pedro Andrés, 171, 172.
POUSSIN, Nicolas, 223.
PRIETO MORENO, Francisco, 34, 35, 37, 45, 47, 50, 51.
PRÍNCIPE DE LA PAZ (*see* GODOY, Manuel).
PRIOLI, Juan B., 99.
PUEBLA DEL MAESTRE, Countess de la, 134.
PUTHOIS, Pierre (*see* PITUÉ, Pierre).

QUER Y MARTÍNEZ, José, 171, 173.
QUEVEDO Y VILLEGAS, Francisco de, 129.
QUINT ZAFORTEZA family, 214.
QUIÑONES DE LEÓN, Fernando, 199.

RABAGLIO, Virgilio, 163.
RAMÍREZ DE LA PISCINA, Francisco Antonio, 115.
RECCHO, Nardo Antonio, 170, 194.
RENQUIFO, Francisco, 175.
REUGEL, 121.
REY, 156.
REYNA, Juan, 149.
RIBERA, Catalina de, 69.
RIBERA, Fernanda de, 67.
RIBERA, José de, 135.
RIBERA, María de, 67.
RICHARD, gardener to Louis XV, 149, 224.
RIEUX, Louis de, 187.
RIGAUD Y ROS, Jacinto, 141.
RIO, Brígida del, 135.
RIOJA Y RODRÍGUEZ, Francisco de, 67.
RIQUEUR, 171.
RIUDOR, Luis, 251, 257.
RIVAS, Duke of, 57, 61, 65, 71.
RIVERO DE AGUILAR family, 207.
RIVIÈRE, Fernando, 256.
RIZO, Salvador, 182.
RODRÍGUEZ, Cecilio, 247, 254, 255.
RODRÍGUEZ, Ventura, 97, 144, 173, 226, 239, 240.
RODRÍGUEZ ACOSTA, José, 48, 49.
RODRÍGUEZ ARIAS, Cipriano, 96.
ROGER II OF SICILY, 33.
ROLAND, Piche, 261.
ROMANONES, Count of, 97, 219, 220.
ROMERO, Juan Bautista (*see* SAN JUAN, Marqués de).
ROMERO MURUBE, Joaquín, 64, 250.
ROSELLÓN, Conde de, 210.
ROUSSEAU, Jean Jacques, 223.
ROVIRALTA, Raúl, 256.
ROVIRALTA DE SANTA CLOTILDE, Marqueses de, 256.
ROZ, Juan, 115.
RUBENS, Peter Paul, 129, 138.
RUBIÓ LÓPEZ, Hipólito, 172, 174 a 179, 182, 187, 211.
RURÓN, Pedro, 235.
RUSIÑOL, Santiago, 225, 232.

SAAVEDRA, Angel (*see* RIVAS, Duke of).
SABATINI, Francisco, 149, 150, 163, 173, 239.
SACCHETTI, Juan Bautista, 155, 239.
SÁENZ SANTA MARÍA, 54.
SAHAGÚN, Fr. Bernardino de, 189.
SAINT-SIMON, Luis de Bouvroy, Duke of, 122, 160.
SAINZ DE ROBLES, F. C., 81.
SALVADOR, Jaime, 170, 171.
SALVATIERRA, Marqueses de, 253.
SAMÁ, Salvador (*see* MARIANAO, Marqués de).
SAINT ANTHONY of Padua, 205.
SAINT AUGUSTINE, 82.
SAINT BENEDICT, 78, 80, 82.
SAINT BERNARD, 80.
SAINT FERDINAND, 20, 24.
SAINT FERDINAND DE QUIROGA, Dukes of, 240.
SAINT JAMES, Apostle, 207.
SAINT JERÓME, 82.
SANCHO, King, 213.
SANCHO OF LEÓN, 30.
SAND, George (Aurora DUPIN), 212, 213, 214.

SANDOVAL Y ROJAS, Cardinal de, 220.
SAN ESTEBAN DEL MAR, Duquesa de (*see* VALDÉS Y RAMÍREZ DE JOVE, Rosario).
SAN JUAN, Marqués de, 232.
SAN FRANCISCO CARACCIOLO, 219.
SAN JUAN DE LA CRUZ, 48.
SAN MARTÍ, 211.
SANTA CRUZ DE RIVADULLA, Marqués de (*see* ARMADA Y FERNÁNDEZ DE CÓRDOBA, Iván).
SANTA CRUZ Y DEL VISO, Marqués de, 98, 99, 233.
SANTO DOMINGO, Marqués de, 254.
SANTO TOMÁS, Fr. Alonso de, 111, 112.
SEBASTIÁN, Mariscal, 46.
SECO DE LUCENA, Luis, 54.
SEDEÑO, Santos Martín, 162.
SEGOVIA, Andrés, 39.
SERT, José María, 251.
SERRANO, Manuel, 149.
SERRANO, María, 264.
SESSÉ, Martín, 187, 189.
SIGÜENZA, Fr. José de, 84, 92, 106, 107, 108, 170.
SILUS, King, 19.
SILVA Y SARMIENTO, María Ana de (*see* ARCOS, Dowager Duchess of).
SOLÍS, (French gardens), 155.
SOMA, Duchess of, 84.
SOPHIA OF BOURBON, 109.
STANILAS OF NANCY, King, 145.
STIRLING, William, 92.
SUÁREZ DE FIGUEROA, Lorenzo, 119.
SUBIRATS, architect, 258.
SVENSON SVENTENIUS, E. R., 262.

TACCA, Pedro, 103, 129, 138.
TADEY, Angel María, 231.
TARACENA, Blas, 15.
TARAY, Pedro, 125.
TARIFA, Marqués de, 66.
TASCHER DE LA PAGERIE, Alejandrina María, 53.
TÉLLEZ GIRÓN Y BEAUFORT, Mariano (*see* OSUNA, Duke of).
TEMBURY, Juan, 111, 112.
TENDILLA, Count of, 48.
TENREIRO family, 209.
TEOFRASTO, 22.
TERRANOVA, Duke of, 126.
TERRANOVA, Duchess of, 84.
TESTARD, Pedro, 238.
TEXEIRA, gardener, 121, 133, 239.
THIERRY, Juan, 155, 156, 159, 160, 162.
TICKNOR, George, 33, 71.
TIRSO DE MOLINA, 220.
TOGORES Y ZANGLADA, José (*see* AYAMANS, Conde de).
TOLEDO, Juan Bautista de, 103, 121, 122.
TORRES MOLINA, Manuel, 47.
TOURNEFORT, José de, 171.
TOVAR, Simón, 170.
TREVOR ROPER, Hugh, 20.
TUDOR, Mary, 121.
TUPAC AMARO, 52, 176.
TURGOT, Roberto, 173.
TURRIANO, Juanelo, 90, 91.

ULLOA, Antonio de, 173.
ULLOA, Violante de, 208.
URBANO VIII, Pope, 67.
URSINS, Princesse des, 130, 132, 133.

VÁCARO, Antonio, 177.
VALDECASAS family, 265.
VALDÉS, Antonio de, 182.
VALDÉS Y RAMÍREZ DE JOVE, Rosario, 202.
VALENCIA, Duke of (*see* NARVÁEZ, Ramón María de), 53.
VALSECA, Gabriel, 212.
VALLABRIGA, Teresa, 226.
VALLADARES, Marqueses de, 199.
VALLE-INCLÁN, Ramón del, 198.
VANVITELLI, Luis, 163.
VARGAS, Fadrique de, 103.
VARRO, Marcos Terencius, 9, 10, 12.
VASARI, Jorge, 169.
VÁZQUEZ, Mateo, 170.
VEDEL, Domingo Honorio María Antonio, Conde de (General), 235.
VEGA, Gaspar de la, 121.
VEGA, Luis, 103, 119.
VEGA CARPIO, Lope Félix de, 94, 127, 129.
VEGA DE ARMIJO, Marqués de la (*see* MESSÍA DE LA CERDA, Pedro).
VEGA INCLÁN, Marqués de la, 64.
VELÁZQUEZ, Diego, 95, 106, 122, 127, 129, 134, 135, 138.
VÉLEZ ULIBARBI DE OLAZO, José Manuel, 173.
VENTURA LLOVERA, Francisco, 149.
VERDAGUER, Mosén Jacinto, 258.
VERGEL, Marqués de, 210.
VESPUCIO, Américo, 212.
VIANA, Marqués de, 70, 251.
VIANA, Marquesa de, 71.
VICTORIA I, 246.
VICTORIA EUGENIE, Queen, 163, 258.
VIDA family, 215.
VIET, François, 241.
VIGNOLA, Jacobo Barozio da Vignola, 169.
VILLACASTÍN, Fr. Antonio de, 90.
VILLALBA, Bartolomé de, 93.
VILLALCÁZAR DE SIRGA, Count of, 111-114.
VILLALONGA family, 210.
VILLALONGA, Rafael, 215.
VILLAMEDIANA, Count of, 122, 123.
VILLANUEVA, Juan de, 150, 171, 173, 224, 228.
VILLANUEVA DEL PRADO, Marqués de, 172.
VILLAR, Marqués del, 179.
VILLARÍAS, Marqués de, 159.
VILLARS, Marquise of, 122.
VILLASECA, Marquis of, 70.
VILLENA, Marqués de, 97.
VILLENA, Melchor de, 172.
VILLIERS STUART, Mrs., 27, 28, 60, 65, 70, 211, 215.
VIÑAS, botanist, 172.
VITRUVIUS, 5, 8, 9.
VIVES RIPOLL, Luisa, 214.

WALSH, Gualterio, 121.
WALLACE, Richard, 253.
WARD, Kingdon, 246.
WELLINGTON, Arthur Wellesley, Duke of, 133, 207.
WIFREDO II, 79.
WILLIAM OF ORANGE, 61.
WILLKOMM, Moritz, 193.
WINCKELMANN, Juan Joaquín, 223.
WINDSOR, Duke and Duchess of, 253.
WINTHUYSEN, Javier, 95, 137, 226, 234.
WITTE, Carlos de, 145.
WOEVODSKY family, 256.
WOLFE, Charles, 207.
WYTS, Lamberto, 121.

XIMENES DE SOLÍS, Sancho, 54.
XIMÉNEZ, Fr. Francisco, 170.

YARNOZ, 76.
YUSUF I, 36, 38, 45.
YUSUF ABEN, Aber, 54.

ZAFORTEZA TAGAMENT family, 211.
ZEA, Francisco Antonio, 182.
ZORAYYA, (Estrellita de la Mañana), 54.
ZULOAGA, Ignacio, 219.
ZÚÑIGA Y SOTOMAYOR, Francisco de (*see* BÉJAR, Duke of).

INDEX OF PLACES

Abad, Plaza del (Granada), 48.
Abadía (Cáceres), 111.
Abadía, Estate of (Béjar), 93, 95.
Abalos, Garden of (Haro, Rioja) 115.
Acequia, Patio of the (Generalife), 42, 43.
Acequia Real (Royal Canal) (Granada), 40.
Acomayo, 175.
Adarves, Garden of the (Alhambra), 37.
Agreda, 110.
Aguila, Fountain of (El Escorial), 104.
Aguilar, 54.
Alameda, Orchard of the, 149.
Alameda de Osuna (Madrid), 231, 232, 235, 245.
Alba, Duke of, Palace of (Seville), 68, 93.
Albaicín (Granada), 40, 42, 46-48, 51.
  Alcazaba of the, 36.
Albani, Palacio (Urbano), 163.
Albéniz Palace (Montjuich), 258.
Alberca, Patio of the (Alhambra), 37.
Albufera, La (Valencia), 22.
Alcalá de Henares, 11, 46, 168.
Alcarria, 11, 82, 156, 241.
Alcoba, Garden of the (Alcázar de Sevilla), 63.
Alcora, 145.
Alcorcón, 255.
Aldeanueva de Camino, 93.
Aldehuela, 115.
Alexandria, 20, 121, 238.
  Lighthouse of, 20.
Alfabia, La, 210, 211, 215.
Alfonso el Magnánimo, Plaza de (Valencia), 232.
Alfonso XIII, Garden of (Alcázar of Seville), 62.
Algeciras, 37, 190.
Alicante, 156, 263, 278.
Almagro, 99.
Almería, 23, 24, 33, 41, 149, 255, 269, 278.
Almuñécar, 33.
Ambo, 175.
Anceis, Pazo de, 207.
Andalusia, 41, 46, 65, 71, 76, 156, 226, 236.
András, 201.
Andròmeda, Fountain of (La Granja), 160.
Antequeruela Alta, District of (Granada), 49.
Antioquía, 220.
Apollo, Fountain of (Aranjuez), 124, 224, 235.
Aragón, 14, 20, 25, 27.
Aranjuez, 52, 61, 95, 97, 119-122, 127, 130, 133, 138, 141, 142, 147, 149, 150, 153, 155-157, 163, 170-172, 224-226, 234-240.
  Alcázar of, 141.
  Botanical gardens of, 114, 169.
  Nurseries, 238.
  Palace, 119, 130, 141, 143, 239.
  Plaza de, 145.
Araxa, Estate of (*see* Raxa).
Arco, Duke del, Estate of (El Pardo, Madrid), 111, 114, 134.
Ariccia, 211.
Armería, Plaza de la (Madrid), 239.
Army Museum (Madrid), 127.
Arrayanes, Patio de los (Alhambra), 21.
Arrecife, 262,
Arruzafa, Garden (Córdoba), 24.
Arucas (Grand Canary), 245.
Asturias, 12, 20, 75, 198.
Atenas, 3.
  Agora de, 3.
Atocha Railway Station (Madrid), 131.
Audenarde, 121.
Augsburg, 212.
Avila, 226, 254, 255.
Ay, 150.
Ayabaca, 182.

Babylon, 23, 83.
Bacchus:
  Fountain of (Aranjuez), 126.
  Plaza (Aranjuez), 149.
Bagatelle:
  Garden of, 253.
  Rose Garden, 273.
Balearic Islands, 12, 176, 273.
Balsaín, 76, 142, 147, 154, 155, 156.
Banderas, Patio de (Alcázar of Seville), 58, 60.
Bañolas, 258.
Barajas, 235.
  Airport, 231, 232.
Barcas, Bridge of (Aranjuez), 141.
Barcelona, 11, 19, 79, 171, 176, 229, 231, 245, 248, 251, 254, 256, 261.
  Gothic quarter, 79.
  Cathedral, 79.
  La Murta de, 92.
Bargas, Garden of, 93.
Bastida, La, 218.
Baths of:
  Diana, Fountain of (La Granja), 156, 158-161.
  María Padilla, Garden of the (Alcázar of Seville), 58, 60, 62, 63.
Bayonne, 149, 235.
Béjar, 93, 95.
Bellver, Castle of, 212.
Bengal, 238.
Berga, Son, 214.
Bergondo, Estate of, 208.
Betanzos:
  Bay of, 209.
  Mariñas de, 198, 208.
Bigarrambla, 167.
Bilbao, 142.
Bílbilis, 13, 25.
Bishop's Palace (Córdoba), 28.
Bizancio, 20.
Blanes, 256.
Boadilla del Monte, 149, 226, 235, 255.
  Gardens of the Palace of, 240.
Boboli Gardens (Florence), 95, 127.
Bois de Boulogne (Paris), 253.
Bolivia, Forests of, 176.
Bosque, El:
  Old path of (Salamanca), 95.
  Garden of (Salamanca), 96.
  Palace of, 95.
  Park of, 97.

Braga, 7.
Brihuega, 227.
Bucarelli, Bahía de, 189.
Buenavista, Cigarral de, 97, 220.
Buen Retiro, (Madrid), 126, 133, 138, 143, 171, 235, 236, 241.
Garden, 127, 129, 131, 132.
Palace, 127, 129, 141.
Park, 153, 155.
Buen Suceso, Church of (Madrid), 239.
Burgos, 9, 82, 93.
Burgundy, 80, 150.

Cabra, 156.
Cabrera, La, 198.
Cáceres, 23, 111.
Cachicanía (Monastery of the Escorial), 108.
Cadalso de los Vidrios, 93, 97, 219.
Palace of, 220.
Cádiz, 12, 171, 178, 179.
Cairo, 84.
Cala Ratjada, Bay of, 261.
Calatayud, 25.
Caleiro, 201.
California, 187.
Gulf of, 189.
Peninsula of, 189.
Callao (Chile), Port of, 176, 178, 187.
Cambados, 201.
Campo, Casa de (Madrid), 95, 103-105, 121, 122, 138, 170, 194, 233, 238, 241, 255.
Campo del Moro, Gardens (Madrid), 104, 127, 147, 237, 239-241.
Canary Islands, 176, 256, 261, 262, 273.
Canet, Estate of, 213.
Canton, 183.
Cap Roig, Garden of (Palafrugell), 256.
Capua, 68.
Carbón, Casa del (Granada), 66.
Carmona, Caños de, 60, 67.
Carrara, 62, 68, 214, 232.
Carrera de Caballos, Pools of (La Granja), 159.
Cartagena, 11, 150, 171.
Cartagena de Indias, 182.
Carthage, 12, 13, 20.
Casa Real (Granada), 36.
Casa Real (Madrid), 103.
Caserta, Gardens, 163.
Casino, (Madrid), 241.
Casón, El (Buen Retiro, Madrid), 127, 129, 131, 133, 134.
Castellaus, 238.
Castille, 19, 80, 82, 89, 92, 106, 108, 120, 274-276.
Castilleja de Guzmán, 250.
Castrelos, Pazo de, 199.
Castro de Coaña, 12.
Catalonia, 78, 256, 257.
Cayenne, 187.
Ceylon, 174, 187.
Champagne, 150.
Chancay, 176.
Chapiz (Granada):
Casa del, 66.
Hill of, 47, 48.
Palace Hotel, 48.
Chapultepec, 149.
Charing Cross (London), 129.
Charles V, Garden of (Seville), 60, 63, 64.
Chatsworth Palace (Derbyshire), 246.
Chavanilles (Peru), 176.
Chinchao, 176. 179.
Choisy-le-Roy, 149.
Churriana, 111, 112.
Clairvaux, 80.
Cloth Factory, Garden of the (Brihuega), 227.
Clunia, 9, 23.
Cluny, 80.
Coimbra, 171.
Colegiata (Madrid), 163.
Colmenar, 145.
Comares (Alhambra de Granada):
Patio of, 38, 40.
Tower of, 36-38, 54.
Throne of, 36, 37.
Concepción (Chile), 176, 177.
Conchas, Fuente de las (Madrid) — (Fountain of the Shells), 104, 240.
Concorde, Place de la (Paris), 147.
Conde:
Garden of, (Pazo de San-Thomé), 199.
Pazo do, 207.
Conímbriga, 7, 9.
Constantinople, 23.
Cónsula, La (Málaga), 112, 115.
Córdoba, 15, 19, 22-24, 28, 30, 33, 44, 65, 70, 71, 75, 111.
Alcázar, 30.
Cathedral, 99.
Gardens, 167.
Mosque, 20, 27, 28, 248.
Corella, 167.
Coruña, 190, 207-209.
Costa:
Blanca, 278.
Brava, Gardens of the, 256.
del Sol, 278.
Crucero, Garden (Alcázar of Seville), 58.
Cruz:
Camino de la (Way of the Cross), (Seville), 66.
del Campo (Carmona), 67.
Cuchero, 175, 176, 178, 179.
Cuenca, 156.
Cuzco, 52, 175.
Palace (Granada), 51.
Cypress of the Sultana, Patio of the (Generalife, Granada), 43, 44.
Cypresses, Carmen of the, 47.

Damas, Las (Ladies):
Garden of, 60, 62.
Tower of, (Alhambra), 51.
Damascus, 84, 217.
Dance, Garden of the (Alcázar de Sevilla), 62.
Daraxa, Garden of (Alhambra), 40.
Debod, Temple of (Madrid), 110.
Defla, Castle of, 216.
Deya, 259.
Diana, Fountain of (La Granja), 161, 162.
Dijon, 80.
Diputación, Palace (Barcelona), 79.
Donay, 103.
Doña Maria, Tower of, 70.
Don Juan of Austria, Fountain of (Aranjuez), 125.
Don Pedro, Walk of (Seville), 60.
Doria Pamphili, Villa (Rome), 126.
Dos Hermanas, 70.
Dragons, Fountain of the (La Granja), 161.
Dueñas (Sisters), Palace of the (Seville), 69.

Efeso, 20.
Eight Water Spouts, Fountain of (El Bosque), 96.
Eight Paths, Square of (La Granja), 159.
El Chafariz, Fountain (Pazo San-Thomé), 199.
Elche, 22, 263, 264, 278.
Municipal Park, 264.
Palm Groves, 245, 262, 263, 279.
Emparrado, Garden of (Aranjuez), 112, 237

Escorial, El, 105, 106, 108, 121, 170, 228, 241.
Cloister of the Evangelists, 84.
Library, 169, 193.
Monastery, 82, 90, 106, 107, 154, 155.
University, 104.
Escorial de la Vera de Plasencia, 92, 93.
Esmeraldas (Quito), 174.
Es Moli, Hotel Garden (Deya), 259.
España, Plaza de (Seville), 251.
Esperanza, Quinta de la, 238.
Espinardo, Garden (Murcia), 108.
Esporlas, 212, 215.
Establisments, 214, 215.
Estrada, La, 204.

Falkland Islands, 190.
Fama:
Fountain of the (La Granja), 156, 157, 161.
Parterre de la (La Granja), 157, 159, 160.
Faramello, Pazo del, 206, 207.
Flanders, 76, 94, 108, 120, 121.
Florence, 50, 95, 129, 138.
Florida, Orchard of La (Madrid), 109, 234.
Florida, La (Vitoria), 110, 149, 245.
Flowers, Garden of the (Buen Retiro, Madrid), 127.
Fonseca, Cloister of (Santiago de Compostela), 84, 172.
Fontainebleau, 76.
Formentor, Hotel Garden (Deya), 259.
Forteza de Puigpunyent, Son ("El Salt"), 215, 216.
Fortuny, La Granja de (Mallorca), 215.
Fountain:
Blanca (White), Garden (Madrid), 137
del Berro, Quinta de la (Madrid), 247.
Garden of the (Churriana), 112, 114, 136.
Negra (Black), Garden of (Madrid), 136.
Fountains, Avenue of the (Aranjuez), 124.
Fr. Tomás, Garden (Málaga), 114.
Fresneda, La (El Escorial), 105, 107, 108.
Friars, Garden of the (El Escorial), 84, 85, 106, 170.
Frogs, Fountain of the (La Granja), 159.
Fuencarral, 134, 137.
Gate of, 137.
Old, 137.

Gades (Cádiz), 11.
Galeras, Garden of (Alcázar of Seville), 62.
Galiana, Palace (Toledo), 25, 27.
Galicia, 12, 198-200, 208, 216.
Gardens, 197, 202.
Gamberaia, Villa (Settignano), 95.
Gandía, 22.
Gante, 90, 169.
Gaudí Museum, 248.
Geese, Fountain of the, 79.
Generalife, 23, 24, 27, 33-36, 40-44, 46, 51, 58, 89, 114, 210, 228, 248.
Geneva, 190.
Genoa, 45, 110, 145, 155, 214.
Gibraltar, 22.
Campo de, 190.
Gimonde, House of (Santiago de Compostela), 204.
Giralda, Tower, 60.
Giverny, 251.
Gixon, 183.
Gomis, Casa (Barcelona), 229.
Granada, 22-24, 30, 33-37, 39-47, 49, 51, 52, 54, 60, 65, 89, 121, 155, 163, 167, 210, 220, 240, 253.
Alhambra of, 21, 33, 35-42, 46-48, 50, 57, 60, 63, 89, 92, 248.
Archaeological Museum, 42.
Chapel of St. Michael in the Cathedral, 52.
Municipality of, 48.
Royal Palace, 46.
School of Arab Studies, 41, 48.
Grand Canary, 245, 262, 273, 279.
Granja, La, 53, 113, 114, 134, 142, 147, 150, 163, 223.
Gardens, 130, 153, 155-159, 162, 171.
Park, 160.
Granjilla, La, 106, 108.
Grand Trianón de Versailles, Gardens, 158.
Guadalajara, 11, 77.
Guadalupe Monastery, 83.
Guadix, 54.
Guanacamba, 182.
Guantánamo Commission, 190.
Guimarans, House of (Santiago de Compostela), 204.
Guimarey, House of (Santiago de Compostela), 204.
Guipúzcoa, 198.
Gumiel, 28.

Hague, The, 142, 149.
Hamlet de Marie Antoinette (Versailles), 149, 223.
Haro (Rioja), 115.
Harpies, Arbour of the (Aranjuez), 125.
Havre, Le, 142.
Herculaneum, 7, 10, 223, 234.
Hercules and Antaeus, Fountain of (Aranjuez), 235.
Hermitage, The (Aranjuez), 236.
Herrería (Monastery of El Escorial), 108.
Hierro, Puerta de (Madrid), 134, 173.
Higueruela, 45, 54.
Honda, 187.
Hornachuelos (Córdoba), 251.
Hort del Chocolater (Elche), 264.
Hort del Gat (Elche), 264.
Horta (Barcelona), 245.
Horta, Labyrinth of, 229, 230.
Hotel, Alfonso XIII (Seville), 251.
Hours, Fountain of the (Aranjuez), 124.
Hoya, La (Málaga), 114.
Huánuco, 175, 176, 178, 179.
Huerta Real (Granada), 40.

Ibiza, 12.
Icod de los Vinos (Tenerife), 245.
Ile de France, 157.
Incarnation, Convent of the (Madrid), 239.
Independencia, Plaza de la (Madrid), 173.
Infantado, Palace (Guadalajara), 77.
Infante, Casita del ("de Arriba"), (House of the Prince), (El Escorial), 228.
Infante Don Francisco, Garden of (Aranjuez), 237.
Infantes, Casa de (Aranjuez), 237.
Insane Asylum (*see* Maristán).
Institute of Hispanic Culture, 187.
Iola, 187.
Isla Española (Cuba), 168.
Island Gardens (Aranjuez), 127, 147.
Fountains of the, 235.
Island Gardens, 119-123, 126, 143, 144, 149, 235, 236, 239.
Itálica (Seville), 4, 5, 7, 8, 23.
Iznájar, 53.

Jadraque, 132.
Jameos del Agua, Club de los, 262.
Jardin des Plantes (Paris), 174.
Játiva, 22.
Jaz, Casa de, 209.
Jerez, 22.
Jerusalem, 66, 115, 207.
Juana la Loca, Bath of (Alcázar of Seville), 64.
Juliá, Son, 261.
Junquera, Palace (Puebla del Caramiñal), 205.

Kashmir, Gardens, 42, 62.
Kew Gardens, 246.
Kingdom of:
  Cochin, 187.
  Granada (Colombia), 173.
  New Spain (México), 173.
Kutubiya (Marrakesh), 58.

Labrador, Casa del (Aranjuez), 224, 235.
Labyrinth (La Granja), 156.
La Cadena, Cigarral de, 217, 218.
La Concepción, Gardens (Málaga), 245.
La Coronela, Puerta (Madrid), 133.
La Florera, Jardincillo (Aranjuez), 225.
La Flamenca, Huerta (Aranjuez), 237.
La Glorieta, Garden (Valencia), 232.
Lahore, Gardens, 42.
La Laguna, Seminary of, Garden, 245.
Lanzarote Island, 261.
Laredo, 121.
Las Rejas de Don Gome, Palace of, 70, 71.
Latona of Versailles, Fountain of, 159.
Leganitos, Heights of (Madrid), 239.
León, 19, 75.
Lerma, 130.
Licugé (Vienne), Abbey of, 80.
Lima, 174-176, 178, 179, 187.
Lindaraxa, Patio de la (Alhambra), 39, 89.
Linnaeus, Temple of, 256.
Lions:
  Fountain of the (Alhambra), 39.
  Court of the (Alhambra), 36, 38-40, 58.
Liria, Palace of (Madrid), 253.
Lisbon, 7, 19, 58, 121, 168, 171, 236.
Little Garden of Delights (Vergelillo de los Deleytes), 150.
Lloret de Mar, 256.
Lluchmayor, 261.
Loja, 52, 53, 175, 179, 182, 187.
Lombardy, 83.
London, 129, 149, 223.
Lonja de Palma, 211.
Love, Temple of (Versailles), 224.
Lucca, 220.
Luque, 44.
Lyon, 235.

Macael (Almería), 149, 156.
Macarena, District of La (Sevilla) 69.
Machuca:
  Palace of (Granada), 89.
  Patio of (Alhambra), 37.
Madrid, 10, 93, 97, 106, 108, 109, 114, 119, 121, 127, 129, 132, 133, 135, 137, 138, 147, 149, 150, 154, 157, 171-174, 179, 225, 228, 231, 232, 234, 238, 241, 245, 247, 265, 276.
  Alcázar of, 129, 239.
  Archaeological Museum, 15.
  Archives of the Botanical Garden, 193.
  Botanical Garden, 171, 173, 179, 182, 183, 187, 189, 190, 211, 234-236.
  Colegio Máximo de los Jesuitas de (Institute of San Isidro), 170.
  Gate of, 137.
  National Library of, 168.
  Natural Science Museum, 187.
  Naval Museum, 99.
  Royal Palace, 81, 127, 129, 130, 133, 173, 237, 238, 241, 245, 254.
  Royal Palace Archives, 130, 136.
Magdalene:
  Hermitage of (Buen Retiro, Madrid), 129.
  Palace (Santander), 163.
Malabar, 187.
Málaga, 22, 52, 69, 111, 112, 150, 245.
  Alcazabas of, 24, 255.
Mallorca, 79, 82, 210, 212, 215, 216, 256, 259.
  Gardens of, 209, 259.
Manises, 20.
Manuel de Falla, Carmen de, 49.
Manzanares, 103.
Marañon, Cigarral de, 218.
María Cristina, Royal College of (El Escorial), 241.
María de la Salud, 214.
María Luisa, Park, 248, 250.
Marimurtra, Botanical Garden, 256.
Mariñan, Pazo de, 207.
Mariners, House of (Aranjuez), 225.
Mariquita, 182.
Maristán, 40.
Marly, 131, 153, 159.
Maroig, Son, 214.
Martyrs, Garden of the (Granada), 48.
Maspalomas, 279.
Massa, 110.
Medina Al-Zahra, 24, 28, 30, 37.
Medinaceli, Duke of, Palace of (Seville), 66.
Mérida, 4, 7, 15, 23.
Mexico, 149, 170, 172, 177, 187, 189, 241, 259, 261.
  National University of, 170.
Mexuar, Patio de (Alhambra), 37, 39, 89.
"Mi Capicho" (Estate of the Dukes of Osuna), 231, 235.
Migas Calientes, 149, 171.
  Garden of, 171.
Mihrab, 20.
Mirador del Alcalde, 257, 259.
Mira-el-Rey, 149.
Miraflores:
  Catuja de, 82.
  Park (Aranjuez), 237.
Miramar (Mallorca):
  Palace, 214.
  Son, 214.
Molucca Islands, 187.
Mombello, Palace (Italy), 109.
Moncloa (Madrid):
  Estate of, 234.
  Garden of, 234.
  Palace of, 110, 137, 149, 232, 233, 255.
Mondragón, Casa de (Ronda), 253.
Monforte (Valencia), 245.
  Garden, 232.
Montánchez, 23.
Montaña:
  Barracks of La (Madrid), 110.
  Suiza (Aranjuez), 224.
Montevideo, 190.
Montjuich, 257, 258, 261.
  Castle, 257.
  Hill, 251.
  Park, 251.
Montpellier, 171, 174.

Moragues, Son, 214.
Moratalla, Estate of, 251.
Moravia, 197.
Mosul, Huerta del, 93.
Motril, 22, 33.
Muña, Mountains of, 179.
Murcia, 23, 24, 33, 108, 269.
Museum of Natural Sciences of Madrid, 173.
Muxo, 183.

Na Foradada Rocks, 214.
Naples, 10, 68, 133, 163.
Narcissus, Fountain of (Aranjuez), 224.
Navarre, 19, 76.
Neptune, Fountain of (Aranjuez), 126.
New Spain (Mexico), 169, 173, 187, 189, 194, 198.
New Granada, 187.
New Orleans, 149.
New Plaza (Granada), 47.
New Batzán (Madrid), 163.
New Kingdom of Granada, 182.
Nomentum (Rome), 13.
Nôtre Dame (Paris), 220.
Numancia, 12.

Oaxaca (México), 171.
Oca:
  Palace, 203, 205.
  Pazo de, 202, 203.
Ocaña, 119.
Oeste, Parque del (Madrid), 110, 247.
  Rose Garden, 255.
Olite:
  Castle of, 76.
  Gardens of, 76.
Oporto, 190.
Oran, 144.
Orange Garden (Son Berga), 214.
Orangery (La Granja), 156.
Orange Trees, Patio of (Mosque of Córdoba), 27, 28.
Orense, 202, 205.
Oriente, Plaza de (Madrid), 129, 239, 241.
Oro Tower, 60.
Orotava, La, 171, 172.
  Acclimatisation garden, 273.
Ostia, 4, 8.
Our Lady of Sorrows, Carmen of, 47.
Oviedo, 19.

Padres Agonizantes, Garden of the (Lima), 179.
Padrón, 206, 207.
Padua, Botanical Gardens, 169.
Paestum, 14.
Painters, Garden of the (Alhambra), 37.
Palafrugell, 256.
Palavicini, Garden (Genoa), 214.
Palestine, 190.
Palma de Mallorca, 211-215, 261.
Pampa del Sacramento, 178.
Pamplona:
  Palace, 76.
  Tower, 76.
Pardo, El, 106, 108, 110, 111, 134, 135, 149, 171, 233, 234.
  Palace, 105, 106.
  Gate of, 137.
Paredas, Palace of (Córdoba), 111.
Paris, 131, 142, 147, 155, 158, 168, 235, 241, 253.
  Botanical Gardens, 171, 174.
  Cabinet d'Estampes, 131.
  National Library, 130.
  Plaza de (Madrid), 145.
  Pont Neuf, 104.
  Science Institute, 187.
Parterre (Aranjuez), 235.
Partal (Alhambra):
  Pool of the, 40.
  Gardens, 40.
Parthenon (Athens), 223.
Pasco, Hills of, 178.
Paseo:
  de Coches (Coach Road), (Retiro, Madrid), 228.
  de la Castellano (Madrid), 251.
  del Prado (Madrid), 235.
  Garden, 193.
Patagonia, 190.
Patriarca (Valencia):
  Huerta del, 77.
  Garden, 108.
Paular, El, 156, 158.
Peciña, 115.
Pedroches, Los, 30.
Pegli (Genoa), 214.
Peking, 187.
Peñaranda, 135.
Pescador, Casita del (El Retiro, Madrid), 228.
Philip II, Gardens of (Aranjuez), 61.
Piacenza, 142.
Picos, Torre de los (Granada), 40.
Pico-Tagus, Orchards of, 144, 169.

Piedrahíta, Palace, 226.
Pilatos (Pilate):
  Casa de (Seville), 58, 66, 67-69, 84.
  House of (Jerusalem), 66.
Pillao (Peru), 179.
Pinya de Rosa, Garden (Lloret de Mar), 256.
Pisa, Botanical Gardens of, 169.
Pitti Gallery (Florence), 138.
Plantío Walk (Valencia), 172.
Plasencia, 90, 93.
Poblet, Monastery, 81.
Poets, Garden of the (Alcázar of Seville), 65.
Pompeii, 4, 8, 10, 223, 224, 234.
Pontevedra, 84.
  Museum, 84.
Poor Clares, Convent of the, 78, 79.
Poyo Monastery (Pontevedra), 84.
Pozuzo, 178, 179.
Prado Gallery (Madrid), 127, 173.
Prado Museum (Madrid), 127, 138.
Prado, Nuevo (Madrid), 110.
Prague, 109.
Primavera (Aranjuez):
  Fountain, 147, 149.
  Garden, 147, 149.
Príncipe (Prince):
  Casita del ("de Abajo"), (El Escorial), 228.
  Fountain (Aranjuez), 235.
  Garden of the (Alcázar de Sevilla), 62.
  Garden of the (Aranjuez), 147, 149, 150, 171, 224, 225, 232, 235, 236, 237.
Príncipe Pío, Monaña del (Madrid), 109, 233, 234, 241.
Prioress, Orchard of the (Madrid), 170, 194, 239.
Puebla de Montalbán, La, 217.
Puebla del Caramiñal, La, 201, 205.
Puentedeume, 209.
Puente Ulla, 205.
Puente Verde, 236.
Puerta del Sol (Aranjuez), 235.
Puerto de Santa María, El, 171.
Puigpunyent, 215.
Purification, Carmen of the, 47.

Quexigal, 108.
Quito, 174, 175, 182, 187.
Quixos, 187.

Rakka, 20.
Ramalete, Soto del (Tudela), 15

Raxa, Estate of (Mallorca), 211, 212, 215.
Real:
Gardens (Valencia), 108, 232.
Alcázar, (Madrid), 170.
Florida (Madrid), 110, 234, 241.
Reina (Queen):
Avenida de la (Aranjuez), 224.
Fountain (La Granja), 161.
Garden (Aranjuez), 120.
Reja, Patio de la (Alhambra), 39, 40, 66, 89.
Rejas, Las, de Don Gome (Cordoba):
Garden of, 71.
Palace of, 70, 71, 72.
Patio of, 71.
Retiro:
Gardens (Madrid), 240, 255.
Gardens (Málaga), 111, 114, 115.
Park (Madrid), 110, 130, 134, 228, 234.
Rose Garden, 246.
Rey, Huerta del, (Toledo), 25.
Rey Moro, Casa del (Ronda), 253.
Rey Naser, Botanical Garden (Guadix), 167.
Rhages, 20.
Riad, Patio of the (Generalife) 27, 36, 40, 42, 43, 210.
Riofrío, Palace of, 163.
Rioja, 19, 20, 83, 115.
Robledo de Chavela, 108.
Romanée, 150.
Rome, 3-5, 8-11, 13, 14, 24, 46, 50, 68, 78, 126, 155, 156, 162, 169, 175, 202, 220.
Ronda, 193, 238, 253.
Roqueta (Mallorca), 214.
Rotterdam, 142.
Royal Bath (Alhambra), 36.
Rubianes, Manor House of, 200.
Chapel of, 200, 201.
Rusafa, Palace of (Arruzafa), 30.

Sábana, Fountain of la (El Bosque), 96.
Sabatini, Gardens (Madrid), 254.
Sacramento, Colony of, 190.
Sacrificial pool of Bethsaida (Jerusalem), 115.
Sacromonte, 36, 48.
Sada, 208.
Saétabis (Játiva), 12.
S'Agaró, 256.
Sagrada Familia (Barcelona), 248.
Sagunto, 12.
Saint Cloud, 131, 153.
Park, 136.
Saint Martin, Tower of (Tervel), 20.
Salamanca, 19.
Saldeñuela, 93.
Salesas Reales (Madrid), 145.
Salobreña, 22, 33.
Salón, El (Buen Retiro), 127.
Salvador, Church of El (Granada), 48.
Samá, Park (Tarragona), 247, 248.
Samaria, 20.
San Augustín, Carmen of, 48, 51.
San Andrés, District of (Córdoba), 22.
San Antón, Castle (La Coruña), 190.
San Antonio:
Chapel of (Aranjuez), 144.
de los Portugueses, Hermitage of (Buen Retiro), 129, 133.
Plaza de (Aranjuez), 226.
San Bartolomé de Lupiana, Monastery, 82.
San Baudelio de Berlanga, 19.
San Bruno, Hermitage of (Buen Retiro), 129.
San Carlos, Garden (La Coruña), 207.
San Cugat del Vallés, Cloister, 78.
San Fernando, Academia de Bellas Artes de (Madrid), 173.
San Francisco de Palma, Monastery, 82.
San Francisco, Parador de (Granada), 50, 51.
San Francisco de Sevilla, Convent, 84.
Sangre, Hospital de la (Seville), 69, 94.
San Ildefonso, 142, 153, 155, 158, 171, 235.
Capilla de, 163.
San Isidro:
Hermitage of (Madrid), 129
Farm of (Málaga), 114.
San Jerónimo:
Cuarto Real de (Buen Retiro), 127.
Iglesia de, 133.
Prado de, 131.
San Juan, Hermitage of (Buen Retiro), 129.
San Juan Despí, 171.
San Lázaro, Huerto del Hospital de (Valencia), 172.
San Lorenzo, Monastery of (Santiago de Compostela), 84.
Sanlúcar de Barrameda, 65, 172.
San Martín de Valdeiglesias, 97.
San Miguel de Escalada, 19, 75.
San Millán de la Cogolla (Suso), 19, 20, 83.
San Pablo, Hermitage of (Buen Retiro), 129, 130.
San Pablo del Campo, Parish of (Barcelona), 79.
San Paolo Fuora Muri, Cloister, 78.
San Pedro de Cea, 201.
San Sebastián Convent (Valencia), 172.
Santa Clara Convent (Tordesillas), 75.
Santa Clotilde, Garden (Lloret de Mar), 256.
Santa Creus Cloisters, 81.
Santa Cruz de Mudela, 98.
Santa Cruz de Rivadulla, Pazo de, 202, 203, 206.
Sante Fe, 175, 182, 183, 187.
Santa Juana (Chile), 177.
Santa María (Mallorca), 216.
Church of (Elche), 264.
de la Piscina, monument (Rioja), 115.
de Lebeña, 19.
de Naranco, Palace of, 19.
de Sisla, Monastery of, 254.
Santander, 19, 198.
Santa Pola, 263.
San Telmo, Gardens of (Seville), 248.
San-Thomé, Estate of (*called* La Pastora), 199.
Santiago (Chile), 177.
Santiago, Parish of (Madrid), 240.
Santiago de Compostela, 84, 172, 198, 200-207, 220.
School of Pharmacy of, 84, 172.
Santianes de Pravia, 19.
Santi Cuattro Coronatti, Cloister, 78.
Santo Domingo, Convent (Málaga), 111.
Santo Domingo de Silos, Monastery, 80.
Santo Tomás, House of, 112.
Santo Tomás del Monte, Estate of, 114.
San Vicente, Hill of, 149, 150.
Sarracín, 93.
S'Avall, 259, 261.
Sax, Castle of, 263.
Segovia, 76, 157, 220.
Alcázar of, 37.
Monastery of Parral, 154.
Selva, Garden of the (La Granja), 162.
Sepúlveda, 160, 161.

Settignano, 95.
Seville, 20, 22, 24, 58, 62-68, 70, 84, 170, 248, 250, 251.
  Alcázar de, 57, 58, 60-65, 70, 71, 90, 92, 114, 155, 163.
  Giralda, 20, 75.
Shalimar, Gardens of, 42.
Siagoga, Paso de la, 201.
Sierra, Callejón de la (Granada), 49.
Sineu, 216.
Sirens, Fountain of the (Churriana), 112.
Sisla (Toledo), 90.
Sol, Cerro del (Granada), 23, 40.
Sóller, 211.
Somosaguas (Madrid), 264, 265, 266.
Sorano, 138.
Sordo, Quinta del, 234.
Soria, 19, 93, 255.
Stourhead, Gardens of (Wiltshire), 246.
  Park of (Wiltshire), 230.
Subiaco, 78.
Surinam, 183.
Syllery, 150.

Tafalla, Gardens of, 76.
Tafira, Alta, 262.
  Jardin Canario de (Grand Canary), 273.
Taj Mahal, Fountains of the, 42.
Talavera, 93, 145, 220, 254.
Talca, 177.
Tarma, 174, 175, 178.
Tarragona, 4, 12, 81, 247, 248, 278.
  Cathedral, 81.
Tarrasa, 238.
Tavera, Hospital de, (Toledo), 135.
Tazas (Cups), Fountain of Las (La Granja), 159, 161.
Temixitán (México), 168.
Tenerife, 171-173, 217.
Tervel, 20.
Tetuán, 28.
Thorn:
  Boy with (Aranjuez), 125.
  Fountain (Aranjuez), 235.
Three Graces, Fountain of the (La Granja), 160.
Thuya, 65.
Tivoli, 5, 25, 224, 230.
Toledo, 22, 25,33, 90, 97, 168, 217, 219, 220, 254, 255.
  Alcázar of, 90.
  Cigarrales of, 216.
Toluca, 189.
Tordesillas, 75.
Toronjales, Garden of, 76.
Torrella, Son, 216.
Toulouse, 81.
Tounay, 121.
Trevenque, 51.
Tritons:
  Fountain of the (Aranjuez), 95, 126, 127.
  Fountain of the (Madrid), 104, 147, 240.
Tucumán, 52.
Tunis, 92.

Uffizi Gallery (Florence), 138.
Unabra, 177.
University Residence (Santiago de Compostela), 172.
Urbano, 163.

Valdivia (Chile), 177.
Valence, 220.
Valencia, 12, 22, 23, 108, 121, 171, 172, 232, 245.
  Cathedral, 24.
  Real de, 76, 77.
Valldemosa, 212, 216.
  Cartuja de, 213, 214.
Valle-Inclán, Estate of, 201.
Valparaíso (Chile), 177.
Vatican, 126.
Vega, Cuesta de la (Madrid), 255.
Vela, Tower (Alhambra), 37, 47.
Venerables of Seville, Hospital de, 112.
Venice, 25, 44, 220.
Venus, Temple of (Aranjuez), 224.
Veracruz, 171.
Versailles, 76, 122, 130, 132, 133, 143, 149, 150, 153, 154, 156, 157, 159, 161, 162, 225, 235.
  Royal Palace, 131.
  Park of, 146, 160.
Vía Flaminia, 169.
Viera y Clavijo, Garden (Canaries), 262.
Vigo, 199, 200.
Vila Nova de Gaia (Porto), 197.
Villa of Pope Julius, 169.
Villagarcía de Arosa, 200, 201.
Villajuán, 201.
Villa Lante, 211.
Villanueva de los Infantes, 99.
Villaviciosa, 163, 238.
  Castle, 147.
Villena, Castle, 263.
Viscainhos, Casa dos (Braga), 197.
Viso, Palace, 99.
Viso del Marqués, 98, 99.
Vista Alegre, Real Quinta de, 240, 241.
Vistillas, Palace, 150.
Vizcaya, 198.
Víznar, 51, 52.

Wiltshire, 230, 246.

Yunnan (China), 197.
Yuso, Monastery, 83.
Yuste, 105.
  Monastery, 82, 85, 90, 92.

Zarzuela, Palace (Madrid), 108, 237.
Zoelia, 12.
Zubia, 51.

ANTIQUE COLLECTORS' CLUB

The Antique Collectors' Club was formed in 1966 and now has a five figure membership spread throughout the world. It publishes the only independently run monthly antiques magazine *Antique Collecting* which caters for those collectors who are interested in widening their knowledge of antiques, both by greater awareness of quality and by discussion of the factors which influence the price that is likely to be asked. The Antique Collectors' Club pioneered the provision of information on prices for collectors and the magazine still leads in the provision of detailed articles on a variety of subjects.

It was in response to the enormous demand for information on "what to pay" that the price guide series was introduced in 1968 with the first edition of *The Price Guide to Antique Furniture* (completely revised, 1978), a book which broke new ground by illustrating the more common types of antique furniture, the sort that collectors could buy in shops and at auctions rather than the rare museum pieces which had previously been used (and still to a large extent are used) to make up the limited amount of illustrations in books published by commercial publishers. Many other price guides have followed, all copiously illustrated, and greatly appreciated by collectors for the valuable information they contain, quite apart from prices. The Antique Collectors' Club also publishes other books on antiques, including horology and art reference works, and a full book list is available.

Club membership, which is open to all collectors, costs £14.95 per annum. Members receive free of charge *Antique Collecting,* the Club's magazine (published every month except August), which contains well-illustrated articles dealing with the practical aspects of collecting not normally dealt with by magazines. Prices, features of value, investment potential, fakes and forgeries are all given prominence in the magazine.

Among other facilities available to members are private buying and selling facilities, the longest list of "For Sales" of any antiques magazine, an annual ceramics conference and the opportunity to meet other collectors at their local antique collectors' clubs. There are nearly eighty in Britain and so far a dozen overseas. Members may also buy the Club's publications at special pre-publication prices.

As its motto implies, the Club is an amateur organisation designed to help collectors get the most out of their hobby: it is informal and friendly and gives enormous enjoyment to all concerned.

For Collectors — By Collectors — About Collecting

The Antique Collectors' Club, 5 Church Street, Woodbridge, Suffolk

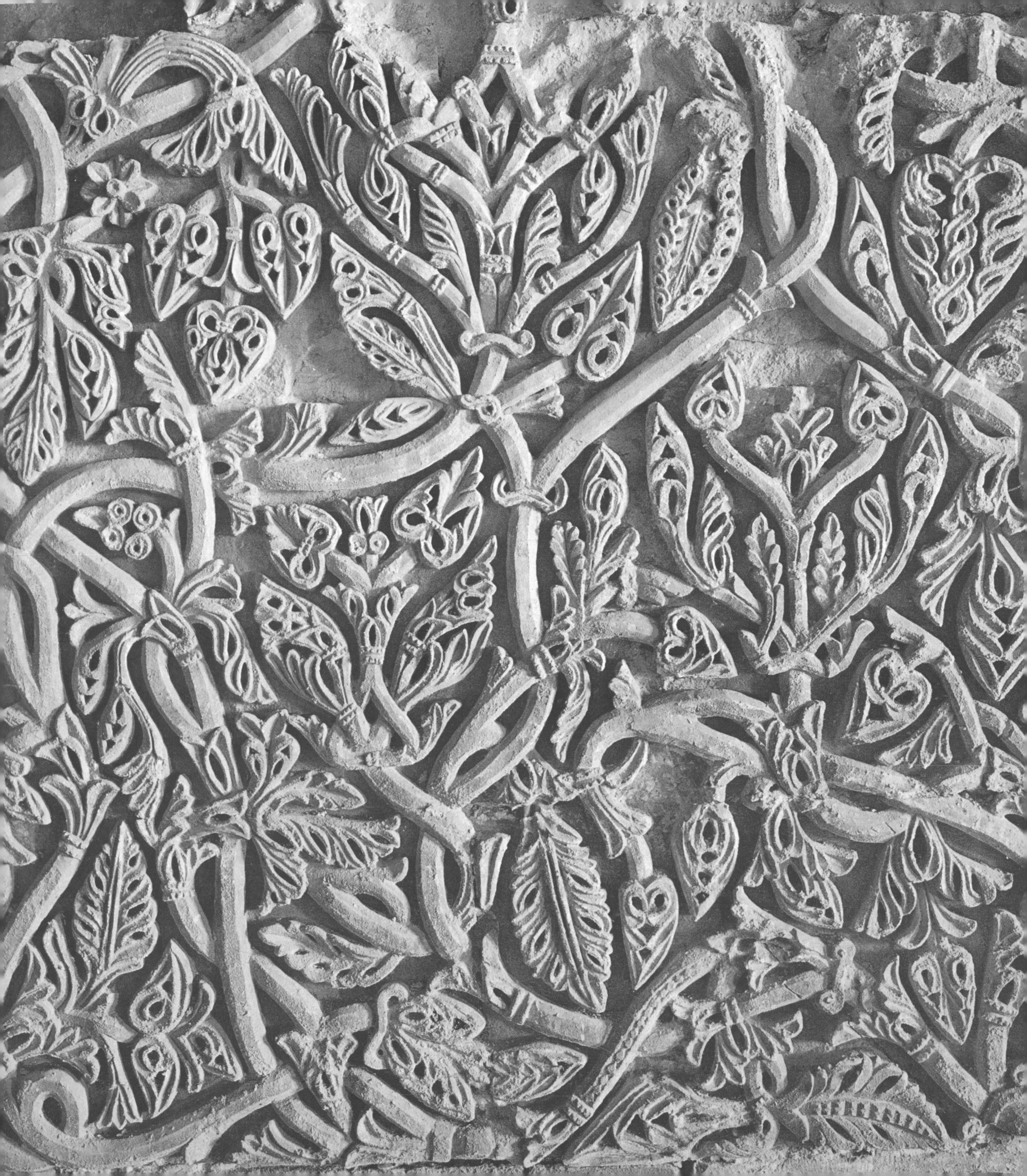

Life stage group	Potassium (g/d)	Chloride (g/d)	Calcium (mg/d)	Phosphorus (mg/d)	Magnesium (mg/d)	Iron (mg/d)	Zinc (mg/d)	Selenium (μg/d)	Iodine (μg/d)	Copper (μg/d)	Manganese (mg/d)	Fluoride (mg/d)	Chromium (μg/d)	Molybdenum (μg/d)	Water (L/d)[8]
Infants															
0-6 mo	0.4*	0.18*	200	100*	30*	0.27*	2*	15*	110*	200*	0.003*	0.01*	0.2*	2*	0.7*
7-12 mo	0.7*	0.57*	260	275*	75*	11	3*	20*	130*	220*	0.6*	0.5*	5.5*	3*	0.8*
Children															
1-3 y	3.0*	1.5*	700	460	80	7	3	20	90	340	1.2*	0.7*	11*	17	1.3*
4-8 y	3.8*	1.9*	1000	500	130	10	5	30	90	440	1.5*	1*	15*	22	1.7*
Males															
9-13 y	4.5*	2.3*	1,300	1,250	240	8	8	40	120	700	1.9*	2*	25*	34	2.4*
14-18 y	4.7*	2.3*	1,300	1,250	410	11	11	55	150	890	2.2*	3*	35*	43	3.3*
19-30 y	4.7*	2.3*	1,000	700	400	8	11	55	150	900	2.3*	4*	35*	45	3.7*
31-50 y	4.7*	2.3*	1,000	700	420	8	11	55	150	900	2.3*	4*	35*	45	3.7*
51-70 y	4.7*	2.0*	1,200	700	420	8	11	55	150	900	2.3*	4*	30*	45	3.7*
>70 y	4.7*	1.8*	1,200	700	420	8	11	55	150	900	2.3*	4*	30*	45	3.7*
Females															
9-13 y	4.5*	2.3*	1,300	1,250	240	8	8	40	120	700	1.6*	2*	21*	34	2.1*
14-18 y	4.7*	2.3*	1,300	1,250	360	15	9	55	150	890	1.6*	3*	24*	43	2.3*
19-30 y	4.7*	2.3*	1,000	700	310	18	8	55	150	900	1.8*	3*	25*	45	2.7*
31-50 y	4.7*	2.3*	1,000	700	320	18	8	55	150	900	1.8*	3*	25*	45	2.7*
51-70 y	4.7*	2.0*	1,200	700	320	8	8	55	150	900	1.8*	3*	20*	45	2.7*
>70 y	4.7*	1.8*	1,200	700	320	8	8	55	150	900	1.8*	3*	20*	45	2.7*
Pregnancy															
≤18 y	4.7*	2.3*	1,300	1,250	400	27	12	60	220	1,000	2.0*	3*	29*	50	3.0*
19-30 y	4.7*	2.3*	1,000	700	350	27	11	60	220	1,000	2.0*	3*	30*	50	3.0*
31-50 y	4.7*	2.3*	1,000	700	360	27	11	60	220	1,000	2.0*	3*	30*	50	3.0*
Lactation															
≤18 y	5.1*	2.3	1,300	1,250	360	10	13	70	290	1,300	2.6*	3*	44*	50	3.8*
19-30 y	5.1*	2.3	1,000	700	310	9	12	70	290	1,300	2.6*	3*	45*	50	3.8*
31-50 y	5.1*	2.3	1,000	700	320	9	12	70	290	1,300	2.6*	3*	45*	50	3.8*

Sources: Data compiled from *Dietary Reference Intakes for Calcium, Phosphorus, Magnesium, Vitamin D, and Fluoride.* Washington, DC: National Academies Press; 1997. *Dietary Reference Intakes for Thiamin, Riboflavin, Niacin, Vitamin B_6, Folate, Vitamin B_{12}, Pantothenic Acid, Biotin, and Choline.* Washington, DC: National Academies Press; 1998. *Dietary Reference Intakes for Vitamin C, Vitamin E, Selenium, and Carotenoids.* Washington, DC: National Academies Press; 2000. *Dietary Reference Intakes for Vitamin A, Vitamin K, Arsenic, Boron, Chromium, Copper, Iron, Manganese, Molybdenum, Nickel, Silicon, Vanadium, and Zinc.* Washington, DC: National Academies Press; 2000. *Dietary Reference Intakes for Water, Potassium, Sodium, Chloride, and Sulfate.* Food and Nutrition Board. Washington, DC: National Academies Press; 2005. *Dietary Reference Intakes for Calcium and Vitamin D.* Washington, DC: National Academies Press; 2011. These reports may be accessed via http://nap.edu.

Nutrition

Fourth Edition

MyPlate Update

Paul Insel
Stanford University

Don Ross
California Institute of Human Nutrition

Kimberley McMahon
Utah State University

Melissa Bernstein
Rosalind Franklin University of Medicine and Science

JONES & BARTLETT
LEARNING

World Headquarters
Jones & Bartlett Learning
5 Wall Street
Burlington, MA 01803
978-443-5000
info@jblearning.com
www.jblearning.com

Jones & Bartlett Learning books and products are available through most bookstores and online booksellers. To contact Jones & Bartlett Learning directly, call 800-832-0034, fax 978-443-8000, or visit our website, www.jblearning.com.

Substantial discounts on bulk quantities of Jones & Bartlett Learning publications are available to corporations, professional associations, and other qualified organizations. For details and specific discount information, contact the special sales department at Jones & Bartlett Learning via the above contact information or send an email to specialsales@jblearning.com.

Production Credits

Chief Executive Officer: Ty Field
President: James Homer
SVP, Editor-in-Chief: Michael Johnson
SVP, Chief Technology Officer: Dean Fossella
SVP, Chief Marketing Officer: Alison M. Pendergast
Publisher, Higher Education: Cathleen Sether
Executive Editor: Shoshanna Goldberg
Managing Editor: Amy L. Bloom
Editorial Assistant: Agnes Burt
Production Manager: Julie Champagne Bolduc
Production Assistant: Emma Krosschell
Marketing Manager: Jody Yeskey
Composition: Publishers' Design and Production Services, Inc.
Interior Design: Kristin E. Parker
Cover Designer: Scott Moden
Cover and Title Page Image: © Andrey Kiselev/Dreamstime.com
Printing and Binding: Courier Companies
Cover Printing: Courier Companies

To order this product, use ISBN: 978-1-4496-7522-6

Library of Congress Cataloging-in-Publication Data unavailable at time of printing.

ISBN: 978-1-4496-7494-6

6048

Printed in the United States of America
16 15 14 13 12 10 9 8 7 6 5 4 3 2 1

Dedication

To Michelle with love.
— Paul Insel

To Donna and Mackinnon for their sustenance of love, support, and patience.
— Don Ross

To Tom, Dawson, Emmett, and Quincy for your encouragement, patience, support, and love.

— Kimberley McMahon

To my family, with all my love.
— Melissa Bernstein

Brief Contents

Chapter 1 Food Choices: Nutrients and Nourishment 1

Chapter 2 Nutrition Guidelines and Assessment 29

Spotlight on Complementary and Alternative Nutrition: Functional Foods and Dietary Supplements 73

Chapter 3 Digestion and Absorption 105

Chapter 4 Carbohydrates 145

Chapter 5 Lipids 181

Chapter 6 Proteins and Amino Acids 225

Chapter 7 Metabolism 267

Chapter 8 Alcohol 309

Chapter 9 Energy Balance, Body Composition, and Weight Management 335

Chapter 10 Fat-Soluble Vitamins 387

Chapter 11 Water-Soluble Vitamins 429

Chapter 12 Water and Major Minerals 467

Chapter 13 Trace Minerals 507

Chapter 14 Sports Nutrition: Eating for Peak Performance 551

Spotlight on Eating Disorders 595

Chapter 15 Diet and Health 619

Chapter 16 Life Cycle: Maternal and Infant Nutrition 669

Chapter 17 Life Cycle: From Childhood Through Adulthood 711

Chapter 18 Food Safety and Technology: Microbial Threats and Genetic Engineering 749

Chapter 19 World View of Nutrition: The Faces of Global Malnutrition 783

Contents

Preface xvii

About the Authors xxvii

Chapter 1 Food Choices: Nutrients and Nourishment 1

Why Do We Eat the Way We Do? 2

Sensory Influences: Taste, Texture, and Smell 3
Cognitive Influences 3
Environmental Influences 7

Going Green 7

Cultural Influences 8
The American Diet 10

Introducing the Nutrients 10

Definition of Nutrients 11
Carbohydrates 13
Lipids 13
Proteins 13
Vitamins 13
Minerals 14
Water 14
Nutrients and Energy 14
Energy in Foods 15
Obesity: A Public Health Crisis 16

Applying the Scientific Process to Nutrition 17

Epidemiological Studies 17
Animal Studies 18
Cell Culture Studies 18
Human Studies 18

FYI: Are Nutrigenomics in Your Future? 19

More on the Placebo Effect 21

From Research Study to Headline 22

Publishing Experimental Results 22
Sorting Facts and Fallacies in the Media 22

FYI: Evaluating Information on the Internet 24

***Learning Portfolio* 25**

Key Terms 25
Study Points 25
Study Questions 25
Try This 26
What About Bobbie? 26
References 27

Chapter 2 Nutrition Guidelines and Assessment 29

Linking Nutrients, Foods, and Health 30

Planning How You Will Eat 30

Going Green: *Is the American Diet Contributing to a Warmer Planet?* 32

Dietary Guidelines 34

Dietary Guidelines for Americans 34
Key Recommendations from the *Dietary Guidelines for Americans* 35
Canada's Guidelines for Healthy Eating 42

From Dietary Guidelines to Planning: *What* You Will Eat 43

A Brief History of Food Group Plans 43
MyPlate 44
Eating Well with Canada's Food Guide 44
Using MyPlate or *Canada's Food Guide* in Diet Planning 46

Exchange Lists 48

Using the Exchange Lists in Diet Planning 49

FYI: MyPlate: Foods, Serving Sizes, and Tips 50

FYI: Portion Distortion 52

Recommendations for Nutrient Intake: The DRIs 53

Understanding Dietary Standards 53
A Brief History of Dietary Standards 53
Dietary Reference Intakes 53
Use of Dietary Standards 56

Food Labels 57

Ingredients and Other Basic Information 57
Nutrition Facts Panel 58
Daily Values 60
Nutrient Content Claims 60

FYI: Definitions for Nutrient Content Claims on Food Labels 61

Health Claims 62
Qualified Health Claims 63

Structure/Function Claims 63
Using Labels to Make Healthful Food Choices 63

Nutrition Assessment: Determining Nutritional Health 64

The Continuum of Nutritional Status 64
Nutrition Assessment of Individuals 65
Nutrition Assessment of Populations 65

Nutrition Assessment Methods 65

Anthropometric Measurements 65
Biochemical Tests 67
Clinical Observations 67
Dietary Intake 67

Learning Portfolio 70

Key Terms 70
Study Points 70
Study Questions 70
Try This 71
What About Bobbie? 71
References 72

Spotlight on Complementary and Alternative Nutrition: Functional Foods and Dietary Supplements 73

Functional Foods 74

Phytochemicals Make Foods Functional 74
Foods Enhanced with Functional Ingredients 78
Regulatory Issues for Functional Foods 78

Food Additives 79

Regulation by the FDA 79
Delaney Clause 81

FYI: The Saccharin Story 81

Additives in Functional Foods 82

Claims for Functional Foods 82

Structure/Function Claims for Functional Foods 83

Strategies for Functional Food Use 83

Dietary Supplements: Vitamins and Minerals 83

Moderate Supplementation 85
Megadoses in Conventional Medical Management 86
Megadosing Beyond Conventional Medicine: Orthomolecular Nutrition 86

FYI: Shopping for Supplements 87

Drawbacks of Megadoses 88

Dietary Supplements: Natural Health Products 89

Helpful Herbs, Harmful Herbs 89
Other Dietary Supplements 92

Dietary Supplements in the Marketplace 92

The FTC and Supplement Advertising 93
The FDA and Supplement Regulation 93
Supplement Labels 95
Canadian Regulations 95
Choosing Dietary Supplements 96
Fraudulent Products 98

Complementary and Alternative Medicine 99

Where Does Nutrition Fit In? 99

Learning Portfolio 102

Key Terms 102
Study Points 102
Study Questions 103
Try This 103
References 103

Chapter 3 Digestion and Absorption 105

Taste and Smell: The Beginnings of Our Food Experience 106

The Chemosenses 106

The Gastrointestinal Tract 107

Organization of the GI Tract 108
A Closer Look at Gastrointestinal Structure 108

Overview of Digestion: Physical and Chemical Processes 110

The Physical Movement and Breaking Up of Food 110
The Chemical Breakdown of Food 111

Overview of Absorption 112

The Four Roads to Nutrient Absorption 112

Going Green: ***Air + Water + Brown Stuff + Green Stuff = Compost! 113***

Assisting Organs 115

Salivary Glands 115
Liver 116
Gallbladder 116
Pancreas 117

Putting It All Together: Digestion and Absorption 117

Mouth 117
Stomach 117
Small Intestine 119

FYI: Lactose Intolerance 122

The Large Intestine 124

Regulation of Gastrointestinal Activity 126

Nervous System 126
Hormonal System 126

Nutrition Science in Action Gum Chewing After Surgery 128

Circulation of Nutrients 129

Vascular System 129
Lymphatic System 129

Influences on Digestion and Absorption 130
Psychological Influences 130
Chemical Influences 131
Bacterial Influences 131
Nutrition and GI Disorders 131
Constipation 133
FYI: Bugs in Your Gut? Health Effects of Intestinal Bacteria 134
Diarrhea 134
Diverticulosis 135
Heartburn and Gastroesophageal Reflux 135
Irritable Bowel Syndrome 136
Colorectal Cancer 137
Gas 138
Ulcers 138
Functional Dyspepsia 139
Learning Portfolio 141
Key Terms 141
Study Points 141
Study Questions 141
Try This 142
What About Bobbie? 142
References 143

Chapter 4 Carbohydrates 145

What Are Carbohydrates? 146
Simple Sugars: Monosaccharides and Disaccharides 147
Monosaccharides: The Single Sugars 147
Disaccharides: The Double Sugars 149
Complex Carbohydrates 150
Oligosaccharides 150
Polysaccharides 151
Carbohydrate Digestion and Absorption 155
Digestion 155
Absorption 157
Carbohydrates in the Body 157
Normal Use of Glucose 157
Regulating Blood Glucose Levels 160
High Blood Glucose Levels: Diabetes Mellitus 161
Carbohydrates in the Diet 161
FYI: The Glycemic Index of Foods: Useful or Useless? 162
Recommendations for Carbohydrate Intake 164
Current Consumption 164
Choosing Carbohydrates Wisely 165
Going Green: *Whole Grains: Delicious, Easy to Prepare, Affordable, Good for Your Health, and Good for the Environment 166*
Moderating Sugar Intake 167
Nutrition Science in Action Sugar and Children's Behavior 169
FYI: Unfounded Claims Against Sugars 172
Carbohydrates and Health 173
Sugar and Nutrient Intake 173
Fiber and Obesity 174
Fiber and Type 2 Diabetes 174
Fiber and Cardiovascular Disease 174
Fiber and Gastrointestinal Disorders 175
Negative Health Effects of Excess Fiber 175
Learning Portfolio 177
Key Terms 177
Study Points 177
Study Questions 178
Try This 178
What About Bobbie? 178
References 179

Chapter 5 Lipids 181

What Are Lipids? 182
Fatty Acids Are Key Building Blocks 183
Chain Length 183
Saturation 184
Geometric and Positional Isomers 186
Omega-3, Omega-6, and Omega-9 Fatty Acids 186
Nonessential and Essential Fatty Acids 187
Building Eicosanoids, Omega-3, and Omega-6 Fatty Acids 188
Triglycerides 190
Triglyceride Structure 190
Triglyceride Functions 190
Triglycerides in Food 193
Commercial Processing of Fats 194
Going Green: *Fish: Good for You and the Environment 195*
FYI: Fats on the Health Store Shelf 196
FYI: Which Spread for Your Bread? 198
Phospholipids 198
Phospholipid Structure 198
Phospholipid Functions 199
Phospholipids in Food 201

Sterols 201

Sterol Structure 201
Cholesterol Functions 202
Cholesterol Synthesis 202
Sterols in Food 202

Lipid Digestion and Absorption 204

Digestion of Triglycerides and Phospholipids 204
Digestibility 204
Lipid Absorption 205
Digestion and Absorption of Sterols 208

Lipids in the Body 208

Chylomicrons 208
Very Low Density Lipoprotein 209
Intermediate-Density Lipoprotein 209
Low-Density Lipoprotein 209
High-Density Lipoprotein 210

Lipids in the Diet 210

Recommended Intakes 210
Essential Fatty Acid Requirements 212
Omega-6 and Omega-3 Balance 212
Current Dietary Intakes 213
Role of Fat Replacers 213
FYI: Does "Reduced Fat" Reduce Calories? That Depends on the Food 215

Lipids and Health 216

Obesity 216
Heart Disease 216
Nutrition Science in Action A Matter of Fat 217
Cancer 218

Learning Portfolio 220

Key Terms 220
Study Points 220
Study Questions 221
Try This 221
What About Bobbie? 221
References 222

Chapter 6
Proteins and Amino Acids 225

Why Is Protein Important? 226

Amino Acids Are the Building Blocks of Proteins 226

Amino Acids Are Identified by Their Side Groups 227
Protein Structure: Unique Three-Dimensional Shapes and Functions 228
Protein Denaturation: Destabilizing a Protein's Shape 230

Functions of Body Proteins 230

Structural and Mechanical Functions 230
FYI: Scrabble Anyone? 231
Enzymes 233
Hormones 233
Going Green: *Send in the Proteins* 234
Immune Function 234
Fluid Balance 235
Acid–Base Balance 235
Transport Functions 236
Source of Energy and Glucose 237

Protein Digestion and Absorption 237

Protein Digestion 237
Amino Acid and Peptide Absorption 239

Proteins in the Body 241

Protein Synthesis 241
The Amino Acid Pool and Protein Turnover 242
Synthesis of Nonprotein Molecules 242
Protein and Nitrogen Excretion 243
Nitrogen Balance 243

Proteins in the Diet 244

Recommended Intakes of Protein 244
FYI: Do Athletes Need More Protein? 246
Protein Consumption 246
Protein Quality 247
Evaluating Protein Quality 248
Estimating Your Protein Intake 250
Proteins and Amino Acids as Additives and Supplements 251

Vegetarian Diets 251

Why People Become Vegetarians 251
Types of Vegetarians 252
Health Benefits of Vegetarian Diets 253
Health Risks of Vegetarian Diets 253
Dietary Recommendations for Vegetarians 253
FYI: High-Protein Plant Foods 254

The Health Effects of Too Little or Too Much Protein 256

Protein-Energy Malnutrition 257
Excess Dietary Protein 258
Nutrition Science in Action Protein and Gout 260

Learning Portfolio 263

Key Terms 263
Study Points 263
Study Questions 264
Try This 264
What About Bobbie? 264
References 264

Chapter 7
Metabolism 267

Energy: Fuel for Work 268

Transferring Food Energy to Cellular Energy 268
What Is Metabolism? 270
The Cell Is the Metabolic Processing Center 270

Who Are the Key Energy Players? 272

ATP: The Body's Energy Currency 272
NADH and $FADH_2$: The Body's Energy Shuttles 274
NADPH: An Energy Shuttle for Biosynthesis 274

Breakdown and Release of Energy 275

Extracting Energy from Carbohydrate 275
Extracting Energy from Fat 281
Fat Burns in a Flame of Carbohydrate 283

Going Green: *Biofuel Versus Fossil Fuel* 284

Extracting Energy from Protein 285

Biosynthesis and Storage 285

Making Carbohydrate (Glucose) 286
Making Fat (Fatty Acids) 288
Making Ketone Bodies 291

FYI: Do Carbohydrates Turn into Fat? Marc Hellerstein, MD, PhD 291

Making Protein (Amino Acids) 293

FYI: Key Intersections Direct Metabolic Traffic 294

Regulation of Metabolism 294

Hormones of Metabolism 295

Special States 296

Feasting 296
Fasting 297

FYI: Metabolic Profiles of Important Sites 298

Psychological Stress 302
Diabetes and Obesity 303
Exercise 303

Nutrition Science in Action Fuel for Distance Walking 304

Learning Portfolio 305

Key Terms 305
Study Points 305
Study Questions 306
Try This 306
References 307

Chapter 8
Alcohol 309

History of Alcohol Use 310

The Character of Alcohol 311

Alcohol: Is It a Nutrient? 311

Alcohol and Its Sources 311

Alcohol Absorption 314

Alcohol Metabolism 314

Metabolizing Small Amounts of Alcohol 314
Metabolizing Large Amounts of Alcohol 314
Removing Alcohol from Circulation 316
Individual Differences in Alcohol Metabolism 318

When Alcohol Becomes a Problem 319

Alcohol in the Brain and the Nervous System 319

FYI: Myths About Alcohol 320

FYI: Changing the Culture of Campus Drinking 322

Alcohol's Effect on the Gastrointestinal System 324
Alcohol and the Liver 324
Fetal Alcohol Syndrome 325

Alcoholics and Malnutrition 325

Poor Diet 326
Vitamin Deficiencies 326
Mineral Deficiencies 327
Macronutrients 327
Body Weight 328

Does Alcohol Have Benefits? 328

Learning Portfolio 333

Key Terms 333
Study Points 333
Study Questions 333
Try This 333
References 333

Chapter 9
Energy Balance, Body Composition, and Weight Management 335

Energy In 336

Regulation of Food Intake 337
Control by Committee 338

Energy Out: Fuel Uses 341

Major Components of Energy Expenditure 341

FYI: What's Neat About NEAT? 345

The Measurement of Energy Expenditure 346
Estimating Total Energy Expenditure 348
DRIs for Energy: Estimated Energy Requirements 348

FYI: How Many Calories Do I Burn? 349

Body Composition: Understanding Fatness and Weight 350

Assessing Body Weight 350

Assessing Body Fatness 352
Body Fat Distribution 354

Overweight and Obesity 355

Factors in the Development of Obesity 355
FYI: U.S. Obesity Trends: 1985 to 2007 359
Health Risks of Overweight and Obesity 360

Weight Management 362

The Perception of Weight 362
What Goals Should I Set? 364
Adopting a Healthy Weight-Management Lifestyle 364
Going Green: *Salad Days* *365*
Diet and Eating Habits 366
FYI: High-Protein, Low-Carbohydrate Diets for Weight Loss: Helpful or Harmful? 368
Physical Activity 369
Thinking and Emotions 370
FYI: Learning Weight Management from Some of the "Biggest" Weight Experts: Sumo Wrestlers 371
Weight-Management Approaches 373
FYI: Behaviors That Will Help You Manage Your Weight 374

Underweight 378

Causes and Assessment 378
Weight-Gain Strategies 380

Learning Portfolio 381

Key Terms 381
Study Points 381
Study Questions 382
Try This 382
What About Bobbie? 383
References 384

Chapter 10 Fat-Soluble Vitamins 387

Understanding Vitamins 388

Anatomy of the Vitamins 388
Fat-Soluble Versus Water-Soluble Vitamins 389
Storage and Toxicity 390
Provitamins 390
Vitamins in Foods 391

Vitamin A: The Retinoids 391

Forms of Vitamin A 391
Storage and Transport of Vitamin A 392
Functions of Vitamin A 392
FYI: A Short History of Vitamins 395
Dietary Recommendations for Vitamin A 396
Sources of Vitamin A 397
Vitamin A Deficiency 398
Vitamin A Toxicity 400

The Carotenoids 401

Functions of Carotenoids 401
Carotenoids as Antioxidants 401
Carotenoids and the Immune System 402
Carotenoids and Vision 402
Carotenoids and Cancer 402
Absorption and Storage of Carotenoids 402
Sources of Carotenoids 404
Carotenoid Supplementation 404

Vitamin D 405

Going Green: *Resisting Oxidative Stress* *405*
Forms and Formation of Vitamin D 407
Functions of Vitamin D 407
Nutrition Science in Action Vitamin D and Colon Cancer 408
Dietary Recommendations for Vitamin D 409
Sources of Vitamin D 410
Vitamin D Deficiency 411
Vitamin D Toxicity 413

Vitamin E 413

Forms of Vitamin E 413
Functions of Vitamin E 414
Dietary Recommendations for Vitamin E 416
Sources of Vitamin E 417
Vitamin E Deficiency 418
Vitamin E Toxicity 418

Vitamin K 419

Functions of Vitamin K 419
Dietary Recommendations for Vitamin K 421
Sources of Vitamin K 421
Vitamin K Deficiency 421
Vitamin K Toxicity 424

Learning Portfolio 425

Key Terms 425
Study Points 425
Study Questions 425
Try This 426
What About Bobbie? 426
References 426

Chapter 11 Water-Soluble Vitamins 429

The Water-Soluble Vitamins: Eight Bs and a C 430

The B Vitamins 431

Thiamin 431

Functions of Thiamin 432
Dietary Recommendations for Thiamin 432
Sources of Thiamin 432
FYI: Fresh, Frozen, or Canned? Raw or Cooked? 433
Thiamin Deficiency 434
Thiamin Toxicity 435
Riboflavin 435
Functions of Riboflavin 435
Dietary Recommendations for Riboflavin 436
Sources of Riboflavin 436
Riboflavin Deficiency 436
Riboflavin Toxicity 437
Niacin 437
Functions of Niacin 438
Dietary Recommendations for Niacin 438
Sources of Niacin 438
Niacin Deficiency 440
Niacin Toxicity and Medicinal Uses of Niacin 440
Pantothenic Acid 441
Functions of Pantothenic Acid 441
Dietary Recommendations for Pantothenic Acid 441
Sources of Pantothenic Acid 441
Pantothenic Acid Deficiency 441
Pantothenic Acid Toxicity 442
Biotin 442
Functions of Biotin 442
Dietary Recommendations for Biotin 443
Sources of Biotin 443
Biotin Deficiency 443
Biotin Toxicity 443
Vitamin B_6 443
Functions of Vitamin B_6 444
Dietary Recommendations for Vitamin B_6 445
Sources of Vitamin B_6 445
Vitamin B_6 Deficiency 445
Vitamin B_6 Toxicity and Medicinal Uses of Vitamin B_6 446
Folate 447
Functions of Folate 447
Dietary Recommendations for Folate 448
Sources of Folate 448
Folate Deficiency 449
Folate Toxicity 451
Going Green: *Vitamin Buddies* 452
Vitamin B_{12} 452
Functions of Vitamin B_{12} 452
Absorption of Vitamin B_{12} 453
Dietary Recommendations for Vitamin B_{12} 454
Sources of Vitamin B_{12} 454
Vitamin B_{12} Deficiency 454
Vitamin B_{12} Toxicity 456
Vitamin C 456
Functions of Vitamin C 456
Dietary Recommendations for Vitamin C 457
Sources of Vitamin C 457
Vitamin C Deficiency 459
Vitamin C Toxicity 459
Choline: A Vitamin-like Compound 459
Conditional Nutrients 460
Carnitine 460
Inositol 460
Taurine 461
Lipoic Acid 461
Bogus Vitamins 461
Learning Portfolio 463
Key Terms 463
Study Points 463
Study Questions 463
Try This 464
What About Bobbie? 464
References 465

Chapter 12
Water and Major Minerals 467

Water: The Essential Ingredient for Life 468
Functions of Water 468
Electrolytes and Water: A Delicate Equilibrium 469
Intake Recommendations: How Much Water Is Enough? 470
Sports Drinks and Water Absorption 471
Water Excretion: Where Does the Water Go? 471
Water Balance 472
Alcohol, Caffeine, and Common Medications Affect Fluid Balance 476
Dehydration 476
Going Green: *The Thirst for Water Resources* 477
FYI: Tap, Filtered, or Bottled: Which Water Is Best? 478
Water Intoxication 479
Major Minerals 480
Minerals in Foods 481
Bioavailability 481
Sodium 481
Functions of Sodium 481
Dietary Recommendations for Sodium 482
Sources of Sodium 482

Hyponatremia 483
Hypernatremia 483
Hypertension 483

Nutrition Science in Action Exercise and Sodium Sensitivity 484

Potassium 485

Functions of Potassium 485
Dietary Recommendations for Potassium 485
Sources of Potassium 486
Hypokalemia 487
Hyperkalemia 487

Chloride 487

Functions of Chloride 488
Dietary Recommendations for Chloride 488
Sources of Chloride 488
Hypochloremia 488

Calcium 489

Functions of Calcium 489
Regulation of Blood Calcium 490
Dietary Recommendations for Calcium 492
Sources of Calcium 492
Calcium Absorption 493

FYI: Calcium Supplements: Are They Right for You? 494

Hypocalcemia 495
Hypercalcemia 495
Osteoporosis 495

Phosphorus 496

Functions of Phosphorus 496
Dietary Recommendations for Phosphorus 496
Sources of Phosphorus 496
Hypophosphatemia 498
Hyperphosphatemia 498

Magnesium 499

Functions of Magnesium 499
Dietary Recommendations for Magnesium 499
Sources of Magnesium 499
Hypomagnesemia 500
Hypermagnesemia 500

Sulfur 502

Learning Portfolio 503

Key Terms 503
Study Points 503
Study Questions 504
Try This 504
What About Bobbie? 504
References 505

Chapter 13
Trace Minerals 507

What Are Trace Elements? 508

Why Are Trace Elements Important? 508
Other Characteristics of Trace Elements 509

Iron 510

Functions of Iron 510
Enzymes 510
Regulation of Iron in the Body 511
Dietary Recommendations for Iron 515
Sources of Iron 516
Iron Deficiency and Measurement of Iron Status 516
Iron Toxicity 518

Going Green: *Could Iron Help Cool Global Warming? 519*

Zinc 520

Functions of Zinc 520
Regulation of Zinc in the Body 521
Dietary Recommendations for Zinc 523
Sources of Zinc 523
Zinc Deficiency 524
Zinc Toxicity 525

FYI: Zinc and the Common Cold 525

Selenium 527

Functions of Selenium 527
Regulation of Selenium in the Body 528
Dietary Recommendations for Selenium 529
Sources of Selenium 530
Selenium Deficiency 530
Selenium Toxicity 530

Iodine 530

Functions of Iodine 531
Iodine Absorption and Metabolism 531
Dietary Recommendations for Iodine 531
Sources of Iodine 531
Iodine Deficiency 532
Iodine Toxicity 532

Copper 533

Functions of Copper 533
Copper Absorption, Use, and Metabolism 533
Dietary Recommendations and Food Sources for Copper 533
Copper Deficiency 534
Copper Toxicity 535

Manganese 535

Functions of Manganese 535
Manganese Absorption, Use, and Homeostasis 536

Dietary Recommendations and Food Sources for Manganese 536
Manganese Deficiency 536
Manganese Toxicity 536

Fluoride 536

Functions of Fluoride 537
Fluoride Absorption and Excretion 538
Dietary Recommendations for Fluoride 538
Sources of Fluoride 538
Fluoride Deficiency, Toxicity, and Pharmacological Applications 539

Chromium 539

Functions of Chromium 539
Chromium Absorption, Transport, and Excretion 539
Dietary Recommendations and Food Sources for Chromium 540
Chromium Deficiency 540
Chromium Toxicity 540

Molybdenum 541

Molybdenum Absorption, Use, and Metabolism 541
FYI: Chromium, Exercise, and Body Composition 541
Dietary Recommendations and Food Sources for Molybdenum 542
Molybdenum Deficiency and Toxicity 542

Other Trace Elements and Ultratrace Elements 542

Arsenic 542
Boron 543
Nickel 543
Silicon 544
Vanadium 544

Learning Portfolio 546

Key Terms 546
Study Points 546
Study Questions 547
Try This 547
What About Bobbie? 547
References 548

Chapter 14 Sports Nutrition: Eating for Peak Performance 551

Nutrition and Physical Performance 552

Energy Systems, Muscles, and Physical Performance 555

ATP–CP Energy System 555
Lactic Acid Energy System 556
Oxygen Energy System 556
Teamwork in Energy Production 556
Glycogen Depletion 557
Endurance Training 557
Muscles and Muscle Fibers 559
FYI: Lactate Is Not a Metabolic Dead End 560

Optimal Nutrition for Athletic Performance 561

Going Green: *Exercise High* 562

Energy Intake and Exercise 562

Carbohydrate and Exercise 563

Carbohydrate Loading 563
Carbohydrate Intake Before Exercise 564
Carbohydrate Intake During Exercise 564
Carbohydrate Intake Following Exercise 564
Nutrition Science in Action Fourth-Quarter Performance 566

Dietary Fat and Exercise 567

Fat Intake and the Athlete 567
FYI: Nutrition Periodization: Tailoring Nutrition Intake to Exercise Goals 568

Protein and Exercise 569

Protein Recommendations for Athletes 569
Protein Intake and the Athlete 569
Protein Intake After Exercise 570
Dangers of High Protein Intake 570

Vitamins, Minerals, and Athletic Performance 570

B Vitamins 571
Calcium 571
Iron 571
Other Trace Minerals 571

Fluid Needs During Exercise 572

Hydration 574

Nutrition Needs of Young Athletes 577

Nutrition Supplements and Ergogenic Aids 577

Regulation and Concerns About Dietary and Herbal Supplements 579
Convenience Supplements 580
Weight-Gain Powders 580
Amino Acids 580
Creatine 581
Antioxidants 582
Caffeine 582
Ephedrine 583
Sodium Bicarbonate 583
Chromium 584
Iron 584

Weight and Body Composition 584

Weight Gain: Build Muscle, Lose Fat 585
Weight Loss: The Panacea for Optimal Performance? 585
Weight Loss: Negative Consequences for the Competitive Athlete? 586
Female Athlete Triad 587

Learning Portfolio 590

Key Terms 590
Study Points 590
Study Questions 591
Try This 591
What About Bobbie? 591
References 592

Spotlight on Eating Disorders 595

The Eating Disorder Continuum 596

History of a Modern Malady 597

No Simple Causes 598

Anorexia Nervosa 599

Causes of Anorexia Nervosa 600
Warning Signs 601
Treatment 601

Bulimia Nervosa 603

Causes of Bulimia 604
Obsessed by Thoughts of Food 605

FYI: Diary of an Eating Disorder 605

Treatment 606

Binge-Eating Disorder 607

Stress and Conflict Often Trigger Binge Eating 607
Treatment 608

Body Dysmorphic Disorder 608

Night-Eating Syndrome 609

Males: An Overlooked Population 610

An Unrecognized Disorder 610

Anorexia Athletica 611

The Female Athlete Triad 611

Vegetarianism and Eating Disorders 612

Smoking and Eating Disorders 612

Diabulimia 612

Baryophobia 612

Infantile Anorexia 613

Combating Eating Disorders 613

Learning Portfolio 616

Key Terms 616
Study Points 616
Study Questions 616
Try This 617
What About Bobbie? 617
References 617

Chapter 15
Diet and Health 619

Nutrition and Chronic Disease 620

Healthy People 2010 620
Obesity and Chronic Disease 621

FYI: Overweight and Obesity: Health Consequences 622

Physical Inactivity and Chronic Disease 622

Genetics and Disease 624

The Workings of DNA and Genes 625

Cardiovascular Disease 626

The Cardiovascular System and Cardiovascular Disease 626
What Is Atherosclerosis? 627
Risk Factors for Atherosclerosis 629
Dietary and Lifestyle Factors for Reducing Atherosclerosis Risk 630

Nutrition Science in Action Coronary Heart Disease 632

Putting It All Together 636

Hypertension 636

What Is Blood Pressure? 637
What Is Hypertension? 637
Risk Factors for Hypertension 638
Dietary and Lifestyle Factors for Reducing Hypertension 638
Putting It All Together 641

Cancer 642

What Is Cancer? 642
Risk Factors for Cancer 643
Dietary and Lifestyle Factors for Reducing Cancer Risk 644

Going Green: *What Do Smokers Eat? 645*

Putting It All Together 647

Diabetes Mellitus 648

What Is Diabetes? 649
Low Blood Glucose Levels: Hypoglycemia 651
Risk Factors for Diabetes 652
Dietary and Lifestyle Factors for Reducing Diabetes Risk 653

FYI: The Pima Indians 654

Management of Diabetes 655
Putting It All Together 656

Metabolic Syndrome 656

Osteoporosis 657

What Is Osteoporosis? 658
Risk Factors for Osteoporosis 658
Dietary and Lifestyle Factors for Reducing Osteoporosis Risk 659
Putting It All Together 661

Learning Portfolio 663

Key Terms 663
Study Points 663
Study Questions 663
Try This 664
What About Bobbie? 664
References 664

Chapter 16 Life Cycle: Maternal and Infant Nutrition 669

Pregnancy 670

Nutrition Before Conception 670
Physiology of Pregnancy 673
Maternal Weight Gain 677
Energy and Nutrition During Pregnancy 678
Nutrition Science in Action Eating for Two 679

FYI: Vegetarianism and Pregnancy 681

Food Choices for Pregnant Women 682
Substance Use and Pregnancy Outcome 684
Special Situations During Pregnancy 684

Lactation 687

Breastfeeding Trends 687
Physiology of Lactation 688
Nutrition for Breastfeeding Women 689
Energy 689
Practices to Avoid During Lactation 691
Benefits of Breastfeeding 691
Contraindications to Breastfeeding 692

Resources for Pregnant and Lactating Women and Their Children 693

Infancy 693

Infant Growth and Development 693
Energy and Nutrient Needs During Infancy 695
Newborn Breastfeeding 697
Alternative Feeding: Infant Formula 698

Going Green: *How Safe Are Plastics? 699*

Breast Milk or Formula: How Much Is Enough? 700
Feeding Technique 700
Introduction of Solid Foods into the Infant's Diet 700
Feeding Problems During Infancy 703

FYI: Fruit Juices and Drinks 705

Learning Portfolio 707

Key Terms 707
Study Points 707
Study Questions 708
Try This 708
What About Bobbie? 709
References 709

Chapter 17 Life Cycle: From Childhood Through Adulthood 711

Childhood 712

Energy and Nutrient Needs During Childhood 712

FYI: Food Hypersensitivities and Allergies 716

Influences on Childhood Food Habits and Intake 717
Nutritional Concerns of Childhood 718
Malnutrition and Hunger in Childhood 718

Going Green: *Farmers' Markets 719*

FYI: Overweight in Children and Teens: Whose Problem Is It? 720

Vegetarianism in Childhood 721

Adolescence 722

Physical Growth and Development 722
Nutrient Needs of Adolescents 723
Nutrition-Related Concerns for Adolescents 725

Staying Young While Growing Older 727

Weight and Body Composition 728
Physical Activity 729
Immunity 730
Taste and Smell 730
Gastrointestinal Changes 730

Nutrient Needs of the Mature Adult 731

Energy 731
Protein 731
Carbohydrate 733
Fat 733
Water 733
Vitamins and Minerals 733
To Supplement or Not to Supplement 735

Nutrition-Related Concerns of Mature Adults 736

Drug–Drug and Drug–Nutrient Interactions 736
Depression 738
Anorexia of Aging 738
Arthritis 738
Bowel and Bladder Regulation 739
Dental Health 740
Vision Problems 740
Osteoporosis 740
Alzheimer's Disease 741

Meal Management for Mature Adults 741
Managing Independently 741
Wise Eating for One or Two 742
Finding Community Resources 743
Learning Portfolio 744
Key Terms 744
Study Points 744
Study Questions 744
Try This 745
What About Bobbie? 745
References 745

Chapter 18
Food Safety and Technology: Microbial Threats and Genetic Engineering 749

Food Safety 750
Harmful Substances in Foods 750
FYI: Seafood Safety 754
Going Green: *Ocean Pollution and Mercury Poisoning 760*
Keeping Food Safe 762
FYI: At War with Bioterrorism 764
Who's at Increased Risk for Foodborne Illness? 767
FYI: Safe Food Practices 768
A Final Word on Food Safety 768
Food Technology 769
Food Preservation 770
Genetically Modified Foods 772
A Short Course in Plant Genetics 772
Genetically Modified Foods: An Unstoppable Experiment? 773
Benefits of Genetic Engineering 776
Risks 777
Regulation 777
Learning Portfolio 780
Key Terms 780
Study Points 780
Study Questions 781
Try This 781
References 781

Chapter 19
World View of Nutrition: The Faces of Global Malnutrition 783

Malnutrition in the United States 784
The Face of American Malnutrition 784
Prevalence and Distribution 785
The Working Poor 786
FYI: Hungry and Homeless 788
Attacking Hunger in America 788
Malnutrition in the Developing World 791
Going Green: *Can Chocolate Help the Planet? 792*
The World Food Equation 792
The Fight Against Global Hunger 793
Social and Economic Factors 793
Infection and Disease 795
Political Disruptions 795
FYI: AIDS and Malnutrition 796
Agriculture and Environment: A Tricky Balance 797
FYI: Tough Choices 798
Malnutrition: Its Nature, Its Victims, and Its Eradication 798
Learning Portfolio 803
Key Terms 803
Study Points 803
Study Questions 804
Try This 804
References 804

Appendices

A Food Composition Tables
B Exchange Lists for Diabetes
C USDA Food Intake Patterns
D Nutrition and Health for Canadians
E The Gastrointestinal Tract
F Biochemical Structures
G Major Metabolic Pathways
H Calculations and Conversions
I Growth Charts

Glossary

Index

Photo Credits

On Web Site

Feeding Infants and Toddlers
Information Resources
Answers to Study Questions

Preface

Because changes in nutrition-related information occur so rapidly, and because we are committed to providing comprehensive, current, and accurate information on the most pressing issues, we have prepared this *Fourth Edition* of *Nutrition*. The overall content, organization, and features remain, but within this framework, key topics and issues have been updated with new features and the most recent information available. Our goals in writing this book can be stated simply:

- To present scientifically based, accurate, up-to-date information in an accessible format
- To involve students in taking responsibility for their nutrition, health, and well-being
- To instill a sense of competence and personal power in students

The first of these goals means making expert knowledge about nutrition available to the individual. *Nutrition* presents current information to students about topics and issues that concern them—a balanced diet, nutritional supplements, weight management, exercise, and a multitude of others. Current, complete, and straightforward coverage is balanced with "user-friendly" features designed to make the text appealing.

Our second goal is to involve students in taking responsibility for their nutrition and health. To encourage students to think about the material they're reading and how it relates to their own lives, *Nutrition* uses innovative pedagogy and unique interactive features. We invite students to examine the issues and to analyze their nutrition-related behaviors.

Perhaps our third goal in writing *Nutrition* is the most important: stimulate a sense of competence and personal power in the students who read this book. Everyone has the ability to monitor, understand, and affect his or her own nutritional behaviors.

Dietary Guidelines for Americans

The seventh edition of *Dietary Guidelines for Americans* places a stronger emphasis on improving poor diets and increasing physical activity, two of the most important factors for combating the obesity epidemic. Eating a healthy balance of nutritious foods continues as a central point in the *Dietary Guidelines*, but balancing nutrients is not enough for health. Total calories also count, especially as more Americans are gaining weight. Because almost two-thirds of Americans are overweight or obese, and more than half get too little physical activity, the *2010 Dietary Guidelines* place a stronger emphasis on calorie balance for a healthy body weight and consumption of nutrient-dense foods and beverages. The report identifies several key recommendations. As you read the chapters, look for these recommendations highlighted in the margins.

USDA MyPlate

MyPlate, which replaces MyPyramid, is part of an overall food guidance system that emphasizes the need for a more individualized approach to improving diet and lifestyle. MyPlate incorporates recommendations from the *Dietary Guidelines for Americans* and uses interactive technology found at http://www.ChooseMyPlate.gov. These interactive activities allow individuals to obtain a more personalized recommendation on their daily calorie level based on the *Dietary Guidelines for Americans*. It also allows individuals to find general food guidance and suggestions for making smart choices from each food group. Concepts from MyPlate and the *Dietary Guidelines* are carried throughout the book and fully integrated into the chapter text. MyPlate intake recommendations are summarized in Appendix C.

Trans Fat Labeling

Nutrition delivers the tools for students to understand food labels, including trans fat information, and to incorporate positive nutritional behaviors into their everyday lives. The *Dietary Guidelines for Americans* recommend reducing the intake of trans fats and saturated fats. The recent United States labeling requirement for trans fat provides a more complete picture of fat content in foods—allowing students and other consumers to choose foods low in trans fat, saturated fat, and cholesterol. The FDA estimates that trans fat labeling will prevent from 600 to 1200 cases of coronary heart disease and 250 to 500 deaths each year.

Going Green

A new feature to the *Fourth Edition*, *Going Green* boxes address the nutrition community's concern about the importance of environmental issues in our time. This environmental theme runs through each chapter and expands our nutrition

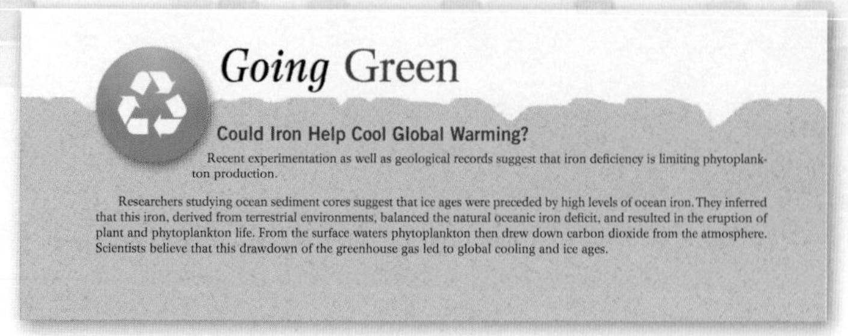

Going Green

Could Iron Help Cool Global Warming?

Recent experimentation as well as geological records suggest that iron deficiency is limiting phytoplankton production.

Researchers studying ocean sediment cores suggest that ice ages were preceded by high levels of ocean iron. They inferred that this iron, derived from terrestrial environments, balanced the natural oceanic iron deficit, and resulted in the eruption of plant and phytoplankton life. From the surface waters phytoplankton then drew down carbon dioxide from the atmosphere. Scientists believe that this drawdown of the greenhouse gas led to global cooling and ice ages.

focus to show that we are all citizens of an endangered planet with opportunities to reduce our environmental footprint.

Nutrition Science in Action

Nutrition Science in Action is an exciting feature that walks students through science experiments involving nutrition. Each *Nutrition Science in Action* presents observations and hypotheses, an experimental plan, and results, conclusions, and discussions that allow students to apply their knowledge of nutrition to real-life experiments outside of the classroom.

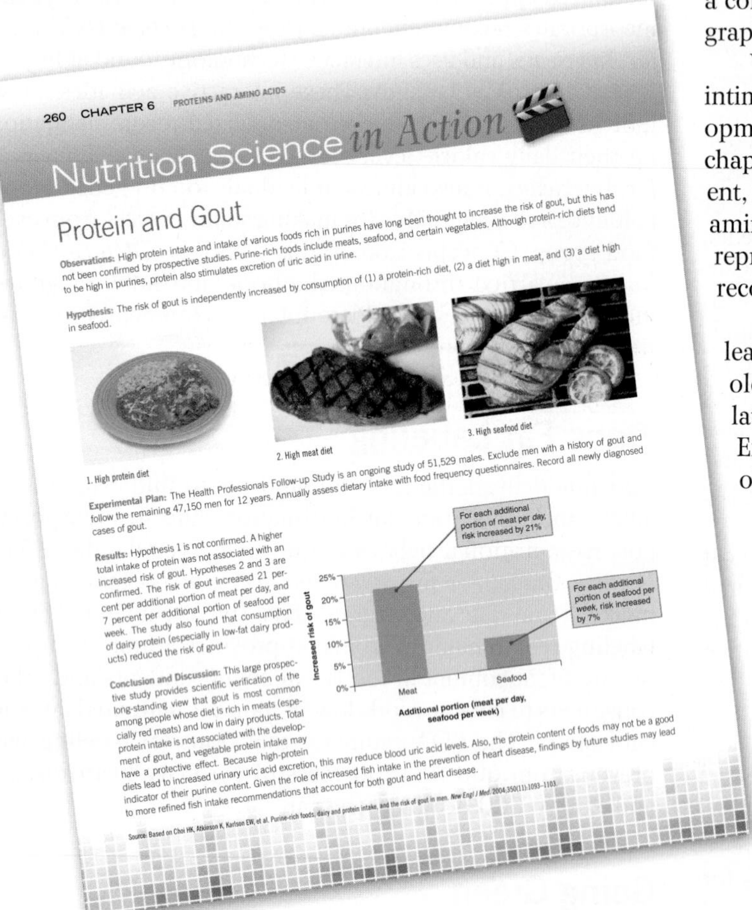

260 CHAPTER 6 PROTEINS AND AMINO ACIDS

Nutrition Science *in Action*

Protein and Gout

Observations: High protein intake and intake of various foods rich in purines have long been thought to increase the risk of gout, but this has not been confirmed by prospective studies. Purine-rich foods include meats, seafood, and certain vegetables. Although protein-rich diets tend to be high in purines, protein also stimulates excretion of uric acid in urine.

Hypothesis: The risk of gout is independently increased by consumption of (1) a protein-rich diet, (2) a diet high in meat, and (3) a diet high in seafood.

1. High protein diet

2. High meat diet

3. High seafood diet

Experimental Plan: The Health Professionals Follow-up Study is an ongoing study of 51,529 males. Exclude men with a history of gout and follow the remaining 47,150 men for 12 years. Annually assess dietary intake with food frequency questionnaires. Record all newly diagnosed cases of gout.

Results: Hypothesis 1 is not confirmed. A higher total intake of protein was not associated with an increased risk of gout. Hypotheses 2 and 3 are confirmed. The risk of gout increased 21 percent per additional portion of meat per day, and 7 percent per additional portion of seafood per week. The study also found that consumption of dairy protein (especially in low-fat dairy products) reduced the risk of gout.

For each additional portion of meat per day, risk increased by 21%

For each additional portion of seafood per *week*, risk increased by 7%

Increased risk of gout

25%
20%
15%
10%
5%
0%

Meat

Seafood

Additional portion (meat per day, seafood per week)

Conclusion and Discussion: This large prospective study provides scientific verification of the long-standing view that gout is most common among people whose diet is rich in meats (especially red meats) and low in dairy products. Total protein intake is not associated with the development of gout, and vegetable protein intake may have a protective effect. Because high-protein diets lead to increased urinary uric acid excretion, this may reduce blood uric acid levels. Also, the protein content of foods may not be a good indicator of their purine content. Given the role of increased fish intake in the prevention of heart disease, findings by future studies may lead to more refined fish intake recommendations that account for both gout and heart disease.

Source: Based on Choi HK, Atkinson K, Karlson EW, et al. Purine-rich foods, dairy and protein intake, and the risk of gout in men. *New Engl J Med.* 2004;350(11):1093–1103.

Bioterrorism and the Food Supply

How safe is our food supply? In the aftermath of the terrorist attacks on the World Trade Center in September 2001 and the spread of anthrax through the mail, there is heightened concern over the vulnerability of our food supply to bioterrorism. *Nutrition* explores past attacks on U.S. and Canadian food supplies, points of vulnerability, and food safety strategies that students can use to help protect themselves.

Additional updates to this edition include the latest DRIs, revised macronutrient chapters, updated references, expanded coverage of diet and health, a new focus on nutrition and the environment, and a full chapter devoted to alcohol. This text has also been redesigned to improve organization and ease of use.

Accessible Science

Nutrition makes use of the latest in learning theory and balances the behavioral aspects of nutrition with an accessible approach to scientific concepts. You will find the book to be a comprehensive resource that communicates nutrition both graphically and personally.

We present technological concepts in an engaging, nonintimidating way with an appealing, stepwise, parallel development of text and annotated illustrations. Illustrations in all chapters use consistent representations. Each type of nutrient, for example, has a distinct color and shape. Icons of an amino acid, a protein, a triglyceride, and a glucose molecule represent "characters" in the nutrition story and are instantly recognizable as they appear throughout the book.

This textbook is unique in the field of nutrition and leads the way in depicting important biological and physiological phenomena, such as emulsification, glucose regulation, digestion and absorption, and fetal development. Extensive graphic presentations make nutrition and physiological principles come alive.

The Pedagogy

Nutrition focuses on teaching behavioral change, personal decision making, and up-to-date scientific concepts in a number of novel ways. This interactive approach addresses different learning styles, making it the ideal text to ensure mastery of key concepts. Beginning with Chapter 1, the material engages students in considering their own behavior in light of the knowledge they are gaining. The pedagogical aids that appear in most chapters include the following:

Think About It questions at the beginning of each chapter present realistic nutrition-related situations and ask students to consider how they would behave in such circumstances.

CHAPTER 1
Food Choices
Nutrients and Nourishment
THINK About It
1 How many different foods have you eaten in the last 24 hours? The last week?
2 Do you have a preference for sweets? Chocolate? Ice cream? If so, where do you think it comes from?
3 What do you think is driving the popularity of vitamins and other supplements?
4 Where do you get the majority of your information about nutrition?
Visit nutrition.jbpub.com

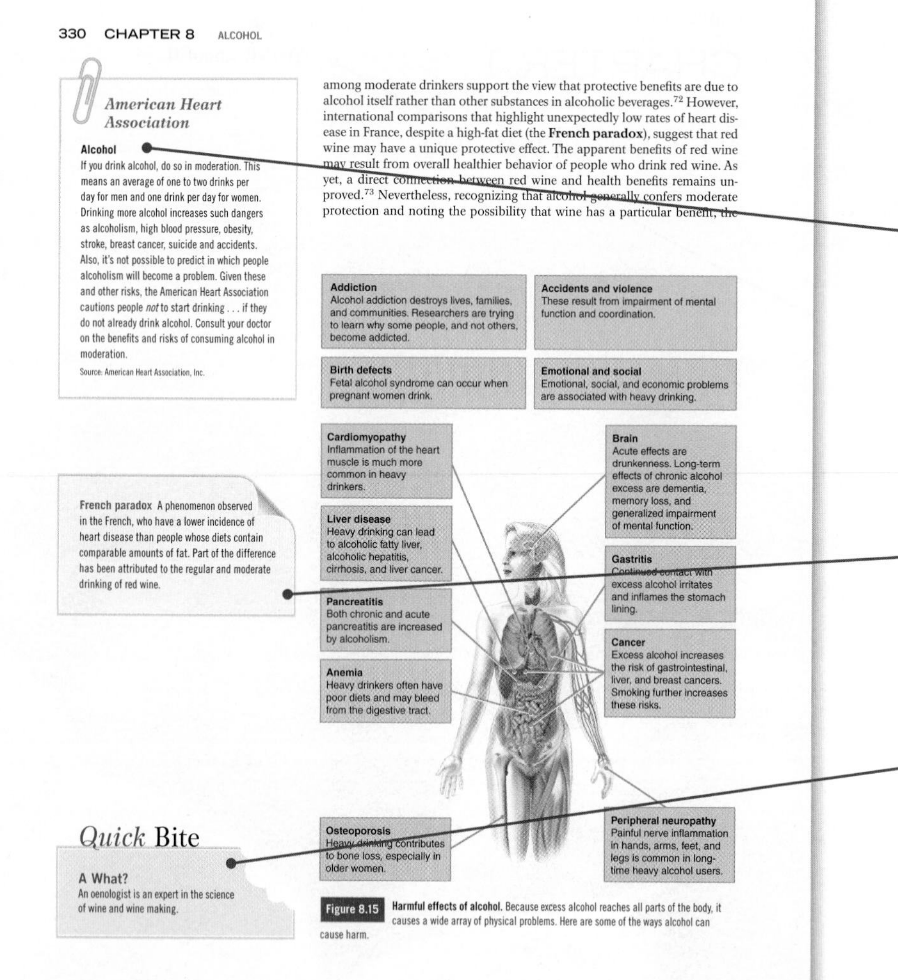

Position Statements from distinguished organizations such as the Academy of Nutrition and Dietetics, the American College of Sports Medicine, and the American Heart Association relate to the chapter topics and bolster the assertions made by the authors by showcasing concurrent opinions held by some of the leading organizations in nutrition and health.

Key Terms are in boldface type the first time they are mentioned. Their definitions also appear in the margins near the relevant textual discussion, making it easy for students to review material.

Quick Bites sprinkled throughout the book offer fun facts about nutrition-related topics such as exotic foods, social customs, origins of phrases, folk remedies, medical history, and so on.

For Your Information offers more in-depth treatment of controversial and timely topics, such as unfounded claims about the effects of sugar, whether athletes need more protein, and usefulness of the glycemic index.

622 CHAPTER 15 DIET AND HEALTH

excess body weight that is linked to increased risks. Waist circumference, for example, can be a valuable screening tool for identifying excess abdominal fatness. Public health objectives, such as those in Healthy People 2010, emphasize the need for healthful eating behaviors, beginning in childhood, that help us achieve and maintain a healthy weight.

Physical Inactivity and Chronic Disease

A sedentary lifestyle is also a significant risk factor for chronic disease. Physically active people generally outlive those who are inactive, and inactivity is

FYI For Your Information

Overweight and Obesity: Health Consequences

Health problems resulting from overweight and obesity could reverse many health gains achieved in the United States in recent decades. Overweight and obesity may soon cause as much preventable disease and death as cigarette smoking. The primary concern of overweight and obesity is one of health, not appearance.

Potential consequences of overweight and obesity are summarized here. In many cases, a small amount of weight loss can reverse chronic disease risks. (See Chapter 9, "Energy Balance, Body Composition, and Weight Management.")

Premature Death

- An estimated 300,000 deaths per year may be attributable to obesity.
- The risk of death rises with increasing weight.
- Even moderate weight excess (10 to 20 pounds for a person of average height) increases the risk of death, particularly among adults aged 30 to 64 years.
- Individuals who are obese (BMI > 30 kg/m²) have a 50 to 100 percent increased ris... of premature death from ...pared with individuals ...ight.

...art disease (heart ...art failure, sudden ... or chest pain, ...ythm) is in... ...o are overweight ...m²). ...ice as com... ...ese than in ... weight.

- Obesity is associated with elevated triglycerides (blood fat) and decreased HDL cholesterol ("good cholesterol").

Diabetes

- A weight gain of 11 to 18 pounds increases a person's risk of developing type 2 diabetes to twice that of individuals who have not gained weight.
- Over 80 percent of people with diabetes are overweight or obese.

Cancer

- Overweight and obesity are associated with an increased risk for some types of cancer, including endometrial (cancer of the lining of the uterus), colon, gallbladder, prostate, kidney, and postmenopausal breast cancer.
- Women who gain more than 20 pounds from age 18 to midlife double their risk of postmenopausal breast cancer compared with women whose weight remains stable.

Breathing Problems

- Sleep apnea (interrupted breathing while sleeping) is more common in obese persons.
- Obesity is associated with a higher prevalence of asthma.

Arthritis

- For every 2-pound increase in weight, the risk of developing arthritis is increased by 9 to 13 percent.
- Symptoms of arthritis can improve with weight loss.

Reproductive Complications

- Obesity in premenopausal women is associated with irregular menstrual cycles and infertility.
- Complications of pregnancy
  - Obesity during pregnancy is associated with increased risk of death in both the baby and the mother, and increases the risk of maternal high blood pressure by 10 times.

Key Concepts summarize previous text and highlight important information.

Label to Table helps students apply their new decision-making skills at the supermarket. It walks students through the various types of information that appear on food labels, including government-mandated terminology, misleading advertising phrases, and amounts of ingredients.

424 CHAPTER 10 FAT-SOLUBLE VITAMINS

Vitamin K Toxicity

Vitamin K is stored primarily in the liver and is also found in bone. Because the body excretes vitamin K much more rapidly than the other fat-soluble vitamins, toxicity from food is rare and thus no UL has been set for vitamin K. A vitamin K overdose can cause hemolytic anemia. This condition has been seen in newborns who receive vitamin K in the form of menadione rather than the recommended form, phylloquinone.

Key Concepts *Vitamin K deficiencies are extremely rare. Because it takes several weeks before the intestinal bacteria that produce vitamin K begin to flourish in the intestine, newborns are routinely given injections of vitamin K at birth. Vitamin K toxicity is rare because the body excretes the nutrient more readily than the other fat-soluble vitamins.*

It is well known that milk is an excellent source of calcium, but did you know that milk also contains three of the four fat-soluble vitamins? Let's take a look at the Nutrition Facts from a carton of nonfat milk.

Nonfat Milk	
Calories	90
Total Fat	0
Cholesterol	less than 5mg
Sodium	130mg
Total Carbohydrate	13g
Dietary Fiber	0g
Sugars	12g
Protein	9g
Vitamin A	10% DV
Vitamin C	4% DV
Calcium	30% DV
Iron	0% DV
Vitamin D	25% DV

Milk contains the fat-soluble vitamins A and D. Vitamin A is found naturally in whole milk and is added to reduced-fat milks. All milks are fortified with vitamin D. Although it is true that fat-soluble vitamins can be toxic in large doses because they are stored in the body, the amounts added to milk are not of concern. Vitamin K is not listed on the label, but milk is a good source of this fat-soluble vitamin as well. (Each cup of milk provides 10 micrograms, which is 12.5 percent of the Daily Value.)

A one-cup serving of fortified milk provides 10 percent of the 5,000 IU Daily Value of vitamin A. If you drank three cups of milk per day, you would get about one-third of your recommended amount of vitamin A. That's good news because dietary vitamin A is not always easy to obtain. One form, retinol, is found mainly in liver and fish liver oil, which are not always staples of the typical American diet. The provitamin forms of vitamin A, the carotenoids, are found in green leafy and dark-orange vegetables.

Vitamin D is important because it helps with the absorption of calcium and phosphorus, both important for bone health. Fish liver oil, sardines, and some fortified cereals are also good sources of vitamin D. As shown in the nutrition label, just one cup of milk gives you one-quarter of the vitamin D Daily Value. That's 25 percent of 10 micrograms, or 2.5 micrograms.

Keep in mind when selecting milk that nonfat (skim) milk contains vitamins A and D just like the higher-fat 2% and whole milk. Don't let the large banner "Vitamin A and D" printed on containers of whole milk trick you into thinking it contains more. It doesn't!

Nutrition Facts
Serving Size: 1 cup (240mL)
Servings Per Container about 8

Amount Per Serving	
Calories 90 Calories from fat 0	
	% Daily Value*
Total Fat 0g	0%
Saturated Fat 0g	0%
Trans Fat 0g	
Cholesterol less than 5mg	1%
Sodium 130mg	5%
Total Carbohydrate 13g	4%
Dietary Fiber 0g	0%
Sugars 12g	
Protein 9g	18%
Vitamin A 10% • Vitamin C 4%	
Calcium 30% • Iron 0%	
Vitamin D 25%	

* Percent Daily Values are based on a 2,000 calorie diet. Your daily values may be higher or lower depending on your calorie needs:

		Calories: 2,000	2,500
Total Fat	Less Than	65g	80g
Sat Fat	Less Than	20g	25g
Cholesterol	Less Than	300mg	300mg
Sodium	Less Than	2,400mg	2,400mg
Total Carbohydrate		300g	375g
Dietary Fiber		25g	30g
Protein		50g	65g

Calories per gram:
Fat 9 • Carbohydrate 4 • Protein 4

AMOUNTS PER 1 CUP SERVING:	FAT
WHOLE MILK	8g
FAT FREE MILK	0g

INGREDIENTS: GRADE A FAT FREE MILK, VITAMIN A PALMITATE, VITAMIN D_3.

The **Learning Portfolio** at the end of each chapter collects, in one place, all aspects of nutrition information that students need to solidify their understanding of the material. The various formats will appeal to students according to their individual learning and studying styles.

Learning Portfolio

Key Terms

	page		page
amino acids	13	lipids	13
antioxidant	11	macrominerals	14
calorie	15	macronutrients	11
carbohydrates	13	microminerals	14
case control studies	18	micronutrients	11
circulation	13	minerals	14
clinical trials	18	neophobia	2
control group	18	nutrients	10
correlations	18	nutrigenomics	18
double-blind study	21	nutrition	2
energy	14	organic	12
epidemiology	17	peer review	22
essential nutrients	10	phytochemicals	11
experimental group	18	pica	5
experiments	18	placebo	21
flavor	3	placebo effect	21
hormones	13	proteins	13
hypotheses	17	social facilitation	6
inorganic	12	trace minerals	14
kilocalories (kcal) [KILL-oh-kal-oh-rees]	15	triglycerides	13
legumes	13	umami [ooh-MA-mee]	3
		vitamins	13

Study Points

- Most people make food choices for reasons other than nutrient value.
- Taste and texture are the two most important factors that influence food choices.
- In all cultures, eating is the primary way of maintaining social relationships.
- Although most North Americans know about healthful food choices, their eating habits do not always reflect this knowledge.
- Food is a mixture of chemicals. Essential chemicals in food are called nutrients.
- Carbohydrates, lipids, proteins, vitamins, minerals, and water are the six classes of nutrients found in food.
- Nutrients have three general functions in the body: they serve as energy sources, structural components, and regulators of metabolic processes.
- Vitamins regulate body processes such as energy metabolism, blood clotting, and calcium balance.
- Minerals contribute to body structures and to regulating processes such as fluid balance.
- Water is the most important nutrient in the body. We can survive much longer without the other nutrients than we can without water.
- Energy in foods and the body is measured in kilocalories. Carbohydrates, fats, and proteins are sources of energy.
- Carbohydrate and protein have a potential energy value of 4 kilocalories per gram, and fat provides 9 kilocalories per gram.
- Scientific studies are the cornerstone of nutrition. The scientific method uses observation and inquiry to test hypotheses.
- Double-blind, placebo-controlled clinical trials are considered the "gold standard" of nutrition studies.
- Research designs used to test hypotheses include epidemiological, animal, cell culture, and human studies.
- Information in the public media is not always an accurate or complete representation of the current state of the science on a particular topic.

Study Questions

1. Name three sensory aspects of food that influence our food choices.
2. How do our health beliefs affect our food choices?
3. List the six classes of nutrients.
4. List the 13 vitamins.
5. What determines whether a mineral is a macromineral or a micro- (trace) mineral?
6. How many kilocalories are in 1 gram of carbohydrate, of protein, and of fat?
7. What is an epidemiological study?
8. What is the difference between an experimental and control group?
9. What is a placebo?

Key Terms list all new vocabulary alphabetically with the page number of the first appearance. This arrangement allows students to review any term they do not recall and turn immediately to the definition and discussion of it in the chapter. This approach also promotes the acquisition of knowledge, not simply memorization.

Study Points summarize the content of each chapter with a synopsis of each major topic. The points are in the order in which they appear in the chapter, so related concepts flow together.

Study Questions encourage students to probe deeper into the chapter content, making connections and gaining new insights. Although these questions can be used for pop quizzes, they will also help students to review, especially students who study by writing out material. They can check their work by looking at the **Answers to Study Questions** on the *Nutrition* Web site, go.jblearning.com/insel4

The **Learning Portfolio** (continued)

Try This activities are for curious students who like to experiment. These suggestions for hands-on activities encourage students to put theory into practice. It will especially help students whose major learning style is experimental.

What About Bobbie? tracks the eating habits and health-related decisions of a typical college student so that students can apply the material they have learned in the chapter to a typical situation. Following the individual case of Bobbie takes students from the general concepts to the specific application of new information. As a complement to this textual feature, the EatRight Analysis software programs allow students to track the various choices Bobbie makes as well as their own food choices.

26 CHAPTER 1 FOOD CHOICES

Try This

Try a New Cuisine Challenge

Expand your culinary taste buds and try a new cuisine. Take your local phone book and see how many ethnic restaurants are near campus. Choose a cuisine you are not very familiar with and take some friends along for dinner so you can order and share several dishes. While you're there, don't be afraid to ask questions about the menu, so you can gain a better understanding of the foods, preparation techniques, spices, and even the cultural meaning attached to some of the dishes.

Food Label Puzzle

The purpose of this exercise is to put the individual pieces of the food label together to determine how many kilocalories are in a serving. Pick six foods in your dorm room or apartment that have complete food labels. Ask a friend to write down the value for calories on each label and then black out these numbers on the labels. Remember that the term *calories* on a food label really is referring to kilocalories. Your job is to determine how many kilocalories are in a serving of each of these foods. You can do this by putting together the individual pieces (carbohydrate, protein, and fat). If you need help, review this chapter and pay close attention to the section on the energy-yielding nutrients. How many kilocalories does each have per gram? You may find that the results of your calculations don't exactly match the numbers on the label. Within labeling guidelines, food manufacturers can round values.

What About Bobbie?

The "What About Bobbie?" feature appears in most chapters. Bobbie is a college student whom you'll follow throughout this text to learn the strengths and weaknesses of her diet. Look for this feature to see how the information you learn in each chapter can be applied to real life.

Bobbie is a 20-year-old college sophomore. She lives on campus and has one roommate. She has the standard meal plan with her university, so she eats most of her meals in the cafeteria. Sometimes she'll get a snack from the local coffee shop or a vending machine. Her schedule is fairly typical, with classes spread out in both the morning and afternoon. Occasionally at night, she and her friends will order pizza or go out for ice cream.

Bobbie weighs 155 pounds and is 5 feet, 4 inches tall. She gained 10 pounds her freshman year in college and would like to lose it because she feels that her ideal weight is more like 145 pounds. She exercises infrequently but likes to walk with her friends and take an occasional aerobics class. Here is a typical day of eating for Bobbie:

Sample one-day menu from Bobbie's diet

7:45 A.M.
1 raisin bagel, toasted
3 tablespoons light cream cheese
10 fluid ounces regular coffee
  2 packets of sugar
  2 tablespoons of 2% milk
10:15 A.M.
1 banana
12:15 P.M.
Turkey and cheese sandwich
2 slices sourdough bread
2 ounces sliced turkey lunch meat
2 teaspoons regular mayonnaise
2 teaspoons mustard
2 slices tomato
2 slices dill pickle
Shredded lettuce
Salad from cafeteria salad bar
  2 cups shredded iceberg lettuce
  2 tablespoons each:
    Shredded carrot
    Chopped egg
    Croutons
    Kidney beans
    Italian salad dressing
12 fluid ounces diet soda
1 small chocolate chip cookie
3:30 P.M.
16 fluid ounces water
1.5 ounces regular tortilla chips
½ cup salsa
6:00 P.M.
Spaghetti with meatballs
  1.5 cups pasta
  3 ounces ground beef (meatballs)
  3 ounces spaghetti sauce
  2 tablespoons Parmesan cheese
1 piece garlic bread
½ cup green beans
  1 teaspoon butter
12 fluid ounces diet soda
10:15 P.M.
1 slice cheese pizza

The Integrated Learning and Teaching Package

Integrating the text and ancillaries is crucial to deriving their full benefit. Based on feedback from instructors and students, Jones & Bartlett Learning offers the following supplements.

The **Instructor's ToolKit CD** is a comprehensive teaching resource available to adopters of the book. It includes:

- PowerPoint Lecture Presentation Slides
- Image and Table Bank: Provides art and tables that can be imported into PowerPoints, tests, or used to create transparencies
- Instructor's Manual: Includes chapter outlines and strategies for teaching difficult concepts

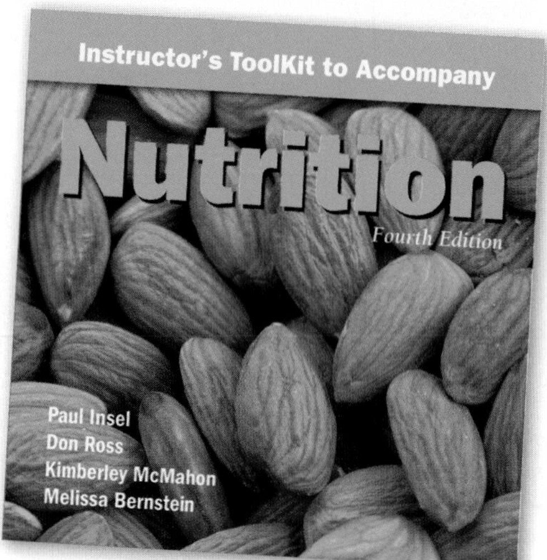

The resources on the Instructor's ToolKit CD have been formatted so that instructors can integrate them into many popular online course management systems. Consult the CD packaging booklet for more information on this feature. Please feel free to contact Jones & Bartlett technical support with questions.

Diet analysis software is an important component of the behavioral change and personal decision-making focus of a nutrition course. **EatRight Analysis**, developed by ESHA Research, provides software that enables students to analyze their diets by calculating their nutrient intake and comparing it to recommended intake levels. EatRight Analysis offers dietary software online at http://EatRight.jblearning.com. With this online tool, you and your students can access personal records from any computer with Internet access. Through a variety of reports, students learn to make better choices regarding their diet and activity habits.

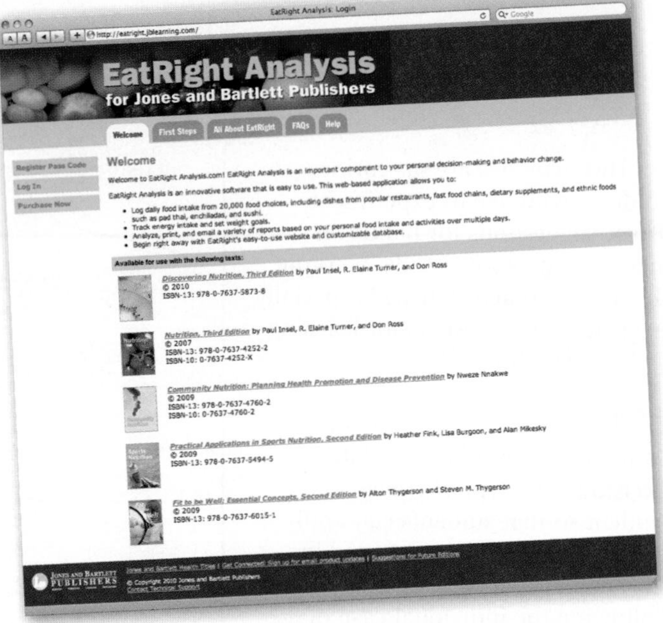

Contact your Publisher's Representative at www.jblearning.com for discount package opportunities.

Nutrition Science Animations are scientifically based animations that give nutrition students an accurate, accessible explanation of the major scientific concepts and physiological principles presented in *Nutrition*. More than thirty of the most difficult processes are graphically presented in an interactive, easy-to-understand format. These animations, available at go.jblearning.com/nutritionanimations, complement online courses, classroom lectures, and independent studying. Access is free and does not require a password. The Nutrition Science Animations are also available on CD (ISBN-13: 978-0-7637-4497-7 / ISBN-10: 0-7637-4497-2).

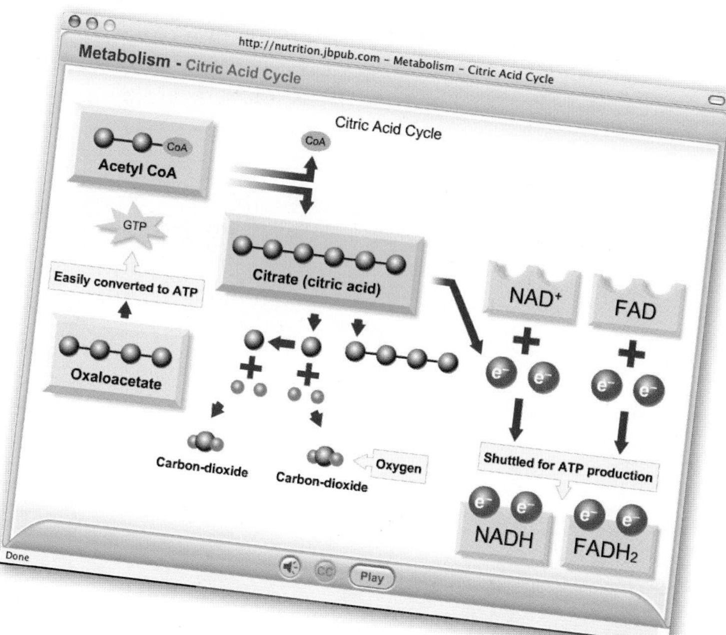

Contact your Publisher's Representative at www.jblearning.com.

The **Online Student Study Guide to Accompany Nutrition** provides a powerful learning tool to students using *Nutrition*. The online Student Study Guide follows the chapter topics and offers fill-in-the-blank questions and summaries so that students can test themselves. Also included are exercises for students to gain familiarity with the key terms in each chapter and tips for making assessments of their own dietary habits. Each new text includes an online access code to the Student Study Guide at no additional cost to students.

The **Web site** for *Nutrition*, go.jblearning.com/insel4, offers students and instructors an unprecedented degree of integration between the text and the online world through many useful study tools, activities, and supplementary health information, including a Chemistry Review, Healthy Recipes, Practice Quizzes, and much more.

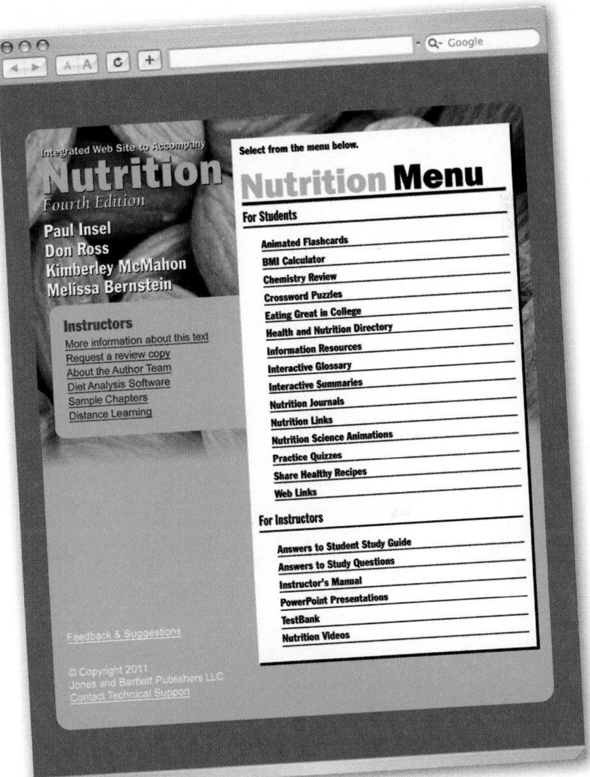

Contact your Publisher's Representative at www.jblearning.com.

About the Authors

The *Nutrition* author team represents a culmination of years of teaching and research in psychology and nutrition science. The combined experience of the authors yields a balanced presentation of both the science of nutrition and the components of behavioral change.

Dr. Paul Insel is Adjunct Clinical Associate Professor of Psychiatry and Behavioral Sciences at Stanford University (Stanford, California). In addition to being the principal investigator on several nutrition projects for the National Institutes of Health (NIH), he is the senior author of the seminal text in health education and has co-authored several best-selling nutrition books.

Don Ross is Director of the California Institute of Human Nutrition (Redwood City, California). For more than 20 years, he has co-authored multiple textbooks and created educational materials about health and nutrition for consumers, professionals, and college students. He has special expertise in communicating complicated physiological processes with easily understood graphical presentations. The National Institutes of Health selected his *Travels with Cholesterol* for distribution to consumers. His multidisciplinary focus brings together the fields of psychology, nutrition, biochemistry, biology, and medicine.

Kimberley McMahon is a Registered Dietitian and Adjunct Instructor in the Nutrition, Dietetics, and Food Sciences Department at Utah State University (Logan, Utah). She has taught basic nutrition, nutrition for exercise and sport, dietetics administration, and clinical nutrition courses and assists with the online Masters of Dietetics Administration program. She co-authored *Eat Right! Healthy Eating in College and Beyond*. Her interests and experience are in the areas of wellness, weight management, sports nutrition, and eating disorders.

Dr. Melissa Bernstein is a Registered Dietitian, Licensed Dietitian, and Assistant Professor in the Department of Nutrition at Rosalind Franklin University of Medicine and Science (North Chicago, Illinois). She received her doctoral degree from the Gerald J. and Dorothy R. Friedman School of Nutrition Science and Policy at Tufts University. Dr. Bernstein has been teaching courses in nutrition for more than 15 years and is innovative in creating engaging and challenging online nutrition courses. Her interests include geriatric nutrition, physical activity, and nutritional biochemistry. In addition to co-authoring *Nutrition for the Older Adult*, Dr. Bernstein has contributed to and authored textbook chapters and peer-reviewed journal publications on the topics of nutrition and nutrition for older adults.

Contributors

The following people contributed to this project:

Janine T. Baer, PhD, RD
University of Dayton
Chapter 14 Sports Nutrition
Chapter 16 Life Cycle: Maternal and Infant Nutrition

Toni Bloom, MS, RD, CDE
San Jose State University
Pedagogy

Boyce W. Burge, PhD
California Institute of Human Nutrition
Chapter 18 Food Safety and Technology

Eileen G. Ford, MS, RD
Drexel University
Chapter 16 Life Cycle: Maternal and Infant Nutrition

Ellen B. Fung, PhD, RD
University of Pennsylvania
Chapter 13 Trace Minerals

Michael I. Goran, PhD
University of Southern California
Chapter 9 Energy Balance, Body Composition, and Weight Management

Nancy J. Gustafson, MS, RD, FADA
Director, Sawyer County Aging Unit, WI
Chapter 4 Carbohydrates
Chapter 6 Proteins and Amino Acids

Rita H. Herskovitz, MS
University of Pennsylvania
Chapter 13 Trace Minerals

Nancy I. Kemp, MD
University of California, San Francisco
Chapter 12 Water and Major Minerals

Sarah Harding Laidlaw, MS, RD, MPA
Editor, Nutrition in Complementary Care, *DPG 18*
Chapter 17 Life Cycle: From Childhood Through Adulthood

Rick D. Mattes, MPH, PhD, RD
Purdue University
Chapter 1 Food Choices

Maye Musk, MS, RD
Past President of the Consulting Dietitians of Canada
Chapter 19 World View of Nutrition

Joyce D. Nash, PhD
Chapter 9 Energy Balance, Body Composition, and Weight Management

Rachel Stern, MS, RD, CNS
North Jersey Community Research Initiative
Chapter 5 Lipids
Chapter 8 Alcohol
Chapter 19 World View of Nutrition

Lisa Stollman, MA, RD, CDE, CDN
State University of New York, Stony Brook
Chapter 3 Digestion and Absorption

Barbara Sutherland, PhD
University of California, Davis
Chapter 7 Metabolism

Debra M. Vinci, PhD, RD, CD
Appalachian State University
Chapter 14 Sports Nutrition

Stella L. Volpe, PhD, RD, FACSM
University of Massachusetts
Chapter 9 Energy Balance, Body Composition, and Weight Management

The authors also would like to acknowledge the valuable contributions of:

C.J. Nieves
Coordinator of Nutrition Education Programs
University of Florida

Reviewers

Namanjeet Ahluwalia, PhD
Pennsylvania State University

Nancy K. Amy, PhD
University of California, Berkeley

R. James Barnard, PhD
University of California, Los Angeles

Susan I. Barr, PhD, RDN
University of British Columbia

Richard C. Baybutt, PhD
Kansas State University

Beverly A. Benes, PhD, RD
University of Nebraska, Lincoln

Marion Birdsall, PhD, RD
University of Pennsylvania

Melanie Tracy Burns, PhD, RD
Eastern Illinois University

N. Joanne Caid, PhD
California State University, Fresno

Jau-Jiin Chen, PhD, RD
University of Nevada, Las Vegas

Jo Carol Chezem, PhD, RD
Ball State University

Beverly E. Conway, MS
Williston State College

Jane B. Dennis, PhD, RD
Tarleton State University

Holly A. Dieken, PhD, MS, BS, RD
University of Tennessee, Chattanooga

Betty J. Forbes, RD, LD
West Virginia University

Debra K. Goodwin, PhD, RD
Jacksonville State University

Margaret Gunther, PhD
Palomar Community College

Shelley R. Hancock, MS, RD, LD
University of Alabama

Donna V. Handley, MS, RD
University of Rhode Island

Jeffrey Harris, DrPH, MPH, CNS, RD
West Chester University

Nancy Gordon Harris, MS, RD, LDN
East Carolina University

Diana Himmel, RDH, MS
Tunxis Community College

Sharon Himmelstein, PhD, MNS, RD, LD
Central New Mexico University

Georgette Howell, MS, RD
Montgomery County Community College

Michael Jenkins
Kent State University

Simon Jenkins, DPhil
University of Bath

Mary Beth Kavanagh, MS, RD, LD
Case Western Reserve University

Zaheer Ali Kirmani, PhD, RD, LD
Sam Houston State University

Anda Lam, MS, RD
Pasadena City College

Samantha R. Logan, DrPH, RD
University of Massachusetts

Colleen Loveland, MS, RD, LD, CDE
Dallas County Community College

Mary-Pat Maciolek, MBA, RD
Middlesex County College

Patricia Z. Marincic, PhD, RD, LD, CLE
College of Saint Benedict/Saint John's University

Melissa J. Martilotta, MS, RD
Pennsylvania State University

Keith R. Martin, PhD
Pennsylvania State University

Glen F. McNeil, MS, RD/LD
Fort Hays State University

Liza Merly, MS
Florida International University, University Park

Mark S. Meskin, PhD, RD, FADA
California State Polytechnic University, Pomona

Kristin Moline, MSEd
Lourdes College

Katherine O. Musgrave, MS, RD, CAS
University of Maine, Orono

Deborah Myers, MS, RD, LD
Bluffton University

J. Dirk Nelson, PhD
Missouri Southern State College

Anne O'Donnell, MS, MPH, RD
Santa Rosa Junior College

Martha Olson, RN, BSN, MS
Iowa Lakes Community College

Rebecca S. Pobocik, PhD, RD
Bowling Green State University

John A. Polagruto, PhD, MS
Sacramento City College

Alayne Ronnenberg, ScD
University of Massachusetts, Amherst

Susan T. Saylor, RD, EdD
Shelton State University

Brian Luke Seaward, PhD
Paramount Wellness Institute

Mohammad R. Shayesteh, PhD, RD, LD
Youngstown State University

LuAnn Soliah, PhD, RD
Baylor University

Bernice Gales Spurlock, PhD
Hinds Community College

Tammy J. Stephenson, PhD
University of Kentucky

James H. Swain, PhD, RD, LD
Case Western Reserve University

Joy E. Swanson, PhD
Cornell University

Priya Venkatesan, MS, RD, CLE
Pasadena City College

Sharonda Wallace, PhD, MPH, RD
California State Polytechnic University

Janelle Walter, PhD
Baylor University

Shahla M. Wunderlich, PhD
Montclair State University

Joseph J Zielinski, MPH, RD
State University of New York, Brockport

Nancy Zwick, MED, RD, LD
Northern Kentucky University

Acknowledgments

We would like to thank the following people for their hard work and dedication. They have helped make this new edition a reality. Thank you to Cindy Kogut for a thorough and careful copyedit; to Julie Bolduc of Jones & Bartlett Learning for shepherding the book through to completion; and to Mark Bergeron, Gail Farrar, and the team at Publishers' Design and Production Services for making this book look so great. We would also like to thank Shoshanna Goldberg, Amy Bloom, Agnes Burt, and Jody Yeskey for giving us help and direction when we needed it.

Thanks also to Virginia Bragg of Utah State University, Anda Lam of Pasadena City College, Betty Forbes of West Virginia University, Marion Birdsall of the University of Pennsylvania, Pamela Fletcher of Albuquerque Technical Vocational Institute, Jeffrey Harris of West Chester University, Janet Anderson of Utah State University, and R. James Barnard of the University of California, Los Angeles, for their insightful reviews of the previous edition.

CHAPTER 1

Food Choices

Nutrients and Nourishment

THINK About It

1 How many different foods have you eaten in the last 24 hours? The last week?

2 Do you have a preference for sweets? Chocolate? Ice cream? If so, where do you think it comes from?

3 What do you think is driving the popularity of vitamins and other supplements?

4 Where do you get the majority of your information about nutrition?

Visit nutrition.jbpub.com

Figure 1.1 **Adventures in eating.** Babies and toddlers are generally willing to try new things.

Friends go out for pizza every Thursday night. A college freshman greets his girlfriend with a box of chocolates. A 5-year-old imitates her parents after they salt their food. A firefighter who is asked to explain why hot dogs are his favorite food says it has something to do with going to baseball games with his father. A professor recently recruited from a Chinese university feels dissatisfied unless she eats a bowl of rice daily. A parent punishes a misbehaving child by withholding dessert. What do these people have in common? They are all using food for something other than its nutrient value. Can you think of a holiday that is not celebrated with food? For most of us, food is more than a collection of nutrients. Many factors affect what we choose to eat. Many of the foods people choose are nourishing and contribute to good health. The same, of course, may be true of the foods we reject.

The science of **nutrition** helps us improve our food choices by identifying the amounts of nutrients we need, the best food sources of those nutrients, and the other components in foods that may be helpful or harmful. Learning about nutrition will help us make better choices and not only improve our health, but also reduce our risk of disease and increase our longevity. Keep in mind, though, that no matter how much you know about nutrition, you are still likely to choose some foods simply for their taste or just because they make you feel good.

nutrition The science of foods and their components (nutrients and other substances), including the relationships to health and disease (actions, interactions, and balances); processes within the body (ingestion, digestion, absorption, transport, functions, and disposal of end products); and the social, economic, cultural, and psychological implications of eating.

neophobia A dislike for anything new or unfamiliar.

Why Do We Eat the Way We Do?

Do you "eat to live" or "live to eat"? For most of us, the first is certainly true—you must eat to live. But there may be times when our enjoyment of food is more important to us than the nourishment we get from it. Factors such as age, gender, genetic makeup, occupation, lifestyle, family, and cultural background affect our daily food choices. We use food to project a desired image, forge relationships, express friendship, show creativity, and disclose our feelings. We cope with anxiety or stress by eating or not eating; we reward ourselves with food for a good grade or a job well done; or, in extreme cases, we punish failures by denying ourselves the benefit and comfort of eating.

Food preferences begin early in life and then change as we interact with parents, friends, and peers. Further experiences with different people, places, and situations often—but not always—cause us to expand or change our preferences. Taste and other sensory factors such as texture are the most important things that influence our food choices; next are cost and convenience.[1] Although what we eat reveals much about who we are, a preference for sweet, salty, and high-fat foods appears to be universal.

Age is a factor in food preferences. Young children prefer sweet or familiar foods; babies and toddlers are generally willing to try new things. (See **Figure 1.1**.) Experimental evidence suggests infants exposed to a variety of flavors are even more likely to accept novel foods.[2] Preschoolers typically go through a period of food **neophobia** (a dislike for anything new or unfamiliar), school-aged children tend to accept a wider array of foods, and teenagers are strongly influenced by the preferences and habits of their peers. If you track the kinds of foods you have eaten in the past year, you might be surprised to discover how few basic foods your diet includes. By the time we reach adulthood, we have formed a core group of foods we prefer. Of this group, only about 100 basic items account for 75 percent of our food intake.

Like many aspects of human behavior, food choices are influenced by both inborn (biological) and environmental factors, and it's not always easy to separate them. However, we can look at food preferences in terms of the

Figure 1.2 **Factors that affect food choices.** We often select a food to eat automatically, without thought. But in fact, our choices are complex events involving the interactions of a multitude of factors.

sensory properties of foods, cognitive factors that influence our choices, and environmental influences such as culture. Exploring each of these areas may help you understand why you prefer certain foods. (See **Figure 1.2**.)

flavor The collective experience that describes both taste and smell.

umami [ooh-MA-mee] A Japanese term that describes a delicious meaty or savory sensation. Chemically, this taste detects the presence of glutamate.

Sensory Influences: Taste, Texture, and Smell

In making food choices, we are drawn to what appeals to our senses. People often refer to **flavor** as a collective experience that describes both taste and smell. Texture is also part of the picture.[3] You may prefer foods that have a crisp, chewy, or smooth texture. You may reject foods that feel grainy, slimy, or rubbery. Other sensory characteristics that affect food choice are color, moisture, and temperature.

We are familiar with the classic four tastes—sweet, sour, bitter, and salty—but studies show that there are more. One of these additional taste sensations is **umami**, which is a Japanese term for the taste produced by glutamate.[4] Glutamate is an amino acid (a building block of protein) that is found in monosodium glutamate (MSG). It gives food a distinctive meaty or savory taste. The way we experience different tastes can be affected by our genetic makeup. Researchers have identified a single gene that determines whether a person can taste a certain intensely bitter substance. This may help explain why some people love broccoli but others cannot bear the bitter taste.[5]

Cognitive Influences

Along with our experiences, our thoughts and feelings about food influence decisions about what to eat and when. We call these factors *cognitive* influences because they affect our thinking and the decisions we make.

Quick Bite

Sweetness and Salt

Salt can do more than just make your food taste salty. Researchers at the Monell Chemical Senses Center demonstrated that salt also suppresses the bitter flavors in foods. When combined with chocolate, in a chocolate-covered pretzel, for example, salt blocks some of the bitter flavor, making the chocolate taste sweeter. This may explain why people in many cultures salt their fruit.

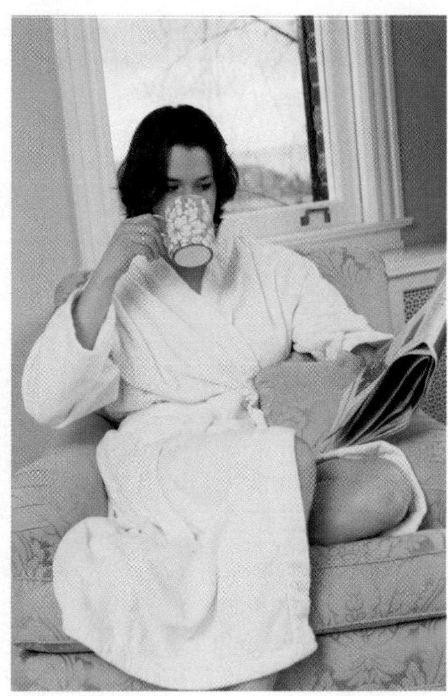

Figure 1.3 **Comfort foods.** Depending on your childhood food experiences, a bowl of traditional soup, a remembered sweet, or a mug of hot chocolate can provide comfort in times of stress.

Day-to-Day Influences on Food Choices: Habits

Your eating and cooking habits are likely to reflect what you learned from your parents. We typically learn to eat three meals a day, at about the same times each day. Quite often we eat the same foods, particularly for breakfast (e.g., cereal and milk) and lunch (e.g., sandwiches). This routine makes life convenient, and we don't have to think much about when or what to eat. But we don't have to follow this routine! How would you feel about eating mashed potatoes for breakfast and cereal for dinner? Some people might get a stomachache just thinking about it, whereas others may enjoy the prospect of doing things differently. Look at your eating habits and see how often you make the same choices every single day.

Comfort and Discomfort Foods

Our desire for particular foods is often based on behavioral motives, even though we are not always aware of them. For some people, food becomes an emotional security blanket. Consuming our favorite foods can make us feel better, relieve stress, and allay anxiety. (See **Figure 1.3**.) Starting with the first days of life, food and affection are intertwined. Infants experience both physical and psychological satisfaction when eating. As we grow older, this experience is continually reinforced. For example, chicken soup and hot tea with honey are favorites when we feel under the weather because Mom and Dad fixed them especially for us. If we were rewarded for good behavior with a particular food (e.g., ice cream, candy, cookies), our positive feelings about that food may persist for a lifetime. The foods that we associate with positive childhood experiences often continue to generate secure and supportive feelings.

In contrast, children who have negative associations with certain foods are unlikely to choose those foods as adults. Maybe you avoid a certain food

Quick Bite

What Is an Ice Cream Headache?

After ingesting a cold substance quickly, such as when you take a big bite of ice cream, you may experience what is commonly known as an ice cream headache, or brain freeze. When cold substances touch the back part of the palate, blood vessels, including those that go to the brain, constrict (tighten), resulting in a sharp pain in the mid-frontal part of the brain. About one-third of the population experience this phenomenon.

because you know it will make you sick. Chances are that at some point in your childhood, you got sick soon after eating that food, and consequently the two events are linked forever in your mind. Repeated power struggles with your parents over a helping of broccoli or zucchini may have turned you away from eating those vegetables. Fortunately, these behaviors can be reversed. Psychologists have shown us that negative associations are easier to extinguish than positive ones. Thus, time and the knowledge that vegetables are beneficial may help us overcome negative associations.

Food Cravings

THINK About It 2

Chocolates for breakfast? Only if you are one of those people who can't survive more than one waking hour without a chocolate rush. Is the intense desire or craving for a particular food psychological or physiological? It's likely to be both, and these factors may interact to increase the intensity of the desire. Add ice cream to chocolate and you have the top two candidates on the food craver's agenda. The use of chocolate and ice cream as rewards in early childhood often sets the stage for later cravings.

Some people offer a nutritional explanation for food cravings: the body senses a nutrient deficit that triggers the desire for a food rich in that nutrient. Some claim that the practice of eating nonfood items such as dirt, clay, and laundry starch results from nutrient deficits. The craving for and consumption of such substances is called **pica** and is often associated with pregnancy. It has been suggested that iron deficiency drives the pregnant woman's craving so that she seeks iron in any form possible, including dirt. In some groups, family traditions and cultural acceptance of pica have made it an expected behavior during pregnancy. Although research has shown an association between lowered iron status and pica,[6] it has not shown conclusively whether pica is a cause or an effect of iron deficiency.[7]

pica The craving for and consumption of nonfood items such as dirt, clay, or laundry starch.

Advertising and Promotion

It may not surprise you that some of the most popular food products are high-fat and high-sugar baked goods and alcoholic beverages. Aggressive and sometimes deceptive advertising programs can influence people to buy foods of poor nutritional quality. However, we are seeing more innovative and aggressive advertising from the commodity boards that promote milk, meat, cranberries, and other more nutrient-dense products.

Consumers make an estimated 70 percent of their food purchase decisions while shopping, rather than before arriving at the market. Accurate nutritional information in the supermarket aisles can improve food choices.[8] Advertising like that in **Figure 1.4**, for example, can be helpful, especially to consumers whose diets need improvement. In the mid-1980s, Kellogg's launched a print and television ad campaign for All-Bran cereal to suggest that a high-fiber diet would reduce the risk of cancer. Not only did sales of All-Bran increase dramatically in the months that followed, but also the sales of all high-fiber cereals increased.[9] When the oat bran craze first hit in the late 1980s, sales of oat bran products by the Quaker Oats Company increased 700 percent in one year.

The popularity of different diets drives changes in food products. Beginning in the late 1980s, low-fat diets became popular and were accompanied by an explosion of reduced-fat, low-fat, and fat-free products. In fact, between 1987 and 2004 over 35,000 such products were introduced.[10] When the "low-carb" diet swung back into popularity, so did the rise in low-carb or no-carb products—nearly 3,500 in 2003 and 2004 alone.

Quick Bite

Dining on Clay

Can geophagy, the practice of eating clay, actually improve nutritional status? When the clay eaten by some West African and black American groups was chemically analyzed, scientists found high levels of calcium, magnesium, potassium, copper, zinc, and iron. However, in a test that simulates the effects in the gastrointestinal tract, the soil reduced absorption of iron, copper, and zinc.

Figure 1.4 **Healthy advertising.** An example of a successful healthy advertising campaign.

Social Factors

Social factors exert a powerful influence on food choice. By observing their parents, infants and children learn which foods and combinations of foods are appropriate to consume and under what circumstances. Perhaps even more influential, though, are the messages from peers about what to eat or how to eat.[11] Although food neophobia is common among children, it can often be overcome when they see another child enjoying a food they have yet to sample. With age and increased social contact, children and teens are likely to adopt not only food preferences from peers, but also their eccentric preparations: "Mark eats his sandwiches in triangles; that's the way I want mine!"

As **Figure 1.5** illustrates, eating is also a social event that brings together different people for a variety of purposes (e.g., religious or cultural celebrations, business meetings, and family dinners). Thanks to **social facilitation**, food intake increases because of the social climate surrounding its consumption.[12] Social pressures, however, can also restrict our food intake and selection. We might, for example, order nonmeat dishes when dining with a group of vegetarian friends.

social facilitation Encouragement of the interactions between people.

Nutrition and Health Beliefs

Who do you turn to for reliable nutrition advice? (See **Figure 1.6**.) Information about food and nutrition is abundant. Why do some people ignore health information and indulge themselves with foods that may lead to health problems, whereas others take the same information and commit themselves to a healthful diet? To examine these questions, we need to consider the health beliefs of consumers, their perceptions of susceptibility to disease, and whether they can take action to prevent or delay its onset. For instance, if people feel vulnerable to disease and believe that dietary change will lead to positive results, they are more likely to pay attention to information about links between dietary choices, dietary fat, and risks for heart disease and cancer. A desire to lose weight can be a powerful force shaping decisions to accept or reject particular foods.[13] Information about nutrient content on food labels along with health claims that describe links between food components and diseases aid consumers who are trying to make positive choices.

Figure 1.5 **Social facilitation.** Interactions with others can affect your eating behavior.

Key Concepts *Many factors influence our decisions about what to eat and when to eat. The four main factors are taste, texture, cost, and convenience. Habits, experiences, social factors, advertising, and knowledge of relationships between food and health also influence our food decisions.*

Environmental Influences

Your environment—where you live, how you live, who you live with—has a lot to do with what you choose to eat. People around us influence our food choices, and we prefer the foods we grew up eating. Environmental factors that influence our food choices include economics, lifestyle, culture, and religion.

Economics

Where you live and the surrounding climate influence which foods are most accessible to you. Environmental factors such as location and climate also affect food costs, a major determinant of food choice. You may have "lobster taste" but a "hot dog budget." The types of foods purchased and the percentage of income used for food are affected by total income. Wealthier households spend only about 7 percent of their after-tax income on food, whereas low-income families spend nearly 25 percent of their income on food.[14] We often assume that wealthier households have more nutritious diets because they can afford to purchase higher-quality lean meats, more fish and seafood, and more fruits and vegetables. Analysis of fruit and vegetable expenditures shows that low-income households spend significantly less on fruits and vegetables; in any given week, nearly 20 percent of low-income households bought no fruits or vegetables.[15] This supports theories that limited finances shift food

Figure 1.6 **Where do you get your nutrition information?** We are constantly bombarded by food messages. Which sources do you find most influential? Are they also the most reliable?

Going Green

Are you familiar with the terms *eco-friendly*, *carbon footprint*, *greenhouse gases*, *global climate*, and *global warming*? These recently coined phrases reflect new perspectives on our interrelated world, signaling our recent awareness of an environment in trouble. Our continuing abuse of our environment has resulted in a global climatic backlash, with widespread disruptions threatening irreversible damage to our planet. The result would be a far less livable planet that is inhospitable to a way of life we have taken for granted for much too long. Some green protesters are taking action. For example, to stop Brazilian planters from destroying more rainforest to cultivate their soy plantations, some soya traders refuse to sell soy from deforested areas of the Amazon.

In this revision of *Nutrition* we focus on our nutrition environment. In each chapter you will see a brief feature entitled "Going Green," which will relate an environmental concern to the chapter's topic. Here are several examples of the new green technology. Only three kinds of plants supply 65 percent of the global food supply. You might be surprised to learn that they are rice, wheat, and corn. With amazing efficiency farmers can turn plant products into animal protein with aquaculture, a fancy word for fish farming, which has realized the fastest growth of global food production and now accounts for more than 30 percent of fish consumption in the world. Again, whereas modern agricultural methods depend heavily on fertilizers, pesticides, and herbicides, newer ecologically friendly farming technologies are increasingly being used to lower costs and preserve the quality of soils. And although surrounded by controversy, genetically modified crops and foods are used to resist pests and increase yields and are finding a niche in our nutrition environment.

Are you taking part in the green revolution? What are your environmental concerns?

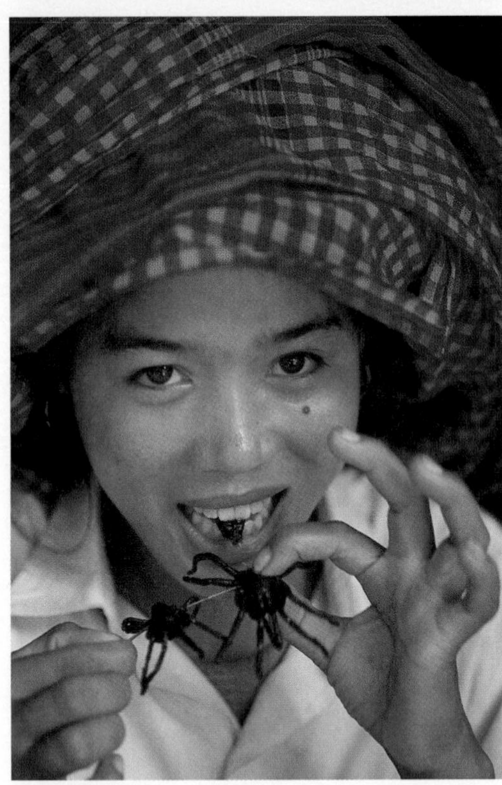

Figure 1.7 **Cultural influences.** If you were visiting China, would you sample the local delicacy—deep-fried scorpion?

choices toward inexpensive high-fat, high-sugar choices.[16] But does a healthier diet necessarily cost more? Analysis by the U.S. Department of Agriculture found that consumers can eat three servings of fruits and four servings of vegetables daily for only 64 cents.[17]

Lifestyle

Another influential factor is lifestyle. Our fast-paced society has little time or patience for food preparation. Forty percent of our food dollars are spent away from home. Convenience foods, from frozen entrees to complete meals "in a box," saturate supermarket shelves. Current trends suggest that we're eating at home more often, but what we eat there frequently is store-bought ready-to-eat or heat-and-eat food.[18]

Cultural Influences

One of the strongest influences on food preferences is tradition or cultural background. In all societies, no matter how simple or complex, eating is the primary way of initiating and maintaining human relationships. Sometimes these culturally acquired preferences can seem quite peculiar to those of a different culture. The college student who serves pickled herring to her friends may have learned to enjoy it from her Jewish parents, who introduced it to her as a child in comforting surroundings. Likewise, it is not uncommon for people of Mexican heritage to enjoy eating hot peppers, which were introduced to them early in life in highly gregarious social settings.

The Japanese boast the longest life spans in the world. Can we attribute their increased longevity to nutrition? In part, yes! Studies have shown that Japanese immigrants to the United States who have acquired Western tastes in food also have an increased incidence of heart disease and cancer.[19] What do the Japanese eat? Consumed with almost every meal, rice is an important food in Japan. Equally important in the Japanese diet are fish and the heart-healthy oils it contains. People in Japan consume an average of 3 ounces of fish per day.[20]

Rice is also an important staple in China. A traditional Chinese breakfast is a bowl of rice congee (rice gruel cooked with bits of meat) served with pickles or another salty side dish and tea. Lunch includes soup, rice, and dishes of vegetables mixed with fish, meat, or poultry. Lunch can also be a bowl of noodle soup. Dinner, the main meal of the day, is a larger version of lunch. Meals are communal; dishes are placed in the center of the table and shared by all.

To a large extent, culture defines our attitudes. "One man's food is another man's poison." Look at **Figure 1.7**. How does the photo make you feel? Insects, maggots, and entrails are delicacies to some, whereas just the thought of ingesting them is enough to make others retch. So powerful are cultural forces that if you were permitted only a single question to establish someone's food preferences, a good choice would be "What is your ethnic background?"[21]

Knowledge, beliefs, customs, and habits all are defining elements of human culture.[22] Although genetic characteristics tie people of ethnic groups together, culture is a learned behavior and consequently can be modified through education, experience, and social and political trends.[23]

In many cultures, food has symbolic meanings related to family traditions, social status, and even health.[24] Indeed, many folk remedies rely on food. Some of these have gained wide acceptance, such as the use of spices and herbal teas for purposes ranging from allaying anxiety to preventing cancer

Quick Bite

Nerve Poison for Dinner?

The puffer fish is a delicacy in Japan. Danger is part of its appeal: eating a puffer fish can be life threatening! The puffer fish contains a poison called tetrodotoxin (TTX), which blocks the transmission of nerve signals and can lead to death. Chefs who prepare the puffer fish must have special training and licenses to prepare the fish properly, so diners feel nothing more than a slight numbing feeling.

and heart disease.[25] Traditional medical practices in many cultures follow the belief that nature is composed of two opposing forces (e.g., yin and yang in traditional Chinese medicine). It is typically believed that good health reflects a balance of the two opposing forces. Excesses in either direction cause illness, which then must be treated by giving foods of the opposite force. This idea of balance, accompanied by terms describing illness and foods as either "hot" or "cold," is also found in other Asian cultures, including India and the Philippines, and in Latin American cultures.

Just as cultural distinctions eventually blur when ethnic groups take part in the larger American culture, so do many of the unique expectations about the ability of certain foods to prevent disease, restore health among those with various afflictions, or enhance longevity. These beliefs are still apparent, however, in older, less assimilated groups. Food habits are among the last practices to change when an immigrant adapts to a new culture.[26]

Quick Bite

The Lima Bean

The lima bean has been in cultivation in Peru since 6000 B.C.E. Not so coincidentally, Peru's capital is Lima.

Religion

Food is an important part of religious rites, symbols, and customs. Some religious rules apply to everyday eating, whereas others are concerned with special celebrations.

Christianity, Judaism, Hinduism, Buddhism, and Islam all have distinct dietary laws, but within each religion different interpretations of these laws give rise to variations in dietary practices. For example, Jewish dietary laws specify the foods that are "fit and proper," or *kosher*, to eat. To be kosher, meat must come from clean animals that chew their cud and have cloven hooves. Fish must have fins and scales. Pork, crustaceans and shellfish, and birds of prey are not acceptable. The Orthodox laws of Judaism prohibit eating meat and milk at the same meal or even preparing or serving them with the same dishes and utensils. Islam identifies acceptable foods as *halal* and has rules similar to those of Judaism for slaughtering animals. Islamic faith prohibits the consumption of pork, the flesh of clawed animals, alcohol, and other intoxicating drugs. Intoxicating beverages are also prohibited in Buddhism.[27] The Church of Jesus Christ of Latter Day Saints disapproves of coffee, tea, and alcoholic beverages. Most Hindus are vegetarians and do not eat eggs. The Jain religion (in India) forbids eating meat or animal products (milk, eggs, etc.) and anything grown in darkness (e.g., potatoes or garlic).

Religious rules may also define when and how often we eat. During the holy month of Ramadan, Muslims fast from dawn to sunset. They consume two meals per day, one before the sunrise and one after sunset.[28] Religious laws (e.g., the traditional Catholic practice of substituting fish for meat on Fridays during Lent) also define the types of foods eaten on specific occasions.[29]

Cultural Cuisine

Diet and culture affect each other. Each contributes to the identity of the other, and both help to define our values, preferences, and practices. As a result, neither is abandoned easily or quickly, even in the face of changing world events. Even so, the question arises: What impact will our increasing mobility have on food choice? Cultural interactions and exposure to various cuisines will undoubtedly increase. Will this ultimately lead to a heightened appreciation and preservation of different culinary practices or the formation of a single new hybrid cuisine?

Key Concepts *The cultural environments in which people grow up have a major influence on what foods they prefer, what foods they consider edible, and what foods they eat* *in combination and at what time of day. Many factors work to define a group's culture: economics, geographic location, traditions, and religious beliefs. As people from other cultures immigrate to new lands, they will adopt new behaviors consistent with their new homes. However, food habits are among the last to change.*

Quick Bite

America's Favorite Vegetables

When Americans eat vegetables, they are most likely to eat potatoes (especially french fries), tomatoes (usually part of tomato sauce or ketchup), onions, and iceberg lettuce.

The American Diet

What, then, is a typical *American* diet? As a country influenced by the practices of both Native Americans and immigrants, there is no easy, single answer to this question. The U.S. diet is as diverse as Americans themselves. Many people around the world imagine that the American diet consists mainly of hamburgers, french fries, and cola drinks! Our fondness for fast food and the marketability of such restaurants overseas make them seem like icons of American culture. And many of the stereotypes are true. The most commonly consumed grain product in the United States is white bread, the favorite meat is beef, and the most frequently eaten vegetable is the potato, usually as french fries. Despite the variety available to us, the American diet is still heavy on meat and potatoes and light on fruits and whole grains. We also are eating more cereals, snack foods, soft drinks, and noncitrus juices than ever before.[30]

So, how healthful is the "American" diet? Although we are bombarded with information about health and nutrition, this doesn't necessarily translate into better food choices. People are not "natural nutritionists"; that is, they don't know instinctively which foods to choose for good health. The majority of the population has never taken a course in nutrition. They probably will never take the time to become well-informed consumers—not just of food, but also of information about food and nutrition. So it is probably not surprising when national surveys indicate that although Americans *know* that nutrition and food choices are important factors in health, few have made the recommended changes (e.g., eating less fat, sugar, and salt and more fruits and vegetables).[31]

You are in a position to gather more information than the average consumer. By taking this course in nutrition, you will be getting the full story: the nutrients we need for good health, the science behind the health messages, and the food choices it will take to implement them. Whether you use this information is up to you, but at least you will be a well-informed consumer!

Key Concepts *"American" cuisine is truly a melting pot of cultural contributions to foods and tastes. Although Americans receive and believe many messages about the role of diet in good health, these beliefs do not always translate into better food choices.*

Introducing the Nutrients

Although we give food meaning through our culture and experience and make dietary decisions based on many factors, ultimately the reason for eating is to obtain nourishment—nutrition.

Just like your body, food is a mixture of chemicals, some of which are essential for normal body function. These essential chemicals are called **nutrients**. You need nutrients for normal growth and development, for maintaining cells and tissues, for fuel to do physical and metabolic work, and for regulating the hundreds of thousands of body processes that go on inside you every second of every day. Further, food must provide these nutrients; the body either cannot make these **essential nutrients** or cannot make enough of

nutrients Any substances in food that the body can use to obtain energy, synthesize tissues, or regulate functions.

essential nutrients Substances that must be obtained from the diet because the body either cannot make them or cannot make adequate amounts of them.

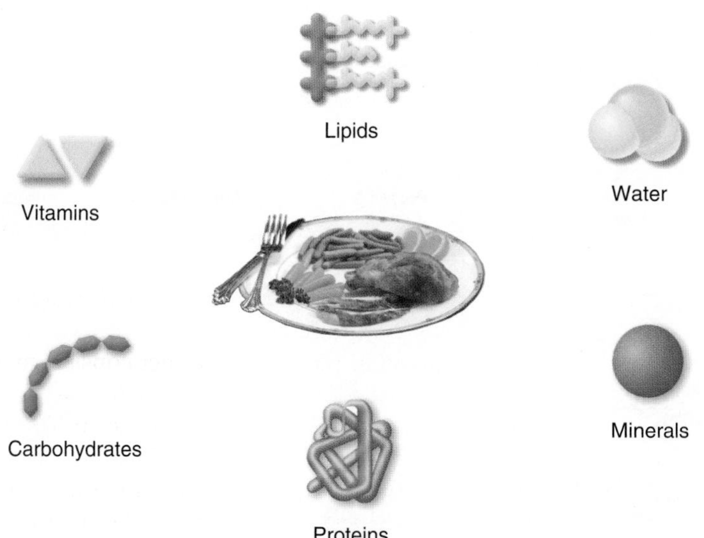

Figure 1.8 **The six classes of nutrients.** Water is our most important nutrient, and we cannot survive long without it. Because our bodies need large quantities of carbohydrate, protein, and fat, they are called macronutrients. Our bodies need comparatively small amounts of vitamins and minerals, so they are called micronutrients.

them. There are six classes of nutrients in food: *carbohydrates, lipids* (fats and oils), *proteins, vitamins, minerals,* and *water*. (See **Figure 1.8**.) The minimum diet for human growth, development, and maintenance must supply about 45 essential nutrients.

Definition of Nutrients

In studying nutrition, we focus on the functions of nutrients in the body so that we can see why they are important in the diet. However, to define a nutrient in technical terms, we focus on what happens in its absence. A nutrient is a chemical whose absence from the diet for a long enough time results in a specific change in health; we say that a person has a deficiency of that nutrient. A lack of vitamin C, for example, will eventually lead to scurvy. A diet with too little iron will result in iron-deficiency anemia. To complete the definition of a nutrient, it also must be true that putting the essential chemical back in the diet will reverse the change in health, if done before permanent damage occurs. If taken early enough, supplements of vitamin A can reverse the effects of deficiency on the eyes. If not, prolonged vitamin A deficiency can cause permanent blindness.

Nutrients are not the only chemicals in food. Other substances add flavor and color, some contribute to texture, and others, such as caffeine, have physiological effects on the body. Some substances in food, such as fiber, have important health benefits (as you will discover in Chapter 4) but do not fit the classical definition of a nutrient. One of the newest areas of research in nutrition is the area of **phytochemicals**. Although these "plant chemicals" are not nutrients, they have important health functions, such as **antioxidant** activity, which may reduce risk for heart disease or cancer (see "Spotlight on Complementary Nutrition").

The six classes of nutrients serve three general functions: they provide energy (fuel), regulate body processes, and contribute to body structures (see **Figure 1.9**). Although virtually all nutrients can be said to regulate body processes, and many contribute to body structures, only proteins, carbohydrates, and fats are sources of energy. Because the body needs large quantities of carbohydrates, proteins, and fats, they are called **macronutrients** (see Chapters 4, 5, and 6); vitamins and minerals are called **micronutrients** because the body needs comparatively small amounts of these nutrients (see Chapters 10, 11, 12, and 13).

phytochemicals Substances in plants that may possess health-protective effects, even though they are not essential for life.

antioxidant A substance that combines with or otherwise neutralizes a free radical, thus preventing oxidative damage to cells and tissues.

macronutrients Nutrients, such as carbohydrate, fat, or protein, that are needed in relatively large amounts in the diet.

micronutrients Nutrients, such as vitamins and minerals, that are needed in relatively small amounts in the diet.

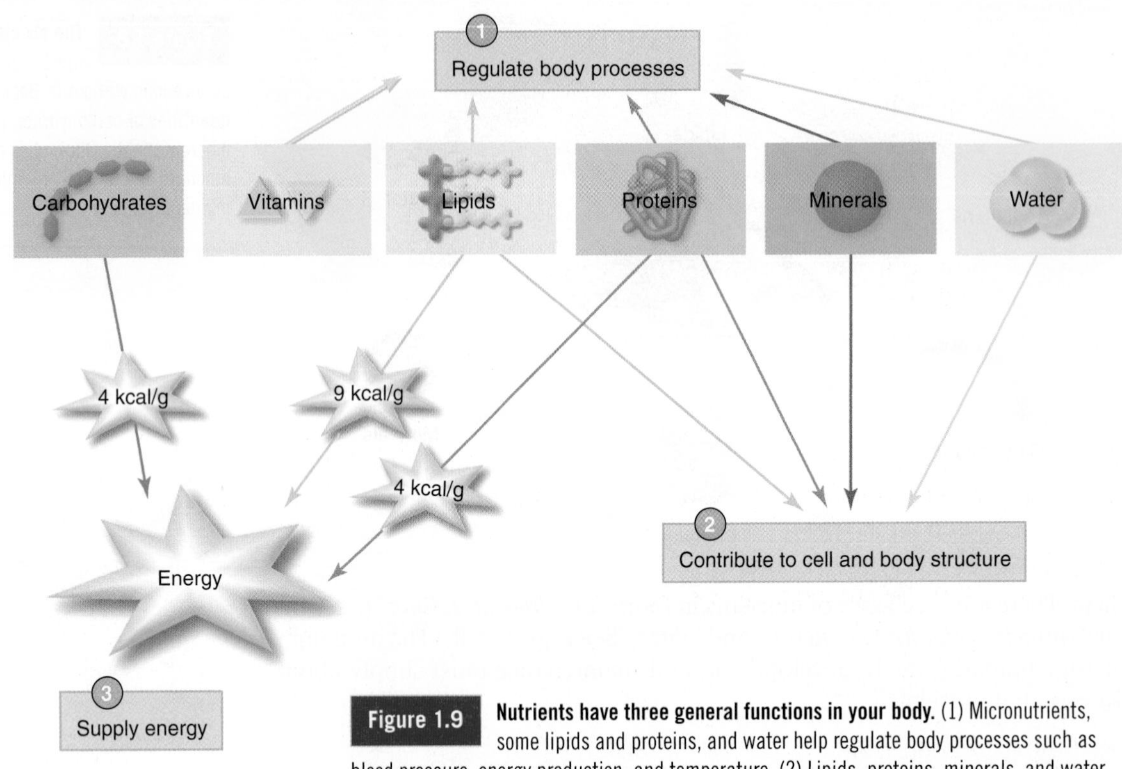

Figure 1.9 **Nutrients have three general functions in your body.** (1) Micronutrients, some lipids and proteins, and water help regulate body processes such as blood pressure, energy production, and temperature. (2) Lipids, proteins, minerals, and water help provide structure to bone, muscle, and other cells. (3) Macronutrients supply energy to power muscle contractions and cellular functions.

organic In chemistry, any compound that contains carbon, except carbon oxides (e.g., carbon dioxide) and sulfides and metal carbonates (e.g., potassium carbonate). The term *organic* also is used to denote crops that are grown without synthetic fertilizers or chemicals.

inorganic Any substance that does not contain carbon, excepting certain simple carbon compounds such as carbon dioxide and monoxide. Common examples include table salt (sodium chloride) and baking soda (sodium bicarbonate).

In addition to their functions, there are several other key differences among the classes of nutrients. First, the chemical composition of nutrients varies widely. One way to divide the nutrient groups is based on whether the compounds contain the element carbon. Substances that contain carbon are **organic** substances; those that do not are **inorganic**. Carbohydrates, lipids, proteins, and vitamins are all organic; minerals and water are not. Structurally, nutrients can be very simple—minerals such as sodium are single elements, although we often consume them as larger compounds (e.g., sodium chloride, which is table salt). Water is also very simple in structure. The organic nutrients have more complex structures—the carbohydrates, lipids, and proteins we eat are made of smaller building blocks, whereas the vitamins are elaborately structured compounds.

It is rare for a food to contain just one nutrient. Meat is not just protein any more than bread is solely carbohydrate. Foods contain mixtures of nutrients, although in most cases protein, fat, or carbohydrate dominates. So although bread is certainly rich in carbohydrates, it also contains some protein, a little fat, and many vitamins and minerals. If it's whole-grain bread you're eating, you also get fiber, which is not technically a nutrient, but is an important compound for good health nonetheless.

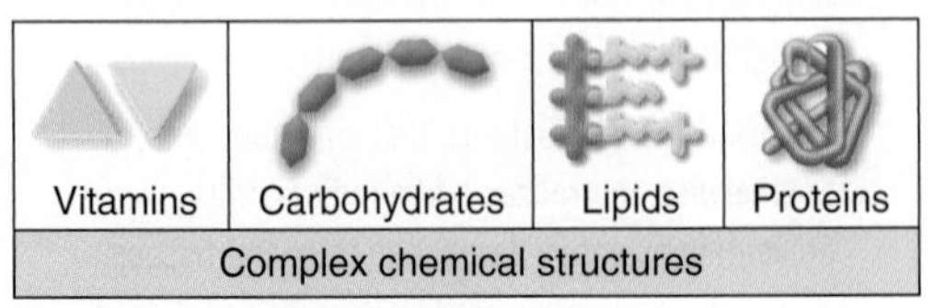

Organic – contains carbon

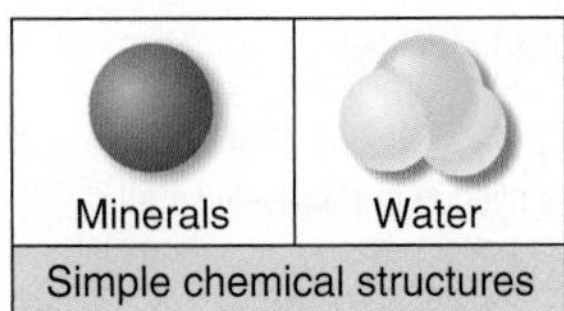

Inorganic – no carbon

Key Concepts *Nutrients are the essential chemicals in food that the body needs for normal functioning and good health and that must come from the diet because they either cannot be made in the body or cannot be made in sufficient quantities. Six classes of nutrients—carbohydrates, proteins, lipids, vitamins, minerals, and water—can be described by their composition or by their function in the body.*

Carbohydrates

If you think of water when you hear the word *hydrate*, then the word *carbohydrate*, or literally "hydrate of carbon," tells you exactly what this nutrient is made of. **Carbohydrates** are made of carbon, hydrogen, and oxygen and are a major source of fuel for the body. Dietary carbohydrates are the starches and sugars found in grains, vegetables, legumes (dry beans and peas), and fruits. We also get carbohydrates from dairy products, but practically none from meats. Your body converts most dietary carbohydrates to glucose, a simple sugar compound. It is glucose that we find in **circulation**, providing a source of energy for cells and tissues. (See Chapter 4, "Carbohydrates.")

Whenever you see this icon, we'll be talking about **carbohydrates**

Provide:
Energy (4 kcal/g)

Lipids

The term **lipids** refers to substances we know as fats and oils, but also to fatlike substances in foods, such as cholesterol and phospholipids. Lipids are organic compounds and, like carbohydrates, contain carbon, hydrogen, and oxygen. Fats and oils—or, more correctly, **triglycerides**—are another major fuel source for the body. In addition, triglycerides, cholesterol, and phospholipids have other important functions: providing structure for body cells, carrying the fat-soluble vitamins (A, D, E, and K), and providing the starting material (cholesterol) for making many **hormones**. Dietary sources of lipids include the fats and oils we cook with or add to foods, the naturally occurring fats in meats and dairy products, and less obvious plant sources, such as coconut, olives, and avocado. (See Chapter 5, "Lipids.")

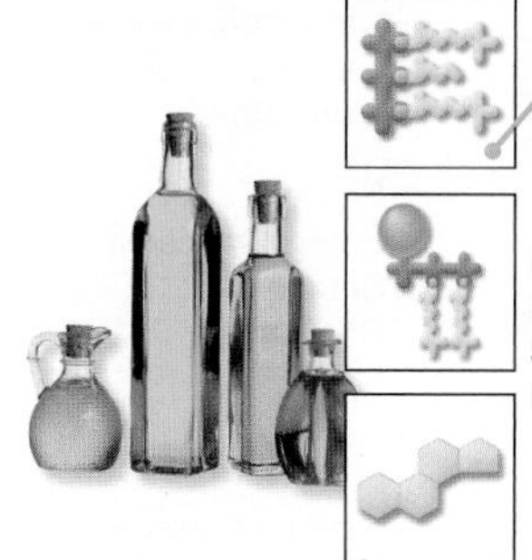

Whenever you see one of these 3 icons, we'll be talking about **lipids**

Provide:
Energy (9 kcal/g)
Structure
Regulation (hormones)

Proteins

Proteins are organic compounds made of smaller building blocks called **amino acids**. Unlike carbohydrates and lipids, amino acids contain nitrogen as well as carbon, hydrogen, and oxygen. Some amino acids also contain the mineral sulfur. The amino acids that we get from dietary protein combine with the amino acids made in the body to make hundreds of different body proteins. Body proteins help build and maintain body structures and regulate body processes. Protein also can be used for energy.

Proteins are found in a variety of foods, but meats and dairy products are among the most concentrated sources. Grains, **legumes**, and vegetables all contribute protein to the diet, while fruits contribute negligible amounts. (See Chapter 6, "Proteins and Amino Acids.")

Vitamins

Vitamins are organic compounds that contain carbon, hydrogen, and perhaps nitrogen, oxygen, phosphorus, sulfur, or other elements. Vitamins regulate body processes such as energy production, blood clotting, and calcium balance. Vitamins help to keep organs and tissues functioning and healthy. Because vitamins have such diverse functions, a lack of a particular vitamin can have widespread effects. Although the body does not break down vitamins to yield energy, vitamins have vital roles in the extraction of energy from carbohydrate, fat, and protein.

Vitamins are usually divided into two groups: fat-soluble and water-soluble. The four fat-soluble vitamins—A, D, E, and K—have very diverse roles. What they have in common is the way they are absorbed and transported in the body and the fact that they are more likely to be stored in larger quantities than the water-soluble vitamins. The water-soluble vitamins include vitamin C

carbohydrates Compounds, including sugars, starches, and dietary fibers, that usually have the general chemical formula $(CH_2O)n$, where *n* represents the number of CH_2O units in the molecule. Carbohydrates are a major source of energy for body functions.

circulation Movement of substances through the vessels of the cardiovascular or lymphatic system.

lipids A group of fat-soluble compounds that includes triglycerides, sterols, and phospholipids.

triglycerides Fats composed of three fatty acid chains linked to a glycerol molecule.

hormones Chemical messengers that are secreted into the blood by one tissue and act on cells in another part of the body.

proteins Large, complex compounds consisting of many amino acids connected in varying sequences and forming unique shapes.

amino acids Organic compounds that function as the building blocks of protein.

legumes A family of plants with edible seed pods, such as peas, beans, lentils and soybeans; also called pulses.

vitamins Organic compounds necessary for reproduction, growth, and maintenance of the body. Vitamins are required in miniscule amounts.

and eight B vitamins: thiamin (B_1), riboflavin (B_2), niacin (B_3), pyridoxine (B_6), cobalamin (B_{12}), folate, pantothenic acid, and biotin. Most of the B vitamins are involved in some way with the pathways for energy metabolism.

Vitamins are found in a wide variety of foods, not just fruits and vegetables—although these are important sources—but also meats, grains, legumes, dairy products, and even fats. Choosing a well-balanced diet usually makes vitamin supplements unnecessary. In fact, when taken in large doses, vitamin supplements—especially those containing vitamins A, D, B_6, or niacin—can be harmful. (See Chapters 10 and 11.)

THINK About It 3

Whenever you see this icon, we'll be talking about **proteins**

Provide:
Energy (4 kcal/g)
Structure
Regulation

Whenever you see these icons, we'll be talking about **vitamins**

Provide:
Regulation

Whenever you see this icon, we'll be talking about **minerals**

Provide:
Structure
Regulation

Minerals

Structurally, **minerals** are simple inorganic substances. At least 16 minerals are essential to health; among them are sodium, chloride, potassium, calcium, phosphorus, and magnesium. Because the body needs these minerals in relatively large quantities compared with other minerals, they are often called **macrominerals**. The body needs the remaining minerals only in very small amounts. These **microminerals**, or **trace minerals**, include iron, zinc, copper, manganese, molybdenum, selenium, iodine, and fluoride. As with vitamins, the functions of minerals are diverse. Minerals can be found in structural roles (e.g., calcium, phosphorus, and fluoride in bones and teeth) as well as regulatory roles (e.g., control of fluid balance and regulation of muscle contraction).

Food sources of minerals are just as diverse. Although we often associate minerals with animal foods, such as meats and milk, plant foods are important sources as well. Deficiencies of minerals, except iron and perhaps calcium, are uncommon. A balanced diet provides enough minerals for most people. However, individuals with iron-deficiency anemia may need iron supplements, and others may need calcium supplements if they cannot or will not drink milk or eat dairy products. As is true for vitamins, excessive intake of some minerals as supplements can be toxic. (See Chapters 12 and 13.)

Water

Next to the mineral elements, water is chemically the simplest nutrient. Water is also the most important nutrient! We can survive far longer without any of the other nutrients in the diet—indeed, without food at all—than we can without water. Water has many roles in the body, including temperature control, lubrication of joints, and transportation of nutrients and wastes.

Because your body is nearly 60 percent water, regular fluid intake to maintain adequate hydration is important. Water is found not only in beverages, but also in most food products. Fruits and vegetables in particular are high in water content. Through many chemical reactions, the body makes some of its own water, but this is only a fraction of the amount needed for normal function. (See Chapter 12, "Water and Major Minerals.")

Key Concepts *The body needs larger amounts of carbohydrates, lipids, and proteins (macronutrients) than vitamins and minerals (micronutrients). Carbohydrates, lipids, and proteins provide energy; proteins, vitamins, minerals, water, and some fatty acids regulate body processes; and proteins, lipids, minerals, and water contribute to body structure.*

minerals Inorganic compounds needed for growth and for regulation of body processes.

macrominerals Major minerals required in the diet and present in the body in large amounts compared with trace minerals.

microminerals See *trace minerals.*

trace minerals Trace minerals are present in the body and required in the diet in relatively small amounts compared with major minerals. Also known as microminerals.

energy The capacity to do work. The energy in food is chemical energy, which the body converts to mechanical, electrical, or heat energy.

Nutrients and Energy

One major reason we eat food, and the nutrients it contains, is for **energy**. Every cellular reaction, every muscle movement, every nerve impulse requires energy. Three of the nutrient classes—carbohydrates, lipids (triglycerides only), and proteins—are energy sources. When we speak of the energy in foods, we are really talking about the *potential* energy that foods contain. Energy itself is not a food component.

Different scientific disciplines use different measures of energy. In nutrition, we discuss the potential energy in food, or the body's use of energy, in units of heat called **kilocalories** (1,000 calories). One kilocalorie (or kcal) is the amount of energy (heat) it would take to raise the temperature of 1 kilogram (kg) of water by 1 degree Celsius. For now, this may be an abstract concept, but as you learn more about nutrition, you will discover how much energy you likely need to fuel your daily activities. You will also learn about the amounts of potential energy in various foods.

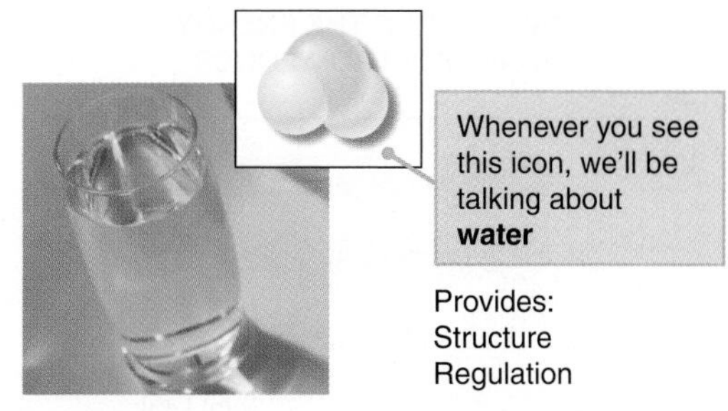

kilocalories (kcal) [KILL-oh-kal-oh-rees] Units used to measure energy. Food energy is measured in kilocalories (1,000 calories = 1 kilocalorie).

calorie The general term for energy in food, used synonymously with the term *energy.* Often used instead of *kilocalorie* on food labels, in diet books, and in other sources of nutrition information.

Energy in Foods

Energy is available from foods because foods contain carbohydrate, fat, and protein. These nutrients can be broken down completely (metabolized) to yield energy in a form that cells can use. When completely metabolized in the body, carbohydrate and protein yield 4 kilocalories of energy for every gram (g) consumed; fat yields 9 kilocalories per gram; and alcohol contributes 7 kilocalories per gram. (See **Figure 1.10**.) Therefore, the energy available from a given food or from a total diet is reflected by the amount of each of these substances consumed. Because fat is a concentrated source of energy, adding or removing fat from the diet can have a big effect on available energy.

When Is a Kilocalorie a Calorie?

Many people inappropriately use the terms **calorie** and *kilocalorie* interchangeably. To clear up this confusing situation, you should use the term *calorie* as a general term for energy, and *kilocalorie* as a specific measurement or unit of that energy. *Calories* is like referring to gas for a car, and *kilocalories* is like referring to gallons of fuel. When in doubt, substitute the word *energy* for *calories*. The following sentence illustrates the use of *kilocalorie* and *calorie*: Because fat contains 9 *kilocalories* per gram, more than double that of protein or carbohydrate, foods high in fat are rich in *calories* (energy).

You'll find that food labels, diet books, and other sources of nutrition information use the term *calorie*, not *kilocalorie*. Technically, the potential energy in foods is best measured in kilocalories; however, the term *calorie* has become familiar and commonplace.

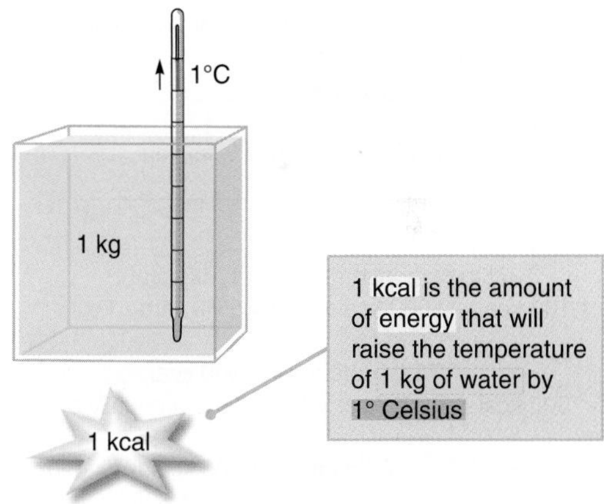

How Can We Calculate the Energy Available from Foods?

To calculate the energy available from food, multiply the number of grams of fat, carbohydrate, and protein by 9, 4, and 4, respectively, and then add the results. For example, if we assume that one bagel plus one and a half ounces of cream cheese contains 39 grams of carbohydrate, 10 grams of protein, and 16 grams of fat, we can determine the available energy from each component:

$$39 \text{ g carbohydrate} \times 4 \text{ kcal/g} = 156 \text{ kcal}$$
$$10 \text{ g protein} \times 4 \text{ kcal/g} = 40 \text{ kcal}$$
$$16 \text{ g fat} \times 9 \text{ kcal/g} = 144 \text{ kcal}$$
$$\text{Total} = 340 \text{ kcal}$$

To calculate the *percentage* of calories each of these components contributes to the total, divide the individual results by the total, and then multiply

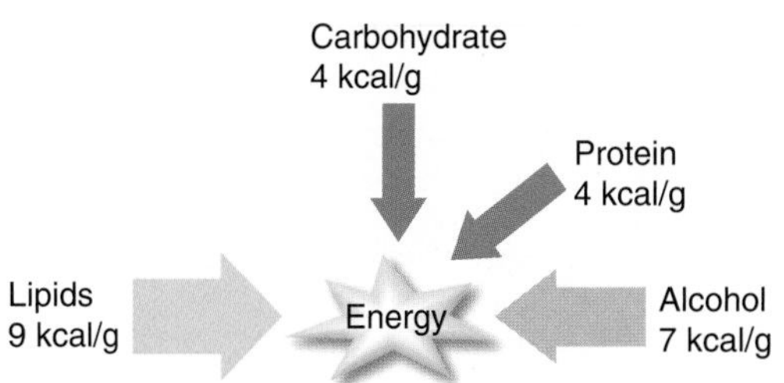

Figure 1.10 **Energy sources.** Carbohydrate, fat, protein, and alcohol provide different amounts of energy per gram.

CALCULATING THE ENERGY AVAILABLE FROM FOODS

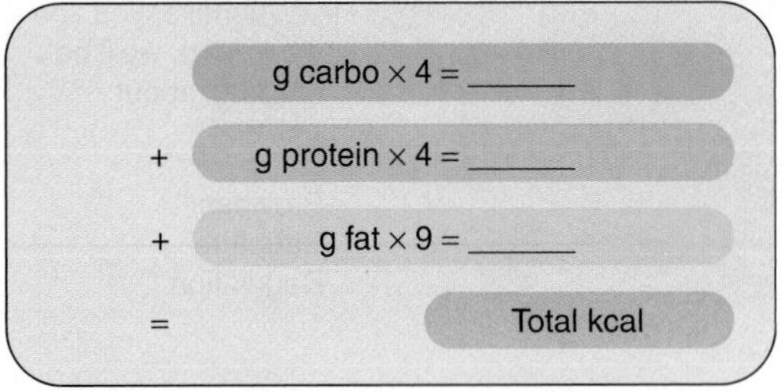

Example:
275 g carbohydrate × 4 kcal/g = 1,100 kcal

75 g protein × 4 kcal/g = 300 kcal

67 g fat × 9 kcal/g = 600 kcal (rounded from 603 kcal)

Total = 2,000 kcal

CALCULATING THE PERCENTAGE OF KILOCALORIES FROM NUTRIENTS

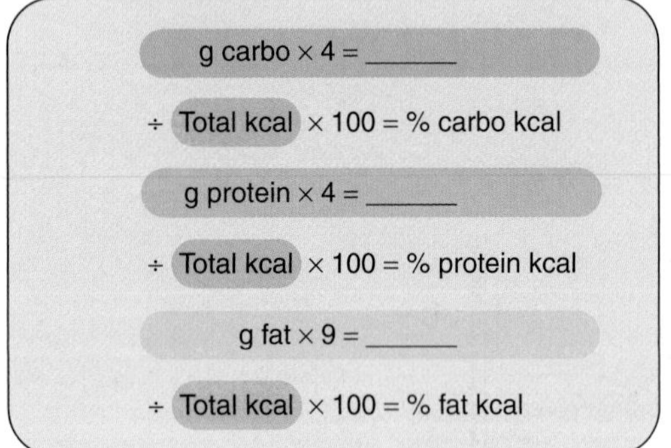

Example:
275 g carbohydrate × 4 = 1,100 kcal
1,100 kcal ÷ 2,000 kcal × 100 = 55% carbo. kcal

75 g protein × 4 = 300 kcal
300 kcal ÷ 2,000 kcal × 100 = 15% protein kcal

67 g fat × 9 = 600 kcal (rounded from 603 kcal)
600 kcal ÷ 2,000 kcal × 100 = 30% fat kcal

by 100. For example, to determine the percentage of calories from fat in this example, divide the 144 fat kilocalories by the total of 340 kilocalories and then multiply by 100 (144 ÷ 340 × 100 = 42%).

Be Food Smart: Calculate the Percentages of Calories in Food

Current health recommendations suggest limiting fat intake to about 20 to 35 percent of *total* energy intake. You can monitor this for yourself in two ways. If you like counting fat grams, you can first determine your suggested maximum fat intake. For example, if you need to eat 2,000 kilocalories each day to maintain your current weight, at most 35 percent of those calories can come from fat.

2,000 kcal × 0.35 = 700 kcal from fat

700 kcal from fat ÷ 9 kcal/g = 77.8 g of fat

Therefore, your maximum fat intake should be about 78 grams. You can check food labels to see how many fat grams you typically eat.

Another way to monitor your fat intake is to know the percentage of calories that come from fat in various foods. If the proportion of fat in each food choice throughout the day exceeds 35 percent of calories, then the day's total of fat will be too high as well. Some foods contain virtually no fat calories (e.g., fruits and vegetables), whereas others are nearly 100 percent fat calories (e.g., margarine, salad dressing). Being aware that a snack such as a bagel and cream cheese provides 42 percent of its calories from fat can help you select lower-fat foods at other times of the day.

Obesity: A Public Health Crisis

Americans and Canadians are getting fatter. Statistics show that more than half are overweight or obese, and that number has grown dramatically over the last decade, most alarmingly in children. Results from the 2005–2006 National Health and Nutrition Examination Survey (NHANES), using measured heights and weights, indicate that 34 percent of U.S. adults are obese.[32]

This obesity epidemic poses a major threat to public health due to the clear association between obesity and a variety of chronic diseases, such as type 2 diabetes, heart disease, cancer, stroke, gallbladder disease, and hypertension. (See Chapter 9, "Energy Balance, Body Composition, and Weight Management.") However, standard public health measures (as seen in the war against tobacco) have not helped to reduce the weight of North Americans. Many people prefer a sedentary lifestyle and have a dependence on fast food.

One of the national health objectives for the year 2010 is to reduce the prevalence of obesity among American adults from 30 percent to less than 15 percent.[33] Research indicates, however, that the situation is worsening rather than improving. A number of factors influence overweight or obesity, including the following:

- *Behavior:* Eating too many calories while not getting enough physical activity.
- *Environment:* Home, work, school, or community can provide barriers to or opportunities for an active lifestyle.
- *Genetics:* Heredity plays a large role in determining how susceptible people are to overweight and obesity. Genes also influence how the body burns calories for energy or stores fat.

Behavioral and environmental factors are the main contributors to overweight and obesity and provide the greatest opportunity for prevention and treatment.

The foods we choose do more than provide us with an adequate diet. The balance of energy sources can affect our risk of chronic disease. For example, high-fat diets have been linked to heart disease and cancer. Excess calories contribute to obesity, which also increases disease risk. Other nutrients, such as the minerals sodium, chloride, calcium, and magnesium, affect blood pressure, while lack of the vitamin folate prior to conception and in early pregnancy can cause serious birth defects. Non-nutrient components in the diet (e.g., phytochemicals) may have antioxidant or immune-enhancing properties that can also keep us healthy. The choices we make can reduce our disease risk, as well as provide energy and essential nutrients.

Key Concepts *All cells and tissues need energy to keep the body functioning. Energy in foods and in the body is measured in kilocalories. The carbohydrates, lipids, and proteins in food are potential sources of energy, meaning that the body can extract energy from them. Triglycerides (fats) are the most concentrated source of energy, with 9 kilocalories per gram. Carbohydrates and proteins provide 4 kilocalories per gram, while alcohol has 7 kilocalories per gram. Excess energy intake is a contributing factor to obesity, a major public health issue.*

Applying the Scientific Process to Nutrition

Whether it's identifying essential nutrients, establishing recommended intake levels, or exploring the effects of vitamins on cancer risk, scientific studies are the cornerstone of nutrition. Although we may use creative, artistic talents to choose and serve a pleasing array of healthful foods, the fundamentals of nutrition are developed through the scientific process of observation and inquiry.

The scientific process enables researchers to test the validity of **hypotheses** that arise from observations of natural phenomena. For example, it was common knowledge in the eighteenth century that sailors on long voyages would likely develop scurvy (which we now know results from a deficiency of vitamin C). Scurvy had been recognized since ancient times, and its common symptoms—pinpoint skin hemorrhages, swollen and bleeding gums, joint pain, fatigue and lethargy, and psychological changes such as depression and hysteria—were well known. Native populations discovered plant foods that would cure this illness; among Native Americans these included cranberries in the Northeast and many tree extracts in other parts of the country. From observations such as this come questions that lead to hypotheses, or "educated guesses," about factors that might be responsible for the observed phenomenon. Scientists then test hypotheses using appropriate research designs. Poorly designed research produces useless results or false conclusions.

Epidemiological Studies

An epidemiological study compares disease rates among population groups and attempts to identify related conditions or behaviors such as diet and smoking habits. The observation that scurvy developed during prolonged time at sea is an example of one aspect of **epidemiology**. Another example is the association between dietary intakes of soy and breast cancer rates. For example, Japanese women have high dietary intakes of soy and low breast

hypotheses Scientists' "educated guesses" to explain phenomena.

epidemiology The science of determining the incidence and distribution of diseases in different populations.

cancer rates, whereas American women have comparatively low dietary intakes of soy and high breast cancer rates.

Epidemiological studies provide information about relationships but do not clarify cause and effect. The results of these studies show **correlations**—relationships between two factors. For example, with soy and breast cancer, epidemiological studies show only that populations with higher soy intake (Japanese women) have lower breast cancer rates; they do not establish that soy intake prevents breast cancer. However, epidemiological studies provide clues and insights that lead to animal and human studies that can further clarify diet and disease relationships.

Animal Studies

Animal studies can provide preliminary data that lead to human studies or can be used to study hypotheses that cannot be tested on humans. It was shown in the 1890s that feeding polished (refined) rice to chickens led to a disease similar to beriberi (thiamin-deficiency disease), but a diet of rice with the hull intact did not. It's important to keep in mind that although animal studies give scientists important information that furthers nutrition knowledge, the results of animal studies cannot be transferred directly to humans. Animal studies need to be followed with cell culture studies or human clinical studies to determine specific effects in humans.

Cell Culture Studies

Another way to study nutrition is to isolate specific types of cells and grow them in a laboratory. Scientists can then use these cells to study the effects of nutrients or other components on metabolic processes in the cell. An important area of nutrition research, called **nutrigenomics**, explores the effect of specific nutrients and other chemical compounds on gene expression. (See the FYI feature "Are Nutrigenomics in Your Future?") This area of molecular biology will help us to explain individual differences in chronic disease risk factors and may lead to designing diets based on an individual's genetic profile, rather than on guidelines for the population in general.[34]

Human Studies

Case control studies and clinical trials are the two primary types of **experiments** used to test hypotheses in humans. Case control studies are small-scale epidemiological studies in which one group of individuals who have a condition (e.g., breast cancer) is compared with a similar group of individuals who do not have the condition. Researchers then identify factors other than the disease in question, such as fruit and vegetable intake, that differ between the two groups. These factors provide researchers with clues about the cause, progression, and prevention of the disease. It is important that the two groups be matched as closely as possible for major characteristics such as age, gender, and race.

Clinical trials are controlled studies in which some type of intervention—a nutrient supplement, controlled diet, or exercise program—is used to determine its impact on certain health parameters. These studies include an **experimental group** (the people who are given the intervention) and a **control group** (similar people who are not treated). Scientists measure aspects of health or disease in each group and compare the results.

James Lind's experiments with sailors aboard the *Salisbury* in 1747 are considered to be the first dietary clinical trial. (See **Figure 1.11**.) His obser-

correlations Connections, co-occurring more frequently than can be explained by chance or coincidence, but without a proven cause.

nutrigenomics The study of how nutrition interacts with specific genes to influence a person's health.

case control studies An investigation that uses a group of people with a particular condition, rather than a randomly selected population. These cases are compared with a control group of people who do not have the condition.

experiments Tests to examine the validity of a hypothesis.

clinical trials Studies that collect large amounts of data to evaluate the effectiveness of a treatment.

experimental group A set of people being studied to evaluate the effect of an event, substance, or technique.

control group A set of people used as a standard of comparison to the experimental group. The people in the control group have characteristics similar to those in the experimental group and are selected at random.

vation that oranges and lemons were the only dietary elements that seemed to cure scurvy was an important finding. However, it took more than 40 years before the British Navy began routinely giving all sailors citrus juice or fruit, such as lemons or limes—a practice that led to the nickname "limeys" when referring to British sailors. It took nearly 200 years (until the 1930s)

Are Nutrigenomics in Your Future?

Nutritional genomics, or nutrigenomics, is the study of how different foods can interact with particular genes to alter a person's risk of developing diseases such as type 2 diabetes, obesity, heart disease, and cancers.

Many of these diseases are especially common among minority populations. African American men, for example, have a 60 percent higher risk of being diagnosed with prostate cancer than do Caucasian men.[1] Half of all adult Pima Indians in the United States have type 2 diabetes, compared with 6.5 percent of adult Americans of Caucasian descent. Genetics, diet, economic and social conditions, culture, and behavior may all contribute to these differences.[2]

Thanks to human genomics research, we now know that all people share the vast majority of human genetic information. Indeed, any two individuals share 99.9 percent of their DNA sequence—or about 1 difference in every 1,000 base pairs. Similarly, all racial and ethnic groups share most genetic variations. The small differences that do exist are responsible for diverse human characteristics such as hair and skin colors, height and weight potential, and other "gene-based" variations, such as susceptibility to disease. The incidence of disease or patterns of progression differ among different groups. Risk factors for common diseases such as obesity, coronary heart disease, diabetes, prostate cancer, and birth defects must take into account both genetic and environmental/behavioral/social factors. The science of nutrigenomics studies how genes, diet, and disease interact to create health disparities for certain human populations that evolved from different geographic regions.

While diet can be a serious risk factor for a number of diseases, the exact effect of different components of food may depend on a person's genetic makeup. Thus, it is not a question of whether your genes are good or bad, but rather how they interact with your environment. A single-letter change in DNA in people from Scandinavia 10,000 years ago, for example, allows most Caucasian adults today to drink cow's milk without getting sick due to lactose intolerance.[3]

The nutrigenomics effort seeks to identify genes controlled by nutrients and other naturally occurring chemicals in food and to study how some of these genes can tip the balance between health and disease. Nutrients alter molecular processes such as DNA structure formation, gene expression, and metabolism, which in turn may alter disease initiation, development, or progression. Individual genetic variations can influence how nutrients are assimilated, metabolized, stored, and excreted by the body. Nutritional genomics will enable individuals to better manage their health and well-being by precisely matching their diets to their unique genetic makeup.

The conceptual basis for this new branch of genomic research can best be summarized by the following Five Tenets of Nutrigenomics:[4]

1. Under certain circumstances and in some individuals, diet can be a serious risk factor for a number of diseases.
2. Common dietary chemicals can act on the human genome, either directly or indirectly, to alter gene expression or structure.
3. The degree to which diet influences the balance between healthy and disease states may depend on an individual's particular genetic makeup.
4. Some diet-regulated genes (and their normal, common variants) are likely to play a role in the onset, incidence, progression, and/or severity of chronic diseases.
5. Dietary intervention based on knowledge of nutritional requirements, nutritional status, and genotype (i.e., "intelligent nutrition") can be used to prevent, mitigate, or cure chronic disease.

Personalized Nutrition

Just as pharmacogenomics has inspired the concepts of "personalized medicine" and "designer drugs," the new field of nutrigenomics is opening the way for "personalized nutrition."[5] In other words, by understanding our nutritional needs, our nutritional status, and our genotype, nutrigenomics should enable people to better manage their health and well-being by precisely matching their diets with their unique genetic makeup. Stay tuned!

1 University of California–Davis. New center will probe links between diet, genes, and disease. Press release; January 21, 2003.

2 Ibid.

3 Enattah NS, et al. Identification of a variant associated with adult-type hypolactasia. *Nat Genet.* 2002;30(2): 233–237.

4 NCMHD Center of Excellence for Nutritional Genomics. What is nutrigenomics and how does it relate to me? University of California–Davis. http://nutrigenomics.ucdavis.edu. Accessed 10/28/08.

5 McCarthy JJ, Hilfiker R. The use of single-nucleotide polymorphism maps in pharmacogenomics. *Nat Biotechnol.* 2000;18(5):505–508.

Key

Controlled variables
Experimental variables
Results
Conclusions

1. **Observation**
   Sailors on long voyages all became ill with scurvy.
2. **Hypothesis**
   Lack of certain foods causes scurvy.
3. **Experimentation**
   Experiment to test hypothesis.
   Predicts that some dietary element will cure scurvy.

James Lind: A Treatise of the Scurvy in Three Parts. Containing an inquiry into the Nature, Causes and Cure of that Disease, together with a Critical and Chronological View of what has been published on the subject. A. Millar, London, 1753.

On the 20th May, 1747, I took twelve patients in the scurvy on board the Salisbury at sea. Their cases were as similar as I could have them. They all in general had putrid gums, the spots and lassitude, with weakness of their knees. They lay together in one place, being a proper apartment for the sick in the fore-hold; and had one diet in common to all, viz., water gruel sweetened with sugar in the morning; fresh mutton broth often times for dinner; at other times puddings, boiled biscuit with sugar etc.; and for supper barley, raisins, rice and currants, sago and wine, or the like. Two of these were ordered each a quart of cyder a day. Two others took twenty five gutts of elixir vitriol three times a day upon an empty stomach, using a gargle strongly acidulated with it for their mouths. Two others took two spoonfuls of vinegar three times a day upon an empty stomach, having their gruels and their other food well acidulated with it, as also the gargle for the mouth. Two of the worst patients, with the tendons in the ham rigid (a symptom none the rest had) were put under a course of sea water. Of this they drank half a pint every day and sometimes more or less as it operated by way of gentle physic. Two others had each two oranges and one lemon given them every day. These they eat with greediness at different times upon an empty stomach. They continued but six days under this course, having consumed the quantity that could be spared. The two remaining patients took the bigness of a nutmeg three times a day of an electuray recommended by an hospital surgeon made of garlic, mustard seed, rad. raphan., balsam of Peru and gum myrrh, using for common drink barley water well acidulated with tamarinds, by a decoction of wich, with the addition of cremor tartar, they were gently purged three or four times during the course.

The consequence was that the most sudden and visible good effects were perceived from the use of the oranges and lemons; one of those who had taken them being at the end of six days fit four duty. The spots were not indeed at that time quite off his body, nor his gums sound; but without any other medicine than a gargarism or elixir of vitriol he became quite healthy before we came into Plymouth, which was on the 16th June. The other was the best recovered of any in his condition, and being now deemed pretty well was appointed nurse to the rest of the sick ...

As I shall have occasion elsewhere to take notice of the effects of other medicines in this disease, I shall here only observe that the result of all my experiments was that oranges and lemons were the most effectual remedies for this distemper at sea. I am apt to think oranges preferable to lemons...

4. **Publication**
   Publication subjects the findings to peer review by fellow scientists.
5. **More experiments**
   Further experiments replicate the findings and extend knowledge.
6. **Theory**
   Scientists consolidate acquired knowledge into a theory that explains the observed phenomenon.

Figure 1.11 **The first clinical trial.** In 1758, physician James Lind reported the careful process of his clinical trial among British sailors afflicted with scurvy.

for scientists to isolate the compound we call vitamin C and show that it had antiscurvy activity.[35] The chemical name for vitamin C, ascorbic acid, comes from its role as an antiscorbutic (antiscurvy) compound.

There are several important elements in a modern clinical trial: random assignment to groups, use of placebos, and the double-blind method. Subjects are assigned randomly—for example, by the flip of a coin—to the experimental group or the control group. This reduces the risk of introducing bias into either group. People in the experimental group receive the treatment or specific protocol (e.g., consuming a certain nutrient at a specific level). People in the control group do not receive the treatment but usually receive a placebo. A **placebo** is an imitation treatment (such as a sugar pill) that looks the same as the experimental treatment but has no effect. The placebo is also important for reducing bias because subjects do not know whether they are receiving the intervention and are less inclined to alter their responses or reported symptoms based on what they think should happen.

When the members of neither the experimental nor the control groups know what treatment they are receiving, we say the subjects are "blinded" to the treatment. If a clinical trial is designed so neither the subjects nor the researchers collecting data are aware of the subjects' group assignments (experimental or control), the study is called a **double-blind study**. This reduces the possibility that researchers will see the results they want to see even if these results do not occur. In this case, another member of the research team holds the code for subject assignments and does not participate in the data collection. Double-blind, placebo-controlled clinical trials are considered the "gold standard" of nutrition studies. These studies can show clear cause-and-effect relationships, but often require large numbers of subjects and are expensive and time consuming to conduct.

More on the Placebo Effect

Because the **placebo effect** can exert a powerful influence, research studies must take it into account. For example, when researchers tested the effectiveness of a medication in reducing binge eating among people with bulimia, they used a double-blind, placebo-controlled study to eliminate the placebo effect.[36] After a baseline number of binge-eating episodes was determined, 22 women with bulimia were given the medication or a placebo. After a period of time, the number of binge-eating episodes was reassessed. The study found a 78 percent reduction in binge-eating episodes among those taking the medication and a 70 percent reduction in the placebo group. This showed that the *expectation* that the medication would be effective was nearly as effective as the medication itself. However, a review of placebo or no-treatment clinical trials concluded that placebos do not generally have significant effects in studies with objective outcomes, but may have small benefits in studies where the outcome measures were subjective, such as pain intensity.[37] Based on this information, the often-quoted value that one-third of patients show improvement after receiving a placebo is probably an overstatement.

Key Concepts *The scientific method is used to expand our nutrition knowledge. Hypotheses are formed from observations and are then tested by experiments. Epidemiological studies observe patterns in populations. Animal and cell culture studies can test effects of various treatments. For human studies, randomized, double-blind, placebo-controlled clinical trials are the best research tools for determining cause-and-effect relationships.*

placebo An inactive substance that is outwardly indistinguishable from the active substance whose effects are being studied.

double-blind study A research study set up so that neither the subjects nor the investigators know which study group is receiving the placebo and which is receiving the active substance.

placebo effect A physical or emotional change that is not due to properties of an administered substance. The change reflects participants' expectations.

From Research Study to Headline

What about the nutrition and health headlines we see in the newspapers, hear on TV, or read on the Internet daily? Consumers are often confused by what they see as the "wishy-washiness" of scientists—for example, coffee is good, then coffee is bad. Margarine is better than butter—no, wait, maybe butter is better after all. These contradictions, despite the confusion they cause, show us that nutrition is truly a science: dynamic, changing, and growing with each new finding.

Publishing Experimental Results

peer review An appraisal of research against accepted standards by professionals in the field.

Once an experiment is complete, scientists publish the results in a scientific journal to communicate new information to other scientists. Generally, before articles are published in scientific journals, other scientists who have expert knowledge of the subject critically review them. **Peer review** ensures that only high-quality research findings are published. Unfortunately, peer-reviewed journals such as the *American Journal of Clinical Nutrition* and the *Journal of the Academy of Nutrition and Dietetics* are not the main sources of information presented in the popular media.

Each time research findings are summarized and reported, some degree of opinion is introduced into the report. A large-scale clinical trial or a long-term observational study produces mountains of data. Researchers must decide, using their experience and judgment, which data-analysis methods to use and which results to summarize for peer-reviewed publication. The journalist who regularly scans scientific journals for potential headlines decides which studies will get media attention and then summarizes study results in nontechnical terms. A news article becomes a 30-second sound bite that often is far removed from the original data. In some cases, the study may be distorted, with its results misstated or overstated. (See **Figure 1.12**.)

Sorting Facts and Fallacies in the Media

People tend to believe what they hear repeatedly. Even when it has no basis in fact, a claim can seem credible if heard often enough. For example, do you believe that sugar makes kids hyperactive? There is no *scientific* evidence to support this claim! The public is surrounded by messages from various media: TV, radio, newspapers, magazines, books, and the Internet. Because a larger audience translates into higher ratings or sales and subsequently high advertising rates, the media make money attracting viewers, listeners, and readers. To increase the number of viewers or listeners, media may sensationalize and oversimplify nutrition-related topics. This is particularly true of stories related to obesity, cancer, vitamins and minerals, and food safety. Although news stories may be based on reports in the scientific literature, the media may

SCIENTISTS DISPUTE CLAIMS OF GINKGO BILOBA EFFECTIVENESS

There have been over four hundred scientific

Researchers Link Caffeine and Cancer

Some Say Ginkgo Biloba Improves Memory

Cancer and Vitamin E Link Disputed

Besides causing a multitude of other offenses against human health, free radicals are the main

hardening of the arteries. Briefly, here's how it works: Excess free radicals in the bloodstream oxidize particles of LDL. Immune system cells in the arterial walls recognize the oxidized LDLs as toxic to the body and gobble them up. When the immune cells become overloaded with LDLs, they break down

Vitamin E Reduces Risk of Cancer

The walls recognize the risk of oxidized LDLs as toxic to the body and gobble them up. This vitamin has been shown to be instrumental in reducing some forms of cancer in certain

Vitamin E reduces the risk of LDL cholesterol being oxidized and therefore attaching to the cell wall. Because it is fat soluble, Vitamin E can get

logical cells called foam cells. The foam cells attach readily to the vessel wall and start the

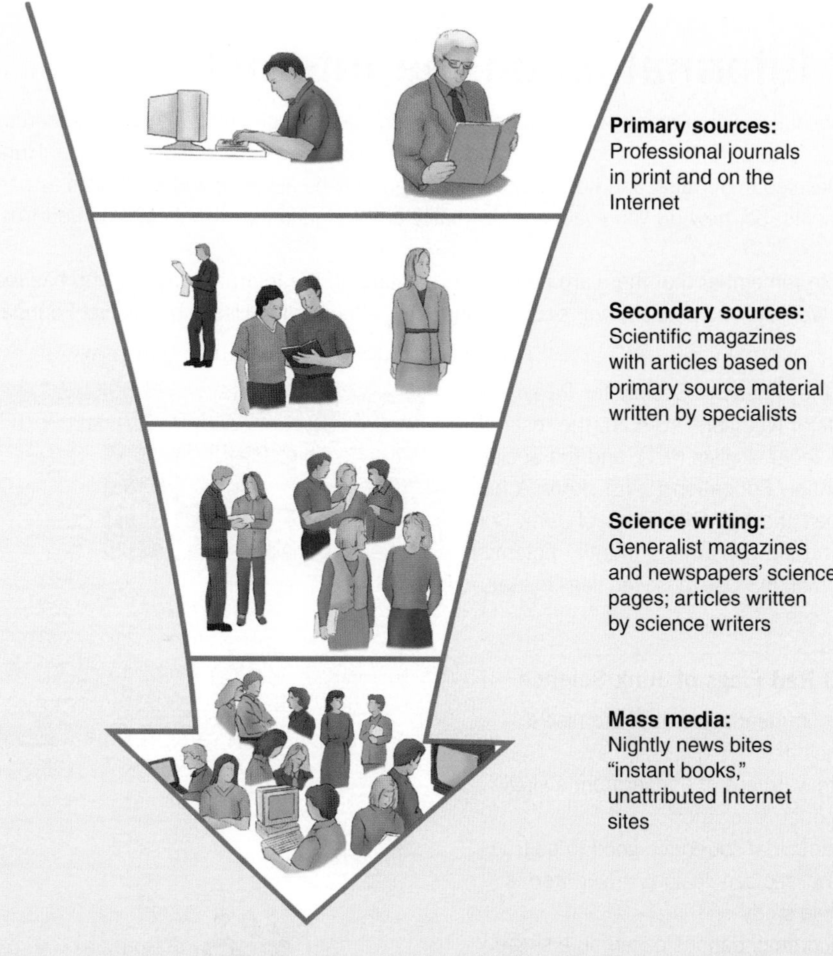
As scientific information is made accessible to more and more people, less detail is provided and more opinion and sensationalism are introduced.
Primary sources: Professional journals in print and on the Internet
Secondary sources: Scientific magazines with articles based on primary source material written by specialists
Science writing: Generalist magazines and newspapers' science pages; articles written by science writers
Mass media: Nightly news bites "instant books," unattributed Internet sites

Figure 1.12 **Sifting facts and fallacies.** From original research to the evening news, each step along the way introduces biases as information is summarized and restated. Whether on television, radio, the Internet, or in print, the best consumer information cites sources for reported facts.

distort the facts through omission of details. (See the FYI feature "Evaluating Information on the Internet.")

As you learn about nutrition, you will undoubtedly be more aware not only of your eating and shopping habits but also of nutrition-related information in the media. As you see and hear reports, stop to think carefully about what you are hearing. Headlines and news reports often overstate the findings of a study. You may want to find the scientific article and read it for yourself. At first, reading journal articles will be difficult, but with experience (and growing nutrition knowledge) you will understand more of the information presented. Talk to your instructor for ideas about journal articles that might help you evaluate headlines. Two other things to keep in mind: one study does not provide all the answers to our nutrition questions; and if it sounds too good to be true, it probably is!

Your study of nutrition is just beginning. As you learn about the essential nutrients, their functions and food sources, be alert to your food choices and the factors that influence them. When the discussion turns to the role of diet in health, think about your preconceived ideas and evaluate your beliefs in the light of current scientific evidence. Keep an open mind, but also think critically. Most of all, remember that food is more than the nutrients it provides; it is part of the way we enjoy and celebrate life!

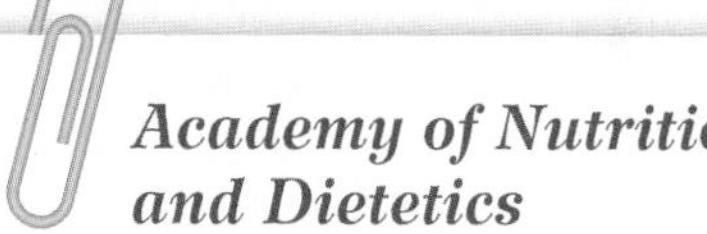

Academy of Nutrition and Dietetics

Food and Nutrition Misinformation

It is the position of the Academy of Nutrition and Dietetics that food and nutrition misinformation can have harmful effects on the health and economic status of consumers. Nationally credentialed dietetics professionals working in health care, academia, public health, nutrition communications, media, and the food industry and serving in policy-making/regulatory roles are uniquely qualified to advocate for and promote sound, science-based nutrition information to the public, function as primary nutrition educators to health professionals, and actively counter and correct food and nutrition misinformation.

Source: Reproduced from Position of the American Dietetic Association: food and nutrition misinformation. *J Am Diet Assoc.* 2006;106(4):601–607. Copyright 2006. Reprinted with permission from Elsevier.

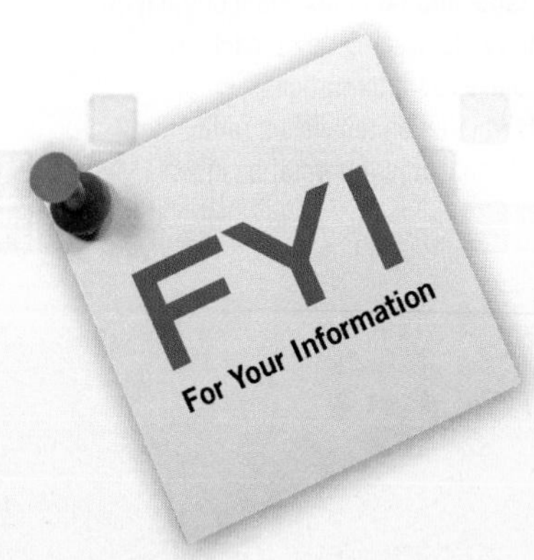

Evaluating Information on the Internet

Surfing the Web has made life easier in many ways. You can buy a car, check stock prices, search out sources for a paper you're writing, chat with like-minded people, and stay up to date on news or sports scores. Hundreds of Web sites are devoted to nutrition and health topics, and you may be asked to visit such sites as part of your course requirements. So, how do you evaluate the quality of information on the Web? Can you trust what you see?

First, it's important to remember that there are no rules for posting on the Internet. Anyone who has the equipment can set up a Web site and post any content he or she likes. Although the Health on the Net Foundation has set up a Code of Conduct for medical and health Web sites, following their eight principles is completely voluntary.[1]

Second, consider the source, if you can tell what it is! Many Web sites do not specify where the content came from, who is responsible for it, or how often it is updated. If the site lists the authors, what are their credentials? Who sponsors the site itself? Educational institutions (.edu), government agencies (.gov), and organizations (.org) generally have more credibility than commercial (.com) sites, where selling rather than educating may be the motive.[2] Identifying the purpose for a site can give you more clues about the validity of its content.

Third, when you see claims for nutrients, dietary supplements, or other products, and results of studies or other information, keep in mind the scientific method and the basics of sound science. Who did the study? What type of study was it? How many subjects? Was it double-blind? Were the results published in a peer-reviewed journal? Think critically about the content, look at other sources, and ask questions of experts before you accept information as truth. What is true of books, magazines, and newspapers also applies to the Internet: just because it is in print or online doesn't mean it's true.

Finally, be on the lookout for "junk science"—sloppy methods, interpretations, and claims that lead to public misinformation. The Food and Nutrition Science Alliance (FANSA) is a coalition of six professional societies: the American College of Nutrition (ACN), the Academy of Nutrition and Dietetics (AND), the American Society for Nutrition (ASN), the American Society for Parenteral and Enteral Nutrition (ASPEN), the Institute of Food Technologists (IFT), and the Society for Nutrition Education (SNE). FANSA has developed the "10 Red Flags of Junk Science" to help consumers identify potential misinformation.[3] Use these red flags to evaluate Web sites.

The 10 Red Flags of Junk Science

1. Recommendations that promise a quick fix
2. Dire warnings of danger from a single product or regimen
3. Claims that sound too good to be true
4. Simplistic conclusions drawn from a single study
5. Recommendations based on a single study
6. Dramatic statements that are refuted by reputable scientific organizations
7. Lists of "good" and "bad" foods
8. Recommendations made to help sell a product
9. Recommendations based on studies published without peer review
10. Recommendations from studies that ignore differences among individuals or groups

Use the Internet; it's fun and can be educational. Don't forget about the library, though; many scientific journals are not available online. Treat claims as "guilty until proven innocent"—in other words, don't accept what you read at face value until you have evaluated the science behind it. If it sounds too good to be true, it probably is!

Note: The Academy of Nutrition and Dietetics provides links to several reliable Internet resources for dietetics professionals—see the AND Web site at http://www.eatright.org/cps/rde/xchg/ada/hs.xsl/nutrition.html.

1 Health on the Net Foundation. HONcode: principles. http://www.hon.ch/HONcode/Conduct.html. Accessed 10/28/08.

2 The wheat from the chaff: sorting out nutrition information on the Internet. *J Am Diet Assoc.* 1998;98:1270–1272.

3 "The 10 Red Flags of Junk Science" from Food and Nutrition Science Alliance (FANSA) of which the AND is a member. Reprinted with permission from the Academy of Nutrition and Dietetics. http://www.eatright.org/cps/rde/xchg/ada/hs.xsl/media_2922_ENU_HTML.htm. Accessed 10/28/08.

Learning Portfolio

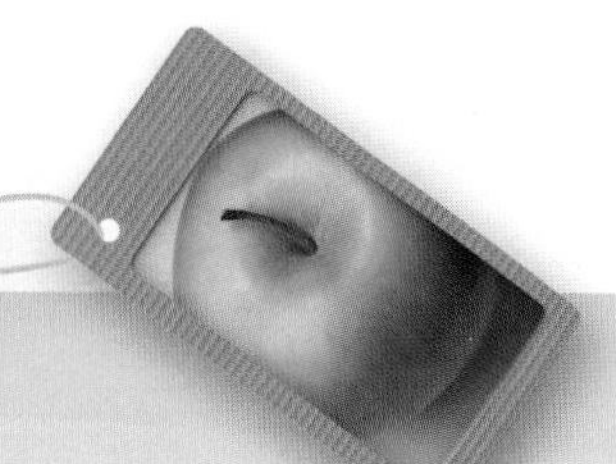

Key Terms

	page		page
amino acids	13	lipids	13
antioxidant	11	macrominerals	14
calorie	15	macronutrients	11
carbohydrates	13	microminerals	14
case control studies	18	micronutrients	11
circulation	13	minerals	14
clinical trials	18	neophobia	2
control group	18	nutrients	10
correlations	18	nutrigenomics	18
double-blind study	21	nutrition	2
energy	14	organic	12
epidemiology	17	peer review	22
essential nutrients	10	phytochemicals	11
experimental group	18	pica	5
experiments	18	placebo	21
flavor	3	placebo effect	21
hormones	13	proteins	13
hypotheses	17	social facilitation	6
inorganic	12	trace minerals	14
kilocalories (kcal) [KILL-oh-kal-oh-rees]	15	triglycerides	13
		umami [ooh-MA-mee]	3
legumes	13	vitamins	13

Study Points

- Most people make food choices for reasons other than nutrient value.
- Taste and texture are the two most important factors that influence food choices.
- In all cultures, eating is the primary way of maintaining social relationships.
- Although most North Americans know about healthful food choices, their eating habits do not always reflect this knowledge.
- Food is a mixture of chemicals. Essential chemicals in food are called nutrients.
- Carbohydrates, lipids, proteins, vitamins, minerals, and water are the six classes of nutrients found in food.
- Nutrients have three general functions in the body: they serve as energy sources, structural components, and regulators of metabolic processes.
- Vitamins regulate body processes such as energy metabolism, blood clotting, and calcium balance.
- Minerals contribute to body structures and to regulating processes such as fluid balance.
- Water is the most important nutrient in the body. We can survive much longer without the other nutrients than we can without water.
- Energy in foods and the body is measured in kilocalories. Carbohydrates, fats, and proteins are sources of energy.
- Carbohydrate and protein have a potential energy value of 4 kilocalories per gram, and fat provides 9 kilocalories per gram.
- Scientific studies are the cornerstone of nutrition. The scientific method uses observation and inquiry to test hypotheses.
- Double-blind, placebo-controlled clinical trials are considered the "gold standard" of nutrition studies.
- Research designs used to test hypotheses include epidemiological, animal, cell culture, and human studies.
- Information in the public media is not always an accurate or complete representation of the current state of the science on a particular topic.

Study Questions

1. Name three sensory aspects of food that influence our food choices.
2. How do our health beliefs affect our food choices?
3. List the six classes of nutrients.
4. List the 13 vitamins.
5. What determines whether a mineral is a macromineral or a micro- (trace) mineral?
6. How many kilocalories are in 1 gram of carbohydrate, of protein, and of fat?
7. What is an epidemiological study?
8. What is the difference between an experimental and control group?
9. What is a placebo?

Try This

Try a New Cuisine Challenge

Expand your culinary taste buds and try a new cuisine. Take your local phone book and see how many ethnic restaurants are near campus. Choose a cuisine you are not very familiar with and take some friends along for dinner so you can order and share several dishes. While you're there, don't be afraid to ask questions about the menu, so you can gain a better understanding of the foods, preparation techniques, spices, and even the cultural meaning attached to some of the dishes.

Food Label Puzzle

The purpose of this exercise is to put the individual pieces of the food label together to determine how many kilocalories are in a serving. Pick six foods in your dorm room or apartment that have complete food labels. Ask a friend to write down the value for calories on each label and then black out these numbers on the labels. Remember that the term *calories* on a food label really is referring to kilocalories. Your job is to determine how many kilocalories are in a serving of each of these foods. You can do this by putting together the individual pieces (carbohydrate, protein, and fat). If you need help, review this chapter and pay close attention to the section on the energy-yielding nutrients. How many kilocalories does each have per gram? You may find that the results of your calculations don't exactly match the numbers on the label. Within labeling guidelines, food manufacturers can round values.

What About Bobbie?

The "What About Bobbie?" feature appears in most chapters. Bobbie is a college student whom you'll follow throughout this text to learn the strengths and weaknesses of her diet. Look for this feature to see how the information you learn in each chapter can be applied to real life.

Bobbie is a 20-year-old college sophomore. She lives on campus and has one roommate. She has the standard meal plan with her university, so she eats most of her meals in the cafeteria. Sometimes she'll get a snack from the local coffee shop or a vending machine. Her schedule is fairly typical, with classes spread out in both the morning and afternoon. Occasionally at night, she and her friends will order pizza or go out for ice cream.

Bobbie weighs 155 pounds and is 5 feet, 4 inches tall. She gained 10 pounds her freshman year in college and would like to lose it because she feels that her ideal weight is more like 145 pounds. She exercises infrequently but likes to walk with her friends and take an occasional aerobics class. Here is a typical day of eating for Bobbie:

Sample one-day menu from Bobbie's diet

7:45 A.M.
1 raisin bagel, toasted
3 tablespoons light cream cheese
10 fluid ounces regular coffee
  2 packets of sugar
  2 tablespoons of 2% milk

10:15 A.M.
1 banana

12:15 P.M.
Turkey and cheese sandwich
2 slices sourdough bread
2 ounces sliced turkey lunch meat
2 teaspoons regular mayonnaise
2 teaspoons mustard
2 slices tomato
2 slices dill pickle
Shredded lettuce
Salad from cafeteria salad bar
  2 cups shredded iceberg lettuce
  2 tablespoons each:
    Shredded carrot
    Chopped egg
    Croutons
    Kidney beans
    Italian salad dressing
12 fluid ounces diet soda
1 small chocolate chip cookie

3:30 P.M.
16 fluid ounces water
1.5 ounces regular tortilla chips
½ cup salsa

6:00 P.M.
Spaghetti with meatballs
  1.5 cups pasta
  3 ounces ground beef (meatballs)
  3 ounces spaghetti sauce
  2 tablespoons Parmesan cheese
1 piece garlic bread
½ cup green beans
  1 teaspoon butter
12 fluid ounces diet soda

10:15 P.M.
1 slice cheese pizza

In later chapters, we will return to this one-day food record and examine Bobbie's intake in more detail.

References

1 Kittler PG, Sucher KP. *Food and Culture*. 5th ed. Belmont, CA: Wadsworth, 2008.

2 Gerrish CJ, Mennella JA. Flavor variety enhances food acceptance in formula-fed infants. *Am J Clin Nutr*. 2001;73(6):1080–1085.

3 Smith DV, Margolskee RF. Making sense of taste. *Sci Am*. 2001;284(3):32–39.

4 Yamaguchi S, Ninomiya K. Umami and food palatability. *J Nutr*. 2000;130:921S–926S.

5 Kim U, Jorgenson E, Coon H, et al. Positional cloning of the human quantitative trait locus underlying taste sensitivity to phenylthiocarbamide. *Science*. 2003;299:1221–1226.

6 Corbett RW, Ryan C, Weinrich SP. Pica in pregnancy: does it affect pregnancy outcome? *Am J Matern Child Nurs*. 2003;28:183–189.

7 Sandstead HH. Syndrome of iron deficiency anemia, hepatosplenomegaly, hypogonadism, dwarfism, and geophagia. *J Trace Elements Exp Med*. 2001; 14(2):145–155.

8 Connell D, Goldberg JP, Folta SC. An intervention to increase fruit and vegetable consumption using audio communications: in-store public service announcements and audiotapes. *J Health Commun*. 2001;6(1):31–43.

9 Stewart-Brown S. *What Is the Evidence on School Health Promotion in Improving Health or Preventing Disease and, Specifically, What Is the Effectiveness of the Health Promoting Schools Approach?* Copenhagen: WHO Regional Office for Europe, 2006. Health Evidence Network report. http://www.chdf.org.au/i-cms_file?page=3/WHOHPSeffectivenessreport.pdf. Accessed 4/16/09.

10 Kuchler F, Golan E. Is there a role for government in reducing the prevalence of overweight and obesity? *Choices*, Fall 2004. http://choicesmagazine.org/2004-3/obesity/2004-3-03.htm. Accessed 1/22/10.

11 Wansink B. Environmental factors that increase the food intake and consumption volume of unknowing consumers. *Ann Rev Nutr*. 2004;24:455–479.

12 De Castro JM, Brewer ME. The amount eaten in meals by humans is a power function of the number of people present. *Physiol Behav*. 1991;51:121–125; and Patel KA, Schlundt DG. Impact of moods and social context on eating behavior. *Appetite*. 2001;36(2):111–118.

13 Mooney K, Walbourn L. When college students reject food: not just a matter of taste. *Appetite*. 2001;36(1):41–50.

14 Drewnowski A, Spencer SE. Poverty and obesity: the role of energy density and energy costs. *Am J Clin Nutr*. 2004;79:6–16.

15 Blisard N, Stewart H, Jolliffee D. *Low-Income Households' Expenditures on Fruits and Vegetables*. Washington, DC: US Department of Agriculture, Economic Research Service, 2004. Agricultural Economic Report No. 833. http://www.ers.usda.gov/publications/AER833. Accessed 1/22/10.

16 Drewnowski, Spencer. Poverty and obesity.

17 Reed J, Frazão E, Itskowitz R. *How Much Do Americans Pay for Fruits and Vegetables?* Washington, DC: US Department of Agriculture, 2004. Agriculture Information Bulletin No. 790.

18 Sloan AE. What, when, and where Americans eat: 2008. *Food Tech*. 2008;62(1):20–29.

19 Ueshima H, Okayama A, Saitoh S, et al. Differences in cardiovascular disease risk factors between Japanese in Japan and Japanese-Americans in Hawaii: the INTERLIPID study. *J Hum Hypertens*. 2003;17(9):631–639.

20 Boyles S. Japan's heart healthy diet: fish is key. MedicineNet.com. http://www.medicinenet.com/script/main/art.asp?articlekey=91403. Accessed 1/22/10.

21 Fieldhouse P. *Food and Nutrition: Customs and Culture*. 2nd ed. London: Chapman and Hall, 1996.

22 Kittler, Sucher. *Food and Culture*.

23 Bryant CA, DeWalt KM, Courtney A, Schwartz J. *The Cultural Feast: An Introduction to Food and Society*. 2nd ed. Belmont, CA: Wadsworth, 2004.

24 Ibid.

25 Sloan AE. Top 10 food trends. *Food Tech*. 2007:61(4):22–38.

26 Kittler, Sucher. *Food and Culture*.

27 Ibid.

28 Ibid.

29 Bryant, DeWalt, Courtney, Schwartz. *The Cultural Feast*.

30 Sloan. Top 10 food trends.

31 Guenther PM, Juan WY, Reedy J, et al. *Diet Quality of Americans in 1994–96 and 2001–02 as Measured by the Healthy Eating Index 2005*. Washington DC: Center for Nutrition Policy and Promotion, 2008. Nutrition Insight No. 37. http://www.cnpp.usda.gov/Publications/NutritionInsights/Insight37.pdf. Accessed 1/22/10.

32 Ogden CL, Carroll MD, McDowell MA, Flegal KM. *Obesity Among Adults in the United States—No Change Since 2003–2004*. Hyattsville, MD: National Center for Health Statistics, 2007. NCHS Data Brief No. 1.

33 US Department of Health and Human Services. *Healthy People 2010*. 2nd ed. Washington, DC: US Government Printing Office, November 2000. http://www.healthypeople.gov/. Accessed 1/22/10.

34 Kauwell GPA. Emerging concepts in nutrigenomics: a preview of what is to come. *Nutr Clin Pract*. 2005;20:75–87.

35 Levine M, Katz A, Padayatty SJ. Vitamin C. In: Shils ME, Shike M, Ross AC, et al., eds. *Modern Nutrition in Health and Disease*. 10th ed. Philadelphia: Lippincott Williams & Wilkins, 2006.

36 Alger SA, Schwalberg MD, Bigaouette JM, et al. Effect of a tricyclic antidepressant and opiate antagonist on binge-eating behavior in normal weight, bulimic, and obese binge-eating subjects. *Am J Clin Nutr*. 1991;53:865–871.

37 Hrobjartsson A, Gotzsche PC. Is the placebo powerless? An analysis of clinical trials comparing placebo with no treatment. *N Engl J Med*. 2001;344:1594–1602.

CHAPTER 2

Nutrition Guidelines and Assessment

THINK About It

1 Do you and your friends discuss food and diet?

2 Have you ever taken a very large dose of a vitamin or mineral? If so, why? How did you determine whether it was safe?

3 Do you eat the same foods most days, or do you like variety?

Visit nutrition.jbpub.com

Quick Bite

Early "Laws of Health"
Galen may be the best-known physician who ever lived. During the second century, Galen expounded his "laws of health"—eat proper foods, drink the right beverages, exercise, breathe fresh air, get enough sleep, have a daily bowel movement, and control your emotions.

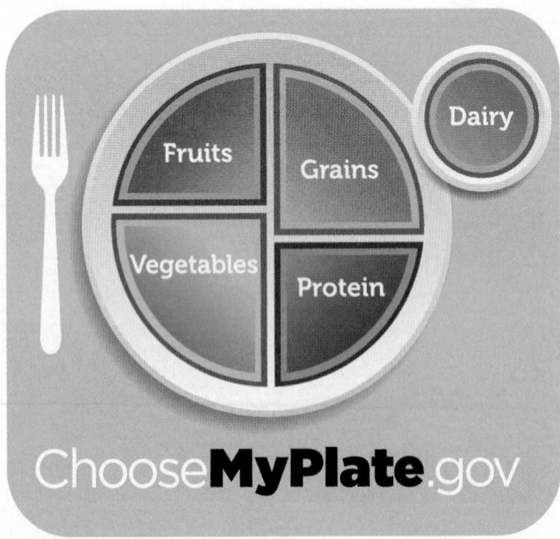

MyPlate Icon. Courtesy of USDA.

So, you want to be healthier—maybe that's why you are taking this course! You probably already know that a well-planned diet is one important element of being healthy. Although most of us know that the foods we choose to eat have a major impact on our health, we aren't always certain about what choices to make. Choosing the right foods isn't made any easier when we are bombarded by headlines and advertisements: Eat less fat! Get more fiber in your diet! Moderation is the key! Build strong bones with calcium!

For many Americans, nutrition is simply a lot of hearsay, or maybe the latest slogan coined from last week's news headlines. Conversations about nutrition start off with "*They* say you should..." or "Now *they* think that..." Have you ever wondered who "they" are and why "they" are telling you what to eat or what not to eat?

It's no secret that a healthy population is a more productive population, so many of our nutrition guidelines come from the federal government's efforts to improve our overall health. Thus, the government is one "they." Undernutrition and overnutrition are examples of two nutrition problems that government policy has helped to correct.

Many important elements of nutrition policy focus on relieving undernutrition in some population groups. Let's look at some examples. To prevent widespread deficiencies, the government requires food manufacturers to add nutrients to certain foods: iodine to salt, vitamin D to milk, and thiamin, riboflavin, niacin, iron, and folic acid to enriched grains. Another example is the publication of dietary standards, such as the Dietary Reference Intakes, which make it easier to define adequate diets for large groups of people.

Overnutrition has led to changes in public policy as well. Health researchers have discovered links between diet and obesity, high blood pressure, cancer, and heart disease; as a result, nutritionists suggest that we make informed food choices by reducing our intake of excess calories, sodium, saturated fats, and trans fats, while being physically active. Another example is the public's need to know what is in the food they eat, which has led to increased nutrition information on food labels. Public education efforts have resulted in the development of teaching tools such as MyPlate.

New information about diet and health will continue to drive public policy. This chapter explores diet-planning tools, dietary guidelines, and current dietary standards and discusses how to evaluate nutritional health. How does your diet compare with these current guidelines and standards?

Linking Nutrients, Foods, and Health

We all know that what we eat affects our health. Nutrition science has made many advances in identifying essential nutrients and the foods in which they are found. Eating foods with all the essential nutrients prevents nutritional deficiencies such as scurvy (vitamin C deficiency) or pellagra (deficiency of the B vitamin niacin). In the United States, few people suffer nutritional deficiencies as a result of dietary inadequacies. More often, Americans suffer from chronic diseases such as heart disease, cancer, hypertension, and diabetes—all linked to overconsumption and lifestyle choices. Your future health depends on today's lifestyle choices, including your food choices.

Planning How You Will Eat

Living in a high-tech world, we expect immediate solutions to long-term problems. It would be nice if we could avoid the consequences of overeating by taking a pill, drinking a beverage, or getting a shot. But no magic food, nutrient, or drug exists. Instead, we have to rely on healthful foods, exercise, and lifestyle choices to reduce our risk of chronic disease.

Many tools are available to help us select healthful foods to eat. The U.S. Department of Agriculture's MyPlate food guidance system and the Exchange Lists are two common and comprehensive tools. Although different, these tools rely on the same core nutrition concepts: adequacy, balance, calorie (energy) control, nutrient density, moderation, and variety. Furthermore, these resources use a total diet approach to ensure nutritional adequacy and choices of healthful food.[1]

Adequacy

Having an adequate diet means that the foods you choose to eat provide all of the essential nutrients, fiber, and energy in amounts sufficient to support growth and maintain health.[2] Many Americans consume more calories than they need without getting 100 percent of the recommended intakes for a number of nutrients. Take, for example, a meal of soda pop, two hard-shell beef tacos, and cinnamon sticks. Although this meal provides foods from different food groups, it is high in sugar and fat, and low in many vitamins and minerals found in fruit and vegetables. Occasionally skipping fruits and vegetables at a meal will not create a vitamin or mineral deficiency; however, dietary habits that skimp on fruit and vegetables most of the time will provide an overall inadequate diet. Most people could improve the adequacy of their diet by choosing meals and snacks that are high in vitamins and minerals but low to moderate in energy (calorie) content. Doing so offers important benefits: normal growth and development of children, health promotion for people of all ages, and reduction of risk for a number of chronic diseases that are major public health problems.[3]

Balance

A healthful diet requires a balance of food groups (grains, vegetables, fruits, oil, milk, and meat and beans), energy sources (carbohydrates, protein, and fat), and other nutrients (vitamins and minerals). Your diet is balanced if the amount of energy (calories) you eat equals the amount of energy you expend in daily activities and exercise. Your diet is also balanced when the foods you choose to eat provide you with adequate nutrients. The trick is to consume enough, but not too much, from all the different food groups.

Calorie Control

Identifying the amount of calories you need to maintain or achieve a healthy weight and then being able to choose an adequate diet that balances the calories you eat with the amount of calories your body uses to sustain its metabolic and physical activities can be challenging. The formula for weight maintenance seems simple: If you eat the same amount of calories that you use each day, your weight will stay the same. If you eat more than you use, you will gain weight, and if you eat less than you use, you will lose weight. Energy balance and weight management are discussed in Chapter 9. Here we continue our focus on how to choose the foods you eat by learning how to get the most nutrients without wasting calories, which is like a lesson on budgeting.

Nutrient Density

The concern that Americans' diets are becoming increasingly energy rich but nutrient poor has focused attention on the nutrient content of individual foods relative to the energy they provide.[4] The Dietary Guidelines Advisory Committee report and the *Dietary Guidelines for Americans* confirm that

Quick Bite

How Much Do Doctors and Dentists Know About Nutrition?

Nutrition training in medical schools and residency programs has been identified as an essential component of medical education by numerous organizations, including the American Society for Clinical Nutrition, the American Medical Student Association, the National Academy of Sciences, and the U.S. Congress, which passed the National Nutritional Monitoring and Related Research Act of 1990 mandating nutrition as a part of the medical school curriculum. Findings indicate, however, that significant variation in nutrition knowledge of the U.S. medical students exists and that the amount of time medical schools spend on nutrition education varies significantly, ranging from a mandatory course in nutrition to nutrition education being a component of another required course.

Sources: National Nutritional Monitoring and Related Research Act of 1990. Public law 1101-445/HR 1608, section 302; and *Education for Health: Change in Learning and Practice.* 2006;(19)3:321–330.

nutrient density A description of the healthfulness of foods. Foods high in nutrient density are those that provide substantial amounts of vitamins and minerals and relatively few calories; foods low in nutrient density are those that supply calories but relatively small amounts of vitamins and minerals (or none at all).

many Americans are overweight or obese, yet many are also undernourished.[5] Understanding nutrient density can help you meet your nutrient needs without getting too many calories.

Just as each of us has a monetary budget—a certain amount of money to spend on things such as food, rent, books, and transportation—in a sense we all have a calorie budget as well. Once you determine how many calories your body uses each day and how to manipulate your calorie expenditure to reach certain health goals (as discussed in Chapter 9), you will be making food choices to match your calorie needs. Every time you eat, you are choosing to spend some of your calorie budget for that day. Those who spend their budget wisely tend to be healthier than those who do not.

The **nutrient density** of food provides a clue to how "healthy" a food is. Nutrient-dense foods are those foods that provide substantial amounts of vitamins and minerals and relatively few calories.[6] Foods that are low in nutrient density are foods that supply calories but relatively small amounts

Going Green

Is the American Diet Contributing to a Warmer Planet?

Our food choices, which include production, transport, processing, packaging, storage, and preparation, may be a significant contributor to global warming. The food sector in America accounts for 19 percent of total U.S. energy use each year. The average American diet creates 2.8 tons of carbon dioxide (CO_2) emissions per person per year, which far surpasses the 2.2 tons of CO_2 emissions generated by Americans driving.[1]

The highly processed foods that have become a big part of our diets often require barrels of oil to create and deliver to our dinner plates, and are often low in nutrient value as well. Your food choices not only contribute to your state of health, both current and future, but also are a significant part of your overall carbon footprint. The good news is that healthy, flavorful, and good-to-eat foods are entirely possible while also easing the load of your carbon footprint.

Here are some tips for lean and green eating:

- *Eat less red meat.* The amount of beef in your diet is one of the biggest factors in your global impact.
- *Ban the bottled water.* Liquids are one of the heaviest items to ship, and their plastic containers are filling landfills.
- *Snack sustainably.* This is good for your waist as well as your waste. Ditch the processed snack foods and choose whole, real foods instead.
- *Be an efficient shopper.* Minimize shopping trips to different stores if possible, reuse bags, and shop the bulk bins.
- *Become a locavore.* Eat locally (or regionally) and seasonally to the extent that you can.
- *Compost your food waste.* Food scraps are about 12 percent of a family's household waste and emit powerful warming gases in landfill. Regenerate them into healthy soil instead!
- *Cook in more, take out less.* Dining out significantly increases a food's carbon footprint, especially if there is packaging.
- *Practice "hara hachi bu."* The Okinawan phrase *hara hachi bu* translates as "eat until you are eight parts full." Slow down while you eat, and give your stomach time to tell your brain you are full.
- *Limit highly packaged, single-serving snacks, foods, and beverages.* Hit the bulk aisle and bulk up instead.
- *Pack a PB&J for lunch.* Make your own lunch and bring it with you. If it's peanut butter and jelly or almond butter with local jam on whole-grain bread, it's fast, easy, healthy, and greener too.

[1]Eshel G, Martin PA. Diet, energy and global warming. *Earth Interactions.* 2006;10(9):1–17.

Source: Geagan K. *Go Green, Get Lean: Trim Your Waistline with the Ultimate Low-Carbon Footprint Diet.* Emmaus, PA: Rodale, 2009.

of vitamins and minerals, sometimes none at all.[7] If a food is high in calories but low in vitamins and minerals, we say that food is less nutrient dense than one that has a high vitamin and mineral content compared with its overall calories.

Take, for example, a potato. Potatoes are presented to us to eat in many different forms. We can eat baked potatoes, mashed potatoes with butter or sauces, or french fries. Regardless of how it is cooked, the potato is still a potato, but depending on how it is cooked and what is added to it before we eat it, the nutrient density of that potato changes. The most nutrient-dense form of this potato would be a plain baked potato, which provides the most amount of vitamins and minerals with relatively few calories. The least nutrient-dense version of this potato is the french fries, because frying a food adds a lot more calories without adding more vitamins and minerals, producing a product that has a relatively low amount of vitamins and minerals compared to its overall (higher) calorie content.

Foods with little or no added sugar or fat are high-nutrient-dense food choices. For example, you might decide to eat a pear instead of a handful of caramel corn. Both provide about the same amount of calories. By choosing to eat the pear instead of the caramel corn, you are working toward meeting your daily nutrient needs on a lower energy budget. These choices over time will result in a diet that is healthier overall.

Moderation

THINK About It 2

Not too much or too little—that's what moderation means. Moderation does not mean that you have to eliminate low-nutrient-dense foods from your diet, but rather that you can include them occasionally. Moderation also means not taking anything to extremes. You probably have heard that vitamin C has positive effects, but that doesn't mean huge doses of this essential nutrient are appropriate for you. It's also important to remember that substances that are healthful in small amounts can sometimes be dangerous in large quantities. For example, the body needs zinc for hundreds of chemical reactions, including those that support normal growth, development, and immune function. Too much zinc, however, can cause deficiency of another essential mineral, copper, which can lead to impaired immune function. Being moderate in your diet means that you do not restrict or completely eliminate any one type of food, but rather that all types of food can fit into a healthful diet.

Food guides and their graphics convey the message of moderation by showing suggested amounts of different food groups. Appearing in diverse shapes, food guides from other countries reflect their cultural contexts. Korea, for example, uses the shape of a pagoda. (See **Figure 2.1**.)

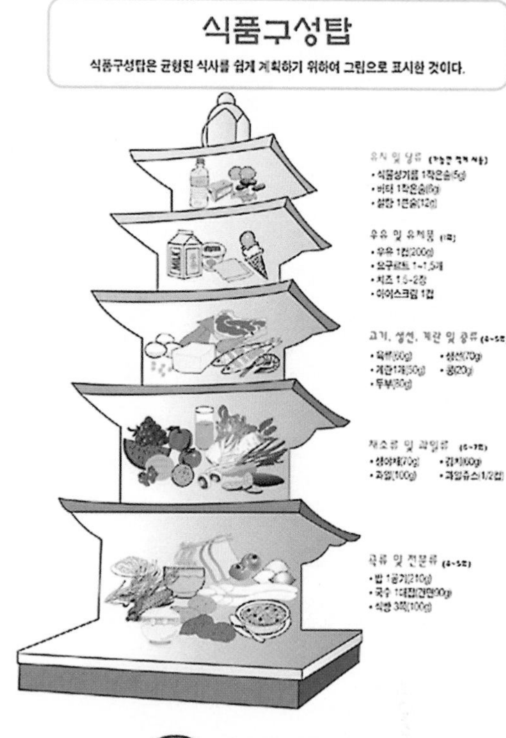

Figure 2.1 **Korean Dietary Guidelines.** Around the world, countries have adopted food guide presentations tailored to their individual cultures as well as physical needs. Both Korea and China use the pagoda shape for their food guides. The United States uses a plate, and Canada uses a rainbow. Mexico and most European countries use a circular form.

Source: Painter J, Jee-Hyun R, Yeon-Kyung L. Comparison of international food guide pictorial representations. *J Am Diet Assoc.* 2002;102:483–489. © The American Dietetic Association. Reprinted with permission.

Variety

How many *different* foods do you eat on a daily basis? Ten? Fifteen? Would it surprise you that one of Japan's dietary guidelines suggests eating 30 different foods each day?[8] Now *that's* variety!

THINK About It 3

Variety means including lots of different foods in the diet: not just different food groups such as fruits, vegetables, and grains but also different foods from each group. Eating two bananas and three carrots each and every day may give you the minimum number of recommended daily servings for fruits and vegetables, but it doesn't add much variety.

Variety is important for a number of reasons. Eating a variety of fruits, for example, will provide a broader mix of vitamins, minerals, and phytochemicals than just including one or two fruits. Choosing a variety of protein sources will give you a different balance of fats and other nutrients. Variety can add interest and excitement to your meals while preventing boredom with your diet. Perhaps most important, variety in your diet helps ensure that you get all the nutrients you need. Studies have shown that people who have varied diets are more likely to meet their overall nutrient needs.[9]

So remember, there are no magic diets, foods, or supplements. Instead, your overall, long-term food choices can bring you the benefits of a healthful diet. A healthful diet is something you create over time, not the way you eat on any given day. Using the principles of adequacy, balance, calorie (energy) control, nutrient density, moderation, and variety will help you attain and achieve healthy eating habits, which in turn will contribute to your overall healthy lifestyle. Let's take a look at some general guidance for making those food choices.

Key Concepts *Food and nutrient intake play a major role in health and risk of disease. For most Americans, overnutrition is more of a problem than undernutrition. The diet-planning principles of adequacy, balance, calorie (energy) control, nutrient density, moderation, and variety are important concepts in choosing a healthful diet.*

Dietary Guidelines

To help citizens improve their overall health, many countries have developed dietary guidelines—simple, easy-to-understand statements about food choices, food safety, and physical activity. This section examines dietary guidelines for the United States and Canada.

Dietary Guidelines for Americans

In 1980 the **U.S. Department of Agriculture (USDA)** and the **U.S. Department of Health and Human Services (DHHS)** jointly released the first edition of the ***Dietary Guidelines for Americans***. Revised guidelines have been released every five years as scientific information about links between diet and chronic disease is updated. The purpose of the *Dietary Guidelines for Americans* is to provide science-based advice to promote health and to reduce risk for chronic diseases through diet and physical activity.[10] The food and physical activity choices you make every day affect your health—how you feel today, tomorrow, and in the future. You'll find additional recommendations for specific population groups highlighted in later chapters.

The *Dietary Guidelines for Americans, 2010* (**Figure 2.2**) offers a roadmap intended to guide personal choices and help individuals make informed food and activity decisions. The result of a systematic, evidence-based review of the scientific literature, the *Dietary Guidelines for Americans, 2010* is based on what experts have determined to be the best advice for Americans to reduce the risk for chronic diseases and reduce the prevalence of overweight and obesity through improved nutrition and physical activity. These guidelines are the cornerstone of federal nutrition policy and education. They are used to develop educational materials and to aid in the design and implementation of nutrition-related programs, such as the National School Lunch Program and Meals on Wheels. The *Dietary Guidelines for Americans* serves as the basis for nutrition messages and consumer materials developed by nutrition educators and health professionals for the general public.[11]

Lifestyle choices, including a poor diet and lack of physical activity, are the most important factors that contribute to the overweight and obesity epidemic

U.S. Department of Agriculture (USDA) The government agency that monitors the production of eggs, poultry, and meat for adherence to standards of quality and wholesomeness. The USDA also provides public nutrition education, performs nutrition research, and administers the WIC program.

U.S. Department of Health and Human Services (DHHS) The principal federal agency responsible for protecting the health of all Americans and providing essential human services. The agency is especially concerned with those Americans who are least able to help themselves.

Dietary Guidelines for Americans The *Dietary Guidelines for Americans* are the foundation of federal nutrition policy and are developed by the U.S. Department of Agriculture (USDA) and the Department of Health and Human Services (DHHS). These science-based guidelines are intended to reduce the number of Americans who develop chronic diseases such as hypertension, diabetes, cardiovascular disease, obesity, and alcoholism.

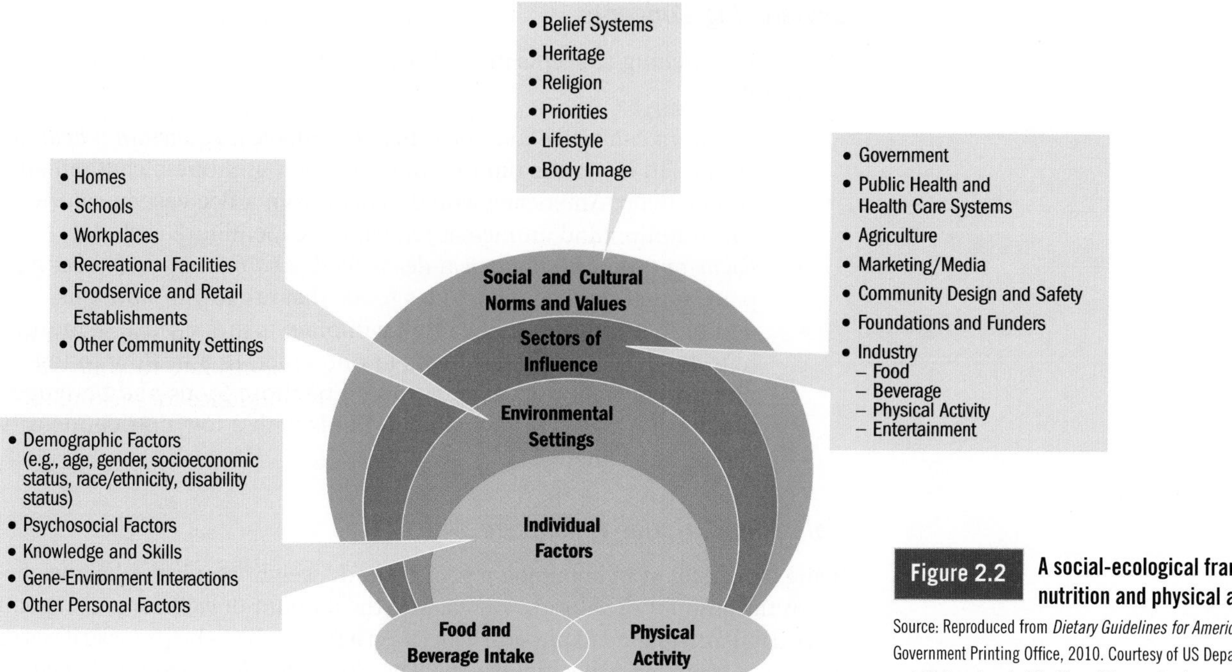

Figure 2.2 **A social-ecological framework for nutrition and physical activity decisions.**

Source: Reproduced from *Dietary Guidelines for Americans 2010*, 7th ed., US Government Printing Office, 2010. Courtesy of US Department of Agriculture and US Department of Health and Human Services.

that is currently affecting men, women, and children throughout the United States. Even in individuals who are not overweight, a poor diet and physical inactivity are well known to be associated with the major causes of morbidity and mortality. Currently the number of Americans who are overweight or obese is at an all-time high; as a consequence, the risk for various chronic diseases is also on the rise. In an effort to address this growing problem, the *Dietary Guidelines for Americans, 2010* focuses on the integration of government, agriculture, health care, business, educators, and communities working together to encourage individuals to make healthy lifestyle changes.[12] The main objective of these guidelines is to encourage Americans to balance calorie intake with physical activity to manage weight. This means helping Americans make the choices they need to eat a healthier diet by promoting the consumption of more vegetables, fruits, whole grains, fat-free and low-fat dairy products, and seafood; the consumption of foods with less sodium, saturated and trans fats, added sugars, and refined grains; and an increase in daily physical activity.

Key Recommendations from the *Dietary Guidelines for Americans*

The six chapters of the *Dietary Guidelines for Americans, 2010* contain two overarching concepts and 23 key recommendations for the general population, as well as 6 additional key recommendations for specific population groups. The recommendations within the *Dietary Guidelines for Americans, 2010* are intended for people age 2 years or older together with those who are at an increased risk of chronic disease.

This section reviews the overarching concepts and key recommendations from each chapter of the *Dietary Guidelines for Americans, 2010*. You can access the full report at www.dietaryguidelines.gov.

Overarching Concepts

The two overarching concepts in the *Dietary Guidelines for Americans, 2010* are as follows:

- *Maintain calorie balance over time to achieve and sustain a healthy weight.* To lower the number of overweight and obese children and adults, many Americans would benefit from a decrease in calorie consumption and an increase in calorie expenditure each day.
- *Focus on consuming nutrient-dense foods and beverages.* An eating pattern that frequently includes foods that are low in nutrients and high in calories (unhealthy) will often take the place of more nutrient-dense (healthier) foods in one's diet. In a healthy eating pattern, the majority of foods should be those foods and beverages that have a high nutrient content; foods with a low nutrient density should be limited.

Balancing Calories to Manage Weight

Being successful at maintaining a healthy body weight requires a balance between the amount of calories you eat and the amount of calories you expend every day. Participating in physical activity on a regular basis helps make it easier for you to maintain a healthy weight. The *2008 Physical Activity Guidelines for Americans* suggests that adults should do the equivalent of 150 minutes of moderate-intensity aerobic activity each week—that's an average of only 30 minutes a day, five days a week. For children and adolescents age 6 years or older, the recommendation is 60 minutes or more of physical activity per day.[13]

The environment in which many Americans now live, work, learn, and play may be a roadblock for many people trying to achieve or maintain a healthy body weight. An obesogenic environment is a significant contributor to America's obesity epidemic because it affects both sides of the calorie balance equation.[14] In our modern lifestyle, the availability of high-calorie, palatable, inexpensive food is coupled with many mechanized labor-saving devices. The result is that we live in an environment that often promotes overeating while at the same time discourages physical activity.

Key Recommendations

The following are key recommendations intended to help each of us balance calories to manage weight:

- Prevent and/or reduce overweight and obesity through improved eating and physical activity behaviors.
- Control total calorie intake to manage body weight. For people who are overweight or obese, this will mean consuming fewer calories from foods and beverages.
- Increase physical activity and reduce time spent in sedentary behaviors.
- Maintain appropriate calorie balance during each stage of life—childhood, adolescence, adulthood, pregnancy and breastfeeding, and older age.

Foods and Food Components to Reduce

This chapter of the *Dietary Guidelines for Americans, 2010* focuses on several foods and food components that Americans typically consume in excess. These foods and food components include sodium, solid fats, added sugars, and refined grains. Consistently eating too much of these foods and food components may increase the risk of certain chronic diseases, such as cardiovascular disease, diabetes, and certain types of cancer. In addition, when these foods and food components are a regular part of a person's diet, they tend to replace more nutrient-dense foods in the diet, making it even more difficult to meet recommended nutrient and calorie levels.

Key Recommendations

The following are key recommendations intended to help each of us reduce our intake of certain foods and food components:

- Reduce daily sodium intake to less than 2,300 milligrams (mg) (equals 1 teaspoon) and further reduce intake to 1,500 mg among persons who are 51 or older and those of any age who are African American or have hypertension, diabetes, or chronic kidney disease. The 1,500 mg recommendation applies to about half of the U.S. population, including children, and the majority of adults.
- Consume less than 10 percent of calories from saturated fatty acids by replacing them with monounsaturated and polyunsaturated fatty acids.
- Consume less than 300 mg per day of dietary cholesterol.
- Keep trans fatty acid consumption as low as possible by limiting foods that contain synthetic sources of trans fats, such as partially hydrogenated oils, and by limiting other solid fats.
- Reduce the intake of calories from solid fats and added sugars.
- Limit the consumption of foods that contain refined grains, especially refined grain foods that contain solid fats, added sugars, and sodium.
- If alcohol is consumed, it should be consumed in moderation—up to one drink per day for women and two drinks per day for men—and only by adults of legal drinking age.

Foods and Nutrients to Increase

In this chapter of the *Dietary Guidelines for Americans, 2010*, the focus is on food choices that many Americans should adopt to move toward more healthful eating. In the United States, intakes of vegetables, fruits, whole grains, milk and milk products, and oils are lower than recommended. As a result, dietary intakes of several nutrients, such as potassium, dietary fiber, calcium, and vitamin D, are low enough to be of public concern for both adults and children. Choosing healthful foods that provide these nutrients has been found to aid in preventing disease and be beneficial for overall well-being.

Keep in mind that recommendations for a healthy eating pattern will generally group foods based on commonalities in the nutrients provided, their effects on health, and how the foods are viewed and used by consumers. When trying to adopt the following recommendations as part of a healthy eating pattern, it is important that you also consider the recommendations from the previous section to help ensure that you are staying within your calorie needs. Some examples of the health benefits as well as tips for helping you to adopt the *Dietary Guidelines*' key recommendations can be found in Table 2.1.

Key Recommendations

The following are key recommendations intended to help each of us increase particular foods and nutrients:

- Increase vegetable and fruit intake.
- Eat a variety of vegetables, especially dark-green and red and orange vegetables and beans and peas.

Table 2.1 ***Dietary Guidelines for Americans:* Benefits, Behaviors, and Tips**

Dietary Guideline Recommendation	Benefits to Your Health	Goals or Behaviors That Could Make You Healthier	How-to Tips
Control total calorie intake to manage body weight.	Helps you to achieve and sustain a healthy weight. Benefits your physical health by improving blood pressure. Benefits your physical health by improving your blood cholesterol levels. Benefits your physical health by improving your blood sugar levels. Improves your energy level. Improves your physical mobility. Improves your overall general mood and self-confidence.	Consume foods and drinks to meet, not exceed, calorie needs. Plan ahead to make better food choices. Track food and calorie intake. Reduce portion sizes, especially of high-calorie foods. Cook and eat more meals at home, instead of eating out. Choose healthy options when eating out.	Know your calorie needs. Prepare and pack healthy snacks at home to be eaten at school or work. Track and evaluate what you eat using a food journal or an online food planner. Pay attention to feelings of hunger. Eat only until you are satisfied, not full. Limit eating while watching television, which often leads to overeating. Choose smaller plates and smaller portions. To feel satisfied with fewer calories, replace large portions of high-calorie foods with lower-calorie foods, like vegetables and fruits. Cook and eat at home more often. When eating out, choose a smaller size option or take home part of your meal. Choose dishes that include vegetables, fruits, and/or whole grains, and avoid choosing foods with the following words: creamy, fried, breaded, battered, or buttered.
Increase physical activity and reduce time spent in sedentary behaviors.	Helps to control your weight. Promotes psychological well-being. Reduces feelings of pressure and anxiety. Helps reduce your risk for chronic diseases such as diabetes, metabolic syndrome, high blood pressure, and some cancers. Helps build and maintain healthy bones, muscles, and joints. Improves your ability to do daily activities. Helps older adults become stronger and better able to move about without falling. Increases your chances of living longer.	Limit screen time. Be more active daily. Avoid couch time. Some physical activity is better than none. Slowly build up the amount of physical activity you choose.	Limit the amount of time you spend watching television or using other media such as computers and video games. Pick activities you like and that fit into your life. Be active with family and friends. Having a support network can help you stay active. Keep track of your physical activity and gradually increase it to meet the recommendations of the *2008 Physical Activity Guidelines for Americans*. Start by being active for longer each time you exercise, and then do more by exercising more often. Adults should do the equivalent of 150 minutes of moderate-intensity aerobic activity each week.
Increase vegetable and fruit intake.	Eating vegetables and fruits as part of a reduced-calorie diet can be of benefit to your body weight. Is associated with a decreased risk for many chronic diseases such as cardiovascular disease and many cancers. Contributes to healthy aging.	Eat five or more servings of vegetables and fruit daily, made up of a variety of choices.	Add dark-green, red, and orange vegetables to soups, stews, casseroles, and stir-fries and other main and side dishes. Add beans or peas to salad, soups, and side dishes, or serve as a main dish. Have raw, cut-up vegetables and fruit handy for a quick side dish, snacks, salad, or desserts. When eating out, choose a vegetable as a side dish.
Increase intake of fat-free or low-fat milk and milk products, such as milk, yogurt, cheese, or fortified soy beverages.	Milk and milk products contribute many nutrients to the diet, including calcium and vitamin D, which help to build and maintain strong bones and teeth. Adequate milk intake is associated with decreased chance of developing metabolic syndrome and high blood pressure.	Choose two to three servings of low-fat dairy products every day. Replace higher-fat milk and milk products with lower-fat options.	Drink fat-free (skim) or low-fat (1%) milk. When drinking beverages such as cappuccino or latte, request fat-free or low-fat milk. When recipes call for sour cream, substitute plain fat-free or low-fat yogurt.

Table 2.1 ***Dietary Guidelines for Americans:* Benefits, Behaviors, and Tips (Continued)**

Dietary Guideline Recommendation	Benefits to Your Health	Goals or Behaviors That Could Make You Healthier	How-to Tips
Limit the consumption of foods that contain refined grains and added sugars.	Eating foods that contain whole grains offers a good source of antioxidants such as vitamin E, magnesium, iron, and fiber to your diet. Eating foods that contain fiber helps lower blood cholesterol levels, control blood glucose levels for people with diabetes, and causes a feeling of satiety. A diet high in sugar is associated with being overweight/obese.	Increase whole-grain intake. Consume at least half of all grains as whole grains. Whenever possible, replace refined grains with whole grains. Choose foods and drinks with added sugars or caloric sweeteners (sugar-sweetened beverages) less frequently. Drink more water.	Choose 100 percent whole-grain breads, crackers, rice, and pasta. Use the Nutrition Facts label to choose whole grains that are a good or excellent source of dietary fiber. Eat fewer refined grain products, such as cakes, cookies, other desserts, and pizza. Replace white bread, rolls, bagels, muffins, pasta, and rice with whole-grain versions. To increase fiber in your diet, choose foods such as oat bran, barley, kidney beans, fruits, vegetables, wheat bran, and whole grains. Drink few or no regular sodas, sports drinks, energy drinks, and fruit drinks. Eat less cake, cookies, ice cream, other desserts, and candy. Choose water, fat-free milk, 100 percent fruit juice, or unsweetened tea or coffee as drinks rather than sugar-sweetened drinks.
Keep trans fatty acid consumption as low as possible.	Eating a diet that includes saturated fat, *trans* fat, and dietary cholesterol raises low-density lipoprotein (LDL), or "bad" cholesterol, levels, which increases the risk of coronary heart disease (CHD).	Be aware of the most likely sources of *trans* fat in your diet, such as many pastry items and donuts, deep-fried foods, many types of snack chips, cookies, and crackers.	When using spreads, choose soft margarines with zero *trans* fats made from liquid vegetable oil, rather than stick margarine or butter. Use vegetable oils such as olive, canola, corn, or sunflower oil rather than solid fats (butter, stick margarine, shortening, lard). Check the Nutrition Facts label to choose foods with little or no saturated fat and no *trans* fat. Limit foods that contain partially hydrogenated oils and other solid fats.
If alcohol is consumed, it should be consumed in moderation.	Excessive drinking has no benefits, and the health and social hazards of heavy alcohol intake are numerous and well known.	If you are of legal drinking age you should drink alcoholic beverages in moderation. Avoid alcohol in situations that can put you at risk.	Limit alcohol to no more than one drink per day for women and two drinks per day for men. Avoid excessive (heavy or binge) drinking. Avoid alcohol if you are pregnant or may become pregnant.
Follow food safety recommendations when preparing and eating foods to reduce the risk of foodborne illnesses.	Prevents foodborne illness.	Learn proper food handling techniques. When in doubt, throw it out. Cook food to a safe temperature. Store food safely.	Clean: Wash hands, utensils, and cutting boards before and after contact with raw meat, poultry, seafood, and eggs. Separate: Keep raw meat and poultry apart from foods that won't be cooked. Cook: Use a food thermometer. Chill: Chill leftovers and takeout foods within 2 hours and keep the refrigerator at 40 degrees Fahrenheit or below.

Source: Modified from *Dietary Guidelines for Americans 2010*, 7th ed., US Government Printing Office, 2010. Courtesy of US Department of Agriculture and US Department of Health and Human Services.

- Consume at least half of all grains as whole grains. Increase whole-grain intake by replacing refined grains with whole grains.
- Increase intake of fat-free or low-fat milk and milk products, such as milk, yogurt, cheese, or fortified soy beverages.
- Choose a variety of protein foods, which include seafood, lean meat and poultry, eggs, beans and peas, soy products, and unsalted nuts and seeds.
- Increase the amount and variety of seafood consumed by choosing seafood in place of some meat and poultry.
- Replace protein foods that are higher in solid fat with choices that are lower in solid fats and calories and/or are sources of oils.
- Use oils to replace solid fats where possible.
- Choose foods that provide more potassium, dietary fiber, calcium, and vitamin D, which are nutrients of concern in U.S. diets. These foods include vegetables, fruits, whole grains, and milk and milk products.

Recommendations for Specific Population Groups

The "Foods and Nutrients to Increase" chapter describes unique recommendations for specific population groups. These recommendations are designed to improve the food choices and health outcomes of certain individuals, such as pregnant and lactating women and older adults who have specific nutritional needs. These recommendations are as follows:

- Women capable of becoming pregnant
  - Choose foods that supply heme iron, which is more readily absorbed by the body, additional iron sources, and enhancers of iron absorption such as vitamin C–rich foods.
  - Consume 400 micrograms (mcg) per day of synthetic folic acid (from fortified foods and/or supplements) in addition to food forms of folate from a varied diet.
- Women who are pregnant or breastfeeding
  - Consume 8 to 12 ounces of seafood per week from a variety of seafood types.
  - Due to their methyl mercury content, limit white (albacore) tuna to 6 ounces per week and do not eat the following four types of fish: tilefish, shark, swordfish, and king mackerel.
  - If pregnant, take an iron supplement as recommended by an obstetrician or other health care provider.
- Individuals age 50 years or older
  - Consume foods fortified with vitamin B_{12}, such as fortified cereals, or dietary supplements.

Building Healthy Eating Patterns

The *Dietary Guidelines for Americans, 2010* also shows you how the recommendations and principles described in its previous chapters can be combined into a healthy overall eating pattern. Culture, ethnicity, tradition, personal preferences, food cost, and food availability are all factors people consider when creating the way they choose to eat. Americans have flexibility in the choices they make when forming their own healthy eating patterns. Americans also have access to established eating plans, such as the USDA Food Patterns and DASH Eating Plan, to assist in such efforts.

In addition, this chapter of the guidelines focuses on eating patterns that prevent foodborne illness and identifies how the four basic food safety principles—clean, separate, cook, and chill—work together to reduce the risk of foodborne illnesses.

Key Recommendations

The following are key recommendations intended to help each of us build healthy eating patterns:

- Select an eating pattern that meets nutrient needs over time at an appropriate calorie level.
- Account for all foods and beverages consumed and assess how they fit within a total healthy eating pattern.
- Follow food safety recommendations when preparing and eating foods to reduce the risk of foodborne illnesses.

Helping Americans Make Healthy Choices

This chapter focuses on two important factors. The first is that people make choices about what to eat and how physically active they will be every day. Second, all elements of society, including individuals and families, communities, business and industry, and various levels of government, should have a positive and productive role in the efforts to make America healthy. The *Dietary Guidelines for Americans, 2010* employs the social-ecological model (**Figure 2.3**) as a tool to illustrate how all elements of society combine to shape an individual's food and physical activity choices.

This chapter also includes the *2010 Dietary Guidelines*' Call to Action, which includes three guiding principles:

1. Ensure that all Americans have access to nutritious foods and opportunities for physical activity.
2. Facilitate individual behavior change through environmental strategies.
3. Set the stage for lifelong healthy eating, physical activity, and weight management behaviors.

The *Dietary Guidelines for Americans, 2010* also provides resources that can be used in developing policies, programs, and educational materials. These include the following:

- Guidelines for Specific Population Groups
- Key Consumer Behaviors and Potential Strategies for Professionals to Use
- Food Safety Principles and Guidance for Consumers
- Using the Food Label to Track Calories, Nutrients, and Ingredients

Ways to Incorporate the Dietary Guidelines into Your Daily Life

Think about your diet and consider your overall food intake to determine whether it is consistent with the *Dietary Guidelines for Americans, 2010*. Choose more fruits, vegetables, and whole grains to make sure you are getting all the nutrients you need while lowering your intake of saturated fat, trans fat, and cholesterol. Eat fewer high-fat toppings and fried foods to help you balance energy intake and expenditure. Exercise regularly. Use the extra things—sugar, salt, and alcohol—in moderation. Drink water more often than soft drinks, and if you choose to drink alcohol at all, use caution.

By using the *Dietary Guidelines* as your roadmap for finding a healthier way of eating, you may not only find it easier to meet your nutrition needs, but also will be protecting your health and achieving or maintaining a healthy

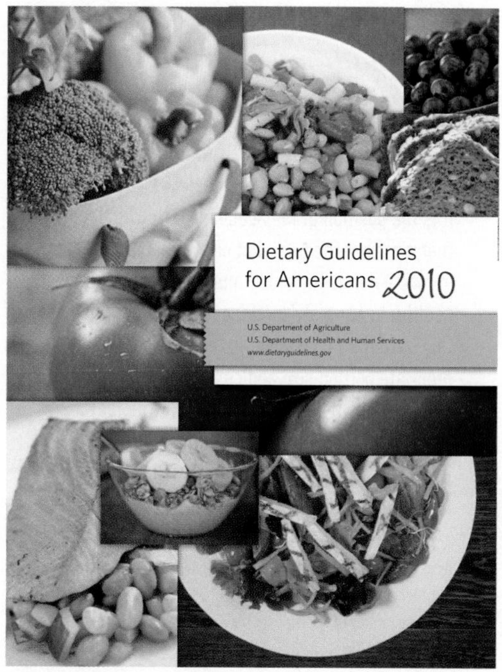

Figure 2.3 ***Dietary Guidelines for Americans.*** A revised *Dietary Guidelines for Americans* was released in 2010.

Source: Reproduced from *Dietary Guidelines for Americans 2010*, 7th ed., US Government Printing Office, 2010. Courtesy of US Department of Agriculture and US Department of Health and Human Services.

Quick Bite

How Well Do School Cafeterias Follow Nutrition Guidelines?

About one in three kids and teenagers is obese, and high-fat school lunches may be part of the problem. Until recently, the UDSA's nutritional standards for school meals had not been updated in more than 15 years. With the majority of school-age kids and teens getting 30 to 50 percent of their total calories from cafeteria meals each day, it's important that these meals be as healthy as possible. The Healthy, Hunger-Free Kids Act is a plan that will (1) boost the nutrition quality of school lunch by requiring fewer calories and sodium and more fresh fruits, vegetables, and whole grains; (2) expand the number of students enrolled in free- and reduced-cost meals; and (3) put into place a plan to eliminate things like unhealthy vending machines from school cafeterias.

Academy of Nutrition and Dietetics

Total Diet Approach to Communicating Food and Nutrition Information

It is the position of the Academy of Nutrition and Dietetics that the total diet or overall pattern of food eaten is the most important focus of a healthful eating style. All foods can fit within this pattern, if consumed in moderation with appropriate portion size and combined with regular physical activity. The Academy of Nutrition and Dietetics strives to communicate healthful eating messages to the public that emphasize a balance of foods, rather than any one food or meal.

American Dietetic Association. Position of the American Dietetic Association: total diet approach to communicating food and nutrition information. *J Am Diet Assoc.* 2007;107: 1224–1232. Reprinted with permission from the American Academy of Nutrition and Dietetics.

weight along the way. Table 2.1 offers suggestions of things that you may be able to change in your own diet or lifestyle. Pick one or two of these suggestions, or come up with some simple changes of your own to try to incorporate the *Dietary Guidelines for Americans, 2010* into your daily life. Table 2.2 gives a summary of daily limits or targets for a number of nutrients addressed in the *Dietary Guidelines*.

Canada's Guidelines for Healthy Eating

Promoting healthy eating habits among Canadians has been a priority of Health Canada for many years. Health Canada is the federal department responsible for helping the people of Canada maintain and improve their health. In the 1980s, a high priority was given to developing a single set of dietary guidelines. The result of this effort was the **1990 Nutrition Recommendations for Canadians**. This report updated the existing dietary standards and provided a scientific description of the characteristics of a healthy dietary pattern. Also published in 1990 was ***Canada's Guidelines for Healthy Eating***, a set of five positive, action-oriented messages for healthy Canadians over the age of 2.

The 2007 revision of Canada's guidelines, *Eating Well with Canada's Food Guide*, recommends that Canadians do the following:[15]

- Eat at least one dark-green and one orange vegetable each day.
- Enjoy vegetables and fruit prepared with little or no added fat, sugar, or salt.
- Have vegetables and fruits more often than juice.
- Select whole grains for at least half of one's grain products.
- Choose grain products that are low in fat, sugar, or salt.
- Drink skim, 1 percent, or 2 percent milk each day.
- Consume meat alternatives, such as beans, lentils, and tofu, often.
- Eat at least two *Food Guide* servings of fish each week.
- Select lean meat and alternatives prepared with little or no added fat or salt.

Nutrition Recommendations for Canadians A set of scientific statements that provide guidance to Canadians for a dietary pattern that will supply recommended amounts of all essential nutrients while reducing the risk of chronic disease.

Canada's Guidelines for Healthy Eating Key messages that are based on the 1990 *Nutrition Recommendations for Canadians* and provide positive, action-oriented, scientifically accurate eating advice to Canadians.

Table 2.2 Daily Targets for Nutrients as Addressed in the *Dietary Guidelines for Americans, 2010*

Nutrient or Food Group	Target for Adults Ages 19–50
Total fat (% of calories)	20–35
Saturated fat (% of calories)	<10%
Cholesterol (mg)	<300
Calcium (mg)	1,000
Potassium (mg)	4,700
Sodium (mg)	<2,300
Vitamin D (mcg) Note: 1 mcg of vitamin D is equivalent to 40 IU	15
Fiber (g)	14 g per 1,000 calories or 28–34 g/day
Vegetables and fruit (cups per day)	At least 4–5
Refined grains (oz per day)	>3
Physical activity	150 minutes of moderate-intensity aerobic activity each week

Source: Data from *Dietary Guidelines for Americans 2010*, 7th ed., US Government Printing Office, 2010. Courtesy of US Department of Agriculture and US Department of Health and Human Services.

Quick Bite

Pass Up the Salt

We require only a few hundred milligrams of sodium each day, but this would be unpalatable. Given our current high-salt food environment, it would also be difficult to achieve. The guideline is to eat less sodium, but not down to the level of actual requirements.

- Include a small amount of unsaturated fat each day.
- Satisfy thirst with water.
- Limit foods and beverages high in calories, fat, sugar, or salt.
- Be active every day.

The companion document, *Canada's Physical Activity Guide*, recommends 30 to 60 minutes of physical activity a day for children and youth.

Dietary guidelines in the United States and Canada address similar issues: less fat; more fruits, vegetables, and grains; less salt; and achieving healthy weights. In addition, both countries have developed graphic depictions of a healthful diet by showing the balance of food groups to be consumed each day. You can read about the USDA's MyPlate and Canada's *Food Guide* in the next section, "From Dietary Guidelines to Planning."

Key Concepts *Dietary guidelines are statements based on current science that "guide" people toward more healthful choices. The* Dietary Guidelines for Americans, 2010 *provides two overarching themes and 23 key recommendations for making food choices that promote good health, a healthy weight, and help prevent disease for healthy Americans age 2 or over. Six additional key recommendations target specific population groups. Behavioral strategies and creating a healthy environment are important for adopting the recommendations in the* Dietary Guidelines for Americans, 2010. *Both the United States and Canada have guidelines that embody the basic principles of balance, variety, moderation, and calorie control.*

From Dietary Guidelines to Planning: *What* You Will Eat

By understanding the *Dietary Guidelines for Americans*, you will be able to identify characteristics that will make your diet and your lifestyle healthy. The next step is to translate those healthy choices into the foods that you choose to eat. For many years, nutritionists and teachers have used **food groups** to illustrate the proper combination of foods in a healthful diet. Even young children can sort food into groups and fill a plate with foods from each group. The foods within each group are similar because of their origins—fruits, for example, all come from the same part of different plants. But from a nutritional perspective, what fruits have in common is the balance of macronutrients and the similarities in micronutrient composition. Even so, the foods in one group may differ significantly in their vitamin and mineral profiles. Some fruits (e.g., citrus, strawberries, and kiwi) are rich in vitamin C, and others (e.g., apples and bananas) have very little. Here again, we can see the importance of variety, of not simply including different food groups but also choosing a variety of foods *within* each group.

food groups Categories of similar foods, such as fruits or vegetables.

A Brief History of Food Group Plans

When the U.S. Department of Agriculture published its first dietary recommendations in 1894, specific vitamins and minerals had not even been discovered.[16] The initial guide stressed the importance of consuming enough fat and sugar and energy-rich foods to support daily activity. Because people performed more manual labor in those days, many people were simply not getting enough calories! Canada's Official Food Rules (1942) recommended a weekly serving of liver, heart, or kidney and regular doses of fish liver oils—good sources of vitamins A and D. Later food group plans, including the Basic Four that was popular from the 1950s through the 1970s, focused on fruits, vegetables, grains, dairy products, and meats and their substitutes. The Basic

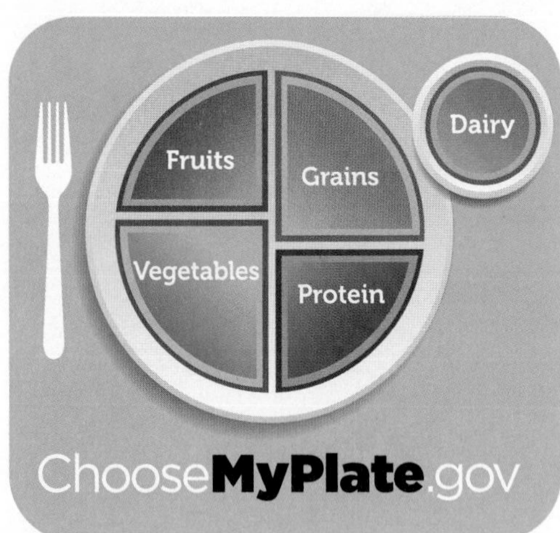

Figure 2.4 **MyPlate.** Released in 2011, MyPlate is an Internet-based educational tool that helps consumers implement the principles of the 2010 *Dietary Guidelines for Americans* and other nutritional standards.

Source: Courtesy of USDA.

MyPlate An educational tool that translates the principles of the *Dietary Guidelines for Americans* and other nutritional standards to help consumers in making healthier food and physical activity choices.

Eating Well with Canada's Food Guide Recommendations to help Canadians select foods to meet energy and nutrient needs while reducing the risk of chronic disease. The *Food Guide* is based on the *Nutrition Recommendations for Canadians* and Canada's Guidelines for Healthy Eating and is a key nutrition education tool for Canadians aged 4 years and older.

Four was usually illustrated as either a circle or a square, with each group having an equal share. The implication was that people should consume equal amounts of food from each group. Nutrition science now tells us that those proportions give us a diet too high in fat and protein for our modern lifestyle, and not high enough in carbohydrates and fiber.

After the development of the *Dietary Guidelines for Americans* in 1980, the USDA developed a new food guide that would promote overall health and be consistent with the *Dietary Guidelines*. To bring this new food guide and its key messages to the attention of consumers, the colorful Food Guide Pyramid was developed. The Pyramid was designed to illustrate the *Dietary Guidelines for Americans* in terms of food groups and recommended numbers of daily servings. Updated again and renamed in 2005, the USDA MyPyramid food guidance system was intended to be a visual reminder for individuals to make healthy food choices and be physically active every day. Based on the *Dietary Guidelines for Americans* and the Dietary Reference Intakes, the goal of MyPyramid was to translate dietary guidance into a total diet that met nutrient needs from food sources and aimed to limit dietary components often consumed in excess. By law, the *Dietary Guidelines for Americans* is reviewed, updated if necessary, and published every five years. In the current version, the *Dietary Guidelines for Americans, 2010*, MyPlate and ChooseMyPlate.gov were created (**Figure 2.4**).

MyPlate

MyPlate is the USDA's current icon and primary food group symbol to accompany the *Dietary Guidelines for Americans, 2010*. As part of the government's healthy eating initiative, MyPlate is designed to convey the seven key messages from the *Dietary Guidelines for Americans, 2010*: Enjoy food but eat less; avoid oversized portions; make half your plate fruits and vegetables; drink water instead of sugary drinks; switch to fat-free or low-fat (1 percent) milk; compare sodium in foods; and make at least half your grains whole grains.

MyPlate is an easy-to-understand visual image intended to empower people with the information they need to make healthy food choices and create eating habits consistent with the *Dietary Guidelines for Americans, 2010*. Because we eat on plates, the design of MyPlate icon identifies visually how much room on a plate each food group should occupy. It is the objective of this tool to remind people to think about, create, and make better, more balanced food choices. MyPlate uses the image of a dinner plate divided into four sections: fruits, vegetables, grains, and proteins, with a smaller plate (or glass) representing a serving of dairy. MyPlate is accompanied by a supporting Web site: www.ChooseMyPlate.gov. ChooseMyPlate.gov provides tools, resources, and practical information on dietary assessment, nutrition education, and other user-friendly nutrition information.

Unlike the USDA's former food guide systems, MyPlate does not suggest particular foods or specific serving sizes and does not even mention desserts or sweets. The purpose behind these changes is clear—this food guide is different! It is not intended to tell people what to eat, but to empower them to make their own healthy choices and to use this visual icon as a sensible guide.[17]

Eating Well with Canada's Food Guide

As science advanced and nutritional concerns changed, Canada's Official Food Rules evolved into **Eating Well with Canada's Food Guide** (see **Figure 2.5**). The amounts and types of foods recommended in the *Food Guide* are based on the nutrient reference values of the Dietary Reference Intakes (DRIs).

10 tips
Nutrition Education Series

liven up your meals with vegetables and fruits

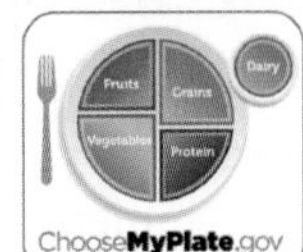

10 tips to improve your meals with vegetables and fruits

Discover the many benefits of adding vegetables and fruits to your meals. They are low in fat and calories, while providing fiber and other key nutrients. Most Americans should eat more than 3 cups—and for some, up to 6 cups—of vegetables and fruits each day. Vegetables and fruits don't just add nutrition to meals. They can also add color, flavor, and texture. Explore these creative ways to bring healthy foods to your table.

1 fire up the grill
Use the grill to cook vegetables and fruits. Try grilling mushrooms, carrots, peppers, or potatoes on a kabob skewer. Brush with oil to keep them from drying out. Grilled fruits like peaches, pineapple, or mangos add great flavor to a cookout.

2 expand the flavor of your casseroles
Mix vegetables such as sauteed onions, peas, pinto beans, or tomatoes into your favorite dish for that extra flavor.

3 planning something Italian?
Add extra vegetables to your pasta dish. Slip some peppers, spinach, red beans, onions, or cherry tomatoes into your traditional tomato sauce. Vegetables provide texture and low-calorie bulk that satisfies.

4 get creative with your salad
Toss in shredded carrots, strawberries, spinach, watercress, orange segments, or sweet peas for a flavorful, fun salad.

5 salad bars aren't just for salads
Try eating sliced fruit from the salad bar as your dessert when dining out. This will help you avoid any baked desserts that are high in calories.

6 get in on the stir-frying fun
Try something new! Stir-fry your veggies—like broccoli, carrots, sugar snap peas, mushrooms, or green beans—for a quick-and-easy addition to any meal.

7 add them to your sandwiches
Whether it is a sandwich or wrap, vegetables make great additions to both. Try sliced tomatoes, romaine lettuce, or avocado on your everday sandwich or wrap for extra flavor.

8 be creative with your baked goods
Add apples, bananas, blueberries, or pears to your favorite muffin recipe for a treat.

9 make a tasty fruit smoothie
For dessert, blend strawberries, blueberries, or raspberries with frozen bananas and 100% fruit juice for a delicious frozen fruit smoothie.

10 liven up an omelet
Boost the color and flavor of your morning omelet with vegetables. Simply chop, saute, and add them to the egg as it cooks. Try combining different vegetables, such as mushrooms, spinach, onions, or bell peppers.

Go to www.ChooseMyPlate.gov for more information.

Source: Reproduced from Dietary Guidelines TipSheet No. 10, US Government Printing Office, 2011. Courtesy of US Department of Agriculture and US Department of Health and Human Services.

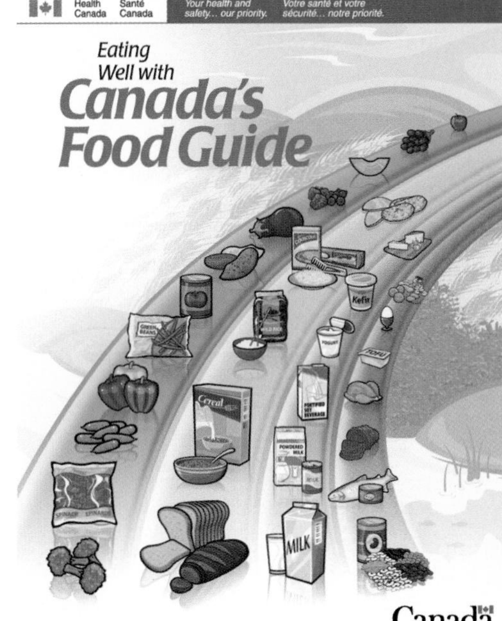

Figure 2.5 ***Eating Well with Canada's Food Guide.*** The rainbow portion of *Canada's Food Guide* sorts food into groups from which people can make wise food choices. For the complete guide, see Appendix D.

Source: *Eating Well with Canada's Food Guide*, Health Canada, 2007. Reproduced with the permission of the Minister of Public Works and Government Services Canada, 2010.

The foods pictured in the *Food Guide* document essentially incorporate both the recommended eating pattern and associated dietary guidance.

The "rainbow" of the *Food Guide* places foods into four groups: Grain Products, Vegetables and Fruits, Milk Products, and Meat and Alternatives. The *Food Guide* describes the kinds of foods to choose from each group. For example, under the Vegetables and Fruit group, the *Food Guide* suggests "Drink fortified soy beverages if you do not drink milk." *Canada's Food Guide* illustrates that vegetables, fruits, and grains should be the major part of the diet, with milk products and meats consumed in smaller amounts.

The "bar" side of the *Food Guide* (see Appendix D) shows how many daily servings are recommended from each group and gives examples of serving sizes. The *Food Guide* also provides specific advice for different ages and stages. Limiting foods and beverages high in calories, fat, sugar, or salt is recommended. Label reading is recommended, and a list of steps to healthy living is provided. The Health Canada Web site (www.healthcanada.gc.ca/foodguide) includes a link to My Food Guide, an interactive tool for personalizing the information in the *Food Guide*.

2–4 servings of fruit

6–11 servings of bread, rice, and cereal.

Using MyPlate or *Canada's Food Guide* in Diet Planning

The first step in using MyPlate or *Canada's Food Guide* for diet planning is to determine the amount of calories you should eat each day. Table 2.3 shows the recommended amounts of food for three calorie-intake levels. It will also give you an idea of how MyPlate varies with different energy needs. Next, become familiar with the types of food in each group, the number of recommended servings, and the appropriate serving sizes. (For an intuitive guide to serving sizes, see Table 2.4.) Finally, plan your meals and snacks using the suggested serving sizes for your appropriate calorie level.

Let's start to plan a 2,000-calorie diet. Beginning with breakfast, you could plan to have the following: 1 cup (1 oz) of ready-to-eat cereal, ½ cup of skim milk, 1 slice of whole wheat toast with 1 teaspoon of butter, and 1 cup of orange juice.

Continue to plan your meals and snack for the rest of the day with the amount of servings you have remaining for each food group. In this case it would be as shown in Table 2.5.

Table 2.3 Food Group Recommendations for a 2,000-Calorie Diet

Food Group	Total Recommended for 2,000-Calorie Diet	Amount Used at Breakfast	Amount Left for Remainder of the Day
Grains	6 oz eq	2 oz eq	4 oz eq
Vegetables	2½ cups	0	2½ cups
Fruits	2 cups	1 cup	1 cup
Dairy	3 cups	½ cup	2½ cups
Protein	5½ oz eq	0	5½ oz
Oils	6 tsp	1 tsp	5 tsp
Empty Calories Allowed	267 calories	0	267 calories

Source: Data from *Dietary Guidelines for Americans 2010*, 7th ed., US Government Printing Office, 2010. Courtesy of US Department of Agriculture and US Department of Health and Human Services.

Table 2.4 USDA Food Patterns: Suggested Daily Amounts for Three Levels of Energy Intake

	Energy Intake Level		
Food Group	*Low (1,400 kcal)*[a]	*Moderate (2,000 kcal)*[b]	*High (2,800 kcal)*[c]
Grains	5 oz eq	6 oz eq	10 oz eq
Vegetables	1½ cups	2½ cups	3½ cups
Fruits	1½ cups	2 cups	2½ cups
Dairy	2.5 cups	3 cups	3 cups
Protein foods	4 oz eq	5½ oz eq	7 oz eq
Oils	17 g	27 g	36 g

[a]1,400 kilocalories is about right for many young children.

[b]2,000 kilocalories is about right for teenaged girls, active women, and many sedentary men.

[c]2,800 kilocalories is about right for teenaged boys, and many active men.

Note: Your calorie needs may be higher or lower than those shown. Women may need more calories when they are pregnant or breastfeeding. Recommended average daily intake amounts at more calorie levels for each food group or subgroup can be found in Appendix C.

Source: Modified from *Dietary Guidelines for Americans 2010*, 7th ed., US Government Printing Office, 2010. Courtesy of US Department of Agriculture and US Department of Health and Human Services.

Table 2.5

Playing with Portions

Your favorite sports and games can help you visualize MyPlate portion sizes.

GRAINS	1 cup dry cereal 4 golf balls	2 ounce bagel 1 hockey puck	½ cup cooked cereal, rice, or pasta tennis ball
VEGETABLES	1 cup of vegetables 1 baseball or 1 Rubik's cube		
FRUITS	1 medium fruit (equivalent of 1 cup of fruit) 1 baseball		
OILS	1 teaspoon vegetable oil 1 die (11⁄16″ size)	1 tablespoon salad dressing 1 jacks ball	
MILK	1½ ounces of hard cheese 6 dice (11⁄16″ size)	⅓ cup of shredded cheese 1 billiard ball or racquetball	
MEAT AND BEANS	3 ounces cooked meat 1 deck of playing cards	2 tablespoons hummus 1 ping pong ball	

Keep in mind that what you consider a serving may differ from the sizes defined in MyPlate. Research shows that Americans' serving sizes for common foods such as pasta, cookies, cereal, soft drinks, and french fries have increased significantly.[18] Do large portions promote overeating and obesity? See the FYI feature "Portion Distortion" for a scientific exploration related to this question.

Sometimes it's difficult to figure out how to account for foods that are mixtures of different groups—lasagna, casseroles, or pizza, for example. Try separating such foods into their ingredients (e.g., pizza contains crust, tomato sauce, cheese, and toppings, which might be meats or vegetables) to estimate the amounts. You should be able to come up with a reasonable approximation. All in all, MyPlate and *Canada's Food Guide* are easy-to-use guidelines that can help you select a variety of foods.

Watch the empty calories, too. Note in Table 2.5 that for a 2,000-calorie food plan, 267 calories are unused even when all the other food groups are accounted for. However, this accounting with leftover calories assumes that all food choices are fat-free or low-fat and do not have added sugars. What does this all mean? If you are already in the habit of choosing low-fat and low-sugar options, you have a few calories to play with each day. These calories can be used for a higher-fat choice or for some sugar in your iced tea. But watch out! Those calories get used up quickly. One regular 12-ounce soft drink would take up 150 discretionary calories; an extra tablespoon of dressing on your salad would be 100 calories.

Using the ChooseMyPlate.gov Web site is easy and informative. Getting a personalized plan, learning healthy eating tips, getting weight loss information, planning a healthy menu, and analyzing your diet are examples of what ChooseMyPlate.gov offers. The Web site is an excellent way to help guide you through the necessary steps of putting the *Dietary Guidelines* into practice, while at the same time teaching good nutrition and providing appropriate physical activity information.

Key Concepts: *MyPlate is a complete food guidance system based on the* Dietary Guidelines for Americans *and Dietary Reference Intakes to help Americans make healthy food choices and remind them to be active every day. The interactive tools on the ChooseMyPlate.gov Web site can help you monitor your food choices.* Eating Well with Canada's Food Guide *illustrates the dietary guidelines for Canadians and the Dietary Reference Intakes. These graphic tools show the appropriate balance of food groups in a healthful diet: more whole grains, vegetables, and fruits and less dairy, meat, and added fats and sugars.*

Exchange Lists

Exchange Lists Lists of foods that in specified portions provide equivalent amounts of carbohydrate, fat, protein, and energy. Any food in an Exchange List can be substituted for any other without markedly affecting macronutrient intake.

Another tool for diet planning that uses food groups is called the **Exchange Lists**. Like MyPlate, the Exchange Lists divide foods into groups. Diets can be planned by choosing a certain number of servings, or exchanges, from each group each day. The original purpose of the Exchange Lists was to help people with diabetes plan diets that would provide consistent levels of energy and carbohydrates—both of which are essential for dietary management of diabetes. For this reason, foods are organized into groups or lists not only by the type of food (e.g., fruits or vegetables) but also by the amount of macronutrients (carbohydrate, protein, and fat) in each portion. The portions are defined so that each "exchange" has a similar composition. For example, 1 fruit exchange is ½ cup of orange juice or 17 small grapes or 1 medium apple or ½ cup of applesauce. All of these exchanges have approximately

60 kilocalories, 15 grams of carbohydrate, 0 grams of protein, and 0 grams of fat. In the Exchange Lists, starchy vegetables such as potatoes, corn, and peas are grouped with breads and cereals instead of with other vegetables because their balance of macronutrients is more like bread or pasta than carrots or tomatoes.

Figure 2.6 shows the amounts of carbohydrate, protein, fat, and kilocalories in one exchange from each group, along with a sample serving size. For a complete set of the Exchange Lists, see Appendix B or go to nutrition.jbpub.com.

Using the Exchange Lists in Diet Planning

In addition to their use by people with diabetes, Exchange Lists are used in many weight-control programs. Planning a diet using the Exchange Lists is done in much the same manner as using MyPlate. The first step is to become very familiar with the components of each group, the variations in fat content for the dairy and meat lists, and ways that other foods may be included. Then, an individual diet plan can be used to select meals and snacks throughout the day. An exchange-based diet plan specifies the number of exchanges to be consumed from each group at each meal. For example, a 1,500-kilocalorie weight reduction diet plan might have the following meal pattern:

Breakfast: 2 starch, 1 fruit, 1 milk, 1 fat
Lunch: 3 meat, 2 starch, 1 fruit, 1 vegetable, 1 fat
Snack: 1 milk, 1 starch, 1 fat
Dinner: 2 meat, 1 starch, 2 vegetable, 2 fat
Snack: 2 starch, 1 fruit

Using this pattern and a complete set of the Exchange Lists, you could then plan out a day or week of menus. Here's one sample:

Breakfast: ½ cup orange juice, ¾ cup corn flakes, 1 cup 2% milk, 1 slice toast, 1 tsp margarine
Lunch: 3 oz cooked hamburger on bun, 1 tsp mayonnaise, ½ cup baby carrots, 1 medium apple
Snack: ¾ cup low-fat yogurt, ½ bagel with 1 tbsp cream cheese
Dinner: 2 oz cooked pork chop, ½ cup rice with 1 tsp margarine, ½ cup yellow squash and ½ cup zucchini stir-fried in 1 tsp vegetable oil
Snack: 1 toasted English muffin, 1 medium pear

Key Concepts *The Exchange Lists are a diet-planning tool that uses the idea of food groups, but defines groups specifically in terms of macronutrient (carbohydrate, fat, and protein) content. Individual diet plans can be developed for people who need to control energy or carbohydrate intake, such as for weight control or management of diabetes mellitus.*

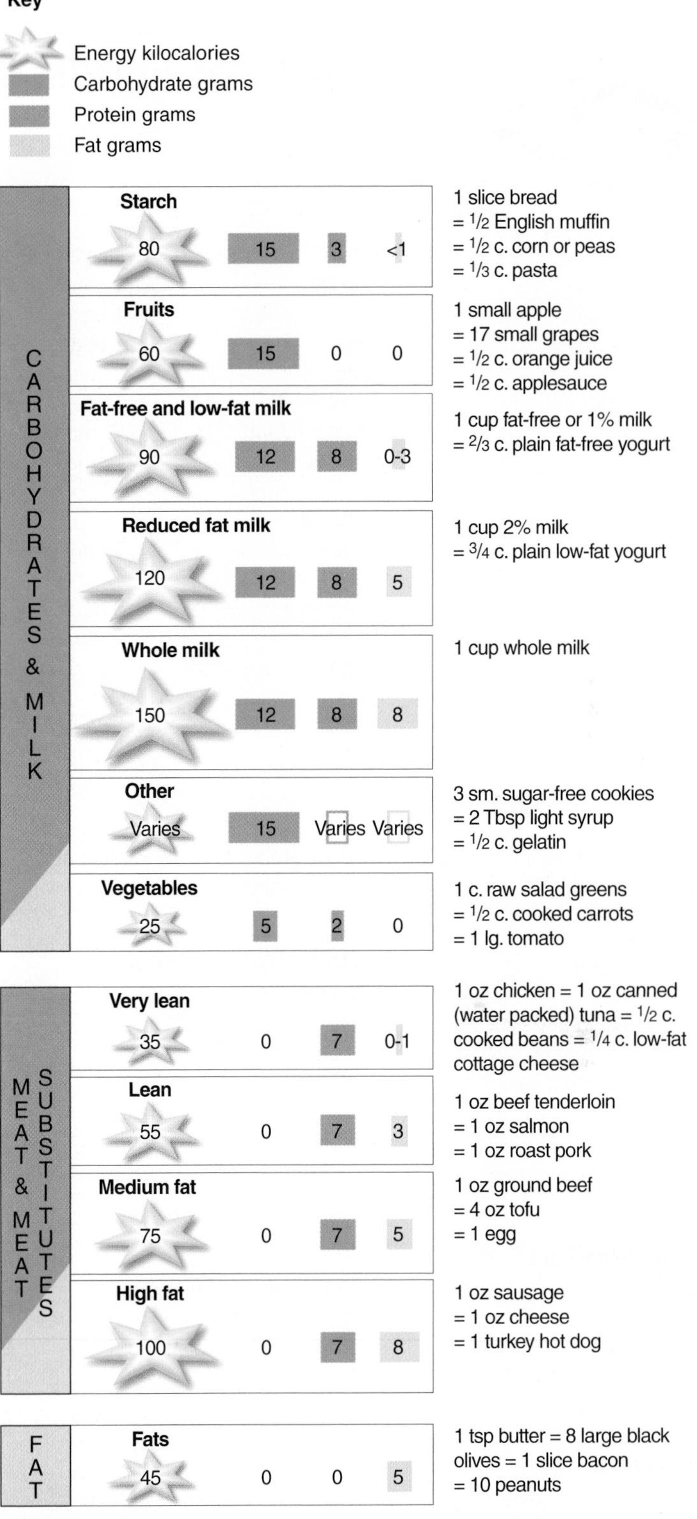

Key
Energy kilocalories
Carbohydrate grams
Protein grams
Fat grams
CARBOHYDRATES & MILK
Starch
80 15 3 <1
1 slice bread = 1/2 English muffin = 1/2 c. corn or peas = 1/3 c. pasta
Fruits
60 15 0 0
1 small apple = 17 small grapes = 1/2 c. orange juice = 1/2 c. applesauce
Fat-free and low-fat milk
90 12 8 0-3
1 cup fat-free or 1% milk = 2/3 c. plain fat-free yogurt
Reduced fat milk
120 12 8 5
1 cup 2% milk = 3/4 c. plain low-fat yogurt
Whole milk
150 12 8 8
1 cup whole milk
Other
Varies 15 Varies Varies
3 sm. sugar-free cookies = 2 Tbsp light syrup = 1/2 c. gelatin
Vegetables
25 5 2 0
1 c. raw salad greens = 1/2 c. cooked carrots = 1 lg. tomato
MEAT & MEAT SUBSTITUTES
Very lean
35 0 7 0-1
1 oz chicken = 1 oz canned (water packed) tuna = 1/2 c. cooked beans = 1/4 c. low-fat cottage cheese
Lean
55 0 7 3
1 oz beef tenderloin = 1 oz salmon = 1 oz roast pork
Medium fat
75 0 7 5
1 oz ground beef = 4 oz tofu = 1 egg
High fat
100 0 7 8
1 oz sausage = 1 oz cheese = 1 turkey hot dog
FAT
Fats
45 0 0 5
1 tsp butter = 8 large black olives = 1 slice bacon = 10 peanuts

Figure 2.6 **Exchange Lists.** The Exchange Lists are a widely used system for meal planning for people with diabetes. They are also helpful for people interested in healthy eating and weight control. See Appendix B for the complete set of Exchange Lists.

Source: American Diabetes Association and the American Dietetic Association. *Exchange Lists for Meal Planning.* Alexandria, VA: American Diabetes Association, 2003. Reprinted with permission.

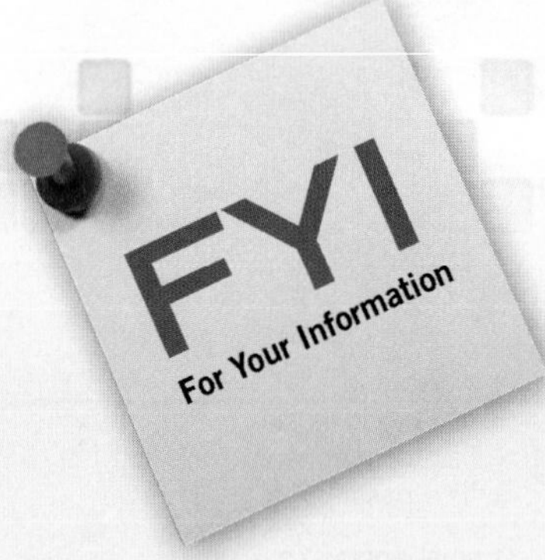

MyPlate: Foods, Serving Sizes, and Tips

Grains	Amount Equal to 1 Ounce	Common Portions and Ounce Equivalents
Bagels	1 "mini" bagel	1 large bagel = 4 ounce equivalents
Biscuits	1 small (2″ diameter)	1 large (3″) = 2 ounce equivalents
Breads	1 regular slice	2 regular slices = 2 ounce equivalents
Bulgur	½ cup cooked	
Cornbread	1 small piece (2½″ × 1¼″ × 1¼″)	1 medium piece = 2 ounce equivalents
English muffin	½ muffin	1 muffin = 2 ounce equivalents
Muffins	1 small (2½″ diameter)	1 large (3½″ diameter) = 3 ounce equivalents
Oatmeal	½ cup cooked	
Pancakes	1 pancake (4½″ diameter)	3 pancakes (4½″ diameter) = 3 ounce equivalents
Popcorn	3 cups, popped	1 microwave bag, popped = 4 ounce equivalents
Ready-to-eat cereals	1 cup flakes; 1¼ cups puffed	
Rice	½ cup cooked (1 ounce dry)	1 cup cooked = 2 ounce equivalents
Pasta	½ cup cooked (1 ounce dry)	1 cup cooked = 2 ounce equivalents
Tortillas	1 small (6″ diameter)	1 large (12″ diameter) = 4 ounce equivalents

Tips: Make at least half your grains whole grains. Choose foods that name one of the following first on the label's ingredient list: brown rice, bulgur, graham flour, oatmeal, whole oats, whole rye, whole wheat, wild rice. Go easy on high-fat or sugary toppings.

Vegetables	Amount Equal to 1 Cup of Vegetables	Vegetables	Amount Equal to 1 Cup of Vegetables
Dark-Green Vegetables		**Starchy Vegetables**	
Spinach, romaine, collards, mustard greens, kale, other leafy greens	2 cups raw or 1 cup cooked	Corn	1 cup or 1 large ear (8″ to 9″ long)
Broccoli	1 cup chopped or florets	Green peas	1 cup
		White potatoes	1 cup diced or mashed 1 medium potato, boiled or baked
Orange Vegetables		**Other Vegetables**	
Carrots	1 cup, raw or cooked 2 medium whole 1 cup baby carrots (about 12)	Bean sprouts Green beans Mushrooms	1 cup cooked 1 cup cooked 1 cup raw or cooked
Pumpkin, sweet potato, winter squash	1 cup, cooked	Tomatoes	1 large raw whole (3″) 1 cup chopped, sliced, or cooked
Dry Beans and Peas			
Black, garbanzo, kidney, pinto, soybeans; black-eyed peas, split peas	1 cup whole or mashed, cooked		
Tofu	1 cup of ½″ cubes		

Tips: Vary your veggies. Make half your plate fruits and vegetables. Eat more dark-green vegetables, more orange vegetables, and more dry beans. Buy fresh vegetables in season for best taste and lowest cost. Buy vegetables that are easy to prepare.

Fruit	Amount Equal to 1 Cup of Fruit
Apple	1 small
Applesauce	1 cup
Banana	1 large (8″ to 9″ long)
Melon	1 cup diced or melon balls
Grapes	1 cup whole; 32 seedless grapes
Canned fruit or diced raw fruit	1 cup
Orange or peach	1 large
Strawberries	About 8 large berries
100% fruit juice	1 cup

Tips: Focus on fruit. Make half your plate fruits and vegetables. Eat a variety of fruit. Choose fresh, frozen, canned, or dried fruit. Go easy on juices. When choosing a juice, look for "100% juice" on the label.

Milk	Amount Equal to 1 Cup of Milk
Milk	1 cup
Yogurt	1 regular container (8 ounces) or 1 cup yogurt
Cheese	1½ ounces hard cheese
	⅓ cup shredded cheese
	2 ounces processed cheese
	2 cups cottage cheese
Milk-based desserts	1 cup pudding made with milk
	1 cup frozen yogurt
Soymilk	1 cup calcium-fortified soymilk

Tips: Get your calcium-rich foods. Switch to fat-free or low-fat milk. If you don't or can't consume milk, get your calcium rich foods by choosing lactose-free or other calcium sources such as calcium-fortified juices, cereals, breads, soy beverages, or rice beverages.

Meat and Beans	Amount Equal to 1 Ounce	Common Portions and Ounce Equivalents
Cooked lean beef, pork, ham	1 ounce	1 small steak = 3½ to 4 ounce equivalents
Cooked chicken or turkey, without skin	1 ounce	1 small lean hamburger = 2 to 3 ounce equivalents
		1 small chicken breast half = 3 ounce equivalents
Cooked fish or shellfish	1 ounce	1 can tuna, drained = 3 to 4 ounce equivalents
		1 salmon steak = 4 to 6 ounce equivalents
		1 small trout = 3 ounce equivalents
Eggs	1 egg	
Nuts and seeds	½ ounce of nuts (12 almonds, 24 pistachios, 7 walnut halves)	
	½ ounce of seeds, roasted	
	1 tablespoon of peanut butter	
Dry beans and peas	¼ cup cooked beans or peas	
	¼ cup baked beans, refried beans	
	¼ cup tofu	
	1 ounce tempeh	
	2 tablespoons hummus	

Tips: Go lean with protein. Choose low-fat or lean meats and poultry. Bake it, broil it, or grill it. Vary your choices, with more fish, beans, peas, nuts, and seeds.

Oils

Common oils: Vegetable oils (canola, corn, cottonseed, olive, safflower, soybean, sunflower)

Foods naturally high in oils:

- Nuts
- Olives
- Some fish
- Avocados

Tips: Know your oils. Oils are not a food group, but they provide essential nutrients. Make most of your fat sources from fish, nuts, and vegetable oils. Limit solid fats such as butter, stick margarine, shortening, and lard.

Source: US Department of Agriculture. MyPlate. http://www.ChooseMyPlate.gov. Accessed 10/10/11.

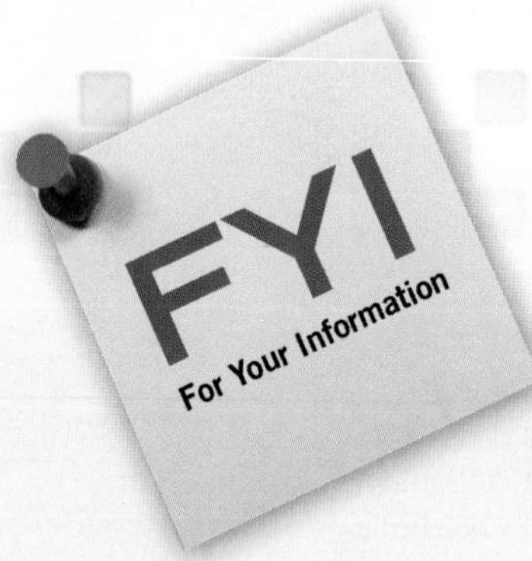

Portion Distortion

The prevalence of obesity continues to be of great concern to both adults and children in the United States. A notable increase in obesity can be observed over the past 20 years. In 2007 only one state (Colorado) had a prevalence of obesity less than 20 percent. Thirty states had a prevalence equal to or greater than 25 percent; three of these states (Alabama, Mississippi, and Tennessee) had a prevalence of obesity equal to or greater than 30 percent.[1]

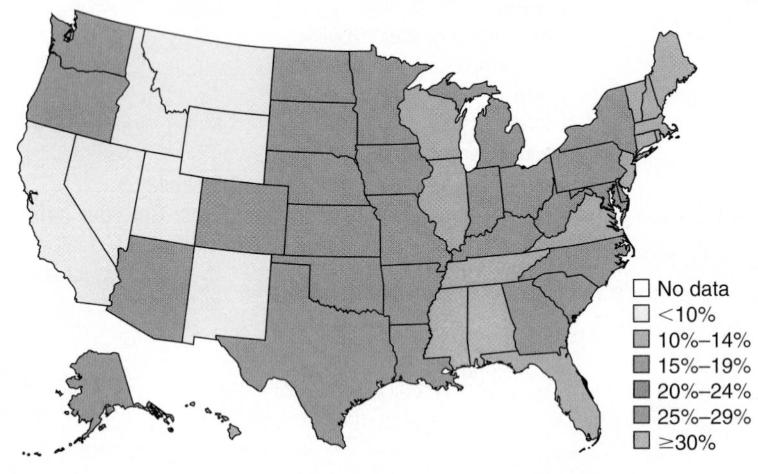

Source: Centers for Disease Control and Prevention.

Many factors contribute to Americans' growing waistlines, but one observation in particular cannot be overlooked: the incidence of obesity has increased in parallel with increasing portion sizes.[2] In almost every eating situation, we are now confronted by huge portions, which are perceived as "normal" or "a great value." This perception that large portion sizes are appropriate has created an environment of *portion distortion*.[3] We find portion distortion in supermarkets, where the number of larger sizes has increased 10-fold between 1970 and 2000.We find portion distortions in restaurants, where the jumbo-sized portions are consistently 250 percent larger than the regular portions.[4] We even find portion distortions in our homes, where the sizes of our bowls and glasses have steadily increased and where the surface area of the average dinner plate has increased 36 percent since 1960.[5] Research shows that people unintentionally consume more calories when faced with larger portions. In addition, research also shows that portion distortion seems to affect the portion sizes selected by young adults and children for some foods.[6] Consuming larger portion sizes can contribute to positive energy balance, which, over time, leads to weight gain and ultimately may result in obesity.

The phenomenon of portion distortion has the potential to hinder weight loss, weight maintenance, and health improvement efforts. Food and nutrition professionals must develop ways to "undistort" what people perceive to be typical portion sizes and help individuals recognize what is an appropriate amount to eat at a single eating occasion.[7]

To see whether you know how today's portions compare to the portions available 20 years ago, take the interactive portion distortion quizzes on the National Heart, Lung and Blood Institute's Portion Distortion Web page (http://hp2010.nhlbihin.net/portion/). You can also learn about the amount of physical activity required to burn off the extra calories provided by today's portions.

1 Centers for Disease Control and Prevention. U.S. obesity trends: trends by state, 1985–2008. http://www.cdc.gov/nccdphp/dnpa/Obesity/trend/maps/index.htm. Accessed 4/29/09.

2 Schwartz J, Byrd-Bredbenner C. Portion distortion: typical portion sizes selected by young adults. *J Am Diet Assoc.* 2006;106(9):1412–1418.

3 Wansink B, van Ittersum K. Portion size me: downsizing our consumption norms. *J Am Diet Assoc.* 2007;7(7):1103–1106.

4 Ibid.

5 Ibid.

6 Schwartz, Byrd-Bredbenner. Portion distortion; and Lawhun SA, Starkoff B, Sundararajan S, et al. Influence of larger portion sizes on the diet of overweight children and adolescents. *J Am Diet Assoc.* 2008;108(9):A38.

7 Schwartz, Byrd-Bredbenner. Portion distortion.

Recommendations for Nutrient Intake: The DRIs

So far, the tools we have described (*Dietary Guidelines for Americans*, Canada's Guidelines for Healthy Eating, MyPlate, *Eating Well with Canada's Food Guide*, and Exchange Lists) have dealt with whole foods and food groups rather than individual nutrient values; after all, foods are what we think about in planning our daily meals and shopping lists. Sometimes, though, we need more specific information about our nutritional needs—a healthful diet is healthful because of the balance of *nutrients* it contains. Before we can choose foods that meet our needs for specific nutrients, we need to know how much of each nutrient we require daily. This is what **dietary standards** do—they define healthful diets in terms of specific amounts of the nutrients.

dietary standards Set of values for recommended intake of nutrients.

Dietary Reference Intakes (DRIs) A framework of dietary standards that includes Estimated Average Requirement (EAR), Recommended Dietary Allowance (RDA), Adequate Intake (AI), and Tolerable Upper Intake Level (UL).

Recommended Nutrient Intakes (RNIs) Canadian dietary standards that have been replaced by Dietary Reference Intakes.

Recommended Dietary Allowances (RDAs) The nutrient intake levels that meet the nutrient needs of almost all (97 to 98 percent) individuals in a life-stage and gender group.

Food and Nutrition Board A board within the Institute of Medicine of the National Academy of Sciences. It is responsible for assembling the group of nutrition scientists who review available scientific data to determine appropriate intake levels of the known essential nutrients.

Understanding Dietary Standards

Dietary standards are sets of recommended intake values for nutrients. These standards tell us how much of each nutrient we should have in our diets. In the United States and Canada, the **Dietary Reference Intakes (DRIs)** are the current dietary standards.

Consider the following scenario. You are running a research center located in Antarctica and staffed by 60 people. Because they will not be able to leave the site to get meals, you must provide all of their food. You must keep the group adequately nourished; you certainly don't want anyone to become ill as a result of a nutrient deficiency. How would you (or the nutritionist you hire) start planning? How can you be sure to provide adequate amounts of the essential nutrients? The most important tool would be a set of dietary standards! Essentially the same scenario faces those who plan and provide food for groups of people in more routine circumstances—the military, prisons, and even schools. To assess nutritional adequacy, diet planners can compare the nutrient composition of their food plans to recommended intake values.

A Brief History of Dietary Standards

Beginning in 1938, Health Canada published dietary standards called **Recommended Nutrient Intakes (RNIs)**. In the United States, the **Recommended Dietary Allowances (RDAs)** were first published in 1941. By the 1940s, nutrition scientists had been able to isolate and identify many of the nutrients in food. They were able to measure the amounts of these nutrients in foods and to recommend daily intake levels. These levels became the first RNI and RDA values. Committees of scientists regularly reviewed the standards and published revised editions; for example, the tenth (and final) edition of RDAs was published in 1989.

In the mid-1990s, the **Food and Nutrition Board** of the National Academy of Sciences began a partnership with Health Canada to make fundamental changes in the approach to setting dietary standards and to replace the RDAs and RNIs. In 1997, the first set of DRIs was published.

Dietary Reference Intakes

Since the inception of the RDAs and RNIs, we have learned more about the relationships between diet and chronic disease, and nutrient-deficiency diseases have become rare in the United States and Canada. The new DRIs reflect not just intake levels for dietary adequacy but also for optimal nutrition.

requirement The lowest continuing intake level of a nutrient that prevents deficiency in an individual.

Estimated Average Requirement (EAR) The intake value that meets the estimated nutrient needs of 50 percent of individuals in a specific life-stage and gender group.

The DRIs are reference values for nutrient intakes to be used in assessing and planning diets for healthy people. (See **Figure 2.7**.) The DRIs include four basic elements: Estimated Average Requirement (EAR), Recommended Dietary Allowance (RDA), Adequate Intake (AI), and Tolerable Upper Intake Level (UL). Underlying each of these values is the definition of a **requirement** as the "lowest continuing intake level of a nutrient that, for a specific indicator of adequacy, will maintain a defined level of nutriture in an individual."[19] In other words, a requirement is the smallest amount of a nutrient you should take in on a regular basis to remain healthy. In the DRI report on macronutrients, two other concepts were introduced: the Estimated Energy Requirement (EER) and the Acceptable Macronutrient Distribution Ranges (AMDRs).[20]

Estimated Average Requirement

The **Estimated Average Requirement (EAR)** reflects the amount of a nutrient that would meet the needs of 50 percent of the people in a particular life-stage (age) and gender group. For each nutrient, this requirement is defined using a specific indicator of dietary adequacy. This indicator could be

THE DRIs: DIETARY REFERENCE INTAKES

All DRI values refer to intakes averaged over time

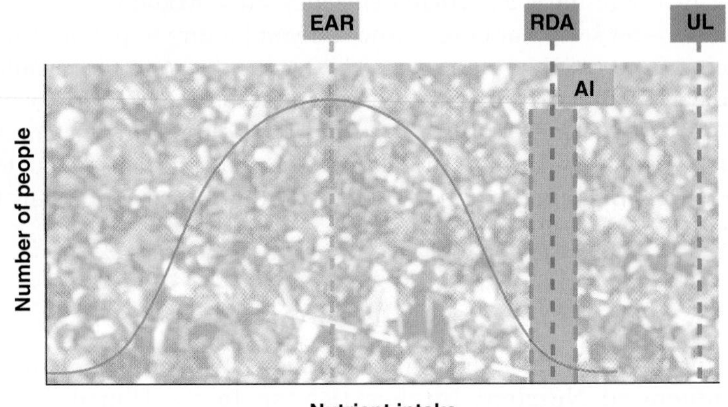

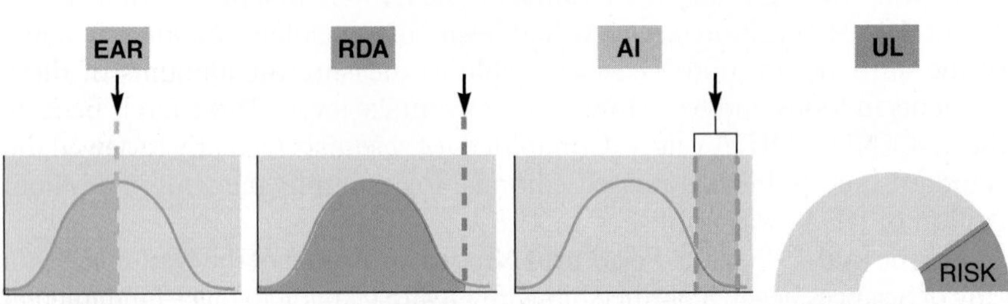

The **Estimated Average Requirement** is the nutrient intake level estimated to meet the need of 50% of the individuals in a life-stage and gender group.

The **Recommended Dietary Allowance** is the nutrient intake level that is sufficient to meet the need of 97–98% of the individuals in a life-stage and gender group. The RDA is calculated from the EAR.

Adequate Intake is based upon expert estimates of nutrient intake by a defined group of healthy people. These estimates are used when there is insufficient scientific evidence to establish an EAR. AI is not equivalent to RDA.

Tolerable Upper Intake Level is the maximum level of daily nutrient intake that poses little risk of adverse health effects to almost all of the individuals in a defined group. In most cases, supplements must be consumed to reach a UL.

Figure 2.7 **Dietary Reference Intakes.** The Dietary Reference Intakes are a set of dietary standards that include Estimated Average Requirement (EAR), Recommended Dietary Allowance (RDA), Adequate Intake (AI), and Tolerable Upper Intake Level (UL).

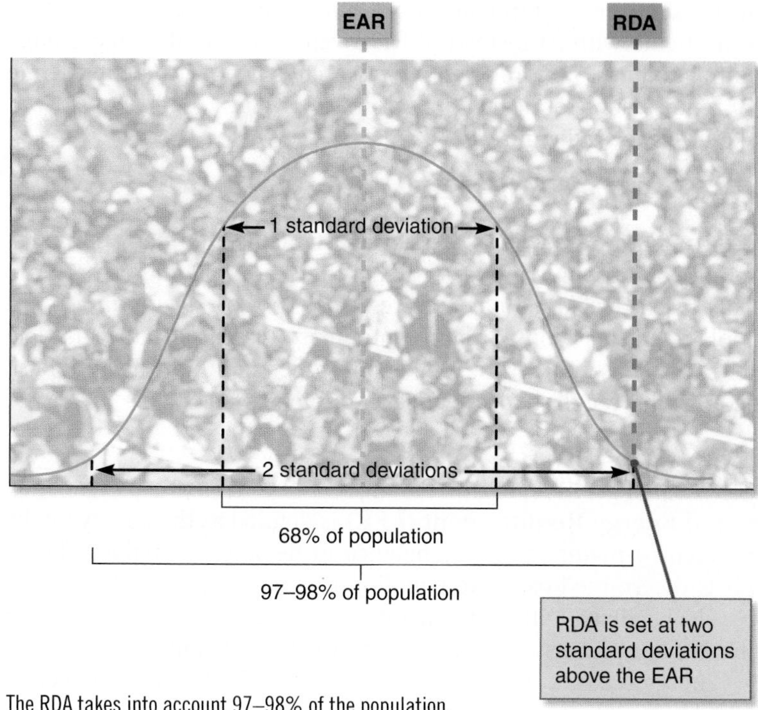

The RDA takes into account 97–98% of the population.

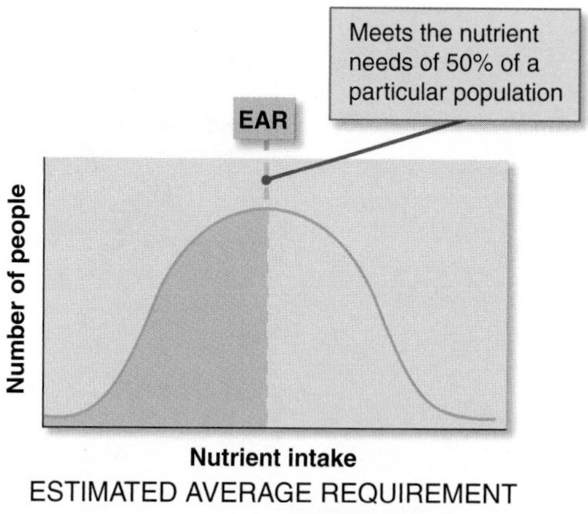

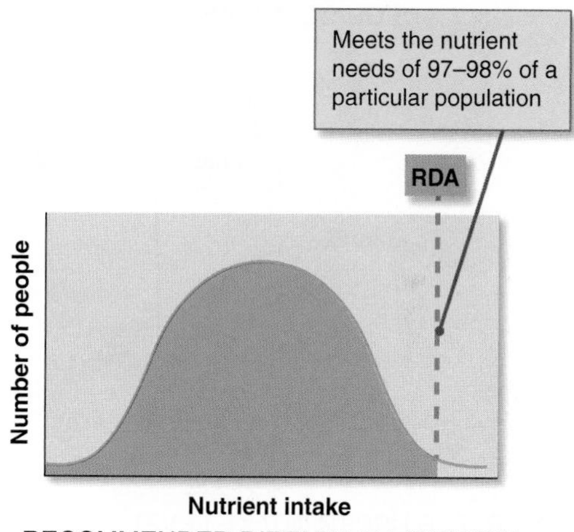

the level of the nutrient or one of its breakdown products in the blood, or the amount of an enzyme associated with that nutrient.[21] The EAR is used to set the RDA, and EAR values can also be used to assess dietary adequacy or plan diets for groups of people.

Recommended Dietary Allowance

The Recommended Dietary Allowance (RDA) is the daily intake level that meets the needs of most people (97 to 98 percent) in a life-stage and gender group. The RDA is set at two standard deviations above the EAR. A nutrient will not have an RDA value if there are not enough scientific data available to set an EAR value.

People can use the RDA value as a target or goal for dietary intake, and make comparisons between actual intake and RDA values. It is important to remember, however, that the RDAs do not define an *individual's* nutrient requirements. Your actual nutrient needs may be much lower than average, and therefore the RDA would be much more than you need. An analysis of your diet might show, for example, that you consume 45 percent of the RDA for a certain vitamin, but that might be adequate for your needs. Only specific laboratory or other tests can determine a person's true nutrient requirements and actual nutritional status. An intake that is consistently at or near the RDA level is highly likely to be meeting your needs.

Adequate Intake

If not enough scientific data are available to set an EAR level, a value called an **Adequate Intake (AI)** is determined instead. AI values are determined in part by observing healthy groups of people and estimating their dietary intake. All the current DRI values for infants are AI levels because there have been too few scientific studies to determine specific requirements in infants. Instead, AI values for infants are usually based on nutrient levels in human breast milk, a complete food for newborns and young infants. Values for older

Adequate Intake (AI) The nutrient intake that appears to sustain a defined nutritional state or some other indicator of health (e.g., growth rate or normal circulating nutrient values) in a specific population or subgroup. AI is used when there is insufficient scientific evidence to establish an EAR.

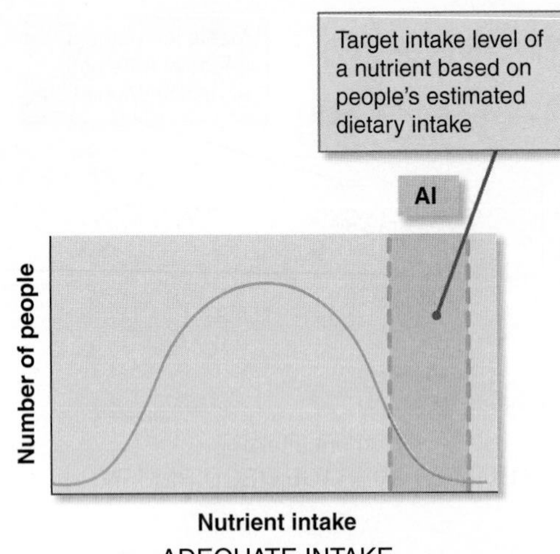

ADEQUATE INTAKE

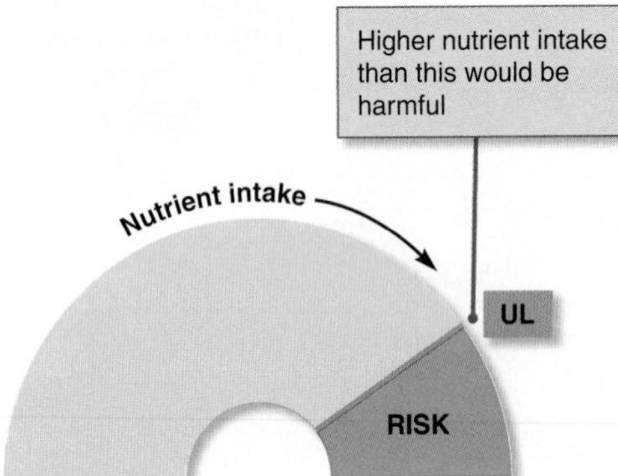

TOLERABLE UPPER INTAKE LEVEL

infants and children are extrapolated from human milk and from data on adults. For nutrients with AI instead of RDA values for all life-stage groups (e.g., calcium, vitamin D), more scientific research is needed to better define the nutrient requirements of population groups. AI values can be considered target intake levels for individuals.

Tolerable Upper Intake Level

Tolerable Upper Intake Levels (ULs) have been defined for many nutrients. Consumption of a nutrient in amounts higher than the UL could be harmful. The ULs have been developed partly in response to the growing interest in dietary supplements that contain large amounts of essential nutrients. The UL is *not* to be used as a target for intake, but rather should be a cautionary level for people who regularly take nutrient supplements.

Estimated Energy Requirement

The **Estimated Energy Requirement (EER)** is defined as the energy intake that is estimated to maintain energy balance in healthy, normal-weight individuals. It is determined using an equation that considers weight, height, age, and physical activity. Different equations are used for males and females and for different age groups. These equations are described in more detail in Chapter 9, "Energy Balance, Body Composition, and Weight Management."

Acceptable Macronutrient Distribution Ranges

Acceptable Macronutrient Distribution Ranges (AMDRs) indicate the recommended balance of energy sources in a healthful diet. These values consider the amounts of macronutrients needed to provide adequate intake of essential nutrients while reducing the risk for chronic disease. The AMDRs are shown in Table 2.6.

Use of Dietary Standards

The most appropriate use of DRIs is to plan and evaluate diets for large groups of people. Remember the North Pole scenario at the beginning of this section? If you had planned menus and evaluated the nutrient composition of the foods that would be included and if the average nutrient levels of those daily menus met or exceeded the RDA/AI levels, you could be confident that your group would be adequately nourished. If you had a very large group—thousands of soldiers, for instance—the EAR would be a more appropriate guide.

Tolerable Upper Intake Levels (ULs) The maximum levels of daily nutrient intakes that are unlikely to pose health risks to almost all of the individuals in the group for whom they are designed.

Estimated Energy Requirement (EER) Dietary energy intake that is predicted to maintain energy balance in a healthy adult of a defined age, gender, weight, height, and level of physical activity consistent with good health

Acceptable Macronutrient Distribution Ranges (AMDRs) Range of intakes for a particular energy source that are associated with reduced risk of chronic disease while providing adequate intakes of essential nutrients.

Table 2.6 Acceptable Macronutrient Distribution Ranges for Adults

Fat	20–35
Carbohydrate	45–65
Protein	10–35
n-6 Polyunsaturated fatty acids	5–10
α-Linolenic acid	0.6–1.2

Note: All values are percentage of energy intake.
Source: Institute of Medicine, Food and Nutrition Board. *Dietary Reference Intakes for Energy, Carbohydrate, Fiber, Fat, Fatty Acids, Cholesterol, Protein, and Amino Acids.* Copyright © 2005 by the National Academy of Sciences, courtesy of the National Academies Press, Washington, DC.

Dietary standards are also used to make decisions about nutrition policy. The Special Supplemental Food Program for Women, Infants, and Children (WIC), for example, takes into account the DRIs as it provides food or vouchers for food. The goal of this federally funded supplemental feeding program is to improve the nutrient intake of low-income pregnant and breastfeeding women, their infants, and young children. The guidelines for school lunch and breakfast programs are also based on DRI values.

Often, we use dietary standards as comparison values for individual diets, something you may be doing in class. It can be interesting to see how your daily intake of a nutrient compares with the RDA or AI. However, an intake that is less than the RDA/AI doesn't necessarily mean deficiency; your individual requirement for a nutrient may be less than the RDA/AI value. You can use the RDA/AI values as targets for dietary intake, while avoiding nutrient intake that exceeds the UL.

Key Concepts *Dietary standards are levels of nutrient intake recommended for healthy people. These standards help the government set nutrition policy and also can be used to guide the planning and evaluation of diets for groups and individuals. The Dietary Reference Intakes are the dietary standards for the United States and Canada. These standards focus on maintaining optimal health and lowering the risks of chronic disease, rather than simply on dietary adequacy.*

Food Labels

Now that you understand diet-planning tools and dietary standards, let's focus on your use of these tools—for example, when making decisions at the grocery store. One of the most useful tools in planning a healthful diet is the **food label**.

Specific federal regulations control what can and cannot appear on a food label and what *must* appear on it. The **Food and Drug Administration (FDA)** is responsible for ensuring that foods sold in the United States are safe, wholesome, and properly labeled. The Health Products and Food Branch of Health Canada has similar responsibilities. The FDA's jurisdiction does not include meat, meat products, poultry, or poultry products; the USDA regulates these foods.

As information about the role of diet in chronic disease grew during the 1970s and 1980s, so did the demand for nutrition labels on all food products. As a result, in 1990 Congress passed the **Nutrition Labeling and Education Act (NLEA)**. Once the necessary regulations had been developed, "Nutrition Facts" labels began appearing on foods in 1994. By 1997, 96.5 percent of food products had nutrition labels.[22] Voluntary nutrition labeling was introduced in Canada in 1988, and final regulations to make nutrition labeling mandatory were released in 2002. Canadian nutrition labels now are similar in format to U.S. nutrition labels.

Ingredients and Other Basic Information

The label on a food you buy today has been shaped by many sets of regulations. As **Figure 2.8** shows, food labels have five mandatory components:

1. A statement of identity
2. The net contents of the package
3. The name and address of the manufacturer, packer, or distributor
4. A list of ingredients
5. Nutrition information

The **statement of identity** requirement means that the product must prominently display the common or usual name of the product or identify

food label Labels required by law on virtually all packaged foods and having five requirements: (1) a statement of identity; (2) the net contents (by weight, volume, or measure) of the package; (3) the name and address of the manufacturer, packer, or distributor; (4) a list of ingredients; and (5) nutrition information.

Food and Drug Administration (FDA) The federal agency responsible for ensuring that foods sold in the United States (except for eggs, poultry, and meat, which are monitored by the USDA) are safe, wholesome, and labeled properly. The FDA sets standards for the composition of some foods, inspects food plants, and monitors imported foods. The FDA is an agency of the Department of Health and Human Services (DHHS).

Nutrition Labeling and Education Act (NLEA) An amendment to the Food, Drug, and Cosmetic Act of 1938. The NLEA made major changes to the content and scope of the nutrition label and to other elements of food labels. Final regulations were published in 1993 and went into effect in 1994.

statement of identity A mandate that commercial food products prominently display the common or usual name of the product or identify the food with an "appropriately descriptive term."

Figure 2.8 **The five mandatory requirements for food labels.** Federal regulations determine what can and cannot appear on food labels.

Nutrition Facts A portion of the food label that states the content of selected nutrients in a food in a standard way prescribed by the Food and Drug Administration. By law, Nutrition Facts must appear on nearly all processed food products in the United States.

the food with an "appropriately descriptive term." For example, it would be misleading to label a fruit beverage containing only 10 percent fruit juice as a "juice." The statement of net package contents must accurately reflect the quantity in terms of weight, volume, measure, or numerical count. Information about the manufacturer, packer, or distributor gives consumers a way to contact someone in case they have questions about the product.

Ingredients must be listed by common or usual name, in descending order by weight; thus, the first ingredient listed is the primary ingredient in that food product. Let's compare two cereals:

Cereal A ingredients: Milled corn, sugar, salt, malt flavoring, high-fructose corn syrup

Cereal B ingredients: Sugar, yellow corn flour, rice flour, wheat flour, whole oat flour, partially hydrogenated vegetable oil (contains one or more of the following oils: canola, soybean, cottonseed), salt, cocoa, artificial flavor, corn syrup

In Cereal B, the first ingredient listed is sugar, which means this cereal contains more sugar by weight than any other ingredient. Cereal A's primary ingredient is milled corn. If we were to read the nutrition information, we would find that a 1-cup serving of Cereal A contains 2 grams of sugars, whereas a similar amount of Cereal B contains 12 grams of sugars. Quite a difference!

As you probably have noticed, when the ingredient list includes the artificial sweetener aspartame, it also displays a warning statement. Also, preservatives and other additives in foods must be listed, along with an explanation of their function. Accurate and complete ingredient information is vital for people with food allergies who must avoid certain food components. As of January 2006, the labels of foods that contain any of the eight major food allergens (egg, wheat, peanuts, milk, tree nuts, soy, fish, and crustaceans) have been required to include common names when listing these ingredients. For example, an ingredient list might show "albumen (egg)."

Nutrition Facts Panel

The **Nutrition Facts** panel contains the most important label information for the health-conscious consumer. The Food Marketing Institute's 2004 survey *Shopping for Health* indicated that 83 percent of shoppers regularly check the Nutrition Facts panel when buying a product for the first time, and 91 percent will make a purchasing decision based on nutrition information.[23] Although fat content is the most frequently sought piece of information, consumers are also looking for foods that are "low calorie," "whole grain," and "low salt/sodium." The Nutrition Facts panel not only is a source of information about the nutritional value of a food product but also can be used to compare similar products.

Let's take a closer look at the elements of the Nutrition Facts panel. It was designed so that the nutrition information would be easy to find on the label. The heading "Nutrition Facts" stands out clearly (see **Figure 2.9**). Just under the heading is information about the serving size and number of servings per container. It is important to note the serving size, because all of the nutrient information that follows is based on that amount of food, and the listed serving size may be different from what you usually eat. An 8-ounce bag of potato chips may be a small snack to a hungry college student, but according to the manufacturer the bag really contains eight servings! Serving sizes are standardized according to reference amounts developed by the FDA. Similar products (cereals, for instance) will have similar serving sizes (1 ounce). This should make it easier to compare products, as the serving size on the food label will likely be the same.

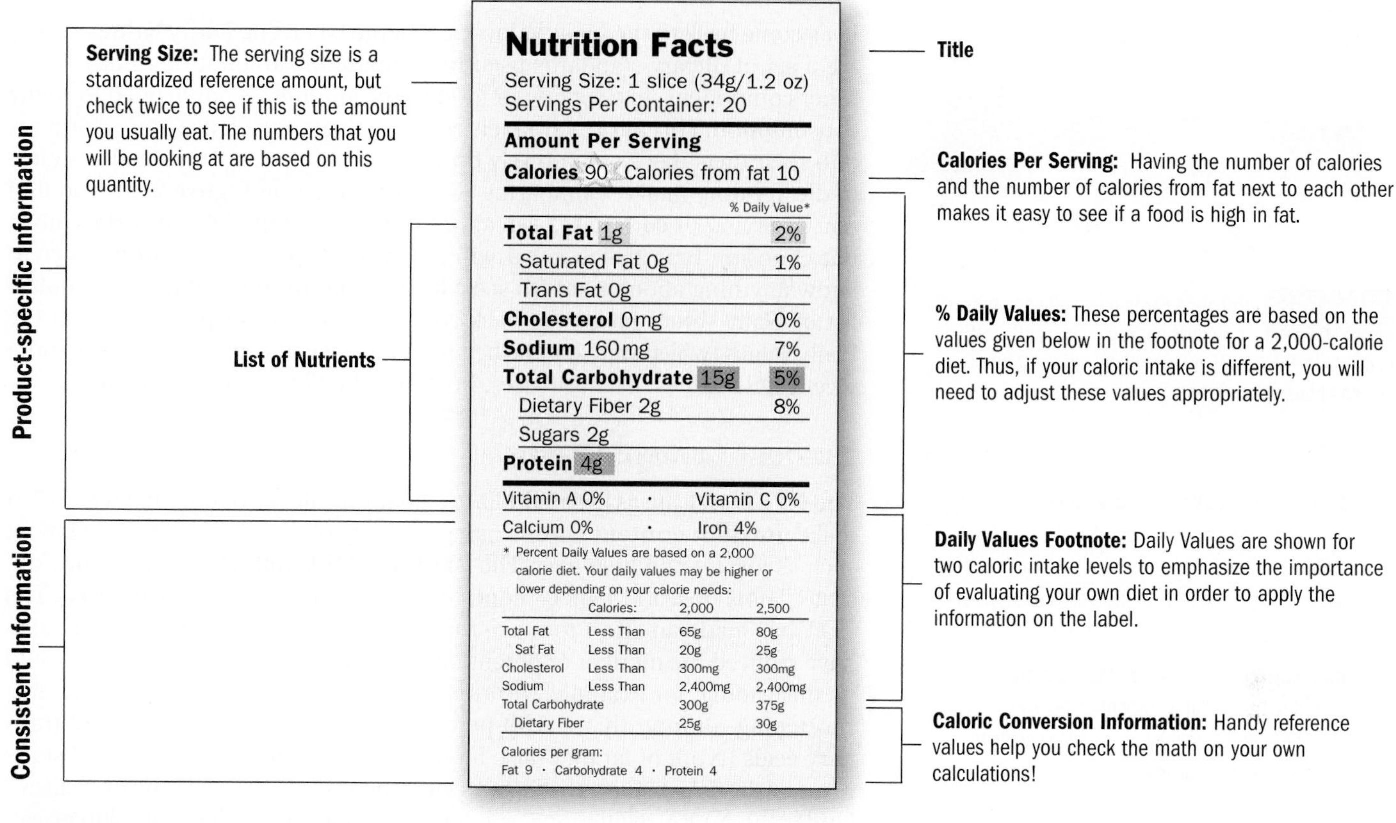

Product-specific Information
Serving Size: The serving size is a standardized reference amount, but check twice to see if this is the amount you usually eat. The numbers that you will be looking at are based on this quantity.
List of Nutrients
Consistent Information
Nutrition Facts
Serving Size: 1 slice (34g/1.2 oz)
Servings Per Container: 20
Amount Per Serving
Calories 90 Calories from fat 10
% Daily Value*
Total Fat 1g 2%
Saturated Fat 0g 1%
Trans Fat 0g
Cholesterol 0mg 0%
Sodium 160mg 7%
Total Carbohydrate 15g 5%
Dietary Fiber 2g 8%
Sugars 2g
Protein 4g
Vitamin A 0% • Vitamin C 0%
Calcium 0% • Iron 4%
* Percent Daily Values are based on a 2,000 calorie diet. Your daily values may be higher or lower depending on your calorie needs:
Calories: 2,000 2,500
Total Fat Less Than 65g 80g
Sat Fat Less Than 20g 25g
Cholesterol Less Than 300mg 300mg
Sodium Less Than 2,400mg 2,400mg
Total Carbohydrate 300g 375g
Dietary Fiber 25g 30g
Calories per gram:
Fat 9 • Carbohydrate 4 • Protein 4
Title
Calories Per Serving: Having the number of calories and the number of calories from fat next to each other makes it easy to see if a food is high in fat.
% Daily Values: These percentages are based on the values given below in the footnote for a 2,000-calorie diet. Thus, if your caloric intake is different, you will need to adjust these values appropriately.
Daily Values Footnote: Daily Values are shown for two caloric intake levels to emphasize the importance of evaluating your own diet in order to apply the information on the label.
Caloric Conversion Information: Handy reference values help you check the math on your own calculations!

Figure 2.9 **The Nutrition Facts panel.** Consumers can use the Nutrition Facts panel to compare the nutritional values of different products.

The next part of the label shows the calories per serving and the calories that come from fat. This information reveals at a glance whether a food product is high or low in fat. If most of the calories in a product come from fat, it is a high-fat food. Following this is a list of the amounts of total fat, saturated fat, trans fat, cholesterol, sodium, total carbohydrate, dietary fiber, sugars, and protein in one serving. This information is given both in quantity (grams or milligrams per serving) and as a percentage of the Daily Value—a comparison standard specifically for food labels (this standard is described in the following section). Listed next are percentages of Daily Values for vitamins A and C, calcium, and iron, which are the only micronutrients that must appear on all standard labels. Manufacturers may choose to include information about other nutrients, such as potassium, polyunsaturated fat, additional vitamins, or other minerals, in the Nutrition Facts panel. However, if they make a claim about an optional component (e.g., "good source of vitamin E") or **enrich** or **fortify** the food, the manufacturers must include specific nutrition information for these added nutrients. This information must be included even when government regulations require enrichment or fortification, such as the fortification of milk with vitamin D to prevent rickets (a bone disease in children that results from vitamin D deficiency) and the fortification of grain products with folic acid to reduce the risk of birth defects. Food products that come in small packages (e.g., gum, candy, and tuna) or that have little nutritional value (e.g., diet soft drinks) can have abbreviated versions of the Nutrition Facts on the label, as **Figure 2.10** shows.

enrich To add vitamins and minerals lost or diminished during food processing, particularly the addition of thiamin, riboflavin, niacin, folic acid, and iron to grain products.

fortify Refers to the addition of vitamins or minerals that were not originally present in a food.

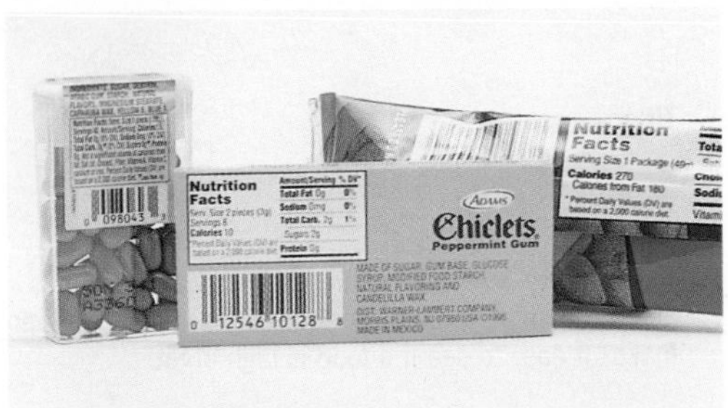

Figure 2.10 **Nutrition Facts on small packages.** When a product package has insufficient space to display a full Nutrition Facts panel, manufacturers may use an abbreviated version.

Daily Values (DVs) A single set of nutrient intake standards developed by the Food and Drug Administration to represent the needs of the "typical" consumer; used as standards for expressing nutrient content on food labels.

nutrient content claims These claims describe the level of a nutrient or dietary substance in the product, using terms such as *good source*, *high*, or *free*.

Daily Values

Let's come back to the Daily Values part of the label. The **Daily Values (DVs)** are a set of dietary standards used to compare the amount of a nutrient (or other component) in a serving of food to the amount recommended for daily consumption. This information lets consumers see at a glance how a food fits into their diets. Let's say you rely on your breakfast cereal as a major source of dietary fiber intake. Comparing two packages, as in **Figure 2.11**, you find that a serving of corn flakes cereal has 4 percent of the DV for dietary fiber, but choosing bran flakes cereal will give you 20 percent. You don't have to know anything about grams to see which has more! You can find a complete list of Daily Values inside the back cover of this text. Keep in mind that the Daily Values (which were established in 1993) may not exactly match the more recent DRI values; in most cases, however, the differences are small.

Nutrient Content Claims

The NLEA and the associated FDA regulations allow food manufacturers to make **nutrient content claims** using a variety of descriptive terms on labels, such as *low fat* and *high fiber*. The FYI feature "Definitions for Nutrient Content Claims on Food Labels" contains a list of terms that may be used. The FDA has made an effort to make the terms meaningful, and the regulations have reduced the number of potentially misleading label statements. It would be misleading, for example, to print "cholesterol free" on a can of vegetable shortening—a food that is 100 percent fat and high in saturated and trans fatty acids (types of fat that raise blood cholesterol levels). This type of statement misleads consumers who associate "cholesterol free" with "heart healthy." Under the NLEA regulations, statements about low cholesterol content can

Figure 2.11 **Comparing cereals.** These cereal labels come from different types of breakfast cereal: cornflakes cereal (left) and bran-flakes cereal (right). What might influence your decision to buy one over the other?

Nutrition Facts

Serving Size: 1 Cup (28g/1.0 oz.)
Servings Per Container: About 18

Amount Per Serving	Cereal	with 1/2 cup Skim Milk
Calories	100	140
Fat Calories	0	0
	% Daily Value	
Total Fat 0g	0%	0%
Saturated Fat 0g	0%	0%
Trans Fat 0g		
Cholesterol 0mg	0%	0%
Sodium 300mg	13%	15%
Potassium 25mg	1%	7%
Total Carbohydrate 24g	8%	10%
Dietary Fiber 1g	4%	4%
Sugars 2g		
Other Carbohydrates 21g		
Protein 2g		
Vitamin A	15%	20%
Vitamin C	25%	25%
Calcium	0%	15%
Iron	45%	45%
Vitamin D	10%	25%
Thiamin	25%	30%
Riboflavin	25%	35%
Niacin	25%	25%
Vitamin B_6	25%	25%
Folate	25%	25%
Vitamin B_{12}	25%	35%

Nutrition Facts

Serving Size: 3/4 Cup (30g)
Servings Per Container: About 15

Amount Per Serving	Cereal	with 1/2 cup Skim Milk
Calories	100	140
Calories from fat	5	5
	% Daily Value	
Total Fat 0.5g	1%	1%
Saturated Fat 0g	0%	0%
Trans Fat 0g		
Cholesterol 0mg	0%	0%
Sodium 210mg	9%	12%
Potassium 200mg	6%	11%
Total Carbohydrate 24g	8%	10%
Dietary Fiber 5g	20%	20%
Sugars 5g		
Other Carbohydrates 14g		
Protein 3g		
Vitamin A	15%	20%
Vitamin C	0%	2%
Calcium	0%	15%
Iron	45%	45%
Vitamin D	10%	25%
Thiamin	25%	30%
Riboflavin	25%	35%
Niacin	25%	25%
Vitamin B_6	25%	25%
Folate	25%	25%
Vitamin B_{12}	25%	35%

Definitions for Nutrient Content Claims on Food Labels

Free: Food contains no amount (or trivial or "physiologically inconsequential" amounts). May be used with one or more of the following: fat, saturated fat, cholesterol, sodium, sugar, and calories. Synonyms include *without, no,* and *zero.*

- ***Fat-free:*** Less than 0.5 g of fat per serving
- ***Saturated fat-free:*** Less than 0.5 g of saturated fat per serving, and less than 0.5 grams of trans fatty acids per serving
- ***Cholesterol-free:*** Less than 2 mg of cholesterol and 2 g or less of saturated fat per serving
- ***Sodium-free:*** Less than 5 mg of sodium per serving
- ***Sugar-free:*** Less than 0.5 g of sugar per serving
- ***Calorie-free:*** Fewer than 5 calories per serving

Low: Food can be eaten frequently without exceeding dietary guidelines for one or more of these components: fat, saturated fat, cholesterol, sodium, and calories. Synonyms include *little, few,* and *low source of.*

- ***Low-fat:*** 3 g or less per serving
- ***Low saturated-fat:*** 1 g or less of saturated fat per serving; no more than 15 percent of calories from saturated fat
- ***Low-cholesterol:*** 20 mg or less and 2 g or less of saturated fat per serving
- ***Low-sodium:*** 140 mg or less per serving
- ***Very low sodium:*** 35 mg or less per serving
- ***Low-calorie:*** 40 calories or less per serving

Lean and extra lean: Describe the fat content of meal and main dish products, seafood, and game meat products.

- ***Lean:*** Less than 10 g fat, 4.5 g or less saturated fat, and less than 95 mg of cholesterol per serving and per 100 g
- ***Extra lean:*** Less than 5 g fat, less than 2 g saturated fat, and less than 95 mg of cholesterol per serving and per 100 g

High: Food contains 20 percent or more of the Daily Value for a particular nutrient in a serving.

Good Source: Food contains 10 to 19 percent of the Daily Value for a particular nutrient in one serving.

Reduced: Nutritionally altered product containing at least 25 percent less of a nutrient or of calories than the regular or reference product. (*Note:* A "reduced" claim cannot be used if the reference product already meets the requirement for "low.")

Less: Food, whether altered or not, contains 25 percent less of a nutrient or of calories than the reference food. *Fewer* is an acceptable synonym.

Light: This descriptor can have two meanings:

1. A nutritionally altered product contains one-third fewer calories or half the fat of the reference food. If the reference food derives 50 percent or more of its calories from fat, the reduction must be 50 percent of the fat.
2. The sodium content of a low-calorie, low-fat food has been reduced by 50 percent. Also, *light in sodium* may be used on a food in which the sodium content has been reduced by at least 50 percent.

Note: The term *light* can still be used to describe such properties as texture and color as long as the label clearly explains its meaning (e.g., *light brown sugar* or *light and fluffy*).

More: A serving of food, whether altered or not, contains more of a nutrient that is at least 10 percent of the Daily Value more than the reference food. This also applies to *fortified, enriched,* and *added* claims, but in those cases, the food must be altered.

Healthy: A *healthy* food must be low in fat and saturated fat and contain limited amounts of cholesterol (less than 60 mg) and sodium (less than 360 mg for individual foods and less than 480 mg for meal-type products). In addition, a single-item food must provide at least 10 percent or more of one of the following: vitamin A or C, iron, calcium, protein, or fiber. A meal-type product, such as a frozen entrée or dinner, must provide 10 percent of two or more of these vitamins or minerals, or protein or fiber, in addition to meeting the other criteria. Additional regulations allow the term *healthy* to be applied to raw, canned, or frozen fruits and vegetables and enriched grains even if the 10 percent nutrient content rule is not met. However, frozen or canned fruits or vegetables cannot contain ingredients that would change the nutrient profile.

Fresh: Food is raw, has never been frozen or heated, and contains no preservatives. *Fresh frozen, frozen fresh,* and *freshly frozen* can be used for foods that are quickly frozen while still fresh. Blanched foods also can be called fresh.

Percent fat-free: Food must be a low-fat or a fat-free product. In addition, the claim must reflect accurately the amount of nonfat ingredients in 100 g of food.

Implied claims: These are prohibited when they wrongfully imply that a food contains or does not contain a meaningful level of a nutrient. For example, a product cannot claim to be made with an ingredient known to be a source of fiber (such as "made with oat bran") unless the product contains enough of that ingredient (e.g., oat bran) to meet the definition for "good source" of fiber. As another example, a claim that a product contains "no tropical oils" is allowed, but only on foods that are "low" in saturated fat, because consumers have come to equate tropical oils with high levels of saturated fat.

Source: Food and Drug Administration. http://www.cfsan.fda.gov/~dms/lab-nutr.html. Accessed 5/01/09.

health claim Any statement that associates a food or a substance in a food with a disease or health-related condition. The FDA authorizes health claims.

be used only when the product is also low in saturated fat (less than 2 grams per serving). In addition to the content claims defined in the regulations, companies may submit to the FDA a notification of a new nutrient content claim based on "an authoritative statement from an appropriate scientific body of the United States Government or the National Academy of Sciences."[24]

Health Claims

With the passage of the NLEA, manufacturers also were allowed to add health claims to food labels. A **health claim** is a statement that links one or more dietary components to reduced risk of disease—such as a claim that calcium helps reduce the risk of osteoporosis. Before the NLEA was passed, products making such claims were considered drugs, not foods.

A health claim must be supported by scientifically valid evidence for it to be approved for use on a food label. Regulations require a finding of "significant scientific agreement" before the FDA may authorize a new health claim. In addition, there are specific criteria for the use of claims. For example, a high-fiber food that is also high in fat is not eligible for a health claim. So far, the FDA has approved the following health claims:

- *Calcium, vitamin D, and osteoporosis:* Adequate calcium and Vitamin D along with regular exercise may reduce the risk of osteoporosis.
- *Dietary fat and cancer:* Low-fat diets may reduce the risk for some types of cancer.
- *Dietary fiber, such as that found in whole oats, barley, and psyllium seed husk, and coronary heart disease (CHD):* Diets low in fat and rich in these types of fiber can help reduce the risk of heart disease.
- *Dietary noncarcinogenic carbohydrate sweeteners and dental caries (tooth decay):* Foods sweetened with sugar alcohols do not promote tooth decay.
- *Dietary saturated fat and cholesterol and coronary heart disease (CHD):* Diets high in saturated fat and cholesterol increase risk for heart disease.
- *Dietary saturated fat, cholesterol, and trans fat and heart disease:* Diets low in saturated fat and cholesterol and as low as possible in trans fat may reduce the risk of heart disease.
- *Fiber-containing grain products, fruits, and vegetables and cancer:* Diets low in fat and rich in high-fiber foods may reduce the risk of certain cancers.
- *Fluoridated water and dental caries:* Drinking fluoridated water may reduce the risk of dental caries.
- *Folate and neural tube defects:* Adequate folate intake prior to and early in pregnancy may reduce the risk of neural tube defects (a birth defect).
- *Fruits and vegetables and cancer:* Diets low in fat and rich in fruits and vegetables may reduce the risk of certain cancers.
- *Fruits, vegetables, and grain products that contain fiber, particularly pectins, gums, and mucilages, and CHD:* Diets low in fat and rich in these types of fiber may reduce the risk of heart disease.
- *Plant sterol/stanol esters and CHD:* Diets low in saturated fat and cholesterol that contain significant amounts of these additives may reduce the risk of heart disease.
- *Potassium and high blood pressure/stroke:* Diets that contain good sources of potassium may reduce the risk of high blood pressure and stroke.

- *Sodium and hypertension (high blood pressure):* Low-sodium diets may help lower blood pressure.
- *Soy protein and CHD:* Foods rich in soy protein as part of a low-fat diet may help reduce the risk of heart disease.
- *Substitution of saturated fat with unsaturated fat and heart disease:* Replacing saturated fat with similar amounts of unsaturated fats may reduce the risk of heart disease.
- *Whole-grain foods and CHD or cancer:* Diets high in whole-grain foods and other plant foods and low in total fat, saturated fat, and cholesterol may help reduce the risk of heart disease and certain cancers.

A new health claim may be proposed at any time, so this list may expand. The most current information on label statements and claims can be found on the following FDA Web site: www.cfsan.fda.gov.[25]

structure/function claims These statements may claim a benefit related to a nutrient-deficiency disease (e.g., *vitamin C prevents scurvy*) or describe the role of a nutrient or dietary ingredient intended to affect a structure or function in humans (e.g., *calcium helps build strong bones*).

Qualified Health Claims

Through an initiative called Consumer Health Information for Better Nutrition, the FDA hopes to facilitate the flow of information about sound dietary choices to consumers by allowing additional claims for foods and supplements. For many relationships between food components and the reduction of disease risk, the current scientific evidence is supportive but doesn't rise to the level of "significant scientific agreement" required for health claims. Consequently, the FDA will now allow manufacturers to submit for approval health claims for which the "weight of the evidence" supports the claimed relationship.[26] Such qualified health claims may also be made for dietary supplements.[27]

When a qualified health claim is approved, the allowed language and acceptable range of products are very specific. For example, the claim "Scientific evidence suggests but does not prove that eating 1.5 ounces per day of most nuts [such as almonds, hazelnuts, peanuts, and pecans] as part of a diet low in saturated fat and cholesterol may reduce the risk of heart disease."

Structure/Function Claims

Food labels also may contain **structure/function claims** that describe potential effects of a food, food component, or dietary supplement component on body structures or functions, such as bone health, muscle strength, and digestion. As long as the label does not claim to diagnose, cure, mitigate, treat, or prevent a disease, a manufacturer can claim that a product "helps promote immune health" or is an "energizer" if *some* evidence can be provided to support the claim. Currently, structure/function claims on foods must be related to the food's nutritive value. Many scientists are concerned about the lack of a consistent scientific standard for both health claims and structure/function claims. For more on structure/function claims, see the "Spotlight on Complementary Nutrition."

Using Labels to Make Healthful Food Choices

What's the best way to start using the information on food labels to make food choices? Let's look at a couple of examples. Perhaps one of your goals is to add more iron to your diet. Compare the cereal labels in Figure 2.11. Which cereal contains a higher percentage of the Daily Value for iron? How do they compare in terms of sugar content? What about vitamins and other minerals?

Maybe it's a frozen entrée you're after. Look at the two examples in **Figure 2.12**. Which is the best choice nutritionally? Are you sure? Sometimes

Nutrition Facts
Serving Size: 1 Entree (240g)
Servings Per Container: 1

Amount Per Serving	
Calories 400	Calories from fat 150
	% Daily Value*
Total Fat 16g	25%
Saturated Fat 2.5g	13%
Trans Fat 1g	
Cholesterol 10mg	3%
Sodium 780mg	33%
Total Carbohydrate 56g	19%
Dietary Fiber 2g	8%
Sugars 2g	
Protein 8g	
Vitamin A 2%	Vitamin C 4%
Calcium 6%	Iron 4%

Product A

Nutrition Facts
Serving Size: 1 package (269g)
Servings Per Container: 1

Amount Per Serving	
Calories 400	Calories from fat 140
	% Daily Value*
Total Fat 16g	24%
Saturated Fat 6g	30%
Trans Fat 2g	
Cholesterol 40mg	14%
Sodium 690mg	29%
Total Carbohydrate 48g	16%
Dietary Fiber 2g	9%
Sugars 5g	
Protein 15g	
Vitamin A 10%	Vitamin C 8%
Calcium 20%	Iron 15%

Product B

Figure 2.12 **Comparing product labels.** Labels may look similar, but appearances can be deceptive. Compare the amounts of saturated fat and sodium in these two products.

the answer is not clear-cut. Product A is higher in sodium, whereas Product B has more saturated and trans fat. It would be important to know about the rest of your dietary intake before making a decision. Do you already have quite a bit of sodium in your diet, or are you likely to add salt at the table? Maybe you never salt your food, so a bit extra in your entrée is okay. If you know that your saturated fat intake is already a bit high, however, Product A might be a better choice. To make the best choice, you should know which substances are most important in terms of your own health risks. The label is there to help you make these types of food decisions.

Key Concepts *Making food choices at the grocery store is your opportunity to implement the* Dietary Guidelines for Americans *and your MyPlate-planned diet. The Nutrition Facts panel on most packaged foods contains not only the specific amounts of nutrients shown in grams or milligrams, but also comparisons between the amounts of nutrients in a food and the recommended intake values. These comparisons are reported as %DV (Daily Values). The %DV information can be used to compare two products or to see how individual foods contribute to the total diet.*

Nutrition Assessment: Determining Nutritional Health

In a nutritional sense, what does it mean to be healthy? Nutritional health is quite simply obtaining all of the nutrients in amounts needed to support body processes. We can measure nutritional health in a number of ways. Taken together, such measurements can give you insight into your current and long-term well-being. The process of measuring nutritional health is usually termed **nutrition assessment**.

Nutrition assessment serves a variety of purposes. It may help evaluate nutrition-related risks that may jeopardize a person's current or future health. Nutrition assessment is a routine part of the nutritional care of hospitalized patients. In this setting, nutrition assessment not only identifies risks, but also measures the effectiveness of treatment. In public health, nutrition assessment helps to identify people in need of nutrition-related interventions and to monitor the effectiveness of intervention programs. Sometimes, assessments determine the nutritional health of an entire population—identifying health risks common in a population group so that specific policy measures can be developed to combat them.

nutrition assessment Measurement of the nutritional health of the body. It can include anthropometric measurements, biochemical tests, clinical observations, and dietary intake, as well as medical histories and socioeconomic factors.

undernutrition Poor health resulting from depletion of nutrients due to inadequate nutrient intake over time. It is now most often associated with poverty, alcoholism, and some types of eating disorders.

overnutrition The long-term consumption of an excess of nutrients. The most common type of overnutrition in the United States is due to the regular consumption of excess calories, fats, saturated fats, and cholesterol.

The Continuum of Nutritional Status

Your nutritional status can be seen as a point along a continuum, with undernutrition and overnutrition at the extremes. Chronic undernutrition results in the development of nutritional deficiency diseases, as well as conditions of energy and protein malnutrition, and can lead to death. Unlike starvation, **undernutrition** is a condition in which *some* food is being consumed, but the intake is not nutritionally adequate. Although chronic undernutrition and associated deficiency diseases were common in the United States in the 1800s and early 1900s, today they are rare. Undernutrition now is most often associated with extreme poverty, alcoholism, illness, or some types of eating disorders.

Overnutrition is the chronic consumption of more than is necessary for good health. Specifically, overnutrition is the regular consumption of excess calories, fats, saturated fats, or cholesterol—all of which increase risk for chronic disease. Today, nutrition-related chronic diseases such as heart disease, cancer, stroke, and diabetes are among the 10 leading causes of death in the United States. All of these problems have been linked to dietary excess.

(Remember that epidemiological [population] studies can show associations between various factors and diseases, but these correlations do not necessarily indicate cause and effect.)

Between these two extremes lies a region of good health. In 1988, the U.S. Surgeon General wrote, "for the two out of three adult Americans who do not smoke and do not drink excessively, one personal choice seems to influence long-term health prospects more than any other: what we eat."[28] Good food and lifestyle choices, a balanced diet, and regular exercise help to reduce the risk of chronic disease and delay its onset, keeping us in a region of good health for more of our lifetime.

Nutrition Assessment of Individuals

In health care settings, a registered dietitian or physician may do an individual nutrition assessment of a patient or client. Depending on the purpose of the nutrition assessment, the measures may be very comprehensive and detailed. A dietitian can then use this information to plan individualized nutrition counseling. Nutrition assessment measures are often repeated in order to assess the effectiveness of nutrition counseling or a change in diet.

Nutrition Assessment of Populations

Typically, nutrition assessment of populations is not as comprehensive as an assessment of an individual. One of the largest ongoing nationwide surveys of dietary intake and health status is the National Health and Nutrition Examination Survey (NHANES). The survey is unique in that it combines interviews and physical examinations.

The NHANES program began in the early 1960s and has been conducted as a series of surveys focusing on different population groups or health topics. In 1999, the survey became a continuous program to meet emerging needs, with a changing focus on a variety of health and nutrition measurements.[29] Data from NHANES have told us a great deal about the nutritional status and dietary intake of our population. This information is released periodically as the *What We Eat in America* report.

Nutrition Assessment Methods

Just as there is not one measure of physical fitness, there is not just one indicator of nutritional health. Nutrients play many roles in the body, so measures of nutritional status must look at many factors. Often these factors are termed the **ABCDs of nutrition assessment**: anthropometric measurements, biochemical tests, clinical observations, and dietary intake. (See Table 2.7.)

Anthropometric Measurements

Anthropometric measurements are physical measurements of the body, such as height and weight, head circumference, girth measurement, or skinfold measurements.

Height and Weight

To provide useful information, height and weight must be accurately measured. For infants and very young children, measurement of height is really measurement of recumbent length (that is, length when they are lying down). Careful measurement of length at each checkup gives a clear indication of

ABCDs of nutrition assessment Nutrition assessment components: anthropometric measurements, biochemical tests, clinical observations, and dietary intake.

anthropometric measurements Measurements of the physical characteristics of the body, such as height, weight, head circumference, girth, and skinfold measurements. Anthropometric measurements are particularly useful in evaluating the growth of infants, children, and adolescents and in determining body composition.

Table 2.7 **The ABCDs of Nutrition Assessment**

Assessment Method	Why It's Done
Anthropometric measures	Measure growth in children; show changes in weight that can reflect diseases (e.g., cancer or thyroid problems); monitor progress in fat loss
Biochemical tests	Measure blood, urine, and feces for nutrients or metabolites that indicate infection or disease
Clinical observations	Assess change in skin color and health, hair texture, fingernail shape, etc.
Dietary intake	Evaluate diet for nutrient (e.g., fat, calcium, protein) or food (e.g., number of fruits and vegetables) intake

To convert inches to centimeters, multiply the number of inches by 2.54

inches × 2.54 = centimeters

To convert pounds to kilograms, divide the number of pounds by 2.2

pounds ÷ 2.2 = kilograms

a child's growth rate. Standard growth charts show how the child's growth compares with that of others of the same age and sex. For children 2 to 20 years old, charts illustrating growth are based on standing height, or stature. (See Appendix H.)

The standing height of older children and adults can be determined with a tape measure fixed to a wall and a sliding right-angle headboard for reading the measurement. Aging adults lose some height due to bone loss and curvature, so it is important to *measure* height and not simply rely on remembered values.

Weight is a critical measure in nutrition assessment. It is used to assess children's growth, predict energy expenditure and protein needs, and determine body mass index. Weight should be measured using a calibrated scale. For assessments that need a high degree of precision, subtract the weight of the clothing. Because many calculations and standards use metric measures of height and weight, it's important to be familiar with standard conversion factors.

For the anthropometric assessment of infants and young children, a third measurement is common: head circumference. This is measured using a flexible tape measure placed snugly around the head. Head circumference measures are compared with standard growth charts and are another useful indicator of normal growth and development, especially during rapid growth from birth to age 3.

Skinfolds

Skinfold measurements serve a variety of purposes. Because a significant amount of the body's fat stores is located right beneath the skin (subcutaneous fat), skinfold measurements at various sites around the body can give a good indication of body fatness. This information may be used to evaluate the physical fitness of an athlete or predict the risk of obesity-related disorders. Skinfold measurements are also useful in cases of illness; the maintenance of fat stores in a patient's body may be a valuable indicator of dietary adequacy. Skinfold measurements are done with special calipers (see **Figure 2.13**). For reliable measurements, training in the use of calipers is essential. Skinfold measurements can be used to estimate the percentage of body fat or can be compared with percentile tables for specific sex and age categories. Other methods for estimating body fat and body composition are discussed in Chapter 9, "Energy Balance, Body Composition, and Weight Management."

skinfold measurements A method to estimate body fat by measuring with calipers the thickness of a fold of skin and subcutaneous fat,

Biochemical Tests

Because of their relation to growth and body composition, anthropometric measurements give a broad picture of nutritional health—whether the diet contains enough calories and protein to maintain normal patterns of growth, normal body composition, and normal levels of lean body mass. However, anthropometric measures do not give specific information about *nutrients*. For that information, a variety of biochemical tests are useful.

Biochemical assessment measures a nutrient or metabolite (a related compound) in one or more body fluids, such as blood or urine, or in feces. For example, the concentration of albumin (an important transport protein) in the blood can be an indicator of the body's protein status. If little protein is eaten, the body produces smaller amounts of body proteins such as albumin.

Biochemical assessments may include measurements of a nutrient metabolite, a storage or transport compound, an enzyme that depends on a vitamin or mineral, or another indicator of the body's functioning in relation to a particular nutrient. These measures usually are a better indicator of nutritional status than directly measuring blood levels of nutrients such as vitamin A or calcium. The levels of nutrients excreted in the urine or feces also provide valuable information.

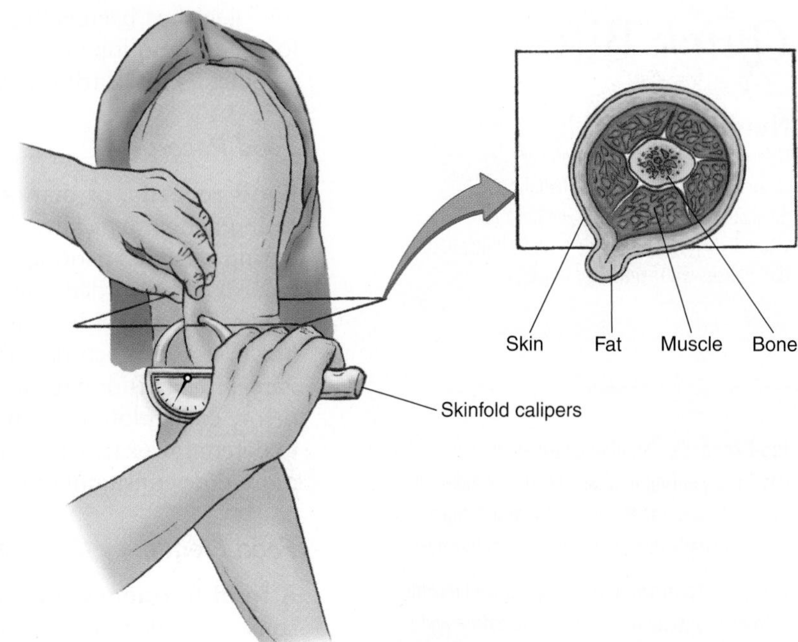

Figure 2.13 **Skinfold measurements.** A significant amount of the body's fat stores lie just beneath the skin, so when done correctly, skinfold measurements can provide an indication of body fatness. An inexperienced or careless measurer, however, can easily make large errors. Skinfold measurements usually work better for monitoring malnutrition than for identifying overweight and obesity. They are also widely used in large population studies.

Clinical Observations

Clinical observations—the characteristics of health that can be seen during a physical exam—help to complete the picture of nutritional health. Although often nonspecific, clinical signs are clues to nutrient deficiency or excess that can be confirmed or ruled out by further testing. In a clinical nutrition examination, a clinician observes the hair, nails, skin, eyes, lips, mouth, bones, muscles, and joints. Specific findings, such as cracking at the corners of the mouth (suggestive of riboflavin, vitamin B_6, or niacin deficiency) or petechiae (small, pinpoint hemorrhages on the skin indicative of vitamin C deficiency), need to be followed by other assessments.

Dietary Intake

A picture of nutritional health would not be complete without information about dietary intake. Dietary information may confirm the lack or excess of a dietary component suggested by anthropometric, biochemical, or clinical evaluations.

There are a number of ways to collect dietary intake data. Each has strengths and weaknesses. It is important to match the method to the type and quantity of data needed. Remember, too, that the quality of information obtained about people's diets often relies heavily on people's memories, as well as their honesty in sharing those recollections. How well do you remember *everything* you ate yesterday?

Diet History

The most comprehensive form of dietary intake data collection is the **diet history**. In this method, a skilled interviewer finds out not only what

biochemical assessment Assessment by measuring a nutrient or its metabolite in one or more body fluids, such as blood and urine, or in feces. Also called laboratory assessment.

clinical observations Assessment by evaluating the characteristics of well-being that can be seen in a physical exam. Nonspecific, clinical observations can provide clues to nutrient deficiency or excess that can be confirmed or ruled out by biochemical testing.

diet history Record of food intake and eating behaviors that includes recent and long-term habits of food consumption. Done by a skilled interviewer, the diet history is the most comprehensive form of dietary intake data collection.

Quick Bite

Nutrition and Nails

Do your nails have white marks or ridges? Contrary to popular belief, that does not necessarily mean you have a vitamin deficiency. Usually a slight injury to the nail causes white marks or ridges.

food records Detailed information about day-to-day eating habits; typically includes all foods and beverages consumed for a defined period, usually three to seven consecutive days.

weighed food records Detailed food records obtained by weighing foods before eating and then weighing leftovers to determine the exact amount consumed.

food frequency questionnaire (FFQ) A questionnaire for nutrition assessment that asks how often the subject consumes specific foods or groups of foods, rather than what specific foods the subject consumes daily. Also called food frequency checklist.

24-hour dietary recall A form of dietary intake data collection. The interviewer takes the client through a recent 24-hour period (usually midnight to midnight) to determine what foods and beverages the client consumed.

the client has been eating in the recent past but also the client's long-term food consumption habits. The interviewer's questions may also address other risk factors for nutrition-related problems, such as economic issues.

Food Record

Food records, or diaries, provide detailed information about day-to-day eating habits. Typically, a person records all foods and beverages consumed during a defined period, usually three to seven consecutive days. Because food records are recorded concurrently with intake, they are less prone to inaccuracy from lapses in memory. Because the data are completely self-reported, however, food records will not be accurate if the person fails to record all items. To make food records more precise, the items in a meal can be weighed before consumption. Remaining portions are weighed at the end of the meal to determine exactly how much was eaten. **Weighed food records** are much more time consuming to complete.

Food Frequency Questionnaire

A **food frequency questionnaire (FFQ)** asks how often the subject consumes specific foods or groups of foods, rather than what specific foods the subject consumes daily. A food frequency questionnaire may ask, for example, "How often do you drink a cup of milk?" with the response options of daily, weekly, monthly, and so on. This information is used to estimate that person's average daily intake.

Although food frequency questionnaires do not require a trained interviewer and can be relatively quick to complete, there are disadvantages to this method of data collection. One problem is that it is often difficult to translate people's response to how often they drink milk, or how many cups of milk they drink per week, into specific nutrient values without more detailed information. More important, food frequency questionnaires require a person to average, over a long period, foods that may be consumed erratically in portions that are sometimes large and sometimes small.

24-Hour Dietary Recall

The **24-hour dietary recall** is the simplest form of dietary intake data collection. In a 24-hour recall, the interviewer takes the client through a recent 24-hour period (usually midnight to midnight) to determine what foods and beverages the client consumed. To get a complete, accurate picture of the subject's diet, the interviewer must ask probing questions such as "Did you put anything on your toast?" but not leading questions such as "Did you put butter and jelly on your toast?" Comprehensive population surveys frequently use 24-hour recalls as the main method of data collection. Although a single 24-hour recall is not very useful for describing the nutrient content of an individual's overall diet (there's too much day-to-day variation), in large-scale studies it gives a reasonably accurate picture of the average nutrient intake of a population. Multiple dietary recalls also are useful for estimating the nutrient intake of individuals.

Methods of Evaluating Dietary Intake Data

Once the data are collected, the next step is to determine the nutrient content of the diet and evaluate that information in terms of dietary standards or other reference points. This is commonly done using nutrient analysis software. Computer programs remove the tedium of looking up foods in tables of nutrient composition; large databases allow for simple access to food composition, and the computer does the math automatically.

Comparison to Dietary Standards It is possible to compare a person's nutrient intake to dietary standards such as the RDA or AI values. Although this will give a quantitative idea of dietary adequacy, it cannot be considered a definitive evaluation of a person's diet because we don't know that individual's specific nutrient requirements. The bottom line is that comparisons of individual diets to RDA or AI values should be interpreted with caution.[30]

Comparison to MyPlate and the *Dietary Guidelines for Americans* The MyPlate system has several online tools for assessment of dietary intake. Individuals (or evaluators) can use the Analyze My Diet feature on the ChooseMyPlate Web site to compare a typical day's intake to the MyPlate groups and *Dietary Guidelines*. Although these evaluations usually are not specific, they give a general idea of whether the subject's diet is high or low in saturated fat, or whether the subject is eating enough fruits, vegetables, and whole grains.

Outcomes of Nutrition Assessment When taken together, anthropometric measures, biochemical tests, clinical exams, and dietary evaluation, along with the individual's family history, socioeconomic situation, and other factors, give a complete picture of nutritional health. A client's assessment may lead to a recommendation for a diet change to reduce weight or blood cholesterol, the addition of a vitamin or mineral supplement to treat a deficiency, the identification of abnormal growth due to inadequate infant feeding, or simply the affirmation that dietary intake is adequate for current nutrition needs.

Key Concepts *Nutrition assessment involves the collection of various types of data—anthropometric measurements, biochemical tests, clinical observations, and dietary intake—for a complete picture of one's nutritional health. Such data are compared to established standards to diagnose nutritional deficiencies, identify dietary inadequacies, or evaluate progress as a result of dietary changes.*

Learning Portfolio

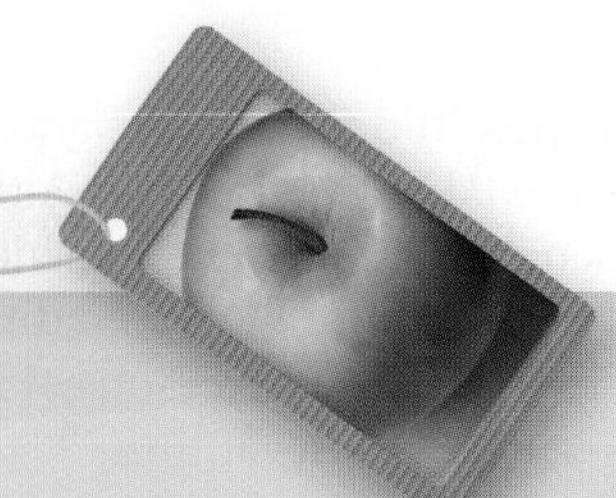

Key Terms

	page
ABCDs of nutrition assessment	66
Acceptable Macronutrient Distribution Ranges (AMDRs)	57
Adequate Intake (AI)	56
anthropometric measurements	66
biochemical assessment	68
Canada's Guidelines for Healthy Eating	43
clinical observations	68
Daily Values (DVs)	61
diet history	68
Dietary Guidelines for Americans	34
Dietary Reference Intakes (DRIs)	54
dietary standards	54
Eating Well with Canada's Food Guide	45
enrich	60
Estimated Average Requirement (EAR)	55
Estimated Energy Requirement (EER)	57
Exchange Lists	49
Food and Drug Administration (FDA)	58
food frequency questionnaire (FFQ)	69
food groups	44
food label	58
Food and Nutrition Board	54
food records	69
fortify	60
health claim	63
MyPlate	45
nutrient content claims	61
nutrient density	32
nutrition assessment	65
Nutrition Facts	59
Nutrition Labeling and Education Act (NLEA)	58
Nutrition Recommendations for Canadians	43
overnutrition	65
Recommended Dietary Allowances (RDAs)	54
Recommended Nutrient Intakes (RNIs)	54
requirement	55
skinfold measurements	66
statement of identity	58
structure/function claims	64
Tolerable Upper Intake Levels (ULs)	57
24-hour dietary recall	69
undernutrition	65
U.S. Department of Agriculture (USDA)	34
U.S. Department of Health and Human Services (DHHS)	34
weighed food records	69

Study Points

- The diet-planning principles of adequacy, balance, calorie (energy) control, nutrient density, moderation, and variety are important concepts in choosing a healthful diet.
- The *Dietary Guidelines for Americans* gives consumers advice regarding general components of the diet.
- MyPlate is a graphic representation of a food guidance system that supports the principles of the *Dietary Guidelines for Americans*.
- Each food group in MyPlate has a recommended daily amount based on calorie needs. Choose a variety of foods from each group to obtain all the nutrients.
- The Exchange Lists are a diet-planning tool most often used for diabetic or weight-control diets.
- Servings for each food in the Exchange Lists are grouped so that equal amounts of carbohydrate, fat, and protein are provided by each choice.
- Dietary standards are values for individual nutrients that reflect recommended intake levels. These values are used for planning and evaluating diets for groups and individuals.
- The Dietary Reference Intakes are the current dietary standards in the United States and Canada. The DRIs consist of several types of values: EAR, RDA, AI, UL, EER, and AMDR.
- Nutrition information on food labels can be used to select a more healthful diet.
- Label information not only provides the gram or milligram amounts of the nutrients present, but also gives a percentage of Daily Values so that the consumer can compare the amount in the food to the amount recommended for consumption each day.
- Nutrition information, label statements, and health claims are specifically defined by the regulations that were developed after passage of the Nutrition Labeling and Education Act of 1990.
- Nutrition assessment is a process of determining the overall health of a person as related to nutrition.
- Nutrition assessment involves four major factors: anthropometric measurements, biochemical tests, clinical observations, and dietary intake.

Study Questions

1. Define undernutrition and overnutrition.
2. What is the purpose of the *Dietary Guidelines for Americans*? List the two overarching concepts of the 2010 *Dietary Guidelines for Americans*.
3. What are the recommended amounts for each food group of MyPlate for a 2,000-calorie diet?
4. Describe how the exchange system works and why people with diabetes might use it.
5. List and define the four main Dietary Reference Intake categories.
6. List the five mandatory components found on all food labels.
7. The standard Nutrition Facts panel shows information on which nutrients?
8. What is the purpose of the "% Daily Value" listed next to most nutrients on food labels?
9. Define the three types of claims that may be found on food labels.

Try This

Are You a MyPlate Pleaser?

Keep a detailed food diary for three days. Make sure to include things you drink, along with the amounts (cups, ounces, tablespoons, etc.) of each food or beverage. How well do you think your intake matches the *Dietary Guidelines* and MyPlate recommendations? To find out, go to ChooseMyPlate.gov and click on Analyze My Diet, and then on Assess Your Food Intake. This feature allows you to do an online assessment of your food intake. Follow the directions to register and then enter your Personal Profile. Then click on Proceed to Food Intake and enter each food you ate for one day. Once you are done, you can click on Analyze Your Food Intake and see the comparisons to the *Dietary Guidelines* and MyPlate.

How did you do? From which groups did you tend to eat more than is recommended? Were there any groups for which you did not meet the recommendations? Was there a day-to-day variation in the number of servings you ate of each group? Use the results of this activity to plan ways you can improve your diet. You may want to visit this site frequently to monitor changes you are making in your food intake.

Grocery Store Scavenger Hunt

On your next trip to the grocery store, find a food item that has any number other than a "0" listed for the two vitamins and minerals required to be listed on the food label %DV. It doesn't matter whether you choose a cereal, soup, cracker, or snack item, as long as it has numbers other than "0" for all four items. Once you're home, review the Daily Values (inside the back cover) and calculate the number of milligrams of calcium, iron, and vitamin C found in each serving of your food. Next, take a look at vitamin A: How many International Units (IUs) does each serving of your product have? If you can calculate these, you should have a better understanding of % Daily Values.

What About Bobbie?

Now that you have learned something about the recommendations for a healthful diet, how do you think Bobbie did? Review her one-day food record in Chapter 1. How closely does Bobbie's intake fit MyPlate? Do you think she met most of the *Dietary Guidelines*? What about the RDA and AI values? Was her diet balanced enough to meet most of these recommendations? The following table summarizes the results of a computerized nutrient analysis of Bobbie's diet.

You may be completing a similar analysis of your own diet as part of your course requirements. In further chapters, you will explore many of these nutrients further and look at the foods in Bobbie's diet that contributed various nutrients. Keep in mind that this is only a one-day food record and may or may not represent her typical diet.

How do you think Bobbie's food choices fit with the *Dietary Guidelines for Americans* and MyPlate? Can you classify all of Bobbie's foods into one of the MyPlate groups? Some items, like the cheese pizza, have elements from more than one group. Others, like the dill pickle, don't seem to fit anywhere.

When Bobbie entered her food intake into the diet analyzer on the MyPlate Web site, she learned her diet was low in milk, fruits, and meat and beans. She was high in the Grains group, but without much whole grain. Her fat intake was also a little high, as was sodium. It's probably not fair to evaluate just this single day of eating, though. We would need to know more about Bobbie's usual diet and lifestyle before making specific recommendations.

	Bobbie	RDA/AI	%RDA/AI
Calories	2,300	2,290*	100%
Carbohydrates	292 g	130 g	225%
Fiber	25 g	25 g	100%
Fat	86 g	25 g	—
Cholesterol	261 mg	—	—
Protein	96 g	46 g	209%
Vitamin A	493 mcg RAE	700 mcg RAE	70%
Vitamin D	0.5 mcg	5 mcg	10%
Vitamin E	9 mg	15 mg	60%
Thiamin	2.0 mg	1.1 mg	182%
Riboflavin	2.2 mg	1.1 mg	200%
Niacin	27.5 mg	14 mg	196%
Vitamin B_6	2.0 mg	1.3 mg	154%
Folate	650 mcg	400 mcg	163%
Vitamin B_{12}	3.7 mcg	2.4 mcg	154%
Vitamin C	42 mg	75 mg	56%
Pantothenic acid	3.7 mg	5 mg	74%
Sodium	4,820 mg	1,500 mg	321%
Potassium	2,890 mg	4,700 mg	61%
Calcium	710 mg	1,000 mg	71%
Phosphorus	1,230 mg	700 mg	176%
Magnesium	310 mg	310 mg	100%
Iron	20 mg	18 mg	111%
Zinc	12 mg	8 mg	125%
Copper	1,560 mcg	900 mcg	173%
Manganese	2.8 mg	1.8 mg	156%
Selenium	152 mcg	55 mcg	276%

*EER for 19-year-old female, 155 pounds, 5′4″, low active.

References

1 Nitzke S, Freeland-Graves J. Position of the American Dietetic Association: total diet approach to communicating food and nutrition information. *J Am Diet Assoc.* 2007;107(7):1224–1232.

2 US Department of Agriculture and US Department of Health and Human Services. *Dietary Guidelines for Americans, 2010.* 7th ed. Washington, DC: US Government Printing Office, December 2010.

3 Ibid.

4 Ibid.

5 Ibid.

6 Pennington J, Kandiah J, Nicklas T, et al. Practice paper of the American Dietetic Association: nutrient density: meeting nutrient goals within calorie needs. *J Am Diet Assoc.* 2007;107(5):860–869.

7 Ibid.

8 Uauy R, Hertrampf E, Dangour AD. Food-based dietary guidelines for healthier populations: international considerations. In: Shils ME, Shike M, Ross AC, et al., eds. *Modern Nutrition in Health and Disease.* 10th ed. Baltimore, MD: Lippincott Williams & Wilkins, 2006.

9 Foote JA, Murphy SP, Wilkens LR, et al. Dietary variety increases the probability of nutrient adequacy among adults. *J Nutr.* 2004;134:1779–1785.

10 US Department of Agriculture and US Department of Health and Human Services. *Dietary Guidelines for Americans, 2010.*

11 Ibid.

12 Ibid.

13 US Department of Health and Human Services. *2008 Physical Activity Guidelines for Americans.* Washington, DC: US Department of Health and Human Services, 2008. Office of Disease Prevention and Health Promotion publication U0035. http://www.health.gov/paguidelines. Accessed 5/6/11.

14 US Department of Agriculture and US Department of Health and Human Services. *Dietary Guidelines for Americans, 2010.*

15 Health Canada. Canada's guidelines for healthy eating. http://www.cfsan.fda.gov/~dms/nuttftoc.html. Accessed 5/01/09.

16 Davis C, Saltos E. *Dietary Recommendations and How They Have Changed Over Time.* http://www.ers.usda.gov/publications/aib750/aib750b.pdf. Accessed 6/26/11.

17 First Lady, agriculture secretary launch MyPlate icon as a new reminder to help consumers to make healthier food choices. US Department of Agriculture press release; June 2, 2011.

18 Burger KS, Kern M, Coleman KJ. Characteristics of self-selected portion size in young adults. *J Am Diet Assoc.* 2007;3:611–618.

19 Institute of Medicine, Food and Nutrition Board. *Dietary Reference Intakes for Calcium, Phosphorus, Magnesium, Vitamin D, and Fluoride.* Washington, DC: National Academies Press, 1997; Institute of Medicine, Food and Nutrition Board. *Dietary Reference Intakes for Thiamin, Riboflavin, Niacin, Vitamin B-6, Folate, Vitamin B-12, Pantothenic Acid, Biotin, and Choline.* Washington, DC: National Academies Press, 1998; Institute of Medicine, Food and Nutrition Board. *Dietary Reference Intakes for Vitamin C, Vitamin E, Selenium, and Carotenoids.* Washington, DC: National Academies Press, 2000; and Institute of Medicine, Food and Nutrition Board. *Dietary Reference Intakes for Vitamin A, Vitamin K, Arsenic, Boron, Chromium, Copper, Iodine, Iron, Molybdenum, Nickel, Silicon, Vanadium, and Zinc.* Washington, DC: National Academies Press, 2001.

20 Institute of Medicine, Food and Nutrition Board. *Dietary Reference Intakes for Energy, Carbohydrate, Fiber, Fat, Fatty Acids, Cholesterol, Protein, and Amino Acids.* Washington, DC: National Academies Press, 2005.

21 American Dietetic Association. Practice paper of the American Dietetic Association: using the Dietary Reference Intakes. *J Am Dietetic Assoc.* 2011;111:762–770.

22 Brecher SJ, Bender MM, Wilkening VL, et al. Status of nutrition labeling, health claims, and nutrient content claims for processed foods: 1997 food label and package survey. *J Am Diet Assoc.* 2000;100:1057–1062.

23 Food Marketing Institute. Shoppers demand healthier foods and more nutrition information from nation's supermarkets and manufacturers, according to "2004 Shopping for Health." FMI press release; November 22, 2004. http://www.fmi.org/news_releases/index.cfm?fuseaction=mediatext&id=684. Accessed 5/01/09.

24 US Food and Drug Administration. Guidance for industry: notification of a health claim or nutrient content claim based on an authoritative statement of a scientific body. http://www.cfsan.fda.gov/~dms/hclmguid.html. Accessed 5/01/09.

25 US Food and Drug Administration Center for Food Safety and Applied Nutrition. http://www.cfsan.fda.gov/~dms/lab-ssa.html. Accessed 4/28/09.

26 Turner RE, Degnan FH, Archer DL. Label claims for foods and supplements: a review of the regulations. *Nutr Clin Pract.* 2005;20:21–32.

27 US Food and Drug Administration. FDA's consumer health information for better nutrition initiative. http://www.fda.gov/oc.nutritioninitiative/whitepaper.html. Accessed 5/01/09.

28 US Department of Health and Human Services. *The Surgeon General's Report on Nutrition and Health.* Washington, DC: US Government Printing Office, 1988.

29 US Department of Health and Human Services. National Health and Nutrition Examination Survey, 2005–2006: overview. http://www.cdc.gov/nchs/data/nhanes/OverviewBrochureEnglish_May05.pdf. Accessed 5/01/09.

30 Barr SI, Murphy SP, Poos MI. Interpreting and using the Dietary Reference Intakes in dietary assessment of individuals and groups. *J Am Diet Assoc.* 2002;102:780–788.

Spotlight on Complementary and Alternative Nutrition

Functional Foods and Dietary Supplements

THINK About It

1. When choosing food, what consideration do you give to health benefits beyond basic nutrition?
2. What are your feelings about the safety of high doses of nutrient supplements?
3. Would you ask your physician before taking an herbal supplement?
4. If a friend told you about a new herbal extract that is guaranteed to tone muscles, would you try it?

Visit nutrition.jbpub.com

Quick Bite

Take out the Bad, Leave in the Good

In Japan, the development of functional foods minimizes undesirable qualities as well as maximizes desirable food factors. This has led to the removal of allergens and the development of hypoallergenic foods.

When she feels down, Jana takes the herbal St. John's wort to help pull her out of the doldrums. Whenever she has the option, Sherina chooses calcium-fortified foods. Carlos swears by creatine in his muscle-building regime. Jason tries a new energy bar with added ginkgo biloba, hoping it will improve his memory. Others in search of better health turn to massage therapy, magnets, macrobiotic diets, homeopathy, acupuncture, and many other practices.

Any trip to the grocery store will tell you that a new era in product development is here—one in which food products are more often touted for what they contain (e.g., soy **isoflavones**, vitamins and minerals, herbal ingredients) than for what they lack (e.g., fat, cholesterol). Beverages, energy bars, and teas marketed as foods sit side by side on the shelf with similar products labeled as **dietary supplements**. And the market for dietary supplements—which are much more than the simple vitamins and minerals our parents knew—continues to grow.

This chapter looks at functional foods, dietary supplements, and the role of nutrition in **complementary and alternative medicine (CAM)**. We will look at the claims made for products and therapies in terms of current scientific knowledge; we'll also consider regulatory and safety issues. Making decisions about nutrition and health requires consumers and professionals alike to stay informed and consult reliable sources before trying a new product or embarking on a new health regimen.

isoflavones Plant chemicals that include genistein and daidzein and may have positive effects against cancer and heart disease. Also called phytoestrogens.

dietary supplements Products taken by mouth in tablet, capsule, powder, gelcap, or other nonfood form that contain one or more of the following: vitamins, minerals, amino acids, herbs, enzymes, metabolites, or concentrates.

complementary and alternative medicine (CAM) A broad range of healing philosophies, approaches, and therapies that include treatments and health care practices not taught widely in medical schools, not generally used in hospitals, and not usually reimbursed by medical insurance companies.

functional food A food that may provide a health benefit beyond basic nutrition.

lycopene One of a family of plant chemicals, the carotenoids. Others in this big family are alpha-carotene and beta-carotene.

Functional Foods

What do garlic, tomato sauce, tofu, and oatmeal all have in common? They aren't in the same food group, nor do they have the same nutrient composition. Instead, all of these foods could be considered "functional foods." Although there is not yet a legal definition for the term, a **functional food** is widely considered to be a food or food component that provides a health benefit beyond basic nutrition.[1] Garlic contains sulfur compounds that may reduce heart disease risk, and tomato sauce is rich in **lycopene**, a compound that may reduce prostate cancer risk. The soy protein in tofu and the fiber in oatmeal can help reduce the risk of heart disease. (See **Figure SAN.1**.) The functional food industry has grown rapidly since its birth in Japan in the late 1980s. In the United States, the functional food industry is predicted to grow from \$20 billion per year in 2002 to nearly \$60 billion in 2009.[2]

THINK About It 1

All the functional foods just mentioned get their health-promoting properties from naturally occurring compounds that are not considered nutrients but are called phytochemicals. While the word *phytochemical* itself may sound futuristic, its meaning is simple: "plant chemical." It seems you can't pick up a health magazine these days without seeing an article about phytochemicals. But what do we really mean when we talk about phytochemicals, and why is there so much interest in these compounds?

Phytochemicals Make Foods Functional

A vitamin is a food substance essential for life. Phytochemicals, in contrast, are substances in plants that may promote good health, even though they are not essential for life. Phytochemicals are complex chemicals that vary from plant to plant. They include pigments, antioxidants, and thousands of other compounds, many of which have been associated with protection from heart disease, hypertension, cancer, and diabetes. Table SAN.1 lists many examples of phytochemicals and their potential benefits.

Figure SAN.1 **Soy is rich in phytochemicals.** Soybeans contain phytochemicals called isoflavones. High intake of soy products such as tofu is linked to a lower incidence of heart disease and cancer.

Table SAN.1 **Examples of Functional Components**

Class/Components	Source(s)[a]	Potential Benefit(s)
Carotenoids		
Beta-carotene	Carrots, pumpkin, sweet potato, cantaloupe	Neutralizes free radicals that may damage cells; bolsters cellular antioxidant defenses; can be made into vitamin A in the body
Lutein, zeaxanthin	Kale, collards, spinach, corn, eggs, citrus	May contribute to maintenance of healthy vision
Lycopene	Tomatoes and processed tomato products, watermelon, red/pink grapefruit	May contribute to maintenance of prostate health
Dietary (Functional and Total) Fiber		
Insoluble fiber	Wheat bran, corn bran, fruit skins	May contribute to maintenance of a healthy digestive tract; may reduce the risk of some types of cancer
Beta glucan[b]	Oat bran, oatmeal, oat flour, barley, rye	May reduce risk of coronary heart disease (CHD)
Soluble fiber[b]	Psyllium seed husk, peas, beans, apples, citrus fruit	May reduce risk of CHD and some types of cancer
Whole grains[b]	Cereal grains, whole-wheat bread, oatmeal, brown rice	May reduce risk of CHD and cancer; may contribute to maintenance of healthy blood glucose levels
Fatty Acids		
Monounsaturated fatty acids (MUFAs)[b]	Tree nuts, olive oil, canola oil	May reduce risk of CHD
Polyunsaturated fatty acids (PUFAs)—omega-3 fatty acids—ALA	Walnuts, flax	May contribute to maintenance of heart health; may contribute to maintenance of mental and visual function
PUFAs—omega-3 fatty acids—DHA/EPA[b]	Salmon, tuna, marine, and other fish oils	May reduce risk of CHD; may contribute to maintenance of mental and visual function
PUFAs—conjugated linoleic acid (CLA)	Beef and lamb; some cheese	May contribute to maintenance of desirable body composition and healthy immune function
Flavonoids		
Anthocyanidins—cyanidin, delphinidin, malvidin	Berries, cherries, red grapes	Bolster cellular antioxidant defenses; may contribute to maintenance of brain function
Flavanols—catechins, epicatechins, epigallocatechin, procyanidins	Tea, cocoa, chocolate, apples, grapes	May contribute to maintenance of heart health
Flavanones—hesperetin, naringenin	Citrus foods	Neutralize free radicals that may damage cells; bolster cellular antioxidant defenses
Flavonols—quercetin, kaempferol, isorhamnetin, myricetin	Onions, apples, tea, broccoli	Neutralize free radicals that may damage cells; bolster cellular antioxidant defenses
Proanthocyanidins	Cranberries, cocoa, apples, strawberries, grapes, wine, peanuts, cinnamon	May contribute to maintenance of urinary tract health and heart health
Isothiocyanates		
Sulforaphane	Cauliflower, broccoli, broccoli sprouts, cabbage, kale, horseradish	May enhance detoxification of undesirable compounds and bolster cellular antioxidant defenses
Phenolic Acids		
Caffeic acid, ferulic acid	Apples, pears, citrus fruits, some vegetables, coffee	May bolster cellular antioxidant defenses; may contribute to maintenance of healthy vision and heart health

(Continues)

Table SAN.1 Examples of Functional Components *(Cont.)*

Class/Components	Source(s)[a]	Potential Benefit(s)
Plant Stanols/Sterols		
Free stanols/sterols[b]	Corn, soy, wheat, wood oils, fortified foods and beverages	May reduce risk of CHD
Stanol/sterol esters[b]	Fortified table spreads, stanol ester dietary supplements	May reduce risk of CHD
Polyols		
Sugar alcohols[b]—xylitol, sorbitol, mannitol, lactitol	Some chewing gums and other food applications	May reduce risk of dental caries
Prebiotics		
Inulin, fructo-oligosaccharides (FOS), polydextrose	Whole grains, onions, some fruits, garlic, honey, leeks, fortified foods and beverages	May improve gastrointestinal health; may improve calcium absorption
Probiotics		
Yeast, *Lactobacilli, Bifidobacteria,* and other specific strains of beneficial bacteria	Certain yogurts and other cultured dairy and nondairy applications	May improve gastrointestinal health and systemic immunity; benefits are strain-specific
Phytoestrogens		
Isoflavones—daidizein, genistein	Soybeans and soy-based foods	May contribute to maintenance of bone health, healthy brain, and immune function; for women, may contribute to maintenance of menopausal health
Lignans	Flax, rye, some vegetables	May contribute to maintenance of heart health and healthy immune function
Soy Protein		
Soy protein[b]	Soybeans and soy-based foods	May reduce risk of CHD
Sulfides/Thiols		
Diallyl sulfide, allyl methyl trisulfide	Garlic, onions, leeks, scallions	May enhance detoxification of undesirable compounds; may contribute to maintenance of heart health and healthy immune system
Dithiolthiones	Cruciferous vegetables	Contribute to maintenance of healthy immune function

[a]Examples are not an all-inclusive list.

[b]FDA-approved health claim established for component.

Source: Reproduced from IFIC Foundation. Background on functional foods. November 2006. http://www.ific.org/nutrition/functional/index.cfm. Accessed 10/28/08. Reprinted with permission from the International Food Information Council Foundation, 2006.

Plants contain phytochemicals in abundance because these substances are of benefit to the plant itself. For example, an orange has at least 170 distinct phytochemicals. Singly and together, these compounds help plants resist the attacks of bacteria and fungi, the ravages of free radicals, and high levels of ultraviolet light from the sun. When we eat these plants, the phytochemicals end up in our tissues and provide many of the same protections that plants enjoy.

Phytochemicals are part of the reason why the *Dietary Guidelines for Americans* recommends ample servings of fruits and vegetables each day. In the MyPlate food plans, 2 cups of fruits and 2½ cups of vegetables are recommended daily for a 2,000-calorie diet. Of course, fruits and vegetables are also naturally low in fat and calories and tend to be rich in fiber, potassium, and vitamins. In addition, studies show that groups of people who consume more fruits and vegetables tend to have lower rates of common chronic diseases.

Benefits of Phytochemicals

What are some of the specific benefits of phytochemicals? People who eat tomatoes and processed tomato products take in lycopene, which is associated with a decreased risk of chronic diseases such as cancer and cardiovascular diseases.[3] Scientists believe that the large consumption of soy products in Asian countries contributes to lower rates of cancers of the colon, prostate, uterus, and breast.[4] In fact, a study of over 3,000 Chinese women suggests that high soy intake during adolescence may reduce the risk of breast cancer in later life.[5] However, some suggest that the biological effects of traditional Asian soy foods may differ from processed forms of soy or soy isoflavone supplements.[6] The foods and herbs with the highest anticancer activity include garlic, soybeans, cabbage, ginger, and licorice, as well as the family of vegetables that includes celery, carrots, and parsley.

How do phytochemicals work to prevent chronic disease? A number of phytochemicals, including those from soybeans and from the cabbage family, are able to modify estrogen metabolism or block the effect of estrogen on cell growth. Such compounds are known as **phytoestrogens**. Because levels of estrogen and other hormones are closely linked to the development of breast, ovarian, and prostate tumors, it is clear how phytochemicals might inhibit development of such cancers. However, some studies suggest that high intake of purified soy isoflavones may stimulate breast cancer cell growth; therefore, women at high risk for breast cancer and breast cancer survivors are cautioned against using soy isoflavone supplements.[7]

Other phytochemicals neutralize **free radicals**. Free radicals (active oxidants) are continually produced in our cells and over time can result in damage to DNA and important cell structures. Eventually, this damage can promote both cancer and cell aging. Free radical oxidation of lipids contributes to heart disease risk. Many different plant chemicals, such as the pigments in grapes and red wine (see **Figure SAN.2**), are able to neutralize or reduce concentrations of free radicals, thus protecting us against the development of both cancer and heart disease.

Phytochemicals in fruits and vegetables have a number of other potential benefits. Lutein and zeaxanthin are carotenoids (plant pigments) found in dark-green leafy vegetables, corn, and egg yolks. Increased consumption of these compounds is associated with a lower incidence of age-related macular degeneration, the leading cause of blindness in older people.[8] The phytochemicals in whole grains are generally similar to those found in fruits and vegetables and are also important in prevention of both cancer and heart disease. One class of grain phytochemicals, the terpenoids, produces a significant reduction in total and LDL cholesterol levels, thus reducing the risk of heart disease. Before you reach for your next slice of bread, it is worth remembering that refined wheat, the source of white flour, has lost more than 99 percent of its phytochemical content, and only four vitamins and one mineral are added back when refined grains are enriched.

Adding Phytochemicals to Your Diet

Since phytochemicals are so beneficial, why can't we just purify the important ones and add them to our diet as supplements, the way we put vitamins back

Quick Bite

Functional Food Decisions

Are you a health-conscious consumer who seeks out functional foods? According to a 1999 survey, nearly two-thirds of Canadian grocery shoppers reported that their desire to ensure overall good health has replaced balanced nutrition or lowering fat intake as the number one motivating factor to purchase "healthy" foods. In contrast, a 2000 survey found that although over 90 percent of U.S. consumers believe certain foods have health benefits beyond basic nutrition, only one-third add particular foods or ingredients to their diet in an effort to improve or maintain their health.

phytoestrogens Plant compounds that have weak estrogen activity in the body.

free radicals Short-lived, highly reactive chemicals often derived from oxygen-containing compounds, which can have detrimental effects on cells, especially DNA and cell membranes.

Figure SAN.2 **Grapes, red wine, and heart disease.** Grapes and red wine contain phytochemicals that appear to reduce the risk of heart disease. Studies show that moderate consumption of alcohol independently reduces heart disease risk.

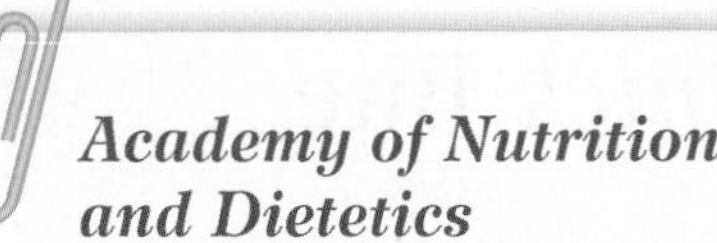

Academy of Nutrition and Dietetics

Functional Foods

It is the position of the Academy of Nutrition and Dietetics (AND) that functional foods, including whole foods and fortified, enriched, or enhanced foods, have a potentially beneficial effect on health when consumed as part of a varied diet on a regular basis, at effective levels. The Association supports research to define further the health benefits and risks of individual functional foods and their physiologically active components. Dietetics professionals will continue to work with the food industry, the government, the scientific community, and the media to ensure that the public has accurate information regarding this emerging area of food and nutrition science.

Source: Position of the American Dietetic Association: functional foods. *J Am Diet Assoc.* 2004;104(5):814–826. Copyright 2004. Reprinted with permission from Elsevier.

additives Substances added to food to perform various functions, such as adding color or flavor, replacing sugar or fat, improving nutritional content, or improving texture or shelf life.

Figure SAN.3 **The National Fruit and Vegetable Program.** This program encourages Americans to increase their consumption of fruits and vegetables for better health. It is a public–private partnership consisting of government agencies, nonprofit groups, and industry. For more information, visit www.fruitsandveggiesmorematters.gov.

Source: Reproduced from Department of Health and Human Services, Centers for Disease Control and Prevention. http://www.fruitsandveggiesmatter.gov.

into white flour after processing? The short answer is that we don't know enough about how phytochemicals function.

Many phytochemicals appear to act in concert, both fighting free radicals and blocking the negative effects of hormones. It is not surprising, then, that when a single pure phytochemical, such as beta-carotene, is given as a long-term supplement, only minor benefits are seen. In fact, some studies have shown no health benefits from such purified supplements and have even found higher lung cancer rates in smokers taking beta-carotene supplements. Yet there is no doubt that consumption of plant foods containing multiple antioxidants is strongly associated with health benefits. The weight of evidence and experience strongly favors finding a place for more fruits and vegetables in the diet. (See **Figure SAN.3**.) The FDA allows the dietary guidance message "Diets rich in fruits and vegetables may reduce the risk of some types of cancer and other chronic diseases" on food labels. The new "Fruits & Veggies—More Matters" logo also encourages fruit and vegetable consumption. The advice of MyPlate to "Make at least half your grains whole grains" will ensure intake of disease-fighting phytochemicals found in whole grains.

Changing your diet to include more functional foods and fewer empty calories needn't be painful if you use your imagination. Sometimes you can have your pizza and eat it too. The next time you indulge, ask for a pizza with minimum cheese and maximum vegetables. Whole-wheat crust would be a plus. The combination of lycopene from tomato sauce, quercetin from onions, glucarates from green peppers, and carotenoids from basil and spinach can turn a potential nutritional train wreck into a phytochemical cornucopia.

Foods Enhanced with Functional Ingredients

Another type of functional food is one that gets its health-promoting properties from what has been added during processing. Calcium-fortified orange juice, breakfast cereals fortified with folic acid, yogurt with live active cultures, and margarines with added plant sterol and plant stanol esters are examples. Health properties come from added nutrients, bacteria, fiber, or other substances. Some functional foods are foods and beverages that contain added herbal compounds, such as those sold in pill form as dietary supplements. The result is a wide variety of products making an often confusing array of label statements and health claims.

Regulatory Issues for Functional Foods

The FDA defines foods as "articles used for food or drink, chewing gum, and articles used for components of any other such article."[9] While this may sound a little confusing, a food is a product that we eat or drink, as well as all the components of that product. This definition distinguishes a food from a drug, which is a substance intended to diagnose, cure, mitigate, treat, or prevent disease. Foods also are distinct from dietary supplements, which are products intended to supplement the diet but that do not represent themselves as a conventional food, meal, or diet. You will learn more about dietary supplements later in this chapter.

Although some manufacturers have tried to market functional products as dietary supplements rather than foods to take advantage of broader allowances for label claims, the FDA's position is that products that are conventional foods and beverages are subject to the regulations for food and not for dietary supplements. A substance added to a food for health benefits must still conform to FDA regulations for food **additives**.

Key Concepts *Functional foods provide health benefits beyond basic nutrition. They get their health-promoting properties from naturally occurring compounds called phytochemicals. Phytochemicals are "plant chemicals" that include thousands of compounds, pigments, and natural antioxidants, many of which are associated with protection from heart disease, hypertension, cancer, and diabetes. Just like conventional foods, functional foods are subject to FDA regulations for claims and safety.*

Food Additives

Food additives work in many different ways to give us a safe, plentiful, varied, and relatively inexpensive food supply. Food additives can be either direct or indirect. **Direct additives** are added to a food for a specific reason. Aspartame, saccharin, and sucralose are direct food additives, used instead of sugar to sweeten. Direct additives are identified in the ingredient list on the food label. **Indirect additives** are substances that unintentionally become part of the food in trace amounts—for example, chemicals from a food's packaging can become part of the food. The FDA evaluates both direct and indirect additives for safety.

Direct additives are used in foods for five main reasons:

1. *To maintain product consistency.* Emulsifiers give products such as peanut butter a consistent texture and prevent them from separating. Stabilizers and thickeners give ice cream a smooth, uniform texture. Anticaking agents help substances such as salt to flow freely.
2. *To improve or maintain nutritional value.* Vitamins and minerals are added to many common foods such as milk, flour, cereal, and margarine to make up for elements likely to be lacking in a person's diet, replace those lost in processing, or improve shelf life.
3. *To keep the food appetizing and wholesome.* Preservatives help protect against mold, air, bacteria, fungi, or yeast, which all can cause food to spoil.
4. *To provide leavening or control acidity and alkalinity.* Leavening agents help cakes, biscuits, and other baked goods to rise during baking. Other additives modify the acidity and alkalinity of foods for flavor, taste, and color.
5. *To enhance flavor or give a desired color.* Many spices and added flavors enhance the taste of foods. Colors likewise enhance the appearance of certain foods to make them more appealing or meet consumer expectations.

Although most people think additives are complex chemicals with unfamiliar names, the three most common additives are sugar, salt, and corn syrup. These three, plus citric acid (found naturally in oranges and lemons), baking soda, vegetable colors, mustard, and pepper account for more than 98 percent by weight of all food additives used in the United States and Canada.

Regulation by the FDA

Although additives serve important functions (see **Figure SAN.4**), you might be skeptical about their safety. Additives fall into four regulatory categories: food additives, color additives, Generally Recognized as Safe (GRAS) substances, and prior-sanctioned substances. The FDA must approve a new food additive before it can be put on the market. The manufacturer must provide convincing research evidence that the additive not only performs its intended

Quick Bite

Early Food Laws
In 1202, King John of England proclaimed the first English food law, the Assize of Bread, which prohibited adulteration of bread with such ingredients as ground peas or beans.

direct additives Substances added to foods for a specific purpose.

indirect additives Substances that become part of the food in trace amounts due to its packaging, storage, or other handling.

Figure SAN.4 **Common foods that contain additives.** Substances may be added to foods to improve texture, shelf life, nutritional quality, and safety.

Maturing and bleaching agents such as bromates, peroxides, and ammonium chloride speed up the natural aging and whitening processes of milled flour, allowing it to be used more quickly for baking products.
Leavening agents such as yeast, baking powder, and baking soda produce carbon dioxide bubbles, which create a light texture in breads and cakes.

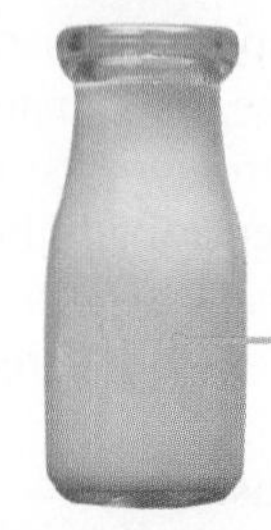
Vitamin D is added to milk to improve its nutritional quality. Many other vitamins and minerals are added to a variety of other foods.

Curing and pickling agents such as nitrates and nitrites are added to bacon, ham, hot dogs, and other cured meats primarily to prevent the growth of *Clostridium botulinum*, the bacterium that causes botulism. Nitrates also give these meats their characteristic pink color. When consumed, nitrates are converted by the body to nitrosamines, which are carcinogenic. Other additives, such as vitamin C, inhibit this conversion.

function but also is not harmful at expected consumption levels. Based on this and other scientific information, the FDA decides whether to approve the additive and determines the types of foods that may contain the additive, the quantities that can be used, and the way the substance will be identified on labels.

A **color additive** is any dye, pigment, or substance that can give color when added to a food or drug. Colors allowed for use in food are classified as either certified or exempt from certification. Certified colors are synthetic. The manufacturer and the FDA test each batch to ensure their purity. Certified colors added to a food must be listed on the food's ingredient list by common name. Colors exempt from certification include natural substances derived from vegetables, minerals, or animals. These colors also must be produced according to specifications that ensure purity.

A third type of additive falls under the category **Generally Recognized as Safe**, or **GRAS**. Congress first defined GRAS substances in 1958 when it passed the Food Additives Amendment to the Food, Drug, and Cosmetic Act. If a substance is classified as GRAS, experts generally consider it safe to use, either because it was safely used in food before 1958 or because there is published scientific evidence for its safety. Salt, sugar, spices, vitamins, and monosodium glutamate (MSG), along with several hundred other substances, are considered GRAS. Manufacturers themselves may assert that a food has GRAS status or petition the FDA to have a new additive be considered GRAS. In either case, the manufacturer must have evidence of safety and a basis for concluding that this evidence is known and accepted by qualified experts.

If the FDA or USDA had determined that an additive was safe for use in a specific food before the 1958 legislation, then it is a **prior-sanctioned substance**,

color additive Any dye, pigment, or other substance that can impart color when added or applied to a food, drug, or cosmetic or to the human body.

Generally Recognized as Safe (GRAS) Refers to substances that are "generally recognized as safe" for consumption and can be added to foods by manufacturers without establishing their safety by rigorous experimental studies. Congress established the GRAS list in 1958.

prior-sanctioned substance All substances that the FDA or the U.S. Department of Agriculture (USDA) had determined were safe for use in specific foods before passage of the 1958 Food Additives amendment are designated as prior-sanctioned substances. These substances are exempt from the food additive regulation process.

the fourth category of additives. Examples include sodium nitrite and potassium nitrite to preserve luncheon meats.

Delaney Clause The part of the 1960 Color Additives Amendment to the Federal Food, Drug, and Cosmetic Act that bars the FDA from approving any additives shown in laboratory tests to cause cancer.

Delaney Clause

Food additives and color additives cannot be approved if they cause cancer in humans or animals. This provision of the law is often referred to as the **Delaney Clause**, named for the congressman who sponsored it.

Although the Delaney Clause sounds good in principle, it has become one of the most controversial food laws on the books. To determine a chemical's safety, researchers often administer massive doses to rodents. Many experts question whether an additive that causes cancer in laboratory animals at extremely high levels should be banned from use in foods at low levels.

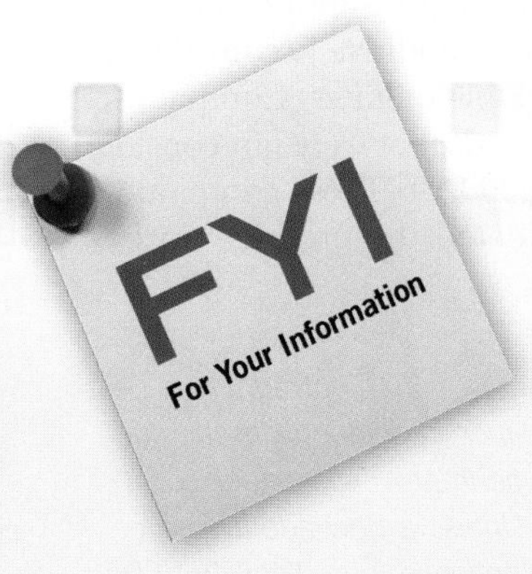

The Saccharin Story

The granddaddy of all sugar substitutes is saccharin. Discovered in 1879, it was used during both world wars to sweeten foods, helping to compensate for sugar shortages and rationing. It is 300 times sweeter than sugar.

In 1907, an early attempt to ban saccharin was thwarted when President Theodore Roosevelt proclaimed the top safety official behind the effort to be "an idiot." Safety questions resurfaced in 1911 when a board of federal scientists called the artificial sweetener "an adulterant" that should not be used in foods. This same board later decided to limit saccharin just to products "intended for invalids," a restriction that was lifted after sugar shortages developed during World War I.

In 1958, when Congress passed the Food Additives Amendment to the Food, Drug, and Cosmetic Act, saccharin was one of the ingredients "generally recognized as safe," or GRAS. That same year the saccharin-based product Sweet 'N Low took the public by storm. Food and beverage companies scrambled to offer saccharin-sweetened products, which came to include the diet soda Tab and a plethora of gelatins, candies, and baked goods.

By the early 1970s, studies of rats who had been fed saccharin raised concerns about the sweetener's role in causing bladder cancer, but scientists later suggested that impurities, not saccharin, may have caused the tumors. Then, in 1977, a Canadian study looked specifically at the role of saccharin in test animals. Researchers fed rats high doses of saccharin equivalent to 5 percent of their diet. The results again showed that saccharin caused bladder cancer in rats.

Because the Delaney Clause prohibits the use of any additive shown to cause cancer in animals or humans, the FDA proposed an immediate ban on saccharin. The FDA proposal prompted a public outcry, fueled in part by media reports that the test rats were fed the equivalent of as many as 800 diet sodas a day.[1] Congress responded by passing the Saccharin Study and Labeling Act, which placed a two-year moratorium on any ban of the sweetener while additional safety studies were conducted. Congress extended the moratorium several times over the years. The law also required that any foods containing saccharin must carry a label that reads "Use of this product may be hazardous to your health. This product contains saccharin, which has been determined to cause cancer in laboratory animals."

In May 2000, the National Toxicology Program (NTP) removed saccharin from its list of possible human carcinogens. The NTP concluded that the types of tumors caused by saccharin in rats arose from a mechanism that is not relevant to humans. This ruling is in keeping with the opinion of other scientific bodies. The National Cancer Institute (NCI) states in its *Cancer Facts* that "epidemiological studies do not provide clear evidence" of a link between saccharin and human cancer. Regina Ziegler, Ph.D., an NCI epidemiologist, says, "Typical intakes of saccharin at normal levels for adults show no evidence of a public health problem."[2] Other health groups, including the American Medical Association, the American Cancer Society, and the Academy of Nutrition and Dietetics, agree that saccharin use is acceptable. And in 2000, Congress repealed the warning label requirements for saccharin-containing foods.

Saccharin remains on the market and continues to have a fairly large appeal as a tabletop sweetener, particularly in restaurants, where it is available in single-serving packets under trade names such as Sweet 'N Low.

1 Henkel J. Sugar substitutes: Americans opt for sweetness and lite. *FDA Consumer*. Nov/Dec 1999.

2 Ibid.

Quick Bite

Old Concept, New Frontier
Functional foods are a new frontier of nutrition and food science, but the idea has been around for centuries. Hippocrates, the father of modern medicine, proclaimed, "Let food be your medicine, and let your medicine be your food."

They argue that feeding animals large doses of a substance over their entire lifetimes may have little relevance to human consumption of trace amounts of that same substance.

For now, the Delaney Clause remains part of our food safety laws. Future scientific techniques might decrease reliance on animal testing and improve accuracy in predicting the effects of food additives on human health.

Additives in Functional Foods

Using additives to create functional foods raises questions of how much should be used and how much is safe. In addition, although there are guidelines for the use of vitamins and minerals in the fortification of food and for the use of approved food additives, little is known about what happens to many novel ingredients, such as botanical extracts, when they are put into a food.[10]

Because so many products with added herbal and other novel ingredients have appeared on the market, the FDA has been reminding manufacturers that food additives not Generally Recognized as Safe require approval before being sold. Any food containing an unapproved food additive is considered adulterated and cannot legally be marketed in the United States. Companies that have marketed foods containing herbal compounds that were not considered GRAS have received warning letters from the FDA.[11] These companies were warned that as formulated, the FDA considered the products to be adulterated.

Key Concepts *Direct additives are used for specific purposes. Indirect additives become part of the food in trace amounts when the food comes in contact with the substance. Additives are used for many reasons; these include improving product quality, maintaining freshness, and improving nutritional value. Unless a new additive meets the requirements to be considered GRAS or is a prior-sanctioned ingredient, the FDA demands that it undergo extensive testing to be proved safe and effective. The FDA is responsible for approving and regulating additives. The Delaney Clause prohibits the approval of an additive if it is found to cause cancer in humans or animals.*

Claims for Functional Foods

In Chapter 2, "Nutrition Guidelines and Assessment," you learned about the wide variety of nutrient content and health claims allowed on food labels and the restrictions on the use of these claims. When a functional food meets the appropriate FDA guidelines, it may make a nutrient content claim or health claim on the label. For example, tofu containing at least 6.25 grams of soy protein per serving may make a health claim about the role of soy protein in reducing the risk of heart disease. However, research conducted since the approval of this health claim in 1999 has not supported more than a minimal role for soy protein or its isoflavones in reducing LDL cholesterol or other heart disease risk factors.[12] Oatmeal with an adequate amount of beta-glucan fiber can highlight its benefit in reducing risk of heart disease. Another health claim applies to a functional food created through the addition of plant sterol or plant stanol esters to a vegetable-oil-based spread. The Benecol and Take Control product lines (spreads and salad dressings) contain these plant esters, which have been shown to reduce cholesterol levels when consumed daily in adequate amounts. (See **Figure SAN.5**.) Certain types of nuts (e.g., almonds, hazelnuts, peanuts, pecans, pistachio nuts, and walnuts) may make a qualified health claim on the label linking nut consumption with reduced risk of heart disease.

Structure/Function Claims for Functional Foods

Structure/function claims must be based on the food's nutritive value. An example is orange juice with added vitamin C, vitamin E, and zinc to "support your natural defenses." However, the phrase "nutritive value" is not clearly defined in the regulations. At present, therefore, many manufacturers are making claims about non-nutrients in foods and their effects on body structure or function. For example, a cereal with added St. John's wort and kava extract is "accented with herbs to support emotional and mental balance," and a bottled tea is "infused with mind-enhancing ginkgo biloba and Panax ginseng." The FDA has sent letters to manufacturers of herbal-enhanced products charging that structure/function claims related to the herbal ingredients mislead consumers and may, if a specific disease is mentioned, make the product an unapproved drug.[13]

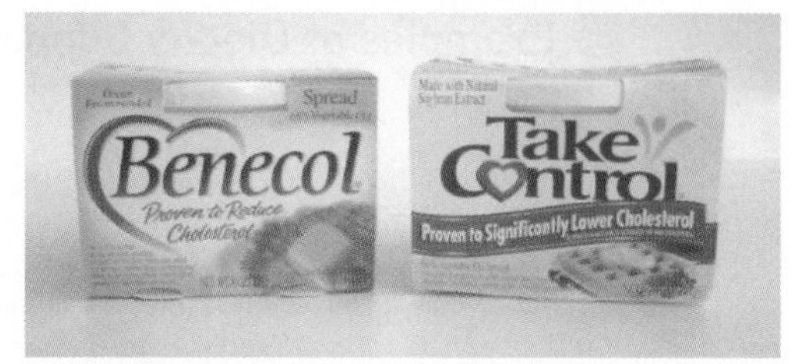

Figure SAN.5 **Some functional foods can make health claims.** Manufacturers have obtained approval from the FDA to make health claims for these margarine products.

Key Concepts *Under FDA guidelines, a functional food's label may have a nutrient content claim, health claim, or structure/function claim. A structure/function claim promotes a substance's effect on the structure or function of the body. For foods, the claimed effect must be based on the food's "nutritive value," a phrase without a clear regulatory definition. Currently, many manufacturers make structure/function claims about non-nutrients in foods.*

Strategies for Functional Food Use

So, should you go all out and fill your shopping cart with functional foods? Which ones would you buy? The best course of action is to stick with what scientists have agreed upon so far. First, fruits and vegetables promote health and reduce disease risk through a whole host of natural phytochemicals. Use the list of foods and phytochemicals in Table SAN.1 to enhance your shopping list with nature's functional foods. Second, consider nutrient-fortified products when a particular nutrient is lacking in your diet and you either don't like or can't eat good food sources of that nutrient. For example, if you are allergic to milk and dairy products, consider calcium-fortified orange juice as a nutritious way to get the calcium that you need. Third, read, read, read about functional foods, and not just what's on the Internet. Do your homework by looking at scientific articles—your instructor can help you find and interpret studies of functional food components. Finally, be critical of advertising and hype—if it sounds too good to be true, it probably is!

Dietary Supplements: Vitamins and Minerals

Dietary supplements come in various forms—vitamins, minerals, amino acids, herbs, glandular extracts, enzymes, and many others. The marketplace includes a wide variety of products claiming to do everything from enhancing immune function to improving mood. Table SAN.2 lists many popular supplements, claims, and important cautions. Despite the enticing claims made for many non-nutrient supplements, scientific evidence of efficacy and long-term safety is often lacking.

"Should I take a vitamin (or mineral) supplement?" Apparently many people already have answered that question for themselves: multivitamin/mineral supplements and other single vitamin or mineral supplements are the most popular supplements and are taken by a substantial percentage of Americans.[14] (See **Figure SAN.6.**) We will look at two levels of vitamin and mineral supplementation: (1) moderate doses that are in the range of

Table SAN.2 Examples of Dietary Supplements and Their Claims

Supplement	Claimed Benefits	Current Research Caveats
Beta-carotene	Prevents cancer and heart disease; boosts immunity; improves eye health	Diets rich in beta-carotene-containing fruits and vegetables reduce heart disease and cancer risk. Supplements have not been shown to be beneficial. Taking supplements may increase lung cancer risk in smokers. In combination with vitamin C, vitamin E, and zinc, may slow progression of age-related macular degeneration.
Chromium picolinate	Builds muscle, helps with blood glucose control in diabetes, promotes weight loss, reduces cholesterol	No solid evidence that chromium picolinate supplements perform as claimed or benefit healthy people. Some evidence that they may harm cells.
Coenzyme Q_{10}	Prevents heart disease, improves health of people with heart disease and hypertension, cure-all	May have value in preexisting heart disease, but benefits for healthy people are unproved.
Cranberry	Prevents and treats urinary tract infections (UTIs)	Regular consumption of juice may reduce UTI incidence; limited evidence for supplements.
Creatine	Increases muscle strength and size, improves athletic performance	May enhance power and strength for some athletes, but is meaningless for casual exercisers and distance athletes.
Echinacea	Protects against and cures colds, boosts immunity	Inconsistent evidence of benefit. Many varieties exist; products on the market are unstandardized.
Ephedra	Weight control, herbal "high," decongestant	Ephedra raises heart rate and blood pressure and is dangerous for people with diabetes, hypertension, or heart disease. The FDA has prohibited sales of ephedra-containing supplements.
Feverfew	Prevents migraines	Some evidence of reduced severity and frequency of migraines, but high drop-out rates in studies.
Garlic	Lowers blood pressure and blood cholesterol, reduces cancer risk	Some evidence that garlic reduces cholesterol and blood pressure. Conflicting results related to cancer risk reduction.
Ginkgo biloba	Improves blood flow and circulatory disorders; prevents or cures absentmindedness, memory loss, dementia	Limited benefits for some Alzheimer's patients. No proven benefit for others.
Ginseng	Improves athletic performance, fights fatigue, helps control blood glucose in people with diabetes, reduces cancer risk	No evidence that ginseng has any beneficial effects. Many products on the market contain no ginseng.
Glucosamine and chondroiton sulfate	Relieves arthritis pain, slows progression of arthritis	Some evidence of reduced pain and improved symptoms, although more studies are needed. Does not reverse arthritis. Variable amounts in products.
Kava	Promotes relaxation and relieves anxiety	May cause liver damage. Banned in Switzerland, Germany, and Canada.
Melatonin	Promotes sleep, counters jet lag, improves sex life, prevents migraine	May be effective for jet lag, studies are contradictory relative to sleep. No evidence for anti-aging or sex-drive claims. No data on long-term safety.
Milk thistle	Reduces liver damage in alcoholic liver disease, promotes general liver health	No evidence of general liver health benefit, some evidence of benefit in those with alcoholic liver cirrhosis.
Saw palmetto	Shrinks prostate, reduces symptoms of benign prostatic hyperplasia, prevents prostate cancer	May improve urinary tract symptoms associated with prostate enlargement. No evidence for prevention of prostate cancer. May affect PSA test and diagnosis of prostate cancer.
St. John's wort	Alleviates depression, promotes emotional well-being	Studies in Europe suggest efficacy for mild depression. Clinical studies in the United States show no effect on major depression of moderate severity. Should not be taken with prescription antidepressants.
Valerian	Enhances sleep, reduces stress and anxiety	Inconclusive results to date, much more research is needed.

Source: Adapted from The Wellness Guide to Dietary Supplements. *UC Berkeley Wellness Letter.* August 1998; and Sarubin Fragakis A. *The Health Professional's Guide to Popular Dietary Supplements.* 3rd ed. Chicago, IL: American Dietetic Association, 2007.

the Daily Values (DVs) or levels you might eat in a nutrient-rich diet and (2) **megadoses**, or high levels that are typically multiples of the DVs and much greater amounts than diet alone could supply.

Figure SAN.6 **Increasing popularity of dietary supplements.** Two-thirds of adult Americans regularly purchase dietary supplements.

megadoses Doses of a nutrient that are 10 or more times the recommended amount.

Moderate Supplementation

Health care practitioners often recommend moderate nutrient supplementation for people with elevated nutrient needs and people who may not always eat well.[15] Some examples include the following:

- *Pregnant and breastfeeding women.* Taking supplemental folic acid prior to and during pregnancy can reduce the incidence of birth defects. During pregnancy, it's hard to meet the increased needs for iron and other nutrients through diet alone. "Morning sickness" makes it even harder. When a woman breastfeeds, some of her nutrient needs are even higher than they were in pregnancy.
- *Women with heavy menstrual bleeding.* Women with high iron losses may need a supplement, but they should not take high doses of iron without a doctor's recommendation. Lab tests can show whether a woman gets enough blood-building nutrients or whether she needs supplements.
- *Children.* A supplement can help balance the diets of picky eaters or children on a food jag (eating only a few specific foods), and it can ease parental worries.
- *Infants.* If their access to sunlight is restricted, infants may need supplemental vitamin D. Doctors also may prescribe fluoride in areas where water is not fluoridated.
- *People with severe food restrictions, either self-imposed or prescribed.* Supplements may help people on a strict weight-loss diet, those who have eating disorders, those who have mental illnesses, and those who limit their eating because of social or emotional situations.
- *Strict vegetarians who abstain from animal foods and dairy products.* People who don't eat meat or dairy products may need supplemental vitamin B_{12}, vitamin D, and perhaps calcium, zinc, iron, and other minerals.
- *Elders.* Because inadequate stomach acid (which is needed for normal absorption of vitamin B_{12}) is common among older people, elders may need extra vitamin B_{12}. When elders have limited exposure to the sun and their diets lack dairy products, they should take supplements of vitamin D, calcium, and possibly other nutrients to help maintain bone health.

Many people take nutrient supplements to ensure that they meet their nutritional needs. However, taking supplements to "fix" a poor diet is a bad idea. Foods provide not only nutrients but also fiber and other health-promoting phytochemicals. Whenever possible, meet your nutritional needs with food.

Many supplements contain multiple vitamins and minerals. If you are one of those who should take multivitamin/mineral supplements, look for brands that contain at least 20 vitamins and minerals, each no more than 150 percent of its Daily Value. (See **Figure SAN.7**.) For some minerals, even 50 percent of the DV in a tablet would make a multivitamin/mineral supplement too large to swallow, so people take these supplements separately. Although most products have appropriate nutrient levels, some formulas are irrational and unbalanced, with less than 10 percent of the Daily Value of some nutrients and more than 1,000 percent of others.

Academy of Nutrition and Dietetics

Fortification and Nutritional Supplements

It is the position of the Academy of Nutrition and Dietetics (AND) that the best nutritional strategy for promoting optimal health and reducing the risk of chronic disease is to wisely choose a wide variety of foods. Additional nutrients from fortified foods and/or supplements can help some people meet their nutritional needs as specified by science-based nutrition standards such as the Dietary Reference Intakes.

Source: Position of the American Dietetic Association: fortification and nutritional supplements. *J Am Diet Assoc.* 2005;105(8):1300–1311. Copyright 2005. Reprinted with permission from Elsevier.

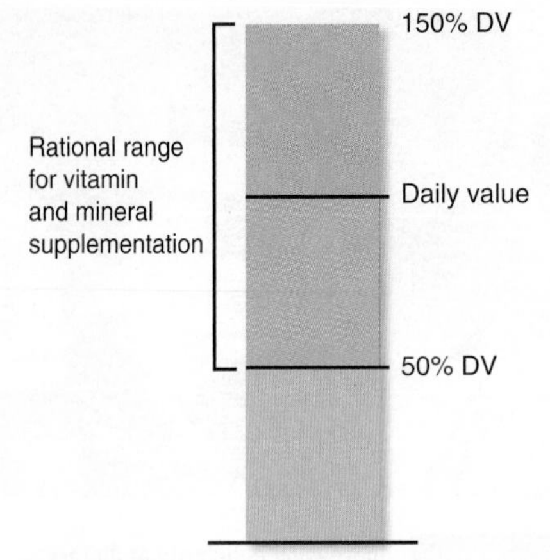

Figure SAN.7 **Moderate supplementation.** Health care practitioners often recommend moderate nutrient supplementation for people with elevated nutrient needs and for people who have consistently poor diets.

nucleic acids A family of more than 25,000 molecules found in chromosomes, nucleoli, mitochondria, and the cytoplasm of cells.

malabsorption syndromes Conditions that result in imperfect, inadequate, or otherwise disordered gastrointestinal absorption.

orthomolecular medicine The preventive or therapeutic use of high-dose vitamins to treat disease.

American Heart Association

Dietary Supplements, Powders, and Other Formulas

The American Heart Association does not recommend using vitamin, mineral, or herbal supplements to treat or prevent heart disease and stroke. To avoid developing nutrient deficiencies, the AHA recommends eating a variety of foods including five or more servings of fruits and vegetables per day.

Source: American Heart Association, Inc.

Key Concepts *Vitamin and mineral supplements are popular; however, it is better to obtain nutrients from food. Some conditions and circumstances make it difficult to meet nutritional needs through food alone or to consume enough food to accommodate increases in nutrient needs. Multivitamin/mineral supplements should be well balanced, with doses no greater than about 150% DV of each nutrient.*

Megadoses in Conventional Medical Management

High doses of vitamins and minerals have become so much a part of treating certain illnesses that when physicians prescribe these nutrients, many see themselves as following "standard medical practice" rather than as "practicing nutrition." Here are some situations in which physicians prescribe megadoses.

- When a medication dramatically depletes or destroys the stores or blocks the functions of vitamins or minerals, megadosing can overcome these effects. For example, folic acid and vitamin B_6 are used during long-term treatment with some tuberculosis drugs. B vitamins also may be prescribed along with seizure medications or medicines that block the metabolism of **nucleic acids**.[16]
- People with **malabsorption syndromes** often take large nutrient doses to compensate for nutritive losses and to override intestinal barriers to absorption. Megadoses routinely are given to patients with colitis or cystic fibrosis, for example.
- Megadoses of vitamin B_{12} can overcome the malabsorption seen in pernicious anemia, a condition in which a key substance needed for vitamin B_{12} absorption is lacking. Ordinarily, an intricate series of steps during digestion prepares B_{12} for normal intestinal absorption; if there is a malfunction during any of these steps, the vitamin is lost. Megadoses allow a small amount of the vitamin to diffuse across the intestine, thus overriding the normal mechanism and preventing deficiency.[17]

A vitamin at megadose levels can have "pharmacological activity"—that is, it acts as a drug. Nicotinic acid (niacin) is the best example. At usual levels (around 10 or 20 milligrams), it functions as a vitamin, but at levels 50 or 100 times higher, it acts as a drug to lower blood lipid levels. Like any drug, though, it can have serious side effects.[18]

Benefits from high doses of other vitamins are not clear-cut. Researchers have tried prescribing B vitamins, including niacin, for emotional problems and mental illnesses; they work well when there's an underlying deficiency, but otherwise results have been mixed and often disappointing. Vitamin E has been tried for some neurological illnesses, to minimize complications of diabetes mellitus, and to reduce the risk of coronary artery disease. A combination supplement of vitamin C, vitamin E, beta-carotene, and zinc (with cupric oxide) has been shown to slow the progression of age-related macular degeneration but is not effective for cataracts.[19] Supplementation with vitamins B_6, B_{12}, and folic acid has been linked to reduced heart disease risk. However, an independent panel of medical experts has concluded that evidence is insufficient to recommend for or against the use of supplements of vitamins A, C, or E, multivitamins with folic acid, or combinations of antioxidants for the prevention of cancer or heart disease.[20]

Megadosing Beyond Conventional Medicine: Orthomolecular Nutrition

In 1968, Linus Pauling, the best-known advocate of megadosing, coined the term **orthomolecular medicine**. To him, *orthomolecular* meant achieving the optimal nutrient levels in the body.[21] Few nutritionists argue with the importance of optimum nutrition. In fact, some nutritionists share Pauling's concerns that the typical diet is too refined to provide adequate nutrients and that intake equal to RDA values may not be high enough to achieve optimal body levels.

Most nutritionists would argue, however, with the high doses Pauling recommended to attain those optimal body levels and with the therapeutic value he and his followers attributed to those doses. Most notably, Pauling suggested in the early 1970s that an optimal daily intake of vitamin C was 2,000 milligrams—more than 30 times the current Daily Value. (See

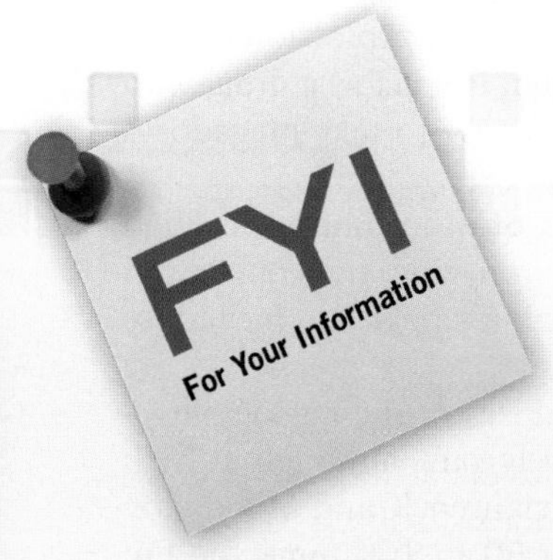

Shopping for Supplements

Thinking about buying a dietary supplement? Before you do, ask yourself, "Why do I need this supplement?" and "Is it suitable for me?" Think about your typical diet and what it may be lacking. Remember, the word *supplement* means just that—a product meant to supplement your food. A well-chosen supplement can be beneficial under some circumstances, especially if your diet is limited. However, if you're healthy and eat a good balance of healthful foods, supplements won't help you much.

It's a good idea to let your doctor know your supplement plans. Some supplements are contraindicated during pregnancy or lactation; others should not be used with certain chronic illnesses. Supplements sometimes interfere with the action of medicines. Some slow blood clotting, which is a concern if surgery is planned.

To a great extent, you'll need to rely on your own understanding of diet and nutrition to make your selection. And you must rely on the supplement manufacturer for the product's safety, its purity and cleanliness, and the label's accuracy. If you're concerned about potential side effects or contraindications, you'll probably need to contact the manufacturer or distributor.

Choose Quality

The FDA has finalized guidelines for current good manufacturing practices by supplement manufacturers. Until standards are fully implemented in 2010, you can use tip-offs to judge a quality company—the kind you'd expect to have good quality control procedures and to manufacture, store, and transport products safely and carefully.

A quality company will not promise miracles on its Web site, in catalogues, in commercials or advertisements, or in in-store promotions. Promises to make you smarter or thinner (unless you cut calories along with taking the supplement), to keep you young, to increase or decrease the size of various body parts, and so forth, should raise a red flag. A quality company will not manipulate statistics or distort research findings in an attempt to mislead you.

A quality company will take care with its labels, print materials, and Web information. Misspelling of terms; confusion of milligrams, grams, and micrograms; and omission on labels of important or required information are indicators of the manufacturer's carelessness or ignorance.

Confirm Supplement Ingredients

Use resources that analyze and confirm supplement content, dose, and purity. ConsumerLab.com (www.consumerlab.com/) is one such service. Pharmaceutical researchers also report findings on supplement label accuracy; a search on PubMed (www.nlm.nih.gov/) can lead you to this information.

Look for the U.S. Pharmacopeia (USP) logo (USP verification mark) on supplement labels. The mark certifies that the USP has found the ingredients consistent with those stated on the label; that the supplement has been manufactured in a safe, sanitary, controlled facility; and that the product dissolves or disintegrates to release nutrients in the body. (However, the USP does not test the supplement's efficacy.)

Choose Freshness

Finding the freshest supplement is often easier if you shop in a retail store. Avoid dust-covered containers. Choose a store where turnover is likely to be quick. Supplements should be displayed away from direct sunlight, bright lights, or nearby heat sources, because heat ages many supplements. Expiration dates can also give you a clue regarding freshness.

Expect Accountability

How easily can you obtain information about the product? Look for a phone number on the label so you can call with questions or to report side effects. On Web sites, look for a domestic address and phone number, in addition to an e-mail contact. Does a knowledgeable company representative respond to your questions, or is the only person available one who reads a scripted response?

If you're shopping online but are uncertain the supplement is right for you, check the Web retailer's return policy. A Web retailer that also has a brick-and-mortar outlet near your locale may be preferable.

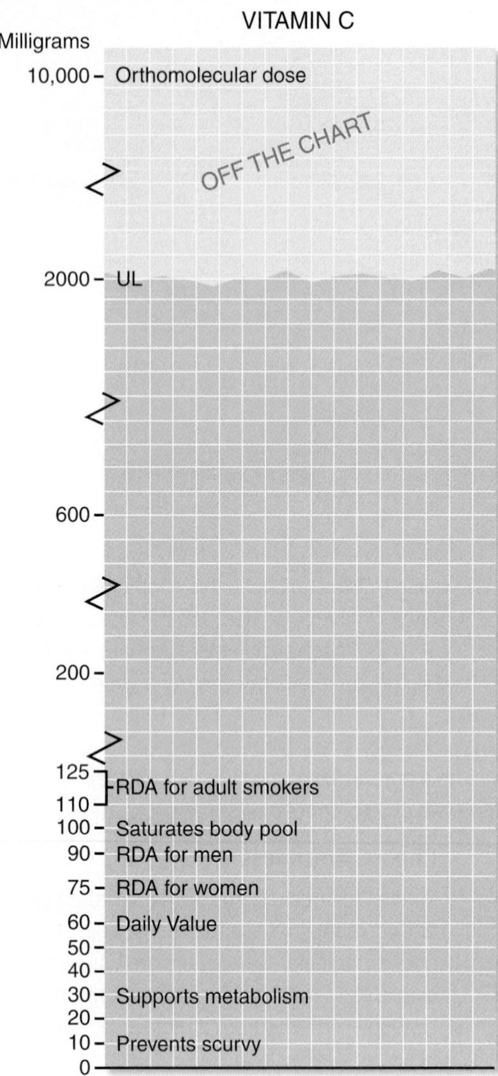

Figure SAN.8 Megadoses of vitamin C are much higher intakes than currently recommended.

Figure SAN.8.) Some advocates of vitamin C recommend even higher doses, relying on intravenous administration to avoid causing diarrhea. Dr. Pauling claimed megadoses of vitamin C prevented or cured the common cold. Although many researchers have attempted to confirm this theory, studies do not support the idea that vitamin C prevents colds. A few studies found that colds were slightly less severe or less frequent in certain people, but most studies found no beneficial effect.[22] The most controversial claim for vitamin C was its purported ability to prevent and treat cancer. Well-controlled studies have failed to support this claim.[23]

Drawbacks of Megadoses

Megadose vitamins and minerals remain popular. But when taken without recommendation or prescription from a qualified health professional, they can cause problems. Because high doses of a nutrient can act as a drug, with a drug's risk of adverse side effects, people who choose to take megadoses should always check first with their doctors. THINK About It 2

Excesses of some nutrients can create deficits of other nutrients. High doses of supplemental minerals, especially calcium, iron, zinc, and copper, can interfere with absorption of the others.[24] In general, it's riskier to megadose with minerals than with vitamins.

It's easy to reach toxic levels if you use high doses of the fat-soluble vitamins A and D. Vitamins E and K appear relatively safe, although at high doses vitamin E can interfere with normal use of vitamin K and blood clotting. Megadosing with water-soluble vitamin B_6 at 50 to 100 times the DV can cause nerve damage. You may want to review the DRI tables for Tolerable Upper Intake Levels (ULs) for vitamins and minerals (see the inside of the back cover).

Megadoses often are recommended for sick people, but sick people may be least able to tolerate them. Supplemental iron is very hard on a sensitive digestive system, for example, and high doses of vitamin C can cause diarrhea. Although people who drink a lot of alcohol often are deficient in vitamin A, supplements not much greater than the DV produce undesirable liver changes in alcoholics.[25]

Megadoses can also interfere with medications and treatments. Although some people who take antiseizure medications also may need folic acid supplementation, too much folic acid can allow "breakthrough seizures." Vitamin K interferes with medication to control blood clotting and should be taken only under a doctor's direction. People undergoing surgery should describe their nutritional supplements to their doctor, because high-dose vitamin E, especially if accompanied by blood thinners such as ginkgo biloba, aspirin, or fish oil, can cause bleeding problems in the operating room. Antioxidant nutrients may counteract chemotherapy or radiation aimed at oxidative destruction of cancer cells.

Key Concepts *High doses (megadoses) of vitamins or minerals turn nutrients into drugs—chemicals with pharmacological activity. Although there may be medical reasons for prescribing high-dose supplements, they should be taken under a physician's supervision. Many claims for high-dose supplements, such as claims that vitamin C prevents cancer, are not supported by clinical studies.*

Dietary Supplements: Natural Health Products

Supplementation with herbal and other "natural" products is a popular form of complementary medicine. (See **Figure SAN.9**.) The 1990s saw a dramatic rise in the popularity of dietary supplements. In the United States, two-thirds of adults use dietary supplements, accounting for $21.4 billion in annual sales.[26] Health Canada estimates that 71 percent of Canadians have consumed natural health products: herbs, vitamins and minerals, and homeopathic products.[27] **Herbal therapy (phytotherapy)** is nothing new, however. Most cultures have long traditions of using plants (and some animal products) to treat illness or sustain health. For centuries there were no other medicines. Even now, most of the world's people depend primarily on plants for medications; in some remote areas, modern medicines are just not obtainable.

In the Western world, the feeling that "natural" is better than "chemical" or "synthetic" has launched the expansion of the herbalism industry.[28] Herbalists reason that natural products are likely to contain a complex of healing ingredients, whereas a purified pharmaceutical product contains only one or two. They believe that when active ingredients are combined with many other plant components, their side effects may be blunted or neutralized. Using herbal medicine sounds simple and easy, but in fact herbalism calls for a great deal of skill. Traditional healers typically serve long apprenticeships and acquire a subjective "feel" for their therapies after much experience. They must learn to judge the safety and potency of individual plants, which vary from season to season, location to location, part of the plant, and age of the plant. They must know how to prepare the plant—whether to extract it and with what, or how to make it into a salve or an oral preparation. They must know how to blend it with other herbs and with other therapies. In traditional Chinese medicine, for example, a blend of herbs, sometimes 30 or more, can be used at once; the mixture usually is simmered in water and taken as a tea or "soup." Other herbal traditions use only one or two carefully chosen herbs at a time.

Traditional herbalists know their patients and individualize their herbal remedies accordingly. In the United States that includes knowing results of diagnostic testing; in other cultures it includes recognizing and understanding symptoms. But those who turn to the mass market for herbal supplements rarely receive such attention.

Figure SAN.9 **Use of herbal supplements is growing in popularity.** Use of herbal supplements grew nearly eightfold during the last decade.

herbal therapy (phytotherapy) The therapeutic use of herbs and other plants to promote health and treat disease.

National Center for Complementary and Alternative Medicine (NCCAM) An NIH organization established to stimulate, develop, and support objective scientific research on complementary and alternative medicine for the benefit of the public.

Helpful Herbs, Harmful Herbs

THINK About It 3 People who decide to use herbs instead of conventional medicines must choose their practitioners carefully. Herbalists must know their herbs, but they also must know when to tell patients to seek conventional care. People who use both an herbalist and a conventional doctor should tell both practitioners about the other and disclose all treatments.

Until recently, most research on herbs was published in obscure or foreign-language journals that were hard to locate or read. Traditional herbal medical practices are difficult to study in a controlled manner because they use plants to make teas or soups, a far cry from the purified extracts and herbal blends sold in a supermarket. Nevertheless, for some herbs, researchers have enough data to plan carefully controlled studies. The **National Center for Complementary and Alternative Medicine (NCCAM)** within the National Institutes of Health (NIH) (see **Figure SAN.10**) funded a large study of St. John's wort, based on preliminary evidence that it fights mild depression and sleeplessness.[29] However, the study found that St. John's wort was no better than a placebo in treating moderately severe major depression.[30] Milk thistle may be helpful for liver disease, but more research is needed.[31] Ginkgo biloba appears to help blood circulation, and some evidence suggests it may help in treating Alzheimer's disease, although efficacy has not been established.[32] Short-term studies indicate that saw palmetto extract improves urinary tract function in men with benign prostate enlargement,[33] but a one-year supple-

Quick Bite

Culinary Herbs Are Not Medicinal Herbs—Or Are They?

Herbs used in cooking are called *culinary herbs* to distinguish them from medicinal herbs. But culinary herbs are also rich in phytochemicals. Some examples are beta-carotene in paprika, the antioxidants in rosemary, the mild antibiotic allicin in garlic, and the mild antiviral curcumin in turmeric.

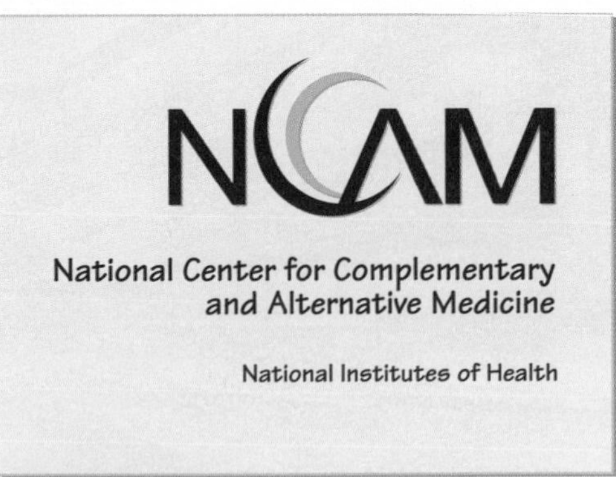

Figure SAN.10 National Center for Complementary and Alternative Medicine. In 1998, Congress established the NCCAM at the National Institutes of Health (NIH) to stimulate, develop, and support research on complementary and alternative medicine (CAM) for the benefit of the public. The NCCAM is an advocate for quality science, rigorous and relevant research, and open and objective inquiry into which CAM practices work, which do not, and why. Explore the NCCAM Web site at http://nccam.nih.gov/.

Source: Courtesy of the National Center for Complementary and Alternative Medicine.

mentation study found no difference between saw palmetto and the placebo.[34] Drinking cranberry juice discourages urinary tract infections by inhibiting harmful bacteria from sticking to the urinary tract's lining.[35]

The suggested benefits of other herbs are based not on scientific study but on years of informal observation: mint helps indigestion; ginger helps nausea and motion sickness; lemon perks appetite; chamomile helps insomnia.

THINK About It 4

If you're considering using an herb, remember this important rule of thumb: any herb that is strong enough to help you can be strong enough to hurt you. Like any medicine, herbs can have side effects, and herbs can be contraindicated. Ginkgo biloba is a blood thinner and has caused harmful bleeding in some people.[36] Just like any other new, unusual substance, herbs can cause sudden allergic reactions.

Herbs can interfere with standard medicines,[37] and they can make people with underlying health problems quite sick. For example, licorice extract—even as a flavoring in chewing tobacco—flushes potassium from the body, raises blood pressure, and can interfere with blood pressure medication.[38] (Most licorice candy is now flavored synthetically; naturally flavored licorice has little effect unless routinely eaten in large amounts.) The FDA has issued a public health advisory warning of interactions between St. John's wort and some prescription medications, including several used in the treatment of HIV/AIDS.[39] Table SAN.3 lists some possible interactions of herbs and drugs.

Some herbs and herbalist treatments are downright dangerous. (See Table SAN.4.) Some hazardous therapies even use lead or arsenic, known poisons.[40] The herbs yohimbe, ephedra (ma huang), chaparral, and comfrey have been shown to be dangerous.[41] Senna, cascara, and rhubarb are powerful laxatives used in products described as "colon cleansers," "colon purifiers," or even "blood purifiers"; their overuse is as damaging as overuse of conventional laxatives. In fact, in November 2002 the FDA ruled that aloe and cascara sagrada are not GRAS and therefore cannot be used in over-the-counter laxatives. In February 2004, the FDA issued a final rule prohibiting the sale of dietary supplements containing ephedra. Health Canada requested a recall of

Table SAN.3 Selected Herb–Drug Interactions

Herb	Drug	Interaction
Feverfew, garlic, ginger, ginkgo biloba, guarana, and pau d'Arco	Warfarin, aspirin	Increases anticoagulant effect by inhibiting platelet aggregation.
Hawthorn and horse chestnut	Digoxin, diuretics	Affects cardiac function and blood pressure; should not be taken with digoxin and diuretics.
Aloe, senna (laxative), cascara, and licorice	Digoxin, diuretics	Causes electrolyte imbalance; true licorice increases blood pressure. Do not take with diuretics and digoxin.
Kava and valerian	Anxiolytics, narcotics, and alcohol	Increases sedative effects.
St. John's wort	Antidepressants, crixivan (indinavir) and other protease inhibitors, cyclosporine	Should not be taken with prescription antidepressants; risk of hypertensive crisis if taken with antidepressants. St. John's wort makes several prescription medications used in the treatment of AIDS less effective. The herb speeds up activity in a key pathway responsible for breaking down these drugs in the body. When the medications are taken with St. John's wort, blood levels of the drugs decrease because the body breaks them down faster.

Table SAN.4 **Potential Adverse Effects of Selected Herbs**

Herb	Adverse Effects
Chamomile (tea)	Allergic reaction; digestive upset
Chaparral	Liver toxicity
Comfrey	Liver and kidney disease
Echinacea	Allergic reaction; stimulation of immune system: not for use by those with systemic/autoimmune diseases
Ephedra	Insomnia, headaches, nervousness, seizures, increased blood pressure, stroke, death
Ginkgo biloba	Inhibits blood clotting; do not take with aspirin, anticoagulants, vitamin E; mild gastrointestinal upset, headaches, dizziness
Ginseng	Headaches, insomnia, diarrhea, heart palpitations, increased bleeding time
Kava	Slowed reaction time; scaly dermatitis; liver damage
Licorice	Headaches, fluid retention, increased blood pressure, electrolyte imbalance, heart failure
Pau d'Arco	Severe nausea, vomiting; anemia; bleeding tendencies
Pennyroyal	Liver damage, convulsions, abortions, coma, death; oil is very toxic
St. John's wort	Adverse interactions with antidepressant and HIV/AIDS medications; possible photosensitivity; gastrointestinal symptoms, headaches, dizziness
Senna	Laxative dependency, diarrhea, cramps, electrolyte disturbances
Valerian	Drowsiness; withdrawal symptoms if abruptly discontinued

Source: Data from McGuffin M, Hobbs C, Upton R, Goldberg A. American Herbal Products Association Botanical Safety Handbook. Boca Raton, FL: CRC Press, 1997; Sarubin Fragakis A. *The Health Professional's Guide to Popular Dietary Supplements.* 3rd ed. Chicago, IL: American Dietetic Association, 2007; and Foster S, Tyler VE. *Tyler's Honest Herbal: A Sensible Guide to the Use of Herbs and Related Remedies.* Binghamton, NY; Haworth Herbal Press, 1999.

similar products in 2002. Also in 2002, both Health Canada and the FDA issued advisories warning consumers not to use products containing kava due to European reports of liver toxicity. In the United States, the ban on ephedra was overturned in a federal court in 2005, a ruling that the FDA subsequently appealed. In 2007 the FDA was granted a summary judgment in its favor.

Herbal blends marketed for specific conditions, such as "healthy bone formula" or "female blend," do not always make sense in light of current scientific knowledge. For example, pennyroyal and St. John's wort—herbs that should not be used during pregnancy—have shown up in some "prenatal formulas." Also, a popular blend used to treat prostate cancer actually had hormonal (estrogenic) activity, which promotes the growth of cancer cells.[42]

Quality control is a big issue in herbal medicines. Contaminants have caused acute illness and death.[43] A common problem is poorly standardized strength, or potency. There can be as much as a 17-fold difference in potency of the popular over-the-counter St. John's wort supplements.[44] One analysis showed that the quantity of active ingredient in ginseng supplements varied from the amount stated on the label by as much as 200-fold.[45]

To correct these problems, in 2007 the FDA issued final regulations requiring current good manufacturing practices (cGMPs) for the manufacturing, packaging, labeling, and storage of dietary supplements. Under the regulations, manufacturers are required to evaluate the identity, purity, strength, and composition of their products and ensure proper labeling.[46]

To guarantee quality, each step from field to market must be monitored carefully. However, monitoring the production of herbal supplements poses special challenges. Herbs are grown and harvested in far-flung, sometimes remote areas of the world. Extraction or preparation of the herbs may take place somewhere else. Mixing the herbs and putting them in capsules, tonics, or teas typically takes place in yet another location.

Quick Bite

Office of Dietary Supplements
The Office of Dietary Supplements (ODS) is a congressionally mandated office in the National Institutes of Health (NIH). The mission of ODS is to strengthen knowledge and understanding of dietary supplements by evaluating scientific information, stimulating and supporting research, disseminating research results, and educating the public to foster an enhanced quality of life and health for the U.S. population.

Other Dietary Supplements

The supplement market used to include only vitamins, minerals, and a handful of other products such as brewer's yeast and sea salt. Today there are hundreds of products, with new ones continuously popping up. Although some are useful, many are of dubious benefit.

Supplement categories now include protein powders, amino acids, carotenoids, **bioflavonoids**, digestive aids, fatty acid formulas and special fats, lecithin and phospholipids, probiotics, products from sharks and other sea animals, algae, metabolites such as coenzyme Q_{10} and nucleic acids, glandular extracts, garlic products, and fibers, such as guar gum. Supplement producers also blend these products with herbs and nutrients, resulting in the countless array of individual and combination supplements sold today. In many cases, labeling and advertising claims go beyond current knowledge about these products.

bioflavonoids Naturally occurring plant chemicals, especially from citrus fruits, that reduce the permeability and fragility of capillaries.

Key Concepts *Herbal products are among the many dietary supplements available today. Herbal medicine has a long history in many cultures. Although there is anecdotal support for the use of many herbal products, there is little scientific evidence to back it up. The FDA has set standards for the production and sale of herbal supplements. It is important to remember that any herb that is strong enough to help you can also be strong enough to hurt you. Before taking any supplements, it's a good idea to consult your health care practitioner.*

Dietary Supplements in the Marketplace

Although some dietary supplements have druglike actions (e.g., reducing cholesterol levels), government agencies regulate supplements differently from drugs. Manufacturers are allowed to make a wide variety of claims for product effects without having to provide scientific evidence to support those claims. The freedoms of speech and press prevail; in practical terms, almost anything goes. Promotional books, magazine articles, audio- and videotapes, lectures, staged interviews, and messages posted on Internet chat rooms—all are protected by the First Amendment, and their authors have the freedom to inform or to deceive. It's up to the listener or reader to distinguish fact from fiction. (See **Figure SAN.11**.)

Quick Bite

Pronouncing the Acronym
The Dietary Supplement Health and Education Act of 1994 is better known by its acronym DSHEA, pronounced "da-shay."

The FTC and Supplement Advertising

The Federal Trade Commission (FTC) in the U.S. Department of Commerce is responsible for ensuring that advertisements and commercials are truthful and do not mislead. The agency depends on and encourages self-monitoring by the supplement industry. In pursuing companies that skirt the regulations,

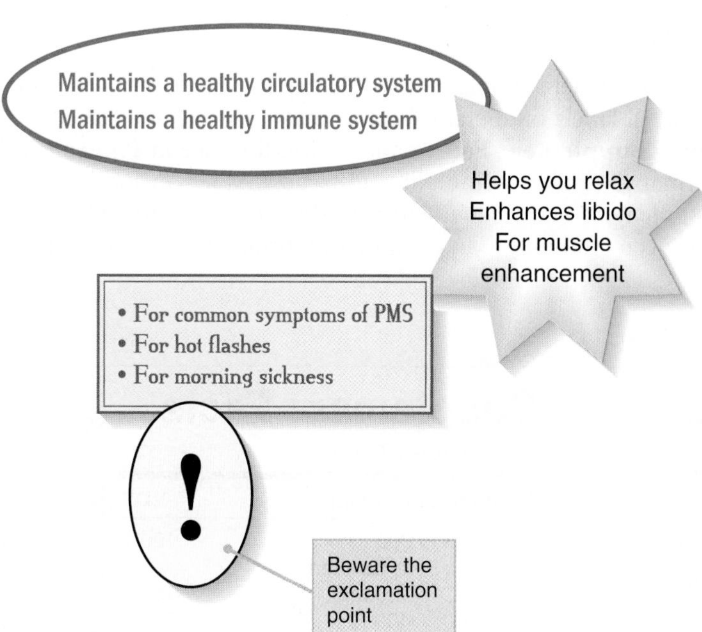

Figure SAN.11 **Dietary supplement label claims.** Although claims such as these appear on dietary supplement labels, they do not have to be approved by the FDA. All should be viewed with skepticism.

the FTC gives priority to cases that seriously put people's health and safety at risk or that affect sick and vulnerable consumers.[47] The FTC's Operation Cure All targets false and unsubstantiated claims on the Internet.

The FDA and Supplement Regulation

The Food and Drug Administration has primary responsibility for regulating the labeling and content of dietary supplements under the Federal Food, Drug, and Cosmetic Act, as amended by the 1994 **Dietary Supplement Health and Education Act (DSHEA).**[48] How do you know a product is a "dietary supplement"? Simple. DSHEA defines any product intended to supplement the diet as a dietary supplement and requires that the word *supplement* be clearly stated on the label. Dietary supplements include vitamins, minerals, herbs, and amino acids as well as other substances, such as enzymes, organ tissues, metabolites, extracts, or concentrates.

Dietary Supplement Health and Education Act (DSHEA) Legislation that regulates dietary supplements.

Dietary supplements are *not* drugs. A drug is intended to diagnose, cure, mitigate, treat, or prevent disease. Before marketing, drugs must undergo extensive studies of effectiveness, safety, interactions with other substances, and dosing. The FDA gives formal premarket approval to a drug and monitors its safety after the drug is on the market. If a drug is subsequently shown to be dangerous, the FDA can act quickly to have it removed from the market. None of this is true for dietary supplements.

Dietary supplements and their ingredients are also *not* food additives, which are also subject to premarket approval. For new ingredients in dietary supplements, the manufacturer finds information (usually not scientific proof) to show the substance is safe if used as directed and submits this information to the FDA 75 days before the supplement is first marketed. However, formal approval by the FDA is not required. A new dietary supplement that contains ingredients already in use does not require such advance notification. Unlike pharmaceutical manufacturers, who must prove the safety and efficacy of their products before they sell them, supplement manufacturers can market their products without the FDA's approval. To restrict the sale and use of a dietary supplement, the FDA must prove that it isn't safe after it is on the market, a process that can take years.

Supplement Facts Content label that must appear on all dietary supplements.

Supplement Labels

Like food labels, supplement labels require mandatory and optional information. All labels on dietary supplements must include ingredient information and a **Supplement Facts** panel.[49] You'll notice in **Figure SAN.12** that the format is similar to the Nutrition Facts panel on food labels. However, a Supplement Facts panel can include substances for which no Daily Value has been established. In combination products, any nutrients with Daily Val-

Figure SAN.12

Supplement Facts panel. Similar to the Nutrition Facts panel on food labels, the Supplement Facts panel required on dietary supplement labels shows the product composition.

Source: Data from US Food and Drug Administration.

Serving Size is the manufacturer's suggested serving expressed in the appropriate unit (tablet, capsule, softgel, packet, teaspoonful).

Each Tablet Contains heads the listing of dietary ingredients contained in the supplement.

Each dietary ingredient is followed by the quantity in a serving. For proprietary blends, total weight of the blend is listed, with components listed in descending order by weight.

Dietary ingredients that have no Daily Value are listed below this line.

Botanical supplements must list the part of plant present and its common name (Latin name if common name not listed in *Herbs of Commerce*).

%DV indicates the percentage of the Daily Value of each nutrient that a serving provides.

An **asterisk** under %DV indicates that a Daily Value is not established for that ingredient.

Supplement Facts

Serving Size 1 Tablet

Each Tablet Contains		**%DV**
Vitamin A	5,000 IU	100%
50% as Beta-Carotene		
Vitamin C	90 mg	150%
Vitamin D	400 IU	100%
Vitamin E	45 IU	150%
Thiamin	1.5 mg	100%
Riboflavin	1.7 mg	100%
Niacin	20 mg	100%
Vitamin B_6	2 mg	100%
Folate	400 mcg	100%
Vitamin B_{12}	6 mcg	100%
Calcium	100 mg	10%
Iron	18 mg	100%
Iodine	150 mcg	100%
Magnesium	100 mg	25%
Zinc	15 mg	100%
Ginseng Root (*Panax ginseng*)	25 mg	*
Ginkgo Biloba Leaf (*Ginkgo biloba*)	25 mg	*
Citrus Bioflavonoids Complex	10 mg	*
Lecithin (*Glycine max*) (bean)	10 mg	*
Nickel	5 mcg	*
Silicon	2 mcg	*
Boron	60 mcg	*

* Daily Value (%DV) not established

List of Ingredients shows the nutrients and other ingredients used to formulate the supplement, in decreasing order by weight.

INGREDIENTS: Dicalcium Phosphate, Magnesium Oxide, Ascorbic Acid, Cellulose, Vitamin A Acetate, Beta-Carotene, Vitamin D, dl-Alpha Tocopherol Acetate, Ginseng Root (*Panax ginseng*), Gelatin, Ginkgo Biloba Leaf (*Ginkgo biloba*), Ferrous Fumarate, Niacinamide, Zinc Oxide, Silicon Dioxide, Lecithin, Citrus Bioflavonoids Complex, Pyridoxine Hydrochloride, Riboflavin, Thiamin Mononitrate, Folic Acid, Potassium Iodine, Boron, Cyanocobalamin, Nickelous Sulfate

Contact Information shows the manufacturer's or distributor's name, address, and zip code.

DISTRIBUTED BY COMPANY NAME
P.O. BOX XXX
CITY, STATE 00000-0000

ues are listed first, followed by other dietary ingredients. Herbal ingredients must list the plant part, such as the root or leaf.

Supplement labels, like food labels, may contain health claims, structure/function claims, and nutrient content claims. However, only a few of the health claims approved for foods are appropriate for dietary supplements. "Adequate calcium may reduce risk of osteoporosis" and "adequate folate intake by women reduces risk of neural tube defects in newborns" are examples of health claims that could appear on supplement labels. (See **Figure SAN.13**.) Qualified health claims may also apply to dietary supplements. For more information about health claims, see Chapter 2, "Nutrition Guidelines and Assessment."

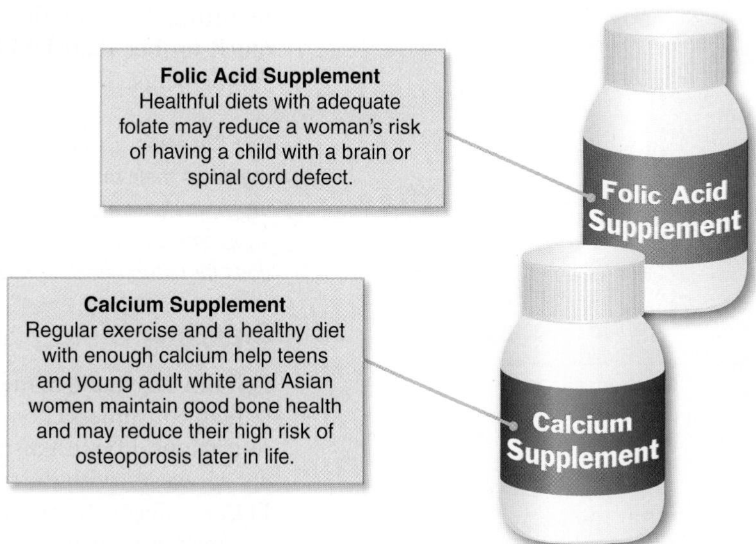

Folic Acid Supplement
Healthful diets with adequate folate may reduce a woman's risk of having a child with a brain or spinal cord defect.
Folic Acid Supplement
Calcium Supplement
Regular exercise and a healthy diet with enough calcium help teens and young adult white and Asian women maintain good bone health and may reduce their high risk of osteoporosis later in life.
Calcium Supplement

Figure SAN.13 **Health claims for supplements.** Calcium and folic acid supplements may carry health claims similar to these model statements.

Source: US Food and Drug Administration.

"Antioxidants maintain cell integrity," "fiber maintains bowel regularity," and "St. John's wort enhances mood" are examples of structure/function claims that might appear on supplement labels. Structure/function claims also may describe the link between a nutrient and a deficiency disease (such as vitamin C and scurvy), as long as the statement also mentions the prevalence of the disease in the United States. Manufacturers can use structure/function claims without FDA authorization and can base their claims on their own review and interpretation of the scientific literature.

Structure/function claims are easy to spot because they are accompanied by the disclaimer "This statement has not been evaluated by the Food and Drug Administration. This product is not intended to diagnose, treat, cure, or prevent any disease." There is often a fine line between structure/function claims and claims that would make the product an unauthorized drug. For example, the claim "promotes urinary tract health" on a bottle of cranberry extract capsules would be allowable, whereas "prevents urinary tract infections" would not. A dietary supplement with a label claiming to cure or treat a specific condition is considered an unapproved drug.

Nutrient content claims must be consistent with definitions approved for foods. With few exceptions, nutrient content claims can be made only for a nutrient or dietary substance that has an established Daily Value. For dietary ingredients without a Daily Value, manufacturers may describe the amount of the ingredient. Examples include simple percentage statements, such as "40% omega-3 fatty acids, 10 mg per capsule," and comparative percentage claims, such as "twice the omega-3 fatty acids per capsule (80 mg) as in 100 mg of menhaden oil (40 mg)."[50]

Canadian Regulations

In June 2003, Health Canada's Natural Health Products Directorate published regulations for natural health products.[51] By definition, natural health products include vitamins, minerals, herbal remedies, and homeopathic medicines. Health Canada has developed a product approval system whereby each product acquires a license after it is authorized for sale by the Natural Health Products Directorate. Authorization requires evidence of safety and efficacy. The regulations also include provisions on site licensing, good manufacturing practices, labeling and packaging requirements, and adverse reaction reporting. The Canadian regulations took effect on January 1, 2004, and go much further than DSHEA in terms of ensuring the safety and efficacy of supplements.

Key Concepts *Dietary supplements are neither foods nor drugs, and the government regulates their manufacture and sale differently than it does for foods, additives, and drugs. In the United States, the FTC and FDA monitor advertising and labeling of dietary supplements. A Supplement Facts panel is now required on labels. Canada's regulations for natural health products require premarket approval and product licensing.*

Choosing Dietary Supplements

DSHEA has made many improvements, such as the Supplement Facts panel, to help consumers choose dietary supplements wisely. By loosening previous restrictions, DSHEA also has made many more products available to consumers. However, with the resulting array of supplements, it is a challenge for the FDA to effectively monitor claims, quality, and safety. Because manufacturers can market their products without prior approval, you need to be wary. For tips on choosing supplements, see the FYI feature "Shopping for Supplements." Knowledge of nutrition science is your most valuable tool for evaluating a supplement. Read each label and judge each implied claim in light of what you know. Ask the following questions:

- *Is the quantity enough to have an effect or is it trivial?* Consider amino acids, for example. A product contains 25 milligrams of glycine. How does this compare with the amount of glycine you would obtain from a diet with 70 grams of protein? Has glycine been added to the product, or is it a component of the gelatin capsule? Is glycine an essential or a nonessential amino acid? What will happen if you take more than you need?
- *Is the product new to you?* Learn about it from the many reliable resources listed on the Web site for this book. Evaluate the product in light of scientific research. Has it been studied in humans, rodents, or other animals, or only in cell cultures or in vitro? If in humans, was the study controlled to eliminate a placebo effect? For case report studies, could the placebo effect influence the results? Consider also the type of preparation and the route of administration. An injected herbal extract may have a very different effect than the same herb in a pill.
- *Consider the dose used in the study. Is it reasonable and an amount found in over-the-counter products?* For example, researchers studied dehydroepiandrosterone (DHEA) and found it may help some immune disorders, but at doses 20 to 50 times greater than the dosage of DHEA sold in health food stores.[52] A consumer who chooses to take 20 of these pills daily to match the dosage used in studies would risk side effects and magnify effects of potential contaminants. Another example is shark cartilage. In the best-controlled study to date of shark cartilage and cancer, the dose was equivalent to about 75 capsules of shark cartilage daily; even at that high dose, patients with advanced cancer were not helped.[53]
- *Can the supplement cross the intestine and travel to its presumed site of action in the body?* The body digests enzyme preparations, for example, along with other proteins. There are little data on the absorption and **bioavailability** of herbal preparations and other types of non-nutrient supplements.

- *Does the product promise too much?* A product touted to control high blood cholesterol, hangnails, psoriasis, and insomnia is unlikely to do much of anything. Neither will a "low-calorie, high-energy" drink. It's possible that the same results can be achieved more cheaply and more enjoyably by eating regular foods. Why take lycopene capsules when you can eat tomatoes, even ketchup? Why take bilberry extract when blueberries (the American equivalent to European bilberries) are delicious and low in calories?
- *Who is selling the product?* Alternative practitioners, dietitians, and even physicians sometimes sell the supplements they recommend—which is a possible conflict of interest that could compromise their objectivity. The Academy of Nutrition and Dietetics has issued guidelines for practitioners' recommendations and sales of supplements.[54] In **multilevel marketing**, someone at each level in the system takes a commission on the supplements you buy, so expect to pay extra. When you buy a supplement over the phone, by catalogue, or over the Web, you lose the chance to examine it before you buy it.

Figure SAN.14 **The USP Verified Mark for Dietary Supplements.** Finding this mark on a supplement indicates that it has been verified by USP to meet established quality, purity, and potency standards.

A good indicator of supplement quality is the **U.S. Pharmacopeia (USP)** Verified Mark (see **Figure SAN.14**), which signifies that a product meets USP's standards for product purity, accuracy of ingredient labeling, and proper manufacturing practices.[55] Established in 1820, USP is an independent, nonprofit organization that establishes quality standards for a wide range of health care products, including prescription and over-the-counter medicines, biotechnology drugs, medical devices, vitamins and minerals, and other dietary supplements. USP is recognized in federal law as an official standards-setting body for dietary supplements in the United States. Products that bear the USP Verified Mark have been voluntarily submitted to USP by their manufacturers and have passed USP's comprehensive testing and review processes. The mark helps assure consumers, health care professionals, and supplement retailers that the product

- Contains the ingredients listed on the label, in the declared potency and amounts
- Does not contain harmful levels of specified contaminants such as, but not limited to, heavy metals, microbes, and pesticides
- Will break down and release into the body within a specified amount of time
- Has been made according to the FDA's current good manufacturing practices (cGMPs), using sanitary and well-controlled procedures

Many nationally known food and drug manufacturers have established their own standards, quality control, and manufacturing practices that they are likely to apply to their dietary supplements as well. Contact the company with your questions; you'll learn a lot, although maybe not what you expected. The "technical representative" may be unable to give you any more information than a brief readout from a computer database. Some companies respond to queries by sending a long printout of journal citations, most of them inappropriate, without text or even abstracts; many references are in a foreign language. However, some dietary supplement companies have on-site quality control and on-site nutritionists who are knowledgeable and happy to supply helpful information. Full implementation of cGMPs will reduce concerns about quality issues.

bioavailability A measure of the extent to which a nutrient becomes available to the body after ingestion and thus is available to the tissues.

multilevel marketing A system of selling in which each salesperson recruits assistants, who then recruit others to help them. The person at each level collects a commission on sales made by the later recruits.

U.S. Pharmacopeia (USP) Established in 1820, the USP is a voluntary, nonprofit health care organization that sets quality standards for a range of health care products.

Quick Bite

Jell-O and Your Nails
You may have heard that taking gelatin can make your nails stronger. Not true. Fingernails get their strength from sulfur in amino acids. Gelatin has no sulfur-containing amino acids.

Even the best-intentioned, most carefully considered supplement can prove ineffective or even risky. Take the example of beta-carotene supplements. Even though diets rich in beta-carotene are linked with reduced cancer risk, several large well-controlled studies found that beta-carotene supplements had no protective effect. For some groups of people, such as smokers, these supplements actually increased risk.[56] The results disappointed advocates of beta-carotene, but these studies demonstrate the value of carefully controlled studies and the risk of unproved assumptions about dietary supplements.

Fraudulent Products

Some health advocates consider the burgeoning market of dietary supplements an unwelcome return to the "snake oil" era of the late nineteenth and early twentieth centuries, when "magic" potions and cures were sold door to door and at county fairs and markets. Most manufacturers work hard to ensure the quality of their products, yet some supplements on the market are nothing more than a mixture of ineffective ingredients.

In the *FDA Consumer* magazine, the agency had this to say about fraudulent products:

> You often can identify fraudulent products by the types of claims made in their labeling, advertising, and promotional literature. Stephen Barrett, M.D., a board member of the National Council Against Health Fraud, points to the following indicators of possible fraud:
>
> - Claims that the product is a secret cure and use of such terms as *breakthrough*, *magical*, *miracle cure*, and *new discovery*. "If the product were a cure for a serious disease, it would be widely reported in the media and used by health-care professionals," he says.
> - "Pseudomedical" jargon, such as *detoxify*, *purify*, and *energize* to describe a product's effects. "These claims are vague and hard to measure," Barrett says. "So, they make it easier for success to be claimed, even though nothing has actually been accomplished," he says.
> - Claims that the product can cure a wide range of unrelated diseases. "No product can do that," he says.
> - Claims that the supplement has only benefits—and no side effects. "A product potent enough to help people will be potent enough to cause side effects," Barrett says.
> - Claims that a product is backed by scientific studies, but with no list of references or references that are inadequate. For instance, if a list of references is provided, the citations cannot be traced, or if they are traceable, the studies are out-of-date, irrelevant, or poorly designed.
> - Accusations that the medical profession, drug companies, and the government are suppressing information about a particular treatment. "It would be illogical," Barrett says, "for large numbers of people to withhold information about potential medical therapies when they or their families and friends might one day benefit from them."[57]

Supplement users who suffer a serious harmful effect or illness that they think is related to supplement use should call a doctor or other health care provider. Practitioners can report problems to FDA MedWatch by calling 1-800-FDA-1088 or by going to the MedWatch Web site (www.fda.gov/Safety/MedWatch/). Consumers can call the toll-free MedWatch number or go to www.fda.gov/Safety/MedWatch/HowToReport/ucm53074.htm on the MedWatch Web site to report an adverse reaction.

Key Concepts *When considering a dietary supplement, it is important to consider the product and its claims carefully. Be aware that some products may promise more than they can deliver. A good indicator of quality is the USP verification mark, but even this does not guarantee that a product will fulfill its claims.*

Quick Bite

Mayonnaise Protects Against Strokes

Is this claim science or snake oil? Studies show that foods rich in vitamin E help protect against heart disease and stroke. In one study of stroke reduction in postmenopausal women, mayonnaise was the most concentrated food source of vitamin E. But to claim that mayonnaise prevents strokes is unwarranted and overstates the evidence.

Complementary and Alternative Medicine

Complementary and alternative medicines (CAM) are therapies and treatments outside the medical mainstream. They tend to be based mainly or solely on observation or anecdotal evidence rather than controlled research. One widely used definition is "treatments or health-care practices neither taught widely in U.S. medical schools nor generally available in U.S. hospitals."[58] This definition, however, may need updating; many medical schools and conventional health care providers have begun to teach or use these therapies, sometimes with insurance reimbursement.[59]

The term *alternative* suggests practices that *replace* conventional ones. *Complementary* implies practices that are used *in addition* to conventional ones. For example, using only herbs and megavitamins to treat AIDS would be "alternative," whereas using herbs to combat diarrhea caused by conventional AIDS medications and taking supplements to replace lost vitamins would be "complementary." Many people find the terms *complementary* and *integrative* more acceptable than *alternative*, although all these terms often are used interchangeably. CAM includes a broad range of healing therapies and philosophies. Several among them involve nutrition, including special diet therapies, phytotherapy (herbalism), orthomolecular medicine, and other biologic interventions.

Approximately one-third of adult Americans use some form of CAM therapy.[60] When prayer specifically for health reasons is included in the definition of CAM, reported use rises to 62 percent of U.S. adults. The most commonly used CAM therapies other than prayer are natural products, deep breathing exercises, meditation, chiropractic care, yoga, massage, and diet-based therapies. People seek out CAM for numerous reasons, including fear of aging, personal beliefs, and distrust of institutional medicine.

Where Does Nutrition Fit In?

A number of alternative therapies involve nutrition, and sometimes the line between standard and alternative nutrition is not clear. A variety of health conditions, such as diabetes, gastrointestinal disorders, and kidney disease, require special diets. Alternative nutrition practices include diets to prevent and treat diseases not shown to be diet-related. (See **Figure SAN.15**.) What often makes these practices "alternative" is the limited nature of the diet, the lack of rigorous scientific evidence showing effectiveness, and the divergence from science-based healthy eating patterns such as the DASH diet or MyPlate. Other practices outside the nutritional mainstream include reliance on only raw foods and the extensive use of herbal and botanical supplements as well as megadoses of vitamin/mineral supplements, which we have already discussed.

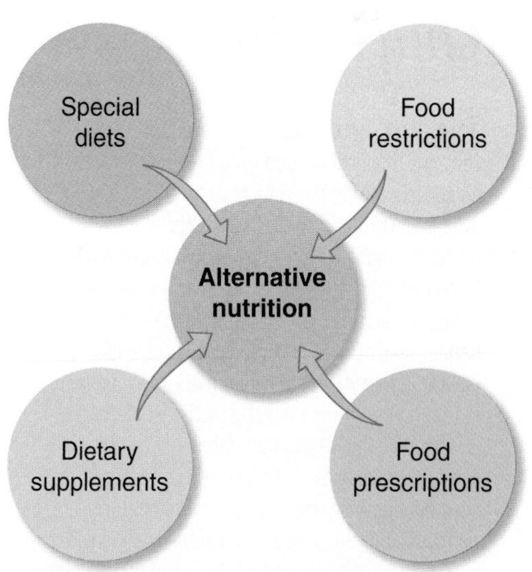

Figure SAN.15 **Alternative nutrition practices.** Although many mainstream medical practices may involve special dietary regimens, alternative nutrition practices often are overly restrictive, depart from established dietary guidelines, and lack rigorous scientific evidence.

Vegetarian Diets

The specifics of vegetarianism are described in Chapter 6, "Proteins and Amino Acids." Most nutritionists consider vegetarianism a routine variation of a normal diet, particularly if the vegetarian's motivation is religious or philosophical, the result of a concern for animals, or an aversion to animal products. When a meat-eater goes vegetarian in an attempt to prevent or cure disease, that's "alternative."

Figure SAN.16 The symbol of yin and yang. In traditional Chinese medicine, practitioners strive to balance the opposing life forces of yin and yang through the use of food and herbs.

Macrobiotic Diet

Aside from vegetarianism, the **macrobiotic diet** probably is the best-known alternative diet. The original version of this primarily vegetarian diet progressed in 10 increasingly restrictive stages, with the "highest level" consisting of little more than brown rice and water. The diet has since evolved to a simpler one-level regimen based on whole-grain cereals and vegetables, a small amount of fish, no other animal products, and no fruit.[61]

Proponents tout the macrobiotic diet as a cure for a variety of illnesses, most notably cancer. To use it as a cancer treatment, the practitioner individualizes the diet according to Eastern philosophy (yin and yang, whose symbol is shown in **Figure SAN.16**) and location of the cancer. Critics say macrobiotic restrictions interfere with legitimate cancer treatment by causing weight loss in people who are already too thin from their illness. The diet is so limited that it just can't meet the increased nutritional needs of the cancer patient. Advocates of macrobiotics argue that undernutrition may help fight the cancer by starving it.[62] Neither opinion is correct: macrobiotic diets appear to have no clear effect, good or bad, on cancer progression or survival.

Compared with the general public, those who follow a macrobiotic diet tend to have healthier blood lipid levels and higher blood levels of phytochemicals, which reflects vegetable intake.[63] However, the diet is low in calcium and vitamin D, which contributes to the risk for osteoporosis. Pediatricians caution against this diet for children.

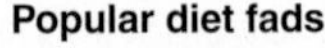

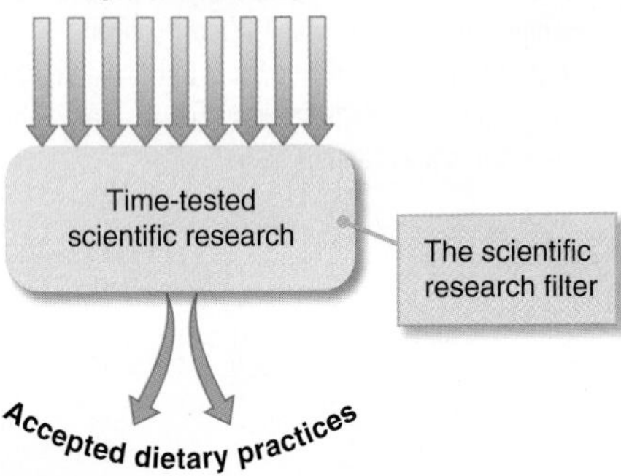

Figure SAN.17 Many apply but few are chosen. Dietary practices with a scientific basis and proven efficacy are incorporated into conventional nutrition and diet therapy.

macrobiotic diet A highly restrictive dietary approach applied as a therapy for risk factors or chronic disease in general.

Food Restrictions and Food Prescriptions

Societies throughout the world commonly use dietary changes to treat or prevent illness. The specifics vary from place to place, however, which suggests that they are based on cultural factors rather than science.

In recent years, we have seen yeast-free diets, dairy-free diets, sugar-free diets, white-flour-free diets, both low-carbohydrate and high-carbohydrate diets, both low-red-meat and high-red-meat diets, caffeine-free diets, salicylate-free diets, and more. We have been advised to load up on molasses, yogurt, honey, vinegar, oysters, mushrooms, and soy nuts. People with subjective symptoms such as headaches, fatigue, or back pain have been instructed to avoid irrational lists of "allergenic foods" based on "blood screening." We've also seen illogical instructions on how to combine foods, such as "don't eat applesauce and asparagus at the same meal." For weight loss, we've had grapefruit diets, hard-boiled-egg diets, cottage-cheese diets, water diets, high-fat diets, low-fat diets, and blue-foods-only diets; the list goes on and on.

Such diets come and go. They are not based on science and eventually fall out of favor when they don't work. Those few that prove effective and have a scientific basis become integrated into conventional nutrition and diet therapy. (See **Figure SAN.17**.)

Quick Bite

The Yin and Yang of Food

The early theory of yin and yang had its genesis during the Yin and Zhou dynasties (1766 B.C.E.–256 B.C.E.). The yin force is passive, downward flowing, and cold. Conversely, the yang force is aggressive, upward rising, and hot. The concept of balance and harmony between these life forces is the basis upon which food and herbs are used as medicine. In traditional Chinese healing methods, disease is viewed as the result of an imbalance of these energies in the body. To balance these energies, according to this view, your diet should balance yin foods and yang foods. Yin (cold) foods include milk, honey, fruit, and vegetables; yang (hot) foods include beef, poultry, seafood, eggs, and cheese. Foods are also classified as sweet (earth), bitter (fire), sour (wood), pungent (metal), and salty (water). Each class supposedly has specific effects on different parts of the body.

Key Concepts *Many types of diets can be described as alternative. Their origins and claims vary, and their proponents often cannot show that they improve health. Some alternative diets can actually be harmful by restricting foods and thereby lowering the body's intake of necessary nutrients.*

If you picked up a multivitamin/mineral container from your drugstore shelf, would you know how to read the label? Look at this Supplement Facts panel from a basic multivitamin/mineral supplement. Here are some questions that you might have.

1. If you were a 20-year-old woman who knew she wasn't consuming enough calcium, would this supplement allow you to get your recommended intake?
2. If 25 percent of the vitamin A in this supplement comes from beta-carotene, where does the rest come from?
3. What trend do you see in the amounts of B vitamins?
4. What trend do you see in the amounts of bone minerals?
5. What trend do you see in the amounts of antioxidant vitamins?
6. Does the USP statement make this supplement "legitimate"?

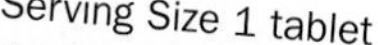

Supplement Facts

Daily Multivitamin/Mineral Dietary Supplement

USP USP has tested and verified ingredients, product and manufacturing process. USP sets official standards for Dietary Supplements. Laboratory tested to dissolve within 60 minutes.

USP DIETARY SUPPLEMENT VERIFIED

Serving Size 1 tablet

Each Tablet Contains	%DV	Each Tablet Contains	%DV
Vitamin A 10,000 I.U. 25% as beta-carotene	200%	Iodine 150 mcg	100%
Vitamin C 120 mg	200%	Magnesium 100 mg	25%
Vitamin D 400 IU	100%	Zinc 22.5 mg	150%
Vitamin E 60 IU	200%	Selenium 45 mcg	64%
Vitamin K 25 mcg	31%	Copper 3 mg	150%
Thiamin (vit. B_1) 1.5 mg	100%	Manganese 2.5 mg	125%
Riboflavin (vit. B_2) 1.7 mg	100%	Chromium 100 mcg	83%
Niacin 20 mg	100%	Molybdenum 25 mcg	33%
Vitamin B_6 2 mg	100%	Chloride 36.3 mg	1%
Folate (folic acid) 400 mcg	100%	Sodium less than 5 mg	less than 1%
Vitamin B_{12} 6 mcg	100%	Potassium 40 mg	1%
Biotin 30 mcg	10%	Nickel 5 mcg	*
Pantothenic acid 10 mg	100%	Tin 10 mcg	*
Calcium 162 mg	16%	Silicon 2 mg	*
Iron 9 mg	50%	Vanadium 10 mcg	*
Phosphorus 109 mg	11%	Boron 150 mcg	*

* Daily Value (%DV) not established

Answers to Questions

1. No. This supplement provides only 162 milligrams, and the Adequate Intake (AI) for a 20-year-old woman is 1,000 milligrams. You may need a calcium supplement if you can't eat enough calcium-rich foods.
2. The other 7,500 IU of vitamin A is most likely retinol in the form of retinyl acetate or retinyl palmitate; check the list of ingredients.
3. With the exception of biotin, this supplement provides 100 percent of the Daily Value for the B vitamins. The 30 micrograms of biotin provides 100 percent of the current AI.
4. This supplement contains very low percentages of the Daily Values for calcium, magnesium, and phosphorus (16 percent, 11 percent, and 25 percent, respectively). Adding more of these minerals would make the pill huge and impossible to swallow! A nutritious diet should provide the rest of these minerals.
5. This supplement contains 200 percent of the Daily Value for each of the antioxidant vitamins C and E, and one-fourth (50% DV) of its vitamin A content comes from the antioxidant beta-carotene.
6. By listing the U.S. Pharmacopeia "stamp of approval," you can be confident that this supplement underwent a test to see how quickly it dissolves. If pills do not dissolve, their contents cannot be absorbed. In this case, the supplement took 60 minutes to dissolve. The USP sets standards for the quality, purity, and potency of supplements.

Learning Portfolio

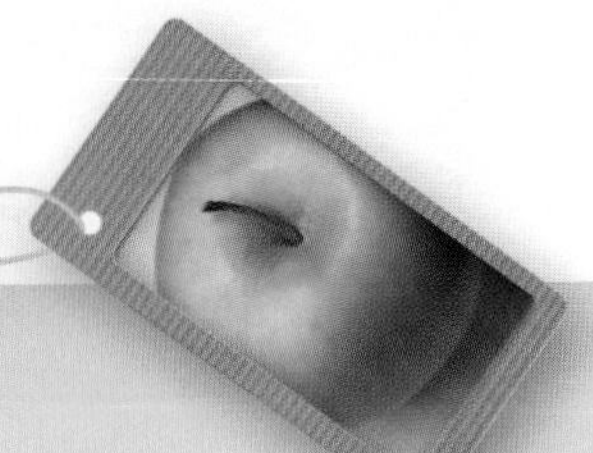

Key Terms

	page		page
additives	78	indirect additives	79
bioavailability	97	isoflavones	74
bioflavonoids	92	lycopene	74
color additive	80	macrobiotic diet	100
complementary and alternative medicine (CAM)	74	malabsorption syndromes	86
Delaney Clause	81	megadoses	85
Dietary Supplement Health and Education Act (DSHEA)	93	multilevel marketing	97
dietary supplements	74	National Center for Complementary and Alternative Medicine (NCCAM)	89
direct additives	79	nucleic acids	86
free radicals	77	orthomolecular medicine	86
functional food	74	phytoestrogens	77
Generally Recognized as Safe (GRAS)	80	prior-sanctioned substance	80
herbal therapy (phytotherapy)	89	Supplement Facts	95
		U.S. Pharmacopeia (USP)	97

Study Points

- A functional food is considered to be a food that may provide a health benefit beyond basic nutrition.
- Phytochemicals are plant chemicals responsible for the health-promoting properties of many functional foods.
- Consumption of plant foods containing multiple antioxidants is strongly associated with health benefits. Scientific evidence strongly supports eating at least five servings of fruits and vegetables daily and emphasizing whole grains.
- The federal government reviews the safety of new additives before they can be used in foods sold on the market.
- The Delaney Clause is a controversial food law that prohibits the approval of an additive if it has been found to cause cancer in humans or laboratory animals, even if massive doses are required to produce the disease.
- Dietary supplements encompass vitamins, minerals, herbal products, amino acids, glandular extracts, enzymes, and many other products.
- Vitamin and mineral supplements may be warranted in certain circumstances, although the preferred mode of obtaining adequate nutrition is through foods.
- Megadose vitamin or mineral therapy has not been proved effective in the treatment of cancer, colds, or heart disease. Moreover, such megadoses act more like drugs than nutrients in the body and should be approached with caution.
- Herbal medicine is a traditional form of healing in many cultures. Some herbal medicines have shown enough promise to warrant large-scale clinical studies involving supplements. However, herbal products can have side effects and can interfere with prescription medications.
- Dietary supplements are regulated according to the provisions of the Dietary Supplement Health and Education Act of 1994. Unlike drugs and additives, dietary supplements do not need premarket approval.
- Claims for dietary supplements can include health claims, structure/function claims, and nutrient content claims.
- Dietary supplements must have a Supplement Facts panel on the label.
- Consumers should carefully evaluate claims and evidence for dietary supplements and consult their physician before taking a supplement.
- Complementary and alternative medicine (CAM) comprises practices outside the medical mainstream that are becoming increasingly popular. CAM includes a broad range of therapies, many of which include nutrition. People seek them for a variety of reasons, including environmental concerns and a fear of aging.

Study Questions

1. What are phytochemicals, and how do they benefit plants and humans?
2. Name three chronic diseases that consuming functional foods may help prevent.
3. What purpose(s) do additives serve?
4. What is the purpose of the Delaney Clause? What are the complications surrounding this food law?

5. How do you know a product is a dietary supplement?
6. If a dietary supplement product label contains the words "High in vitamin E," what type of claim is it making? What other claims can a supplement make?
7. What things should someone do before purchasing supplements?
8. What are some of the possible complications involved in using herbal medicines?
9. What is a macrobiotic diet?

Try This

Finding Functional Beverages

This exercise will familiarize you with the many beverages that contain functional ingredients now available to consumers. Take a trip to your grocery store and spend some time in the beverage aisles. You may want to check out the chilled juice section in addition to the bottled teas and juice beverages. Pick out about 10 different products that have either a nutrient or herbal compound added and try to identify how many have nutrient content claims, health claims, and structure/function claims. Note the prices of these products. How does their nutritional content compare to a 100 percent fruit juice such as orange juice? How does it compare to soda?

Take a Walk on the "Web Side"

This exercise will familiarize you with various Web sites that promote and sell supplements. Log on to the Internet and start doing searches with key words affiliated with supplements. Try *vitamins*, *minerals*, *supplements*, *herbs*, and even some specific terms like *chromium picolinate* and *ginseng*. On the Web sites you visit, how is the nutrition information presented? Do the supplement's benefits sound too good to be true? See if you can spot a fraud. Use the information in the "Fraudulent Products" section of this chapter to identify the accuracy of the product information you find.

References

1 Institute of Food Technologists. *Expert Report on Functional Foods: Opportunities and Challenges*. March 2005. http://www.ift.org/cms/?pid=1001247. Accessed 5/01/09.

2 Heasman M. Addressing the functional food paradox. *Nutraceuticals World*. November 2003. http://www.nutraceuticalsworld.com/articles/2003/11/addressing-the-functional-foods-paradox.php. Accessed 5/01/09; and Sloan AE. Top 10 functional food trends. *Food Tech*. 2008;60:23–40.

3 Rao AV, Rao LG. Carotenoids and human health. *Pharmacol Res*. 2007;55:207–216.

4 Messina M, Gardner C, Barnes S. Gaining insight into the health effects of soy but a long way still to go: commentary on the fourth International Symposium on the Role of Soy in Preventing and Treating Chronic Disease. *J Nutr*. 2002;132:542S–551S.

5 Shu XO, Jin F, Dai Q, et al. Soyfood intake during adolescence and subsequent risk of breast cancer among Chinese women. *Cancer Epidemiol Biomarkers Prev*. 2001;10:483–488.

6 Maskarinec G. Soy foods for breast cancer survivors and women at high risk for breast cancer? *J Am Diet Assoc*. 2005;105:1524–1528.

7 Duffy C, Perez K, Partridge A. Implications of phytoestrogen intake for breast cancer. *CA Cancer J Clin*. 2007;57:260–277.

8 Stahl W. Macular carotenoids: lutein and zeaxanthin. *Dev Ophthalmol*. 2005;38:70–88.

9 Turner RE, Degnan FH, Archer DL. Label claims for food and supplements: a review of the regulations. *Nutr Clin Pract*. 2005;20(1):21–32.

10 Percival SS, Turner RE. Applications of herbs to functional foods. In: Wildman REC, ed. *Handbook of Nutraceuticals and Functional Foods*. 2nd ed. Boca Raton, FL: CRC Press, 2006.

11 US Food and Drug Administration. Letter to manufacturers regarding botanicals and other novel ingredients in conventional foods. January 30, 2001. http://www.cfsan.fda.gov/~dms/ds-ltr15.html. Accessed 10/27/08; and US Food and Drug Administration. Concerns about botanical and other novel ingredients in conventional foods. June 4–5, 2001. http://www.cfsan.fda.gov/~dms/ds-bot5.html. Accessed 5/01/09.

12 Sacks FM, Lichtenstein A, Van Horn L, et al. Soy protein, isoflavones, and cardiovascular health: an American Heart Association Science Advisory for professionals from the Nutrition Committee. *Circulation*. 2006;113:1034–1044.

13 Turner, Degnan, Archer. Label claims for food and supplements.

14 Ervin RB, Wright JD, Reed-Gillette D. *Prevalence of Leading Types of Dietary Supplements Used in the Third National Health and Nutrition Examination Survey, 1988–1994*. Hyattsville, MD: National Center for Health Statistics, 2004. Advance Data from Vital and Health Statistics, No. 349.

15 Multivitamin-mineral supplements: take one—but which one? *The Dietary Supplement*. 2002;3(5,6).

16 *Physicians' Desk Reference, 2008*. 62nd ed. Montvale, NJ: Thomson Healthcare, 2007.

17 Carmel R. Cobalamin (vitamin B_{12}). In: Shils ME, Shike M, Ross AC, et al. eds. *Modern Nutrition in Health and Disease*. 10th ed. Philadelphia: Lippincott Williams & Wilkins, 2006.

18 *Physicians' Desk Reference, 2008*.

19 Seddon JM. Multivitamin–multimineral supplements and eye disease: age-related macular degeneration and cataract. *Am J Clin Nutr*. 2007;85(suppl):304S–307S.

20 US Preventive Services Task Force. Routine vitamin supplementation to prevent cancer and cardiovascular disease: recommendations and rationale. *Ann Intern Med*. 2003;139:51–55.

21 *Alternative Medicine, Expanding Medical Horizons: A Report to the National Institutes of Health on Alternative Medical Systems and Practices in the United States*. Washington, DC: US Government Printing Office, 1994:230–232, 237. NIH publication 94-066.

22 Institute of Medicine, Food and Nutrition Board. *Dietary Reference Intakes for Vitamin C, Vitamin E, Selenium and Carotenoids*. Washington, DC: National Academies Press, 2000.

23 Byers T, Guerrero N. Epidemiologic evidence for vitamin C and vitamin E in cancer prevention. *Am J Clin Nutr*. 1995;62(suppl):1385S–1392S.

24 Institute of Medicine, Food and Nutrition Board. *Dietary Reference Intakes for Vitamin A, Vitamin K, Arsenic, Boron, Chromium, Copper, Iron, Manganese,*

Molybdenum, Nickel, Silicon, Vanadium, and Zinc. Washington, DC: National Academies Press, 2001.

25 Leo MA, Lieber CS. Alcohol, vitamin A, and beta-carotene: adverse interactions, including hepatotoxicity and carcinogenicity. *Am J Clin Nutr*. 1999;69:1071–1085.

26 Council for Responsible Nutrition. Dietary supplements: safe, regulated and beneficial. http://www.crnusa.org/pdfs/CRN_FACT_DSSafeRegulatedBeneficial_07.pdf. Accessed 5/01/09.

27 Health Canada. Baseline natural health products survey among consumers, March 2005. http://www.hc-sc.gc.ca/dhp-mps/pubs/natur/eng_cons_survey_e.html. Accessed 5/01/09.

28 Elvin-Lewis M. Should we be concerned about herbal remedies? *J Ethnopharmacol*. 2001;75:141–164.

29 St. John's wort study launched. NIH news release; October 1, 1997.

30 Hypericum Depression Trial Study Group. Effect of *Hypericum perforatum* (St. John's wort) in major depressive disorder: a randomized controlled trial. *JAMA*. 2002;287:1807–1814.

31 Agency for Healthcare Research and Quality. *Milk Thistle: Effects on Liver Disease and Cirrhosis and Clinical Adverse Effects*. Rockville, MD: Author, 2000. http://www.ahrq.gov/clinic/epcsums/milktsum.htm. Accessed 10/27/08.

32 Evans JG, Wilcock G, Birks J. Evidence-based pharmacotherapy of Alzheimer's disease. *Int J Neuropsychopharmacol*. 2004;7:351–369.

33 Gordon AE, Shaughnessy AF. Saw palmetto for prostate disorders. *Am Fam Physician*. 2003;67:1281–1283.

34 Bent S, Kane C, Shinohara K, et al. Saw palmetto for benign prostatic hyperplasia. *N Engl J Med*. 2006;354:557–566.

35 Howell AB. Bioactive compounds in cranberries and their role in prevention of urinary tract infections. *Mol Nutr Food Res*. 2007;51:732–737.

36 Rosenblatt M, Mindel J. Spontaneous hyphema associated with ingestion of ginkgo biloba extract. *N Engl J Med*. 1997;336:15, 1108.

37 Boullata J. Natural health product interactions with medication. *Nutr Clin Pract*. 2005;20(1):33–51.

38 Edwards C. Lessons from licorice. *N Engl J Med*. 1991;325:1242–1243.

39 US Food and Drug Administration. Risk of drug interactions with St. John's wort, indinavir and other drugs. FDA public health advisory; February 10, 2000. http://www.fda.gov/cder/drug/advisory/stjwort.htm. Accessed 5/01/07.

40 Gallagher RE. Arsenic: new life for an old potion. *N Engl J Med*. 1998;339:1389–1390; and Centers for Disease Control and Prevention. Lead poisoning associated with use of traditional ethnic remedies—California, 1991–1992. *MMWR*. 1993;42:521–523.

41 Gordon DW, Rosenthal G, Hart J, et al. Chaparral ingestion: the broadening spectrum of liver injury caused by herbal medications. *JAMA*. 1995;273:489–490.

42 DiPaola RS, Zhang H, Lambert GH, et al. Clinical and biologic activity of an estrogenic herbal combination (PC-SPES) in prostate cancer. *N Engl J Med*. 1998;339:785–791.

43 Centers for Disease Control and Prevention. Anticholinergic poisoning associated with herbal tea—New York City, 1994. *MMWR*. 1995;44:193–195; and Plantain adulteration with foxglove. FDA press release; June 12, 1997.

44 Good Housekeeping Consumer Safety Symposium on Dietary Supplements and Herbal Remedies. March 3, 1998; New York, NY.

45 Harkey MR, Henderson GL, Gershwin ME, et al. Variability in commercial ginseng products: an analysis of 25 preparations. *Am J Clin Nutr*. 2001;73(6):1101–1106.

46 US Food and Drug Administration. FDA issues dietary supplements final rule. FDA press release; June 22, 2007. http://www.fda.gov/bbs/topics/NEWS/2007/NEW01657.html. Accessed 5/01/09.

47 Business guide for dietary supplement industry. Federal Trade Commission press release; November 18, 1998.

48 US Food and Drug Administration. Dietary Supplement Health and Education Act of 1994, Public Law 103-417. http://www.fda.gov/opacom/laws/dshea.html. Accessed 5/01/09.

49 US Food and Drug Administration. Overview of dietary supplements. January 3, 2001. http://www.cfsan.fda.gov/~dms/ds-oview.html. Accessed 5/01/09.

50 US Food and Drug Administration. Claims that can be made for conventional foods and dietary supplements. September 2003. http://www.cfsan.fda.gov/~dms/hclaims.html. Accessed 5/01/09.

51 Health Canada, Natural Health Products Directorate. About natural health product regulation in Canada. http://www.hc-sc.gc.ca/dhp-mps/prodnatur/about-apropos/index_e.html. Accessed 5/01/09.

52 Salvato P, Thompson C, Keister R. Viral load response to augmentation of natural dehydroepiandrosterone (DHEA). Presented at: International Conference on AIDS; July 7–12, 1996; Vancouver, BC, Canada.

53 Miller DR, Anderson GT, Stark JJ, et al. Phase I/II trial of the safety and efficacy of shark cartilage in the treatment of advanced cancers. *J Clin Oncol*. 1998;16:3649–3655.

54 Thomson C, Diekman C, Sarubin Fragakis A, et al. Guidelines regarding the recommendation and sale of dietary supplements. *J Am Diet Assoc*. 2002;102:1158–1164.

55 USP Dietary Supplementation Verification Program. http://www.usp.org/. Accessed 10/27/08.

56 The Alpha-Tocopherol, Beta-Carotene and Cancer Prevention Study Group. The effect of vitamin E and beta-carotene on the incidence of lung cancer and other cancers in male smokers. *N Engl J Med*. 1994;330:1029–1035.

57 Kurtzweil P. An FDA guide to dietary supplements. *FDA Consumer*. Sept–Oct 1998, revised January 1999. http://www.cfsan.fda.gov/~dms/fdsupp.html. Accessed 5/01/09.

58 Eisenberg DM, Kessler RC, Foster C, et al. Unconventional medicine in the United States: prevalence, costs, and patterns of use. *N Engl J Med*. 1993;328:246–252.

59 Pelletier KR, Marie A, Krasner M, Haskell WL. Current trends in the integration and reimbursement of complementary and alternative medicine by managed care, insurance carriers, and hospital providers. *Am J Health Promotion*. 1997;12:112–123.

60 Barnes PM, Powell-Griner E, McFann K, Nahin RL. *Complementary and Alternative Medicine Use Among Adults: United States, 2002*. Hyattsville, MD: National Center for Health Statistics, 2004. Advance Data from Vital and Health Statistics, No. 343; and Kelly JP, Kaufman DW, Kelly K, et al. Recent trends in use of herbal and other natural products. *Arch Intern Med*. 2005;165:281–286.

61 *Alternative Medicine, Expanding Medical Horizons*.

62 Ibid.

63 Ibid.

CHAPTER 3

Digestion and Absorption

THINK About It

1 Your friend warns you that eating some foods together is not healthful. Is this likely to change your eating behavior?

2 How good are you at identifying tastes?

3 Have you ever noticed that food sometimes tastes sweeter after chewing it for awhile?

4 You feel particularly happy and you find that a meal prepared by your friend tastes especially good. Any connection?

Visit nutrition.jbpub.com

Quick Bite

How Many Taste Buds Do You Have?
We have almost 10,000 taste buds in our mouths, including those on the roofs of our mouths. In general, females have more taste buds than males.

The aroma of a roasting turkey floats past your nose. You haven't eaten for six or seven hours. Anticipating a delicious experience, your mouth waters, and your digestive juices are turned on. Is this virtual reality? Not at all! Before you eat a morsel of food, fleeting thoughts from your brain signal your body to prepare for the feast to come.

The body's machinery to process food and turn it into nutrients is not only efficient but elegant. The action unfolds in the digestive tract in two stages: **digestion**—the breaking apart of foods into smaller and smaller units—and **absorption**—the movement of those small units from the gut into the bloodstream or lymphatic system for circulation. Your digestive system is designed to digest carbohydrates, proteins, and fats simultaneously, while at the same time preparing other substances—vitamins, minerals, and cholesterol, for example—for absorption. Remarkably, your digestive system doesn't need any help! Despite promotions for enzyme supplements and diet books that recommend consuming food or nutrient groups separately, scientific research does not support these claims. Unless you have a specific medical condition, your digestive system is ready, willing, and able to digest and absorb the foods you eat, in whatever combination you eat them.

THINK About It 1

But go back to the aroma of that roast turkey for a moment. Before we begin digesting and absorbing, our senses of taste and smell first attract us to foods we are likely to consume.

Taste and Smell: The Beginnings of Our Food Experience

You probably wouldn't eat a food if it didn't appeal in some way to your senses. Smell and taste belong to our chemical sensing system, or the **chemosenses**. The complicated processes of smelling and tasting begin when tiny molecules released by the substances around us bind to receptors on special cells in the nose, mouth, or throat. These special sensory cells transmit messages through nerves to the brain, where specific smells or tastes are identified.

The Chemosenses

Olfactory (smell) **cells** are stimulated by the odors around us, such as the fragrance of a gardenia or the smell of bread baking. These nerve cells are found in a small patch of tissue high inside the nose, and they connect directly to the brain.

Gustatory (taste) **cells** react to food and beverages. These surface cells in the mouth send taste information along their nerve fibers to the brain. The taste cells are clustered in the taste buds of the mouth and throat. Many of the visible small bumps on the tongue contain taste buds.

THINK About It 2

A third chemosensory mechanism, the **common chemical sense**, contributes to our senses of smell and taste. In this system, thousands of nerve endings—especially on the moist surfaces of the eyes, nose, mouth, and throat—give rise to sensations such as the sting of ammonia, the coolness of menthol, and the irritation of chili peppers.

In the mouth, along with texture, temperature, and the sensations from the common chemical sense, tastes combine with odors to produce a perception of flavor. It is flavor that lets us know whether we are eating a pear or an apple. You recognize flavors mainly through the sense of smell. If you hold your nose while eating chocolate, for example, you will have trouble identifying it—even though you can distinguish the food's sweetness or bitterness. That's because the familiar flavor of chocolate is sensed largely by odor, as is the well-known flavor of coffee.

digestion The process of transforming the foods we eat into units for absorption.

absorption The movement of substances into or across tissues; in particular, the passage of nutrients and other substances into the walls of the gastrointestinal tract and then into the bloodstream.

chemosenses [key-mo-SEN-sez] The chemical sensing system in the body, including taste and smell. Sensory cells in the nose, mouth, or throat transmit messages through nerves to the brain, where smells and tastes are identified.

olfactory cells Nerve cells in a small patch of tissue high in the nose connected directly to the brain to transmit messages about specific smells. Also called smell cells.

gustatory cells Surface cells in the throat and on the taste buds in the mouth that transmit taste information. Also called taste cells.

common chemical sense A chemosensory mechanism that contributes to our senses of smell and taste. It comprises thousands of nerve endings, especially on the moist surfaces of the eyes, nose, mouth, and throat.

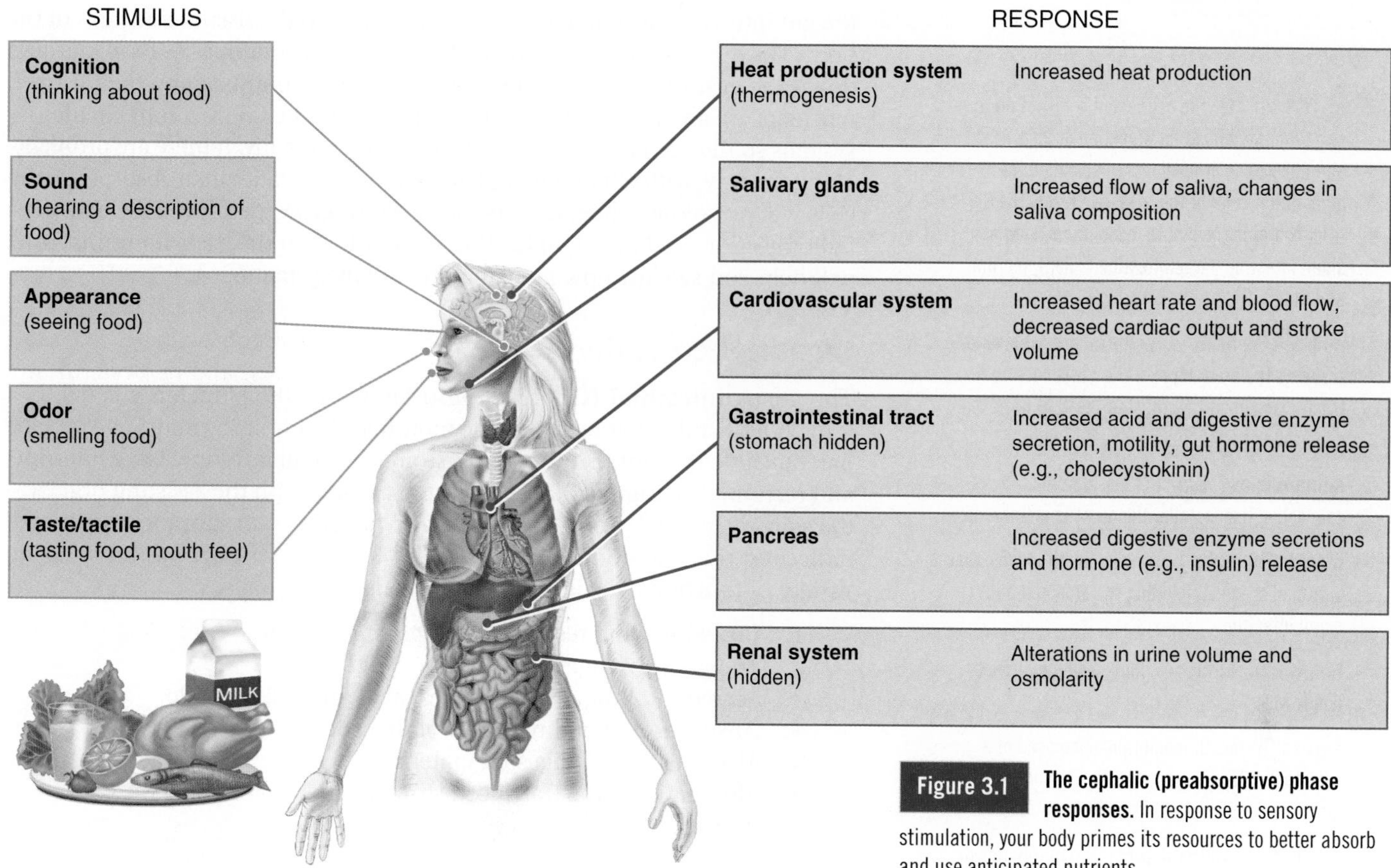

Figure 3.1 **The cephalic (preabsorptive) phase responses.** In response to sensory stimulation, your body primes its resources to better absorb and use anticipated nutrients.

Many nutritionists have suggested that fat has no taste and that its appeal is due solely to its texture. However, this may not be the case. Animal studies have found a taste receptor for fat, and essential fatty acids (fatty acids that must be obtained from the diet) elicit the strongest taste response.[1]

The sight, smell, thought, taste, and in some cases even the sound of food can trigger a set of physiologic responses known as the **cephalic phase responses**.[2] These responses (see **Figure 3.1**) involve more than just the digestive tract, and they follow rapidly on the heels of sensory stimulation. In the digestive tract, salivary and gastric secretions flow, preparing for the consumption of food. If no food is consumed, the response diminishes; eating, however, continues the stimulation of the salivary and gastric cells.

cephalic phase responses The responses of the parasympathetic nervous system to the sight, smell, thought, and sound of food. Also called preabsorptive phase responses.

Key Concepts *Taste and smell are the first interactions we have with food. The flavor of a particular food is really a combination of olfactory, gustatory, and other stimuli. Smell (olfactory) receptors receive stimuli through odor compounds. Taste (gustatory) receptors in the mouth sense flavors. Other nerve cells (the common chemical senses) are stimulated by other chemical factors. If one of these stimuli is missing, our sense of flavor is incomplete.*

The Gastrointestinal Tract

If, instead of teasing the body with mere sights and smells, we actually sit down to a meal and experience the full flavor and texture of foods, the real work of the digestive tract begins. For the food we eat to nourish our bodies, we need to digest it (break it down into smaller units); absorb it (move it from

gastrointestinal (GI) tract [GAS-troh-in-TES-tin-al] The connected series of organs and structures used for digestion of food and absorption of nutrients; also called the alimentary canal or the digestive tract. The GI tract contains the mouth, esophagus, stomach, small intestine, large intestine (colon), rectum, and anus.

mucosa [myu-KO-sa] The innermost layer of a cavity. The inner layer of the gastrointestinal tract, also called the intestinal wall. It is composed of epithelial cells and glands.

submucosa The layer of loose, fibrous connective tissue under the mucous membrane.

circular muscle Layers of smooth muscle that surround organs, including the stomach and the small intestine.

longitudinal muscle Muscle fibers aligned lengthwise.

serosa A smooth membrane composed of a mesothelial layer and connective tissue. The intestines are covered in serosa.

sphincters [SFINGK-ters] Circular bands of muscle fibers that surround the entrance or exit of a hollow body structure (e.g., the stomach) and act as valves to control the flow of material.

the gut into circulation); and finally transport it to the tissues and cells of the body. The digestive process starts in the mouth and continues as food journeys down the gastrointestinal, or GI, tract. At various points along the GI tract, nutrients are absorbed, meaning they move from the GI tract into circulatory systems so they can be transported throughout the body. If there are problems along the way, with either incomplete digestion or inadequate absorption, the cells will not receive the nutrients they need to grow, perform daily activities, fight infection, and maintain health. A closer look at the gastrointestinal tract will help you see just how amazing this organ system is.

Organization of the GI Tract

The **gastrointestinal (GI) tract**, also known as the alimentary canal, is a long, hollow tube that begins at the mouth and ends at the anus. The specific parts include the mouth, esophagus, stomach, small intestine, large intestine, and rectum. (See **Figure 3.2**.) The GI tract works with the assisting organs—the salivary glands, liver, gallbladder, and pancreas—to turn food into small molecules that the body can absorb and use. The GI tract has an amazing variety of functions, including the following:

1. Ingestion—the receipt and softening of food
2. Transport of ingested food
3. Secretion of digestive enzymes, acid, mucus, and bile
4. Absorption of end products of digestion
5. Movement of undigested material
6. Elimination—the transport, storage, and excretion of waste products

A Closer Look at Gastrointestinal Structure

Although it's convenient to describe the GI tract as a hollow tube, its structure is really much more complex. As you can see in **Figure 3.3**, there are several layers to this tube:

- The innermost layer, called the **mucosa**, is a layer of epithelial (lining) cells and glands.
- Next is the **submucosa**, a layer of loose, fibrous connective tissue.
- Continuing outward are two layers of muscle fibers:
  - First is a layer of **circular muscle**, where muscle fibers go around the tube.
  - Next is a layer of **longitudinal muscle**, where fibers lie lengthwise along the tube.
- Finally the outer surface, or **serosa**, provides a covering for the entire GI tract.

At several points along the tract, where one part connects with another (e.g., where the esophagus meets the stomach), the muscles are thicker and form **sphincters**. As you can see in **Figure 3.4**, by alternately contracting and relaxing, a sphincter acts as a valve controlling the movement of food material so that it goes in only one direction.

Key Concepts *The gastrointestinal tract consists of the mouth, esophagus, stomach, small intestine, large intestine, and rectum. The function of the GI tract is to ingest, digest, and absorb nutrients and eliminate waste. The general structure of the GI tract consists of many layers, including an inner mucosal lining, a layer of connective tissue, layers of muscle fibers, and an outer covering layer. Sphincters are muscular valves along the GI tract that control movement from one part to the next.*

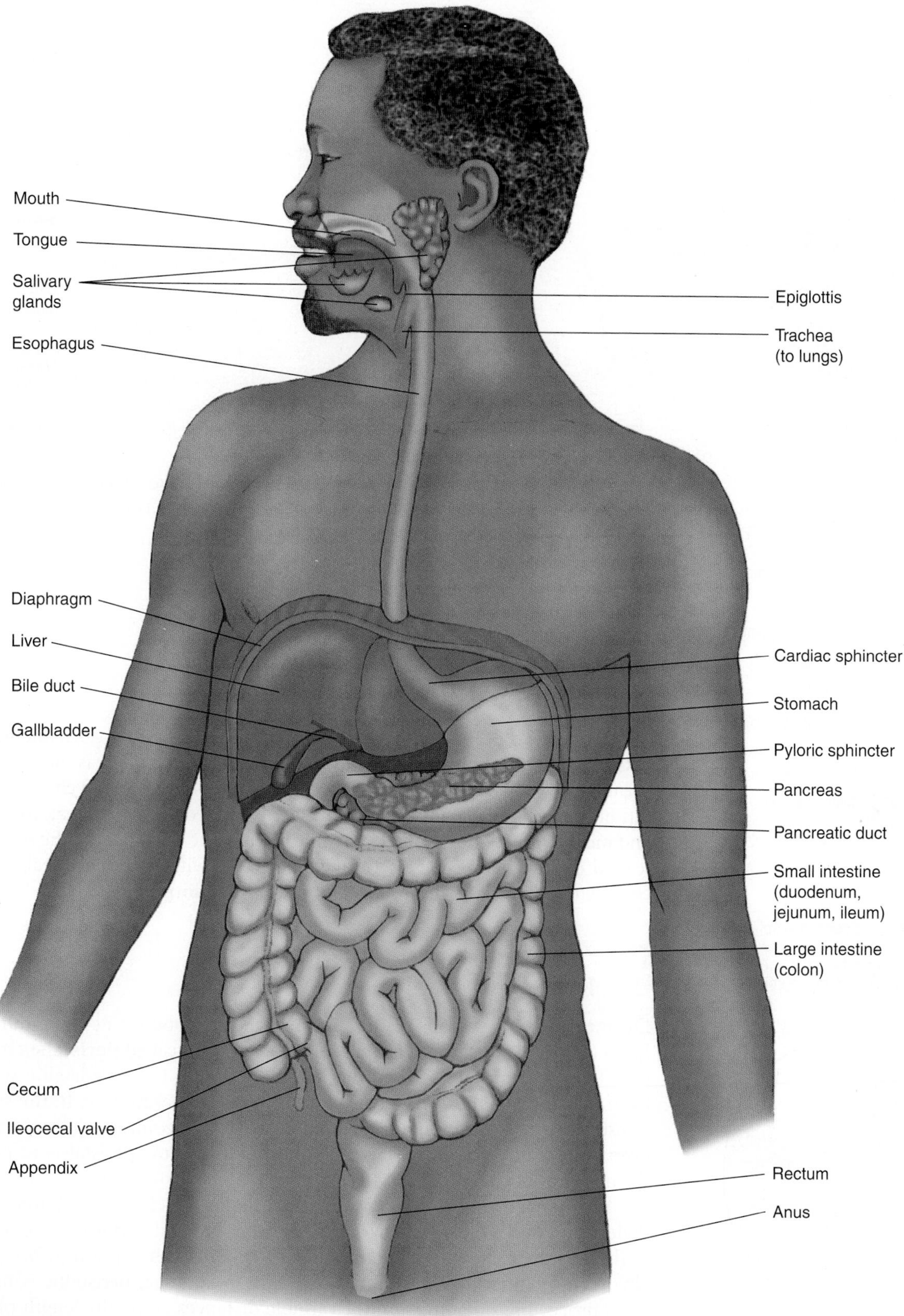

Figure 3.2 **Anatomic and functional organization of the GI tract.** Although digestion begins in the mouth, most digestion occurs in the stomach and small intestine. Absorption primarily takes place in the small and large intestines.

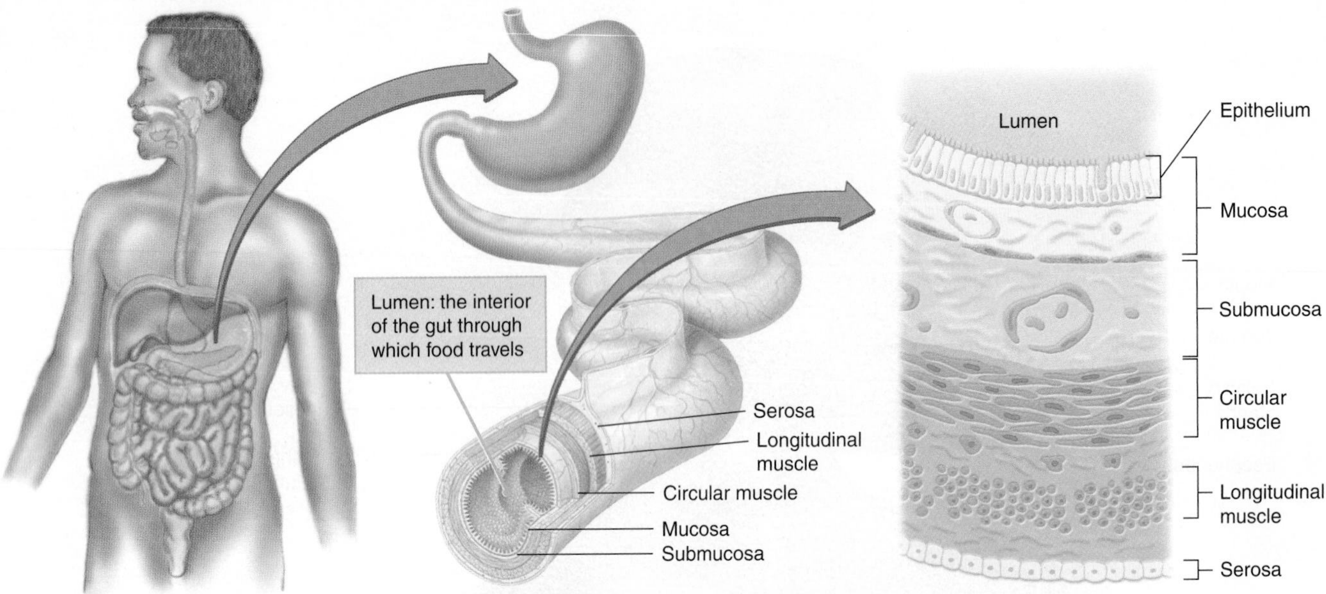

Figure 3.3 **Structural organization of the GI tract wall.** Your intestinal tract is a long, hollow tube lined with mucosal cells and surrounded by layers of muscle cells.

chyme [KIME] A mass of partially digested food and digestive juices moving from the stomach into the duodenum.

peristalsis [per-ih-STAHL-sis] The wavelike, rhythmic muscular contractions of the GI tract that propel its contents down the tract.

segmentation Periodic muscle contractions at intervals along the GI tract that alternate forward and backward movement of the contents, thereby breaking apart chunks of the food mass and mixing in digestive juices.

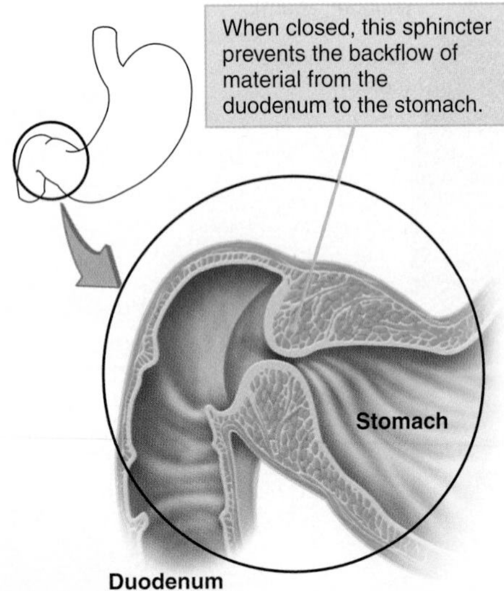

Figure 3.4 **Sphincters in action.** Movement from one section of the GI tract to the next is controlled by muscular valves called sphincters.

Overview of Digestion: Physical and Chemical Processes

The breakdown of food into smaller units and finally into absorbable nutrients involves both chemical and physical processes. First, there is the physical breaking of food into smaller pieces, such as happens when we chew. In addition, the muscular contractions of the GI tract continue to break food up and mix it with various secretions, while at the same time moving the mixture (called **chyme**) along the tract. Enzymes, along with other chemicals, help complete the breakdown process and promote absorption.

The Physical Movement and Breaking Up of Food

Distinct muscular actions of the GI tract take the food on its long journey. From mouth to anus, wavelike muscular contractions called **peristalsis** transport food and nutrients along the length of the GI tract. Peristaltic waves from the stomach muscles occur about three times per minute. In the small intestine, circular and longitudinal bands of muscle contract approximately every four to five seconds. The large intestine uses slow peristalsis to move the end products of digestion (feces).

Segmentation, a muscular movement that occurs in the small intestine, divides and mixes the chyme by alternating forward and backward movement of the GI tract contents. Segmentation also enhances absorption by bringing chyme into contact with the intestinal wall. In contrast, peristaltic contractions proceed in one direction for variable distances along the length of the intestine. Some even travel the entire distance from the beginning of the small intestine to the end. Peristaltic contractions of the small intestine often are continuations of contractions that began in the stomach. **Figure 3.5** shows peristalsis and segmentation.

The Chemical Breakdown of Food

Chemically, it is the action of enzymes that divide nutrients into compounds small enough for absorption. **Enzymes** are proteins that **catalyze**, or speed up, chemical reactions but are not altered in the process. Most enzymes can catalyze only one or a few related reactions, a property called enzyme specificity. Enzymes act in part by bringing the reacting molecules close together. In digestion, these chemical reactions divide substances into smaller compounds by a process called **hydrolysis** (breaking apart by water), as **Figure 3.6** shows. Most of the digestive enzymes can be identified by name; they commonly end in *–ase* (amylase, lipase, and so on). For example, the enzyme needed to digest sucr*ose* is sucr*ase*.

In addition to enzymes, other chemicals support the digestive process. These include acid in the stomach, a neutralizing base in the small intestine, bile that prepares fat for digestion, and mucus secreted along the GI tract. This mucus does not break down food but lubricates it and protects the cells that line the GI tract from the strong digestive chemicals. Along the GI tract, fluids containing various enzymes and other substances are added to the consumed food. In fact, the volume of fluid secreted into the GI tract is about 7,000 milliliters (about 7½ quarts) per day.[3] Table 3.1 shows the average daily fluids in the GI tract.

Key Concepts *Digestion involves both physical and chemical activity. Physical activity includes chewing and the movement of muscles along the GI tract that divide food into smaller pieces and mix it with digestive secretions. Chemical digestion is the breaking of bonds in nutrients, such as carbohydrates or proteins, to produce smaller units. Enzymes—proteins that encourage chemical processes—catalyze these hydrolytic reactions.*

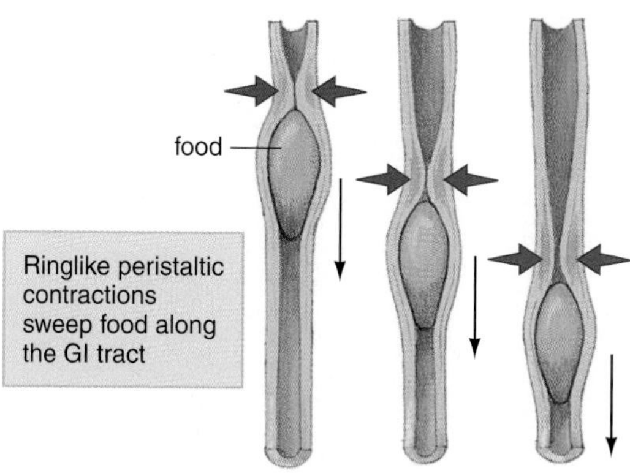
PERISTALSIS
food
Ringlike peristaltic contractions sweep food along the GI tract

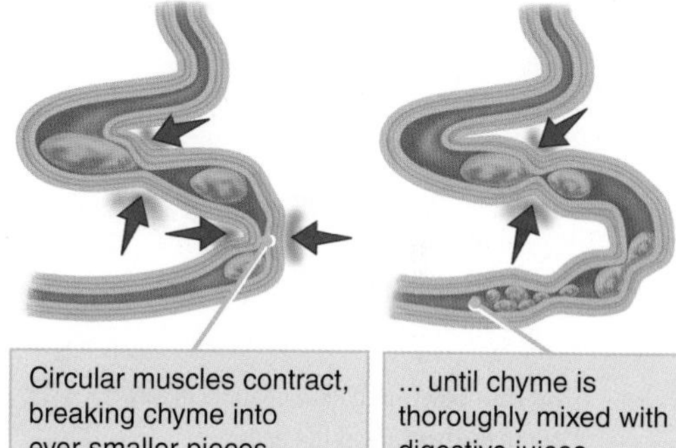
SEGMENTATION
Circular muscles contract, breaking chyme into ever smaller pieces...
... until chyme is thoroughly mixed with digestive juices

Figure 3.5 **Peristalsis and segmentation.** Peristalsis and segmentation help break up, mix, and move food through the GI tract.

enzymes [EN-zimes] Large proteins in the body that accelerate the rate of chemical reactions but are not altered in the process.

catalyze To speed up a chemical reaction.

hydrolysis A reaction that breaks apart a compound through the addition of water.

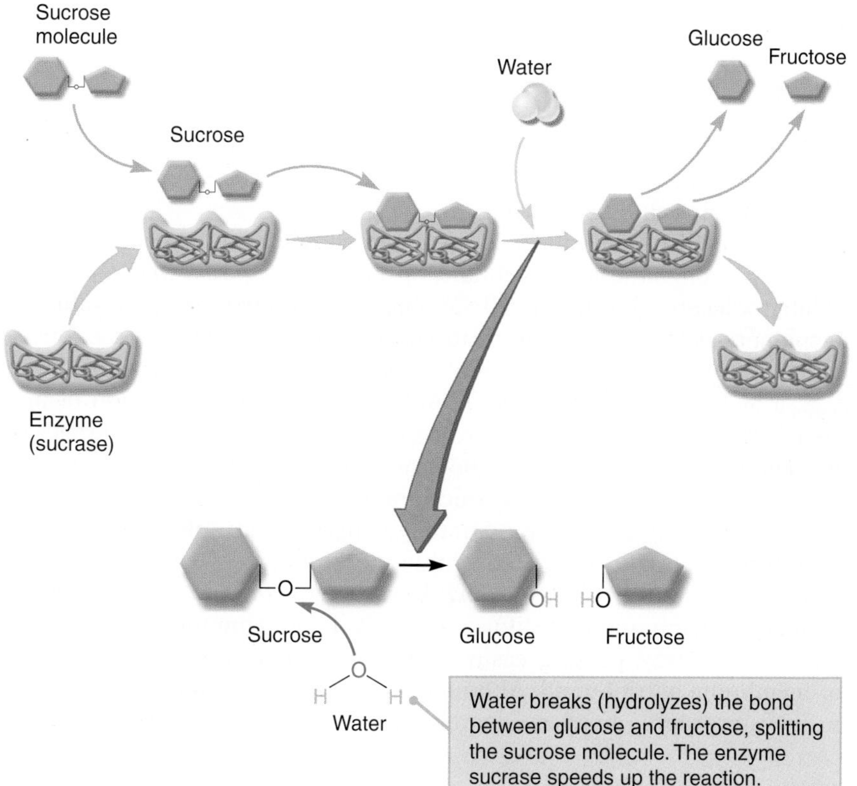
Sucrose molecule
Sucrose
Water
Glucose
Fructose
Enzyme (sucrase)
O
OH
HO
Sucrose
Glucose
Fructose
H
O
H
Water
Water breaks (hydrolyzes) the bond between glucose and fructose, splitting the sucrose molecule. The enzyme sucrase speeds up the reaction.

Figure 3.6 **Water and enzymes in chemical reactions.** Enzymes speed up (catalyze) chemical reactions. When water breaks a chemical bond, the action is called hydrolysis.

Table 3.1 Average Daily Fluid Input and Output

Source	Amount (mL)
Fluid input	
Food and beverages	2,000
Saliva	1,500
Gastric secretions	2,500
Pancreatic secretions	1,500
Bile	500
Small intestine secretions	1,000
Total input	9,000
Fluid output	
Small intestine absorption	7,500
Large intestine absorption	1,400
Feces	100
Total output	9,000

Source: Data from Klein S, Cohn SM, Alpers DH. Alimentary tract in nutrition. In: Shils ME, Shike M, Ross AC, et al., eds. *Modern Nutrition in Health and Disease.* 10th ed. Philadelphia: Lippincott Williams & Wilkins, 2006:1115–1142.

lumen Cavity or hollow channel in any organ or structure of the body.

passive diffusion The movement of substances into or out of cells without the expenditure of energy or the involvement of transport proteins in the cell membrane. Also called simple diffusion.

concentration gradients Differences between the solute concentrations of two substances.

Overview of Absorption

Food is broken apart during digestion and moved from the GI tract into circulation and on to the cells. Many of the nutrients—vitamins, minerals, and water—do not need to be digested before they are absorbed. But the energy-yielding nutrients—carbohydrate, fat, and protein—are too large to be absorbed intact and must be digested first. At this point, we need to outline how nutrients are moved from the interior, or **lumen**, of the gut through the lining cells (mucosa) and into circulation.

The Four Roads to Nutrient Absorption

There are four processes by which nutrients are absorbed: passive diffusion, facilitated diffusion, active transport, and endocytosis (see **Figure 3.7**). Let's take a look at each one in turn.

Passive diffusion is the movement of molecules without the expenditure of energy through the cell membrane, through either special watery channels or intermolecular gaps in the cell membrane. Molecules cross permeable cell membranes as a result of random movements that tend to equalize the concentration of substances on both sides of a membrane. **Concentration gradients** (e.g., a high outside concentration and a low inside concentration of molecules) drive passive diffusion. The larger the concentration of molecules on one side of the cell membrane, the faster those molecules move across the membrane to the area of lower concentration.

Because the cell membrane mainly consists of fat-soluble substances, it welcomes fats and other fat-soluble molecules. Oxygen, nitrogen, carbon dioxide, and alcohols are highly soluble in fat and readily dissolve in the cell membrane and diffuse across it. Large amounts of oxygen are delivered this way, passing easily into a cell's interior almost as if it had no membrane barrier at all. Although water crosses cell membranes easily, most water-soluble nutrients (carbohydrates, amino acids, vitamins, and

Going Green

Air + Water + Brown Stuff + Green Stuff = Compost!

Composting is the way to recycle your yard and kitchen wastes: it is planned decomposition of plants and once-living materials to create enriched soil. It is also a critical step in disposing of garbage needlessly sent to landfills. Compost makes an earthy-smelling, dark, crumbly substance rich in nutrients for house plants or garden soil. Finished compost can be applied to lawns and gardens to help condition the soil and replenish nutrients.

What's in Compost

The recipe for successful compost is fairly simple. Microorganisms (some too small to see, and others such as millipedes, sowbugs, and earthworms) turn yard and food waste into compost. Air, water, carbon, and nitrogen are the other ingredients needed to make useful compost material. Compost is made in the following way:

- "Brown stuff," such as dead dried plant parts (leaves, pine needles), newspaper, or sawdust, provides carbon.
- "Green stuff," such as fresh, living items like freshly cut grass, kitchen vegetable scraps, weeds, and other plants, provides nitrogen.
- Air is incorporated into the mixture by way of churning (via the microorganisms at work as well as by mixing with a shovel or using a rotating movement).
- Water is added to each layer of compost mixture as it is assembled. Water may also be added during the decomposition process to keep the microorganisms alive and to prevent the mixture from drying out.

The Benefits of Compost

Compost can do the following:

- Suppress plant diseases and pests
- Reduce or eliminate the need for chemical fertilizers
- Promote higher yields of agricultural crops
- Facilitate reforestation, wetlands restoration, and habitat revitalization efforts by amending contaminated, compacted, and marginal soils
- Cost-effectively remediate soils contaminated by hazardous waste
- Remove solids, oil, grease, and heavy metals from stormwater runoff
- Capture and destroy 99.6 percent of industrial volatile organic chemicals (VOCs) in contaminated air
- Provide cost savings of at least 50 percent over conventional soil, water, and air pollution remediation technologies, where applicable

What to Compost

Not all items can be composted. Those items in the "In" list can be included in a compost pile, whereas those in the "Out" list should be excluded.

The "In" List

- Animal manure
- Clean paper, shredded newspaper, cardboard rolls
- Coffee grounds, filters, tea bags
- Cotton rags, wool rags
- Dryer and vacuum cleaner lint
- Eggshells, nut shells
- Fireplace ashes
- Fruits and vegetables
- Grass clippings, yard trimmings, leaves, houseplants, hay, and straw
- Hair and fur
- Sawdust, wood chips

The "Out" List

- Black walnut tree leaves or twigs (might release substances harmful to plants)
- Coal or charcoal ash (might contain substances harmful to plants)
- Dairy products (create odor problems and attract pests such as rodents and flies)
- Diseased or insect-ridden plants (infect other plants)
- Fats, grease, lard, or oils (create odor problems; attract pests such as rodents and flies)
- Meat or fish bones and scraps (create odor problems; attract pests such as rodents and flies)
- Pet wastes, such as dog or cat feces or soiled cat litter (might contain parasites, bacteria, germs, pathogens, and viruses harmful to humans)
- Yard trimmings treated with chemical pesticides (might kill beneficial composting organisms)

Source: US Environmental Protection Agency. Basic information: composting. http://www.epa.gov/wastes/conserve/rrr/composting/basic.htm. Accessed 5/08/09.

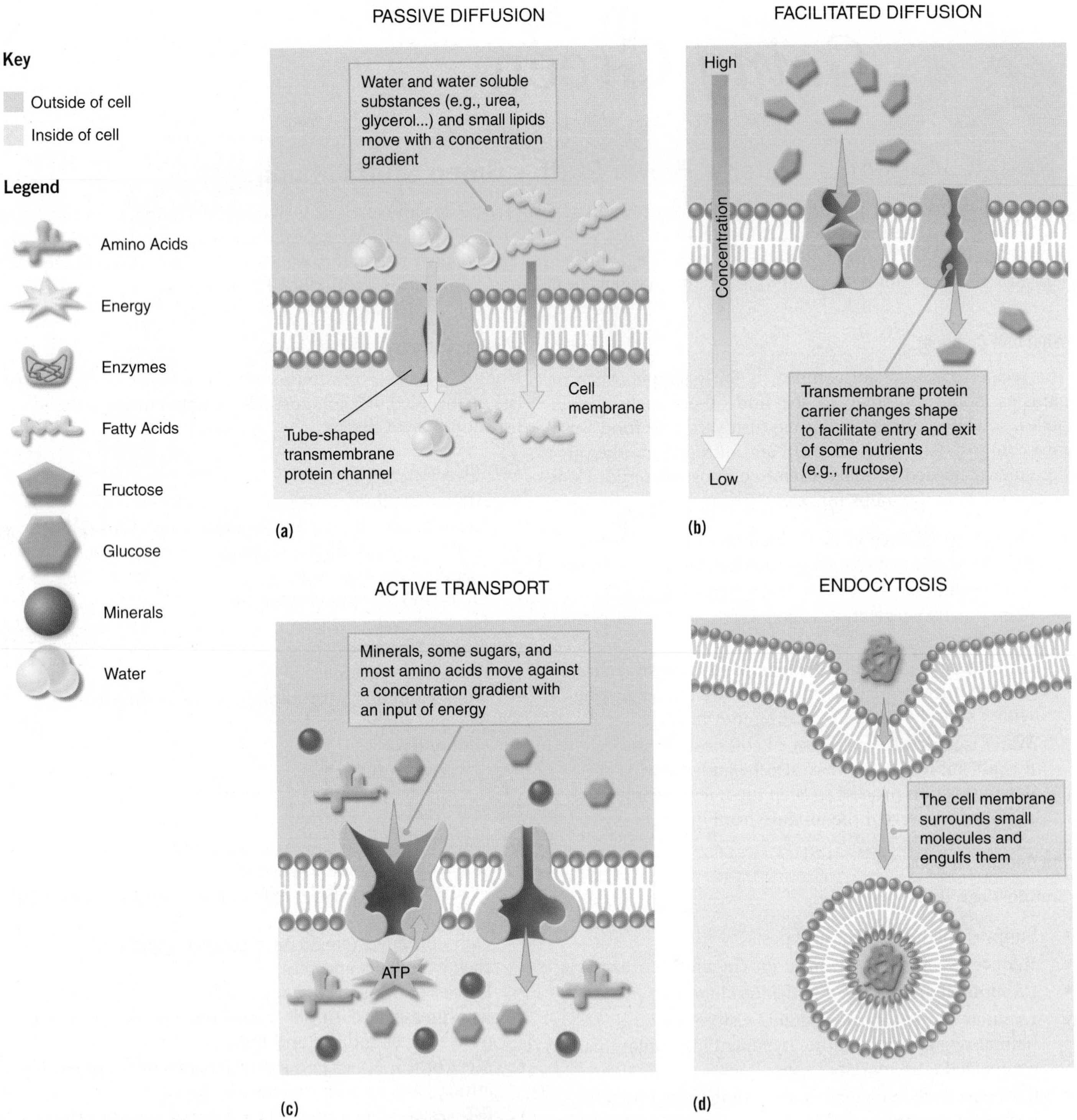

Key

Outside of cell

Inside of cell

Legend

Amino Acids

Energy

Enzymes

Fatty Acids

Fructose

Glucose

Minerals

Water

PASSIVE DIFFUSION

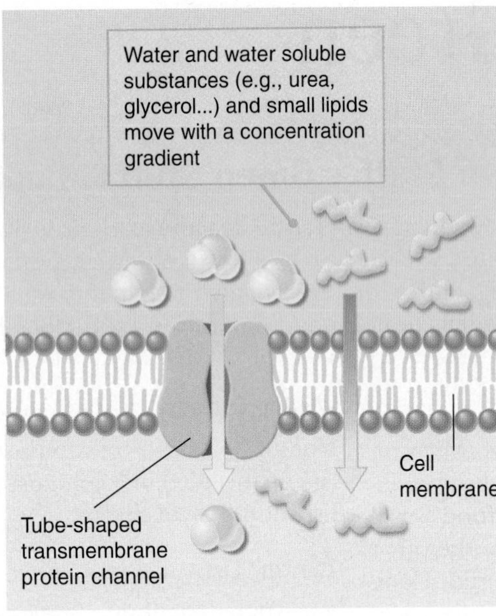
Water and water soluble substances (e.g., urea, glycerol...) and small lipids move with a concentration gradient
Cell membrane
Tube-shaped transmembrane protein channel

(a)

FACILITATED DIFFUSION

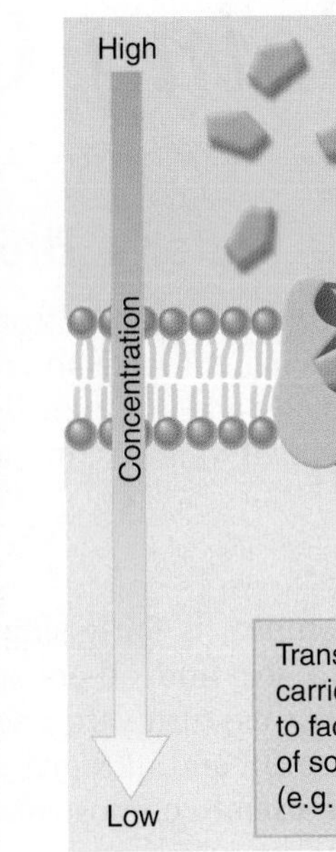
High
Concentration
Low
Transmembrane protein carrier changes shape to facilitate entry and exit of some nutrients (e.g., fructose)

(b)

ACTIVE TRANSPORT

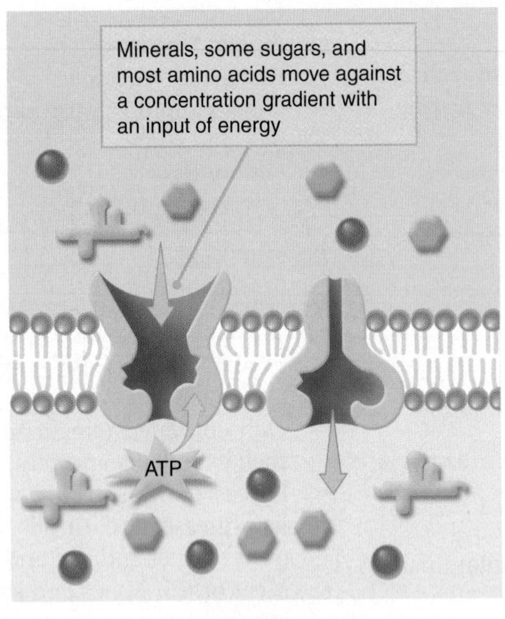
Minerals, some sugars, and most amino acids move against a concentration gradient with an input of energy
ATP

(c)

ENDOCYTOSIS

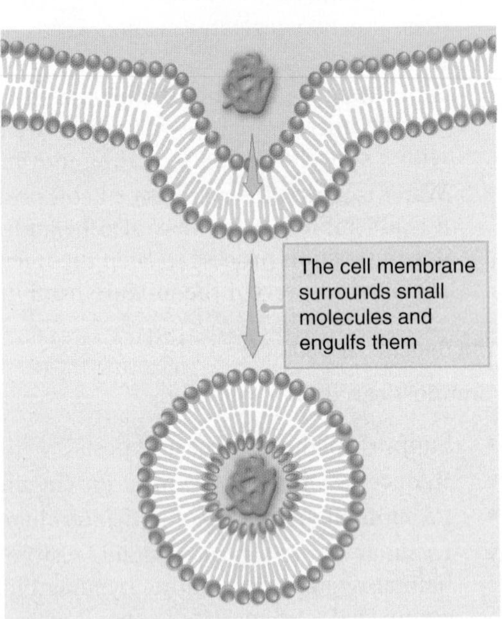
The cell membrane surrounds small molecules and engulfs them

(d)

Figure 3.7 (a) **Passive diffusion.** Using passive diffusion, some substances easily move in and out of cells, either through protein channels or directly through the cell membrane. (b) **Facilitated diffusion.** Some substances need a little assistance to enter and exit cells. A transmembrane protein helps out by changing shape. (c) **Active transport.** Some substances need a lot of assistance to enter cells. Similar to swimming upstream, energy is needed for the substance to penetrate despite an unfavorable concentration gradient. (d) **Endocytosis.** Cells can use their cell membranes to engulf a particle and bring it inside the cell. The engulfing portion of the membrane separates from the cell wall and encases the particle in a vesicle.

minerals) cannot be absorbed via passive diffusion. They need help to cross into the intestinal cells. This help comes in the form of a carrier, and may also require energy.

In **facilitated diffusion**, special carriers help transport a substance (such as the simple sugar fructose) across the cell membrane. The facilitating carriers are proteins that reside in the cell membrane. The diffusing molecule becomes lightly bound to the carrier protein, which changes its shape to open a pathway for the diffusing molecules to move into the cell. Concentration gradients also help to drive facilitated diffusion, which is passive and can move substances only from a region of higher concentration to one of lower concentration.

Energy is required for **active transport** of substances in an unfavorable direction. Substances cannot diffuse "uphill" against an unfavorable gradient, whether the difference is one of concentration, electrical charge, or pressure. Substances that usually require active transport across some cell membranes include many minerals (sodium, potassium, calcium, iron, chloride, and iodide), several sugars (glucose and galactose), and most amino acids (simple components of protein). These substances can move from the intestine even though their concentration in the intestinal lumen is lower than their concentration in the absorptive cell.

Most substances either diffuse or are actively transported across cell membranes, but some are engulfed and ingested in a process known as **endocytosis**. This occurs, for example, when a newborn infant absorbs antibodies from breast milk.[4] In endocytosis, a portion of the cell membrane forms a sac around the substance to be absorbed, pulling it into the interior of the cell. When cells ingest small molecules and fluids, the process is known as **pinocytosis**. A similar ingestion process, **phagocytosis**, is used by specialized cells to absorb large particles.

Key Concepts *Absorption through the GI cell membranes occurs by one of four basic processes. Passive diffusion occurs when nutrients (e.g., water) permeate the intestinal wall without a carrier or energy expenditure. Facilitated diffusion occurs when a carrier brings substances (e.g., fructose) into the absorptive intestinal cell without expending energy. Active transport requires energy (ATP) to transport a substance (e.g., glucose or galactose) across a cell membrane in an unfavorable direction. Endocytosis (phagocytosis or pinocytosis) occurs when the absorptive cell's membrane engulfs particles or fluids (e.g., absorption of antibodies from breast milk).*

Assisting Organs

The salivary glands, liver, gallbladder, and pancreas all have critical roles in the digestive process. The GI tract works in concert with these organs, which assist digestion by providing fluid, acid neutralizers, enzymes, and **emulsifiers**.

Salivary Glands

Three pairs of **salivary glands** (parotid, sublingual, and submandibular) located in or near the mouth secrete saliva into the oral cavity (see **Figure 3.8**). Saliva moistens food, lubricating it for easy swallowing. Saliva also contains enzymes that begin the process of chemical digestion. We secrete approximately 1,500 milliliters (about 1.5 quarts) of saliva each day. The mere sight, smell, or thought of food can start the flow of saliva.

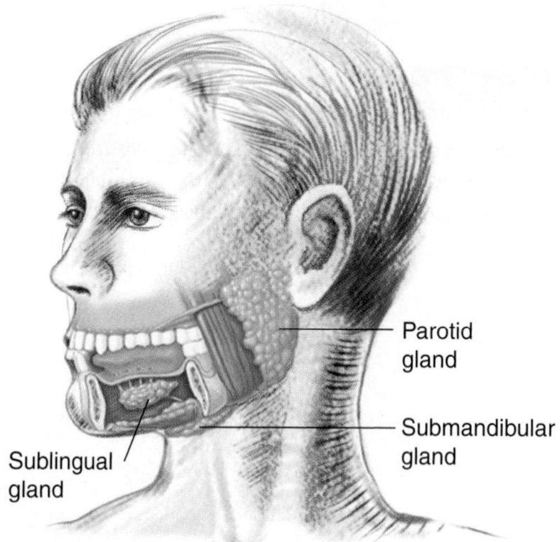

Figure 3.8 **The salivary glands.** The three pairs of salivary glands supply saliva, which moistens and lubricates food. Saliva also contains salivary enzymes that begin the digestion of starch.

facilitated diffusion A process by which carrier (transport) proteins in the cell membrane transport substances into or out of cells down a concentration gradient.

active transport The movement of substances into or out of cells against a concentration gradient. Active transport requires energy (ATP) and involves carrier (transport) proteins in the cell membrane.

endocytosis The uptake of material by a cell by the indentation and pinching off of its membrane to form a vesicle that carries material into the cell.

pinocytosis The process by which cells internalize fluids and macromolecules. To do so, the cell membrane invaginates and forms a pocket around the substance. From *pino*, "drinking," and *cyto*, "cell."

phagocytosis The process by which cells engulf large particles and small microorganisms. Receptors on the surface of cells bind these particles and organisms to bring them into large vesicles in the cytoplasm. From *phago*, "eating," and *cyto*, "cell."

emulsifiers Agents that blend fatty and watery liquids by promoting the breakup of fat into small particles and stabilizing their suspension in aqueous solution.

salivary glands Glands in the mouth that release saliva.

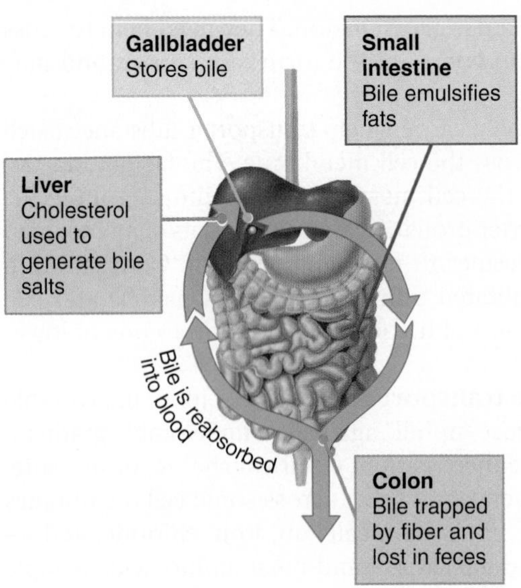

Figure 3.9 **Enterohepatic circulation.** During this recycling process, bile travels from the liver to the gallbladder and then to the small intestine, where it assists digestion. In the small intestine, most of the bile is reabsorbed and sent back to the liver for reuse.

Liver

The **liver** produces and secretes 600 to 1,000 milliliters of **bile** daily. Bile is a yellow-green, pasty material that contains water, bile salts and acids, pigments, cholesterol, phospholipids (a type of fat molecule), and electrolytes (electrically charged minerals). Bile tastes bitter, which is why the word *bile* has come to denote bitterness. Bile acts as an emulsifier by reducing large globs of fat to smaller globs. This process breaks no bonds in fat molecules, but rather increases the surface area of fat, allowing more contact between fat molecules and enzymes in the small intestine.

Bile is concentrated in your gallbladder and released to the small intestine on demand. After it has done its work, most bile salts are reabsorbed and returned to the liver for recycling. This recirculation is known as the **enterohepatic** (*entero* meaning "intestines," and *hepatic* referring to the liver) **circulation** of bile salts (see **Figure 3.9**).

The liver also is a detoxification center that filters toxic substances from the blood and alters their chemical forms. These altered substances may be sent to the kidney for excretion or carried by bile to the small intestine and removed from the body in feces. The liver is a chemical factory—performing over 500 chemical functions that include the production of blood proteins, cholesterol, and sugars. The liver is also a dynamic warehouse that stores vitamins, hormones, cholesterol, minerals, and sugars, releasing them to the bloodstream as needed.

Gallbladder

The primary function of the **gallbladder** is to store and concentrate bile from the liver. The gallbladder is a small, muscular, pear-shaped sac nestled in a depression on the right underside of the liver. This organ holds about a quarter of a cup of bile and is the storage stop for bile between the liver and the small intestine. The gallbladder fills with bile and thickens it until a hormone released after eating signals the gallbladder to squirt out its colorful contents.

The gallbladder is normally relaxed and full between meals. When dietary fats enter the small intestine, they stimulate the production of **cholecystokinin (CCK)**, a hormone, in the intestinal wall. Cholecystokinin causes the gallbladder to contract and the sphincter of Oddi, which is at the end of the common bile duct, to relax. Like a squeeze bulb, the gallbladder squirts bile into the duodenum (the upper part of the small intestine), about 500 milliliters each day. The common bile duct also carries digestive enzymes from the pancreas.

liver The largest glandular organ in the body, it produces and secretes bile, detoxifies harmful substances, and helps metabolize carbohydrates, lipids, proteins, and micronutrients.

bile An alkaline, yellow-green fluid that is produced in the liver and stored in the gallbladder. The primary constituents of bile are bile salts, bile acids, phospholipids, cholesterol, and bicarbonate. Bile emulsifies dietary fats, aiding fat digestion and absorption.

enterohepatic circulation [EN-ter-oh-heh-PAT-ik] Recycling of certain compounds between the small intestine and the liver. For example, bile acids move from the liver to the gallbladder, and then into the small intestine, from whence they are absorbed into the portal vein and transported back to the liver.

gallbladder A pear-shaped sac that stores and concentrates bile from the liver.

cholecystokinin (CCK) [ko-la-sis-toe-KY-nin] A hormone produced by cells in the small intestine that stimulates the release of digestive enzymes from the pancreas and bile from the gallbladder.

Pancreas

The **pancreas** secretes enzymes that affect the digestion and absorption of nutrients. During the course of a day, the pancreas secretes about 1,500 milliliters of fluid, which contains mostly water, bicarbonate, and digestive enzymes. The pancreas also releases hormones that are involved in other aspects of nutrient use by the body. For example, the pancreatic hormones insulin and glucagon regulate blood glucose levels. The combination of these two functions makes the pancreas one of the most important organs in the digestion and use of food.

Key Concepts *The salivary glands, liver, gallbladder, and pancreas all make important contributions to the digestive process. The salivary glands release saliva, which contains mucus and enzymes, into the mouth. The liver produces bile, which is stored in the gallbladder and released into the small intestine, where bile helps to prepare fats for digestion. The pancreas also secretes liquid that contains bicarbonate and several types of enzymes into the small intestine.*

As you swallow, the epiglottis closes off the air passage and prevents choking
Bolus
Airway
Esophagus

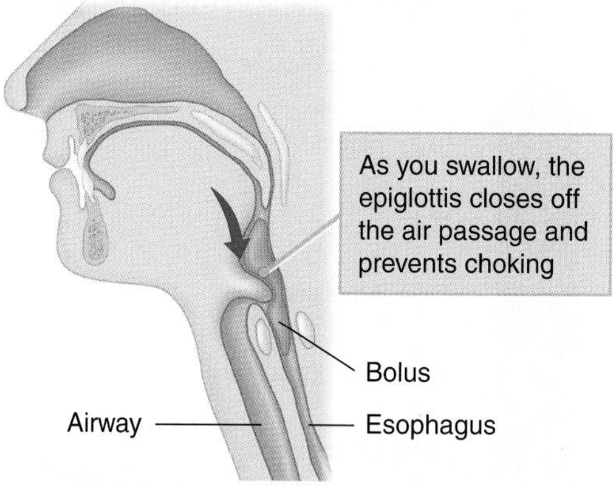

Figure 3.10 **Swallowing.** Your epiglottis didn't completely do its job if you have ever had a drink go "down the wrong pipe" and choked.

Putting It All Together: Digestion and Absorption

Up to this point, our discussion has centered on structures, mechanisms, and processes to give you a general idea of the workings of the GI tract. Now you're ready for a complete tour, a journey along the GI tract to see what happens and how digestion and absorption are accomplished. Detailed descriptions of specific enzymes and actions on individual nutrients are covered in later chapters.

Mouth

As soon as you put food in your mouth the digestive process begins. As you chew, you break down the food into smaller pieces, increasing the surface area available to enzymes. Saliva contains the enzyme salivary **amylase** (ptyalin), which breaks down starch into small sugar molecules. Food remains in the mouth only for a short time, so only about 5 percent of the starch is completely broken down. The next time you eat a cracker or a piece of bread, chew slowly and notice the change in the way it tastes. It gets sweeter. That's the salivary amylase breaking down the starch into sugar. Salivary amylase continues to work until the strong acid content of the stomach deactivates it. To start the process of fat digestion, the cells at the base of the tongue secrete another enzyme, **lingual lipase**. The overall impact of lingual lipase on fat digestion, though, is small.

THINK About It 3

Saliva and other fluids, including mucus, blend with the food to form a **bolus**, a chewed, moistened lump of food that is soft and easy to swallow. When you swallow, the bolus slides past the epiglottis, a valvelike flap of tissue that closes off your air passages so you don't choke. The bolus then moves rapidly through the **esophagus** to the stomach, where it will be digested further. **Figure 3.10** shows the process of swallowing.

Stomach

The bolus enters the **stomach** through the **esophageal sphincter**, also called the cardiac sphincter, which immediately closes to keep the bolus from sliding back into the esophagus. Quick and complete closure by the esophageal sphincter is essential to prevent the acidic stomach contents from backing up into the esophagus, causing the pain and tissue damage called heartburn.

pancreas An organ that secretes enzymes that affect the digestion and absorption of nutrients and that releases hormones, such as insulin, that regulate metabolism as well as the disposition of the end products of food in the body.

amylase [AM-ih-lace] A salivary enzyme that catalyzes the hydrolysis of amylose, a starch. Also called ptyalin.

lingual lipase A fat-splitting enzyme secreted by cells at the base of the tongue.

bolus [BOH-lus] A chewed, moistened lump of food that is ready to be swallowed.

esophagus [ee-SOFF-uh-gus] The food pipe that extends from the pharynx to the stomach, about 25 centimeters long.

stomach The enlarged, muscular, saclike portion of the digestive tract between the esophagus and the small intestine, with a capacity of about 1 quart.

esophageal sphincter The opening between the esophagus and the stomach that relaxes and opens to allow the bolus to travel into the stomach, and then closes behind it. Also acts as a barrier to prevent the reflux of gastric contents. Commonly called the cardiac sphincter.

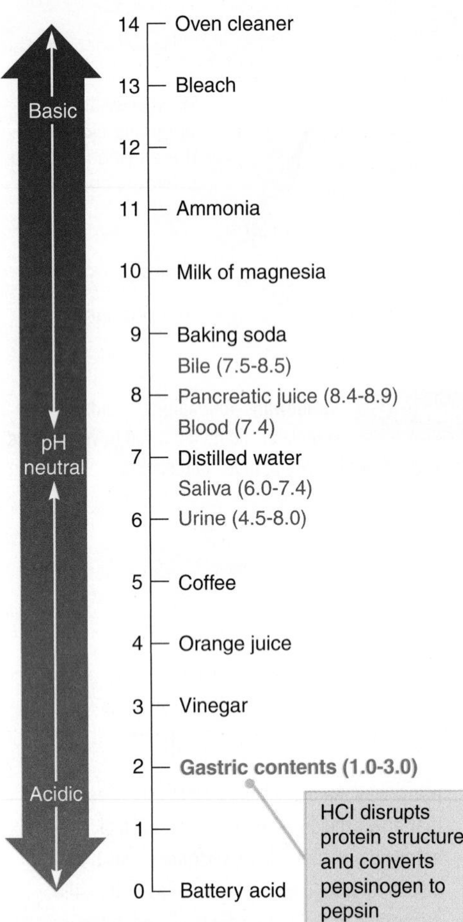

Figure 3.11 **The pH scale.** Because pancreatic juice has a pH around 8, it can neutralize the acidic chyme, which leaves the stomach with a pH around 2.

hydrochloric acid An acid of chloride and hydrogen atoms made by the gastric glands and secreted into the stomach. Also called gastric acid.

pH A measurement of the hydrogen ion concentration, or acidity, of a solution. It is equal to the negative logarithm of the hydrogen ion (H^+) concentration expressed in moles per liter.

mucus A slippery substance secreted in the GI tract (and other body linings) that protects cells from irritants such as digestive juices.

pepsinogen The inactive form of the enzyme pepsin.

pepsin A protein-digesting enzyme produced by the stomach.

Nutrient Digestion in the Stomach

The stomach cells produce secretions that are collectively called gastric juice. Included in this mixture are water, hydrochloric acid, mucus, pepsinogen (the inactive form of the enzyme pepsin), the enzyme gastric lipase, the hormone gastrin, and intrinsic factor.

- **Hydrochloric acid** makes the stomach contents extremely acidic, dropping the **pH** to 2, compared with a neutral pH of 7. (See **Figure 3.11**.) This acidic environment kills many pathogenic (disease-causing) bacteria that may have been ingested, and also aids in the digestion of protein. **Mucus** secreted by the stomach cells coats the stomach lining, protecting these cells from damage by the strong gastric juice. Hydrochloric acid works in protein digestion in two ways. First, it demolishes the functional, three-dimensional shape of proteins, unfolding them into linear chains; this increases their vulnerability to attacking enzymes. Second, it promotes the breakdown of proteins by converting the enzyme precursor **pepsinogen** to its active form, **pepsin**.
- Pepsin then begins breaking the links in protein chains, cutting dietary proteins into smaller and smaller pieces.
- Stomach cells also produce an enzyme called **gastric lipase**. It has a minor role in the digestion of lipids, specifically triglycerides with an abundance of short-chain fatty acids.
- **Gastrin**, another component of gastric juice, is a hormone that stimulates gastric secretion and motility.
- **Intrinsic factor** is a substance necessary for the absorption of vitamin B_{12} that occurs farther down the GI tract, near the end of the small intestine. In the absence of intrinsic factor, only about one-fiftieth of ingested vitamin B_{12} is absorbed.

After swallowing, salivary amylase continues to digest carbohydrates. After about an hour, acidic stomach secretions become well mixed with the food. This increases the acidity of the food and effectively blocks further salivary amylase activity.

Do you sometimes feel your stomach churning? An important action of the stomach is to continue mixing food with GI secretions to produce the semiliquid chyme. To accomplish this, the stomach has an extra layer of diagonal muscles. These, along with the circular and longitudinal muscles, contract and relax to mix food completely. When the chyme is ready to leave the stomach, about 30 to 40 percent of carbohydrate, 10 to 20 percent of protein, and less than 10 percent of fat have been digested.[5] The stomach slowly releases the chyme through the **pyloric sphincter** and into the small intestine. The pyloric sphincter then closes to prevent the chyme from returning to the stomach (see **Figure 3.12**).

The stomach normally empties in one to four hours, depending on the types and amounts of food eaten. Carbohydrates speed through the stomach in the shortest time, followed by protein and fat. Thus, the higher the fat content of a meal, the longer it will take to leave the stomach.

Nutrient Absorption in the Stomach

Although a substantial fraction of digestion has been accomplished by the time chyme leaves the stomach, very little absorption has occurred. Only some lipid-soluble compounds and weak acids, such as alcohol and aspirin, are absorbed through the stomach. Chyme moves on to the small intestine, the digestive and absorptive workhorse of the gut.

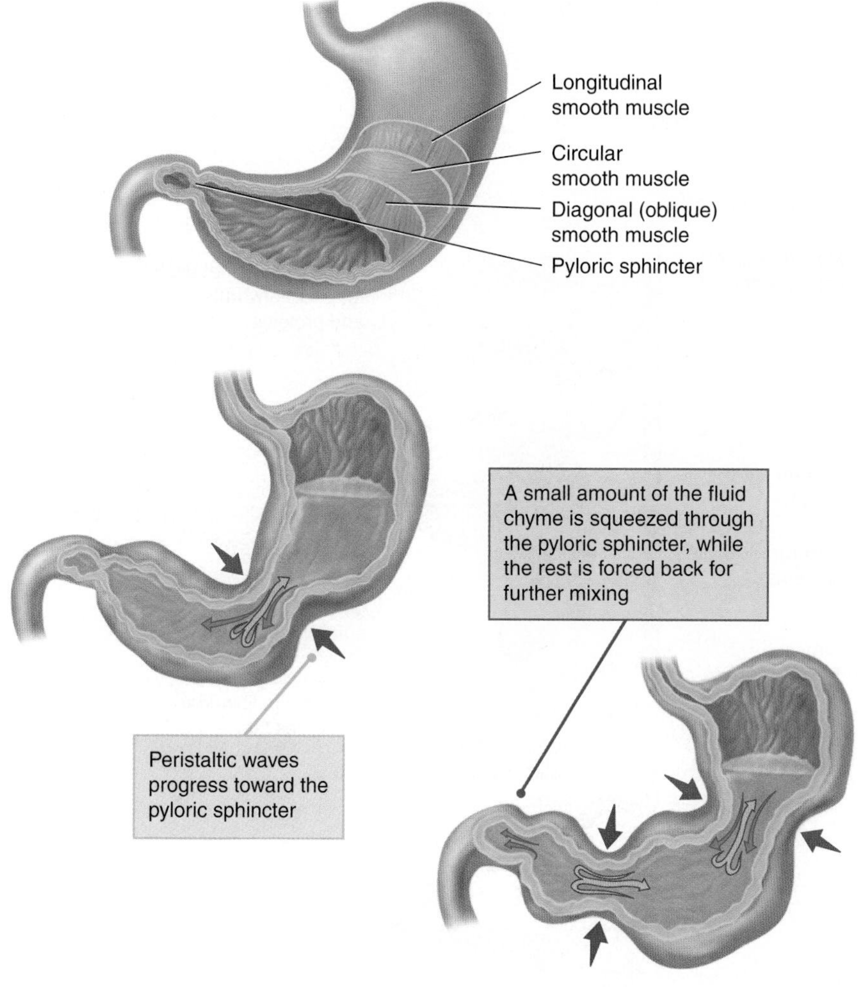
Longitudinal smooth muscle
Circular smooth muscle
Diagonal (oblique) smooth muscle
Pyloric sphincter
A small amount of the fluid chyme is squeezed through the pyloric sphincter, while the rest is forced back for further mixing
Peristaltic waves progress toward the pyloric sphincter

Figure 3.12 **The stomach.** The stomach churns and mixes food with stomach secretions. Hydrochloric acid unfolds proteins and stops salivary amylase action, while pepsin begins protein digestion. The pyloric sphincter controls movement of chyme from the stomach to the small intestine.

gastric lipase An enzyme in the stomach that hydrolyzes certain triglycerides into fatty acids and glycerol.

gastrin [GAS-trin] A polypeptide hormone released from the walls of the stomach mucosa and duodenum that stimulates gastric secretions and motility.

intrinsic factor A glycoprotein released from parietal cells in the stomach wall that binds to and aids in absorption of vitamin B_{12}.

pyloric sphincter [pie-LORE-ic] A circular muscle that forms the opening between the stomach and the duodenum. It regulates the passage of food into the small intestine.

small intestine The tube (approximately 10 feet long) where the digestion of protein, fat, and carbohydrate is completed, and where the majority of nutrients are absorbed. The small intestine is divided into three parts: the duodenum, the jejunum, and the ileum.

duodenum [doo-oh-DEE-num, or doo-AH-den-um] The portion of the small intestine closest to the stomach. The duodenum is 10 to 12 inches long and wider than the remainder of the small intestine.

jejunum [je-JOON-um] The middle section (about 4 feet) of the small intestine, lying between the duodenum and ileum.

ileum [ILL-ee-um] The terminal segment (about 5 feet) of the small intestine, which opens into the large intestine.

digestive secretions Substances released at different places in the GI tract to speed the breakdown of ingested carbohydrates, fats, and proteins into smaller compounds that can be absorbed by the body.

secretin [see-CREET-in] An intestinal hormone released during digestion that stimulates the pancreas to release water and bicarbonate.

Small Intestine

The **small intestine** is where the digestion of protein, fat, and nearly all carbohydrate is completed and where most nutrients are absorbed. As you can see in **Figure 3.13**, the small intestine is a tube about 3 meters long (about 10 feet), divided into three parts:

- **Duodenum** (the first 25 to 30 centimeters—10 to 12 inches)
- **Jejunum** (about 120 centimeters—about 4 feet)
- **Ileum** (about 150 centimeters—about 5 feet)

Most digestion occurs in the duodenum, where the small intestine receives **digestive secretions** from the pancreas, gallbladder, and its own glands. The remainder of the small intestine primarily absorbs previously digested nutrients.

Nutrient Digestion in the Small Intestine

In the duodenum, the acidic chyme from the stomach is neutralized by a base, bicarbonate, from the pancreas. The slow delivery of chyme through the pyloric sphincter (about 2 milliliters per minute) allows chyme to be adequately neutralized. This is important because the enzymes of the small intestine need a more neutral environment to work effectively. The stimulus for release of bicarbonate from the pancreas is the hormone **secretin**. This

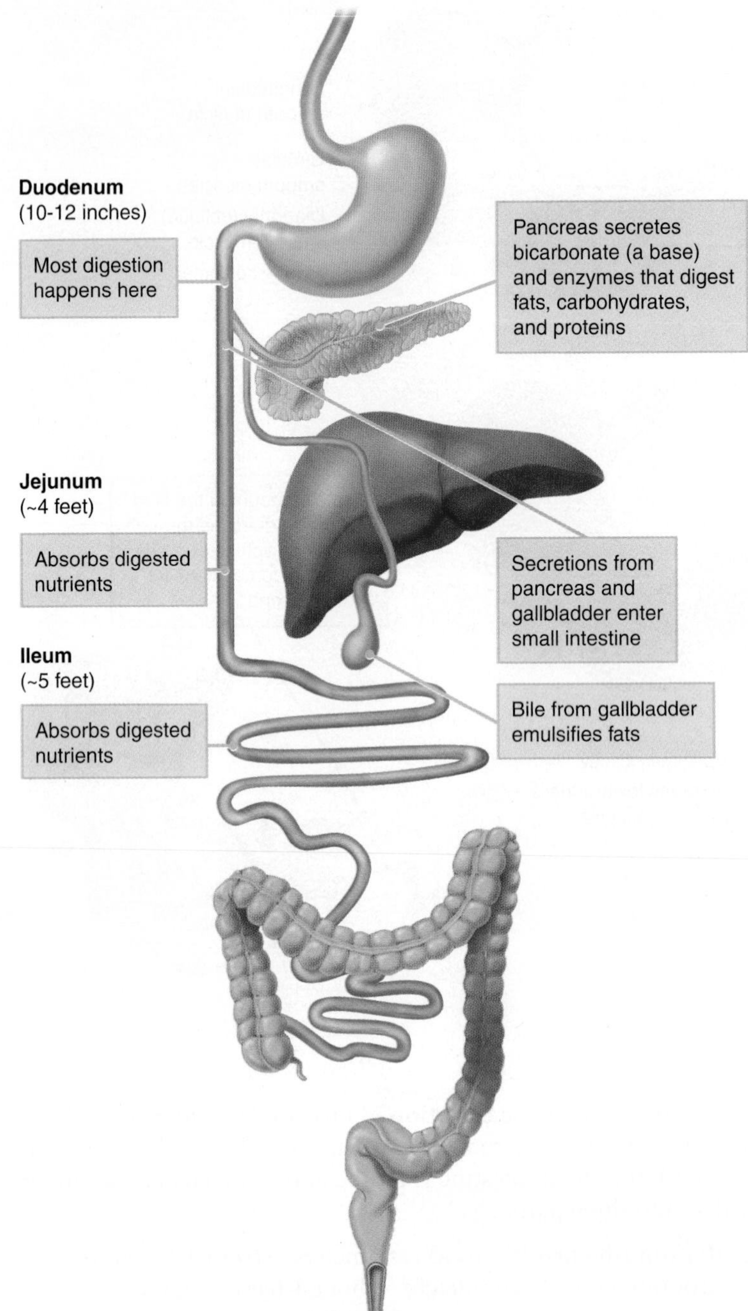
Duodenum
(10-12 inches)
Most digestion happens here
Pancreas secretes bicarbonate (a base) and enzymes that digest fats, carbohydrates, and proteins
Jejunum
(~4 feet)
Absorbs digested nutrients
Secretions from pancreas and gallbladder enter small intestine
Ileum
(~5 feet)
Absorbs digested nutrients
Bile from gallbladder emulsifies fats

Figure 3.13 **The small intestine.** The duodenum is mainly responsible for digesting food; the jejunum and ileum primarily deal with the absorption of food. The duodenum secretes mucus, enzymes, and hormones along with other digestive juices from assisting organs to aid digestion. All along the intestinal walls, nutrients are absorbed into blood and lymph. Undigested materials are passed on to the large intestine.

hormone is released from intestinal cells in response to the appearance of chyme. Pancreatic juice contains a variety of digestive enzymes that help to digest fats, carbohydrates, and proteins. Secretions from the intestinal wall cells add enzymes to complete carbohydrate digestion.

The presence of fat in the duodenum stimulates the release of stored bile by the gallbladder. The specific signal comes from the intestinal hormone cholecystokinin. Lipids ordinarily do not mix with water, but bile acts as an emulsifier, keeping lipid molecules mixed with the watery chyme and digestive secretions. Without the action of bile, lipids might not come into contact with pancreatic lipase, and digestion would be incomplete.

With the pancreatic and intestinal enzymes working together, digestion progresses nicely, leaving smaller protein, carbohydrate, and lipid compounds ready for absorption. Other nutrients, such as vitamins, minerals, and cholesterol, are not digested and generally are absorbed unchanged.

Just as the small intestine accomplishes much of the nutrient digestion, it is also responsible for most nutrient absorption. Its structure makes the process of absorption efficient and complete. In most cases, more than 90 percent of ingested carbohydrate, fat, and protein is absorbed. To see how this is possible, we need to examine the structure of the small intestine.

Absorptive Structures of the Small Intestine

The small intestine packs a gigantic surface area into a small space. As you can see in **Figure 3.14**, the interior surface of the small intestine is wrinkled into folds, tripling the absorptive surface area. These folds are carpeted with

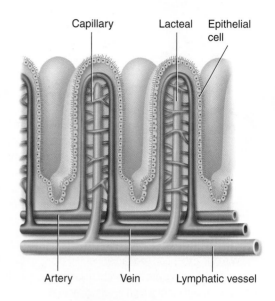

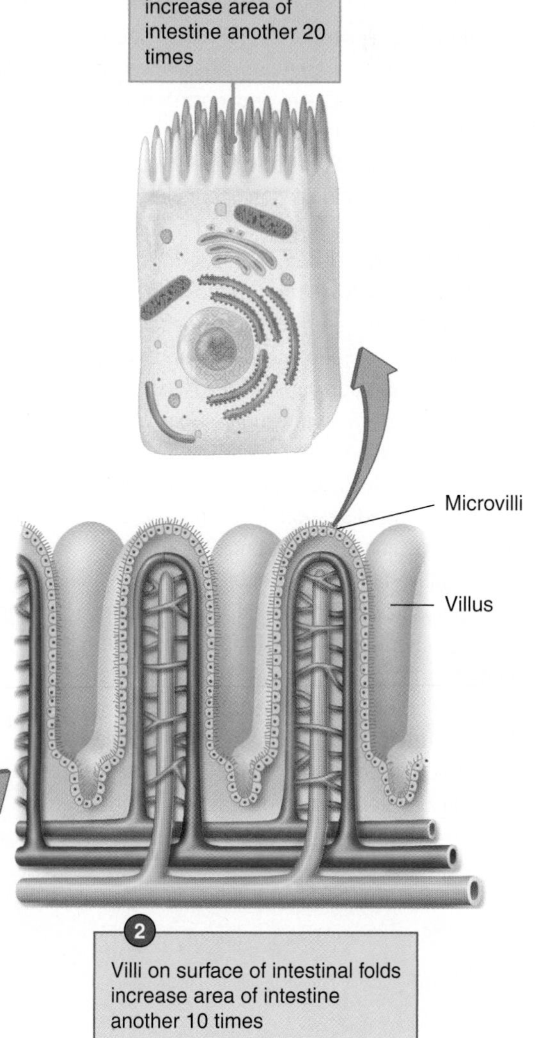

Figure 3.14 **The absorptive surface of the small intestine.** To maximize the absorptive surface area, the small intestine is folded and lined with fingerlike villi. You have a surface area the size of a tennis court packed into your gut.

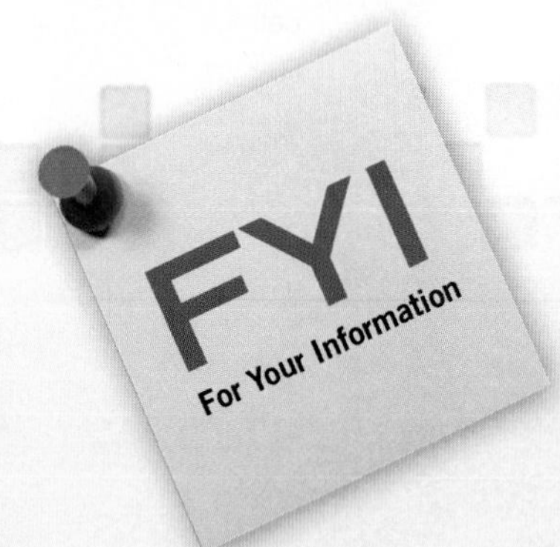

Lactose Intolerance

When drinking a milkshake is followed shortly by bloating, gas, abdominal pain, and diarrhea, it could be lactose intolerance—the incomplete digestion of the lactose in milk due to low levels of the intestinal enzyme lactase. Lactose is the primary carbohydrate in milk and other dairy foods. Nondairy foods—such as instant breakfast mixes, cake mixes, mayonnaise, luncheon meats, medications, and vitamin supplements—also contain small amounts of lactose. Lactase is necessary to digest lactose in the small intestine. If lactase is deficient, undigested lactose enters the large intestine, where it is fermented by colonic bacteria, producing short-chain organic acids and gases (hydrogen, methane, carbon dioxide).

With the exception of a rare inherited disorder in which infants are born without lactase, infants have sufficiently high levels of lactase for normal digestion. However, lactase activity declines with weaning in many racial/ethnic groups. This normal, genetically controlled decrease in lactase activity, called lactose maldigestion, is prevalent among Asians, Native Americans, and African Americans. However, among U.S. Caucasians and northern and central Europeans, lactose maldigestion is far less common because lactase activity tends to persist. Lactose maldigestion occurs in about 25 percent of the U.S. population and in 75 percent of the worldwide population.

In addition to primary lactose intolerance, lactose intolerance can be secondary to diseases or conditions (e.g., inflammatory bowel disease such as Crohn's disease or celiac disease, gastrointestinal surgery, and certain medications) that injure the intestinal mucosa where lactase is expressed. Secondary lactose maldigestion is temporary, and lactose digestion improves once the underlying causative factor is corrected.

Lactose intolerance is far less prevalent than commonly believed. Many factors unrelated to lactose, including strong beliefs, can contribute to this condition. Studies have demonstrated that among self-described lactose-intolerant individuals, one-third to one-half develop few or no gastrointestinal symptoms following intake of lactose under well-controlled, double-blind conditions.

Self-diagnosis of lactose intolerance is a bad idea because it could lead to unnecessary dietary restrictions, expense, nutritional shortcomings, and failure to detect or treat a more serious gastrointestinal disorder. If lactose maldigestion is suspected, tests are available to diagnose this condition.

People with real or perceived lactose intolerance may limit their consumption of dairy foods unnecessarily and jeopardize their intake of calcium and other essential nutrients. A low intake of calcium is associated with increased risk of osteoporosis (porous bones), hypertension, and colon cancer.

With the exception of the few individuals who are sensitive to even very small amounts of lactose, avoiding all lactose is neither necessary nor recommended because some lactase is still being produced. Lactose maldigestors need to determine the amount of lactose they can comfortably consume at any one time. Here are some strategies for including milk and other dairy foods in your diet without developing symptoms:

1. Initially, consume small servings of lactose-containing foods such as milk (e.g., ½ cup). Gradually increase the serving size until symptoms begin to appear, then back off.
2. Consume lactose with a meal or other foods (e.g., milk with cereal) to improve tolerance.
3. Adjust the type of dairy food. Whole milk may be tolerated better than low-fat milk, and chocolate milk may be tolerated better than unflavored milk. Many cheeses (e.g., Cheddar, Swiss, Parmesan) contain considerably less lactose than does milk. Aged cheeses generally have negligible amounts of lactose. Yogurts with live, active cultures are another option; these bacteria will digest lactose. Sweet acidophilus milk, yogurt milk, and other nonfermented dairy foods may be tolerated better than regular milk by lactose maldigestors. However, factors such as the strain of bacteria used may influence tolerance to these dairy foods.
4. Lactose-hydrolyzed dairy foods and/or commercial enzyme preparations (e.g., lactase capsules, chewable tablets, solutions) are another option. Lactose-reduced (70 percent less lactose) and lactose-free (99.9 percent less lactose) milks are available, although at a higher cost than regular milk.

Lactose maldigestion need not be an impediment to meeting the needs for calcium and other essential nutrients provided by milk and other dairy foods.

Distribution of lactose intolerance worldwide.

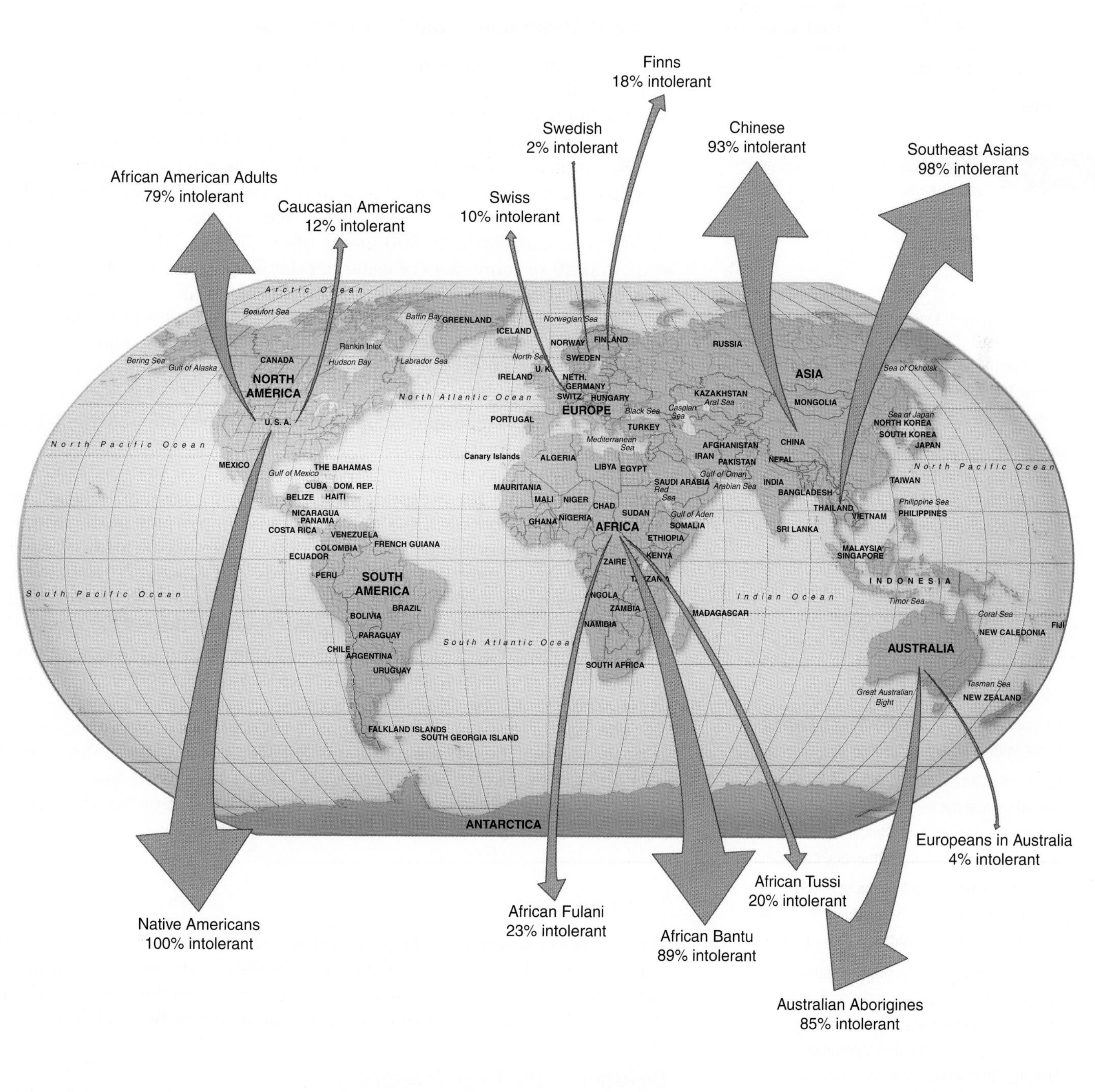

Source: Data from National Institute of Diabetes and Digestive and Kidney Diseases (NIDDK), NIH. Washington, DC; and Enattah NS, Sahi T, Savilahti E, et al. Identification of a variant associated with adult-type hypolactasia. *Nat Genet.* 2002;30(2):233–237.

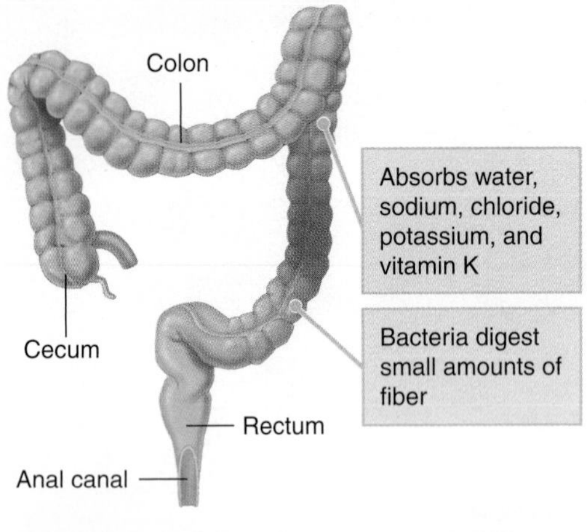

Figure 3.15 **The large intestine.** In the large intestine, bacteria break down dietary fiber and other undigested carbohydrates, releasing acids and gas. The large intestine absorbs water and minerals, and forms feces for excretion.

villi Small, fingerlike projections that blanket the folds in the lining of the small intestine. Singular is *villus.*

microvilli Minute, hairlike projections that extend from the surface of absorptive cells facing the intestinal lumen. Singular is *microvillus.*

lymph Fluid that travels through the lymphatic system, made up of fluid drained from between cells and large fat particles.

lacteal A small lymphatic vessel in the interior of each intestinal villus that picks up chylomicrons and fat-soluble vitamins from intestinal cells.

ileocecal valve The sphincter at the junction of the small and large intestines.

large intestine The tube (about 5 feet) extending from the ileum of the small intestine to the anus. The large intestine includes the appendix, cecum, colon, rectum, and anal canal.

cecum The blind pouch at the beginning of the large intestine into which the ileum opens from one side and which is continuous with the colon.

colon The portion of the large intestine extending from the cecum to the rectum. It is made up of four parts—the ascending, transverse, descending, and sigmoid colons. Although often used interchangeably with the term *large intestine*, these terms are not synonymous.

fingerlike projections called **villi** that expand the absorptive area another 10-fold. Each cell lining the surface of each villus is covered with a "brush border" containing as many as 1,000 hairlike projections called **microvilli**. The microvilli increase the surface area another 20 times. Taken together, the folds plus the villi and microvilli yield a 600-fold increase in surface area. In fact, your 10-foot (3 meters) long intestine has an absorptive surface area of more than 300 square yards (250 or more square meters)—equivalent to the surface of a tennis court!

Nutrient Absorption in the Small Intestine

As nutrients journey through the small intestine, they are trapped in the folds and projections of the intestinal wall and absorbed through the microvilli into the lining cells. Depending on your diet, each day your small intestine absorbs several hundred grams of carbohydrate, 60 or more grams of fat, 50 to 100 grams of amino acids, 3 to 5 grams of vitamins and minerals, and 7 to 8 liters of water. But the total absorptive capacity of the healthy small intestine is far greater. It actually has the capacity to absorb as much as several kilograms of carbohydrate, 500 grams of fat, 500 to 700 grams of amino acids, and 20 or more liters of water per day.[6] Approximately 85 percent of the water absorption by the gut occurs in the jejunum.[7]

Nutrients absorbed through the intestinal lining pass into the interior of the villi. Each villus contains blood vessels (veins, arteries, and capillaries) and a **lymph** vessel (known as a **lacteal**) that transport nutrients to other parts of your body. Water-soluble nutrients are absorbed directly into the bloodstream. Fat-soluble lipid compounds are absorbed into the lymph rather than directly into the blood.

Absorption takes place along the entire length of the small intestine. Most minerals, with the exception of the electrolytes sodium, chloride, and potassium, are absorbed in the duodenum and upper part of the jejunum. Carbohydrates, amino acids, and water-soluble vitamins are absorbed along the jejunum and upper ileum, whereas lipids and fat-soluble vitamins are absorbed primarily in the ileum. At the very end of the small intestine, the terminal ileum is the site of vitamin B_{12} absorption. If there is damage to the lower small intestine, or surgical removal of this section in the treatment of cancer and other diseases, malabsorption of fat-soluble vitamins and vitamin B_{12} is likely.

The small intestine suffers constant wear and tear as it propels and digests the chyme. The intestinal lining is renewed continually as the mucosal cells are replaced every two to five days. When the chyme has completed its 3- to 10-hour journey through the small intestine, it passes through the **ileocecal valve**, the connection to the large intestine.

The Large Intestine

The chyme's next stop is the **large intestine**. As **Figure 3.15** shows, this tube is about 5 feet (1.5 meters) long and includes the **cecum**, **colon**, rectum, and anal canal. As chyme fills the cecum, a local reflex signals the ileocecal valve to close, preventing material from reentering the ileum of the small intestine.

Digestion in the Large Intestine

The peristaltic movements of the large intestine are sluggish compared with those of the small intestine. Normally 18 to 24 hours are required for material to traverse its length. During that time, the colon's large population of

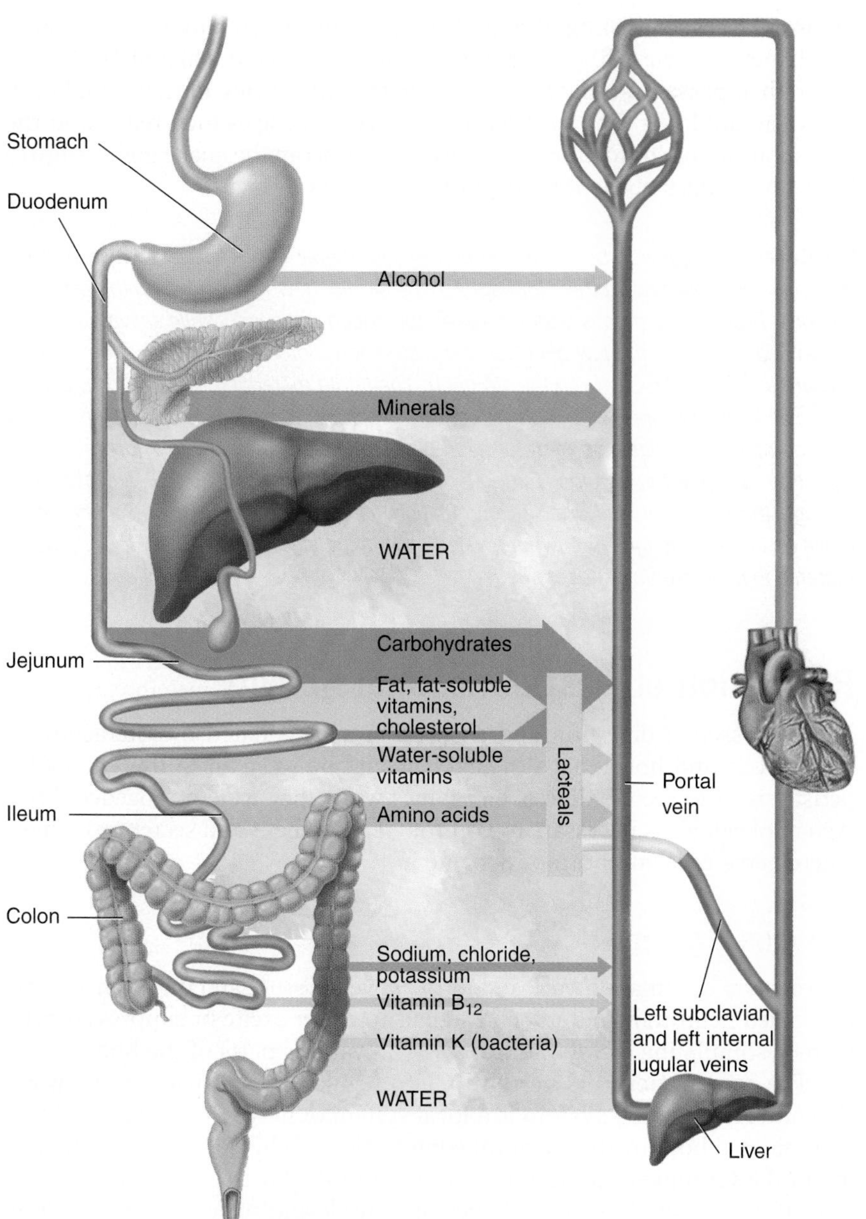

Figure 3.16 Absorption of nutrients.

bacteria digests small amounts of fiber, providing a negligible number of calories daily.[8] Of more significance are the other substances formed by this bacterial activity, including vitamin K, vitamin B_{12}, thiamin, riboflavin, biotin, and various gases that contribute to flatulence.[9] Other than bacterial action, no further digestion occurs in the large intestine.

Nutrient Absorption in the Large Intestine

Minimal nutrient absorption takes place in the large intestine, limited to water, sodium, chloride, potassium, and some of the vitamin K produced by bacteria. Although vitamin B_{12} is also produced by colonic bacteria, it is not absorbed. The colon dehydrates the watery chyme, removing and absorbing most of the remaining fluid. Of the approximately 1,000 milliliters of material that enter the large intestine, only about 150 milliliters remain for excretion as feces. The

Quick Bite

The Clever Colon
Though it has been presumed that the colon has no digestive function, recent research shows that the human colon can be an important digestive site in patients who are missing significant sections of their intestines. These patients can actually absorb energy from starch and nonstarch polysaccharides in the colon.

semisolid feces, consisting of roughly 60 percent solid matter (food residues, which include dietary fiber, bacteria, and digestive secretions) and 40 percent water, then passes into the rectum. In the **rectum**, strong muscles hold back the waste until it is time to defecate. The rectal muscles then relax, and the anal sphincter opens to allow passage of the stool out the anal canal.[10] **Figure 3.16** summarizes nutrient absorption along the GI tract.

Key Concepts *Digestion begins in the mouth with the action of salivary amylase. Food material next moves down the esophagus to the stomach, where it mixes with gastric secretions. Protein digestion is begun through the action of pepsin, while salivary amylase action ceases due to the low pH level of the stomach. Some substances, such as alcohol, are absorbed directly from the stomach. The liquid material (chyme) next moves to the small intestine. Here, secretions from the gallbladder, pancreas, and intestinal lining cells complete the digestion of carbohydrates, proteins, and fats. The end products of digestion, along with vitamins, minerals, water, and other compounds, are absorbed through the intestinal wall and into circulation. Undigested material and some liquid move on to the large intestine, where water and electrolytes are absorbed, leaving waste material to be excreted as feces.*

Regulation of Gastrointestinal Activity

The processes of digestion and absorption are regulated by interaction of the nervous and hormonal systems. It would be wasteful to use energy for peristalsis or to secrete digestive enzymes when they were not needed. So, a system of signals is necessary to control GI movement and secretions. That's where nerve cells and hormones come in.

Nervous System

Nerves carry information back and forth between tissues and the brain. Chemicals called neurotransmitters send signals to either excite or suppress nerves, thereby stimulating or inhibiting activity in various parts of the body.

The **central nervous system (CNS)** regulates GI activity in two ways. The **enteric nervous system** is a local system of nerves in the gut wall that is stimulated both by the chemical composition of chyme and by the stretching of the GI lumen that results from food in the GI tract. This stimulation leads to nerve impulses that enhance the muscle and secretory activity along the tract. The enteric nervous system plays an essential role in the control of motility, blood flow, water and electrolyte transport, and acid secretion in the GI tract. A branch of the **autonomic nervous system** (the portion of the CNS that controls organ function) responds to the sight, smell, and thought of food. This branch of the CNS carries signals to and from the GI tract via the vagus nerve, and also enhances GI motility and secretion. In the past, treatments for some ulcers and other GI ailments included severing the vagus nerve, a measure that brought temporary, but not long-term, relief.

rectum The muscular final segment of the intestine, extending from the sigmoid colon to the anus.

central nervous system (CNS) The brain and the spinal cord. The central nervous system transmits signals that control muscular actions and glandular secretions along the entire GI tract.

enteric nervous system A network of nerves located in the gastrointestinal wall.

autonomic nervous system The part of the central nervous system that regulates the automatic responses of the body; consists of the sympathetic and para-sympathetic systems.

Hormonal System

Hormones are also involved in GI regulation (see **Figure 3.17**). Hormones are chemical messengers that are produced at one location and travel in the bloodstream to affect another location in the body. Some GI hormones, however, are secreted by and active in the same tissue.

Gastrointestinal hormonal signals increase or decrease GI motility and secretions, and influence your appetite by sending signals to the central nervous

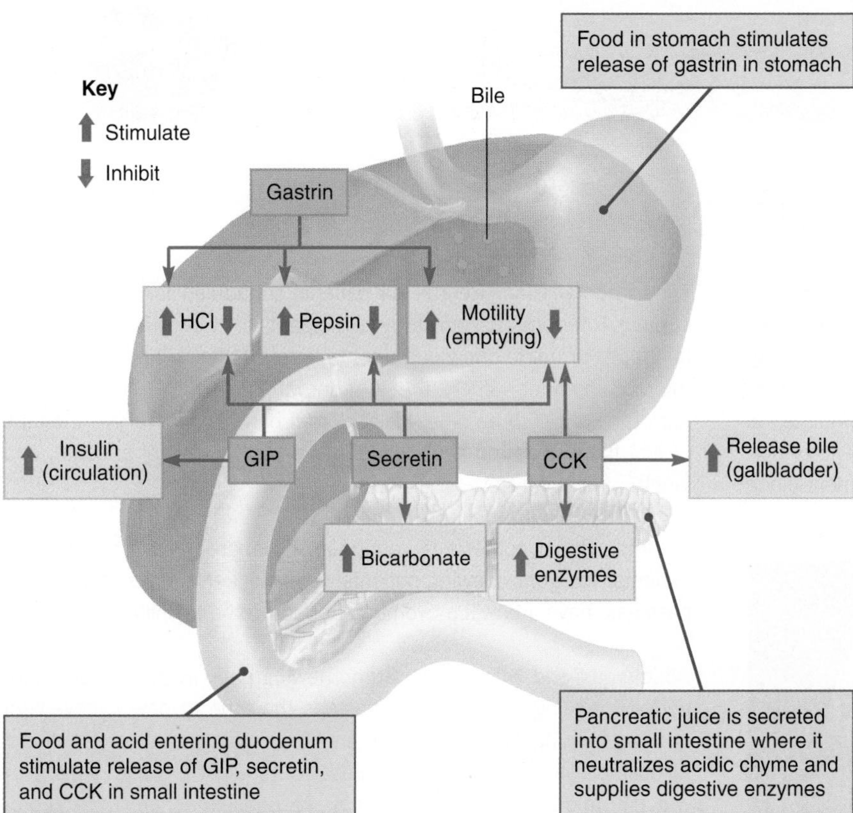
Key
Stimulate
Inhibit
Food in stomach stimulates release of gastrin in stomach
Bile
Gastrin
HCl
Pepsin
Motility (emptying)
Insulin (circulation)
GIP
Secretin
CCK
Release bile (gallbladder)
Bicarbonate
Digestive enzymes
Food and acid entering duodenum stimulate release of GIP, secretin, and CCK in small intestine
Pancreatic juice is secreted into small intestine where it neutralizes acidic chyme and supplies digestive enzymes

Figure 3.17 **Hormonal regulation of digestion.** In response to food moving through the digestive tract, hormones control the increase and decrease of digestive activities.

system. Some GI hormones function as growth factors for the gastrointestinal mucosa and pancreas.

The four major hormones that regulate the GI function are gastrin, secretin, cholecystokinin, and gastric inhibitory peptide.

- Gastrin is released by cells in the stomach in response to distention of the stomach, nerve impulses from the vagus nerve, and the presence of chemicals such as alcohol and caffeine. Gastrin increases muscle movement in the stomach and enhances release of hydrochloric acid and pepsinogen to encourage digestion.
- Secretin is released by cells along the duodenal wall when acidic chyme begins to move into the duodenum. Secretin opposes the action of gastrin; it reduces gastric secretion and motility, and stimulates the pancreas to release bicarbonate so as to neutralize chyme.
- Cholecystokinin (CCK) is released by cells along the small intestine as amino acids and fatty acids from digestion begin to enter the small intestine. CCK stimulates the pancreas to secrete enzymes, stimulates the gallbladder to contract and release bile, and slows gastric emptying.
- **Gastric inhibitory peptide (GIP)** is also released from the intestinal mucosal cells in response to fat and glucose in the small intestine. As its name implies, GIP inhibits gastric secretion, motility, and emptying. In addition, GIP stimulates the release of insulin, which is necessary for glucose utilization.

Taken together, nerve cells and hormones coordinate the movement and secretions of the GI tract so that enzymes are released when and where they are needed and chyme moves at a rate that will optimize digestion and ab-

gastric inhibitory peptide (GIP) [GAS-trik in-HIB-ihtor-ee PEP-tide] A hormone released from the walls of the duodenum that slows the release of the stomach contents into the small intestine and also stimulates release of insulin from the pancreas.

Nutrition Science *in Action*

Gum Chewing After Surgery

Observations: Any abdominal surgery, including colon surgery, can cause a marked decrease or stoppage of intestinal function (ileus). Immediate consequences include pain, vomiting, and bloating. Ileus also can lead to longer hospital stays, increased risk of infection, and breathing difficulties. Chewing gum may stimulate the same nerves in the body as eating, promoting the release of hormones that stimulate muscular contractions and movement along the bowel.

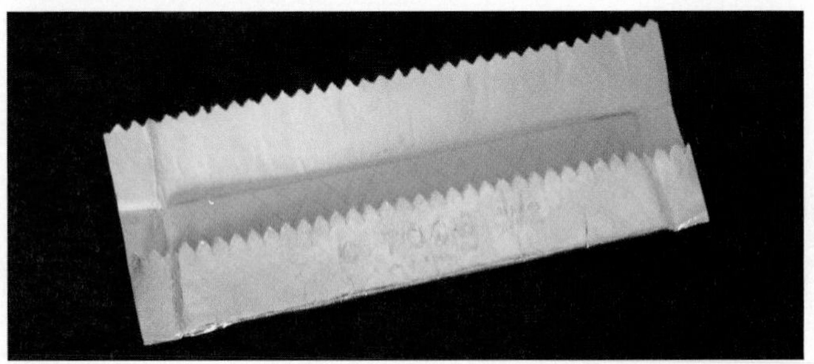

Hypothesis: Chewing gum after colon surgery will shorten hospital stays and the time for appetite and bowel function to return.

Experimental Plan: Recruit 34 patients scheduled for elective colon surgery. Randomly assign study participants to chew gum (experimental group) or not to chew gum (control group) after surgery. Beginning the morning after surgery, the gum-chewing group will chew sugarless gum (one stick) three times daily. For all participants, record the time of first flatus (passing gas), bowel movement, return of appetite, and length of hospital stay.

Results: The hypothesis is confirmed. Compared with control group patients, the gum-chewing patients were quicker to have an appetite, pass gas, have a bowel movement, and leave the hospital.

Conclusion and Discussion: Gum chewing early in the postoperative period following colon surgery hastens the time to bowel movement and first feeding. Gum chewing is an inexpensive and effective adjunct to postoperative care. Future studies may reveal the mechanism by which gum chewing activates cephalic response mechanisms and promotes bowel function.

Source: Data from Shuster R, Grewal N, Greaney GC, Waxman K. Gum chewing reduces ileus after elective open sigmoid colectomy. *Arch Surg.* 2006;141:174–176.

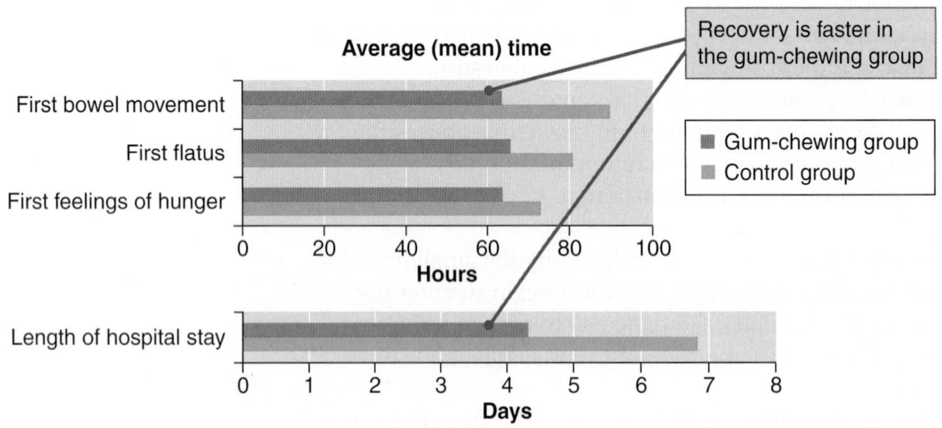

Does chewing gum after colon surgery shorten a hospital stay?

sorption. Side effects from abdominal surgery can slow or halt movement through the GI tract for hours or days. Researchers are investigating strategies for stimulating the release of hormones to improve postoperative GI movement and speed recovery. (See Nutrition Science in Action, "Gum Chewing After Surgery.")

Key Concepts *Both hormonal and nervous system signals regulate gastrointestinal activity. Nerve cells in both the enteric and autonomic nervous systems control muscle movement and secretory activity. Key hormones involved in regulation are gastrin, secretin, cholecystokinin, and gastric inhibitory peptide. The net effect of these regulators is to coordinate GI movement and secretion for optimal digestion and absorption of nutrients.*

Quick Bite

Short Bowel Syndrome

Patients who suffer from short bowel syndrome commonly have difficulty absorbing fat-soluble vitamins. To enhance absorption, treatment includes taking a fat-soluble vitamin supplement that easily mingles with water. These patients may also need to take intramuscular shots of B_{12} because they are unable to absorb this water-soluble vitamin.

Circulation of Nutrients

After foods are digested and nutrients are absorbed, they are transported via the vascular and lymphatic systems to specific destinations throughout the body. Let's take a closer look at how each of these circulatory systems delivers nutrients to the places they are needed.

Vascular System

The **vascular system** is a network of veins and arteries through which the blood carries nutrients (see **Figure 3.18**). The heart is the pump that keeps the blood circulating through the body. From intestinal cells, water-soluble nutrients are absorbed directly into tiny capillary tributaries of the bloodstream, where they travel to the liver before being dispersed throughout the body. Blood carries oxygen from the lungs and nutrients from the GI system to all body tissues. Once the destination cells have used the oxygen and nutrients, carbon dioxide and waste products are picked up by the blood and transported to the lungs and kidneys, respectively, for excretion.

Lymphatic System

The **lymphatic system** is a network of vessels that drain lymph, the clear fluid formed in the spaces between cells. Lymph moves through this system and eventually empties into the bloodstream near the neck. Lymph vessels in the small intestine absorb fat-soluble nutrients and most end products of fat digestion. After a fatty meal, lymph can become as much as 1 to 2 percent fat. Nutrients absorbed into the lymphatic system, unlike those absorbed directly into the vascular system, bypass the liver before entering the bloodstream. We'll discuss the specific process for absorption of lipids into the lymphatic system in Chapter 5, "Lipids."

Unlike the vascular system, the lymphatic system has no pumping organ. The major lymph vessels contain one-way valves; when the vessels are filled with lymph, smooth muscles in the vessel walls contract and pump the lymph forward. The succession of valves allows each segment of the vessel to act as an independent pump. Lymph also is moved along by skeletal muscle contractions that squeeze the vessels.

The lymphatic system also performs an important cleanup function. Proteins and large particulate matter in tissue spaces cannot be absorbed directly into the blood capillaries, but they easily enter the lymphatic system, where they are carried away for removal. This removal process is essential—without it a person would die within 24 hours from buildup of fluid and materials around the cells.[11]

vascular system A network of veins and arteries through which the blood carries nutrients. Also called the circulatory system.

lymphatic system A system of small vessels, ducts, valves, and organized tissue (e.g., lymph nodes) through which lymph moves from its origin in the tissues toward the heart.

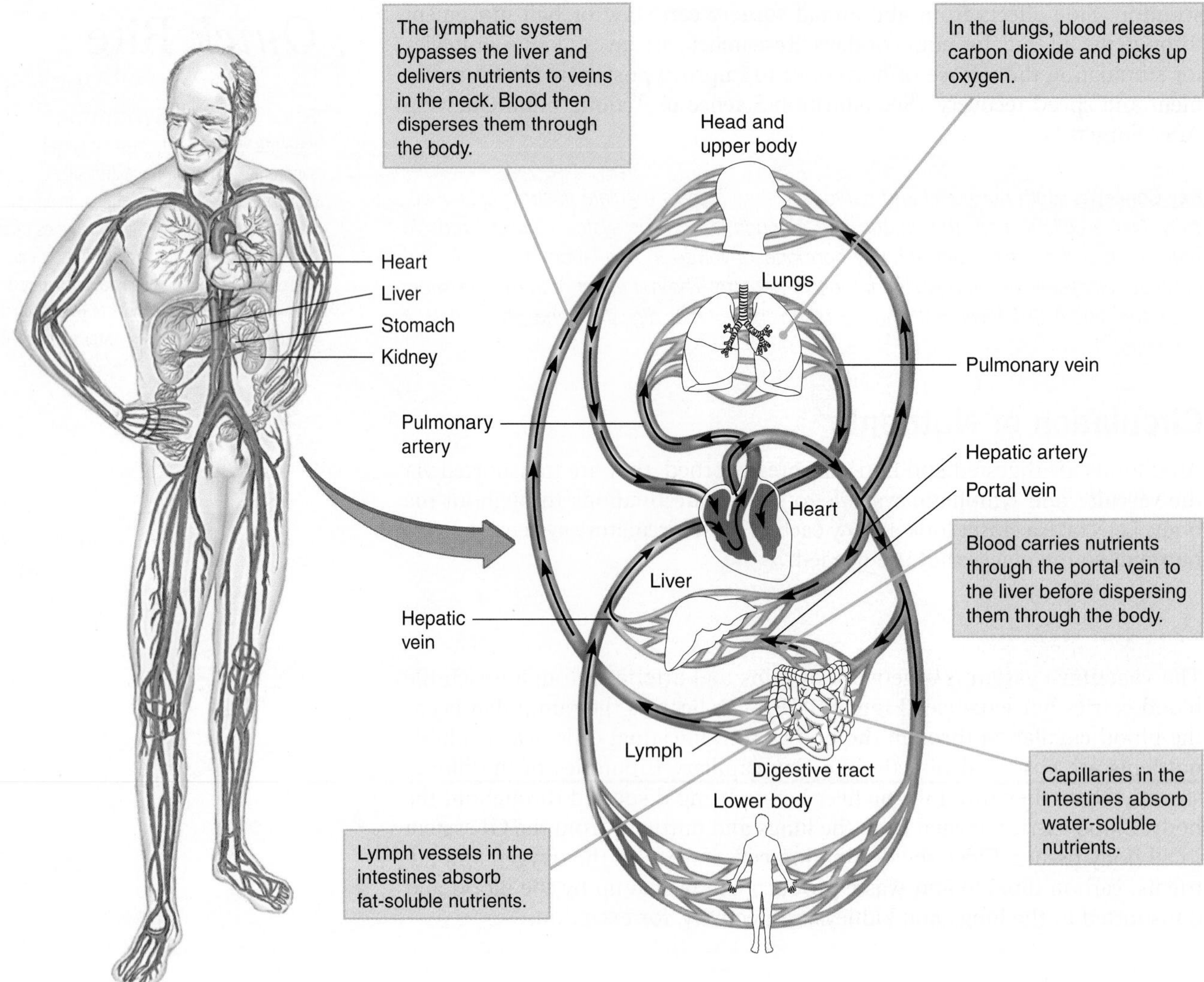
The lymphatic system bypasses the liver and delivers nutrients to veins in the neck. Blood then disperses them through the body.
In the lungs, blood releases carbon dioxide and picks up oxygen.
Head and upper body
Heart
Liver
Stomach
Kidney
Lungs
Pulmonary vein
Pulmonary artery
Hepatic artery
Portal vein
Heart
Blood carries nutrients through the portal vein to the liver before dispersing them through the body.
Liver
Hepatic vein
Lymph
Digestive tract
Lower body
Capillaries in the intestines absorb water-soluble nutrients.
Lymph vessels in the intestines absorb fat-soluble nutrients.

Figure 3.18 **Circulation.** Blood carries oxygen from the lungs and nutrients from the GI system to all body tissues. Intestinal cells absorb water-soluble nutrients and deliver them directly into tiny capillary tributaries of the bloodstream. From there, they travel to the liver before being dispersed throughout the body. Intestinal cells absorb fat-soluble nutrients and deliver most to the lymphatic system, a circulatory system that bypasses the liver before connecting to the bloodstream.

Key Concepts *Absorbed nutrients are carried by either the vascular or lymphatic system. Water-soluble nutrients are absorbed directly into the bloodstream, carried to the liver, and then distributed around the body. Fat-soluble vitamins and large lipid molecules are absorbed into the lymphatic vessels and carried by this system before entering the vascular system.*

Quick Bite

Gastrointestinal Flora Abound

Your entire body has about 100 trillion cells, but this is only one-tenth the number of protective microorganisms normally living in your body. More than 500 bacterial species live in your GI tract.

Influences on Digestion and Absorption

Psychological Influences

The taste, smell, and presentation of foods can have a positive effect on digestion. Just the thought of food can trigger saliva production and peristalsis. Stressful emotions such as depression and fear can have the reverse effect (see **Figure 3.19**): they stimulate the brain to activate the autonomic nervous system. This results in decreased gastric acid secretion, reduced blood flow to

THINK About It 4

the stomach, inhibition of peristalsis, and reduced propulsion of food.[12] The next time you sit down to a holiday meal, notice how you feel at the sight of your family's traditional foods as well as smells from your childhood. Happiness and positive memories add to the enjoyment of food, whereas sadness can bring on a poor appetite or stomach upset.

Chemical Influences

The type of protein you eat and the way it is prepared affect digestion. Plant proteins tend to be less digestible than animal proteins. Cooking food usually denatures protein (uncoils its three-dimensional structure), which increases digestibility. Cooking meat softens its connective tissue, making chewing easier and increasing the meat's accessibility to digestive enzymes.

Food processing produces chemicals that may influence digestive secretions. For example, frying foods in fat at very high temperatures produces small amounts of **acrolein**,[13] which decreases the flow of digestive secretions; in contrast, meat extracts may stimulate digestion. The physical condition of a food sometimes causes problems with digestion. Cold foods may cause intestinal spasms in people who suffer from irritable bowel syndrome or Crohn's disease. Stomach contents can affect absorption. When food is consumed on an empty stomach, it has more contact with gastric secretions and will be absorbed faster than if it were consumed on a full stomach. Certain medicines may inhibit nutrient absorption, and in turn, certain foods may interact with medicines, making the drugs less effective or toxic. (See Chapter 17, "Life Cycle: From Childhood Through Adulthood.")

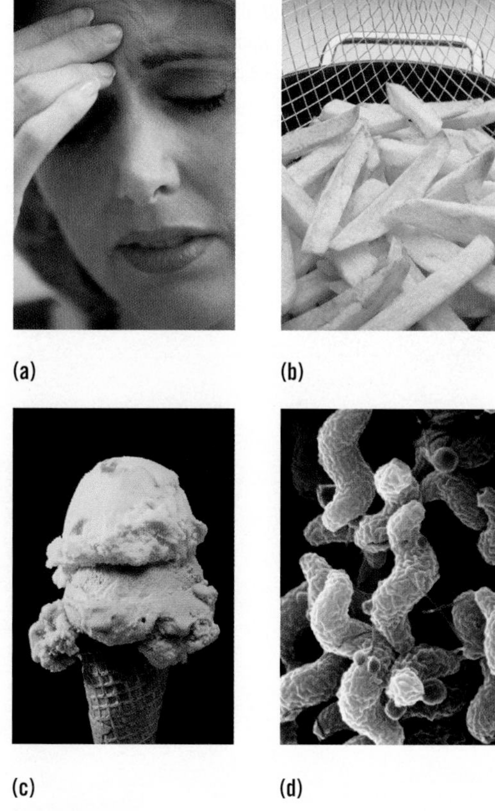

Figure 3.19 **Negative factors for digestion.** (a) Stress. (b) High-temperature fat frying. (c) Cold foods. (d) Bacteria.

Bacterial Influences

In the healthy stomach, hydrochloric acid kills most bacteria. In conditions where there is a lower concentration of hydrochloric acid, more bacteria can survive and multiply; harmful bacteria can cause gastritis (an inflammation of the stomach lining) and peptic ulcer (a wound in the mucous membranes lining the stomach or duodenum). Bacteria that cause foodborne illness resist the germicidal effects of hydrochloric acid, so they survive to wreak havoc on the digestive process.

The large intestine maintains a large population of bacteria. These bacteria can form several vitamins and digest small amounts of fiber, producing a small amount of energy. These bacteria also synthesize gases, such as hydrogen, ammonia, and methane, as well as acids and various substances that contribute to the odor of feces. If the digestion and absorption of food in the small intestine are incomplete, the undigested material enters the large intestine, where bacterial action produces excessive gas, and possibly bloating and pain.

acrolein A pungent decomposition product of fats, generated from dehydrating the glycerol components of fats; responsible for the coughing attacks caused by the fumes released by burning fat. This toxic water-soluble liquid vaporizes easily and is highly flammable.

Key Concepts *Psychological, chemical, and bacterial factors can influence the processes of digestion and absorption. Emotions can influence GI motility and secretion. The temperature and form of food can also affect digestive secretions. Although stomach acid kills many types of bacteria, some are resistant to acid and cause foodborne illness. Helpful bacteria in the large intestine can cause bloating and gas if they receive and begin to digest food components that are normally digested in the small intestine.*

Nutrition and GI Disorders

"I have butterflies in my stomach." "It was a gut-wrenching experience." Our language contains many references to the connection between emotional

Quick Bite

Halt! Who Goes There?
Be they friend or foe, antibiotics kill microorganisms in your GI tract, frequently causing diarrhea. About half of pharmaceutical drugs have gastrointestinal side effects.

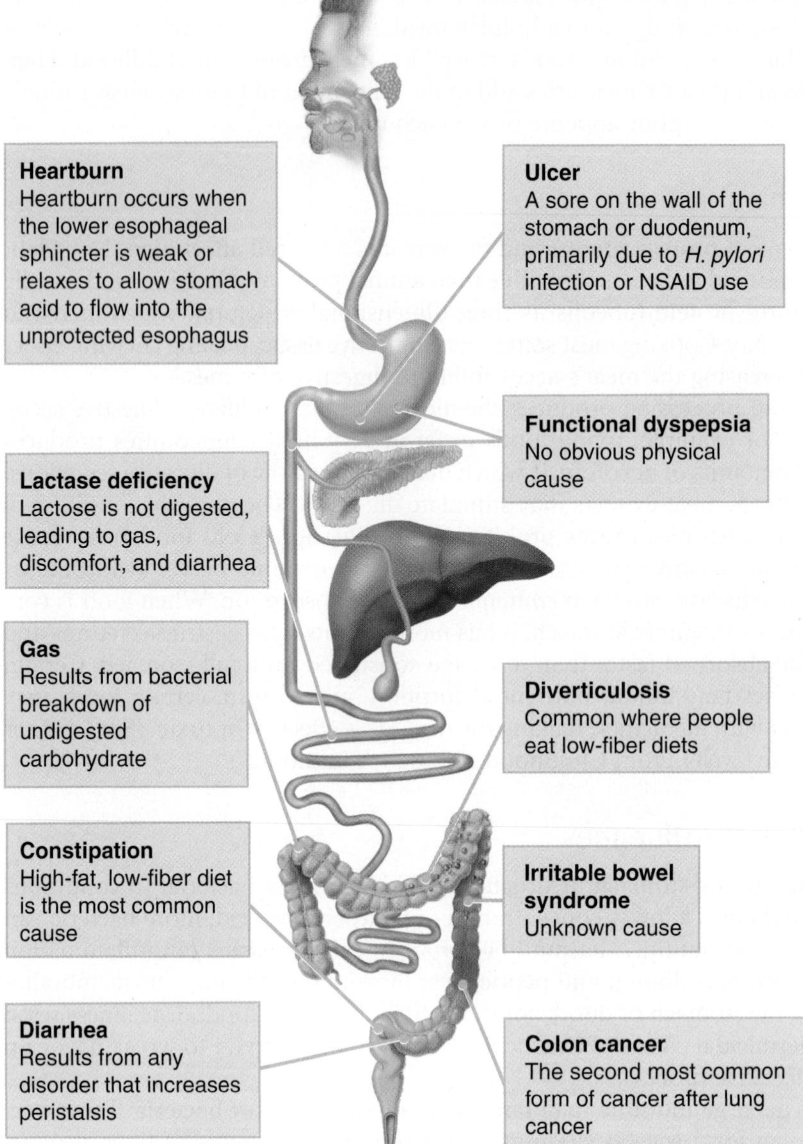
Heartburn
Heartburn occurs when the lower esophageal sphincter is weak or relaxes to allow stomach acid to flow into the unprotected esophagus
Ulcer
A sore on the wall of the stomach or duodenum, primarily due to H. pylori infection or NSAID use
Functional dyspepsia
No obvious physical cause
Lactase deficiency
Lactose is not digested, leading to gas, discomfort, and diarrhea
Gas
Results from bacterial breakdown of undigested carbohydrate
Diverticulosis
Common where people eat low-fiber diets
Constipation
High-fat, low-fiber diet is the most common cause
Irritable bowel syndrome
Unknown cause
Diarrhea
Results from any disorder that increases peristalsis
Colon cancer
The second most common form of cancer after lung cancer

Figure 3.20 **Common GI ailments.** Beans are familiar culprits in what is perhaps the most common GI ailment—gas. Rice is the only starch that does not cause gas.

distress and the GI tract. Most of us have experienced intestinal cramping right before a big date or job interview, or a queasy stomach in response to something very disgusting. The brain, through numerous neurochemical connections with the gut, exerts a profound influence on GI function. Nearly all GI disorders are influenced to some degree by emotional state. On the other hand, a number of illnesses that were once attributed largely to emotional stress, such as peptic ulcer disease, have been shown to be caused primarily by infection and other physical causes. **Figure 3.20** shows some common ailments that affect the GI tract.

Although stress management may help and medical intervention can be required, we can prevent and manage most GI disorders with diet. For instance, adding fiber-rich foods (see Table 3.2) and water to the diet reduces intestinal pressure, decreases the time food by-products remain in the colon, and promotes bowel regularity. You can avoid most problems and keep your

Table 3.2 **Fiber Content of Foods**

Food Group	Serving Size	Fiber (g)
Legumes		
Kidney beans	1 cup, cooked	11.3
Lentils	1 cup, cooked	15.6
Split peas	1 cup, cooked	16.3
Fruit		
Dried plums	½ cup	4.7
Apple with skin	1 small	2.5
Peach with skin	1 large	2.4
Vegetables		
Broccoli	1 cup, raw	2.4
Carrot	2 medium, raw	3.4
Tomato	1 large, raw	2.2
Grains		
Wheat-bran-flake cereal	1 ounce	4.9
Bulgur wheat	½ cup, cooked	4.1
Whole-wheat bread	1 slice	1.1
Brown rice	½ cup, cooked	1.8
Spaghetti, enriched white	½ cup, cooked	1.3
White bread	1 slice	0.6
White rice	½ cup, cooked	0.3

Source: Data from US Department of Agriculture, Agricultural Research Service. USDA National Nutrient Database for Standard Reference, Release 18. 2005. http://www.nal.usda.gov/fnic/foodcomp. Accessed 3/13/06.

GI tract operating at peak efficiency if you regularly eat a healthful diet, exercise, and maintain a healthy weight.

constipation Infrequent and difficult bowel movements, followed by a sensation of incomplete evacuation.

Constipation

Constipation is defined as having a bowel movement fewer than three times per week.[14] With constipation, stools are usually hard, dry, small in size, and difficult to eliminate. People who are constipated may find it painful to have a bowel movement and often experience straining, bloating, and the sensation of a full bowel.

Constipation is a symptom, not a disease. Almost everyone experiences constipation at some point, and a poor diet (low in fiber and water and high in fats) typically is the cause. Some fibers, such as the pectins in fruits and gums in beans, dissolve easily in water and take on a soft, gel-like texture in the intestines. Other fibers, such as the cellulose in wheat bran, pass almost unchanged through the intestines. The bulk and soft texture of fiber help prevent hard, dry stools that are difficult to pass. People who eat plenty of high-fiber foods are not likely to become constipated.

Liquids such as water and juice add fluid to the colon and bulk to stools, making bowel movements softer and easier to pass. The caffeine in many liquids (e.g., coffee, tea, and many soft drinks) is a mild diuretic (a substance that increases urine production).

Although treatment depends on the cause, severity, and duration, in most cases dietary changes help relieve symptoms and prevent constipation.

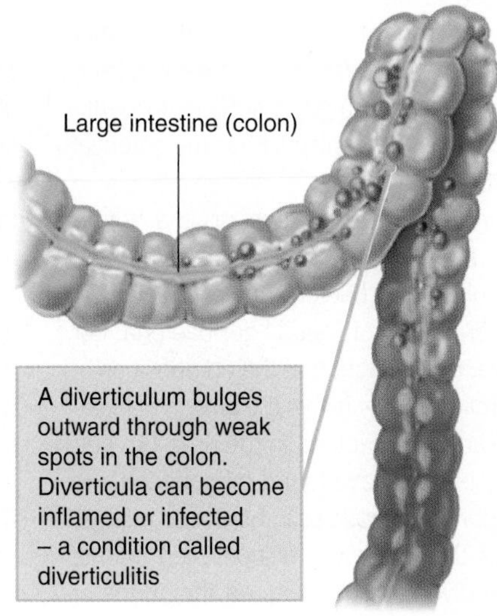
Large intestine (colon)
A diverticulum bulges outward through weak spots in the colon. Diverticula can become inflamed or infected – a condition called diverticulitis

diarrhea Watery stools due to reduced absorption of water.

Diarrhea

Diarrhea—loose, watery stools that occur more than three times in one day—is caused by digestive products moving through the large intestine too rapidly for sufficient water to be reabsorbed.

Diarrhea is a symptom of many disorders that cause increased peristalsis. Culprits include stress, intestinal irritation or damage, and intolerance to gluten, fat, or lactose. Eating food contaminated with bacteria or viruses often causes diarrhea when the digestive tract speeds the offending food along the alimentary canal and out of the body.

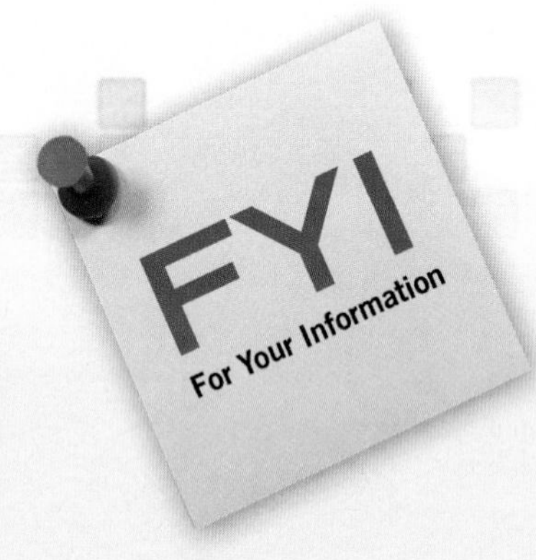

Bugs in Your Gut? Health Effects of Intestinal Bacteria

Unseen and unnoticed, millions and millions of bacteria call your GI tract home. Although we often associate bacteria with illness, the right kinds of bacteria in the gut actually protect us from disease. The normal microflora of the gut, specifically strains of lactobacilli and bifidobacteria, have been linked to improved digestion, intestinal regularity, enhanced GI immune function, improved lactose tolerance, reduced risk of developing allergies, and even reduced risk of colorectal cancer. So how can we be good hosts to our intestinal guests, keeping them well fed and happy? The answer may be in food products and dietary supplements known as probiotics and prebiotics.

Probiotics are foods (or supplements) that contain live microorganisms such as *Lactobacillus acidophilus*. Such lactic-acid-producing bacteria have been used for centuries to ferment milk into yogurt, cheeses, and other products. The bacteria convert lactose into lactic acid, which causes the milk to gel and imparts a tart flavor to the product. The resulting product has a much longer shelf life than fresh milk and is associated with good health and longevity in many societies. Other probiotics are *Bifidobacterium* organisms and yeast. When consumed in sufficient quantities, these microorganisms have the potential to improve health.

The term *prebiotic* describes a nondigestible food product that can be fermented by gastrointestinal bacteria and stimulates the growth or activity of "good" gut bacteria. For example, it is thought that the composition of breast milk strongly favors the growth of lactobacilli and bifidobacteria in the newborn gut. Some scientists have found bifidobacteria to be the dominant species in breastfed infants, whereas the microflora of bottle-fed infants is more diverse. The reduced incidence of GI infections in breastfed infants has been attributed to the dominance of bifidobacteria. Substances that may be effective prebiotics include fructooligosaccharides, polydextrose, arabinogalactan, polyols, and inulin.

So how does feeding the bacteria in your gut improve your health? Successful colonization of helpful bacteria allows them to outnumber (and outeat) disease-causing bacteria, thus reducing the likelihood of foodborne illness and other infections. Studies in young children show that supplementation with *Lactobacillus* reduced the severity and duration of diarrhea due to rotavirus, a common infectious agent in daycare centers. Some probiotics enhance the ability of the gut as a barrier to infectious agents and may also adjust the activity of the immune system.

"Good" bacteria can digest the lactose that enters the colon of a person with lactose intolerance, reducing symptoms and discomfort. Intestinal bacteria metabolize both indigestible and incompletely digested food material. Probiotics may produce by-products that reduce disease risk. For example, acids produced by probiotic colon bacteria change the pH of the colon, which may interfere with carcinogenesis (development of cancer).

In addition to promoting the growth and function of beneficial bacteria, prebiotics may have other health effects. Some prebiotics have been shown to enhance absorption of calcium and magnesium. Others may inhibit growth of lesions in the gut, which in turn reduces colorectal cancer risk. Although lipid-lowering effects have been attributed to prebiotics, the limited data available show inconsistent effects on cholesterol and triglycerides.

Fermented milk products such as yogurt or kefir are one way to keep your gut happy. Look for a seal adopted by the National Yogurt Association to identify products that contain a minimum of 100 million live lactic acid bacteria per gram of yogurt. Not all brands of yogurt contain live, active cultures. Supplemental probiotics must have sufficient numbers of live bacteria to be useful; currently, identification and standardization procedures are lacking. Prebiotics are found in whole grains, onions, bananas, garlic, artichokes, and a variety of fortified foods, beverages, and dietary supplements. Although results are preliminary, food and supplement sources of probiotics and prebiotics may be another useful way to improve gut microflora and overall health.

Diarrhea can cause dehydration, which means the body lacks enough fluid to function properly. Dehydration is particularly dangerous in children and the elderly, and it must be treated promptly to avoid serious health problems.

A diet of broth, tea, and toast and avoidance of lactose, caffeine, and sorbitol can reduce diarrhea until it subsides. As stools form, you can gradually introduce more foods. Pectin, a form of dietary fiber found in apples and citrus peel, may be helpful. Also, include foods high in potassium, if tolerated, to replace lost electrolytes. Fluid replacement is also important to avoid dehydration.

Diverticulosis

Like an inner tube that pokes through weak places in an old tire, the colon develops small pouches that bulge outward through weak spots as people age. Known as diverticulosis, this condition afflicts about half of all Americans aged 60 to 80, and almost everyone over age 80. Although it usually causes few problems, in 10 to 25 percent of these people the pouches become infected or inflamed—a condition called diverticulitis.

Diverticulosis and diverticulitis are common in developed or industrialized countries—particularly the United States, England, and Australia—where low-fiber diets are common. Diverticular disease is rare in Asian and African countries, where people eat high-fiber, vegetable-based diets.

A low-fiber diet can make stools hard and difficult to pass. If the stool is too hard, muscles must strain to move it. This is the main cause of increased pressure in the colon, which causes weak spots to bulge outward.

Increasing the amount of fiber in the diet may reduce symptoms of diverticulosis and prevent complications such as diverticulitis. Fiber keeps stools soft and lowers pressure inside the colon so bowel contents can move through easily. Additional benefits of fiber are listed in Table 3.3.

Until recently, many doctors suggested avoiding foods with small seeds, such as tomatoes or strawberries, because they believed that particles could lodge in the diverticula and cause inflammation. However, this is now a controversial hypothesis, and no evidence supports this recommendation.

If cramps, bloating, and constipation are problems, a doctor may prescribe a short course of pain medication. However, many medications cause either diarrhea or constipation, undesirable side effects for people with diverticulosis.

Heartburn and Gastroesophageal Reflux

Heartburn occurs when the lower esophageal sphincter (LES) relaxes inappropriately, allowing the stomach's contents to flow back into the esophagus. Unlike the stomach, the esophagus has no protective mucous lining, so acid can damage it quickly and cause pain. Many people experience occasional heartburn, but for some, heartburn is a chronic, often daily, event and a symptom of a more serious disorder called **gastroesophageal reflux disease (GERD)**. GERD, along with obesity, is a key risk factor for esophageal cancer, a type of cancer that is on the rise in North America.[15] GERD has a variety of causes, and many treatment strategies involve lifestyle and nutrition.

Doctors recommend avoiding foods and beverages that can weaken the LES, including chocolate, peppermint, fatty foods, coffee, and alcoholic beverages. Foods and beverages that can irritate a damaged esophageal lining, such as citrus fruits and juices, tomato products, and pepper, also should be avoided.

Table 3.3 Benefits of Fiber

1. Helps control weight by delaying gastric emptying and providing a feeling of fullness.
2. Improves glucose tolerance by delaying the movement of carbohydrate into the small intestine.
3. Reduces risk for heart disease by binding with bile (which contains cholesterol) in the intestine and causing it to be excreted, which in turn helps to lower blood cholesterol levels.
4. Promotes regularity and reduces constipation by increasing stool weight and decreasing transit time.
5. Reduces the risk of diverticulosis by decreasing pressure within the colon, decreasing transit time, and increasing stool weight.

Source: Modified from Institute of Medicine, Food and Nutrition Board. *Dietary Reference Intakes for Energy, Carbohydrate, Fiber, Fat, Fatty Acids, Cholesterol, Protein, and Amino Acids.* Washington, DC: National Academies Press. Copyright © 2002, National Academy of Sciences.

gastroesophageal reflux disease (GERD) A condition in which gastric contents move backward (reflux) into the esophagus, causing pain and tissue damage.

Decreasing both the portion size and the fat content of meals may help. High-fat meals remain in the stomach longer than low-fat meals. This creates back pressure on the lower esophageal sphincter. Eating meals at least two to three hours before bedtime may lessen reflux by allowing partial emptying and a decrease in stomach acidity. Elevating the head of the bed or sleeping on a specially designed wedge reduces heartburn by allowing gravity to minimize reflux of stomach contents into the esophagus.

In addition, cigarette smoking weakens the LES, and being overweight often worsens symptoms. Stopping smoking is important, and many overweight people find relief when they lose weight.

Irritable Bowel Syndrome

irritable bowel syndrome (IBS) A disruptive state of intestinal motility with no known cause. Symptoms include constipation, abdominal pain, and episodic diarrhea.

About 20 percent of people in Western countries suffer from **irritable bowel syndrome (IBS)**, a poorly understood condition that causes abdominal pain, altered bowel habits (such as diarrhea or constipation), and cramps.[16] Often IBS is just a mild annoyance, but for some people it can be disabling.

The cause of IBS remains a mystery, but emotional stress and specific foods clearly aggravate the symptoms in most sufferers.[17] Beans, chocolate, milk products, and large amounts of alcohol are frequent offenders. Fat in any form (animal or vegetable) is a strong stimulus of colonic contractions after a meal. Caffeine causes loose stools in many people, but it is more likely to affect those with IBS. Women with IBS may have more symptoms during their menstrual periods, suggesting that reproductive hormones can increase IBS symptoms.

The good news about IBS is that although its symptoms can be uncomfortable, it does not shorten life span or progress to more serious illness. IBS

As you've learned in this chapter, fiber is one of the few things you do not digest fully. Instead, fiber moves through the GI tract and most of it leaves the body in feces. If it's not digested, then why all the fuss about eating more fiber? You'll learn later in this textbook (in the carbohydrates chapter) that a healthy intake of fiber may lower your risk of cancer and heart disease and help with bowel regularity. So how do you know which foods have fiber? You have to check out the food label!

This Nutrition Facts panel is from the label on a loaf of whole-wheat bread. The highlighted sections show you that every slice of bread contains 3 grams of fiber. The 12% listed to the right of that refers to the Daily Values below. Look at the Daily Values at the far right of the label, and note that there are two numbers listed for fiber. One (25 g) is for a person who consumes about 2,000 kilocalories per day, and the other (30 g) is for a 2,500-kilocalorie level. It should be no surprise that if you are consuming more calories, you should also be consuming more fiber. The 12% Daily Value is calculated using the 2,000-kilocalorie fiber guideline as follows:

$$\frac{\textbf{3 grams fiber per slice}}{\textbf{25 grams Daily Value}} = \textbf{0.12, or 12\%}$$

This means if you make a sandwich with two slices of whole-wheat bread, you're getting 6 grams of fiber and almost one-quarter (24% Daily Value) of your fiber needs per day. Not bad! Be careful, though; many people inadvertently buy wheat bread thinking that it's as high in fiber as *whole-wheat* bread, but it's not. Whole-wheat bread contains the whole (complete) grain, but wheat bread often is stripped of its fiber. Check the label before you buy your next loaf.

can usually be controlled with diet and lifestyle modifications and judicious use of medication. Stress management is an important part of treatment for IBS and includes stress reduction (relaxation) training and relaxation therapies, such as meditation; counseling and support; regular exercise; changes to stressful situations in your life; and adequate sleep.[18]

Many researchers are convinced that IBS sufferers have abnormal patterns of intestinal motility, but studies show no consistent differences in the GI motion patterns of IBS patients compared with normal control subjects. Some researchers have postulated that IBS sufferers may be hypersensitive to GI stimuli, but, again, research results are inconclusive. We are a long way from understanding what causes IBS, but it is likely that a number of physical and psychosocial factors combine to trigger this disorder.

Colorectal Cancer

After lung cancer, colorectal cancer—cancer of the colon or rectum—is the second leading cause of cancer-related deaths in the United States.[19] According to the World Health Organization, "Review of the relationships between diet and colorectal cancer suggests that risk is increased by high intakes of meat and fat, and decreased by high intakes of fruit, vegetables, folate, and calcium. Overweight and obesity increase risk while regular physical activity reduces risk."[20] A study of nearly 149,000 American adults found that those who ate the most red meat and processed meat had a 30 to 40 percent higher risk of developing colorectal cancer.[21]

Observational and case control studies support the idea that fiber-rich diets reduce colorectal cancer risk, and scientists have hypothesized a number of possible ways that fiber might be protective.[22] These include dilution of

Nutrition Facts

Serving Size: 1 slice (43g)
Servings Per Container: 16

Calories 100
Calories from Fat 15

Amount Per Serving	% Daily Value*
Total Fat 2g	**3%**
Saturated Fat 0g	**0%**
Trans Fat 0g	
Cholesterol 0mg	**0%**
Sodium 230mg	**9%**
Total Carbohydrate 18g	**6%**
Dietary Fibers 3g	**12%**
Sugars 2g	
Protein 5g	

Vitamin A 0% · Vitamin C 0% · Calcium 6% · Iron 6%
Thiamin 10% · Riboflavin 4% · Niacin 10% · Folate 10%

* Percent Daily Values are based on a 2,000 calorie diet. Your daily values may be higher or lower depending on your calorie needs:

	Calories:	2,000	2,500
Total Fat	Less Than	65g	80g
Sat Fat	Less Than	20g	25g
Cholesterol	Less Than	300mg	300mg
Sodium	Less Than	2,400mg	2,400mg
Total Carbohydrate		300g	375g
Dietary Fiber		25g	30g

INGREDIENTS: STONE GROUND WHOLE WHEAT FLOUR, WATER, HIGH FRUCTOSE CORN SYRUP, WHEAT GLUTEN, WHEAT BRAN. CONTAINS 2% OR LESS OF EACH OF THE FOLLOWING: YEAST, SALT, PARTIALLY HYDROGENATED SOYBEAN OIL, HONEY, MOLASSES, RAISIN JUICE CONCENTRATE, DOUGH CONDITIONERS (MAY CONTAIN ONE OR MORE OF EACH OF THE FOLLOWING: MONO- AND DIGLYCERIDES, CALCIUM AND SODIUM STEAROYL LACTYLATES, CALCIUM PEROXIDE), WHEAT GERM, WHEY, CORNSTARCH, YEAST NUTRIENTS (MONOCALCIUM PHOSPHATE, CALCIUM SULFATE, AMMONIUM SULFATE).

carcinogens in a bulkier stool, more rapid transit of carcinogens through the GI tract, and lower colon pH due to bacterial fermentation of fiber.

Although there are logical reasons why a high fiber intake may be beneficial, studies in humans and animals fail to support these theories. Fiber has not been shown to reduce risk of colorectal cancer[23] or to prevent recurrence of the colorectal polyps that are precursors to many cancers.[24]

Quick Bite

Flatulence Facts

Researchers studying pilots and astronauts during the 1960s made some interesting discoveries. The average person inadvertently swallows air with food and drink, and subsequently expels approximately one pint of gas per day, composed of 50 percent nitrogen. Another 40 percent is composed of carbon dioxide and the products of aerobic bacteria in the intestine.

Gas

Everyone has gas and eliminates it by burping or passing it through the rectum. Gas is made primarily of odorless vapors. The unpleasant odor of flatulence comes from bacteria in the large intestine that release small amounts of gases that contain sulfur. Although having gas is common, it can be uncomfortable and embarrassing.

Gas in the stomach is commonly caused by swallowing air. Everyone swallows small amounts of air when they eat and drink. However, eating or drinking rapidly, chewing gum, smoking, or wearing loose dentures can cause some people to take in more air. Burping, or belching, is the way most swallowed air leaves the stomach. The remaining gas moves into the small intestine, where it is partially absorbed. A small amount travels into the large intestine for release through the rectum. (The stomach also releases carbon dioxide when stomach acid and bicarbonate mix, but most of this gas is absorbed into the bloodstream and does not enter the large intestine.)

Frequent passage of rectal gas may be annoying, but it's seldom a symptom of serious disease. **Flatus** (lower intestinal gas) composition depends largely on dietary carbohydrate intake and the activity of the colon's bacterial population.

flatus Lower intestinal gas that is expelled through the rectum.

ulcer A craterlike lesion that occurs in the lining of the stomach or duodenum; also called a peptic ulcer to distinguish it from a skin ulcer.

Most foods that contain carbohydrates can cause gas. By contrast, fats and proteins cause little gas. In the large intestine, bacteria partially break down undigested carbohydrate, producing hydrogen, carbon dioxide, and, in about one-third of people, methane. Eventually these gases exit through the rectum.

Foods that produce gas in one person may not cause gas in another. Some common bacteria in the large intestine can destroy the hydrogen that other bacteria produce. The balance of the two types of bacteria may explain why some people have more gas than others.

Carbohydrates that commonly cause gas are raffinose and stachyose, found in large quantities in beans; lactose, the natural sugar in milk; fructose, a common sweetener in soft drinks and fruit drinks; and sorbitol, found naturally in fruits and used as an artificial sweetener.

Most starches, including potatoes, corn, noodles, and wheat, produce gas as they are broken down in the large intestine. Rice is the only starch that does not cause gas.

The fiber in oat bran, beans, peas, and most fruits is not broken down until it reaches the large intestine, where digestion causes gas. In contrast, the fiber in wheat bran and some vegetables passes essentially unchanged through the intestines and produces little gas.

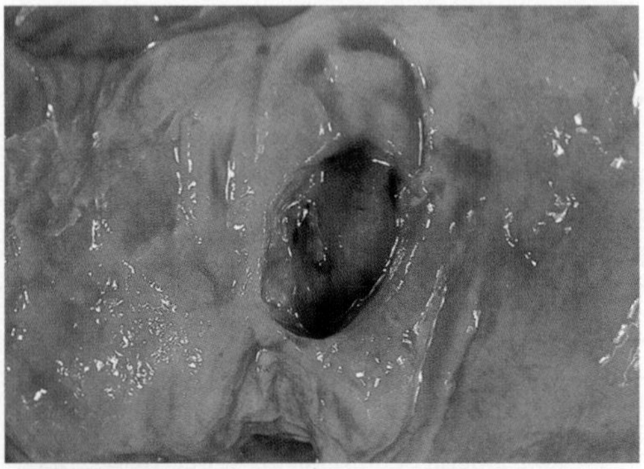

Ulcers

A gnawing, burning pain in the upper abdomen is the classic sign of a peptic ulcer, which also can cause nausea, vomiting, loss of appetite, and weight loss. A peptic **ulcer** is a sore that forms in the duodenum (duodenal ulcer) or the lining of the stomach (gastric ulcer) (see **Figure 3.21**).

Figure 3.21 Stomach ulcer.

It was once assumed that stress was a major factor in the development of peptic ulcer disease, particularly in people with "intense" personalities. Diet was also thought to be important, with spicy foods often cast as a major villain. But much to the amazement of most of the medical community, research over the last 10 years has confirmed that the vast majority of ulcers are actually caused by infection with a bacterium, *Helicobacter pylori* (see **Figure 3.22**). Excessive use of nonsteroidal anti-inflammatory drugs (NSAIDs), such as aspirin, ibuprofen, and naproxen sodium, is also a common cause of ulcers.

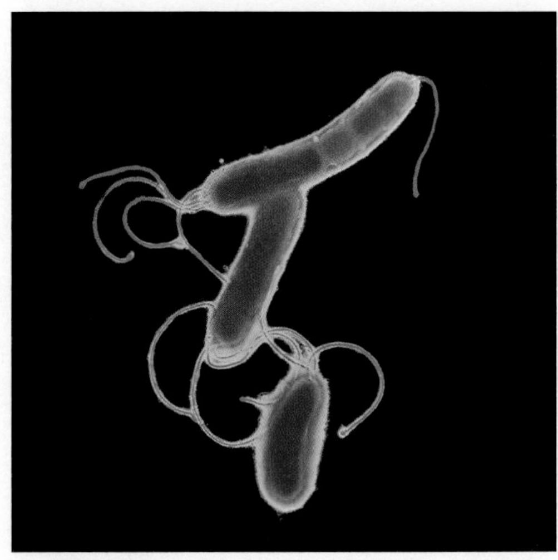

Figure 3.22 ***Helicobacter pylori.***

H. pylori causes 80 percent of gastric ulcers and more than 90 percent of duodenal ulcers. These bacteria weaken the protective mucous coating, allowing acid to penetrate to the sensitive lining beneath. Both the acid and the bacteria irritate the lining and cause a sore, or ulcer. *H. pylori* is able to survive in stomach acid because it secretes enzymes that neutralize the acid. This mechanism allows *H. pylori* to make its way to the "safe" area—the protective mucous lining. Once there, the bacterium's spiral shape helps it burrow through the mucous lining.[25]

NSAIDs cause ulcers by interfering with the GI tract's ability to protect itself from acidic stomach juices. Normally the stomach and duodenum employ three defenses against digestive juices: mucus that coats the lining and shields it from stomach acid; the chemical bicarbonate, which neutralizes acid; and blood circulation, which aids in cell renewal and repair. NSAIDs hinder all these protective mechanisms. With the defenses down, digestive juices can cause ulcers by damaging the sensitive lining of the stomach and duodenum. Fortunately, NSAID-induced ulcers usually heal once the person stops taking the medication.

If you had ulcers in the 1950s, you would have been told to quit your high-stress job and switch to a bland diet. Today, ulcer sufferers are usually treated with an antimicrobial regimen aimed at eradicating *H. pylori*.[26] Although personality and life stress are no longer considered significant factors in the development of most ulcers, relapse after treatment is more common in people who are emotionally stressed or suffering from depression.

Functional Dyspepsia

Chronic pain in the upper abdomen not due to any obvious physical cause (such as inflammation of the esophagus, peptic ulcer, or gallstones) is referred to as **functional dyspepsia**. Like IBS, the cause of functional dyspepsia is unknown. Hypersensitivity to GI stimuli, abnormal GI motility, and psychosocial problems have all been postulated as causes of dyspepsia.[27] *H. pylori* may also be a factor in some cases of functional dyspepsia.

functional dyspepsia Chronic pain in the upper abdomen not due to any obvious physical cause.

The treatment of functional dyspepsia includes drugs that speed up the transit of food through the upper part of the intestinal tract, agents that decrease stomach acid production, and antibiotics. Just as with IBS, stress reduction techniques such as meditation and biofeedback can often improve the symptoms of functional dyspepsia.

Key Concepts *GI disorders generally produce uncomfortable symptoms such as abdominal pain, gas, bloating, and change in elimination patterns. Some GI disorders, such as diarrhea, are generally symptoms of some other illness. Although medications are useful in reducing symptoms, many GI disorders are treatable with changes in diet, especially getting adequate fiber and fluids in the diet.*

Figure 3.23 **Fate of a piece of pizza.** When you eat a piece of pizza, what happens to the carbohydrate, fat, and protein?

Carbohydrate. Enzymes in the mouth begin the breakdown of starch. Stomach acid halts carbohydrate digestion. In the small intestine, enzymes break down carbohydrate, which is absorbed into the blood. In the large intestine, bacteria digest small amounts of fiber. The remainder is eliminated in feces.

Fat. The stomach absorbs a few short-chain fatty acids into the blood. But most fat is broken down and absorbed in the small intestine, where it enters the lymphatic system.

Protein. Stomach acid unfolds proteins, and enzymes begin protein breakdown. The small intestine completes the breakdown to amino acids, which enter the blood.

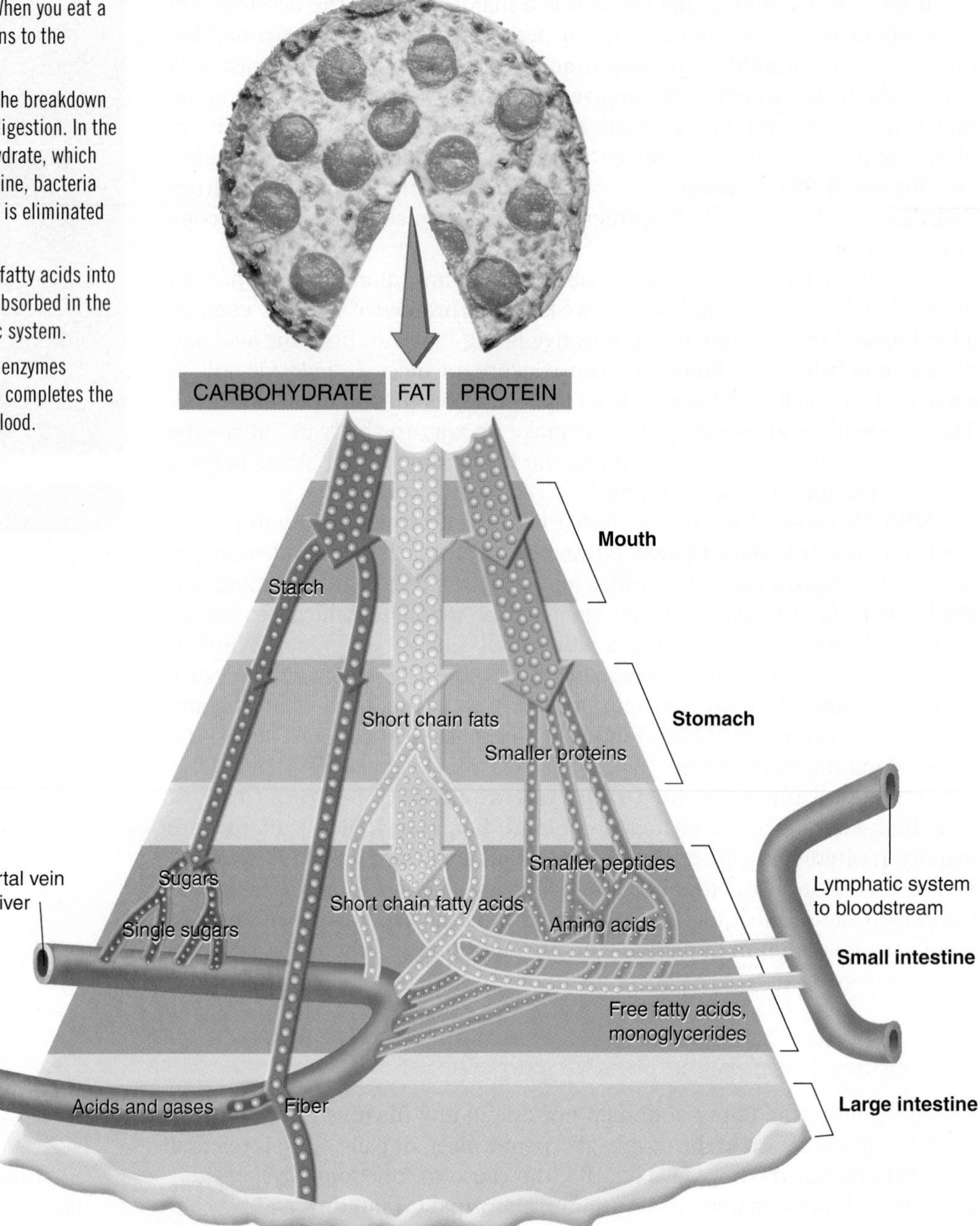

As you have seen, the gastrointestinal tract is the key to turning food and its nutrients into nourishment for our bodies. **Figure 3.23** shows the sites for digestion and absorption of the macronutrients using a piece of pizza as an example of a food that contains substantial amounts of carbohydrate, fat, and protein. A healthy GI tract is an important factor in our overall health and well-being.

Learning Portfolio

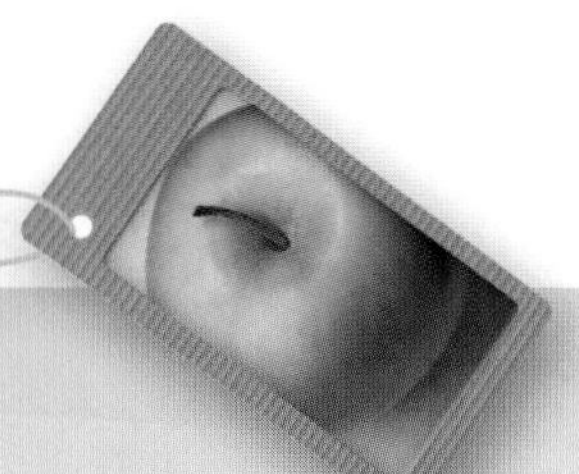

Key Terms

	page
absorption	106
acrolein	131
active transport	115
amylase [AM-ih-lace]	117
autonomic nervous system	126
bile	116
bolus [BOH-lus]	117
catalyze	111
cecum	124
central nervous system (CNS)	126
cephalic phase responses	107
chemosenses [key-mo-SEN-sez]	106
cholecystokinin (CCK) [ko-la-sis-toe-KY-nin]	116
chyme [KIME]	110
circular muscle	108
colon	124
common chemical sense	106
concentration gradients	112
constipation	133
diarrhea	134
digestion	106
digestive secretions	119
duodenum [doo-oh-DEE-num, or doo-AH-den-um]	119
emulsifiers	115
endocytosis	115
enteric nervous system	126
enterohepatic circulation [EN-ter-oh-heh-PAT-ik]	116
enzymes [EN-zimes]	111
esophageal sphincter	117
esophagus [ee-SOFF-uh-gus]	117
facilitated diffusion	115
flatus	138
functional dyspepsia	139
gallbladder	116
gastric inhibitory peptide (GIP) [GAS-trik in-HIB-ihtor-ee PEP-tide]	127
gastric lipase	119
gastrin [GAS-trin]	119
gastroesophageal reflux disease (GERD)	135
gastrointestinal (GI) tract [GAS-troh-in-TES-tin-al]	108
gustatory cells	106
hydrochloric acid	118
hydrolysis	111
ileocecal valve	124
ileum [ILL-ee-um]	119
intrinsic factor	119
irritable bowel syndrome (IBS)	136
jejunum [je-JOON-um]	119
lacteal	124
large intestine	124
lingual lipase	117
liver	116
longitudinal muscle	108
lumen	112
lymph	124
lymphatic system	129
microvilli	124
mucosa [myu-KO-sa]	108
mucus	118
olfactory cells	106
pancreas	117
passive diffusion	112
pepsin	118
pepsinogen	118
peristalsis [per-ih-STAHL-sis]	110
pH	118
phagocytosis	115
pinocytosis	115
pyloric sphincter [pie-LORE-ic]	119
rectum	126
salivary glands	115
secretin [see-CREET-in]	119
segmentation	110
serosa	108
small intestine	119
sphincters [SFINGK-ters]	108
stomach	117
submucosa	108
ulcer	138
vascular system	129
villi	124

Study Points

- The GI tract is a tube that can be divided into regions: the mouth, esophagus, stomach, small intestine, large intestine, and rectum.
- Digestion and absorption of the nutrients in foods occur at various sites along the GI tract.
- Digestion involves both physical processes (e.g., chewing, peristalsis, and segmentation) and chemical processes (e.g., the hydrolytic action of enzymes).
- Absorption is the movement of molecules across the lining of the GI tract and into circulation.
- Four mechanisms are involved in nutrient absorption: passive diffusion, facilitated diffusion, active transport, and endocytosis.
- In the mouth, food is mixed with saliva for lubrication. Salivary amylase begins the digestion of starch.
- Secretions from the stomach lower the pH of stomach contents and begin the digestion of proteins.
- The pancreas and gallbladder secrete material into the small intestine to help with digestion.
- Most chemical digestion and nutrient absorption occur in the small intestine.
- Electrolytes and water are absorbed from the large intestine. Remaining material, waste, is excreted as feces.
- Both the nervous system and the hormonal system regulate GI tract processes.
- Numerous factors affect GI tract functioning, including psychological, chemical, and bacterial factors.
- Problems that occur along the GI tract can affect digestion and absorption of nutrients. Dietary changes are important in the treatment of GI disorders.

Study Questions

1. The contents of which organ has the lowest pH? Which organ produces an alkaline or basic solution to buffer this low pH?
2. Where in the GI tract does the majority of nutrient digestion and absorption take place?

3. Describe the path food follows as it travels through the digestive system. Summarize the muscular actions that take place along the way.
4. Name three "assisting" organs that are not part of the GI tract but are needed for proper digestion. What are their roles in digestion?
5. List the four major hormones involved in regulating digestion and absorption. What are their roles?
6. What is gastroesophageal reflux disease?

Try This

The Saltine Cracker Experiment

This experiment will help you understand the effect of salivary amylase. Remember, salivary amylase is the starch-digesting enzyme produced by the salivary glands. Chew two saltine crackers until a watery texture forms in your mouth. You have to fight the urge to swallow so you can pay attention to the taste of the crackers. Do you notice a change in the taste?

The crackers first taste salty and "starchy," but as amylase is secreted it begins to break the chains of starch into sugar. As it does this, the saltines begin to taste sweet like animal crackers!

What About Bobbie?

Because both fluid and fiber are important for a healthy gastrointestinal tract, let's check out Bobbie's intake of these. Refresh your memory regarding her day of eating (see Chapter 1). How do you think Bobbie did in terms of fiber? She did pretty well! At 25 grams of fiber, she's right at the Adequate Intake (AI) for fiber for women for her age—25 grams per day. Here are her best fiber sources:

Food	Fiber Grams
Spaghetti (pasta)	3.5
Tortilla chips	3
Banana	3
Salsa	2
Sourdough bread	2

Are you surprised by the tortilla chips and the amount of fiber they add? Don't misinterpret this to mean that tortilla chips are a great source of fiber. There are two reasons why the chips rank so high. First, the other grain choices were not whole wheat and therefore didn't contribute a lot of fiber. Second, her afternoon snack consisted of just over 200 calories of tortilla chips.

What could Bobbie have done differently if she wanted to keep her fiber intake high, but reduce calories and fat by avoiding the tortilla chips? Here are a few small changes that she could make:

- By choosing a whole-wheat bagel, she'd add 4 grams of fiber.
- By having her sandwich on whole-wheat bread, she'd add at least 3 grams of fiber.
- By substituting the 2 tablespoons of croutons with 2 more tablespoons of kidney beans, she'd add 1.5 grams of fiber.
- If she ate another piece of fruit as a snack sometime in her day, it would add 1 to 3 grams of fiber.

Now let's look at Bobbie's fluid intake. Remember, when you increase your fiber, it is critical to increase your fluid intake so you don't become constipated. Here's a list of Bobbie's drinks:

Breakfast—10 ounces coffee
Snack—none
Lunch—12 ounces diet soda
Snack—16 ounces water
Dinner—12 ounces diet soda
Snack—none

How do you think she did? Her total fluid intake is 50 ounces (1,500 milliliters). Her food also contains fluids and contributes another 1,000 milliliters. The AI for total fluid intake for adult women is 2,700 milliliters per day. If Bobbie's intake is assumed to be about 2,500 milliliters, this is close to the AI. She could add another beverage with one or both of her snacks and be right on target. She also could improve her fluid choices, since most contain caffeine, which is a mild diuretic.

What suggestions do you have that will improve Bobbie's fluid intake? Any of the following would work:

- Carry a water bottle to sip throughout the day.
- Wash down the morning banana snack with a cup or two of water.
- Consider decaffeinated coffee or decaffeinated soda.
- Drink more water with the tortilla chips in the afternoon.
- Add a fluid to dinner.
- Drink water with the piece of pizza at night.

References

1 Gilbertson TA, Fontenot DT, Lui L, et al. Fatty acid modulation of K+ channels in taste receptor cells: gustatory cues for dietary fat. *Am J Physiol.* 1997;272:(4 pt 1):C1203–1210.

2 Mattes RD. Physiologic responses to sensory stimulation by food: nutritional implications. *J Am Diet Assoc.* 1997;97:406–410.

3 Klein S, Cohn SM, Alpers DH. Alimentary tract in nutrition. In: Shils ME, Shike M, Ross AC, et al., eds. *Modern Nutrition in Health and Disease*. 10th ed. Philadelphia: Lippincott Williams & Wilkins, 2006:1115–1142.

4 Caspary WF. Physiology and pathophysiology of intestinal absorption. *Am J Clin Nutr.* 1992;55:299S–307S; and Yamada T, Alpers DH. *Textbook of Gastroenterology*. New York: JB Lippincott, 1995.

5 Guyton AC, Hall JE. *Textbook of Medical Physiology*. 11th ed. Philadelphia: WB Saunders, 2006.

6 Ibid.

7 Klein, Cohn, Alpers. Alimentary tract in nutrition.

8 Scheppach W, Luehrs H, Menzel T. Beneficial health effects of low-digestible carbohydrate consumption. *Br J Nutr.* 2001;85(suppl 1):S23–S30.

9 Guyton, Hall. *Textbook of Medical Physiology*.

10 Ibid.

11 Ibid.

12 Mahan LK, Escott-Stump S. *Krause's Food Nutrition and Diet Therapy*. 12th ed. Philadelphia: WB Saunders, 2008.

13 US Department of Health and Human Services, Agency for Toxic Substances and Disease Registry. *Toxicological Profile for Acrolein (Updated)*. Atlanta, GA: US Public Health Service, 2007. http://www.atsdr.cdc.gov/toxprofiles/tp124.html. Accessed 05/01/09.

14 National Digestive Diseases Information Clearinghouse. Constipation. February 2006. NIH publication 06-2754. http://digestive.niddk.nih.gov/ddiseases/pubs/constipation/index.htm. Accessed 05/01/09.

15 Mayne ST, Navarro SA. Diet, obesity, and reflux in the etiology of adenocarcinomas of the esophagus and gastric cardia in humans. *J Nutr*. 2002;132(11):3467S–3470S.

16 Ringel Y, Sperber AD, Drossman DA. Irritable bowel syndrome. *Annu Rev Med*. 2001;52:319–338.

17 National Institute of Diabetes and Digestive and Kidney Diseases. Irritable bowel syndrome. April 2003. NIH publication 03-693. http://digestive.niddk.nih.gov/ddiseases/pubs/ibs/. Accessed 05/01/09.

18 Ibid.

19 Centers for Disease Control and Prevention. Colorectal cancer: the importance of prevention and early detection. 2004/2005 fact sheet. http://www.cdc.gov/cancer/colorctl/about2004.htm. Accessed 05/01/09.

20 World Health Organization. *Diet, Nutrition and the Prevention of Chronic Diseases: A Report of a Joint WHO/FAO Expert Consultation*. Geneva, Switzerland: World Health Organization, 2003. WHO Technical Report Series 916.

21 Chao A, Thun MJ, Connell CJ, et al. Meat consumption and risk of colon cancer. *JAMA*. 2005;293:172–182.

22 Institute of Medicine, Food and Nutrition Board. *Dietary Reference Intakes for Energy, Carbohydrate, Fiber, Fat, Fatty Acids, Cholesterol, Protein, and Amino Acids*. Washington, DC: National Academies Press, 2005.

23 Terry P, Giovannucci E, Michels KB, et al. Fruit, vegetables, dietary fiber, and risk of colorectal cancer. *J Natl Cancer Inst*. 2001;93(7):525–533.

24 Schatzkin A, Lanza E, Corle D, et al. Lack of effect of a low-fat, high-fiber diet on the recurrence of colorectal adenomas. Polyp Prevention Trial Study Group. *N Engl J Med*. 2000;342(16):1149–1155.

25 National Institute of Diabetes and Digestive and Kidney Diseases. *H. pylori* and peptic ulcer. October 2004. NIH publication 05-4225. http://digestive.niddk.nih.gov/ddiseases/pubs/hpylori/index.htm. Accessed 03/13/06.

26 Ibid.

27 Barry S, Dinan TG. Functional dyspepsia: are psychosocial factors of relevance? *World J Gastro*. 2006;12(17):2701–2707.

CHAPTER 4

Carbohydrates

THINK About It

1 When you think of the word *carbohydrate*, what foods come to mind?

2 How does your dietary fiber intake stack up?

3 Many people choose honey instead of white sugar because they think it's more "natural." What do you think?

4 Do you prefer artificial sweeteners to sugar? Explain your preference.

Visit nutrition.jbpub.com

Does sugar causes diabetes? Will too much sugar make a child hyperactive? Does excess sugar contribute to criminal behavior? What about starch? Does it really make you fat? These and other questions have been asked about sugar and starch—dietary carbohydrates—over the years. But where do these ideas come from? What is myth and what is fact? Are carbohydrates important in the diet? Or, as some popular diets suggest, should we eat only small amounts of carbohydrates? What links, if any, are there between carbohydrate in your diet and health?

Most of the world depends on carbohydrate-rich plant foods for daily sustenance. In some countries, 80 percent or more of daily calorie intake is carbohydrate. Rice provides the bulk of the diet in Southeast Asia, as does corn in South America, cassava in certain parts of Africa, and wheat in Europe and North America. (See **Figure 4.1**.) Besides providing energy, foods rich in carbohydrates, such as whole grains, legumes, fruits, and vegetables, are also good sources of vitamins, minerals, dietary fiber, and phytochemicals that can help lower the risk of chronic diseases.

THINK About It 1

Quick Bite

Is Pasta a Chinese Food?
Noodles were used in China as early as the first century; Marco Polo did not bring them to Italy until the 1300s.

Generous carbohydrate intake should provide the foundation for any healthful diet. Carbohydrates contain only 4 kilocalories per gram, compared with 9 kilocalories per gram for fat. Thus, a diet rich in carbohydrates provides fewer calories and a greater volume of food than the typical fat-laden American diet. As you explore the topic of carbohydrates, think about some claims you have heard for and against a high carbohydrate intake.

What Are Carbohydrates?

Plants use carbon dioxide from the air, water from the soil, and energy from the sun to produce carbohydrates and oxygen through a process called photosynthesis. (See **Figure 4.2**.) Carbohydrates are organic compounds that contain carbon (C), hydrogen (H), and oxygen (O) in the ratio of two hydrogen atoms and one oxygen atom for every one carbon atom (CH_2O). The sugar glucose, for example, contains 6 carbon atoms, 12 hydrogen atoms, and 6 oxygen atoms, giving this vital carbohydrate the chemical formula $C_6H_{12}O_6$.

Figure 4.1 **Cassava, rice, wheat, and corn.** These carbohydrate-rich foods are dietary staples in many parts of the world.

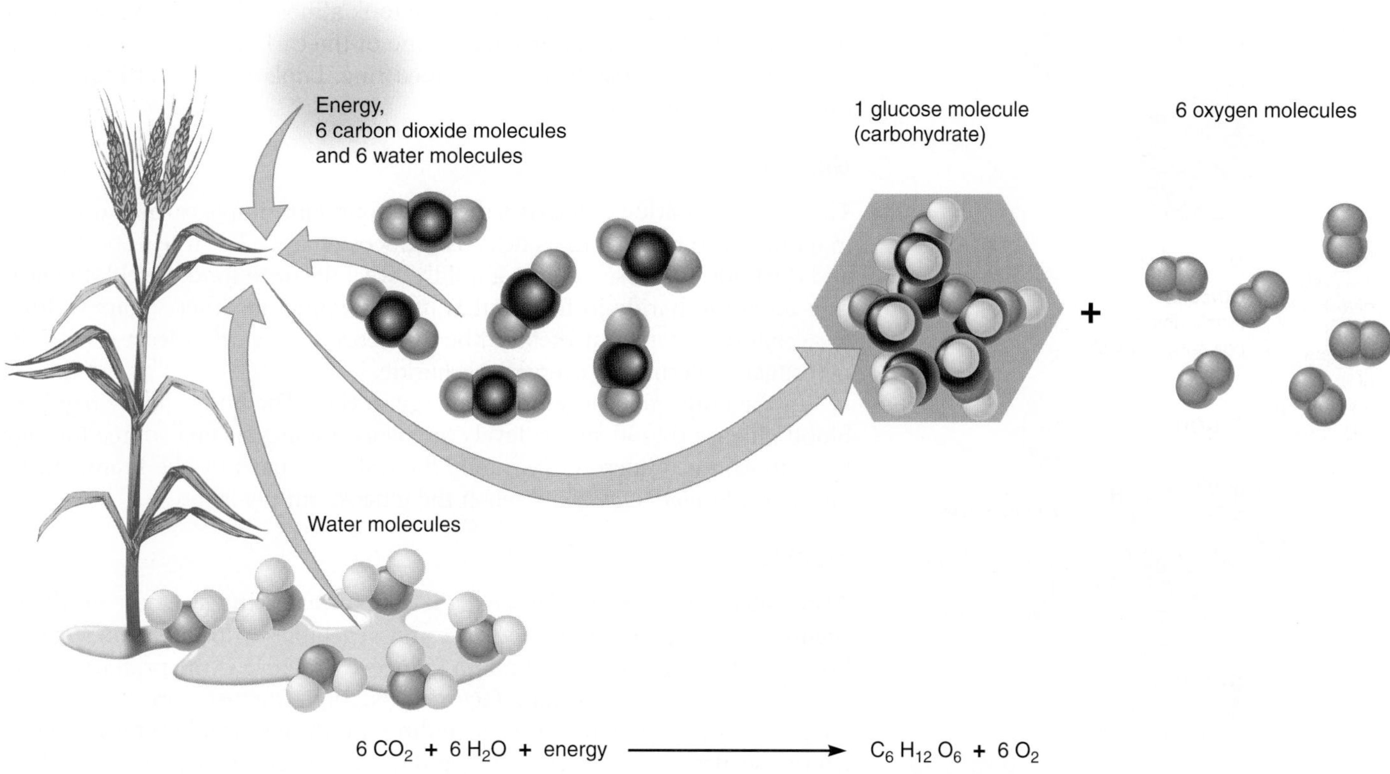

Figure 4.2 **Plants make carbohydrates.** Plants release oxygen as they use water, carbon dioxide, and energy from the sun to make carbohydrate (glucose) molecules.

Two or more sugar molecules can be assembled to form increasingly complex carbohydrates. The two main types of carbohydrates in food are simple carbohydrates (sugars) and complex carbohydrates (starches and fiber).

Simple Sugars: Monosaccharides and Disaccharides

Simple carbohydrates are naturally present as simple sugars in fruits, milk, and other foods. Plant carbohydrates also can be refined to produce sugar products such as table sugar or corn syrup. The two main types of sugars are monosaccharides and disaccharides. **Monosaccharides** consist of a single sugar molecule (*mono* meaning "one" and *saccharide* meaning "sugar"). **Disaccharides** consist of two sugar molecules chemically joined together (*di* meaning "two"). Monosaccharides and disaccharides give various degrees of sweetness to foods.

simple carbohydrates Sugars composed of a single sugar molecule (a monosaccharide) or two joined sugar molecules (a disaccharide).

monosaccharides Any sugars that are not broken down during digestion and have the general formula $C_nH_{2n}O_n$, where $n = 3$ to 7. The common monosaccharides glucose, fructose, and galactose all have six carbon atoms ($n = 6$).

disaccharides [dye-SACK-uh-rides] Carbohydrates composed of two monosaccharide units linked by a glycosidic bond. They include sucrose (common table sugar), lactose (milk sugar), and maltose.

Monosaccharides: The Single Sugars

The most common monosaccharides in the human diet are the following:

- Glucose
- Fructose
- Galactose

All three monosaccharides have six carbons, and all have the chemical formula $C_6H_{12}O_6$, but each has a different arrangement of these atoms. The carbon and oxygen atoms of glucose and galactose form a six-sided ring.

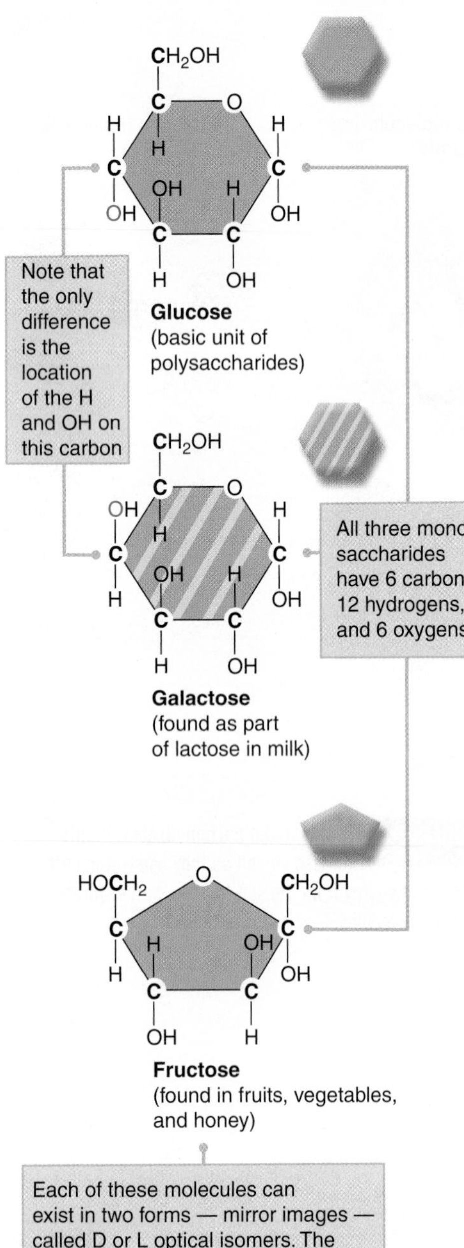
CH2OH
Glucose
(basic unit of polysaccharides)
Note that the only difference is the location of the H and OH on this carbon
Galactose
(found as part of lactose in milk)
All three monosaccharides have 6 carbons, 12 hydrogens, and 6 oxygens
HOCH2
Fructose
(found in fruits, vegetables, and honey)
Each of these molecules can exist in two forms — mirror images — called D or L optical isomers. The body can only use one of these forms, the D isomer

Figure 4.3 **The monosaccharides: glucose, galactose, and fructose.** Since glucose and galactose share similar six-sided hexagonal structures, they can be difficult to tell apart. Fructose's five-sided pentagon stands out.

The structures of glucose and galactose look almost identical except for the reversal of the OH and H groups on one of the carbon atoms. The carbons and oxygen of fructose form a five-sided ring. Look carefully at **Figure 4.3** to find all six carbons.

Glucose

The monosaccharide **glucose** is the most abundant simple carbohydrate unit in nature. Also referred to as dextrose, glucose plays a key role in both foods and the body. Glucose imparts a mildly sweet flavor to food. It seldom exists as a monosaccharide in food but is usually joined to other sugars to form disaccharides, starch, or dietary fiber. Glucose makes up at least one of the two sugar molecules in every disaccharide.

In the body, glucose supplies energy to cells. The body closely regulates blood glucose (blood sugar) levels to ensure a constant fuel source for vital body functions. Glucose is virtually the only fuel used by the brain, except during prolonged starvation, when the glucose supply is low.

Fructose

Also called levulose or fruit sugar, **fructose** tastes the sweetest of all the sugars and occurs naturally in fruits and vegetables. Although the sugar in honey is about half fructose and half glucose, fructose is the primary source of the sweet taste. Food manufacturers use high-fructose corn syrup as an additive to sweeten many foods, including soft drinks, fruit beverages such as lemonade, desserts, candies, jellies, and jams. The term *high-fructose* is a little misleading—the fructose content of this sweetener is around 50 percent.

Galactose

Galactose rarely occurs as a monosaccharide in food. It usually is chemically bonded to glucose to form lactose, the primary sugar in milk.

Other Monosaccharides and Derivative Sweeteners

Pentoses are single sugar molecules that contain five carbons. Although they are present in foods in only small quantities, they are essential components of nucleic acids, the genetic material of life. (See **Figure 4.4**.) The five-carbon sugar ribose is part of ribonucleic acid, or RNA. Another five-carbon sugar,

glucose [GLOO-kose] A common monosaccharide containing six carbons that is present in the blood; also known as dextrose or blood sugar. It is a component of the disaccharides sucroses, lactose, and maltose and various complex carbohydrates.

fructose [FROOK-tose] A common monosaccharide containing six carbons that is naturally present in honey and many fruits; often added to foods in the form of high-fructose corn syrup. Also called levulose or fruit sugar.

galactose [gah-LAK-tose] A monosaccharide containing six carbons that can be converted into glucose in the body. In foods and living systems, galactose usually is joined with other monosaccharides.

pentoses Sugar molecules containing five carbon atoms.

sugar alcohols Compounds formed from monosaccharides by replacing a hydrogen atom with a hydroxyl group (–OH); commonly used as nutritive sweeteners. Also called polyols.

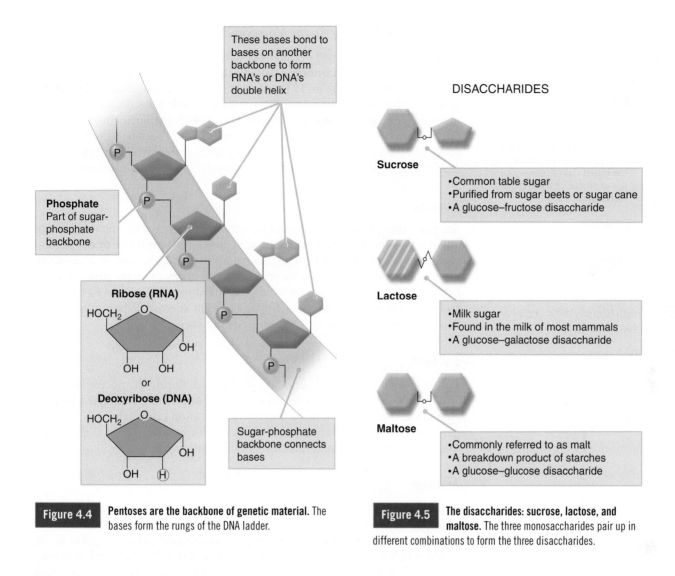

These bases bond to bases on another backbone to form RNA's or DNA's double helix

Phosphate Part of sugar-phosphate backbone

Ribose (RNA)
HOCH$_2$ O OH OH OH
or
Deoxyribose (DNA)
HOCH$_2$ O OH OH H

Sugar-phosphate backbone connects bases

Figure 4.4 **Pentoses are the backbone of genetic material.** The bases form the rungs of the DNA ladder.

DISACCHARIDES

Sucrose
- Common table sugar
- Purified from sugar beets or sugar cane
- A glucose–fructose disaccharide

Lactose
- Milk sugar
- Found in the milk of most mammals
- A glucose–galactose disaccharide

Maltose
- Commonly referred to as malt
- A breakdown product of starches
- A glucose–glucose disaccharide

Figure 4.5 **The disaccharides: sucrose, lactose, and maltose.** The three monosaccharides pair up in different combinations to form the three disaccharides.

deoxyribose, is a part of deoxyribonucleic acid, or DNA. Some pentoses also are components of indigestible gums and mucilages, which are classified as part of the dietary fiber component of foods.[1] Pentoses are synthesized in the body, and therefore are not needed in the diet.

Sugar alcohols are derivatives of monosaccharides. Like other sugars, they taste sweet and supply energy to the body. However, they are absorbed more slowly than sugars, and the body processes them differently. Some fruits naturally contain minute amounts of sugar alcohols. Sugar alcohols such as sorbitol, mannitol, lactitol, and xylitol also are used as nutritive sweeteners in foods. For example, sorbitol, which is derived from glucose, sweetens sugarless gum, breath mints, and candy. For more information on sugar alcohols, see the "Nutritive Sweeteners" section later in this chapter.

Disaccharides: The Double Sugars

Disaccharides consist of two monosaccharides chemically joined by a process called condensation. The following disaccharides (see **Figure 4.5**) are important in human nutrition:

- Sucrose (common table sugar)
- Lactose (major sugar in milk)
- Maltose (product of starch digestion)

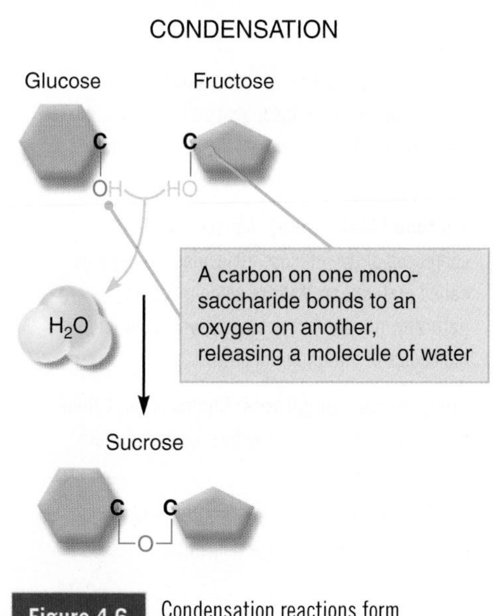

Figure 4.6 Condensation reactions form disaccharides.

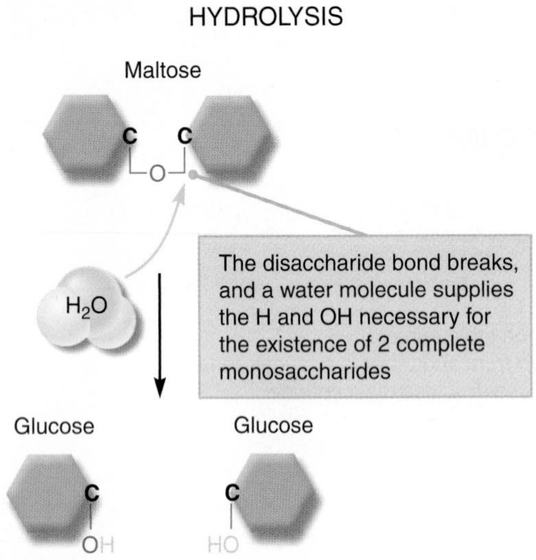

HYDROLYSIS

Maltose

The disaccharide bond breaks, and a water molecule supplies the H and OH necessary for the existence of 2 complete monosaccharides

H_2O

Glucose Glucose

Figure 4.7 Hydrolysis reactions split disaccharides into monosaccharides.

Joining and Cleaving Sugar Molecules

Sugar molecules are joined or separated (cleaved) by the removal or addition of a molecule of water. A **condensation** reaction chemically joins two monosaccharides while removing an H from one sugar molecule and an OH from the other to form water (H_2O) (see **Figure 4.6**). A hydrolysis reaction separates disaccharides into monosaccharides (see **Figure 4.7**). During hydrolysis, the addition of a molecule of water splits the bond between the two sugar molecules, providing the H and OH groups necessary for the sugars to exist as monosaccharides. The digestion of carbohydrates involves hydrolysis reactions.

Sucrose

Sucrose, most familiar to us as table sugar, is composed of one molecule of glucose and one molecule of fructose. Sucrose provides some of the natural sweetness of honey, maple syrup, fruits, and vegetables. Manufacturers use a refining process to extract sucrose from the juices of sugar cane or sugar beets. Full refining removes impurities; white sugar and powdered sugar are so highly refined they are virtually 100 percent sucrose. When a food label lists *sugar* as an ingredient, the term refers to sucrose.

Lactose

Lactose, or milk sugar, is composed of one molecule of glucose and one molecule of galactose. Lactose gives milk and other dairy products a slightly sweet taste. Human milk has a higher concentration (approximately 7 grams per 100 milliliters) of lactose than cow's milk (approximately 4.5 grams per 100 milliliters), so human milk tastes sweeter than cow's milk.

Maltose

Maltose is composed of two glucose molecules. Maltose seldom occurs naturally in foods, but is formed whenever long molecules of starch break down. Human digestive enzymes in the mouth and small intestine break down starch into maltose. When you chew a slice of fresh bread, you may detect a slightly sweet taste as starch breaks down into maltose. Starch also breaks down into maltose in germinating seeds. Maltose is fermented in the production of beer.

Key Concepts *Carbohydrates are composed of carbon, hydrogen, and oxygen and can be categorized as simple or complex. Simple carbohydrates include monosaccharides and disaccharides. The monosaccharides glucose, fructose, and galactose are single sugar molecules. The disaccharides sucrose, lactose, and maltose are double sugar molecules. A condensation reaction joins two monosaccharides to form a disaccharide.*

Complex Carbohydrates

Complex carbohydrates are chains of more than two sugar molecules. Short carbohydrate chains may have as few as three monosaccharide molecules, but long chains, the polysaccharides, can contain hundreds or even thousands.

Oligosaccharides

Oligosaccharides (*oligo* meaning "scant") are short carbohydrate chains of 3 to 10 sugar molecules. Dried beans, peas, and lentils contain the two most

condensation In chemistry, a reaction in which a covalent bond is formed between two molecules by removal of a water molecule.

sucrose [SOO-crose] A disaccharide composed of one molecule of glucose and one molecule of fructose joined together. Also known as table sugar.

lactose [LAK-tose] A disaccharide composed of glucose and galactose; also called milk sugar because it is the major sugar in milk and dairy products.

maltose [MALL-tose] A disaccharide composed of two glucose molecules; sometimes called malt sugar. Maltose seldom occurs naturally in foods but is formed whenever long molecules of starch break down.

complex carbohydrates Chains of more than two monosaccharides. May be oligosaccharides or polysaccharides.

oligosaccharides Short carbohydrate chains composed of 3 to 10 sugar molecules.

common oligosaccharides—raffinose and stachyose.[2] Raffinose is formed from three monosaccharide molecules—one galactose, one glucose, and one fructose. Stachyose is formed from four monosaccharide molecules—two galactose, one glucose, and one fructose. The body cannot break down raffinose or stachyose, but they are readily broken down by intestinal bacteria and are responsible for the familiar gaseous effects of foods such as beans.

Human milk contains more than one hundred different oligosaccharides, which vary according to the length of a woman's pregnancy, how long she has been nursing, and her genetic makeup.[3] For breastfed infants, oligosaccharides serve a function similar to dietary fiber in adults—making stools easier to pass. Some of these oligosaccharides also protect infants from disease-causing agents by binding to them in the intestine. Oligosaccharides in human milk also provide sialic acid, a compound essential for normal brain development.[4]

polysaccharides Long carbohydrate chains composed of more than 10 sugar molecules. Polysaccharides can be straight or branched.

starch The major storage form of carbohydrate in plants; starch is composed of long chains of glucose molecules in a straight (amylose) or branching (amylopectin) arrangement.

Polysaccharides

Polysaccharides (*poly* meaning "many") are long carbohydrate chains of monosaccharides. Some polysaccharides form straight chains, whereas others branch off in all directions. Such structural differences affect how the polysaccharide behaves in water and with heating. The way monosaccharides are linked make them digestible (e.g., starch) or nondigestible (e.g., fiber).

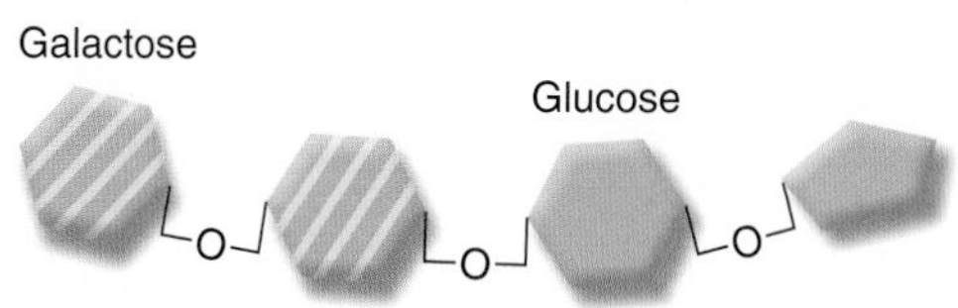

Stachyose

Starch

Plants store energy as **starch** for use during growth and reproduction. Rich sources of starch include (1) grains such as wheat, rice, corn, oats, millet, and barley, (2) legumes such as peas, beans, and lentils, and (3) tubers such as potatoes, yams, and cassava (**Figure 4.8**). Starch imparts a moist, gelatinous

Figure 4.8 A scanning electron micrograph of a potato tuber cell shows the starch granules where energy is stored.

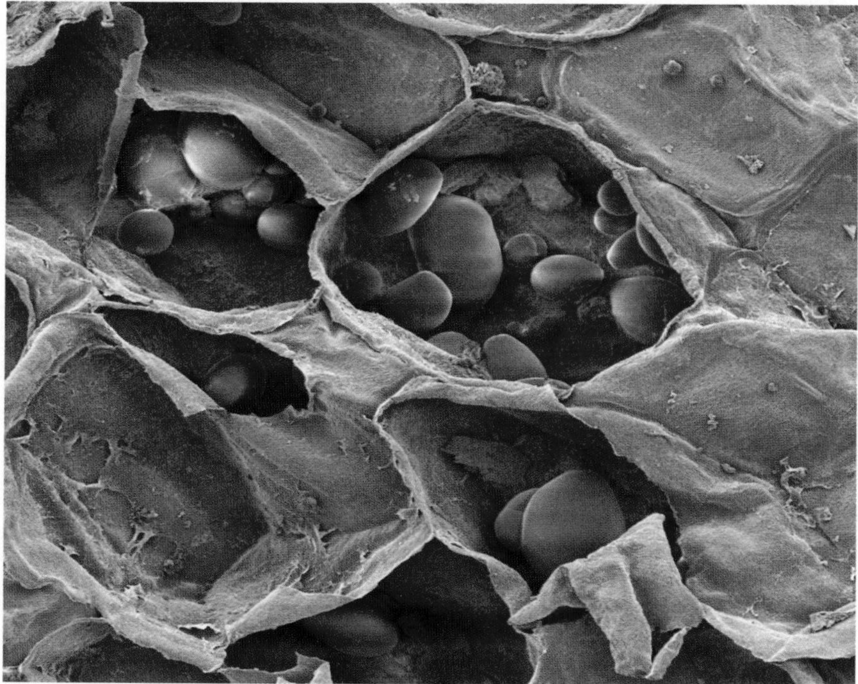

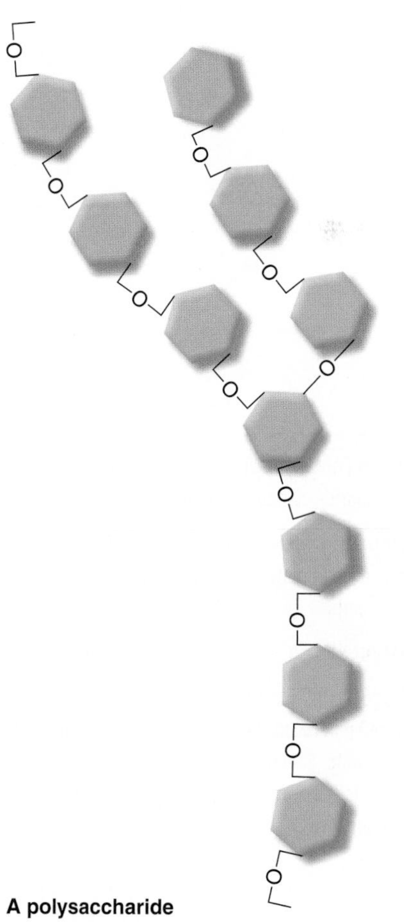

A polysaccharide

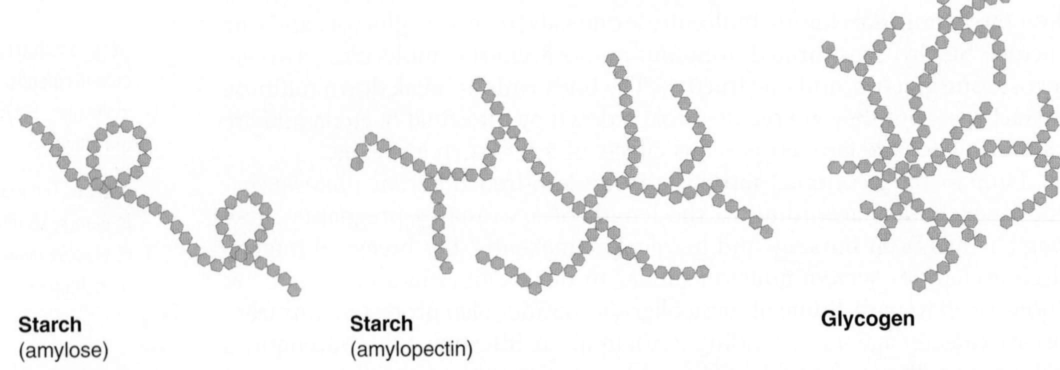

Figure 4.9 **Starch and glycogen.** Plants have two main types of starch—amylose, which has long unbranched chains of glucose, and amylopectin, which has branched chains. Animals store glucose in highly branched chains called glycogen.

texture to food. For example, it makes the inside of a baked potato moist, thick, and almost sticky. The starch in flour absorbs moisture and thickens gravy.

Starch takes two main forms in plants: amylose and amylopectin. **Amylose** is made up of long, unbranched chains of glucose molecules, whereas **amylopectin** is made up of branched chains of glucose molecules. (See **Figure 4.9**.) Amylose and amylopectin typically occur in a ratio of about 1:4 in plants, although this proportion can vary.[5] Wheat flour contains a higher proportion of amylose, whereas cornstarch contains a higher proportion of amylopectin.

The proportion of amylose to amylopectin in a food affects its functional properties. For example, food manufacturers often thicken gravies for frozen foods with cornstarch (rich in branched amylopectin) because it forms thicker, more stable gels than gravies thickened with wheat flour (rich in unbranched amylose).

In the body, amylopectin is digested more rapidly than amylose.[6] Although the body easily digests most starches, a small portion of the starch in plants may remain enclosed in cell structures and escape digestion in the small intestine. Starch that is not digested is called **resistant starch**.[7] Some legumes, such as white beans, contain large amounts of resistant starch. Resistant starch also is formed during the processing of starchy foods.

Glycogen

Glycogen, also called animal starch, is the storage form of carbohydrate in living animals. (See Figure 4.9.) After slaughter, tissue enzymes break down most glycogen within 24 hours. Although some organ meats, such as kidney, heart, and liver, contain small amounts of carbohydrate, meat from muscle contains none.[8] Since plant foods also contain no glycogen, it is a negligible carbohydrate source in our diets. Glycogen does, however, play an important role in our bodies as a readily mobilizable store of glucose.

Glycogen is composed of long, highly branched chains of glucose molecules. Its structure is similar to amylopectin, but glycogen is much more highly branched. When we need extra glucose, glycogen in our cells can be broken down rapidly into single glucose molecules. Because enzymes can attack only the ends of glycogen chains, the highly branched structure of glycogen multiplies the number of sites available for enzyme activity.

amylose [AM-ih-los] A straight-chain polysaccharide composed of glucose units.

amylopectin [am-ih-low-PEK-tin] A branched-chain polysaccharide composed of glucose units.

resistant starch A starch that is not digested.

glycogen [GLY-ko-jen] A very large, highly branched polysaccharide composed of multiple glucose units. Sometimes called animal starch, glycogen is the primary storage form of glucose in animals.

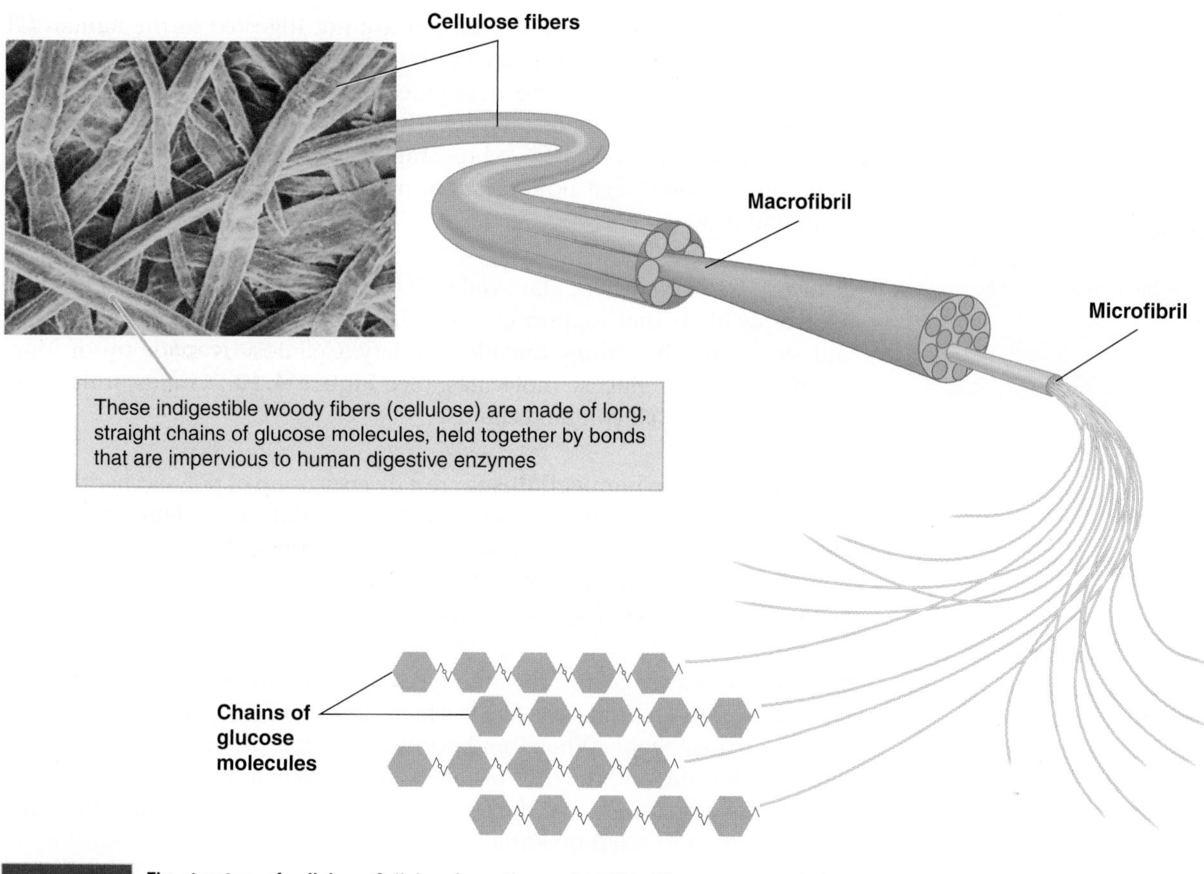
Cellulose fibers
Macrofibril
Microfibril
These indigestible woody fibers (cellulose) are made of long, straight chains of glucose molecules, held together by bonds that are impervious to human digestive enzymes
Chains of glucose molecules

Figure 4.10 **The structure of cellulose.** Cellulose forms the nondigestible, fibrous component of plants and is part of grasses, trees, fruits, and vegetables.

Skeletal muscle and the liver are the two major sites of glycogen storage. In muscle cells, glycogen provides a reservoir of glucose for strenuous muscular activity. Liver cells also use glycogen to regulate blood glucose levels. If necessary, liver glycogen can provide as much as 100 to 150 milligrams of glucose per minute to the blood at a sustained rate for up to 12 hours.[9]

Normally, the body can store only about 200 to 500 grams of glycogen at a time.[10] Some athletes practice a carbohydrate-loading regimen by gradually tapering off rigorous training and emphasizing high-carbohydrate meals a few days to one week before competition. This can increase the amount of stored glycogen by 20 to 40 percent above normal, providing a competitive edge for marathon running and other endurance events.[11] (See Chapter 14, "Sports Nutrition.")

Fiber

The Food and Nutrition Board redefined *fiber* as part of the DRI report on macronutrients.[12] **Dietary fiber** consists of nondigestible carbohydrates and lignins that are intact and intrinsic in plants. **Functional fiber** refers to isolated, nondigestible carbohydrates that have beneficial physiological effects in humans. **Total fiber** is the sum of dietary fiber and functional fiber.

All types of plant foods—including fruits, vegetables, legumes, and whole grains—contain dietary fiber. Many types of dietary fiber resemble

dietary fiber Carbohydrates and lignins that are naturally in plants and are nondigestible; that is, they are not digested and absorbed in the human small intestine.

functional fiber Isolated nondigestible carbohydrates, including some manufactured carbohydrates, that have beneficial effects in humans.

total fiber The sum of dietary fiber and functional fiber.

Quick Bite

"An Apple a Day Keeps the Doctor Away"
Most likely this adage persisted over time because of the actual health benefits from apples. Apples have a high pectin content, a soluble fiber known to be an effective GI regulator.

cellulose [SELL-you-los] A straight-chain polysaccharide composed of hundreds of glucose units linked by beta bonds. It is nondigestible by humans and a component of dietary fiber.

hemicelluloses [hem-ih-SELL-you-los-es] A group of large polysaccharides in dietary fiber that are fermented more easily than cellulose.

pectins A type of dietary fiber found in fruits.

gums Dietary fibers, which contain galactose and other monosaccharides, found between plant cell walls.

mucilages Gelatinous soluble fibers containing galactose, mannose, and other monosaccharides; found in seaweed.

psyllium The dried husk of the psyllium seed.

lignins [LIG-nins] Insoluble fibers composed of multi-ring alcohol units that constitute the only noncarbohydrate component of dietary fiber.

β-glucans Functional fiber, consisting of branched polysaccharide chains of glucose, that helps lower blood cholesterol levels. Found in barley and oats.

chitin A long-chain structural polysaccharide of slightly modified glucose. Found in the hard exterior skeletons of insects, crustaceans, and other invertebrates; also occurs in the cell walls of fungi.

chitosan Polysaccharide derived from chitin.

starches—they are polysaccharides, but are not digested in the human GI tract. Examples of these nonstarch polysaccharides include cellulose, hemicellulose, pectins, gums, and beta-glucans (β-glucans). Oligosaccharides also are considered to be dietary fiber. Examples of functional fiber include extracted plant pectins, gums and resistant starches, chitin and chitosan, and commercially produced nondigestible polysaccharides. Fiber is not found in animal foods.

Cellulose **Cellulose** gives plant cell walls their strength and rigidity. It forms the woody fibers that support tall trees. It also forms the brittle shafts of hay and straw and the stringy threads in celery. Cellulose is made up of long, straight chains of glucose molecules. (See **Figure 4.10**.) Grains, fruits, vegetables, and nuts all contain cellulose.

Hemicelluloses The **hemicelluloses** are a diverse group of polysaccharides that vary from plant to plant. They are mixed with cellulose in plant cell walls.[13] Hemicelluloses are composed of a variety of monosaccharides with many branching side chains. The outer bran layer on many cereal grains is rich in hemicelluloses, as are legumes, vegetables, and nuts.

Pectins **Pectins** are gel-forming polysaccharides found in all plants, especially fruits. The pectin in fruits acts like a cement that gives body to fruits and helps them keep their shape. When fruit becomes overripe, pectin breaks down into monosaccharides and the fruit becomes mushy. When mixed with sugar and acid, pectin forms a gel that the food industry uses to add firmness to jellies, jams, sauces, and salad dressings.

Gums and Mucilages Like pectin, **gums** and **mucilages** are thick, gel-forming fibers that help hold plant cells together. The food industry uses plant gums such as gum arabic, guar gum, locust bean gum, and xanthan gum and mucilages such as carrageenan to thicken, stabilize, or add texture to foods such as salad dressings, puddings, pie fillings, candies, sauces, and even drinks. **Psyllium** (the husk of psyllium seeds) is a mucilage that becomes very viscous when mixed with water. It is the main component in the laxative Metamucil, and is being added to some breakfast cereals.

Lignins **Lignins** are not actually carbohydrates. Rather, these nondigestible substances make up the woody parts of vegetables such as carrots and broccoli and the seeds of fruits such as strawberries.

β-Glucans **β-Glucans** are polysaccharides of branched glucose units. These fibers are found in large amounts in barley and oats. β-Glucan fiber is especially effective in lowering blood cholesterol levels (see the section "Carbohydrates and Health" later in this chapter).

Chitin and Chitosan **Chitin** and **chitosan** are polysaccharides found in the exoskeletons of crabs and lobsters, and in the cell walls of most fungi. Chitin and chitosan are primarily consumed in supplement form. Although they are marketed as being useful for weight control, published research does not support this claim.

Foods rich in dietary fiber include whole-grain foods such as brown rice, rolled oats, and whole-wheat breads and cereals; legumes such as kidney beans, garbanzo beans (chickpeas), peas, and lentils; fruits; and vegetables.

Table 4.1 lists foods rich in dietary fiber, and Table 3.2 lists the fiber content of common foods.

Key Concepts *Complex carbohydrates include starch, glycogen, and fiber. Starch is composed of straight or branched chains of glucose molecules and is the storage form of energy in plants. Glycogen is composed of highly branched chains of glucose molecules and is the storage form of energy in animals. Fibers include many different substances that cannot be digested by enzymes in the human intestinal tract and are found in plant foods, such as whole grains, legumes, vegetables, and fruits.*

Table 4.1 **Foods Rich in Dietary Fiber**

Fruits	
Apples	Grapefruit
Bananas	Mango
Berries	Oranges
Cherries	Pears
Cranberries	
Vegetables	
Asparagus	Green peppers
Broccoli	Red cabbage
Brussels sprouts	Spinach
Carrots	Sprouts
Nuts and Seeds	
Almonds	Sesame seeds
Peanuts	Sunflower seeds
Pecans	Walnuts
Legumes	
Most legumes	
Grains	
Brown rice	Wheat-bran cereals
Oat bran	Whole-wheat breads
Oatmeal	

Source: Adapted from Shils ME, Olson JA, Shike M, Ross AC, eds. *Modern Nutrition in Health and Disease.* 10th ed. Philadelphia: Lippincott Williams & Wilkins, 2006.

Carbohydrate Digestion and Absorption

Although glucose is a key building block of carbohydrates, you can't exactly find it on the menu at your favorite restaurant or campus hideout. You must first drink that chocolate milkshake or eat that hamburger bun so that your body can convert the food carbohydrate into glucose in the body. Let's see what happens to the carbohydrate foods you eat!

Digestion

Figure 4.11 provides an overview of the digestive process. Carbohydrate digestion begins in the mouth, where the starch-digesting enzyme salivary amylase hydrolyzes starch into shorter polysaccharides and maltose. Chewing stimulates saliva production and mixes salivary amylase with food. Disaccharides, unlike starch, are not digested in the mouth. In fact, only about 5 percent of the starches in food are broken down by the time the food is swallowed.

When carbohydrate enters the stomach, the acidity of stomach juices eventually halts the action of salivary amylase by denaturing it, which causes the enzyme (a protein) to lose its shape and function. This denaturation stops carbohydrate digestion, which will restart in the small intestine. Certain fibers, such as pectins and gums, provide a feeling of fullness and tend to delay digestive activity by slowing stomach emptying.

Most carbohydrate digestion takes place in the small intestine. As the stomach contents enter the small intestine, the pancreas secretes pancreatic amylase into the small intestine. **Pancreatic amylase** continues the digestion of starch, breaking it into many units of the disaccharide maltose.

Meanwhile, enzymes attached to the brush border (microvilli) of the mucosal cells lining the intestinal tract go to work. (See Chapter 3 for a detailed explanation of the complex structure of the small intestine.) These digestive enzymes, called brush border disaccharidases, break disaccharides into monosaccharides for absorption. The enzyme maltase splits maltose into two glucose molecules. The enzyme sucrase splits sucrose into glucose and fructose. The enzyme lactase splits lactose into glucose and galactose.

The bonds that link glucose molecules in complex carbohydrates are called glycosidic bonds. The two forms of these bonds, **alpha (α) bonds** and **beta (β) bonds**, have important differences. (See **Figure 4.12**.) Human enzymes easily break alpha bonds, making glucose available from the polysaccharides starch and glycogen. Our bodies don't have enzymes to break most beta bonds, such as those that link the glucose molecules in cellulose, a nondigestible polysaccharide. Beta bonds also link the galactose and glucose molecules in the disaccharide lactose, but the enzyme lactase is specifically tailored to attack this small molecule. People with a sufficient supply of the enzyme lactase can break these bonds. When lactase is lacking, however, the

pancreatic amylase Starch-digesting enzyme secreted by the pancreas.

alpha (α) bonds Chemical bonds linking two monosaccharides (glycosidic bonds) that can be broken by human intestinal enzymes, releasing the individual monosaccharides. Maltose and sucrose contain alpha bonds.

beta (β) bonds Chemical bonds linking two monosaccharides (glycosidic bonds) that cannot be broken by human intestinal enzymes. Cellulose contains beta bonds.

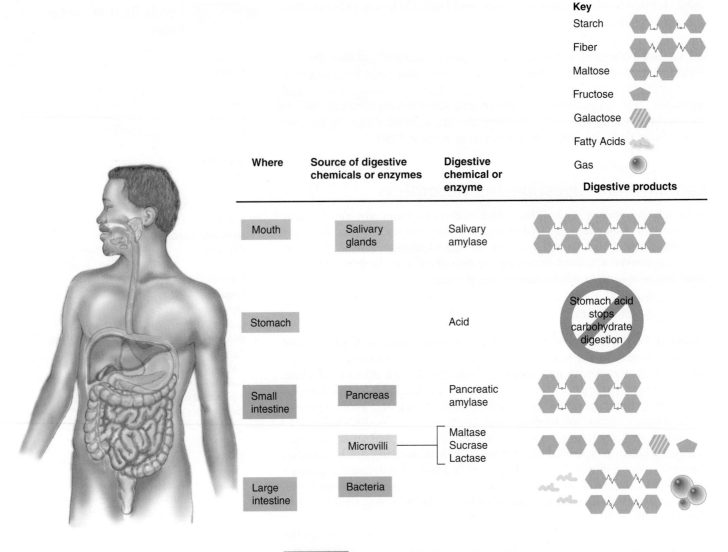

Key: Starch, Fiber, Maltose, Fructose, Galactose, Fatty Acids, Gas

Where	Source of digestive chemicals or enzymes	Digestive chemical or enzyme	Digestive products
Mouth	Salivary glands	Salivary amylase	
Stomach		Acid	Stomach acid stops carbohydrate digestion
Small intestine	Pancreas	Pancreatic amylase	
	Microvilli	Maltase Sucrase Lactase	
Large intestine	Bacteria		

Figure 4.11 **Carbohydrate digestion.** Most carbohydrate digestion takes place in the small intestine.

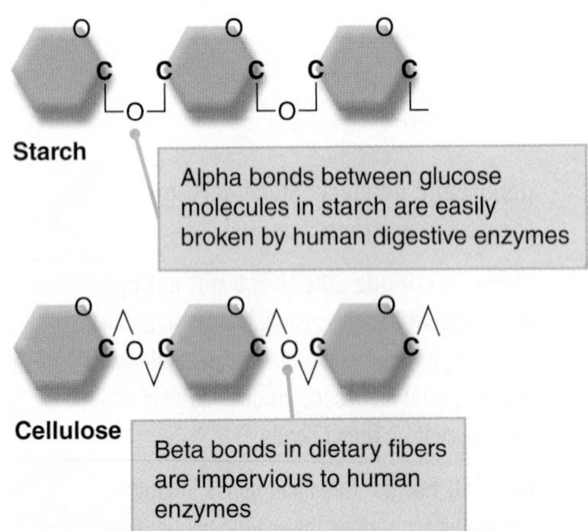

Figure 4.12 **Alpha bonds and beta bonds.** Human digestive enzymes can easily break the alpha bonds in starch, but they cannot break the beta bonds in cellulose.

beta bonds remain unbroken and lactose remains undigested until bacteria in the colon can attack it. (See Chapter 3 for more on lactose maldigestion.)

Enzymes are highly specific; they speed up only certain reactions and work on only certain molecules. Humans lack the digestive enzymes needed to break down the oligosaccharides raffinose and stachyose, for example. The commercial product Beano is an enzyme preparation. When taken immediately before eating beans or other gas-forming vegetables, Beano helps break oligosaccharides into monosaccharides so that the body can absorb them.

Some carbohydrate remains intact as it enters the large intestine. This carbohydrate may be fiber or resistant starch, or the small intestine may have lacked the necessary enzymes to break it down. In the large intestine, bacteria partially ferment (break down) undigested carbohydrate and produce gas plus a few short-chain fatty acids. These fatty acids are absorbed into the colon and are used for energy by the colon cells. In addition, these fatty acids may reduce the risk of developing gastrointestinal disorders, cancers, and cardiovascular disease.[14]

Some fibers, particularly cellulose and psyllium, pass through the large intestine unchanged and therefore produce little gas. Instead, these fibers add to the stool weight and water content, making it easier to pass.

Absorption

Monosaccharides are absorbed into the mucosal cells lining the small intestine by two different mechanisms that you learned about in Chapter 3. Fructose is absorbed by facilitated diffusion, whereas glucose and galactose depend on an active transport mechanism. A sodium-dependent glucose transport protein helps move glucose and galactose across the intestinal cell's membrane. The carrier protein in the cell membrane is first loaded with sodium, and then either glucose or galactose can attach to it.[15] Energy for this process is provided by the hydrolysis of adenosine triphosphate (ATP). Fructose absorption is slower than that of glucose or galactose. In the villi, absorbed monosaccharides pass through the intestinal mucosal cells and enter the bloodstream. Glucose, galactose, and fructose molecules travel to the liver via the portal vein, where galactose and fructose are converted into glucose or used for energy. The liver stores and releases glucose as needed to maintain constant blood glucose levels. **Figure 4.13** illustrates the digestion and absorption of carbohydrates.

Key Concepts *Carbohydrate digestion takes place primarily in the small intestine, where digestible carbohydrates are broken down and absorbed as monosaccharides. Bacteria in the large intestine partially ferment resistant starch and some types of fiber, producing gas and a few short-chain fatty acids that can be absorbed through the large intestine and used for energy. The liver converts absorbed monosaccharides into glucose.*

Carbohydrates in the Body

Through the processes of digestion and absorption, our varied diet of carbohydrates from vegetables, fruits, grains, and milk becomes glucose. Glucose has one major role—to supply energy for the body.

Normal Use of Glucose

Cells throughout the body depend on glucose for energy to drive chemical processes. Although most—but not all—cells can also burn fat for energy, the body needs some glucose to burn fat efficiently.

When we eat food, our bodies immediately use some glucose to maintain normal blood glucose levels. We store excess glucose as glycogen in liver and muscle tissue. Insulin and glucagon, two hormones produced by the pancreas, closely regulate blood glucose levels.

Glucose

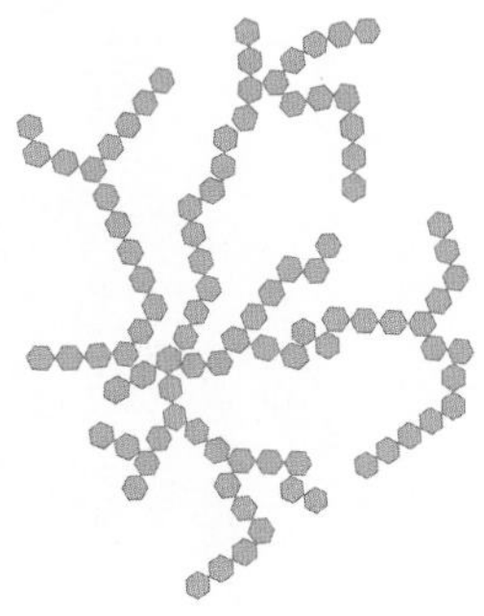
Glycogen

Using Glucose for Energy

Glucose is the primary fuel for most cells in the body and the preferred fuel for the brain, red blood cells, nervous system, fetus, and placenta. Even when fat is burned for energy, a small amount of glucose is needed to break down fat completely. To obtain energy from glucose, cells must take up glucose from the blood. Once glucose enters cells, a series of metabolic reactions break it down into carbon dioxide and water, releasing energy in a form that the body can use.[16] (See Chapter 7, "Metabolism.")

Storing Glucose as Glycogen

To store excess glucose, the body assembles it into the long, branched chains of glycogen. Glycogen can be broken down quickly, releasing glucose for energy as needed. Liver glycogen stores are used to maintain normal blood glucose levels and account for about one-third of the body's total glycogen stores. Muscle glycogen stores are used to fuel muscle activity and account for about two-thirds of the body's total glycogen stores.[17] The body can store only limited amounts of glycogen—usually enough to last from a few hours to one day, depending on activity level.[18]

Sparing Body Protein

In the absence of carbohydrate, both proteins and fats can be used for energy. Although most cells can break down fat for energy, brain cells and developing red blood cells require a constant supply of glucose.[19] (After an extended period of starvation, the brain adapts and is able to use ketones from fat breakdown for part of its energy needs.) If glycogen stores are depleted and glucose is not provided in the diet, the body must make its own glucose from protein to maintain blood levels and supply glucose to the brain. Adequate consumption of dietary carbohydrate spares body proteins from being broken down and used to make glucose.

Preventing Ketosis

Even when fat provides the fuel for cells, cells require a small amount of carbohydrate to completely break down fat to release energy. When no carbohydrate is available, the liver cannot break down fat completely. Instead,

Figure 4.13 **Travels with carbohydrate.** (1) Carbohydrate digestion begins in the mouth. (2) Stomach acid halts carbohydrate digestion. (3) Carbohydrate digestion resumes in the small intestine, where monosaccharides are absorbed. (4) Monosaccharides enter intestinal cells through a variety of transport proteins and use facilitated diffusion to leave the cells and enter the bloodstream. (5) The liver converts fructose and galactose to glucose, which it can assemble into chains of glycogen, release to the blood, or use for energy.

Key

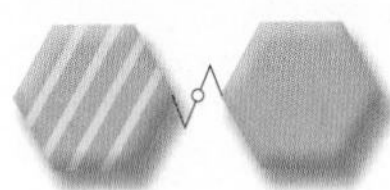
Lactose

Sucrose

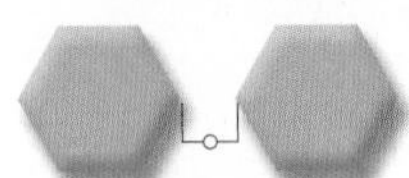
Maltose

Fructose

Galactose

Glucose

Enzymes

Na^+

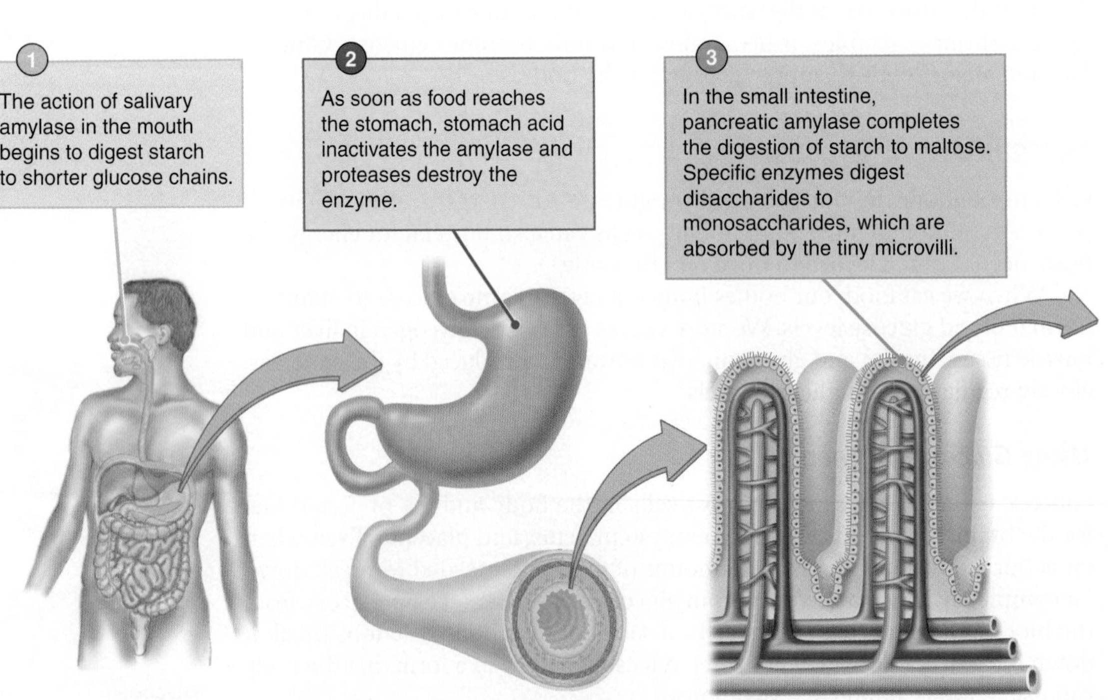
1
The action of salivary amylase in the mouth begins to digest starch to shorter glucose chains.
2
As soon as food reaches the stomach, stomach acid inactivates the amylase and proteases destroy the enzyme.
3
In the small intestine, pancreatic amylase completes the digestion of starch to maltose. Specific enzymes digest disaccharides to monosaccharides, which are absorbed by the tiny microvilli.

it produces small compounds called **ketone bodies**.[20] Most cells can use ketone bodies for energy.

When ketone bodies are produced more quickly than the body can use them, ketone levels build up in the blood and can cause a condition known as **ketosis**. People vulnerable to ketosis include those who consume only small amounts of carbohydrate or who cannot metabolize blood glucose normally. Ketosis is most commonly caused by very low carbohydrate diets, starvation, uncontrolled diabetes mellitus, and chronic alcoholism. Ketosis also can develop when fluid intake is too low to allow the kidneys to excrete excess ketone bodies. As the concentration of ketone bodies increases, the blood becomes too acidic. The body loses water as it excretes excess ketones in urine, and dehydration is a common consequence of ketosis. To prevent

ketone bodies Molecules formed when insufficient carbohydrate is available to completely metabolize fat. Formation of ketone bodies is promoted by a low glucose level and high acetyl CoA level within cells. Acetone, acetoacetate, and beta-hydroxybutyrate are ketone bodies. Beta-hydroxybutyrate is sometimes improperly called a ketone.

ketosis [kee-TOE-sis] Abnormally high concentration of ketone bodies in body tissues and fluids.

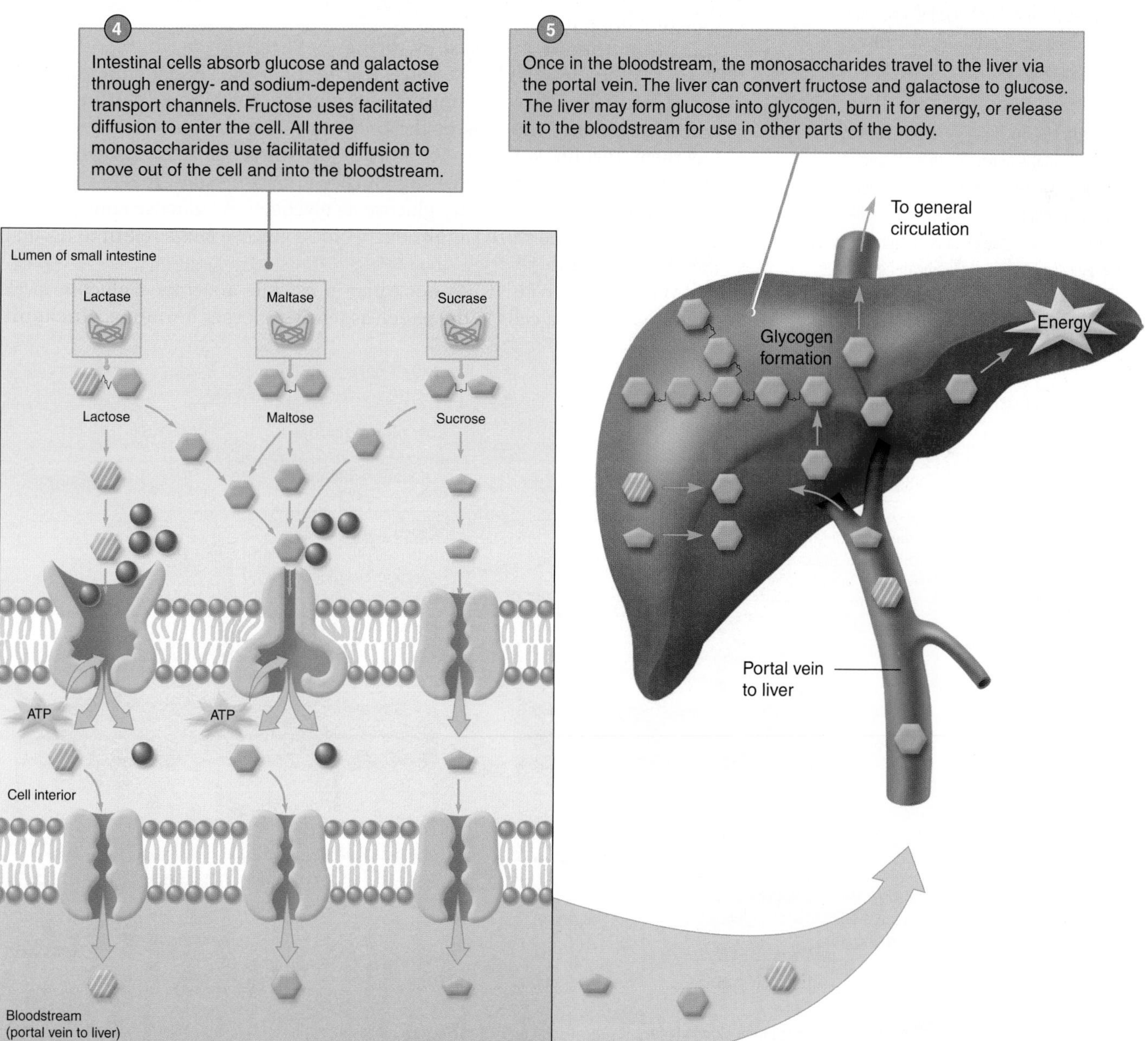
4
Intestinal cells absorb glucose and galactose through energy- and sodium-dependent active transport channels. Fructose uses facilitated diffusion to enter the cell. All three monosaccharides use facilitated diffusion to move out of the cell and into the bloodstream.
5
Once in the bloodstream, the monosaccharides travel to the liver via the portal vein. The liver can convert fructose and galactose to glucose. The liver may form glucose into glycogen, burn it for energy, or release it to the bloodstream for use in other parts of the body.
Lumen of small intestine
Lactase
Maltase
Sucrase
Lactose
Maltose
Sucrose
ATP
ATP
Cell interior
Bloodstream
(portal vein to liver)
To general
circulation
Glycogen
formation
Energy
Portal vein
to liver

ketosis, the body needs a minimum of 50 to 100 grams of carbohydrate daily.[21] (See Chapter 7, "Metabolism," for more details on ketosis.)

Key Concepts *Glucose circulates in the blood to provide immediate energy to cells. The body stores excess glucose in the liver and muscle as glycogen. The body needs adequate carbohydrate intake to prevent the breakdown of body proteins to fulfill glucose or energy needs. The body needs some carbohydrate to completely break down fat and prevent the buildup of ketone bodies in the blood.*

blood glucose levels The amount of glucose in the blood at any given time. Also known as blood sugar levels.

insulin [IN-suh-lin] Produced by beta cells in the pancreas, this polypeptide hormone stimulates the uptake of blood glucose into muscle and adipose cells, the synthesis of glycogen in the liver, and various other processes.

glucagon [GLOO-kuh-gon] Produced by alpha cells in the pancreas, this polypeptide hormone promotes the breakdown of liver glycogen to glucose, thereby increasing blood glucose. Glucagon secretion is stimulated by low blood glucose levels and by growth hormone.

Regulating Blood Glucose Levels

The body closely regulates **blood glucose levels** (also known as blood sugar levels) to maintain an adequate supply of glucose for cells. If blood glucose levels drop too low, a person becomes shaky and weak. If blood glucose levels rise too high, a person becomes sluggish and confused, and may have difficulty breathing.

Two hormones produced by the pancreas tightly control blood glucose levels.[22] When blood glucose levels rise after a meal, special pancreatic cells called beta cells release the hormone insulin into the blood. **Insulin** acts like a key, "unlocking" the cells of the body and allowing glucose to enter and fuel them. Insulin works on receptors on the surface of cells, increasing their affinity for glucose and increasing glucose uptake by cells. It also stimulates liver and muscle cells to store glucose as glycogen. As glucose enters cells to deliver energy or be stored as glycogen, blood glucose levels return to normal. (See **Figure 4.14a**.)

When an individual has not eaten in a while and blood glucose levels begin to fall, alpha cells in the pancreas release another hormone, **glucagon**.

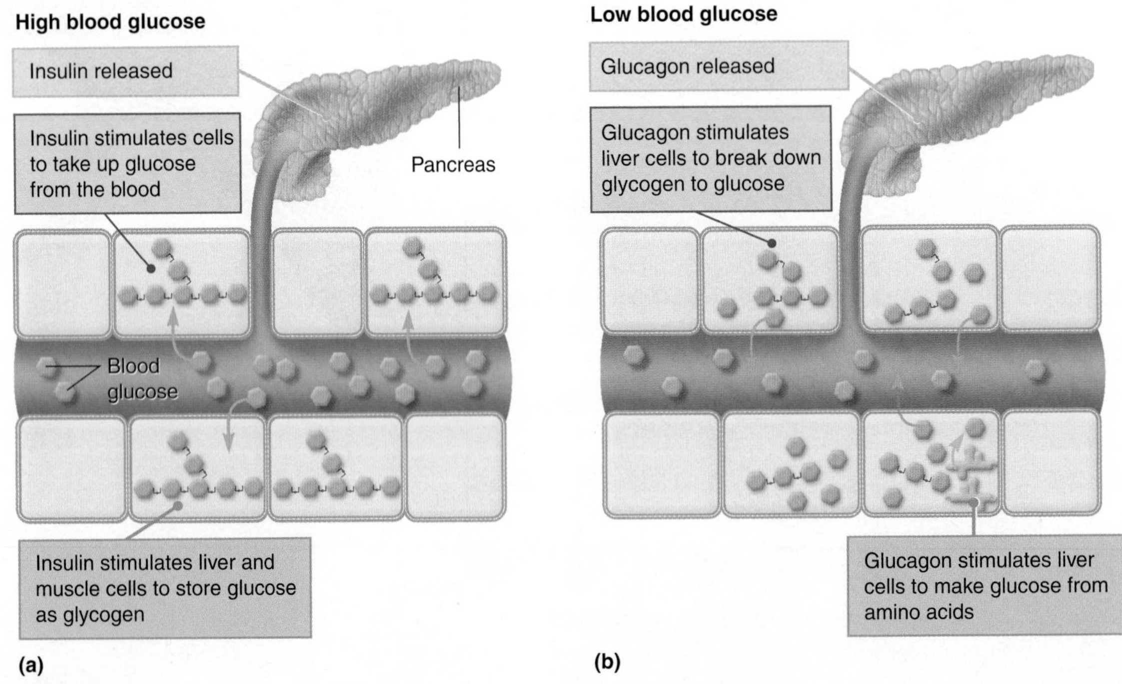

Figure 4.14 **Regulating blood glucose levels.** Insulin and glucagon have opposing actions. (a) Insulin acts to lower blood glucose levels, and (b) glucagon acts to raise them.

Glucagon stimulates the breakdown of glycogen stores to release glucose into the bloodstream. (See **Figure 4.14b**.) It also stimulates gluconeogenesis, or the synthesis of glucose from protein. Another hormone, **epinephrine** (also called adrenaline), exerts effects similar to glucagon to ensure that all body cells have adequate energy for emergencies. Released by the adrenal glands in response to sudden stress or danger, epinephrine is called the fight-or-flight hormone.

Different foods vary in their effect on blood glucose levels. Foods rich in simple carbohydrates or starch but low in fat or fiber tend to be digested and absorbed rapidly. This rapid absorption causes a corresponding large and rapid rise in blood glucose levels.[23] The body reacts to this rise by pumping out extra insulin, which in turn can lower blood sugar levels too far before finally stabilizing. Other foods—especially those rich in dietary fiber, resistant starch, or fat—cause a less dramatic blood glucose response accompanied by smaller swings in blood glucose levels.

The **glycemic index** measures the effect of a food on blood glucose levels. Foods with a high glycemic index cause a faster and higher rise in blood glucose, whereas foods with a low glycemic index cause a slower rise in blood glucose.[24]

epinephrine A hormone released in response to stress or sudden danger, epinephrine raises blood glucose levels to ready the body for "fight or flight." Also called adrenaline.

glycemic index A measure of the effect of food on blood glucose levels. It is the ratio of the blood glucose value after eating a particular food to the value after eating the same amount of white bread or glucose.

diabetes mellitus A chronic disease in which uptake of blood glucose by body cells is impaired, resulting in high glucose levels in the blood and urine. Type 1 is caused by decreased pancreatic release of insulin. In type 2, target cells (e.g., fat and muscle cells) lose the ability to respond normally to insulin.

High Blood Glucose Levels: Diabetes Mellitus

When people have **diabetes mellitus**, their bodies either do not produce enough insulin or do not use insulin properly. If diabetes is not treated and controlled, blood glucose levels are chronically elevated, causing serious complications and premature death.[25] Although scientists don't completely understand the causes of diabetes, both genetics and environmental factors (obesity and lack of exercise, for example) appear to be involved (see Chapter 15 for a complete discussion of diabetes mellitus).

Type 2 Diabetes in Youth

Type 2 diabetes mellitus has emerged as a diagnosis among adolescents in the United States. It is well known that the prevalence of overweight and central adiposity in children and adolescence has increased dramatically in recent years.[26] Excess adiposity is considered a major risk factor for development of type 2 diabetes in youth.[27] The Diabetes Prevention Program[28] and the Finnish Diabetes Prevention Study[29] provide clear evidence for the efficacy of moderate weight loss to reduce risk for type 2 diabetes in adult populations.[30] Key dietary goals in these trials included reduced calorie intake consistent with moderate weight loss and reduced intake of fat as a percentage of energy. Increased physical activity was also a key focus of the interventions. Clinical trials of lifestyle approaches to facilitate weight management via diet and physical activity and to improve insulin sensitivity in youth at high risk for type 2 diabetes have been successful on a small scale.[31] The occurrence of type 2 diabetes within the population of youth is indeed alarming. A child with type 2 diabetes is at high risk for obesity, dyslipidemia, hypertension, or a combination of these, and management of the disease is critical.[32]

Carbohydrates in the Diet

What foods supply our dietary carbohydrates? **Figure 4.15** shows many foods rich in carbohydrates. Plant foods are our main dietary sources of carbohydrates: grains, legumes, and vegetables provide starches and fibers; fruits provide sugars and fibers. Additional sugar (mainly lactose) is found in dairy foods, and various sugars are found in beverages, jams, jellies, and candy.

Quick Bite

Carbohydrate Companions

The word *companion* comes from the Latin *companio*, meaning "one who shares bread."

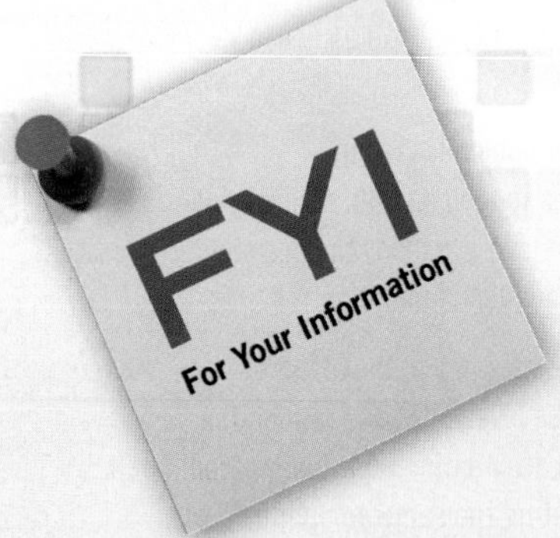

The Glycemic Index of Foods: Useful or Useless?

The glycemic index is a valuable and easy-to-use concept, claim some researchers.[1] Others contend that although it is promising, more definitive data are needed before this concept should be promoted for widespread public use.[2] Several popular weight-loss diets use the glycemic index to guide food choices.

How Is Glycemic Index Measured?

The glycemic index classifies foods or meals based on their potential to raise blood glucose levels. It is expressed as a percentage of the response to a standard food or carbohydrate, usually white bread or pure glucose.[3]

Foods with a high glycemic index trigger a sharp rise in blood glucose, followed by a dramatic fall, often to levels that are transiently below normal. In contrast, low-glycemic-index foods trigger slower and more modest changes in blood glucose levels.

What Factors Affect the Glycemic Index of a Food or Meal?

The glycemic index of a food is not always easy to predict. Would you expect a high-sugar food such as ice cream to have a high glycemic index? Ice cream actually has a low index because its fat slows sugar absorption. On the other hand, wouldn't you expect complex carbohydrate foods such as bread or potatoes to have a low glycemic index? In fact, the starch in white bread and cooked potatoes is readily absorbed, so each has a high value.[4] The glycemic indices of some common foods are listed in **Table 1**, and lower-glycemic-index substitutions are given in **Table 2**.

The type of carbohydrate, the cooking process, and the presence of fat and dietary fiber all affect a food's glycemic index.[5] In a person's diet, it is the glycemic index of mixed meals, referred to as the glycemic load of a meal, rather than the individual foods, that counts.[6]

Table 1 Glycemic Index Compared with Pure Glucose*

Food	Glycemic Index	Food	Glycemic Index
Bakery products		**Fruits**	
Angel food cake	67	Apples	38
Waffles	76	Bananas	52
Breads		Pineapple	59
White bread	73	**Legumes**	
Wheat bread, whole meal flour	71	Black-eyed peas	42
		Lentils	29
Breakfast cereals		**Pasta**	
All bran	42	Spaghetti	42
Corn flakes	81	Macaroni	47
Oatmeal	58	**Vegetables**	
Cereal grains		Carrots	47
Barley	25	Baked potatoes	85
Sweet corn	53	Green peas	48
White rice, long grain	56	**Candy**	
Bulgur	48	Jelly beans	78
Dairy foods		Life Savers	70
Ice cream	61		
Skim milk	32		

*Glycemic response to pure glucose is 100.

Source: Data compiled from Foster-Powell K, Holt SHA, Brand-Miller JC. International table of glycemic index and glycemic load values: 2002. *Am J Clin Nutr.* 2002;76:5–56.

Why Do Some Researchers Believe the Glycemic Index Is Useful?

Health benefits can be significant. Diets that emphasize low-glycemic-index foods decrease the risk of developing type 2 diabetes and improve blood sugar control in people who are already afflicted.[7] Epidemiological studies suggest that such diets also reduce the risk of colon and other cancers[8] and may help reduce the risk of heart disease as well. Diets with a low glycemic load are associated with higher HDL cholesterol levels,[9] and with reduced incidence of heart attack.[10] Also, studies indicate that the effectiveness of low-fat, high-carbohydrate diets for weight loss can be improved by reducing the glycemic load.[11]

Why Do Some Researchers Believe the Glycemic Index Is Useless?

Some researchers question the usefulness of conclusions drawn primarily from epidemiological studies.[12] Epidemiological studies can show association, but cannot prove causation. Also, researchers worry about the inconsistencies in the use of glucose or white bread as the standard and the wide variations in measured glycemic responses to individual foods.

Table 2 **Sample Substitutions for High-Glycemic-Index Foods**

High-Glycemic-Index Food	Low-Glycemic-Index Alternative	High-Glycemic-Index Food	Low-Glycemic-Index Alternative
Bread, wheat or white	Oat bran, rye, or pumpernickel bread	Plain cookies and crackers	Cookies made with nuts and whole grains such as oats
Processed breakfast cereal	Unrefined cereal such as oats (either museli or oatmeal); bran cereals	Cakes and muffins	Cakes and muffins made with fruit, oats, or whole grains
		Bananas	Apples
		Potatoes	Pasta or legumes

Low glycemic index = 55 or less, medium = 56–69, high = 70 or more.

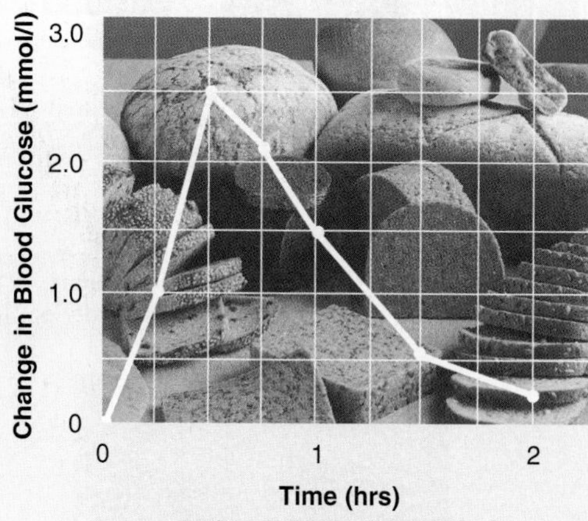

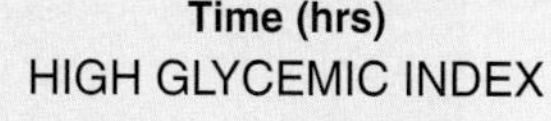

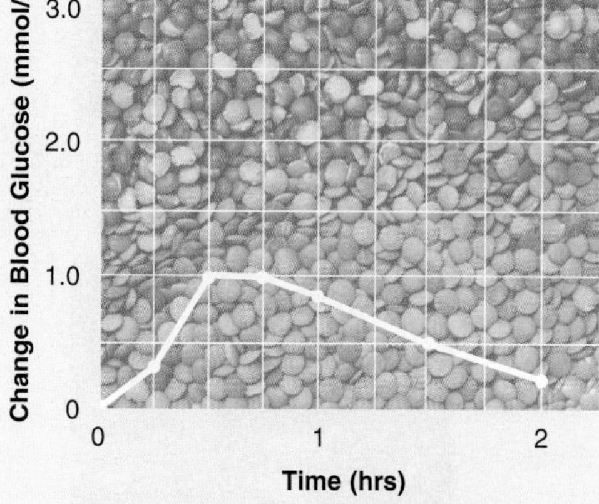

Many believe the glycemic index is too complex for most people to use effectively. After reviewing current research, the 2010 Dietary Guidelines Advisory Committee has determined that strong evidence does not exist for the association between glycemic index and body weight and therefore it is not necessary to consider for weight management.[13] The American Diabetes Association has not yet endorsed widespread adoption of low-glycemic-index diets, stating that "although the use of low-glycemic index food may reduce postprandial **hyperglycemia**, there is not sufficient evidence of long-term benefit to recommend use of low-glycemic index diets as a primary strategy in food/meal planning for individuals with type 1 diabetes, or for general use by type 2 diabetes patients."[14]

What's the Bottom Line?

Like many other nutrition issues, the glycemic index needs further study. We need to continue to identify the influence of processing techniques on the glycemic index, and agree on methodologies and standards for measuring it. Most researchers also call for prospective, long-term clinical trials to evaluate the effects of low-glycemic-index and low-glycemic-load diets in chronic disease risk reduction and treatment.[15] Until then, encouraging the consumption of whole-grain, minimally refined cereal products and other low-glycemic-index foods won't hurt, and it may help to improve health!

1 Miller JB, Colagiuri S, Foster-Powell K. The glycemic index is easy and works in practice. *Diabetes Care*. 1997;20:1628–1629.

2 Pi-Sunyer FX. Glycemic index and disease. *Am J Clin Nutr*. 2002;76(suppl):290S–298S.

3 Jenkins DJA, Kendall CWC, Augustin LSA, et al. Glycemic index: overview of implications in health and disease. *Am J Clin Nutr*. 2002;76(suppl):266S–273S.

4 Foster-Powell K, Holt SH, Brand-Miller JC. International table of glycemic index and glycemic load values: 2002. *Am J Clin Nutr*. 2002;76:5–56.

5 Pi-Sunyer. Glycemic index and disease.

6 Willett W, Manson J, Liu S. Glycemic index, glycemic load, and risk of type 2 diabetes. *Am J Clin Nutr*. 2002;76(suppl):274S–280S.

7 Ibid.

8 Jenkins, Kendall, Augustin, et al. Glycemic index.

9 Leeds AR. Glycemic index and heart disease. *Am J Clin Nutr*. 2002;76(suppl):286S–289S.

10 Jenkins, Kendall, Augustin, et al. Glycemic index.

11 Pawlak DB, Ebbeling CB, Ludwig DS. Should obese patients be counseled to follow a low-glycaemic index diet? Yes. *Obes Rev*. 2002;3:235–243.

12 Raben A. Should obese patients be counseled to follow a low-glycaemic index diet? No. *Obes Rev*. 2002;3(4):245–256; and Pi-Sunyer. Glycemic index and disease.

13 US Department of Agriculture and US Department of Health and Human Services. *Dietary Guidelines for Americans, 2010*. 7th ed. Washington, DC: US Government Printing Office, December 2010.

14 Franz MJ, Bantle JP, Beebe CA, et al. Evidence-based nutrition principles and recommendations for the treatment and prevention of diabetes and related complications. *Diabetes Care*. 2002;25(1):148–198.

15 Ludwig DS, Eckel RH. The glycemic index at 20 y. *Am J Clin Nutr*. 2002;76(suppl):264S–265S.

hyperglycemia [HIGH-per-gly-SEE-me-uh] Abnormally high concentration of glucose in the blood.

Table sugar, corn syrup, and brown sugar are rich in sucrose, a simple carbohydrate

Milk and milk products are rich in lactose, a simple carbohydrate

Fruits and vegetables provide simple sugars, starch, and fiber

Bread, flour, cornmeal, rice, and pasta are rich in starch and, sometimes, dietary fiber

Figure 4.15 **Carbohydrate sources.**

Recommendations for Carbohydrate Intake

The minimum amount of carbohydrate required by the body is based on the brain's requirement for glucose. This glucose can come either from dietary carbohydrate or from synthesis of glucose from protein in the body. Relying on protein alone is not recommended, however, because adaptation to using protein for glucose and ketone bodies for energy may be incomplete.[33] Therefore, an RDA for carbohydrate of 130 grams per day has been set for individuals aged 1 year and older. The RDA for carbohydrate rises to 175 grams per day for pregnancy and 210 grams per day during lactation.

Most Americans eat more carbohydrate than this amount. In fact, health-promoting diets *should* contain more carbohydrate. In its report on DRIs for macronutrients, the Food and Nutrition Board developed recommended ranges of intake for the energy-yielding nutrients based on evidence of increased risk for heart disease with very high carbohydrate intakes, and increased risk for obesity and heart disease with high fat intake. The Acceptable Macronutrient Distribution Range (AMDR) for carbohydrate is 45 to 65 percent of kilocalories. For an adult who eats about 2,000 kilocalories daily, this represents 225 to 325 grams of carbohydrate. The Daily Value for carbohydrates is 300 grams per day, representing 60 percent of the calories in a 2,000-kilocalorie diet.

The *Dietary Guidelines for Americans* suggests that we "consume at least half of all grains as whole grains. Increase whole-grain intake by replacing refined grains with whole grains."[34] One key recommendation is to choose and prepare foods and beverages with little added sugar. Although the AMDR for added sugars is no more than 25 percent of daily energy intake, a point at which the micronutrient quality of the diet declines, many sources suggest that added sugar intake should be lower. In its 2003 report on diet and chronic disease, the World Health Organization suggested a limit of 10 percent of energy from added sugars.[35] The "empty calories" in the USDA's MyPlate food guidance system covers calories from added sugars, alcohol, and higher-fat meat or milk choices. For someone consuming 2,000 kilocalories daily, about 250 kilocalories are "empty calories." If no alcohol is consumed, added sugar must then be balanced with extra fat. If fat intake is low (close to 20 percent of energy intake), added sugar could be as much as 18 teaspoons, equivalent to two cans of regular soft drink each day. But if fat intake is higher (35 percent of energy intake), allowable added sugar drops to 0 teaspoons.

The *Dietary Guidelines for Americans* also recommends that we "increase vegetable and fruit intake and eat a variety of vegetables, especially dark-green and red and orange vegetables." Fruits, vegetables, and whole grains, along with legumes, are good sources of fiber. The Adequate Intake (AI) value for total fiber is 38 grams per day for men aged 19 to 50 years, and 25 grams per day for women in the same age group. This AI value is based on a level of intake (14 grams per 1,000 kilocalories) that provides the greatest risk reduction for heart disease.[36] The Daily Value for fiber used on food labels is 25 grams.

Current Consumption

Adult Americans currently consume about 49 to 50 percent of their energy intake as carbohydrate. Dietary fiber averages around 18 grams per day for women and 22 grams per day for men.[37] Added sugar intake ranges widely, from 40 to 120 grams per day for adults; on average, sugar intake is about 16 percent of daily energy intake. Although these values for total carbohydrate

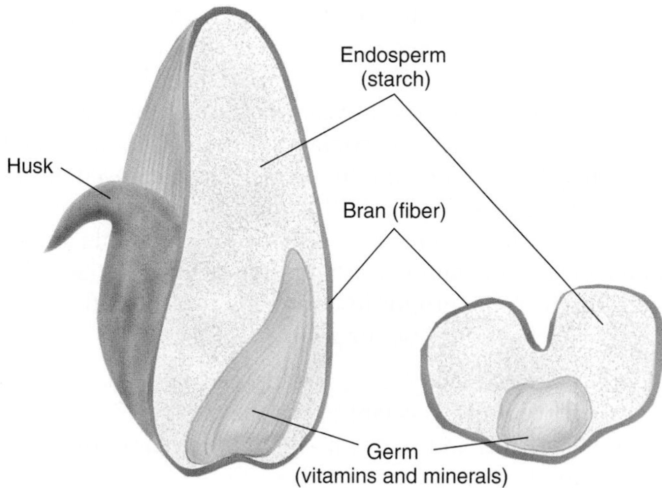

Figure 4.16 **Anatomy of a kernel of grain.** Whole kernels of grains consist of four parts: germ, endosperm, bran, and husk.

and added sugar are within the AMDRs, fiber consumption is lower than recommended.

Natural sugars in milk, fruits, and grains make up about half of our sugar intake; refined sugars added to foods make up the other half. About one-third of our added sugar intake comes from nondiet soft drinks. This is of concern because as soft drink intake rises, so does energy intake, while consumption of milk and the vitamin and mineral quality of the diet declines.[38] Many studies suggest that rising soft drink consumption is a factor in overweight and obesity, even among very young children.[39]

germ The innermost part of a grain, located at the base of the kernel, that can grow into a new plant. The germ is rich in protein, oils, vitamins, and minerals.

endosperm The largest, middle portion of a grain kernel. The endosperm is high in starch to provide food for the growing plant embryo.

bran The layers of protective coating around the grain kernel that are rich in dietary fiber and nutrients.

husk The inedible covering of a grain kernel. Also known as the chaff.

Choosing Carbohydrates Wisely

The *Dietary Guidelines for Americans* encourages us to increase our intake of fruits, vegetables, whole grains, and fat-free or low-fat milk while keeping calorie intake under control. These foods are all good sources of carbohydrates and many other nutrients. Choosing a variety of fruits and vegetables, and particularly including choices from all five vegetable subgroups (dark-green vegetables, orange vegetables, legumes, starchy vegetables, and other vegetables), provides vitamin A, vitamin C, folate, potassium, and fiber.

Strategies for Increasing Fiber Intake

Along with fruits and vegetables, whole grains are important sources of fiber. Whole kernels of grains consist of four parts: germ, endosperm, bran, and husk. (See **Figure 4.16**.) The **germ**, the innermost part at the base of the kernel, is the portion that grows into a new plant. It is rich in protein, oils, vitamins, and minerals. The **endosperm** is the largest, middle portion of the grain kernel. It is high in starch and provides food for the growing plant embryo. The **bran** is composed of layers of protective coating around the grain kernel and is rich in dietary fiber. The **husk** is an inedible covering.

When grains are refined—making white flour from wheat, for example, or making white rice from brown rice—the process removes the outer husk and bran layers and sometimes the inner germ of the grain kernel. Because the bran and germ portions of the grain contain much of the dietary fiber, vitamins, and minerals, the nutrient content of whole grains is far superior to that of refined grains. Although food manufacturers add iron, thiamin, riboflavin, and niacin back to white flour through enrichment, they usually do not add back dietary fiber and nutrients such as vitamin B_6, calcium, phosphorus, potassium, magnesium, and zinc, which are also lost in processing.

Read labels carefully to choose foods that contain whole grains. Terms such as *whole-wheat*, *whole-grain*, *rolled oats*, and *brown rice* indicate that the entire grain kernel is included in the food. Even better, look for the words *100 percent whole grain* or *100 percent whole wheat*. Several "whole-grain" products on the market may contain some whole grains, but the total amount of whole grains may be very low or refining may have removed most of certain whole-grain components. In early 2006, the FDA proposed that anything labeled as containing whole grains must contain a comparable amount of the fibrous, protein-dense, and nutrient-rich portions of grains—the endosperm, germ, and bran—in the same proportion normally present in the intact grain.[40]

To increase your fiber intake:

- Eat more whole-grain breads, cereals, pasta, and rice, as well as more fruits, vegetables, and legumes.
- Eat fruits and vegetables with the peel, if possible. The peel is high in fiber.
- Add fruits to muffins and pancakes.
- Add legumes—such as lentils and pinto, navy, kidney, and black beans—to casseroles and mixed dishes as a meat substitute.
- Substitute whole-grain flour for all-purpose flour in recipes whenever possible.
- Use brown rice instead of white rice.
- Substitute oats for flour in crumb toppings.
- Choose high-fiber cereals.
- Choose whole fruits rather than fruit juices.

When increasing your fiber intake, do so gradually and drink plenty of fluids to allow your body to adjust. Add just a few grams a day; otherwise, abdominal cramps, gas, bloating, and diarrhea or constipation may result. Parents and caregivers should also emphasize foods rich in fiber for children older than 2 years, but must take care that these foods do not fill a child up before energy and nutrient needs are met. Table 4.2 lists various foods that are high in simple and complex carbohydrates.

Going Green

Whole Grains: Delicious, Easy to Prepare, Affordable, Good for Your Health, and Good for the Environment

Whole-grain products are the perfect fit for a healthy body and a healthy environment. Remember that by definition, whole grains are not processed. These "whole" foods require ingestion and digestion in the way that they come in nature—together. Whole grains can claim an array of health benefits that other foods cannot. Studies show that people who eat whole grains have a lower body mass index, lower total cholesterol, and lower waist-to-hip ratio. In addition, as a less processed food, whole grains save on CO_2 production and lighten your carbon footprint.

Whole grains are convenient, easy to prepare, generally inexpensive, and found in a number of delicious foods. Many options are available for adding whole grains to your diet. A simple way to include more grains is to substitute them for the more processed version, such as using whole-grain bread instead of white bread, or brown rice instead of white rice. Foods rich in whole grains also make great snack foods. Whole-grain ready-to-eat cereal, snack crackers, and popcorn are all great choices. So, the next time you are tempted to choose a highly processed snack, such as potato chips, a doughnut, or chocolate chip cookies, consider a whole-grain option instead. Such a change just may add years to your life, and life to the planet!

Table 4.2 High-Carbohydrate Foods

High in Complex Carbohydrates	High in Simple Carbohydrates
Bagels	***Naturally Present***
Tortillas	Fruits
Cereals	Fruit juices
Crackers	Skim milk
Rice cakes	Plain nonfat yogurt
Legumes	
Corn	***Added***
Potatoes	Angel food cake
Peas	Soft drinks
Squash	Sherbet
Popcorn	Syrups
	Sweetened nonfat yogurt
	Candy
	Jellies
	Jams
	Gelatin
	High-sugar breakfast cereals
	Cookies
	Frosting

Table 4.3 Forms of Sugar Used in Foods

Brown rice syrup
Brown sugar
Concentrated fruit juice sweetener
Confectioners sugar
Corn syrup
Dextrose
Fructose
Galactose
Glucose
Granulated sugar
High-fructose corn syrup
Invert sugar
Lactose
Levulose
Maltose
Mannitol
Maple sugar
Molasses
Natural sweeteners
Raw sugar
Sorbitol
Turbinado sugar
White sugar
Xylitol

Although health food stores, pharmacies, and even grocery stores sell many types of fiber supplements, most experts agree that you should get fiber from food rather than from a supplement. Foods rich in dietary fiber contain a variety of fibers as well as vitamins, minerals, and other phytochemicals that offer important health effects.

Moderating Sugar Intake

Most of us enjoy the taste of sweet foods, and there's no reason why we should not. But for some individuals, habitually high sugar intake crowds out foods that are higher in fiber, vitamins, and minerals.

To reduce added sugars in your diet:

- Use less of all nutritive sugars, including white sugar, brown sugar, honey, and syrups.
- Limit consumption of soft drinks, high-sugar breakfast cereals, candy, ice cream, and sweet desserts.
- Use fresh or frozen fruits and fruits canned in natural juices or light syrup for dessert and to sweeten waffles, pancakes, muffins, and breads.

Read ingredient lists carefully. Food labels list the total grams of sugar in a food, which includes both sugars naturally present in foods and sugars added to foods. Many terms for added sweeteners appear on food labels. Foods likely to be high in sugar list some form of sweetener as the first, second, or third ingredient on labels. Table 4.3 lists various forms of sugar used in foods.

Sugar substitutes can help many people lower sugar intake, but foods with these substitutes may not provide less energy than similar products containing nutritive sweeteners. Rather than sugar, other energy-yielding

Quick Bite

Liquid Candy

In the United States, corn sweeteners are primarily consumed in carbonated soft drinks (25.4 pounds per year), fruitades and drinks (8.2 pounds), and syrup and sweet toppings (4.1 pounds). In all, 36.3 percent of sugar and corn sweeteners is consumed in carbonated soft drinks, fruitades, and other nonalcoholic drinks.

Quick Bite

Sugar Overload

In many affluent countries, sugar consumption is nearly 100 pounds per capita per year. The United States averages 103 pounds of sugar per person per year—roughly half as refined sugar and half as corn sweeteners (especially high-fructose corn syrup). Boys aged 12 to 19 years consume nearly 160 pounds per year, and girls the same ages consume 114 pounds annually.

nutrients, such as fat, are the primary source of the calories in these foods. Also, as sugar substitute use in the United States has increased, so has sugar consumption—an interesting paradox!

Key Concepts *Current recommendations suggest that Americans consume at least 130 grams of carbohydrate per day. An intake of total carbohydrates representing between 45 and 65 percent of total energy intake and a fiber intake of 14 grams per 1,000 kilocalories are associated with reduced heart disease risk. Added sugar should account for no more than 25 percent of daily energy and ideally should be much less. Americans generally eat too little fiber. An emphasis on consuming whole grains, legumes, fruits, and vegetables would help to increase fiber intake.*

nutritive sweeteners Substances that impart sweetness to foods and that can be absorbed and yield energy in the body. Simple sugars, sugar alcohols, and high-fructose corn syrup are the most common nutritive sweeteners used in food products.

refined sweeteners Composed of monosaccharides and disaccharides that have been extracted and processed from other foods.

Nutritive Sweeteners

Nutritive sweeteners are digestible carbohydrates and therefore provide energy. They include monosaccharides, disaccharides, and sugar alcohols from either natural or refined sources. White sugar, brown sugar, honey, maple syrup, glucose, fructose, xylitol, sorbitol, and mannitol are just some of the many nutritive sweeteners used in foods. One slice of angel food cake, for example, contains about 5 teaspoons of sugar. Fruit-flavored yogurt contains about 7 teaspoons of sugar. Even two sticks of chewing gum contain about 1 teaspoon of sugar. Whether sweeteners come from natural sources or are refined, all are broken down in the small intestine and absorbed as monosaccharides and provide energy. Because all these absorbed monosaccharides end up as glucose, the body cannot tell whether the monosaccharides came from honey or table sugar.

The sugar alcohols in sugarless chewing gums and candies are also nutritive sweeteners, but the body does not digest and absorb them fully, so they provide only about 2 kilocalories per gram, compared with the 4 kilocalories per gram that other sugars provide.

Natural Sweeteners Natural sweeteners such as honey and maple syrup contain monosaccharides and disaccharides that make them taste sweet. Honey contains a mix of fructose and glucose—the same two monosaccharides that make up sucrose. Bees make honey from the sucrose-containing nectar of flowering plants. Real maple syrup contains primarily sucrose and is made by boiling and concentrating the sap from sugar maple trees. Most maple-flavored syrups sold in grocery stores, however, are made from corn syrup with maple flavoring added.

Many fruits also contain sugars that impart a sweet taste. Usually the riper the fruit, the higher its sugar content—a ripe pear tastes sweeter than an unripe one.

Quick Bite

Why Is Honey Dangerous for Babies?

Because honey and Karo syrup (corn syrup) can contain spores of the bacterium *Clostridium botulinum*, they should never be fed to infants younger than 1 year. Infants do not produce as much stomach acid as older children and adults, so these spores can germinate in an infant's GI tract and cause botulism, a deadly foodborne illness.

Refined Sweeteners **Refined sweeteners** are monosaccharides and disaccharides that have been extracted from plant foods. White table sugar is sucrose extracted from either sugar beets or sugar cane. Molasses is a by-product of the sugar-refining process. Most brown sugar is really white table sugar with molasses added for coloring and flavor.

Manufacturers make high-fructose corn syrup by treating cornstarch with acid and enzymes to break down the starch into glucose. Then different enzymes convert about half the glucose to fructose. High-fructose corn syrup has about the same sweetness as table sugar but costs less to produce. An increase in high-fructose corn syrup in soft drinks and other processed foods accounts for much of the increased use of sweeteners in the United States

Nutrition Science *in Action*

Sugar and Children's Behavior

Observations: Many parents and child-care professionals observe that eating sugary foods "sets some children off." Parents cite cane sugar as the most frequent trigger of hyperactive behavior and provide anecdotal evidence with reports of children who become restless, irritable, and uncontrollable after eating sugar.

Hypothesis: Dietary sucrose adversely affects behavior in children.

Experimental Plan: Conduct a double-blind trial with 23 school-aged children (6 to 10 years) described by parents as sensitive to sugar. For each of three consecutive 3-week periods, provide the children and their families with a different diet (see below). The children, their families, and the research staff are unaware of the sequence of the diets, and all diets are essentially free of additives, artificial food coloring, and preservatives. Use standardized assessments to evaluate each child's behavior at the start and weekly during the experimental diets. The assessments measure 39 variables, such as attention, impulsivity, hyperactivity, aggression, social skills, mood, memory, and learning. Each week, ask the parents to attempt identification of the children's diets.

Results: The hypothesis that dietary sugar causes adverse behavior is not confirmed. In this group of school-aged children thought to be sensitive to sugar, none of the 39 measured variables differed significantly among the three dietary periods or with the baseline assessment. Only one parent correctly identified the sequence of diets.

Conclusion and Discussion: Overall, comparisons among the three diets and baseline measures are resoundingly negative and do not support opinions and uncontrolled observations that sugar intake affects children's behavior. Additional studies have yielded similar negative results. Sugar-free diets, which can be burdensome and socially inhibiting, should not be endorsed on the basis of unsupported anecdotal evidence.

Source: Based on Wolraich ML, Lindgren SD, Stumbo PJ, et al. Effects of diets high in sucrose or aspartame on the behavior and cognitive performance of children. *New Engl J Med.* 1994;330:301–307.

Does eating sugar affect a child's behavior?

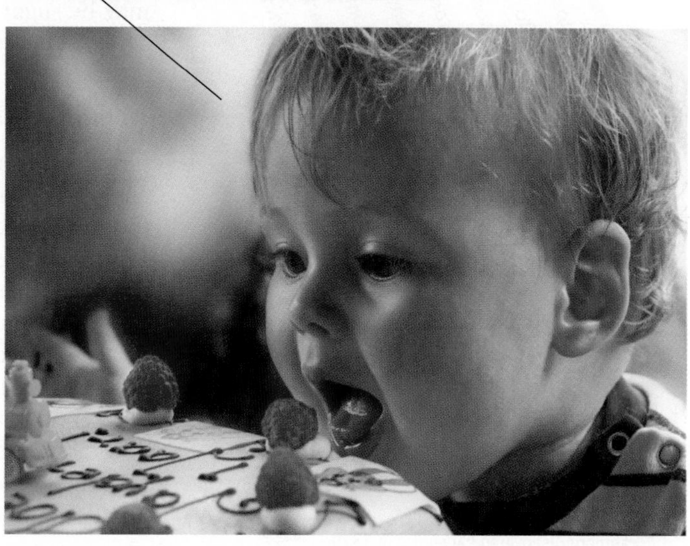

Experimental Diets

Diet 1
High sucrose; no artificial sweeteners

Diet 2
Low sucrose; sweeten with aspartame

Diet 3
Low sucrose; sweeten with saccharin

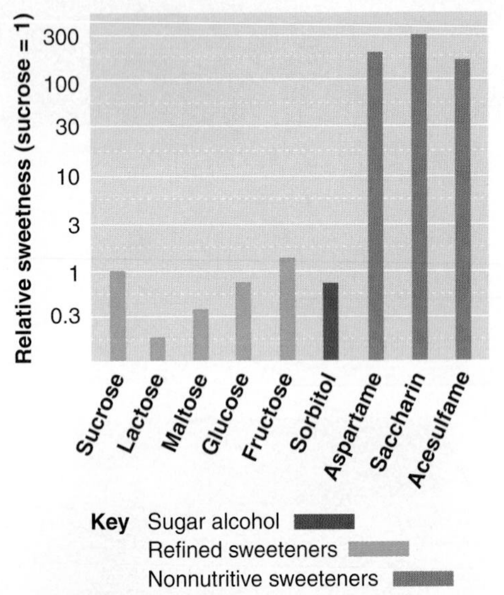

Figure 4.17 **Comparing the sweetness of sweeteners.** Artificial sweeteners are much sweeter than table sugar.

Quick Bite

The Discovery of Saccharin

A German student named Constantine Fahlberg discovered saccharin in 1879, while working with organic chemicals in the lab of Ira Remsen at Johns Hopkins University. One day, while eating some bread, he noticed a strong sweet flavor. He deduced that the flavor came from the compound on his hands, $C_6H_4CONHSO_2$. Fahlberg then patented saccharin by himself, without Remsen.

polyols See *sugar alcohols.*

nonnutritive sweeteners Substances that impart sweetness to foods but supply little or no energy to the body; also called artificial or alternative sweeteners. They include acesulfame, aspartame, saccharin, and sucralose.

saccharin [SAK-ah-ren] An artificial sweetener that tastes about 300 to 700 times sweeter than sucrose.

aspartame [AH-spar-tame] An artificial sweetener composed of two amino acids and methanol. It is 200 times sweeter than sucrose. Its trade name is NutraSweet.

since the 1970s.[41] High fructose consumption may contribute to obesity and high triglyceride levels.[42]

Sugar Alcohols The sugar alcohols sorbitol, xylitol, and mannitol occur naturally in a wide variety of fruits and vegetables and are commercially produced from other carbohydrates such as sucrose, glucose, and starch. Also known as **polyols**, these sweeteners are not as sweet as sucrose, but they do have the advantage of being less likely to cause tooth decay. Manufacturers use sugar alcohols to sweeten sugar-free products, such as gum and mints, and to add bulk and texture, provide a cooling sensation in the mouth, and retain moisture in foods. When sugar alcohols are used as the sweetener, the product may be sugar- (sucrose-) free, but it is not calorie-free. Check the label to be sure. An excessive intake of sugar alcohols may cause diarrhea.[43]

Nonnutritive Sweeteners

Gram for gram, most **nonnutritive sweeteners** (also called artificial sweeteners) are many times sweeter than nutritive sweeteners. As a consequence, food manufacturers can use much less artificial sweetener to sweeten foods. **Figure 4.17** compares the sweetness of sweeteners. Although some nonnutritive sweeteners do provide energy, their energy contribution is minimal given the small amounts used.

The most common nonnutritive sweeteners in the United States are saccharin, aspartame, and acesulfame K. Cyclamates, which were banned in the United States in 1969 because of cancer concerns, are still used in Canada and many other countries. For people who want to decrease their intake of sugar and energy while still enjoying sweet foods, artificial sweeteners offer an alternative. Also, artificial sweeteners do not contribute to tooth decay.

Saccharin Discovered in 1879 and used in foods ever since then, **saccharin** tastes about 300 times sweeter than sucrose. In the 1970s, research indicated that very large doses of saccharin were associated with bladder cancer in laboratory animals. As a result, in 1977 the U.S. Food and Drug Administration (FDA) proposed banning saccharin from use in food. Widespread protests by consumer and industry groups, however, led Congress to impose a moratorium on the saccharin ban. Every few years, the moratorium was extended, and products containing saccharin had to display a warning label about saccharin and cancer risk in animals. In 2000, convincing evidence of safety led to saccharin's removal from the National Toxicology Program's list of potential cancer-causing agents, and the U.S. Congress repealed the warning label requirement.[44] In Canada, although saccharin is banned from food products, it can be purchased in pharmacies and carries a warning label.

Aspartame The artificial sweetener **aspartame** is a combination of two amino acids: phenylalanine and aspartic acid. When digested and absorbed, it provides 4 kilocalories per gram. However, aspartame is so many times sweeter than sucrose that the amount used to sweeten foods contributes virtually zero calories to the diet, and it does not promote tooth decay. The FDA approved aspartame for use in some foods in 1981 and for use in soft drinks in 1983. More than 90 countries allow aspartame in products such as beverages, gelatin desserts, gums, and fruit spreads. Because heating destroys the sweetening power of aspartame, this sweetener cannot be used in products that require cooking.

Several safety concerns have been raised regarding aspartame. Some groups claim that aspartame could cause high blood levels of phenylalanine.

In reality, high-protein foods such as meats contain much more phenylalanine than foods sweetened with aspartame. The amounts of phenylalanine in aspartame-sweetened foods are not high enough to cause concern for most people. However, people with a genetic disease called **phenylketonuria (PKU)** cannot properly metabolize the amino acid phenylalanine, so they must carefully monitor their phenylalanine intake from all sources, including aspartame.

Although some people report headaches, dizziness, seizures, nausea, or allergic reactions with aspartame use, scientific studies have failed to confirm these effects, and most experts believe aspartame is safe for healthy people.[45] The FDA sets a maximum allowable daily intake of aspartame of 50 milligrams per kilogram of body weight.[46] This amount of aspartame equals the amount in sixteen 12-ounce diet soft drinks for adults and eight diet soft drinks for children.

Acesulfame K Marketed under the brand name Sunette, **acesulfame K** is about 200 times sweeter than table sugar. The FDA approved its use in the United States in 1988. Acesulfame K provides no energy, because the body cannot digest it. Food manufacturers use acesulfame K in chewing gum, powdered beverage mixes, nondairy creamers, gelatins, and puddings. Heat does not affect acesulfame K, so it can be used in cooking.

Sucralose Sold under the trade name Splenda, **sucralose** was approved for use in the United States in 1998 and has been used in Canada since 1992. Sucralose is made from sucrose, but the resulting compound is nonnutritive and about 600 times sweeter than sugar. Sucralose has been approved for use in a wide variety of products, including baked goods, beverages, gelatin desserts, and frozen dairy desserts. It also can be used as a "tabletop sweetener," with consumers adding it directly to food.

Other Sweeteners

The FDA has accepted the manufacturers' determinations that the sweet substances known as **D-tagatose** and **trehalose** are GRAS (Generally Recognized as Safe) and can be added to foods. Small amounts of tagatose are found naturally in some dairy foods, and tagatose is derived from lactose. Although it has only 75 to 92 percent of the sweetness of sugar, tagatose is incompletely absorbed and provides only 1.5 kilocalories per gram. Trehalose, which is only half as sweet as sucrose, is found naturally in mushrooms, lobster, shrimp, and foods produced using baker's or brewer's yeast. It is made commercially from starch. In foods, trehalose is probably used more often for its textural properties than for sweetness. Trehalose is absorbed completely and provides 4 kilocalories per gram, but produces a lower glycemic response than glucose.[47]

Neotame was approved as a food additive in 2002. It can be used as a tabletop sweetener or added to foods. Neotame is a derivative of a dipeptide containing aspartic acid and phenylalanine—the same two amino acids that make up aspartame. However, chemical modifications to the structure make it 30 to 40 times sweeter than aspartame, or about 7,000 to 13,000 times sweeter than sucrose.

Stevioside (also known as **stevia**) is derived from the stevia plant found in South America. Stevia leaves have been used for centuries to sweeten beverages and make tea. In Japan, stevioside has been used as a sweetener since the 1970s. This substance is 300 times sweeter than sucrose, but its metabolism in the body has not been completely investigated. Because the FDA has not approved stevioside as a food additive nor accepted it as a GRAS substance,

Academy of Nutrition and Dietetics

Use of Nutritive and Nonnutritive Sweeteners

It is the position of the Academy of Nutrition and Dietetics that consumers can safely enjoy a range of nutritive and nonnutritive sweeteners when consumed in a diet that is guided by current federal nutrition recommendations, such as the *Dietary Guidelines for Americans* and the Dietary References Intakes, as well as individual health goals.

Source: Position of the American Dietetic Association: use of nutritive and nonnutritive sweeteners. *J Am Diet Assoc.* 2004;104:255–275. Copyright 2004. Reprinted with permission from Elsevier.

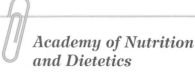

phenylketonuria (PKU) An inherited disorder caused by a lack or deficiency of the enzyme that converts phenylalanine to tyrosine.

acesulfame K [ay-SUL-fame] An artificial sweetener that is 200 times sweeter than common table sugar (sucrose). Because it is not digested and absorbed by the body, acesulfame contributes no calories to the diet and yields no energy when consumed.

sucralose An artificial sweetener made from sucrose; it was approved for use in the United States in 1998, and has been used in Canada since 1992. Sucralose is nonnutritive and about 600 times sweeter than sugar.

D-tagatose An artificial sweetener derived from lactose that has the same sweetness as sucrose with only half the calories.

trehalose A disaccharide of two glucose molecules, but with a linkage different from maltose. Used as a food additive and sweetener.

neotame An artificial sweetener similar to aspartame, but one that is sweeter and does not require a warning label for phenylketonurics.

stevioside A dietary supplement, not approved for use as a sweetener, that is extracted and refined from *Stevia rebaudiana* leaves.

stevia See *stevioside.*

glycyrrhizin Nonnutritive sweetener derived from licorice root. Has a licorice flavor and is 50 to 100 times sweeter than sucrose.

it cannot be used in food in the United States. Although stevia may be sold as a dietary supplement, its labels may not promote its use as a sweetener. With recent demands for low-carbohydrate, low sugar, all-natural food products, stevia has gained attention as a natural sweetener.

Some sweet food additives are GRAS flavoring agents but are not approved as sweeteners. **Glycyrrhizin**, an extract of licorice root, is 50 to 100 times sweeter than sucrose, but its pronounced licorice flavor and tendency to

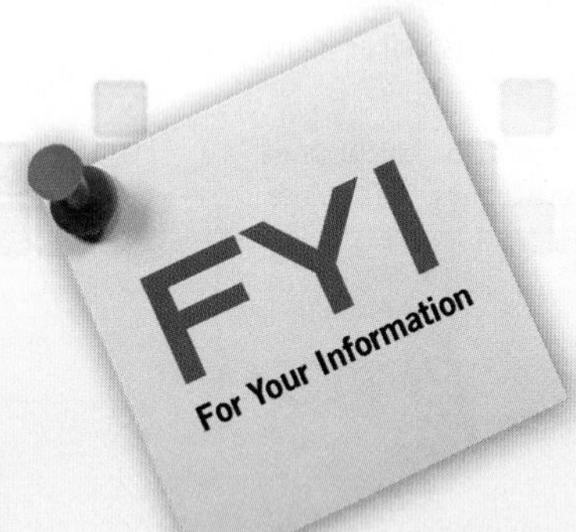

Unfounded Claims Against Sugars

Sugar has become the vehicle for diet zealots to create a new crusade. Cut sugar to trim fat! Bust sugar! Break the sugar habit! These battle cries falsely demonize sugar as a dietary villain. But what are the facts?

Sugar and Obesity

Many people believe that sugar is fattening and causes obesity. Sugar is a carbohydrate, and all carbohydrates provide 4 kilocalories per gram. High fat—not sugar—intakes are associated with a greater risk of obesity.[1] Fat is a more concentrated source of energy, and provides 9 kilocalories per gram. However, many foods high in sugar, such as doughnuts and cookies, are also high in fat. Excess energy intake from any source will cause obesity, but sugar by itself is no more likely to cause obesity than starch or protein. The increased availability of low-fat and fat-free foods has not reduced obesity rates in the United States; in fact, the incidence of obesity is still climbing. Some speculate that consumers equate fat-free with calorie-free and eat more of these foods, not realizing that fat-free foods often have a higher sugar content, which makes any calorie savings negligible. Also, foods high in added sugars often have low nutrient value and become "extras" in the diet. High intake of added sugar is associated with increased total energy intake.[2]

Sugar and Heart Disease

Risk factors for heart disease include a genetic predisposition, smoking, high blood pressure, high blood cholesterol levels, diabetes, and obesity. Sugar by itself does not cause heart disease.[3] However, if intake of high-sugar foods contributes to obesity, then risk for heart disease increases. In addition, excessive intake of refined sugar can alter blood lipids in carbohydrate-sensitive people, increasing their risk for heart disease. However, a high fat intake is more likely to promote obesity than a high sugar intake. Thus, total fats, saturated fat, cholesterol, and obesity have a significantly more important relationship to heart disease than sugar.

Sugar and Behavior

Parents continue to talk about kids "bouncing off the walls" at birthday parties because of "all that sugar." So, what's going on? Most likely, the event (a party, trick-or-treating for Halloween, a carnival) is enhancing kids' normal levels of excitement and enthusiasm. From a brain chemistry perspective, carbohydrates actually have a calming effect by increasing production of the sleep-inducing chemical serotonin! Well-controlled research studies have found no link between sugar and hyperactivity, so blame the excitement of the party, but not the sugar, for kids' "wild" behavior.[4] (See the Nutrition Science in Action feature "Sugar and Children's Behavior.")

In 1978 Dan White blamed his gunning down the mayor of San Francisco on an emotional state created by eating too many Hostess Twinkies, a legal strategy that became known as the Twinkie defense. Claims that sugar causes criminal behavior in adults are unfounded. Studies show no association between high sugar intake and adult behavior.[5]

1 Lichtenstein AH, Kennedy E, Barrier P, et al. Dietary fat consumption and health. *Nutr Rev.* 1998;56:S3–S19.

2 US Department of Agriculture and US Department of Health and Human Services. *Dietary Guidelines for Americans, 2010.* 7th ed. Washington, DC: US Government Printing Office, December 2010.

3 Institute of Medicine, Food and Nutrition Board. *Dietary Reference Intakes for Energy, Carbohydrate, Fiber, Fat, Fatty Acids, Cholesterol, Protein, and Amino Acids.* Washington, DC: National Academies Press, 2005.

4 White JW, Wolraich M. Effect of sugar on behavior and mental performance. *Am J Clin Nutr.* 1995;62:S242–S249; Wolraich ML, Lindgren SD, Stumbo PJ, et al. Effects of diets high in sucrose or aspartame on the behavior and cognitive performance of children. *N Engl J Med.* 1994;330:301–307; and Institute of Medicine, Food and Nutrition Board. *Dietary Reference Intakes for Energy, Carbohydrate.*

5 White, Wolraich. Effect of sugar on behavior and mental performance.

increase blood pressure limit widespread use. **Dihydrochalcones (DHCs)**, derived from citrus fruits, can be 300 to 2,000 times sweeter than sucrose. **Thaumatin**, a mixture of sweet-tasting proteins from a West African fruit, is about 2,000 times sweeter than sucrose. DHCs and thaumatin have a delayed sweet taste and licorice aftertaste. Thaumatin cannot be used in products to be baked or boiled.

Key Concepts *Sweeteners add flavor to foods. Nutritive sweeteners provide energy, whereas nonnutritive sweeteners provide little or no energy. The body cannot tell the difference between sugars derived from natural and refined sources.*

Carbohydrates and Health

Carbohydrates contribute both positively and negatively to health. On the up side, foods rich in fiber help keep the gastrointestinal tract healthy and may reduce the risk of heart disease and cancer. On the down side, excess sugar can contribute to weight gain, poor nutrient intake, and tooth decay.

Sugar and Nutrient Intake

Foods high in sugar are popular in American diets. These empty-calorie foods (e.g., candy, soft drinks, sweetened gelatin, and some desserts) provide most of their energy from sugar but contain little or no dietary fiber, vitamins, or minerals. Studies link the rising prevalence of obesity in children to consumption of sugar-sweetened drinks.[48] On average, Americans drink 53 gallons of soda per year—40 percent more than two decades ago.[49] Consider that one 12-ounce soft drink contains 10 to 12 teaspoons of sugar. Would you add that much sugar to a glass of iced tea?

People with high energy needs, such as active teenagers and young adults, can afford to get a bit more of their calories from high-sugar foods. People with low energy needs, such as some elderly or sedentary people or people trying to lose weight, cannot afford as many calories from high-sugar foods. Most people can include moderate amounts of sugar in their diet and still meet other nutrient needs. But as the amount of added sugar in the diet increases, intake of vitamins and minerals tends to decrease.[50]

Sugar and Dental Caries

High sugar intake contributes to **dental caries**, or cavities. (See **Figure 4.18**.) When bacteria in the mouth feed on sugars, they produce acids that eat away tooth enamel and dental structure, causing dental caries. Although these bacteria quickly metabolize sugars, they feed on any carbohydrate, including starch.

The longer a carbohydrate remains in the mouth or the more frequently it is consumed, the more likely it will promote dental caries. Foods that stick to the teeth, such as caramel, licorice, crackers, sugary cereals, and cookies, are more likely to cause dental caries than foods that are quickly washed out of the mouth. High-sugar beverages such as soft drinks are more likely to cause dental caries when they are sipped slowly over an extended period of time. A baby should never be put to bed with a bottle, because the warm milk or juice may remain in the mouth all night, providing a ready source of carbohydrate for bacteria to break down.

Snacking on high-sugar foods throughout the day provides a continuous intake of carbohydrate that nourishes the bacteria in your mouth, promoting

Dietary Guidelines for Americans, 2010
Key Recommendations

Foods and Food Components to Reduce

- Reduce the intake of calories from solid fats and added sugars.
- Limit the consumption of foods that contain refined grains, especially refined grain foods that contain solid fats, added sugars, and sodium.

Foods and Nutrients to Increase

- Increase vegetable and fruit intake.
- Eat a variety of vegetables, especially dark-green and red and orange vegetables and beans and peas.
- Consume at least half of all grains as whole grains. Increase whole-grain intake by replacing refined grains with whole grains.
- Increase intake of fat-free or low-fat milk and milk products, such as milk, yogurt, cheese, or fortified soy beverages.
- Choose foods that provide more potassium, dietary fiber, calcium, and vitamin D, which are nutrients of concern in American diets. These foods include vegetables, fruits, whole grains, and milk and milk products.

dihydrochalcones (DHCs) Nonnutritive sweeteners derived from bioflavonoids of citrus fruits. Approximately 300 to 2,000 times sweeter than sucrose and have a a licorice aftertaste.

thaumatin Mixture of sweet-tasting proteins from a West African fruit. Approximately 2,000 times sweeter than sucrose and has a licorice aftertaste. Breaks down when heated to cooking temperatures.

dental caries [KARE-ees] Destruction of the enamel surface of teeth caused by acids resulting from bacterial breakdown of sugars in the mouth.

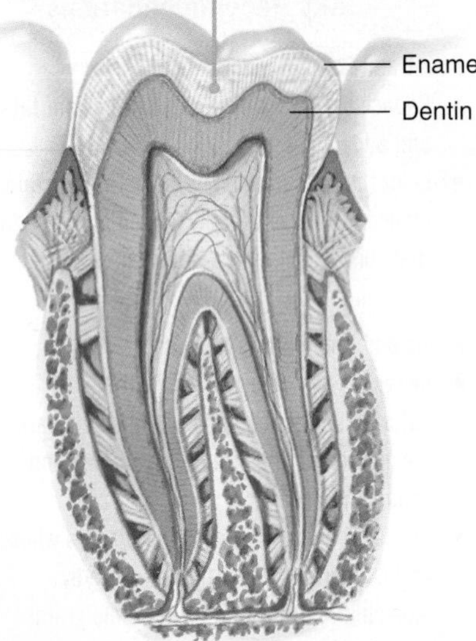
Bacteria feeding on sugar and other carbohydrates produce acids that eat away tooth enamel
Enamel
Dentin

Figure 4.18 **Dental health.** Good dental hygiene, adequate fluoride, and proper nutrition help maintain healthy teeth. A well-balanced diet contains vitamins and minerals crucial for healthy bones and teeth. To help prevent dental caries, avoid continuous snacking on high-sugar foods, especially those that stick to the teeth.

the formation of dental caries. Good dental hygiene, adequate fluoride, and a well-balanced diet for strong tooth formation can help prevent cavities.[51]

Fiber and Obesity

Foods rich in fiber are usually low in fat and energy. They are also more filling, offer a greater volume of food for fewer calories, and take longer to eat. Once eaten, foods high in dietary fiber take longer to leave the stomach and they attract water, giving a feeling of fullness. Consider the following three apple products, which have the same energy content but different fiber content: a large apple containing 5 grams of dietary fiber; ½ cup of applesauce containing 2 grams of fiber; and ¾ cup of apple juice containing 0.2 gram of fiber. For most of us, the whole apple would be more filling and satisfying than the applesauce or apple juice.

Studies show that people who consume more fiber weigh less than those who consume less fiber, suggesting that fiber intake has a role in weight control. Although research supports a role for dietary fiber in reducing hunger and promoting satiety, studies on specific types of fiber have produced inconsistent results.[52]

Fiber and Type 2 Diabetes

Populations with a high intake of dietary fiber have a low incidence of type 2 diabetes (see Chapter 15 for a description of type 2 diabetes). Epidemiological evidence suggests that intake of certain fibers may delay glucose uptake and smooth out the blood glucose response, thus providing a protective effect against diabetes.[53] Current dietary recommendations for people with type 2 diabetes advise a high intake of foods rich in dietary fiber.[54]

Fiber and Cardiovascular Disease

High blood cholesterol levels increase risk for heart disease. Dietary trials using high doses of oat bran, which is high in dietary fiber, show blood cholesterol reductions of 2 percent per gram of intake.[55] Because every 1 percent decrease in blood cholesterol levels decreases the risk of heart disease by 2 percent, high fiber intake can decrease the risk of heart disease substantially. Studies show a 20 to 40 percent difference in heart disease risk between the highest and lowest fiber intake groups.[56]

Fiber from oat bran, legumes, and psyllium may lower serum cholesterol levels by binding bile acids in the gastrointestinal tract and preventing their reabsorption into the body. Bile acids are made from cholesterol in the liver and are secreted into the intestinal tract to aid with fat absorption. (See Chapter 3, "Digestion and Absorption.") When dietary fiber prevents their reabsorption, new bile acids must be made in the liver from cholesterol, reducing blood cholesterol levels. The short-chain fatty acids produced from bacterial fermentation of fiber in the large intestine may also inhibit cholesterol synthesis.[57]

Studies also show an association between high intake of whole grains and low risk of heart disease.[58] Whole grains contain not only fiber but also antioxidants, which may protect against cellular damage that promotes heart disease. It is likely that the combination of compounds found in grains, rather than any one component, explains the protective effects against heart disease.[59] Consuming at least three 1-ounce servings of whole grains each day can reduce heart disease risk.[60]

Academy of Nutrition and Dietetics

Health Implications of Dietary Fiber

It is the position of the Academy of Nutrition and Dietetics (AND) that the public should consume adequate amounts of dietary fiber from a variety of plant foods.

Source: Position of the American Dietetic Association: health implications of dietary fiber. *J Am Diet Assoc.* 2002;102:993–1000. Copyright 2000. Reprinted with permission from Elsevier.

Fiber and Gastrointestinal Disorders

Fiber, particularly cellulose from cereal grains, helps promote healthy gastrointestinal functioning. High fiber intake also helps in treating certain gastrointestinal disorders.[61]

Diets rich in fiber add bulk and increase water in the stool, softening the stool and making it easier to pass. Fiber also accelerates passage of food through the intestinal tract, promoting regularity. If fluid intake is also ample, high fiber intake helps prevent and treat constipation, hemorrhoids (swelling of rectal veins), and diverticular disease (development of pouches on the intestinal wall).

Negative Health Effects of Excess Fiber

Despite its health advantages, high fiber intake can cause problems, especially for people who drastically increase their fiber intake in a short period of time. If you increase your fiber intake, you also should increase your water intake to prevent the stool from becoming hard and impacted. A sudden increase

Quick Bite

Fierce Fiber and Flatulence

The Jerusalem artichoke surpasses even dry beans in its capacity for facilitating flatulence. This artichoke contains large amounts of nondigestible carbohydrate. After passing through the small intestine undigested, the fiber is attacked by gas-generating bacteria in the colon.

This label highlights all the carbohydrate-related information you can find on a food label. Look at the center of the Nutrition Facts label and you'll see the Total Carbohydrates along with two of the carbohydrate "subgroups": Dietary Fiber and Sugars. Recall that carbohydrates are classified into simple carbohydrates and the two complex carbohydrates starch and fiber.

Using this food label, you can determine all three of these components. There are 19 total grams of carbohydrate, with 14 grams coming from sugars and 0 grams from fiber. This means the remaining 5 grams must be from starch, which is not required to be listed separately on the label. Without even knowing what food this label represents, you can decipher that it contains a high proportion of sugar (14 of the 19 grams) and is probably sweet. If this is a fruit juice, that level of sugar would be expected; but if this is cereal, you'd be getting a lot more sugar than complex carbohydrates, and probably not be making the best choice!

Do you see the 6% listed to the right of "Total Carbohydrates"? This doesn't mean that the food item contains 6 percent of its calories from carbohydrate. Instead, it refers to the daily allotment (or Daily Value) of carbohydrates listed at the bottom of the label. There you can see that a person consuming 2,000 kilocalories per day should consume 300 grams of carbohydrates each day. This product contributes 19 grams per serving, which is just 6 percent of the Daily Value of 300 grams per day. Note that the % Daily Value for fiber is 0% because this food item lacks fiber.

The last highlighted section on this label, at the bottom of some Nutrition Facts labels, is the number of calories in a gram of carbohydrate. Recall that carbohydrates contain 4 kilocalories per gram. Armed with this information and the product's calorie information, can you calculate the percentage of calories that come from carbohydrate?

Here's how:

19 g carbohydrate × 4 kcal per g = 76 carbohydrate kcal

76 carbohydrate kcal ÷ 154 total kcal = 0.49 or 49% carbohydrate kcal

Nutrition Facts

Serving Size: 1 cup (248g)
Servings Per Container: 4

Amount Per Serving

Calories 154 Calories from fat 35

	% Daily Value*
Total Fat 4g	6%
Saturated Fat 2.5g	12%
Trans Fat 0.5g	
Cholesterol 20mg	7%
Sodium 170mg	7%
Total Carbohydrate 19g	6%
Dietary Fiber 0g	0%
Sugars 14g	
Protein 11g	

Vitamin A 4% · Vitamin C 6%
Calcium 40% · Iron 0%

* Percent Daily Values are based on a 2,000 calorie diet. Your daily values may be higher or lower depending on your calorie needs:

	Calories:	2,000	2,500
Total Fat	Less Than	65g	80g
Sat Fat	Less Than	20g	25g
Cholesterol	Less Than	300mg	300mg
Sodium	Less Than	2,400mg	2,400mg
Total Carbohydrate		300g	375g
Dietary Fiber		25g	30g

Calories per gram:
Fat 9 · Carbohydrate 4 · Protein 4

in fiber intake also can cause increased intestinal gas and bloating. These problems can be prevented both by increasing fiber intake gradually over several weeks and by drinking plenty of fluids.

High fiber intake may also bind small amounts of minerals in the GI tract and prevent them from being absorbed. In particular, fiber binds the minerals zinc, calcium, and iron. For people who get enough of these minerals, the recommended amounts of dietary fiber will not significantly affect mineral status.[62]

If the diet contains high amounts of fiber, some people, such as young children and the elderly, may become full before meeting their energy and nutrient needs. Because of a limited stomach capacity, they must be careful that their fiber intake does not interfere with their ability to consume adequate energy and nutrients.

Due to the bulky nature of fibers, excess consumption is likely to be self-limiting. Although a high fiber intake may cause occasional adverse gastrointestinal symptoms, serious chronic adverse effects have not been observed. As part of an overall healthy diet, a high intake of fiber will not produce significant deleterious effects in healthy people. Therefore, a Tolerable Upper Intake Level (UL) is not set for fiber.

Key Concepts *High sugar intake promotes dental caries and can contribute to nutrient deficiencies by replacing more nutritious foods in the diet. High intake of foods rich in dietary fiber offers many health benefits, including reduced risk of obesity, type 2 diabetes, cardiovascular disease, and gastrointestinal disorders. Increase fiber intake gradually while drinking plenty of fluids; children and the elderly with small appetites should take care that their energy needs are still met. The DRIs do not contain a UL for fiber.*

Learning Portfolio

Key Terms

	page
acesulfame K [ay-SUL-fame]	171
alpha (α) bonds	155
amylopectin [am-ih-low-PEK-tin]	152
amylose [AM-ih-los]	152
aspartame [AH-spar-tame]	170
beta (β) bonds	155
β-glucans	154
blood glucose levels	160
bran	165
cellulose [SELL-you-los]	154
chitin	154
chitosan	154
complex carbohydrates	150
condensation	150
dental caries [KARE-ees]	173
diabetes mellitus	161
dietary fiber	153
dihydrochalcones (DHCs)	173
disaccharides [dye-SACK-uh-rides]	147
endosperm	165
epinephrine	161
fructose [FROOK-tose]	148
functional fiber	153
galactose [gah-LAK-tose]	148
germ	165
glucagon [GLOO-kuh-gon]	160
glucose [GLOO-kose]	148
glycemic index	161
glycogen [GLY-ko-jen]	152
glycyrrhizin	172
gums	154
hemicelluloses [hem-ih-SELL-you-los-es]	154
hyperglycemia [HIGH-per-gly-SEE-me-uh]	163
husk	165
insulin [IN-suh-lin]	160
ketone bodies	159
ketosis [kee-TOE-sis]	159
lactose [LAK-tose]	150
lignins [LIG-nins]	154
maltose [MALL-tose]	150
monosaccharides	147
mucilages	154
neotame	171
nonnutritive sweeteners	170
nutritive sweeteners	168
oligosaccharides	150
pancreatic amylase	155
pectins	154
pentoses	148
phenylketonuria (PKU)	171
polyols	170
polysaccharides	151
psyllium	154
refined sweeteners	168
resistant starch	152
saccharin [SAK-ah-ren]	170
simple carbohydrates	147
starch	151
stevia	171
stevioside	171
sucralose	171
sucrose [SOO-crose]	150
sugar alcohols	148
D-tagatose	171
thaumatin	173
total fiber	153
trehalose	171

Study Points

- Carbohydrates include the simple sugars and complex carbohydrates.
- Monosaccharides are the building blocks of carbohydrates.
- Three monosaccharides are important in human nutrition: glucose, fructose, and galactose.
- The monosaccharides combine to make disaccharides: sucrose, lactose, and maltose.
- Starch, glycogen, and fiber are long chains (polysaccharides) of glucose units.
- Carbohydrates are digested by enzymes from the mouth, pancreas, and small intestine and absorbed as monosaccharides.
- The liver converts the monosaccharides fructose and galactose to glucose.
- Blood glucose levels rise after eating and fall between meals. Two pancreatic hormones, insulin and glucagon, regulate blood glucose levels, preventing extremely high or low levels.
- The main function of carbohydrates in the body is to supply energy. In this role, carbohydrates spare protein for use in making body proteins, and allow for the complete breakdown of fat as an additional energy source.
- Carbohydrates are found mainly in plant foods as starch, fiber, and sugar.
- In general, Americans consume more sugar and less starch and fiber than is recommended.
- Carbohydrate intake can affect health. Excess sugar can contribute to low nutrient intake, excess energy intake, and dental caries.
- Diets high in complex carbohydrates, including fiber, have been linked to reduced risk for GI disorders, heart disease, and cancer.

Study Questions

1. Describe the difference between starch and fiber.
2. How will eating excessive amounts of carbohydrate affect health?
3. What are the consequences of eating too little carbohydrate?
4. List the benefits of eating more fiber. What are the consequences of eating too much? Too little?
5. Which foods contain carbohydrates?
6. What advantage does the branched-chain structure of glycogen provide compared with a straight chain of glucose?
7. Which blood glucose regulation hormone is secreted in the recently fed state? The fasting state?
8. Describe the structure of a monosaccharide, disaccharide, and polysaccharide.
9. In an effort to lose weight, you decide to follow a diet of 1,200 calories with 225 grams of carbohydrate. Calculate the percentage of carbohydrate in this diet and compare this amount to the Daily Value recommendations. Daily Value recommendations for carbohydrate are 300 grams per day. Compare this amount to the recommendation for the overall percentage of carbohydrate, which is 45 to 65 percent of total calories.

Try This

The Fiber-Type Experiment

This experiment is to help you understand the difference between sources of dietary fiber. Go to the store and buy a small amount of raw bran. It is usually sold in a bin at a health food store or near the hot cereals in a grocery store. Also purchase some pectin (near the baking items) or some Metamucil (in the pharmacy section). Once you're home, fill two glasses with water and put the raw bran in one glass and the pectin or Metamucil in the other. Stir each glass for a minute or two and watch what happens. Describe the differences. What would happen in your GI tract?

The Sweetness of Soda

This experiment is to help you understand the amount of sugar found in a can of soda. Take a glass and fill it with 12 ounces (1½ cups) of water. Using a measuring spoon, add 10 to 12 teaspoons of sugar to the water. Stir the sugar water until all the sucrose has dissolved. Now sip the water. Does it taste sweet? It shouldn't taste any sweeter than a can of regular soda. This is the amount of sugar found in one 12-ounce can!

What About Bobbie?

Refer to Chapter 1 to see the complete list of food and drinks from Bobbie's recorded intake. Let's examine her day of eating using the guidelines you've learned in this chapter. How well did Bobbie do? Did she meet her overall carbohydrate goal? Did she consume 45 to 65 percent of her calories from carbohydrates? Was her diet made up mostly of complex carbohydrates or simple sugars? Let's take a look.

Her overall carbohydrate intake was 292 grams or 1,168 kilocalories. Her total energy intake was 2,300 kilocalories, which means 51 percent of her calories were from carbohydrate. This is within the Acceptable Macronutrient Distribution Range (AMDR) for carbohydrate. Here are the biggest contributors, which supply more than 80 percent of Bobbie's carbohydrate intake:

Food	Carbohydrate (g)	Percentage of calorie intake (%)
Spaghetti	60	10
Bread (lunch and dinner)	53	9
Bagel	39	7
Banana	27	5
Tortilla chips	27	5
Pizza	24	4
Spaghetti sauce	10	1.7
Cookie	9	1.5

Review the list of Bobbie's foods again. Do you think her carbohydrate intake comes mostly from complex sources or simple sugars? Very few of her carbohydrate sources are high in sugars: just the banana, the sugar for the coffee, and the chocolate chip cookie.

Let's take a closer look at Bobbie's carbohydrate intake. Which food groups contribute the most to her carbohydrate intake? To answer this question, let's divide her carbohydrate-dense foods into the three carbohydrate-rich food groups:

Food Group	Number of Servings	
	Bobbie's	*Recommended**
Grains Group		
Bagel	2	
Bread (lunch)	2	
Bread (dinner)	1	
Tortilla chips	2	
Pasta	3	
Pizza	1	
Total	11 oz eq	7 oz eq (3.5 as a whole grain)
Fruit Group		
Banana	1 cup	
Total	1 cup	2 cups
Vegetable Group		
Lettuce	1 cup	
Sandwich and salad toppings	½ cup	
Salsa	½ cup	
Green beans	½ cup	
Total	2½ cups	3 cups

*Based on USDA's MyPlate food intake patterns for 2,200 kilocalories.

So, now that you've reviewed Bobbie's food group totals, what can you conclude about her carbohydrate intake? Her total carbohydrate calories are within the recommended range, but her diet still could use some improvement. Bobbie has plenty of servings for grains, but no whole grains. She is low in fruits, and her vegetable choices could be a little more varied. Adding a half-cup of orange juice for breakfast and another piece of fresh fruit during the day would help. Choosing spinach or romaine lettuce for her salad would broaden her vegetable choices, and a whole-wheat bagel instead of cinnamon raisin would be a good start for adding more whole grains.

References

1 Eastwood M. *Principles of Human Nutrition*. New York: Chapman & Hall, 1997.

2 Institute of Medicine, Food and Nutrition Board. *Dietary Reference Intakes for Energy, Carbohydrate, Fiber, Fat, Fatty Acids, Cholesterol, Protein, and Amino Acids (Macronutrients)*. Washington, DC: National Academies Press, 2005.

3 Newburg DS, Ruiz-Palacios GM, Morrow AL. Human milk glycans protect infants against enteric pathogens. *Annu Rev Nutr.* 2005;25:37–58.

4 Wang B, McVeagh P, Petocz P, Brand-Miller J. Brain ganglioside and glycoprotein sialic acid in breastfed compared with formula-fed infants. *Am J Clin Nutr.* 2003;78(5):1024–1029.

5 Eliasson AC. *Carbohydrates in Food*. New York: Marcel Dekker, 1996; and GMO Compass. Amylose, amylopectin (starch). http://www.gmo-compass.org/eng/glossary/104.amylose-amylopectin-starch.html. Accessed 5/08/09.

6 Institute of Medicine, Food and Nutrition Board. *Dietary Reference Intakes for Energy, Carbohydrate*.

7 Murphy MM, Douglass JS, Birkett A. Resistant starch intake in the United States. *J Am Diet Assoc.* 2008;108:67–78.

8 Meat processing. *Encyclopaedia Britannica* [online]. http://www.britannica.com/eb/article?eu5120856. Accessed 5/08/09.

9 Robyt JF. *Essentials of Carbohydrate Chemistry*. New York: Springer, 1998.

10 Keim NL, Levin RJ, Havel PJ. Carbohydrates. In: Shils ME, Shike M, Ross AC, et al., eds. *Modern Nutrition in Health and Disease*. 10th ed. Philadelphia: Lippincott Williams & Wilkins, 2006.

11 Newburg, Ruiz-Palacios, Morrow. Human milk glycans protect infants against enteric pathogens.

12 Institute of Medicine, Food and Nutrition Board. *Dietary Reference Intakes for Energy, Carbohydrate*.

13 Graham LE, Graham JM, Wilcox LW. *Plant Biology*. Upper Saddle River, NJ: Prentice Hall, 2003.

14 Wong JM, de Souza R, Kendall CW, et al. Colonic health: fermentation and short chain fatty acids. *J Clin Gastroenterol.* 2006;40(3):235–243.

15 Martini FH. *Fundamentals of Anatomy and Physiology*. 6th ed. San Francisco: Benjamin Cummings, 2004.

16 Ibid.; and Berg JM, Tymoczko JL, Stryer L. *Biochemistry*. 6th ed. New York: WH Freeman, 2007.

17 Martini. *Fundamentals of Anatomy and Physiology*.

18 Ibid.

19 Ibid.

20 Berg, Tymoczko, Stryer. *Biochemistry*.

21 Institute of Medicine, Food and Nutrition Board. *Dietary Reference Intakes for Energy, Carbohydrate*.

22 Martini. *Fundamentals of Anatomy and Physiology*.

23 Institute of Medicine, Food and Nutrition Board. *Dietary Reference Intakes for Energy, Carbohydrate*.

24 Jenkins DJA, Kendall CWC, Augustin LSA, et al. Glycemic index: overview of implications in health and disease. *Am J Clin Nutr.* 2002;76(suppl):266S–273S.

25 National Digestive Diseases Information Clearinghouse. *National Diabetes Statistics*. November 2005. NIH publication 06-3892. http://diabetes.niddk.nih.gov/dm/pubs/statistics/index.htm. Accessed 5/08/09.

26 Thompson DR, Obarzanek E, Franko DL, et al. Childhood overweight and cardiovascular disease risk factors: the National Heart, Lung and Blood Institute Growth and Health Study. *J Pediatr.* 2007;150:18–25.

27 Libman IM, Arslanian SA. Prevention and treatment of type 2 diabetes in youth. *Horm Res.* 2007;67:22–34.

28 Knowler, Barrett-Connor, Fowler, et al. Reduction in the incidence of type 2 diabetes with lifestyle intervention or metformin. *N Engl J Med.* 2002;346:393–403.

29 Tuomilehto J, Lindstrom J, Eriksson JG, et al. Prevention of type 2 diabetes mellitus by changes in lifestyle among subjects with impaired glucose tolerance. *N Engl J Med.* 2001;344:1343–1350.

30 Mayer-Davis E. Type 2 diabetes in youth: epidemiology and current research toward prevention and treatment. *J Am Diet Assoc.* 2008;8(4):S45–S49.

31 Ibid.

32 Ibid.

33 Institute of Medicine, Food and Nutrition Board. *Dietary Reference Intakes for Energy, Carbohydrate.*

34 US Department of Agriculture and US Department of Health and Human Services. *Dietary Guidelines for Americans, 2010.* 7th ed. Washington, DC: US Government Printing Office, December 2010.

35 World Health Organization. *Diet, Nutrition and the Prevention of Chronic Diseases: A Report of a Joint WHO/FAO Expert Consultation.* Geneva, Switzerland: World Health Organization, 2003. WHO Technical Report Series 916.

36 Institute of Medicine, Food and Nutrition Board. *Dietary Reference Intakes for Energy, Carbohydrate.*

37 Ibid.

38 US Department of Agriculture and US Department of Health and Human Services. *Dietary Guidelines for Americans, 2010.*

39 Welsh JA, Cogswell ME, Rogers S, et al. Overweight among low-income preschool children associated with the consumption of sweet drinks: Missouri, 1999–2002. *Pediatrics.* 2005;115:223–229.

40 US Food and Drug Administration. Whole grain label statements—draft guidance. February 17, 2006. http://www.cfsan.fda.gov/~dms/flgragui.html. Accessed 5/7/06.

41 Giboney M, Sigman-Grant M, Stanton JL, Keast DR. Consumption of sugars. *Am J Clin Nutr.* 1995;62(suppl):178S–194S; and Coulston AM, Johnson RK. Sugar and sugars: myth and realities. *J Am Diet Assoc.* 2002;102:351–353.

42 Havel PJ. Dietary fructose: implications for dysregulation of energy homeostasis and lipid/carbohydrate metabolism. *Nutr Rev.* 2005; 63:133–157.

43 American Dietetic Association. Position of the American Dietetic Association: use of nutritive and nonnutritive sweeteners. *J Am Diet Assoc.* 2004;104:255–275.

44 US Department of Health and Human Services, National Toxicology Program. *Report on Carcinogens.* 11th ed. January 31, 2005. http://ntp.niehs.nih.gov/index.cfm?objectid532BA9724-F1F6-975E-7FCE50709CB4C932. Accessed 5/08/09.

45 Butchko HH, Stargel WW, Comer CP, et al. Aspartame: review of safety. *Regul Toxicol Pharmacol.* 2002;35:S1–S93.

46 American Dietetic Association. Position of the American Dietetic Association: use of nutritive and nonnutritive sweeteners.

47 Ibid.

48 Murray R, Frankowski B, Taras H. Are soft drinks a scapegoat for childhood obesity? *J Pediatr.* 2005;146(5):586–590.

49 Capps JRO, Caluson A, Guthrie J, et al. *Contributions of Nonalcoholic Beverages to the U.S. Diet.* March 2005. US Department of Agriculture Economic Research Service Report No. 1. http//www.ers.usda.gov/publication/err1.pdf. Accessed 05/08/09.

50 US Department of Agriculture and US Department of Health and Human Services. *Dietary Guidelines for Americans, 2010.*

51 American Dental Association. *Fluoridation Facts.* Chicago: American Dental Association, 2005. http://www.ada.org/public/topics/fluoride/facts/index.asp. Accessed 05/08/09.

52 Slavin JL. Position of the American Dietetic Association: health implications of dietary fiber. *J Am Diet Assoc.* 2008;108(10):1716–1731.

53 Institute of Medicine, Food and Nutrition Board. *Dietary Reference Intakes for Energy, Carbohydrate.*

54 Anderson JW, Randles KM, Kendall CW, et al. Carbohydrate and fiber recommendations for individuals with diabetes: a quantitative assessment and meta-analysis of the evidence. *J Am Coll Nutr.* 2004;23:5–17.

55 Institute of Medicine, Food and Nutrition Board. *Dietary Reference Intakes for Energy, Carbohydrate.*

56 Ibid.

57 Wong JM, de Souza R, Kendall CW, et al. Colonic health: fermentation and short chain fatty acids. *J Clin Gastroenterol.* 2006;40(3):235–243.

58 Jacobs DR, Meyer KA, Kushi LH, Folsom AR. Whole-grain intake may reduce the risk of ischemic heart disease death in postmenopausal women: the Iowa Women's Health Study. *Am J Clin Nutr.* 1998;68:248–257; and Willet WC, Hu FB. Optimal diets for prevention of coronary heart disease. *JAMA.* 2002;288(20):2569–2578.

59 Slavin JL, Jacobs D, Marquart L, Wiemer K. The role of whole grains in disease prevention. *J Am Diet Assoc.* 2001;101:780–785.

60 US Department of Agriculture and US Department of Health and Human Services. *Dietary Guidelines for Americans, 2010.*

61 Institute of Medicine, Food and Nutrition Board. *Dietary Reference Intakes for Energy, Carbohydrate.*

62 Ibid.

CHAPTER 5

Lipids

THINK About It

1 How important is fat to the foods you think of as tasty?

2 Can one have too little body fat?

3 What's your take on the differences between fat and cholesterol?

4 What's your understanding of "good" versus "bad" cholesterol?

Visit nutrition.jbpub.com

A generic fatty acid

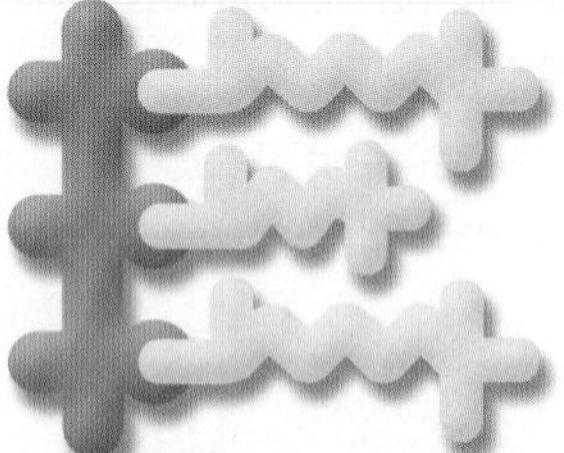
A generic triglyceride

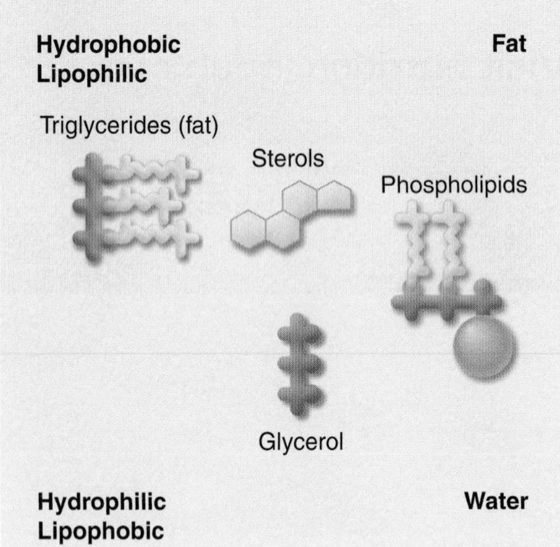

hydrophobic Insoluble in water.

lipophilic Attracted to fat and fat solvents; fat-soluble.

hydrophilic [high-dro-FILL-ik] Readily interacting with water (literally, "water-loving"). Hydrophilic compounds are polar and soluble in water.

lipophobic Adverse to fat solvents; insoluble in fat and fat solvents.

phospholipids Compounds that consist of a glycerol molecule bonded to two fatty acid molecules and to a phosphate group with a nitrogen-containing component. Phospholipids have both hydrophilic and hydrophobic regions that make them good emulsifiers.

sterols A category of lipids that includes cholesterol. Sterols are hydrocarbons with several rings in their structures.

Maria and Rachel are trying to lose weight. Maria swears by a new diet program that allows you to eat all the fat you want, but no high-carbohydrate, "starchy" foods. Her diet is working—she's already lost 10 pounds! Then there's Rachel, whose goal in life is to eat zero grams of fat. She's fat-obsessed—always insisting on "fat-free" everything, and driving her friends nuts with information about the number of fat grams in whatever they eat. As you listen to the two of them compare dieting stories, you wonder which one has the right approach to fat consumption, or even whether there *is* a right approach. On the one hand, it seems that you hear a lot about American high-fat diets and high rates of obesity and heart disease. On the other hand, can a "no-fat" diet be healthy? Are all low-fat and no-fat products really more nutritious?

Fat is an essential nutrient. Although our bodies are very good at making and storing fat in the form of triglycerides, they cannot make some types of fatty acids (a component of triglycerides), so these compounds must come from the diet. Triglycerides—the fats we associate with fried foods, cream cheese, vegetable oil, or salad dressing—are one type of a larger group of compounds called lipids. Cholesterol, another lipid, is familiar to most Americans, but you may not realize that your body makes cholesterol and that your dietary cholesterol makes only a small contribution to the total amount in your body. All lipids have important roles, but at the same time, too much triglyceride or too much cholesterol can increase the risk for chronic disease.

Fats contribute greatly to the flavor and texture of foods. When you take out the fat, sometimes you have to boost the flavor with sugar, sodium, or other additives to have a tasty product. This means that fat-free foods sometimes aren't any lower in calories than regular food—so Rachel can't eat the whole box of fat-free cookies and still expect to lose weight!

Once you have an idea of the role of lipids in the body and in foods, you'll be able to apply the principles of balance, variety, and moderation in selecting a healthful, enjoyable diet with neither too much nor too little fat.

What Are Lipids?

The term *lipids* applies to a broad range of organic molecules that dissolve easily in organic solvents such as alcohol, ether, or acetone, but are much less soluble in water. Lipids generally are **hydrophobic** (averse to water; literally "water-fearing") and **lipophilic** (soluble in fat and fat solvents; literally "fat-loving"). In contrast, water-soluble substances are, not surprisingly, **hydrophilic** (attracted to water, "water loving") and **lipophobic** (averse to fat solvents, "fat fearing"). Lipids vary in their solubilities, with some being very hydrophobic and others less so. The main classes of lipids found in foods and in the body are triglycerides, phospholipids, and sterols.

Triglycerides are the largest category of lipids. In the body, fat cells store triglycerides in adipose tissue. In foods, we call triglycerides "fats and oils," with fats usually being solid and oils being liquid at room temperature. Overall, however, the choice of terminology—*fat, triglyceride, oil*—is somewhat arbitrary, and the terms are often used interchangeably. In this chapter, when we use the word *fat* or *oil*, we are referring to triglycerides.

About 2 percent of dietary lipids are **phospholipids**. They are found in foods of both plant and animal origin, and the body also makes those that it needs. Unlike other lipids, phospholipids are soluble in both fat and water. These versatile molecules play crucial roles as a major constituent in cell membranes, and in blood and body fluids, where they help keep fats suspended.

Only a small percentage of our dietary lipids are **sterols**, yet one infamous member, cholesterol, generates much public concern. The body makes cholesterol, which is an important component of cell membranes and a precursor in the synthesis of sex hormones, adrenal hormones (e.g., cortisol), vitamin D, and bile salts.

Lipids share similar functional properties, solubility, and transport mechanisms, although the composition and structure of individual molecules vary. Fatty acids are components of both triglycerides and phospholipids and are often attached to cholesterol.

Fatty Acids Are Key Building Blocks

Fatty acids determine the characteristics of a fat, such as whether it is solid or liquid at room temperature. Fatty acids that are not joined to another compound, such as the glycerol of a triglyceride, are sometimes called "free" fatty acids, to emphasize that they are unattached. Some free fatty acids have their own distinct flavor. Butyric acid, for example, is the fatty acid that gives butter its flavor (see **Figure 5.1**). Caproic, caprylic, and capric acids, all named after the Greek word for "goat," have the undesirable "goaty" flavors and odors that their names suggest. Contributing to a strong unpleasant odor, they may be present as free fatty acids in spoiled foods.

Although there are many kinds of fatty acids, they are basically chains of carbon atoms with an organic acid (carboxyl) group (–COOH) at one end and a methyl group (–CH_3) at the other end.

Chain Length

Fatty acids differ in **chain length** (the number of carbons in the chain). Foods contain fatty acids with chain lengths of 4 to 24 carbons, and most have an even number of carbons. They are grouped as short-chain (fewer than 6 carbons), medium-chain (6 to 10 carbons), and long-chain (12 or more carbons) fatty acids. (See **Figure 5.2**.) The shorter the carbon chain, the more liquid the fatty acid (the lower its melting point). (See **Figure 5.3**.) Shorter fatty acids are also more water-soluble, a property that affects their absorption in the digestive tract.

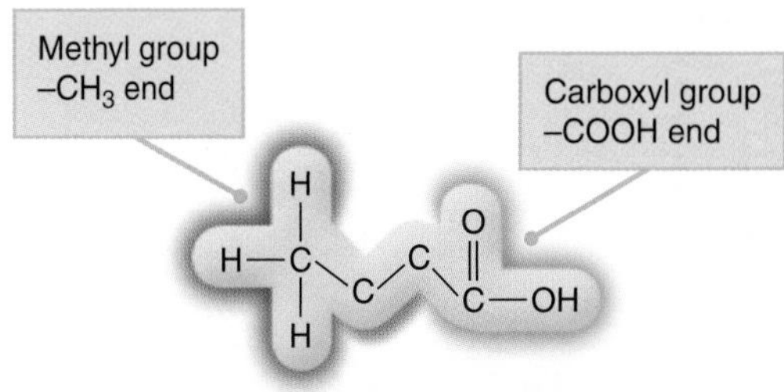

Butyric acid

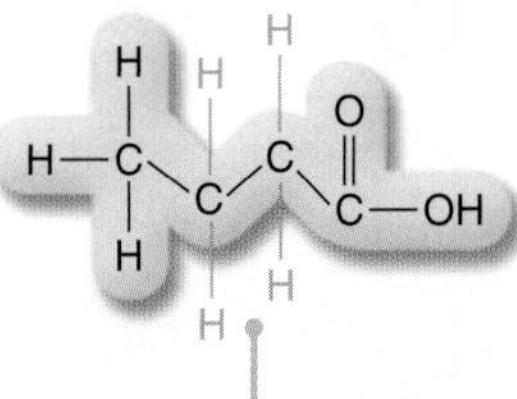

For simplicity in most of these pictures the hydrogens are omitted from all but the end carbons

Figure 5.1 **Fatty acid structure.** The basic structure of a fatty acid is a carbon chain with a methyl end (–CH_3) and an acid (carboxyl) end (–COOH). Butyric acid (shown here) is a fatty acid found in butter fat.

fatty acids Compounds containing a long hydrocarbon chain with a carboxyl group (COOH) at one end and a methyl group (CH_3) at the other end.

chain length The number of carbons that a fatty acid contains. Foods contain fatty acids with chain lengths of 4 to 24 carbons, and most have an even number of carbons.

Short-chain fatty acid
(2–4 carbons)

Butyric C4:0

Medium-chain fatty acid
(6–10 carbons)

Caprylic C8:0

Long-chain fatty acid
(12 or more carbons)

Palmitic C16:0

Figure 5.2 **Fatty acid chain lengths.** Fatty acids can be classified by their chain length as short-, medium-, or long-chain fatty acids.

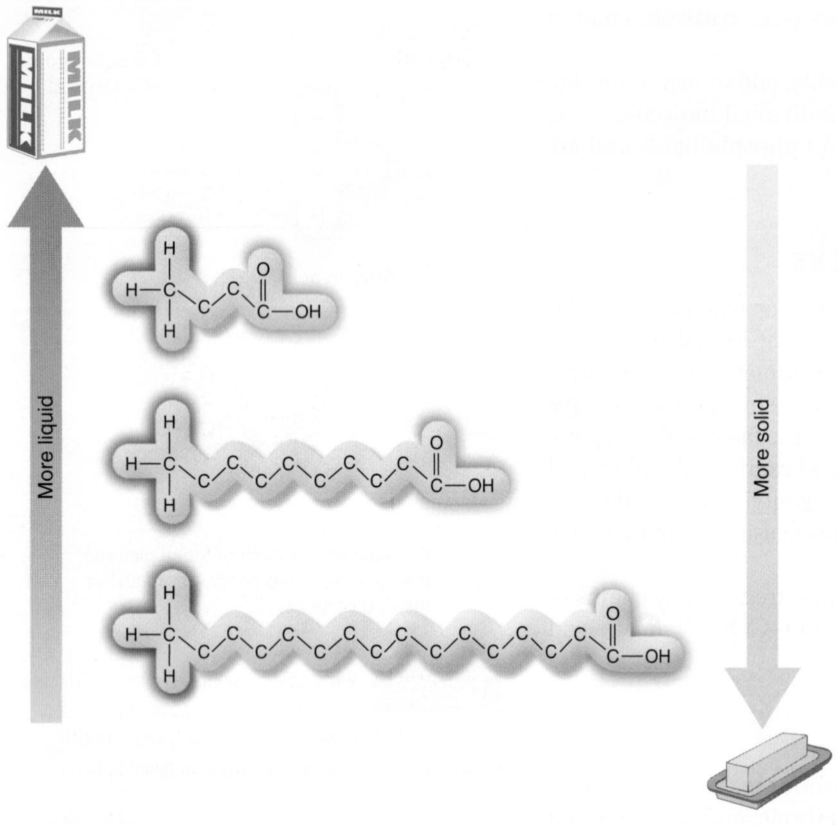

Figure 5.3 **Fatty acid chain lengths and liquidity.** As the chain length of saturated fatty acids increases, they become more solid at room temperature.

Figure 5.4 **Fatty acid nomenclature.** The carbons are identified by their locations in the chain. Although some disciplines count from the alpha carbon, nutritionists count from the omega carbon.

Each carbon in these chains can be numbered for identification, but it's important to know from which end the counting begins. In organic chemistry the scientific naming of fatty acids counts from the carbon at the acid (–COOH) end. This carbon is the alpha carbon, and the carbon at the methyl (–CH_3) end is the omega carbon. They are named after the first and last letters of the Greek alphabet, respectively. (See **Figure 5.4**.) As you'll see later, nutritionists identify double bonds by their location relative to the omega carbon.

saturated fatty acid A fatty acid completely filled by hydrogen with all carbons in the chain linked by single bonds.

unsaturated fatty acid A fatty acid in which the carbon chain contains one or more double bonds.

monounsaturated fatty acid A fatty acid in which the carbon chain contains one double bond.

polyunsaturated fatty acid A fatty acid in which the carbon chain contains two or more double bonds.

Saturation

Within a fatty acid chain, each carbon atom has four bonds. When a carbon is joined to adjacent carbons with single bonds (–C–C–C–), it still has two bonds available for other atoms, such as hydrogen atoms. If all the carbons in the chain are joined with single bonds and the remaining bonds are filled with hydrogen, the fatty acid is called a **saturated fatty acid**. It is fully loaded (saturated) with hydrogen.

However, if adjoining carbons are connected by a double bond (C=C), there are two fewer bonds holding hydrogen, so the chain is not saturated with hydrogen. This is an **unsaturated fatty acid**. A fatty acid with one double bond is a **monounsaturated fatty acid**; one with two or more double bonds is a **polyunsaturated fatty acid** (often abbreviated MUFA and PUFA, respectively). **Figure 5.5** illustrates the three types of fatty acids.

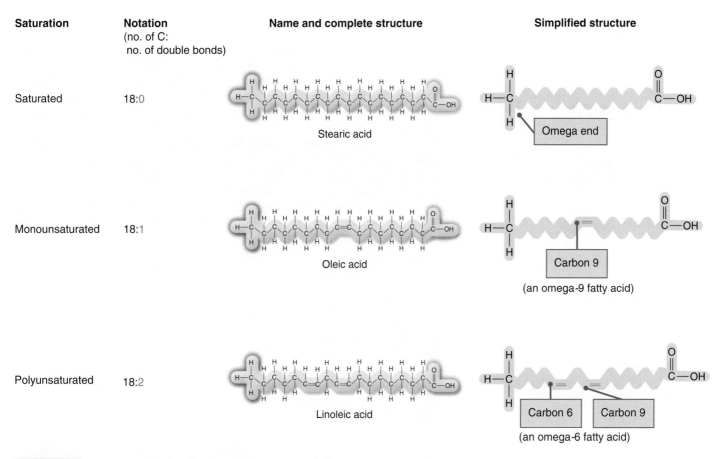

Saturation	Notation (no. of C: no. of double bonds)	Name and complete structure	Simplified structure
Saturated	18:0	Stearic acid	Omega end
Monounsaturated	18:1	Oleic acid	Carbon 9 (an omega-9 fatty acid)
Polyunsaturated	18:2	Linoleic acid	Carbon 6, Carbon 9 (an omega-6 fatty acid)

Figure 5.5 **Saturated, monosaturated, and polyunsaturated fatty acids.** Hydrogens saturate the carbon chain of a saturated fatty acid. Unsaturated fatty acids are missing some hydrogens and have one (mono) or more (poly) carbon–carbon double bonds.

Foods never contain only unsaturated or only saturated fatty acids. Instead, food fats are a mixture of fatty acid types, so it is technically wrong to refer to a particular food fat as a "saturated fat." However, food fats with more unsaturated fatty acids typically have lower melting points and are more likely to be liquid at room temperature. Foods rich in saturated fatty acids tend to be solid at room temperature and have higher melting points. (See **Figure 5.6**.) For example, stearic acid, an 18-carbon saturated fatty acid, is abundant in chocolate and meat fats, both of which are solid at room temperature. The major fatty acid of olive oil is 18-carbon monounsaturated oleic acid. Olive oil is a thick liquid at room temperature, but may solidify under refrigeration. The major fatty acid of soybean oil is an 18-carbon fatty acid with two double bonds called linoleic acid, and soybean oil is a thin liquid at room temperature. And 18-carbon alpha-linolenic acid, a fatty acid with three double bonds, is abundant in flaxseed oil, a very thin liquid at room temperature.

Key Concepts *The term lipids refers to a group of organic molecules that are soluble in organic solvents and less soluble in water, including triglycerides, phospholipids, and sterols. Fatty acids are key structural components of both triglycerides and phospholipids and are sometimes attached to cholesterol. Fatty acids are carbon chains of varying lengths. Those with no double bonds between carbon atoms are called saturated, whereas those with at least one double bond are called unsaturated.*

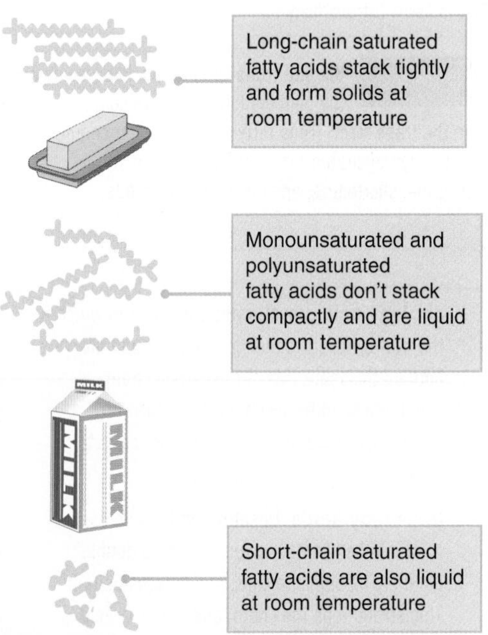

Figure 5.6 **Liquid or solid at room temperature?** Short-chain and unsaturated fatty acids cannot pack tightly together and tend to be more liquid than long-chain saturated fatty acids.

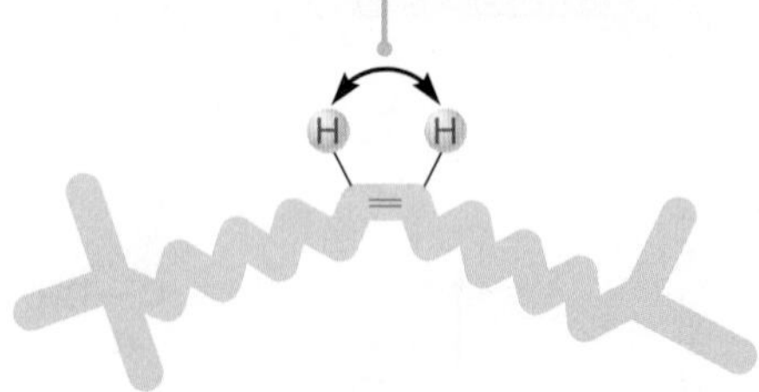
These two neighboring hydrogens repel each other, causing the carbon chain to bend
Cis form (bent)

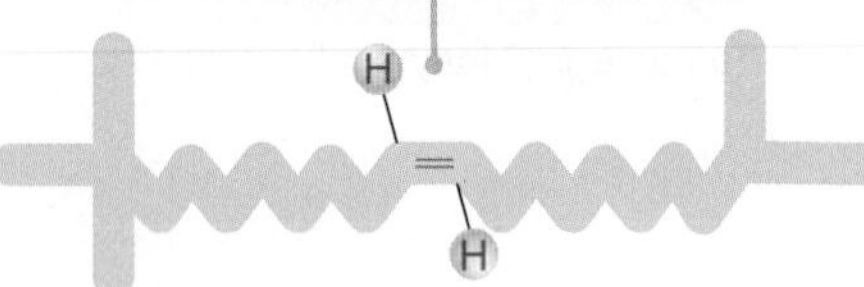
These two hydrogens are already as far apart as they can get
Trans form (straighter)

Figure 5.7 **Cis and trans fatty acids.** Fatty acids with the bent cis form are more common in food than the trans form. Trans fatty acids are most commonly found in hydrogenated fats, such as those in stick margarine, shortening, and deep-fat fried foods.

Geometric and Positional Isomers

Otherwise identical unsaturated fatty acids can exist in different geometric forms, or isomers. In most naturally occurring unsaturated fatty acids, the hydrogens next to double bonds are on the same side of the carbon chain. This is called a cis formation. The carbon chain of a **cis fatty acid** is bent. If the double bond is altered, moving the hydrogens across from each other, the formation is called trans and the carbon chain is straighter. (See **Figure 5.7**.) There are small amounts of **trans fatty acids** in meats and dairy products from cows and sheep, but the commercial process of **hydrogenation**, or adding hydrogens where some of the double bonds are located in the unsaturated fatty acid, creates most of our dietary trans fatty acids.[1] Most trans fatty acids are monounsaturated, but a small number are fatty acids with two double bonds. Trans fatty acids have become a health concern because they have been shown to raise low-density lipoprotein (LDL) cholesterol levels and therefore increase one's risk for heart disease.

Conjugated linoleic acid (CLA) is a collective term for a group of geometric and positional isomers of linoleic acid in which the double bonds (trans or cis) are conjugated; that is, the double bonds occur without an intervening carbon atom that is not part of a double bond. Although present in only trace amounts in cow's milk, conjugated linoleic acid is being studied for potential positive health effects and is under study for potential anticancer benefits.[2]

Small amounts of trans fatty acids and conjugated linoleic acid are present in all diets. They can serve as a source of fuel energy for the body. However, there are no known requirements for trans fatty acids and conjugated linoleic acid for specific body functions.[3]

Omega-3, Omega-6, and Omega-9 Fatty Acids

The location of the double bond closest to the omega (methyl) end of the fatty acid chain identifies a fatty acid's family. Oleic acid has one double bond, at carbon 9 (counting from the omega end of the chain) and is classified as an **omega-9 fatty acid**. Linoleic acid has double bonds both at carbon 6 and carbon 9. Because the first double bond occurs at carbon 6, it is an **omega-6 fatty acid**. **Omega-3 fatty acids** such as alpha-linolenic acid have a double bond at carbon 3, plus two or more additional double bonds. (See **Figure 5.8**.) All of these fatty acids can be burned for energy. When the body

cis fatty acid Unsaturated fatty acid in which the hydrogens surrounding a double bond are both on the same side of the carbon chain, causing a bend in the chain. Most naturally occurring unsaturated fatty acids are cis fatty acids.

trans fatty acids Unsaturated fatty acids in which the hydrogens surrounding a double bond are on opposite sides of the carbon chain. This straightens the chain, and the fatty acid becomes more solid.

hydrogenation [high-dro-jen-AY-shun] A chemical reaction in which hydrogen atoms are added to carbon–carbon double bonds, converting them to single bonds. Hydrogenation of monounsaturated and polyunsaturated fatty acids reduces the number of double bonds they contain, thereby making them more saturated.

conjugated linoleic acid A polyunsaturated fatty acid in which the position of the double bonds has moved, so that a single bond alternates with two double bonds.

omega-9 fatty acid Any polyunsaturated fatty acid in which the first double bond starting from the methyl (CH_3) end of the molecule lies between the ninth and tenth carbon atoms.

omega-6 fatty acid Any polyunsaturated fatty acid in which the first double bond starting from the methyl (CH_3) end of the molecule lies between the sixth and seventh carbon atoms.

omega-3 fatty acids Any polyunsaturated fatty acid in which the first double bond starting from the methyl (CH_3) end of the molecule lies between the third and fourth carbon atoms.

uses them to synthesize new compounds, however, the omega-3, omega-6, and omega-9 classes behave quite differently.

Nonessential and Essential Fatty Acids

The body is a good chemist, synthesizing most fatty acids as it needs them. The liver adds carbons in a process called **elongation** to build storage and structural fats, to manufacture the fat in breast milk, or to make fatty acids for use in other compounds. The body also synthesizes oleic acid, an omega-9 fatty acid, by removing hydrogens from carbons 9 and 10 of saturated stearic acid, thus creating a double bond at carbon 9. This process is called **desaturation**. Oleic acid can be elongated further and desaturated to create other necessary fatty acids.

Because your body can make saturated and omega-9 fatty acids, it is not essential to get them in your diet. We therefore call them **nonessential fatty acids**. (Do not confuse "nonessential" with "unimportant." Your body ensures an adequate supply of nonessential fatty acids by making them when they are needed.)

Our bodies cannot produce carbon–carbon double bonds before the ninth carbon from the methyl end, so we cannot manufacture certain fatty acids such as omega-6 linoleic or omega-3 alpha-linolenic acids. They must come from food, so they're called **essential fatty acids** (EFA). (See **Figure 5.9**.) Deficiency of essential fatty acids is extremely rare. It typically occurs only with severe fat malabsorption or prolonged intravenous feeding without supplemental fat. A lack of linoleic acid leads to a scaly skin rash and dermatitis, poor growth in children, and a lowered immune response. In the few human cases where alpha-linolenic acid was lacking, neuropathy, visual problems, and poor growth were the results.[4]

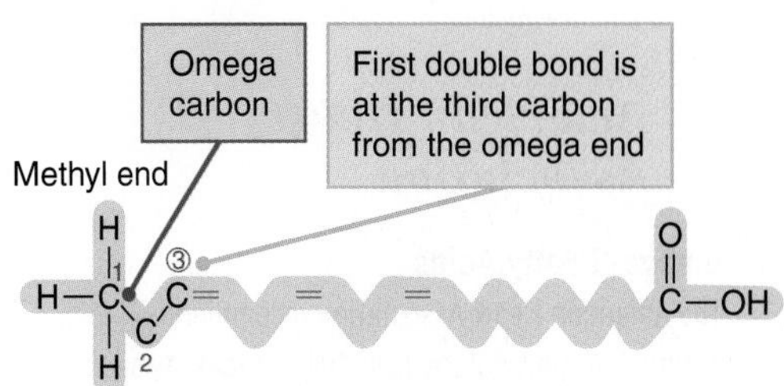

Alpha-linolenic, an omega-3 fatty acid

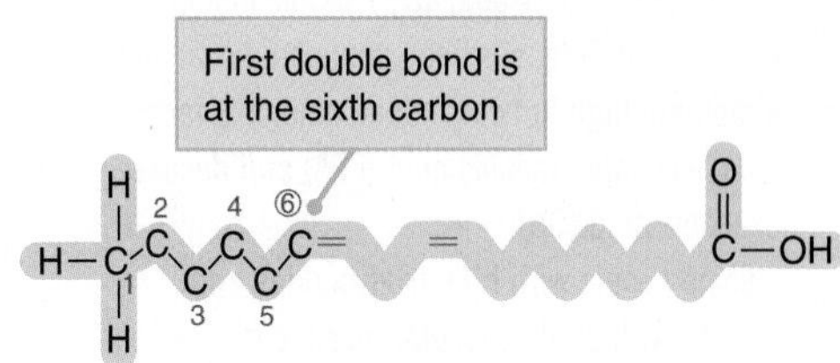

Linoleic, an omega-6 fatty acid

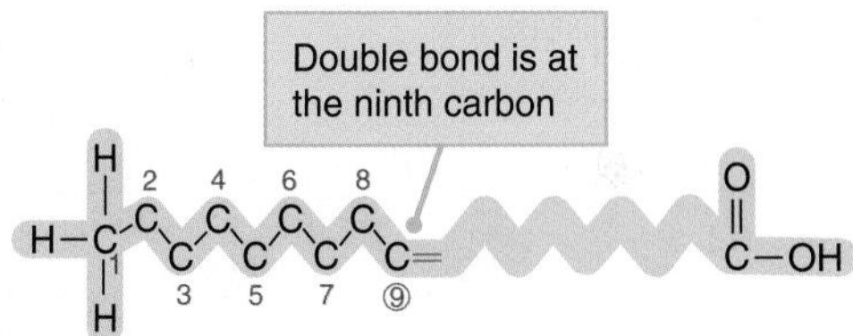

Oleic, an omega-9 fatty acid

Figure 5.8 **Omega-3, omega-6, and omega-9 fatty acids.** Unsaturated fatty acids can be classified by counting from the omega carbon to the location of the first double bond.

Your body cannot form C=C double bonds **before** the 9th carbon

Your body can form C=C double bonds **after** the 9th carbon

Fatty acids with double bonds before the 9th carbon are ESSENTIAL

Linolenic acid

Linoleic acid

Fatty acids with no double bonds before the 9th carbon are NONESSENTIAL

Oleic acid

Figure 5.9 **Essential and nonessential fatty acids.** Your body makes some types of fatty acids, but others are essential in your diet.

elongation Addition of carbon atoms to fatty acids to lengthen them into new fatty acids.

desaturation Insertion of double bonds into fatty acids to change them into new fatty acids.

nonessential fatty acids The fatty acids that your body can make when they are needed. It is not necessary to consume them in the diet.

essential fatty acids The fatty acids that the body needs but cannot synthesize, and which must be obtained from diet.

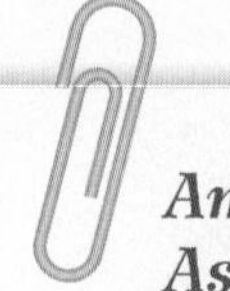

American Heart Association

Omega-3 Fatty Acids

The American Heart Association recommends eating fish (particularly fatty fish) at least two times a week. Fish is a good source of protein and doesn't have the high saturated fat that fatty meat products do. Fatty fish like mackerel, lake trout, herring, sardines, albacore tuna, and salmon are high in two kinds of omega-3 fatty acids: eicosapentaenoic acid (EPA) and docosahexaenoic acid (DHA).

Some people with high triglycerides and patients with cardiovascular disease may benefit from more omega-3 fatty acids than they can easily get from diet alone. These people should talk to their doctor about taking supplements to reduce heart disease risk.

Source: American Heart Association, Inc.

Building Eicosanoids, Omega-3, and Omega-6 Fatty Acids

You metabolize most of the fatty acids you eat to supply your energy needs, but a small proportion become crucial chemical regulators. The **eicosanoids** (also called prostanoids) are one such group of regulators. These signaling molecules contain 20 or more carbons (*eikosi* is the Greek word for "twenty"). They have profound localized effects through their influence on inflammatory processes, blood vessel dilation and constriction, blood clotting, and more. Because they don't circulate throughout the body as hormones do, scientists sometimes call eicosanoids "local" hormones.

Eicosanoids are made from unsaturated long-chain fatty acids from membrane phospholipids or circulating free fatty acids. The liver elongates these fatty acids 2 carbons at a time until the carbon chains have 20 or 22 carbons. Elongation alternates with desaturation. Once the fatty acid reaches 20 carbons, the body can convert it to one or more of the eicosanoids, such as thromboxanes, prostaglandins, prostacyclins, lipoxins, and leukotrienes. Eicosanoids can have opposing physiologic effects depending on whether they are derived from omega-3, omega-6, or omega-9 fatty acids. Here, we will concentrate on eicosanoids derived from the essential fatty acids—that is, from the omega-3s and omega-6s, over which we probably have the most dietary control and where most interest currently lies.

The Omega-6 Fatty Acids

Linoleic acid, an 18-carbon essential fatty acid with two double bonds (18:2), is our main dietary omega-6 fatty acid. In a sequence of elongation and desaturation steps, our bodies convert linoleic acid to arachidonic acid, a 20-carbon fatty acid with four double bonds (20:4). To simplify a very complex picture, a series of eicosanoids is then formed from arachidonic acid (see Table 5.1), and these eicosanoids have the overall effect of constricting blood vessels, promoting blood clotting, and promoting inflammation.

Table 5.1 **Omega-6 to Eicosanoids**

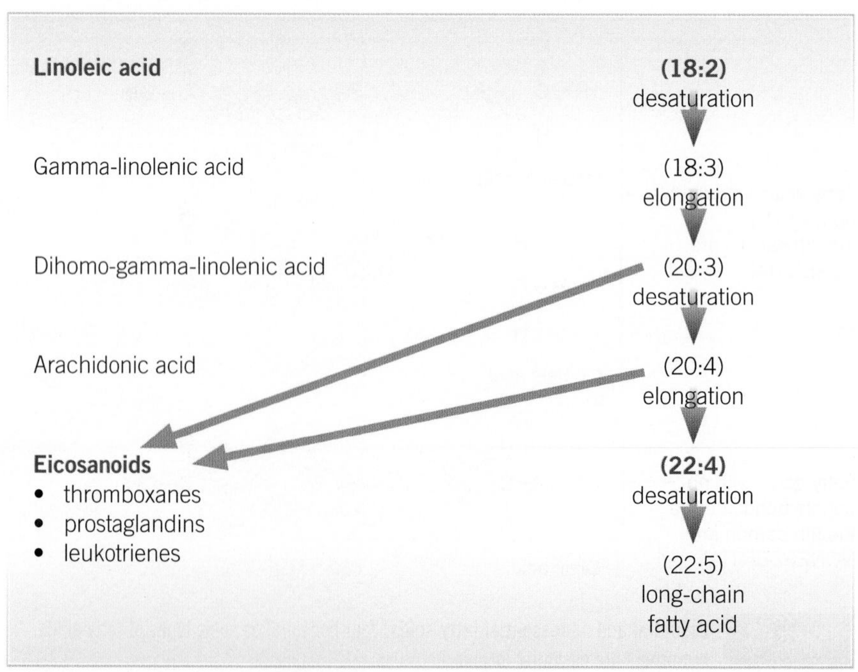

eicosanoids A class of hormonelike substances formed in the body from long-chain fatty acids.

linoleic acid [lin-oh-LAY-ik] An essential omega-6 fatty acid that contains 18 carbon atoms and two carbon–carbon double bonds (18:2).

The Omega-3 Fatty Acids

Alpha-linolenic acid is an 18-carbon essential fatty acid with three double bonds (18:3). It can ultimately be elongated and desaturated to EPA (eicosapentaenoic acid), with 20 carbons and five double bonds (20:5), and DHA (docosahexaenoic acid), with 22 carbons and six double bonds (22:6). (See Table 5.2.) However, for these reactions to take place, it must compete with the omega-6s (and even with polyunsaturated trans fatty acids) for the same enzymes, so only a portion of alpha-linolenic acid is converted to EPA and DHA. The eicosanoids derived from EPA have the overall effect of dilating blood vessels, discouraging blood clotting, and reducing inflammation. Because of these properties, omega-3 fatty acids have attracted interest as a potential factor in reducing risk for vascular disease.[5] Additional health benefits that have been associated with omega-3 fatty acids include the secondary prevention of chronic diseases and an association with the following:[6]

- *Inflammatory conditions:* Improves rheumatoid arthritis, psoriasis, asthma, and some skin conditions.
- *Ulcerative colitis and Crohn's disease:* Reduces the severity of symptoms.
- *Cardiovascular disease:* Lowers triglycerides and raises high-density lipoprotein cholesterol levels, improves blood circulation, reduces clotting, improves vascular function, and lowers blood pressure.
- *Type 2 diabetes mellitus:* Reduces hyperinsulinemia and insulin resistance.
- *Renal disease:* Preserves renal function in AgA nephropathy; potentially reduces vascular access thrombosis in hemodialysis patients and is cardioprotective.
- *Mental function:* Reduces severity of several mental conditions such as Alzheimer's disease, depression, and bipolar disorder;

alpha-linolenic acid [al-fah lin-oh-LEN-ik] An essential omega-3 fatty acid that contains 18 carbon atoms and three carbon–carbon double bonds (18:3).

Table 5.2 **Omega-3 to Eicosanoids**

Alpha-linolenic acid	**(18:3)**
	desaturation ↓
	(18:4)
	elongation ↓
	(20:4)
	desaturation ↓
EPA (eicosapentaenoic acid) → Eicosanoids	(20:5)
	elongation ↓
Eicosanoids • thromboxanes • prostaglandins • leukotrienes	**(22:5)**
	desaturation ↓
DHA (docosahexaenoic acid)	(22:6)

A generic triglyceride

A generic glycerol

improvement in children with attention deficit hyperactivity disorder and dyslexia has also been noted.

- *Growth and development:* Neurodevelopment and function of the brain and also the retina of the eye where visual function is affected.

As a result of the findings regarding growth and development, DHA (along with omega-6 arachidonic acid) is now being added to selected infant formulas.

Key Concepts *Unsaturated fatty acids can have cis or trans double bonds. The body can make many of the fatty acids it needs, but it cannot make linoleic or alpha-linolenic acids, so these are dietary essentials. The body can elongate and desaturate essential fatty acids to form other important compounds, such as eicosanoids.*

Triglycerides

Triglycerides are the major lipids in both the diet and in the body. Triglycerides add flavor and texture (and calories!) to foods and are an important source of the body's energy.

Triglyceride Structure

A triglyceride consists of three fatty acids attached to a molecule of glycerol. Both in food and in the body, most fatty acids exist as part of a triglyceride molecule. Alone, **glycerol** is a thick, smooth liquid often used in the food industry. Chemically it is an alcohol, a simple three-carbon molecule with an alcohol (hydroxyl) group (–OH) at each carbon. Glycerol is the backbone of a triglyceride. It is always the same, whereas the fatty acids attached to it can vary considerably. Chemically speaking, a triglyceride is an **ester**, a combination of an alcohol and a fatty acid. An ester forms when a hydrogen and an oxygen from the fatty acid's carboxyl (acid) group combine with a hydrogen from the alcohol's hydroxyl (alcohol) group. Because the reaction produces a molecule of water, it is called a condensation reaction. An ester linkage now chemically joins the altered fatty acid and alcohol, a process called **esterification**.

Esterification produces triglycerides, **diglycerides** (two fatty acids attached to a glycerol), and **monoglycerides** (one fatty acid attached to a glycerol). **Figure 5.10** illustrates the formation of a triglyceride. Our foods contain relatively small amounts of mono- and diglycerides, mostly as food additives used for their emulsifying or blending qualities.

glycerol [GLISS-er-ol] An alcohol that contains three carbon atoms, each of which has an attached hydroxyl group (–OH). It forms the backbone of mono-, di-, and triglycerides.

ester A chemical combination of an organic acid (e.g., fatty acid) and an alcohol. When hydrogen from the alcohol combines with the acid's hydrogen and oxygen, water is released and an ester linkage is formed. A triglyceride is an ester of three fatty acids and glycerol.

esterification [e-ster-ih-fih-KAY-shun] A condensation reaction in which an organic acid (e.g., fatty acid) combines with an alcohol with the loss of water, creating an ester.

diglycerides Molecules composed of glycerol combined with two fatty acids.

monoglycerides Molecules composed of glycerol combined with one fatty acid.

Triglyceride Functions

Although some of us, like Rachel at the beginning of this chapter, think of fat as something to avoid, fat is a key nutrient with important body functions. **Figure 5.11** shows the functions of triglycerides.

Energy Source

Fat is a rich and efficient source of calories. Under normal circumstances, dietary and stored fat supply about 60 percent of the body's resting energy needs. Like carbohydrate, fat is *protein-sparing*; that is, fat is burned for energy, sparing valuable proteins for their important roles as muscle tissue, enzymes, antibodies, and other functions. Different body tissues preferentially use dif-

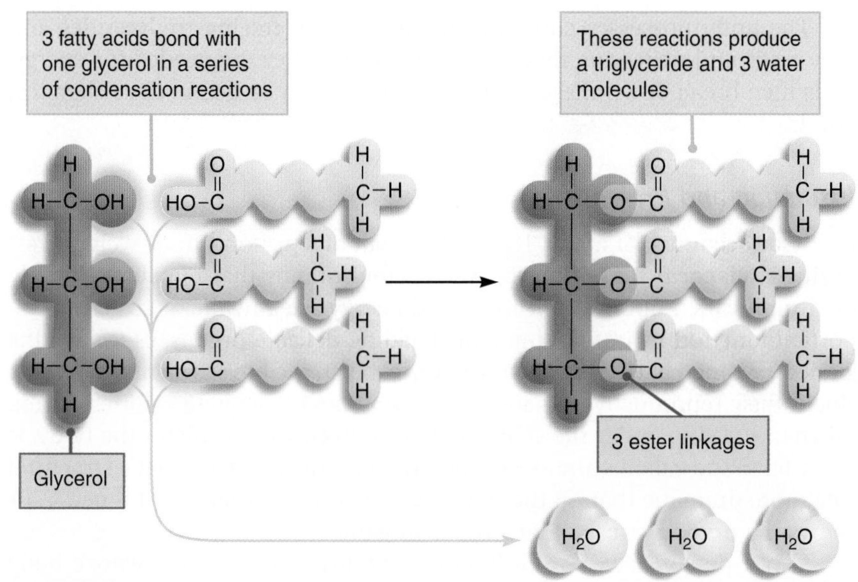

Figure 5.10 **Forming a triglyceride.** Condensation reactions attach three fatty acids to a glycerol backbone to form a triglyceride. These reactions release water.

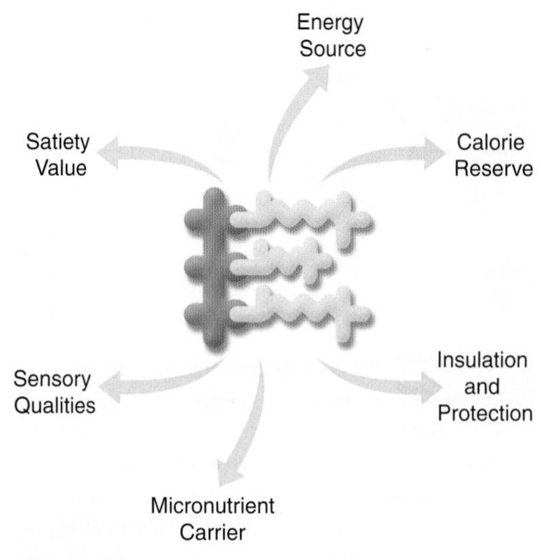

Figure 5.11 **Functions of triglycerides.** Fat performs a number of essential functions in the body.

Figure 5.12 **Fat is a major energy source.** When at rest, muscles prefer to use fat for fuel.

ferent sources of calories. Glucose is virtually the sole fuel for the brain except during prolonged starvation, and fat is the preferred fuel of muscle tissue at rest (see **Figure 5.12**). During physical activity, glucose and glycogen join fat in supplying energy.

High-fat foods are higher in calories than either high-protein or high-carbohydrate foods. One gram of fat contains 9 kilocalories, compared with only 4 kilocalories in a gram of carbohydrate or protein, or 7 kilocalories per gram for alcohol. For example, a tablespoon of corn oil (pure fat) has 120 kilocalories, whereas a tablespoon of sugar (pure carbohydrate) has only 50 kilocalories.

Fat's caloric density is especially important when energy needs are high. An infant, for example, who needs ample energy for fast growth but whose stomach can hold only a limited amount of food, needs the high fat content of breast milk or infant formula to get enough calories. When inappropriately put on a low-fat diet, infants and young children do not grow and develop properly. Other people with high-energy needs include athletes, individuals who are physically active in their jobs, and people who are trying to regain weight lost due to illness.

Of course, fat's caloric density has a negative side. In practical terms, 9 kilocalories per gram translates to about 115 to 120 kilocalories per tablespoon of pure fat (e.g., vegetable oil). That makes it very easy to get too many fat calories, and dietary fat in excess of a person's energy needs is a major contributor to obesity.

Energy Reserve

We store excess dietary fat as body fat to tide us over during periods of calorie deficit. Fat's caloric density comes in handy for this task, storing energy away in a small space. The fat is stored inside fat cells called **adipocytes**, which form body fat tissue, technically called **adipose tissue**. (See **Figure 5.13**.) Hibernating animals have perfected this process; the fat stores they build in autumn can see them through a winter's fast.

adipocytes Fat cells.

adipose tissue Body fat tissue.

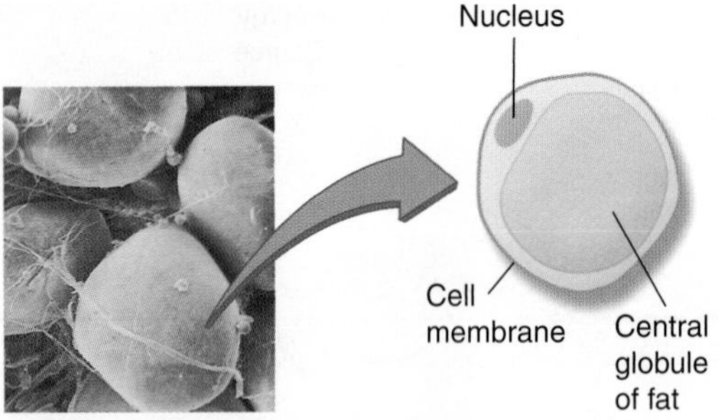

Figure 5.13 **Fat is an efficient storage medium.** Evolution has selected fat, rather than glycogen, as its primary energy storage medium. A gram of fat stores more than six times as much energy as a gram of glycogen. If a 155-pound man (with 20 pounds of fat) could store all his energy reserves as glycogen and none as fat, he would weigh 255 pounds!

Quick Bite

The Marvelous Storage Efficiency of Fat

Why do you think we don't store all our extra energy as readily available glycogen? It would take more than six pounds of glycogen to store the same energy as one pound of fat. Just imagine how much bulkier we would be! How cumbersome it would be to move about! That's why only a very small portion of the body's energy reserve is glycogen.

The body possesses complex mechanisms for freeing triglycerides and fatty acids and delivering them when and where they are needed for energy. Cells then break down these lipids to release energy stored in their chemical bonds.

Insulation and Protection

Fat tissue accounts for about 15 to 30 percent of a person's body weight. Part of this is **visceral fat**, adipose tissue around organs that remains relatively inert until called upon to release stored energy. Meanwhile, it serves an important function by cushioning and shielding delicate organs, especially the kidneys. Women have extra fat, most noticeably in the breasts and hips, to help shield their reproductive organs and to guarantee adequate calories during pregnancy. Lying under the skin, where it protects and insulates the body, is other fat tissue called **subcutaneous fat**. Perhaps nowhere is fat's structural role more dramatic than in the brain, which is 60 percent fat.[7] **Figure 5.14** shows the primary areas of fat storage in women and men.

Can a person have too little body fat? Just ask someone whose body fat has been depleted by illness. It hurts to sit and it hurts to lie down. For people without enough body fat, cool temperatures are intolerable and even room temperature may be uncomfortably cool. Women stop menstruating and become infertile. Children stop growing. Skin deteriorates from pressure sores or from fatty acid deficiency and may become covered with fine hair called **lanugo**. Illness, involuntary starvation, and famine can deplete fat to this extent, as can excessive dieting and exercise. THINK About It 2

Carrier of Fat-Soluble Compounds

As you can see in **Figure 5.15**, dietary fats dissolve and transport micronutrients such as fat-soluble vitamins and fat-soluble phytochemicals such as

Figure 5.14 **Sites for fat storage differ for men and women.** Whereas men often store excess fat in their abdomens, women tend to store it in their hips.

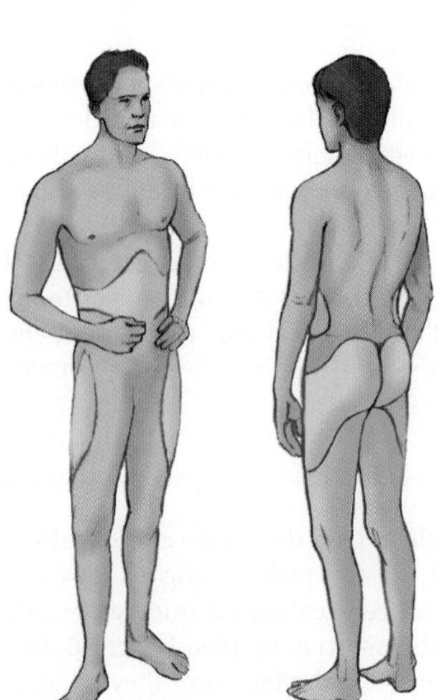

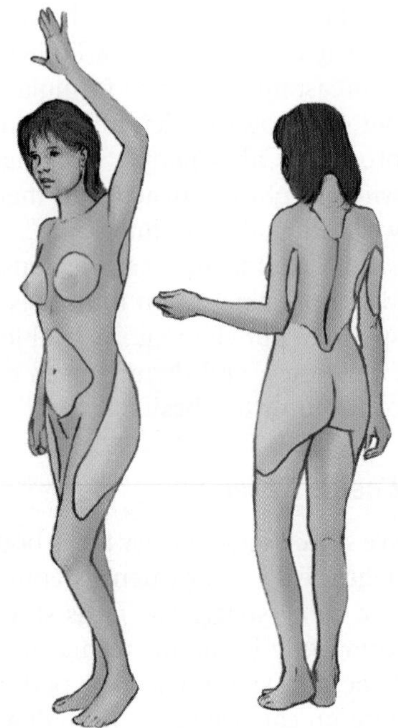

visceral fat Fat stores that cushion body organs.

subcutaneous fat Fat stores under the skin.

lanugo [lah-NEW-go] Soft, downy hair that covers a normal fetus from the fifth month but is shed almost entirely by the time of birth. It also appears on semistarved individuals who have lost much of their body fat, serving as insulation normally provided by body fat.

carotenoids. Phytochemicals, although not essential (their lack will not cause a deficiency disease), have emerged as contributors to optimal health.

Dietary fats carry other fat-soluble substances through the digestive process, improving intestinal absorption or bioavailability. For example, the body absorbs more lycopene, the healthful red-colored phytochemical in tomatoes, if the tomatoes are served with oil or salad dressing. People who suffer from fat malabsorption disorders risk deficiency of fat-soluble micronutrients, so many must use supplements.

Removing a food's lipid portion—for example, removing butterfat from milk—also removes fat-soluble vitamins. In the case of most dairy products, vitamin A is usually replaced. But the natural vitamin E of whole wheat (vitamin E is in the germ) is not replaced after the lipid-rich germ portion of wheat grain is removed during refinement to white flour. Fat-soluble vitamins may be destroyed in fat processing; for example, some vitamin E is lost in processing vegetable oils.

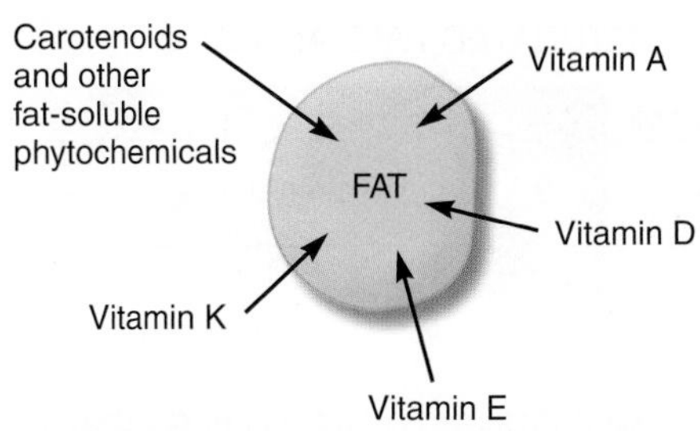

Figure 5.15 **Fat is a micronutrient carrier.** Fat holds more than just energy. It also carries important nutrients, such as fat-soluble vitamins and carotenoids.

Sensory Qualities

As a food component or as an ingredient, fat contributes greatly to the flavor, odor, and texture of food (see **Figure 5.16**). Simply put, it makes food taste good. Flavorful volatile chemicals are dissolved in the fat of a food; heat sends them into the air, producing mouth-watering odors that perk up appetites. Fats have a rich, satisfying feeling in the mouth. Fats make baked goods tender and moist. And fats can be heated to high temperatures for frying, which seals in flavors and cooks food quickly. These are all good qualities—but too good for many people who find high-fat foods irresistible and eat too much of them. Alas, fat's most appealing attributes are also serious drawbacks to maintaining a healthful diet.

Figure 5.16 Fat imparts a rich, sensory quality to food.

Key Concepts *Triglycerides are formed when a glycerol molecule combines with three fatty acids. Dietary triglycerides add texture and flavor to food and are a concentrated source of calories. The body stores excess calories as adipose tissue. While storing energy, adipose tissue also insulates the body and cushions its organs. The fats in food carry valuable fat-soluble nutrients into the body and help with their absorption.*

Triglycerides in Food

Dietary triglycerides are found in a variety of fats and oils and in foods that contain them, such as salad dressing and baked goods. Some food fats are obvious, such as butter, margarine, cooking oil, and fat along a cut of meat or under the skin of chicken. Baked goods, snack foods, nuts, and seeds also provide fat, but less noticeably.

Fats and oils are mixtures of many triglycerides, but we often categorize them by their most prevalent type of fatty acid—saturated, monounsaturated, or polyunsaturated. (See **Figure 5.17**.) Canola oil, for example, often is classified as a monounsaturated fat. Its fatty acids are mostly monounsaturated oleic acid; however, 10 percent of its fatty acids are the essential alpha-linolenic acid. Although these classifications are useful, they do not always tell the whole story. For example, saturated stearic acid appears to affect blood cholesterol differently than saturated palmitic acid does. As we've seen, omega-3 and omega-6 fatty acids also behave differently in the body, even though both classes are polyunsaturated. Their food sources often differ as well.

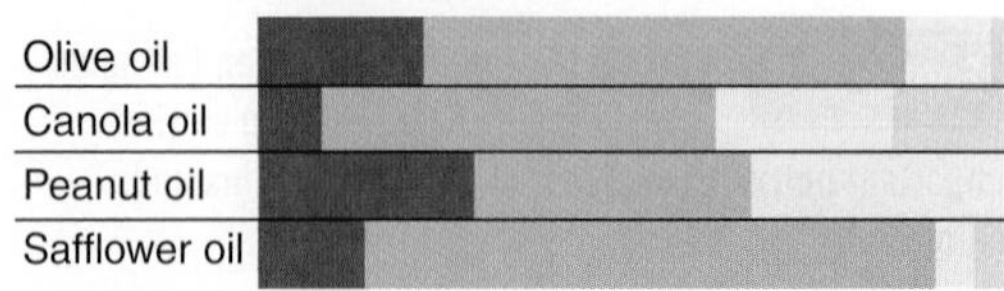

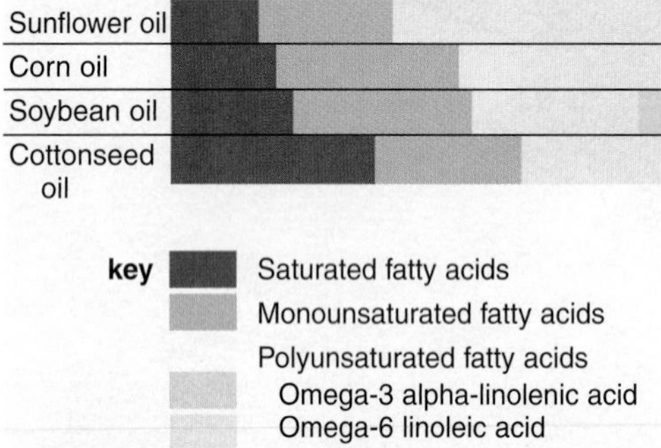

Figure 5.17 **The diversity of fats.** Fats are mixtures of saturated and unsaturated fatty acids. Depending on which type of fatty acid is most prevalent, the fat is classified as saturated, monounsaturated, or polyunsaturated.

Source: Adapted from *Nutrition Today*, May/June 1996;31(3).

Sources of Omega-3 Fatty Acid

Plant foods are generally rich in polyunsaturated fatty acids. Soybean oil, canola oil, and walnuts contain alpha-linolenic acid, the essential omega-3 fatty acid. However, the most generous source is flaxseed (or linseed) oil, which is more than 50 percent alpha-linolenic acid. Longer-chain omega-3s—EPA and DHA—are found in fatty fish (e.g., salmon, tuna, and mackerel) and in fish oil supplements. Because fish oil supplements can have potent effects, children, pregnant women, and nursing mothers should not take them without medical supervision.[8] See the FYI feature "Fats on the Health Store Shelf." Table 5.3 lists the omega-3 fatty acids in some foods.

Sources of Omega-6 Fatty Acid

Good sources of the 18-carbon omega-6 fatty acid linoleic acid include seeds, nuts, and the richest sources, common vegetable oils such as corn oil. Small amounts of arachidonic acid, a 20-carbon omega-6 fatty acid, are found in meat, poultry, and eggs, but not in plant foods.

Commercial Processing of Fats

In nature, almost all fats exist in combination with other macronutrients: they generally occur along with starches in plant foods, and with proteins in animal foods. In earlier times, the only concentrated fats and oils available to people were obtained by very simple processing: rendering fats from meats and poultry; skimming or churning the butterfat from milk; skimming the oil from ground nuts; or pressing a few oil-rich plant parts such as coconuts or olives.

Table 5.3 **Omega-3 Fatty Acids in Selected Foods**

	18:3 (mg)	20:5 (EPA) (mg)	22:6 (DHA) (mg)
1 Tbsp canola oil	1,302		
1 Tbsp soybean oil	925		
1 Tbsp walnut oil	1,414		
1 Tbsp flaxseed oil	7,249		
3 oz canned sockeye salmon (fatty fish)		418	564
3 oz cooked mackerel (fatty fish)		555	1,016
3 oz flounder (lean fish)		207	219
3 oz cooked shrimp		145	122
1 Tbsp cod liver oil		938	1,492
1 Tbsp salmon oil		1,771	2,480

Fish and seafood also contain small amounts of 18:3, which are not included on this table.

It sounds like a lot of omega-3. But remember, these are milligrams! Dietary fat is usually measured in grams. The 267 milligrams (0.267 g) of EPA and DHA in a serving of shrimp is not much in relation to a diet that has 50+ grams of fat and is a bit less than half the recommendation for daily intake.

Source: Based on data from US Department of Agriculture, Agricultural Research Service. USDA Nutrient Database for Standard Reference, Release 18. 2005. http://www.nal.usda.gov/fnic/foodcompindex.html. Accessed 5/24/06.

Technology that came into use in the 1920s allowed production of pure vegetable oils.[9] By efficiently removing edible oil from its source, processing has increased the availability of calories worldwide. Processing reduces waste and prevents spoilage during normal use and storage. It does so by inhibiting the destructive processes of hydrolysis and oxidation.

oxidation Oxygen attaches to the double bonds of unsaturated fatty acids. Rancid fats are oxidized fats.

Hydrolysis Products containing unrefined fats and oils also contain enzymes that hydrolyze oil by splitting fatty acids from triglycerides. Free fatty acids then perpetuate the damaging hydrolysis. Refining destroys the hydrolytic enzymes and removes most free fatty acids.

Oxidation The more unsaturated an oil (the more double bonds it has), the more vulnerable it is to **oxidation**. Oxidation occurs when an unsaturated fat comes in contact with air, and oxygen atoms attach at double-bond sites on the fatty acid chain. Oxidation rapidly turns fats rancid, and oxidized fats damage body tissues, particularly blood vessels.[10] Fortunately, people avoid bad-tasting rancid fats. Exposure to light increases the rate of oxidation and shortens shelf life. The presence of small amounts of metals, which typically

Going Green

Fish: Good for You and the Environment

What is a "good" source of fat, a lean protein high in vitamins and minerals, that does not contribute to the production of methane greenhouse gas? Fish! Methane, produced by farm animals, is a powerful greenhouse gas and is considered 20 times more powerful than carbon dioxide at trapping solar energy. Choosing to eat fish while decreasing your beef intake will not only give you all of the health benefits associated with omega-3 fatty acids but also will potentially decrease dangerous greenhouse gas production. An American Heart Association scientific statement on fish consumption, fish oils, omega fatty acids, and cardiovascular disease emphasizes the benefits of eating fish and recommends at least two servings of fish per week. Eicosapentaenoic acid (EPA) and docosahexaenoic acid (DHA) are the omega-3 fatty acids found in oily fish, with mackerel, salmon, trout, sardines, and herring being excellent sources. Approximately 1 gram of EPA/DHA can be obtained from 100 grams (3.5 ounces) of oily fish.[1]

What If I Don't Like to Eat Fish?

Remember that there are three types of omega-3 fatty acids used by the body: alpha-linolenic acid (ALA), EPA, and DHA. Once eaten, the body converts ALA to EPA and DHA, the two types of omega-3 fatty acids most readily used by the body. Although fish are an excellent source of EPA and DHA, plants are excellent sources of ALA. Sources of ALA include oils from flaxseed and canola, soybeans, walnuts, and wheat germ. Adding flaxseed or wheat germ to ready-to-eat cereals or using canola oil for cooking are ways you could incorporate more omega-3 fatty acids into your diet. Examples of foods fortified with omega-3 fatty acids include milk-based products, juices, table spreads, salad dressings, sauces, breakfast cereals, baked goods, sauces, infant formulas, and baby foods and juices, among others.[2] Omega-3 fatty acids are also available in the form of dietary supplements.

There are many healthy choices when it comes to incorporating healthful fats into your diet. Just remember, even though these fatty acids provide a "good" source of fat, don't go overboard. Fat is still fat, even if it is good for you and for the environment, so make your choices wisely.

1 Rigby A. Omega-3 choices: fish or flax? *Today's Dietitian*. 2004;6(1):37.

2 Hernandez E. Omega-3 oils as food ingredients [Web cast]. 2007. Institute of Food Technologists; and Mantzioris E, Cleland LG, Gibson RA, et al. Biochemical effects of a diet containing foods enriched with n-3 fatty acids. *Am J Clin Nutr.* 2000;72:42–48.

are removed by refining, also promotes oxidation. Naturally occurring vitamin E inhibits oxidation, which explains why it and other antioxidants are often added to oils.

Unfortunately, processing also has a negative side. To achieve stability and uniform taste, potentially healthful phospholipids, plant sterols, and other phytochemicals are removed, and a significant portion of the natural vitamin E is lost. Oils have become so familiar that we often forget they are highly processed, highly refined foods. Further processing of oils into solid fats such as margarine or shortening also produces some undesirable changes.

Hydrogenation To get a liquid vegetable oil to act like a solid fat, it must be at least partially hydrogenated. Hydrogenation involves breaking some of the double bonds in unsaturated fatty acids and adding hydrogen. This process produces a harder, more saturated fat—one that is more effective for making

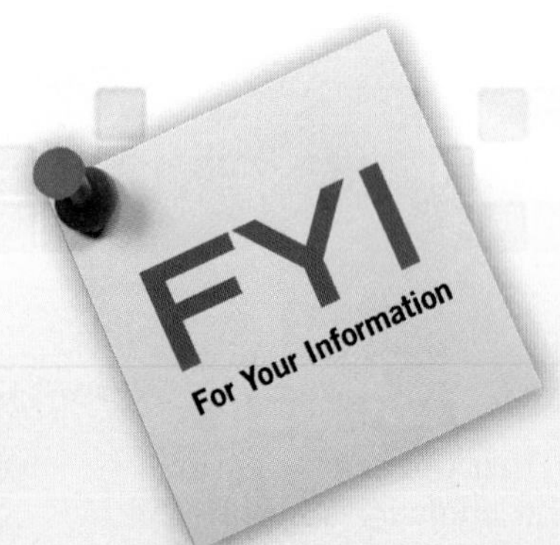

Fats on the Health Store Shelf

Many claims made for lipid products sold as supplements may not hold up under scientific scrutiny. You may not even recognize these products as lipids, especially because their long, complicated names are often abbreviated. The amount of lipid and calories in most of these products is quite small.

EPA and DHA in Fish Oil Capsules

These omega-3 fatty acids are thought to help lower blood pressure, reduce inflammation, reduce blood clotting, and lower high serum triglyceride levels.[1] They were thought to help psoriasis, but studies proved disappointing.[2] Dietary supplementation with omega-3 fatty acids is unlikely to reduce the risk of cancer. A large body of scientific literature has failed to find a significant association between omega-3 fatty acid consumption and cancer incidence.[3]

EPA (eicosapentaenoic acid) and DHA (docosahexaenoic acid) usually make up only about one-third of the fatty acids in fish oil capsules, and research studies often use multiple doses. These should not be taken without close medical supervision, because their blood-thinning properties can cause bleeding. Because fish oil is highly unsaturated, antioxidant vitamins are included to prevent oxidation. Another problem, though not health related, is that fish oil capsules often leave a fishy aftertaste.

Flaxseed Oil Capsules

Flaxseed oil is an unusually good source of omega-3 alpha-linolenic acid, which accounts for about 55 percent of its fatty acids. Like fish oil, flaxseed oil is highly unsaturated, and thus very susceptible to rancidity. Capsules protect the oil from oxygen, but limit the dose. A half-tablespoon of canola oil has about as much omega-3 as a capsule of flaxseed oil, but adds more calories. DHA and EPA are considered more potent omega-3 fatty acids than alpha-linolenic.

GLA in Borage, Evening Primrose, or Black Currant Seed Oil Capsules

These oils contain 9 to 24 percent GLA (gamma-linolenic acid), the omega-6 desaturation product of linoleic acid. Studies of GLA's effects on skin diseases and heart conditions have been disappointing, and research on potential benefits of GLA supplements in rheumatoid arthritis has been conflicting.[4]

Medium-Chain Triglycerides

Medium-chain triglycerides (MCTs) can be purchased as such, or found as ingredients in "sports" drinks and foods. Because MCTs are absorbed easily, they are marketed to athletes as a noncarbohydrate source of quick,

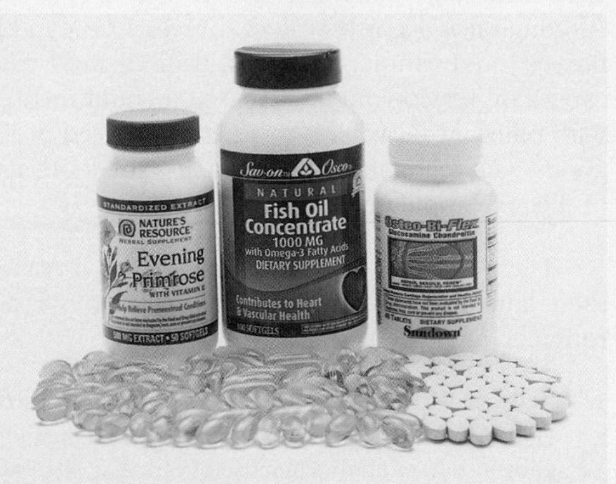

baked goods and snack foods, and one that spreads like butter (most of us recoil at the thought of putting pure corn oil on toast!). Although hydrogenation protects the fat from oxidation and rancidity, it also changes some of the double bonds in the fat's structure to the trans configuration. Combined with the increase in saturated fatty acids, this has led many to wonder whether margarine is a better alternative to butter (see the FYI feature "Which Spread for Your Bread?").

Key Concepts *Triglycerides are found mainly in foods we think of as fats and oils, but also in nuts, seeds, meats, and dairy products. Saturated fatty acids are found mainly in animal foods and tropical oils, whereas polyunsaturated fatty acids are found in vegetable oils and other plant foods. Unsaturated fatty acids are susceptible to spoilage by oxidation. Hydrogenation of oils protects fats from oxidation but creates trans fatty acids, which increase risk for heart disease.*

concentrated energy. However, they have no specific performance benefits. A tablespoon of MCT contains about 100 kilocalories.

Lecithin Oil or Granules

Lecithin supplements are derived from soybeans and are a mixture of phospholipids. They are often promoted as emulsifiers that lower cholesterol, but since dietary phospholipids are broken down by the enzyme lecithinase in the intestine, they cannot have this effect. They may be useful as a source of choline. Because choline is the precursor of acetylcholine (a neurotransmitter), lecithin is promoted for treating Parkinson's and Alzheimer's diseases, which are associated with low levels of acetylcholine in the brain. Unfortunately, these claims have little scientific support.[5]

Monolaurin Capsules

Monolaurin is an ester of lauric acid, a 12-carbon fatty acid found in coconut oil. Lauric acid is said to have anti-infective effects, but the amount in these capsules is probably too small to be significant.

CLA

Conjugated linoleic acid (CLA) is linoleic acid with only one saturated bond between its two double bonds. It is promoted as an aid for reducing body fat and has been suggested to have anticancer properties. Studies show promising results,[6] but more work is needed to identify specific functions of CLA and evaluate its long-term safety.[7]

DHEA

Dehydroepiandrosterone (DHEA) is a testosterone precursor formed from cholesterol. It is present in the body in large quantities during adolescence, peaks in the 20s, and gradually declines with age. Many elderly people have low levels, and levels also dip during serious illnesses. With only a few exceptions, attempts to use DHEA for illnesses or to slow aging have been disappointing. Researchers generally use doses many times greater than those in over-the-counter supplements, levels that may cause hairiness in women and, more seriously, a risk of liver problems.[8]

Shark Liver Oil and Squalene Capsules

Squalene, an intermediary compound in the synthesis of cholesterol in the body, and shark liver oil, which contains squalene, are said to help liver, skin, and immune function. The basis for these claims is unclear.

1 Connor SL, Connor WE. Are fish oils beneficial in disease prevention and treatment? *Am J Clin Nutr.* 1997;66:S1020–S1031.

2 Soyland E, Funk J, Rajka G, et al. Effect of dietary supplementation with very-long-chain n-3 fatty acids in patients with psoriasis. *N Engl J Med.* 1993:328:1812–1816.

3 MacLean CH, Newberry SJ, Mojica WA, et al. Effects of omega-3 fatty acids on cancer risk: a systematic review. *JAMA.* 2006;295(4):403–416.

4 Sarubin Fragakis A. *The Health Professional's Guide to Popular Dietary Supplements.* 2nd ed. Chicago: American Dietetic Association, 2003.

5 Higgins JP, Flicker L. Lecithin for dementia and cognitive impairment. *Cochrane Database Syst Rev.* 2000;4:CD001015.

6 Larsson SC, Bergkvist L, Wolk A. High-fat dairy food and conjugated linoleic acid intakes in relation to colorectal cancer incidence in the Swedish mammography cohort. *Am J Clin Nutr.* 2005;82(4):894–900.

7 Belury MA. Dietary conjugated linoleic acid in health: physiological effects and mechanisms of action. *Annu Rev Nutr.* 2002;22:505–531.

8 Khaw KT. Dehydroepiandrosterone, dehydroepiandrosterone sulphate and cardiovascular disease. *J Endocrinol.* 1996;150:S149–S153.

Phospholipids

Phospholipids are similar to triglycerides in that they contain both glycerol and fatty acids. However, important differences in their structure make phospholipids entirely different in terms of function. Phospholipids are synthesized by the body and not needed in the diet.

phosphate group A chemical group ($-PO_4$) on a larger molecule, where the phosphorus is single-bonded to each of the four oxygens, and the other bond of one of the oxygens is attached to the rest of the molecule. Often hydrogen atoms are attached to the oxygens. Sometimes there are double bonds between the phosphorus and an oxygen.

Phospholipid Structure

Phospholipids have a chemical structure similar to that of triglycerides, except that one of the fatty acids is replaced by another compound. Phospholipids are diglycerides—two fatty acids attached to a glycerol backbone. A **phosphate group** with a nitrogen-containing component, such as choline, occupies the third attachment site. **Figure 5.18** shows the structure of a phospholipid.

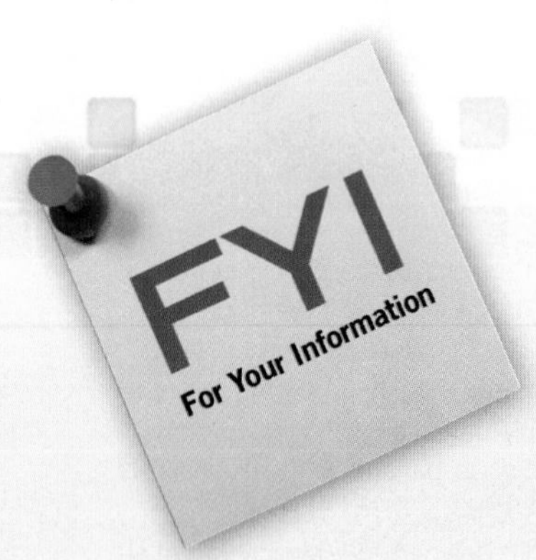

Which Spread for Your Bread?

Okay, it's time to see if you can put some of your new knowledge about lipids to work. You're standing in front of the dairy case ready to pick out the best spread. But, wow! So many choices. Of course, there's butter, the traditional spread—wholesome, natural, and creamy; sometimes there's just no substitute for the real thing. Margarine is the choice of many, and has come to be more familiar than butter to some consumers. Then what's this "vegetable oil spread"? Here's one that says it "helps promote healthy cholesterol levels."

Butter

When it comes to heart health, butter has some serious disadvantages: (1) it's high in cholesterol-raising saturated fat, (2) it contains cholesterol, and (3) like other fats, it's high in calories.

Here are the facts: 1 tablespoon of butter provides

100 kcal
11 g fat
7 g saturated fat
0 g trans fat
30 mg cholesterol
85 mg sodium
8% Daily Value for vitamin A

The ingredients are simple: "cream, salt, annatto (added seasonally)." Annatto is a natural coloring (a carotenoid) that is used to keep the color of butter consistent, despite what dairy cows might have been grazing on.

If you like the taste of butter, but want a bit less saturated fat and cholesterol, you can buy "whipped butter." The ingredients are the same, but the incorporation of air reduces calories, fat, saturated fat, cholesterol, and sodium by 60 to 70 percent.

Margarine

Margarine was developed to be a substitute for butter. Made from vegetable oils, it appears to be more healthful; as a plant-derived food, it's certainly cholesterol-free, and vegetable oils contain more unsaturated fatty acids than butter. Inconveniently, though, unsaturated oils are liquid, and without extra processing, margarine would run right off any slice of bread. Hydrogenated oils are needed to produce a spreadable consistency. But, as you know, hydrogenation increases the number of saturated and trans fatty acids in a fat, and both of these are associated with higher blood cholesterol levels.

Looking at the label of a standard stick of margarine, you'll find the following per tablespoon:

100 kcal
11 g fat
2 g saturated fat
2 g trans fat
3.5 g polyunsaturated fat
3.5 g monounsaturated fat
0 mg cholesterol
115 mg sodium
10% Daily Value for vitamin A

So compared with butter, we have the same amount of calories and fat (a fact unknown to many consumers!), less saturated fat and cholesterol, and a bit more sodium and vitamin A. The PUFA and MUFA content of butter is not listed, because these are not required elements of the Nutrition Facts label.

Turning to the list of ingredients, we find "liquid soybean oil, partially hydrogenated

The phosphate–nitrogen component of phospholipids is hydrophilic, so a phospholipid is compatible with both fat and water: fatty acids in its diglyceride area attract fats, while its phosphate–nitrogen component attracts water-soluble substances.

Phospholipid Functions

Because phospholipids have both hydrophobic and hydrophilic regions, they are ideal emulsifiers (compounds that help keep fats suspended in a watery environment) and are often used in foods to keep oil and water mixed. This same property makes phospholipids a perfect structural element for cell membranes—able to communicate with the watery environments of blood and cell fluids, yet with a lipid portion that allows other lipids to enter and exit cells.

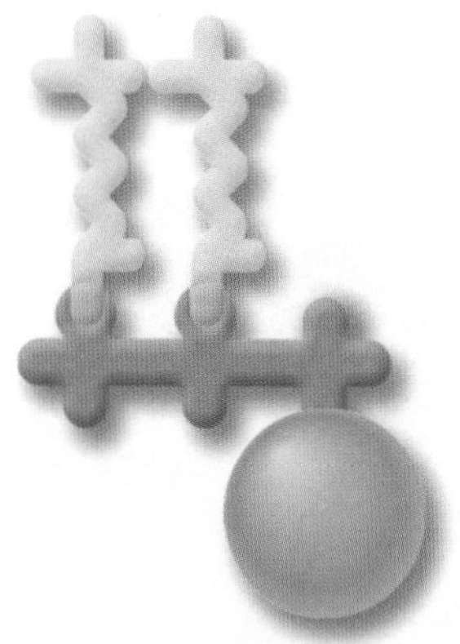

A generic phospholipid

soybean oil, water, whey, salt, soy lecithin, and vegetable mono- and diglycerides (emulsifiers), sodium benzoate (a preservative), vitamin A palmitate, beta carotene (color)." Nothing terribly unusual, especially now that you know what lecithin and mono- and diglycerides are.

Spreads and Other Butter Imitators

Beyond the traditional stick margarine, there are numerous "light," "soft," "whipped," "squeeze," and "spread" products. These items do not fit the legal definition of "margarine," and so the term *vegetable oil spread* is generally used. In terms of ingredients, these products have more liquid oil and water and less partially hydrogenated oils than margarine. More emulsifiers may be needed, along with flavors (including salt) and colors. The result typically is fewer calories, saturated fat, and still no cholesterol.

Some products tout the inclusion of canola or olive oil for more healthful MUFA. Others indicate "no trans fatty acids" and have no hydrogenated oils on the list. Several spreads contain plant sterols or stanols that reduce intestinal absorption of cholesterol.[1] Another product, still under development, will contain the soluble fiber psyllium, also meant to lower cholesterol absorption.[2]

Cholesterol-Lowering Margarines

Stanols are plant sterols similar in structure to cholesterol. Ingested plant sterols compete with and inhibit cholesterol absorption. Studies show that consumption of stanols reduces total blood cholesterol levels and LDL cholesterol levels.[3] HDL cholesterol levels increased or remained unchanged.[4]

The "cholesterol-lowering" margarines Benecol and Take Control contain plant sterols. Consumption of 3 grams of stanol per day, which is equivalent to three pats of these margarines, can effectively improve lipid profiles and may reduce cardiovascular risk. When consumed as part of a controlled diet, sterol/stanol esters do not change blood levels of fat-soluble vitamins or carotenoids.[5] Unfortunately, these margarines are expensive, about five times the cost of regular margarine.

Making Choices

The spread you choose may depend on your purpose. There are times, and foods, where nothing but real butter will do. If you've ever tried baking cookies with a soft, reduced-fat spread, you know the outcome—and probably will use butter, margarine, or vegetable shortening next time.

Remember, your goal is to limit total fats as well as saturated and trans fatty acids. Using less butter or margarine overall will do that. Choosing a margarine or spread with liquid vegetable oil as the first ingredient (meaning that the amount of hydrogenated oil is less) will reduce not only saturated fat but trans fat as well. Moderation is the key—making choices that consider your whole diet will help you stay in line with heart-healthy recommendations.

1 Hollingsworth P. Margarine: the over-the-top functional food. *Food Tech.* 2001;55(1):59–62.

2 Ostlund RE. Phytosterols in human nutrition. *Annu Rev Nutr.* 2002;22:533–549.

3 Jones PJ, Ntanios FY, Raeini Sarjaz M, Vanstone CA. Cholesterol-lowering efficacy of a sitostanol-containing phytosterol mixture with a prudent diet in hyperlipidemic men. *Am J Clin Nutr.* 1999;69(6):1144–1150; Gylling H, Miettinen TA. Cholesterol reduction by different plant stanol mixtures and with variable fat intake. *Metabolism.* 1999;48:(5):575–580; and Jones PJ, MacDougall DE, Ntanios F, Vanstone CA. Dietary phytosterols as cholesterol-lowering agents in humans. *Can J Physiol Pharmacol.* 1997;75:(3):217–227.

4 Gylling, Miettinen. Cholesterol reduction by different plant stanol mixtures and with variable fat intake.

5 Raeini-Sarjaz M, Ntanios FY, Vanstone CA, Jones PJ. No changes in serum fat-soluble vitamin and carotenoid concentrations with the intake of plant sterol/stanol esters in the context of a controlled diet. *Metabolism.* 2002;51(5):652–656.

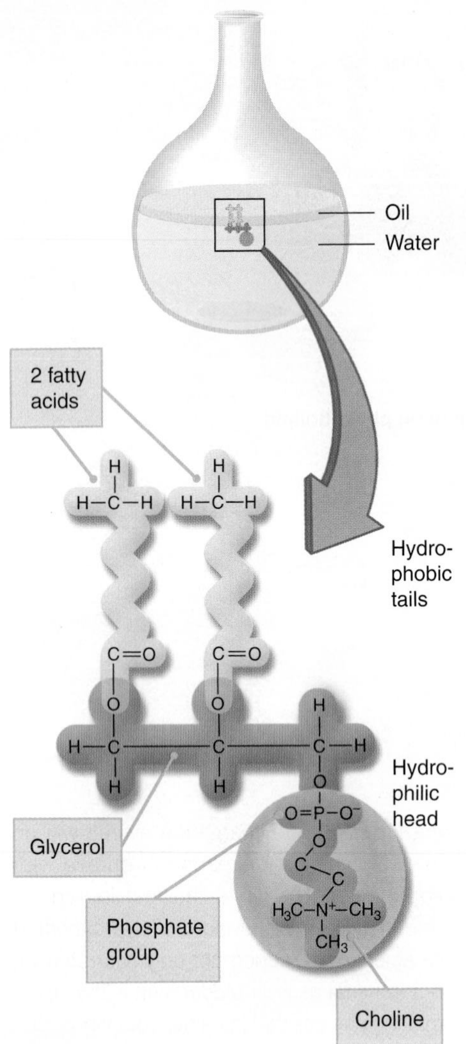

Figure 5.18 **Phospholipid.** A phospholipid is soluble in both oil and water. This is a useful property for transporting fatty substances in the body's watery fluids.

Cell Membranes

Phospholipids are major components of cell membranes. Cell membranes are a double layer of phospholipids that selectively allow both fatty and water-soluble substances into the cell. (See **Figure 5.19**.) They also provide a temporary store of fatty acids, donating them for short-term energy needs or for synthesis into regulatory chemicals (e.g., eicosanoids). Phosphatidylcholine (a phospholipid), whose **choline** is the precursor to the major neurotransmitter acetylcholine, plays an especially important role in nerve cells. By keeping fatty acids, choline, and other biologically active substances bound in phospholipids and freeing them only as needed, the body is able to regulate them closely.

Lipid Transport

The ability of phospholipids to combine both fatty and watery substances comes in handy throughout the body. In the stomach, dietary phospholipids help break fats into tiny particles for easier digestion. In the intestine, phospholipids from bile continue emulsifying. And in the watery environment of blood, phospholipids coat the surface of the lipoproteins that carry lipid particles to their destinations in the body.

Emulsifiers (Lecithins)

In the body and in foods of animal origin, phosphatidylcholine is also called **lecithin**. However, for food additives or supplements, the term *lecithin* is used for a mix of phospholipids derived from plants (usually soybeans). Understandably, this inconsistent terminology has caused confusion.

Lecithins are used by the food industry as emulsifiers to combine two ingredients that don't ordinarily mix, such as oil and water. (See **Figure 5.20**.) In high-fat powdered products (e.g., dry milk, milk replacers, and coffee creamers), lecithins help to mix hydrophobic compounds with water. Lecithins in salad dressing, chili, and sloppy-joe mixes increase dispersion and reduce fat separation. Lecithin is even added to chewing gum to increase its shelf life, prolong flavor release, and prevent the gum from sticking to teeth and dental work.

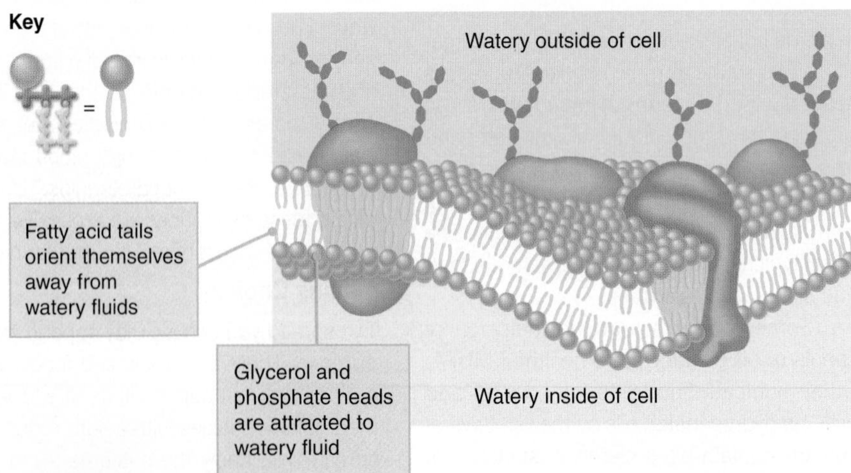

Figure 5.19 **Cell membranes are phospholipid bilayers.** Although proteins and other substances are embedded in cell membranes, these membranes primarily consist of phospholipids.

choline A nitrogen-containing compound that is part of phosphatidylcholine, a phospholipid. Choline is also part of the neurotransmitter acetylholine. The body synthesizes choline from the amino acid methionine.

lecithin In the body, a phospholipid with the nigrogenous component choline. In foods, lecithin is a blend of phospholipids with different nitrogenous components

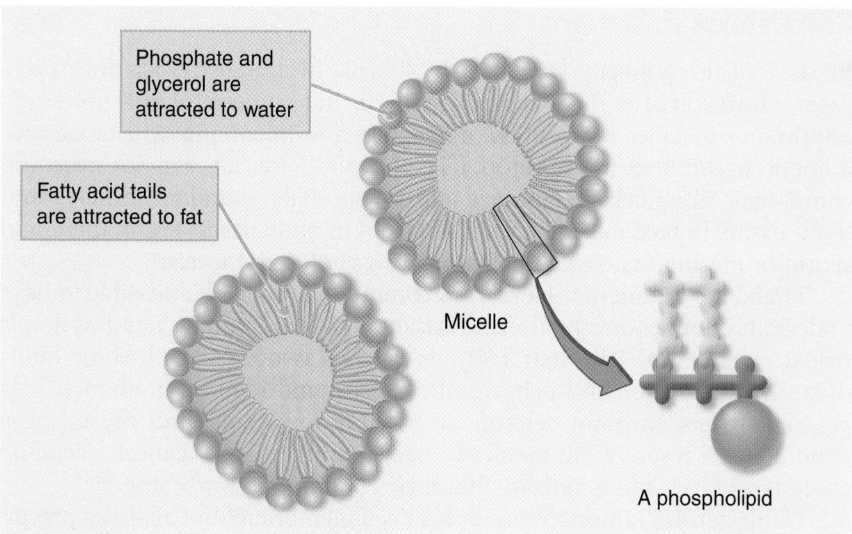

Figure 5.20 **Phospholipids and emulsification.** Phospholipids form water-soluble packages called micelles that suspend fat-soluble compounds in watery media. In a micelle, the phospholipids form into a water-soluble ball with a fatty core. The hydrophilic head of each phospholipid molecule points outward in contact with the watery medium, whereas the hydrophobic tails point inward in contact with the fatty core.

Quick Bite

The Power of Yolk

A single raw egg yolk is capable of emulsifying many cups of oil. Cooks take advantage of the natural emulsifying ability of egg yolk phospholipids to emulsify and stabilize preparations such as mayonnaise (oil and vinegar emulsion) and hollandaise sauce (butter and lemon juice emulsion). Food producers use phospholipid emulsifiers in processed foods, which today provide much of our intake.

Phospholipids in Food

Phospholipids occur naturally throughout the plant and animal world, albeit in small amounts compared with triglycerides. They are most abundant in egg yolks, liver, soybeans, and peanuts. Naturally occurring phospholipids are often lost when foods are processed, but other phospholipids are frequently used as food additives. Overall, a typical diet contains only about 2 grams per day. However, phospholipids are not dietary essential because your body can readily synthesize them from available raw materials.

Key Concepts *Phospholipids are diglycerides (glycerol plus two fatty acids) with a molecule containing a phosphate–nitrogen group attached at the third attachment point of glycerol. This structure gives the phospholipid both hydrophobic and hydrophilic regions, contributing to its functional properties. Phospholipids are major components of cell membranes and act as emulsifiers. They also store fatty acids for release into the cell and serve as a source of choline. Phospholipids are not needed in the diet because the body can synthesize them.*

Sterols

Although classified as lipids, sterols are quite different from triglycerides and phospholipids, both in structure and function. The best-known sterol is cholesterol.

THINK About It 3

Sterol Structure

Whereas triglycerides and phospholipids have fingerlike structures, sterols are hydrocarbons with a multiple-ring structure. (See **Figure 5.21**.) Like triglycerides, sterols are lipophilic and hydrophobic. Unlike triglycerides and phospholipids, most sterols contain no fatty acids.

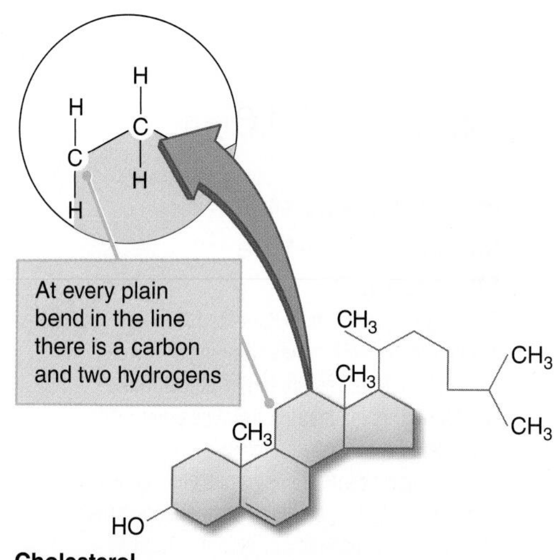

Figure 5.21 **Sterols.** Sterols are multi-ring structures. Because of its role in heart disease, cholesterol has become the best known sterol.

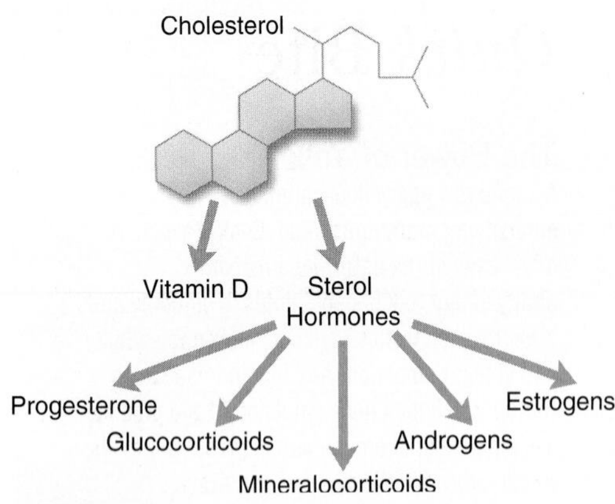

Figure 5.22 Cholesterol is a precursor of vitamin D and sterol hormones.

cholesterol [ko-LES-te-rol] A waxy lipid (sterol) whose chemical structure contains multiple hydrocarbon rings.

Quick Bite

Would You Pay More for Cholesterol-Free Mushrooms?

Several years ago, some plant foods were promoted with labels claiming they were "cholesterol free." As you might expect, the FDA found this misleading because plant foods never contain cholesterol unless an animal product such as butter or egg has been added. Regulations no longer allow the implication that cholesterol has been removed from a naturally cholesterol-free food. Rather than saying "cholesterol-free mushrooms," labels must now say "mushrooms, a cholesterol-free food."

Cholesterol Functions

Because of the publicity generated by its role in atherosclerosis (heart disease), **cholesterol** is the best-known sterol. But cholesterol is a necessary, important substance in the body; it becomes a problem only when excessive amounts accumulate in the blood. Like phospholipids, it is a major structural component of all cell membranes and is especially abundant in nerve and brain tissue. In fact, most cholesterol resides in body tissue, not in the blood serum or plasma that is routinely tested for cholesterol levels.

High blood cholesterol levels are common, but it is also possible to have undesirably low cholesterol levels. Although less common, very low levels (usually defined as less than 160 mg/dL) are associated with some kinds of stroke; lung, liver, and behavioral illnesses; and reduced immunity.[11] As yet, researchers have not determined whether low cholesterol causes these conditions or results from them. For people with AIDS or cancer, declining cholesterol levels often indicate that their condition is worsening.[12]

Cholesterol is important not only in cell membranes but also as a precursor molecule. For example, vitamin D is synthesized from cholesterol. Cholesterol is the precursor of five major classes of sterol hormones: progesterones, glucocorticoids, mineralocorticoids, androgens, and estrogens. (See **Figure 5.22**.) Progesterone is essential for maintaining a healthy pregnancy. Glucocorticoids (such as cortisol) increase the formation of liver glycogen and the breakdown of fat and protein. Mineralocorticoids (primarily aldosterone) help control blood pressure. Androgens (such as testosterone) promote the development of male sex characteristics, and estrogens promote the development of female sex characteristics. When testosterone is synthesized from cholesterol, an intermediate called DHEA (dehydroepiandrosterone) is formed. DHEA has become a popular nutritional supplement, marketed with the largely unfulfilled promise that it will boost potency and restore youth.

The liver uses cholesterol to manufacture bile salts, which are secreted in bile. The gallbladder stores and concentrates the bile. On demand, the gallbladder releases the bile into the small intestine, where bile salts emulsify dietary fats.

Cholesterol Synthesis

Because the body can synthesize cholesterol, it is not needed in the diet. Although researchers believe all cells synthesize at least some cholesterol, the liver is the primary cholesterol-manufacturing site, and the intestines contribute appreciable amounts. In fact, your body produces approximately 1,000 milligrams of cholesterol per day, far more than is found in the average diet. This production level attests to cholesterol's biological importance. In the lens of the eye, which has a high concentration of cholesterol, on-site cholesterol synthesis may be essential for preventing cataracts.[13] Animal studies suggest that the brain makes almost all the cholesterol incorporated into it during development.[14] Increasing dietary cholesterol reduces synthesis somewhat, but not by an equivalent amount.[15] Less cholesterol is produced when we eat frequent small meals rather than a few large meals. Fasting markedly reduces cholesterol production.[16]

Sterols in Food

Cholesterol occurs only in foods of animal origin. It is distributed based on its biological roles: it is highest in the brain, high in the liver and other organ meats, and moderate in muscle tissue. Because it is fat-soluble, cholesterol is found in the butterfat portion of dairy products. Egg yolks are high in cho-

Table 5.4 **Cholesterol in Selected Foods**

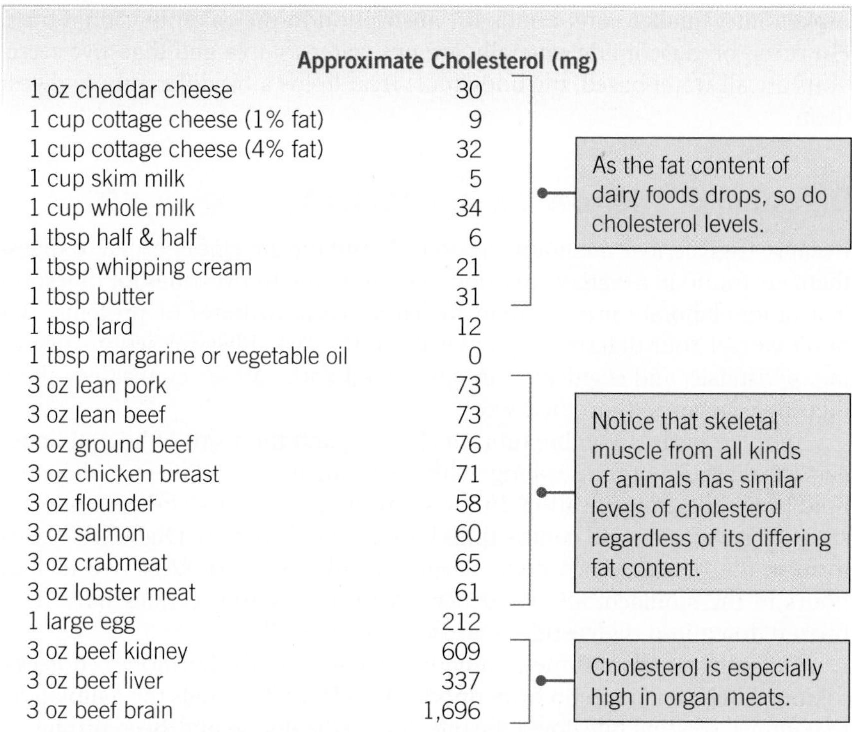

	Approximate Cholesterol (mg)
1 oz cheddar cheese	30
1 cup cottage cheese (1% fat)	9
1 cup cottage cheese (4% fat)	32
1 cup skim milk	5
1 cup whole milk	34
1 tbsp half & half	6
1 tbsp whipping cream	21
1 tbsp butter	31
1 tbsp lard	12
1 tbsp margarine or vegetable oil	0
3 oz lean pork	73
3 oz lean beef	73
3 oz ground beef	76
3 oz chicken breast	71
3 oz flounder	58
3 oz salmon	60
3 oz crabmeat	65
3 oz lobster meat	61
1 large egg	212
3 oz beef kidney	609
3 oz beef liver	337
3 oz beef brain	1,696

As the fat content of dairy foods drops, so do cholesterol levels.

Notice that skeletal muscle from all kinds of animals has similar levels of cholesterol regardless of its differing fat content.

Cholesterol is especially high in organ meats.

The values here give only a general idea of amounts in foods. Cholesterol values are quite variable, differing by time of the year; the animal's origin, species, or breed; processing; and more. One thing is always true, though: cholesterol is never found in plant foods.

Source: Based on data from US Department of Agriculture, Agricultural Research Service. USDA National Nutrient Database for Standard Reference, Release 18. 2005. http://www.nal.usda.gov/fnic/foodcompindex.html. Accessed 5/24/06.

lesterol, with about 212 milligrams per large egg (the egg white contains no cholesterol), and breast milk is moderately high, suggesting the importance of cholesterol during early growth and development.[17] Table 5.4 lists the amounts of cholesterol in some common foods.

Aside from cholesterol and vitamin D, few dietary sterols have nutritional significance. Whale liver and plants contain the cholesterol precursor **squalene**. Although whale liver is not a common item in U.S. grocery stores, squalene capsules are sold as dietary supplements with the unproved claim that squalene speeds healing. Plants contain a number of other sterols (phytosterols) that are poorly absorbed. **Phytosterols** are of current interest because they reduce intestinal absorption of cholesterol and are used as a cholesterol-lowering food ingredient in certain vegetable oil spreads.

squalene A cholesterol precursor found in whale liver and plants.

phytosterols Sterols found in plants. Phytosterols are poorly absorbed by humans and reduce intestinal absorption of cholesterol. They have been used as a cholesterol-lowering food ingredient.

Key Concepts *Sterols are hydrocarbons with a distinctive ring structure. Cholesterol is the best-known sterol; other sterols are hormones or hormone precursors. Cholesterol is an important precursor compound and a key component of cell membranes. High levels of blood cholesterol increase the risk of heart disease. Cholesterol is found only in foods of animal origin. Because the body can make all it needs, cholesterol is not a dietary essential.*

Lipid Digestion and Absorption

Like the other macronutrients (carbohydrates and proteins), most lipids are broken into smaller compounds for absorption in the gastrointestinal tract. However, because lipids generally are not water-soluble and digestive secretions are all water-based, the body must treat lipids a bit differently to digest them.

Digestion of Triglycerides and Phospholipids

Because triglycerides are not water-soluble and the enzymes needed to digest them are found in a watery environment, preparing triglycerides for digestion is a more elaborate process than for either carbohydrates or proteins. But don't worry! Your digestive system is up to the task. Physical actions (chewing, peristalsis, and segmentation) combined with various emulsifiers allow digestive enzymes to do their work.

In the mouth, a combination of chewing and the work of lingual lipase gets the digestive process rolling, with the small amount of dietary phospholipid providing emulsification. In the stomach, gastric lipase joins in, and the stomach's churning and contractions keep the fat dispersed. Diglycerides that form in the breakdown process become emulsifiers, too. After two to four hours in the stomach, about 30 percent of dietary triglycerides have been broken down into diglycerides and free fatty acids.[18]

Fat in the small intestine stimulates the release of the hormones cholecystokinin (CCK) and secretin from duodenal cells. CCK signals the gallbladder to contract, sending bile down the bile duct to the duodenum. Secretin signals the pancreas to release pancreatic juice rich in pancreatic lipase, which joins bile just before it reaches the duodenum, where the two substances mix with the watery chyme.

Bile contains a large quantity of bile salts and the phospholipid lecithin. These components are the key elements that emulsify fat, breaking globules into smaller pieces so that water-soluble pancreatic lipase can attack the surface. This emulsification process increases the total surface area of fats by as much as 1,000-fold.[19] Many common household detergents remove grease with this same action of emulsification.

As bile breaks up clumps of triglycerides into small pieces and keeps them suspended in solution, pancreatic lipase breaks off one fatty acid at a time. Pancreatic juice contains enormous amounts of pancreatic lipase—enough to digest all accessible triglycerides within minutes. When the lipase has completed its work, most of the dietary triglycerides have been split into monoglycerides and free fatty acids. (See **Figure 5.23**.)

Bile salts surround the products of fat digestion, forming **micelles**—water-soluble globules with a fatty core. The micelles transport the monoglycerides and free fatty acids through the watery intestinal environment to the brush border of the intestinal mucosal cells for absorption.

Phospholipid digestion follows a similar pathway, with phospholipases as well as other lipases participating in the process and with the added release of the phospholipid's phosphate and nitrogen components.

micelles Tiny emulsified fat packets that can enter enterocytes. The complexes are composed of emulsifier molecules oriented with their hydrophobic part facing inward and their hydrophilic part facing outward toward the surrounding aqueous environment.

steatorrhea Production of stools with an abnormally high amount of fat.

Digestibility

Normally, triglyceride digestion and absorption are very efficient. It is abnormal to find more than 6 or 7 percent of ingested lipids still intact in fecal matter. Production of fatty stools, called **steatorrhea**, indicates fat malabsorption, a condition that may follow radiation therapy or digestive surgery and often accompanies diseases of malabsorption such as cystic fibrosis or Crohn's disease.

Triglycerides of medium-chain fatty acids (medium-chain triglycerides, or MCTs) are used in products developed for people with fat malabsorption.[20] Medium-chain fatty acids—those with 6 to 10 carbons—are more water-soluble than longer-chain fatty acids and thus are more readily emulsified, with less need for bile. Because the fatty acid chains are shorter and therefore more water-soluble, MCTs are digested quickly and absorbed efficiently.

Breast milk is easily digestible. It is rich in medium-chain fatty acids and contains its own lipase, which enhances fat digestion despite the immaturity of the baby's digestive system. Some free medium-chain fatty acids released by hydrolysis are even absorbed directly through the baby's stomach lining.

Short-chain fatty acids, with the exception of butyric acid in milk fat, are almost never found in foods. Instead, they are produced by bacteria in the colon from undigested food, especially certain types of fiber. These fatty acids enter the cells of the large intestine (**enterocytes**), where they can be used for energy. A lack of short-chain fatty acids, which can occur when prolonged and exclusive intravenous feeding bypasses bacterial activity, is thought to damage intestinal cells, and nutritionists are studying the use of short-chain fatty acid supplements for these cases. Some research also suggests that butyric acid stimulates colon cells to suppress cancer growth, a finding that helps explain how dietary fiber may discourage colon cancer.[21]

enterocytes Intestinal cells.

Lipid Absorption

Most fat absorption takes place in the duodenum or jejunum of the small intestine. Micelles carry the monoglycerides and long-chain fatty acids to the

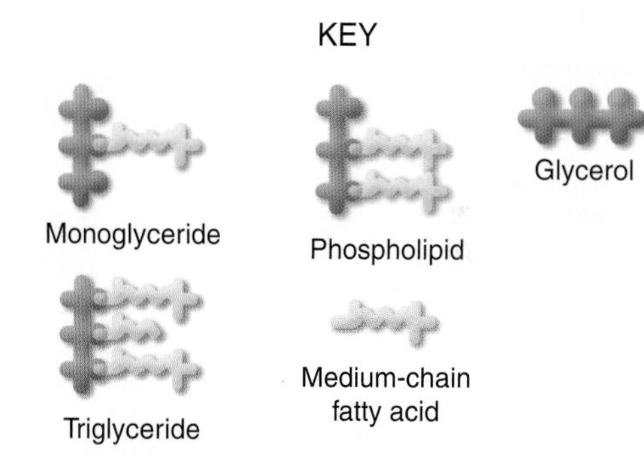

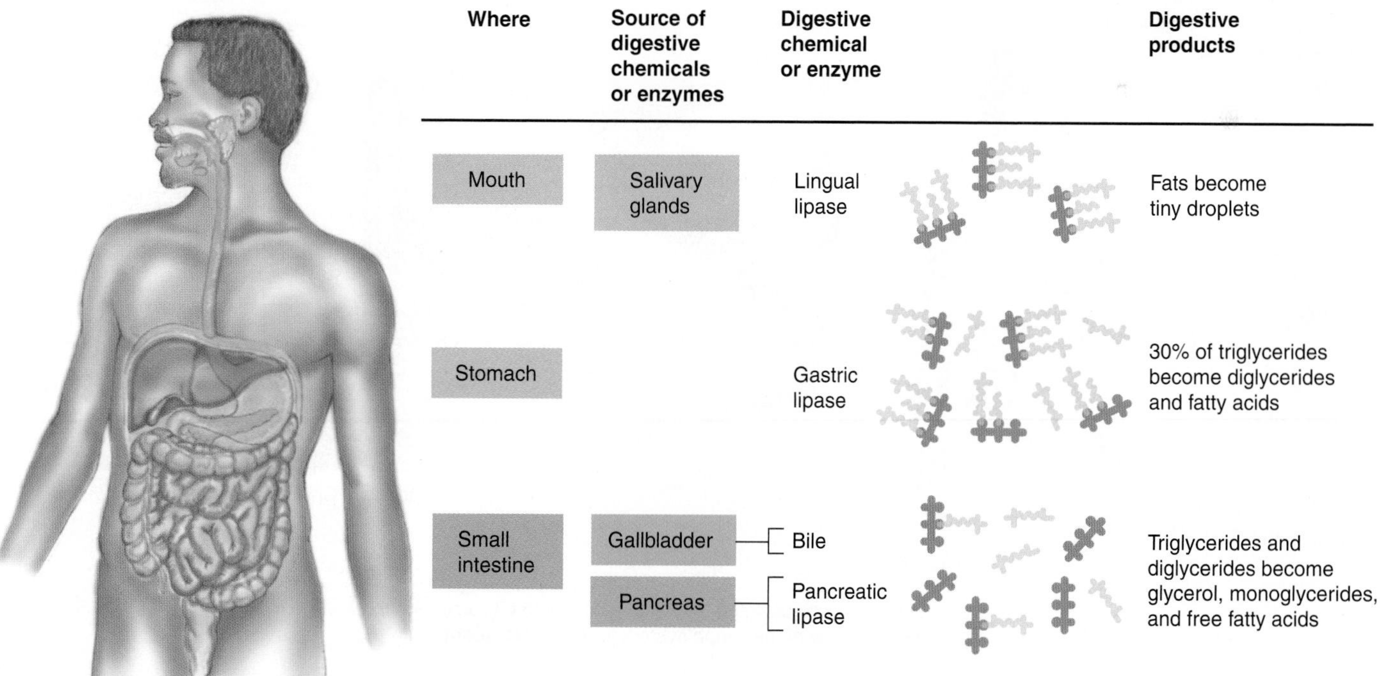

Where
Source of digestive chemicals or enzymes
Digestive chemical or enzyme
Digestive products
Mouth
Salivary glands
Lingual lipase
Fats become tiny droplets
Stomach
Gastric lipase
30% of triglycerides become diglycerides and fatty acids
Small intestine
Gallbladder
Bile
Pancreas
Pancreatic lipase
Triglycerides and diglycerides become glycerol, monoglycerides, and free fatty acids

Figure 5.23 **Triglyceride digestion.** Most triglyceride digestion takes place in the small intestine.

surfaces of the microvilli in the brush border, even penetrating the recesses between individual microvilli. Here, the monoglycerides and long-chain fatty acids immediately diffuse into the intestinal cells (enterocytes). The unabsorbed bile salts return to the interior of the small intestine to ferry another load of monoglycerides and fatty acids. In the last section of the small intestine (the ileum), bile salts are absorbed. They return via the portal vein to the

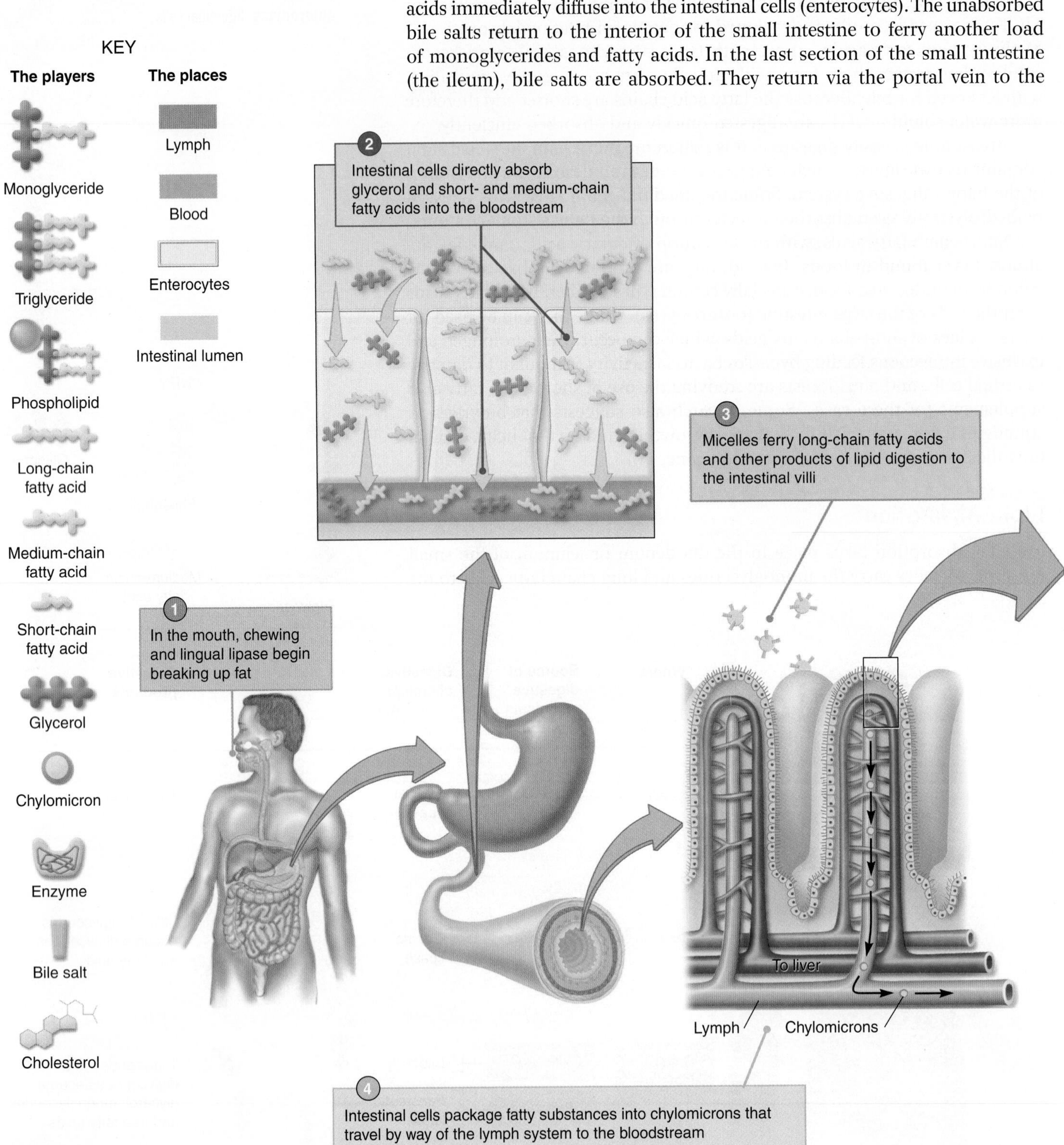

Figure 5.24 **Digestion and absorption of triglycerides.** Minimal fat digestion takes place in the mouth and stomach. In the small intestine, bile salts and lecithin break up and disperse fatty lipids in tiny globules. Enzymes attack these globules, breaking down triglycerides and phospholipids to fatty acids and other component parts. Glycerol and short- and medium-chain fatty acids are absorbed directly into the bloodstream. Bile salts surround the remaining products of fat digestion, forming water-soluble micelles that carry fat to intestinal cells, where it is absorbed and repackaged for transport by the lymphatic system.

liver, where they are once again secreted as part of bile. This bile recycling pathway—the liver to the intestine, and the intestine to the liver—is called enterohepatic circulation. Figure 3.9 in Chapter 3, "Digestion and Absorption," illustrates enterohepatic circulation.

As monoglycerides and fatty acids pass into the intestinal cells, they re-form into triglycerides. Most of the triglycerides, cholesterol, and phospholipids join protein carriers to form a **lipoprotein**. When this assemblage leaves the intestinal cell, it is called a **chylomicron**. The chylomicrons make their way to the central lacteal of the villi, where they enter the lymph system, to be propelled through the thoracic duct and emptied into veins in the neck.

Absorption of glycerol and of short-chain and medium-chain fatty acids is more direct. They are absorbed directly into the bloodstream rather than forming triglycerides and entering the lymph system. These fatty acids can diffuse directly into the capillaries of the villi because they are more water-soluble than longer-chain fatty acids. **Figure 5.24** illustrates the digestion and absorption of triglycerides.

One or two hours after you eat, dietary fat begins to appear in the bloodstream. Fat levels peak after 3 to 5 hours, and fats are generally cleared by 10 hours. That's why health professionals instruct people to fast for 12 hours before having blood drawn for lipid testing.

lipoprotein Complexes that transport lipids in the lymph and blood. They consist of a central core of triglycerides and cholesterol surrounded by a shell composed of proteins and phospholipids. The various types of lipoproteins differ in size, composition, and density.

chylomicron [kye-lo-MY-kron] A large lipoprotein particle formed in intestinal cells following the absorption of dietary fats. A chylomicron has a central core of triglycerides and cholesterol surrounded by phospholipids and proteins.

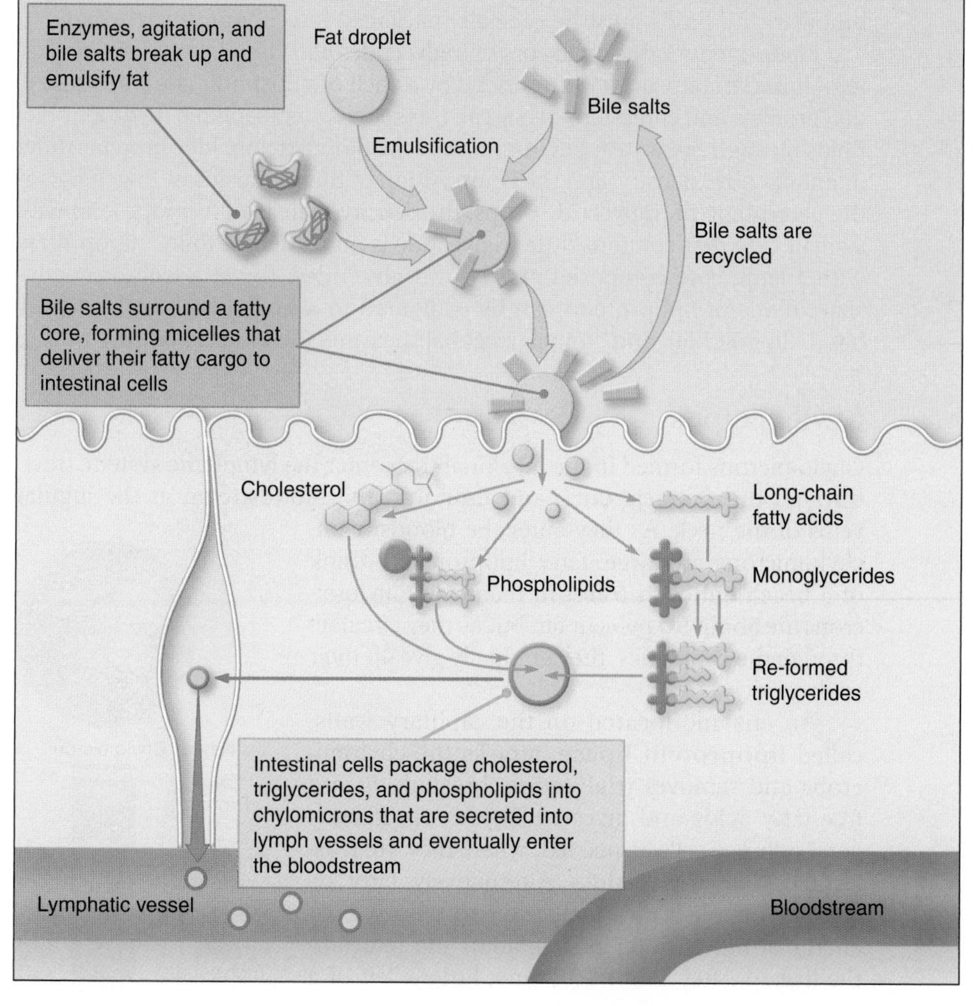
Enzymes, agitation, and bile salts break up and emulsify fat
Fat droplet
Bile salts
Emulsification
Bile salts are recycled
Bile salts surround a fatty core, forming micelles that deliver their fatty cargo to intestinal cells
Cholesterol
Long-chain fatty acids
Phospholipids
Monoglycerides
Re-formed triglycerides
Intestinal cells package cholesterol, triglycerides, and phospholipids into chylomicrons that are secreted into lymph vessels and eventually enter the bloodstream
Lymphatic vessel
Bloodstream

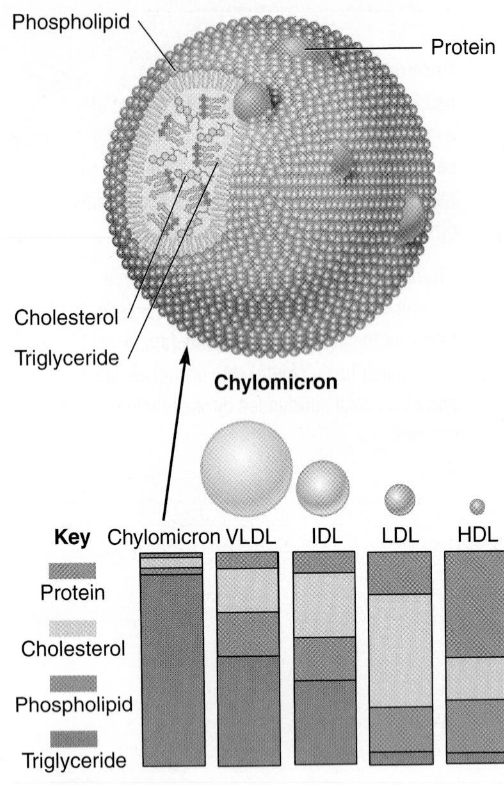

Figure 5.25 **Lipoprotein sizes and composition.** Lipoproteins become less dense as they increase in size. LDL is about double the size of HDL. VLDL is about 60 times larger than HDL. Chylomicrons range from 500 to 1,000 times larger than HDL.

Digestion and Absorption of Sterols

Digestion does little to change cholesterol and other sterols, which are poorly absorbed compared with triglycerides. Cholesterol may be esterified (attached to a fatty acid) prior to absorption. When there is dietary fat in the intestine, cholesterol absorption increases. When there are plenty of plant sterols and dietary fiber in the intestine, especially fiber from fruits, vegetables, oats, peas, and beans, cholesterol absorption decreases. Overall, only about 50 percent of dietary cholesterol is absorbed, and that proportion decreases as cholesterol intake increases. Because certain fibers bind bile salts and cholesterol and carry them out of the colon, health professionals often recommend eating foods rich in soluble fiber to lower blood cholesterol.

Key Concepts *Digestion breaks most lipids down into glycerol, free fatty acids, monoglycerides, and, in the case of phospholipids, a nitrogenous compound. In the small intestine, long-chain fatty acids and monoglycerides are absorbed primarily into the lymphatic system. Glycerol, short-chain fatty acids, and medium-chain fatty acids are absorbed directly into the blood. Sterols are mostly unchanged by digestion, and their absorption is relatively poor.*

Lipids in the Body

The digestive tract is not the only place where lipids need special handling to move in a water-based environment. To be transported around the body in the bloodstream, lipids must be specially packaged into lipoprotein carriers.

Lipoproteins have a lipid core of triglycerides and cholesterol esters (cholesterol linked to fatty acids) surrounded by a shell of phospholipids with embedded proteins and cholesterol. They can transport water-insoluble (hydrophobic) lipids through the watery environment of the bloodstream. Lipoproteins differ mainly by size, density, and the composition of their lipid cores. In general, as the percentage of triglyceride drops, the density increases. A lipoprotein with a small core that contains little triglyceride is much denser than a lipoprotein with a large core composed mostly of triglycerides. To get a feel for relative sizes, different lipoproteins can be compared to a huge beach ball, softball, baseball, golf ball, and ¾-inch steel ball bearing. (See **Figure 5.25**.)

Chylomicrons

Chylomicrons formed in the intestinal tract enter the lymphatic system, travel through the thoracic duct, and flow into the bloodstream at the jugular veins of the neck. As they enter the bloodstream, chylomicrons are large, fatty lipoproteins—think of a beach ball 3 to 6 feet in diameter. Chylomicrons are about 90 percent fat, but as they circulate through the capillaries, they gradually give up their triglycerides.

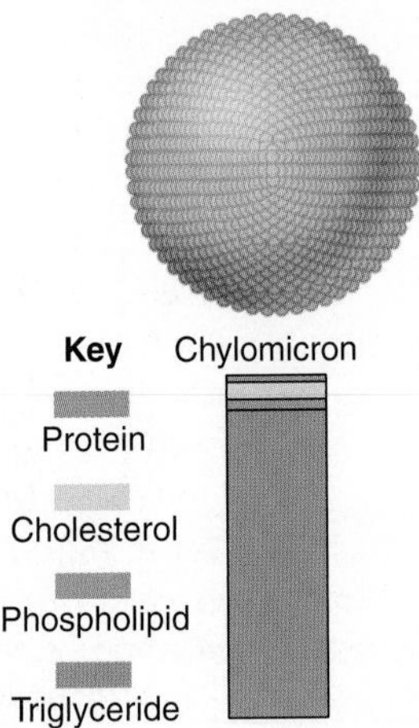

An enzyme located on the capillary walls, called **lipoprotein lipase**, attacks the chylomicrons and removes triglyceride, breaking it into free fatty acids and glycerol. These components enter adipose cells as needed, where they are reassembled into triglycerides. Alternatively, fatty acids may be taken up by muscle and oxidized for energy or may remain in circulation and return to the liver.[22] After about 10 hours, little is left of a

lipoprotein lipase The major enzyme responsible for the hydrolysis of plasma triglycerides.

circulating chylomicron except cholesterol-rich remnants. It's as if the air were let out of our beach ball, shrinking it to about the size of a 4½-inch diameter softball. The liver picks up these chylomicron remnants and uses them as raw material to build very low density lipoproteins.

very low density lipoproteins (VLDL) The triglyceride-rich lipoproteins formed in the liver. VLDL enters the bloodstream and is gradually acted upon by lipoprotein lipase, releasing triglyceride to body cells.

intermediate-density lipoproteins (IDL) The lipoproteins formed when lipoprotein lipase strips some of the triglycerides from VLDL. Containing about 40 percent triglycerides, this type of lipoprotein is more dense than VLDL and less dense than LDL. Also called a VLDL remnant.

low-density lipoproteins (LDL) The cholesterol-rich lipoproteins that result from the breakdown and removal of triglycerides from intermediate-density lipoprotein in the blood.

Very Low Density Lipoprotein

The liver and intestines assemble **very low density lipoproteins (VLDL)** with a triglyceride-rich core—for relative size, think of a softball. VLDL has a very low density because it is nearly two-thirds triglyceride. As with chylomicrons, lipoprotein lipase splits off and hydrolyzes triglycerides from VLDL as it circulates through the capillaries of the bloodstream. As VLDL loses triglycerides, it becomes denser, gradually becoming an intermediate-density lipoprotein. Our softball has shrunk to about the size of a 2¾-inch diameter baseball. When the diet is high in saturated and trans fat, more VLDL and triglycerides are released from the liver.[23]

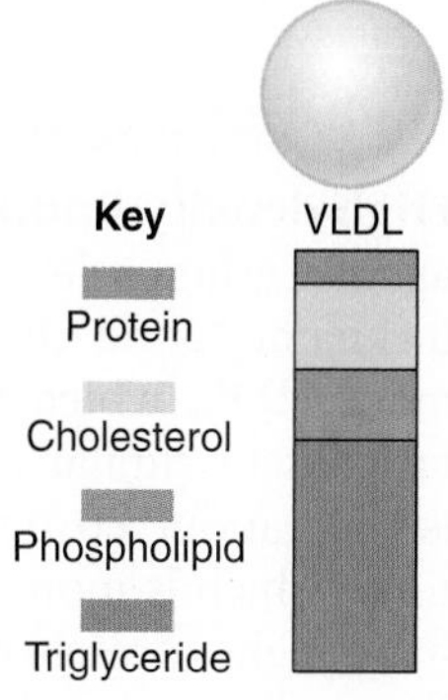

Intermediate-Density Lipoprotein

Intermediate-density lipoproteins (IDL) are about 40 percent triglyceride. As IDL travels through the bloodstream, it acquires cholesterol from another lipoprotein (see "High-Density Lipoprotein," later in this chapter), and circulating enzymes remove some phospholipids. IDL returns to the liver, where liver cells convert it to low-density lipoproteins.

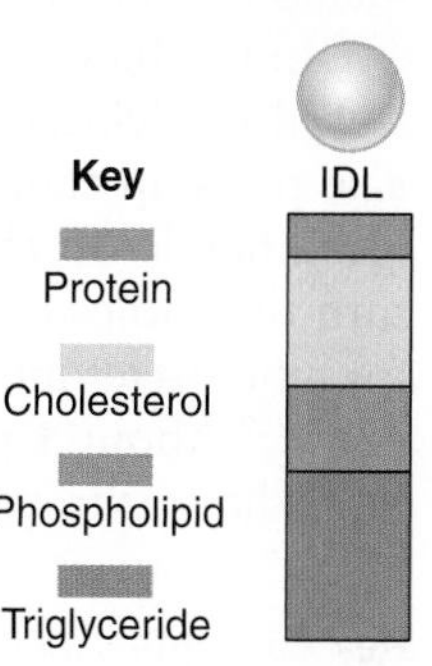

Low-Density Lipoprotein

THINK About It 4

Elevated levels of **low-density lipoproteins (LDL)** in the blood increase the risk of atherosclerosis and heart disease, earning LDL cholesterol the nickname "bad cholesterol." LDL delivers cholesterol to body cells, which use it to synthesize membranes, hormones, and other vital compounds. LDL is more than half cholesterol and cholesterol esters; triglycerides make up only 6 percent. For a relative size, think of a golf ball about 1⅝ inches in diameter.

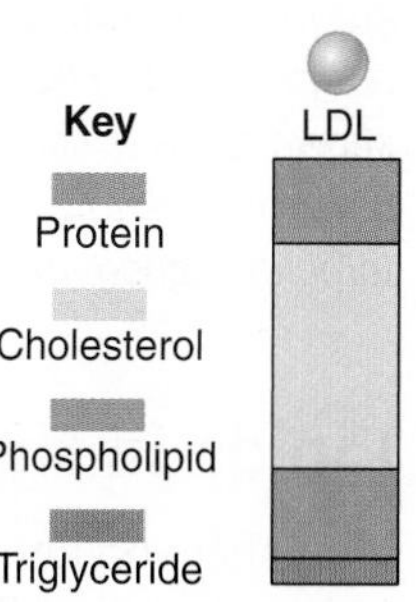

Special receptors on the cell walls bind low-density lipoproteins, which the cell engulfs and ingests via endocytosis. Inside the cell, LDL is broken into its component parts, releasing its load of cholesterol.

When the LDL receptors on liver cells bind LDL, they help control blood cholesterol levels.[24] A lack of LDL receptors reduces the uptake of cholesterol, forcing it to remain in circulation at dangerously high levels. Some research suggests that saturated fats block LDL receptors, limiting their clearance of cholesterol from the blood.[25] However, the main effect of saturated (and also trans) fats appears to be on VLDL production, which then leads to elevated LDL levels in the blood.[26]

Low-density lipoprotein also is picked up by scavenger receptors. These are a different type of receptor, one that has a particular affinity for altered (oxidized) LDL. When smoking, diabetes, high blood pressure, or infections

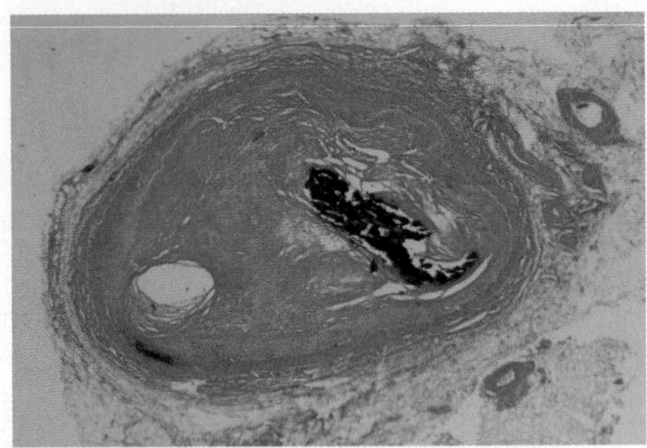

Figure 5.26 Plaque buildup in a coronary artery.

injure blood vessel walls, the body's emergency repair team swings into action. It mobilizes white blood cells, which travel to the site of the injury and bury themselves in the blood vessel wall. Certain white blood cells with scavenger receptors bind and ingest LDL. As LDL degrades, it releases its cholesterol. Over several years, this process leads to an accumulation of cholesterol and the development of plaque that thickens and narrows the artery, a condition known as atherosclerosis (**Figure 5.26**).

High-Density Lipoprotein

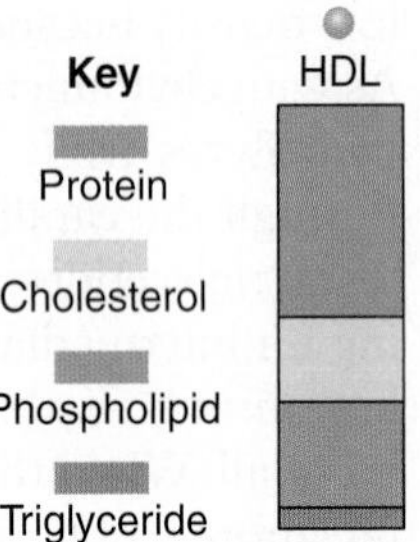

High-density lipoproteins (HDL) appear to protect against atherosclerosis, earning HDL cholesterol the nickname "good cholesterol." The liver and intestines make HDL, which is about 5 percent triglyceride, a fat content similar to LDL. On the other hand, HDL is only about 20 percent cholesterol, much less than LDL, which is more than 50 percent cholesterol. HDL has a higher protein content than any other lipoprotein. For a relative size, think of a steel ball bearing about ¾ inches in diameter.

In the bloodstream, HDL picks up cholesterol released by dying cells and from cell membranes as they are renewed. HDL also picks up cholesterol from arterial plaques, reducing their accumulation. HDL hands off cholesterol to other lipoproteins, especially IDL, which return the cholesterol to the liver for recycling. Low HDL levels increase risk for atherosclerotic heart disease, whereas high HDL levels have a protective effect.[27] About 1 percent of the population who have extremely high HDL levels have extremely low rates of heart disease and stroke.[28]

high-density lipoproteins (HDL) The blood lipoproteins that contain high levels of protein and low levels of triglycerides. Synthesized primarily in the liver and small intestine, HDL picks up cholesterol released from dying cells and other sources and transfers it to other lipoproteins.

Key Concepts *Lipoprotein carriers transport lipids in the blood. Chylomicrons, formed in the intestinal mucosal cells, transport lipids from the digestive tract into circulation. VLDL carries lipids from the liver to the other body tissues, delivering triglycerides and gradually becoming IDL. The liver takes up IDL and assembles LDL, the main carrier of cholesterol. High blood levels of LDL cholesterol, the "bad cholesterol," have been shown to be a risk factor for heart disease. Circulating HDL picks up cholesterol and sends it back to the liver for recycling or excretion. A relatively high level of HDL cholesterol, the "good cholesterol," reduces risk for heart disease.*

Lipids in the Diet

Now that you know something about lipids and their importance in the body, you can see that Rachel's no-fat approach to life has serious flaws. However, consumption of too much dietary fat can contribute unwanted calories, and high intake of saturated and trans fat has been linked to heart disease. Let's discuss the recommended amounts and balance of lipids in a healthful diet.

Recommended Intakes

In the 1990s, the American Heart Association (AHA), the National Cholesterol Education Program (NCEP) of the National Institutes of Health, and the *Dietary Guidelines for Americans* set specific target levels for intake of lipids. These guidelines set limits on total fat and saturated fat intake as a percentage of calories and on the total amount of cholesterol in the diet.

In 2006, the AHA released revised diet and lifestyle recommendations. (See Table 5.5.) One of the most significant changes from prior guidelines

Quick Bite

Doctors, Name Your Fat Syndrome

There are several conditions of high blood fats:

- Hypercholesterolemia—high total cholesterol.
- Hypertriglyceridemia—high triglycerides.
- Hyperlipidemia—may be high triglycerides, high cholesterol, or both. The term is often used along with a more detailed classification, such as "hyperlipidemia type II." It is sometimes shortened to "lipidemia."
- Dyslipidemia—abnormal lipid levels, usually too high.

Table 5.5 **American Heart Association Diet and Lifestyle Recommendations**

Improving diet and lifestyle is a critical component of the AHA's strategy for cardiovascular disease risk reduction.
• Balance calorie intake and physical activity to achieve or maintain a healthy body weight.
• Consume a diet rich in vegetables and fruit.
• Choose whole-grain, high-fiber foods.
• Consume fish, especially oily fish, at least twice a week.
• Limit your intake of saturated fat to <7% of energy, trans fat to <1% of energy, and cholesterol to <300 mg per day.
• Minimize your intake of beverages and foods with added sugars.
• Choose and prepare foods with little or no salt.
• If you consume alcohol, do so in moderation.
• When you eat food that is prepared outside of the home, follow the ADA Diet and Lifestyle Recommendations.

Source: Lichtenstein AH, Appel LJ, Brands M, et al. Diet and lifestyle recommendations revision 2006: a scientific statement from the American Heart Association Nutrition Committee. *Circulation*. 2006;114:82–96.

Dietary Guidelines for Americans, 2010
Key Recommendations

Foods and Food Components to Reduce

- Consume less than 10 percent of calories from saturated fatty acids by replacing them with monounsaturated and polyunsaturated fatty acids.
- Consume less than 300 mg per day of dietary cholesterol.
- Keep trans fatty acid consumption as low as possible by limiting foods that contain synthetic sources of trans fats, such as partially hydrogenated oils, and by limiting other solid fats.
- Reduce the intake of calories from solid fats and added sugars.

Foods and Nutrients to Increase

- Replace protein foods that are higher in solid fats with choices that are lower in solid fats and calories and/or are sources of oils.
- Use oils to replace solid fats where possible.

was a recommendation to consume at least two weekly servings of oily fish, such as tuna or salmon. These recommendations support the AHA's Diet and Lifestyle Goals for Cardiovascular Disease Risk Reduction.[29] Consuming an overall healthy diet and aiming for a healthy body weight are two of the AHA's goals.

Recently, researchers also have focused on the balance of calories from fat and carbohydrate rather than just targeting a reduction in fat. A high-fat, low-carbohydrate diet tends to contribute extra calories that lead to weight gain. When high-fat diets are high in saturated and trans fat, increased LDL cholesterol levels and higher heart disease risk result.[30] On the other hand, low-fat, high-carbohydrate diets are associated with lower HDL cholesterol and higher blood triglyceride levels—also increasing heart disease risk. Very low fat intake can make it difficult to get adequate amounts of vitamin E and essential fatty acids.[31]

In 2002, the National Academy of Sciences published its report on Dietary Reference Intakes (DRIs) for the macronutrients.[32] This report recommends an Acceptable Macronutrient Distribution Range (AMDR) for fat of 20 to 35 percent of calories for adults. This is balanced with 45 to 65 percent of calories from carbohydrates and 10 to 35 percent of calories from protein. Because children have higher energy needs, the AMDR for younger ages is more liberal: 30 to 40 percent of calories for children aged 1 to 3 years, and 25 to 35 percent of calories for those aged 4 to 18 years. For infants, the Adequate Intake (AI) for fat is 31 grams per day from birth to 6 months of age, and 30 grams per day for ages 7 to 12 months. AIs or RDAs were not set for older children and adults because there is no defined fat intake level that promotes optimal growth, maintains fat balance, or reduces chronic disease risk. In short, scientists suggest that humans can adapt to a wide range of fat intakes.

Many nutritionists were surprised to find that the DRI committee did not set upper limit (UL) levels for fat or cholesterol. The committee concluded

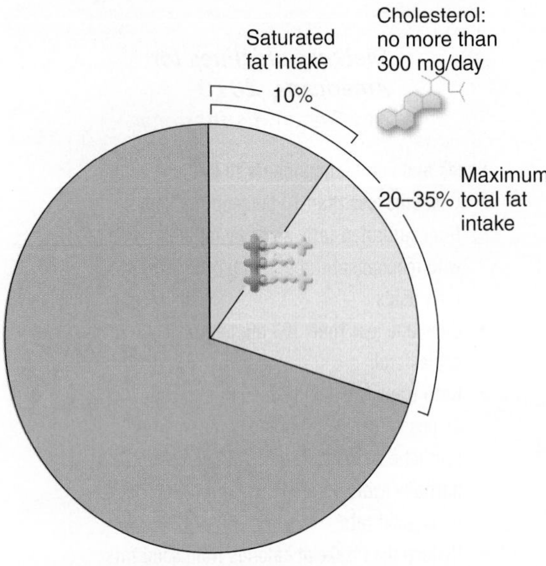

Figure 5.27 **Recommended fat intake.** The *Dietary Guidelines for Americans* recommends a maximum fat intake of 20 to 35 percent of total calories. Saturated fat should supply no more than 10 percent of our total calories, or about one-third of our fat calories.

that there were no defined levels of intake that separated "healthful" from "harmful" and that any increase in saturated fat, trans fat, or cholesterol in the diet increased LDL cholesterol levels and heart disease risk. Because it would be virtually impossible to completely exclude these lipids from the diet, the committee recommended that saturated fat, trans fat, and cholesterol intake be minimized. Substituting monounsaturated and polyunsaturated sources improves blood lipid values, with the most favorable results produced by replacing saturated fat with monounsaturated fat.[33]

The 2010 *Dietary Guidelines* merges recommendations from the DRI committee with those of the American Heart Association. (See **Figure 5.27**.) The recommendation for total fat intake is the AMDR: 20 to 35 percent of calories for adults. Saturated fat should be limited to no more than 10 percent of calories, and cholesterol intake limited to less than 300 milligrams per day. The *Dietary Guidelines* also suggests that we keep trans fat intake as low as possible. The Daily Values on food labels are 65 grams of total fat (29 percent of the calories in a 2,000-kilocalorie diet), 20 grams of saturated fat (9 percent of calories), and 300 milligrams of cholesterol. Although trans fat information is now required on food labels, no Daily Value has been set; consumers should choose foods to minimize trans fat intake along with saturated fat and cholesterol.[34] Complete or near-complete avoidance of industrially produced trans fats—consumption of less than 0.5 percent of total energy intake—may be necessary to avoid adverse effects and would be prudent to minimize health risks.[35]

Essential Fatty Acid Requirements

Although too much fat in the diet is not healthful, we still need to get enough fat to meet our need for essential fatty acids. Because essential fatty acid deficiency is virtually nonexistent in the United States and Canada, the DRI committee relied on median intake levels of essential fatty acids to set AI levels. For adults aged 19 to 50, the AI for linoleic acid is 17 grams per day for men and 12 grams per day for women. The AI for alpha-linolenic acid is 1.6 grams per day for men and 1.1 grams per day for women. To fulfill our need for omega-6 fatty acids, linoleic acid should provide about 2 percent of our calories. Average U.S. consumption is much more than that. Two teaspoons of corn oil, which is a little more than half linoleic acid, would supply more than 2 percent of the calories in a 2,000-kilocalorie diet.

Because science has recognized the importance of omega-3 fatty acids only recently, we know less about our requirements for those substances.

Omega-6 and Omega-3 Balance

It is important to have the right balance of omega-3 and omega-6 fatty acids in your diet. These two substances work together to promote health. Omega-3 fatty acids help reduce inflammation, whereas omega-6 fatty acids tend to promote inflammation. A proper balance between these two essential fatty acids helps to maintain, and even improve, health; an improper balance may contribute to the development of disease.

Some researchers suggest that to reduce cardiovascular disease risk we should get about 0.75 percent of our calories as alpha-linolenic acid (about 1.7 grams per day for a 2,000-kilocalorie diet) and increase EPA and DHA intake to 0.25 to 0.5 percent of calories, or about 500 to 1,000 milligrams per day for a 2,000-kilocalorie diet.[36] A ratio of 6:1 for omega-6 fatty acids to omega-3 fatty acids is also recommended.[37] To meet these recommendations, most people need to eat more fish than meat. The American Heart Association recommends at least two servings of fish per week.[38] The typical American diet contains 14 to 25 times more omega-6 fatty acids than omega-3 fatty acids, and many researchers believe this imbalance is a significant factor in the rising rate of inflammatory disorders in the United States.[39]

Figure 5.28 gives an overview of the dietary sources of fatty acids. Because shark, swordfish, king mackerel, and tilefish contain high levels of mercury, the FDA and EPA recommend that women who may become pregnant, pregnant women, nursing mothers, and young children avoid eating these fish.[40]

It is important to remember that consuming too much of the omega-3 fatty acids can suppress immune function and prolong bleeding time, so we should be cautious about the high levels of these fatty acids found in some supplements. The DRI committee set an AMDR for omega-6 fatty acids of 5 to 10 percent of energy and an AMDR for alpha-linolenic acid of 0.6 to 1.2 percent of energy.

BASIC FATTY ACIDS

Saturated
Animal products (including dairy products), palm and coconut oils, and cocoa butter.

Polyunsaturated
Sunflower, corn, soybean, and cottonseed oils.

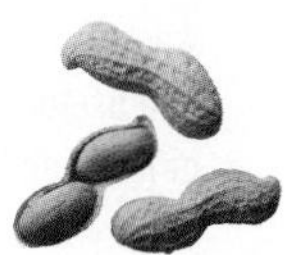

Monounsaturated
Most nuts and olive, canola, peanut, and safflower oils.

TRANS FATTY ACIDS

Stick margarine (not soft or liquid margarine) and many fast foods and baked goods.

ESSENTIAL FATTY ACIDS

Omega-3 fatty acids

Alpha-linolenic acid
Canola oil, soybeans, olive oil, many nuts (e.g., walnuts, peanuts, filberts, pistachios, pecans, almonds), seeds, and purslane (a green, leafy vegetable).

DHA and EPA
Fish such as mackerel, tuna, salmon, herring, trout, and cod liver oil. The fish with the lowest amount of total fat include Atlantic cod, haddock, and pink salmon. Other fish high in omega-3 but also high in total fat are sardines and bluefish. Human milk.

Omega-6 fatty acids

Linoleic acid
Plants (flax) and some vegetable oils (soybean and canola oil).

Figure 5.28 Overview of dietary sources of fatty acids.

Source: Adapted from Cancer smart. *Scientific American.* 1998;4(3):9.

Current Dietary Intakes

Dietary surveys report that mean fat intake is just under 33 percent of calories.[41] Although this value is within the recommended AMDR, about 25 percent of the population has a fat intake greater than 35 percent of calories. Fat intake as a percentage of calories is down from 36 percent in the early 1970s, and down markedly from 45 percent in 1965. See "What About Bobbie?" at the end of this chapter to see how to calculate the percentage of calorie intake from fat.

Although the percentage of calories from fat dropped, average calorie intake increased, which means Americans actually are consuming more total grams of fat. Americans are consuming more beverages (especially soft drinks), food mixtures, grain snacks, and pastries.[42] Although intake of whole milk and fats and oils declined, intake of fat from food mixtures (e.g., prepared and convenience foods) was higher.[43] Snacks contribute a significant percent of daily calories. Among the most frequently reported snacks are cookies, candies, crackers, popcorn, and potato chips, all generally high in fat.[44]

Current intake of saturated fat is about 11 percent of calories, a little higher than recommended. Cholesterol intake averages 341 milligrams per day for adult men, and 242 milligrams per day for adult women.[45] Intake of linoleic acid is estimated to be 6 percent of calories, with alpha-linolenic acid providing 0.75 of calories, and EPA plus DHA another 0.1 percent of calories. By keeping total fat intake within the AMDR and getting most of our fat from vegetable oils, fish, and nuts, we can move closer to meeting recommendations.

Role of Fat Replacers

The food industry responded to the public health challenge of the 1990s to lower fat intake by making low-fat, low-calorie goodies that still taste good. More than 15 different types of **fat replacers** have been developed, and over the years, thousands of fat-free, low-fat, and reduced-fat foods have hit grocery shelves.[46]

Fat Replacers: What Are They Made Of?

Some fat replacers are carbohydrates: generally starches and fibers such as vegetable gums, cellulose, maltodextrins, and Oatrim (a fat replacer made from oats). Some are more digestible than others, but all provide far fewer than the 9 kilocalories per gram of fat. They also incorporate extra water into

fat replacers Compounds that imitate the functional and sensory properties of fats, but contain less available energy than fats.

Academy of Nutrition and Dietetics

Fat Replacers

It is the position of the Academy of Nutrition and Dietetics that the majority of fat replacers, when used in moderation by adults, can be safe and useful adjuncts to lowering the fat content of foods and may play a role in decreasing total dietary energy and fat intake. Moderate use of low-calorie, reduced-fat foods, combined with low total energy intake, could potentially promote dietary intake consistent with the objectives of Healthy People 2010 and the 2010 *Dietary Guidelines for Americans*.

Source: Position of the American Dietetic Association: fat replacers. *J Am Diet Assoc*. 2005;105:266–275. Copyright 2005. Reprinted with permission from Elsevier.

olestra A fat replacer that can withstand heat and is stable at frying temperatures. Olestra, whose trade name is Olean, is a sucrose polyester: sucrose (instead of glycerol) is the "backbone" molecule, with six to eight fatty acids attached (instead of triglyceride's three). The fatty acid arrangement prevents hydrolysis by digestive lipases, so the fatty acids are not absorbed.

food by binding with it, which further dilutes calories. With their moist, thick textures, they mimic fat's richness and smooth "mouth feel."

Proteins are the raw ingredients of other fat replacers. Food manufacturers can modify egg whites and whey from milk so that they are thick and smooth and hold water. Because this protein and water combination has fewer calories per gram than fat, it cuts calories. However, high heat denatures the protein structure, which changes the properties of these replacers and limits their usefulness. Manufacturers used the protein-based product Simplesse in frozen desserts, but it was not well accepted by consumers.

The most high-tech fat replacers—and the most controversial—are the "fat-based" replacers. This group includes Olean and the poorly digested Caprenin and Salatrim (or Benefat). Caprenin is a blend of medium-chain fatty acids and a 22-carbon fatty acid. Salatrim is primarily a blend of 18-carbon stearic acid and short-chain fatty acids. The fatty acids are arranged on glycerol in a way that inhibits digestion. They provide about half the calories of fat, although this is only an estimate because people differ in their ability to digest them. Manufacturers use these fat replacers in reduced-fat candies and baked goods.

One advantage of fat-based fat replacers is their ability to withstand heat. That's fortunate for **olestra** (Olean), because few food ingredients have had to take as much "heat." Technically, olestra is a sucrose polyester: sucrose (instead of glycerol) is the "backbone" molecule, with six to eight fatty acids attached (instead of triglyceride's three). (See **Figure 5.29**.) The number and arrangement of fatty acids and the length and saturation of each fatty acid determine the characteristics of the sucrose polyester. This allows manufacturers to vary properties such as melting point and consistency, to make olestra appropriate for each intended use. The fatty acid arrangement prevents hydrolysis by digestive lipase, so the fatty acids are not absorbed. This makes olestra calorie-free, even though its fatty acids give it the flavor and cooking performance of fat. It is stable even at frying temperatures.

The Olestra Controversy: Are Fat Replacers Safe?

Consumers have expressed few safety concerns about carbohydrate- and protein-based fat replacers. Most safety issues center on olestra, which aroused controversy long before it received FDA approval as a food additive in January 1996. The approval process itself was controversial,[47] and even after FDA approval, olestra continued to evoke strong, conflicting opinions.[48]

Because the GI tract does not absorb olestra, some people suffer fat malabsorption symptoms—diarrhea, gas, and cramps. Olestra also acts as a solvent for fat-soluble nutrients. Thus, when it leaves the body unabsorbed, it carries these nutrients with it. Manufacturers are required to replace fat-soluble vitamins, but critics counter that healthful phytochemicals such as the carotenoids are lost and not replaced.

The FDA, concerned about malabsorption and nutrient loss, has limited olestra's use to just a few snack foods. Critics would like to see olestra eliminated altogether, whereas the food industry wants to expand its usage. Postmarketing surveillance (mandated by the FDA) shows that only a small percentage (5 percent) of those surveyed were "heavy consumers" with an average intake of more than 2.0 grams per day.[49] The calorie savings from even a small amount (1 to 2 grams per day) of fat replacement with olestra may be enough to prevent gradual weight gain in adulthood.[50] Surveillance has also not found evidence of reduced blood levels of carotenoids and fat-soluble vitamins.[51]

The power of suggestion, brought on by adverse publicity, may be responsible for some consumers' digestive discomfort after eating olestra-containing chips. In fact, in a large double-blind study of volunteers that pitted olestra-containing chips against regular chips, more people had indigestion after eating the regular chips. Will using olestra subtly encourage people to eat more? In another study, when subjects ate unlabeled olestra-containing potato chips, they ate fewer total calories and less fat than when they ate unlabeled

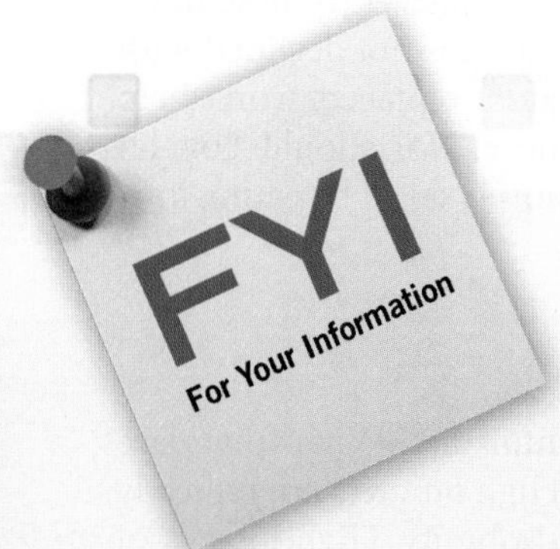

Does "Reduced Fat" Reduce Calories? That Depends on the Food

Reducing fat intake is a common dietary recommendation, one that can help reduce risk for heart disease, cancer, and obesity. Given that fat is our most concentrated source of calories, we expect that a reduced-fat or low-fat food would have fewer calories than its unmodified counterpart. But is this always true?

Sometimes low-fat and fat-free foods make a big difference in calories.

Food	Kilocalories
1 oz American cheese	105
1 oz low-fat cheese product	50
2 oz bologna	180
2 oz fat-free bologna	45
1 tbsp mayonnaise	100
1 tbsp fat-free mayonnaise/dressing	12

But sometimes they make almost no difference at all.

Food	Kilocalories
1 cup canned chicken vegetable soup	75
1 cup reduced-fat chicken vegetable soup	95
3 chocolate cookies (30 g)	145
3 reduced-fat chocolate chip cookies (30 g)	135
2 tbsp peanut butter	190
2 tbsp reduced-fat peanut butter	170
1 oz potato chips	150
1 oz reduced-fat potato chips	135

Many reduced-fat products contain added sugar. Although sugar has fewer calories per gram than fat, the amount added may negate any difference in calories. If fat is your concern, low-fat or fat-free makes sense. But if you're trying to reduce fat *and* calories, modified products may not be a big help. So, be a smart shopper—check the label before you check out with a cartload of reduced-fat foods.

Source: US Department of Agriculture, Agricultural Research Service. USDA National Nutrient Database for Standard Reference, Release 18. 2005. http://www.nal.usda.gov/fnic/foodcomp. Accessed 6/8/06.

Light mayonnaise

Nutrition Facts
Serving Size: 1 Tbsp (14g)
Servings: 32
Calories 50
Fat Cal 45

Amount/serving	%DV
Total Fat 5g	8%
Saturated Fat 1g	4%
Trans Fat 0g	
Cholesterol 5mg	2%
Sodium 115mg	5%
Total Carbohydrate 0g	0%
Protein 0g	

* Percent Daily Values (DV) are based on a 2,000 calorie diet.
Not a significant source of dietary fiber, vitamin A, vitamin C, calcium, and iron.
INGREDIENTS: WATER, SOYBEAN OIL, VINEGAR, FOOD STARCH-MODIFIED*, EGG YOLKS, SUGAR, SALT, LEMON JUICE, MUSTARD FLOUR, XANTHAN GUM*, BETA-CAROTENE (COLOR)*, AND NATURAL FLAVORS, POTASSIUM SORBATE, AND CALCIUM DISODIUM SULFATE EDTA USED TO PROTECT QUALITY.
*INGREDIENTS NOT FOUND IN MAYONNAISE.

Regular mayonnaise

Nutrition Facts
Serving Size: 1 Tbsp (14g)
Servings: 32
Calories 100
Fat Cal 100

Amount/serving	%DV
Total Fat 11g	17%
Saturated Fat 1.5g	8%
Trans Fat 0g	
Cholesterol 5mg	2%
Sodium 80mg	3%
Total Carbohydrate 0g	0%
Protein 0g	

* Percent Daily Values (DV) are based on a 2,000 calorie diet.
INGREDIENTS: SOYBEAN OIL, WHOLE EGGS AND EGG YOLKS, WATER, VINEGAR, SALT, SUGAR, LEMON JUICE, NATURAL FLAVORS, CALCIUM DISODIUM SULFATE EDTA USED TO PROTECT QUALITY.

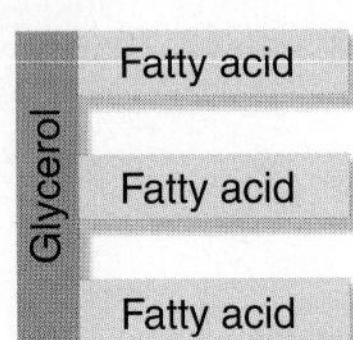

A triglyceride has three fatty acids attached to a glycerol backbone

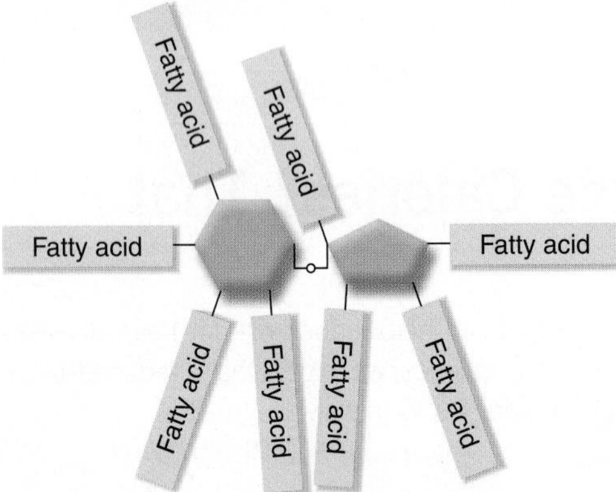

Olestra has six to eight fatty acids attached to a sucrose backbone

Figure 5.29 **Olestra's structure.** The structure of olestra is unlike the structure of a triglyceride. Although olestra imparts triglyceride-like qualities to food, your digestive enzymes cannot break it down.

regular potato chips. But when they knew the chips they were eating were fat-free, the subjects ate more.[52] If consumers eat too many olestra-containing snacks, they may be more likely to suffer side effects.

When used in moderation, fat replacers pose no specific risks to adult consumers. There is still a need for research to determine whether long-term consumption increases health risks or if there are specific risks to children.[53]

Do Fat Replacers Save Calories? Do They Reduce Total Fat Intake?

Considering the American population as a whole, the answer to these questions seems to be "no." American fat and calorie intake has not declined with the growth in the fat-replacer market. It is clear that fat replacers won't help if people treat them simply as an excuse to eat more. Nor should "low-fat foods" be confused with "low-calorie foods"; the calories saved by eating low-fat foods are often negligible.[54]

Lipids and Health

Moderation and balance are the keys to a healthful diet. When diets are consistently high in fat, several problems emerge. High-fat diets are typically high in calories and contribute to weight gain and obesity. High intakes of saturated fat and trans fat increase risk for heart disease, and high-fat diets have been weakly linked to several types of cancer.[55] The dietary recommendations discussed earlier suggest levels of fat intake that should reduce risk for these conditions.

Obesity

Obesity is defined as the excessive accumulation of body fat leading to a body weight in relation to height that is substantially greater than some accepted standard (see Chapter 9, "Energy Balance, Body Composition, and Weight Management"). More than one-third of U.S. adults are obese. This includes 33.3 percent of men and 35.3 percent of women.[56] Sixteen percent of U.S. children are obese.[57] After a quarter century of increases, obesity prevalence in adults has not measurably increased in the past few years, but the levels are still high. On the other hand, the increased prevalence of obesity is a concern for children and adolescents. Data from NHANES surveys show that the prevalence of obesity has significantly increased over the past 30 years.[58]

Eating large amounts of dietary fat contributes to this obesity epidemic.[59] Fat is a dense source of calories, it makes food taste good, and it's often unnoticed or "hidden" in restaurant and convenience foods. Table 5.6 shows how fat increases the calorie content of foods. Standard advice to Americans trying to attain or maintain normal weight usually includes cutting back on fats and fatty foods, along with increasing physical activity and eating fewer calories. For more on obesity and weight management, see Chapter 9.

Quick Bite

What Does the Color of Beef Fat Reveal?

Yellow-tinged fat indicates that a steer was grass fed, whereas white fat suggests that the animal was fed corn or cereal grain, at least during its final months. Thus, steak surrounded by pearly white fat should be more tender and, consequently, more expensive.

Heart Disease

Heart disease is the leading cause of death in the United States and Canada, and fat intake is a key factor in its development. High saturated and trans fat intake raises blood cholesterol levels, particularly LDL cholesterol.[60] High blood cholesterol is one of the major risk factors for atherosclerosis, a type of heart disease in which arteries become progressively clogged with deposits of fatty material. To reduce the risk of heart disease, reducing intakes of saturated and trans fats appears more important than modifying total fat intake.[61] See

Nutrition Science *in Action*

A Matter of Fat

Observations: Cardiovascular disease (CVD) is the leading cause of death in women in the United States, Canada, and throughout most of the world. Clinical trials and observational studies have identified strong associations between diet and CVD risk factors. To confirm that reducing fat intake reduces risk of CVD, long-term intervention data are needed.

Hypothesis: A dietary intervention that reduces intake of total fat and increases intakes of fruits, vegetables, and grains will reduce the risk of cardiovascular disease.

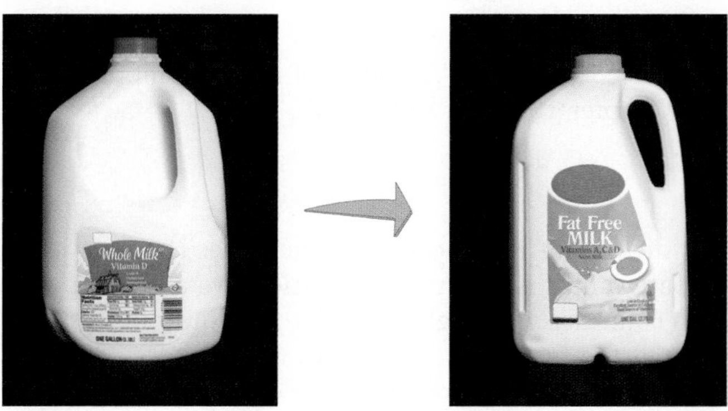

Whole milk Fat-free alternative

Experimental Plan: The Women's Health Initiative (WHI) enrolled 48,835 women (mean age 62.3 years; 20 percent nonwhite). Investigators randomly assigned 19,541 women to an intervention group that participated in a behavioral modification program aimed at reducing intake of total fat and increasing intakes of grains and fruits and vegetables; the remainder were the control group. For both groups, dietary adherence and health outcomes were recorded for eight years.

Results: The hypothesis was not confirmed. The main CVD findings were that the intervention had no effect on risk of coronary heart disease, stroke, or overall cardiovascular disease. Compared with the control group, the intervention group reported significant changes in all dietary components, resulting in an 8.2 percent reduction in total fat intake and increased intakes of fiber, vegetables and fruits, grains, and soy.

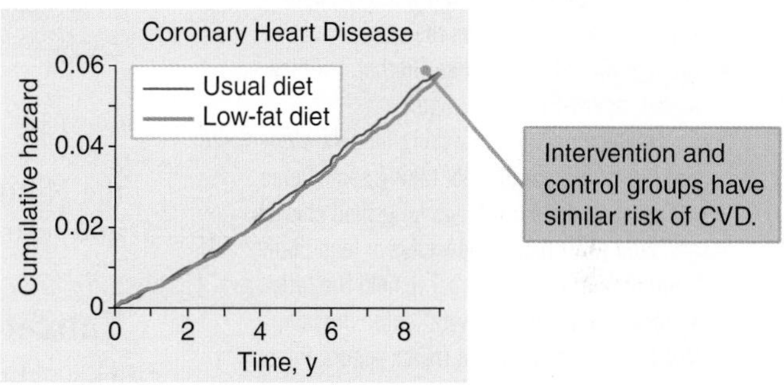

Conclusion and Discussion: The intervention focused on total fat, thus reducing intakes of fats that increase CVD risk (saturated and trans fat) *and* those that may reduce risk (unsaturated fats). Since this study was initiated, scientific thinking has evolved to focus on modifying intakes of specific types of fat. Future dietary intervention studies of dietary fat and CVD risk could examine changes in the intakes of different types of dietary fat or other dietary factors, such as fish and fish oil, for which a compelling body of evidence suggests protective effects.

Source: Based on Howard BV, Van Horn L, Hsia J, et al. Low-fat dietary pattern and risk of cardiovascular disease: the Women's Health Initiative Randomized Controlled Dietary Modification Trial. *JAMA.* 2006;295:655–666.

Quick Bite

NCEP Tips for Healthful Eating Out

- Choose restaurants that have low-fat, low-cholesterol menu items.
- Don't be afraid to ask for foods that follow your eating pattern.
- Select poultry, fish, or meat that is broiled, grilled, baked, steamed, or poached rather than fried.
- Choose lean deli meats like fresh turkey or lean roast beef instead of higher-fat cuts like salami or bologna.
- Look for vegetables seasoned with herbs or spices rather than butter, sour cream, or cheese. Ask for sauces on the side.
- Order a low-fat dessert like sherbet, fruit ice, sorbet, or low-fat frozen yogurt.
- Control serving sizes by asking for a small serving, sharing a dish, or taking some home.
- At fast food restaurants, go for grilled chicken and lean roast beef sandwiches or lean plain hamburgers (but remember to hold the fatty sauces), salads with low-fat salad dressing, low-fat milk, and low-fat frozen yogurt. Pizza topped with vegetables and minimum cheese is another good choice.

Table 5.6 Fat Can Markedly Increase Calories in Food

	Approximate Kcalories	Approximate Fat (g)
4 oz fried potatoes	188	5.8
4 oz boiled potatoes	98	0.1
½ cup creamed cottage cheese	108	4.7
½ cup 1% low-fat cottage cheese	82	1.2
½ cup green beans + 1 tsp butter	56	4.0
½ cup green beans without butter	22	0.2
3 oz T-bone steak, untrimmed	260	19.4
3 oz T-bone steak, trimmed	161	7.4
½ cup vanilla ice cream	145	7.92
½ cup fat-free vanilla ice cream	105	0.0

Source: Based on data from US Department of Agriculture, Agricultural Research Service. USDA National Nutrient Database for Standard Reference, Release 18. 2005. http://www.nal.usda.gov/fnic/foodcompindex.html. Accessed 5/24/06.

the Nutrition Science in Action feature "A Matter of Fat." For more on diet and heart disease, see Chapter 15, "Diet and Health."

Cancer

The evidence linking dietary fat to cancer is inconclusive. The case looks strong when we compare cancer rates among countries: overall cancer rates are generally higher in countries with high fat intake, and lower in countries where people eat less fat. But in population studies within those countries, the evidence linking fat to cancer is weaker. For more on diet and cancer, see Chapter 15, "Diet and Health."

Key Concepts *Current recommendations suggest eating 20 to 35 percent of calories from fat, while keeping saturated fat, trans fat, and cholesterol intake as low as possible. Over the years, Americans have reduced their percentage of calories from fat but are eating more total calories and, as a result, more grams of fat. This is in spite of the increased availability of a wide variety of fat substitutes and lower-fat foods. Excessive fat intake has been linked to obesity, heart disease, and cancer.*

The Nutrition Facts panel shown here highlights all of the lipid-related information you can find on a food label. Look at the top of the label, where it states that this product contains 35 calories from fat. Do you know how you can estimate this number from another part of the label? Recall (or look at the bottom of the label) that each gram of fat contains 9 kilocalories. If this food item has 4 grams of fat, then it should make sense that there are approximately 36 kilocalories provided by fat.

Total fat is the second thing you'll see, along with saturated and trans fat. Manufacturers are required to list only saturated and trans fat content on the label, but they can voluntarily list monounsaturated and polyunsaturated fat. Using this food label, you can estimate the amount of unsaturated fat by simply looking at the highlighted sections. There are 4 total grams of fat: 2.5 of them are saturated and 0.5 are trans. That means the remaining 1.0 gram is either polyunsaturated, monounsaturated, or a mix of both. Without even knowing what food item this label represents, you can see that it contains more saturated and trans fat than unsaturated fat (3.0 grams versus 1.0 gram).

Do you see the "6%" to the right of "Total Fat"? It does not mean that the food item contains 6 percent of its calories from fat. In fact, this food item contains 23 percent of its calories from fat (35 fat kilocalories ÷ 154 total kilocalories = 0.23, or 23% fat kilocalories). The 6% refers to the Daily Values, found below. You can see that a person who consumes 2,000 kilocalories per day could consume up to 65 grams of fat per day. This product contributes just 4 grams per serving, which is 6 percent of that amount (4 ÷ 65 = 0.06, or 6%). Note that the % Daily Value for saturated fat is 12 percent, which means that just a few servings of this food can contribute quite a bit of saturated fat to your diet. There is no DV for trans fat, but intake should be kept as low as possible. Cholesterol is also highlighted on this label (20 mg), along with its Daily Value contribution (7%).

Nutrition Facts
Serving Size: 1 cup (248g)
Servings Per Container: 4

Amount Per Serving	
Calories 154	Calories from fat 35
	% Daily Value*
Total Fat 4g	6%
Saturated Fat 2.5g	12%
Trans Fat 0.5g	
Cholesterol 20mg	7%
Sodium 170mg	7%
Total Carbohydrate 19g	6%
Dietary Fiber 0g	0%
Sugars 14g	
Protein 11g	
Vitamin A 4% ·	Vitamin C 6%
Calcium 40% ·	Iron 0%

* Percent Daily Values are based on a 2,000 calorie diet. Your daily values may be higher or lower depending on your calorie needs:

	Calories:	2,000	2,500
Total Fat	Less Than	65g	80g
Sat Fat	Less Than	20g	25g
Cholesterol	Less Than	300mg	300mg
Sodium	Less Than	2,400mg	2,400mg
Total Carbohydrate		300g	375g
Dietary Fiber		25g	30g

Calories per gram:
Fat 9 · Carbohydrate 4 · Protein 4

Learning Portfolio

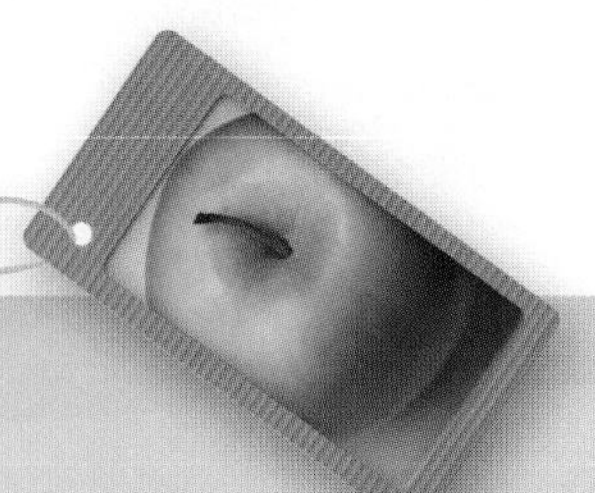

Key Terms

	page
adipocytes	191
adipose tissue	191
alpha-linolenic acid [al-fah lin-oh-LEN-ik]	189
chain length	183
cholesterol [ko-LES-te-rol]	202
choline	200
chylomicron [kye-lo-MY-kron]	207
cis fatty acid	186
conjugated linoleic acid	186
desaturation	187
diglycerides	190
eicosanoids	188
elongation	187
enterocytes	205
essential fatty acids	187
ester	190
esterification [e-ster-ih-fih-KAY-shun]	190
fat replacers	213
fatty acids	183
glycerol [GLISS-er-ol]	190
high-density lipoproteins (HDL)	210
hydrogenation [high-dro-jen-AY-shun]	186
hydrophilic [high-dro-FILL-ik]	182
hydrophobic	182
intermediate-density lipoproteins (IDL)	209
lanugo [lah-NEW-go]	192
lecithin	200
linoleic acid [lin-oh-LAY-ik]	188
lipophilic	182
lipophobic	182
lipoprotein	207
lipoprotein lipase	208
low-density lipoproteins (LDL)	209
micelles	204
monoglycerides	190
monounsaturated fatty acid	184
nonessential fatty acids	187
olestra	214
omega-3 fatty acids	186
omega-6 fatty acid	186
omega-9 fatty acid	186
oxidation	195
phosphate group	198
phospholipids	182
phytosterols	203
polyunsaturated fatty acid	184
saturated fatty acid	184
squalene	203
steatorrhea	204
sterols	182
subcutaneous fat	192
trans fatty acids	186
unsaturated fatty acid	184
very low density lipoproteins (VLDL)	209
visceral fat	192

Study Points

- Lipids are a group of compounds that are soluble in organic solvents but not in water. Fats and oils are part of the lipids group.
- There are three main classes of lipids: triglycerides, phospholipids, and sterols.
- Fatty acids—long carbon chains with methyl and carboxyl groups on the ends—are components of both triglycerides and phospholipids and are often attached to cholesterol.
- Saturated fatty acids have no double bonds between carbons in the chain, monounsaturated fatty acids have one double bond, and polyunsaturated fatty acids have more than one double bond.
- Two polyunsaturated fatty acids, linoleic acid and alpha-linolenic acid, are essential; they must be supplied in the diet. Phospholipids and sterols are made in the body and do not have to be supplied in the diet.
- Essential fatty acids are elongated and desaturated in the process of making "local hormones" called eicosanoids. These compounds regulate many body functions.
- Triglycerides are food fats and storage fats. They are composed of glycerol and three fatty acids.
- In the body, triglycerides are an important source of energy. Stored fat provides an energy reserve.
- Phospholipids are made of glycerol, two fatty acids, and a phosphate group with a nitrogen-containing component.
- Phospholipids are components of cell membranes and lipoproteins. Their unique affinity for both fat and water allows them to be effective emulsifiers in foods and in the body.
- Cholesterol is found in cell membranes and is used to synthesize vitamin D, bile salts, and steroid hormones. High levels of blood cholesterol are associated with heart disease risk.
- For adults, the Acceptable Macronutrient Distribution Range (AMDR) for fat is 20 to 35 percent of calories.

- Diets high in fat and saturated fat tend to increase blood levels of LDL cholesterol and increase risk for heart disease.
- Excess fat in the diet is linked to obesity, heart disease, and some types of cancer.

Study Questions

1. How can different oils contain a mixture of polyunsaturated, monounsaturated, and saturated fats?
2. What does the hardness or softness of a triglyceride typically signify?
3. What is the most common form of lipid found in food?
4. What are the positive and negative consequences of hydrogenating a fat?
5. List the many functions of triglycerides.
6. Describe the difference between LDL and HDL in terms of cholesterol and protein composition.
7. What foods contain cholesterol?
8. Name the two essential fatty acids.

Try This

The Fat = Fullness Challenge

The goal of this experiment is to see whether fat affects your desire to eat between meals. Do this experiment for two consecutive breakfasts. Each meal is to include *only* the foods listed here. Try to eat normally for the other meals of the day and to eat around the same time of day. Each of these breakfasts has approximately the same calories, but one has a high percentage of them from fat, the other from carbohydrate. After each breakfast, take note of how many hours pass before you feel hungry again.

Day 1 (~420 kilocalories; 1.5 grams fat)
One 3-oz bagel with 3 Tbsp of jelly
Day 2 (~430 kilocalories; 28 grams fat)
2 eggs fried
1 biscuit (2½-inch diameter) with 1 tsp butter or margarine

What About Bobbie?

Let's take a look at Bobbie's fat intake. Review her day of eating (see Chapter 1) and pay special attention to the foods you know contain fat. What percentage of her calories do you think came from fat? Did she eat more saturated or unsaturated fat? How about her cholesterol intake? Do you think she came in below the guideline?

Bobbie's total fat intake was 86 grams. Here are the foods that contributed the most fat:

Food	Fat (g)
Salad dressing	13
Meatballs	11
Tortilla chips	11
Garlic bread	10
Cream cheese	8
Mayonnaise	7
Pizza	6

Bobbie's diet has 34 percent of its calories from fat, which is within the AMDR for fat. Here's how to calculate this:

86 grams fat × 9 kcal/g = 774 kcal fat
774 kcal fat ÷ 2,300 total kcal = 0.34, or 34% kcal from fat

Are you surprised her fat intake is on the high end of the recommended range? Her intake doesn't look too unusual, but you can see how the "extras" along the way add up. Look at the list of fat-containing foods again. Do you think her diet is higher in saturated or unsaturated fat? Well, three of the foods listed are animal products (meatballs, pizza, and cream cheese), so you know they contribute to the amount of saturated fat. Both the tortilla chips and garlic bread contain a mixture of saturated and unsaturated fats, and the Italian dressing contains mostly unsaturated fat. Her overall saturated fat intake is 27 grams. That's about 11 percent of her caloric intake, which is more than recommended by the *Dietary Guidelines for Americans* (no more than 10 percent of energy as saturated fat). If Bobbie wanted to lower her saturated fat and total fat intake, what changes could she make? Here are some suggestions.

Bobbie can lower her saturated fat intake by

- Topping her bagel with peanut butter instead of cream cheese
- Decreasing the number of meatballs on her pasta
- Snacking on pizza less often

Bobbie can lower her overall fat intake by

- Using cream cheese on only half her bagel and using jelly on the other half
- Using only mustard on her sandwich, not mustard and mayonnaise
- Reducing the amount of tortilla chips she eats by half and having a piece of fruit in their place
- Reducing the amount of Italian dressing she puts on her salad (2 tablespoons contain 11 grams of fat and more than 100 kilocalories!)
- Having a plain piece of bread with dinner, not the garlic bread made with butter or margarine

In terms of cholesterol, how do you think Bobbie did? She consumed 261 milligrams during this day. If she follows the tips to lower her saturated fat intake, she'll find that her overall cholesterol intake will be cut in half!

References

1 Mozaffarian D, Katan MB, Ascherio A, et al. Trans fatty acids and cardiovascular disease. *New Engl J Med.* 2006;354(15):1601–1613.

2 Bhattacharya A, Banci J, Rahman M, et al. Biological effects of conjugated linoleic acids in health and disease. *J Nutr Biochem.* 2006;17:789–810.

3 Institute of Medicine, Food and Nutrition Board. *Dietary Reference Intakes for Energy, Carbohydrate, Fiber, Fat, Fatty Acids, Cholesterol, Protein, and Amino Acids.* Washington, DC: National Academies Press, 2005.

4 Ibid.

5 Connor WE. Importance of n-3 fatty acids in health and disease. *Am J Clin Nutr.* 2000;71(suppl):171S–175S; and Djoussé L, Arnett DK, Carr AJ, et al. Dietary linolenic acid is inversely associated with calcified atherosclerotic plaque in the coronary arteries: the National Heart, Lung and Blood Institute Family Heart Study. *Circulation.* 2005;111:2921–2926.

6 Rigby A. Omega-3 choices: fish or flax? *Today's Dietitian.* 2004;6(1):37.

7 Der G, Batty GD, Deary J. Effect of breastfeeding on intelligence in children: prospective study, sibling pairs analysis, and meta-analysis. *BMJ.* 2006;333:945–949.

8 Hendler SS, Rorvik D, eds. *PDR for Nutritional Supplements.* Montvale, NJ: Medical Economics/Thompson Healthcare, 2001.

9 Wan PJ, Hron RJ. Extraction solvents for oilseeds. *Inform.* July 1998;9:707–709.

10 Seidner DL. Clinical uses for omega-3 polyunsaturated fatty acids and structured triglycerides. *Support Line.* June 1994;16:7–11.

11 Neaton JD, Blackburn H, Jacobs D, et al. Serum cholesterol level and mortality findings for men screened in the Multiple Risk Factor Intervention Trial. Multiple Risk Factor Intervention Trial Research Group. *Arch Intern Med.* 1992;152:1490–1500; and El-Sadr WM, Mullin CM, Carr A, et al. Effects of HIV disease on lipid, glucose and insulin levels: results from a large antiretroviral-naïve cohort. *HIV Med.* 2005;6:114–121.

12 El-Sadr, Mullin, Carr, et al. Effects of HIV disease on lipid, glucose and insulin levels.

13 Mason RP, Tulenko TN, Jacob RF. Direct evidence for cholesterol crystalline domains in biological membranes: role in human pathobiology. *Biophysica Acta.* 2003;1610:198–207.

14 Saher G, Brugger B, Lappe-Siefke C, et al. High cholesterol level is essential for myelin membrane growth. *Nat Neurosci.* 2005;8:468–475.

15 Jones PJH, Kubow S. Lipids, sterols and their metabolites. In: Shills ME, Shike M, Ross CA, et al., eds. *Modern Nutrition in Health and Disease.*10th ed. Philadelphia: Lippincott Williams & Wilkins, 2006:92–135.

16 Ibid.

17 Dietschy JM, Turley SD. Cholesterol metabolism in the central nervous system during early development and in the mature animal. *J Lipid Res.* 2004;45:1375–1397.

18 Jones PJH, Kubow S. Lipids, sterols, and their metabolites. In: Shils ME, Shike M, Ross CA, et al., eds. *Modern Nutrition in Health and Disease.* 10th ed. Philadelphia: Lippincott Williams & Wilkins, 2006:92–122.

19 Guyton AC, Hall JE. *Textbook of Medical Physiology.* 11th ed. Philadelphia: WB Saunders, 2006.

20 Craig GB, Darnell DE, Weinsier RL, et al. Decreased fat and nitrogen losses in patients with AIDS receiving medium-chain-triglyceride-enriched formula vs those receiving long-chain-triglyceride-containing formula. *J Am Diet Assoc.* 1997;97(6):605–611.

21 Nkondjock A, Shatenstein B, Maisonneuve P, Ghadirian P. Specific fatty acids and human colorectal cancer: an overview. *Cancer Detect Prev.* 2003;27:55–66.

22 Institute of Medicine, Food and Nutrition Board. *Dietary Reference Intakes for Energy, Carbohydrate.*

23 Lin J, Yang R, Tarr PT. Hyperlipidemic effects of dietary saturated fats mediated through PGC-1β coactivation of SREBP. *Cell.* 2005;120:261–273.

24 Jeon H, Blacklow SC. Structure and physiologic function of the low-density lipoprotein receptor. *Ann Rev Biochem.* 2005;74:535–562.

25 Kolovou GD, Anagnostopoulou KK, Cokkinos DV. Pathophysiology of dyslipidaemia in the metabolic syndrome. *Postgrad Med J.* 2005;81:358–366.

26 Wijendran V, Hayes KC. Dietary n-6 and n-3 fatty acid balance and cardiovascular health. *Ann Rev Nutr.* 2004;24:597–615.

27 Lichtenstein AH, Appel LJ, Brands M, et al. Diet and lifestyle recommendations revision 2006: a scientific statement from the American Heart Association Nutrition Committee. *Circulation.* 2006;114:82–96.

28 National Cholesterol Education Program. *Detection, Evaluation, and Treatment of High Blood Cholesterol in Adults (Adult Treatment Panel III) Final Report.* Washington, DC: National Institutes of Health, 2002.

29 Lichtenstein, Appel, Brands, et al. Diet and lifestyle recommendations revision 2006.

30 Mozafarrian, Katan, Ascherio, et al. Trans fatty acids and cardiovascular disease.

31 Ibid.

32 Institute of Medicine, Food and Nutrition Board. *Dietary Reference Intakes for Energy, Carbohydrate.*

33 Ibid.

34 Nettleton J. Striving to increase compliance with dietary guidelines for fatty acid intake: a call for a multifaceted dietary approach. *J Am Diet Assoc.* 2007;107(10):1723–1725.

35 Mozaffarian, Katan, Ascherio, et al. Trans fatty acids and cardiovascular disease.

36 Wijendran, Hayes. Dietary n-6 and n-3 fatty acid balance and cardiovascular health.

37 Ibid.

38 Kris-Etherton PM, Harris WS, Appel LJ. Fish consumption, fish oil, omega-3 fatty acids, and cardiovascular disease. *Circulation.* 2002;106:2747–2757.

39 Aronson WJ, Glaspy JA, Reddy ST, et al. Modulation of omega-3/omega-6 polyunsaturated ratios with dietary fish oils in men with prostate cancer. *Urology.* 2001;58(2):283–288.

40 US Department of Health and Human Services and Environmental Protection Agency. *What You Need to Know About Mercury in Fish and Shellfish.* March 2004. http://www.cfsan.fda.gov/~dms/admehg3.html. Accessed 12/3/06.

41 Briefel RR, Johnson CL. Secular trends in dietary intake in the United States. *Ann Rev Nutr.* 2004;24:401–431.

42 Chanmugam P, Guthrie J, Cecilio S, et al. Did fat intake in the United States really decline between 1989–1991 and 1994–1996? *J Am Diet Assoc.* 2003;103:867–872.

43 Ibid.

44 McBride J. Today's kids eating more. August 11, 2000. http://www.ars.usda.gov/is/pr/2000/000811.htm. Accessed 5/15/09.

45 Briefel, Johnson. Secular trends in dietary intake in the United States.

46 American Dietetic Association. Position of the American Dietetic Association: fat replacers. *J Am Diet Assoc.* 2005;105:266–275.

47 Neuhouser ML, Rock CL, Kristal AR, et al. Olestra is associated with slight reductions in serum carotenoids but does not markedly influence serum fat-soluble vitamin concentrations. *Am J Clin Nutr.* 2006;83:624–631.

48 Satia-Abouta J, Kristal AR, Patterson RE, et al. Is olestra consumption associated with changes in dietary intake, serum lipids, and body weight? *Nutrition.* 2003;19:754–759.

49 Ibid.

50 Eldridge AL, Cooper DA, Peters JC. A role for olestra in body weight management. *Obes Rev.* 2002;3:17–25.

51 Neuhouser, Rock, Kristal, et al. Olestra is associated with slight reductions in serum carotenoids.

52 Miller DL, Casteollanos VH, Shide DJ, et al. Effect of fat-free potato chips with and without nutrition labels on fat and energy intakes. *Am J Clin Nutr.* 1998;68:282–290.

53 American Dietetic Association. Position of the American Dietetic Association: fat replacers.

54 Ibid.

55 Prentice RL, Caan B, Chleobowski RT, et al. Low-fat dietary pattern and risk of invasive breast cancer: the Women's Health Initiative Randomized Controlled Dietary Modification Trial. *JAMA.* 2006;29:529–642.

56 National Center for Health Statistics. *Prevalence of Overweight and Obesity Among Adults: United States, 2005–2006.* http://www.cdc.gov. Accessed 5/15/09.

57 Ibid.

58 US Department of Health and Human Services. Trends in childhood obesity. 2009. http://www.cdc.gov/obesity/childhood/prevalence.htm. Accessed 5/15/09.

59 Lavizzo-Mourey R. Building the evidence to reverse an epidemic. *Am J Prevent Med.* 2007;33(suppl 4):S162–S164.

60 Mozaffarian, Katan, Ascherio, et al. Trans fatty acids and cardiovascular disease.

61 Anderson CA, Appel LJ. Dietary modification and CVD prevention. *JAMA.* 2006;295(6):693–695.

CHAPTER 6

Proteins and Amino Acids

THINK About It

1 What's your understanding of the term *protein-sparing*?

2 Do you take amino acid supplements? If so, do you know how well they are absorbed?

3 What's your estimate of the percentage of your energy intake that comes from protein?

4 Have you ever considered a vegetarian diet?

Visit nutrition.jbpub.com

Quick Bite

Bugburger, Anyone?

Did you know that bugs provide 10 percent of the protein consumed worldwide? What creepy crawler would you choose for your dinner plate? A grasshopper is 15 to 60 percent protein. Pound for pound, spiders have more protein than any other bug.

Think of your favorite meal—perhaps a holiday feast, the foods you always ask for on your birthday, or something from a special restaurant. If you are like most Americans, you have probably conjured up something along the lines of steak and baked potato; a lobster feast with corn on the cob; turkey with dressing, mashed potatoes, and all the trimmings; or maybe something simpler—a juicy hamburger and fries. What do all these meals have in common? In each case you imagine a meat item as the focus of the plate, surrounded by various grain or vegetables.

From a young age, we're taught that meat is an important source of protein and that protein helps us grow big and strong. Many traditional ways of eating in the United States emphasize meat as the most important ingredient of the meal, and protein as the most important nutrient. But do such meals conform to your body's needs? Could a different style of eating be more healthful? For example, what about adding just a small amount of meat to a stir-fry of vegetables over rice? Or what about eliminating meat entirely from the diet? What makes the most sense nutritionally?

From the body's perspective, protein is critically important. Protein is part of every cell, it is needed in thousands of chemical reactions, and it keeps us "together" structurally. But, as you are about to learn, the human body is so good at using the protein we feed it that our actual needs for dietary protein are relatively small—meat doesn't need to be at the center of the plate to keep you healthy!

Why Is Protein Important?

The word *protein* was coined by the Dutch chemist Gerardus Mulder in 1838, and comes from the Greek word *protos*, meaning "of prime importance." Mulder discovered that proteins are a major component of all plant and animal tissues, second only to water. Today we know that these intricately constructed molecules are vital to many aspects of health and play an integral role in every living cell. Our bodies constantly assemble, break down, and use proteins, so we count on our diet to provide enough protein each day to replace what is being used. When we eat more protein than we need, the excess is either used to make energy or is stored as fat.

Most people associate protein with animal foods such as beef, chicken, fish, or milk. However, plant foods such as dried beans and peas, grains, nuts, seeds, and vegetables also provide protein. Many protein-rich plant foods are also rich in vitamins and minerals. These plant foods usually are low in fat and calories.

People living in poverty may suffer from a shortage of both protein and energy in the diet. When the diet lacks protein, the body breaks down tissue such as muscle and uses it as a protein source. This causes loss, or **wasting**, of muscles, organs, and other tissues. Protein deficiency also increases susceptibility to infection, and impairs digestion and absorption of nutrients. In the United States and other industrialized countries, most people are able to get more than enough protein to meet their physiological needs. In fact, a more common problem in these areas is excess intake of protein.

wasting The breakdown of body tissue such as muscle and organ for use as a protein source when the diet lacks protein.

indispensable amino acids Amino acids that the body cannot make at all or cannot make enough of to meet physiological needs. Indispensable amino acids must be supplied in the diet.

Amino Acids Are the Building Blocks of Proteins

R
O
H—N—C—C—OH
H H

Just as glucose is the basic building block of carbohydrates, amino acids are the basic building blocks of proteins. Proteins are sequences of amino acids. When building these sequences, your body has 20 different amino acids from which to choose. Nine of these amino acids are called **indispensable amino acids** because your body cannot make them and must get them in the diet. Your body can manufacture the remaining 11, called **dispensable amino acids**, when enough nitrogen, carbon, hydrogen, and oxygen are available. Dispensable amino acids do not need to be supplied in your diet.

Sometimes, certain dispensable amino acids can become indispensable. This is true of dispensable amino acids that are synthesized from other amino acids or when synthesis is limited due to special physiological conditions.[1] Tyrosine and cysteine are both considered **conditionally indispensable amino acids**. Under normal circumstances, your body makes tyrosine from the indispensable amino acid phenylalanine, and cysteine from either methionine or serine. If a disease or condition interferes with your ability to synthesize tyrosine or cysteine from its amino acid precursors, then your body will need tyrosine or cysteine from the diet. Table 6.1 lists the indispensable, dispensable, and conditionally indispensable amino acids.

Tyrosine becomes an indispensable amino acid for people with phenylketonuria (PKU), a rare genetic disorder that impairs phenylalanine metabolism (see Chapter 4, "Carbohydrates"). Because people with PKU lack sufficient amounts of an enzyme needed to convert phenylalanine to tyrosine, tyrosine must be supplied in the diet. Phenylalanine intake must be carefully controlled because excess phenylalanine and its metabolic by-products (phenylketones) can build up and contribute to irreversible brain damage.[2] Because foods that have aspartame contain phenylalanine, they can be dangerous for people with PKU. When babies with PKU receive treatment starting at birth, their IQ development is unaffected. Without treatment, they suffer severe mental retardation.

Other amino acids also can become indispensable under certain circumstances. The amino acid glutamine is the main fuel for rapidly dividing cells and plays a key role in transporting nitrogen between organs.[3] Although normally considered dispensable, glutamine can become indispensable after trauma or during periods of critical illness that increase the body's need for it.[4] The amino acid arginine can also become indispensable in conditions of intestinal metabolic dysfunction or severe physiological stress.[5]

dispensable amino acids Amino acids that the body can make if supplied with adequate nitrogen. Dispensable amino acids do not need to be supplied in the diet.

conditionally indispensable amino acids Amino acids that are normally made in the body (dispensable) but become indispensable under certain circumstances, such as during critical illness.

Amino Acids Are Identified by Their Side Groups

Amino acids (with the exception of proline) uniformly consist of a central carbon atom chemically bonded to one hydrogen atom (H), one carboxylic acid group (–COOH), one amino (nitrogen-containing) group ($-NH_2$), and

Table 6.1 Indispensable, Dispensable, and Conditionally Indispensable Amino Acids

Indispensable	Dispensable	Conditionally Indispensable
Histidine	Alanine	
Isoleucine	Arginine	Arginine
Leucine	Asparagine	
Lysine	Aspartic acid	
Methionine	Cysteine	Cysteine
Phenylalanine	Glutamic acid	
Threonine	Glutamine	Glutamine
Tryptophan	Glycine	Glycine
Valine	Proline	Proline
	Serine	
	Tyrosine	Tyrosine

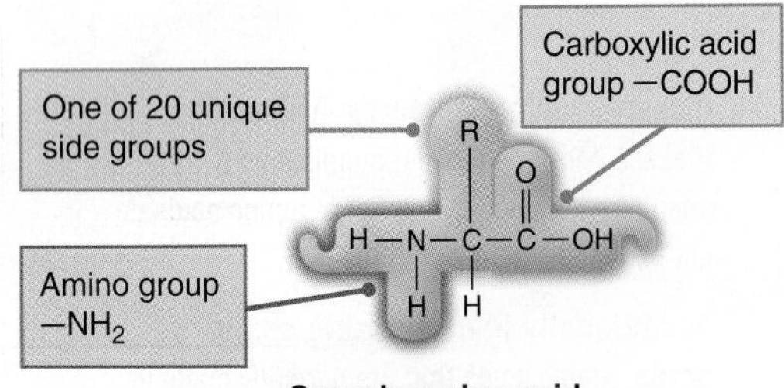

Generic amino acid

Glycine

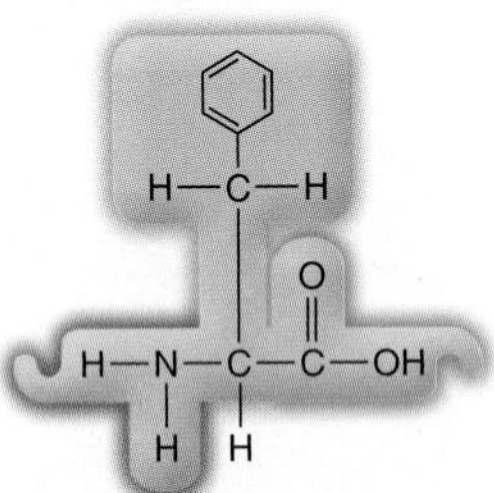

Phenylalanine

Figure 6.1 **Structure of an amino acid.** All amino acids have a similar structure. Attached to a carbon atom is a hydrogen (H), shown here but not in later illustrations of amino acids; an amino group (–NH_2); an acid group (–COOH); and a side group (R). The side group gives each amino acid its unique identity.

one side group unique to each amino acid (R). The side group gives each amino acid its identity. It can vary from a simple hydrogen atom, as in glycine, to a complex ring of carbon and hydrogen atoms, as in phenylalanine. The side groups mean that amino acids differ in shape, size, composition, electrical charge, and pH. When amino acids are linked to form a protein, these characteristics work together to determine that protein's specific function. **Figure 6.1** shows the structure of an amino acid.

Key Concepts *Amino acids, which consist of a central carbon atom bonded to a hydrogen, a carboxyl group, an amino group, and a side group, are the building blocks of proteins. Indispensable amino acids cannot be made by the body and must be supplied in the diet. Dispensable amino acids can be made in the body, given an adequate supply of nitrogen, carbon, hydrogen, and oxygen.*

Protein Structure: Unique Three-Dimensional Shapes and Functions

Proteins are very large molecules. Their chains of linked amino acids twist, fold, or coil into unique shapes. Just as we combine letters of the alphabet in different sequences to form an infinite variety of words, the body combines amino acids in different sequences to form a nearly infinite variety of proteins. For this reason, protein molecules are more diverse than either carbohydrates or lipids.

Amino Acid Sequence

Amino acids link in specific sequences to form strands of protein (often called peptides) up to hundreds of amino acids long. One amino acid is joined to the next by a **peptide bond.** To form a peptide bond, the carboxyl (–COOH) group of one amino acid bonds to the amino (–NH_2) group of another amino acid, releasing water (H_2O) in the process. (See **Figure 6.2.**) A **dipeptide** is two amino acids joined by a peptide bond, and a **tripeptide** is three amino

peptide bond The bond between two amino acids formed when a carboxyl (–COOH) group of one amino acid joins an amino (–NH_2) group of another amino acid, releasing water in the process.

dipeptide Two amino acids joined by a peptide bond.

tripeptide Three amino acids joined by peptide bonds.

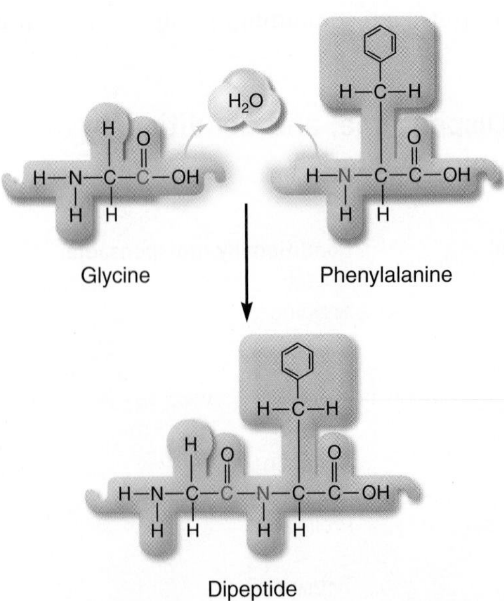

Figure 6.2 **Forming a peptide bond.** Imagine a row of people facing forward with their hands joined—the right hand joined to the left hand. Similarly, when two amino acids join together, the carboxyl group of one amino acid is matched with the amino group of another. A condensation reaction forms a peptide bond and releases water.

acids joined by peptide bonds. The term **oligopeptide** refers to a chain of 4 to 10 amino acids, whereas a **polypeptide** contains more than 10 amino acids.[6] Proteins in the body and in the diet are long polypeptides, most with hundreds of linked amino acids.

oligopeptide Four to 10 amino acids joined by peptide bonds.

polypeptide More than 10 amino acids joined by peptide bonds.

hemoglobin [HEEM-oh-glow-bin] The oxygen-carrying protein in red blood cells that consists of four heme groups and four globin polypeptide chains. The presence of hemoglobin gives blood its red color.

hydrophilic amino acids Amino acids that are attracted to water (water-loving).

Protein Shape

As its amino acids are assembled in the cell's cytoplasm, each protein chain assumes a unique three-dimensional shape that derives from the sequence and properties of its amino acids. The three-dimensional shape of a protein determines its function and its interaction with other molecules. As an example, **Figure 6.3** illustrates the unique folded and twisted shape of **hemoglobin**, the iron-carrying protein in red blood cells. In the lungs, hemoglobin binds oxygen and releases carbon dioxide. It then travels throughout the body, delivering oxygen to other tissues and picking up carbon dioxide for the return trip to the lungs.

Some amino acids carry electrical charges and therefore are attracted to the charged ends of water molecules (**hydrophilic amino acids**). In

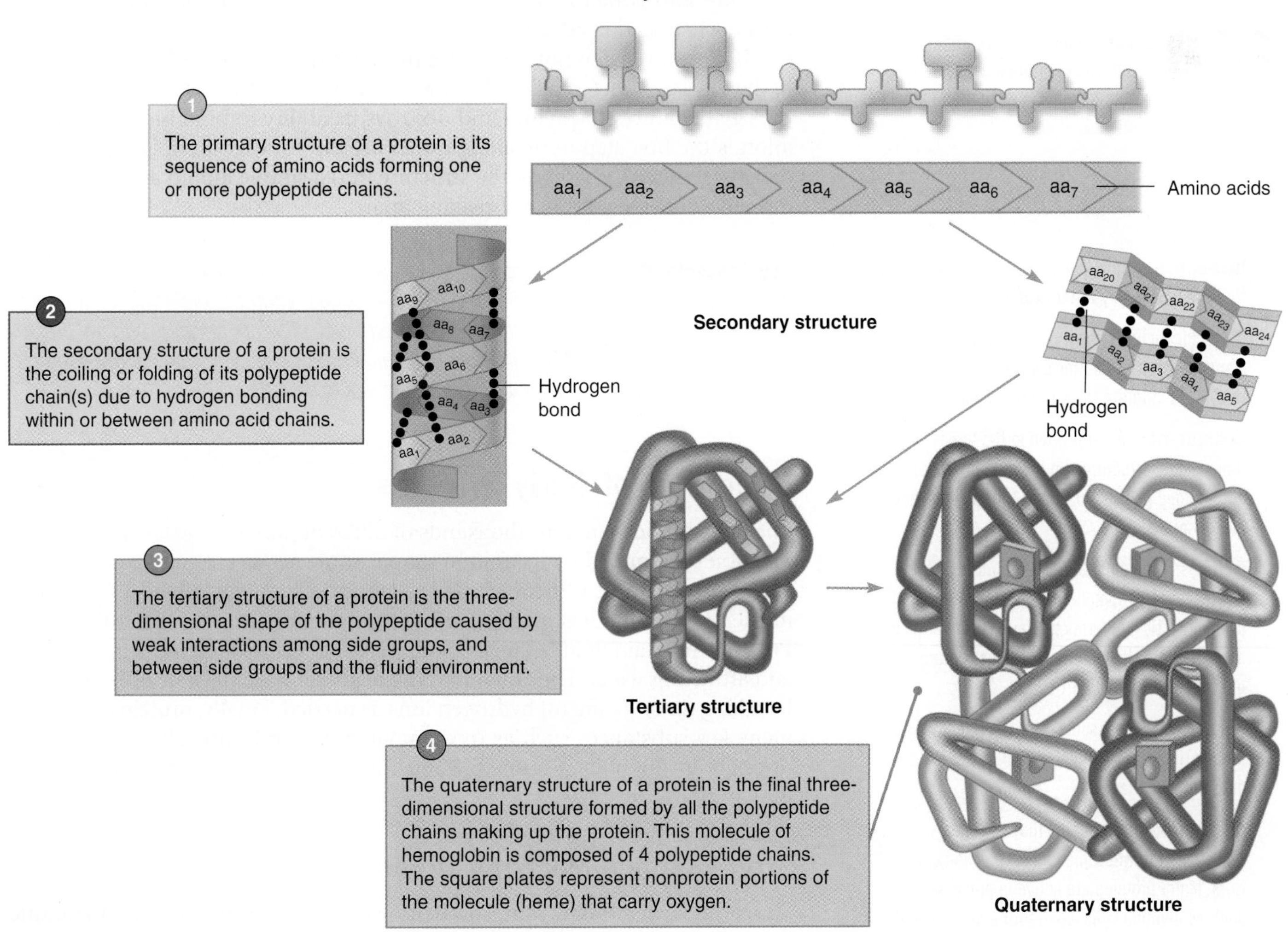

Primary structure
1
The primary structure of a protein is its sequence of amino acids forming one or more polypeptide chains.
aa1 aa2 aa3 aa4 aa5 aa6 aa7
Amino acids
2
The secondary structure of a protein is the coiling or folding of its polypeptide chain(s) due to hydrogen bonding within or between amino acid chains.
Secondary structure
Hydrogen bond
Hydrogen bond
3
The tertiary structure of a protein is the three-dimensional shape of the polypeptide caused by weak interactions among side groups, and between side groups and the fluid environment.
Tertiary structure
4
The quaternary structure of a protein is the final three-dimensional structure formed by all the polypeptide chains making up the protein. This molecule of hemoglobin is composed of 4 polypeptide chains. The square plates represent nonprotein portions of the molecule (heme) that carry oxygen.
Quaternary structure

Figure 6.3 **Hemoglobin.** Each protein becomes folded, twisted, and coiled into a shape all its own. This shape defines how a protein functions in your body. The simplest depiction of a protein reveals its unique sequence of amino acids.

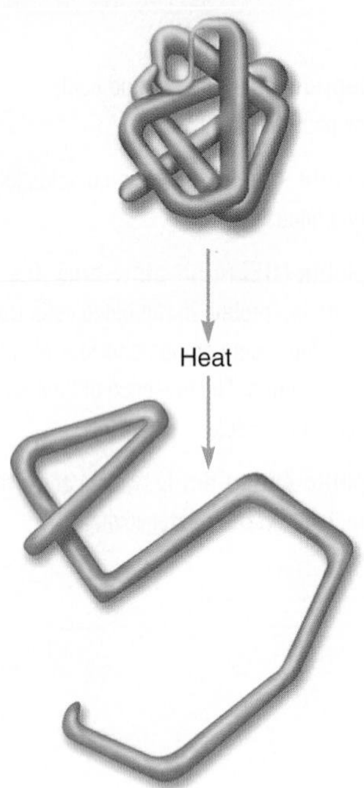

Figure 6.4 **Denaturation.** Heat, pH, oxidation, and mechanical agitation are some of the forces that can denature a protein, causing it to unfold and lose its functional shape.

a watery environment, hydrophilic amino acids orient themselves on the outside of the folded protein chain in close contact with water molecules. Other amino acids are electrically neutral and do not interact with water (**hydrophobic amino acids**). In a watery environment, hydrophobic amino acids fold to the inside of the protein molecule. The amino acid cysteine, which has sulfur atoms in its side group, sometimes will chemically bond to another cysteine in the chain, creating a **disulfide bridge**, which helps stabilize the protein's structure.

Protein Denaturation: Destabilizing a Protein's Shape

Acidity, alkalinity, heat, alcohol, oxidation, and agitation can all disrupt the chemical forces that stabilize a protein's three-dimensional shape, causing it to unfold and lose its shape (denature), as shown in **Figure 6.4**. Because a protein's shape determines its function, denatured proteins lose their ability to function properly.

If you've ever cooked an egg, you've witnessed protein **denaturation**. As the egg cooks, some of its protein bonds break. As these proteins unfold, they bump into and bind to each other. Eventually, as these interconnections increase, the liquid egg coagulates to form a solid. Raw egg white proteins denature and stiffen as they are whipped, and milk proteins denature and curdle when acid is added.

If an egg is eaten raw, its avidin protein can bind to the B vitamin biotin in the digestive tract, making the vitamin unavailable for absorption. Cooking the egg denatures the avidin and destroys its ability to bind biotin. Denaturation is the first step in breaking down protein for digestion. Stomach acids denature protein, uncoiling the structure into a simple amino acid chain that digestive enzymes can start breaking apart.

Key Concepts *Proteins are large molecules made up of amino acids joined in various sequences. Amino acids are joined by peptide bonds. Each protein assumes a unique three-dimensional shape depending on the sequence of its amino acids and the properties of their side groups. Acid, alkaline, heat, alcohol, and agitation can disrupt chemical forces that stabilize proteins, causing the proteins to denature, or lose their shape.*

Functions of Body Proteins

The human body contains thousands of different proteins, each with a specific function determined by its unique shape. Some act as enzymes, speeding up chemical reactions. Others act as hormones, which are a kind of chemical messenger. Antibodies made of protein protect us from foreign substances. Proteins maintain fluid balance by pumping molecules across cell membranes and attracting water. They maintain the acid and base balance of body fluids by taking up or giving off hydrogen ions as needed. Finally, proteins transport many key substances such as oxygen, vitamins, and minerals to target cells throughout the body. **Figure 6.5** illustrates the functions of proteins in the human body.

Structural and Mechanical Functions

Structures such as bone, skin, and hair owe their physical properties to unique proteins. **Collagen**, which appears microscopically as a densely packed long rod, is the most abundant protein in mammals and gives skin and bone their

hydrophobic amino acids Amino acids that are repelled by water (water-fearing).

disulfide bridge A bond between the sulfur components of two sulfur-containing amino acids that helps stabilize the structure of protein.

denaturation An alteration in the three-dimensional structure of a protein resulting in an unfolded polypeptide chain that usually lacks biological activity.

collagen The most abundant fibrous protein in the body. Collagen is the major constituent of connective tissue, forms the foundation for bones and teeth, and helps maintain the structure of blood vessels and other tissues.

keratin A water-insoluble fibrous protein that is the primary constituent of hair, nails, and the outer layer of the skin.

motor proteins Proteins that use energy and convert it into some form of mechanical work. Motor proteins are active in processes such as dividing cells, contracting muscle, and swimming sperm.

elastic strength. Hair and nails are made of **keratin**, which is another dense protein made of coiled helices. Protein is essential for building these anatomical structures; therefore, protein deficiencies during a child's development can be disastrous. **Figure 6.6** shows structural proteins.

Motor proteins are exactly what their name implies: proteins that turn energy into mechanical work. In fact, these proteins are the final step in converting our food into physical work. When you bike down a road or up a mountain, you are using your stored food energy to power minuscule molecular motors in your muscles. These molecular motors slide muscle proteins past each other, causing muscles to contract. As you pump the pedals, proteins turn that energy bar you ate into work! Similarly, specialized motor proteins are involved in a variety of processes, including cell division, muscle contraction, and sperm swimming.

Quick Bite

How to Beat the Stiffest Egg Whites

Whenever you want the greatest possible lightness or fluffiness, beat egg whites alone. A single drop of yolk or fat may reduce the foam's maximum volume by as much as two-thirds. Also, avoid plastic bowls because plastics tend to retain fatty material on their surfaces.

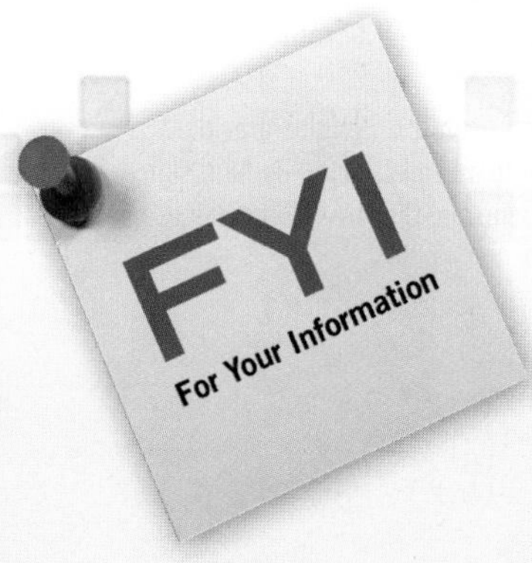

Scrabble Anyone?

Scrabble tile = amino acid

word = protein chain

Making a meaningful word from available Scrabble tiles is a good analogy for the making of a functional protein chain from available amino acids. Just as we can make many different words from the same tiles, cells can make many different proteins from the same amino acids.

If your cells have all 20 amino acids at their disposal, these can be arranged in a bewildering number of combinations to create tens of thousands of different protein chains, just as all the letters of the alphabet can be used to make an almost unlimited number of words.

Key

Amino Acid		Scrabble Tile
Glutamic Acid	Glu	E
Isoleucine	Ile	I
Asparagine	Asn	N
Serine	Ser	S
Threonine	Thr	T
Lysine	Lys	K
Arginine	Arg	R

E I N S T K R
Glu Ile Asn Ser Thr Lys Arg

T I N K E R S
Thr Ile Asn Lys Glu Arg Ser

R E S T K I N
Arg Glu Ser Thr Lys Ile Asn

R E K N I T S
Arg Glu Lys Asn Ile Thr Ser

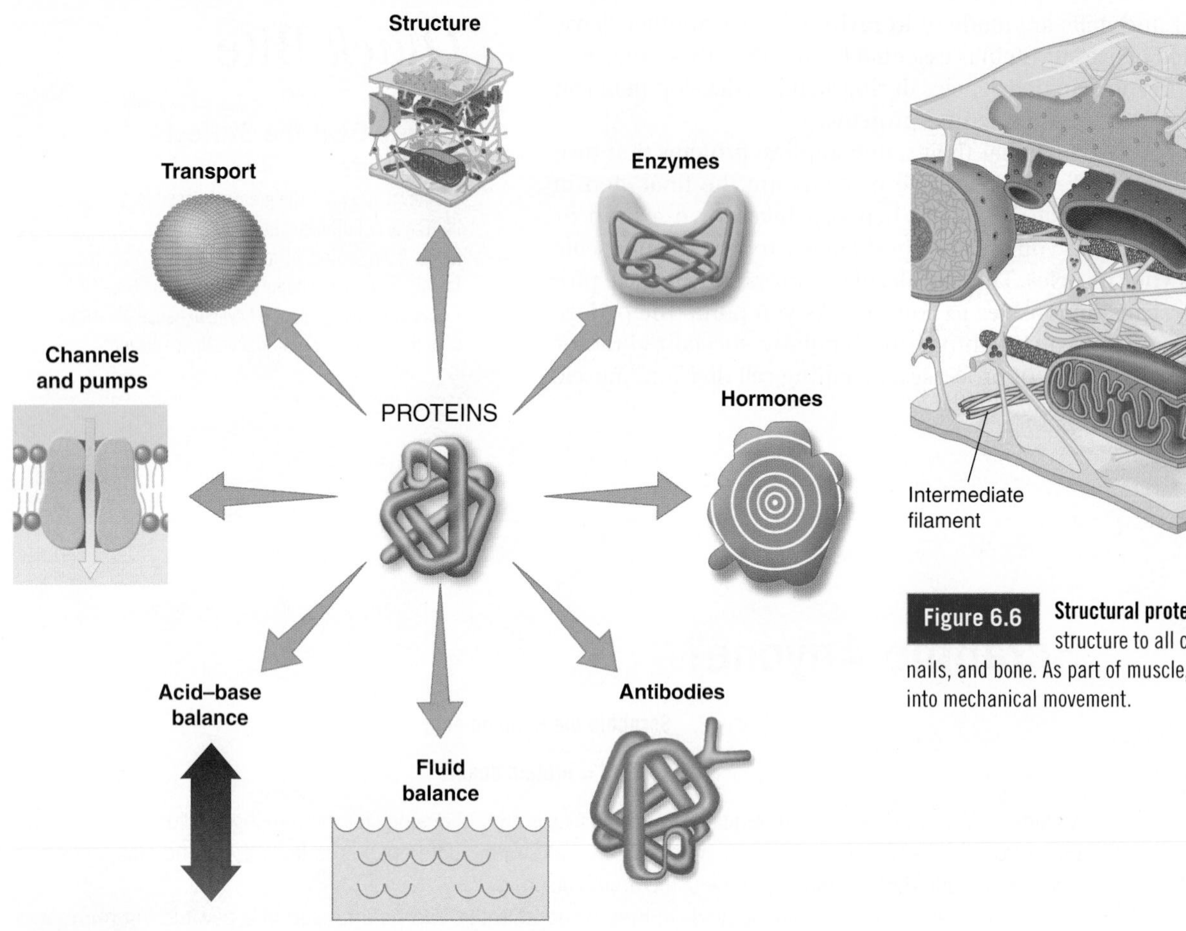
Structure
Transport
Enzymes
Channels and pumps
PROTEINS
Hormones
Acid–base balance
Fluid balance
Antibodies

Figure 6.5 **Functions of proteins.** There are many different types of proteins, each with its particular role in the body.

Intermediate filament
Microfilament
Microtubule

Figure 6.6 **Structural proteins.** Proteins provide structure to all cells, including hair, skin, nails, and bone. As part of muscle, they transform energy into mechanical movement.

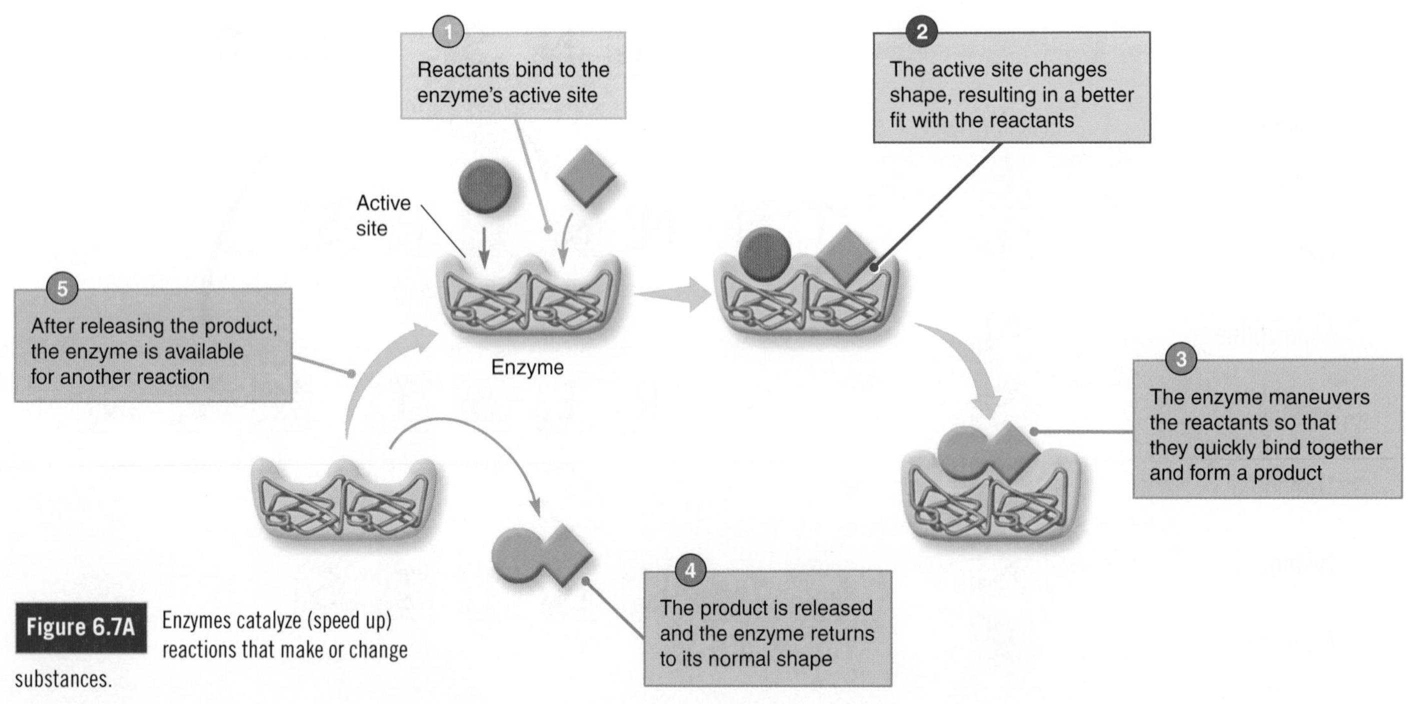
1 Reactants bind to the enzyme's active site
2 The active site changes shape, resulting in a better fit with the reactants
Active site
Enzyme
3 The enzyme maneuvers the reactants so that they quickly bind together and form a product
4 The product is released and the enzyme returns to its normal shape
5 After releasing the product, the enzyme is available for another reaction

Figure 6.7A Enzymes catalyze (speed up) reactions that make or change substances.

Enzymes

Enzymes are proteins that catalyze chemical reactions without being destroyed in the process. (See **Figure 6.7A** and **B**.) Every cell contains thousands of types of enzymes, each with its own purpose. During digestion, for example, enzymes help break down carbohydrates, proteins, and fats into monosaccharides, amino acids, and fatty acids for absorption into the body. Cellular enzymes release energy from these nutrients to fuel thousands of body processes. Enzymes also trigger the reactions that build muscle and tissue.

Our foods also contain enzymes, but these are inactivated (denatured) by cooking. Stomach acid denatures the enzymes in raw foods. You may notice special purified enzymes being sold as supplements to enhance digestion. Most of the time, stomach acid denatures these enzymes so that they are unable to function in the intestinal tract. However, some enzyme supplements are coated with a special substance to protect them from stomach acid. For example, a specially coated tablet form of the enzyme lactase can help people with lactose intolerance. Coated enzymes temporarily help break down foods in the small intestine but eventually are digested themselves.

Hormones

Hormones are chemical messengers that are made in one part of the body but act on cells in other parts of the body. (See **Figure 6.8**.) Many are proteins with important regulatory functions. Insulin, for example, is a protein hormone that plays a key role in regulating the amount of glucose in the blood. It is released from the pancreas in response to a rise in blood glucose levels, and functions to lower those levels (see Chapter 4, "Carbohydrates"). People with type 1 diabetes must take insulin injections to control blood glucose. Insulin cannot be taken as a pill—if it were, it would be denatured and digested just like any other protein.

Thyroid-stimulating hormone (TSH) and leptin are two other protein hormones. The pituitary gland produces TSH, which stimulates the thyroid

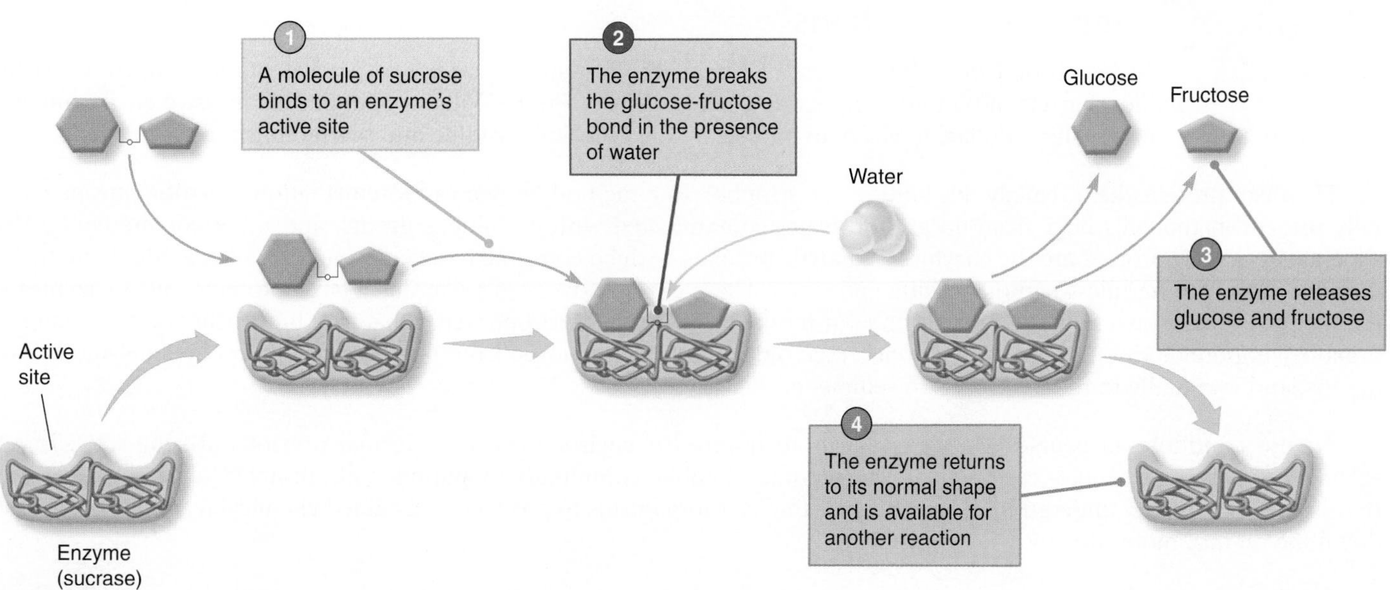
1
A molecule of sucrose binds to an enzyme's active site
2
The enzyme breaks the glucose-fructose bond in the presence of water
Glucose
Fructose
Water
3
The enzyme releases glucose and fructose
Active site
4
The enzyme returns to its normal shape and is available for another reaction
Enzyme (sucrase)

Figure 6.7B Enzymes catalyze reactions that break down molecules.

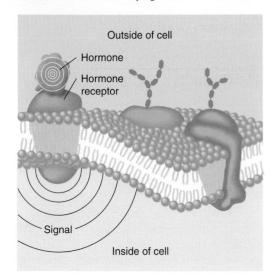

Figure 6.8 **Hormones.** Hormones are formed in one part of the body and carried in the blood to a different location where they signal cells to alter activities.

gland to produce the hormone thyroxine. Thyroxine, a modified form of the amino acid tyrosine, increases the body's metabolic rate. Leptin is produced by fat cells and plays an important role in body weight regulation.[7] For more information on leptin, see Chapter 9, "Energy Balance, Body Composition, and Weight Management."

Immune Function

Proteins play an important role in the immune system, which is responsible for fighting invasion and infection by foreign substances. (See **Figure 6.9**.)

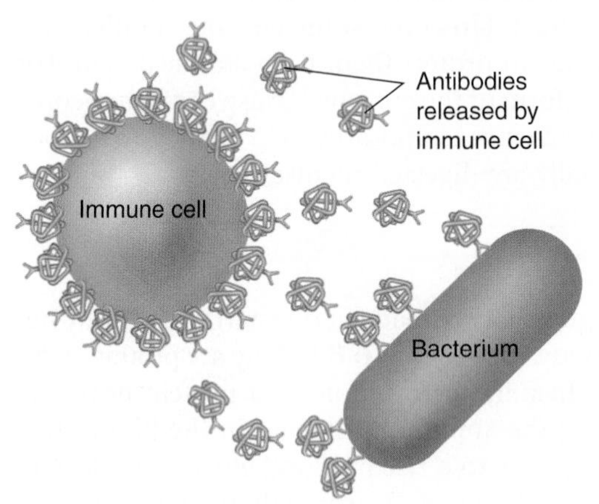

Figure 6.9 **Proteins and the immune system.** Protein antibodies are a crucial line of defense against invading bacteria and viruses.

Going Green

Send in the Proteins

In March of 1989, off the coast of Alaska, the oil tanker *Exxon Valdez* accidentally dumped a quarter million barrels of oil into the pristine environment of Prince William Sound. This massive environmental disaster cost more than a billion dollars to clean up. Worse, it killed precious wildlife and scarred unspoiled landscape.

How can proteins help remedy this kind of catastrophe? In a method known as bioremediation, microorganisms naturally present in the soils help clean up ground water contaminated with gasoline, solvents, and other contaminants. The superagents in this process are the enzymes—catalytic proteins—which consume toxic compounds and degrade them, transforming them into harmless carbon dioxide and water. These enzymes work just like those large proteins—also enzymes—that help us break down nutrients in digesting our food. This process is just one step in nature's biogeochemical recycling of organic compounds through the carbon cycle: reservoirs of carbon are moved from plants to freshwater systems and soil to oceans, and eventually to the fossil fuels in sediments.

Nature's antidote, of course, takes many years to restore the environment to its former previous pristine state. To accelerate the process, scientists can stimulate the natural microbial community by pumping air, proteins, and other nutrients (fertilizers or molasses) underground, and then use the microorganisms to produce a sustained chemical reaction that breaks down the oil into molecules and base elements.

Similarly, wastewater treatment using bioremediation relies on the nutritional abilities of microbes to maintain clean water for us. Scientists continue to study and improve bioremediation technology and techniques, not only to clean up after oil spills but also to restore many other environments that have been degraded.

Antibodies are blood proteins that attack and inactivate bacteria and viruses that cause infection. When your diet does not contain enough protein, your body cannot make as many antibodies as it needs. Your immune response is weakened and your risk of infection and illness increases. Each protein antibody has a specific shape that allows it to attack and destroy a specific foreign invader. Once your immune system learns how to make a certain kind of antibody, your body can protect itself by quickly making that antibody the next time the same germ invades.

Viruses, such as those that cause the common cold, take over cells to replicate. In a series of steps known as the **immune response**, your body mobilizes its defenses against the viral invaders. As part of the defense strategy, you produce protein antibodies that bind to the viruses, marking them for destruction. Even when the viruses are gone, special cells retain a memory of the particular virus so that a faster immune response can be mounted against future invasions. When people are immunized for a disease such as measles or mumps, they are actually getting a small amount of dead or inactivated virus in the injection. The dead virus cannot cause infection, but it does cue the body to make antibodies to the disease.

Fluid Balance

Fluids in the body are found inside cells (**intracellular fluid**) or outside cells (**extracellular fluid**). There are two types of extracellular fluid: fluid between cells (called intercellular fluid, or **interstitial fluid**) and fluid in the blood (**intravascular fluid**). These interior and exterior fluid levels must stay in balance for body processes to work properly.

Proteins in the blood help to maintain appropriate fluid levels in the vascular system. (See **Figure 6.10**.) The force of the heart's beating pushes fluid and nutrients from the capillaries out into the fluid surrounding the cells. But blood proteins such as albumin and globulin are too large to leave the capillary beds. These proteins remain in the capillaries, where they attract fluid. This provides a balancing and partially counteracting force that keeps fluid in the circulatory system.

If the diet lacks enough protein to maintain normal levels of blood proteins, fluid will leak into the surrounding tissue and cause swelling, also called **edema**. Children with protein malnutrition often suffer from severe edema. Reestablishing a diet adequate in protein and energy will allow the edema to subside.

Acid–Base Balance

Using a scale of 0 to 14, pH is a measure of the concentration of hydrogen ions in a substance. The higher the concentration of hydrogen ions, the lower the pH. Acids, with a high concentration of hydrogen ions, have a pH lower than 7; bases, with a low concentration of hydrogen ions, have a pH higher than 7. The lower the pH, the stronger the acid. The higher the pH, the stronger the base. The body works hard to keep the pH of the blood near 7.4, or nearly neutral. We can tolerate only small blood pH fluctuations without disastrous physiological consequences. Only a few hours with a blood pH above 8.0 or below 6.8 will cause death.

Proteins help maintain stable pH levels in body fluids by serving as **buffers**; they pick up extra hydrogen ions when conditions are acidic, and they donate hydrogen ions when conditions are alkaline. (See **Figure 6.11**.) If

antibodies [AN-tih-bod-ees] Large blood proteins produced by B lymphocytes in response to exposure to particular antigens (e.g., a protein on the surface of a virus or bacterium). Each type of antibody specifically binds to and helps eliminate its matching antigen from the body. Once formed, antibodies circulate in the blood and help protect the body against subsequent infection.

immune response A coordinated set of steps, including production of antibodies, that the immune system takes in response to an antigen.

intracellular fluid The fluid in the body's cells. It usually is high in potassium and phosphate and low in sodium and chloride. It constitutes about two-thirds of total body water.

extracellular fluid The fluid located outside of cells. It is composed largely of the liquid portion of the blood (plasma) and the fluid between cells in tissues (interstitial fluid), with fluid in the GI tract, eyes, joints, and spinal cord contributing a small amount. It constitutes about one-third of body water.

interstitial fluid [in-ter-STISH-ul] The fluid between cells in tissues. Also called intercellular fluid.

intravascular fluid The fluid portion of the blood (plasma) contained in arteries, veins, and capillaries. It accounts for about 15 percent of the extracellular fluid.

edema Swelling caused by the buildup of fluid between cells.

buffers Compounds or mixtures of compounds that can take up and release hydrogen ions to keep the pH of a solution constant. The buffering action of proteins and bicarbonate in the bloodstream plays a major role in maintaining the blood pH at 7.35 to 7.45.

Blood from heart to body
Capillary bed
Blood from body back to heart
Force of pumping blood from heart pushes fluids from blood into interstitial fluid
Proteins that remain in blood attract interstitial fluid back into bloodstream

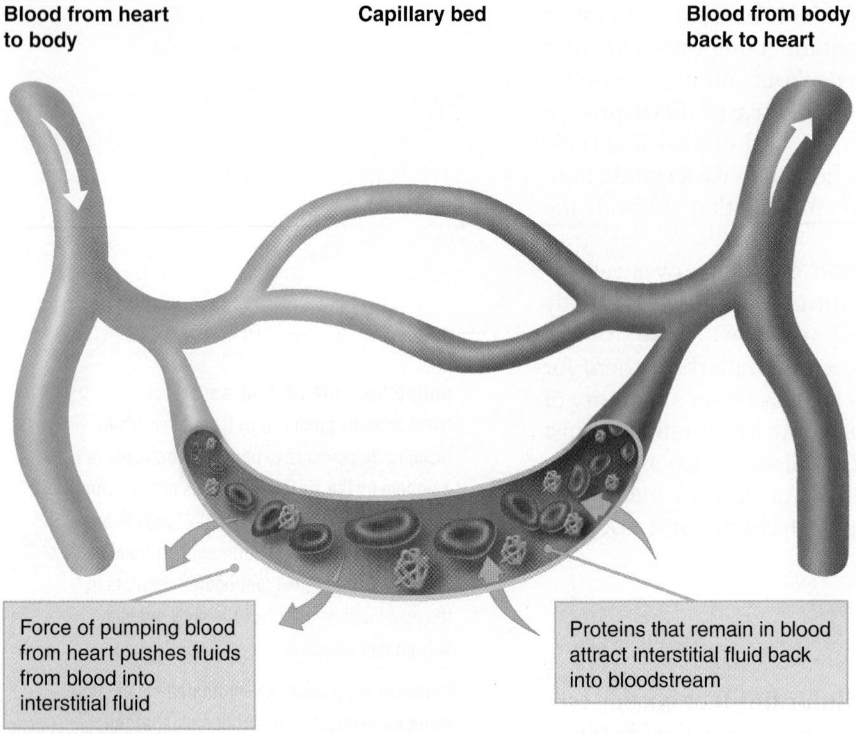

Figure 6.10 **Proteins in the blood.** Blood proteins attract fluid into capillaries. This counteracts the force of the heart beating, which pushes fluid out of capillaries.

The measure of hydrogen ions in a substance
pH
14
Alkalosis
Ideal blood pH
8
7.35–7.45
6.8
Blood pH range
Acidosis
0
Bases
Acids
Proteins can either donate or accept hydrogen ions to maintain stable pH levels
High hydrogen ion concentration = low pH

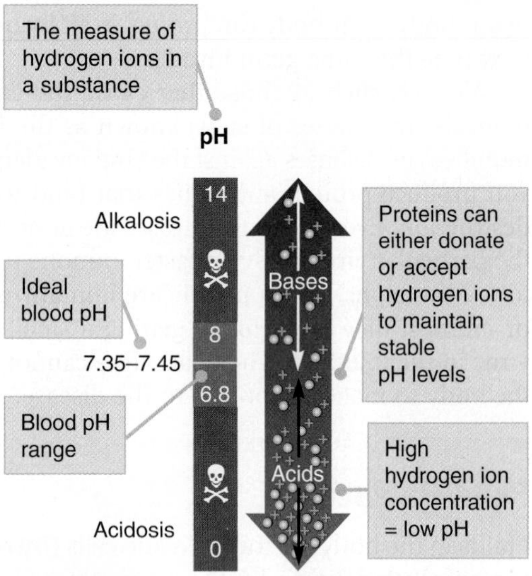

Figure 6.11 **Proteins help maintain stable pH levels.** Proteins act as buffers. When conditions are acidic, they pick up extra hydrogen ions. When conditions are alkaline, they donate hydrogen ions.

proteins are not available to buffer acidic or alkaline substances, the blood can become too acidic or too alkaline, resulting in either **acidosis** or **alkalosis**. Both conditions can be serious; either can cause proteins to denature, which can lead to coma or death.

Transport Functions

Many substances pass in and out of cells via proteins that cross cell membranes and act as channels and pumps. Channels allow substances to flow rapidly through the membranes by passive diffusion and require no input of energy. Pumps (active transporters), in contrast, must use energy to drive the transport of substances across membranes. In fact, sodium–potassium pumps—proteins that control cell volume and nerve impulses and drive the active transport of monosaccharides and amino acids—use more than one-third of the energy your body consumes at rest.[8] **Figure 6.12** shows a transmembrane protein.

Proteins also act as carriers, transporting many important substances in the bloodstream for delivery throughout the body. Lipoproteins, for example, package proteins with lipids so that lipid particles can be carried in the blood. (See **Figure 6.13**.) Other proteins carry fat-soluble vitamins, such as vitamin A, and certain other vitamins and minerals. Because protein carries vitamin A in the blood, protein deficiency contributes to vitamin A deficiency. The protein transferrin carries iron in the blood. In the liver, iron is stored as part of ferritin, a different protein.

acidosis An abnormally low blood pH (below about 7.35) due to increased acidity.

alkalosis An abnormally high blood pH (above about 7.45) due to increased alkalinity.

Source of Energy and Glucose

THINK About It 1

Although your body preferentially burns carbohydrate and fat for energy, if necessary it can use protein for energy or to make glucose. Thus, carbohydrate and fat are protein-sparing: they spare amino acids from being burned for energy and allow them to be used for protein synthesis.

If the diet does not provide enough energy to sustain vital functions, the body will sacrifice its own protein from enzymes, muscle, and other tissues to make energy and glucose for use by the brain, lungs, and heart. This is what happens in cases of starvation. (See Chapter 7, "Metabolism.")

When the body uses protein for energy, it first breaks the protein into individual amino acids. To release energy from an amino acid, the body removes the nitrogen group—a process called **deamination**. It can use the remaining carbon skeleton for energy. The carbon skeleton from most amino acids can be used to make glucose.

If the diet contains more protein than is needed for protein synthesis, most of the excess is converted to glucose or stored as fat. Thus, people who take protein supplements or eat high-protein diets in hopes of increasing muscle mass may instead be expensively adding to their body fat.

This review of protein functions illustrates that protein is of "prime importance," just as the Greeks believed. For proteins to perform all these functions, the diet must provide adequate amounts of protein components. In addition, the body needs adequate energy from carbohydrates and fats, and adequate digestibility of protein foods.

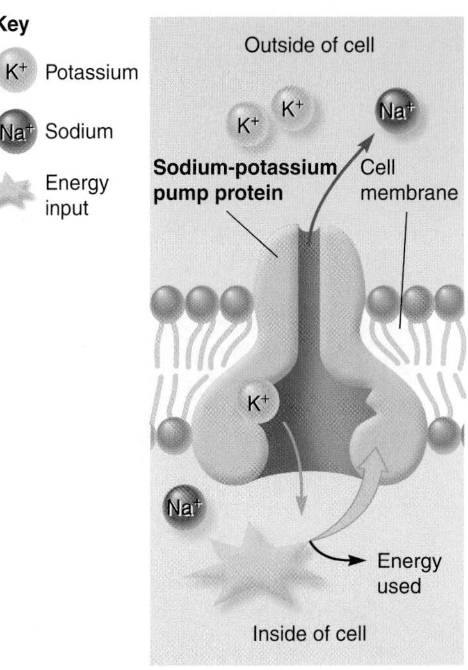

Figure 6.12 **A transmembrane protein.** Proteins form channels and pumps that help move substances in and out of cells.

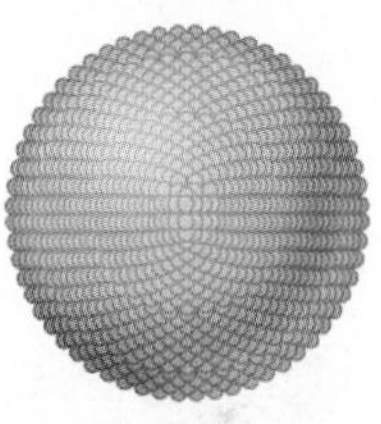

Figure 6.13 **Proteins act as carriers.** Lipoproteins have embedded proteins that help them transport fat and cholesterol in the blood.

Key Concepts *In the body, proteins perform numerous vital functions that are determined by each protein's shape. As enzymes, they speed up chemical reactions; as hormones, they are chemical messengers. Protein antibodies protect the body from infection and illness; proteins also maintain fluid balance and acid–base balance, and transport substances throughout the body. If needed, protein can also be used as a source of energy or glucose.*

Protein Digestion and Absorption

Before your body can make a body protein from food protein, it must digest and absorb the protein you eat. **Figure 6.14** shows the process of protein digestion and absorption.

Protein Digestion

The first step in using dietary protein is digesting its long polypeptide chains into amino acids. As with the other energy-yielding nutrients, digestion requires enzymes from a number of sources. Digestion of protein begins in the stomach.

In the Stomach

In the stomach, hydrochloric acid (HCl) denatures a protein, unfolding it and making the amino acid chain more accessible to the action of enzymes. Glands in the stomach lining produce the proenzyme pepsinogen, an inactive **precursor** of the enzyme pepsin. When pepsinogen comes in contact with hydrochloric acid, it is converted to the active enzyme pepsin. Gastric juices must be acidic for this enzyme to be active; it is most active at a (very acidic) pH of 2.5 and is inactive at a pH above 5.0. Gastric glands secrete hydrochloric acid at a pH of approximately 0.8. Once the acid is mixed with the

deamination The removal of the amino group ($-NH_2$) from an amino acid.

precursor A substance that is converted into another active substance. Enzyme precursors are also called proenzymes.

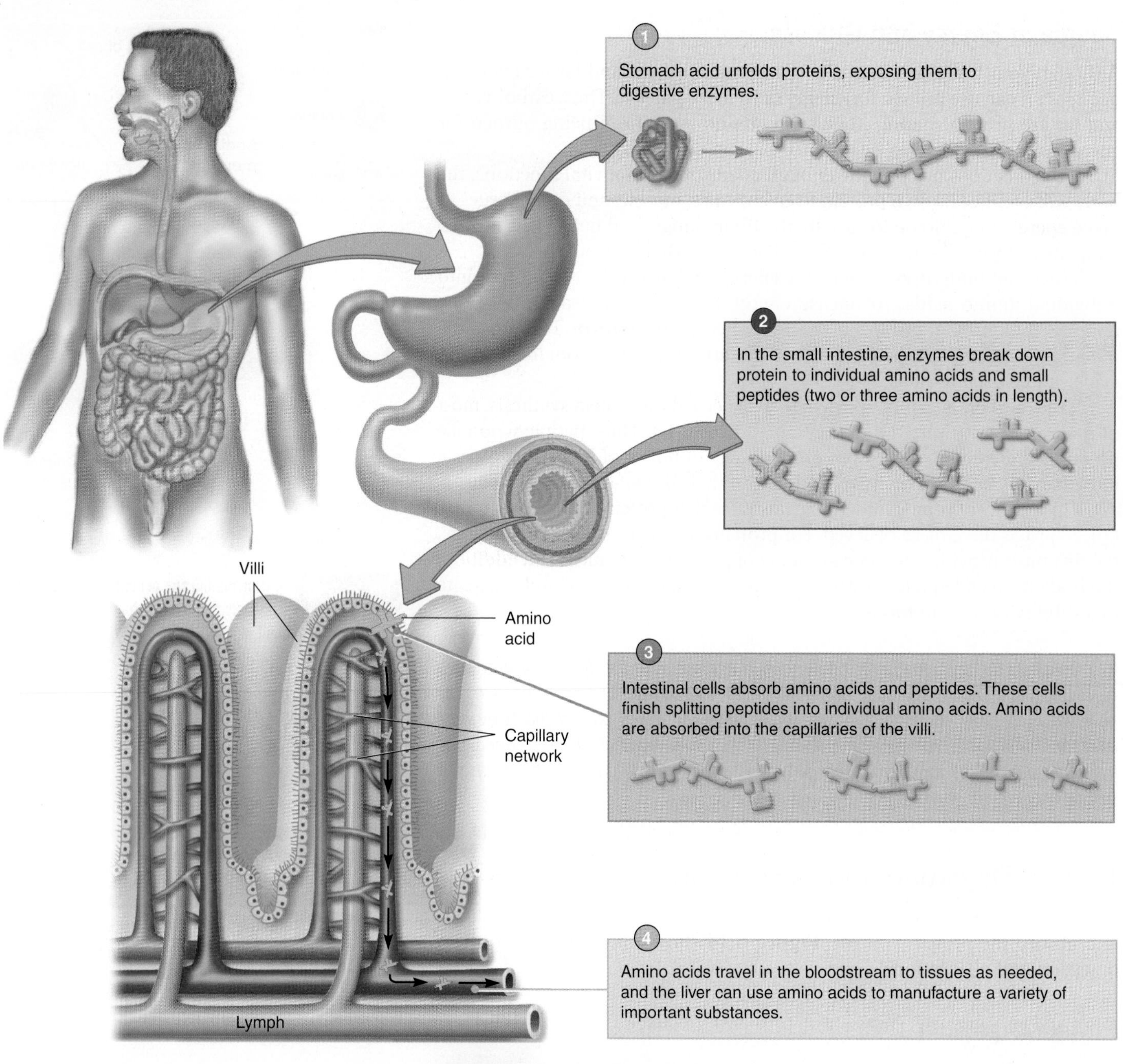

1
Stomach acid unfolds proteins, exposing them to digestive enzymes.
2
In the small intestine, enzymes break down protein to individual amino acids and small peptides (two or three amino acids in length).
Villi
Amino acid
3
Intestinal cells absorb amino acids and peptides. These cells finish splitting peptides into individual amino acids. Amino acids are absorbed into the capillaries of the villi.
Capillary network
4
Amino acids travel in the bloodstream to tissues as needed, and the liver can use amino acids to manufacture a variety of important substances.
Lymph

Figure 6.14 **The breakdown of protein in the body.** Digestion breaks down protein to amino acids that can be absorbed into the bloodstream.

gastric contents, the pH of the gastric juices falls to 2.5—the ideal medium for pepsin activity. By the time dietary protein leaves the stomach, pepsin has broken it down into individual amino acids and peptides of various lengths. Pepsin is responsible for about 10 to 20 percent of protein digestion.[9]

proteases [PRO-tea-ace-ez] Enzymes that break down protein into peptides and amino acids.

In the Small Intestine

From the stomach, amino acids and polypeptides pass into the small intestine, where most protein digestion takes place. In the small intestine, **proteases** (protein-digesting enzymes) break down large peptides into smaller peptides.

If a cell produces active forms of proteases, it will digest itself and break down its own cellular protein. However, cells employ a protective strategy. They produce and secrete most proteases as **proenzymes**, inactive forms of the enzymes, for later activation. This delayed activation protects the integrity of the cell.

Both the pancreas and the small intestine make digestive proenzymes. The pancreas makes **trypsinogen** and **chymotrypsinogen**, which are secreted into the small intestine in response to the presence of protein. Here, these proenzymes are cleaved into their active forms: **trypsin** and **chymotrypsin**, respectively. These activated proteases then break polypeptides into smaller peptides. Pancreatic enzymes completely digest only a small percentage of proteins into individual amino acids; most of the proteins at this point are dipeptides, tripeptides, and still larger polypeptides.

The final stages of protein digestion take place on the surface of the intestine's lining and require enzymes secreted by the intestinal lining cells. Brush border (microvilli) **peptidases** react with intestinal fluids that come in contact with the cell surface and split the remaining larger polypeptides into tripeptides, dipeptides, and individual amino acids. These smaller units are transported across the microvilli membranes into the cell. Inside the cell, many other peptidases specifically attack the linkages between the amino acids. Within minutes, these peptidases digest virtually all the remaining dipeptides and tripeptides into individual amino acids for absorption into the bloodstream.

Undigested Protein

Any parts of proteins not digested and absorbed in the small intestine continue through the large intestine and pass out of the body in the feces. Normally the body efficiently digests and absorbs protein. Diseases of the intestinal tract, however, decrease the efficiency of absorption and increase nitrogen losses in the feces.[10] People with **celiac disease**, for example, cannot properly digest gluten—a protein found in wheat, rye, and oats. Unless treated with a gluten-free diet, people with celiac disease show poor growth, weight loss, and other symptoms resulting from poor absorption of protein and other nutrients. When people have **cystic fibrosis**, thick, sticky mucus prevents digestive enzymes, including proteases, from reaching the small intestine and results in poor digestion and absorption of protein and other nutrients.[11] Special enzyme preparations that contain protease, lipase, and amylase are needed to prevent malnutrition.

Amino Acid and Peptide Absorption

Absorption of some amino acids requires active transport, whereas other amino acids are absorbed via facilitated diffusion. (See **Figure 6.15**.) Although the active transport process is the same for amino acids as it is for glucose and galactose, amino acids and monosaccharides use different transport proteins.

Although there are several active transport mechanisms, similar amino acids share the same active transport system. The amino acids leucine, isoleucine, and valine, for example, all depend on the same carrier molecule for absorption. Normally proteins in foods supply a mix of many amino acids, so amino acids that share the same transport system are absorbed fairly equally. If a person consumes a large amount of one particular amino acid, however, absorption of other amino acids that share the same transport system will be deficient. Thus, if you take a supplement of one amino acid, you may be interfering with the absorption of another amino acid from your diet.

THINK About It 2

Quick Bite

Softening Tough Meat

Cooking tough meat in liquid for hours helps dissolve the source of its toughness, fibrous protein called connective tissue.

proenzymes Inactive precursors of enzymes.

trypsinogen/trypsin A protease produced by the pancreas that is converted from the inactive proenzyme form (trypsinogen) to the active form (trypsin) in the small intestine.

chymotrypsinogen/chymotrypsin A protease produced by the pancreas that is converted from the inactive proenzyme form (chymotrypsinogen) to the active form (chymotrypsin) in the small intestine.

peptidases Enzymes that act on small peptide units by breaking peptide bonds.

celiac disease [SEA-lee-ak] A disease that involves an inability to digest gluten, a protein found in wheat, rye, oats, and barley. If untreated, it causes flattening of the villi in the intestine, leading to severe malabsorption of nutrients. Symptoms include diarrhea, fatty stools, swollen belly, and extreme fatigue.

cystic fibrosis An inherited disorder that causes widespread dysfunction of the exocrine glands, resulting in chronic lung disease, abnormally high levels of electrolytes (e.g., sodium, potassium, chloride) in sweat, and deficiency of pancreatic enzymes needed for digestion.

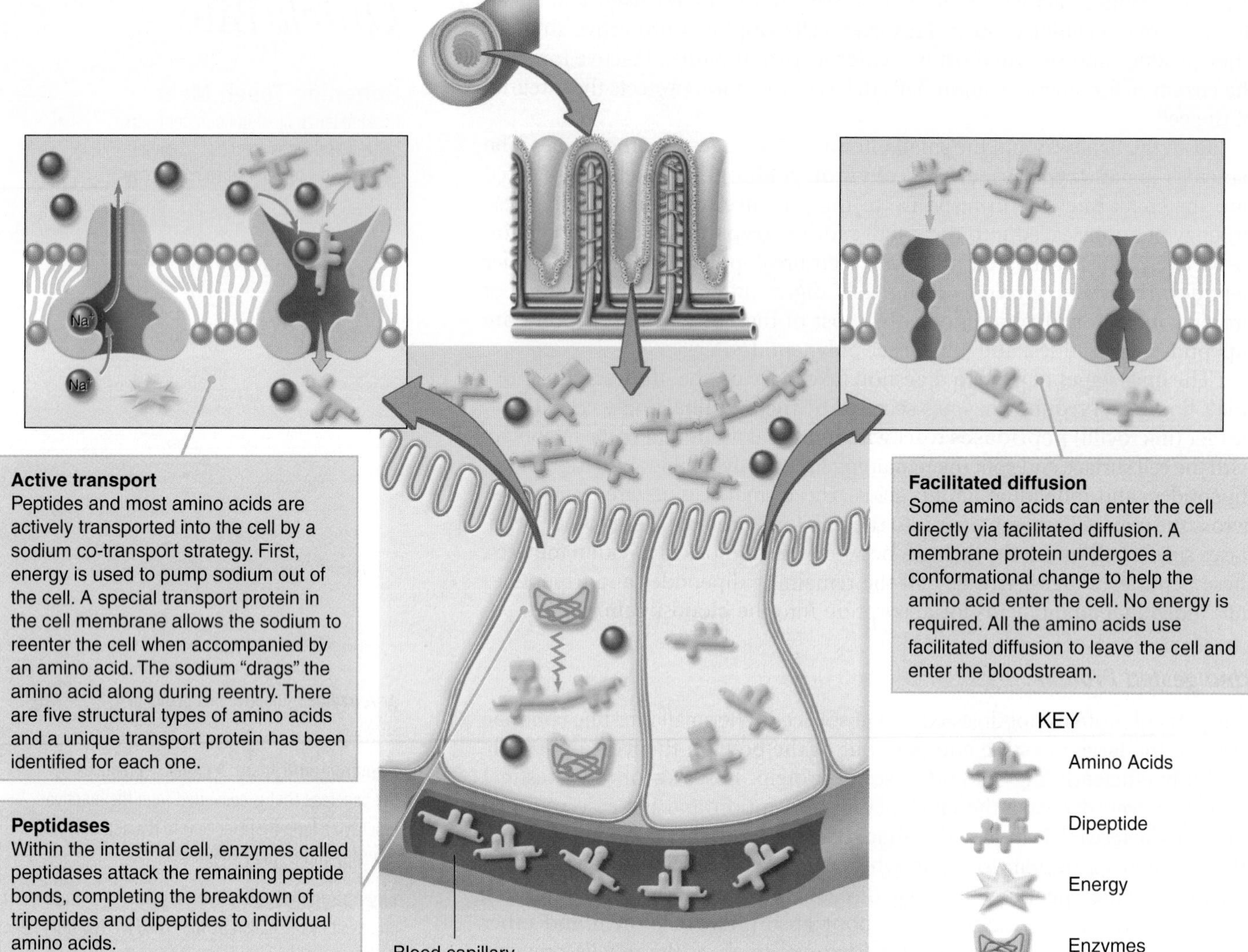

Na+
Na+
Active transport
Peptides and most amino acids are actively transported into the cell by a sodium co-transport strategy. First, energy is used to pump sodium out of the cell. A special transport protein in the cell membrane allows the sodium to reenter the cell when accompanied by an amino acid. The sodium "drags" the amino acid along during reentry. There are five structural types of amino acids and a unique transport protein has been identified for each one.
Peptidases
Within the intestinal cell, enzymes called peptidases attack the remaining peptide bonds, completing the breakdown of tripeptides and dipeptides to individual amino acids.
Blood capillary
Facilitated diffusion
Some amino acids can enter the cell directly via facilitated diffusion. A membrane protein undergoes a conformational change to help the amino acid enter the cell. No energy is required. All the amino acids use facilitated diffusion to leave the cell and enter the bloodstream.
KEY
Amino Acids
Dipeptide
Energy
Enzymes

Figure 6.15 **Protein absorption into an intestinal cell.** Intestinal cells use active transport and facilitated diffusion to absorb amino acids.

Most protein absorption takes place in the cells that line the duodenum and jejunum. After they are absorbed, most amino acids and the few absorbed peptides are transported via the portal vein to the liver and then released into general circulation. Some amino acids remain in the intestinal cells and are used to synthesize intestinal enzymes and new cells. More than 99 percent of protein enters the bloodstream as individual amino acids. Peptides are rarely absorbed, and whole proteins that escape digestion hardly ever are. The absorption of only a few molecules of whole protein can cause a severe allergic reaction or immune dysfunction.[12]

Key Concepts *Protein digestion begins in the stomach, where the enzyme pepsin breaks proteins into smaller peptides. Digestion continues in the small intestine, where proteases break polypeptides into smaller peptide units, which are then absorbed into cells, where additional enzymes complete digestion to amino acids. Key enzymes are pepsin in the stomach, and trypsin and chymotrypsin from the pancreas. Proteases (protein-digesting enzymes) are synthesized and secreted as inactive proenzymes, so that cells do not digest themselves.*

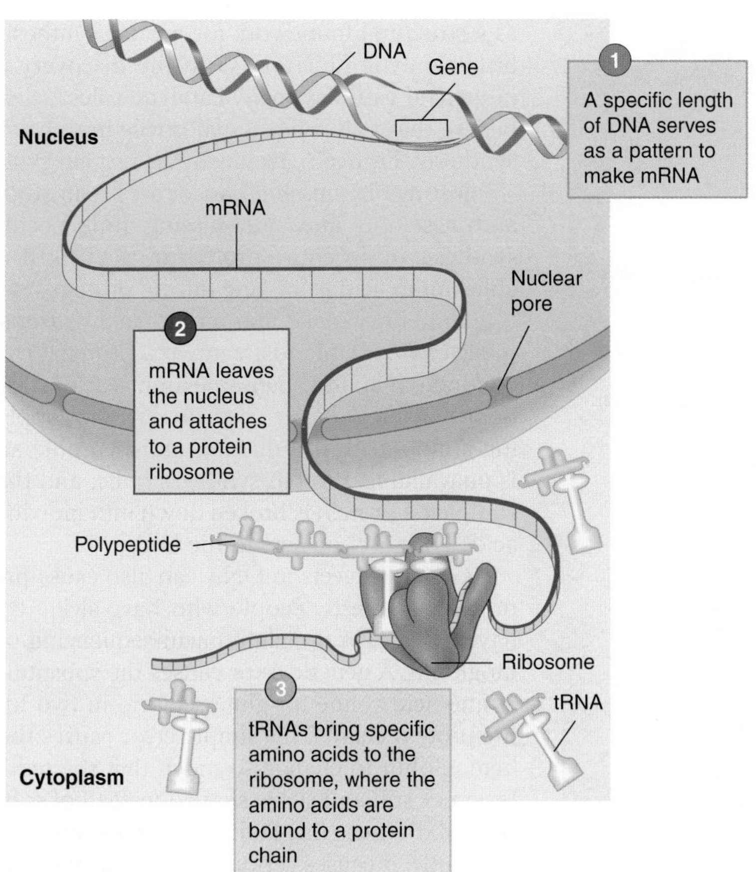

Figure 6.16 **Protein synthesis.** Ribosomes are our protein synthesis factories. mRNA carries manufacturing instructions from DNA in the cell nucleus to the ribosomes. tRNA collects amino acids in the correct sequence, and rRNA in the ribosome directs protein synthesis.

Proteins in the Body

Once in the bloodstream, amino acids are transported throughout the body and are available for synthesizing cellular proteins. To build proteins, cells use peptide bonds to link amino acids.

Protein Synthesis

Genetic material in the nucleus of every cell is the blueprint for the thousands of proteins needed to perform life functions. This is also what makes each of us unique. Cells receive the genetic material at the time of conception, and store it in the form of long, coiled molecules of **DNA (deoxyribonucleic acid)** in each cell's nucleus.

To synthesize a protein, the cell uses a specific length of the DNA in the cell nucleus, called a gene, as a pattern to make a special type of ribonucleic acid (RNA) called **messenger RNA (mRNA).** This mRNA carries the code for the sequence of amino acids needed in the protein. The mRNA leaves the nucleus of the cell and attaches itself to one of the **ribosomes**, or protein-making machines, in the cell's cytoplasm.

Another type of RNA, **transfer RNA (tRNA)**, then gathers the necessary amino acids from cell fluid and carries them to the mRNA, where enzymes bind each amino acid to the growing protein chain. During protein synthesis, thousands of tRNAs each carry their own specific amino acid to the site of protein synthesis, but only one mRNA controls the sequencing of amino acids for a given protein.

A third type of RNA, **ribosomal RNA (rRNA)**, is the major component of ribosomes. For many years, scientists assumed that rRNA primarily served

DNA (deoxyribonucleic acid) The carrier of genetic information. Specific regions of each DNA molecule, called genes, act as blueprints for the synthesis of proteins.

messenger RNA (mRNA) Long, linear, single-stranded molecules of ribonucleic acids formed from DNA templates that carry the amino acid sequence of one or more proteins from the cell nucleus to the cytoplasm, where the ribosomes translate mRNA into proteins.

ribosomes Cell components composed of protein located in the cytoplasm that translate messenger RNA into protein sequences.

transfer RNA (tRNA) A type of ribonucleic acid that is composed of a complementary RNA sequence and an amino acid specific to that sequence. It inserts the appropriate amino acid when the messenger RNA sequence and the ribosome call for it.

ribosomal RNA (rRNA) A type of ribonucleic acid that is a major component of ribosomes. It provides a structural framework for protein synthesis and orchestrates the process.

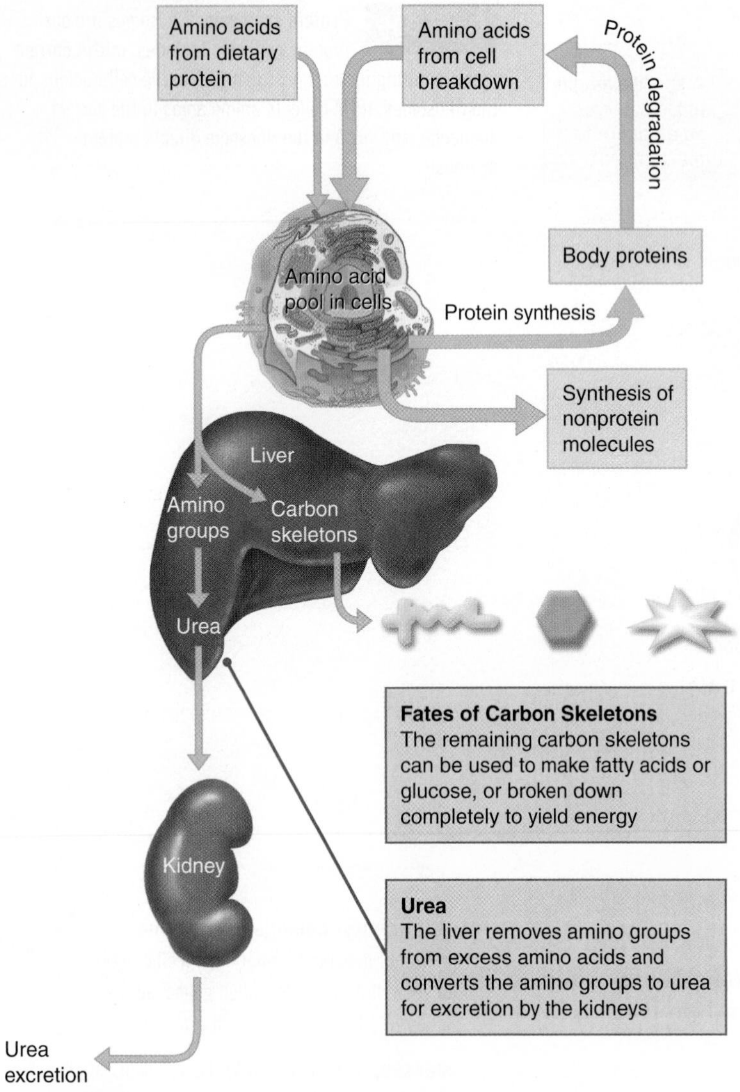

Amino acids from dietary protein
Amino acids from cell breakdown
Protein degradation
Body proteins
Amino acid pool in cells
Protein synthesis
Synthesis of nonprotein molecules
Liver
Amino groups
Carbon skeletons
Urea
Kidney
Urea excretion

Fates of Carbon Skeletons
The remaining carbon skeletons can be used to make fatty acids or glucose, or broken down completely to yield energy

Urea
The liver removes amino groups from excess amino acids and converts the amino groups to urea for excretion by the kidneys

Figure 6.17 **Protein turnover.** Cells draw upon their amino acid pools to synthesize new proteins. These small pools turn over quickly, and must be replenished by amino acids from dietary protein and degradation of body protein. Dietary protein supplies about one-third and the breakdown of body protein supplies about two-thirds of the amino acids needed to synthesize roughly 300 grams of body protein daily.

as a structural framework for protein synthesis and had little catalytic function. With the discovery that RNA in general can play many catalytic roles, scientists now believe that rRNA has a major role in directing protein synthesis. **Figure 6.16** illustrates protein synthesis.

Just as one missing part of a car can stop an entire auto assembly line, one missing amino acid can stop synthesis of an entire protein in the cell. If a dispensable amino acid is missing during protein synthesis, the cell will either make that amino acid or obtain it from the liver via the bloodstream, and protein synthesis will continue. If an indispensable amino acid is missing, the body may break its own protein down to supply the missing amino acid. If a missing indispensable amino acid is unavailable, protein synthesis halts, and the partially completed protein is broken down into individual amino acids for use elsewhere in the body.

Genetic defects in DNA can also cause problems in protein synthesis. People who have sickle cell anemia have a defect in the amino acid sequencing of their hemoglobin. A genetic error causes the substitution of the amino acid valine for glutamic acid in two locations in the protein chain. This simple error causes the shape of hemoglobin to change so much that the red blood cell becomes stiff and sickle-shaped instead of soft and disk-shaped. Because this faulty protein cannot carry oxygen efficiently, it causes serious medical problems.

The Amino Acid Pool and Protein Turnover

Cells throughout the body constantly and simultaneously synthesize and break down protein. When cells break down protein, the protein's amino acids return to circulation. (See **Figure 6.17**.) These available amino acids, found throughout body tissues and fluids, are collectively referred to as the **amino acid pool**.[13] Some of these amino acids may be used for protein synthesis; others may have their amino group removed and be used to produce energy or nonprotein substances such as glucose.

The constant recycling of proteins in the body is known as **protein turnover**.[14] Each day, more amino acids in your body are recycled than are supplied in your diet. Of the approximately 300 grams of protein synthesized by the body each day, 200 grams are made from recycled amino acids. This remarkable recycling capacity is the reason we need so little protein in our diet. Although our requirements are small, dietary protein is extremely important. When dietary protein is inadequate, increased breakdown of body protein replenishes the amino acid pool. This can lead to the breakdown of essential body tissue.

amino acid pool The amino acids in body tissues and fluids that are available for new protein synthesis.

protein turnover The constant synthesis and breakdown of proteins in the body.

Synthesis of Nonprotein Molecules

Amino acids have roles other than as components of peptides and proteins; they are precursors of many molecules with important biological roles. Your body makes nonprotein molecules from amino acids and the nitrogen they contain. The vitamin niacin, for example, is made from the amino acid tryptophan. Precursors of DNA, RNA, and many coenzymes derive in part from amino acids. Your body also uses amino acids to make **neurotransmitters**, chemicals that send signals from nerve cells to other parts of the body. The neurotransmitter serotonin, which helps regulate mood, is made from tryptophan. Norepinephrine and epinephrine (also called noradrenaline and adrenaline, respectively), which ready the body for action, are neurotransmitters made from tyrosine. Your body also uses tyrosine to make the skin pigment melanin and a hormone called thyroxine. The simple amino acid glycine combines with many toxic substances to make less harmful substances that the body can excrete. Your body uses the amino acid histidine to make histamine, a potent vasodilator (dilator of blood vessels) and a culprit in allergic reactions.

neurotransmitters Substances released at the end of a stimulated nerve cell that diffuse across a small gap and bind to another nerve cell or muscle cell, stimulating or inhibiting it.

urea The main nitrogen-containing waste product in mammals. Formed in liver cells from ammonia and carbon dioxide, urea is carried via the bloodstream to the kidneys, where it is excreted in the urine.

positive nitrogen balance Nitrogen intake exceeds the sum of all sources of nitrogen excretion.

negative nitrogen balance Nitrogen intake is less than the sum of all sources of nitrogen excretion.

nitrogen balance Nitrogen intake minus the sum of all sources of nitrogen excretion.

nitrogen equilibrium Nitrogen intake equals the sum of all sources of nitrogen excretion; nitrogen balance equals zero.

Protein and Nitrogen Excretion

Cells break down and recycle amino acids. Breakdown of an amino acid yields an amino group ($-NH_2$). This NH_2 molecule is unstable and is quickly converted to ammonia (NH_3). However, ammonia is toxic to cells, so it is expelled into the bloodstream as a waste product and carried to the liver. In the liver, an amino group and an ammonia group react with carbon dioxide through a series of reactions (known collectively as the urea cycle) to generate **urea** and water. The nitrogen-rich urea is transported from the liver by way of the bloodstream to the kidneys, where it is filtered from the blood and sent to the bladder for excretion in the urine. Small amounts of other nitrogen-containing compounds, such as ammonia, uric acid, and creatinine, are excreted in the urine as well. Some nitrogen is also lost through skin, sloughed-off GI cells, mucus, hair and nail cuttings, and body fluids.

Nitrogen Balance

Because nitrogen is excreted as proteins are recycled or used, we can use the balance of nitrogen in the body to evaluate whether the body is getting enough protein. (See **Figure 6.18.**) We can estimate the balance of nitrogen, and therefore protein, in the body by comparing nitrogen intake to the sum of all sources of nitrogen excretion (urine, feces, skin, hair, and body fluids).[15]

nitrogen balance = grams of nitrogen intake − grams of nitrogen output

If nitrogen intake exceeds nitrogen excretion, the body is said to be in **positive nitrogen balance**. Positive nitrogen balance means that the body is adding protein, as is the case for growing children, pregnant women, or people recovering from protein deficiency or illnesses. If nitrogen excretion exceeds nitrogen intake, the body is in **negative nitrogen balance**. This means that the body is losing protein. People who are starving or on extreme weight-loss diets or who suffer from fever, severe illnesses, or infections are in a state of negative nitrogen balance. If nitrogen intake equals nitrogen excretion, **nitrogen balance** is zero and the body is in **nitrogen equilibrium**. Healthy adults are in nitrogen equilibrium, which means that their dietary protein intake is adequate to maintain and repair tissue. They have no net gain or loss of body protein, and they simply excrete excess dietary nitrogen.

Key Concepts *The information that allows a cell to make a particular protein is stored in cellular DNA. Three forms of RNA—mRNA, tRNA, and rRNA—are needed to build body proteins. Cells throughout the body constantly synthesize and break down protein simultaneously, a process known as protein turnover. Nitrogen-containing end products of protein metabolism are excreted in urine via the kidneys. Comparison of nitrogen intake (from dietary protein) to nitrogen excretion gives a measure of nitrogen balance and indicates protein status in the body.*

Figure 6.18 **Protein (nitrogen) balance.** Nitrogen balance reflects whether a person is gaining or losing protein.

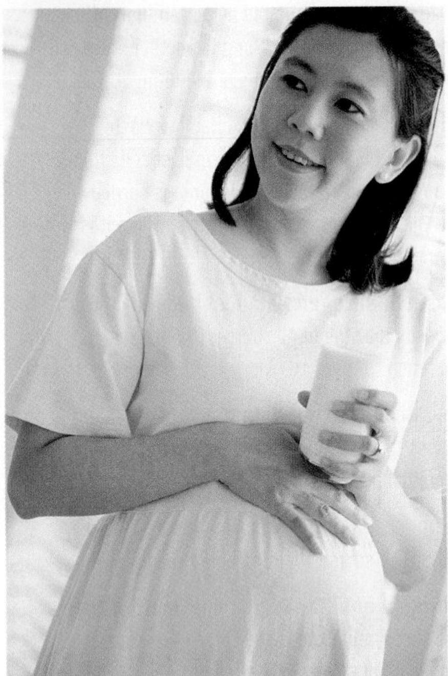

A pregnant woman is adding protein so she has a positive nitrogen balance.

A healthy person who is neither gaining nor losing protein is in nitrogen equilibrium.

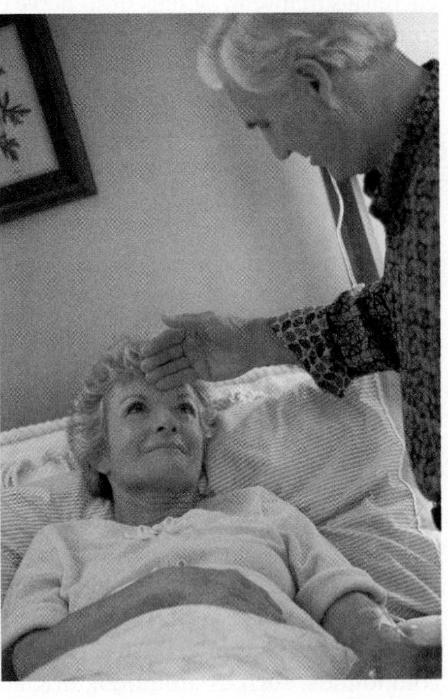

A person who is severely ill and losing protein has a negative nitrogen balance.

Proteins in the Diet

Many government and health organizations have made recommendations about the amount of protein in a healthful diet, just as they have for other nutrients. Meat, eggs, milk, legumes, grains, and vegetables are all sources of protein. Fruits contain minimal amounts and, along with fats, are not considered protein sources. **Figure 6.19** shows some good sources of protein.

Recommended Intakes of Protein

In the United States and Canada, the Recommended Dietary Allowance (RDA; see Chapter 2, "Nutrition Guidelines and Assessment") is the accepted dietary standard for protein. RDAs are set to meet the nutritional needs of most healthy people, so most people actually require somewhat less protein than the RDA. RDA values also assume that people are consuming adequate energy and other nutrients to allow their bodies to use dietary protein for protein synthesis, rather than for energy.

Based on evidence of increased heart disease risk when diets are low in fat and high in carbohydrate, and increased risk of obesity and heart disease when diets are high in fat, the Food and Nutrition Board developed Acceptable Macronutrient Distribution Ranges (AMDRs) for the energy-yielding nutrients.[16] For adults, the AMDR for fat is 20 to 35 percent of energy intake, and the AMDR for carbohydrate is 45 to 65 percent of energy intake. This leaves about 10 to 35 percent of energy intake from protein, a level that is typically higher than the RDA. Protein currently provides about 14 to 15 percent of the energy for adults in the United States.[17]

Adults

For adults, the RDA for protein intake is 0.8 gram per kilogram of body weight.[18] In clinical situations that require precise assessments, ideal body weight (rather than actual body weight) is typically used to determine protein needs. The RDA for adults translates into a daily protein recommendation of 56 grams for the average adult male and 46 grams for the average adult female aged 19 to 24. When calculated as a percentage of average energy intake, the protein RDA for adults provides about 8 to 11 percent of energy intake.

THINK About It 3

Convert weight to kg (pounds ÷ 2.2) Multiply kg by 0.8 = Protein RDA in g

Male, 19–24 years old, 70 kg (154 lb)
70 kg × 0.8 g/kg = 56 g protein

Female, 19–24 years old, 57 kg (125 lb)
57 kg × 0.8 g/kg = 46 g protein

Other Life Stages

Infants have the highest protein needs relative to body weight of any time of life (see Table 6.2). Protein is needed to support rapid growth during infancy. The Adequate Intake (AI) value for infants 0 to 6 months of age is based on the protein content of human milk and the average milk consumption of breastfed babies. Protein requirements per kilogram body weight gradually fall throughout childhood and adolescence until a person reaches adulthood.

Both pregnancy and lactation (production of breast milk) increase a woman's need for protein. The RDA for pregnant and lactating women is 1.1 grams per kilogram. This is an increase of about 25 grams per day over the female RDA for protein. Most American women already consume more than enough protein to support pregnancy and lactation.

The RDA for protein for all adults, regardless of age, is set at 0.8 gram protein per kilogram body weight. There is evidence, however, that the RDA for people over the age of 50 may be greater than 0.8 g/kg/day. Evidence indicates that protein intake greater than the RDA can improve muscle mass, strength, and function in this population. Immune status, wound healing, blood pressure, and bone health may be improved by increasing protein intake above the RDA.[19] In addition, elderly people on average have less lean body mass to maintain than younger people, so the body becomes less efficient at digesting, absorbing, and using protein as it ages.[20] It appears that an intake of 1.5 grams protein per kilogram per day, or about 15 to 20 percent of total caloric intake, is a reasonable target for individuals older than 50 years in terms of health and function.[21]

Physical Stress

Severe physical stress can increase the body's need for protein. Infections, burns, fevers, and surgery all increase protein losses, and the diet must re-

Table 6.2 Protein AI or RDA for Infants, Children, and Teens

Age	Protein AI or RDA (g/kg body weight)
0–6 months	1.52
7–12 months	1.2
1 to 3 years	1.05
4 to 8 years	0.95
9 to 13 years	0.95
14 to 18 years	0.85

Source: Institute of Medicine, Food and Nutrition Board. *Dietary Reference Intakes for Energy, Carbohydrate, Fiber, Fat, Fatty Acids, Cholesterol, Protein, and Amino Acids.* Washington, DC: National Academies Press. Copyright 2002. Reprinted with permission from the National Academy of Sciences.

Figure 6.19 Protein sources.

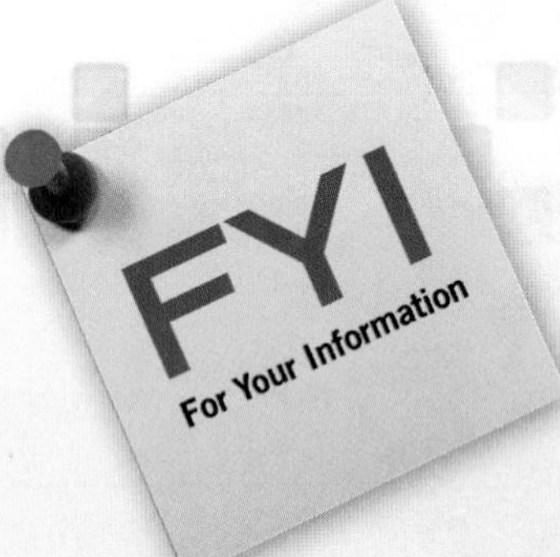

Quick Bite

Mother's Milk

Because it contains less protein than cow's milk, and in particular less casein protein, infants digest human milk more readily than cow's milk. Milks high in casein protein tend to form curds (clumps) in the stomach upon exposure to stomach acid. These tough curds are hard for digestive enzymes to break apart.

place that lost protein. A severe infection can increase protein requirements by one-third. Severe burns can increase requirements two to four times. Less severe physical stressors, such as a viral illness with a mild fever lasting only a few days, rarely increase protein requirements. Muscle-building activities, such as intense weight training, increase protein need much less than most people think. In fact, the typical American diet supplies an ample amount of protein for most people, even for bodybuilders. (See the FYI feature "Do Athletes Need More Protein?")

Protein Consumption

According to national survey data, the median daily intake of protein for adult males ranges from 71 to 101 grams. This is approximately 1.0 to 1.4 grams

FYI For Your Information

Do Athletes Need More Protein?

Athletes are not just pumping iron these days; they're also pumping protein supplements in hopes of building muscle and improving performance. Look inside many sports magazines and you'll see ads for protein or amino acid supplements targeted to athletes. You cannot force your body to build muscle by pumping in more protein than you need, any more than you can make your car run faster by adding more gas to a full tank. Extra protein does not build muscles; only regular workouts fueled by a mix of nutrients can achieve this goal.

Protein Requirements for Athletes

Many people assume that because muscle fibers are protein, building muscle must require protein. This is only partially true. The heavy resistance-type exercise that is needed to stimulate muscle growth must first be fueled by glucose and fatty acids (glucose will be the predominant fuel). People who regularly engage in low-intensity exercise do not need additional protein above the RDA of 0.8 gram per kilogram per day;[1] however, studies suggest that endurance athletes involved in heavy training require 1.2 to 1.4 grams of protein per kilogram of body weight per day.[2] Resistance-trained athletes may need as much as 1.6 to 1.7 grams per kg body weight.[3] Protein intake of 1.4 to 2.0 grams per kilogram per day for physically active individuals is not only safe, but also may improve adaptations to exercise training.[4]

Because Americans, on average, consume much more protein than they actually need, any increased need for athletes is most likely already being met. An athlete in training (let's make his weight 70 kilograms) might consume as many as 5,000 kilocalories per day. Even if his diet contained only 10 percent of calories as protein (the low side of the AMDR for protein, and lower than average), he would be getting about 126 grams of protein daily, about 1.8 grams per kilogram. It is unlikely that an athlete would not be able to meet his or her protein needs from a normal, mixed diet—especially one that follows the MyPlate food guidance system recommendations.

Risks of Supplements

Maybe there's no benefit to taking protein or amino acid supplements, but there's no harm either, right? Not necessarily. If excess protein means excess calories, it adds weight as fat, not muscle, which can slow down your performance. Purified protein supplements can contribute to calcium losses, thereby harming bone health. Excess protein means excess nitrogen that must be excreted, which poses a risk for dehydration if fluid intake is inadequate. Supplements of single amino acids can interfere with absorption of other amino acids and can alter neurotransmitter activity.

If you are a weekend athlete, there's no need to increase the protein in your diet, and no reason to expect that doing so will help your performance. If you are a competitive athlete, choosing adequate calories from a wide variety of foods will ensure an adequate protein intake. Supplements are unnecessary and expensive, and they may disrupt normal protein balance in the body. Play it safe; choose a healthful diet to fuel your exercise.

1 Carroll C. Protein and exercise. In: Dunford M, ed. *Sports Nutrition: A Practice Manual for Professionals*. 4th ed. Chicago: American Dietetic Association, 2006.

2 Lemon PW. Dietary protein requirements in athletes. *J Nutr Biochem*. 1997;8:52.

3 Gibala MJ. Dietary protein, amino acid supplements, and recovery from exercise. *GSSI Sports Science Exchange*. 2002;15(4):1–4.

4 Ibid.

per kilogram using a reference body weight of 70 kilograms. For females, the median protein intake is 55 to 62 grams per day, or 0.96 to 1.1 grams per kilogram using a reference body weight of 57 kilograms.[22] Generally speaking, Americans eat more protein than the adult RDA and more than the Daily Value, which is 50 grams per day.

Key Concepts *Infants, who are growing rapidly, have the highest protein needs relative to body weight. The recommended intakes (AIs or RDAs) decline from 1.52 grams per kilogram for infants 0 to 6 months old to 0.8 gram per kilogram for adults. Pregnancy, lactation, and severe physical stress all can alter protein requirements. Adults currently consume about 15 percent of their energy as protein, a level that provides ample protein for most people.*

Protein Quality

Although both animal and plant foods contain protein, the quality of protein in these foods differs. Foods that supply all the indispensable amino acids in the proportions needed by the body are called **complete**, or **high-quality**, **proteins**. Foods that lack adequate amounts of one or more indispensable amino acids are called **incomplete**, or **low-quality**, **proteins**.

When a variety of foods provides ample dietary protein, the protein quality of foods is not a primary dietary concern. But whenever protein or energy intake is marginal, or when only one or a few plant foods are the main protein sources in the diet, protein quality is a critical issue.

Complete Proteins

Animal foods generally provide complete protein; that is, they provide all the indispensable amino acids in approximately the right proportions. One exception is gelatin, a protein derived from animal collagen that lacks the indispensable amino acid tryptophan.

Red meats, poultry, fish, eggs, milk, and milk products (all animal foods) contain complete protein. More than 20 percent of these foods' energy content is protein. Protein provides about 80 percent of the energy in water-packed tuna. The protein isolated from soybeans also provides a complete, high-quality protein equal to that of animal protein.[23] Although soy protein contains a lower proportion of the amino acid cysteine than animal protein, the amount of soy typically consumed provides all the amino acids in sufficient amounts to meet the body's needs. Moreover, soybeans contain no cholesterol or saturated fat.

Americans, on the average, obtain about 63 percent of their protein intake from animal foods.[24] (See Table 6.3.) In other parts of the world, animal proteins play a smaller role. In Africa and East Asia, for example, animal foods provide only 20 percent of protein intake.[25]

Incomplete and Complementary Proteins

With the exception of soy protein, the protein in plant foods is incomplete; that is, it lacks one or more indispensable amino acids and does not match the body's amino acid needs as closely as animal foods do. Although the protein in one plant food may lack certain amino acids, the protein in another plant food may be a **complementary protein** that completes the amino acid pattern. So the protein of one plant food can provide the indispensable amino acid(s) that the other plant food is missing. Table 6.4 lists some examples of complementary food combinations.

complete (high-quality) proteins Proteins that supply all of the indispensable amino acids in the proportions the body needs.

incomplete (low-quality) proteins Proteins that lack one or more amino acids.

complementary protein An incomplete food protein whose assortment of amino acids makes up for, or complements, another food protein's lack of specific indispensable amino acids so that the combination of the two proteins provides sufficient amounts of all the indispensable amino acids.

Quick Bite

Paleolithic Protein

Didn't our ancestors eat a lot of meat, too? Researchers estimate that hunter/gatherer populations' diets were about one-third meat and two-thirds vegetable. The meat from wild game, however, averages only one-seventh the fat of domesticated beef (about 4 g of fat per 100 g of wild meat, compared with 29 g of fat per 100 g of domestic meat). In addition, compared with the meat at your local supermarket, the fat contained in game animals that graze on the free range has five times as much polyunsaturated fat.

Table 6.3 **Top Ten Sources of Protein in the United States**

Rank	Food	% of Protein Contributed
1	Beef	18
2	Poultry	14
3	Milk	9
4	Yeast bread	7
5	Cheese	6
6	Fish/shellfish*	4
7	Eggs	3
8	Pork, fresh	3
9	Ham	3
10	Pasta	2

* Does not include tuna.

Source: US Department of Agriculture. 1989–1991 Continuing Survey of Food Intake by Individuals.

For example, grain products such as pasta are low in the indispensable amino acid lysine but high in the indispensable amino acids methionine and cysteine. Legumes such as kidney beans are low in methionine and cysteine but high in lysine. In a dish that combines these foods, such as a pasta–kidney bean salad, the protein from pasta complements the protein from kidney beans, so together they provide a complete protein. Generally, when you combine grains with legumes, or legumes with nuts or seeds, you will get complete, high-quality protein.

Small amounts of animal foods can also complement the protein in plant foods. For example, Asians often flavor rice with small amounts of beef, chicken, or fish, complementing the protein in the rice. Americans eat breakfast cereal with milk, which complements the protein in the cereal.

Protein complementation is important only for people who consume little to no animal proteins. For these people, eating a wide variety of plant protein sources is the key to obtaining adequate amounts of all the indispensable amino acids. When protein and energy intake are adequate, there is no need to plan complementary proteins at each meal.[26] Complementary proteins may still need to be combined in the same meal for very young children.[27]

Boosting your intake of plant protein foods can provide benefits. High-protein plant foods are usually rich in vitamins, minerals, and dietary fiber. Plant foods contain no cholesterol and little fat, and they usually cost less than animal foods high in protein. Lentil loaf, for example, is substantially cheaper to make than meat loaf.

Table 6.4 **Examples of Complementary Food Combinations**

- Beans and rice
- Beans and corn or wheat tortillas
- Rice and lentils
- Rice and black-eyed peas
- Pea soup with bread or crackers
- Garbanzo beans (chickpeas) with sesame paste
- Pasta with beans
- Peanut butter on bread

Evaluating Protein Quality

A high-quality protein (1) provides all the indispensable amino acids in the amounts the body needs, (2) provides enough other amino acids to serve as nitrogen sources for synthesis of dispensable amino acids, and (3) is easy to digest. If a food protein contains the right proportion of amino acids but cannot be digested and absorbed, it is useless to the body. We can measure protein quality in many ways, but any assessment of protein quality requires, at the least, information about the amino acid composition of the food protein. Protein quality might be assessed to plan a special diet or develop a new product such as infant formula.

Chemical, or Amino Acid, Scoring

A simple way to determine a food's protein quality is to compare its amino acid composition to that of a reference pattern of amino acids. This method is referred to as **chemical scoring**, or **amino acid scoring**. The amino acid composition of the reference pattern closely reflects the amounts and proportions of amino acids that humans need. The Food and Nutrition Board has proposed an amino acid scoring pattern that uses the pattern of amino acids required by children aged 1 to 3 years.[28] If a protein meets the amino acid needs of growing preschool-aged children, then it should also meet the needs of almost all other segments of the population.

For each of the nine indispensable amino acids, researchers take the number of milligrams of the amino acid in one gram of food and divide it by the number of milligrams of that amino acid in the reference pattern. The result is multiplied by 100 to convert the figure to a percentage. For example, if a food contains only 65 percent of the lysine in the reference, the chemical score for the amino acid lysine is 65. The amino acid with the lowest score is the **limiting amino acid** (the amino acid present in the smallest amount relative to biological need). The chemical score of the food protein is the score of its limiting amino acid.

$$\text{chemical score}^{*} = \frac{\text{mg of the essential amino acid in 1 g of test protein}}{\text{mg of the essential amino acid in 1 g of reference protein}}$$

*For a percent value, multiply this result by 100.

Protein Efficiency Ratio

The **protein efficiency ratio (PER)** measures amino acid composition *and* accounts for digestibility. Researchers compare the weight gain of growing animals fed a test protein with the weight gain of growing animals fed a high-quality reference protein (e.g., casein, the main protein in cow's milk). Thus, this method measures how well the body can use the test protein, which reflects amino acid composition, digestibility, and availability. The PER is used to determine the protein quality of infant formulas.

$$\text{protein efficiency ratio (PER)} = \frac{\text{weight gain in grams}}{\text{protein intake in grams}}$$

Net Protein Utilization

Net protein utilization (NPU) measures how much dietary protein the body actually uses. Scientists carefully measure the nitrogen content of a test food, and then give the food to laboratory animals as their sole protein source. They then measure the animals' nitrogen excretion to determine how much of the food's nitrogen content was retained. The more nitrogen the animal retains from a food, the higher the protein quality of that food—that is, the more efficiently the animal was able to use the food protein to make body proteins.

$$\text{net protein utilization (NPU)} = \frac{\text{nitrogen retained}}{\text{nitrogen intake}} \times 100$$

Biological Value

The **biological value (BV)** method determines how much of the nitrogen absorbed from a particular food protein is retained by the body for growth and/or maintenance. Because nitrogen retention is a function of absorption (if it's not absorbed, it can't be retained), measuring nitrogen absorption is a key element of this method. In general, if a protein has an indispensable amino acid composition similar to our needs, it will be more efficiently retained by the body.

Determining biological value is a tedious process because the key measures of urinary and fecal nitrogen output must be measured while subjects (human or animal) are consuming the test protein and again while they are on a nitrogen-free diet. The final value expresses nitrogen retention as a percentage of nitrogen absorption. Egg protein has a biological value of 100.

$$\text{biological value (BV)} = \frac{\text{nitrogen retained}}{\text{nitrogen absorbed}} \times 100$$

This means that all the absorbed egg protein is retained by growing laboratory animals (100 percent). The biological value of the protein in corn is 60, meaning only 60 percent of the absorbed corn protein (and not all of it is absorbed) is retained for use by the body.

Protein Digestibility Corrected Amino Acid Score

PDCAAS =

chemical score × % digestibility of the protein

The **protein digestibility corrected amino acid score (PDCAAS)** accounts for both the amino acid composition of a food and the digestibility of the protein. The first step in determining the PDCAAS is the same as that used to determine the chemical score—divide the amount of the limiting amino acid by the amount of the same amino acid in the reference pattern. Then, instead of multiplying by 100 to get a percentage, multiply by the percentage of digestible food protein. This will produce a score between 0 and 1. Egg protein provides all the amino acids that preschool children need (the reference standard) and is fully digested, so it has a PDCAAS of 1.0.

Thus, if a protein food has a chemical score of 0.70 based on its limiting amino acid, and 80 percent of the protein in that food is digestible, the PDCAAS score would be 80 percent of 0.70, or 0.56. The PDCAAS value of isolated soybean protein is 0.99. The scores for beef, canned garbanzo beans (chickpeas), and whole wheat are 0.92, 0.66, and 0.40, respectively.

The U.S. Food and Drug Administration (FDA) recognizes the PDCAAS as the official method for determining the protein quality of most food.[29] If the %DV for protein is listed on a food label, it must be based on the food's PDCAAS. It would be misleading to say that, for example, 8 grams of protein from tuna and 8 grams of protein from kidney beans would contribute equally to amino acid needs. Consequently, even though the number of grams of protein per serving might be the same, the %DV would be different for these two foods. For baby foods and infant formulas, the PER method is used to determine protein quality.

chemical scoring A method to determine the protein quality of a food by comparing its amino acid composition with that of a reference protein. Also called amino acid scoring.

amino acid scoring A method to determine the protein quality of a food by comparing its amino acid composition with that of a reference protein. Also called chemical scoring.

limiting amino acid The amino acid in shortest supply during protein synthesis. Also the amino acid in the lowest quantity when evaluating protein quality.

protein efficiency ratio (PER) Protein quality calculated by comparing the weight gain of growing animals fed a test protein with growing animals fed a high-quality reference protein. It depends on both the digestibility and the amino acid composition of a protein.

net protein utilization (NPU) Percentage of ingested protein nitrogen retained by the body. It measures the amount of dietary protein the body uses.

biological value (BV) The extent to which protein in a food can be incorporated into body proteins. BV is expressed as the percentage of the absorbed dietary nitrogen retained by the body.

protein digestibility corrected amino acid score (PDCAAS) A measure of protein quality that takes into account the amino acid composition of the food and the digestibility of the protein. It is calculated by multiplying the amino acid score by the percentage of the digestible food protein.

Key Concepts *In general, animal foods provide complete protein that contains the right mix of all the indispensable amino acids. With the exception of soybean protein, plant foods contain incomplete protein—that is, proteins lacking in one or more amino acids. Plant foods can be combined to complement each other's amino acid patterns. Researchers use many methods to determine protein quality, including chemical analysis of amino acid content and biological measures of the protein's digestibility, its retention in the body, or its ability to support growth.*

Estimating Your Protein Intake

By this time, you may be wondering how much protein you consume in a typical day. To be accurate, you would need an inconvenient and expensive chemical analysis of your food intake. Instead, you can estimate your protein intake using more readily available information. First, food labels list the quantity of protein (in grams) in a serving of food. If you have a label for every food you consume, just add up the grams.

Another way to estimate your protein intake is to use the Exchange Lists found in Figure 2.6 and Appendix B. In the Exchange Lists, one starch exchange provides an average of 3 grams of protein, one milk exchange provides 8 grams, one vegetable exchange provides 2 grams, and one meat exchange provides 7 grams. Fruit and fat exchanges contribute 0 grams of protein. You can also use food composition tables or computer software to calculate your protein intake.

As a reference point, if you consume the minimum number of servings recommended in MyPlate (see Chapter 2), you will get an ample amount of protein—more than enough to meet most people's protein needs.

protein hydrolysates Proteins that have been treated with acid or enzymes to break them down into amino acids and polypeptides.

Proteins and Amino Acids as Additives and Supplements

Proteins contribute to the structure, texture, and taste of food. They are often added to foods to enhance these properties. The milk protein casein is added to frozen dessert toppings. Gelatin is added to yogurt and fillings. **Protein hydrolysates**—proteins that have been broken down into amino acids and polypeptides—are added to many foods as thickeners, stabilizers, or flavor enhancers.

Amino acids are also used as additives. Monosodium glutamate (sodium bound to the amino acid glutamic acid) is a flavor enhancer added to many foods. The artificial sweetener aspartame is a dipeptide composed of aspartic acid and phenylalanine.

Protein and amino acid supplements are sold to dieters, athletes, and people who suffer from certain diseases. Despite a lack of scientific evidence, some people buy the amino acid lysine for cold sores and the amino acid tryptophan in the hope that it will relieve pain, depression, and sleep disorders. A number of protein powders and amino acid cocktails are marketed with the claims that they enhance muscle building and exercise performance. Although the anecdotal evidence (stories from friends and health food store clerks) for these products may be convincing, few scientific studies back up these claims. Remember, muscle work builds muscle strength and size, and muscles prefer carbohydrate to fuel this type of work.

There are no documented health benefits from consuming large amounts of individual amino acids, and the risks are unknown. An excess of a single amino acid in the digestive tract can impair absorption of other amino acids that use the same carrier for absorption, which could cause a deficiency of one or more amino acids and an unhealthy excess of the supplemented amino acid.

Key Concepts *You can use food labels to estimate your protein intake. Eating a diet that follows MyPlate will supply adequate amounts of protein. Supplements of protein or amino acids are rarely necessary and might be harmful.*

Vegetarian Diets

What did Socrates, Plato, Albert Einstein, Leonardo da Vinci, William Shakespeare, Charles Darwin, and Mahatma Gandhi have in common? They all advocated a vegetarian lifestyle.[30] George Bernard Shaw, vegetarian, famous writer, and political analyst of the early 1900s, wrote, "A man fed on whiskey and dead bodies cannot do the finest work of which he is capable."[31]

Meat-eaters often contend that vegetarian diets do not provide enough protein and other essential nutrients, but this is not necessarily the case. With careful planning, a diet that contains no animal products can be nutritionally complete and offer many health benefits. Poorly planned vegetarian diets, however, can pose health risks.

Why People Become Vegetarians

In parts of the world where food is scarce, vegetarianism is not a choice but a necessity. Where food is abundant, people choose vegetarianism for many

Table 6.5 Religious Groups with Vegetarian Dietary Practices

Religious Group	Dietary Practices
Buddhism	Some sects lacto-vegetarian, other sects vegan
Hinduism	Generally lacto-vegetarian, but mutton or pork eaten occasionally
Seventh-Day Adventists	Lacto-ovo-vegetarian emphasizing whole-grain foods. Also avoid alcohol, tobacco, and caffeine

reasons. People may choose a vegetarian diet because of religious beliefs, concern for the environment, a desire to reduce world hunger and make better use of scarce resources, an aversion to eating another living creature, or concerns about cruelty to animals. Still others become vegetarians because they believe it is healthier for them. Table 6.5 shows three religious groups and their vegetarian practices. Today, about 3 to 4 percent of Americans consider themselves vegetarians.[32]

THINK About It 4

Types of Vegetarians

Although all vegetarians share the common practice of not eating meat and meat products, they differ greatly in specific dietary practices. Lacto-ovo-vegetarians use animal products such as milk, cheese, and eggs, but abstain from eating the flesh of animals. Vegans eat no animal-based foods and usually avoid products such as cosmetics made with animal-based ingredients. Fruitarians eat only raw fruit, nuts, and green foliage.

Some people eat a semi-vegetarian diet, avoiding red meats but eating small amounts of chicken or fish. The Mediterranean diet, known for reducing the risk of heart disease, is a semi-vegetarian diet rich in grains, pasta, vegetables, cheeses, and olive oil supplemented with small amounts of chicken and fish. Table 6.6 lists the types of vegetarian diets and the foods typically included and excluded.

Table 6.6 Types of Vegetarian Diets

Type	Animal Foods Included	Foods Excluded
Semi-vegetarian	Dairy products, eggs, chicken, fish	Red meats (beef, pork)
Pesco-vegetarian	Dairy products, eggs, and fish	Beef, pork, poultry
Lacto-ovo-vegetarian	Dairy products, eggs	Any animal flesh
Lacto-vegetarian	Dairy products	Eggs, all animal flesh
Ovo-vegetarian	Eggs	Dairy products and animal flesh
Vegan	None	All animal products
Fruitarian	None	All foods except raw fruits, nuts, and green foliage

Zen macrobiotic diets are mostly vegan and stress whole grains, locally grown vegetables, beans, sea vegetables, and soups. Extreme Zen macrobiotic diets can be very limited, such as a diet of primarily brown rice.

Health Benefits of Vegetarian Diets

Vegetarian diets usually contain less fat, saturated fat, and cholesterol and more magnesium and folate than nonvegetarian diets.[33] Vegetarian diets that emphasize fresh fruits and vegetables contain higher amounts of antioxidants such as beta-carotene and vitamins C and E, which protect the body from cell and tissue damage. Fruits and vegetables also contain dietary fiber and phytochemicals—substances that are not essential in the diet but that can have important health effects.

On average, vegetarians have lower blood cholesterol levels and are less likely to develop heart disease than nonvegetarians. Vegetarian diets low in fat and saturated fat combined with other healthy lifestyle habits can reverse the clogging of arteries that eventually can lead to heart attack or stroke.[34]

Vegetarians usually weigh less for their height than nonvegetarians, partly because their diets provide less energy and partly because of other healthful lifestyle factors such as regular exercise. Some studies have shown that hypertension occurs less frequently among vegetarians than among nonvegetarians, regardless of body weight or sodium intake.

Vegetarians, especially vegans, have lower rates of cancer than nonvegetarians, particularly prostate and colorectal cancer.[35] Vegetarian diets generally include more fruits, vegetables, phytochemicals, and fiber, and less fat. Intake of red meat has been linked to a higher risk of colorectal cancer.

Health Risks of Vegetarian Diets

Although vegetarian diets offer many health benefits, certain types of vegetarian diets pose some unique nutritional risks. The more limited the vegetarian diet, the more likely are nutritional problems. Lacto-ovo-vegetarian diets that contain a variety of foods generally are nutritionally adequate but can be high in fat and cholesterol. Iron content may be low if the diet contains large amounts of milk products.

Vegan diets tend to be low in zinc, calcium, vitamin D, riboflavin, and vitamin B_{12}. The best sources of these nutrients are animal foods—red meat for zinc; milk for calcium, vitamin D, and riboflavin; and any animal foods for B_{12}. Because plant foods contain a form of iron called nonheme iron that is not as well absorbed as the heme iron in animal foods, vegetarians need to include more iron in their diets. Vitamin C and other compounds in fruits and vegetables aid iron absorption in the body.

Vegans tend to have higher intakes of phytates (found in whole grains, bran, and soy products), oxalates (found in spinach, rhubarb, and chocolate), and tannins (found in tea). These compounds can bind minerals, making them less available to the body for absorption. Very limited vegan diets, such as fruitarian diets or extreme Zen macrobiotic diets, pose the greatest nutritional risks. These diets are likely to be deficient in many essential nutrients.

Although vegetarian diets may be adequate for most people, vegetarian diets must be planned carefully for periods of rapid growth, such as for infants and young children and for women who are pregnant or breastfeeding.

Dietary Recommendations for Vegetarians

Dietitians from the United States and Canada have developed a food guide for use in planning vegetarian diets.[36] This food guide includes the following

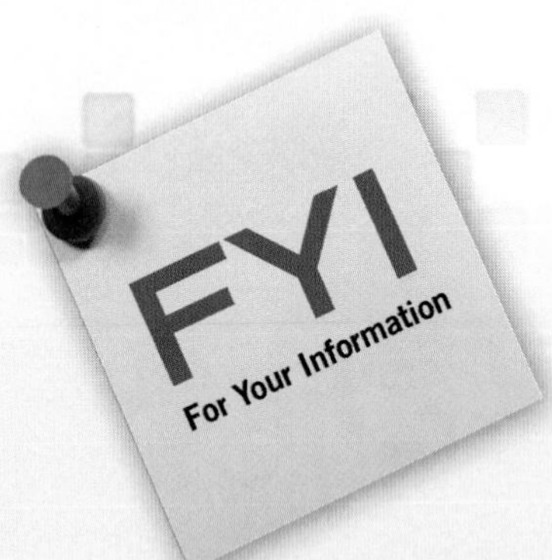

High-Protein Plant Foods

Of the top 10 sources of protein in the American diet, only two sources—yeast breads and pasta—are plant-based (see Table 6.3). Lentils, a dense source of plant protein, don't even make the list. Yet look at the comparison between the nutritional profile of lentils and the profile of beef in **Table 1**.

When we consider these two foods in light of the *Dietary Guidelines for Americans* (see Chapter 2), it's no contest. To reduce fat, saturated fat, and cholesterol while increasing fiber, the lentils win hands down! With all that lentils have going for them, you'd think more Americans would be eating them. Yet dried beans, peas, and lentils combined contribute less than 1 percent of the daily protein intake of Americans, while beef contributes 17.7 percent.

High-protein plant foods also contribute complex carbohydrates, dietary fiber, and vitamins and minerals to the diet. Since these plant foods contain little fat, they are nutrient dense; that is, they provide a high amount of protein and nutrients relative to their energy contribution.

Sources of Plant Protein

Grains and grain products, legumes (lentils and dried beans and peas such as kidney beans or chickpeas), starchy vegetables, and nuts and seeds all provide protein (**Table 2**). A serving of a grain product or starchy vegetable provides an average of about 5 grams of protein, a serving of legumes provides 10 to 20 grams of protein, and a serving of vegetables provides about 3 grams of protein. Although a serving of these foods contains less protein than a serving of meat, you can eat more plant protein foods for fewer calories.

Complementing Plant Proteins

It's important to remember that plant proteins lack one or more of the indispensable amino acids needed to build body proteins, so individual plant proteins need to complement each other. A simple rule to remember in complementing plant proteins is that combining grains and legumes or combining legumes and nuts or seeds provides complete, high-quality protein.

Soy Protein

The protein in soybeans is a notable exception to the rule that most plant proteins are incomplete. Soy provides complete, high-quality protein comparable to that in animal foods. In addition, soybeans provide no saturated fat or cholesterol, and are rich in isoflavonoids—phytochemicals that help reduce risk of heart disease and cancer and improve bone health.

Isoflavonoids act as antioxidants, protecting cells and tissues from damage. One specific isoflavonoid, genistein, inhibits growth of both breast and prostate cancer cells in the laboratory. Isoflavonoids protect LDL cholesterol (the kind of cholesterol associated with greater risk of heart disease) from oxidation. Oxidized LDL cholesterol contributes to the plaque buildup in arteries. The isoflavones in soybeans also act as phytoestrogens, helping to protect older women from cardiovascular disease and osteoporosis. Soy foods that contain most or all of the bean, such as soy milk, sprouts, flour, and tofu, are the best sources of these phytochemicals.

It is easy to incorporate a variety of soy foods into your diet. Tofu, tempeh, ground soy, soy milk, soy flour, and textured soy protein are soy-based products that can be included in many meals and snacks (**Table 3**).

The nutritional benefits of plant protein sources such as soy foods and other legumes, grains, and vegetables deserve a closer look. Most Americans would benefit from emphasizing plant protein foods in their diet. The next time you plan to make meat loaf, make lentil loaf instead.

Table 1 **How Do Lentils Stack Up Against Beef?**

	Cooked Lentils	Lean, Broiled Sirloin
Amount	1 cup	5 ounces
Energy	230 kcal	260 kcal
Protein	18 grams	43 grams
Fat	<1 gram	8 grams
Cholesterol	0	82 milligrams
Carbohydrate	40 grams	0
Dietary fiber	16 grams	0
Percent calories from fat	3%	28%

Source: US Department of Agriculture, Agricultural Research Service. USDA National Nutrient Database for Standard Reference, Release 18. 2005. http://fnic.nal.usda.gov/nal_display/index.php?info_center=4&tax_level=1. Accessed 5/21/09.

Table 2 **Plant Sources of Protein**

Plant Protein Source	Grams of Protein	Kilocalories
Grain Products		
1 oat bran bagel (3 in.)	6	145
1 whole English muffin, mixed grain	6	155
1 large flour tortilla (10 in.)	6	218
1 cup cooked spaghetti	8	221
1 cup cooked brown rice	5	216
1 cup cooked oatmeal	6	147
2 slices whole-wheat bread	5	138
½ cup low-fat granola	5	209
Starchy Vegetables		
1 cup cooked corn	5	177
1 cup baked winter squash	5	102
1 medium baked potato with skin	3	145
Legumes		
½ cup tofu	10	94
1 cup cooked lentils	18	230
1 cup cooked kidney beans	16	219
Vegetables		
1 cup cooked broccoli	4	55
1 cup cooked cauliflower	2	29
1 cup cooked Brussels sprouts	4	56
Nuts and Seeds		
2 tablespoons peanut butter	8	188
¼ cup peanuts	10	216
¼ cup sunflower seeds	7	200

Source: US Department of Agriculture, Agricultural Research Service. USDA National Nutrient Database for Standard Reference, Release 18. 2005. http://www.nal.usda.gov/fnic/foodcompindex.html. Accessed 5/21/09.

Table 3 **Soy Food Products and Uses**

Tofu A solid cake of curdled soy milk similar to soft cheese. Tofu comes in hard and soft varieties. It absorbs the flavors of the foods it is mixed with. Soft tofu can be substituted for cheese in pasta dishes, stuffed in large shell pasta, blended with fruit, or used to make pie filling. Hard tofu can be used in salads, shish-ka-bobs, and in place of meat in stir-fry or mixed dishes.

Tempeh Tempeh is a flat cake made from fermented soybeans. It has a mild flavor and chewy texture. Tempeh can be grilled, included in sandwiches, or combined in casseroles.

Meat Analogues Meat analogues are meat alternatives made primarily of soy protein. Flavored and textured to resemble chicken, beef, and pork, they can be substituted for meat in mixed dishes, pizza, tacos, or sloppy joes.

Soy Milk Soy milk is the liquid of the soybean. It comes in regular and low-fat versions and in different flavors. Soy milk can be used plain or substituted for regular milk on cereals, in hot cocoa, puddings, or desserts.

Soy Flour Soy flour is made from roasted soybeans ground into flour. Soy flour can replace up to one-quarter of the regular flour in a recipe.

Textured Soy Protein Textured soy protein resembles ground beef. It can be rehydrated and substituted for ground beef in any recipe.

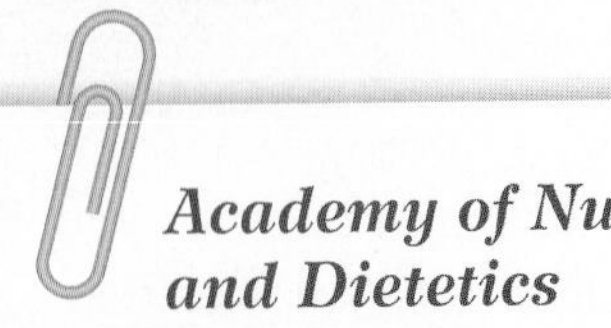

Academy of Nutrition and Dietetics

Vegetarian Diets

It is the position of the Academy of Nutrition and Dietetics and Dietitians of Canada that appropriately planned vegetarian diets are healthful, nutritionally adequate, and provide health benefits in the prevention and treatment of certain diseases.

Source: Position of the American Dietetic Association and Dietitians of Canada: vegetarian diets. *J Am Diet Assoc.* 2003;103:748–765. Copyright 2003. Reprinted with permission from Elsevier.

food groups: grains, vegetables and fruits, legumes, nuts and other protein-rich foods, fats, and calcium-rich foods. Vegetarians who include milk, milk products, and eggs in their diet can easily meet their nutritional needs for protein and other essential nutrients but must take care to choose low-fat milk products and limit eggs to avoid excess saturated fat and cholesterol.

Since grains, vegetables, and legumes (dried beans and peas) all provide protein, vegans who eat a variety of foods also can meet their protein needs easily. Although most plant foods do not contain complete protein, eating complementary plant protein sources during the same day adequately meets the body's needs for protein production.

Vegans who avoid all animal products must supplement their diets with a reliable source of vitamin B_{12}, such as fortified soy milk. Although bacteria in some fermented foods and in the knobby growths of some seaweeds produce vitamin B_{12}, most vegans do not eat enough seaweeds and fermented foods to meet their vitamin B_{12} needs. Vegans also need a dietary source of vitamin D when sun exposure is limited.

The Academy of Nutrition and Dietetics and Dietitians of Canada provide the following nutritional guidelines for vegetarians:[37]

1. Choose a variety of foods, including whole grains, vegetables, fruits, legumes, nuts, seeds, and, if desired, dairy products and eggs.
2. Choose whole, unrefined foods often and minimize intake of highly sweetened, fatty, and heavily refined foods.
3. Choose a variety of fruits and vegetables.
4. If animal foods such as dairy products and eggs are used, choose lower-fat dairy products and use both eggs and dairy products in moderation.
5. Use a regular source of vitamin B_{12} and, if sun exposure is limited, of vitamin D.

Key Concepts *Vegetarian diets eliminate animal products to various degrees. Lacto-ovo-vegetarians include milk and eggs in their diets, whereas vegans eat no animal foods. Vegetarian diets tend to be low in fat and high in fiber and phytochemicals, which may help reduce chronic disease risks. Careful diet planning is necessary for vegans and growing children to ensure that all nutrient needs are met.*

American Heart Association

High-Protein Diets

The American Heart Association doesn't recommend high-protein diets for weight loss. Some of these diets restrict healthful foods that provide essential nutrients and don't provide the variety of foods needed to adequately meet nutritional needs. People who stay on these diets very long may not get enough vitamins and minerals and face other potential health risks.

Source: American Heart Association, Inc.

The Health Effects of Too Little or Too Much Protein

Because protein plays such a vital role in so many body processes, protein deficiency can wreak havoc in numerous body systems. A lack of available protein means insufficient amounts of indispensable amino acids, which stops the synthesis of body proteins.

Protein deficiency occurs when energy and/or protein intake is inadequate. Adequate energy intake spares dietary and body proteins so they can be used for protein synthesis. Without adequate energy intake, the body burns dietary protein for energy rather than using it to make body proteins. Protein deficiency can occur even in people who eat seemingly adequate amounts of protein if the protein they eat is of poor quality or cannot be absorbed.

Although protein deficiency is widespread in poverty-stricken communities and in some nonindustrialized countries, most people in industrialized countries face the opposite problem—protein excess. Although the RDA for a 70-kilogram (154-pound) person is 56 grams, the average American man consumes approximately 100 grams of protein daily, and the average woman about 70 grams. Many meat-loving Americans eat far more protein.

Some research suggests that high protein intake contributes to risk for heart disease, cancer, and osteoporosis. However, because high protein intake often goes hand-in-hand with high intakes of saturated fat and cholesterol, the independent effects of high protein intake are difficult to determine.

Protein-Energy Malnutrition

A deficiency of protein, energy, or both in the diet is called **protein-energy malnutrition (PEM)**. Protein and energy intake are difficult to separate because diets adequate in energy usually are adequate in protein, and diets inadequate in energy inhibit the body's use of dietary protein for protein synthesis.

Although it can occur at all stages of life, PEM is most common during childhood, when protein is needed to support rapid growth. PEM affects every fourth child worldwide and is a factor in more than half of the 104 million annual deaths of children younger than age 5.[38] PEM symptoms can be mild or severe and exist in either acute or chronic forms.

Protein-energy malnutrition occurs in all parts of the world but is most common in Africa, South and Central America, East and Southeast Asia, and the Middle East. In industrialized countries, PEM occurs most often in populations living in poverty, in the elderly, and in hospitalized patients with other conditions such as anorexia nervosa, AIDS, cancer, or malabsorption syndromes.[39]

There are two forms of severe PEM: **kwashiorkor** and **marasmus**. Sometimes people have symptoms of both. Researchers do not understand fully why PEM causes symptoms of kwashiorkor in some people and symptoms of marasmus in others.[40] Historically, kwashiorkor was thought to result from inadequate intake of protein but adequate intake of energy. Marasmus was thought to result from inadequate intake of both protein and energy. Now researchers know that the lines between these two diseases are not so clear and that protein deficiency rarely develops with adequate energy intake.

Researchers believe that kwashiorkor develops from acute PEM, whereas marasmus develops from chronic PEM. Some researchers also believe that kwashiorkor is an abnormal adaptation to PEM, whereas marasmus is a normal adaptation. Other factors, such as infections or toxins in the diet, may trigger the development of kwashiorkor rather than marasmus.[41] See **Figure 6.20** for the signs and symptoms of kwashiorkor and marasmus.

Kwashiorkor

The term *kwashiorkor* is a Ghanian word that describes the "evil spirit that infects the first child when the second child is born." In many cultures, babies are breastfed until the next baby comes along. When the new baby arrives, the first baby is weaned from nutritious breast milk and placed on a watered-down version of the family's diet. In areas of poverty, this diet is often low in protein, or the consumed protein is not digested and absorbed easily.

One symptom of kwashiorkor that sets it apart from marasmus is edema, or swelling of body tissue, usually in the feet and legs. Lack of blood proteins reduces the force that keeps fluid in the bloodstream, allowing fluid to leak out into the tissues. Because proteins are unavailable to transport fat, it accumulates in the liver. Combined with edema, this accumulation produces a bloated belly. Other features of kwashiorkor include stunted weight and

protein-energy malnutrition (PEM) A condition resulting from long-term inadequate intakes of energy and protein that can lead to wasting of body tissues and increased susceptibility to infection.

kwashiorkor A type of malnutrition that occurs primarily in young children who have an infectious disease and whose diets supply marginal amounts of energy and very little protein. Common symptoms include poor growth, edema, apathy, weakness, and susceptibility to infections.

marasmus A type of malnutrition resulting from chronic inadequate consumption of protein and energy that is characterized by wasting of muscle, fat, and other body tissue.

Quick Bite

The Source of Salisbury Steak

Dr. James Salisbury, a London physician who lived in the late 1800s, believed man to be two-thirds carnivorous and one-third herbivorous. He recommended a diet low in starch and high in lean meat, with lots of hot water to rinse out the products of fermentation. His diet regimen included broiled, lean, minced beef three times a day. Although we call it Salisbury steak as a courtesy to Dr. Salisbury's heritage, minced beef patties are really more like hamburgers.

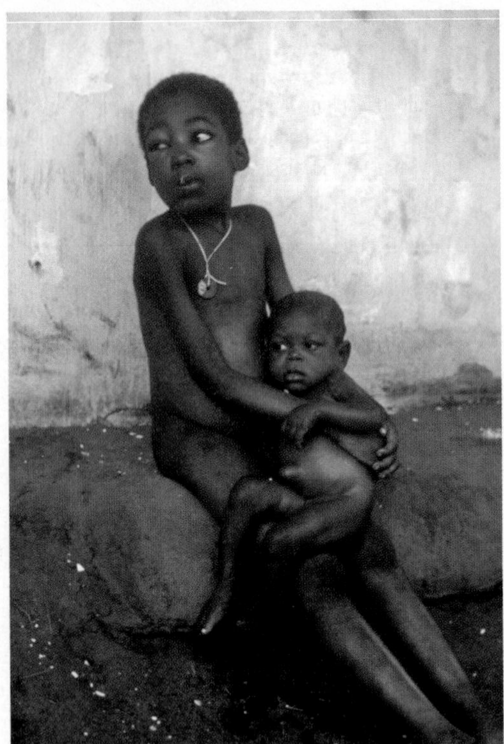

(a)

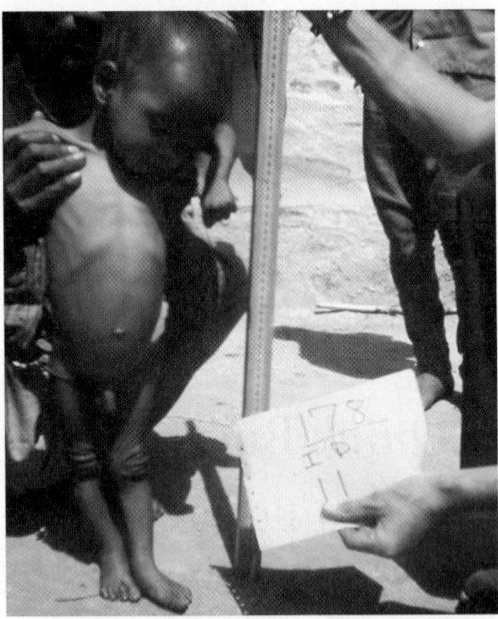

(b)

Figure 6.20 **Kwashiorkor and marasmus.** (a) Edema in the feet and legs and a bloated belly are symptoms of kwashiorkor. (b) Children with marasmus are short and thin for their age and can appear frail and wrinkled.

height; increased susceptibility to infection; dry, flaky skin, and sometimes skin sores; dry, brittle, and unnaturally blond hair; and changes in skin color. Because the energy deficit is usually not as severe (or as longstanding) in kwashiorkor as in marasmus, people with kwashiorkor may still have some body fat stores left.

Kwashiorkor usually develops in children between 18 and 24 months of age, about the time weaning occurs. Its onset can be rapid and is often triggered by an infection or illness that increases the child's protein needs. In hospital settings, kwashiorkor can develop in situations where protein needs are extremely high (e.g., trauma, infection, burns) but dietary intake is poor.

Marasmus

Marasmus is derived from the Greek word *marasmos*, which means "withering" or "to waste away." The condition develops more slowly than kwashiorkor and results from chronic PEM. Protein, energy, and nutrient intake are all grossly inadequate, depleting body fat reserves and severely wasting muscle tissue, including vital organs such as the heart. Growth slows or stops, and children are both short and very thin for their age. Metabolism slows and body temperature drops as the body tries to conserve energy. Children with marasmus are apathetic, often not even crying in an effort to conserve energy. Their hair is sparse and falls out easily. Because muscle and fat are used up, a child with marasmus often looks like a frail, wrinkled, elderly person.

Marasmus occurs most often in infants and children aged 6 to 18 months who are fed diluted or improperly mixed formulas. Because this is a time of rapid brain growth, marasmus can permanently stunt brain development and lead to learning disabilities. Marasmus also occurs in adults during cancer and starvation, including the self-imposed starvation of the eating disorder known as anorexia nervosa.

Nutritional Rehabilitation

To recover, people with PEM need gradual and careful refeeding to correct protein, energy, fluid, and vitamin and mineral imbalances.[42] People with PEM are often dehydrated and have low body potassium stores as a result of diarrhea. These imbalances in fluids and electrolytes are corrected first to raise blood pressure and strengthen the heart. Once these imbalances have been corrected, the patient receives protein and other nutrients in small amounts that are gradually increased as tolerated.

Excess Dietary Protein

In industrialized countries, an excess of protein and energy is more common than a deficiency. Generally, self-selected diets do not contain more than 40 percent of calories from protein.[43] Although high protein intake has been suggested to contribute to kidney problems, osteoporosis, heart disease, and cancer (see **Figure 6.21**), the Food and Nutrition Board did not find the evidence supporting these links to be strong enough to set a UL for protein.[44]

Kidney Function

Since the kidneys must excrete the products of protein breakdown, high protein intake can strain kidney function and is especially harmful for people with kidney disease or diabetes.

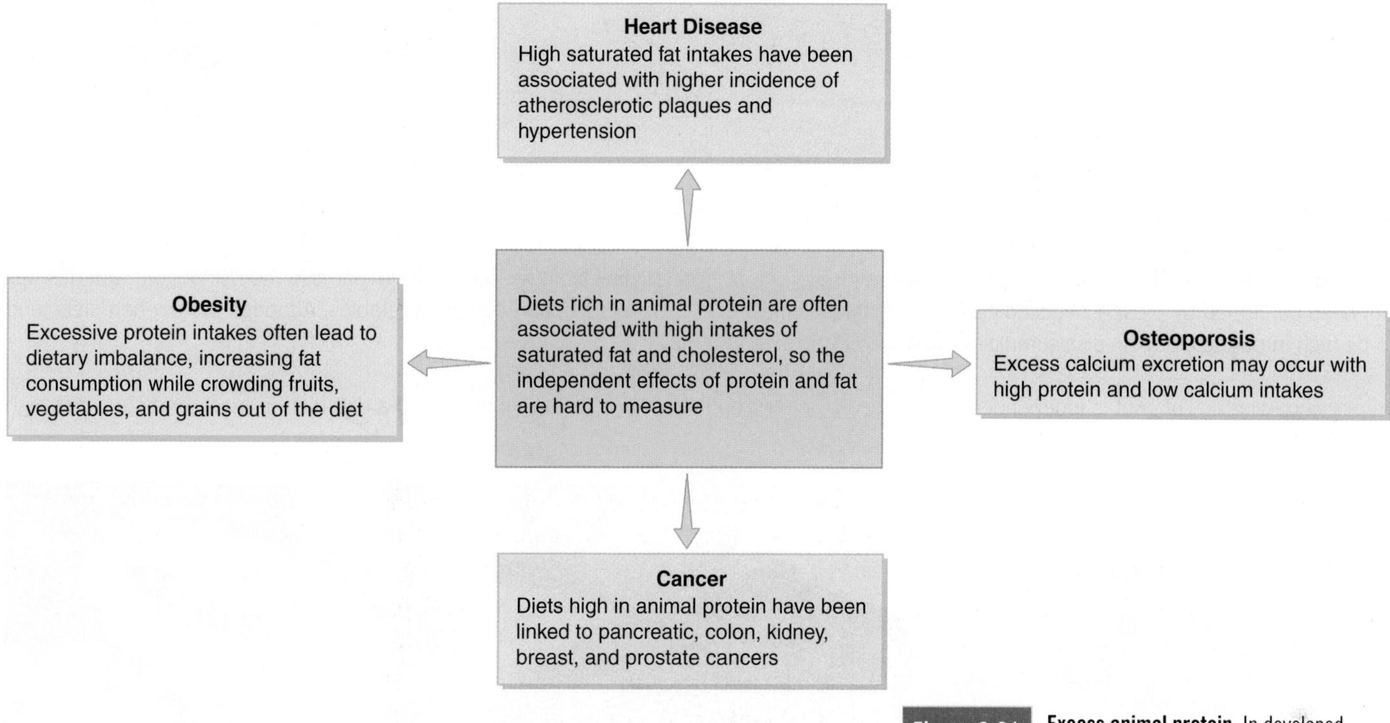

Heart Disease
High saturated fat intakes have been associated with higher incidence of atherosclerotic plaques and hypertension
Obesity
Excessive protein intakes often lead to dietary imbalance, increasing fat consumption while crowding fruits, vegetables, and grains out of the diet
Diets rich in animal protein are often associated with high intakes of saturated fat and cholesterol, so the independent effects of protein and fat are hard to measure
Osteoporosis
Excess calcium excretion may occur with high protein and low calcium intakes
Cancer
Diets high in animal protein have been linked to pancreatic, colon, kidney, breast, and prostate cancers

Figure 6.21 **Excess animal protein.** In developed countries, excess protein and energy are a greater problem than protein deficiency.

To prevent dehydration, it is important to drink plenty of fluids to dilute the by-products of protein breakdown for excretion. Human infants should not be fed unmodified cow's milk until they are at least 1 year old because the high protein concentration in cow's milk combined with an immature kidney system can cause excessive fluid losses and dehydration.

Mineral Losses

The link between high-protein diets and osteoporosis is based on studies showing that a high protein intake increases calcium excretion, which could then contribute to bone mineral losses. However, these studies generally used purified proteins rather than food proteins. Studies of postmenopausal women have shown that a high meat intake combined with a calcium intake of 600 milligrams per day did not result in increased calcium loss[45] and that substitution of soy protein for meat protein had no effect on calcium balance.[46] Other studies of older men and women have found favorable effects on bone mineral density from increasing both protein and calcium intake.[47]

Obesity

Some epidemiological studies have shown a correlation between high protein intake and body fatness.[48] High-protein foods often are high in fat. A diet high in fat and protein may provide too much energy, contributing to obesity. Large amounts of high-protein foods will displace fruits, vegetables, and grains—foods that contain fewer calories. Researchers have suggested that high dietary protein intake alters hormones and the body's response to hormones, including leptin, which regulates feeding centers in the brain to reduce food intake.[49] Some studies suggest that because of this effect on hormones, a high protein intake early in life increases the risk of obesity later in life.[50]

Quick Bite

Protein Makes for Springy Bugs

Resilin is an elastic rubberlike protein in insects, scorpions, and crustaceans. The springiness in the wing hinges of some insects, such as locusts and dragonflies, comes from the unique mechanical properties of resilin. The protein also is found in the stingers of bees and ants, the eardrums and sound organs of cicadas, and the little rubber balls in the hips of jumping fleas. The structural properties of resilin are similar to true rubber, which makes it very unusual among structural proteins.

Nutrition Science *in Action*

Protein and Gout

Observations: High protein intake and intake of various foods rich in purines have long been thought to increase the risk of gout, but this has not been confirmed by prospective studies. Purine-rich foods include meats, seafood, and certain vegetables. Although protein-rich diets tend to be high in purines, protein also stimulates excretion of uric acid in urine.

Hypothesis: The risk of gout is independently increased by consumption of (1) a protein-rich diet, (2) a diet high in meat, and (3) a diet high in seafood.

1. High protein diet

2. High meat diet

3. High seafood diet

Experimental Plan: The Health Professionals Follow-up Study is an ongoing study of 51,529 males. Exclude men with a history of gout and follow the remaining 47,150 men for 12 years. Annually assess dietary intake with food frequency questionnaires. Record all newly diagnosed cases of gout.

Results: Hypothesis 1 is not confirmed. A higher total intake of protein was not associated with an increased risk of gout. Hypotheses 2 and 3 are confirmed. The risk of gout increased 21 percent per additional portion of meat per day, and 7 percent per additional portion of seafood per week. The study also found that consumption of dairy protein (especially in low-fat dairy products) reduced the risk of gout.

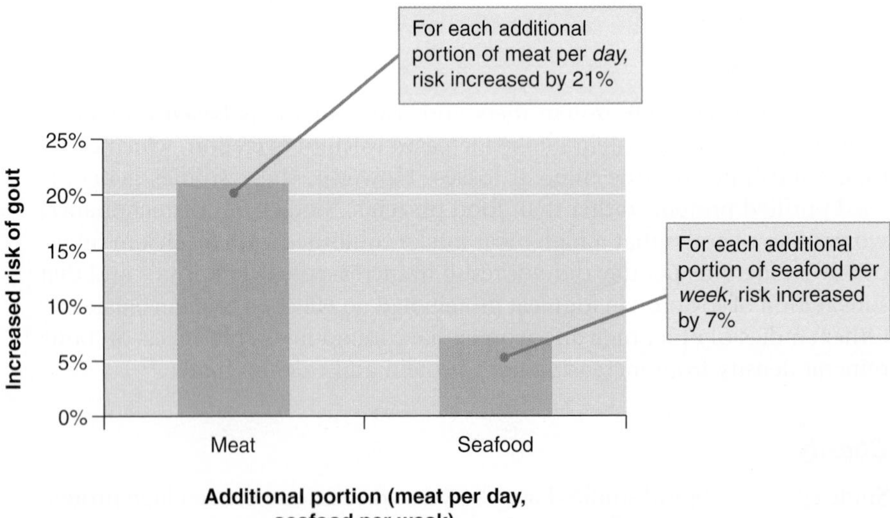

Conclusion and Discussion: This large prospective study provides scientific verification of the long-standing view that gout is most common among people whose diet is rich in meats (especially red meats) and low in dairy products. Total protein intake is not associated with the development of gout, and vegetable protein intake may have a protective effect. Because high-protein diets lead to increased urinary uric acid excretion, this may reduce blood uric acid levels. Also, the protein content of foods may not be a good indicator of their purine content. Given the role of increased fish intake in the prevention of heart disease, findings by future studies may lead to more refined fish intake recommendations that account for both gout and heart disease.

Source: Based on Choi HK, Atkinson K, Karlson EW, et al. Purine-rich foods, dairy and protein intake, and the risk of gout in men. *New Engl J Med.* 2004;350(11):1093–1103.

Heart Disease

Research has linked high intake of animal protein to high blood cholesterol levels and increased risk of heart disease. Foods high in animal protein are also high in saturated fat and cholesterol. Whether protein alone—independent of fat—plays a role in the development of heart disease is less clear. Based on studies that showed beneficial effects from consumption of soy protein,[51] the FDA approved a health claim saying that soy protein is beneficial in reducing the risk of heart disease. A review by the American Heart Association, however, found that consuming soy protein has little or no effect on the risk factors for heart disease.[52] The researchers also concluded that consuming soy protein products, such as tofu, soy butter, soy nuts, and some soy burgers, could be beneficial. Soy protein foods, with their high content of polyunsaturated fats, fiber, vitamins, and minerals and low content of saturated fat, could replace other protein foods that are high in fat.[53]

gout An intensely painful form of inflammatory arthritis that results from deposits of needlelike crystals of uric acid in connective tissue and/or the joint space between bones.

Cancer

Some studies suggest a link between a diet high in animal protein foods and an increased risk for certain types of cancers.[54] The evidence is strongest for a relationship between animal protein and colon cancer.[55] Prolonged high intake of both red meat (beef, pork) and processed meat (ham, smoked meats, sausage, bacon) has been associated with increased colon cancer risk.[56]

Gout

Gout is an immensely painful inflammatory arthritis caused by the accumulation of uric acid crystals in joints. Uric acid forms from the breakdown of nitrogen-containing compounds called purines. Uric acid normally dissolves in the blood and passes through the kidneys into the urine. In people with gout, uric acid builds up and forms sharp crystals that can collect around the joints, causing swelling and intense pain. Diets high in meats (especially red meats) and seafood and low in dairy products significantly increase the risk of gout—the most common form of inflammatory arthritis in men.[57] Total protein intake, however, is not correlated with an increased risk of gout. (See the Nutrition Science in Action feature "Protein and Gout.")

Key Concepts *Protein-energy malnutrition (PEM) is a common form of malnutrition in the developing world, with potentially devastating effects for children. PEM can manifest in two forms: kwashiorkor and marasmus. Among other symptoms, kwashiorkor is distinguished by edema, or swelling of the tissues. Marasmus results from chronic PEM and is distinguished by severe wasting of body fat and muscles. Excess dietary protein may contribute to obesity, heart disease, and certain forms of cancer. These links, however, may be attributable to the high fat intake that often accompanies high protein intake.*

Have you ever visited a health food store and noticed all the protein powders, amino acid supplements, and high-protein bars? Do you believe claims like "protein boosts your energy level" or "amino acid X helps you build muscle" or "protein shakes are the best pre-workout fuel"? You know from this chapter that protein is an important nutrient and that it's used to build and repair tissue. But do you need one of these supplements? Before reaching into your wallet, check out the Nutrition Facts of this protein powder and determine whether it's a good buy.

Take a look at this label and note how far down protein is on the list of nutrients. This de-emphasized placement of protein was intentional to try to get consumers to de-emphasize protein in their diets. You may recall that most Americans eat more protein than they need, and because much of that protein comes from animal foods, they are often getting excess saturated fat. Although there is a DV for protein (50 grams), manufacturers must first determine a food protein's quality by the PDCAAS method before they can determine %DV. Manufacturers are not required to give the %DV for protein on food labels.

Do protein and amino acid supplements do what they claim to do? In terms of building muscle, exercise physiologists agree that it takes consistent muscle work (i.e., weight lifting) and a healthy diet that meets the body's calorie needs. Muscle building does not depend on extra protein. In fact, muscles use carbohydrate and fat for fuel, not protein, so these other nutrients are more important for effective workouts.

In terms of protein's ability to boost your energy level, recall that anything with calories (carbohydrates, proteins, and fats) provides the body with "energy." In fact, unlike carbohydrates and fats, only a small amount of protein is used for energy expenditure. Research shows that the best thing to eat prior to a workout is carbohydrate, not protein, because carbohydrate provides glucose for the muscle cells. Review this label again. What percentage of this protein powder's calories is from protein?

kcal **154**

Protein **11 grams × 4 kcal per gram**

= 44 protein kcal

44 ÷ 154 = 0.28 or 28% protein kcal

Surprise! Surprise! Only one-quarter of the powder's calories are protein anyway, so it's okay as a pre-workout fuel not because of its protein content but because of its ample carbohydrate!

Nutrition Facts
Serving Size: 2 scoops
Servings Per Container: 18

Amount Per Serving
Calories 154 Calories from fat 35

	% Daily Value*
Total Fat 4g	6%
Saturated Fat 2.5g	12%
Trans Fat 0.5g	
Cholesterol 20mg	7%
Sodium 170mg	7%
Total Carbohydrate 19g	6%
Dietary Fiber 0g	0%
Sugars 14g	
Protein 11g	

Vitamin A 4% • Vitamin C 6%
Calcium 40% • Iron 0%

* Percent Daily Values are based on a 2,000 calorie diet. Your daily values may be higher or lower depending on your calorie needs:

	Calories:	2,000	2,500
Total Fat	Less Than	65g	80g
Sat Fat	Less Than	20g	25g
Cholesterol	Less Than	300mg	300mg
Sodium	Less Than	2,400mg	2,400mg
Total Carbohydrate		300g	375g
Dietary Fiber		25g	30g

Calories per gram:
Fat 9 • Carbohydrate 4 • Protein 4

Learning Portfolio

Key Terms

	page
acidosis	236
alkalosis	236
amino acid pool	242
amino acid scoring	250
antibodies [AN-tih-bod-ees]	235
biological value (BV)	250
buffers	235
celiac disease [SEA-lee-ak]	239
chemical scoring	250
chymotrypsinogen/ chymotrypsin	239
collagen	230
complementary protein	247
complete (high-quality) proteins	247
conditionally indispensable amino acids	227
cystic fibrosis	239
deamination	237
denaturation	230
dipeptide	228
dispensable amino acids	227
disulfide bridge	230
DNA (deoxyribonucleic acid)	241
edema	235
extracellular fluid	235
gout	261
hemoglobin [HEEM-oh-glow-bin]	229
hydrophilic amino acids	229
hydrophobic amino acids	230
immune response	235
incomplete (low-quality) proteins	247
indispensable amino acids	226
interstitial fluid [in-ter-STISH-ul]	235
intracellular fluid	235
intravascular fluid	235
keratin	230
kwashiorkor	257
limiting amino acid	250
marasmus	257
messenger RNA (mRNA)	241
motor proteins	230
negative nitrogen balance	243
net protein utilization (NPU)	250
neurotransmitters	243
nitrogen balance	243
nitrogen equilibrium	243
oligopeptide	229
peptidases	239
peptide bond	228
polypeptide	229
positive nitrogen balance	243
precursor	237
proenzymes	239
proteases [PRO-tea-ace-ez]	238
protein digestibility corrected amino acid score (PDCAAS)	250
protein efficiency ratio (PER)	250
protein hydrolysates	251
protein turnover	242
protein-energy malnutrition (PEM)	257
ribosomal RNA (rRNA)	241
ribosomes	241
transfer RNA (tRNA)	241
tripeptide	228
trypsinogen/trypsin	239
urea	243
wasting	226

Study Points

- Many vital compounds are proteins, including enzymes, hormones, transport proteins, and regulators of both acid–base and fluid balance.
- Proteins are long chains of amino acids.
- Amino acids are composed of a central carbon atom bonded to hydrogen, carboxyl, amino, and side groups.
- At least 20 amino acids are important in human nutrition; 9 of these amino acids are considered indispensable (must come from the diet), whereas the body can make the other 11 (dispensable) amino acids.
- The amino acid sequence of a protein determines its shape and function.
- Denaturing of proteins changes their shape and therefore their functional properties.
- Protein digestion begins in the stomach through the action of hydrochloric acid and the enzyme pepsin.
- Proteins are digested completely in the small intestine and absorbed by facilitated diffusion and active transport.
- Dietary protein is found in meats, dairy products, legumes, nuts, seeds, grains, and vegetables.
- In general, animal foods contain higher-quality protein than is found in plant foods.
- Protein needs are highest when growth is rapid, such as during infancy, childhood, and adolescence.
- The protein intake of most Americans exceeds their RDA.
- Protein deficiency is most common in developing countries and results in the conditions known as marasmus and kwashiorkor.
- Protein excess is also harmful and may affect risk for osteoporosis, heart disease, cancer, and gout.

Study Questions

1. List the functions of body proteins.
2. Describe the differences among indispensable, dispensable, and conditionally indispensable amino acids.
3. Among the nutrient molecules, which element is unique to protein and how does it fit into the basic structure of an amino acid?
4. Why are most plant proteins considered incomplete?
5. What are complementary proteins? List three examples of food combinations that contain complementary proteins.
6. What health effects occur if you are protein deficient?
7. How is protein related to immune function?
8. Describe a vegan diet.
9. List the potential health benefits of a vegetarian diet.

Try This

The Sweetness of NutraSweet

The purpose of this experiment is to see the effect of high temperatures on the dipeptide known as NutraSweet (aspartame). Make a cup of hot tea (or coffee) and add one packet of Equal (one brand of aspartame). Stir and taste the tea; note its sweetness. Reheat the tea (via a microwave or stovetop) so that it boils for 30 to 60 seconds. After the tea cools, taste it. Does it still taste sweet? Why or why not?

The Vegetarian Challenge

The purpose of this activity is to eat a completely vegan diet for one day. Begin by making a list of your typical meals and snacks. Once the list is complete, review each food item and determine whether it contains animal products. Cross off items that contain animal products and circle the remaining vegan-friendly options. Double-check the circled list with a friend or roommate. You may have missed something! Create a full day's worth of meals and snacks using your circled foods as well as additional vegan options. Make sure your menu looks complete and nutritionally balanced. Try to stick to this menu for at least one day. Pay attention to deviations you make and whether these are vegan food choices.

What About Bobbie?

Take a minute to review Bobbie's food intake with a special eye on protein. How do you think she did? Do you think she's lower or higher than her RDA? Let's first calculate her protein RDA. Since Bobbie weighs 155 pounds, her protein RDA is as follows:

155 pounds ÷ 2.2 pounds = 70.5 kilograms

70.5 kilograms × 0.8 gram protein = 56.40 grams

Her protein intake is 96 grams. This is quite high compared with her RDA! Are you surprised to learn she eats twice as much protein as she needs? Her diet doesn't look *that* high in protein, does it? Here are the foods that contribute the most protein to her diet:

Food	Protein (grams)
Meatballs	24
Turkey breast	17
Spaghetti	10
Pizza	9
Bagel	7

Another way to evaluate Bobbie's protein intake is in terms of calories. If her total protein intake is 96 grams, then 384 kilocalories come from protein. Remember, her total kilocalorie intake is 2,300, which means protein accounts for 17 percent of her energy intake. General guidelines recommend that 10 to 35 percent of energy come from protein.

So, what's the deal? Is Bobbie eating way too much protein or just the right amount? She's certainly high compared with her RDA of 56 grams, but using the AMDR, she could consume as much as 200 grams at her current energy intake level! We've already seen that her diet could use more servings of fruits and vegetables, and in future chapters we'll see whether her balance of energy sources is appropriate for obtaining all the needed vitamins and minerals.

References

1 Institute of Medicine, Food and Nutrition Board. *Dietary Reference Intakes for Energy, Carbohydrate, Fiber, Fat, Fatty Acids, Cholesterol, Protein, and Amino Acids*. Washington, DC: National Academies Press, 2005.

2 National Institutes of Health. *Phenylketonuria: Screening and Management*. NIH Consensus Statement. 2000;17(3):1–27.

3 Institute of Medicine, Food and Nutrition Board. *Dietary Reference Intakes for Energy, Carbohydrate*.

4 Ibid.

5 Ibid.

6 Voet D, Voet JG. *Biochemistry*. 3rd ed. New York: Wiley, 2004.

7 Greenberg AS, Obin MS. Obesity and the role of adipose tissue in inflammation and metabolism. *Am J Clin Nutr.* 2006;83(2):461S–465S.

8 Berg JM, Tymoczko JL, Stryer L. *Biochemistry: A Short Course*. New York: Macmillan, 2009.

9 Guyton A, Hall J. *Textbook of Medical Physiology*. 11th ed. Philadelphia: WB Saunders, 2006.

10 Kelly DG. Assessment of malnutrition. In: Shils ME, Shike M, Ross AC, et al., eds. *Modern Nutrition in Health and Disease*. 10th ed. Philadelphia: Lippincott Williams & Wilkins, 2006:1143–1151.

11 Ibid.

12 Guyton, Hall. *Textbook of Medical Physiology*.

13 Mathews DE. Proteins and amino acids. In: Shils ME, Shike M, Ross AC, et al., eds. *Modern Nutrition in Health and Disease*. 10th ed. Philadelphia: Lippincott Williams & Wilkins, 2006:23–61.

14 Ibid.

15 Ibid.

16 Institute of Medicine, Food and Nutrition Board. *Dietary Reference Intakes for Energy, Carbohydrate*.

17 Briefel RR, Johnson CL. Secular trends in dietary intake in the United States. *Ann Rev Nutr.* 2004;24:401–431.

18 Institute of Medicine, Food and Nutrition Board. *Dietary Reference Intakes for Energy, Carbohydrate*.

19 Wolfe R, Miller S, Miller K. Optimal protein intake in the elderly. *Clin Nutr.* 2008;27(5):675–684.

20 Millward DJ, Roberts SB. Protein requirements of older individuals. *Nutr Res Rev.* 1996;9:67–87.

21 Wolfe, Miller, Miller. Optimal protein intake in the elderly.

22 Institute of Medicine, Food and Nutrition Board. *Dietary Reference Intakes for Energy, Carbohydrate*.

23 De Mejia E, de Lumen B. Soybean bioactive peptides: a new horizon in preventing chronic disease. *Sexuality Reprod Menopause.* 2006;4(2):91–95.

24 US Department of Agriculture. Nutrient content of the U.S. food supply. http://209.48.219.50/NFSDatabase/QueAV.asp. Accessed 6/8/06.

25 Young VR, Pellett PL. Plant proteins in relation to human protein and amino acid nutrition. *Am J Clin Nutr.* 1994;59:1203S–1212S.

26 Panebranco S. The merits and pitfalls of vegetarianism. *J Sci Healing*. 2007;3(1).

27 Dwyer JT. Nutritional consequences of vegetarianism. *Ann Rev Nutr.* 1991;11:61–91.

28 Institute of Medicine, Food and Nutrition Board. *Dietary Reference Intakes for Energy, Carbohydrate*.

29 Food and Agriculture Organization. *Protein Quality Evaluation: Report of the Joint FAO/WHO Expert Consultation*. Rome: Food and Agriculture Organization of the United Nations, 1991. FAO Food and Nutrition Paper 51; and Sarwar G, McDonough RE. Evaluation of protein digestibility-corrected amino acid score method for assessing protein quality of foods. *J Assoc Official Analytic Chem.* 1990;73:347–356.

30 Ballenntine R. *Transition to Vegetarianism: An Evolutionary Step*. Honesdale, PA: Himalayan International Institute of Yoga Science and Philosophy, 1987; and Null G. *The Vegetarian Handbook: Eating Right for Total Health*. New York: St. Martin's Press, 1987.

31 Null. *The Vegetarian Handbook*.

32 The Vegetarian Resource Group. How many vegetarians are there? *Vegetarian J.* May 21, 2003. http://www.vrg.org/journal/vj2003issue3/vj2003issue3poll.htm. Accessed 5/21/09.

33 American Dietetic Association. Position of the American Dietetic Association and the Dieticians of Canada: vegetarian diets. *J Am Diet Assoc.* 2003;103:748–765.

34 Gould KL, Ornish D, Scherwitz L, et al. Changes in myocardial perfusion abnormalities by positron emission tomography after long-term intense risk factor modification. *JAMA.* 1995;274:894–901; and Leitzman C. Vegetarian diets: what are the advantages? *Forum Nutr.* 2005;57:147–156.

35 American Dietetic Association. Vegetarian diets.

36 Messina V, Melina V, Mangels AR. A new food guide for North American vegetarians. *J Am Diet Assoc.* 2003;103:771–775.

37 American Dietetic Association. Vegetarian diets.

38 Shetty P. Malnutrition and undernutrition. *Medicine*. 2006;34(12):524–529.

39 Akuyam SA. A review of some metabolic changes in protein-energy malnutrition. *Niger Postgrad Med J.* 2007;14:155–162.

40 Manary MJ, Broadhead RL, Yarasheski KE. Whole-body protein kinetics in marasmus and kwashiorkor during acute infection. *Am J Clin Nutr.* 1998;67:1205–1209.

41 Fuhrman MP, Charney P, Mueller CM. Hepatic proteins and nutrition assessment. *J Am Diet Assoc.* 2004;104:1258–1264; and Krawinkel M. Kwashiorkor is still not fully understood. *Bull World Health Organ.* 2003;81:910–911.

42 Hoffer JJ. Metabolic consequences of starvation. In: Shils ME, Shike M, Ross AC, et al., eds. *Modern Nutrition in Health and Disease*. 10th ed. Philadelphia: Lippincott Williams & Wilkins, 2006:730–748.

43 Institute of Medicine, Food and Nutrition Board. *Dietary Reference Intakes for Energy, Carbohydrate*.

44 Ibid.

45 Roughead ZK, Johnson LK, Lykken GI, Hunt JR. Controlled high meat diets do not affect calcium retention or indices of bone status in healthy postmenopausal women. *J Nutr.* 2003;133:1020–1026.

46 Roughead ZK, Hunt JR, Johnson LK, et al. Controlled substitution of soy protein for meat protein: effects on calcium retention, bone, and cardiovascular health indices in postmenopausal women. *J Clin Endocrinol Metab.* 2005;90:181–189.

47 Dawson-Hughes B, Harris SS. Calcium intake influences the association of protein intake with rates of bone loss in elderly men and women. *Am J Clin Nutr.* 2002;75:773–779; and Promislow JH, Goodman-Gruen D, Slymen DJ, Barrett-Connor E. Protein consumption and bone mineral density in the elderly: the Rancho Bernardo Study. *Am J Epidemiol.* 2002;155:636–644.

48 Institute of Medicine, Food and Nutrition Board. *Dietary Reference Intakes for Energy, Carbohydrate*.

49 Schwartz M, Seeley RJ. The new biology of body weight regulation. *J Am Diet Assoc.* 1997;97:54–58; and Weigle DS, Breen PA, Matthys CC, et al. A high-protein diet induces sustained reductions in appetite, ad libitum caloric intake, and body weight despite compensatory changes in diurnal plasma leptin and ghrelin concentrations. *Am J Clin Nutr.* 2005;82(1):41–48.

50 Parizkova J, Rolland-Cachera MF. High proteins early in life as a predisposition for later obesity and further health risks. *Nutrition*. 1997;13:818–819; and Koletzko B, Broekaert I, Demmelmair H, et al. Protein intake in the first year of life: a risk factor for later obesity? The E.U. Childhood Obesity Project. *Adv Exp Med Biol.* 2005;569:69–79.

51 Liao F-H, Shieh M-J, Yang S-C, et al. Effectiveness of a soy-based compared with a traditional low-calorie diet on weight loss and lipid levels in overweight adults. *Nutrition*. 2007;23(7):551–556.

52 Sacks FM, Lichtenstein A, Van Horn L, et al. Soy protein, isoflavones, and cardiovascular health: an American Heart Association science advisory for professionals from the nutrition committee. *Circulation*. 2006;113:1034–1044.

53 Ibid.

54 Giovannuci E. Intake of fat, meat, and fiber in relation to colon cancer in men. *Cancer Res.* 1994;54:2390.

55 Willett WC. Diet and cancer: an evolving picture. *JAMA.* 2005;293:233–234.

56 Chao A, Thun MJ, Connell CJ. Meat consumption and risk of colorectal cancer. *JAMA.* 2005;293:172–182.

57 Choi HK, Atkinson K, Karlson EW, et al. Purine-rich foods, dairy and protein intake, and the risk of gout in men. *New Engl J Med.* 2004;350(11):1093–1103.

CHAPTER 7

Metabolism

THINK About It

1 You are driving on "the energy highway." You stop at the tollbooth. What kind of currency do you need to pay the toll?

2 When you think of "cell power," what comes to mind?

3 What do you think is meant by the saying "Fat burns in a flame of carbohydrate"?

4 When it comes to fasting, what's your body's first priority?

Visit nutrition.jbpub.com

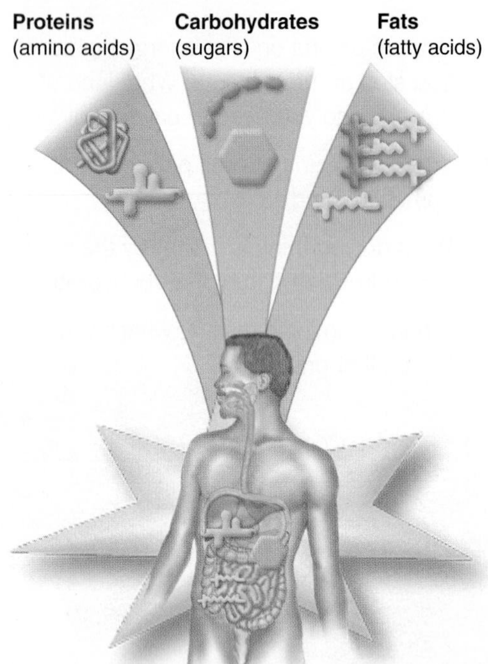

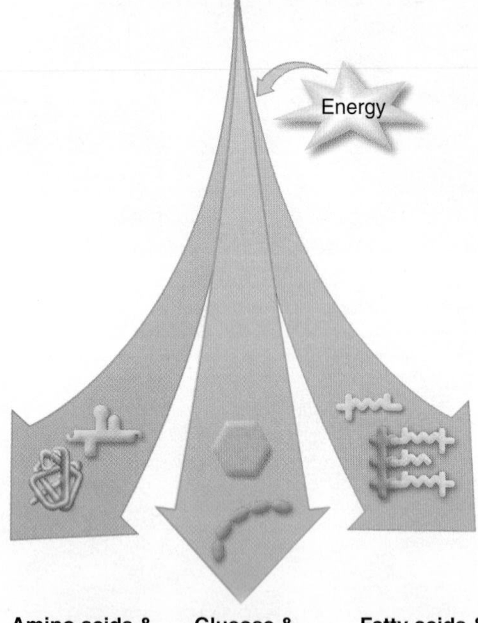

Figure 7.1 **Metabolism.** Cells use metabolic reactions to extract energy from food and to form building blocks for biosynthesis.

Your body is a wonderfully efficient factory. It accepts raw materials (food), burns some to generate power, uses some to produce finished goods, routes the rest to storage, and discards waste and by-products. Constant turnover of your stored inventory keeps it fresh. Your body draws on these stored raw materials to produce compounds, and nutrient intake replenishes the supply.

Do you ever wonder how your biological factory responds to changing supply and demand? Under normal circumstances, it hums along nicely with all processes in balance. When supply exceeds demand, your body stores the excess raw materials in inventory. When supply fails to meet demand, your body draws on these stored materials to meet its needs. Your biological factory never stops; even though a storage or energy-production process may dominate, all your factory operations are active at all times.

Collectively, these processes are known as **metabolism**. (See **Figure 7.1**.) Whereas some metabolic reactions break down molecules to extract energy, others synthesize building blocks to produce new molecules. To carry out metabolic processes, thousands of chemical reactions occur every moment in cells throughout your body. The most active metabolic sites include your liver, muscle, and brain cells.

Energy: Fuel for Work

To operate, machines need energy. Cars use gasoline for fuel, factory machinery uses electricity, and windmills rely on wind power. So what about you? All cells require energy to sustain life. Even during sleep, your body uses energy for breathing, pumping blood, maintaining body temperature, delivering oxygen to tissues, removing waste products, synthesizing new tissue for growth, and repairing damaged or worn-out tissues. When awake, you need additional energy for physical movement (such as standing, walking, and talking) and for the digestion and absorption of foods.

Where does the energy come from to power your body's "machinery"? Biological systems use heat, mechanical, electrical, and chemical forms of energy. Our cells get their energy from **chemical energy** held in the molecular bonds of carbohydrates, fats, and protein—the energy macronutrients—as well as alcohol. The chemical energy in foods and beverages originates as light energy from the sun. Green plants use light energy to make carbohydrate in a process called **photosynthesis**. In photosynthesis, carbon dioxide (CO_2) from the air combines with water (H_2O) from the earth to form a carbohydrate, usually glucose ($C_6H_{12}O_6$), and oxygen (O_2). Plants store glucose as starch and release oxygen into the atmosphere. Plants such as corn, peas, squash, turnips, potatoes, and rice store especially high amounts of starch in their edible parts. In the glucose molecule, the chemical bonds between the carbon (C) and hydrogen (H) atoms hold energy from the sun.[1] When our bodies extract energy from food and convert it to a form that our cells can use, we lose more than half of the total food energy as heat.[2]

Within any system (including the universe), the total amount of energy is constant. Although energy can change from one form to another and can move from one location to another, the system never gains or loses energy. This principle, called the first law of thermodynamics, is known as conservation of energy.

Transferring Food Energy to Cellular Energy

Although burning food releases energy as heat, we cannot use heat to power the many cellular functions that maintain life. Rather than using combustion, we transfer energy from food to a form that our cells can use. (See **Figure 7.2**.) This transfer is not completely efficient; we lose roughly half of the total food energy as heat as our bodies extract energy from food in three stages:[3]

Stage 1: Digestion, absorption, and transportation. Digestion breaks food down into small subunits—simple sugars, fatty acids, monoglycerides, glycerol, and amino acids—that the small intestine can absorb. The circulatory system then transports these nutrients to tissues throughout the body.

Stage 2: Breakdown of many small molecules to a few key metabolites. Inside individual cells, chemical reactions convert simple sugars, fatty acids, glycerol, and amino acids into a few key **metabolites** (products of metabolic reactions). This process liberates a small amount of usable energy.

metabolism All chemical reactions within organisms that enable them to maintain life. The two main categories of metabolism are catabolism and anabolism.

chemical energy Energy contained in the bonds between atoms of a molecule.

photosynthesis The process by which green plants use radiant energy from the sun to produce carbohydrates (hexoses) from carbon dioxide and water.

metabolites Any substances produced during metabolism.

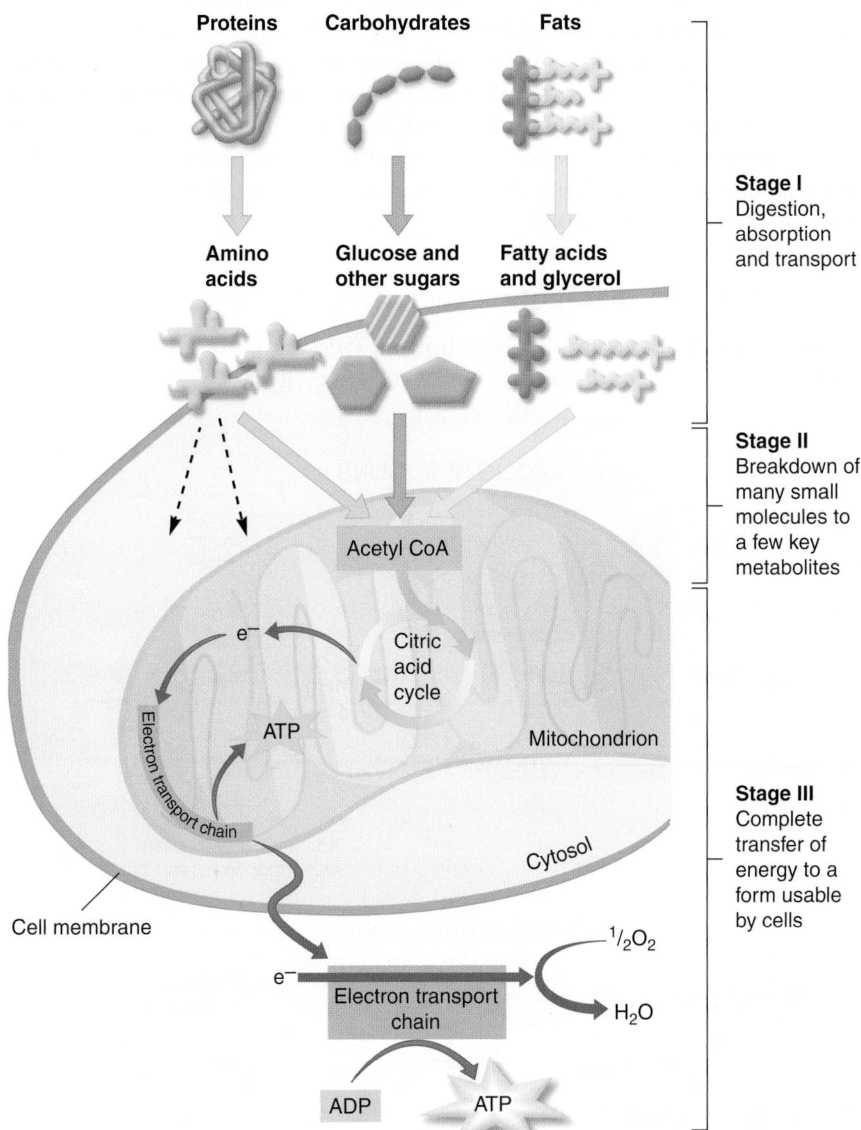

Figure 7.2 **Energy extraction from food.** In the first stage, the body breaks down food into amino acids, monosaccharides, and fatty acids. In the second stage, cells degrade these molecules to a few simple units, such as acetyl CoA, that are pervasive in metabolism. In the third stage, the oxygen-dependent reactions of the citric acid cycle and electron transport chain liberate large amounts of energy in the form of ATP.

metabolic pathway A series of chemical reactions that either break down a large compound into smaller units (catabolism) or synthesize more complex molecules from smaller ones (anabolism).

catabolism [ca-TA-bol-iz-um] Any metabolic process whereby cells break down complex substances into simpler, smaller ones.

anabolism [an-A-bol-iz-um] Any metabolic process whereby cells convert simple substances into more complex ones.

cells The basic structural units of all living tissues, which have two major parts: the nucleus and the cytoplasm.

nucleus The primary site of genetic information in the cell, enclosed in a double-layered membrane. The nucleus contains the chromosomes and is the site of messenger RNA (mRNA) and ribosomal RNA (rRNA) synthesis, the "machinery" for protein synthesis in the cytosol.

cytoplasm The material of the cell, excluding the cell nucleus and cell membranes. The cytoplasm includes the semifluid cytosol, the organelles, and other particles.

cytosol The semifluid inside the cell membrane, excluding organelles. The cytosol is the site of glycolysis and fatty acid synthesis.

organelles Various membrane-bound structures that form part of the cytoplasm. Organelles, including mitochondria and lysosomes, perform specialized metabolic functions.

mitochondria (mitochondrion) The sites of aerobic production of ATP, where most of the energy from carbohydrate, protein, and fat is captured. Called the "power plants" of the cell, the mitochondria contain two highly specialized membranes, an outer membrane and a highly folded inner membrane, that separate two compartments, the internal matrix space and the narrow intermembrane space. A human cell contains about 2,000 mitochondria.

Stage 3: Transfer of energy to a form that cells can use. The complete breakdown of metabolites to carbon dioxide and water liberates large amounts of energy. The reactions during this stage are responsible for converting more than 90 percent of the available food energy to a form that our bodies can use.

What Is Metabolism?

Metabolism is a general term that encompasses all chemical changes occurring in living organisms. The term **metabolic pathway** describes a series of chemical reactions that either break down a large compound into smaller units (**catabolism**) or build more complex molecules from smaller ones (**anabolism**).[4] For example, when you eat bread or rice, the GI tract breaks down the starch into glucose units. Cells can further catabolize these glucose units to release energy for activities such as muscle contractions. Conversely, anabolic reactions take available glucose molecules and assemble them into glycogen for storage. **Figure 7.3** illustrates catabolism and anabolism.

Metabolic pathways are never completely inactive. Their activity continually ebbs and flows in response to internal and external events. Imagine, for example, that your instructor keeps you late and you have only five minutes to get to your next class. As you hustle across campus, your body ramps up energy production to fuel the demand created by your rapidly contracting muscles. As you sit in your next class, your body continues to break down and extract glucose from the banana you recently ate. Your body assembles the glucose into branched chains to replenish the glycogen stores you depleted while running across campus.

The Cell Is the Metabolic Processing Center

Cells are the "work centers" of metabolism. (See **Figure 7.4**.) Although our bodies are made up of different types of cells (e.g., liver cells, brain cells, kid-

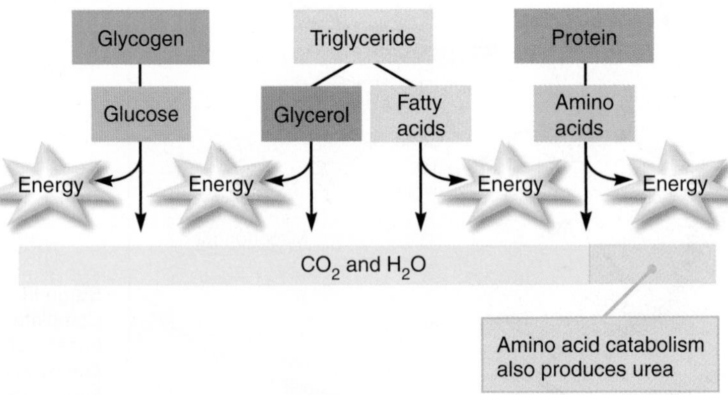

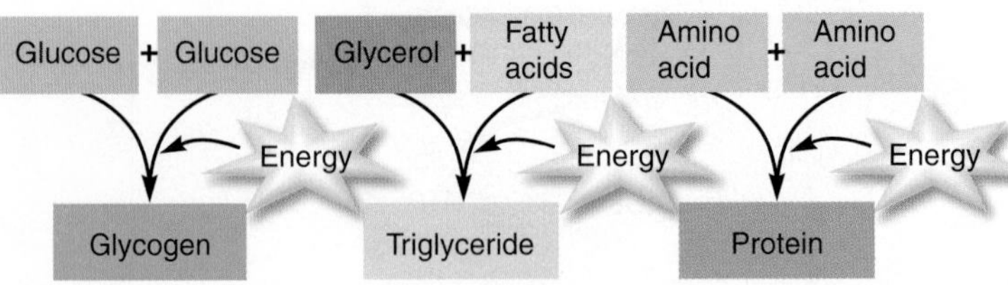

Figure 7.3 **Catabolism and anabolism.** Catabolic reactions break down molecules and release energy and other products. Anabolic reactions consume energy as they assemble complex molecules.

ney cells, muscle cells), most have a similar structure. The basic animal cell has two major parts: the cell **nucleus** and a membrane-enclosed space called the **cytoplasm**. As we zoom in for a closer look, we see that the semifluid **cytosol** fills the cytoplasm. Floating in the cytosol are many organelles, small units that perform specialized metabolic functions. A large number of these **organelles**—the capsule-like **mitochondria**—are power generators that contain many important energy-producing pathways.

Figure 7.4 **Cell structure.** Liver cells, brain cells, kidney cells, muscle cells, and so forth all have a similar structure.

Organelles

Endoplasmic reticulum (ER)
- An extensive membrane system extending from the nuclear membrane.
- Rough ER: The outer membrane surface contains ribosomes, the site of protein synthesis.
- Smooth ER: Devoid of ribosomes, the site of lipid synthesis.

Golgi apparatus
- A system of stacked membrane-encased discs.
- The site of extensive modification, sorting and packaging of compounds for transport.

Lysosome
- Vesicle containing enzymes that digest intracellular materials and recycle the components.

Mitochondrion
- Contains two highly specialized membranes, an outer membrane and a highly folded inner membrane. Membranes separated by narrow intermembrane space. Inner membrane encloses space called mitochondrial matrix.
- Often called the power plant of the cell. Site where most of the energy from carbohydrate, protein, and fat is captured in ATP (adenosine triphosphate).
- About 2,000 mitochondria in a cell.

Ribosome
- Site of protein synthesis.

Nucleus
- Contains genetic information in the base sequences of the DNA strands of the chromosomes.
- Site of RNA synthesis – RNA needed for protein synthesis.
- Enclosed in a double-layered membrane.

Cytoplasm
- Enclosed in the cell membrane and separated from the nucleus by the nuclear membrane.
- Filled with particles and organelles, which are dispersed in a clear semifluid called cytosol.

Cytosol
- The semifluid inside the cell membrane.
- Site of glycolysis and fatty acid synthesis.

Cell membrane
- A double-layered sheet, made up of lipid and protein, that encases the cell.
- Controls the passage of substances in and out of the cell.
- Contains receptors for hormones and other regulatory compounds.

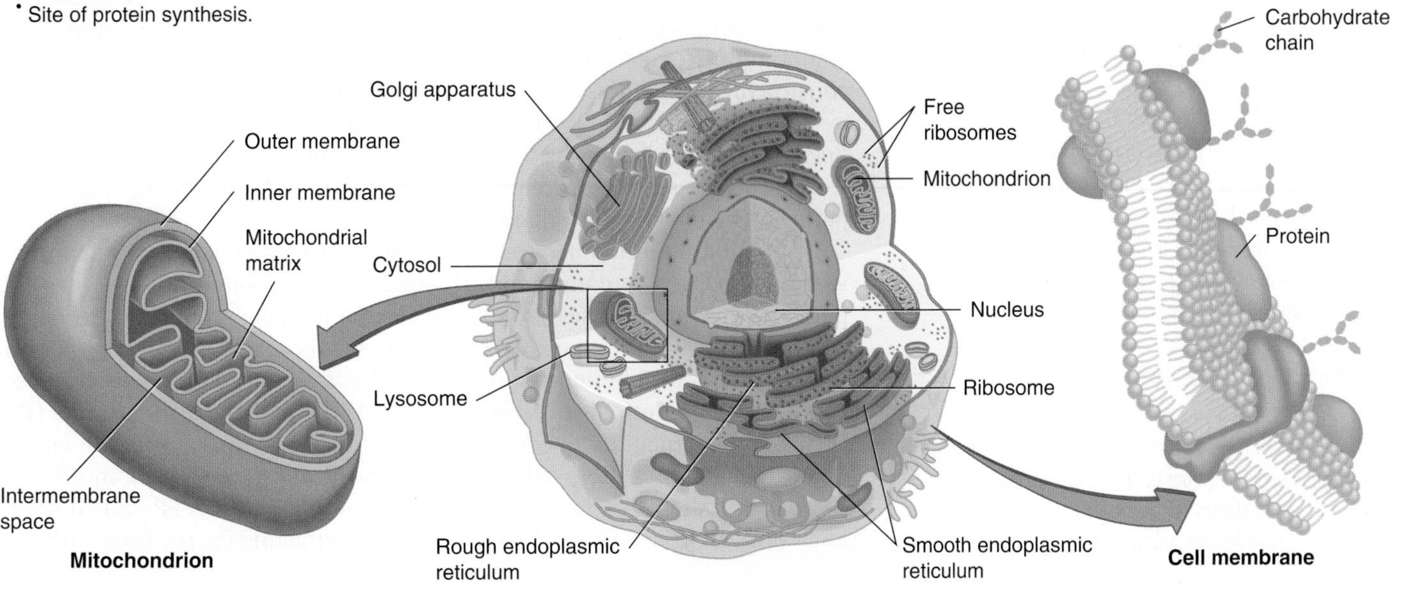

Quick Bite

Key Players in the Energy Game

Each of the "key players" in the energy game has a common acronym by which it is usually called:

ATP: adenosine triphosphate
NAD^+: nicotinamide adenine dinucleotide (oxidized)
NADH: nicotinamide adenine dinucleotide (reduced)
$NADP^+$: nicotinamide adenine dinucleotide phosphate (oxidized)
NADPH: nicotinamide adenine dinucleotide phosphate (reduced)
FAD^+: flavin adenine dinucleotide (oxidized)
$FADH_2$: flavin adenine dinucleotide (reduced)

To remember the major parts of a cell, think about a bowl of thick vegetable soup with a single meatball floating in it. For our example, think of the broth as having a runny, jellylike consistency and the bowl as a thin flexible structure with the consistency of a wet paper bag. The bowl surrounds and holds the mixture, similar to the way a cell membrane encloses a cell. The meatball represents the cell nucleus, and the remaining mixture is the cytoplasm. This cytoplasmic soup is made up of a thick, semiliquid fluid (cytosol) and vegetables (organelles). Among the vegetables, think of those kidney beans as mitochondria.

Enzymes, which are catalytic proteins, speed up chemical reactions in metabolic pathways. Many enzymes are inactive unless they are combined with certain smaller molecules called **cofactors**, which usually are derived from a vitamin or mineral. Vitamin-derived cofactors are also called **coenzymes**. All the B vitamins form coenzymes used in metabolic reactions. (For more on coenzymes, see Chapter 11, "Water-Soluble Vitamins.")

Key Concepts *Metabolism encompasses the many reactions that take place in cells to build tissue, produce energy, break down compounds, and do other cellular work. Anabolism refers to reactions that build compounds, such as protein or glycogen. Catabolism is the breakdown of compounds to yield energy. Mitochondria, the power plants within cells, contain many of the breakdown pathways that produce energy.*

cofactors Compounds required for an enzyme to be active. Cofactors include coenzymes and metal ions such as iron (Fe^{2+}), copper (Cu^{2+}), and magnesium (Mg^{2+}).

coenzymes Organic compounds, often B vitamin derivatives, that combine with an inactive enzyme to form an active enzyme. Coenzymes associate closely with these enzymes, allowing them to catalyze certain metabolic reactions in a cell.

adenosine triphosphate (ATP) [ah-DEN-oh-seen try-FOS-fate] A high-energy compound that is the main direct fuel that cells use to synthesize molecules, contract muscles, transport substances, and perform other tasks.

NADH The reduced form of nicotinamide adenine dinucleotide (NAD^+). This coenzyme, derived from the B vitamin niacin, acts as an electron carrier in cells, and undergoes reversible oxidation and reduction.

$FADH_2$ The reduced form of flavin adenine dinucleotide (FAD). This coenzyme, which is derived from the B vitamin riboflavin, acts as an electron carrier in cells and undergoes reversible oxidation and reduction.

NADPH The reduced form of nicotinamide adenine dinucleotide phosphate. This coenzyme, which is derived from the B vitamin niacin, acts as an electron carrier in cells, undergoing reversible oxidation and reduction. The oxidized form is $NADP^+$.

Who Are the Key Energy Players?

Certain compounds have recurring roles in metabolic activities. **Adenosine triphosphate (ATP)** is the fundamental energy molecule used to power cellular functions, so it is known as the universal energy currency. Two other molecules, **NADH** and **$FADH_2$**, are important couriers that carry energy for the synthesis of ATP. A similar energy carrier, **NADPH**, delivers energy for **biosynthesis**.

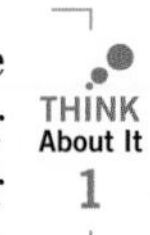

ATP: The Body's Energy Currency

To power its needs, your body must convert the energy in food to a readily usable form—ATP. This universal energy currency kick-starts many energy-releasing processes, such as the breakdown of glucose and fatty acids, and powers energy-consuming processes, such as building glucose from other compounds. Remember that making large molecules from smaller ones, like constructing a building from bricks, requires energy.

Production of ATP is the fundamental goal of metabolism's energy-producing pathways. Just as the ancient Romans could claim that all roads lead to Rome, you can say that, with a few exceptions, your body's energy-producing pathways lead to ATP production.

The ATP molecule has three phosphate groups attached to adenosine, which is an organic compound. Because breaking the bonds between the phosphate groups releases a tremendous amount of energy, ATP is an energy-rich molecule. (See **Figure 7.5**.) Cells can use this energy to power biological work. When a metabolic reaction breaks the first phosphate bond, it breaks down ATP to **adenosine diphosphate (ADP)** and **pyrophosphate (P_i)**. Breaking the remaining phosphate bond releases an equal amount of energy and breaks down ADP to **adenosine monophosphate (AMP)** and P_i.

Because the reaction can proceed in either direction, ATP and ADP are interconvertible, as **Figure 7.6** shows. When extracting energy from carbohy-

ATP, ADP, AMP, AND HIGH-ENERGY PHOSPHATE BONDS

ATP: adenosine triphosphate

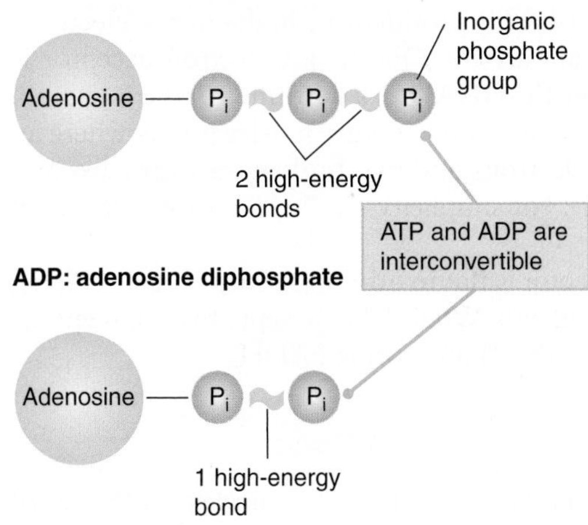

AMP: adenosine monophosphate

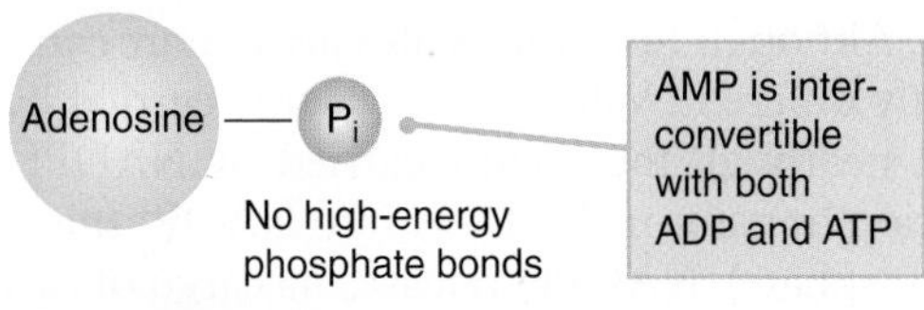

Figure 7.5 **ATP, ADP, and AMP.** Your body can readily use the energy in high-energy phosphate bonds. During metabolic reactions, phosphate bonds form or break to capture or release energy.

Formation of ATP captures energy from the oxidation of energy nutrients

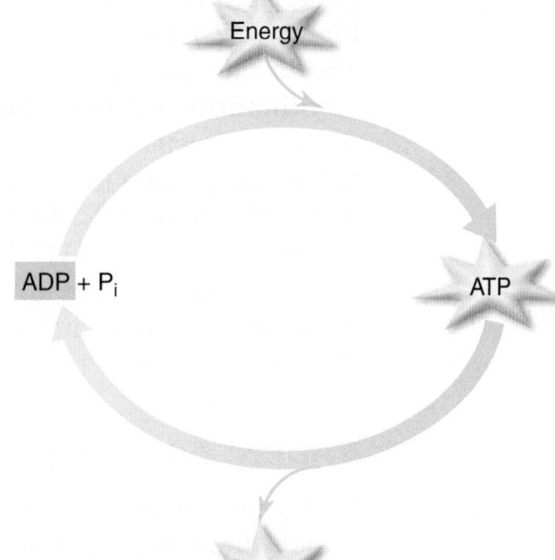

Energy

Breakdown of ATP releases energy to power
Motion
Active transport
Biosynthesis
Signal amplification

Figure 7.6 **The ADP–ATP cycle.** When extracting energy from nutrients, the formation of ATP from ADP + P_i captures energy. Breaking a phosphate bond in ATP to form ADP + P_i releases energy for biosynthesis and work.

ATP **Adenosine–P~P~P**

GTP **Guanosine–P~P~P**

drate, protein, and fat, ADP binds P_i, forming a phosphate bond and capturing energy in a new ATP molecule. When the reaction flows in the opposite direction, ATP releases P_i, breaking a phosphate bond and liberating energy while re-forming ADP. This liberated energy can power biological activities such as motion, active transport across cell membranes, biosynthesis, and signal amplification.

The body's pool of ATP is a small, immediately accessible energy reservoir rather than a long-term energy reserve. The typical lifetime of an ATP molecule is less than one minute, and ATP production increases or decreases in direct relation to energy needs. At rest, you use about 40 kilograms of ATP in 24 hours (an average rate of about 28 grams per minute). In contrast, if you are exercising strenuously, you can use as much as 500 grams per minute! On average, you turn over your body weight in ATP every day.[5]

The molecule **guanosine triphosphate (GTP)** is similar to ATP and holds the same amount of available energy. Like ATP, GTP has high-energy phosphate bonds and three phosphate groups, but they are linked to guanosine rather than to adenosine. Energy-rich GTP molecules are crucial for vision and supply part of the power needed to synthesize protein and glucose. GTP readily converts to ATP.

biosynthesis Chemical reactions that form simple molecules into complex biomolecules, especially carbohydrate, lipids, protein, nucleotides, and nucleic acids.

adenosine diphosphate (ADP) The compound produced upon hydrolysis of ATP, and used to synthesize ATP. Composed of adenosine and two phosphate groups.

pyrophosphate (P_i) Inorganic phosphate. This high-energy phosphate group is an important component of ATP, ADP, and AMP.

adenosine monophosphate (AMP) Hydrolysis product of ADP and of nucleic acids. Composed of adenosine and one phosphate group.

guanosine triphosphate (GTP) A high-energy compound, similar to ATP, but with three phosphate groups linked to guanosine.

NADH and $FADH_2$: The Body's Energy Shuttles

When breaking down nutrients, metabolic reactions release high-energy electrons. Further reactions transfer energy from these electrons to ATP. (See **Figure 7.7**.) To reach the site of ATP production, high-energy electrons hitch a ride on special molecular carriers. One major electron acceptor is **nicotinamide adenine dinucleotide (NAD^+)**, a derivative of the B vitamin niacin. The metabolic pathways have several energy-transfer points where an NAD^+ accepts two high-energy electrons and two **hydrogen ions** (two protons [$2H^+$]) to form NADH + H^+. For simplicity, the "+ H^+" is often dropped when talking about NADH.

The other major electron acceptor is **flavin adenine dinucleotide (FAD)**, a derivative of the B vitamin riboflavin. When FAD accepts two high-energy electrons, it picks up two protons ($2H^+$) and forms $FADH_2$.

$NAD^+ + 2H^+ \leftrightarrow NADH + H^+$

NADH carries two high-energy electrons

$FAD + 2H^+ \leftrightarrow FADH_2$

$FADH_2$ carries two high-energy electrons

NADPH: An Energy Shuttle for Biosynthesis

Energy powers the assembly of building blocks into complex molecules of carbohydrate, fat, and protein. NADPH, an energy-carrying molecule similar to NADH, delivers much of the energy these biosynthetic reactions require. The only structural difference between NADPH and NADH is the presence or absence of a phosphate group. Although both molecules are energy carriers, their metabolic roles are vastly different. Whereas the energy carried by NADH primarily produces ATP, nearly all the energy carried by NADPH drives biosynthesis. When a reaction transforms NADPH into $NADP^+$ (nicotinamide adenine dinucleotide phosphate), NADPH releases its cargo of two energetic electrons.

$NADPH + H^+ \leftrightarrow NADP^+ + 2H^+$

NADPH releases energy for biosynthesis when converted to $NADP^+$

nicotinamide adenine dinucleotide (NAD^+) The oxidized form of nicotinamide adenine dinucleotide. This coenzyme, which is derived from the B vitamin niacin, acts as an electron carrier in cells, undergoing reversible oxidation and reduction. The reduced form is NADH.

hydrogen ions Also called a proton. This lone hydrogen has a positive charge (H^+). It does not have its own electron, but it can share one with another atom.

flavin adenine dinucleotide (FAD) A coenzyme synthesized in the body from riboflavin. It undergoes reversible oxidation and reduction and thus acts as an electron carrier in cells. FAD is the oxidized form; $FADH_2$ is the reduced form.

glycolysis [gligh-COLL-ih-sis] The anaerobic metabolic pathway that breaks a glucose molecule into two molecules of pyruvate and yields two molecules of ATP and two molecules of NADH. Glycolysis occurs in the cytosol of a cell.

Key Concepts *ATP is the energy currency of the body. Your body extracts energy from food to produce ATP. NADH and $FADH_2$ are hydrogen and electron carriers that shuttle energy to ATP production sites. NADPH is also a hydrogen and electron carrier, but it shuttles energy for anabolic processes.*

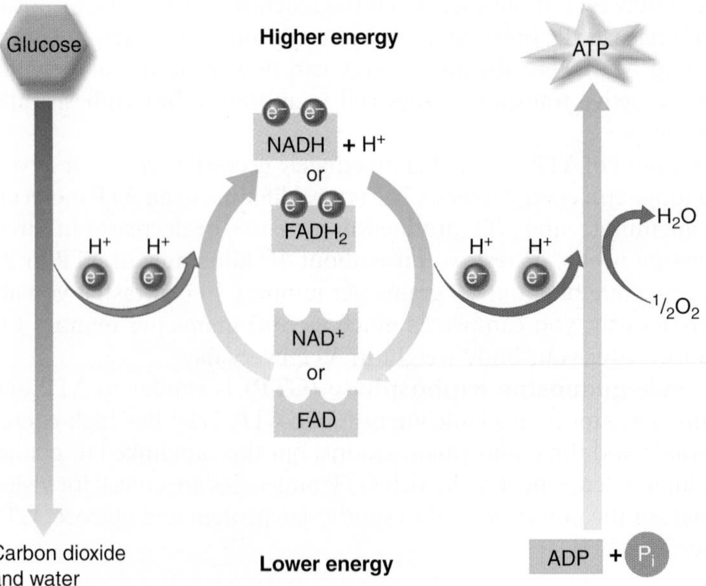

Figure 7.7 **Energy transfer**. As energy moves from glucose to ATP, molecules become high-energy or low-energy as they collect and transfer high-energy electrons and hydrogen ions (protons).

Breakdown and Release of Energy

The complete catabolism of carbohydrate, protein, and fat for energy occurs via several pathways. Although different pathways initiate the breakdown of these nutrients, complete breakdown eventually proceeds along two shared catabolic pathways—the citric acid cycle and the electron transport chain. This section first describes the pathways that catabolize glucose. It then discusses the steps that start the breakdown of fat and protein.

anaerobic [AN-ah-ROW-bic] Referring to the absence of oxygen or the ability of a process to occur in the absence of oxygen.

pyruvate The three-carbon compound that results from glycolytic breakdown of glucose. Pyruvate, the salt form of pyruvic acid, also can be derived from glycerol and some amino acids.

aerobic [air-ROW-bic] Referring to the presence of or need for oxygen. The complete breakdown of glucose, fatty acids, and amino acids to carbon dioxide and water occurs only via aerobic metabolism. The citric acid cycle and electron transport chain are aerobic pathways.

acetyl CoA A key intermediate in the metabolic breakdown of carbohydrates, fatty acids, and amino acids. It consists of a two-carbon acetate group linked to coenzyme A, which is derived from pantothenic acid.

Extracting Energy from Carbohydrate

Cells extract usable energy from carbohydrate via four main pathways: glycolysis, conversion of pyruvate to acetyl CoA, the citric acid cycle, and the electron transport chain. (See Figure 7.8.) Although glycolysis and the citric acid cycle produce small amounts of energy, the electron transport chain is the major ATP production site.

Glycolysis

Glycolysis ("glucose splitting") is an **anaerobic** process; that is, it does not require oxygen. In the cytosol, this sequence of reactions splits each 6-carbon glucose molecule into two 3-carbon **pyruvate** molecules while producing a relatively small amount of energy.

Just as a pump requires priming, glycolysis requires the input of two ATP molecules to get started. In the later stages, various reactions produce energy-rich molecules of NADH and release four ATP molecules. Although glycolysis both consumes and releases energy, it produces more than it uses. Glycolysis is rapid, but it produces a comparatively small amount of ATP. The glycolysis of one glucose molecule yields a net of two NADH and two ATP, along with the two pyruvates. (See Figure 7.9.)

Although most glycolytic reactions can flow in either direction, some are irreversible, one-way reactions. These one-way reactions prevent glycolysis from running backward.

What about the other simple sugars, fructose and galactose? In liver cells, glycolysis usually breaks them down, and normally they are not available to other tissues.[6] Although fructose and galactose enter glycolysis at intermediate points, the end result is the same as for glucose. One molecule of glucose, fructose, or galactose produces two NADH, a net of two ATP, and two pyruvates. Once glycolysis is complete, the pyruvate molecules easily pass from the cytosol to the interior of mitochondria, the cell's power generators, for further processing.

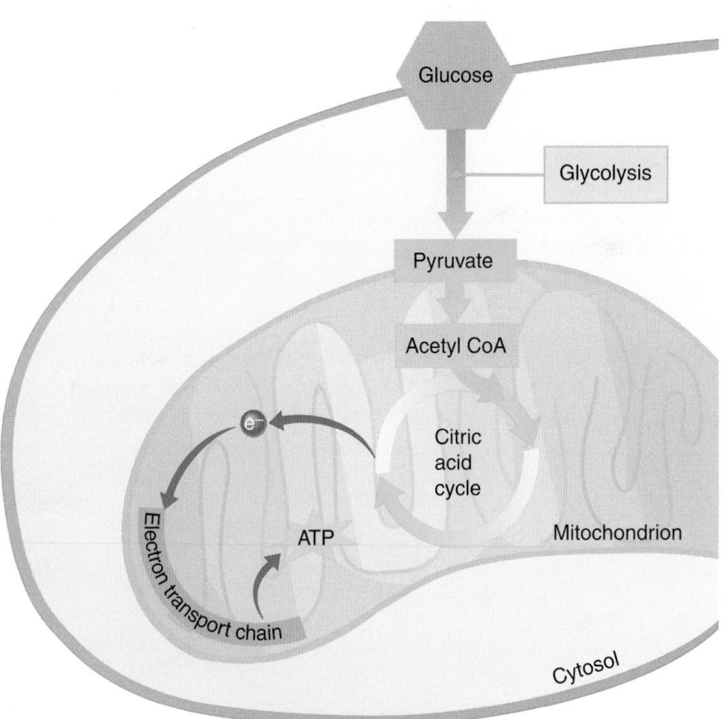

Figure 7.8 **Obtaining energy from carbohydrate.** The complete oxidation of glucose uses four major metabolic pathways: glycolysis, conversion of pyruvate to acetyl CoA, the citric acid cycle, and the electron transport chain. Glycolysis takes place in the cytosol. The remaining reactions take place in the mitochondria.

Conversion of Pyruvate to Acetyl CoA

When a cell requires energy, and oxygen is readily available, **aerobic** reactions in the mitochondria convert each pyruvate molecule to an **acetyl CoA** molecule. These reactions produce CO_2 and transfer a pair of high-energy electrons to form NADH. (See Figure 7.10.) The NADH shuttle carries the electrons to the electron transport chain.

Although many metabolic pathways can proceed either forward or backward, the formation of acetyl CoA is a one-way (irreversible) process. To form

coenzyme A Coenzyme A is a cofactor derived from the vitamin pantothenic acid.

lactate The ionized form of lactic acid, a three-carbon acid. It is produced when insufficient oxygen is present in cells to oxidize pyruvate.

acetyl CoA, reactions remove one carbon from the three-carbon pyruvate and add **coenzyme A**, a molecule derived from the B vitamin pantothenic acid. After combining with oxygen, the carbon is released as part of carbon dioxide. Recall that glycolysis splits glucose into two pyruvate molecules, so we now have two NADH and two acetyl CoA molecules.

In rapidly contracting muscle, oxygen is in short supply, and pyruvate cannot form acetyl CoA. Instead, pyruvate is rerouted to form **lactate**, another three-carbon compound. Lactate is an alternative fuel that muscle cells can

Quick Bite

When Glycolysis Goes Awry

Red blood cells do not have mitochondria, so they rely on glycolysis as their only source of ATP. They use ATP to maintain the integrity and shape of their cell membranes. A defect in red blood cell glycolysis can cause a shortage of ATP, which leads to deformed red blood cells. Destruction of these cells by the spleen leads to a type of anemia called hemolytic anemia.

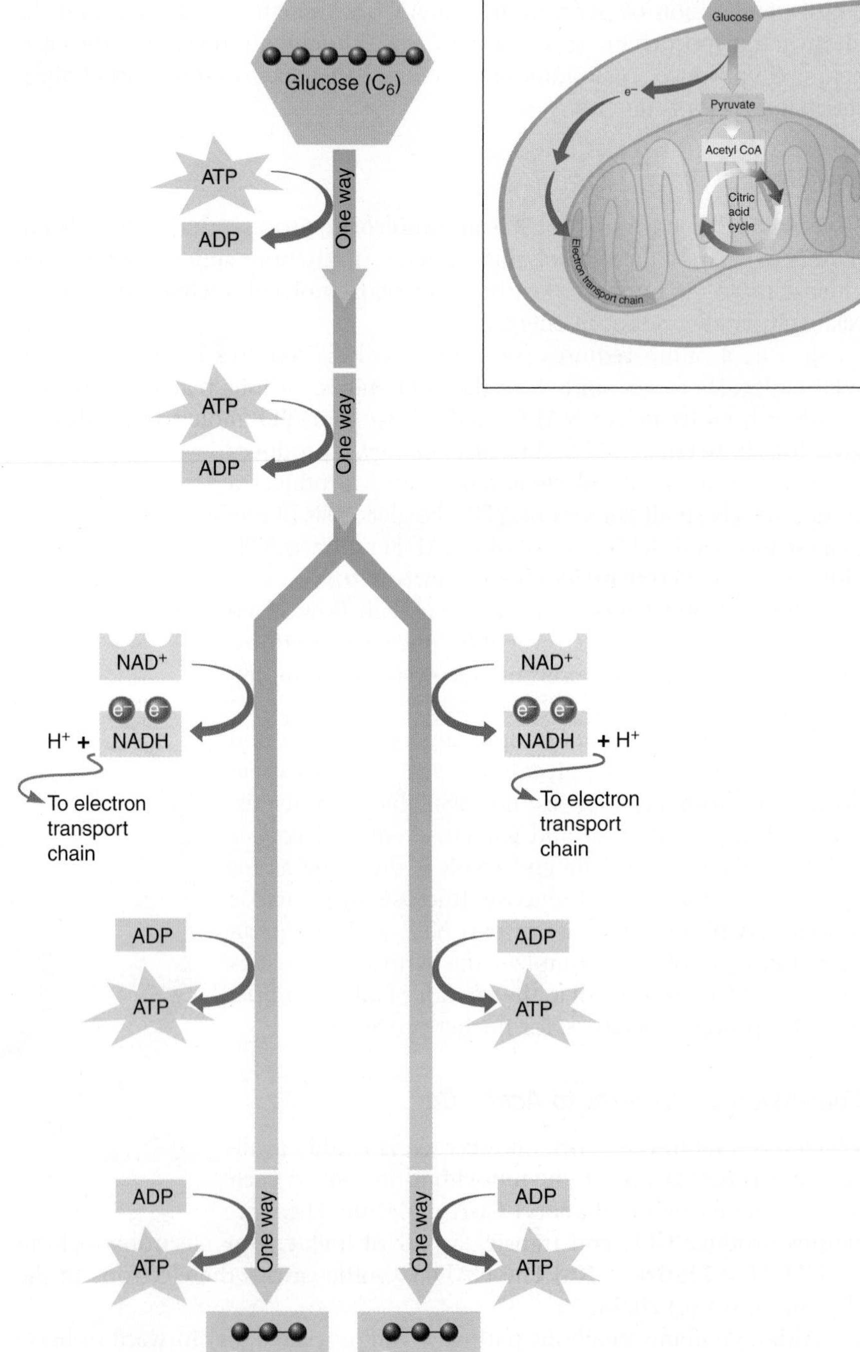

Figure 7.9 **Glycolysis.** The breakdown of one glucose molecule yields two pyruvate molecules, a net of two ATP and two NADH molecules. The two NADH molecules shuttle pairs of high-energy electrons to the electron transport chain for ATP production. Glycolytic reactions do not require oxygen, and some steps are irreversible.

Figure 7.10 **Conversion of pyruvate to acetyl CoA.** When oxygen is readily available, each pyruvate formed from glucose yields one acetyl CoA, one CO_2, and one NADH. The NADH shuttles high-energy electrons to the electron transport chain for ATP production.

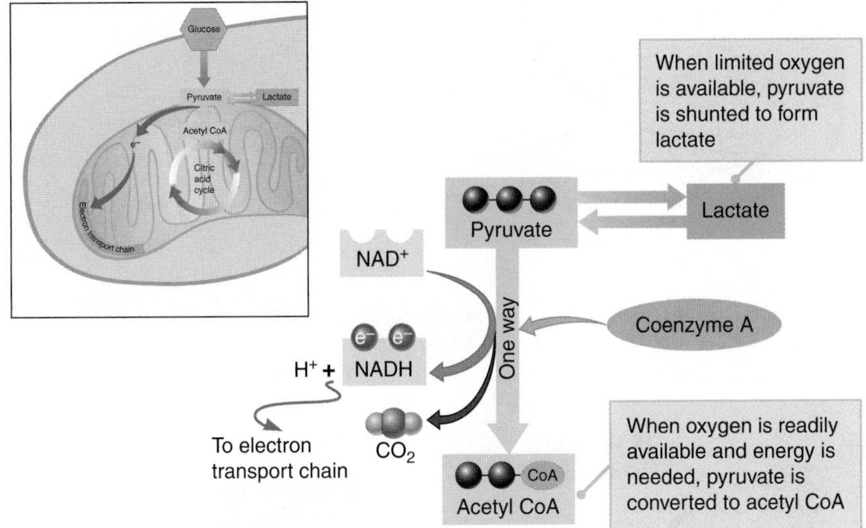

use or that liver cells can convert to glucose. When oxygen again becomes readily available, lactate is converted back to pyruvate, which irreversibly forms acetyl CoA. You will learn more about lactate production, cycling, and use in Chapter 14, "Sports Nutrition."

Although pyruvate passes easily between the cytosol and the mitochondria, the mitochondrial membrane is impervious to acetyl CoA. The acetyl CoA produced from pyruvate is trapped inside the mitochondria, ready to enter the citric acid cycle.

Citric Acid Cycle

The **citric acid cycle** is an elegant set of reactions that proceed along a circular pathway in the mitochondria. To begin the cycle, acetyl CoA combines with **oxaloacetate**, freeing coenzyme A and yielding a six-carbon compound called citrate (citric acid). The coenzyme A leaves the cycle, becoming available to react with another pyruvate and form a new acetyl CoA. Subsequent reactions in the citric acid cycle transform citrate into a sequence of intermediate compounds as they remove two carbons and release them in two molecules of CO_2. Because acetyl CoA adds two carbons to the cycle and the cycle releases two carbons as CO_2, there is no net gain or loss of carbon atoms. The final step in the citric acid cycle regenerates oxaloacetate.

The citric acid cycle extracts most of the energy that ultimately powers the generation of ATP. For each acetyl CoA entering the cycle, one complete "turn" produces one GTP and transfers pairs of high-energy electrons to three NADH and one $FADH_2$. Because the breakdown of one glucose molecule yields two molecules of acetyl CoA, the citric acid cycle "turns" twice for each glucose molecule and produces twice these amounts (i.e., six NADH, two $FADH_2$, and two GTP).

The citric acid cycle goes by many names. It often is called the **Krebs cycle** after Sir Hans Krebs, the first scientist to explain its operation, who was awarded the Nobel Prize in 1953 for his work. It also is called the **tricarboxylic acid (TCA) cycle** because a tricarboxylic acid (citrate)

citric acid cycle The metabolic pathway occurring in mitochondria in which the acetyl portion ($CH_3COO–$) of acetyl CoA is oxidized to yield two molecules of carbon dioxide and one molecule each of NADH, $FADH_2$, and GTP. Also known as the Krebs cycle and the tricarboxylic acid cycle.

oxaloacetate A four-carbon intermediate compound in the citric acid cycle. Acetyl CoA combines with free oxaloacetate in the mitochondria, forming citrate and beginning the cycle.

Krebs cycle See *citric acid cycle.*

tricarboxylic acid (TCA) cycle See *citric acid cycle.*

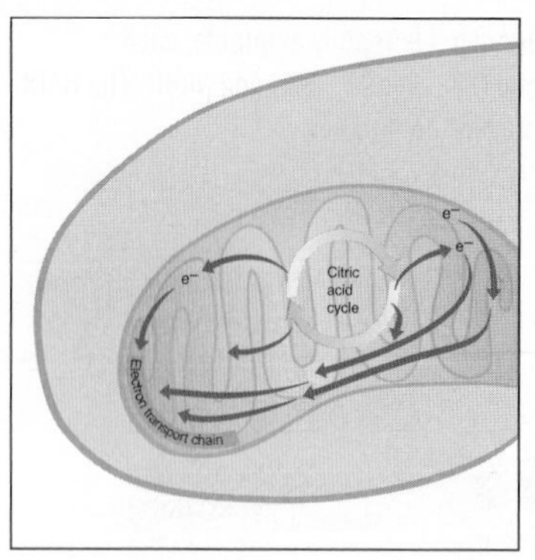

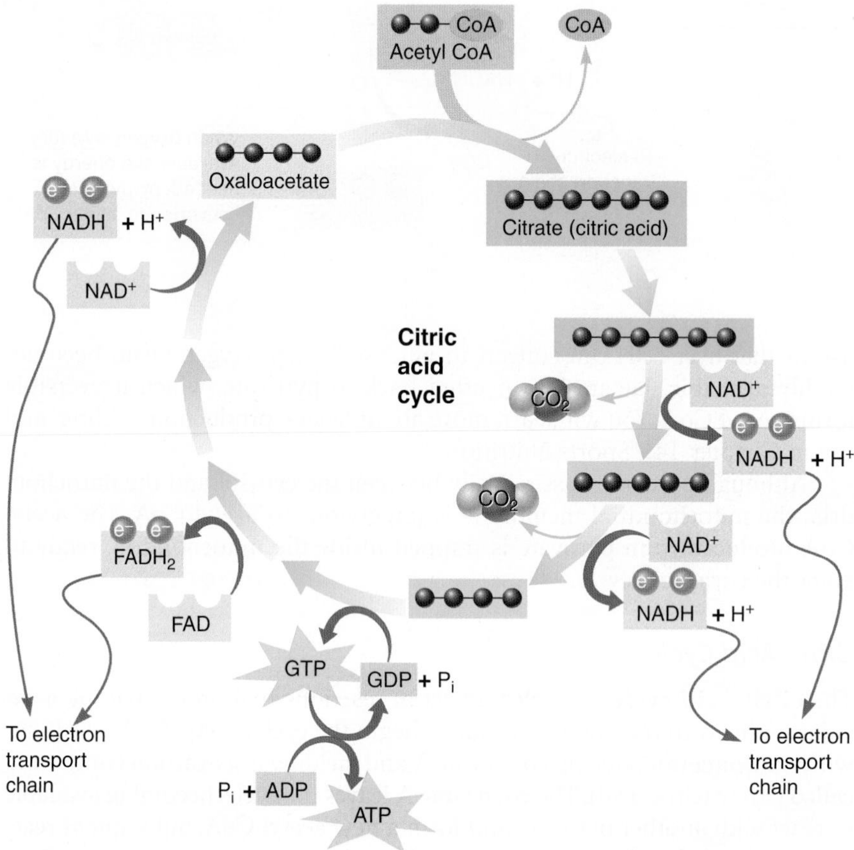

Figure 7.11 **The citric acid cycle.** This circular pathway accepts one acetyl CoA and yields two CO_2, three NADH, one $FADH_2$, and one GTP (readily converted to ATP). The electron shuttles NADH and $FADH_2$ carry high-energy electrons to the electron transport chain for ATP production.

is formed in the first step. Most nutritionists use the term *citric acid cycle*. **Figure 7.11** shows an overview of the citric acid cycle.

The citric acid cycle is also an important source of building blocks for the biosynthesis of amino acids and fatty acids. Rather than using the cycle's intermediate molecules to complete the cycle, the cell may siphon them off for biosynthesis. Cells may use oxaloacetate, for example, to make glucose or certain amino acids. If alternate uses deplete the supply of oxaloacetate, the citric acid cycle can slow or even stop. Fortunately, cells can make oxaloacetate directly from pyruvate, easily replenishing the citric acid cycle's supply.

electron transport chain An organized series of carrier molecules—including flavin mononucleotide (FMN), coenzyme Q, and several cytochromes—that are located in mitochondrial membranes and shuttle electrons from NADH and $FADH_2$ to oxygen, yielding water and ATP.

Electron Transport Chain

The final step in glucose breakdown is a sequence of linked reactions that take place in the **electron transport chain**, which is located in the inner

THINK About It 2 **mitochondrial membrane**. Most ATP is produced here, and as long as oxygen is available, it can dispense ATP and maintain exercise for hours. Because the mitochondrion is the site of both the citric acid cycle and the electron transport chain, it truly is the energy power plant of the cell.

NADH and $FADH_2$ now deliver their cargo of high-energy electrons. NADH produced in the mitochondria by the citric acid cycle delivers its pair of high-energy electrons to the beginning of the chain. In the inner mitochondrial membrane, these electrons are passed along a chain of linked reactions, giving up energy along the way to power the final production of ATP. At the end of the electron transport chain, oxygen accepts the energy-depleted electrons and reacts with hydrogen to form water. This formation of ATP coupled to the flow of electrons along the electron transport chain is called **oxidative phosphorylation** because it requires oxygen and it phosphorylates ADP (joins it to P_i) to form ATP. (See **Figure 7.12**.)

mitochondrial membrane The mitochondria are enclosed by a double shell separated by an intermembrane space. The outer membrane acts as a barrier and gatekeeper, selectively allowing some molecules to pass through while blocking others. The inner membrane is where the electron transport chains are located.

oxidative phosphorylation Formation of ATP from ADP and P_i coupled to the flow of electrons along the electron transport chain.

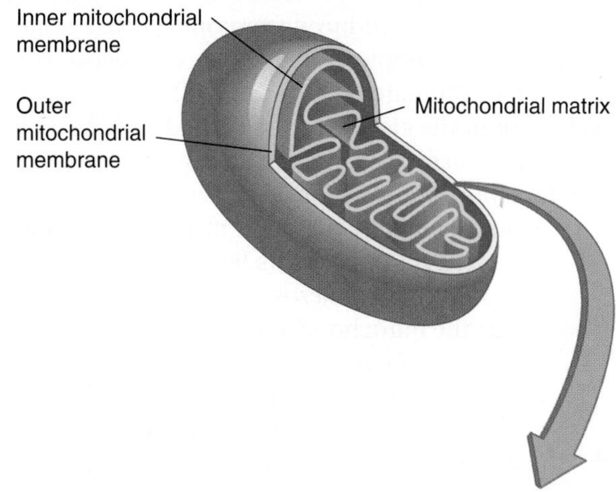

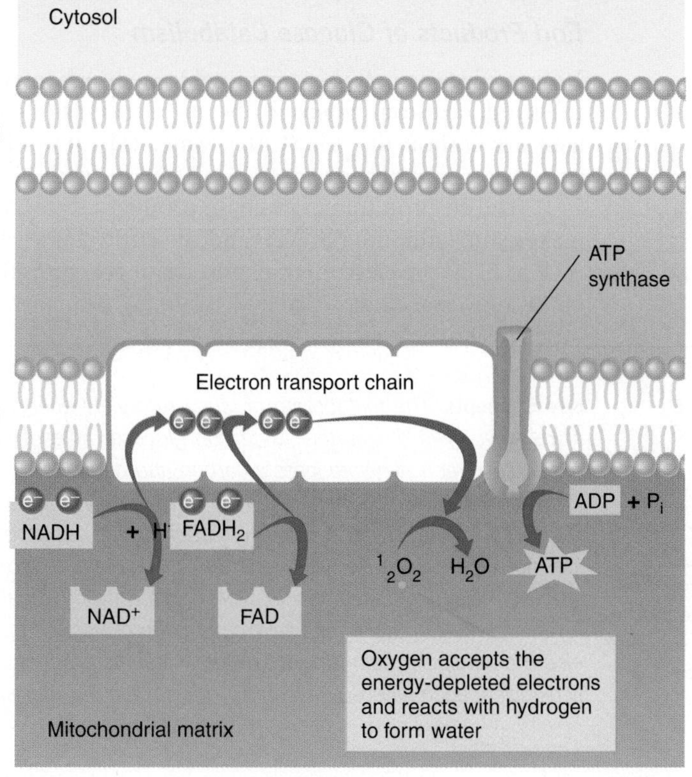

Figure 7.12 **Electron transport chain.** This pathway produces most of the ATP available from glucose. NADH molecules deliver pairs of high-energy electrons to the beginning of the chain. The pairs of high-energy electrons carried by $FADH_2$ enter this pathway farther along and produce fewer ATP than electron pairs carried by NADH. Water is the final product of the electron transport chain.

Quick Bite

The Latest ATP Count

The number of ATP (or GTP) molecules formed directly in glycolysis and the citric acid cycle is unequivocally known, but the number of ATP molecules formed from NADH and $FADH_2$ in the electron transport chain is less certain. Old estimates credited NADH from the citric acid cycle with 3 ATP, and $FADH_2$ with 2 ATP. The best current estimates are 2.5 and 1.5, respectively. "Hence, about 30 ATP are formed when glucose is completely oxidized to CO_2; this value supersedes the traditional estimate of 36 ATP." —*Lubert Stryer, Professor of Biochemistry, Stanford University*

Without an oxygen "basket" at the end to accept the energy-depleted electrons, the transport of electrons down the chain would halt, stopping ATP production. Without ATP, there would be no power for our body's essential functions. If our oxygen supply was not rapidly restored, we would die.

What about $FADH_2$? The high-energy electrons from $FADH_2$ enter the electron transport chain at a later point than the electrons from NADH. Because they travel through fewer reactions, the electrons from $FADH_2$ generate fewer ATP molecules.

Biochemists have revised their estimates of the amount of ATP produced by the electron transport chain. Scientists had estimated that electron pairs from NADH produced 3 ATP and those from $FADH_2$ produced 2 ATP. Experiments have shown, however, that the actual amounts are slightly smaller—2.5 ATP from NADH and 1.5 ATP from $FADH_2$. Because each pair of electrons that traverses the electron transport chain produces slightly fewer ATP molecules than once thought, biochemists have revised their estimates for the total amount of ATP produced from one glucose molecule. Historically, they believed that the complete breakdown of glucose produced 36 to 38 ATP, but the current estimate is 30 to 32 ATP.[7]

What about the electron pairs carried by NADH from glycolysis? Recall that glycolysis takes place in the cytosol, whereas the citric acid cycle and electron transport chain are located in the mitochondria. NADH in the cytosol cannot penetrate the outer mitochondrial membrane. Instead, cytosolic NADH transfers its high-energy electrons to special molecules that shuttle them across the outer mitochondrial membrane. Once inside the mitochondrion, the electron pair may be picked up by the formation of either NADH or $FADH_2$. Depending on which shuttle is formed, an electron pair from glycolytic NADH generates either 2.5 or 1.5 ATP. Because of this difference, the complete oxidation of a glucose molecule does not always produce the same amount of ATP. (See **Figure 7.13**.)

Figure 7.13 **Complete oxidation of glucose.** These metabolic pathways and molecules move energy from glucose to ATP. Complete oxidation of one glucose molecule yields 30 to 32 ATP.

COMPLETE OXIDATION OF GLUCOSE

Pathway	ATP formed by pathway	ATP formed in electron transport chain
Glycolysis (1 Glucose)		
Net 2 ATP (4 produced – 2 used)	2	
2 NADH*		3 to 5
2 Pyruvate to 2 Acetyl CoA		
First pyruvate → Acetyl CoA		
1 NADH		2.5
Second pyruvate → Acetyl CoA		
1 NADH		2.5
Citric Acid Cycle (twice)		
First acetyl CoA → Citric acid cycle		
1 GTP (ATP)	1	
1 $FADH_2$		1.5
3 NADH		7.5
Second acetyl CoA → Citric acid cycle		
1 GTP (ATP)	1	
1 $FADH_2$		1.5
3 NADH		7.5
Subtotal	4	26 to 28
		Total = 30 to 32

*Each NADH formed in the cytosol by glycolysis will produce either 2.5 or 1.5 ATP in the electron transport chain.

End Products of Glucose Catabolism

Now you've seen all the steps in glucose breakdown. What has the cell produced from glucose? The end products of complete catabolism are carbon dioxide (CO_2), water (H_2O), and ATP. Both the conversion of pyruvate to acetyl CoA and the citric acid cycle produce CO_2. The electron transport chain produces water. While glycolysis makes small amounts of ATP and the citric acid cycle makes a little ATP as GTP, the electron transport chain generates the vast majority of this universal energy currency. Table 7.1 summarizes the pathways of glucose metabolism.

Key Concepts *The metabolism of glucose to yield energy occurs in several steps. Glycolysis breaks the six-carbon glucose molecule into two pyruvate molecules. Each pyruvate loses a carbon and combines with coenzyme A to form acetyl CoA, which then enters the citric acid cycle. Two carbons enter the cycle as part of acetyl CoA, and two carbons leave as part of two carbon dioxide molecules. Because two acetyl CoA molecules are formed from a single glucose molecule, the citric acid cycle operates twice. Finally, the NADH and $FADH_2$ formed in these pathways carry pairs of high-energy electrons to the electron transport chain, where ATP and water are produced. When completely oxidized, each glucose molecule yields carbon dioxide, water, and ATP.*

Table 7.1 **Summary of the Major Metabolic Pathways in Glucose Metabolism**

Pathways	Location	Type	Summary	Starting Materials	End Products
Glycolysis	Cytosol	Anaerobic	A series of reactions that convert one glucose molecule to two pyruvate molecules.	Glucose, ATP	Pyruvate, ATP, NADH
Pyruvate to acetyl CoA	Mitochondria	Aerobic	Pyruvate from glycolysis combines with coenzyme A to form acetyl CoA while releasing carbon dioxide.	Pyruvate, coenzyme A	Acetyl CoA, carbon dioxide, NADH
Citric acid cycle	Mitochondria	Aerobic	This cycle of reactions degrades the acetyl portion of acetyl CoA and releases the coenzyme A portion. This cycle releases carbon dioxide and produces most of the energy-rich molecules, NADH and $FADH_2$, generated by the breakdown of glucose.	Acetyl CoA	Carbon dioxide, NADH, $FADH_2$, GTP
Electron transport chain	Mitochondria (membrane)	Aerobic	As the electrons from NADH and $FADH_2$ pass along this chain of transport proteins, they release energy to power the generation of ATP. Oxygen is the final electron acceptor and combines with hydrogen to form water.	NADH, $FADH_2$	ATP, water

Extracting Energy from Fat

To extract energy from fat, the body first breaks down triglycerides into their component parts, glycerol and fatty acids. Glycerol, a small three-carbon molecule, carries a relatively small amount of energy and can be converted by the liver to pyruvate or glucose. Fatty acids store nearly all the energy found in triglycerides.

The breakdown of fatty acids takes place inside the mitochondria. Before a fatty acid can cross into a mitochondrion, it must be linked to coenzyme A, which activates the fatty acid. Just as the input of ATP launched glycolysis, the input of ATP powers fatty acid activation. The breakdown of one ATP molecule to one AMP and two P_i provides the energy to drive this reaction. Although this activation reaction requires only one molecule of ATP, it breaks both of ATP's high-energy phosphate bonds and consumes the energetic equivalent of two ATP molecules (double the amount of energy released from the reaction ATP $\rightarrow$ ADP + P_i).

Carnitine Shuttle

Without assistance, the activated fatty acid cannot get inside the mitochondria where fatty acid oxidation and the citric acid cycle operate. This entry problem is solved by **carnitine**, a compound formed from the amino acid lysine. Carnitine has the unique task of ferrying activated fatty acids across the mitochondrial membrane, from the cytosol to the interior of the mitochondrion. When carnitine is in short supply, the production of ATP slows. Moderate carnitine deficiency in heart or skeletal muscle reduces muscle endurance; more extreme deficiency causes muscular strength to fail more quickly.[8] Based on its role in fatty acid oxidation, some people claim that carnitine supplements act as "fat burners." Research data show that carnitine

carnitine [CAR-nih-teen] A compound that transports fatty acids from the cytosol into the mitochondria, where they undergo beta-oxidation.

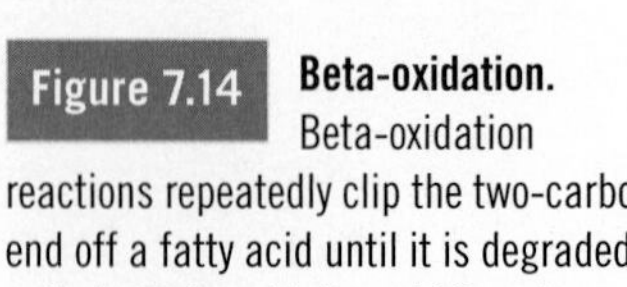

Figure 7.14 Beta-oxidation. Beta-oxidation reactions repeatedly clip the two-carbon end off a fatty acid until it is degraded entirely. Beta-oxidation of 18-carbon stearic acid produces nine acetyl CoA, eight $FADH_2$, and eight NADH.

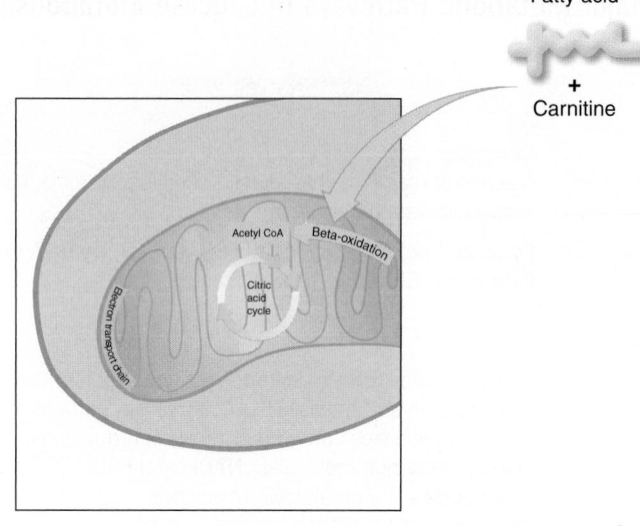
Fatty acid
+
Carnitine
Acetyl CoA
Beta-oxidation
Citric acid cycle
Electron transport chain

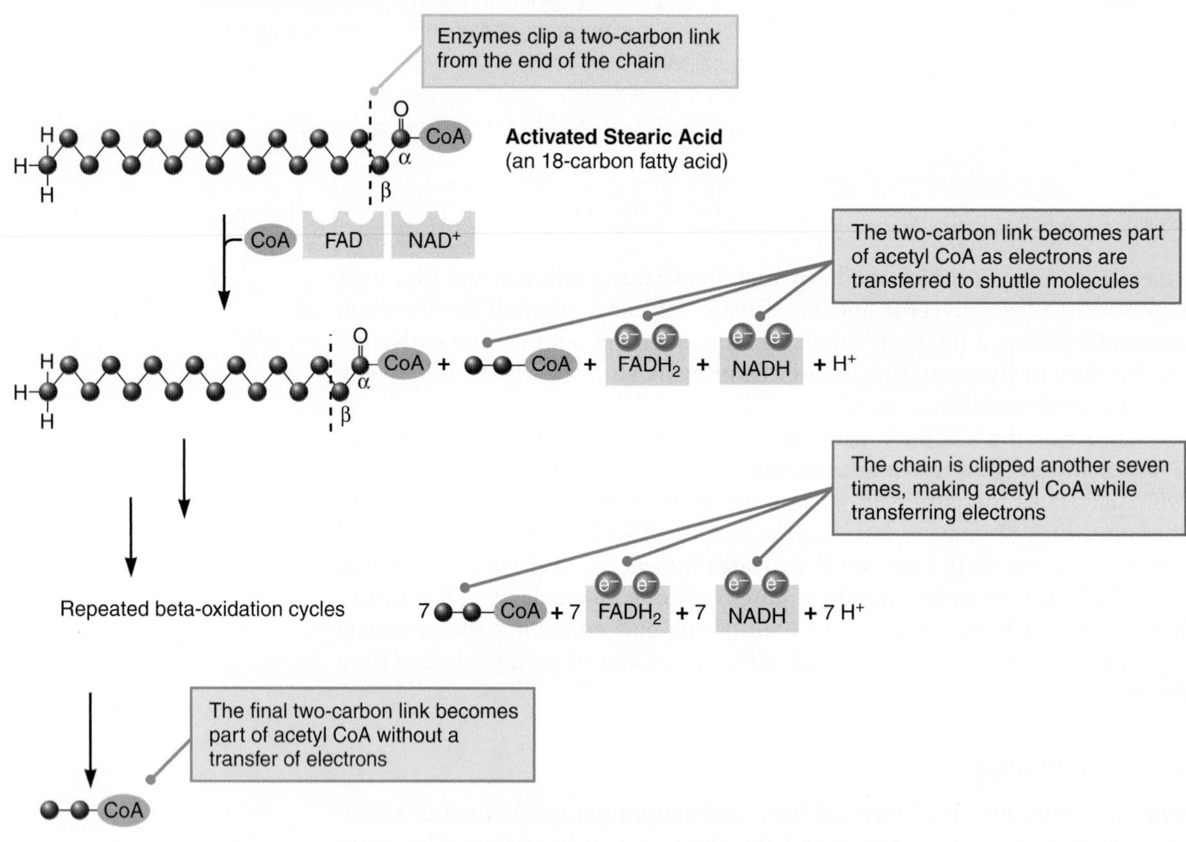
BETA-OXIDATION
Enzymes clip a two-carbon link from the end of the chain
Activated Stearic Acid
(an 18-carbon fatty acid)
CoA FAD NAD+
The two-carbon link becomes part of acetyl CoA as electrons are transferred to shuttle molecules
CoA + CoA + FADH2 + NADH + H+
The chain is clipped another seven times, making acetyl CoA while transferring electrons
Repeated beta-oxidation cycles
7 CoA + 7 FADH2 + 7 NADH + 7 H+
The final two-carbon link becomes part of acetyl CoA without a transfer of electrons
CoA

supplementation in healthy people has little or no effect on fatty acid oxidation rates or athletic performance.[9]

beta-oxidation The breakdown of a fatty acid into numerous molecules of the two-carbon compound acetyl coenzyme A (acetyl CoA).

Beta-Oxidation

Once in the mitochondria, a process called **beta-oxidation** disassembles the fatty acid and converts it into several molecules of acetyl CoA. (See **Figure 7.14**.) Starting at the beta carbon of the fatty acid (the second carbon from the acid end), enzymes clip a two-carbon "link" off the end of the chain. Reactions convert this two-carbon link to one acetyl CoA, while also transferring one pair of electrons to $FADH_2$ and another pair to NADH. This process repeats in stepwise fashion, shortening the chain by two carbons at a time until only one two-carbon segment remains. This final two-carbon link simply becomes one acetyl CoA without producing $FADH_2$ and NADH.

In nature, almost all fatty acids have an even number of carbons. Although they can vary in length from 4 to 26 carbons, they often are 16 or 18 carbons long. If your body encounters an odd-numbered fatty acid, it breaks down this chain in the same way until it reaches a final three-carbon link. Rather than try to clip this link into smaller segments, a reaction joins it with coenzyme A. This three-carbon compound enters the citric acid cycle at a point farther along than acetyl CoA's entry point. Because it skips some of the early citric acid cycle reactions, it has a shorter journey than acetyl CoA and produces two fewer NADH molecules.

The Citric Acid Cycle and Electron Transport Chain Complete Fatty Acid Breakdown

Beta-oxidation of a fatty acid produces a flood of acetyl CoA that can enter the citric acid cycle. The citric acid cycle and electron transport chain complete the extraction of energy from fatty acids. Just as they processed acetyl CoA, NADH, and $FADH_2$ from glucose, these same pathways use acetyl CoA, NADH, and $FADH_2$ from fatty acids to produce ATP.

The end products of fatty acid breakdown are the same as those of glucose breakdown: carbon dioxide, water, and ATP. The exact amount of ATP depends on the length of the fatty acid chain. Because longer chains have more carbon bonds, beta-oxidation of longer chains produces more acetyl CoA and thus more ATP. The complete breakdown of an 18-carbon fatty acid, for example, produces 120 ATP (see **Figure 7.15**), whereas a 10-carbon fatty acid produces only 66 ATP. Because a fatty acid chain typically contains many more carbon atoms than a molecule of glucose, a single fatty acid produces substantially more ATP. For a single triglyceride with three 18-carbon fatty acids, complete breakdown of the fatty acids produces 360 ATP, more than 10 times the 30 to 32 ATP produced from the complete oxidation of glucose.

Pathway	ATP yield
Beta-oxidation – stearic acid (C18:0)	
8 NADH	20
8 $FADH_2$	12
Citric acid cycle – 9 acetyl CoA	
1 GTP x 9 = 9 GTP	9
3 NADH x 9 = 27 NADH	67.5
1 $FADH_2$ x 9 = 9 $FADH_2$	13.5
Subtotal	122
ATP needed to start beta-oxidation	–2
Net yield	**120**

The grand total:
120 ATP from one molecule of stearic acid

Figure 7.15 The complete breakdown of stearic acid. The complete oxidation of one 18-carbon fatty acid yields about four times as much ATP as the complete oxidation of one glucose molecule.

Fat Burns in a Flame of Carbohydrate

Acetyl CoA from beta-oxidation can enter the citric acid cycle only when fat and carbohydrate breakdown are synchronized. Without available oxaloacetate, acetyl CoA cannot start the citric acid cycle. Conditions such as starvation and consumption of high-fat, low-carbohydrate diets can deplete oxaloacetate, blocking acetyl CoA from entry. This reroutes the acetyl CoA to form a family of compounds called ketone bodies. (See the section "Making Ketone Bodies" later in this chapter.) Production of ketone bodies can occur with popular high-protein diets that are low in carbohydrate but also high in fat.

THINK About It 3

For fatty acid oxidation to continue efficiently and unchecked, reactions in the mitochondria must ensure a reliable supply of oxaloacetate. These reactions convert some pyruvate directly to oxaloacetate rather than to acetyl CoA. Since carbohydrate (glucose) is the original source of the pyruvate, and hence this oxaloacetate, scientists coined the adage "Fat burns in a flame of carbohydrate."

Key Concepts *Extracting energy from fat involves several steps. First, triglycerides are separated into glycerol and three fatty acids. Glycerol forms pyruvate and can be broken down to yield a small amount of energy. Beta-oxidation breaks down fatty acid chains to two-carbon links that form acetyl CoA, which enters the citric acid cycle. Beta-oxidation and the citric acid cycle form NADH and $FADH_2$, which carry pairs of high-energy electrons to the electron transport chain, where ATP and water are made. The complete breakdown of one triglyceride molecule yields water, carbon dioxide, and substantially more ATP than the complete breakdown of one glucose molecule.*

Going Green

Biofuel Versus Fossil Fuel

Just as calories provide energy for our bodies, machine fuel supplies the energy for our lifestyles. We obtain calories from varied sources, and we obtain fuel from different sources. The two main fuel sources for machines are biofuel and fossil fuel. Both types of fuels present unique challenges in their impact on the environment, as well as on our carbon footprints.

Fossil fuels come from organisms that died millions of years ago. Coal is an example of a fossil fuel created from dead plant material that settled in swamps and underwent changes over millions of years. Fossil fuels are a nonrenewable resource because their replenishment rate is extremely low relative to their consumption rate. How do fossil fuels affect the environment? The prospecting and extracting, transporting, refining, and distribution of fossil fuel all contribute to greenhouse gas emissions and thus to climate change.

Biofuels can be produced from a number of different food crops that are derived directly or indirectly from photosynthesis. Although considered a renewable resource, this process raises environmental concerns and issues as well. The United States is the world's biggest producer of biofuels, derived mostly from corn. The environmental impacts of corn ethanol are significant. Soil erosion in addition to the heavy use of nitrogen fertilizer and pesticides leads to water and soil pollution. These factors in turn contribute to climate change. In addition, producing each gallon of ethanol requires 1,700 gallons of water (mostly to grow the corn) and generates 6 to 12 gallons of noxious organic effluent.[1]

Are biofuels a better alternative to fossil fuels? Some scientific research has established that some kinds of biofuel generate as much carbon dioxide as the fossil fuels they replace. Additionally, many people are focusing on how best to proceed globally with biofuel production in light of its potential impact on the world's food supply and hunger.[2]

One issue of increasing concern regards the quantity of arable land needed to produce biofuel rather than to produce food crops. Supporters of biofuel contend that biofuels are the only renewable alternative to fossil fuels and do generally result in greenhouse gas emission savings. Although there is great concern about the ultimate impact of biofuel production on hunger among the world's poorest people, the major increase in biofuels does have the potential to benefit the world's population living in poverty.[3]

So, what type of fuel is best for the environment? We do not have a definitive answer yet. Alternatives that have proven to be efficient for biofuel production are cellulose-containing materials, such as trees; grasses; woodchips; and field crop residues from wheat, rice straw, and cornstalks.[4] Until we have more definitive answers, we need to use every technique and strategy available. These will involve, in addition to experimenting with fuel sources, conservation of electricity and other resources. Small steps in energy conservation today can have a significant impact on your carbon footprint of tomorrow!

1 Bournay E. *Atlas Environment du Monde Diplomatique 2007*, as cited in UNEP/GRID-Arendal. Biofuel versus fossil fuel. http://maps.Grida.no/go/graphic/biofuel-versus-fossil-fuel1. Accessed 7/15/09.

2 Stein K. Food vs biofuel. *J Am Diet Assoc.* 2007;107(11):1870.

3 Ibid.

4 Runge CF, Senauer B. How biofuels could starve the poor. *Foreign Affairs* May/June 2007. http://www.foreignaffairs.org/20070501faessay86305/c-ford-runge-benjamin-senauer/how-biofuels-could-starve-the-poor.html. Accessed 8/15/09.

Extracting Energy from Protein

Because protein has vital structural and functional roles, proteins and amino acids are not considered primary sources of energy. The primary and unique role of amino acids is to serve as building blocks for the synthesis of body protein and nitrogen-containing compounds. However, if energy production falters due to a lack of available carbohydrate and fat, protein comes to the rescue. During starvation, for example, energy needs take priority, so the body breaks down protein and extracts energy from the amino acid building blocks.

To use amino acids as an energy source, a process called deamination first strips off the amino group (–NH2), leaving a "carbon skeleton." (See **Figure 7.16**.) The liver quickly converts the amino group first to ammonia and then to urea, which the kidneys excrete in urine. When you eat more protein than you need, your kidneys excrete the excess nitrogen and your liver uses the carbon skeletons to produce energy, glucose, or fat. Much to the dismay of bodybuilders, when they attempt to build muscle by drinking pricey protein drinks, they can end up gaining fat instead!

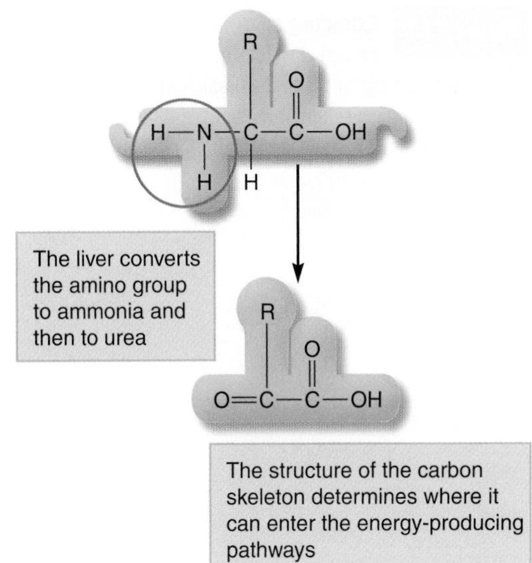
R
O
H—N—C—C—OH
H H
The liver converts the amino group to ammonia and then to urea
R
O
O=C—C—OH
The structure of the carbon skeleton determines where it can enter the energy-producing pathways

Figure 7.16 **Deamination.** A deamination reaction strips the amino group from an amino acid.

Carbon Skeletons Enter Pathways at Different Points

Like a crowd of people streaming into a concert through five different doors rather than one main entrance, carbon skeletons—unlike glucose—can enter the breakdown pathways at several different points. The carbon skeleton from each type of amino acid has a unique structure and number of carbon atoms. These characteristics determine the carbon skeleton's fate, be it pyruvate, acetyl CoA, ketone bodies, or one of the intermediates of the citric acid cycle.

End Products of Amino Acid Catabolism

The complete breakdown of an amino acid yields urea, carbon dioxide, water, and ATP. The carbon skeleton's point of entry into the breakdown pathways determines the amount of ATP it produces. Whereas the complete breakdown of alanine, for example, produces 12.5 ATP, methionine produces only 5 ATP. Compared with glucose and fatty acids, no amino acid produces much ATP. (See **Figure 7.17**.)

Key Concepts *To extract energy from amino acids, first deamination removes the amino groups, leaving behind carbon skeletons. The liver quickly converts these amino groups to urea and sends them to the kidneys for excretion. The carbon skeleton structure determines where it enters the catabolic pathways. Some carbon skeletons become pyruvate, others become acetyl CoA, and still others become intermediate compounds of the citric acid cycle. Complete breakdown of amino acids yields water, carbon dioxide, urea, and ATP.*

Biosynthesis and Storage

Uh oh! Surveying the results of those holiday dinners and treats, you cringe with regret. Your clothes no longer fit, and you hate the idea of stepping on the scale. Your biosynthetic pathways have been hard at work, building fat stores from your excess intake of energy.

You head for the gym. After sweating through many workouts, your body begins to firm. You drop fat and add muscle. Now any problem with clothes fitting is due to muscle gain, not fat gain. To build muscle protein, different biosynthetic pathways have been busy making amino acids and assembling proteins.

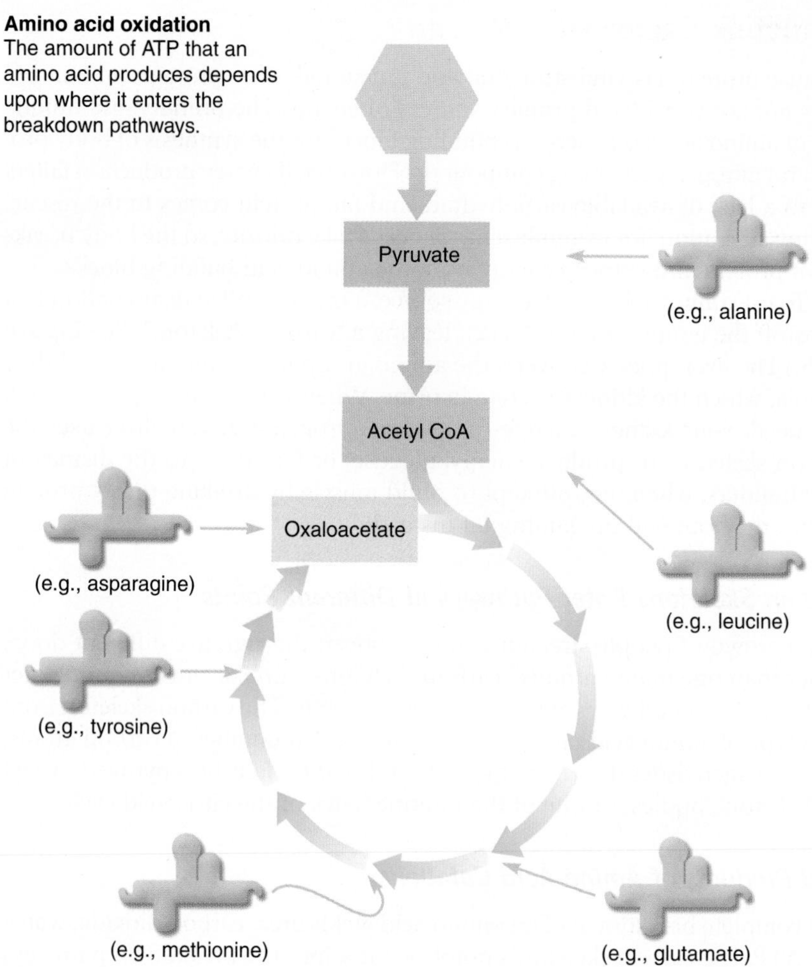

Figure 7.17 **Extracting energy from amino acids.** The carbon skeletons of amino acids have several different entrances to the breakdown pathways. Compared with glucose and fatty acids, amino acids yield much smaller amounts of energy (ATP).

Perhaps you've heard of "carb loading." (See Chapter 14, "Sports Nutrition.") This strategy uses high-carbohydrate meals to pack carbohydrate into your muscle glycogen stores before a race. Biosynthetic pathways assemble glucose into glycogen chains for storage. When needed, your body also can make glucose from certain amino acids and other precursors.

Both the breakdown and biosynthetic pathways are active at all times. While some cells are breaking down carbohydrate, fat, and protein to extract energy, other cells are busy building glucose, fatty acids, and amino acids. When your body needs energy, the breakdown pathways prevail. When it has an excess of nutrients, the biosynthetic pathways dominate. The activities in these pathways ebb and flow so that they proceed at just the right rate, not too rapidly and not too slowly. **Figure 7.18** illustrates the interconnections among the metabolic pathways.

Making Carbohydrate (Glucose)

Your body sets a high priority on maintaining an adequate amount of glucose circulating in the bloodstream. Table 7.2 shows the amount of energy, in kilocalories, that a typical 70-kilogram man has available. Blood glucose is the primary source of energy for your brain, central nervous system, and

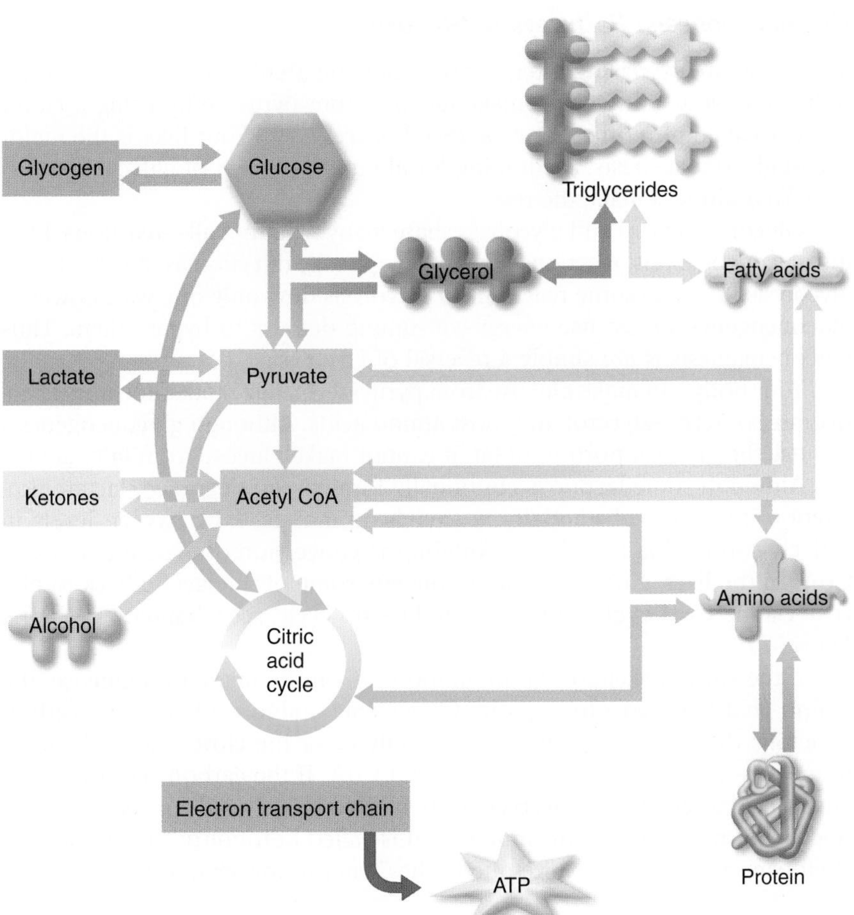

Figure 7.18 **Overview of metabolic pathways.** As if they were traveling through a maze of city streets, molecules move through a network of breakdown and biosynthetic pathways. Not all pathways are available to a molecule. Just as traffic lights and one-way streets regulate traffic flow, cellular mechanisms control the flow of molecules in metabolic pathways. These mechanisms include hormones, irreversible reactions, and the location of the reactions in the cell.

red blood cells. In fact, while you're at rest, your brain consumes about 60 percent of the energy consumed by your entire body.

The brain stores little glucose—only about 8 kilocalories. About 140 kilocalories of glucose circulate in the blood or are stored in adipose tissue. Your primary carbohydrate stores are in the form of glycogen. Muscle tissue holds about 1,200 kilocalories of glycogen, and the liver stores another 400 kilocalories.

Table 7.2 **Available Energy (kcal) in a Typical 70-Kilogram Man**

Organ	Glucose or Glycogen	Triglycerides	Mobilizable Proteins
Blood	60	45	0
Liver	400	450	400
Brain	8	0	0
Muscle	1,200	450	24,000
Adipose tissue	80	135,000	40

Source: Adapted from Berg JM, Tymoczko JL, Stryer L. *Biochemistry.* 5th ed. New York: WH Freeman, 2002.

Quick Bite

Sweet Origins
The word *gluconeogenesis* is derived from the Greek words *glyks*, meaning "sweet," *neo*, meaning "new," and *genesis*, meaning "origin" or "generation."

Gluconeogenesis: Pathways to Glucose

When you are exercising intensely or when you aren't taking in enough carbohydrate, your body can remake glucose from pyruvate by using a clever strategy called **gluconeogenesis**. (See **Figure 7.19**.) Your liver is the major site of gluconeogenesis, accounting for about 90 percent of glucose production. Your kidneys make the rest.

Gluconeogenesis and glycolysis share many—but not all—reactions. During gluconeogenesis, reactions flow in the opposite direction as they do during glycolysis. Because some reactions of glycolysis flow only one way, however, gluconeogenesis must use energy-consuming detours to bypass them. Thus gluconeogenesis is *not* simply a reversal of glycolysis.

Your body can make glucose from pyruvate, lactate, and some noncarbohydrate sources—glycerol and most amino acids. Although gluconeogenesis can use the glycerol portion of fat, it cannot make glucose from fatty acids.

Although some lactate is continually formed and degraded, lactate production increases substantially in exercising muscle. Low oxygen levels in actively contracting muscle cells inhibit the conversion of pyruvate to acetyl CoA. In the liver, gluconeogenesis converts some of the lactate back to glucose via the **Cori cycle**. For more on the Cori cycle, see Chapter 14, "Sports Nutrition."

If the carbon skeleton of an amino acid can be made into glucose, the amino acid is called **glucogenic**. Glucogenic amino acids provide carbon skeletons that become pyruvate or directly enter the citric acid cycle at intermediate points without forming acetyl CoA. If the carbon skeleton of an amino acid directly forms acetyl CoA (which your body can convert to ketone bodies but not glucose), the amino acid is called **ketogenic** (see the section "Ketogenesis: Pathways to Ketone Bodies" later in this chapter).

Key Concepts *Your body can make glucose from pyruvate, lactate, glucogenic amino acids, and glycerol, but not from fatty acids. Although most gluconeogenesis takes place in the liver, the kidneys are responsible for about 10 percent of glucose synthesis.*

gluconeogenesis [gloo-ko-nee-oh-JEN-uh-sis] Synthesis of glucose within the body from noncarbohydrate precursors such as amino acids, lactate, and glycerol. Fatty acids cannot be converted to glucose.

Cori cycle The circular path that regenerates NAD^+ and glucose when oxygen is low and lactate and NADH build up in excess in muscle tissue.

glucogenic In the metabolism of amino acids, a term describing an amino acid broken down into pyruvate or an intermediate of the citric acid cycle; that is, any compound that can be used in gluconeogenesis to form glucose.

ketogenic In the metabolism of amino acids, a term describing an amino acid broken down into acetyl CoA (which can be converted into ketone bodies).

glycogenesis The formation of glycogen from glucose.

glycogenolysis The breakdown of glycogen to glucose.

Storage: Glucose to Glycogen

Our main storage form of glucose is glycogen, a branched-chain polysaccharide made of glucose units (see Chapter 4, "Carbohydrates"). Both the liver and muscle store glycogen. Liver glycogen serves as a glucose reserve for the blood, and muscle glycogen supplies glucose to exercising muscle tissue. Glycogen stores are limited; fasting or strenuous exercise can deplete them rapidly.

A pathway called **glycogenesis** assembles glucose molecules into branched chains for storage as glycogen. When the body needs glucose, a different series of reactions known as **glycogenolysis** breaks down the glycogen chains into individual glucose molecules. In muscle, these glucose molecules enter glycolysis and continue along the metabolic pathways to produce ATP. In the liver, glycogenolysis yields glucose that moves into the bloodstream to maintain blood glucose levels.

Making Fat (Fatty Acids)

Acetyl CoA is the most important ingredient in fatty acid synthesis. Compounds that can be metabolized to form acetyl CoA can feed fatty acid synthesis. Such precursors include ketogenic amino acids, alcohol, and fatty acids themselves.

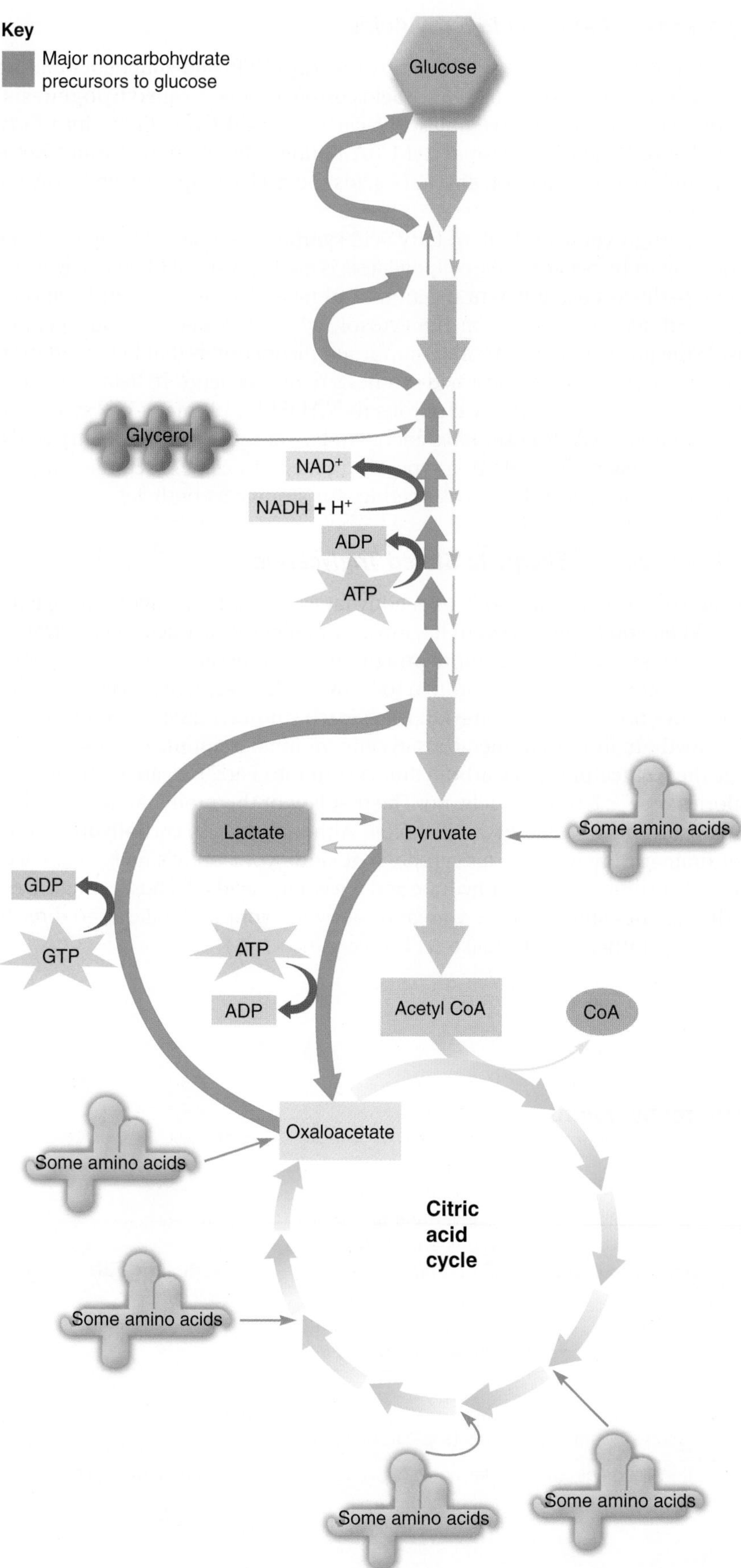

Figure 7.19 **Gluconeogenesis.** Liver and kidney cells make glucose from pyruvate by way of oxaloacetate. Gluconeogenesis is *not* the reverse of glycolysis. Although these pathways share many reactions, albeit in the reverse direction, gluconeogenesis must detour around the irreversible steps in glycolysis.

lipogenesis [lye-poh-JEN-eh-sis] Synthesis of fatty acids, primarily in liver cells, from acetyl CoA derived from the metabolism of alcohol and some amino acids.

Lipogenesis: Pathways to Fatty Acids

When your body has a plentiful supply of energy (ATP) and abundant building blocks, it can make long-chain fatty acids using a process called **lipogenesis**. To do this, your body assembles two-carbon acetyl CoA "links" into fatty acid chains. Where do these acetyl CoA building blocks come from? Ketogenic amino acids, alcohol, and fatty acids themselves supply acetyl CoA for lipogenesis.

Although you can think of fatty acid synthesis as reassembling the links broken apart by beta-oxidation, lipogenesis is *not* the reversal of beta-oxidation. These pathways use different reactions and take place in different locations: fatty acid synthesis occurs in the cytosol, whereas beta-oxidation operates inside the mitochondria. Another important distinction is that beta-oxidation releases energy, whereas fatty acid synthesis requires energy. In beta-oxidation, reactions deliver high-energy electrons to NADH for ultimate ATP synthesis. In lipogenesis, NADPH supplies energy to power the synthesis of fatty acids. Your endoplasmic reticulum, a type of organelle in cells, assembles surplus fatty acids and glycerol into triglycerides for storage as body fat.

Storage: Dietary Energy to Stored Triglyceride

When you overeat, your body uses body fat as a long-term energy storage depot. When you eat an excess of fat, most extra dietary fatty acids head straight to your fat stores. If you eat more protein than your tissues can use, your body converts most of the excess protein to body fat. Interestingly, excess carbohydrate does not readily become fat. In research studies, massive overfeeding of carbohydrate in normal men caused only minimal amounts of fat synthesis. (See the FYI feature "Do Carbohydrates Turn into Fat?") So are carbohydrate calories "free"? Unfortunately, no. The first law of thermodynamics—the law of conservation of energy—still holds. Although excess carbohydrate does not dramatically increase fat synthesis, it shifts your body's fuel preferences toward burning more carbohydrate and fewer fatty acids.[10] Thus, eating excess carbohydrates still can make you fat by allowing your fat intake to go directly to storage rather than to make ATP. (See Table 7.3.)

Table 7.3 Summary of Energy Yield and Interconversions

Dietary Nutrient	Yields Energy?	Convertible to Glucose?	Convertible to Amino Acids and Body Proteins?	Convertible to Fat?
Carbohydrate (glucose, fructose, galactose)	Yes	Yes	Yes, can yield certain amino acids when amino groups are available	Insignificant
Fat (triglycerides)				
Fatty acids	Yes, large amounts	No	No	Yes
Glycerol	Yes, small amounts	Yes, small amounts	Yes (see carbohydrate)	Insignificant
Protein (amino acids)	Yes, generally not much (see starvation in text)	Yes, if insufficient carbohydrate is available	Yes	Yes, from some amino acids
Alcohol (ethanol)	Yes	No	No	Yes

Key Concepts *When ATP is plentiful and the diet supplies an excess of energy, your cells make fatty acids and triglycerides. Energy carried by NADPH powers the synthesis of fatty acids from acetyl CoA building blocks. Glycerol and fatty acids are assembled into triglycerides on the endoplasmic reticulum. Although excess dietary carbohydrate is not readily converted to fat, it does shift the body's selection of fuel and encourages the accumulation of dietary fat in body fat stores.*

ketones [KEE-tones] Organic compounds that contain a chemical group consisting of C=O (a carbon–oxygen double bond) bound to two hydrocarbons. Pyruvate and fructose are examples of ketones. Acetone and acetoacetate are both ketones and ketone bodies. Although beta-hydroxybutyrate is not a ketone, it is a ketone body.

Making Ketone Bodies

Ketone bodies (sometimes incorrectly called **ketones**) include three compounds: acetoacetate, beta-hydroxybutyrate, and acetone. Acetoacetate and

Do Carbohydrates Turn into Fat?

Marc Hellerstein, MD, PhD

Thirty years ago, Jules Hirsch and his colleagues addressed this question indirectly. They found that the composition of fatty acids in adipose tissue closely resembled the subjects' dietary fat intake. Moreover, when they put these subjects on controlled diets of different fatty acid composition for six months, adipose fatty acids slowly changed to reflect the new dietary fatty acid composition. These studies concluded that "we are what we eat" with regard to body fat and that fatty acid synthesis is minimal at best.

The body's ability to make fat from carbohydrate is called *de novo lipogenesis* (DNL). Numerous studies using a technique called indirect calorimetry have shown that net DNL is absent or very low in humans under most dietary conditions, even after a large carbohydrate meal. But could there be concurrent synthesis and use of fat that results in no net change?

Concurrent DNL and burning of fatty acids is called *futile cycling*. About 25 to 28 percent of the carbohydrate energy is lost during the inefficient conversion to fatty acids. Does this costly conversion really happen? Stable isotopic methods have helped answer this question.

Direct Evidence

Direct evidence from stable isotopic methods shows that DNL is minimal in normal (nonobese, nondiabetic, nonoverfed) men. DNL represents less than 1 gram of saturated fat per day, whether the subjects are given large meals, intravenous glucose, or a liquid diet.

Do any circumstances stimulate DNL? Jean-Marc Schwarz gave fructose and glucose orally to lean and obese subjects. The dietary fructose increased DNL up to twentyfold compared with equal calorie loads of glucose. Nevertheless, fat synthesis still represented only a small percentage of the fructose load given (<5 percent). Scott Siler has shown that drinking alcohol stimulates DNL. Again, however, only a small percentage (<5 percent) of the alcohol was converted to fat; the great majority was released from the liver as acetate.

My laboratory studied the effect of five to seven days of carbohydrate overfeeding or underfeeding in normal men. Fat synthesis by the liver was highly sensitive to the degree of dietary carbohydrate excess. In fact, we could determine exactly which diet a person was eating by measuring DNL. Even so, the absolute amount of fat synthesis remained low, even on massively excessive carbohydrate intakes. DNL may be a sensitive *signal* of excess carbohydrate in the diet, but it is not a quantitatively important route for excess carbohydrate disposal.

Other conditions yield similar findings. Very low-fat diets (10 percent of energy as fat; 70 percent as carbohydrate) stimulate lipogenesis, but, again, not a large amount. In young women, lipogenesis increases during the follicular phase of the menstrual cycle, but the amount is small, representing only one to two pounds of extra fat per year. A high rate of DNL has been documented in humans only under conditions of massive carbohydrate overfeeding—for example, 5,000 to 6,000 carbohydrate calories per day for more than a week.

Are Carbohydrate Calories "Free"?

Alas, we still become fatter if we overeat carbohydrate. At rest, our bodies normally burn fat as our primary fuel source. An excess of dietary carbohydrate energy causes a fat-sparing shift in fuel selection as it markedly reduces the use of fat to fuel the body. Dietary fat makes a beeline for body fat storage rather than being burned to release energy. Thus, excess dietary carbohydrate is not "free" when the diet also contains fat, because the carbohydrate spares fat use.

Dr. Hellerstein is Professor of Medicine at the University of California, San Francisco, and Professor of Nutritional Sciences at the University of California at Berkeley.

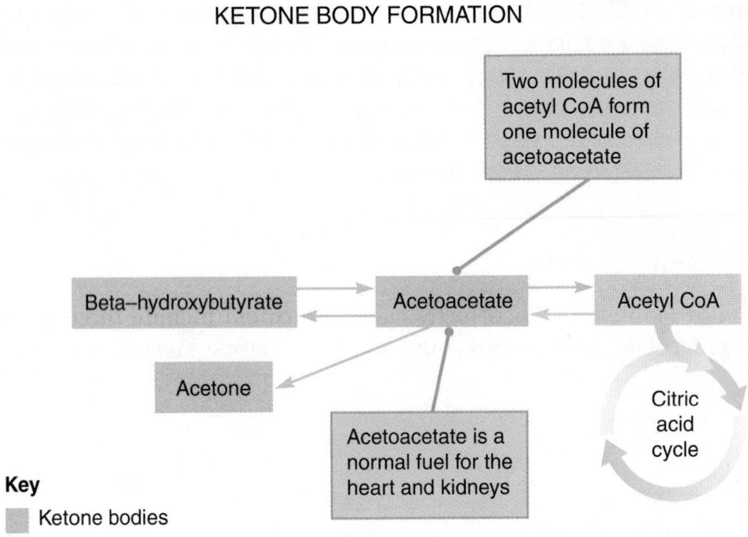

Figure 7.20 **Ketogenesis.** For acetyl CoA from fatty acid oxidation to enter the citric acid cycle, fat and carbohydrate metabolism must be synchronized. When acetyl CoA cannot enter the citric acid cycle, it is shunted to form ketone bodies, a process called ketogenesis.

ketogenesis The process in which excess acetyl CoA from fatty acid oxidation is converted into the ketone bodies acetoacetate, beta-hydroxybutyrate, and acetone.

ketoacidosis Acidification of the blood caused by a buildup of ketone bodies. It is primarily a consequence of uncontrolled type 1 diabetes mellitus and can be life threatening.

beta-hydroxybutyrate are acids, so they are sometimes referred to as keto acids. You may recognize the term *acetone*, since this chemical is a common solvent. In fact, you can smell the strong odor of acetone on the breath of people with high levels of ketone bodies in their blood: their breath smells like some nail polish removers!

Your body makes and uses small amounts of ketone bodies at all times. Although long considered to be just an emergency energy source or the result of an abnormal condition such as starvation or uncontrolled diabetes, ketone bodies are normal, everyday fuels. In fact, your heart and kidneys prefer to use the ketone body acetoacetate rather than glucose as a fuel source.[11]

Ketogenesis: Pathways to Ketone Bodies

During the breakdown of fatty acids, not all acetyl CoA enters the citric acid cycle. Your liver converts some acetyl CoA to ketone bodies, a process called **ketogenesis**. (See **Figure 7.20**.)

Ketogenesis is highly active when fatty acid oxidation in the liver produces such an abundance of acetyl CoA that it overwhelms the available supply of oxaloacetate. Unable to enter the citric acid cycle, the excess acetyl CoA is shunted to ketone body production. When a person has uncontrolled diabetes or is actually starving, ketone bodies help provide emergency energy to all body tissues, especially the brain and the rest of the CNS. Other than glucose, ketone bodies are your central nervous system's only other effective fuel.[12] (See the section "Special States" for more details on starvation and diabetes mellitus.) After the liver makes ketone bodies from acetyl CoA molecules, the ketone bodies travel to other tissues via the bloodstream. Tissue cells can convert the ketone bodies back to acetyl CoA for ATP production via the citric acid cycle and electron transport chain.[13]

To dispose of excess ketone bodies, your kidneys excrete them in urine and your lungs exhale them. If this removal process cannot keep up with the production process, ketone bodies accumulate in the blood—a condition called ketosis. (See Chapter 4, "Carbohydrates.") During even a brief fast, the catabolism of fat and protein increases the production of ketone bodies and results in ketosis.[14] Ketosis is likely to occur in uncontrolled type 1 diabetes mellitus, and in this situation, blood acidity rises quickly. This **ketoacidosis**

Quick Bite

Why Didn't My Cholesterol Levels Drop?

Your body can make cholesterol from acetyl CoA by way of ketone bodies. In fact, all 27 carbons in synthesized cholesterol come from acetyl CoA. The rate of cholesterol formation is highly responsive to cholesterol levels in cells. If levels are low, the liver makes more. If levels are high, synthesis decreases. This is why dietary cholesterol in the absence of dietary fat often has little effect on blood cholesterol levels.

can lead to a coma and eventually death if untreated.[15] During a short fast, ketoacidosis rarely occurs.

Because "fat burns in a flame of carbohydrate," a very high-fat, low-carbohydrate diet promotes ketosis. The lack of carbohydrate inhibits formation of oxaloacetate, slowing entry of acetyl CoA into the citric acid cycle and rerouting acetyl CoA to form ketone bodies. Given time, however, the body can adapt to a very high-fat, low-carbohydrate diet and avoid ketosis. Eskimos, for example, sometimes live almost entirely on fat but do not develop ketosis. Even brain cells can adapt to derive 50 to 75 percent of their fuel from ketone bodies (principally beta-hydroxybutyrate) after a few weeks of a low supply of glucose, their preferred fuel.[16]

Key Concepts *Although some ketone bodies are made and used for energy all the time, a lack of available carbohydrate accelerates ketone body production. Three types of ketone bodies—acetoacetate, beta-hydroxybutyrate, and acetone—can be made from any precursor of acetyl CoA: pyruvate, fatty acids, glycerol, and certain amino acids. Ketone bodies become an important fuel source during starvation, uncontrolled diabetes mellitus, and very high-fat, low-carbohydrate diets. In type 1 diabetes mellitus, an accumulation of ketone bodies can acidify the blood, a dangerous condition known as ketoacidosis.*

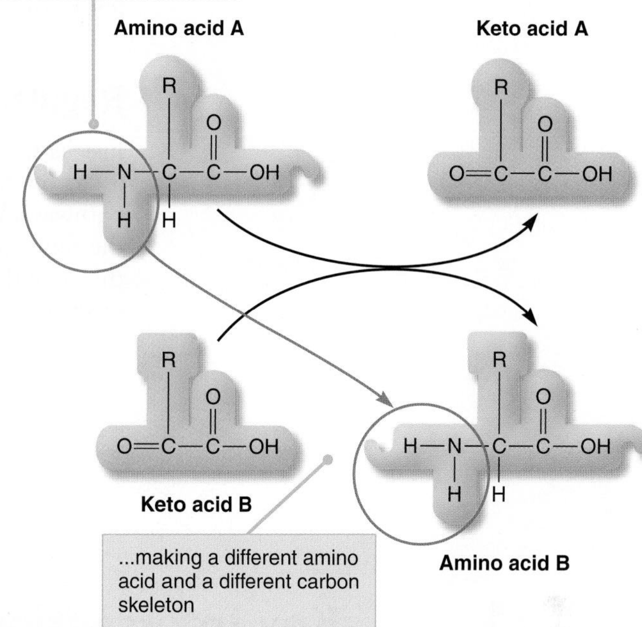

Figure 7.21 **Transamination.** A transamination reaction transfers the amino group from one amino acid to form a different amino acid.

Making Protein (Amino Acids)

Your body rebuilds proteins from a pool of amino acids in your cells. But how is that amino acid pool replenished? Your diet supplies some amino acids, the breakdown of body proteins supplies some, and cells make some. During protein synthesis, your cells can make dispensable amino acids and retrieve indispensable amino acids from the bloodstream. Your cells cannot make indispensable amino acids, however. If a cell lacks an indispensable amino acid and your diet doesn't supply it, protein synthesis stops. The cell breaks down this incomplete protein into its constituent amino acids, which are returned to the bloodstream. (See Chapter 6, "Proteins and Amino Acids," for more details of protein synthesis.)

Biosynthesis: Making Amino Acids

Your body uses many different pathways to synthesize dispensable amino acids. Each pathway is short, involving just a few steps, and builds amino acids from carbon skeletons. Pyruvate, along with intermediates of glycolysis and the citric acid cycle, supplies the carbon skeletons.

To make dispensable amino acids, the body transfers the amino group from one amino acid to a new carbon skeleton, a process called **transamination** (see **Figure 7.21**). To make the amino acid alanine, for example, pyruvate swipes an amino group from the amino acid glutamic acid to yield alanine and alpha-ketoglutaric acid. Transamination requires several enzymes. One group of enzymes, known as the aminotransferases, is derived from the B vitamin pyridoxine (B_6). Although vitamin B_6 deficiency is rare, a lack of B_6 will inhibit amino acid synthesis and impair protein formation.

transamination [TRANS-am-ih-NAY-shun] The transfer of an amino group from an amino acid to a carbon skeleton to form a different amino acid

Key Concepts *Proteins are made from combinations of indispensable and dispensable amino acids. The body synthesizes dispensable amino acids from pyruvate, other glycolytic intermediates, and compounds from the citric acid cycle. To form amino acids, transamination reactions transfer amino groups to carbon skeletons.*

Regulation of Metabolism

Just as the cruise control on your car regulates the vehicle's speed within a narrow range, your body tightly controls the reactions of your metabolic pathways. Whether highly or minimally active, each pathway proceeds at just the right speed, not too fast and not too slow. How does your body achieve this remarkable control? Although a number of strategies operate simultaneously, certain hormones are the master regulators.

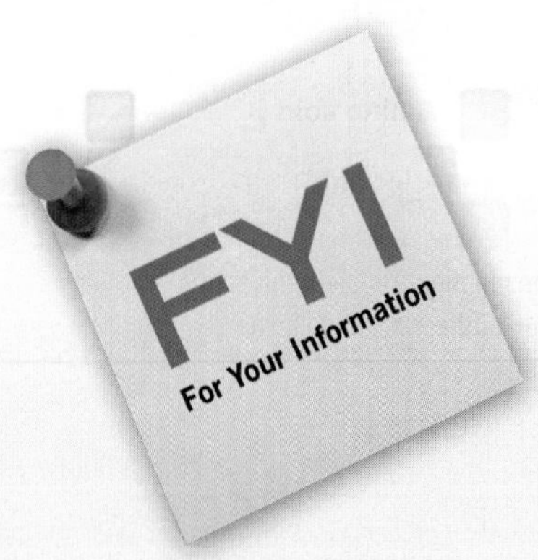

Key Intersections Direct Metabolic Traffic

Pyruvate Is Pivotal

Pyruvate is a pivotal point in the metabolic pathways. How does it select a path? What determines its destination? When ATP levels are low, cellular energy is in short supply, so the metabolic pathways flow toward the production of ATP. Depending on oxygen availability, low ATP routes pyruvate to acetyl CoA or lactate. When ATP is abundant, cells have ample energy, so the biosynthetic pathways prevail as pyruvate is converted to oxaloacetate or the amino acid alanine; oxaloacetate is converted to glucose and stored as glycogen.

To Acetyl CoA

When cells need ATP and have readily available oxygen, they rapidly convert pyruvate to acetyl CoA. This irreversible reaction commits the carbons of carbohydrates to oxidation by the citric acid cycle or to the biosynthesis of lipids. Acetyl CoA cannot be converted to glucose.

To and from Lactate

When cells need ATP but lack readily available oxygen, they reroute most pyruvate to form lactate. Although this route is always at least minimally active, it prevails when oxygen levels are low. Reversible reactions convert pyruvate to lactate, so these substances are interconvertible. For more about lactate and its various fates, see the feature "Lactate Is Not a Metabolic Dead End" in Chapter 14. The reaction that converts pyruvate to lactate uses energy carried by NADH, so it also produces NAD^+. This regeneration of NAD^+ is critical to continued glycolysis. Anaerobic conditions cut off the supply of NAD^+ from other sources, so without the NAD^+ generated in the production of lactate, glycolysis would stop.

To Oxaloacetate

Cells also can convert pyruvate to oxaloacetate, another pivotal molecule. Oxaloacetate can react with acetyl CoA to start the citric acid cycle when ATP is needed, or it can provide the building blocks to make glucose.

Oxaloacetate is essential for acetyl CoA's entry into the citric acid cycle. A steady supply of oxaloacetate is critical to the citric acid cycle's efficient extraction of energy from fatty acids. Carbohydrate feeds the pool of oxaloacetate as reactions break down carbohydrate to pyruvate and irreversibly convert the pyruvate to oxaloacetate. Cells can also make glucose from this oxaloacetate and store energy in the branched glucose chains of glycogen.

When cells have abundant ATP, they restrict the activities of certain enzymes, thus slowing the entry of acetyl CoA into the citric acid cycle. This reroutes the acetyl CoA into energy-storage pathways to form fatty acids so as to store energy as fat.

To and from Alanine

Since a reversible process converts pyruvate to the amino acid alanine, pyruvate and alanine are interconvertible. Although alanine is the only amino acid made from pyruvate, many other amino acids can be converted to pyruvate. Thus, pyruvate is located at a major junction of amino acid and carbohydrate metabolism.

Acetyl CoA at the Crossroads

Acetyl CoA, like pyruvate, stands at a pivotal point in metabolism. The breakdown pathways for glucose, fatty acids, and some amino acids converge at acetyl CoA. Once formed,

Hormones of Metabolism

Hormones are chemical messengers that help determine whether metabolic processing favors catabolic (breakdown) or anabolic (building) pathways. The major regulatory hormones are insulin, glucagon, cortisol, and epinephrine.

The pancreas secretes insulin, the leader of the storage (anabolic) team. Its mission is to decrease the amount of glucose in the blood, so it promotes carbohydrate use and storage (as glycogen). Because insulin stimulates the use of glucose over fat, its actions are said to be *fat-sparing*. In addition, insulin promotes fat storage in adipose tissue, cellular uptake of amino acids, and assembly of these amino acids into proteins. It also inhibits the breakdown of body proteins.

The pancreas also secretes glucagon, the leader of the breakdown (catabolic) team. Glucagon's mission is to increase the amount of glucose in

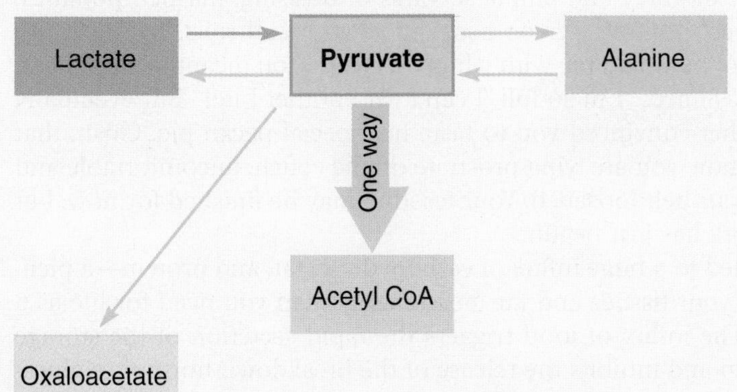

The demand for ATP and the availability of oxygen determine pyruvate's destination.

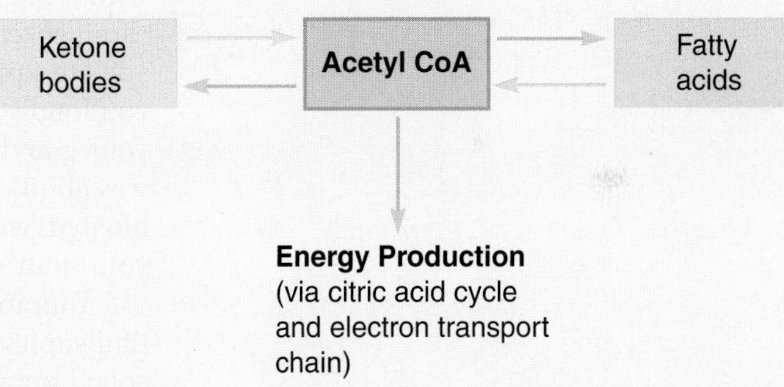

Acetyl CoA sits at a key intersection of the carbohydrate and fatty acid breakdown pathways.

what are acetyl CoA's options? It cannot return to pyruvate or make glucose, but acetyl CoA can enter major energy-producing and biosynthetic pathways. The body's energy status determines the predominant route.

To Energy Production

When cells need ATP and have oxaloacetate available, acetyl CoA enters the citric acid cycle for the ultimate production of ATP by the electron transport chain.

To and from Ketone Bodies

When the production of oxaloacetate does not match acetyl CoA production, acetyl CoA cannot enter the citric acid cycle, so the metabolic pathways shunt acetyl CoA to form ketone bodies.

To and from Fatty Acids

When energy is abundant, acetyl CoA molecules become building blocks for fatty acid chains. The body assembles these fatty acid chains into triglycerides and stores them in adipose tissue.

circulation; it stimulates the breakdown of liver glycogen. The adrenal glands secrete two other members of the breakdown team—the hormones cortisol and epinephrine. Cortisol promotes the breakdown of amino acids for gluconeogenesis and helps increase the activity of the enzymes that drive gluconeogenic reactions.[17] Epinephrine stimulates the conversion of glycogen to glucose in muscle, increasing the amount of glucose available.

The actions of each team ebb and flow in response to the levels of available nutrients.[18] Although both the storage and the breakdown teams are always active, storage dominates in times of plenty, and breakdown dominates in times of need.

Key Concepts *Hormones and other factors regulate the balance of anabolic and catabolic pathways in energy metabolism. The hormone insulin stimulates glycogen, protein, and triglyceride synthesis. The hormones glucagon, cortisol, and epinephrine stimulate breakdown of glycogen and triglycerides.*

Special States

Now you can put your new knowledge of metabolism to work by evaluating case studies of special physiological states: feasting, fasting, stress, diabetes mellitus, and exercising. What happens to your metabolism under each situation? Read on to find out which states stimulate breakdown and which stimulate biosynthesis.

Feasting

You're stuffed. You just ate a huge holiday dinner: two servings of turkey with a big ladle of gravy and ample servings of dressing, mashed potatoes, caramelized sweet potatoes, green peas, and two bread rolls. To top it off, you ate a piece of pumpkin pie with whipped cream. You meant to stop there; you loudly proclaimed, "I'm so full, I can't eat another bite!" But eventually your grandmother convinced you to taste her special pecan pie. Gosh, that was good! But now you are lying prostrate on the couch, uncomfortable and bloated, with your belt loosened. Your feasting may be finished for now, but your body's work has just begun.

Your meal led to a huge influx of carbohydrate, fat, and protein—a plentiful supply for your tissues and far more energy than you need for life as a couch potato. The influx of food triggers the rapid secretion of the storage hormone insulin and inhibits the release of the breakdown hormones glucagon, cortisol, and epinephrine. Insulin is sometimes called the "hormone of plenty" because when energy is abundant, it promotes the replenishment of energy stores (glycogen and fat), the synthesis of protein, and the maintenance and repair of tissues. Its suppression of glucagon and cortisol reduces the rate of breakdown.

The storage hormone insulin signals your cells to "store, store, store!" Consequently, much of your holiday dinner will wind up stored as fat. The surplus carbohydrate first enters glycogen stores, filling their limited capacity. In the short term, excess carbohydrate primarily readjusts your body's fuel preferences.[19] In a fat-sparing shift, your body maximizes its use of carbohydrate and minimizes its use of fat, thus promoting fat storage.[20] Although your body does not directly make appreciable amounts of fat from carbohydrate, the shift in fuel use triggered by excess carbohydrate still leads to increased fat stores and weight gain.

What happens to the surplus fat and protein? Fat tissue is the perfect energy storage package for both. Although some ATP is produced from dietary fat, nearly all excess dietary fat becomes body fat. Excess protein, beyond what's needed to replenish the overall body pool of amino acids, also heads to fat storage. (See **Figure 7.22**.)

The Return to Normal

After this frenzied bout of storage, the amount of glucose and triglyceride circulating in the bloodstream drops to the fasting level. The level of amino acids in the blood also returns to baseline, and the secretion of insulin slows.

Hours later, after a nap and perhaps a game of touch football, a further decline in blood glucose levels signals the pancreas to secrete the breakdown hormone glucagon. Glucagon broadcasts the order "Release the glucose!" and your body swings into action to counteract falling blood glucose levels. The body breaks down liver glycogen to glucose, which is released into the bloodstream. Glucagon also stimulates the production of glucose from amino acids and slows the synthesis of glycogen and fatty acids. If blood glucose levels continue to fall, the adrenal glands secrete epinephrine, which signals the liver to further increase its release of glucose into the bloodstream. Epinephrine also stimulates the breakdown of muscle glycogen to form glucose that muscles can use. This glucose does not enter the bloodstream and is immediately available for muscle tissue to mount a fight-or-flight response to danger.

If low blood glucose levels persist for hours or days, the pituitary and adrenal glands join the battle by secreting growth hormone and cortisol, respectively. These hormones cause most cells to shift their fuel usage from glucose to fatty acids. Cortisol also promotes the breakdown of amino acids, and gluconeogenesis begins to ramp up and make glucose from circulating amino acids.[21] All breakdown hormones work in concert to maintain blood glucose levels and ensure a constant supply of glucose for the central nervous system and red blood cells[22]—until it is time to attack the leftovers!

Key Concepts *Feasting, or taking in too many calories, stimulates anabolic processes such as glycogen and triglyceride synthesis. Insulin is the key hormone that promotes synthesis and storage of glycogen and fat. Your body resists making fat from excess carbohydrate, but shifts its fuel preferences. This shift still leads to the accumulation of fat stores.*

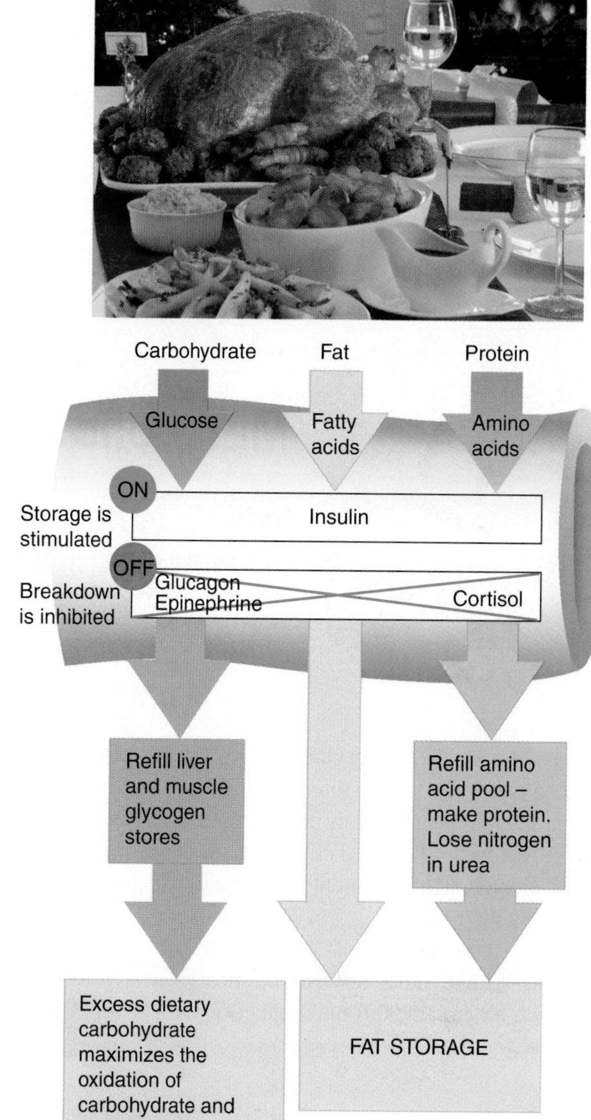

Figure 7.22 **Feasting.** Your body deals with a large influx of energy-yielding nutrients by increasing cellular uptake of glucose and promoting fat storage.

Fasting

Feasting on a holiday dinner floods your body with excess energy that is stored for future use. In contrast, fasting and starvation deprive you of energy, so your body must employ an opposing strategy—the mobilization of fuel. (See **Figure 7.23**.) Whether starvation occurs in a child during a famine, a young woman with anorexia nervosa, a patient with AIDS wasting syndrome, or a person who is intentionally fasting, the body responds in the same way.

Some people deprive themselves of food for a particular purpose—to lose weight, to stage a political protest, to participate in a religious fast, or to "cleanse" their bodies. The cleansing motivation is ironic, because fasting actually unleashes potentially damaging toxins to circulate throughout the body. Over time, fat stores accumulate environmental toxins, such as DDT, PCBs, and benzene.[23] In the case of PCBs, despite the fact that Congress banned their use decades ago, more than 9 of 10 Americans still have traces of these compounds in their body fat.[24] When bound in adipose tissue, toxins are relatively harmless. Fasting, however, breaks down adipose tissue and releases these toxins, giving them a second chance to damage cells. Although the liver—the body's detoxification center—and the intestines remove a small

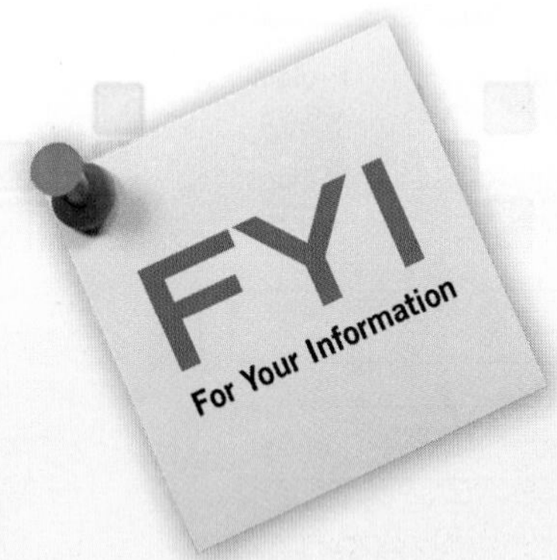

Metabolic Profiles of Important Sites

Brain

What powers your brain? Glucose! But brain cells cannot store glucose, so they need a constant supply. Your brain uses about 120 grams of glucose daily, which corresponds to a dietary energy intake of about 420 kilocalories. When your body's at rest, your brain accounts for about 60 percent of your glucose use.[1]

What happens during starvation? When glucose is in short supply, the liver comes to the rescue by converting fatty acids to ketone bodies. Ketone bodies are a critical source of replacement fuel that augments the supply of glucose to the brain.

Still, some brain cells can use only glucose. These cells survive by breaking down amino acids to make glucose via gluconeogenesis.[2]

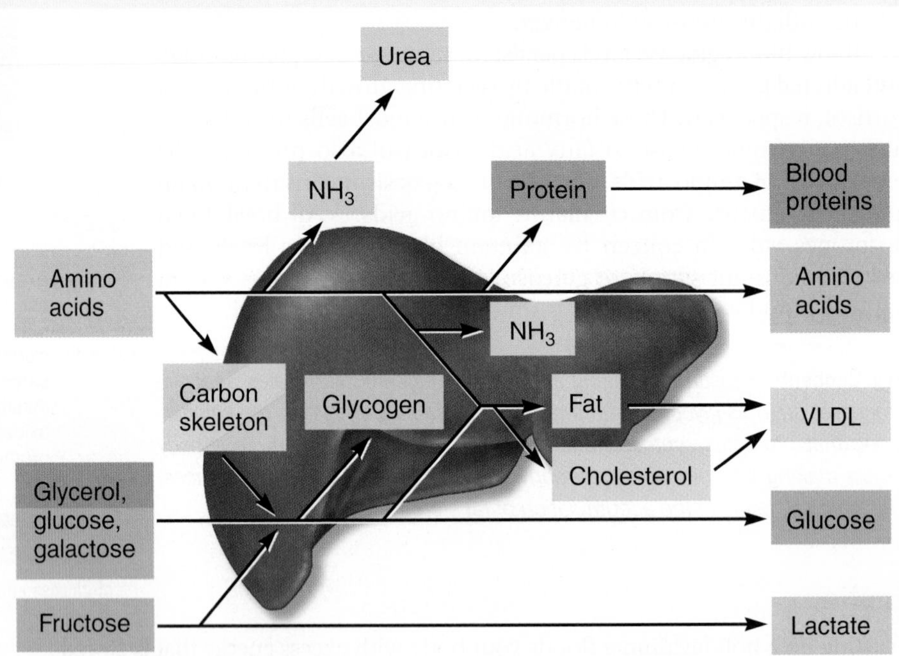

Muscle

Muscle can use a variety of fuels: lactate, fatty acids, ketone bodies, glucose, and pyruvate. Unlike your brain, muscle stores large amounts of carbohydrate fuel—about 1,200 kilocalories—in the form of glycogen. This represents about three-fourths of the glycogen in your body. To fuel bursts of activity, muscle cells readily obtain glucose from glycogen.[3]

When your muscles actively contract, they rapidly deplete available oxygen, thus inhibiting the production of ATP via the aerobic breakdown pathways. ATP formed during glycolysis becomes the primary fuel. Muscle cells use the pyruvate from glycolysis to form lactate. The lactate travels to the liver, which converts it to glucose. The glucose returns to your muscle cells and undergoes anaerobic glycolysis. Known as the Cori cycle, this pathway rapidly produces ATP while shifting part of the metabolic burden from your muscles to your liver.

Whereas fatty acids are the primary fuel for muscles at rest, glycogen and glucose fuel short, intense activity, such as when you are sprinting to arrive at class on time. During prolonged exercise, such as running a marathon, fatty acid oxidation kicks in to help out. Fatty acids can directly supply energy or form ketone bodies to augment the fuel supply.

Your muscle cells are major sites for glycolysis, beta-oxidation, and the common aerobic breakdown pathways: the citric acid cycle and the electron transport chain.

portion of these liberated toxins, the balance remain in circulation, where they can wreak havoc.

Survival Priorities and Potential Energy Sources

Starvation confronts your body with several dilemmas. Where will it get energy to fuel survival needs? Which should it burn first—fat, protein, or

Adipose Tissue

Adipose tissue is your body's primary energy storage depot. A 55-kilogram (121-pound) woman with 25 percent body fat (a healthy body composition) stores about 105,000 kilocalories in adipose tissue, enough energy to run 40 marathons! Your liver assembles fatty acids into triglycerides and sends them to adipose tissue for storage. Eighty to 90 percent of the volume of an adipose cell is pure triglyceride.[4]

To supply fatty acids for energy production, adipose cells break down triglycerides to glycerol and free fatty acids.

Liver

Most substances absorbed by your intestines eventually pass through the liver, the body's main metabolic factory. This versatile organ performs glycolysis, gluconeogenesis, beta-oxidation, lipogenesis, ketogenesis, and cholesterol synthesis.

Your liver can store up to 400 kilocalories of glucose as glycogen. When blood glucose levels are low, the liver breaks down stored glycogen to glucose or makes glucose from noncarbohydrate precursors. Several sources pitch in to provide glucose building blocks: muscle supplies lactate and the amino acid alanine; adipose tissue supplies glycerol; and your diet supplies glucogenic amino acids.

The liver is the traffic cop for lipid metabolism. When energy is abundant, the liver directs fatty acids to storage. When energy is scarce, the liver breaks down fatty acids to form ATP. If an inadequate amount of carbohydrate blocks the entry of acetyl CoA into the citric acid cycle, the liver redirects fatty acids to ketone bodies.

Kidney

Your kidneys are important disposal systems of metabolic wastes. Without rapid elimination, these wastes can build up to toxic levels. When your liver deaminates amino acids (removes amino groups), a cooperative effort eliminates the released nitrogen. Your liver captures the nitrogen in urea, which it releases into the bloodstream. The kidneys filter out the urea and excrete it in urine.

The kidneys can make glucose (gluconeogenesis) from amino acids and other precursors. During prolonged starvation, the kidneys produce glucose in amounts that rival production by the liver![5]

Heart

Your heart relies on an interesting mix of fuels. Rather than glucose, which it uses in only small amounts, your heart relies on free fatty acids, lactate, and ketone bodies. During normal conditions, free fatty acids supply the bulk of its energy.[6] When glucose is in short supply, your heart makes a special effort to spare its use. It uses ketone bodies, then free fatty acids, and finally glucose as its fuel source.[7] During heavy exercise, your body releases large amounts of lactate into the bloodstream. Compared with other types of tissue, your heart is particularly capable of using lactate to supply the energy it needs.[8]

Red Blood Cells

Just like the brain, red blood cells rely primarily on glucose for fuel. In these cells, glycolysis and the pentose phosphate pathway (an alternative energy-producing pathway) extract energy from glucose. Since red blood cells have no mitochondria, they do not contain the pathways for beta-oxidation, the citric acid cycle, or the electron transport chain.

The pentose phosphate pathway generates the NADPH that is critical for a red blood cell's health. Energy carried by NADPH helps maintain cell membrane pliability and ion transport capabilities. NADPH also helps preserve iron in the cell's hemoglobin and prevent premature breakdown of the cell's proteins.[9]

1 Berg JM, Tymoczko JL, Stryer L. *Biochemistry.* 6th ed. New York: WH Freeman, 2007.
2 Guyton AC, Hall JE. *Textbook of Medical Physiology.* 10th ed. Philadelphia: WB Saunders, 2000.
3 Berg, Tymoczko, Stryer. *Biochemistry.*
4 Guyton, Hall. *Textbook of Medical Physiology.*
5 Ibid.
6 Schaap FG, van der Vusse GJ, Glatz JF. Fatty acid-binding proteins in the heart. *Mol Cell Biochem.* 1998;180:1–2, 43–51.
7 Murray RK, et al. *Harper's Biochemistry.* 25th ed. Stamford, CT: Appleton & Lange, 1999.
8 Guyton, Hall. *Textbook of Medical Physiology.*
9 Ibid.

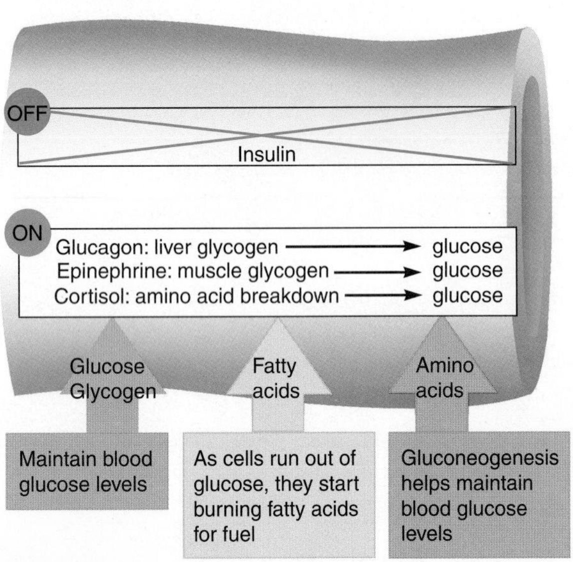

Figure 7.23 **Fasting.** During a short fast, cells first break down liver glycogen to maintain blood glucose levels. They also burn fatty acids and ramp up the production of glucose from amino acids.

carbohydrate? Can it conserve its energy reserves? Which tissues should it sacrifice to ensure survival?

Your body's first priority is to preserve glucose-dependent tissue: red blood cells, brain cells, and the rest of the central nervous system. Your brain will not tolerate even a short interruption in the supply of adequate energy. Once your body depletes its carbohydrate reserves, it begins sacrificing readily available circulating amino acids to make glucose and ATP.

Your body's second priority is to maintain muscle mass. In the face of danger, we rely upon our ability to mount a fight-or-flight response. This survival mechanism requires a large muscle mass, allowing us to move quickly and effectively. Your body grudgingly uses muscle protein for energy and breaks it down rapidly only in the final stages of starvation.

Although your body stores most of its energy reserve in adipose tissue, triglycerides are a poor source of glucose. Although your body can make a small amount of glucose from the glycerol backbone, it cannot make any glucose from fatty acids. As a consequence, your body's primary energy stores—fat—are incompatible with your body's paramount energy priority—glucose for your brain. To meet this metabolic challenge, your body's antistarvation strategies include a glucose-sparing mechanism. It shifts to fatty acids and ketone bodies to fuel its needs. In time, even your brain adapts as most, but not all, brain cells come to rely on ketone bodies for fuel.

The Prolonged Fast: In the Beginning

What happens during the fasting state? Let's take a metabolic look at Fasting Frank, a political activist determined to make a dramatic statement. Frank begins fasting at sundown, planning to drink only water and consume no other foods or liquids.

The first few hours are no different from your nightly fast between dinner and breakfast. As blood glucose drops to fasting baseline levels, the liver breaks down glycogen to glucose. Gluconeogenesis becomes highly active and begins churning out glucose from circulating amino acids. The liver pours glucose into the bloodstream to supply other organs and shifts to fatty acids for its own energy needs. Muscle cells also start burning fatty acids. After about 12 hours, the battle to maintain a constant supply of blood glucose exhausts nearly all carbohydrate stores.[25]

The First Few Days

During the next few days, fat and protein are the primary fuels. To preserve structural proteins, especially muscle mass, Frank's body first turns to easily metabolized amino acids. It uses some to produce ATP and others to make glucose. Glucogenic amino acids, especially alanine, furnish about 90 percent of the brain's glucose supply. Glycerol from triglyceride breakdown supplies the remaining 10 percent. After a couple of days, production of ketone bodies ramps up, augmenting the fuel supply. (See **Figure 7.24**.)

The Early Weeks

As starvation continues, Frank's body initiates several energy-conservation strategies. It ratchets down its energy use by lowering body temperature, pulse rate, blood pressure, and resting metabolism. Frank becomes lethargic, reducing the amount of energy expended in activity. He also begins to have detectable signs of mild vitamin deficiencies as his body depletes its small reserves of vitamin C and most B vitamins.

If Frank's body continued to rapidly break down protein, he would survive less than three weeks. To avoid such a quick demise, protein breakdown slows drastically and gluconeogenesis drops by two-thirds or more.[26] To pick up the slack, Frank's body doubles the rate of fat catabolism to supply fatty acids for fuel and glycerol for glucose. Ketone bodies pour into the bloodstream and provide an important glucose-sparing energy source for the brain and red blood cells. After about 10 days of fasting, ketone bodies meet most of the nervous system's energy needs. Some brain cells, however, can use only glucose. To maintain a small, but essential, supply of blood glucose, protein breakdown crawls along, supplying small amounts of amino acids for gluconeogenesis.

Several Weeks of Fasting

After several weeks of fasting, Frank is increasingly susceptible to disease and infection. His severe micronutrient deficiencies add to his overall poor health.

The average person has about three weeks of fat stores, and the rate of fat depletion is fairly constant. As the later stages of starvation exhaust the final fat stores, the body turns again to protein, its sole remaining fuel source. Normally, Frank's body breaks down about 30 to 55 grams of protein each day, but now it accelerates the rate to several hundred grams daily. (See **Figure 7.25**.) You can see some of the effects of accelerated protein breakdown in

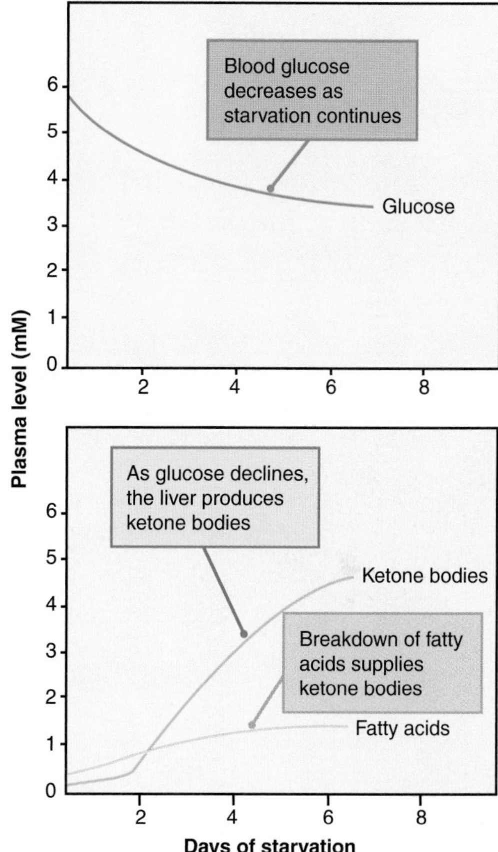

Figure 7.24 **Shifting fuel selection during starvation.** To fuel its needs as blood glucose levels decline, the body shifts from glucose to fatty acids and ketone bodies.

Figure 7.25 **Starvation and fuel sources.** During starvation, carbohydrate is exhausted quickly, and fat becomes the primary fuel. Burning fat without available carbohydrate produces ketone bodies, a by-product that the body can use as fuel. Glucose produced from amino acids and the glycerol portion of fatty acids help fuel the brain. The body conserves protein and breaks it down rapidly only after most fat stores are depleted.

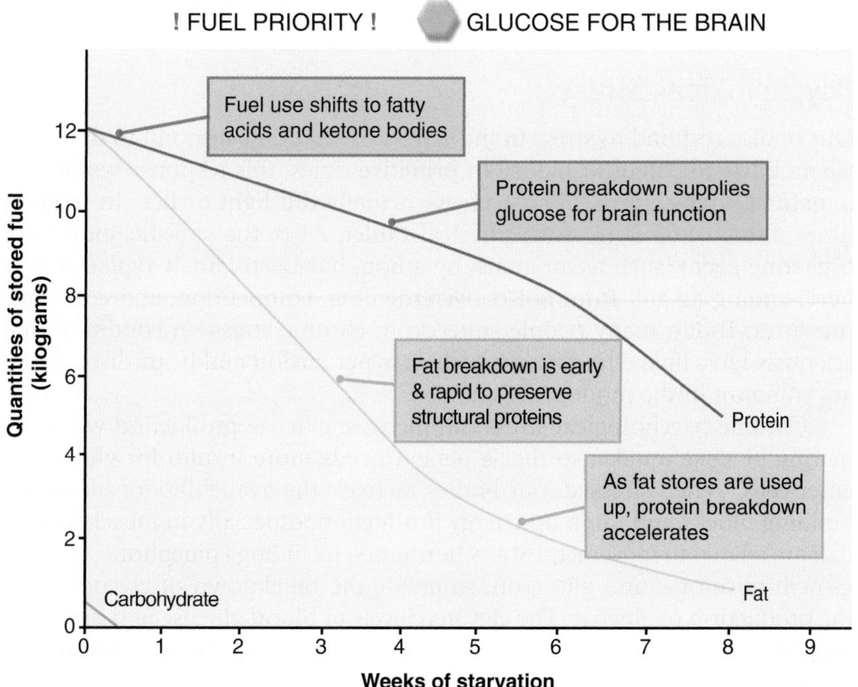

starving children suffering from kwashiorkor. The loss of blood proteins causes the swollen limbs and bulging stomachs that typify this type of protein-energy malnutrition (PEM). (For more detail on PEM, see Chapter 6, "Proteins and Amino Acids.").

The End Is Near

In the final stage of protein depletion, the body deteriorates rapidly. You can see the severe muscle atrophy and emaciation in photos of Holocaust victims. Their bodies sacrificed muscle tissue in attempts to preserve brain tissue. Even organ tissues were not spared. The final stage of starvation attacks the liver and intestines, greatly depleting them. It moderately depletes the heart and kidneys, and even mounts a small attack on the nervous system. Amazingly, starving people can cling to life until they lose about half their body proteins, after which death generally occurs.

How long can a person survive total starvation? A while ago, some Irish prisoners starved themselves to death—the average time was 60 days.[27] Most people survive total starvation for one to three months. Starvation survival factors include the following:

- *Starting percentage of body fat:* Ample adipose tissue prolongs survival.
- *Age:* Middle-aged people survive longer than children and the elderly.
- *Sex:* Women fare better due to their higher proportion of body fat.
- *Energy expenditure levels:* Increased activity leads to an earlier demise.

Key Concepts *Fasting, or underconsumption of energy (calories), favors catabolic pathways. The body first obtains fuel from stored glycogen, and then from stored fat and functional proteins, such as muscle. Over time, the body adapts to using increasing amounts of ketone bodies as fuel because limited carbohydrate is available. Larger stores of fat in adipose tissue extend survival time during starvation. In prolonged starvation, the body catabolizes muscle tissue to continue minimal production of glucose from amino acids.*

Psychological Stress

Our bodies respond to stress in the same way that they respond to danger—we mobilize for "fight or flight." In primitive times, this response would culminate in intense physical activity; we actually did fight or flee. In modern times, there often is no such physical outlet. Also, the specific short-term triggering event, such as an attack by a lion, has been largely replaced by a never-ending assault from noise, overcrowding, competition, and economic pressures. Today, many people suffer from chronic stress—a condition that scientists have linked to diseases such as hypertension and heart disease that are common in the modern world.

Chronic psychological stress can increase glucose production while impairing glucose uptake, so that a person needs more insulin for glucose to enter cells. When stressed, our bodies increase the availability of biological building blocks and ramp up energy production, especially in muscle tissues that are related to movement. Stress hormones, including epinephrine, cortisol, growth hormone, and glucagon, stimulate the breakdown of glycogen and the production of glucose. The elevated levels of blood glucose and increased metabolic rate provide energy to help us respond to threats, whether real or perceived.

Cells prepare for action by taking up glucose at a near maximal rate.[28] This uptake slows the assimilation of new glucose. When the danger passes, cells need higher than normal amounts of insulin to return blood glucose to baseline levels. This condition, called glucose intolerance, is a known complication of chronic stress.[29]

Diabetes and Obesity

In type 1 diabetes mellitus, a lack of insulin limits the cellular uptake of glucose. The starving, glucose-deprived cells signal the liver to make more glucose. This combination of limited uptake and increased production causes abnormally high blood glucose levels. The starving cells turn to fatty acids for energy. Inside the cells, the increased rate of fatty acid oxidation, along with a lack of glucose, leads to the production of ketone bodies. In untreated type 1 diabetes mellitus, ketone bodies accumulate rapidly, causing ketosis and producing the characteristic smell of acetone on the breath. The blood becomes acidic, and the condition of a person with untreated type 1 diabetes mellitus can progress quickly to coma and death.

Obese people and individuals with type 2 diabetes mellitus often have only mildly elevated blood glucose levels, elevated fasting insulin levels, and glucose intolerance. Although insulin levels are adequate, their cells have difficulty taking up glucose, possibly due to a problem with insulin receptors. Because some glucose enters the cells, ketosis is less common among people with type 2 diabetes. (For more details on diabetes, see Chapter 15, "Diet and Health.")

Exercise

Exercise increases not only muscle fitness but also "cell fitness" by enhancing the ability of cells to take up glucose. In fact, regular exercise often can reduce the need for insulin in a person with diabetes.

Carbohydrate and fat are the primary fuels for physical activity, providing more than 90 percent of the energy used by contracting skeletal muscle. During low-intensity aerobic activities, such as walking, fat is a good fuel source. Carbohydrate is better suited to fuel high-intensity anaerobic efforts, such as fast running, that can be maintained for only a few minutes. As exercise intensity moves from low to high, the mix of fuels burned moves gradually from mostly fat to mostly carbohydrate. Which fuel predominates has important implications for how long an activity can be maintained. (See the Nutrition Science in Action feature "Fuel for Distance Walking.")

Key Concepts *Chronic psychological stress can cause glucose intolerance, so that a person needs more insulin for glucose to enter cells. In uncontrolled diabetes mellitus, cells react much as they do in starvation. Untreated type 1 diabetes mellitus can cause a dangerous accumulation of ketone bodies and acidification of the blood. Exercise enhances glucose uptake. Depending on the duration and intensity of exercise, your body chooses different mixes of metabolic fuels.*

Quick Bite

Sweet Urine

The word *diabetes* is Greek for "siphon," from *dia*, meaning "through," and *bainein*, meaning "to go." The word *mellitus* is Latin for "sweetened with honey." Diabetes mellitus means the flow of sweetened water. The disease causes a rise in blood sugar that spills into the urine. As early as the 1600s, some doctors would taste a patient's urine to confirm a diagnosis of diabetes mellitus.

Nutrition Science *in Action*

Fuel for Distance Walking

Observations: Humans naturally select a preferred walking speed (PWS), and the body's fuel selection can be critical to the total distance traveled. The body primarily uses carbohydrate (CHO) to fuel short, intense bursts of activity and uses fat to fuel endurance exercise. Lean humans store far more energy as fat than as CHO, and the choice of fuel may produce a 30-fold difference in the distance traveled.

Hypothesis: Humans select a preferred walking speed that primarily uses fat as fuel and does not deplete carbohydrate stores.

Experimental Plan: Recruit 12 healthy adults. Time the subjects as they walk four laps at their natural rate around a 53-meter track. After resting 10 minutes, subjects walk on a level treadmill for 10-minute increments at 3.2, 4.0, 4.8, 5.6, 6.4, and 7.2 kilometers per hour (kph). Using indirect calorimetry, estimate fat and CHO oxidation during each increment.

Results: The hypothesis is confirmed. The subjects' natural PWS was 4.7 kph. At speeds less than 4.8 kph, CHO oxidation rates remain low and fat oxidation is the primary fuel. At about 4.8 kph and beyond, CHO oxidation increases abruptly and rises rapidly.

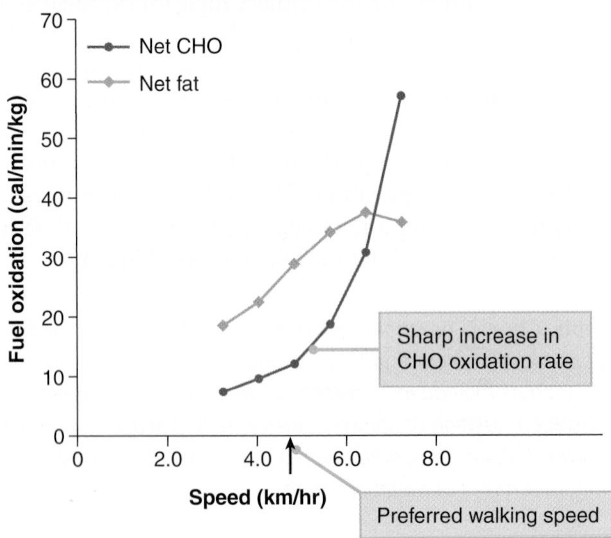

Conclusion and Discussion: The major finding of this study was that able-bodied subjects naturally selected a walking speed just below the speed preceding an abrupt rise in CHO oxidation that would deplete the body's small stores of CHO quickly.

In a historical context, people able to naturally select the walking speed resulting in the greatest range would have a survival advantage when challenged with walking away from a region of food scarcity. Moreover, minimizing CHO depletion would defend the person's ability to engage in burst activity to escape predators or capture prey during the trek.

Source: Based on Willis WT, Ganley KJ, Herman RM. Fuel oxidation during human walking. *Metabolism.* 2005;54(6):793–799.

Learning Portfolio

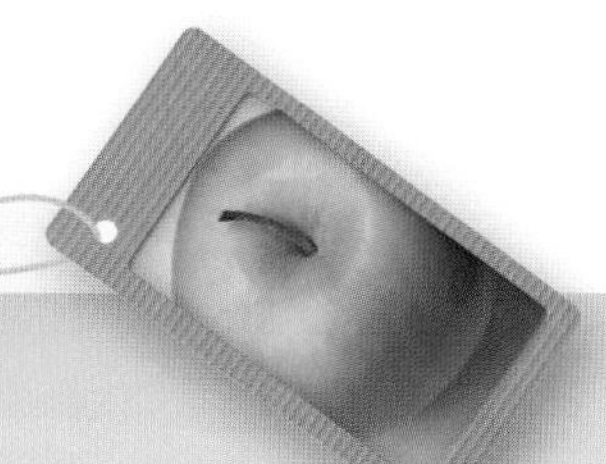

Key Terms

	page
acetyl CoA	275
adenosine diphosphate (ADP)	273
adenosine monophosphate (AMP)	273
adenosine triphosphate (ATP) [ah-DEN-oh-seen try-FOS-fate]	272
aerobic [air-ROW-bic]	275
anabolism [an-A-bol-iz-um]	270
anaerobic [AN-ah-ROW-bic]	275
beta-oxidation	282
biosynthesis	273
carnitine [CAR-nih-teen]	281
catabolism [ca-TA-bol-iz-um]	270
cells	270
chemical energy	269
citric acid cycle	277
coenzyme A	276
coenzymes	272
cofactors	272
Cori cycle	288
cytoplasm	270
cytosol	270
electron transport chain	278
$FADH_2$	272
flavin adenine dinucleotide (FAD)	274
glucogenic	288
gluconeogenesis [gloo-ko-nee-oh-JEN-uh-sis]	288
glycogenesis	288
glycogenolysis	288
glycolysis [gligh-COLL-ih-sis]	274
guanosine triphosphate (GTP)	273
hydrogen ions	274
ketoacidosis	292
ketogenesis	292
ketogenic	288
ketones [KEE-tones]	291
Krebs cycle	277
lactate	276
lipogenesis [lye-poh-JEN-eh-sis]	290
metabolic pathway	270
metabolism	269
metabolites	269
mitochondria (mitochondrion)	270
mitochondrial membrane	279
NADH	272
NADPH	272
nicotinamide adenine dinucleotide (NAD^+)	274
nucleus	270
organelles	270
oxaloacetate	277
oxidative phosphorylation	279
photosynthesis	269
pyrophosphate (P_i)	273
pyruvate	275
transamination [TRANS-am-ih-NAY-shun]	293
tricarboxylic acid (TCA) cycle	277

Study Points

- Energy is necessary to do any kind of work. The body converts chemical energy from food sources—carbohydrates, proteins, and fats—into a form usable by cells.
- Anabolic reactions (anabolism) build compounds. These reactions require energy.
- Catabolic reactions (catabolism) break compounds into smaller units. These reactions produce energy.
- Adenosine triphosphate (ATP) is the energy currency of the body.
- NADH, $FADH_2$, and NADPH are important carriers of hydrogen and high-energy electrons. NADH and $FADH_2$ are used in making ATP, while NADPH is used in biosynthetic reactions.
- Cells extract energy from carbohydrate via four main pathways: glycolysis, conversion of pyruvate to acetyl CoA, the citric acid cycle, and the electron transport chain.
- The citric acid cycle and electron transport chain require oxygen. Glycolysis does not.
- The electron transport chain produces more ATP than other catabolic pathways.
- To extract energy from fat, first triglycerides are separated into glycerol and fatty acids. Next, beta-oxidation breaks down the fatty acids to yield acetyl CoA, NADH, and $FADH_2$. The acetyl CoA enters the citric acid cycle, producing more NADH and $FADH_2$. The NADH and $FADH_2$ molecules deliver their high-energy electrons to the electron transport chain to make ATP.
- To extract energy from an amino acid, first it is deaminated (the amino group is removed). Depending on the structure of the remaining carbon skeleton, it enters the catabolic pathways as pyruvate, acetyl CoA, or a citric acid cycle intermediate. The citric acid cycle and the electron transport chain complete the production of ATP.

- The liver converts the nitrogen portion of amino acids to urea, which the kidneys excrete.
- Tissues differ in their preferred source of fuel. The brain, nervous system, and red blood cells rely primarily on glucose, whereas other tissues use a mix of glucose, fatty acids, and ketone bodies as fuel sources.
- When carbohydrate is available, glucose can be stored as glycogen in liver and muscle tissue.
- Glucose can be produced from the noncarbohydrate precursors glycerol and some (glucogenic) amino acids, but not from fatty acids.
- The hormone insulin regulates metabolism by favoring anabolic pathways. It promotes the uptake of glucose by cells, thus removing it from the bloodstream.
- Glucagon, cortisol, and epinephrine stimulate catabolic pathways. These hormones promote the breakdown of glycogen to glucose and of amino acids to make glucose via gluconeogenesis. The breakdown of liver glycogen increases the amount of glucose in the blood.
- Feasting, or overconsumption of energy, leads to glycogen and triglyceride storage.
- Fasting, or underconsumption of energy, leads to the mobilization of liver glycogen and stored triglycerides. Starvation, the state of prolonged fasting, leads to protein breakdown as well and can be fatal.

Study Questions

1. What is the "universal energy currency"? Where is most of it produced?
2. Name the two energy-equivalent molecules that contain three phosphates as part of their structure. What makes these two molecules different? How many high-energy phosphate bonds do they contain?
3. In the catabolic pathways, which two molecules are major electron acceptors? After they accept electrons, which electron carriers do they become? What is the primary function of the electron carriers?
4. How many pyruvate molecules does glycolysis produce from one glucose molecule? What does the oxidative step after glycolysis produce? What does the citric acid cycle produce from a single glucose molecule?
5. Which two-carbon molecules does beta-oxidation form as it "clips" the links of a fatty acid chain? Which other molecules important to the production of ATP does beta-oxidation produce?
6. What dictates whether an amino acid is considered ketogenic or glucogenic?
7. What are ketone bodies and when are they produced?
8. Name the three tissues where energy is stored. Which contains the largest store of energy?
9. Define gluconeogenesis and lipogenesis. Under what conditions do they predominantly occur? What are their primary inputs and outputs?

Try This

Comparing Fad Diets

The purpose of this exercise is to have you evaluate two fad diets in regard to their metabolic consequences. The two diets, Cabbage Soup and Super Protein, are described below. Once you've reviewed them, answer the following questions: Will these diets result in weight loss? Why or why not? On the seventh day of each diet, which of the following metabolic pathways will be highly active?

- Glycogen breakdown
- Fat breakdown
- Gluconeogenesis
- Ketogenesis

Diet 1: The Cabbage Soup Diet

A person following the Cabbage Soup diet eats only a water-based soup made out of cabbage and a few other vegetables. Three to four meals per day of this restricted diet supply approximately 500 kilocalories per day. The diet is devoid of protein and fat and gets its calories from the small amount of carbohydrate in the vegetables. Think about what happens during starvation.

Diet 2: The Super Protein Diet

In the Super Protein diet, a person can eat an unlimited amount of protein-rich foods such as meat, poultry, eggs, and seafood, but no added fats or carbohydrates are allowed. The average person can consume about 1,400 kilocalories if he or she eats three or four small meals each day. Think about what happens when little carbohydrate is available as a person metabolizes fat and protein.

Fasting for Ketones

The purpose of this experiment is to see whether a day without eating will cause your body to produce measurable ketones in your urine. Before starting your fast, check with your physician to be sure this won't pose any health risks. Go to your local pharmacy and ask the pharmacist for urine ketone strips (often called Ketostix). Bring them home and read the directions. Before you start your one-day fast, test your urine to see whether it has a detectable amount of ketones. Start a 24-hour fast (or fast for as long as you can go without food or calorie-containing fluids, but no longer than 24 hours) and test your urine at 6-hour intervals. Do you detect a color change on the strips as the day goes on? Why? What has happened metabolically as the day progresses?

Remember to drink lots of water!

References

1 Alberts B, Johnson A, Lewis J, et al. *Molecular Biology of the Cell*. 5th ed. New York: Garland, 2008.

2 Butte NF, Cabellero B. Energy needs: assessments and requirements. In: Shils ME, Shike M, Ross AC, et al., eds. *Modern Nutrition in Health and Disease*. 10th ed. Philadelphia: Lippincott Williams & Wilkins, 2006:136–148.

3 Stipanuk MH. *Biochemical and Physiological Aspects of Human Nutrition*. 2nd ed. Philadelphia: WB Saunders, 2006.

4 Nelson DL, Cox MM. *Lehninger Principles of Biochemistry*. 5th ed. New York: WH Freeman, 2008.

5 Berg JM, Tymoczko JL, Stryer L. *Biochemistry*. 6th ed. New York: WH Freeman, 2007.

6 Gropper SS, Smith JL, Groff JL. *Advanced Nutrition and Human Metabolism*. 5th ed. Belmont, CA: Wadsworth, 2009.

7 Nelson, Cox. *Lehninger Principles of Biochemistry*; and Berg, Tymoczko, Stryer. *Biochemistry*.

8 Burge B. Carnitine in energy production. *Healthline*. July 1999.

9 Sarubin-Fragakis A. *The Health Professional's Guide to Popular Dietary Supplements*. 3rd ed. Chicago: American Dietetic Association, 2007.

10 Gropper, Smith, Groff. *Advanced Nutrition and Human Metabolism*.

11 Berg, Tymoczko, Stryer. *Biochemistry*.

12 Stein JH. *Internal Medicine*. 4th ed. St. Louis, MO: Mosby-Yearbook, 1994.

13 Nelson, Cox. *Lehninger Principles of Biochemistry*.

14 Martini FH. *Fundamentals of Anatomy and Physiology*. 6th ed. San Francisco: Benjamin Cummings, 2004.

15 Anderson JW. Prevention and management of diabetes mellitus. In: Shils ME, Shike M, Ross CA, et al., eds. *Modern Nutrition in Health and Disease*. 10th ed. Philadelphia: Lippincott Williams & Wilkins, 2006:1043–1066.

16 Guyton AC, Hall JE. *Textbook of Medical Physiology*. 10th ed. Philadelphia: WB Saunders, 2000.

17 Nelson, Cox. *Lehninger Principles of Biochemistry*.

18 Griffin JE, Ojeda SR. *Textbook of Endocrine Physiology*. 4th ed. New York: Oxford University Press, 2000.

19 Joosen AMCP, Westerterp KR. Energy expenditure during overfeeding. *Nutr Metab*. 2006;3:25.

20 Minehira K, Vega N, Vidal H, et al. Effect of metabolism and expression of lipogenic enzymes in adipose tissue of lean and overweight humans. *Int J Obes*. 2004;28:1291–1298.

21 Nelson, Cox. *Lehninger Principles of Biochemistry*.

22 Martini. *Fundamentals of Anatomy and Physiology*.

23 Scheele JS. A comparison of the concentrations of certain pesticides and polychlorinated hydrocarbons in bone marrow and fat tissue. *J Environ Pathol Toxicol Oncol*. 1998:17(1):65–68.

24 Gower T. The fasting cure. *Health*. April 1999:61–63.

25 Guyton, Hall. *Textbook of Medical Physiology*.

26 Ibid.

27 Ganong WF. *Review of Medical Physiology*. 24th ed. Stamford, CT: McGraw-Hill, 2005.

28 Battilana P, Seematter G, Schneiter P, et al. Effects of free fatty acids on insulin sensitivity and hemodynamics during mental stress. *J Clin Endocrinol Metab*. 2001;86:124–128.

29 Summers RL, Woodward LH, Sanders DY, Hall JE. Graphic analysis for the study of metabolic states. *Adv Physiol Ed*. 1996;15(1):S81–S87.

CHAPTER 8

Alcohol

THINK About It

1 In a word or two, how would you describe alcohol? Is it a nutrient?

2 Compared with beer, what's your impression of the alcohol content of wine? How about compared with vodka?

3 Have you ever thought of alcohol as a poison?

4 After a night of drinking and carousing, your friend awakens with a splitting headache and asks you for a pain reliever. What would you recommend?

Visit nutrition.jbpub.com

Quick Bite

Preferred Beverages
Beer is the national beverage of Germany and Britain. Wine is the national beverage of Greece and Italy.

Think about alcohol. What image comes to mind: Champagne toasts? Elegant gourmet dining? Hearty family meals in the European countryside? Or do you think of wild parties? Or sick, out-of-control drunks? Violence? Car accidents? Broken homes? No other food or beverage has the power to elicit such strong, disparate images—images that reflect both the healthfulness of alcohol in moderation, the devastation of excess, and the political, social, and moral issues surrounding alcohol.

Alcohol has a long and checkered history. More drug than food, alcoholic beverages produce druglike effects in the body while providing little, if any, nutrient value other than energy. Yet it still is important to consider alcohol in the study of nutrition. Alcohol is common to the diets of many people. In moderation, it may impart significant health benefits, yet even small quantities can raise risks for birth defects and breast cancer. In large amounts, it interferes with our intake of nutrients as well as the body's ability to use them, and it causes significant damage to every organ system in the body. The *Dietary Guidelines for Americans* advises us, "If alcohol is consumed, it should be consumed in moderation—up to one drink per day for women and two drinks per day for men—and only by adults of legal drinking age."[1]

For most people, alcohol consumption is a pleasant social activity. Moderate alcohol use does not harm most adults. Nonetheless, many people have serious trouble with drinking. Episodes of heavy drinking are common among adult populations and are on the rise.[2] Adult excessive drinkers and underage drinkers currently account for half of all alcohol consumption and half of consumer spending on alcohol.[3] Heavy drinking can increase the risk for certain cancers. It can also cause liver cirrhosis, brain damage, and harm to the fetus during pregnancy. In addition, drinking increases the number of deaths from automobile crashes, recreational accidents, on-the-job accidents, homicide, and suicide. Underage alcohol use is more likely to kill young people than all illegal drugs combined.[4] An analysis found that alcohol use is the third leading actual cause of death in the United States, after tobacco use and poor diet and/or inactivity.[5]

History of Alcohol Use

Alcohol has had a prominent role throughout history. Old religious and medical writings frequently recommend its use, although with warnings for moderation. Thanks to alcohol's antiseptic properties, fermented drinks were safer than water during the centuries before modern sanitation, especially as people moved to towns and villages where water supplies were contaminated. Even mixing alcohol with dirty water afforded some protection from bacteria.[6]

At a time when life was filled with physical and emotional hardships, people valued alcohol for its analgesic and euphoric qualities. People relied on it to lift spirits, ease boredom, numb hunger, and dull the discomfort, even pain, of daily routine. Before the twentieth century, it was one of the few painkillers available in the Western world.

In sharp contrast to what is allowed today, drinking was often encouraged at the work site. Workers might be given alcohol as an inducement to do boring, painful, or dangerous jobs. Distilled spirits, beer, and wine accompanied sailors and passengers on all long voyages, supplying relatively pathogen-free fluid and calories. Legend has it that even the Puritans, a group known for rigid morality, disembarked at Plymouth Rock because their beer supply was depleted.[7]

alcohol Common name for ethanol or ethyl alcohol. As a general term, it refers to any organic compound with one or more hydroxyl (–OH) groups.

ethanol Chemical name for drinking alcohol. Also known as ethyl alcohol.

ethyl alcohol See *ethanol*.

methanol The simplest alcohol. Also known as methyl alcohol and wood alcohol.

methyl alcohol See *methanol*.

wood alcohol Common name for methanol.

fermentation The anaerobic conversion of various carbohydrates to carbon dioxide and an alcohol or organic acid.

The Character of Alcohol

Although there are many types of alcohol, the term **alcohol** commonly refers to the specific alcohol compound in beer, wine, and spirits. (See **Figure 8.1**.) Its technical name is **ethanol**, or **ethyl alcohol**. Ethanol is commonly abbreviated to "EtOH," shorthand often preferred by health professionals. In this chapter, when we use the term *alcohol*, we are referring to ethanol.

Other types of alcohol are unsafe to drink. The simplest alcohol is **methanol**, also called **methyl alcohol** or **wood alcohol**, a solvent used in paints and for woodworking. Some years ago, down-on-their-luck alcoholics thought they had discovered a way to save money—wood alcohol, used at that time to heat chafing dishes, was intoxicating but considerably cheaper than beer or wine. Unfortunately, methanol caused blindness and death. Methanol is no longer used in these products, but methanol poisoning from other sources still occurs.[8] Today, methanol is used in a number of consumer products, including paint strippers, duplicator fluid, model airplane fuel, and dry gas. Most windshield washer fluids are 50 percent methanol.

Alcohol: Is It a Nutrient?

Alcohol eludes easy classification. Like fat, protein, and carbohydrate, it provides energy when metabolized. Laboratory experiments in the nineteenth century demonstrated that upon oxidation pure alcohol releases 7 kilocalories per gram, but many people doubted it actually produced energy in the body. These doubts were the basis of the controversial conclusion that alcohol was not food—a conclusion used by early Prohibitionists in their fight against alcohol. (See **Figure 8.2**.) However, a classic series of experiments by energy researchers Francis Atwater and Wilbur Benedict showed that alcohol did indeed produce 7 kilocalories per gram in the body—findings that were a great disappointment to the Temperance Movement, because they showed that alcohol was a food.[9]

But alcohol's status as a nutrient is more questionable. It is certainly different from any other substance in the diet. It provides energy but is not essential, performing no necessary function in the body. Unlike the nutrients, alcohol is not stored in the body. And for no nutrient are the dangers of overconsumption so dramatic and the window of safety so narrow. In the small amounts most people usually consume, alcohol acts as a drug, producing a pleasant euphoria. For some people, it is addictive, with the characteristics of tolerance, dependence, and withdrawal symptoms. Certainly, alcohol is a substance available in the diet, but it does not meet the technical definition of a nutrient. (See Chapter 1 for the definition of a nutrient.)

Key Concepts *Alcohol—or, more specifically, the compound ethyl alcohol—has been part of people's diets for thousands of years. Although it provides calories, alcohol performs no essential function in the body and therefore is not a nutrient.*

Alcohol and Its Sources

When yeast cells metabolize sugar, they produce alcohol and carbon dioxide by a process called **fermentation**. If little oxygen is present, these cells produce more alcohol and less carbon dioxide. **Figure 8.3** shows living yeast cells.

Fermentation can occur spontaneously in nature—all that's needed is sugar, water, a warm environment, and yeast (whose spores are present in air

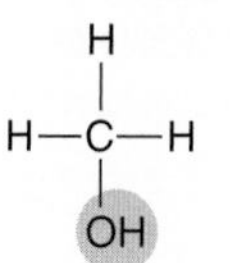

Methanol
(wood alcohol)

Methanol is an alcohol used as an alternative car fuel and in paint strippers, duplicator fluid, and model airplane fuels.

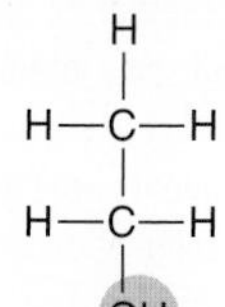

Ethanol
(EtOH)

Ethanol is the alcohol in beer, wine, and liquor.

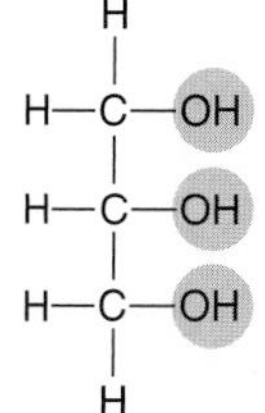

Glycerol

Glycerol is the alcohol that forms the backbone of triglyceride molecules.

Isopropanol
(rubbing alcohol)

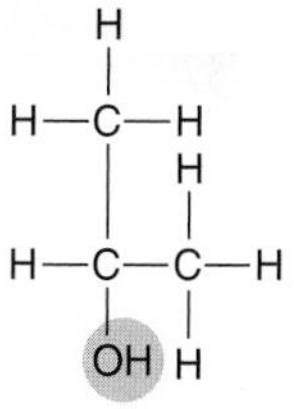

Isopropanol is an alcohol that is used as a disinfectant or solvent, and in making many commercial products.

Figure 8.1 **Alcohols.** Ethanol is not the only alcohol people consume. When people eat fat, they consume the alcohol glycerol. Consuming the alcohol methanol or isopropanol can be deadly.

Quick Bite

Nutrients in Beer?
Most of the carbohydrate used in the production of alcohol is converted to ethanol. In beer, however, some carbohydrate remains, along with a little protein and some vitamins. So although it is technically correct to say there are nutrients in beer, the amounts are small when beer is consumed at recommended low levels.

congeners Biologically active compounds in alcoholic beverages that include nonalcoholic ingredients as well as other alcohols such as methanol. Congeners contribute to the distinctive taste and smell of the beverage and may increase intoxicating effects and subsequent hangover.

standard drink One serving of alcohol (about 15 grams), defined as 12 ounces of beer, 4 to 5 ounces of wine, or 1.5 ounces of liquor.

binge drinking Consuming excessive amounts of alcohol in short periods of time.

and soil). Human experience with alcohol probably began at least 10,000 years ago with spontaneously fermented fruits or honey. Because all humans possess the enzymes to metabolize at least minimal amounts of alcohol,[10] it's reasonable to assume that humans have always had small quantities of alcohol in their diets. Very small amounts of alcohol are even produced by the microorganisms in our intestines.

Humans probably learned to make wine from fruits, mead from honey, and beer from grain about 5,000 years ago. In some areas, people made alcohol-containing dairy products. Using simple yeast fermentation, they could not produce beverages with alcohol levels exceeding 16 percent—the point at which alcohol kills off the yeast, halting alcohol production. Later, seventh-century Egyptian chemists discovered how to use distillation to capture concentrated alcohol, which could be added to drinks to boost alcohol content. Distilled alcoholic beverages (such as rum, gin, and whiskey) are called spirits, liquor, or hard liquor.

Distillation can yield more than just ethanol. Traces of other compounds, such as methanol, evaporate and then condense in the distilled product. Called **congeners**, these biologically active compounds help to create the distinctive taste, smell, and appearance of alcoholic beverages such as whiskey, brandy, and red wine. But congeners are also suspected of causing or contributing to hangovers[11] and may play a role in alcohol's relationship to cancer.

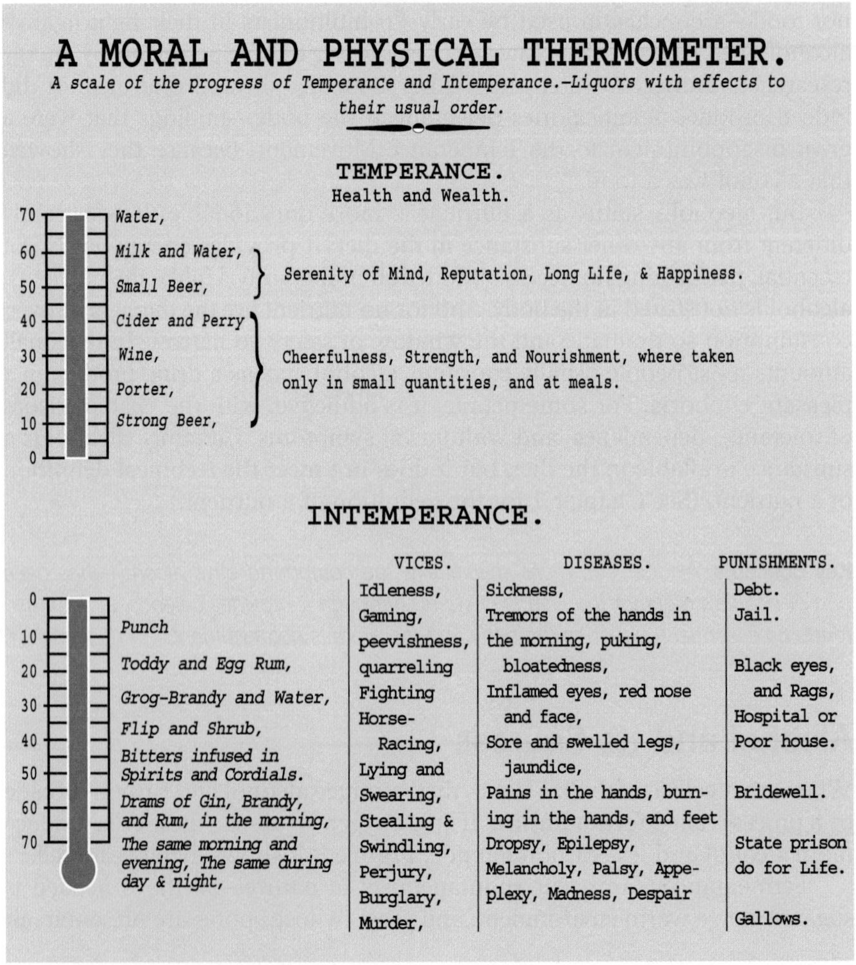

A MORAL AND PHYSICAL THERMOMETER.

A scale of the progress of Temperance and Intemperance.–Liquors with effects to their usual order.

TEMPERANCE.
Health and Wealth.

Scale	Liquors	Effects
70	*Water,*	
60	*Milk and Water,*	Serenity of Mind, Reputation, Long Life, & Happiness.
50	*Small Beer,*	
40	*Cider and Perry*	Cheerfulness, Strength, and Nourishment, where taken only in small quantities, and at meals.
30	*Wine,*	
20	*Porter,*	
10	*Strong Beer,*	
0		

INTEMPERANCE.

Scale	Liquors	VICES.	DISEASES.	PUNISHMENTS.
0		Idleness,	Sickness,	Debt.
10	*Punch*	Gaming, peevishness,	Tremors of the hands in the morning, puking,	Jail.
20	*Toddy and Egg Rum,*	quarreling	bloatedness,	Black eyes,
30	*Grog-Brandy and Water,*	Fighting	Inflamed eyes, red nose and face,	and Rags,
	Flip and Shrub,	Horse-Racing,	Sore and swelled legs,	Hospital or Poor house.
40	*Bitters infused in Spirits and Cordials.*	Lying and	jaundice,	
50		Swearing,	Pains in the hands, burning in the hands, and feet	Bridewell.
60	*Drams of Gin, Brandy, and Rum, in the morning,*	Stealing & Swindling,	Dropsy, Epilepsy,	
70	*The same morning and evening, The same during day & night,*	Perjury, Burglary,	Melancholy, Palsy, Appeplexy, Madness, Despair	State prison do for Life.
		Murder,		Gallows.

Figure 8.2 **A moral and physical thermometer of temperance and intemperance.** As part of a late eighteenth century temperance movement, Philadelphian Dr. Benjamin Rush (1745–1813) created the Moral and Physical Thermometer and distributed it to the clergy in a campaign against heavy drinking.

Source: Reprinted with permission from *Quarterly Journal of Studies on Alcohol*, vol 4, pp. 321–341, 1943 (presently *Journal of Studies on Alcohol*). Copyright Alcohol Research Documentation, Inc., Rutgers Center of Alcohol Studies, Piscataway, NJ 08854.

THINK About It 2

Beer, wine, and liquor have different alcohol levels: most beer is up to 5 percent alcohol, although some beers exceed 6 percent; wine is 8 to 14 percent alcohol; and hard liquor is typically 35 to 45 percent alcohol. Beer and wine are labeled with the percentage of alcohol, but hard liquor is labeled by "proof," which is twice the alcohol percentage (an 80 proof whiskey is 40 percent alcohol).

Pure alcohol—a clear, colorless liquid used in chemistry labs—is 95 percent alcohol. (Even "pure" alcohol contains some water.) The beverage closest to pure alcohol is vodka, which is alcohol, water, and almost nothing else; gin is similar but flavored with juniper berries. Scotch, rum, rye, whiskey, and other liquors have residual flavor traces of the grain from which they were fermented or flavors introduced during storage. All liquors, however, offer little nutritional value besides energy. Beer and wine do contain unfermented carbohydrates and a trace of protein but, like liquor, have negligible minerals. With the exception of niacin in beer (a 12-ounce beer contains 1.8 milligrams of niacin, nearly 10 percent of the Daily Value), alcoholic beverages have negligible vitamins as well. Table 8.1 shows the number of calories in various alcoholic beverages.

One serving of alcohol, or a **standard drink**, is defined as 12 ounces of regular beer, 5 ounces of wine (12 percent alcohol), or 1.5 ounces (a "jigger") of 80 proof liquor.[12] All contain roughly 15 grams (1 measuring tablespoon) of pure alcohol. Most health professionals who speak of "moderate alcohol intake" usually mean no more than one (for women) or two (for men) servings in a day.[13] (See **Figure 8.4**.) Moderate intake is not an average of seven drinks per week, when there are six days of abstinence followed by seven drinks in one night! That's **binge drinking**, and it's dangerous.

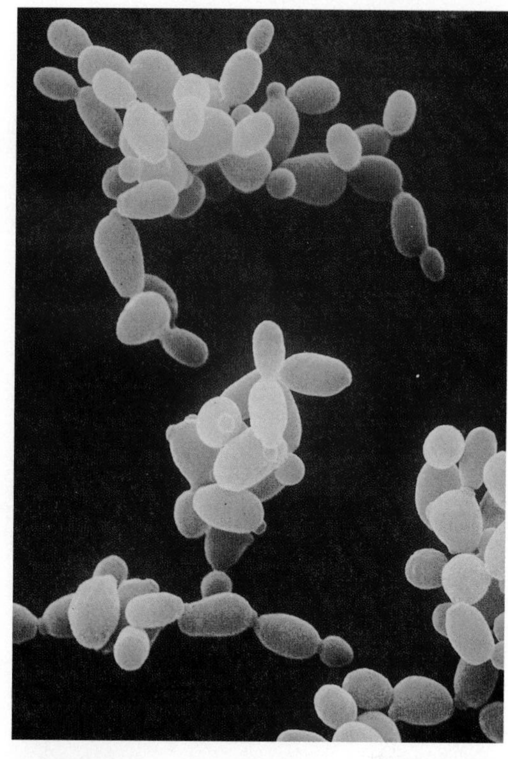

Figure 8.3 A micrograph of yeast.

Key Concepts *Alcohol is formed when yeast ferments sugars to yield energy. Distillation methods produce concentrated solutions containing up to 95 percent alcohol. A typical serving of beer, wine, or distilled spirits contains about 15 grams of alcohol.*

Table 8.1 Calories in Selected Alcoholic Beverages

Beverage	Serving Size	Approximate Kcalories
Beer (regular)	12 fl oz	153
Beer (light)	12 fl oz	103
White wine	5 fl oz	121
Red wine	5 fl oz	125
Sweet dessert wine	3.5 fl oz	165
80 proof distilled spirits (gin, rum, vodka, whiskey)	1.5 fl oz	97

This table is a guide to estimate the caloric intake from various alcoholic beverages. Higher alcohol content and mixing alcohol with other beverages, such as calorically sweetened soft drinks, tonic water, fruit juice, or cream, increases the amount of calories in the beverage. Alcoholic beverages supply calories but provide few essential nutrients.

Source: US Department of Agriculture, Agricultural Research Service. USDA National Nutrient Database for Standard Reference, Release 20. 2007. http://www.ars.usda.gov/ba/bhnrc/ndl. Accessed 3/31/08.

WHAT IS MODERATE DRINKING ?
Women:
No more than 1 drink a day
Men:
No more than 2 drinks a day
COUNT AS A DRINK...

Figure 8.4 **Moderate drinking.**

Source: USDA Center for Nutrition Policy and Promotion.

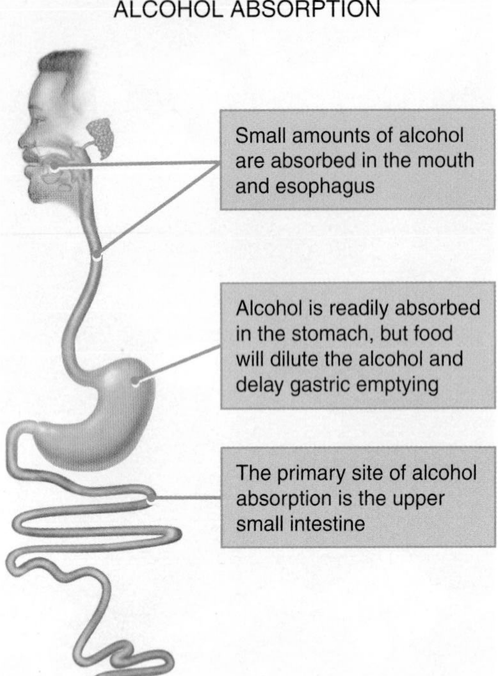
ALCOHOL ABSORPTION
Small amounts of alcohol are absorbed in the mouth and esophagus
Alcohol is readily absorbed in the stomach, but food will dilute the alcohol and delay gastric emptying
The primary site of alcohol absorption is the upper small intestine

Figure 8.5 **Alcohol absorption.** Alcohol easily diffuses in and out of cells, so most alcohol is absorbed unchanged.

Alcohol Absorption

Alcohol absorption begins immediately in the mouth and esophagus, where small quantities enter the bloodstream. Although alcohol absorption continues in the stomach, the small intestine efficiently absorbs most of the alcohol a person consumes.[14] (See **Figure 8.5**.)

You've heard it before: "Don't drink on an empty stomach." Eating before or with a drink slows down the rush of alcohol into the bloodstream in several ways. Food, especially if it contains fat, delays emptying of the stomach into the small intestine. The delay also provides a longer opportunity for oxidizing stomach enzymes to work. And food dilutes the stomach contents, lowering the concentration of alcohol and its rate of absorption.

About 80 to 95 percent of alcohol is absorbed unchanged. However, some oxidation does take place in the digestive tract, mainly in the stomach, and products of this metabolism join alcohol as it diffuses into the gut cells.[15] These products travel via the portal vein directly to the liver, where most alcohol metabolism takes place. When all goes well, metabolism achieves two goals: energy production and protection from the damaging effects of alcohol and its even more toxic metabolite, acetaldehyde.

Alcohol Metabolism

The body cannot store potentially harmful alcohol, and so it works extra hard to get rid of it. To prevent alcohol from accumulating and destroying cells and organs, the body quickly metabolizes it and removes it from the blood. The liver selectively metabolizes alcohol before other compounds and has alternative pathways to handle excess consumption.

Metabolizing Small Amounts of Alcohol

Alcohol dehydrogenase (ADH) is a zinc-containing enzyme that catalyzes the conversion of small to moderate amounts of alcohol to **acetaldehyde**, a toxic substance. To avoid toxic buildup, another enzyme, **aldehyde dehydrogenase (ALDH)**, quickly and effectively converts acetaldehyde to acetate. (See **Figure 8.6**.) People differ in their ability to eliminate toxic acetaldehyde, and small amounts of it are found in the blood of intoxicated people.[16]

Dehydrogenases in the gastrointestinal tract and the liver are responsible for almost all alcohol metabolism. Probably about 4 to 9 percent, but possibly as much as 20 percent, of alcohol is changed to acetaldehyde in the digestive tract.[17] Gastrointestinal aldehyde dehydrogenase does not completely convert acetaldehyde to acetate, however. The remaining acetaldehyde is more destructive than alcohol itself and can damage the mucous membranes lining the gut.[18]

Alcohol breakdown always takes priority over the breakdown of carbohydrates, proteins, and fats. Liver cells detoxify alcohol and use the products to synthesize fatty acids, which are assembled into fats. Fat accumulation in the liver can be seen after a single bout of heavy drinking, and fatty acid synthesis accelerates with chronic alcohol consumption. **Fatty liver** is the first stage of liver destruction in alcoholics.

Metabolizing Large Amounts of Alcohol

Large amounts of alcohol can overwhelm the alcohol dehydrogenase system, the usual metabolic path. As alcohol builds up, the body identifies it

Quick Bite

Alcohol Aversion Therapy

In alcohol aversion therapy, the medication disulfiram (Antabuse) deliberately blocks the conversion of toxic acetaldehyde to acetate (acetic acid). Even small amounts of alcohol trigger the highly unpleasant Antabuse–alcohol reaction, which includes a throbbing headache, breathing difficulties, nausea, copious vomiting, flushing, vertigo, confusion, and a drop in blood pressure.

alcohol dehydrogenase (ADH) The enzyme that catalyzes the oxidation of ethanol and other alcohols.

acetaldehyde A toxic intermediate compound formed by the action of the alcohol dehydrogenase enzyme during the metabolism of alcohol.

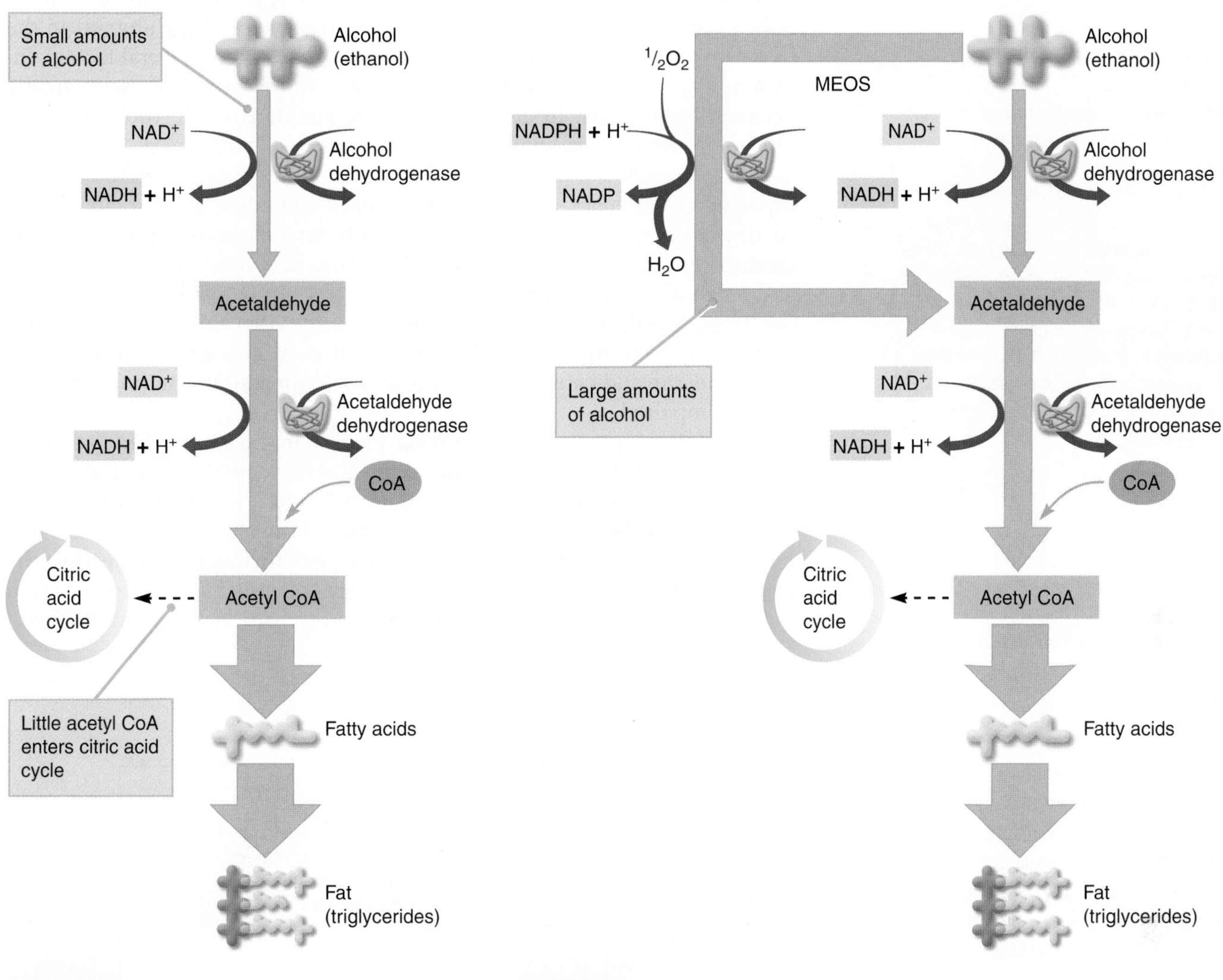

Figure 8.6 **Metabolizing alcohol.** The metabolism of alcohol inhibits the citric acid cycle and primarily forms fat.

Figure 8.7 **The MEOS overflow pathway.** Large amounts of alcohol can overwhelm its typical metabolic route, so excess alcohol enters an overflow pathway called the microsomal ethanol-oxidizing system (MEOS).

as a foreign substance and routes it into the primary overflow pathway, the **microsomal ethanol-oxidizing system (MEOS)**. (See **Figure 8.7**.) The liver ordinarily uses the MEOS bypass pathway to metabolize drugs and detoxify "foreign" substances. Chronic heavy drinking appears to activate MEOS enzymes, which may be responsible for transforming the pain reliever acetaminophen into chemicals that can damage the liver.

To transform alcohol into acetaldehyde, the MEOS pathway uses different enzymes than the alcohol dehydrogenase system. When repeatedly exposed to large doses of alcohol, the MEOS pathway increases its capacity and processing speed. Whether alcoholics metabolize alcohol differently from nonalcoholics is unknown. Clearly, chronic ingestion of alcohol leads to changes in the liver, and the alcohol abuser acquires an increased tolerance to alcohol and to drugs such as sedatives, tranquilizers, and antibiotics.

aldehyde dehydrogenase (ALDH) The enzyme that catalyzes the conversion of acetaldehyde to acetate, which forms acetyl CoA.

fatty liver Accumulation of fat in the liver, a sign of increased fatty acid synthesis.

microsomal ethanol-oxidizing system (MEOS) An energy-requiring enzyme system in the liver that normally metabolizes drugs and other foreign substances. When the blood alcohol level is high, alcohol dehydrogenase cannot metabolize it fast enough, and the excess alcohol is metabolized by MEOS.

Quick Bite

How to Shock Your Surgeon

If a former alcoholic neglects to disclose past alcohol use before undergoing surgery, the surgeon could be in for a big surprise. Even if the patient is now a teetotaler, his or her MEOS could still act like that of an alcoholic—operating at the faster speed it once needed to process alcohol quickly. The overactive MEOS would deplete anesthesia much quicker than expected. Theoretically, the patient could wake up in the middle of surgery, much to the shock of the surgeon. That's why anesthesiologists and surgeons ask their patients about alcohol use, past and present.

Removing Alcohol from Circulation

Despite its multiple alcohol-processing pathways, the liver can metabolize only a certain amount of alcohol per hour, regardless of the amount in the bloodstream. The rate of alcohol metabolism depends on several factors, including the amount of metabolizing enzymes in the liver, and varies greatly between individuals. In general, after one standard drink, the amount of alcohol in the drinker's blood (blood alcohol concentration, or BAC) peaks in 30 to 45 minutes. (See **Figure 8.8**.) When absorption exceeds the liver's capacity, a bottleneck develops, and alcohol enters the general circulation. Alcohol diffuses rapidly, dispersing equally into all body fluids, including cerebrospinal fluid and the brain and, during pregnancy, into the placenta and fetus. About 10 percent of circulating alcohol is lost in urine, through the lungs, and through skin. Consequently, urine tests and breathalyzer tests both reflect concentrations of blood alcohol as well as alcohol levels in the brain and can indicate how much a person's mental and motor functions may be impaired.

Even after a person stops drinking, alcohol in the stomach and small intestine continues to enter the bloodstream and circulate throughout the body. Blood alcohol concentration continues to rise, and it is dangerous to assume the person will be fine by sleeping it off. Rapid binge drinking (which often happens as a result of a bet or a dare) is especially dangerous, because the victim can ingest a fatal dose of alcohol before becoming unconscious. Even if the victim lives, an alcohol overdose can lead to irreversible brain damage.

alcohol poisoning An overdose of alcohol. The body is overwhelmed by the amount of alcohol in the system and cannot metabolize it fast enough.

hangover The collection of symptoms experienced by someone who has consumed a large quantity of alcohol. Symptoms can include pounding headache, fatigue, muscle aches, nausea, stomach pain, heightened sensitivity to light and sound, dizziness, and possibly depression, anxiety, and irritability.

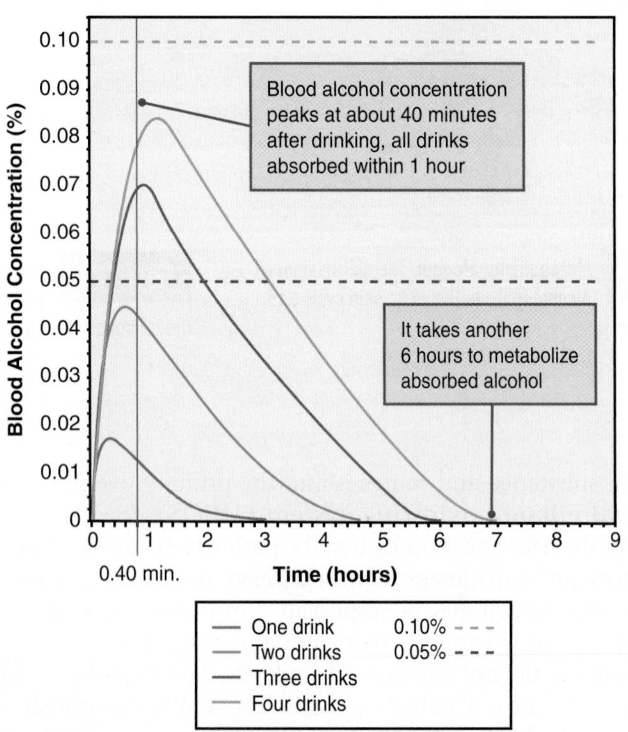

Figure 8.8 **Blood alcohol concentration over time.** Because the body metabolizes alcohol at a relatively constant rate, it clears small amounts faster than large amounts.

Source: National Institute on Alcohol Abuse and Alcoholism. *Alcohol Metabolism.* Bethesda, MD: NIAAA, 1997. Alcohol Alert, No. 35. http://pubs.niaaa.nih.gov/publications/aa35.htm. Accessed 3/31/08.

Quick Bite

Is the Alcoholic Beverage Industry Addicted to Alcohol Abuse?

The combined value of illegal and underage drinking and adult alcohol abuse to the alcoholic beverage industry is estimated to be at least \$48.3 billion, or 37.5 percent of consumer expenditures for alcohol in 2001. Other estimates suggest the value may be closer to \$62.9 billion (48.8 percent of expenditures).

Excessive alcohol consumption deprives the brain of oxygen. The struggle to deal with an overdose of alcohol and lack of oxygen eventually causes the brain to shut down functions that regulate breathing and heart rate. This shutdown leads to a loss of consciousness and, in some cases, coma and death. When a drinker passes out, the body is actually protecting itself: when you lose consciousness, you can't add more alcohol to your system. When you hear of an **alcohol poisoning** death, it usually is the result of consuming such a large quantity of alcohol in such a short period of time that the brain of the victim is overwhelmed. Heart and lung functions shut down, and the person dies.

Quick Bite

Ancient Hangover Helpers

According to the ancient Persians, eating five almonds could prevent a hangover. The Romans and Greeks had a different solution: celery.

The Morning After

After a night of heavy alcohol consumption, the drinker may suffer from a pounding headache, fatigue, muscle aches, nausea, and stomach pain as well as a heightened sensitivity to light and noise—a **hangover** in full force. The sufferer may be dizzy, have a sense that the room is spinning, and be depressed, anxious, and irritable. Usually a hangover begins within several hours after the last drink, when the blood alcohol level is dropping. Symptoms normally peak about the time the alcohol level reaches zero, and they may continue for an entire day.[19]

What causes a hangover? Scientists have identified several causes of the painful symptoms of a hangover. (See **Figure 8.9**.) Alcohol causes dehydration, which leads to headache and dry mouth. Alcohol directly irritates the stomach and intestines, contributing to stomach pain and vomiting. The sweating, vomiting, and diarrhea that can accompany a hangover cause additional fluid loss and electrolyte imbalance. Alcohol's hijacking of the metabolic process diverts liver activity away from glucose production and can lead to low blood glucose (hypoglycemia), causing light-headedness and lack of energy. Alcohol also disrupts sleep patterns, interfering with the dream state and contributing to fatigue. The symptoms of a hangover are largely due to inflammation. During a hangover, blood levels of C-reactive protein are elevated and strongly associated with hangover severity.[20] In general, the greater the amount of alcohol consumed, the more likely a hangover will strike. However, some people experience a hangover after only one drink, whereas some heavy drinkers do not have hangovers.[21]

In addition, factors other than alcohol may contribute to the hangover. A person with a family history of alcoholism has increased vulnerability to hangovers. Mixing alcohol and drugs also is suspected of increasing the likelihood of a hangover. The congeners in most alcoholic beverages can contribute to more vicious hangovers. Research shows that gin and vodka—beverages that contain less of these biologically active compounds—cause fewer headaches.[22]

Treating a Hangover

How can you plan to minimize the symptoms of a hangover? You may want to consider these ways to help minimize the symptoms of a hangover:[23]

- Be sure to eat before you start to drink. Having a full stomach helps slow down the absorption of alcohol and gives the body more time to process the toxins.
- Drink in moderation. Limiting yourself to one drink per hour will give your body more time to process the alcohol.

So what can you do about a hangover? Few treatments have undergone rigorous, scientific investigation. Time works best, however. Hangover symp-

Hangover Symptoms

Constitutional—fatigue, weakness, and thirst
Pain—headache and muscle aches
Gastrointestinal—nausea, vomiting, and stomach pains
Sleep and biological rhythms—decreased sleep, decreased dreaming when asleep
Sensory—vertigo and sensitivity to light and sound
Cognitive—decreased attention and concentration
Mood—depression, anxiety, and irritability
Sympathetic hyperactivity—tremor, sweating, increased pulse, and blood pressure

Possible Contributing Factors

Direct effects of alcohol
- Dehydration
- Electrolyte imbalance
- Gastrointestinal disturbances
- Low blood sugar
- Sleep and biological rhythm disturbances

Alcohol withdrawal
Alcohol metabolism (i.e., acetaldehyde toxicity)
Nonalcohol factors
- Compounds other than alcohol in beverages, especially the congener methanol
- Use of other drugs, especially nicotine
- Personality traits such as neuroticism, anger, and defensiveness
- Negative life events and feelings of guilt about drinking
- Family history for alcoholism

Figure 8.9 **Hangovers.** Factors other than just alcohol contribute to the misery of a hangover.

toms usually disappear in 8 to 24 hours. No matter what you do to help get over your hangover, your body still has to clean up all the toxic by-products left over from the alcohol.[24] Eating bland foods that contain complex carbohydrates, such as toast or crackers, can combat low blood glucose and possibly nausea. Sleep can ease fatigue, and drinking nonalcoholic beverages can alleviate dehydration. Limited research suggests that taking vitamin B_6 or an extract from *Opuntia ficus indica* (a type of prickly pear cactus) before drinking may reduce the severity of hangover symptoms.[25] The prickly pear cactus extract may reduce three symptoms of hangover—nausea, dry mouth, and loss of appetite.[26]

Certain medications also can relieve some symptoms. Antacids, for example, may relieve nausea and stomach pains. Aspirin may reduce headache and muscle aches, but could increase stomach irritation. Avoid acetaminophen because alcohol metabolism enhances its toxicity to the liver.[27] In fact, people who drink three or more alcoholic beverages per day should avoid all over-the-counter pain relievers and fever reducers. These heavy drinkers may have an increased risk of liver damage and stomach bleeding from medicines that contain aspirin, acetaminophen (Tylenol), ibuprofen (Advil), naproxen sodium (Aleve), or ketoprofen (Orudis KT and Actron).[28]

THINK About It 4

People with hangovers should avoid "the hair of the dog that bit you," a remedy that calls for drinking more alcohol. Additional drinking only enhances the toxicity of the alcohol previously consumed and extends the recovery time.

Individual Differences in Alcohol Metabolism

Individuals vary in their ability to metabolize alcohol and acetaldehyde. As a consequence, they differ in their susceptibility to intoxication, hangover, and, in the long term, addiction and organ damage.

The result of individual differences is easiest to see in acute responses to alcohol. For example, when people of Asian descent drink alcohol, about half experience flushing around the face and neck, probably as a result of high blood acetaldehyde levels.[29] These individuals lack gastric alcohol dehydrogenase, and their livers have an inefficient form of aldehyde dehydrogenase. This may explain why their ancestors depended on boiled water (for teas) as a source of safe fluid. In contrast, Europeans are able to metabolize larger quantities of alcohol and historically have relied on fermentation to produce fluids that were safer to drink.[30]

Elderly people often find their tolerance for alcohol is less than it used to be. Due to decreased tolerance, the effects of alcohol, such as impaired coordination, occur at lower intakes in the elderly than in younger people, whose tolerance increases with increased consumption. This reduced tolerance is compounded by an age-related decrease in body water, so that blood alcohol concentrations in older people are likely to rise higher after drinking.[31]

Body composition
Women have a higher percentage of fat than men and thus have less water to dilute alcohol.
Less enzyme activity
Alcohol dehydrogenase, the primary enzyme involved in the metabolism of alcohol, is up to 40% less active in women than in men.
Body size
Women are smaller on average than men (smaller livers and less total water).
Hormonal fluctuations
Women typically have a heightened response to alcohol which is increased when they are about to have their periods, or when taking birth control pills.

Figure 8.10 **Women and men respond differently to alcohol.** Women tend to have a lower capacity for alcohol than men.

Women and Alcohol

Men and women respond differently to alcohol. (See **Figure 8.10**.) Blood alcohol rises faster in women, so they become more intoxicated than men with an equivalent dose of alcohol.[32] Accordingly, moderate drinking is usually defined as "two standard drinks for men and one for women."[33] Women also metabolize alcohol more slowly than men. Several factors are responsible for alcohol's greater effect on women:

- *Body size and composition.* Women, on average, are smaller than men and have smaller livers; thus, they have less capacity for metabolizing alcohol. Women also have lower total body water and higher body fat than men of comparable size. After alcohol is consumed, it diffuses uniformly into all body water, both inside and outside cells. Because of their smaller quantity of body water, women have higher concentrations of alcohol in their blood than men do after drinking equivalent amounts of alcohol.[34]

- *Less enzyme activity.* Women also have less alcohol dehydrogenase (the primary enzyme involved in the metabolism of alcohol) activity than men—about 40 percent less.[35] This contributes to higher blood alcohol concentrations and lengthens the time needed to metabolize and eliminate alcohol. The gender difference in blood alcohol levels is due mainly to the significantly lower activity of gastric enzymes in women.[36]
- *Chronic alcohol abuse.* Alcoholism and other abuses exact a greater physical toll on women than men. Female alcoholics have death rates 50 to 100 percent higher than those of male alcoholics. Furthermore, a higher percentage of female alcoholics die from suicides, alcohol-related accidents, circulatory disorders, and cirrhosis of the liver.

Key Concepts *Alcohol does not need to be digested prior to absorption and moves easily across the GI tract lining into the bloodstream. Once alcohol is absorbed, the liver metabolizes it. The primary metabolic enzymes are alcohol dehydrogenase and aldehyde dehydrogenase. When large amounts of alcohol are consumed, some alcohol is metabolized by the MEOS pathway. Genetic and gender differences in the amount and activity levels of alcohol-metabolizing enzymes influence a person's response to consuming alcohol.*

When Alcohol Becomes a Problem

Alcohol affects every organ system in the body. In the short term, small amounts of alcohol change the levels of neurotransmitters in the brain, reducing inhibitions and physical coordination. In the long term, chronic intake of large amounts of alcohol damages the heart, liver, GI tract, and brain. When a pregnant woman drinks, alcohol can have a devastating effect on the development of her baby.

Alcohol in the Brain and the Nervous System

Alcohol diffuses readily into the brain, and because a small amount is absorbed from the mouth directly into circulating blood, its effects can be almost immediate, reaching the brain in as little as one minute after consumption. Alcohol can produce detectable impairments in memory after only a few drinks and, as the amount of alcohol increases, so does the degree of impairment. Large quantities of alcohol, especially when consumed quickly and on an empty stomach, can produce a blackout—that is, an interval of time for which the intoxicated person cannot recall key details of events, or even entire events. **Figure 8.11** shows the effects alcohol has on the brain.

Because alcohol is soluble in fat, it can easily cross the protective fatty membrane of nerve cells. There, it disrupts the brain's complex system for communicating between nerve cells. Neurotransmitters that excite nerve cells and those that inhibit nerve cells are thrown out of balance. Excess of some neurotransmitters produces sleepiness; high levels of others cause a loss of coordination; an imbalance of others impairs judgment and mental ability;

Figure 8.11 **Effects of alcohol on the brain.** As blood alcohol concentration rises, different parts of the brain are affected.

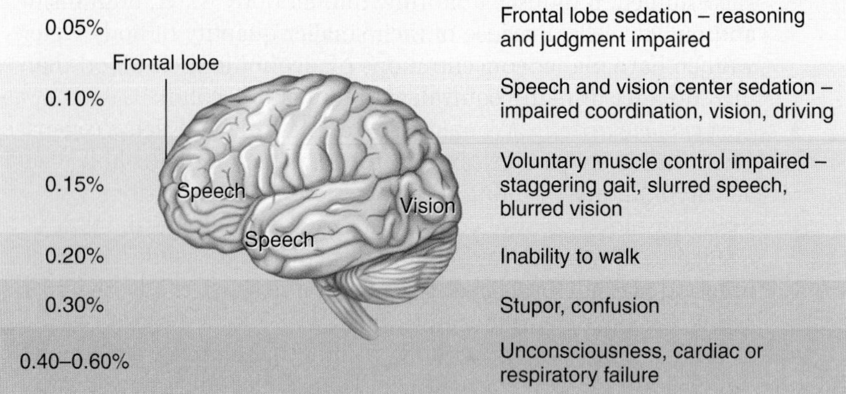

and still other neurotransmitters perpetuate the desire to keep drinking, even when it's clearly time to stop. Changes in these messengers are suspected of leading to addiction and symptoms of alcohol withdrawal.[37] In the short run, they probably contribute to a hangover.

Alcohol's short-term effects are related to how much a person drinks. One or two drinks typically bring alcohol blood levels to 0.04 percent and usually

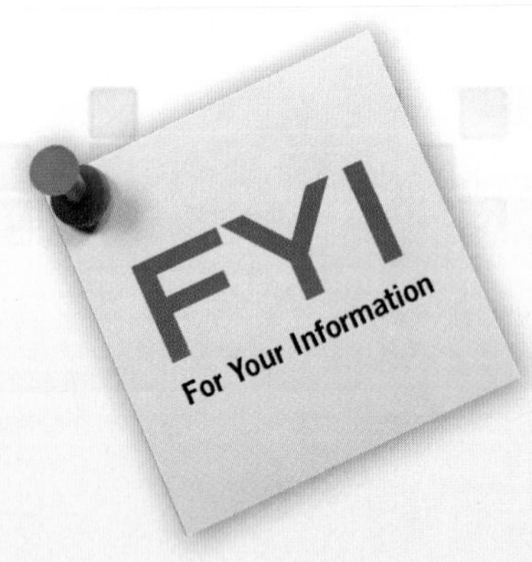

Myths About Alcohol

Myths and misunderstandings just keep circulating about alcohol. Some of these statements are partly true, but most are completely false. You may have heard some of the following:

- *Drinking isn't all that dangerous.* Wrong! One in three 18- to 24-year-olds admitted to emergency rooms for serious injuries is intoxicated. Alcohol use is also associated with homicides, suicides, and drownings.
- *I can manage to drive well enough after a few drinks.* No. About one-half of all fatal traffic crashes among 18- to 24-year-olds involve alcohol.
- *I can sober up quickly if needed.* No. It takes about three hours to eliminate the alcohol content of two drinks, depending on your weight and other factors. Nothing can speed up this process—not even coffee or cold showers.
- *Alcohol is a stimulant.* No. It's actually a depressant, but its initial depressing effect on inhibitions and judgment may make it seem stimulating.
- *Alcohol keeps you warm.* Partly true. It dilates blood vessels near the body's surface, giving a feeling of warmth. But as body heat escapes, alcohol cools the inner body.
- *Alcohol is an aphrodisiac.* Partly true. By suppressing inhibitions, it may loosen behavior. However, sexual function is often compromised by alcohol.
- *Most alcoholics live on skid row.* No. The highly visible skid-row alcoholic represents only a minority of alcoholics.
- *Beer is a source of vitamins.* Partly true. Beer does contain a fair amount of niacin. But you'd need about 1 liter to fulfill daily niacin requirements. Levels of other vitamins are much lower.
- *Alcohol helps you sleep.* No. Alcohol disrupts sleep patterns, leading to a restless, unsatisfying sleep.
- *Laboratory animals love to drink.* No. Alcohol is usually given by tube feeding because most animals refuse to drink it willingly.
- *It's good to have a beer before breastfeeding.* No. Alcohol may be relaxing and allow milk to flow more readily, but alcohol concentrations in breast milk are similar to those in the mother's blood. Alcohol in breast milk reduces milk production by reducing the intensity of the infant's suckling.

cause only mild, pleasant changes in mood and release of inhibitions. With more drinks and rising blood alcohol levels, coordination, judgment, reaction time, and vision are increasingly impaired. In the United States and Canada, it is illegal for a person whose blood level of alcohol has reached or exceeds 0.08 percent to drive a motor vehicle. A review of 112 studies concludes that certain skills required to drive a motor vehicle can become significantly impaired at a blood alcohol concentration as low as 0.05 percent.[38] For commercial drivers, a BAC of 0.04 percent is illegal nationwide. Table 8.2 shows the effects various amounts of alcohol have on mood and behavior.

The acute effect of a large alcohol intake—swallowed accidentally by children, for example—is hypoglycemia (low blood glucose) severe enough to kill.[39] Binge drinking, especially following several days of little food, also can be deadly. The lack of food depletes glycogen stores, and heavy drinking suppresses gluconeogenesis. The resulting severe hypoglycemia is a medical emergency with the potential for coma and death.

Table 8.2 **Alcohol Impairment Chart**

Men — Body Weight in Pounds / Approximate Blood Alcohol Percentage

Drinks	100	120	140	160	180	200	220	240	
0	.00	.00	.00	.00	.00	.00	.00	.00	Only Safe Driving Limit
1	.04	.03	.03	.02	.02	.02	.02	.02	Impairment Begins
2	.08	.06	.05	.05	.04	.04	.03	.03	Driving Skills Affected
3	.11	.09	.08	.07	.06	.06	.05	.05	
4	.15	.12	.11	.09	.08	.08	.07	.06	Possible Criminal Penalties
5	.19	.16	.13	.12	.11	.09	.09	.08	
6	.23	.19	.16	.14	.13	.11	.10	.09	
7	.26	.22	.19	.16	.15	.13	.12	.11	Legally Intoxicated
8	.30	.25	.21	.19	.17	.15	.14	.13	
9	.34	.28	.24	.21	.19	.17	.15	.14	Criminal Penalties
10	.38	.31	.27	.23	.21	.19	.17	.16	

Women — Body Weight in Pounds / Approximate Blood Alcohol Percentage

Drinks	90	100	120	140	160	180	200	220	240	
0	.00	.00	.00	.00	.00	.00	.00	.00	.00	Only Safe Driving Limit
1	.05	.05	.04	.03	.03	.03	.02	.02	.02	Impairment Begins
2	.10	.09	.08	.07	.06	.05	.05	.04	.04	Driving Skills Affected
3	.15	.14	.11	.10	.09	.08	.07	.06	.06	Possible Criminal Penalties
4	.20	.18	.15	.13	.11	.10	.09	.08	.08	
5	.25	.23	.19	.16	.14	.13	.11	.10	.09	
6	.30	.27	.23	.19	.17	.15	.14	.12	.11	
7	.35	.32	.27	.23	.20	.18	.16	.14	.13	Legally Intoxicated
8	.40	.36	.30	.26	.23	.20	.18	.17	.15	
9	.45	.41	.34	.29	.26	.23	.20	.19	.17	Criminal Penalties
10	.51	.45	.38	.32	.28	.25	.23	.21	.19	

Note: Subtract .01% for each 40 minutes of drinking. Your body can get rid of one drink per hour. One drink is 1.25 oz of 80-proof liquor, 12 oz of beer, or 5 oz of table wine. Data supplied by the Pennsylvania Liquor Control Board.

Source: The National Clearinghouse for Alcohol and Drug Information, Substance Abuse and Mental Health Services Administration. http://www.lcb.state.pa.us/edu/cwp/view.asp?a=1346&q=555292. Accessed 9/22/09. Reprinted with permission.

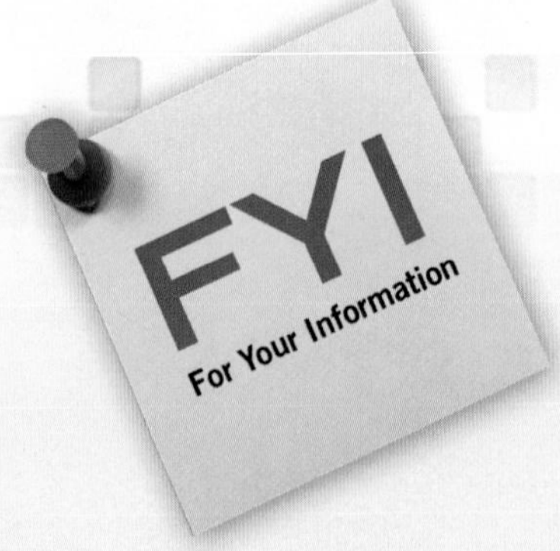

Changing the Culture of Campus Drinking

From car crashes to alcohol poisoning, the culture of drinking on many college campuses puts students at grave risk. Alcohol use is pervasive among college students, many of whom are younger than the legal drinking age.

Annually, at least 1,700 student deaths and nearly 600,000 unintentional injuries involve alcohol.[1] College students who drink are more likely to drink and drive, have failing grades, and have medical and legal problems. Increased rates of crime, traffic crashes, rapes and assaults, property damage, and other alcohol-related consequences affect both drinking and nondrinking students, as well as members of the surrounding community. Each year, for example, students who have been drinking assault more than 696,000 of their classmates.[2]

The Culture of College Drinking

On many campuses, alcohol consumption is a rite of passage, and the influence of peers is an especially powerful force driving college problem drinking.[3] Traditions and beliefs handed down through generations of college drinkers reinforce the perception that alcohol is a necessary component of social success.[4] Many students arrive at college with a history of alcohol consumption and positive expectations about alcohol's effects. Thirty percent of twelfth-graders, for example, report heavy episodic drinking in high school, slightly more report having "been drunk," and almost three-fourths report drinking in the past year.[5]

Rates of excessive alcohol use are highest at colleges and universities where fraternities and sororities are popular, where sports teams have a prominent role, and at schools located in the Northeast.[6] In the local community, tolerance of student drinking may permit alcoholic beverage outlets and advertising to be located near campus. Due to lax enforcement, selling alcohol to students below the legal drinking age often has few consequences. Also, underage students who are caught using fake IDs to obtain alcohol are seldom penalized.[7] Just look at the advertising and sale of alcoholic beverages on or near campuses, and the role of alcohol in college life is evident.

Alcohol Use and Abuse by College Students

Approximately 70 percent of college students consumed some alcohol within 30 days of being surveyed.[8] Although some of these students are problem drinkers (e.g., frequent heavy episodic drinkers or those who display symptoms of dependence), others may drink moderately or may misuse alcohol only occasionally (e.g., drink and drive infrequently). Surveys of drinking patterns show that college students are more likely than nonstudents of similar age to consume any alcohol, to drink heavily, and to engage in heavy episodic drinking. Young people who are not in college, however, are more likely to consume alcohol every day.[9] Even though college students tend to drink more, they are not at greater risk of alcohol-related problems.[10]

A survey questioned students about patterns and consequences of their alcohol use during the past year.[11] Thirty-one percent reported symptoms associated with alcohol abuse (e.g., drinking in hazardous situations and alcohol-related school problems), and 6 percent reported three or more symptoms of alcohol dependence (e.g., drinking more or longer than initially planned and experiencing increased tolerance to alcohol's effects). What happens when these student imbibers leave college? Surprisingly, most high-risk student drinkers reduce their consumption of alcohol. Nevertheless, some continue frequent, excessive drinking, leading to alcoholism or medical problems associated with chronic alcohol abuse.[12]

Binge Drinking

Binge drinking is especially worrisome, and it is widespread on college campuses. What is binge drinking? Binge drinking is defined as the consumption of at least five drinks in a row for men or four drinks in a row for women. Just over two in five students (44 percent) report binge drinking behaviors, and about one in four (23 percent) report bingeing frequently, defined as three or more times in a two-week period. Frequent binge drinkers average more than 14 drinks per week and account for more than two-thirds of the alcohol consumed by college students.[13] Most college binge drinkers drink not for sociability, but solely and purposefully to get drunk.

Binge drinkers often do something they later regret—argue with friends, make fools of themselves, get sick, engage in unplanned (and often unprotected) sexual activity, or drive drunk. Afterward they may forget where they were or what they did, but the consequences of the binge remain. These consequences may include alienated friends, a hangover, and embarrassment. Or the consequences could be much more serious—sexually transmitted disease, hospitalization, permanent injury, rape, pregnancy, or death.

Abstaining

There is a polarizing trend in college drinking, with binge drinkers at one extreme and abstainers at the other. The number of college students who drink no alcohol is rising and now nearly equals the number who binge frequently. About one in five students (19 percent) report consuming no alcohol within the past year.[14] In a survey, one in three college campuses reported banning the use of alcohol on campus by all students regardless of age.[15]

Prevention Strategies and Changing the Culture of Drinking

Changing the culture of college drinking represents the first step toward an effective prevention strategy, according to a task force of college presidents, alcohol researchers, and students established by the National Institute on Alcohol Abuse and Alcoholism. Their report emphasizes the need for collaboration between academic institutions, researchers, and the community to effect lasting change.[16]

The task force strongly supports the use of a "3-in-1 Framework" to target three primary audiences simultaneously: (1) individual students, including high-risk drinkers; (2) the student body as a whole; and (3) the surrounding community.[17] The task force reviewed potentially useful preventive interventions, grouping them into "tiers" according to evidence for their effectiveness.

Tier 1: Strategies Effective Among College Students

Strong evidence supports the following strategies:

1. Simultaneously address alcohol-related attitudes and behaviors (e.g., refuting false beliefs about alcohol's effects while teaching students how to cope with stress without resorting to alcohol).
2. Use survey data to counter students' misperceptions about their fellow students' drinking practices and attitudes toward excessive drinking.
3. Increase student motivation to change drinking habits by providing nonjudgmental advice and progress evaluations.

Programs that combine these three strategies have proved effective in reducing alcohol consumption.[18]

Tier 2: Strategies Effective Among the General Population That Could Be Applied to College Environments

These strategies have proved successful in populations similar to those found on college campuses. Measures include the following:

1. Increase enforcement of minimum legal drinking age laws.[19]
2. Implement, enforce, and publicize other laws to reduce alcohol-impaired driving, such as zero-tolerance laws that reduce the legal blood alcohol concentration for underage drivers to near zero.[20]
3. Increase the prices or taxes on alcoholic beverages.[21]
4. Institute policies and training for servers of alcoholic beverages to prevent sales to underage or intoxicated patrons.[22]

Tier 3: Promising Strategies That Require Research

These strategies make sense intuitively or show theoretical promise, but their usefulness requires further testing. They include more consistent enforcement of campus alcohol regulations and increasing the severity of penalties for violating them, regulating happy hours, enhancing awareness of personal liability for alcohol-related harm to others, establishing alcohol-free dormitories, restricting or eliminating alcohol-industry sponsorship of student events while promoting alcohol-free student activities, and conducting social norms campaigns to correct exaggerated estimates of the overall level of drinking among the student body.

How Can I Say No to Drinking Alcohol and Still Fit in with My Friends?

Drinking alcohol is a personal decision. It is best to make your decision to drink or not to drink based on your own feelings, knowledge, and experiences. You may want to consider the following things before you are put in a position where alcohol is available:[23]

- If you choose to abstain, make up your mind to say no before you are ever in the situation.
- Tell people that you feel better when you drink less.
- Stay away from people who give you a hard time about not drinking.
- Learn to hold a glass or beer bottle for a long time, and refill it with whatever you want (such as water or club soda).

1 Hingson RW, Heeren T, Winter M, et al. Magnitude of alcohol-related mortality and morbidity among U.S. college students ages 18–24: changes from 1998 to 2001. *Ann Rev Pub Health.* 2005;26:259–279.

2 Ibid.

3 Ham LS, Hope DA. Incorporating social anxiety into a model of college student problematic drinking. *Addict Behav.* 2005;30(1):127–150.

4 National Institute on Alcohol Abuse and Alcoholism. *A Call to Action: Changing the Culture of Drinking at U.S. Colleges.* Bethesda, MD: NIAAA, 2002. NIH publication 02-5010; and National Institute on Alcohol Abuse and Alcoholism. *Young Adult Drinking.* Bethesda, MD: NIAAA, 2006. Alcohol Alert, No. 68.

5 Johnston LD, O'Malley PM, Bachman JG. *Monitoring the Future: National Survey Results on Drug Use, 1975–2000. Volume 1: Secondary School Students.* Bethesda, MD: National Institute on Drug Abuse, 2001. NIH publication 01-4924.

6 Presley CA, Meilman PW, Leichliter JS. College factors that influence drinking. *J Studies Alcohol.* 2002;(suppl 14):82–90.

7 Toomey TL, Wagenaar AC. Environmental policies to reduce college drinking: options and research findings. *J Studies Alcohol.* 2002;(suppl 14):193–205.

8 O'Malley PM, Johnston LD. Epidemiology of alcohol and other drug use among American college students. *J Studies Alcohol.* 2002;(suppl 14):23–39.

9 Slutske WS. Alcohol use disorders among US college students and their non-college-attending peers. *Arch Gen Psychiatry.* 2005;62:321–327.

10 Ibid.

11 Knight JR, Wechsler H, Kuo M, et al. Alcohol abuse and dependence among U.S. college students. *J Studies Alcohol.* 2002;63(3):263–270.

12 Schulenberg J, O'Malley PM, Bachman JG, et al. Getting drunk and growing up: trajectories of frequent binge drinking during the transition to young adulthood. *J Studies Alcohol.* 1996;57(3):289–304.

13 Wechsler H, Lee JE, Kuo M, et al. Trends in college binge drinking during a period of increased prevention efforts: findings from 4 Harvard School of Public Health College Alcohol Study surveys: 1993–2001. *J Am Coll Health.* 2002;50(5):203–217.

14 Ibid.

15 Wechsler H, Seibring M, Liu IC, Ahl M. Colleges respond to student binge drinking: reducing student demand or limiting access. *J Am Coll Health.* 2004;52(4):159–168.

16 National Institute on Alcohol Abuse and Alcoholism. *A Call to Action.*

17 Hingson RW, Howland J. Comprehensive community interventions to promote health: implications for college-age drinking problems. *J Studies Alcohol.* 2002;(suppl 14):226–240; and Holder HD, Gruenewald PJ, Ponicki WR, et al. Effect of community-based interventions on high-risk drinking and alcohol-related injuries. *JAMA.* 2000;284:2341–2347.

18 Larimer ME, Cronce JM. Identification, prevention, and treatment: a review of individual-focused strategies to reduce problematic alcohol consumption by college students. *J Studies Alcohol.* 2002;(suppl 14):148–163.

19 Wagenaar AC, Toomey TL. Effects of minimum drinking age laws: review and analyses of the literature from 1960 to 2000. *J Studies Alcohol.* 2002;(suppl 14):206–225.

20 Wagenaar A, O'Malley P, LaFond L. Lowered legal blood alcohol limits for young drivers: effects on drinking, driving, and driving-after-drinking behaviors in 30 states. *Am J Pub Health.* 2001;91(5):801–804.

21 Cook PJ, Moore MJ. The economics of alcohol abuse and alcohol-control policies. *Health Affairs.* 2002;21(2):120–133.

22 Toomey, Wagenaar. Environmental policies to reduce college drinking.

23 Anderson J, Vitale, T. *Eat Right! Healthy Eating in College and Beyond.* San Francisco: Pearson Benjamin Cummings, 2007:87.

A person who drinks heavily over a long period of time may have brain deficits that persist well after he or she achieves sobriety. Exactly how alcohol affects the brain and the likelihood of reversing the impact of heavy drinking on the brain remain hot topics in alcohol research today.[40] Chronic alcoholism produces many different mental disorders. Malnutrition is a probable factor in most of these, even when diet appears adequate. After years of drinking, brain cells become permanently damaged and unable to metabolize nutrients properly.

Alcohol's Effect on the Gastrointestinal System

Years of heavy drinking and ongoing contact with alcohol and acetaldehyde eventually damage the gastrointestinal system, which in turn discourages eating, affects absorption of protective nutrients, and leaves the digestive lining even more vulnerable to damage as the vicious cycle continues.

Chronic irritation from alcohol and acetaldehyde erodes protective mucosal linings, causing inflammation and release of destructive free radicals. **Esophagitis** (inflammation of the esophagus), esophageal stricture (closing), and swallowing difficulties are common among alcoholics. When the stomach is exposed repeatedly to alcohol at high concentrations, **gastritis** (inflammation of the stomach) often develops. Alcoholics frequently have diarrhea and malabsorption, evidence of intestinal damage. The mouth, throat, esophagus, stomach, and small and large intestines are all at greatly increased risk of cancer.[41] Smoking dramatically multiplies this risk.

esophagitis Inflammation of the esophagus.

gastritis Inflammation of the stomach.

Alcohol and the Liver

Metabolizing and detoxifying alcohol is almost entirely the responsibility of the liver. So it's not surprising that too much drinking hurts the liver more than any other site in the body. In the United States, heavy alcohol use is considered the most important risk factor for chronic liver disease. During the 1980s, alcoholic fatty liver, acute alcoholic hepatitis, and alcoholic cirrhosis together accounted for 46 percent of deaths from chronic liver disease and 49 percent of hospitalizations for liver disease.[42]

The earliest evidence of liver damage is fat accumulation, which can appear after only a few days of heavy drinking. Fatty liver (see **Figure 8.12**) recedes with abstinence but persists with continued drinking. Is fatty liver in and of itself harmful? The answer is controversial among liver researchers, with some experts suggesting it's a benign condition. However, studies show that 5 to 15 percent of people with alcoholic fatty liver who continue to drink develop liver fibrosis (excessive fibrous tissue) or cirrhosis (scarring) in only 5 to 10 years.[43]

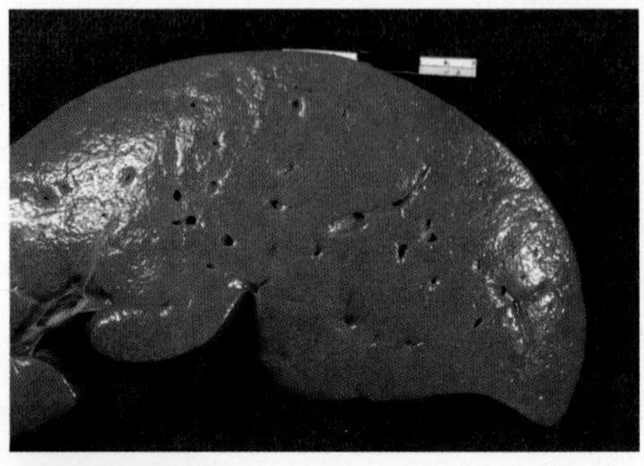

Figure 8.12 Fatty liver.

Fat accumulation is one of several factors resulting in alcoholic liver disease. With regular high intakes of alcohol, alcohol and acetaldehyde continually irritate and inflame the liver, producing alcoholic hepatitis (persistent inflammation of the liver) in 10 to 35 percent of heavy drinkers. The inflammatory process also generates free radicals that batter away at liver cells.[44] The destruction of liver cells becomes self-perpetuating, especially if antioxidant nutrients are unavailable to help break the cycle. If the intestines also have been damaged, toxins, including those produced by the gut's microorganisms, may be able to cross the intestinal barrier into circulation, worsening inflammation.[45]

Alcoholic hepatitis may be treatable, but it's often fatal. Alcoholic hepatitis also predisposes a person to liver cancer and cirrhosis, conditions that are usually fatal. With continued inflammation, the liver makes excessive collagen and becomes fibrous (fibrotic liver disease) and scarred (cirrhosis). This ultimately kills liver cells by choking off tiny blood vessels that nourish them. About 10 to 20 percent of heavy drinkers develop cirrhosis.[46]

Dietary changes may be helpful in treating liver disease, but abstinence from alcohol is essential. Reducing dietary fats somewhat reduces fat accumulation in the liver. Consuming adequate micronutrients and a healthful balance of macronutrients probably speeds recuperation from liver diseases in their earlier stages.[47] In late-stage liver disease, dietary restrictions, often of proteins, may slow disease progression or improve symptoms.

Fetal Alcohol Syndrome

Fetal alcohol syndrome is perhaps the saddest result of alcohol consumption. Victims of this syndrome suffer a variety of congenital defects: mental retardation, coordination problems, and heart, eye, and genitourinary malformations, as well as low birth weight and slowed growth rate. Most apparent are characteristic facial abnormalities. Severe cases of fetal alcohol syndrome are rare, but subtle damage with one or two abnormalities, sometimes called "fetal alcohol effects," is probably much more widespread. Symptoms of the syndrome may not emerge until months after birth and are apt to go undiagnosed.[48] This disorder, a major cause of mental retardation in the United States, is preventable.

fetal alcohol syndrome A set of physical and mental abnormalities observed in infants born to women who abuse alcohol during pregnancy. Affected infants exhibit poor growth, characteristic abnormal facial features, limited hand–eye coordination, and mental retardation.

Alcohol is especially damaging in the early weeks of pregnancy, before a woman may know she's pregnant. It crosses the placenta into the tiny body of the fetus, where its effects are grossly magnified. Both the congeners in alcoholic beverages and the associated disturbed metabolism of vitamin A and folic acid, nutrients clearly required for fetal growth and development, can interfere with embryonic development.[49]

Relatively small amounts of alcohol may cause fetal alcohol syndrome. A safe level during pregnancy is not known; therefore, pregnant women should abstain from alcohol consumption. Unlike most other alcohol-related diseases, fetal alcohol damage does not require chronic intake. A binge—even having several drinks at a party—at the wrong moment of pregnancy can cause serious problems. However, population studies show that babies with neurodevelopmental problems are more common among women who drink more frequently during pregnancy.[50]

Official health advisories warn women against drinking alcohol if they are pregnant or considering becoming pregnant. Labels on alcoholic beverages must carry a warning for pregnant women. In 2002, 10.1 percent of pregnant women consumed alcohol, and 1.9 percent did so frequently.[51] **Figure 8.13** shows the prevalence of binge drinking by women of childbearing age.

Key Concepts *Alcohol affects every organ system of the body. In the brain and nervous system, alcohol impairs coordination, judgment, reaction time, and vision. In the GI tract, alcohol damages cells of the esophagus and stomach and increases the risk for GI cancers. The liver is most affected by alcohol consumption, culminating in alcoholic hepatitis and cirrhosis after years of alcohol abuse. Alcohol intake during pregnancy can have devastating effects on fetal development.*

Alcoholics and Malnutrition

In the United States and Canada, where food is plentiful and fortification of foods with vitamins and minerals is common, overt nutrient deficiencies are rare—except among alcoholics. The results of their poor diet interact with

Figure 8.13 Prevalence of binge drinking among childbearing-aged women (18–44 years), by state: United States, 2002.

Source: Centers for Disease Control and Prevention. Alcohol consumption among women who are pregnant or who might become pregnant—United States, 2002. *MMWR.* 2004;53(50):1178–1181.

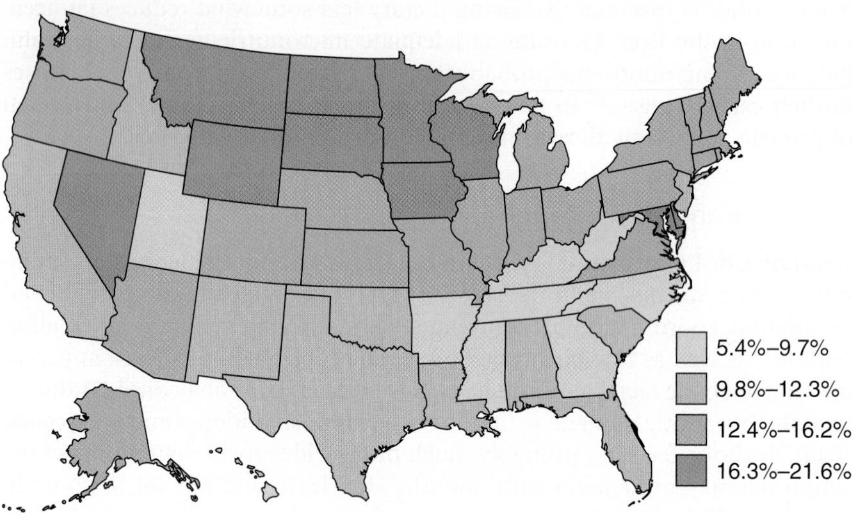

the results of alcohol's toxicity—which include diarrhea, malabsorption, liver malfunction, bleeding, bone marrow changes, and hormonal changes—to worsen malnutrition. (See **Figure 8.14**.) In general, the more a person drinks, the worse the malnutrition.

Poor Diet

A nationally representative study found that as alcohol quantity increased, diet quality worsened, but as alcohol frequency increased, diet quality improved. Diet quality was poorest among the highest-quantity, lowest-frequency drinkers and best among the lowest-quantity, highest-frequency drinkers.[52]

Disordered eating is common among heavy drinkers, especially among alcoholic women.[53] Factors responsible for the poor diet of alcoholics are much easier to identify than to correct. Economic factors include poverty, lack of cooking facilities, and homelessness. Anxiety, depression, loneliness, and isolation are all characteristic of alcoholism, and all contribute to loss of appetite. So can physical pain. Lack of interest in food is common. There may be an aversion to many specific foods or to eating in general, especially after the experience of diarrhea, painful indigestion, or difficulty swallowing.

Heavy drinkers who get about half their calories from alcohol cannot eat enough to obtain adequate vitamins and minerals. Severely malnourished alcoholics often have multiple deficiencies.

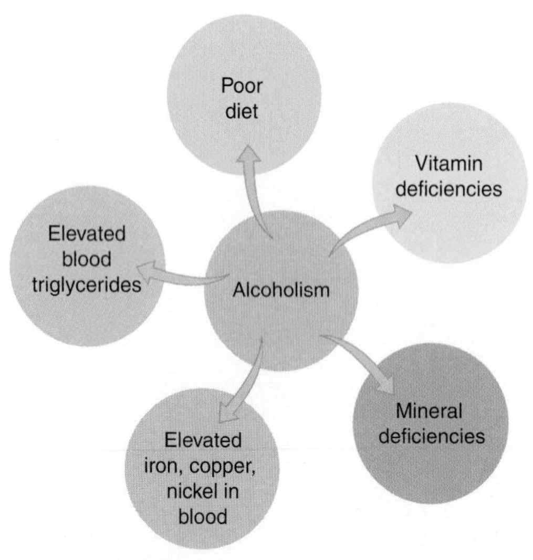

Figure 8.14 **Alcoholism and malnutrition.** Alcoholics' poor diets interact with alcohol's toxicity to worsen their malnutrition.

Vitamin Deficiencies

Inadequate intake, poor absorption, increased vitamin destruction in the body, and urinary losses all contribute to vitamin deficiencies in the alcoholic. Alcohol also interferes with the conversion of vitamin precursors to active forms.

Folate, thiamin, and vitamin A are most often affected by alcoholism. Folate deficiency contributes to malabsorption, anemia, and nerve damage—

all of which worsen malnutrition. Vitamin A deficiency also creates a vicious cycle by damaging gastrointestinal lining and by impairing immunity, leaving the victim susceptible to infections. Thiamin deficiency contributes to classic diseases of alcoholism: the brain damage of Wernicke-Korsakoff syndrome, polyneuropathy (nerve inflammation), and cardiomyopathy (heart inflammation). Alcoholics can have overt scurvy from vitamin C deficiency. Vitamin B_6 and vitamin B_{12} deficiencies are less common.

Alcohol metabolism interferes with the normal metabolism of vitamins and other nutrients. For example, metabolism of ethanol uses up the dehydrogenase enzyme that is also used for metabolism of retinol.[54] Retinol (vitamin A) uses that enzyme for its conversion to other active forms of vitamin A, and the disruption of its metabolism is probably one way that alcohol increases cancer risk. The same disruption may produce fetal birth defects when pregnant women drink.

Alcohol-induced fat malabsorption and metabolic abnormalities contribute to the depletion of fat-soluble vitamins A, D, E, and K. Blood-clotting factors drop with depleted vitamin K, increasing risk of bleeding and anemia. Vitamin E deficiency is not generally recognized as a complication of alcoholism, but its depletion due to fat malabsorption is possible. Optimal vitamin E status is necessary to quench free radicals generated during alcohol metabolism.[55]

Mineral Deficiencies

Alcoholics are commonly deficient in minerals such as calcium, magnesium, iron, and zinc. Alcohol itself does not seem to affect their absorption. Rather, fluid losses and an inadequate diet are the primary culprits. Magnesium deficiency causes "shakes" similar to that seen in alcohol withdrawal. Chronic diarrhea and loss of epithelial tissue (caused by skin rashes or sloughing off of the digestive lining) may seriously deplete zinc, a mineral needed for immune function. In cases of bleeding, especially gastrointestinal blood loss, iron levels fall.

Not all minerals are lower in heavy drinkers than in nondrinkers. If there is no bleeding, a heavy drinker's iron levels tend to be higher than normal in the blood and liver, potentially contributing to harmful oxidation. Copper and nickel levels also may be elevated in advancing disease, but the reason and the effects are unclear.[56]

Macronutrients

Animal experiments can demonstrate a number of ways that alcohol alters digestion and metabolism of carbohydrate, fat, and protein, but the relevance to humans at usual levels of intake is not certain. Alcohol interferes with amino acid absorption, but its overall effect on protein balance appears minimal. It inhibits gluconeogenesis and lowers blood glucose levels, probably contributing to hangovers and, at the most extreme, causing acute, potentially lethal hypoglycemia if a person who drinks heavily neglects to eat.[57]

Alcohol's most dramatic effect is on fats. You have seen that alcohol causes fatty liver. On the one hand, excess alcohol has the undesirable effect of raising blood triglyceride levels, often significantly. Hyperlipidemia (high blood fats) is common among heavy drinkers. Abstinence and a balanced diet can usually return blood lipids to normal.[58] On the other hand, moderate alcohol use increases protective high-density lipoproteins (HDL, or "good cholesterol"), an important factor in alcohol's relationship to the reduced risk for coronary artery disease.

Dietary Guidelines for Americans, 2010
Key Recommendations

Foods and Food Components to Reduce

- If alcohol is consumed, it should be consumed in moderation—up to one drink per day for women and two drinks per day for men—and only by adults of legal drinking age.
- There are many circumstances in which people should not drink alcohol. These include:
  - Individuals who cannot restrict their drinking to moderate levels.
  - Anyone younger than the legal drinking age. Besides being illegal, alcohol consumption increases the risk of drowning, car accidents, and traumatic injury, which are common causes of death in children and adolescents.
  - Women who are pregnant or who may be pregnant. Drinking during pregnancy, especially in the first few months of pregnancy, may result in negative behavioral or neurologic consequences in the offspring. No safe level of alcohol consumption during pregnancy has been established.
  - Individuals taking prescription or over-the-counter medications that can interact with alcohol.
  - Individuals with certain specific medical conditions.
  - Individuals who plan to drive, operate machinery, or take part in other activities that require attention, skill, or coordination or in situations where impaired judgment could cause injury or death.

Body Weight

Although alcoholic beverages provide minimal nutrient value, they do provide calories; alcohol contains 7 kilocalories per gram. Does alcohol consumption contribute to obesity? It appears likely. One reason for weight gain associated with alcohol intake is that the calories in alcohol can easily add up. Some cocktail-type drinks, such as margaritas or piña coladas, contain more than 500 calories per drink! In addition, food choices that accompany drinking are generally low in nutrient density and high in calories, adding to an overall excess calorie intake. The excess calories promote body fat accumulation and weight gain.

In an analysis of data collected from more than 37,000 people, researchers found that overweight drinkers consumed more drinks than leaner drinkers on the days that they drank.[59] Men and women who infrequently consume the greatest quantity of alcohol weigh more than those who frequently drink small amounts. Because smoking and drinking interact to influence body weight, the researchers looked only at current drinkers who had never smoked.

Key Concepts *Alcohol interferes with normal nutrition by reducing the intake of nutrient-dense foods and by affecting the absorption, metabolism, and excretion of many vitamins and minerals. Alcohol contains a significant number of calories (7 kilocalories per gram), and heavy episodic drinkers tend to weigh more than light drinkers.*

Does Alcohol Have Benefits?

Can a potentially harmful drink like alcohol play a role in a healthful diet? The consensus of health experts is that it can—but not for everyone. The question continues to arouse much debate, however, and even those supporting alcohol's usefulness often have reservations. Public health statements on alcohol are typically accompanied by plenty of "ifs" and "buts."

Consistent epidemiological evidence suggests that low to moderate drinking reduces mortality among some groups.[60] (Table 8.3 gives definitions of different levels of drinking.) Compared with nondrinkers or heavy drinkers, middle-aged and older adults who drink moderate amounts of alcohol have a lower risk of mortality from all causes.[61] This includes people with heart disease,[62] diabetes,[63] high blood pressure,[64] or a prior heart attack.[65] Consistent and growing evidence shows that alcohol reduces insulin resistance and may protect against heart disease by improving "good" cholesterol levels and reducing blood clotting.[66]

No evidence has suggested that moderate drinking harmed the people in the studies. In fact, analysis of data from the Nurses' Health Study, which involves more than 12,000 participants, suggests that in women, up to one drink per day does not impair mental functioning and may actually decrease the risk of mental decline with age.[67]

Tracked against alcohol intake, death rates typically follow what statisticians describe as a "U-shaped curve." Compared with people who rarely or never drink, people who drink slightly or moderately have lower total mortality rates. The lowest rate is seen in people who consume one drink per week. Increasing the number of drinks confers no additional benefit. In fact, as the number of drinks increases, the mortality rate rises. People who consume two drinks per day have about the same mortality rate as nondrinkers.[68] Beyond three drinks per day, the death rate rises dramatically.[69] Heavy alcohol consumption increases the risk of stroke, for example, whereas light or moderate drinking appears to reduce that risk.[70] Alcohol's primary benefit

Table 8.3 How Much Is Too Much?

Term	Criterion
Moderate drinking (NIAAA)	Men: ≤ 2 drinks per day
	Women: ≤ 1 drink per day Over 65: ≤ 1 drink per day
At-risk drinking (NIAAA)	Men: > 14 drinks per week or > 4 drinks per occasion Women: > 7 drinks per week or > 3 drinks per occasion
Alcohol abuse (APA)	Maladaptive pattern of alcohol use leading to clinically significant impairment or distress, manifested within a 12-month period by one or more of the following: • Failure to fulfill role obligations at work, school, or home • Recurrent use in hazardous situations • Legal problems related to alcohol • Continued use despite alcohol-related social or interpersonal problems • Symptoms have never met criteria for alcohol dependence
Alcohol dependence (APA)	Maladaptive pattern of alcohol use leading to clinically significant impairment or distress, manifested within a 12-month period by three or more of the following: • Tolerance (either increasing amounts used or diminished effects with the same amount) • Withdrawal (withdrawal symptoms or use to relieve or avoid symptoms) • Use of larger amounts over a longer period than intended • Persistent desire or unsuccessful attempts to cut down or control use • Great deal of time spent obtaining or using or recovering from use • Important social, occupational, or recreational activities given up or reduced • Use despite knowledge of alcohol-related physical or psychological problems
Hazardous use (WHO)	Person at risk for adverse consequences
Harmful use (WHO)	Use resulting in physical or psychological harm

Note: NIAAA = National Institute on Alcohol Abuse and Alcoholism; APA = American Psychiatric Association; WHO = World Health Organization.

Source: O'Connor PG, Schottenfield RS. Patients with alcohol problems. *N Engl J Med.* 1998;338(9):593.

is to raise protective HDL cholesterol levels. It may also inhibit formation of blood clots, but this connection is less clear.[71] In addition, alcohol may have subjective benefits such as stress relief and relaxation.

In most studies, wine, beer, and spirits appear equal in offering protection against heart disease. Findings of reduced rates of nonfatal heart attacks

American Heart Association

Alcohol

If you drink alcohol, do so in moderation. This means an average of one to two drinks per day for men and one drink per day for women. Drinking more alcohol increases such dangers as alcoholism, high blood pressure, obesity, stroke, breast cancer, suicide and accidents. Also, it's not possible to predict in which people alcoholism will become a problem. Given these and other risks, the American Heart Association cautions people *not* to start drinking . . . if they do not already drink alcohol. Consult your doctor on the benefits and risks of consuming alcohol in moderation.

Source: American Heart Association, Inc.

among moderate drinkers support the view that protective benefits are due to alcohol itself rather than other substances in alcoholic beverages.[72] However, international comparisons that highlight unexpectedly low rates of heart disease in France, despite a high-fat diet (the **French paradox**), suggest that red wine may have a unique protective effect. The apparent benefits of red wine may result from overall healthier behavior of people who drink red wine. As yet, a direct connection between red wine and health benefits remains unproved.[73] Nevertheless, recognizing that alcohol generally confers moderate protection and noting the possibility that wine has a particular benefit, the

French paradox A phenomenon observed in the French, who have a lower incidence of heart disease than people whose diets contain comparable amounts of fat. Part of the difference has been attributed to the regular and moderate drinking of red wine.

Addiction
Alcohol addiction destroys lives, families, and communities. Researchers are trying to learn why some people, and not others, become addicted.
Accidents and violence
These result from impairment of mental function and coordination.
Birth defects
Fetal alcohol syndrome can occur when pregnant women drink.
Emotional and social
Emotional, social, and economic problems are associated with heavy drinking.
Cardiomyopathy
Inflammation of the heart muscle is much more common in heavy drinkers.
Liver disease
Heavy drinking can lead to alcoholic fatty liver, alcoholic hepatitis, cirrhosis, and liver cancer.
Pancreatitis
Both chronic and acute pancreatitis are increased by alcoholism.
Anemia
Heavy drinkers often have poor diets and may bleed from the digestive tract.
Osteoporosis
Heavy drinking contributes to bone loss, especially in older women.
Brain
Acute effects are drunkenness. Long-term effects of chronic alcohol excess are dementia, memory loss, and generalized impairment of mental function.
Gastritis
Continued contact with excess alcohol irritates and inflames the stomach lining.
Cancer
Excess alcohol increases the risk of gastrointestinal, liver, and breast cancers. Smoking further increases these risks.
Peripheral neuropathy
Painful nerve inflammation in hands, arms, feet, and legs is common in long-time heavy alcohol users.

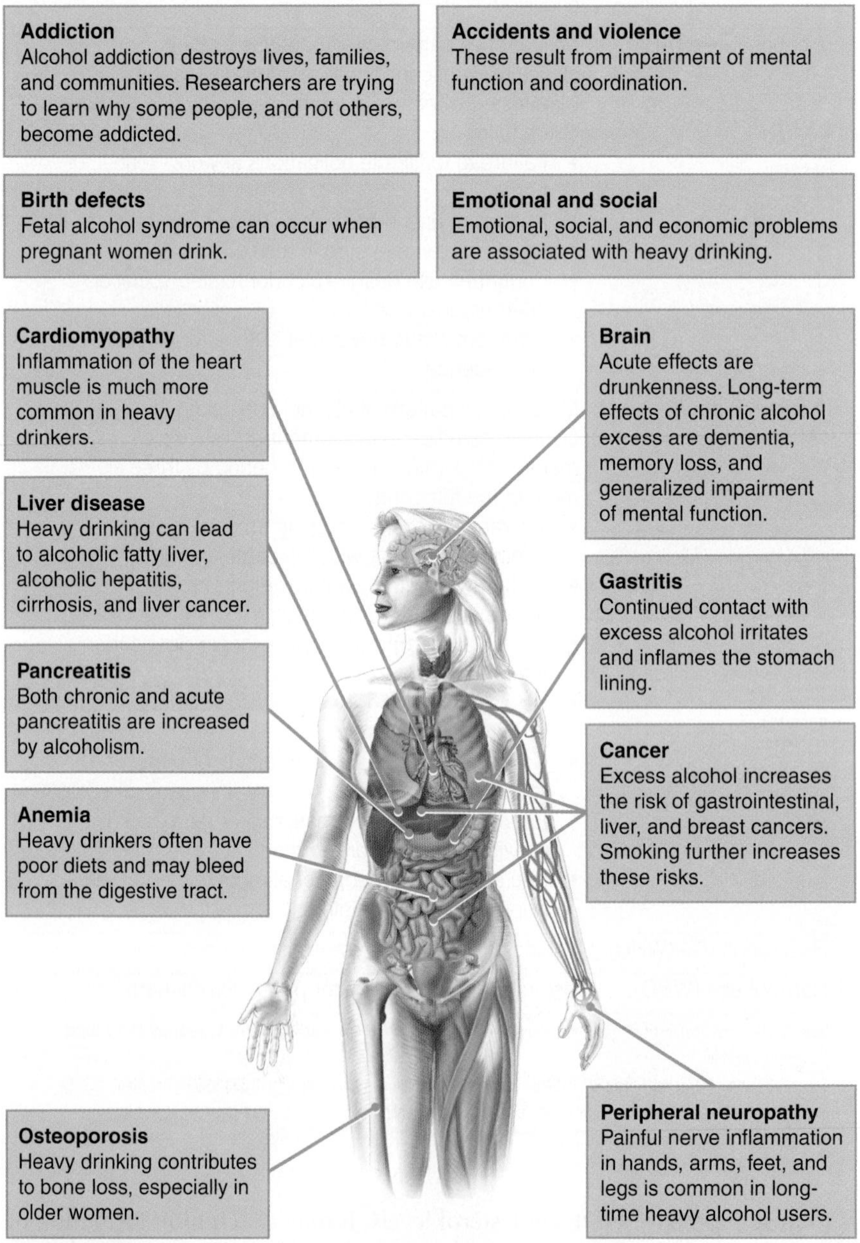

Figure 8.15 **Harmful effects of alcohol.** Because excess alcohol reaches all parts of the body, it causes a wide array of physical problems. Here are some of the ways alcohol can cause harm.

Quick Bite

A What?

An oenologist is an expert in the science of wine and wine making.

Bureau of Alcohol, Tobacco, and Firearms granted permission for wine labels to include one of the following statements:[74]

"The proud people who made this wine encourage you to consult your family doctor about the health effects of wine consumption."

"To learn the health effects of wine consumption, send for the Federal Government's Dietary Guidelines for Americans. . . ."

Because of the many harmful effects of alcohol (see **Figure 8.15**), public health agencies and organizations caution against inappropriate drinking. Although low to moderate alcohol use may offer some benefit, these groups advise people to discuss their alcohol intake with their doctors, and they

Label to Table

Have you ever wondered how much protein, carbohydrate, and fat are in a can of beer? If you've ever looked at a beer label, you know it's quite different from a food label. Look at the following information from a can of light beer and see if you can calculate the calories from carbohydrate, fat, and protein.

Serving size = 12 fl oz
Calories = 103 (kcal)
Carbohydrate = 5 g
Protein = 1 g
Fat = 0 g

First, to figure out how many calories come from the three macronutrients, multiply the number of grams by their respective calorie contribution per gram:

5 g carbohydrate × 4 kcal/g = 20 kcal from carbohydrate
1 g protein × 4 kcal/g = 4 kcal from protein
0 g fat × 9 kcal/g = 0 kcal from fat

Uh oh. Is this adding up correctly? So far we have accounted for only 24 of the 103 kilocalories in this beer. Where are the other 79 kilocalories? Don't forget that many of the calories in beer come from alcohol, and it's easy to calculate just how many grams are in this can of light beer. Remember, alcohol has 7 kilocalories per gram, so the remaining 79 kilocalories come from 11 grams of alcohol (79 ÷ 7 = 11.3).

So, for the 103 kilocalories this beer provides, you get very little (if any) protein, carbohydrate, or fat. Instead, a majority of the calories come from alcohol. This holds true for the micronutrients as well: beer contains negligible amounts of vitamins or minerals.

This is why people say alcoholic beverages have only "empty calories." They provide calories, but almost no nutrient value!

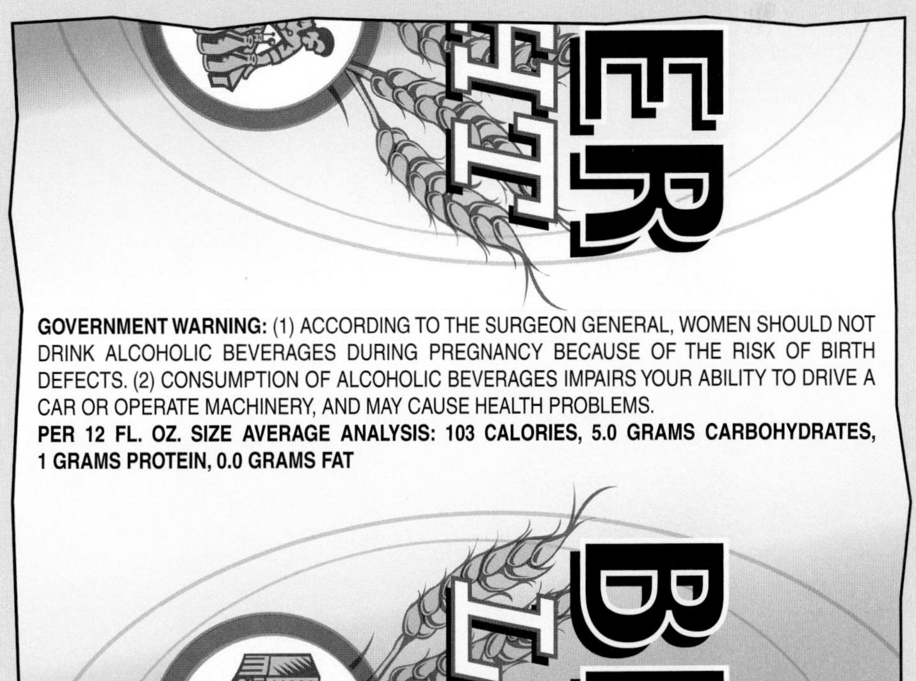
GOVERNMENT WARNING: (1) ACCORDING TO THE SURGEON GENERAL, WOMEN SHOULD NOT DRINK ALCOHOLIC BEVERAGES DURING PREGNANCY BECAUSE OF THE RISK OF BIRTH DEFECTS. (2) CONSUMPTION OF ALCOHOLIC BEVERAGES IMPAIRS YOUR ABILITY TO DRIVE A CAR OR OPERATE MACHINERY, AND MAY CAUSE HEALTH PROBLEMS.
PER 12 FL. OZ. SIZE AVERAGE ANALYSIS: 103 CALORIES, 5.0 GRAMS CARBOHYDRATES, 1 GRAMS PROTEIN, 0.0 GRAMS FAT

urge moderation. The U.S. Preventive Services Task Force recommends that primary care doctors routinely screen patients for unhealthy alcohol use and, when appropriate, intervene with a brief counseling session to reduce alcohol misuse.[75] Public health officials also point out that numerous groups should not drink any alcohol:[76]

- People who cannot restrict their alcohol intake to moderate levels
- Children and adolescents
- People taking medications that can interact with alcohol
- People who have an alcohol-related illness or another illness that will be worsened by alcohol
- People who plan to drive, operate machinery, or take part in other activities that require attention, skill, or coordination
- Women who are pregnant or may become pregnant
- Women who are breastfeeding
- People with a personal or strong family history of alcoholism

Key Concepts *Although alcohol has the potential to reduce risk for heart disease, most health organizations recommend moderate to no drinking. It is too early in the scientific investigation of alcohol's benefits to recommend alcohol intake for all adults. Some people, such as pregnant women, should not drink any alcohol.*

Learning Portfolio

Key Terms

	page
acetaldehyde	314
alcohol	310
alcohol dehydrogenase (ADH)	314
alcohol poisoning	316
aldehyde dehydrogenase (ALDH)	315
binge drinking	312
congeners	312
esophagitis	324
ethanol	310
ethyl alcohol	310
fatty liver	315
fermentation	310
fetal alcohol syndrome	325
French paradox	330
gastritis	324
hangover	316
methanol	310
methyl alcohol	310
microsomal ethanol-oxidizing system (MEOS)	315
standard drink	312
wood alcohol	310

Study Points

- Alcohol provides 7 kilocalories per gram but no essential function for the body; therefore, alcohol is not a nutrient.
- Alcohol requires no digestion and is absorbed easily all along the gastrointestinal tract.
- Fatty liver is apparent even after one night of binge drinking.
- Different rates of alcohol metabolism can be attributed to different levels of the alcohol-metabolizing enzymes; these differences are due to genetic and gender variations.
- Alcohol affects all organs in the body, but the most obvious effects are in the brain and the nervous system, the GI system, and the liver.
- Malnutrition among alcoholics is common due to poor food choices and alcohol's interference with the absorption, metabolism, and excretion of nutrients.
- Fetal alcohol syndrome is one of the most devastating consequences of alcohol consumption, and it is preventable.
- Moderate alcohol consumption has been linked to reduced risk of heart disease.
- The potential benefits of moderate alcohol consumption may be related to effects on lipoprotein levels and the antioxidant components of beverages such as wine.
- Health organizations recommend moderate to no alcohol consumption.

Study Questions

1. How much alcohol is in beer, wine, and liquor?
2. List the ways food helps to delay or avoid inebriation.
3. Where does alcohol metabolism take place?
4. What causes a hangover? Is there any way to relieve one?
5. List some factors that affect our ability to metabolize alcohol.
6. Why do health care professionals advise pregnant women not to drink alcohol?
7. List the positive and the negative effects of alcohol.

Try This

Cruising Through the Medicine Cabinet

This exercise will increase your awareness of the amounts of alcohol in over-the-counter medications. Look through your medicine cabinet and check the ingredient lists of all the products there. In particular, take a close look at any mouthwash or cough syrup. Which products contain alcohol? How much? What do you think its purpose is in these medicines?

References

1 US Department of Health and Human Services and US Department of Agriculture. *Dietary Guidelines for Americans, 2010*. 7th ed. Washington, DC: US Government Printing Office, December 2010.

2 Maimi TS, Brewer RD, Mokdad A, et al. Binge drinking among US adults. *JAMA*. 2003;289:70–75.

3 Foster WE, Vaughan RD, Foster WH, et al. Alcohol consumption and expenditures for underage drinking and adult excessive drinking. *JAMA*. 2003;289:989–995.

4 National Institute on Alcohol Abuse and Alcoholism. *Underage Drinking: A Major Public Health Problem*. Bethesda, MD: NIAAA, 2003. Alcohol Alert, No. 59.

5 Mokdad AH, Marks JS, Stroup DF, et al. Actual causes of death in the United States, 2000. *JAMA*. 2004;291:1238–1245.

6 Roe DA. *Alcohol and the Diet*. Westport, CT: AVI Publishing, 1979.

7 Ibid.

8 Mittal BV, Desai AP, Khade KR. Methyl alcohol poisoning: an autopsy study of 28 cases. *J Postgrad Med*. 1991;37:9–13.

9 Roe. *Alcohol and the Diet*.

10 Zakhari S. Overview: how is alcohol metabolized by the body? *Alcohol Res Health*. 2006;29(4):243–252.

11 Swift R, Davidson D. Alcohol hangover: mechanisms and mediators. *Alcohol Health Res World*. 1998;22:54–60.

12 US Department of Health and Human Services and US Department of Agriculture. *Dietary Guidelines for Americans, 2010*.

13 Doll R, Peto R, Boreham J, et al. Mortality in relation to alcohol consumption: a prospective study among male British doctors. *Int J Epidemiol.* 2005;34:199–204.
14 Seitz HK, Oneta CM. Gastrointestinal alcohol dehydrogenase. *Nutr Rev.* 1998;56:52–60.
15 Ibid.
16 Swift, Davidson. Alcohol hangover.
17 Seitz, Oneta. Gastrointestinal alcohol dehydrogenase.
18 Ibid.
19 Swift, Davidson. Alcohol hangover.
20 Wiese J, McPherson S, Odden MC, et al. Effect of *Opuntia ficus indica* on symptoms of the alcohol hangover. *Arch Intern Med.* 2004;164:1334–1340.
21 Swift, Davidson. Alcohol hangover.
22 Ibid.
23 Anderson J, Vitale T, et al. *Eat Right! Healthy Eating in College and Beyond.* San Francisco: Pearson Benjamin Cummings, 2007:85.
24 Ibid.
25 Wiese, McPherson, Odden, et al. Effect of *Opuntia ficus indica* on symptoms of the alcohol hangover.
26 Ibid.
27 Swift, Davidson. Alcohol hangover.
28 Mayo Clinic. Pain relievers and alcohol: a potential risky combination. *Mayo Clinic Health Letter.* 2006;6(May).
29 National Institute on Alcohol Abuse and Alcoholism. *Alcohol: The Genetics of Alcoholism.* Bethesda, MD: NIAAA, 2003. Alcohol Alert, No. 60.
30 Vallee BL. Alcohol in the Western world. *Scientific American.* June 1998;80–85.
31 National Institute on Alcohol Abuse and Alcoholism. *Alcohol and Aging.* Bethesda, MD: NIAAA, 1998. Alcohol Alert, No. 40.
32 Dufour MC. What is moderate drinking? *Alcohol Res Health.* 1999;23(1):1–14.
33 USDA Center for Nutrition Policy and Promotion. *Does Alcohol Have a Place in a Healthy Diet?* Washington, DC: Center for Nutrition Policy and Promotion, 1997. Nutrition Insights, No. 4.
34 National Institute on Alcohol Abuse and Alcoholism. *Alcohol: An Important Women's Health Issue.* Bethesda, MD: NIAAA, 2004. Alcohol Alert, No. 62.
35 Swift, Davidson. Alcohol hangover.
36 Baraona E, Abbittan CS, Dohmen K, et al. Gender differences in pharmacokinetics of alcohol. *Alcohol Clin Exp Res.* 2001;25:502–507.
37 Pinel JP. *Biopsychology.* Boston: Allyn & Bacon, 2006.
38 National Institute on Alcohol Abuse and Alcoholism. *Alcohol and Transportation Safety.* Bethesda, MD: NIAAA, 2001. Alcohol Alert, No. 52.
39 US Department of Health and Human Services. *Hypoglycemia.* Washington, DC: National Institutes of Health, 2006. NIH publication 03-3926.
40 National Institute on Alcohol Abuse and Alcoholism. *Alcohol's Damaging Effects on the Brain.* Bethesda, MD: NIAAA, October 2004. Alcohol Alert, No. 63.
41 Boffetta P, Hashibe M. Alcohol and cancer. *Lancet Oncol.* 2006;7(2):149–156.
42 Centers for Disease Control and Prevention. Deaths and hospitalizations from chronic liver disease and cirrhosis—United States, 1980–1989. *MMWR.* 1993;41:969–973.
43 Lieber CS. Alcoholic fatty liver: its pathogenesis and mechanism of progression to inflammation and fibrosis. *Alcohol.* 2004;34(1):9–19.
44 Dey A, Cederbaum AI. Alcohol and oxidative liver damage. *Hepatology.* 2006;43(suppl 2):S63–S74.
45 University of Maryland Medical Center. Liver disease: alcohol-induced liver disease. http://www.umm.edu/liver/alcohol.htm. Accessed 1/28/09.
46 Ibid.
47 Teli MR, Day CP, Burt AD, et al. Determinants of progression to cirrhosis or fibrosis in pure alcoholic fatty liver. *Lancet.* 1995;346:987–990.
48 Centers for Disease Control and Prevention. Identification of children with fetal alcohol syndrome and opportunity for referral of their mother for primary prevention, Washington, 1993–1997. *MMWR.* 1998;47:861–864.
49 Roe. *Alcohol and the Diet.*
50 Centers for Disease Control and Prevention. Alcohol consumption among pregnant and childbearing-aged women—United States, 2002. *MMWR.* 2004;53:1178–1181.
51 Ibid.
52 Breslow RA, Guenther PM, Smothers BA. Alcohol drinking patterns and diet quality: the 1999–2000 National Health and Nutrition Examination Survey. *Am J Epidemiol.* 2006;163(4):359–366.
53 Lilenfeld LR, Kaye WH. The link between alcoholism and eating disorders. *Alcohol Health Res World.* 1996;20:94–99.
54 Seitz, Oneta. Gastrointestinal alcohol dehydrogenase; and Wang XD. Chronic alcohol intake interferes with retinoid metabolism and signaling. *Nutr Rev.* 1999;57:51–59.
55 Lieber CS. Nutrition and diet in alcoholism. In: Shils ME, Olson JA, Shike M, eds. *Modern Nutrition in Health and Disease.* 9th ed. Philadelphia: Lippincott Williams & Wilkins, 2004.
56 Ibid.
57 Ibid.
58 Ibid.
59 Breslow RA, Smothers BA. Drinking patterns and body mass index in never smokers. *Am J Epdemiol.* 2005;161:368–376.
60 Klatsky AL. Should patients with heart disease drink alcohol? *JAMA.* 2001;285:2004–2006; and Doll R, Peto R, Boreham J, Sutherland I. Mortality in relation to alcohol consumption: a prospective study among male British doctors. *Int J Epidemiol.* 2005;34:199–204.
61 National Institute on Alcohol Abuse and Alcoholism. *State of the Science Report on the Effects of Moderate Drinking.* Bethesda, MD: NIAAA, 2003; and US Department of Health and Human Services and US Department of Agriculture. *Dietary Guidelines for Americans, 2010.*
62 Klatsky. Should patients with heart disease drink alcohol?
63 Ajani UA, Gaziano JM, Lotufo PA, et al. Alcohol consumption and risk of coronary heart disease by diabetes status. *Circulation.* 2000;102:500–505; and Solomon CG, Hu FB, Stampfer MJ, et al. Moderate alcohol consumption and risk of coronary heart disease among women with type 2 diabetes mellitus. *Circulation.* 2000;102:494–499.
64 Malinski MK, Sesso HD, Lopez-Jimenez F, et al. Alcohol consumption and cardiovascular mortality in hypertensive patients. Paper presented at: 41st Annual Conference on Cardiovascular Disease Epidemiology and Prevention; March 2, 2001; San Antonio, TX.
65 Muntwyler J, Hennekens CH, Buring JE, et al. Mortality and light to moderate alcohol consumption after myocardial infarction. *Lancet.* 1998;352:1882–1885.
66 Fagrell B, De Faire U, Bondy S, et al. The effects of light to moderate drinking on cardiovascular diseases. *J Intern Med.* 1999;246:331–340; and Paoletti R, Klatsky AL, Poli A, Zahari S, eds. *Moderate Alcohol Consumption and Cardiovascular Disease.* Dordrecht: Kluwer; 2000.
67 Stampfer MJS, Kang JH, Chen J, et al. Effects of moderate alcohol consumption on cognitive function in women. *N Engl J Med.* 2005;352:245–253.
68 Gaziano JM, Gaziano TA, Glynn RJ, et al. Light-to-moderate alcohol consumption and mortality in the Physicians' Health Study enrollment cohort. *J Am Coll Cardiol.* 2000;35:96–105.
69 Pearson TA. Alcohol and heart disease. *Circulation.* 1996;94:3023–3025.
70 Reynolds K, Lewis BL, Nolen JD, et al. Alcohol consumption and risk of stroke. *JAMA.* 2003;289:579–588.
71 Klatsky. Should patients with heart disease drink alcohol?
72 Bobak M, Skodova Z, Marmot M. Effect of beer drinking on risk of myocardial infarction: population based case-control study. *BMJ.* 2000;320:1378–1379; and Mukamal KJ, Conigrave KM, Mittleman MA, et al. Roles of drinking pattern and type of alcohol consumed in coronary heart disease in men. *N Engl J Med.* 2003;348:109–118.
73 Tjonneland A, Gronbaek M, Stripp C, Overvad K. Wine intake and diet in a random sample of 48,763 Danish men and women. *Am J Clin Nutr.* 1999;69:49–54.
74 Treasury announces actions concerning labeling of alcoholic beverages. US Treasury Department, Bureau of Alcohol, Tobacco and Firearms press release; February 5, 1999.
75 Saitz R. Unhealthy alcohol use. *N Engl J Med.* 2005;352:596–607.
76 Pearson. Alcohol and heart disease; and US Department of Health and Human Services and US Department of Agriculture. *Dietary Guidelines for Americans, 2010.*

CHAPTER 9

Energy Balance, Body Composition, and Weight Management

THINK About It

1 How often do you reject dessert after a big meal?

2 When it comes to body fat distribution, are you an apple or a pear?

3 What does it mean to be metabolically fit?

4 How much time do you spend talking with your friends about weight?

Visit nutrition.jbpub.com

Quick Bite

Early Energy Balance Experiments

Erasistraus of Chios performed the first recorded experiment on energy balance in 280 B.C.E. Seeking to balance intake with output, he used a jar to fashion a kind of respiration apparatus. He then put two birds in the jar, weighing them and their excreta before and after feeding.

Your body is in the energy exchange business. Here's how it works. You balance the energy you expend with energy from the food in your diet. If you do a fairly good job of equalizing input and output, your body does the rest—maintaining energy equilibrium and keeping your weight steady. But what happens if you bring in more energy than your body can handle? It banks the excess energy as fat, and you gain weight. If your "account" grows too big, you become obese. Losing that extra weight—withdrawing the fat from your account—is not always easy.

Energy intake is the amount of fuel (calories) you take in through consumption of carbohydrate, protein, fat, and alcohol. **Energy output** is the amount you expend—primarily for basic body functions, physical activity, and the processing of food. An average adult consumes 1,800 to 3,000 kilocalories per day. In one year, that adds up to 657,000 to 1,095,000 kilocalories! Amazingly, despite such a huge intake of energy over time, most people maintain roughly the same weight during their adult lives.

People who maintain a relatively constant weight are in **energy equilibrium**. Within limits, your body automatically regulates your weight, thanks to its ability to balance intake and expenditure. Your body can be in energy equilibrium even if your energy intake is very high, as long as your expenditure also is high. Conversely, your body can be in energy equilibrium when you don't expend much energy, as long as your intake also is low.

When you take in more energy than you need, you have a **positive energy balance**. You store the surplus as fat—the major energy reserve—and as glycogen, the short-term carbohydrate energy reserve. Pregnant women and growing children need a positive energy balance to increase energy stores. But the positive energy balance that results from overeating and inactivity, a common occurrence around major holidays, leads to unneeded weight gain.

When you take in less energy than you need, you have a **negative energy balance**. Reduced energy intake can be the result of illness, or it can be an intentional change for weight loss. To obtain fuel, your body uses stores of glycogen and fat (and breaks down body protein too, if the deficit is extreme), and body weight goes down. Thus, body weight change reflects overall **energy balance**. **Figure 9.1** shows different ratios of energy intake to energy expenditure.

Key Concepts *Energy balance is the relationship between energy intake and energy output. Energy intake comes from the calories in food and beverages. Energy output is the amount of fuel used mainly for basic body functions, the processing of food, and physical activity.*

energy intake The caloric or energy content of food provided by the sources of dietary energy: carbohydrate (4 kcal/g), protein (4 kcal/g), fat (9 kcal/g), and alcohol (7 kcal/g).

energy output The use of calories or energy for basic body functions, physical activity, and processing of consumed foods.

energy equilibrium A balance of energy intake and output that results in little or no change in weight over time.

positive energy balance Energy intake exceeds energy expenditure, resulting in an increase in body energy stores and weight gain.

negative energy balance Energy intake is lower than energy expenditure, resulting in a depletion of body energy stores and weight loss.

energy balance The balance in the body between amounts of energy consumed and expended.

bomb calorimeter A device that uses the heat of combustion to measure the energy content of a food.

Energy In

We can measure the energy content of a food with a **bomb calorimeter**, like that shown in **Figure 9.2**. Inside a sealed chamber, the food is completely burned and sensors measure the amount of heat produced by its combustion. Your body is not as efficient as a bomb calorimeter. It does not completely digest all food and is unable to oxidize nitrogen. When calculating the amount of energy your body can extract from food, the number of kilocalories released by complete combustion in a bomb calorimeter is adjusted downward as follows:

4 kilocalories per gram pure carbohydrate
4 kilocalories per gram pure protein
9 kilocalories per gram pure fat
7 kilocalories per gram pure alcohol

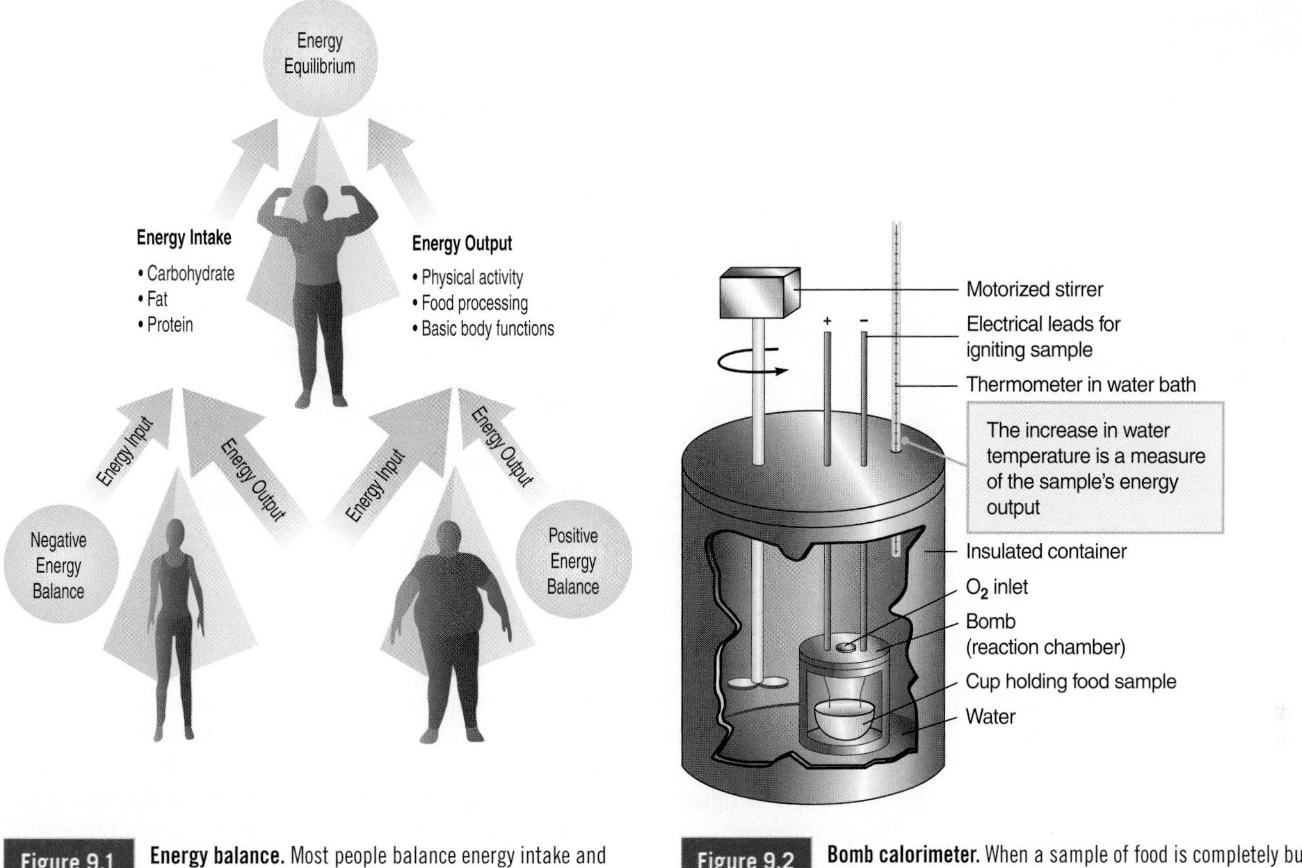

Figure 9.1 **Energy balance.** Most people balance energy intake and output and stay in energy balance. People in negative energy balance lose weight, and those in positive energy balance gain weight.

Figure 9.2 **Bomb calorimeter.** When a sample of food is completely burned inside the sealed chamber of a bomb calorimeter, it causes the temperature of the water surrounding the chamber to rise. This rise in temperature is a measure of the energy content of the food.

If we know a food's carbohydrate, fat, and protein content, we can use these numbers to estimate its calorie content.

Regulation of Food Intake

Internal and external cues help the body regulate food consumption and thus maintain energy equilibrium. Internal cues involve interactions and feedback mechanisms among hormones and hormonelike compounds and organ systems. External cues are stimuli in the eating environment and include the sight, smell, and taste of food. Internal and external cues work together to ensure that we eat enough to survive. However, the complex interplay of these cues makes it difficult to identify specific factors that cause overeating and obesity or disordered eating.

Hunger, Satiation, and Satiety

We experience internal cues as three different sensations that influence our eating behaviors. (See **Figure 9.3**.) The first, **hunger**, prompts eating ("I'm hungry"). Hunger is a physical sensation that includes the gnawing feeling in your stomach and signals the physiological need to eat. The second, **satiation**, tells you to stop eating ("I'm full"). The third, **satiety**, determines the interval between meals ("I'm not ready to eat again"). Satiety means not being hungry; it is influenced in part by how many calories you ate at your last meal.

hunger The internal, physiological drive to find and consume food. Unlike appetite, hunger is usually experienced as a negative sensation, often manifesting as an uneasy or painful sensation.

satiation Feeling of satisfaction and fullness that terminates a meal.

satiety The effects of a food or meal that delay subsequent intake. A feeling of satisfaction and fullness following eating that quells the desire for food.

Figure 9.3 **Hunger, satiation, and satiety.** Hunger helps initiate eating. Satiation brings eating to a halt. Satiety is the state of nonhunger that determines the amount of time until eating begins again.

Hunger signals you to begin eating
Growing hunger
I'm beginning to get hungry
Let's eat
Between meals
Eating
I'm full
Satiety is the satisfaction between meals
Satiation signals you to stop eating

appetite A psychological desire to eat that is related to the pleasant sensations often associated with food.

Appetite

Internal and external cues can stimulate **appetite**, which complicates the workings of hunger, satiation, and satiety. To ensure adequate nourishment, appetite and hunger work in tandem. Appetite is the psychological desire to eat and is related to pleasant sensations associated with food. Hunger is the physiological need for food. In this sense, while appetite reflects our eating experiences, hunger is a basic drive. When you are truly hungry, any food will do, but appetite can trigger your desire for a specific food or type of food, even though you may not be hungry. For example, after a big meal of steak, potato, salad, and bread, you probably wouldn't want a second helping. But you might be tempted by the dessert cart! That's appetite. Even when we are hungry, illness and medication can cause loss of appetite and a lack of interest in food.

THINK About It 1

Key Concepts *Food intake is regulated by sensations of hunger, a physiological drive to eat; satiation, feelings of satisfaction that lead to ending a meal; and satiety, continued feelings of fullness that delay the start of the next meal. Appetite is the psychological urge to eat and often has no relation to hunger.*

Control by Committee

What, then, stimulates hunger, satiation, satiety, and appetite? As you will see, there are multiple players involved. What you eat, the amount that you eat, and responses in the digestive tract, central nervous system, and general circulation influence your eating behavior. Sites throughout the body monitor energy status and send reports to the brain. Even the temperature of our environment affects how much we eat.

Diet Composition

The energy density (kcal/g), balance of energy sources (carbohydrates, lipids, and protein), and the form (liquid vs. solid) of your foods affect the amount you eat. Regardless of its nutrient value, people tend to eat a fairly constant amount of food. Therefore, if your overall diet includes a lot of energy-dense

Quick Bite

Why Do We Have Hunger Pangs?

When the stomach has been without food for at least three hours, intense stomach contractions can begin, sometimes lasting two to three minutes. Healthy young people have the strongest contractions, due to good muscle tone in the GI tract. After 12 to 24 hours, contractions of an empty stomach can cause painful hunger pangs.

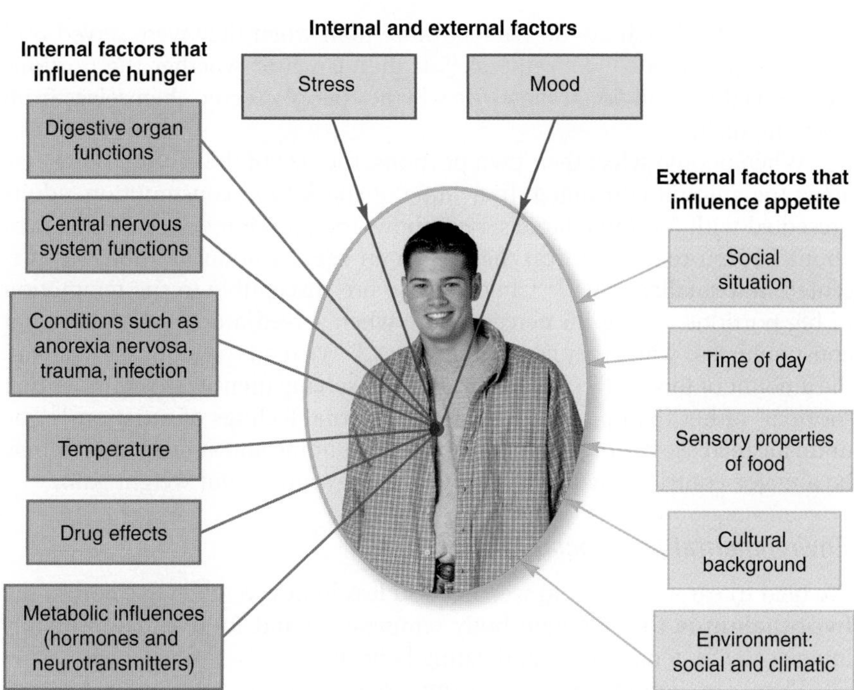

Figure 9.4 Internal and external influences on hunger and appetite.

foods (generally high-fat, high-sugar, low-fiber), your overall diet will likely result in excess energy consumption, and in return, weight gain.

Protein appears to makes a stronger contribution to satiety than fats or carbohydrates.[1] In a small study comparing two breakfast meals, subjects ate less for lunch when their breakfast had more protein (20 percent of calories versus 14 percent of calories).[2] However, it is not clear what role protein plays in long-term energy balance. Bulkier foods, those with higher amounts of fiber and water, also have a higher satiety value.[3] Some types of fiber enhance satiation by slowing the rate at which the stomach empties, whereas others seem to enhance satiation by creating bulk.[4]

Liquid sources of calories (e.g., juices, soft drinks) generally have low satiety value. When people consume liquid or solid snacks with similar amounts of carbohydrates, subsequent food intake is greater following the liquid carbohydrate snacks.[5] In addition, regular sugar-sweetened beverage consumption between meals may put some young children at a greater risk for overweight.[6] On the other hand, soups, despite their liquid form, have relatively high satiety value.[7]

Sensory Properties

The aroma of freshly baked bread or the warmth and chewiness of chocolate chip cookies right out of the oven encourage us to eat more than our hunger dictates. Food's sensory properties—flavor, texture, color, temperature, and presentation—influence its appeal, and such external cues affect food intake.[8] (See **Figure 9.4**.) Taste is usually the reason why people choose a particular food. But foods that are pleasant to eat are often high in fat and are energy dense—properties that can lead to overeating.[9]

Portion Size

Portion size plays a role in how much we eat. In a controlled study of adults, people served a 1,000-gram portion (approximately 33 ounces) of macaroni

Quick Bite

Supersize Me!

Morgan Spurlock wrote, directed, produced, and is the lead character in *Supersize Me!*, a film that documents Spurlock's consumption of a 30-day McDonald's-only diet. Whenever offered the option to "supersize" his order, Spurlock always selected the larger portion size. Starting at 185 pounds, the 6-foot, 2-inch Spurlock packed on 25 pounds and weighed 210 by the end of his experiment. His total cholesterol shot up from 165 to 230, his libido flagged, and he suffered headaches and depression.

hypothalamus [high-po-THAL-ah-mus] A region of the brain involved in regulating hunger and satiety, respiration, body temperature, water balance, and other body functions.

and cheese for lunch ate 30 percent more than when they were served 500 grams (approximately 17 ounces).[10] It didn't matter whether the portions were served on individual plates or whether people served themselves from a serving dish.

When people select their own portions, the size of the serving bowl may affect the amount consumed. In a study of snack food consumption, adults presented with food in a large serving bowl took more food (and consumed about 140 more kilocalories) than when an equal amount of food was presented in a smaller bowl.[11] Children also are susceptible to the temptation of big portions, eating 25 percent more when served a double portion, but consuming less when they serve themselves.[12] We tend to respond visually to the amount of food on a plate or the size of a serving utensil and consider that "normal" rather than paying attention to internal feelings of satiation.[13] The dramatic increase in portion sizes eaten both at home and at restaurants[14] may be a major contributing factor to excess energy intake and weight gain.

Environmental and Social Factors

We tend to eat more in cold weather and less in hot weather. Systems in the **hypothalamus** that regulate body temperature and food intake probably interact to link temperature and eating behavior.

Plate size, lighting, and socializing are other factors that influence consumption.[15] Any change in our surroundings that inhibits our self-monitoring of consumption tends to increase the volume that we eat. Larger plates and bowls encourage larger servings. We tend to eat more in dimly lit situations than when the lights are brighter, perhaps because we are less inhibited and self-conscious.[16] The best predictor of the amount of food that will be eaten at a given time is the number of people present. Studies show that meals eaten with other people last longer and tend to increase consumption by at least one-third compared with eating alone.[17]

Emotional Factors

Many people use food to cope with stress and negative feelings. Eating can provide a powerful distraction from loneliness, anger, boredom, anxiety, shame, sadness, and inadequacy. To combat low moods, low energy levels, and low self-esteem, people often turn to the refrigerator. When we use food and eating to cope with our emotions, binge eating or other disturbed eating patterns can develop.

Gastrointestinal Sensations

As food fills your stomach and small intestine, they stretch and trigger signals to the brain. Your sense of fullness suppresses your urge to eat.[18]

Just passing a reasonable amount of food through the mouth can satisfy hunger temporarily—even if the food never reaches the stomach. When researchers fed large amounts of food to a person with a hole in the esophagus, hunger decreased, even though the food never reached the stomach. As we taste, salivate, chew, and swallow, the brain probably measures the passage of food, much as a water meter measures the flow of water. After a certain amount of food passes through the mouth, hunger diminishes for 20 to 40 minutes.[19]

Neurological and Hormonal Factors

More than 50 different chemicals are thought to be involved in the regulation of feeding. Determining the way these chemical factors work is an active research area that may lead to improved therapies for those either overweight or underweight.

Hormones, hormonelike factors, and some drugs (including appetite suppressants) influence eating behavior through their direct or indirect effects on the brain.[20] **Neuropeptide Y (NPY)** is a hormonelike factor in the brain that powerfully stimulates appetite.[21] Although a number of signals can affect NPY activity, opposing signals from the hormones **ghrelin** and **leptin** link NPY secretion to daily feeding patterns.[22]

Ghrelin, sometimes called the "hunger hormone," is produced in the stomach. Ghrelin levels rise prior to a meal and fall quickly after food is consumed. The rise in ghrelin levels appears to stimulate NPY, thus encouraging feeding.

Leptin, sometimes called the "satiety hormone," is produced in fat cells. Leptin tells the central nervous system how much fat the body is storing. A rise in leptin levels appears to inhibit NPY, thus suppressing appetite.[23] Leptin also appears to signal pathways that enhance energy production to keep body weight in a normal range. Administering leptin to obese experimental animals lacking the hormone causes them to become normal weight.

Unfortunately, when body weight is high, these regulators act inconsistently. Common human obesity is associated with increased, not decreased, leptin levels,[24] and a trial of leptin in obese people produced variable amounts of weight loss.[25] Although obese people tend to have lower fasting ghrelin levels (suggesting that they would experience lower levels of hunger before a meal), they also have smaller reductions of ghrelin levels after a meal (suggesting that overeating may be due to lower levels of satiation).[26]

Key Concepts *Diet composition and factors in the digestive tract and central nervous system influence eating behavior. The brain, especially the hypothalamus, receives signals from all over the body about energy status. External factors, such as portion size, social circumstances, and environmental conditions, as well as the food itself, can enhance or suppress appetite.*

neuropeptide Y (NPY) A neurotransmitter widely distributed throughout the brain and peripheral nervous tissue. NPY activity has been linked to eating behavior, depression, anxiety, and cardiovascular function.

ghrelin A peptide hormone produced by the stomach that stimulates feeding; sometimes called the "hunger hormone."

leptin A hormone produced by adipose cells that signals the amount of body fat content and influences food intake; sometimes called the "satiety hormone."

total energy expenditure (TEE) The total of the resting energy expenditure (REE), energy used in physical activity, and energy used in processing food (TEF); usually expressed in kilocalories per day.

basal energy expenditure (BEE) The basal metabolic rate (BMR) extrapolated to 24 hours. Often used interchangeably with REE.

resting energy expenditure (REE) The minimum energy needed to maintain basic physiological functions (e.g., heart beat, muscle function, respiration). The resting metabolic rate (RMR) extrapolated to 24 hours. Often used interchangeably with BEE.

Energy Out: Fuel Uses

Our bodies use fuel (expend energy) for three primary purposes:

1. To maintain basic physiological functions such as breathing and blood circulation
2. To process the food we eat
3. To power physical activity

We also expend energy to support growth, stay warm in cold environments, metabolize drugs, and deal with physical trauma, fever, and psychological stress. The sum of all energy expended is the **total energy expenditure (TEE)**. **Figure 9.5** illustrates the major components of energy expenditure.

Major Components of Energy Expenditure

Energy Expenditure at Rest

We generally expend most of our energy on the basic body functions needed to sustain life. This **basal energy expenditure (BEE)**, or **resting energy expenditure (REE)**, maintains heartbeat, respiration, nervous function, muscle tone, body temperature, and so on. Resting energy expenditure accounts for 60 to 75 percent of total energy expenditure.[27] The rate of energy expended at rest (kcal/hour) is measured as either the

Figure 9.5 **Major components of energy expenditure.** You expend most of your energy to maintain basic body functions. Energy expended in physical activity can be significant and is the most variable component of total energy expenditure. The thermic effect of food is the energy needed to digest, absorb, transport, metabolize, and store ingested food.

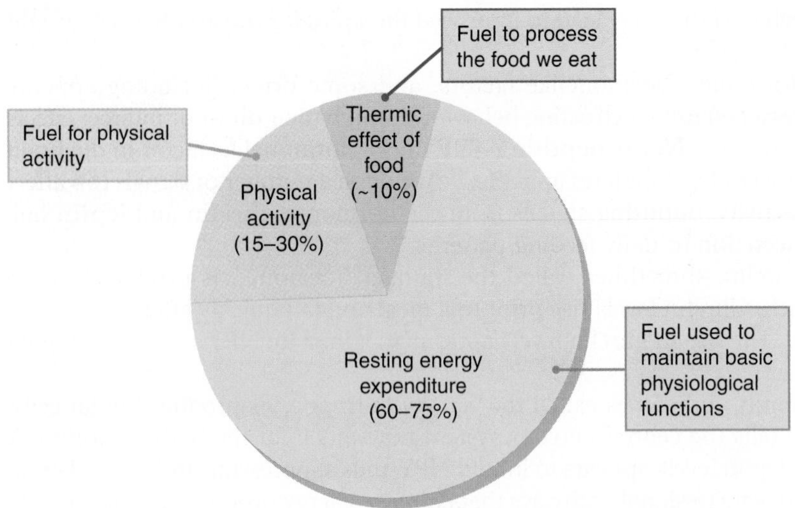

basal metabolic rate (BMR) A clinical measure of resting energy expenditure performed upon awakening, 10 to 12 hours after eating, and 12 to 18 hours after significant physical activity. Often used interchangeably with RMR.

resting metabolic rate (RMR) A clinical measure of resting energy expenditure performed three to four hours after eating or performing significant physical activity. Often used interchangeably with BMR.

lean body mass The portion of the body exclusive of stored fat, including muscle, bone, connective tissue, organs, and water.

basal metabolic rate (BMR) or the **resting metabolic rate (RMR)**. BEE or REE refers to energy expended in a 24-hour period.[28] Researchers measure BMR under the following conditions:

1. The person is lying at rest.
2. The person has just awoken from a normal overnight sleep.
3. Ten to 12 hours have elapsed since the person's last meal.
4. No physical activity has taken place—usually for 12 to 18 hours.

The RMR differs slightly from the BMR. Researchers usually measure RMR three to four hours after a person eats or does significant physical work. RMR tends to be somewhat higher than BMR[29] and is a more practical concept because the ideal conditions for measuring BMR are more difficult to meet. For this reason, in the remainder of this text we will use the terms *resting metabolic rate* and *resting energy expenditure*.

Factors That Affect Resting Metabolic Rate Over time, your RMR varies less than 5 percent. However, among different people, RMR can vary by as much as 25 percent. Individual differences in muscle and organ mass account for most of this variation. Resting muscles and organ tissue make the greatest contribution to RMR because they have greater metabolic activity than other tissue such as fat. (See Table 9.1.) Muscles, organs, bones, and fluids make up most of what is known as the **lean body mass**—the total mass of the body that isn't fat. Differences in lean body mass explain 70 to 80 percent of the variation in resting metabolic rate among individuals.[30] As a result, an extremely muscular person with a large lean body mass would have a higher resting energy expenditure than someone who weighs the same but has a higher proportion of body fat.

Age, gender, degree of muscle development, and, of course, body size are the primary influences on a person's lean body mass. In the aging adult, lean body mass tends to decrease while body fatness rises, resulting in an RMR reduction of about 2 to 3 percent per decade.[31] However, declining lean body mass does not account fully for the age-related decline in RMR, which also may reflect declining organ function.[32] Keeping physically active as we age helps slow loss of lean tissue and discourages accumulation of fat, thus maintaining a higher RMR.

Women usually have lower RMRs than men. Women tend to be smaller than men, and pound for pound they generally have less lean body mass.

Table 9.1 **Approximate Energy Expenditure of Organs in Adults**

Organ	Percentage of RMR
Liver	29
Brain	19
Heart	10
Kidney	7
Skeletal muscles (at rest)	18
Remainder (including bone)	17
	100

Source: Modified from Mahan LK, Escott-Stump S. *Krause's Food, Nutrition and Diet Therapy.* 10th ed. Philadelphia: WB Saunders, 2000:20. Reprinted by permission of Elsevier.

Yet even when differences in lean body mass are taken into account, a man's metabolic rate is still about 50 kilocalories per day higher than that of a woman.[33] The reason is unclear, but this difference is consistent throughout the lives of men and women. RMR also varies during the menstrual cycle, fluctuating from the low point about one week before ovulation to the high point just before the onset of menstruation.[34]

Other factors that influence metabolic rate may be less consistent, of shorter duration, or limited to individual situations. During sleep, RMR falls about 10 percent. RMR relative to lean body mass rises during periods of rapid growth, such as in infancy and adolescence. Hormones, especially thyroxine (thyroid hormone) and norepinephrine, help regulate metabolic rate. Inadequate thyroxine production (hypothyroidism) can slow the metabolic rate; excess thyroxine (hyperthyroidism) can increase the metabolic rate. Physical stress increases the metabolic rate, probably in response to changes in norepinephrine levels. Fever increases RMR by about 7 percent for each degree of temperature over 98.6°F. Environmental temperature also affects the metabolic rate. During exposure to cold, RMR increases. As ambient temperatures rise above normal, RMR first decreases and then plateaus. At much higher temperatures, RMR increases. During starvation, the metabolic rate declines as the body slows basic functions to conserve energy and prolong survival. Finally, some variation in RMR has been attributed to unknown genetic factors.[35] **Figure 9.6** shows the factors that affect RMR.

Key Concepts *We use energy to fuel basic body functions, process the food we eat, and support physical activity. The energy used in these basic functions is called the resting energy expenditure, or REE. Factors that affect resting energy expenditure include body composition, age, gender, fitness, genetics, stage of growth, hormone levels, fever, and environmental temperatures.*

Energy Expenditure for Physical Activity

Physical activity is more than just exercise and sport. It includes work, leisure activities, and other everyday activities—even fidgeting. Depending on whether a person is mostly sedentary or a top athlete in training, energy expended on physical activity accounts for 15 to 30 percent of total energy expenditure.[36] The energy cost of an activity depends on its type (whether it is walking, running, or typing, for example), duration, and intensity. Table 9.2 shows the amounts of energy expended in specific activities.

Body size affects energy cost, too—it takes more energy to move a bigger mass, so a large person expends more calories per minute than a smaller person doing the same activity. Fitness level has an effect as well. A fit person exercises more efficiently, with lower energy costs. However, fit people also can exercise with greater intensity and duration, burning more calories overall.

Mental activity—such as studying for an exam—uses little energy. But if you fidget when you study, you may expend a significant amount of energy. The acronym **NEAT** stands for **nonexercise activity thermogenesis**, which is the energy associated with activities other than exercise, including fidgeting, maintenance of posture, and similar contributors to energy expenditure.[37] (See the FYI feature "What's Neat About NEAT?")

Energy Expenditure to Process Food

Our bodies expend energy to digest, absorb, and metabolize the nutrients we take in, and these processes generate heat. This energy output is collec-

Quick Bite

Brr! Shivering Away Calories

Cold weather increases energy needs. Shivering alone can increase the RMR by 2.5 times. Although shivering bodies use both fat and carbohydrate, carbohydrates are the preferred fuel. In addition, people with less body fat shiver more in the cold.

nonexercise activity thermogenesis (NEAT) The output of energy associated with fidgeting, maintenance of posture, and other minimal physical exertions.

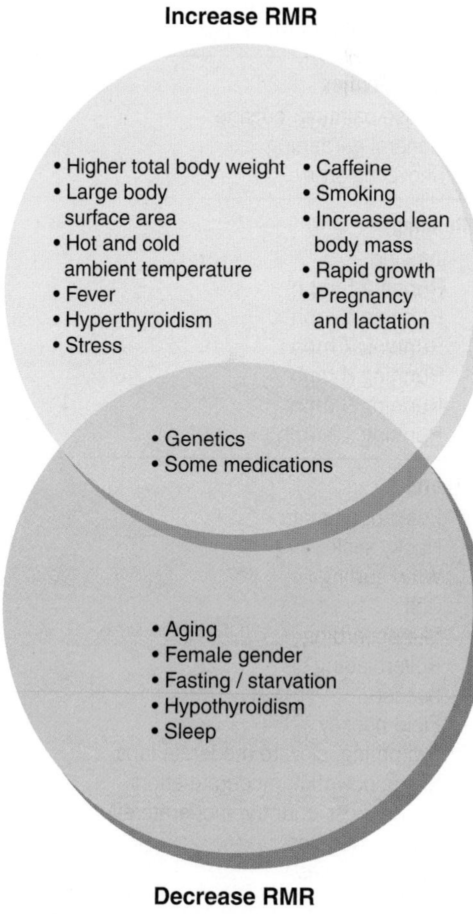

Increase RMR

- Higher total body weight
- Large body surface area
- Hot and cold ambient temperature
- Fever
- Hyperthyroidism
- Stress
- Caffeine
- Smoking
- Increased lean body mass
- Rapid growth
- Pregnancy and lactation

- Genetics
- Some medications

- Aging
- Female gender
- Fasting / starvation
- Hypothyroidism
- Sleep

Decrease RMR

Figure 9.6 **Factors that affect RMR.** Inherited traits determine whether you have a generally high or low RMR. Many environmental and physiological factors may temporarily raise RMR, and other factors may temporarily lower it.

Table 9.2 Amount of Energy Expended in Specific Activities

			kcal/h at Different Body Weights				
Description	*kcal/h/kg*	*kcal/h/lb*	*50 kg 110 lb*	*57 kg 125 lb*	*68 kg 150 lb*	*80 kg 175 lb*	*91 kg 200 lb*
Aerobics							
Light	3.0	1.36	150	170	205	239	273
Moderate	5.0	2.27	250	284	341	398	455
Heavy	8.0	3.64	400	455	545	636	727
Bicycling							
Leisurely <10 mph	4.0	1.82	200	227	273	318	364
Light 10–11.9 mph	6.0	2.73	300	341	409	477	545
Moderate 12–13.9 mph	8.0	3.64	400	455	545	636	727
Fast 14–15.9 mph	10.0	4.55	500	568	682	795	909
Racing 16–19 mph	12.0	5.45	600	682	818	955	1091
BMX or mountain	8.5	3.86	425	483	580	676	773
Daily Activities							
Sleeping	1.2	0.55	60	68	82	95	109
Studying, reading, writing	1.8	0.82	90	102	123	143	164
Cooking, food preparation	2.5	1.14	125	142	170	199	227
Home Activities							
House painting, outside	4.0	1.82	200	227	273	318	364
General gardening	5.0	2.27	250	284	341	398	455
Shoveling snow	6.0	2.73	300	341	409	477	545
Running							
Jogging	7.0	3.18	350	398	477	557	636
Running 5 mph	8.0	3.64	400	455	545	636	727
Running 6 mph	10.0	4.55	500	568	682	795	909
Running 7 mph	11.5	5.23	575	653	784	915	1045
Running 8 mph	13.5	6.14	675	767	920	1074	1227
Running 9 mph	15.0	6.82	750	852	1023	1193	1364
Running 10 mph	16.0	7.27	800	909	1091	1273	1455
Sports							
Frisbee, ultimate	3.5	1.59	175	199	239	278	318
Hacky sack	4.0	1.82	200	227	273	318	364
Wind surfing	4.2	1.91	210	239	286	334	382
Golf	4.5	2.05	225	256	307	358	409
Skateboarding	5.0	2.27	250	284	341	398	455
Rollerblading	7.0	3.18	350	398	477	557	636
Soccer	7.0	3.18	350	398	477	557	636
Field hockey	8.0	3.64	400	455	545	636	727
Swimming, slow to moderate laps	8.0	3.64	400	455	545	636	727
Skiing downhill, moderate effort	6.0	2.73	300	341	409	477	545
Skiing cross country, moderate effort	8.0	3.64	400	455	545	636	727
Tennis, doubles	6.0	2.73	300	341	409	477	545
Tennis, singles	8.0	3.64	400	455	545	636	727
Walking							
Strolling <2 mph, level	2.0	0.91	100	114	136	159	182
Moderate pace ~3 mph, level	3.5	1.59	175	199	239	278	318
Moderate pace ~3 mph, uphill	6.0	2.73	300	341	409	477	545
Brisk pace ~3.5 mph, level	4.0	1.82	200	227	273	318	364
Very brisk pace ~4.5 mph, level	4.5	2.05	225	256	307	358	409

Source: Adapted from Nieman DC. *Exercise Testing and Prescription.* 4th ed. Mountain View, CA: Mayfield Publishing, 1999.

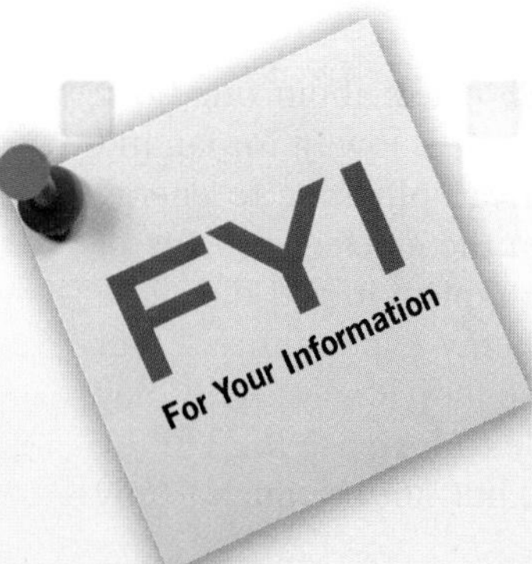

What's Neat About NEAT?

It seems Jan only has to look at food to gain weight. Yet her friend Molly doesn't seem to gain weight no matter what she eats. Both have the same height and frame, eat about the same amount of calories, and get about the same amount of exercise. So what's missing? Research suggests that fidgeting and movements such as posture adjustments may be part of the answer.

Studies in the early 1900s first suggested that weight gained in response to overeating wasn't proportional to the extra calories ingested. Following experiments on himself, the German scientist R. O. Neumann coined the term "luxuskonsumption" to describe his observation that excess calories did not result in weight gain and therefore must be lost as heat.[1] Further studies supported this idea, showing wide individual variation in response to overfeeding. Some suggest that the ease of weight gain is genetically based.[2]

A study at the Mayo Clinic attributes differences in weight gain in response to overfeeding to a mechanism described as NEAT: nonexercise activity thermogenesis.[3] According to the researchers, NEAT is "the thermogenesis [heat production] that accompanies physical activities other than volitional [intentional] exercise, such as the activities of daily living, fidgeting, spontaneous muscle contraction, and maintaining posture when not recumbent."

In the NEAT study, 16 volunteers (12 men and 4 women) were given an extra 1,000 kilocalories per day—roughly equivalent to two double cheeseburgers—for a period of eight weeks. Before the study began, careful measurements were made over a two-week period to determine each participant's maintenance energy requirements. Physical activity during the study was controlled, and meals were provided only through the Mayo Clinic General Clinical Research Center. Questionnaires and interviews were done to ensure compliance.

The average weight gained by the study participants was 4.7 kilograms (10.3 lb), but some gained as much as 7.2 kilograms (15.8 lb), whereas others added only 1.4 kilograms (3.1 lb). The theoretical expected weight gain from an eight-week excess of 56,000 kilocalories would be 7.3 kilograms (16.0 lb) to 9.1 kilograms (20.0 lb)—more than the maximum weight gain of any participant!

After accounting for RMR, TEF, and energy used in physical activity, the remaining energy expenditure was attributed to NEAT. The amount of energy expended as NEAT varied among the participants by nearly 800 kilocalories per day. Participants with higher NEAT resisted weight gain, suggesting that people who can effectively activate NEAT tend not to gain weight, even with overeating. Further, this suggests that obese people may not effectively activate NEAT.

In another study, the Mayo Clinic researchers found that obese individuals sat for two hours longer than lean individuals.[4] This pattern of activity (or lack thereof) didn't change when obese individuals lost weight or lean individuals gained weight.

So is the take-home message "fidget more, stand up straight, and you won't gain weight?" Not exactly. The researchers did not account for factors such as the extra energy needed to move a higher body weight in activity. In addition, in the first study they relied on self-reports and pedometers that lacked precision and accuracy.[5] However, in the comparison of obese and lean individuals, a physical activity monitoring system was used to capture posture and movement data 120 times per minute. Attributing the entire difference in energy expenditure to NEAT ignores heat production by brown adipose tissue, a type of fat tissue that tends to "waste" energy.[6] Clearly, though, some individuals are able to resist weight gain, even when overeating, while others cannot. Further studies to better understand NEAT and the factors that regulate it may help to better understand conditions of energy imbalance—not only obesity, but also anorexia nervosa.[7]

1 Neumann RO. Experimentalle Beitrage zur Lehre von dem taglichen Nahrungsbedarf der Menschen unter besonder Berucksichtigung der notwendigen Eisewissmenge. *Arch Hyg.* 1902;45:1–2.

2 Bouchard C, Tremblay A, Despres JP, et al. The response to long-term overfeeding in identical twins. *N Engl J Med.* 1990;322:1477–1482.

3 Levine JA, Eberhardt NL, Jensen MD. Role of nonexercise activity thermogenesis in resistance to fat gain in humans. *Science.* 1999;283:212–214.

4 Levine JA, Lanningham-Foster LM, McCrady SK, et al. Interindividual variation in posture allocation: possible role in human obesity. *Science.* 2005;307:584–586.

5 Ravussin E, Danforth E. Beyond sloth—physical activity and weight gain. *Science.* 1999;283:184–185.

6 Klaus S. Adipose tissue as a regulator of energy balance. *Curr Drug Targets.* 2004;5:241–250.

7 Levine JA. Nonexercise activity thermogenesis (NEAT): environment and biology. *Am J Physiol Endocrinol Metab.* 2004;286:E675–E685.

Quick Bite

Magic Underwear
James Levine, the endocrinologist and professor of medicine at the Mayo Clinic who coined the term "NEAT," uses what he calls "magic underwear," which contains sensors to measure the research subject's movements and body postures 120 times each minute.

tively called the **thermic effect of food (TEF)**. TEF peaks about one hour after eating and normally dissipates within five hours. It is lowest for fat and highest for protein. Converting excess protein and carbohydrate to energy stores (fat and glycogen) requires more energy than the efficient process of simply storing excess dietary fat as body fat. For a typical mixed diet, TEF accounts for approximately 10 percent of total energy expenditure,[38] but research suggests that TEF may be reduced in obese individuals[39] and may be reduced by irregular eating habits.[40] It's possible to increase the TEF by altering the macronutrient composition of the diet, but not by much—only about 50 kilocalories or so daily.

Key Concepts *An individual's fitness level, weight, and the type, duration, and intensity of activity affect the amount of energy expended in physical activity. The thermic effect of food is the energy needed to process the food we eat and is influenced by the amount and mix of nutrients in the diet.*

The Measurement of Energy Expenditure

Calorimetry, the measurement of energy expenditure, helps us understand individual differences in energy expenditure and the effects of environmental conditions, as well as age, gender, exercise, and other factors.

A Brief History of Calorimetry

Antoine Lavoisier, an eighteenth-century French chemist, was the first to study food combustion in the body.[41] He theorized that just as a burning candle needs oxygen and releases heat, organisms need oxygen to live and release heat as they combust food.

Lavoisier built the first **calorimeter**, quite an achievement at that time. A calorimeter consists of a chamber within a chamber. The inner chamber is large enough to house an animal or human; the outer chamber is sensitive to temperature changes that occur in the inner one. Lavoisier packed ice into a sealed pocket around the inner chamber (his studies were possible only in winter, when ice was plentiful) and then placed it inside the outer chamber, which was insulated to shield it from the outside environment. As the animal in the inner chamber used energy, it produced heat that melted the ice. By collecting the resulting water and measuring its volume, Lavoisier could accurately calculate the amount of heat produced by the animal.

Direct and Indirect Calorimetry

Lavoisier's technique illustrates the principles of **direct calorimetry**. When your body combusts food, it captures some energy while losing the rest as heat. This heat loss is proportional to the body's total energy use and can be measured directly using a chamber like that constructed by Lavoisier. Modern chambers dispense with the ice and instead measure the temperature change in a surrounding layer of water.

Direct calorimetry is expensive and complex. The chamber must be large enough to accommodate a person, yet maintain the precision to measure the relatively small changes in temperature. Since the advent of alternative methods, direct calorimetry is no longer widely used.

Indirect calorimetry is easier and less expensive than direct calorimetry. It is "indirect" because energy production (as heat) is not measured directly. Instead, energy expenditure is estimated from a person's oxygen consumption and carbon dioxide production. Burning (oxidizing) fuel consumes oxygen

thermic effect of food (TEF) The energy used to digest, absorb, and metabolize energy-yielding foodstuffs. It constitutes about 10 percent of total energy expenditure but is influenced by various factors.

calorimetry [kal-oh-RIM-eh-tree] The measurement of the amount of heat given off by an organism. It is used to determine total energy expenditure.

calorimeter A device used to measure quantities of heat generated by various processes.

direct calorimetry Determination of energy use by the body by measuring the heat released from an organism enclosed in a small insulated chamber surrounded by water. The rise in the temperature of the water is directly related to the energy used by the organism.

indirect calorimetry Determination of energy use by the body without directly measuring the production of heat. Methods include gas exchange, the measurement of oxygen uptake and/or carbon dioxide output, and the doubly labeled water method.

and produces carbon dioxide in proportion to the amount of fuel burned and the amount of energy released.

For indirect calorimetry, a technician collects respiratory gases. During short periods of rest or exercise, expired air can be collected using a face mask, mouthpiece, or canopy system. (See **Figure 9.7**.) This cumbersome apparatus makes indirect calorimetry impractical for use during physically demanding activities or normal living conditions.

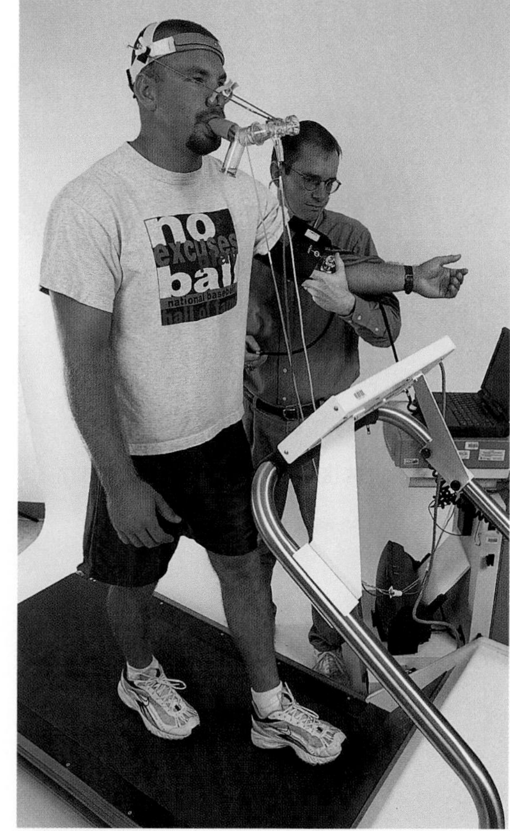

Figure 9.7 **Indirect calorimetry.** A technician collects respiratory gases and then calculates energy expenditure.

Doubly Labeled Water

A relatively new and easier technique to measure total energy expenditure is **doubly labeled water**. (See **Figure 9.8**.) Rather than measuring respiratory gases, this indirect calorimetry technique relies on measuring the **isotopes** (typically a form of an element with a higher than usual atomic mass but the same characteristics as the usual element) of hydrogen and oxygen in excreted water and carbon dioxide. A person swallows a small quantity of two kinds of water, one labeled with the hydrogen isotope deuterium (^2H) and the other labeled with an isotope of oxygen (oxygen-18, or ^{18}O). Both isotopes occur naturally and are nonradioactive. The body excretes oxygen-18 as part of water ($H_2{}^{18}O$) and carbon dioxide ($C^{18}O_2$). It excretes deuterium only as part of water (^2H_2O). Scientists use the difference between the rate of deuterium loss and oxygen-18 loss to calculate carbon dioxide output and determine the total energy expenditure.

The doubly labeled water technique is noninvasive and unobtrusive. Subjects can stay in their normal environment and perform normal activities during the testing period, which typically lasts 7 to 14 days or longer. This method is emerging as the gold standard against which other energy expenditure measurement methods are compared. For best accuracy, doubly labeled water studies should last at least 14 days. Unfortunately, the doubly labeled water technique is not widely available, and it's expensive—the ^{18}O isotope costs about $500 for a 70-kg adult, and the analytic equipment is

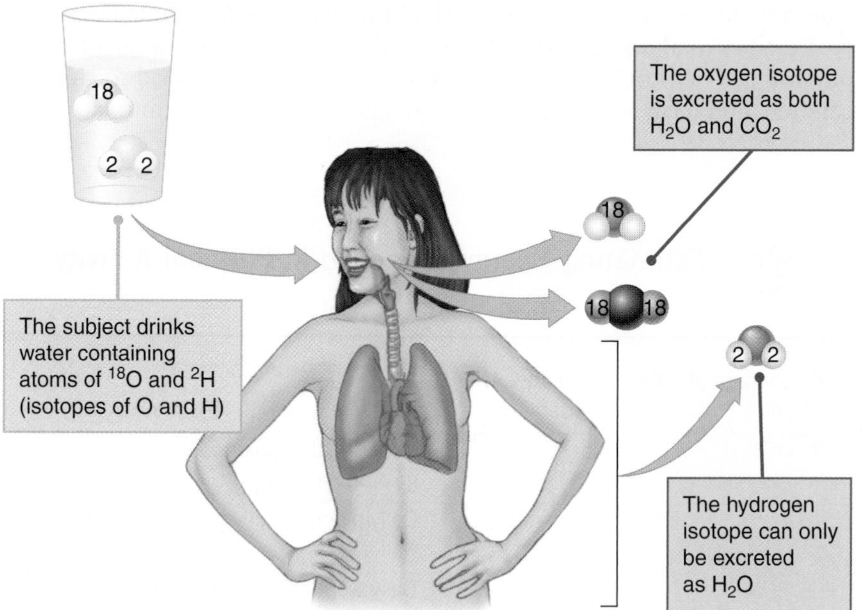
18
2 2
The oxygen isotope is excreted as both H_2O and CO_2
18
18 18
2 2
The subject drinks water containing atoms of ^{18}O and ^2H (isotopes of O and H)
The hydrogen isotope can only be excreted as H_2O

Figure 9.8 **Doubly labeled water.** When using doubly labeled water, scientists measure the excretion rates of the two isotopes to calculate carbon dioxide output and determine total energy expenditure.

doubly labeled water A method for measuring daily energy expenditure over extended time periods, typically 7 to 14 days, while subjects are living in their usual environments. Small amounts of water that is isotopically labeled with deuterium and oxygen-18 (^2H_2O and $H_2{}^{18}O$) are ingested. Energy expenditure can be calculated from the difference between the rates at which the body loses each isotope.

isotopes [EYE-so-towps] Forms of an element in which the atoms have the same number of protons but different numbers of neutrons.

costly. Therefore, the technique is not suited to large-scale studies. It has other limitations as well: it cannot give information about individual days, individual activities, or day-to-day variability.

Estimating Total Energy Expenditure

Abbreviated Method to Estimate REE

For adult men

$$REE = weight\ (kg) \times 1.0\ kcal/kg \times 24\ hr/day$$

$$REE = weight\ (kg) \times 1.0 \times 24$$

For adult women

$$REE = weight\ (kg) \times 0.9\ kcal/kg \times 24\ hr/day$$

$$REE = weight\ (kg) \times 0.9 \times 24$$

Directly measuring a person's total energy expenditure requires sophisticated equipment that is inaccessible to all but a few people in research settings. To determine the energy needs of most people, nutritionists must rely on calculated estimates.

An adult's REE can be estimated using an abbreviated method (see margin). The 1.0 and 0.9 factors for kilocalories per kilogram reflect the differences in body composition between men and women. Men have proportionally more lean body mass and therefore burn more calories per kilogram of body weight. This abbreviated method dramatically underestimates children's REE, however, and somewhat overestimates the REE of older adults.

The abbreviated method estimates only REE. To determine total energy expenditure (TEE), energy for physical activity and the thermic effect of food must be included. Energy expended in physical activity can be estimated as a percentage of REE based on a person's general activity level (see Table 9.3). Most adults in the United States and Canada have a light or moderate activity level. The thermic effect of food can be estimated as roughly 10 percent of the sum of REE plus energy expended in physical activity. Summing the three estimated components—REE, physical activity, and TEF—delivers the estimated total energy expenditure. See the FYI feature "How Many Calories Do I Burn?" for an example of these estimates in action.

DRIs for Energy: Estimated Energy Requirements

Just as there are Dietary Reference Intakes (DRIs) for nutrients, there are also DRIs for energy, called Estimated Energy Requirements (EERs).[42] The EER is defined as the energy intake predicted to maintain energy balance in a healthy person of normal weight. The EER equations for adults (see Table 9.4) predict total energy expenditure from age, height, weight, gender, and physical activity level. Separate equations have been developed for infants, children, and teens, and adjustments are made for pregnancy and lactation.

Table 9.3 Estimating Energy Expended in Physical Activity

Percentage of REE	Activity Level	Description
20–30%	Sedentary	Mostly resting with little or no activity
30–45%	Light	Occasional unplanned activity, e.g., going for a stroll
45–65%	Moderate	Daily planned activity, such as brisk walks
65–90%	Heavy	Daily workout routine requiring several hours of continuous exercise
90–120%	Exceptional	Daily vigorous workouts for extended hours; training for competition

Table 9.4 **Estimated Energy Requirements (EER) for Adults**

Males

EER = 662 – 9.53 × Age [yr] + PA × (15.91 × Weight [kg] + 539.6 × Height [m])

PA =	
1.0	Sedentary
1.11	Low active
1.25	Active
1.48	Very active

Females

EER = 354 – 6.91 × Age [yr] + PA × (9.36 × Weight [kg] + 726 × Height [m])

PA =	
1.0	Sedentary
1.12	Low active
1.27	Active
1.45	Very active

Source: Reproduced from Institute of Medicine, Food and Nutrition Board. *Dietary Reference Intakes for Energy, Carbohydrate, Fiber, Fat, Fatty Acids, Cholesterol, Protein, and Amino Acids.* Washington, DC: National Academies Press, 2005. Reprinted with permission from National Academy of Sciences.

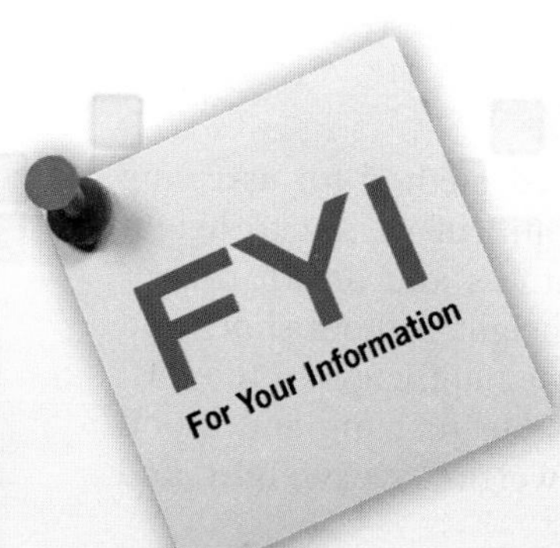

How Many Calories Do I Burn?

You can estimate the amount of energy you use each day by using some simple equations. Remember that there will be quite a lot of individual variation in actual energy output, and so these calculated values are just estimates.

1. Convert your weight in pounds to weight in kilograms. For example, Carol is a 120-pound female. Her weight is 54.5 kilograms (54.5 = 120 ÷ 2.2).

$$\underset{\textbf{weight (lbs)}}{\underline{\qquad\qquad}} \div 2.2 = \underset{\textbf{weight (kg)}}{\underline{\qquad\qquad}}$$

2. Estimate your personal REE.

For adult women:

$$\text{REE} = \underset{\textbf{weight (kg)}}{\underline{\qquad\qquad}} \times 0.9 \times 24$$

For adult men:

$$\text{REE} = \underset{\textbf{weight (kg)}}{\underline{\qquad\qquad}} \times 1.0 \times 24$$

For example, Carol has an estimated REE of 1,177 kilocalories (1,177 = 54.5 × 0.9 × 24).

3. Estimate your energy expended in physical activity (see Table 9.2).

$$\text{energy}_{\text{physical activity}} = \underset{\textbf{from Table 9.2}}{\underline{\qquad\qquad}} \times \text{REE}$$

For example, Carol has a light to moderate physical activity level. She expends about 530 kilocalories in physical activity (530 = 0.45 × 1,177).

4. Estimate your thermic effect of food (TEF).

$$\text{TEF} = 0.1 \times (\underset{\textbf{energy}_{\text{physical activity}}}{\underline{\qquad\qquad}} + \underset{\textbf{REE}}{\underline{\qquad}})$$

For our example, Carol's thermic effect of food is about 171 kilocalories (171 = 0.1 × [530 + 1,177]).

5. Estimate your personal total energy expenditure (TEE).

$$\text{TEE} = \underset{\textbf{REE}}{\underline{\qquad}} + \underset{\textbf{energy}_{\text{physical activity}}}{\underline{\qquad\qquad}} + \underset{\textbf{TEF}}{\underline{\qquad}}$$

For our example, Carol's total energy expenditure is about 1,878 kilocalories (1,177 + 530 + 171).

You may want to calculate your REE using the equations on page 348 and compare that result to this simplified method.

Quick Bite

The Fattest Mammals
Among mammals, humans carry the largest percentage of weight as body fat.

body composition The chemical or anatomical composition of the body. Commonly defined as the proportions of fat, muscle, bone, and other tissues in the body.

body mass index (BMI) Body weight (in kilograms) divided by the square of height (in meters), expressed in units of kg/m^2. Also called Quetelet index.

underweight BMI less than 18.5 kg/m^2.

overweight BMI at or above 25 kg/m^2 and less than 30 kg/m^2.

obesity BMI at or above 30 kg/m^2.

To calculate BMI

$$\text{BMI} = \frac{\text{weight (kg)}}{\text{height (m)}^2}\text{, or}$$

$$\text{BMI} = \frac{\text{weight (lb)}}{\text{height (in)}^2} \times 704.5.$$

Quick Bite

Is Shaq Too Fat?
Although BMI has become the standard reference for determining overweight and obesity, it has limitations at the extremes of body size and composition. Consider Shaquille O'Neal, the talented basketball star. At 7 feet, 1 inch, and 325 pounds, Shaq has a BMI of 32.7—well into the range for obesity. LaDainian Tomlinson, star running back for the NFL's San Diego Chargers, could also be considered obese based on his BMI of 31.8 kg/m^2 (5 feet, 10 inches, 221 pounds)!

Key Concepts *Energy expenditure can be measured using direct or indirect calorimetry. Direct calorimetry measures heat production by the body, whereas indirect calorimetry measures oxygen consumption and carbon dioxide production. The doubly labeled water method is becoming accepted as the gold standard for determining energy expenditure. In most situations, measuring energy expenditure is not practical, so a variety of equations have been developed for predicting energy expenditure.*

Body Composition: Understanding Fatness and Weight

Stepping onto a scale provides quick and easy feedback about your body weight. Yet many people have a distorted notion of their weight—thinking they're too fat when they aren't or thinking their weight is just fine when it isn't. In terms of your health risks, **body composition** is more important than body weight.

Body composition is the relative amount of fat and lean body mass. Excess body fatness is linked with increased risk for heart disease, hypertension, cancer, diabetes, and other chronic diseases. Two people with the same height and high weight may have very different health risks. Whereas one may be obese and have many weight-related health risks, the other could be very fit and muscular, with no increased disease risk.

Assessing Body Weight

Body mass index (BMI) has become the accepted method for assessing body weight for height. This index, which is a ratio of weight to height squared, correlates reasonably well with body fatness and health risks.[43] To determine your BMI, accurately measure your height without shoes and your weight with minimal clothing. Then plug these numbers into the BMI equations in the margin. For adults, the National Heart, Lung and Blood Institute (NHLBI) defines **underweight**, normal weight, **overweight**, and **obesity** as follows:[44]

- *Underweight:* BMI < 18.5 kg/m^2
- *Normal weight:* 18.5 $kg/m^2 \leq$ BMI $<$ 25 kg/m^2
- *Overweight:* 25 $kg/m^2 \leq$ BMI $<$ 30 kg/m^2
- *Obese:* BMI $\geq$ 30 kg/m^2

Table 9.5 can help you determine whether your weight is a healthy weight according to the *Dietary Guidelines for Americans*.

As **Figure 9.9** shows, correlating BMI with mortality produces a J-shaped curve. Studies indicate that underweight (BMI less than 18.5 kg/m^2) is associated with increased mortality, as is obesity (BMI greater than or equal to 30 kg/m^2). Normal weight and overweight are not associated with excess overall mortality.[45] Although your BMI can give you a general idea of your overall health risks, it still doesn't tell you enough about whether you are carrying muscle weight or excess fat. A classic example is the heavy football player or bodybuilder with a large muscle mass who has a BMI greater than 30 kg/m^2 but is not overfat. For someone who has lost muscle mass, perhaps an older adult, BMI can underestimate health risks associated with excess body fat. BMI measurements should be interpreted cautiously when used for people who are petite, who have large body frames, or who are highly muscular.[46]

For children and teens, height and weight measurements can be compared with standard growth charts to see if the child is growing and gaining weight at the appropriate rate. (See Chapter 16 for more on growth charts.)

Table 9.5 Adult BMI Chart

BMI	19	20	21	22	23	24	25	26	27	28	29	30	31	32	33	34	35
Height							Weight in Pounds										
4′10″	91	96	100	105	110	115	119	124	129	134	138	143	148	153	158	162	167
4′11″	94	99	104	109	114	119	124	128	133	138	143	148	153	158	163	168	173
5′	97	102	107	112	118	123	128	133	138	143	148	153	158	163	158	174	179
5′1″	100	106	111	116	122	127	132	137	143	148	153	158	164	169	174	180	185
5′2″	104	109	115	120	126	131	136	142	147	153	158	164	169	175	180	186	191
5′3″	107	113	118	124	130	135	141	146	152	158	163	169	175	180	186	191	197
5′4″	110	116	122	128	134	140	145	151	157	163	169	174	180	186	192	197	204
5′5″	114	120	126	132	138	144	150	156	162	168	174	180	186	192	198	204	210
5′6″	118	124	130	136	142	148	155	161	167	173	179	186	192	198	204	210	216
5′7″	121	127	134	140	146	153	159	166	172	178	185	191	198	204	211	217	223
5′8″	125	131	138	144	151	158	164	171	177	184	190	197	203	210	216	223	230
5′9″	128	135	142	149	155	162	169	176	182	189	196	203	209	216	223	230	236
5′10″	132	139	146	153	160	167	174	181	188	195	202	209	216	222	229	236	243
5′11″	136	143	150	157	165	172	179	186	193	200	208	215	222	229	236	243	250
6′	140	147	154	162	169	177	184	191	199	206	213	221	228	235	242	250	258
6′1″	144	151	159	166	174	182	189	197	204	212	219	227	235	242	250	257	265
6′2″	148	155	163	171	179	186	194	202	210	218	225	233	241	249	256	264	272
6′3″	152	160	168	176	184	192	200	208	216	224	232	240	248	256	264	272	279
	Healthy Weight						Overweight					Obese					

Locate the height of interest in the leftmost column and read across the row for that height to the weight of interest. Follow the column of the weight up to the top row that lists the BMI. BMI of 19 to 24 is the healthy weight range, BMI of 25 to 29 is the overweight range, and BMI of 30 and above is in the obese range. Due to rounding, these ranges vary slightly from the NHLBI values.

Source: US Department of Agriculture and US Department of Health and Human Services. *Dietary Guidelines for Americans.* 6th ed. Washington, DC: US Government Printing Office, 2005.

For children and teens (2 to 20 years old), pediatric growth charts include age- and sex-specific percentile curves for BMI.[47] A BMI-for-age at or above the 95th percentile indicates overweight and the need for further evaluation and possible treatment. Further evaluation may also be indicated if the child's BMI-for-age is at or above the 85th percentile and is accompanied by other risk factors such as high blood pressure, high blood cholesterol, diabetes, and family history of obesity-related disease.[48] A BMI-for-age below the 5th percentile suggests that the child is underweight.

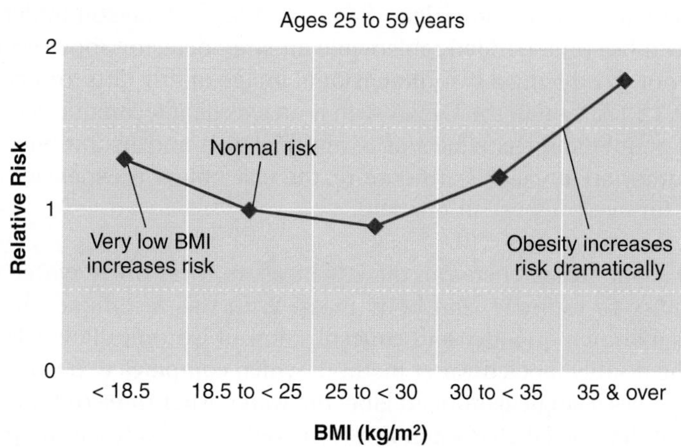

Figure 9.9 **BMI and mortality.** People with a high or very low BMI have a higher relative mortality rate.

Source: Adapted from Flegal KM, Graubard BI, Williamson DF, Gail MH. Excess deaths associated with underweight, overweight, and obesity. *JAMA.* 2005;293:1861–1867.

Figure 9.10 **Underwater weighing.** During underwater weighing, the subject must exhale completely, submerge without taking a breath, and remain motionless until the water is still and the scale is steady.

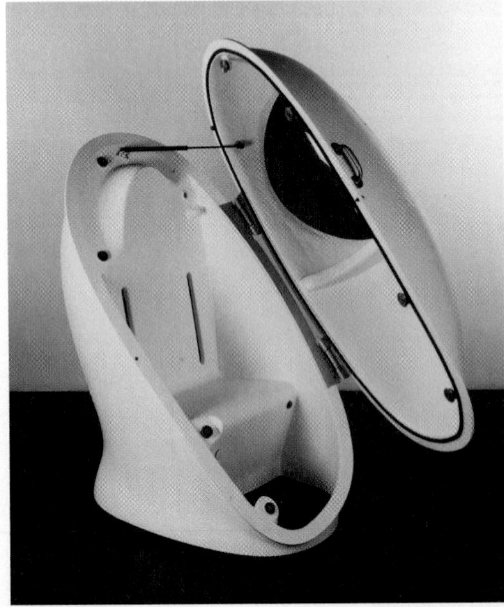

Figure 9.11 **BOD POD.** By using air displacement, the BOD POD provides an alternative to underwater weighing that is easier, cheaper, and of similar accuracy.

Key Concepts *Body composition is a key element in determining energy expenditure and is an important factor in disease risk. Weight and height measures can be used to calculate BMI, which is correlated with body fatness and health risks. Elevated BMI in adults or children can increase health risks.*

Assessing Body Fatness

Fat is stored in the adipose tissue that lies directly under the skin. Fat tissue also surrounds internal organs. Healthy adult females typically have 20 to 35 percent body fat; for men, the range is 8 to 24 percent. Risk of chronic disease rises dramatically when body fat exceeds these levels.

Densitometry is the measure of body density (body mass divided by body volume). Because fat and lean tissues have different densities, if we know the person's volume and weight, we can calculate the ratio of fat to lean body mass. The density of fat doesn't vary, but hydration status, age, gender, and ethnicity all influence the density of lean body mass. For example, bone loss in the elderly leads to a lower density of lean body mass.

Densitometry and Underwater Weighing **Underwater weighing**, also called **hydrostatic weighing**, is an accurate densitometry method that is used in research settings and some sports programs. Because fat is less dense than muscle, a person with more body fat will have a lower underwater weight than a person with the same body weight but less fat. With this technique, a seated person is submerged fully in water and weighed as **Figure 9.10** illustrates. Body density is calculated using the above-water weight, the submerged weight, and the quantity of water displaced during submersion. Underwater weighing often is impractical because it requires a special water tank and other nonportable, expensive equipment. The subject must exhale completely, submerge without taking a breath, and remain motionless until the water is still and the scale is steady—clearly not a comfortable experience for everyone!

Densitometry and Air Displacement The **BOD POD** measures displacement of air to determine relative amounts of fat and fat-free mass for calculating body density. With this technique, a person sits in a sealed chamber of known volume and displaces a certain volume of air. Air displacement uses the same principles as underwater weighing, but it is much faster and easier. **Figure 9.11** shows an air displacement chamber.

Dual-Energy X-Ray Absorptiometry **Dual-energy x-ray absorptiometry (DEXA)**, used to measure bone density, can also be used to analyze body composition by differentiating bone, other lean tissue, and fat.[49] A person undergoing a DEXA scan lies on a padded table while an x-ray detector above scans from head to foot, producing a two-dimensional image of tiny dots, or pixels. (See **Figure 9.12**.) Although the DEXA scan is an excellent technique, its accuracy in obese people and the effects of tissue thickness and hydration status on scan accuracy are unclear. Furthermore, the instrument is expensive and not practical for everyday use in the field.

Isotope Dilution Researchers can directly measure **total body water** and use this quantity to estimate lean body mass. With this technique, the subject swallows a known quantity and concentration of isotopically labeled water. Unlike the doubly labeled water method, which compares two isotopes, this technique uses a single isotope to label the water. After three or four hours, it is assumed that the labeled water is fully mixed in the body's water pool. The

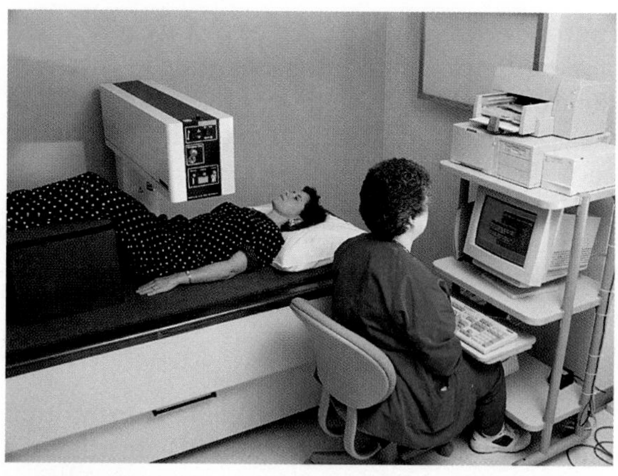

Figure 9.12 **Dual-energy x-ray absorptiometry (DEXA) scan.** The two-dimensional image produced from a DEXA scan can be used to assess body composition.

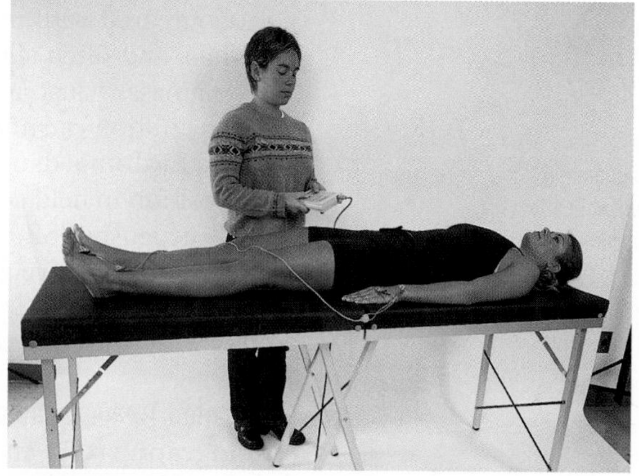

Figure 9.13 **Bioelectrical impedance analysis (BIA).** The measured resistance to a small electrical current passed through the body is used to estimate body composition.

researcher takes a sample of body water (e.g., from plasma, saliva, or urine), measures the concentration of the isotope, and calculates the total volume of body water. Based on the assumption that lean body mass is 73 percent water, researchers can estimate the total lean body mass. Unfortunately, this assumption does not hold true for all people; the amount of water in lean body mass can vary, especially in the elderly. Obesity and dehydration from severe exercise and use of diuretics or laxatives also may influence the results.

Skinfold Thickness As you learned in Chapter 2, "Nutrition Guidelines and Assessment," skinfold thicknesses often are used to measure body fatness. Typically, more than half of body fat is located just under the skin, and the percentage increases as body weight increases.[50]

Skinfold measurements are a low-tech method for assessing body fatness. A special caliper is used to measure skinfold thicknesses at several sites on the body—typically over the triceps muscles on the back of the upper arm, just below the shoulder blade, near the navel, and over the hips. Predictive equations then estimate regional and total body fatness.

Because of its simplicity and relatively low cost (less than $500 for calipers), skinfold anthropometry is popular in health clubs and weight-control programs. Skinfold measures also are widely used in large population studies. When done correctly, body composition estimates from skinfolds correlate well with those from underwater weighing, but an inexperienced or careless measurer can easily make large errors. Skinfold thicknesses are especially useful in tracking changes in subcutaneous fat distribution in an individual over time. They usually work better for assessing malnutrition than for identifying overweight and obesity.

Bioelectrical Impedance Analysis **Bioelectrical impedance analysis (BIA)** measures the rate at which a small electric current flows through the body between electrodes placed on the wrist and ankle. (See **Figure 9.13**.) Fat doesn't conduct electricity well; it resists, or impedes, the current. In contrast, electrolyte-containing fluids readily conduct a current. These fluids are found mostly in lean body tissues, so the leaner the person, the less the resistance. From the impedance reading, the researcher calculates total body water and then estimates total lean body mass and body fatness.

densitometry A method for estimating body composition from measurement of total body density.

underwater weighing Determining body density by measuring the volume of water displaced when the body is fully submerged in a specialized water tank. Also called hydrostatic weighing.

hydrostatic weighing See *underwater weighing.*

BodPod A device used to measure the density of the body based on the volume of air displaced as a person sits in a sealed chamber of known volume.

dual-energy x-ray absorptiometry (DEXA) A body composition measurement technique originally developed to measure bone density.

total body water All of the water in the body, including intracellular and extracellular water, and water in the urinary and GI tracts.

bioelectrical impedance analysis (BIA) Technique to estimate amounts of total body water, lean tissue mass, and total body fat. It uses the resistance of tissue to the flow of an alternating electric current.

Quick Bite

Where's the Fat?

The location of excess abdominal fat may hold information about health risks. Within the abdomen, visceral fat (fat surrounding the organs) may be more harmful than subcutaneous fat (fat under the skin). Only sophisticated imaging techniques, such as CT scans and MRI, can distinguish between the two.

Compared with underwater weighing, the results of BIA usually are as good as, and often slightly better than, skinfold measurements in assessing body fatness.[51] Just as in the isotope dilution method, age, obesity, and altered hydration can affect the accuracy of BIA results. Despite its limitations, bioelectrical impedance is accepted as a valuable tool for measuring body composition in field studies. The equipment is easily portable and only moderately expensive ($2,500–$8,000), making the technique popular at upscale health clubs and weight-loss centers. Similar to BIA, total body electrical conductivity (TOBEC) is an acceptably accurate measure of conductivity, but is less widely used because the equipment is expensive.

Computed Tomography and Magnetic Resonance Imaging Although **computed tomography (CT)** and **magnetic resonance imaging (MRI)** are primarily medical diagnostic techniques, researchers can use them to distinguish and quantify body tissues. CT scans use x-ray beams to produce highly detailed cross-sectional images of body tissues (see **Figure 9.14**). MRI technology uses a magnetic field and radio-frequency waves to both produce cross-sectional images and perform chemical analysis of body tissues. However, CT and MRI are costly techniques limited to research settings, and CT scans entail exposure to radiation.

Near-Infrared Interactance **Near-infrared interactance** uses the principle that materials of different composition absorb, reflect, or transmit infrared light at different rates. With this technique, a probe acts as an infrared transmitter and detector. Placed on the biceps muscle, it transmits infrared light through the skin and detects the amount reflected. Analysis of the transmitted and reflected values can estimate body composition. The method, which became instantly popular in health clubs and athletic departments, has not yet been validated and appears to overestimate body fat in lean subjects and underestimate fatness in the obese. Experts do not currently recommend it for body composition assessment.[52]

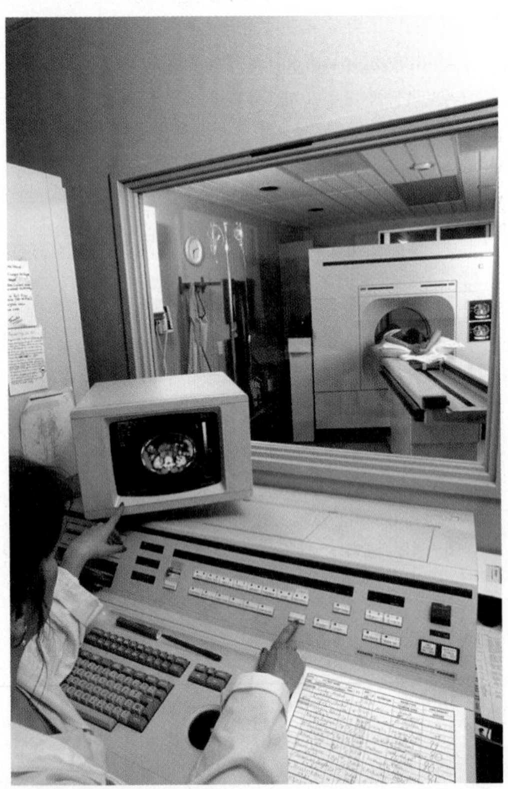

Figure 9.14 **Computed tomography (CT).** CT scans produce detailed cross-sectional images that can be used to quantify body composition.

Body Fat Distribution

Measurements of body fatness tell you more about your health risks than your weight does, but they still don't tell the whole story. Where the fat is located—**body fat distribution**—can be an independent risk factor.[53] The "pear shape," or **gynoid obesity**, more common in women has excess fat distributed predominantly around the hips and thighs. The "apple shape," or **android obesity**, typical of men has extra fat distributed higher up, around the abdomen. **Figure 9.15** shows the gynoid and android distributions of body fat.

THINK About It 2

Excess abdominal fat appears to raise blood lipid levels, which in turn interferes with insulin function. Consequently, android obesity has been linked to high blood lipids, glucose intolerance and insulin resistance, and high blood pressure; it increases the risk of heart disease and diabetes mellitus. These risks exist for both men and women who have excess abdominal fat. In fact, android obesity may indicate an increased breast cancer risk for women.[54]

If your **waist circumference** increases, you are probably gaining abdominal fat. Clinical guidelines from the National Institutes of Health (NIH) suggest that for people with a BMI of 25 kg/m^2 to 34.9 kg/m^2, a waist circumference greater than 40 inches (102 centimeters) in men or greater than 35 inches (88 centimeters) in women is a sign of increased health risk. Combining measures of BMI and waist circumference is more predictive of cardiovascular disease risk than either measure alone.[55] When BMI is 35 kg/m^2 or higher, however, waist circumference measures do not predict health risks accurately.

Key Concepts *Excess body fatness is associated with increased risk for chronic diseases, including heart disease and diabetes. Researchers use a number of different methods to assess body fatness. High cost may limit the usefulness of more sophisticated techniques. Distribution of body fat is important in evaluating risk of disease. Excess body fat around the abdomen is associated with higher disease risk than is excess fat around the hips and thighs. Waist circumference can be used to assess body fat distribution.*

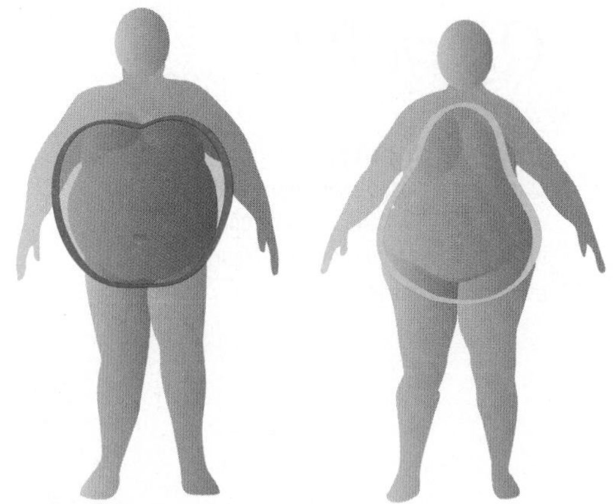

Figure 9.15 **Differences in body fat distribution.** Men tend to carry excess fat around their abdomen (android obesity). Women tend to accumulate excess fat in their hips and thighs (gynoid obesity).

Overweight and Obesity

Obesity has become a global problem[56] and has emerged as the most important contributor to ill health, displacing undernutrition and infectious diseases.[57] Not only is obesity prevalent in Europe and the Americas,[58] but it is also on the rise in Southeast Asia, where Japan and China have seen a marked increase. In North Africa, more than half the women in Morocco and Tunisia are overweight or obese,[59] and in the Middle East, the United Arab Emirates now recognizes obesity as a major public health problem.[60]

In the United States, the prevalence of overweight and obesity has increased dramatically, jumping from one of every four Americans to nearly two of every three![61] Nearly one of six children and teens (ages 6 to 19) are overweight (double the rate from 20 years earlier), and a similar number are at risk of becoming overweight.[62] This escalating problem is blamed on overconsumption of plentiful, tasty, and energy-dense foods, along with decreased physical activity. The goal of Healthy People 2010 is to cut the prevalence of obesity to no more than 15 percent in adults and 5 percent in children and adolescents.[63]

As overweight and obesity have increased, so has society's emphasis on thinness, as well as efforts at weight management. Every year, the diet industry rakes in $40 billion to $50 billion from weight-loss programs, diet books, pills, videos, and supplements. In 2009, 55 percent of adults surveyed said they were trying to lose weight.[64] Children and adolescents also are concerned about weight. In studies of grade-school girls from various socioeconomic backgrounds, 28 to 40 percent reported that they sometimes dieted or were very often worried about being fat.[65]

Key Concepts *Worldwide, the number of overweight or obese people has increased markedly in recent years. The rising rates among children are especially disturbing. At the same time, more people are engaging in weight-control efforts and starting to do so at younger ages.*

Factors in the Development of Obesity

At its simplest, obesity results from a chronic positive energy balance: energy intake regularly exceeds energy output, and weight is gained. But why? As we learn more about the factors that regulate feeding behavior and energy metabolism, scientists are beginning to unravel the specific mechanisms at work and, from there, to determine what may go wrong in people who are obese. Obesity is a complex disorder that probably involves several regulatory mechanisms and the way they interact and respond to biological factors such as heredity, age, and sex; to social and environmental factors; and to behavior and lifestyle choices.

computed tomography (CT) The gathering of anatomical information from cross-sectional images generated by a computer synthesis of x-ray data.

magnetic resonance imaging (MRI) Medical imaging technique that uses a magnetic field and radio-frequency radiation to generate anatomical information.

near-infrared interactance The measurement of body composition using infrared radiation. It is based on the principle that substances of different densities absorb, reflect, or transmit infrared light at different rates.

body fat distribution The pattern of fat distribution on the body.

gynoid obesity Excess storage of fat located primarily in the buttocks and thighs. Also called gynecoid obesity.

android obesity [AN-droyd] Excess storage of fat located primarily in the abdominal area.

waist circumference The waist measurement, as a marker of abdominal fat content; can be used to indicate health risks.

Quick Bite

Island Obesity
Some of the most obese people in the world live in the islands of Micronesia. Among these populations, the Naurus are the most obese.

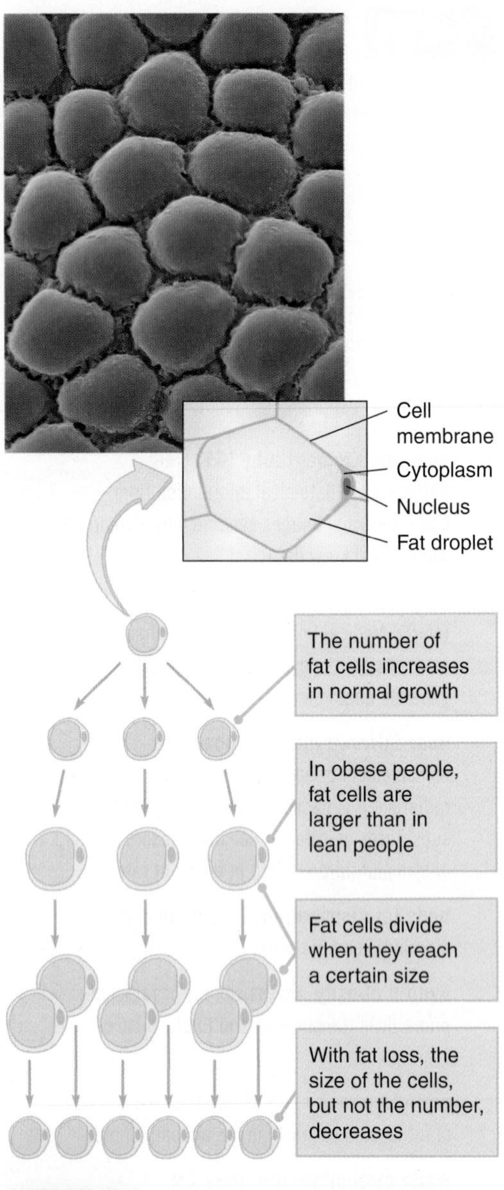
Cell membrane
Cytoplasm
Nucleus
Fat droplet
The number of fat cells increases in normal growth
In obese people, fat cells are larger than in lean people
Fat cells divide when they reach a certain size
With fat loss, the size of the cells, but not the number, decreases

Figure 9.16 **The formation of fat cells.** As body fat accumulates, fat cells enlarge and divide. Fat loss reduces the size of fat cells, but not their number.

Biological Factors

Heredity and Genetics Researchers have long recognized hereditary patterns of obesity. When both parents are morbidly obese (body weight 100 percent above normal), the probability that their children will be obese is high (80 percent); when neither parent is obese, the probability that their children will be obese is relatively low (less than 10 percent). However, about 25 to 30 percent of obese individuals have normal-weight parents.[66]

To what extent are family patterns of obesity caused by the environment rather than heredity? Studies in twins confirm that the response to diet is mediated by a person's genetic makeup.[67] Researchers estimate that genes alone generally account for 50 to 90 percent of variations in the amount of stored body fat.[68]

Fat Cell Development The number and size of fat cells in the body help determine how easily a person gains or loses fat. People with **hypercellular obesity**, an above-average number of fat cells, may have been born with them or may have developed them at certain critical times because of overeating. In **hypertrophic obesity**, fat cells are larger than normal. Fat cells continue to expand as they fill with more fat; when their capacity is reached, the body generates more cells. (See **Figure 9.16**.) Once body fat reaches three to five times the normal amount, fat tissue is likely to have both bigger fat cells *and* more of them, a condition called **hyperplastic obesity (hyperplasia)**.

Even with weight loss, the number of fat cells does not decline (though presumably some could be removed by liposuction). Fat cells do become smaller, but beyond a certain point, they resist further shrinking and the body strives to refill them with fat, making it difficult to maintain weight loss.

Sex and Age In general, males and females set different weight standards for themselves. Beginning in grade school, boys are less likely than girls to consider themselves overweight; in fact, males of all ages accept some degree of overweight. Boys typically are more concerned about becoming taller and more muscular. As adolescents and young adults, most of us worry about body weight and appearance. A survey of college students aspiring to become registered dietitians, for example, found that most adolescent dieters wanted to lose weight to improve appearance and increase self-esteem.[69]

By early adulthood, about the same number of men want to lose or gain weight, whereas almost all women want to lose weight. As adults, men tend to see themselves as overweight at higher weights, whereas women describe themselves as overweight when they are closer to a healthy body weight. (See **Figure 9.17**.) Adult women feel thin only when they weigh less than 90 percent of desirable body weight, whereas men rate themselves as thin even when they are above a healthy body weight.[70]

As we age, we become more concerned with our weight as it relates to health. Both men and women gain the most weight between 25 and 34 years of age. After that, we gain weight more slowly and then start to lose it after we reach age 55.[71] However, it's often important for seniors to maintain weight.

Although women try harder than men to avoid overweight or to slim down,[72] they frequently become obese after pregnancy and at menopause. In pregnancy, fat stores increase to meet the energy demands of breastfeeding. Many women retain this extra weight after they give birth, and become heavier with each child.

Race and Ethnicity In the United States, the prevalence of obesity and attitudes about weight differ among racial and ethnic groups. Black and Hispanic women are more likely to be overweight than white women.[73] Rates of overweight are similar for black, Hispanic, and white men. Because of cultural factors, African Americans, Hispanic Americans, Native Americans, and Pacific Islanders typically value thinness less than white Americans do.[74]

Social and Environmental Factors

Socioeconomic Status Americans are more likely to be obese if they have low socioeconomic status, and the stigma of obesity can impede their upward mobility. But obesity rates are rising among the affluent as well. Statistics show that in the early 1970s, 22.5 percent of low-income adults were obese; this value had risen to 34.7 percent in 2002. In contrast, only 9.7 percent of upper-income adults were obese in the 1970s; now that figure is over 28.7 percent.[75] Rural women tend to be heavier than women living in metropolitan areas, and southern women are the most likely to be overweight.[76]

Education is another factor associated with body weight, but mainly for women. The prevalence of overweight among women ranges from 60 percent of those with less than a high school education to 29 percent of those with postgraduate college degrees.[77] An analysis has shown that race and education interact in their effects on women's body weights.[78] At the lowest level of education, average BMI (approximately 31 kg/m^2) is similar for middle-aged black and white women. But at higher education levels, black women were significantly heavier (BMI = 31.5 kg/m^2) than white women (BMI = 27.8 kg/m^2).

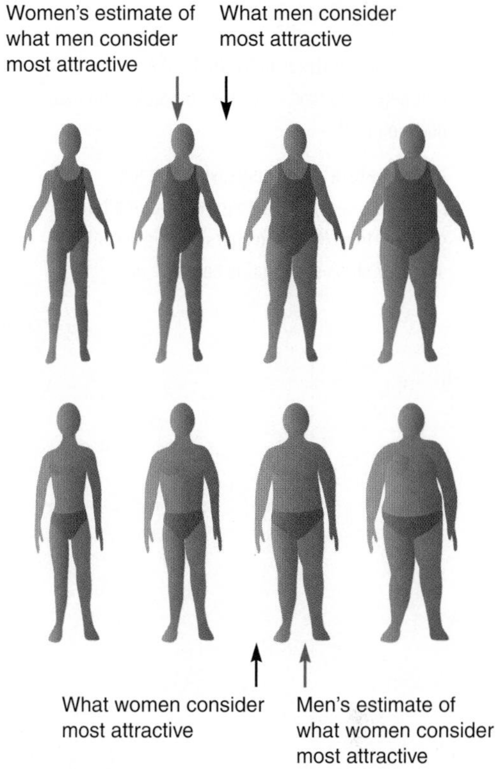

The Built Environment Our immediate surroundings influence our behaviors, and researchers have begun to link aspects of the **built environment** with obesity. The built environment, which can be defined as "human formed, developed, or structured areas," includes buildings, roads, parks, and transportation systems.[79] These environments in which we live and work can either encourage or hinder physical activity and healthful eating.[80]

People who live in neighborhoods with sidewalks and safe streets are more physically active. But when neighborhoods have low "walkability" or are considered unsafe, BMIs tend to be higher. Socioeconomic factors are at work too—lower-income neighborhoods have fewer recreational facilities and healthful eating options. Fast food restaurants and convenience stores are more prevalent in low-income neighborhoods, whereas the number of supermarkets triples in wealthier neighborhoods.[81]

Social Factors Social factors also influence the development of obesity. Abundant high-calorie, highly palatable foods, pervasive advertising promoting their consumption, and the social enjoyment of eating all create pressures to overeat. At the same time, our culture tells us that we should be thin, and we feel unhealthy pressures to diet. Table 9.6 summarizes social characteristics that are key predictors of obesity.

Lifestyle and Behavior Factors

Physical Activity Lack of exercise is a major contributing factor to weight gain and obesity. Only 22 percent of U.S. adults get the recommended amount of regular physical activity; more than 60 percent are not active on a regular basis, and 25 percent are not active at all. Inactivity is more common among

Figure 9.17 What men and women consider attractive. Compared with men, women perceive attractive shapes to be slimmer.

Source: Data compiled from Fallon A, Rozin P. Sex differences in perceptions of desirable body shape. *Abnorm Psychol.* 1985;94:102–105; and Kalat J. *Introduction to Psychology.* 5th ed. Belmont, CA: Wadsworth, 1999.

hypercellular obesity Obesity due to an above-average number of fat cells.

hypertrophic obesity Obesity due to an increase in the size of fat cells.

hyperplastic obesity (hyperplasia) Obesity due to an increase in both the size and number of fat cells.

built environment Any human-formed, developed, or structured areas, including the urban environment that consists of buildings, roads, fixtures, parks, and all other human developments that form its physical character.

restrained eaters Individuals who routinely avoid food as long as possible, and then gorge on food.

binge eaters Individuals who routinely consume a very large amount of food in a brief period of time (e.g., two hours) and lose control over how much and what is eaten.

women, older adults, less affluent adults, and black or Hispanic adults.[82] In both children and adults, research links excessive television viewing to obesity.[83] In addition, adolescents who watch television while eating meals have lower intakes of vegetables, calcium-rich foods, and grains and higher intakes of soft drinks compared with adolescents who do not watch television during meals.[84] For all ages, obesity itself may lead to physical inactivity, although the strength of this relationship is unclear.

Psychological Factors Some people adopt eating as a strategy for dealing with the stresses and challenges of life. (Others use drugs, alcohol, smoking, shopping, gambling, and so on.) Eating also can provide entertainment and alleviate boredom. Some people use eating as a pick-me-up when fatigued, and some use eating to distract themselves from difficult problems or as a means of punishing themselves or others for real or imagined transgressions.

Certain obese people may be more prone to emotional eating than others. These subgroups include **restrained eaters** and **binge eaters**.[85] Restrained

Table 9.6 **Sociocultural Influences on Obesity**

Social Contexts	
Culture	People in developed societies have more body fat than those in developing societies.
History	Fatness is increasing in the United States, but idealized weights are decreasing.
Social Characteristics	
Age and lifestyle	Fatness increases during adulthood, declines in the elderly.
Gender	Obesity is more prevalent in women than in men.
Race and ethnicity	Obesity is more prevalent in African American, Hispanic, Native American, and Pacific Islander women.
Socioeconomic Status	
Income	Obesity is more prevalent in lower-income women.
Education	Less-educated women have a higher incidence of obesity.
Occupational prestige	Obesity is more prevalent in women (people) in less prestigious jobs.
Employment	Women who are not employed have a higher incidence of obesity.
Household composition	Older people who live with others have a higher incidence of obesity.
Marriage	Married men have a higher incidence of obesity.
Residence	Rural women have a higher incidence of obesity.
Region	People residing in the South have a higher incidence of obesity.

Source: Adapted from Dalton S. Body weight terminology, definitions, and measurements. In: Dalton S, ed. *Overweight and Weight Management: The Health Professional's Guide to Understanding and Practice.* Sudbury, MA: Jones and Bartlett, 1997:314.

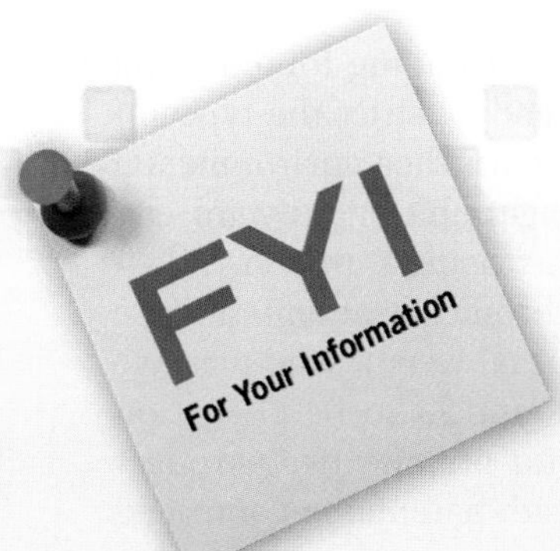

U.S. Obesity Trends: 1985 to 2007

During the past 20 years there has been a dramatic increase in obesity in the United States. The maps in **Figures 1** and **2** illustrate this trend by showing the increased prevalence of obesity across each of the states. In 2007, only one state (Colorado) had a prevalence of obesity less than 20 percent. Thirty states had a prevalence equal to or greater than 25 percent; three of these states (Alabama, Mississippi, and Tennessee) had a prevalence of obesity equal to or greater than 30 percent (see **Table 1**). Refer to the following Web site for a complete slide show of each year during this time period: http://www.cdc.gov/obesity/data/trends.html.

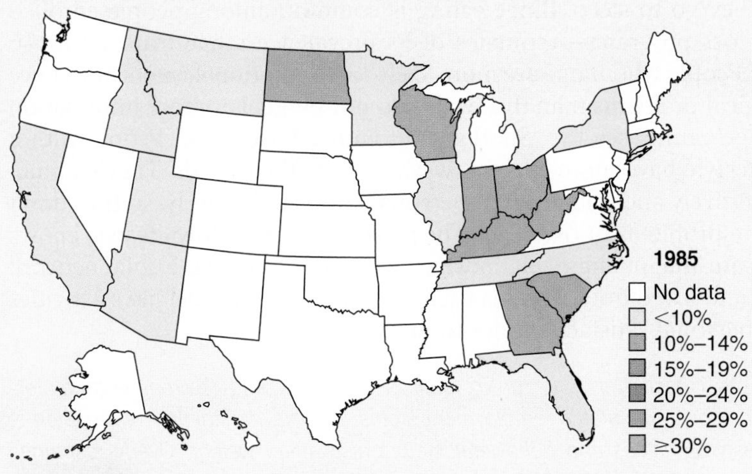

Figure 1 Percentage of obesity (BMI ≥ 30) in U.S. adults, 1985.

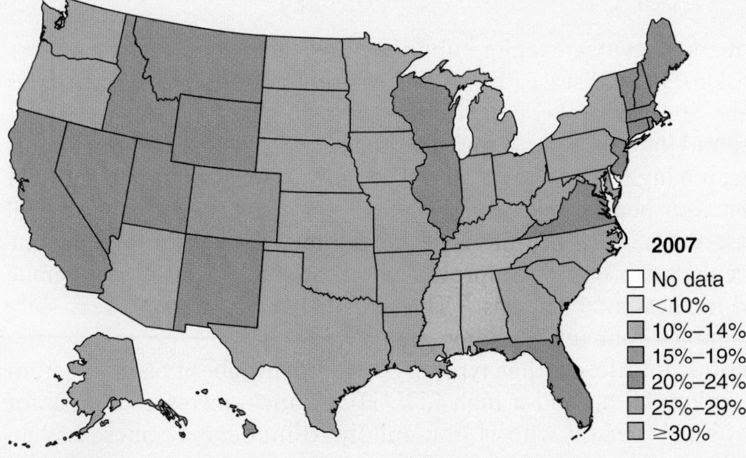

Figure 2 Percentage of obesity (BMI ≥ 30) in U.S. adults, 2007.

Table 1 2007 State Obesity Rates

2007 State Obesity Rates

State	%	State	%
Alabama	30.3	Montana	21.8
Alaska	27.5	Nebraska	26.0
Arizona	25.4	Nevada	24.1
Arkansas	28.7	New Hampshire	24.4
California	22.6	New Jersey	23.5
Colorado	18.7	New Mexico	24.0
Connecticut	21.2	New York	25.0
Delaware	27.4	North Carolina	28.0
Washington DC	21.8	North Dakota	26.5
Florida	23.6	Ohio	27.5
Georgia	28.2	Oklahoma	28.1
Hawaii	21.4	Oregon	25.5
Idaho	24.5	Pennsylvania	27.1
Illinois	24.9	Rhode Island	21.4
Indiana	26.8	South Carolina	28.4
Iowa	26.9	South Dakota	26.2
Kansas	26.9	Tennessee	30.1
Kentucky	27.4	Texas	28.1
Louisiana	29.8	Utah	21.8
Maine	24.8	Vermont	21.3
Maryland	25.4	Virginia	24.3
Massachusetts	21.3	Washington	25.3
Michigan	27.7	West Virginia	29.5
Minnesota	25.6	Wisconsin	24.7
Mississippi	32.0	Wyoming	23.7
Missouri	27.5		

Source: Centers for Disease Control and Prevention. U.S. Obesity Trends: Trends by State 1985–2007. http://www.cdc.gov/obesity/data/trends.html. Accessed 6/22/09.

eaters try to reduce their calorie intake by fasting or avoiding food as long as possible. They skip meals, delay eating, or severely restrict the types of food they eat. Then, like a dam that bursts, they overeat when environmental or emotional stress triggers a complete release of inhibitions toward eating. Although not all obese binge eaters follow this pattern, the "fast, then binge" behavior is common in obese people who chronically attempt to lose weight.[86] This pattern also occurs in women of normal weight who perceive themselves as fat. These restrained eating patterns appear to be passed on from mother to daughter.[87] Parental use of foods for nonnutritive purposes is prevalent in the United States and is associated with parental uncontrolled or emotional eating.[88]

Binge eaters compulsively overeat, sometimes for days. Some people binge only at night, taking in most of their excess calories between 6 P.M. and the time they go to sleep. Binge eating is common among people enrolled in weight-loss programs—estimates of its prevalence range from 23 to 46 percent.[89] People who binge are more likely to be emotional eaters or to have psychological problems than those who do not binge. For more information about binge eating, see the "Spotlight on Eating Disorders." People with a healthy lifestyle have more effective ways to meet their needs. They communicate assertively and manage interpersonal conflict effectively, so they don't shrink from problems or overreact. The person with a healthy lifestyle knows how to create and maintain relationships with others and has a solid network of friends and loved ones. Food is used appropriately—to fuel life's activities and gain personal satisfaction, not to manage stress.

Key Concepts *Obesity tends to run in families. Sex, age, and environmental factors such as socioeconomic status, employment status, and having children are related to weight. Lifestyle choices and behavioral factors also affect weight. Overly restrained eating may result in episodes of overeating and weight gain. Binge eating is common among people in weight-loss programs.*

Health Risks of Overweight and Obesity

Overweight and obesity are major public health challenges. Obese people are at higher risk for heart disease, the leading cause of death in the United States and Canada, and for stroke, diabetes, hypertension, some forms of cancer, gallbladder and joint diseases,[90] and psychosocial problems. The longer obesity persists, the higher the risks. Table 9.7 lists the effects that excess weight can have on your health. Scientists speculate that rising rates of obesity will soon reverse the increases in life expectancy that occurred throughout the twentieth century as a result of improved living conditions, advances in public health, and medical interventions.[91] The costs of obesity-related diseases are staggering—an estimated $75 billion annually.[92]

The blood lipid levels that typically accompany obesity—high serum triglycerides, low HDL, and a high LDL/HDL ratio—increase the risk for atherosclerosis. A person who is only mildly to moderately obese has an elevated risk of coronary heart disease. However, even modest weight loss (about 10 percent of body weight) reduces risk.[93]

Type 2 diabetes, the most common form of diabetes in the United States and Canada, is three times more likely to develop in people who are obese, especially if they have abdominal (android) obesity. Obesity increases insulin resistance and compromises the ability of body cells to take up glucose. Diabetes, in turn, is a risk factor for heart disease, kidney disease, and vascular problems. Again, even modest levels of weight reduction can improve glucose tolerance.

Table 9.7 **What Are the Risks of Being Overweight?**

Heart Disease and Stroke
Hypertension and very high blood levels of cholesterol and triglycerides (blood fats) can lead to heart disease and often are linked to being overweight. Being overweight also contributes to angina (chest pain caused by decreased oxygen to the heart) and sudden death from heart disease or stroke without any signs or symptoms.

Diabetes
Overweight people are twice as likely to develop type 2 diabetes as people who are not overweight. Type 2 diabetes is a major cause of early death, heart disease, kidney disease, stroke, and blindness.

Cancer
Several types of cancer are associated with being overweight. In women, these include cancer of the uterus, gallbladder, cervix, ovary, breast, and colon. Overweight men are at greater risk for developing cancer of the colon, rectum, and prostate. For some types of cancer, such as colon or breast, it is not clear whether the increased risk is due to the extra weight or consumption of a high-fat and high-calorie diet.

Sleep Apnea
Sleep apnea is a serious condition that is closely associated with being overweight. Sleep apnea can cause a person to stop breathing for short periods during sleep and to snore heavily. Sleep apnea may cause daytime sleepiness and even heart failure. The risk for sleep apnea increases with higher body weights. Weight loss usually improves sleep apnea.

Osteoarthritis
Extra weight appears to increase the risk of osteoarthritis by placing extra pressure on weight-bearing joints and wearing away the cartilage (tissue that cushions the joints) that normally protects them. Weight loss can decrease stress on the knees, hips, and lower back and may improve the symptoms of osteoarthritis.

Gallbladder Disease
Gallbladder disease and gallstones are more common if you are overweight. Your risk of disease increases as your weight increases. It is not clear how being overweight may cause gallbladder disease.

Weight loss itself, particularly rapid weight loss or loss of a large amount of weight, can actually increase your chances of developing gallstones. Modest, slow weight loss of about one pound a week is less likely to cause gallstones.

Fatty Liver Disease
Fatty liver disease occurs when fat builds up in the liver cells and damages the liver. It can lead to liver failure. Fatty liver disease is linked to higher than normal blood glucose levels, which are more common in people who are overweight. Weight loss can help with blood glucose control and reduce the build-up of fat in the liver. Also, people who have fatty liver disease should avoid alcohol.

Source: NIDDK Weight Control Information Network. Do you know the health risks of being overweight? http://win.niddk.gov/publications/health_risks.htm. Accessed 12/30/06.

Overweight people are two to six times more likely to develop hypertension.[94] The more you weigh, the more blood you need to supply oxygen and nutrients to your tissues. As the volume of blood circulated through your blood vessels increases, so does the pressure on your artery walls. Increased resistance in the peripheral blood vessels changes the way the kidneys handle sodium, along with other changes in kidney function.[95] Weight loss lowers blood pressure in overweight people with hypertension.

Although the exact reason is unknown, obesity increases the risk of cancer. The same food pattern that contributes to obesity (a diet high in calories and fat, plus low in fiber, fruits, and vegetables) also may be a cancer risk. Inactivity not only encourages obesity but also increases cancer risk. For example, women who are physically active have a lower risk of breast cancer than do sedentary women.[96] People who are obese have increased levels of hormones that influence development of some cancers. Obese women, for example, have more endometrial, gallbladder, cervical, and ovarian cancers.[97]

Obese people are more likely to have obstructive **sleep apnea**, in which the airway collapses during sleep and breathing stops for a short spell. As the body struggles for air, blood pressure spikes upward. Typically, the individual wakes up, gasps for air, begins breathing again, and then falls asleep until the

sleep apnea Periods of absence of breathing during sleep.

weight cycling Repeated periods of gaining and losing weight. Also called yo-yo dieting.

weight management The adoption of healthful and sustainable eating and exercise behaviors that reduce disease risk and improve well-being.

airway collapses again and the cycle repeats. This pattern not only interrupts and prevents a good night's sleep, it also increases the risk of heart attack and stroke. Modest weight loss can alleviate sleep apnea, improve sleep quality, and reduce daytime drowsiness.[98]

Weight Cycling

Weight cycling is a pattern of losing and regaining weight over and over again. You might expect this behavior to be harmful, perhaps harder on the body than overweight itself. However, research suggests that the potential benefits of weight loss for obese individuals still outweigh the potential risks of weight cycling.[99]

Researchers have found that women who repeatedly gain and lose weight, especially obese women, have significantly lower levels of HDL, the "good" cholesterol. Although low HDL levels are a significant risk factor for coronary artery disease (CAD), no direct link between weight cycling and CAD was observed.[100] More research is necessary to observe the health and behaviors of these women over time. Another study has linked weight cycling with an increased risk for hypertension,[101] and research has suggested that weight cycling impairs immune function.[102]

Key Concepts *Obesity is a risk factor for many chronic diseases, including heart disease, cancer, hypertension, and diabetes. In many cases, a modest amount of weight loss (about 10 percent of initial body weight) can improve symptoms and disease management.*

Dietary Guidelines for Americans, 2010
Key Recommendations

Balancing Calories to Manage weight
- Prevent and/or reduce overweight and obesity through improved eating and physical activity behaviors.
- Control total calorie intake to manage body weight. For people who are overweight or obese, this will mean consuming fewer calories from foods and beverages.
- Increase physical activity and reduce time spent in sedentary behaviors.
- Maintain appropriate calorie balance during each stage of life—childhood, adolescence, adulthood, pregnancy and breastfeeding, and older age.

Building Healthy Eating Patterns
- Select an eating pattern that meets nutrient needs over time at an appropriate calorie level.
- Account for all foods and beverages consumed and assess how they fit within a total healthy eating pattern.

Weight Management

Each person has a unique set of interrelated factors that lead to weight gain. Approaches to weight management are just as complex, and to be effective, they must be tailored to the individual. As you continue reading, keep in mind the following definition of **weight management** from the Academy of Nutrition and Dietetics; note that there is no mention of weight loss or ideal weight:

> Weight management is the adoption of healthful and sustainable eating and exercise behaviors indicated for reduced disease risk and improved feelings of energy and well-being.[103]

The Perception of Weight

The weights of celebrity models often mold popular notions about desirable weight. In the early 1960s, as today, thin was "in." (In the 1960s, the trendsetter was supermodel Twiggy, who at 5 feet, 7 inches weighed only 98 pounds; her BMI was a mere 15.4 kg/m^2!) Since then, the number of diet and exercise articles in women's magazines has escalated, and diet books have become best-sellers. Dieting has become an institution with its own magazines, television shows, camps and resorts, and weight-loss gurus. However, the images in **Figure 9.18** show that beauty has not always been associated with thinness.

Despite obesity's link to health risks, a backlash against dieting has emerged. The antidiet advocates' rallying cry is "Diets don't work!" While acknowledging that severe obesity is dangerous, they argue for size acceptance and challenge the notion that mild obesity is unhealthful. In fact, data from the Centers for Disease Control and Prevention show that people who are overweight (BMI 25 to < 30 kg/m^2) had no higher risk of mortality than people of normal weight.[104]

Figure 9.18 **Society's changing standards of beauty.** Over time, society has increasingly valued thinness. (a) Ruben's *The Three Graces*, 1639. (b) Degas's *After the Bath*, 1896. (c) Celebrity Victoria Beckam.

Health professionals now treat obesity as a complex disorder with multiple contributing factors. (See **Figure 9.19**.) They emphasize overall health and fitness rather than a number on the bathroom scale. Dietary recommendations emphasize moderation and a balanced diet that promotes consumption of healthful foods such as fruits, vegetables, and whole grains. Behavior change is still an important part of weight management, but change is seen as an ongoing process that requires new skills for maintaining a healthy lifestyle over the long run. Although vigorous exercise isn't required, substantial increases in moderate exercise are needed for long-term weight management.[105]

There are limitations as to what each of us can look like or what we can weigh. Although we shouldn't abandon efforts to achieve good health, we

Quick Bite

Rising Rates of Childhood Obesity: Kids and Car Seats

An April 2006 *Pediatrics* article, "Tipping the Scales: Obese Children and Child Safety Seats," found that, based on NHANES data, 285,305 children ages 6 and younger would have a difficult time fitting into most child safety seats due to their overweight status. More than half of these children are age 3 and weigh more than 40 pounds. The researchers found only four car seats on the market that could both accommodate these children and keep them safe.

Genetic
Psychological
Physiological
Behavioral
Obesity
Metabolic
Environmental
Hormonal
Sociocultural

Figure 9.19 **Multiple factors contribute to obesity.** Obesity is a complex disorder that is not easy to treat.

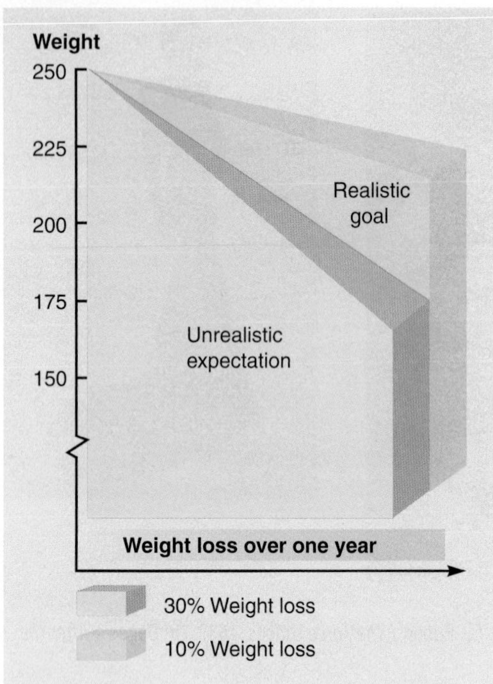

Figure 9.20 **Expectations and reasonable weight goals.** People who establish moderate rather than aggressive goals are more likely to succeed in their weight-loss program.

should balance our desire to lose weight with self-acceptance. If we engage in futile attempts to achieve an "ideal" body shape and weight, we may undermine our self-esteem and be harmed emotionally or even physically.

Key Concepts *Many factors contribute to the complex disorder of obesity. Currently, experts suggest that the best way to manage weight is to improve health by establishing healthy eating and exercise patterns and accepting the limitations of heredity.*

What Goals Should I Set?

What is a reasonable goal for weight management? According to the *Dietary Guidelines for Americans*, adults should aim to achieve and maintain a body weight that optimizes their health.[106] It doesn't take major weight loss to improve health; a modest weight loss of roughly 10 percent is enough to produce health benefits and perhaps to encourage continued success. A key initial goal is to prevent or stop weight gain. Small changes in energy intake and expenditure—for example, an intake reduction of 100 kilocalories per day—may be all that is needed to prevent weight gain.[107] Goals must be realistic and attainable. (See **Figure 9.20**.)

Many health experts suggest that people should aim for **metabolic fitness** rather than a specific weight,[108] especially if they have difficulty achieving or maintaining recommended BMI levels. High metabolic fitness includes an elevated use of fat at rest and during exercise. The capacity for glucose metabolism is also enhanced in trained muscle.[109] If you are metabolically fit, you don't have any of the metabolic or biochemical risk factors associated with obesity—such as high LDL cholesterol, low HDL cholesterol, high levels of triglycerides, elevated blood glucose, insulin resistance, and high blood pressure. Other risk factors include excess abdominal fat.[110] If these risk factors are at normal levels, a person is considered metabolically fit, even if BMI is elevated. If not, the person has an increased risk for coronary heart disease, diabetes, gout, hypertension, and associated conditions. You can reduce these risk factors or even bring them within normal ranges through modest weight loss (5 to 10 percent of initial body weight) achieved by a small reduction in calorie intake and a moderate increase in physical activity (e.g., walking 30 minutes per day, no fewer than five days per week). In fact, researchers estimate that most of the weight gain seen in the U.S. population could be eliminated by as little as a 100 kilocalorie per day shift in intake and expenditure.[111] You also can improve metabolic fitness just by increasing physical activity levels.[112]

THINK About It 3

Don't focus on a particular weight as your goal. Instead, focus on living a lifestyle that includes eating moderate amounts of healthful foods, getting plenty of exercise, thinking positively, and learning to cope with stress. Learn to use your body's hunger and satiation signals to regulate eating and then let the pounds fall where they may. Most people who follow this advice will approach the healthy BMI ranges discussed earlier. Some will still weigh more than societal standards call for—but their weight will be right for them. By letting a healthy lifestyle determine your weight, you can avoid developing unhealthy patterns of eating and a negative body image.

THINK About It 4

metabolic fitness The absence of all metabolic and biochemical risk factors associated with obesity.

Adopting a Healthy Weight-Management Lifestyle

Most weight problems are lifestyle problems. It has been shown that 80 percent of children who were overweight at age 10 to 15 years are obese adults at age 25 years. Even though more and more young people are developing weight problems, many arrive at early adulthood with the advantage of having a "normal" body weight—neither too fat nor too thin. In fact, many young adults get away with terrible eating and exercise habits and don't develop a weight problem. But as the rapid growth of adolescence slows and family and career obligations increase, maintaining a healthy weight becomes a greater challenge. If you develop a lifestyle for successful weight management during early adulthood, healthy behavior patterns have a better chance of taking firm hold.

Permanent weight management is not something you start and stop. You need to adopt healthful behaviors that you can maintain throughout your life. People who have long-term success share common behavioral strategies that include eating a diet low in fat, frequent self-monitoring of body weight and food intake, and high levels of regular physical activity.[113] To maintain your weight over the long term, focus on healthy behaviors and develop coping strategies to deal with the stresses and challenges in your life. **Figure 9.21** shows the necessary components of an effective weight-management program.

Key Concepts *Healthy weight management means focusing on metabolic fitness—healthy levels of blood lipids and blood pressure—rather than on achieving a specific weight. Permanent healthy behaviors are necessary for a long-term weight-management lifestyle.*

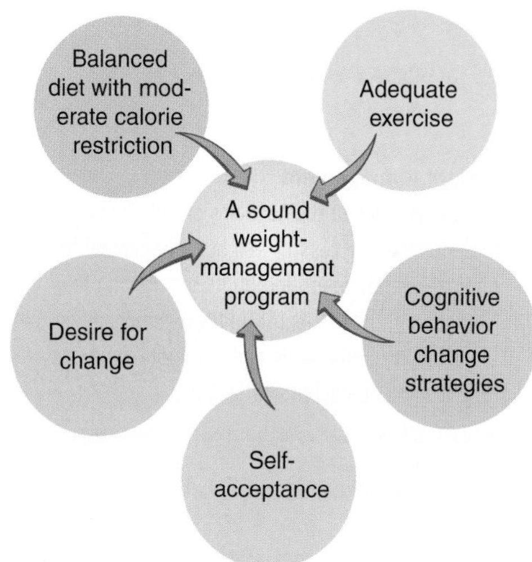

Figure 9.21 **Components of a sound weight-management program.** Recognizing the need for change, establishing reasonable goals, adopting goal-directed activities and self-monitoring them, and rewarding goal attainment can help successfully implement the components of a sound weight-management program.

Going Green

Salad Days

When you graduated from high school four years ago you were an active, lithe 121 pounds. You now tip the scale at 140 and are heading north. Many of your conversations are about those "promising" weight-management plans that fail to work for you. You joke with your friends that you are looking for the Eat More, Weigh Less diet. One of your buddies who is studying nutrition suggests that the plan already exists. It's called the low-energy-dense foods meal plan or the calorie-in, calorie-out diet. Foods with a lower energy density, such as lettuce, provide fewer calories than foods such as french fries. But who wants to substitute lettuce for french fries? At the end of a meal you want to feel satisfied and not heading for the fridge for a midnight snack. Here's how it works: satiety, that feeling of fullness and satisfaction, can be achieved by starting the meal with a low-energy-dense salad with lots of lettuce, veggies, and low-calorie dressing.

A number of studies have shown that eating lower-energy-dense meals can be effective in controlling hunger while reducing calories. Two studies illustrate the point. A study by Bell and colleagues found that adding extra vegetables to meals led to reduced calorie intake.[1] Despite the reduced calorie intake, subjects reported themselves full and satisfied.

In a study by Duncan and associates over five days, subjects were provided with a reduced-fat diet with substantial amounts of fruits, vegetables, whole grains, and beans.[2] In another five-day session they were fed a diet with large amounts of high-fat meats and desserts. Satiety ratings were similar at the end of both sessions.

Did our "starting with salad" friend succeed in getting back to high school trim? Not exactly. But reducing one's carbon footprint and walking to the store to buy smaller pants is a good start.

1 Bell EA, Castellanos VH, Pelkman CL, et al. Energy density of foods affects energy intake in normal-weight women. *Am J Clin Nutr.* 1998;67:412–420.

2 Duncan KH, Bacon JA, Weinsier RL. The effects of high and low energy density diets on satiety, energy intake, and eating time of obese and nonobese subjects. *Am J Clin Nutr.* 1983;37:763–767.

Academy of Nutrition and Dietetics

Weight Management

It is the position of the Academy of Nutrition and Dietetics that successful weight management to improve overall health for adults requires a life-long commitment to healthful lifestyle behaviors emphasizing sustainable and enjoyable eating practices and daily physical activity.

Source: Position of the American Dietetic Association: weight management. *J Am Diet Assoc.* 2002;102:1145–1155. Copyright 2002. Reprinted with permission from Elsevier.

Diet and Eating Habits

In contrast to "dieting," which involves some form of food restriction, "diet" refers to your daily food choices. Everyone has a diet, but not everyone is dieting. You need to develop a balanced diet of moderate caloric intake that includes foods you enjoy and that enables you to maintain a healthy body composition.

Total Calories

If you want to lose weight, you must take in fewer calories than you expend. Over the long term, you are more likely to control your weight successfully by cutting 200 to 300 kilocalories per day rather than drastically restricting your diet to only 1,000 to 1,200 kilocalories per day. Simply eliminating one can of regular soda from your daily routine would reduce your energy intake by about 150 kilocalories. You don't need to make major diet changes; just make small, sustainable changes and focus on the balance of food groups suggested by MyPlate. The Analyze My Diet feature on the ChooseMyPlate Web site (www.choosemyplate.gov) can help you evaluate your intake and find small changes that you can make.

Overconsumption of total calories is closely tied to portion sizes. Most of us significantly underestimate the amount of food we eat; at the same time, the size of portions served as single servings in restaurants and convenience stores has increased.[114] Limiting portion sizes to those recommended in MyPlate is critical for weight management. You'll probably find it easier to monitor and manage your total food intake if you concentrate on portion sizes rather than counting calories.

Crash Diets Don't Work

Don't go on a "crash diet" that contains only minimal calories. You need to consume enough food to meet your need for essential nutrients. Very low calorie intake promotes rapid loss of water, reduced RMR, and potential nutrient deficiencies. Once you lose weight, you probably won't maintain it unless you continue some degree of calorie restriction. So it is important that you adopt a level of food intake that you can live with. A highly restricted diet just won't work over the long term.

Balancing Energy Sources: Fat

In addition to balancing energy intake with energy output, achieving a balanced intake of energy sources is important for successful weight management. Although we all need some dietary fat, you should avoid overeating fatty foods. Because fat is the most concentrated source of calories, limiting fat in the diet can help you limit your total calories. Research suggests that fat calories are more easily converted to body fat than calories from protein or carbohydrate.[115] In a study of older men (ages 55 to 79), higher energy intake from fat was associated with higher BMI levels.[116] Fat should supply about 20 to 35 percent of your average total daily calories, which translates into 45 to 75 grams of fat each day in a 2,000-kilocalorie diet.

Some people are better fat burners than others; that is, they burn more of the fat they take in and therefore have less fat to store. People who burn fat at a relatively slow rate convert more dietary fat to stored body fat. For these people, the tendency to hoard fat may be an important part of the genetic tendency toward obesity, so restricting fat calories may help them manage their weight.

Quick Bite

Double-Checking Dietary Recall

When researchers checked the validity of food diaries and self-reports, they found that obese people underreport their energy intake by 20 to 50 percent and lean people underreport by 10 to 30 percent. Energy expenditure in the obese subjects was normal relative to their body size.

Several large surveys of the relationship between what we eat and how much we weigh have found that eating more fat and fewer complex carbohydrates is associated with excess body fat.[117] High-fat, low-fiber diets tend to delay satiation and encourage overeating. If you eat a diet with lots of whole grains, fresh fruits, and vegetables and reduce your reliance on meats and processed foods, you will reduce fat consumption and increase dietary fiber. Watch out for processed foods labeled "fat-free" or "reduced-fat"; they can be high in calories despite their lower fat content.

Balancing Energy Sources: Carbohydrates

To lose weight, dieters often cut back on bread, pasta, and potatoes. But these foods, along with vegetables, legumes, and other grain products, are rich in the complex carbohydrates and fiber that can help you achieve and maintain a healthy body weight. Fiber-rich foods help provide a feeling of satiation, or fullness, that can keep you from overeating. Carbohydrates should make up 45 to 65 percent of your total daily calories. Avoid mixing your carbohydrate sources with high-fat toppings and sauces, however. Experiment with lower-fat alternatives. Instead of sour cream on your baked potato, try plain yogurt, or even salsa! Rather than cream sauces on your pasta, use tomato-based sauces.

High-sugar foods usually provide calories but few nutrients. You should consume them sparingly, so choose fresh fruits and whole grains instead of candy and sugary cereals.

Balancing Energy Sources: Protein

Many popular diet books promote a high-protein, low-carbohydrate intake. They often proclaim their plan to be a "scientific breakthrough," although most contain speculations that have been recycled since the 1800s. Even though they promise "all you can eat," such diets typically involve significant calorie restriction. This lower energy intake is what actually causes any weight loss that occurs. A high-protein, low-carbohydrate, low-calorie diet does not conform to the *Dietary Guidelines for Americans* and is difficult to maintain. Most authorities recommend diets high in complex carbohydrates and moderate in protein consumption. (See the FYI feature "High-Protein, Low-Carbohydrate Diets for Weight Loss: Helpful or Harmful?")

Although protein promotes a sense of fullness, foods high in protein often are high in fat. Including some lean protein in each meal is a good idea, but stick to the recommended intake: 10 to 35 percent of total daily calories.

Eating Habits

Equally important to weight management is eating small, frequent meals—three or more per day plus snacks—on a dependable, regular schedule. If you skip meals, you are apt to feel excessively hungry and deprived, and you will be more likely to snack or binge on high-calorie, high-fat, or sugary foods. A person who eats on a regular schedule is more likely to reduce total energy intake and improve lipid levels than a person who eats irregularly.[118] Also, a regular meal pattern usually includes breakfast—a benefit when trying to manage weight. Research shows that morning intake is much more satiating than late-night eating and will help reduce overall energy intake.[119] Also, in a study of healthy, lean women, skipping breakfast lowered insulin sensitivity, raised LDL and total cholesterol, and led to higher energy intake.[120]

If you follow a regular pattern of eating and set up some "decision rules" that govern your food choices, you will be able to handle the many details

American Heart Association

Commercial Weight Reduction Programs

Being overweight, even by just 10 to 15 pounds, can lead to health problems. And obesity is a risk factor for cardiovascular disease. That's why the American Heart Association encourages people to achieve and maintain a healthy weight. Effective weight loss programs should include

- informed consent (participant or patient information)
- appropriate health risk screening
- guidelines for who needs to be evaluated by a physician
- individualized nutrition, physical activity, and behavioral components
- counseling by qualified health professionals
- identification of reasonable weight-loss goals
- a maintenance program that lasts for at least two years
- evaluation of the long-term effectiveness and safety of the program

Source: American Heart Association, Inc.

that go into a healthful diet. Decision rules governing breakfast, for example, might be as follows:

- Most of the time, choose a low-sugar, high-fiber cereal with nonfat milk.
- Once in a while, have an egg that's prepared without added fat (e.g., hard-boiled or scrambled).
- Save pancakes and waffles for special occasions.

When you proclaim some foods "off limits," you are setting up a rule to be broken. Instead, adopt the principle of "everything in moderation." Troublesome foods might be placed off limits temporarily until you regain control. If you can learn to eat in moderation, you can achieve a healthy diet and manage your weight successfully; no foods need to be entirely off limits, though some should be eaten prudently. Making the healthier choice more often than not is the essence of moderation.

High-Protein, Low-Carbohydrate Diets for Weight Loss: Helpful or Harmful?

High-protein, low-carbohydrate weight-loss diets are in style. Browse through the weight-loss section of any major bookstore, and you will find books such as *Dr. Atkins' New Diet Revolution, The South Beach Diet, Sugar Busters*, and *Enter the Zone*. All these books promote various high-protein diets for weight loss.

These diets revisit the idea, popular in the 1970s (and with historical roots dating back nearly 200 years), that carbohydrates (starches and sugars) make us fat. Proponents of high-protein diets point to the fact that throughout the high-carb, low-fat 1980s and early 1990s and with the explosion of fat-free foods, Americans got fatter. They fail to note that although the percentage of calories from fat in U.S. diets has decreased, Americans are eating more total fat and total calories (and therefore more total grams of fat) and exercising less—a recipe for weight gain.

Do High-Protein, Low-Carbohydrate Diets Work?

The Atkins diet made headlines in November 2002 when researchers from Duke University presented results of a study comparing the Atkins diet to the American Heart Association's (AHA) low-fat diet at the AHA's annual scientific meeting. Headlines of "Atkins diet meets with success," "Vindication for the Atkins diet?" and "Atkins diet beats low-fat fare" had meat-lovers cheering and dietitians cringing. Skeptics argued that the study, funded by the Atkins Center for Complementary Medicine, included too few people and failed to monitor participants' actual food intake and exercise levels.

Since this report, several studies of low-carbohydrate diets have been published, some of which were funded by government sources. One study compared a low-carbohydrate (≤30 grams per day) diet to a calorie-restricted, low-fat diet (≤30 percent of calories from fat; caloric restriction of 500 kcal per day) for severely obese adults.[1] The study lasted six months and included 132 total subjects. In the other study, 63 obese adults were randomly assigned to either a low-carbohydrate, high-protein, high-fat diet (based on the Atkins diet) or a low-calorie, high-carbohydrate, low-fat diet (60 percent carbohydrate, 25 percent fat, 15 percent protein).[2] Subjects were followed for a one-year period.

At the six-month time point in both studies, people on the low-carbohydrate diets had lost more weight (about 8 pounds more on average). When the subjects were followed for one year, however, difference in weight loss became nonsignificant. Overall weight loss was relatively small compared with the participants' starting weights. Improvements in blood cholesterol levels initially seen on the low-carbohydrate diet also became nonsignificant as time progressed. In both studies, drop-out rates were high—about 60 percent of those who began the studies. This attrition rate makes interpretation of the results difficult, if not impossible.[3] A review of published studies concluded that participant weight loss on low-carbohydrate diets was mainly associated with decreased calorie intake rather than reduced carbohydrate content.[4]

In another study that compared four different types of popular weight-loss diets, overall weight loss at one year was similar regardless of diet.[5] Heart disease risk factors improved for each diet group, but in different ways. The very low fat vegetarian Ornish diet was best for lowering LDL cholesterol, where-

Key Concepts *Balancing energy sources and controlling portion sizes can help reduce overall energy consumption. Reducing fat intake is a major step toward lowering calorie intake. Fiber-rich foods provide a feeling of fullness that can help prevent overeating. When planning a diet, aim for a caloric intake of 20 to 35 percent fat, 10 to 35 percent protein, and 45 to 65 percent carbohydrate.*

Physical Activity

Regular physical activity is a vital component of weight management and promotes fitness and good health. At the same time, it discourages overeating by reducing stress; it produces positive feelings that reinforce self-worth and a sense of accomplishment; and it often includes pleasant socialization. To prevent weight gain and maximize health benefits, adults should aim for 60 minutes of moderate-intensity physical activity each day.[121]

Quick Bite

The Fletcherism Fad

At the turn of the twentieth century, a retired businessman named Horace Fletcher started a dietary craze known as "Fletcherism." Calling the mouth "Nature's Food Filter," he believed that the sense of taste and the urge to swallow are perfect guides to nutrition. Although he recommended chewing food at least 50 times before swallowing, preferably until tasteless, he far exceeded this by once chewing a piece of onion 722 times. His philosophy did lead to some weight loss; people adhering to Fletcherism cut back on energy intake due to the additional mechanical effort of chewing.

as other diets, including Atkins and the Zone, were better at raising HDL cholesterol.

So what explains reports of dramatic weight loss and no hunger while eating pork rinds, bacon, sausage, and steak? Removing carbohydrates from the diet causes the body to deplete glycogen stores, which results in a rapid loss of water. The ketosis that results from low carbohydrate intake can also enhance fluid loss. High protein intake tends to be satiating, and the monotony of the diet also blunts the appetite. Although the effects are small, an increase in protein intake (e.g., 30 to 35 percent of calories) causes a slight increase in energy expenditure, possibly from the extra energy needed to convert protein to glucose.[6]

Are High-Protein, Low-Carbohydrate Diets Safe?

In a review of research on low-carbohydrate diets, Levine and colleagues found insufficient evidence to recommend for or against this approach to weight loss.[7] They note that common concerns include accumulation of ketones, abnormal insulin metabolism, impaired liver and kidney function, salt and water depletion, impaired renal function, and hyperlipidemia resulting from high fat intake. Their analysis of weight outcomes and complications was limited by small sample sizes, high drop-out rates, short study durations, and high variability in measured outcomes. It is likely, though, that people who start a low-carbohydrate diet do not stay on it long enough to develop serious complications, although constipation, nausea, weakness, dehydration, and fatigue are common side effects.

The Best Diet to Follow

Is there a "best" diet? If there were, we wouldn't have so many diet books vying for our attention and money! What we know about our nutrient needs still points to the *Dietary Guidelines for Americans* for guidance: the best diet emphasizes fruits, vegetables, and grains—not high-protein foods. From what we have seen in research studies, it is very difficult for individuals to stick to a particular diet, especially those diets that are most restrictive.[8] And although weight loss may be the goal of many, weight maintenance is the key to reducing the health risks of obesity. Weight maintenance requires permanent changes to eating habits and, more important, increased physical activity. The specific strategies for making those changes, and making them permanent, will vary from person to person. So, instead of a walk through the diet book aisle, save your money and improve your health with a fitness walk through the mall.

1 Samaha FF, Iqbal N, Seshadri P, et al. A low-carbohydrate as compared with a low-fat diet in severe obesity. *N Engl J Med.* 2003;348:2074–2081.

2 Foster GD, Wyatt HR, Hill JO, et al. A randomized trial of a low-carbohydrate diet for obesity. *N Engl J Med.* 2003;348:2082–2090.

3 Ware JH. Interpreting incomplete data in studies of diet and weight loss. *N Engl J Med.* 2003;348:2136–2137.

4 Bravata DM, Sanders L, Huang J, et al. Efficacy and safety of low-carbohydrate diets: a systematic review. *JAMA.* 2003;289(14):1837–1850.

5 Dansinger ML, Gleason JA, Griffith JL, et al. Comparison of the Atkins, Ornish, Weight Watchers, and Zone diets for weight loss and heart disease risk reduction: a randomized trial. *JAMA.* 2005;293:43–53.

6 Buchholz AC, Schoeller DA. Is a calorie a calorie? *Am J Clin Nutr.* 2004;79(suppl):899S–906S.

7 Levine MJ, Jones JM, Lineback DR. Low-carbohydrate diets: assessing the science and knowledge gaps, summary of an ILSI North America workshop. *J Am Diet Assoc.* 2006;106:2086–2094.

8 Dansinger, Gleason, Griffith, et al. Comparison of the Atkins, Ornish, Weight Watchers, and Zone diets.

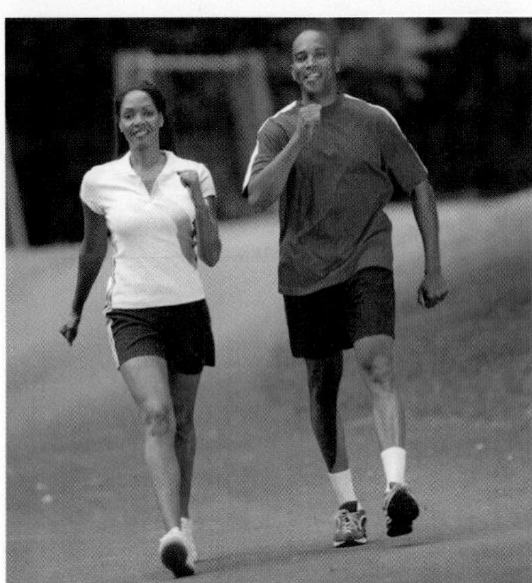

Figure 9.22 **Weight management through lifetime habits.** To achieve long-term weight management, healthy habits must become part of one's daily routine.

Look for ways to incorporate more physical activity into your daily life. (See **Figure 9.22.**) You may not think you have an hour each day to devote to moderate-intensity physical activity, but you don't have to get this exercise all at once; you can break it up throughout the day.[122] Walk the dog for an extra half-hour daily, for example. Use a stairway instead of an elevator. Walk briskly instead of using transportation. Take up an active hobby such as bicycling.

Increasing your activity level by just a small amount can help you maintain your current weight or lose a moderate amount of weight. "Going for the burn" and "no pain, no gain" were the mottos of the aerobics movement during the 1970s and 1980s, but such intense activity is neither necessary nor desirable. Instead, regular exercise of moderate intensity—any activity that expends 4 to 7 kilocalories per minute (240 to 420 kilocalories per hour; see Table 9.2)—provides substantial health benefits.

Once you have increased your everyday activity level, consider beginning a formal exercise program that includes cardiorespiratory endurance exercise, resistance training, and stretching exercises. Regular, moderate cardiorespiratory endurance exercise, sustained for 45 minutes to 1 hour, can help trim body fat permanently. Strength training helps increase fat-free mass, which results in more calorie burning even outside of exercise periods.

One thing is clear: regular exercise, maintained throughout life, makes weight management easier. The sooner you establish good habits, the better. You will succeed in maintaining your weight if you make exercise an integral part of the lifestyle you enjoy now and will enjoy in the future.

Key Concepts *Successful weight management involves regular physical activity as well as healthful food choices. Small increases in activity have significant health benefits and help weight loss and maintenance. To prevent weight gain and maximize health benefits, you should include at least 60 minutes of moderate physical activity in your daily routine.*

Thinking and Emotions

What goes on in your head is another factor in a healthy lifestyle and successful weight management. The way you think about yourself and your world influences, and is influenced by, how you feel and how you act. Certain kinds of thinking produce negative emotions, which can undermine a healthy lifestyle.

When we compare ourselves to an internally held picture of an "ideal self," we are more likely to have low self-esteem and feel negative emotions. The "ideal self" we envision is often the result of having adopted perfectionistic goals and beliefs about how we "should" be. You might know someone who believes "If I don't do things perfectly, I'm a failure" or "It's terrible if I'm not thin." When we accept these irrational beliefs, we may actually cause ourselves stress and emotional conflict. The remedy is to challenge such beliefs and replace them with more realistic ones.

The beliefs and attitudes you hold give rise to self-talk, an internal dialogue you carry on with yourself about events that happen to and around you. When you talk yourself through the steps of a job and then praise yourself when it's successfully completed, you are engaging in **positive self-talk.** When you make self-deprecating remarks or angry and guilt-producing comments and when you blame yourself unnecessarily, you are engaging in **negative self-talk.** Negative self-talk can undermine efforts at self-control and lead to feelings of anxiety and depression.

positive self-talk Constructive mental or verbal statements made to one's self to change a belief or behavior.

negative self-talk Mental or verbal statements made to one's self that reinforce negative or destructive self-perceptions.

ABC model of behavior A behavioral model that includes the external and internal events that precede and follow the behavior. The "A" stands for antecedents, the events that precede the behavior ("B"), which is followed by consequences ("C") that positively or negatively reinforce the behavior.

Your beliefs and attitudes influence how you interpret what happens to you and what you can expect in the future, as well as how you feel and react. Realistic beliefs and goals combined with positive self-talk and problem-solving efforts support a healthy lifestyle.

Stress Management

Stress management can be an important part of weight management.[123] You can use the **ABC model of behavior** (**Figure 9.23**) to help you cope with daily stresses and their effects on eating behavior.

The ABC model helps you manage the events that trigger behaviors and the factors that reinforce them. *Antecedents*, the "A" part of the model, are the events that precede the behavior and trigger it. Overeating is one possible *behavior*, the "B" part of the model. The *consequences*, or "C," follow and reinforce the "B." The "C" may be desirable, such as relief from stress, or undesirable, such as guilt or weight gain. Consequences may be immediate or, like weight gain, occur in the future; consequences that occur immediately have the greatest influence.

Identifying the cues (A) that trigger overeating is the first step to changing or avoiding these triggers. You might remove problem foods from the house or avoid the grocery store's candy aisle. You can sometimes manipulate antecedents to trigger positive behaviors (for example, putting exercise clothes by the door to prompt exercise).

Antecedents

Her mouth starts watering as she passes by a bakery with delicious sights and aromas.

Behavior

She purchases many pastries, intending some for later. Despite this resolve, she succumbs to the need for instant gratification, immediately eating them all.

Consequences

She regrets her behavior and feels guilty. Overeating may leave her feeling ill and nauseated.

Figure 9.23 **The ABC model of eating behavior.** Conquering overeating often requires a psychological strategy for changing ingrained habits and other behaviors.

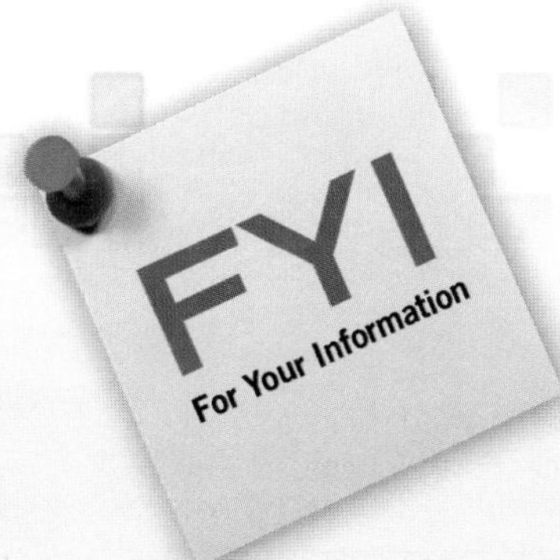

Learning Weight Management from Some of the "Biggest" Weight Experts: Sumo Wrestlers

Is it possible to work out three to five hours a day, seven days a week, eat a relatively low-fat diet, and still gain weight? Yes! This is the training way of Sumo wrestlers, and a way of life which allows them to pack on the pounds. The world's biggest people are experts at putting on fat, which means that the lessons they've learned can help teach us how to keep the weight off. If you do not want to gain weight, follow these tips. The wrestlers, of course, will be doing just the opposite.

- *Make your workouts slow and steady, not fast and frantic.* Sustained moderate workouts lasting 30 to 60 minutes are more helpful at burning calories than exerting yourself in a brief, intense burst of exercise. Sumo wrestlers train to win at a sport whose rules are simple: one of two wrestlers loses when he is forced out of the wrestling ring or if anything other than his feet touch the playing surface. The average sumo wrestler stands about 6 feet tall and weighs 336 pounds. Their training is focused on being powerful enough to push over something the size of a refrigerator. Going for a 3-mile run or riding a bicycle for 60 minutes is not a priority for sumo wrestler workouts.
- *Don't skip breakfast.* Try not to go longer than four to five hours without eating. Your body will adapt to the threat of starvation and decrease your metabolism so that you can survive on less calories. Most sumo wrestlers eat only twice a day.
- *Eat small meals and snacks throughout the day.* Split up your daily calories among breakfast, lunch, dinner, and a couple of snacks. You're less likely to put on weight eating small meals and never overeating, rather than letting yourself get too hungry and then eating too much. Sumo wrestlers eat about one-half of their overall daily food calories at one meal. For a person the size of a sumo wrestler, that can be over 3,000 calories every day just for lunch!
- *Choose a well-balanced diet with a lot of variety.* Remember that balance, variety, and moderation are cornerstones of good nutrition. Sumo wrestlers eat a relatively low-fat diet, but tend to have a diet heavy in complex carbohydrates, protein, and vegetables, with little fruit.

Source: Anderson J, Christensen N, Hoffman E, et al. *Eat Right! Healthy Eating in College and Beyond.* San Francisco: Pearson Benjamin Cummings, 2007:67–79.

Quick Bite

The Beverly Hills Diet

The Beverly Hills diet, introduced in 1980, begins with 10 days of fruit and water only. Many dieters reported an unpleasant side effect: diarrhea.

You can change the behavior of overeating (B) by using positive self-talk to encourage a new behavior and avoiding excuses and rationalizations to eat something inappropriate.

Positive consequences (C) help to reinforce new behaviors. You could sign a contract with a friend that rewards you for deciding not to overeat. Rewards such as time for physical activity not only reinforce behavior but also develop fitness. Table 9.8 summarizes cognitive-behavioral tools for changing habits and behavior patterns.

Balancing Acceptance and Change

It's not enough to change your behavior to manage obesity. Self-acceptance is equally necessary. (See Table 9.9.) Accepting yourself as you are will help your self-esteem and improve your general satisfaction with life. It is destructive to be overly concerned with the importance of body weight and shape or to have unattainable goals of idealized physical appearance. But don't confuse self-acceptance with complacency or a do-nothing attitude that ignores health risks.

If you must diet, do so in combination with exercise, and avoid very low calorie diets. Don't try to lose more than one-half to one pound per week. Realize that most low-calorie diets cause a rapid loss of body water at first. When this phase passes, weight loss declines. As a result, dieters often are misled into believing that their efforts are not working. They then give up, not realizing that smaller losses later in the diet actually are better than the initial big losses. In fact, the later loss is mostly fat loss, whereas the initial loss is primarily fluid loss.

Table 9.8 Cognitive-Behavioral Tools for Changing Behavior

Tool	Description
Self-monitoring	Prospectively recording information about behavior to identify the antecedents (what precedes and elicits a particular action), the behaviors of interest (usually eating behavior), and the consequences (the thoughts, feelings, and reactions that accompany the behavior of interest).
Environmental management	Avoiding or changing cues that trigger undesirable behavior (e.g., not driving by the doughnut shop, putting the cookie jar out of sight), or instituting new cues to elicit new behaviors (e.g., putting your walking shoes by the door as a reminder to exercise); also called "stimulus control."
Alternate behaviors	Learning new ways of responding to old cues or circumstances that can't be changed or avoided (e.g., taking a walk when you get upset instead of getting something to eat).
Reward	Giving yourself, or arranging to be given, rewards for engaging in desired behaviors.
Negative reinforcement	Arranging to give up something desirable (e.g., money) or to endure something undesirable (e.g., wash your friend's car) for engaging in unwanted behaviors.
Social support	Getting others to participate in or otherwise provide emotional and physical support of your weight-management efforts.
Cognitive coping	Reducing negative self-talk, increasing positive self-talk, and challenging beliefs that undermine your resolve and contribute to negative emotions; setting reasonable goals and avoiding "thinking traps."
Managing emotions	Using reframing, disengagement, imagery, and self-soothing to reduce or manage negative emotions.
Relapse prevention and recovery	Identifying high-risk situations that pose a hazard for relapsing, and learning to recover from small indiscretions before they become major relapses.

Source: Modified from Nash JD. *The New Maximize Your Body Potential.* Palo Alto, CA: Bull Publishing Company, 1997. Used with permission.

Key Concepts *Identifying cues that precede overeating can help a person make behavior changes. Long-term weight management should include self-acceptance and enhanced self-esteem. Goals of idealized body size and shape should be replaced with goals that promote good health and a lifetime of fitness.*

Weight-Management Approaches

Do certain weight-loss diets have adverse health consequences? Is it unhealthy to lose weight quickly? Will the weight stay off? What motivates people to lose weight and to maintain weight? What are the barriers to losing weight and/or to maintaining weight?

In a study of popular weight-loss diets, 160 participants with an average BMI of 35 kg/m^2 were randomly assigned to one of four weight-loss diets: Weight Watchers (restriction of portion sizes and calories; 1,200 to 1,600 calories daily), Atkins (low carbohydrate—less than 20 grams daily at onset, gradual increase to 50 grams), Zone (40–30–30 balance of percentage calories from carbohydrate, fat, and protein, respectively), and Ornish (vegetarian, less than 10 percent of calories from fat).[124] Subjects lost weight on all four diets, but no one diet was more effective than any of the others. Compliance was a key factor: only about 25 percent of subjects in each group maintained the diet at a level of 6 on a 10-point scale (1 = no adherence, 10 = perfect adherence), but dietary adherence was strongly associated with weight loss. Those who stuck to the diets best lost on average 7 percent of body weight, a meaningful start in reducing health risks.

A wide range of weight-management approaches is available to the consumer. It's important to investigate your options thoroughly to find the approach best suited to your personal needs.

Self-Help Books and Manuals

Some people respond well to simple information provided in an easy-to-understand format. They are able to change their behavior by referring to good, well-researched self-help manuals and books,[125] and even Internet-based resources. The proliferation of diet books is nothing short of phenomenal, however, and each year dozens of dubious weight-loss diet books reach the market. When evaluating a diet book or Web site diet plan, be alert to the following warning flags:

- Unbalanced diet patterns. The recommended pattern should not stray too far from that of MyPlate (see Chapter 2, "Nutrition Guidelines and Assessment").
- Claims of a "scientific breakthrough" or promises of "quick and easy" weight loss. There is no "quick fix" when it comes to weight management.
- Irrational food instructions, such as food restrictions (e.g., no fruits), illogical overemphasis of some foods (e.g., five grapefruits daily), and irrational food patterns (e.g., don't eat meat and bread at the same meal). Such restrictions set the stage for feelings of deprivation and binge eating.
- The promise of a cure for some disease along with weight loss. That's not only a waste of money, but also potentially dangerous.

Should you decide on the "do-it-yourself" route, develop specific goals for your diet, exercise, and maintenance plans. (See the FYI feature "Behaviors That Will Help You Manage Your Weight.") Keep tabs on your habits and become more involved in activities other than eating, especially fitness activities.

Table 9.9 Basic Tenets of Size Acceptance

- Human beings come in a variety of sizes and shapes. We celebrate this diversity as a positive characteristic of the human race.
- There is no ideal body size, shape, or weight that every individual should strive to achieve.
- Every body is a good body, whatever its size or shape.
- Self-esteem and body image are strongly linked. Helping people feel good about their bodies and about who they are can help motivate and maintain healthy behaviors.
- Appearance stereotyping is inherently unfair to the individual because it is based on superficial factors over which the individual has little or no control.
- We respect the bodies of others even though they might be quite different from our own.
- Each person is responsible for taking care of his/her body.
- Good health is not defined by body size; it is a state of physical, mental, and social well-being.

People of all sizes and shapes can reduce their risk of poor health by adopting a healthy lifestyle.

Source: Modified from *Basic Tenets of Health at Every Size*, developed by dietitians and nutritionists who are advocates of size acceptance; their efforts coordinated by Joanne P. Ikeda, MA, RD, Nutrition Education Specialist, Department of Nutritional Sciences, University of California, Berkeley. Reprinted by permission of Joanne P. Ikeda.

Quick Bite

Diet Revolution?

The Diet Revolution, first promoted by Dr. Atkins in 1972, centered on putting dieters into a state of ketosis by consuming few carbohydrates. In 1973 the American Medical Association called the diet dangerous and required Atkins to testify before the U.S. Senate Select Committee on Nutrition.

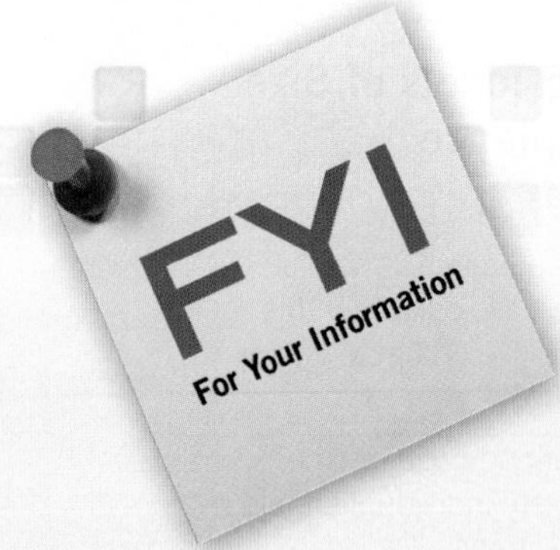

Behaviors That Will Help You Manage Your Weight

Set the Right Goals

Setting the right goals is an important first step. Most people trying to lose weight focus just on weight loss. However, you'll be more successful if you focus on dietary and exercise changes that lead to long-term weight change. Successful weight managers select no more than two or three goals at a time.

Effective goals are (1) specific, (2) attainable, and (3) forgiving. "Exercise more" is a commendable ideal, but it's not specific. "Walk five miles every day" is specific and measurable, but is it attainable if you're just starting out? "Walk 30 minutes every day" is more attainable, but what happens if you're held up at work or there's a thunderstorm? "Walk 30 minutes, five days each week" is specific, attainable, and forgiving. In short, a great goal!

Nothing Succeeds Like Success

Select a series of short-term goals that get you closer and closer to the ultimate goal (for example, consider reducing fat intake from 40 percent of calories to 35 percent and later to 30 percent). Nothing succeeds like success. This strategy employs two important behavioral principles: (1) consecutive goals that move you ahead in small steps are the best way to reach a distant point, and (2) consecutive rewards keep the overall effort invigorated.

Reward Success (But Not with Food)

You're more likely to keep working toward your goal if you are rewarded—especially when goals are difficult to reach. An effective reward is something that is desirable, timely, and contingent on meeting your goal. Your rewards may be tangible (e.g., a movie or music CD or a payment toward buying a more costly item) or intangible (e.g., an afternoon off from studying or just an hour of quiet time away from the daily demands of school). As you meet small goals, give yourself numerous small rewards; don't wait to meet your ultimate goal for a single reward. The long, difficult effort might lead you to give up.

Balance Your (Food) Checkbook

Keeping track of your behavior—observing and recording calorie intake, servings of fruits and vegetables, exercise frequency and duration, or any other wellness behavior—can help alter that behavior. Self-monitoring usually changes a behavior in the desired direction and can produce "real-time" records for you and your health care provider. For example, you can track your exercise progress. A record of increasing exercise encourages you to keep up the good work. If the record shows little or no progress, you know that a change of strategy is needed. Some people find that specific self-monitoring forms make it easier, while others prefer to use their own recording system.

Although you don't need to step on the scale every day, monitoring your weight regularly (once a week) can help you maintain your lower weight. Use a graph rather than a list or calendar notations so that you have a picture of cumulative progress. Changes in your body's water content, rather than fat content, are responsible for most of the up-and-down fluctuations from day to day. A long-term downward trend reflects fat losses.

Avoid a Chain Reaction

Identify the social or environmental cues that seem to encourage undesirable eating, and then change those cues. For example, you may learn from reflection or self-monitoring that you're more likely to overeat while watching television, when treats are on display at the campus café, or when you're around a certain friend. You might then try to break the association between eating and the cue (don't eat while watching television), avoid or eliminate the cue (avoid sitting near the display counter), or change the circumstances surrounding the cue (plan to meet with your friend in nonfood settings). In general, visible and accessible food items often are cues for unplanned eating.

Get the (Fullness) Message

Changing the way you go about eating can make it easier to eat less without feeling deprived. It takes 15 or more minutes for your brain to get the message you've been fed. Slowing the rate of eating can allow satiation (fullness) signals to begin by the end of the meal. Eating lots of vegetables also can make you feel fuller. Another trick is to use smaller plates so that moderate portions do not appear meager. Changing your eating schedule, or setting one, can be helpful, especially if you tend to skip or delay meals and overeat later.

The Backsliding Phenomenon

You've just signed a contract with yourself to avoid high-fat desserts for one month when you're presented with an array of your favorite "to die for" desserts. You say to yourself, "just this once" and satisfy your craving. Most of us have experienced the "backsliding phenomenon" in which we have lost our resolve and slipped back into a former bad habit. When it happens, be prepared for it and move on with your resolve. You're most apt to backslide when you're tempted by something unexpected and your self-control is threatened. You can remove high-fat snacks from your home, but not from other places you eat. Imagine tempting situations in your mind's eye and practice coping with them successfully. If you do slip, don't waste time with self-blame. Learn from the experience and get back on track.

Source: Adapted from National Heart, Lung and Blood Institute. *Guide to Behavior Change.* http://www.nhlbi.nih.gov/health/public/heart/obesity/lose_wt/behavior.htm. Accessed 6/18/09.

Long-term success depends on maintaining the lifestyle changes that helped you lose the weight in the first place.

Quick Bite

Letter on Corpulence

Published in the early 1800s, *Bantry's Letter on Corpulence* was the first popular diet book in the United States. The book advocated restricting intake of carbohydrates.

Meal Replacements

Some people turn to meal replacements—shakes and bars, for example—to help lose weight. Meal replacements are convenient, often contain added vitamins and minerals, and reduce the choices and temptations available at mealtime. When compared with traditional, reduced-calorie diet programs, people using meal replacements lost slightly more weight and were less likely to stop the program.[126] The challenge is to learn long-term eating strategies that will allow weight management without reliance on special products.

Self-Help Groups

Self-help groups, often led by laypeople, help many people cope with their weight. Such groups can share experiences, reduce the isolation and alienation felt by many obese people, and provide an understanding and accepting community.

Commercial Programs

Commercial weight-loss programs provide group or individual counseling and group support. Some sell prepackaged foods or nutritional supplements. Some companies employ dietitians, health educators, psychologists, or physicians to develop and guide the program at the corporate level. The Federal Trade Commission (FTC) encourages commercial programs to release the following information to potential clients:

- Staff training and education
- Risks of overweight and obesity
- Risks of their products or program
- Cost
- Program outcomes: success and failure rates

Be sure to obtain this information before you register for a weight-loss program, and think twice about any program that does not willingly provide it. In a comparison of a structured commercial program (food plan + activity plan + cognitive restructuring behavior modification plan + weekly meetings) to a self-help strategy, the commercial program supported modest levels of weight loss, but more than the self-help strategy achieved over a two-year period.[127]

Several commercial programs, such as Optifast and Health Management Resources (HMR), use **very low calorie diets (VLCD)** containing only 400 to 800 kilocalories per day as the initial phase of treatment. When such diets were first introduced in the 1970s, several deaths resulted from cardiac abnormalities. As a result, VLCD should be undertaken only with close medical supervision.

very low calorie diets (VLCD) Diets supplying 400 to 800 kilocalories per day, which include adequate high-quality protein, little or no fat, and little carbohydrate.

Professional Private Counselors

Private counselors can be physicians, psychotherapists, nutritionists, or registered dietitians. They provide individualized approaches to weight management and the support and attention that some obese people may need. Dietary counseling interventions produce modest weight losses that diminish over time.[128] Some programs use the Internet rather than face-to-face counseling sessions. Internet-based weight-management interventions result in small amounts of weight loss, prevent weight gain, and have potential for widespread dissemination as a population health approach.[129] Regular e-mail behavioral counseling and feedback from a trained counselor can improve weight loss.[130] However, a comparison of a commercial Internet-based weight-loss program to a self-help weight-loss manual found higher weight loss at one year in the self-help group (4 percent of initial body weight versus 1 percent).[131]

Carefully scrutinize the training and credentials of private counselors before committing to any program. Effective weight-loss counselors should do the following:[132]

1. Assess obesity risk.
2. Ask about readiness to lose weight.
3. Advise in designing a weight-control program.
4. Assist in establishing appropriate intervention.
5. Arrange for follow-up.

Antiobesity Prescription Drugs

The pharmaceutical industry has long searched for a "magic bullet" to battle obesity, but a cure has failed to emerge. Two popular antiobesity drugs, fenfluramine (one component of a combination called fen-phen) and dexfenfluramine (Redux), were withdrawn from the market after research found that they were the likely cause of life-threatening lung disease and heart valve problems.[133] With the recognition that obesity involves multiple factors, the focus is shifting to drugs with multiple mechanisms and drugs to be used in conjunction with proper diet and exercise.[134]

Antiobesity prescription drugs approved for short-term use include Dexedrine, other amphetamines, and amphetamine derivatives. For long-term use, only two prescription drugs—Xenical and Meridia—are presently approved for treating obesity. Xenical (orlistat) interferes with pancreatic lipase and reduces fat digestion and absorption. Because Xenical blocks fat absorption by as much as 30 percent, it must be accompanied by a low-fat diet; otherwise, the unabsorbed fat can produce diarrhea and flatulence. The drug also blocks fat-soluble nutrient absorption, so it's necessary to take a vitamin supplement as well.[135] Sales of Xenical fell in 2002 amid research showing that the drug improved weight loss by only 2 to 3 percent.[136]

Meridia (sibutramine) is an appetite suppressant that affects the balance of chemicals in the brain. Meridia was believed to be safer than earlier antiobesity drugs, but like all prescription drugs, it can have side effects—in this case, increased blood pressure and heart rate.[137] Because of questions about its safety, public-interest groups in the United States have asked the FDA to withdraw it from the market, and authorities in Italy have banned it from sale.[138]

The FDA has approved the use of antiobesity drugs only in combination with calorie-restricted diets. Aside from Xenical, antiobesity drugs are addictive and have the potential for abuse. Antiobesity agents shouldn't be used in combination with each other or with other drugs for appetite control, because the safety of such combinations has not been evaluated. The drugs should be used only in people who are obese—not people looking to lose just a few pounds. Are they effective? A review of numerous clinical trials suggests that the benefits of drug therapy over behavioral interventions are modest at best.[139]

With recent advances in the understanding of hormones and other factors that regulate appetite and satiety, scientists have new targets for the development of weight-loss medications. Leptin was a major focus of research until it became clear that leptin therapy is effective only for those with genetic defects in synthesis of leptin or its receptors. Current efforts are exploring compounds that may block the action of ghrelin and suppress NPY production.

In using any medications for weight loss, one needs to understand that prescription medications alone, without behavior modification, are not effective for long-term weight-loss maintenance. Patients who respond to medication typically regain weight when the drug is discontinued.[140]

Over-the-Counter Drugs and Dietary Supplements

Nonprescription (over-the-counter, or OTC) weight-loss pills may contain caffeine, benzocaine, or fiber. Caffeine is a stimulant and diuretic. Benzocaine numbs the tongue, which reduces taste sensations and discourages eating. Pills with fiber are designed to fill the stomach and provide a feeling of fullness. Although moderately effective, fiber pills can lead to dehydration; much of the lost weight is water, which is easily regained when the pills are stopped.

Numerous dietary supplements are marketed for weight loss, with names such as "Weight Away." Common ingredients include chromium picolinate, chitosan, hydroxycitric acid (HCA), glucomannan, and pyruvate. Few studies have evaluated these products for weight loss, and what little evidence exists is not convincing enough to recommend their use.[141]

In 2004, following years of study and an accumulation of reported adverse effects, the FDA banned the use of ephedra in dietary supplements—the government's first ban of a dietary supplement. Ephedra was an ingredient in many supplements marketed for weight loss and enhanced sports performance. Although it promotes modest short-term weight loss,[142] ephedra (also known as ma huang) is dangerous to people with hypertension, heart disease, or diabetes. Safety data from 50 different research studies found two- to threefold increases in risk for adverse events,[143] and the FDA's evidence linked ephedra to 155 deaths and dozens of heart attacks and strokes. The ban was overturned in federal court in 2005, a ruling that the FDA successfully appealed in 2006.

Over-the-counter medicines and dietary supplements are no substitute for exercise and healthful eating. There is no quick, easy way to effectively lose weight.

Surgery

Sometimes, surgery can successfully treat **extreme obesity** (also called **morbid obesity**), defined as a BMI of 40 kg/m^2 or higher. Surgery should be a last-ditch effort, taken only when all legitimate, less-invasive methods have failed. The two most common procedures are gastric banding and gastric bypass. Gastric banding reduces stomach size by creating a smaller upper stomach, or "pouch," thus limiting intake to only a few calories at one time.[144] Gastric bypass also creates a smaller stomach pouch and then connects that pouch to a shortened section of small intestine. (See **Figure 9.24**.) Reducing the size of the stomach reduces food intake, and bypassing the upper part of the small intestine reduces digestion and absorption of caloric foods. The absorption of some micronutrients is also reduced—an obvious drawback. Such surgeries are growing in popularity: in the United States, 220,000 bariatric surgical procedures were performed in 2008 compared to 16,200 in 1994—a more than 13-fold increase that is still rising.[145]

The results are impressive. Patients lose substantially more weight than those who try diet and exercise, or even weight-loss medications. Although weight loss tends to plateau by 18 to 24 months after surgery, it is not un-

Gastric Banding

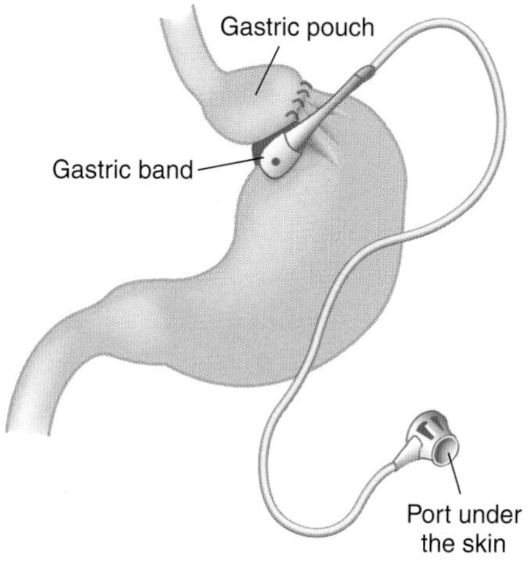

Gastric Bypass

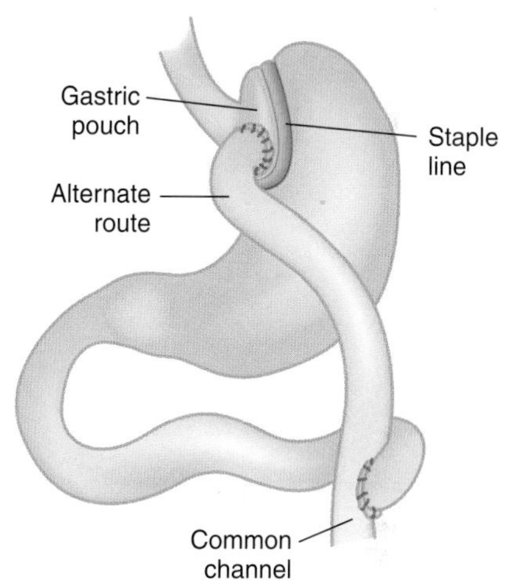

Figure 9.24 Gastric surgery in obesity treatment. In gastric banding, surgery reduces the size of the stomach. The band can be adjusted by an infusion of saline through a port that lies just beneath the skin. In gastric bypass, an alternate route carries food to the jejunum, bypassing the duodenum and most of the stomach.

Source: Reproduced from Steinbrook R. Surgery for severe obesity. *N Engl J Med.* 2004;350:1075–1079.

extreme obesity Obesity characterized by body weight exceeding 100 percent of normal; a condition so severe it often requires surgery.

morbid obesity See *extreme obesity.*

usual for patients to have maintained a 50 percent loss of initial body weight after five years.[146]

The long-term effectiveness of gastric surgery depends on how patients manage their eating. They can defeat the procedure by consuming high-calorie drinks or semisolid foods that overcome stomach size. With time the pouch stretches, allowing more solid foods, but by then, doctors hope that the patient has established healthy eating habits. Also, RMR can decline significantly after gastric surgery, making weight loss more difficult; thus, exercise is important along with diet modifications.[147] Studies show that gastric bypass leads to dramatically lower levels of ghrelin, the gastric hormone that increases food intake.[148] Lower levels of ghrelin likely contribute to the effectiveness of the procedure.

Liposuction is a cosmetic surgical procedure that reshapes the body by removing fat. Although the procedure removes some fat cells, the body still has billions of other fat cells ready to store extra fat. Thus, liposuction is not effective for significant or long-term weight loss. It should not be undertaken casually. Risks include blood clots, perforation injuries, skin and nerve damage, and unfavorable drug reactions.

Summary of Weight-Management Strategies

For best effect, weight-management strategies need to be individualized. Until the science of nutrigenomics advances far enough to match an individual's genetics to the right diet plan, dietary strategies that reduce chronic disease risks (more fruits and vegetables, whole grains, and fish)[149] should be combined with physical activity to achieve a modest but persistent reduction in calories.[150] For individuals who are morbidly obese, consultation with a physician is essential to determine the right approach for managing weight and improving health.

Key Concepts *Books, Internet resources, and commercial programs can help some individuals lose weight. However, consumers should always proceed with caution before spending money. Drugs have potential side effects and must be used with caution and medical supervision. For those who are extremely obese, surgical intervention is an aggressive, last-resort approach to weight management. Liposuction removes fat cells from specific parts of the body but is not considered an effective approach to weight control.*

Underweight

From a public health standpoint, underweight is much less of a problem than obesity, but those who are underweight can find it troublesome and frustrating. Underweight is usually defined as a BMI below 18.5 kg/m^2. When low BMI is simply an inherited pattern, there is no need to worry about health risks as long as diet and other health behaviors are appropriate. But your health is at risk if your underweight results from undernutrition; deficits in protein, vitamins, and minerals, as well as energy, can cause health problems ranging from fatigue to compromised immune function. Underweight women are more likely to suffer amenorrhea, low fertility, and poor pregnancy outcome.

Causes and Assessment

The causes of underweight are as diverse as those of overweight and include the following:

- Altered response to hunger, appetite, satiation, satiety, and external cues (described earlier in this chapter)
- Factors in eating disorders such as distorted body image, compulsive dieting, and compulsive overexercising
- Metabolic and hereditary factors
- Prolonged psychological and emotional stress
- Addiction to alcohol and street drugs
- Bizarre diet patterns or otherwise inadequate diets

Do you believe that by choosing cookies or chips labeled "low-fat" or sticking with certain brand names associated with "diet foods" you are automatically making the right decisions? It may surprise you to know that many low-fat or fat-free products have nearly the same amount of calories as the full-fat versions! After reading this chapter you now know that when it comes to weight loss, total calories are just as important as calories from fat. If you eat a fat-free food, but eat so much of it that your calories are excessive, you will still gain weight. To illustrate this point, let's compare the nutrition labels from some leading cookie manufacturers. The lower-fat cookie label (on the right) claims they are "better for you" and have "50% less fat" compared to the regular cookies. Here are the key facts from the labels:

Regular Cookie	Lower-Fat Cookie
Serving: 2 cookies (29 g)	Serving: 2 cookies (26g)
Calories: 140	Calories: 110
Calories from fat: 50	Calories from fat: 25
Total fat: 6g	Total fat: 3g

True, there is a 50 percent reduction in fat content (6 grams vs. 3 grams), which is an important part of the picture. However, take a look at the Total Calories. The lower-fat cookies only have 30 fewer kilocalories than the regular cookies, which may be a surprise to those who think they are saving more.

There is another interesting piece of information on these labels: the serving size. At first glance, you may think the serving size of the cookies are the same, two cookies. However after further inspection you can see that the lower-fat cookies are slightly smaller. A 10 percent reduction in size/weight is certainly worth noting when you are trying to explain how a product can have fewer calories.

The next time you are in the cookie aisle debating whether you should settle a craving with a low-fat product or its full-fat version, be a smart consumer and read the label before you buy!

Nutrition Facts

Serving Size: 2 cookies (29g)
Servings Per Container about 16

Amount Per Serving	
Calories 140	Calories from fat 50
	% Daily Value*
Total Fat 6g	9%
Saturated Fat 1.5g	8%
Trans Fat 0.5g	
Cholesterol 0mg	0%
Sodium 105mg	4%
Total Carbohydrate 21g	7%
Dietary Fiber less than 1g	3%
Sugars 8g	
Protein 2g	
Vitamin A 0% • Vitamin C 0%	
Calcium 0% • Iron 4%	

* Percent Daily Values are based on a 2,000 calorie diet. Your daily values may be higher or lower depending on your calorie needs:

	Calories:	2000	2,500
Total Fat	Less Than	65g	80g
Sat Fat	Less Than	20g	25g
Cholesterol	Less Than	300mg	300mg
Sodium	Less Than	2,400mg	2,400mg
Total Carbohydrate		300g	375g
Dietary Fiber		25g	30g

Regular cookie

Nutrition Facts

Serving Size: 2 cookies (26g)
Servings Per Container: 18

Amount Per Serving	
Calories 110	Calories from fat 25
	% Daily Value*
Total Fat 3g	5%
Saturated Fat 0.5g	3%
Polyunsaturated Fat 0g	
Monounsaturated Fat 1g	
Trans Fat 0g	
Cholesterol 0mg	0%
Sodium 130mg	5%
Total Carbohydrate 20g	7%
Dietary Fiber 0g	0%
Sugars 10g	
Protein 1g	
Vitamin A 0% • Vitamin C 0%	
Calcium 0% • Iron 2%	

* Percent Daily Values are based on a 2,000 calorie diet. Your daily values may be higher or lower depending on your calorie needs:

	Calories:	2000	2,500
Total Fat	Less Than	65g	80g
Sat Fat	Less Than	20g	25g
Cholesterol 300mg	Less Than	300mg	
Sodium 2,400mg	Less Than	2,400mg	
Total Carbohydrate		300g	375g
Dietary Fiber		25g	30g

Lower-fat cookie

Underweight can be a sign of underlying disease, such as cancer. Illness can speed up metabolic rate, spoil the appetite, or interfere with digestion. Correcting underweight helps improve the quality of life.

Weight-Gain Strategies

The way to gain weight is to create a positive energy balance. Here are some strategies:

- Have small, frequent meals consisting of nutrient-dense and energy-dense foods and beverages.
- Drink fluids at the end of the meal or, better yet, between meals to avoid filling the stomach with liquids of low nutrient density.
- Try high-calorie weight-gain beverages and foods.
- Use timers or other cues (similar to the ABC model in Figure 9.23, but with a different goal) to prompt eating.
- Take a balanced vitamin/mineral supplement to ensure that poor appetite isn't a result of nutritional deficiency.

Sometimes prescription drugs, such as appetite stimulants, are helpful. Medication also can speed stomach emptying, improving appetite for the next meal. Digestive enzyme replacements help people who are underweight due to poor digestion or absorption.

Exercise has a role in weight gain as well. Simple anaerobic or isometric exercise encourages weight gain as lean body mass rather than fat.

Key Concepts *Underweight is not as common as overweight. Gaining weight can be difficult, but the basic concepts of energy balance apply. Changes in diet along with regular physical activity are important strategies for gaining weight.*

Learning Portfolio

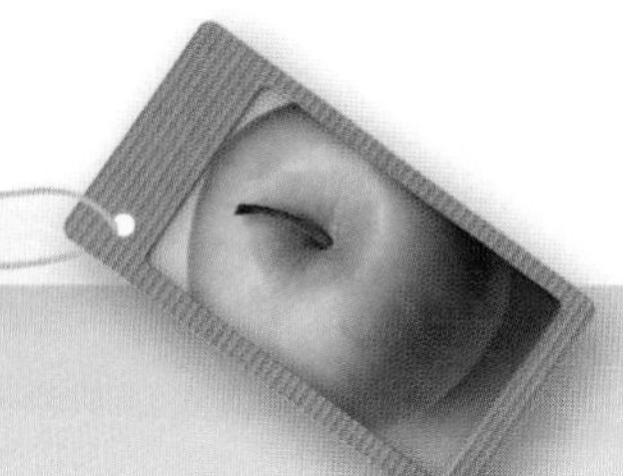

Key Terms

	page
ABC model of behavior	370
android obesity [AN-droyd]	355
appetite	338
basal energy expenditure (BEE)	341
basal metabolic rate (BMR)	342
binge eaters	358
bioelectrical impedance analysis (BIA)	353
BodPod	353
body composition	350
body fat distribution	355
body mass index (BMI)	350
bomb calorimeter	336
built environment	357
calorimeter	346
calorimetry [kal-oh-RIM-eh-tree]	346
computed tomography (CT)	355
densitometry	353
direct calorimetry	346
doubly labeled water	347
dual-energy x-ray absorptiometry (DEXA)	353
energy balance	336
energy equilibrium	336
energy intake	336
energy output	336
extreme obesity	377
ghrelin	341
gynoid obesity	355
hunger	337
hydrostatic weighing	353
hypercellular obesity	357
hyperplastic obesity (hyperplasia)	357
hypertrophic obesity	357
hypothalamus [high-po-THAL-ah-mus]	340
indirect calorimetry	346
isotopes [EYE-so-towps]	347
lean body mass	342
leptin	341
magnetic resonance imaging (MRI)	355
metabolic fitness	364
morbid obesity	377
near-infrared interactance	355
negative energy balance	336
negative self-talk	370
neuropeptide Y (NPY)	341
nonexercise activity thermogenesis (NEAT)	343
obesity	350
overweight	350
positive energy balance	336
positive self-talk	370
resting energy expenditure (REE)	341
resting metabolic rate (RMR)	342
restrained eaters	358
satiation	337
satiety	337
sleep apnea	361
thermic effect of food (TEF)	346
total body water	353
total energy expenditure (TEE)	341
underwater weighing	353
underweight	350
very low calorie diets (VLCD)	375
waist circumference	355
weight cycling	362
weight management	362

Study Points

- Energy balance is the relationship between energy intake and energy output.
- The energy content in food can be measured directly using a bomb calorimeter or estimated using the following factors: 4 kilocalories per gram for carbohydrate and protein, 9 kilocalories per gram for fat, and 7 kilocalories per gram for alcohol.
- Food intake is regulated by hunger, satiation, satiety, and appetite, which are influenced by complex factors. Hunger is the physiological need to eat. Satiation is the feeling of fullness that leads to termination of a meal. Satiety is the feeling of satisfaction and lack of hunger that determines the interval until the next meal. Appetite is a desire to eat that is influenced by external factors such as flavors and smells, and environmental and cultural factors.
- Gastrointestinal stimulation, circulating nutrients, neurotransmitters, and hormones signal the brain to regulate food intake.
- The major components of energy expenditure are resting energy expenditure, the thermic effect of food, and energy for physical activity.
- Calorimetry is the measurement of energy use, either directly by measuring heat production or indirectly by determining oxygen intake and carbon dioxide production.
- Body composition, age, gender, genetics, and hormonal activity affect the amount of energy used for resting metabolism.
- The energy cost of physical activity is affected by a person's size and the intensity and duration of the activity.
- Body composition—the relative amounts of fat and lean body mass—has a major influence on energy expenditure and risk of chronic disease.
- Body mass index—a ratio correlated with total body fatness and risk of chronic disease—is calculated with height and weight measurements.
- The prevalence of obesity and overweight is escalating worldwide, contributing to chronic disease.

- Health risks associated with obesity are more pronounced when excess body fat is located in the abdominal region of the body.
- The factors that cause obesity are not completely understood, but a complex interaction of hormonal and metabolic factors is believed to play a role, along with genetic, sociocultural, and psychological factors.
- Rather than focus on ideal body weight, many professionals now promote health and fitness goals.
- Physical activity improves fitness and helps achieve the negative energy balance needed for weight reduction.
- Abandoning unrealistic ideas of thinness and accepting body weight and shape are important elements in weight management.
- Long-term weight management includes a balanced diet of moderately restricted calorie intake, adequate exercise, cognitive-behavioral strategies for changing habits and behavior patterns, and attention to balancing self-acceptance and the desire for change.
- Surgical approaches to weight control should be considered only as a last resort for the morbidly obese.
- If the cause is not hereditary, being underweight can pose health problems.
- Gaining weight can be difficult for individuals who are underweight.

Study Questions

1. Explain the concept of energy balance.
2. List and describe the three main components of energy expenditure.
3. Explain the three main factors that determine energy expenditure in activity.
4. List the techniques for measuring body composition.
5. Obesity is seen as a complex disorder with multiple contributing factors. List the types of factors involved in the development and maintenance of obesity.
6. What body mass index (BMI) values are associated with being underweight, overweight, and obese? Do these vary for men and women?
7. Describe the concept of metabolic fitness.
8. What is the difference between hyperplastic and hypertrophic obesity?
9. What are the components of a sound approach to weight management?
10. Explain how the ABCs of behavior modification can assist with weight control.
11. Define underweight.

Try This

A One-Week Energy Balance Check

The purpose of this exercise is to see if you're in energy balance by monitoring your body weight for one week. Measure your weight on a Monday morning soon after you wake up. Record your weight. Don't change your normal routine of exercise and food intake. One week later weigh yourself again (on a Monday morning just after waking). Did your weight change? If not, your energy intake closely matched your energy output. If so, did you gain or lose weight? What factors do you think contributed to your body weight change? Try repeating this exercise over a longer period of time. Measure and record your weight every Monday morning for six months. What happens?

Increasing Your Energy Output

Physical activity is the part of your energy output that varies the most. The purpose of this exercise is to increase your energy expenditure by committing to daily exercise for one week. Make each exercise session about 30 minutes long, and remember that the longer the duration, the harder the intensity, and the larger the muscle groups involved, the greater the energy expenditure. Choose an exercise you enjoy—such as walking, jogging, cycling, swimming, or rollerblading. Once your week is complete, ask yourself these questions: How did this week's daily exercise affect my energy balance? Have I gained or lost weight during the week? Did I compensate for the extra energy expenditure by increasing my calorie intake?

Changing Your Energy Input

Would you like to change your weight by a pound or two? The purpose of this exercise is to increase or decrease your energy input (calorie intake) so that you gain or lose 1 pound by the end of a week. How? Make only minor adjustments in your usual diet but try to change the energy content for each of your meals by a small amount. Keep a food log and use Appendix A, EatRight Analysis Software, or Nutritionist Pro software to estimate your calorie total for each of the days. Your goal is to change your calorie total by approximately 500 kilocalories per day. You should not consume fewer than 1,500 kilocalories (for women) or 1,800 kilocalories (for men) per day. Weigh yourself at the start of your week and at the end. What change, if any, do you see?

What About Bobbie?

Remember, Bobbie is a 20-year-old college sophomore who weighs 155 pounds and is 5 feet, 4 inches tall. She gained 10 pounds her freshman year and would like to lose it because she feels healthier when her weight is closer to 145 pounds. She exercises infrequently but likes to walk with her friends and occasionally goes to an aerobics class. How would you suggest she lose the extra 10 pounds? Let's start by reducing her calorie intake slightly. Refer to Bobbie's typical day of eating and some small changes in portion sizes that will save some calories.

As you can see in the righthand column, small changes in Bobbie's diet can result in a 500-kilocalorie deficit, which will translate to approximately 1 pound per week of weight loss. This doesn't take into account any extra exercise she might do. So if she starts to work out more regularly, she can make fewer changes in her calorie intake and still lose 1 pound per week.

Typical Day	Alternative	Kcal
Breakfast		
1 cinnamon-raisin bagel		
3 Tbsp. light cream cheese	1 Tbsp. light cream cheese	70 saved
Coffee, 2 Tbsp. 2% milk, 2 tsp. sugar		
Snack		
1 banana		
Lunch		
2 slices sourdough bread		
2 ounces turkey lunch meat		
2 tsp. regular mayo, 2 tsp. mustard, 1 slice tomato, dill pickle, lettuce leaf		
12 oz. diet cola		
Salad		
2 C iceberg lettuce with 2 Tbsp. each shredded carrot, chopped egg, croutons, kidney beans, Italian dressing	1 Tbsp. Italian dressing	55 saved
1 chocolate chip cookie		
Snack		
1½ oz. tortilla chips, ½ C salsa	1 oz. tortilla chips	70 saved
2 C water		
Dinner		
1½ C pasta	1 C pasta	100 saved
3 oz. meatballs, 3 oz. spaghetti sauce, 2 Tbsp. parmesan cheese		
1 slice garlic bread	delete garlic bread	185 saved
½ C green beans	1 C green beans	25 added
1 tsp. butter	delete butter	30 saved
12 oz. diet cola		
Snack		
1 slice cheese pizza		
Total 500 saved		

References

1 Anderson GH, Moore SE. Dietary proteins in the regulation of food intake and body weight in humans. *J Nutr.* 2004;134:974S–979S; Gerstein DE, Woodward-Lopez G, Evans AE, et al. Clarifying concepts about macronutrients' effects on satiation and satiety. *J Am Diet Assoc.* 2004;104:1151–1153; and Mattes RD, Hollis J, Hayes D, Stunkard AJ. Appetite: measurement and manipulation misgivings. *J Am Diet Assoc.* 2005;105:S87–S97.

2 Vander Wal JS, Marth JM, Khosla P, et al. Short-term effect of eggs on satiety in overweight and obese subjects. *J Am Coll Nutr.* 2005;24(6):510–515.

3 Gerstein DE, Woodward-Lopez G, Evans AE, et al. Clarifying concepts about macronutrients' effects on satiation and satiety. *J Am Diet Assoc.* 2004;104(7): 1151–1153; and Rolls BJ, Drewnowski A, Ledikwe JH. Changing the energy density of the diet as a strategy for weight management. *J Am Diet Assoc.* 2005;105:S98–S103.

4 Willis HJ, Eldridge AL, Beiseigel J, et al. Greater satiety response with resistant starch and corn bran in human subjects. *Nutr Res.* 2009;29:100–105.

5 DiMeglio DP, Mattes RD. Liquid versus solid carbohydrate: effects on food intake and body weight. *Int J Obes.* 2000;24:794–800.

6 Dubois L, Farmer A, Girard M, Peterson K. Regular sugar-sweetened beverage consumption between meals increases risk of overweight among preschool-aged children. *J Am Diet Assoc.* 2007;107:924–934.

7 Mattes R. Soup and satiety. *Physiol Behav.* 2004;83:739–747.

8 Stubbs RJ, Johnstone AM, Mazalan N, et al. Effect of altering the variety of sensorially distinct foods, of the same macronutrient content, on food intake and body weight in men. *Eur J Clin Nutr.* 2001;55:19–28.

9 Gerstein, Woodward-Lopez, Evans, et al. Clarifying concepts about macronutrients' effects on satiation and satiety.

10 Rolls BJ, Morris EL, Roe LS. Portion size of food affects energy intake in normal-weight and overweight men and women. *Am J Clin Nutr.* 2002;76:1207–1213.

11 Wansink B, Cheney MM. Super bowls: serving bowl size and food consumption. *JAMA.* 2005;293:1727–1728.

12 Orlet Fisher J, Rolls BJ, Birch LL. Children's bite size and intake of an entrée are greater with large portions than with age-appropriate or self-selected portions. *Am J Clin Nutr.* 2003;77(5):1164–1170.

13 Wansink B, Painter JE, North J. Bottomless bowls: why visual cues of portion size may influence intake. *Obes Res.* 2005;13:93–100; and Geier AB, Rozin P, Doros G. Unit bias. *Psychol Sci.* 2006;17(6):521–525.

14 Wansink B, Van Ittersum K. Portion size me: downsizing our consumption norms. *J Am Diet Assoc.* 2007;107:1069–1262.

15 Wansink B. Environmental factors that increase the food intake and consumption volume of unknowing consumers. *Ann Rev Nutr.* 2004;24:455–479.

16 Ibid.

17 Ibid.; de Castro JM, Brewer E. The amount eaten in meals by humans is a power function of the number of people present. *Physiol Behav.* 1992;51:121–125; and Stroebele N, de Castro JM. Influence of physiological and subjective arousal on food intake in humans. *Nutrition.* 2006;22:996–1004.

18 Guyton AC, Hall JE. *Textbook of Medical Physiology.* 11th ed. Philadelphia: WB Saunders, 2005.

19 Ibid.

20 Schwartz MW, Woods SC, Porter D Jr., et al. Central nervous system control of food intake. *Nature.* 2000;404(6):661–671.

21 Shioda S, Takenoya F, Yagi M, et al. Neural networks of several novel neuropeptides involved in feeding regulation. *Nutrition.* 2008;24:848–853.

22 Kalra SP, Kalra PS. NPY and cohorts in regulating appetite, obesity and metabolic syndrome: beneficial effects of gene therapy. *Neuropeptides.* 2004;38(4):201–211.

23 MacNeil JS. Study supports leptin's role in regulating appetite. *Family Pract News.* 2005;35(5):75.

24 Brodsky IG. Hormones and growth factors. In: Shils ME, Shike M, Ross AC, et al., eds. *Modern Nutrition in Health and Disease.* 10th ed. Philadelphia: Lippincott Williams & Wilkins, 2006:636–654.

25 Bowles L, Kopelman P. Leptin: of mice and men? *J Clin Pathol.* 2001;54: 1–3.

26 le Roux CW, Patterson M, Vincent RP, et al. Postprandial plasma ghrelin is suppressed proportional to meal calorie content in normal-weight but not obese subjects. *J Clin Endocrinol Metab.* 2004;90:1068–1071.

27 Wilmore JH, Costill DL. *Physiology of Sport and Exercise.* 4th ed. Champaign, IL: Human Kinetics, 2008.

28 Institute of Medicine, Food and Nutrition Board. *Dietary Reference Intakes for Energy, Carbohydrate, Fiber, Fat, Fatty Acids, Cholesterol, Protein, and Amino Acids.* Washington, DC: National Academies Press, 2005.

29 Ibid.

30 Ibid.

31 Poehlman ET, Berke EM, Joseph JR, et al. Influence of aerobic capacity, body composition and thyroid hormones on the age-related decline in resting metabolic rate. *Metabolism.* 1992;41:915–921.

32 Mahan LK, Escott-Stump S. *Krause's Food, Nutrition and Diet Therapy.* 10th ed. Philadelphia: WB Saunders, 2005.

33 Bouchard C, ed. *The Genetics of Obesity.* Boca Raton, FL: CRC Press, 1994:135–145.

34 Mahan, Escott-Stump. *Krause's Food, Nutrition and Diet Therapy.*

35 Arciero PJ, Goran MI, Poehlman ET. Resting metabolic rate is lower in women compared to men. *J Appl Physiol.* 1993;75:2514–2520.

36 Wilmore, Costill. *Physiology of Sport and Exercise.*

37 Levine JA, Eberhardt NL, Jensen MD. Role of nonexercise activity thermogenesis in resistance to fat gain in humans. *Science.* 1999;283:212–214; and Levine JA. Nonexercise activity thermogenesis (NEAT): environment and biology. *Am J Physiol Endocrinol Metab.* 2004;286:E675–E685.

38 Wilmore, Costill. *Physiology of Sport and Exercise.*

39 Granata GP, Brandon LJ. The thermic effect of food and obesity: discrepant results and methodological variations. *Nutr Rev.* 2002;60:223–233; and de Jonge L, Bray GA. The thermic effect of food is reduced in obesity. *Nutr Rev.* 2002;60:295–297.

40 Farshchi HR, Taylor MA, Macdonald IA. Decreased thermic effect of food after an irregular compared with a regular meal pattern in healthy lean women. *Int J Obes.* 2004;28:653–660.

41 Carpenter KJ. A short history of nutritional science: part 1 (1785–1885). *J Nutr.* 2003;133:638–645.

42 Institute of Medicine, Food and Nutrition Board. *Dietary Reference Intakes for Energy, Carbohydrate.*

43 Rippe JM, Crossley S, Ringer R. Obesity as a chronic disease: modern medical and lifestyle management. *J Am Diet Assoc.* 1998(suppl):S9–S15. Theme issue.

44 National Heart, Lung, and Blood Institute. *The Practical Guide: Identification, Evaluation and Treatment of Overweight and Obesity in Adults.* October 2000. NIH publication 00-4084. http://www.nhlbi.nih.gov/guidelines/obesity/prctgd_c.pdf. Accessed 6/16/09.

45 Flegal KM, Graubard BI, Williamson DF, Gail MH. Excess deaths associated with underweight, overweight, and obesity. *JAMA.* 2005;293:1861–1867.

46 USDA Center for Nutrition Policy and Promotion. *Body Mass Index and Health.* Washington, DC: Center for Nutrition Policy and Promotion, 2000. Nutrition Insights, No. 16.

47 National Center for Health Statistics. *2000 CDC Growth Charts: United States.* http://www.cdc.gov/growthcharts. Accessed 7/5/06.

48 Barlow SE, Dietz WH. Obesity evaluation and treatment: expert committee recommendations. *Pediatrics.* 1998;102, E29. http://www.pediatrics.org/cgi/content/full/102/3/e29. Accessed 7/5/06.

49 Pietrobelli A, Formica C, Wang Z, Heymsfield SB. Dual-energy x-ray absorptiometry body composition model: a review of physical concepts. *Am J Physiol.* 1996;34:E941–E951.

50 Pi-Sunyer FX. Obesity. In: Shils ME, Olson JA, Shike M., eds. *Modern Nutrition in Health and Disease*. 9th ed. Philadelphia: Williams & Wilkins, 1999:1395–1418.

51 Lee RD, Nieman DC. *Nutritional Assessment*. 2nd ed. St. Louis: Mosby-Year Book, 1996.

52 Ibid.

53 Heymsfield SB, Baumgartner RN. Body composition and anthropometry. In: Shils ME, Shike M, Ross AC, et al., eds. *Modern Nutrition in Health and Disease*. 10th ed. Philadelphia: Lippincott Williams & Wilkins, 2006:751–770.

54 Ziegler RG. Anthropometry and breast cancer. *J Nutr.* 1997;127(suppl 5):924S–928S; and Pichard C, Plu-Bureau G, Neves-e-Castro M, Gompel A. Insulin resistance, obesity and breast cancer risk. *Maturitas*. 2008;60:19–30.

55 Zhu S, Heshka S, Wang Z, et al. Combination of BMI and waist circumference for identifying cardiovascular risk factors in whites. *Obes Res.* 2004;12:633–645.

56 Lavizzo-Mourey R. Building the evidence to reverse an epidemic. *Am J Prev Med.* 2007;33(4):S162–S164.

57 Kopelman PG. Obesity as a medical problem. *Nature*. 2000;404:635–643.

58 Uauy R, Albala C, Kain J. Obesity trends in Latin America: transitioning from under- to overweight. *J Nutr.* 2001;131:893S–899S.

59 Mokhatar N, Elati J, Chabir R, et al. Diet culture and obesity in northern Africa. *J Nutr.* 2001;131:887S–892S.

60 Kopelman. Obesity as a medical problem.

61 Hedley AA, Ogden CL, Johnson CL, et al. Overweight and obesity among US children, adolescents, and adults, 1999–2002. *JAMA.* 2004;291:2847–2850.

62 Ibid.

63 US Department of Health and Human Services. Leading health indicators. In: *Healthy People 2010: Understanding and Improving Health*. 2nd ed. Washington, DC: US Government Printing Office, 2000.

64 Gallup Consulting. In U.S., more would like to lose weight than are trying to. *Gallup Health and Healthcare Poll*. http://www.gallup.com/poll/12448/in-u.s.-more-lose-weight-than-trying-to.aspx. Accessed 1/24/10.

65 Gustafson-Larson AM, Terry RD. Weight-related behaviors and concerns of fourth-grade children. *J Am Diet Assoc.* 1992;92:818–822.

66 Bouchard C. Genetic factors and body weight regulation. In: Dalton S, ed. *Overweight and Weight Management: The Health Professional's Guide to Understanding and Practice*. Sudbury, MA: Jones and Bartlett, 1997:161–186.

67 Loos RJ, Rankinen T. Gene-diet interactions on body weight changes. *J Am Diet Assoc.* 2005;105:29–34.

68 Barsh GS, Faroogi S, O'Rahilly S. Genetics of body-weight regulation. *Nature*. 2000;404:644–651.

69 McArthur LH, Howard AB. Dietetics majors' weight-reduction beliefs, behaviors, and information sources. *J Am Coll Health*. 2001;49:175–181.

70 Anderson AE. Eating disorders in males. In: Brownell KD, Fairburn CG, eds. *Eating Disorders and Obesity*. New York: Guilford, 1995:177–182.

71 Williamson DF, Kahn HS, Remington PL, Anda RF. The 10-year incidence of overweight and major weight gain in US adults. *Arch Intern Med.* 1990;150:665–672.

72 Pliner P, Chaiken S, Flett GL. Gender differences in concern with body weight and physical appearance over the life span. *Personal Soc Psychol Bull.* 1990;16:262–273.

73 Kopelman. Obesity as a medical problem.

74 James W. The epidemiology of obesity. In: Chadwick D, Cardew G, eds. *The Origins and Consequences of Obesity*. Chichester, England: Wiley, 1996:1–16.

75 Maheshwari N, Robinson J, Kohatsu N, Zimmerman B. Obesity spreading out to all income levels. Paper presented at: American Heart Association's 45th Annual Conference on Cardiovascular Disease Epidemiology and Prevention; May 2, 2005. Abstract 26. http://www.americanheart.org/presenter.jhtml?identifier53030596. Accessed 6/16/09; and Trust for American's Health. *F as in Fat: How Obesity Policies Are Failing America*. 2006. http://wwwrwjf.org/files/research/TFAHObesityReport0806R.PDF. Accessed 6/16/09.

76 Sobal J, Troiano R, Frongillo E. Rural-urban differences in obesity. *Rural Sociol.* 1996;61:289–305.

77 National Center for Health Statistics. Prevalence of overweight and obesity among adults in the United States. http://www.cdc.gov/nchs/products/pubs/pubd/hestats/3and4/overweight.htm. Accessed 7/5/06.

78 Lewis TT, Everson-Rose SA, Sternfeld B, et al. Race, education, and weight change in a biracial sample of women at midlife. *Arch Intern Med.* 2005;165:545–551.

79 Centers for Disease Control and Prevention. *Healthy Places Terminology*. http://www.cdc.gov/healthyplaces/terminology.htm. Accessed 7/5/06.

80 Booth KM, Pinkston MM, Poston WSC. Obesity and the built environment. *J Am Diet Assoc.* 2005;105:S110–S117.

81 Morland K, Wing S, Diez Roux A, Poole C. Neighborhood characteristics associated with the location of food stores and food service places. *Am J Prev Med.* 2002;22:23–29.

82 Keim NL, Blanton CA, Kretsch MJ. America's obesity epidemic: measuring physical activity to promote an active lifestyle. *J Am Diet Assoc.* 2004;104:1398–1409.

83 Hu FB, Li TY, Colditz GA, et al. Television watching and other sedentary behaviors in relation to risk of obesity and type 2 diabetes in women. *JAMA.* 2003;289:1785–1791; and Andersen RE, Crespo CJ, Barlett SJ, et al. Relationship of physical activity and television watching with body weight and level of fatness among children. *JAMA.* 1998;282:1561–1567.

84 Feldman S, Eisenberg M, Neumark-Sztainer D, Story M. Associations between watching TV during family meals and dietary intake among adolescents. *J Nutr Educ Behav.* 2007;39(5):257–263.

85 Faith MS, Allison DB, Geliebter A. Emotional eating and obesity. In: Dalton S, ed. *Overweight and Weight Management: The Health Professional's Guide to Understanding and Practice*. Sudbury, MA: Jones and Bartlett, 1997:439–465.

86 Arnow B, Kenardy J, Agras WS. The emotional eating scale: the development of a measure to assess coping with negative affect by eating. *Int J Eating Dis.* 1995;18:79–90.

87 Cutting TM, Fisher JO, Grimm-Thomas K, Birch LL. Like mother, like daughter: familial patterns of overweight are mediated by mothers' dietary disinhibition. *Am J Clin Nutr.* 1999;69:608–613.

88 de Lauzon-Guillain B, Musher-Eizenman D, Leporc E, et al. Parental feeding practices in the United States and in France: relationships with child's characteristics and parent's eating behavior. *J Am Diet Assoc.* 2009;109:1064–1069.

89 Marcus MD. Binge eating in obesity. In: Fairburn CG, Wilson GT, eds. *Binge Eating: Nature, Assessment, and Treatment*. New York: Guilford, 1993:77–96.

90 Bray GA, Champagne CM. Beyond energy balance: there is more to obesity than kilocalories. *J Am Diet Assoc.* 2005;105:S17–S23.

91 Olshansky SJ, Passaro DJ, Hershow RC. A potential decline in life expectancy in the United States in the 21st century. *N Engl J Med.* 2005;352:1138–1145.

92 Finkelstein EA, Fiebelkorn IC, Wang G. State-level estimates of annual medical expenditures attributable to obesity. *Obes Res.* 2004;12:18–24.

93 Blackburn GL. Effects of weight loss on weight-related risk factors. In: Brownell KD, Fairburn CG, eds. *Eating Disorders and Obesity*. New York: Guilford, 1995:406–410.

94 National High Blood Pressure Education Program (NHBPEP) Working Group. Report on primary prevention of hypertension. *Arch Intern Med.* 1993;153:186.

95 Reisin E, Jack AV. Obesity and hypertension: mechanisms, cardio-renal consequences, and therapeutic approaches. *Med Clin North Am.* 2009;93(3):733–751.

96 Maitre C. Importance of physical activity in the prevention of breast cancer. *Bull Cancer*. 2009;96(5):543–551.

97 Schlienger JL, Luca F, Vinzio S, Pradignac A. Obesity and cancer. *Rev Med Intern.* 2009; June 11.

98 Carter R 3rd, Watenpaugh DE. Obesity and obstructive sleep apnea: or is it OBA and obesity? *Pathophysiology*. 2008;15(2):71–77.

99 Kirschenbaum DS, Fitzgibbon ML. Controversy about the treatment of obesity: criticisms or challenges? *Behav Ther.* 1995;26:43–68.

100 Olson MB, Kelsey SF, Bittner V, et al. Weight cycling and high-density lipoprotein cholesterol in women: evidence of an adverse effect. A report from the NHLBI-sponsored WISE study. *J Am Coll Cardiol.* 2000;36(5):1565–1571.

101 Schulz M, Liese AD, Boeing H, et al. Associations of short-term weight changes and weight cycling with incidence of essential hypertension in the EPIC-Potsdam Study. *J Hum Hypertens.* 2005;19:61–67.

102 Shade ED, Ulrich CM, Wener MH, et al. Frequent intentional weight loss is associated with lower natural killer cell toxicity in postmenopausal women. *J Am Diet Assoc.* 2004;104:903–912.

103 American Dietetic Association. Position of the American Dietetic Association: weight management. *J Am Diet Assoc.* 2009;109(2):330–346.

104 Flegal, Graubard, Williamson, Gail. Excess deaths associated with underweight, overweight, and obesity.

105 Hill JO, Thompson H, Wyatt H. Weight maintenance: what's missing? *J Am Diet Assoc.* 2005;105:S63–S66.

106 US Department of Health and Human Services and US Department of Agriculture. *Dietary Guidelines for Americans, 2010.* 7th ed. Washington, DC: US Government Printing Office, December 2010.

107 Hill, Thompson, Wyatt. Weight maintenance: what's missing?

108 Saltin B, Pilegaard H. Metabolic fitness: physical activity and health [in Danish]. *Ugeskr Laeger.* 2002;164(16):2156–2162.

109 Ibid.

110 Grundy SM, Cleeman JI, Daniels SR, et al. AHA scientific statement: diagnosis and management of metabolic syndrome. *Circulation.* 2005;112:e285–e290.

111 Hill JO, Wyatt HR, Reed GW, Peters JC. Obesity and the environment: where do we go from here? *Science.* 2003;299:853–855.

112 Irwin ML, Mayer-Davis EJ, Addy CL, et al. Moderate-intensity physical activity and fasting insulin levels in women: the Cross-Cultural Activity Participation Study. *Diabetes Care.* 2000;23(4):449.

113 National Weight Control Registry. http:///www.nwcr.ws/Research/default.htm. Accessed 1/24/10.

114 Schwartz J, Byrd-Bredbenner C. Portion distortion: typical portion sizes selected by young adults. *J Am Diet Assoc.* 2006;106:1412–1418.

115 Stubbs RJ, Prentice AM, James WP. Carbohydrates and energy balance. *Ann N Y Acad Sci.* 1997;819:44–69.

116 Satia-About AJ, Patterson RE, Schiller RN, Kristal AR. Energy from fat is associated with obesity in U.S. men: results from the Prostate Cancer Prevention Trial. *Prev Med.* 2002;34:493–501.

117 Miller WC, Niederpruem MG, Wallace JP, Lindeman AK. Dietary fat, sugar, and fiber predict body fat content. *J Am Diet Assoc.* 1994;94:612–615.

118 Farshchi HR, Taylor MA, Macdonald IA. Beneficial metabolic effects of regular meal frequency on dietary thermogenesis, insulin sensitivity, and fasting lipid profiles in healthy obese women. *Am J Clin Nutr.* 2005;81:16–24.

119 de Castro JM. The time of day of food intake influences overall intake in humans. *J Nutr.* 2004;134:104–111.

120 Farshchi HR, Taylor MA, Macdonald IA. Deleterious effects of omitting breakfast on insulin sensitivity and fasting lipid profiles in healthy lean women. *Am J Clin Nutr.* 2005;81:388–396.

121 Institute of Medicine, Food and Nutrition Board. *Dietary Reference Intakes for Energy, Carbohydrate.*

122 Ibid.

123 Greenwald A. Current nutritional treatments of obesity. *Adv Psychosom Med.* 2006;27:24–41.

124 Dansinger ML, Gleason JA, Griffith JL, et al. Comparison of the Atkins, Ornish, Weight Watchers, and Zone diets for weight loss and heart disease risk reduction: a randomized trial. *JAMA.* 2005;293:43–53.

125 Carter JC, Fairburn CG. Cognitive-behavioral self-help for binge eating disorder: a controlled effectiveness study. *J Consult Clin Psychol.* 1998;66:616–623.

126 Berkel LA, Poston WSC, Reeves RS. Behavioral interventions for obesity. *J Am Diet Assoc.* 2005;105:S35–S43.

127 Heshka S, Anderson JW, Atkinson RL, et al. Weight loss with self-help compared with a structured commercial program: a randomized trial. *JAMA.* 2003;289:1792–1798.

128 Dansinger ML, Tatsioni A, Wong JB, et al. Meta-analysis: the effect of dietary counseling for weight loss. *Ann Intern Med.* 2007;147:41–50.

129 Hunter CM, Peterson AL, Alvarez LM, et al. Weight management using the Internet: a randomized controlled trial. *Am J Prev Med.* 2008;34:119–126.

130 Tate DF, Jackvony EH, Wing RR. Effects of Internet behavioral counseling on weight loss in adults at risk for type 2 diabetes: a randomized trial. *JAMA.* 2003;289(14):1833–1836.

131 Womble LG, Wadden TA, McGuckin BG, et al. A randomized controlled trial of a commercial Internet weight loss program. *Obes Res.* 2004;12:1011–1018.

132 Serdula MK, Kahn LK, Dietz WH. Weight loss counseling revisited. *JAMA.* 2003;289(14):1747–1750.

133 Weissman NJ. Appetite suppressants and valvular heart disease. *Am J Med Sci.* 2001;32:285–291.

134 Campfield LA. The role of pharmacological agents in the treatment of obesity. In: Dalton S, ed. *Overweight and Weight Management: The Health Professional's Guide to Understanding and Practice.* Sudbury, MA: Jones and Bartlett, 1997:466–485.

135 Lucas KH, Kaplan-Machlis B. Orlistat—a novel weight loss therapy. *Ann Pharmacother.* 2001;35:314–328.

136 Gura T. Obesity drug pipeline not so fat. *Science.* 2003;299:849–852.

137 Aronne LJ. Modern medical management of obesity: the role of pharmaceutical intervention. *J Am Diet Assoc.* 1998;10(suppl 2):S23–S26.

138 Ibid.

139 Haddock CK, Poston WSC, Dill PL, et al. Pharmacotherapy for obesity: a quantitative analysis of four decades of published randomized clinical trials. *Int J Obes.* 2002;226:262–273.

140 Moyers SB. Medications as adjunct therapy for weight loss: approved and off-label agents in use. *J Am Diet Assoc.* 2005;105:948–959.

141 Pittler MH, Ernst E. Dietary supplements for body-weight reduction: a systematic review. *Am J Clin Nutr.* 2004;79:529–536; and Dwyer JT, Allison DB, Coates PM. Dietary supplements in weight reduction. *J Am Diet Assoc.* 2005;105:S80–S86.

142 Shekelle OG, Mardy ML, Morton SC, et al. Efficacy and safety of ephedra and ephedrine for weight loss and athletic performance: a meta-analysis. *JAMA.* 2003;289:1537–1545.

143 Fontanarosa PB, Rennie D, DeAngelis CD. The need for regulation of dietary supplements—lessons from ephedra. *JAMA.* 2003;289:1568–1570.

144 Wadden TA, Byrne KJ, Krauthamer-Ewing S. Obesity: management. In: Shils ME, Shike M, Ross AC, et al., eds. *Modern Nutrition in Health and Disease.* 10th ed. Philadelphia: Lippincott Williams & Wilkins, 2006:1029–1042.

145 American Society for Metabolic & Bariatric Surgery. Fact sheet:metabolic and bariatric surgery. http://www.asmbs.org/Newsite07/media/ASMBS_Metabolic_Bariatric_Surgery_Overview_FINAL_09.pdf. Accessed 2/18/10; and Robinson MK. Surgical treatment of obesity—weighing the facts. *NEJM.* 2009;361:520–521.

146 Heena P, Santry MD, Gillen DL, Launderdale DS. Trends in bariatric surgical procedures. *JAMA.* 2005;294:1909–1917.

147 NIDDK Weight-Control Information Network. Gastrointestinal surgery for severe obesity. http://www.win.niddk.nih.gov/publications/gastric.htm. Accessed 12/30/06.

148 Cummings DE, Weigle DS, Frayo S, et al. Ghrelin-leptin tango in body-weight regulation. *Gastroenterology.* 2003;124(5):1532–1544.

149 Eyre H, Kahn R, Robertson RM, et al. Preventing cancer, cardiovascular disease, and diabetes: a common agenda for the American Cancer Society, the American Diabetes Association, and the American Heart Association. *Circulation.* 2004;109:3244–3255.

150 Eckel RH. The dietary approach to obesity: is it the diet or the disorder? *JAMA.* 2005;293:96–97.

CHAPTER 10

Fat-Soluble Vitamins

THINK About It

1 How do you feel about taking vitamin supplements?

2 Which food group, if any, supplies most of your vitamin needs?

3 From a well-lighted area, you step into a dark room. Over time, you see details. What's going on?

4 Your grandmother is a strict vegetarian and she seldom goes outdoors. What can you tell her about vitamin D intake?

Visit nutrition.jbpub.com

carotenodermia A harmless yellow-orange cast to the skin due to high levels of carotenoids in the bloodstream resulting from consumption of extremely large amounts of carotenoid-rich foods, such as carrot juice.

You get a panicky call from your sister-in-law: her nine-month-old baby is turning orange! She and her husband have done everything the pediatrician told them to do about feeding; just last month they started giving the baby infant cereal, and now they have started him on strained baby food. They introduced just one food at a time. In fact, they have only fed him one food other than cereal—carrots. Yes, the baby liked them, so much that he eats two to three jars at each meal! Do you think that could be the problem? But aren't vegetables supposed to be good for you?

Vegetables are healthful foods, and carrots are an important source of many nutrients. Carrots are probably best known as a source of beta-carotene, a vitamin A precursor and the pigment that gives carrots their orange color. Your sister-in-law's baby is eating large quantities of carrots, and the excess beta-carotene circulating in his blood gives the skin a yellow-orange cast. This condition is known as **carotenodermia** and is completely harmless. But it has probably given at least one or two new parents a scare!

Understanding Vitamins

Vitamins. Just the word probably makes you think of health and well-being! Children can quickly tell you that fruits and vegetables are good sources of vitamins and can recite some of the best food sources: oranges for vitamin C, carrots for vitamin A, and so on. For many people, however, vitamins have become something to purchase and take in supplement form, rather than a criterion for choosing foods. Americans spend huge amounts of money, billions of dollars each year, on vitamin supplements. Their reasons for taking vitamins are almost as varied as the vitamins themselves. Some people take supplements because they "don't eat right." Some take them for extra "insurance," whereas others look to vitamins to prevent and cure a whole host of conditions, from colds to cancer. Is all this money well spent?

To answer this question, you need to consider several aspects of vitamin supplementation. First, survey data indicate few widespread nutrient deficiencies in the United States. From that perspective, people are probably taking many supplements unnecessarily. A second aspect is the common sentiment that "if a little is good, more must be better." This misguided belief can lead to problems when applied to vitamin supplementation. Although high doses of some vitamins cause no ill effects, others can have serious, life-long consequences. A third consideration is that research continues to identify relationships between vitamins and reduced risk of some diseases, so some supplementation may be warranted.

THINK About It 1

These two chapters on vitamins will help you explore some of the implications of too much or too little of a vitamin in the diet and understand the facts about vitamins: what they are, what they do in the body, and which foods contain them. Armed with this information, you will be able to make wise decisions about food and whether to take supplements.

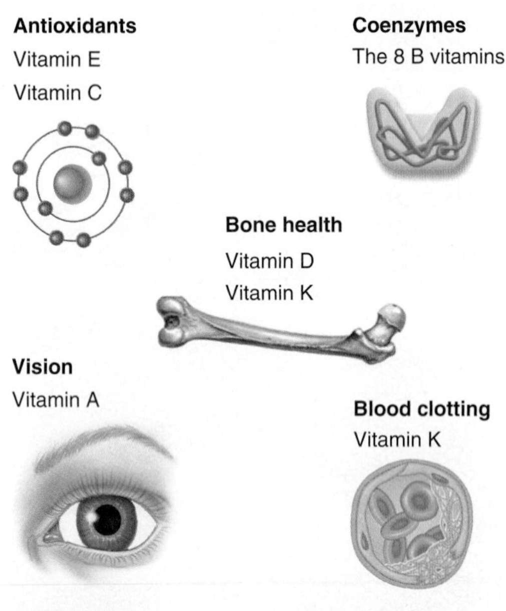

Figure 10.1 **Major roles of vitamins.** Vitamins are crucial for normal functioning, growth, and maintenance of body tissues. Compared to carbohydrate, fat, and protein, the body needs tiny amounts of vitamins.

Anatomy of the Vitamins

Vitamins differ from fat, protein, and carbohydrate in many important ways. For one, the body requires large amounts of carbohydrates, proteins, and fats—amounts measured in grams. By comparison, the daily needs for vitamins are small—a mere microgram or two in some cases. In addition, unlike fat, protein, and carbohydrate, vitamins are not an energy source. However, many vitamins play crucial roles in regulating the chemical reactions that allow us to extract energy from those nutrients. Another difference is structural: vitamins are individual units rather than long chains of smaller units.

Like fat, carbohydrate, and protein, however, vitamins are organic (carbon-containing) compounds essential for normal functioning, growth, and maintenance of the body. The functions of vitamins are often interrelated (see **Figure 10.1**), so a deficiency of just one can cause profound health problems.

Fat-Soluble Versus Water-Soluble Vitamins

Scientists classify vitamins as "fat-soluble" or "water-soluble." Vitamins A, D, E, and K are lipidlike molecules that are soluble in fat. The B vitamins and vitamin C, on the other hand, are soluble in water. This difference in solubility affects the way the body absorbs, transports, and stores vitamins. **Figure 10.2** illustrates the body's absorption of vitamins.

Intestinal cells absorb fat-soluble vitamins along with dietary fat. The amount absorbed typically varies from 40 to 90 percent of the amount consumed; efficiency of absorption generally falls as the dietary intake rises above the body's needs. Just like triglycerides and other dietary lipids, lipoproteins carry absorbed fat-soluble vitamins on their journey through the lymph and bloodstream. As chylomicrons move through the blood, cells take up most

Figure 10.2 **Absorption of vitamins.** Water-soluble vitamins are absorbed in the intestinal cells and delivered directly to the bloodstream. Fat-soluble vitamins are absorbed with fat.

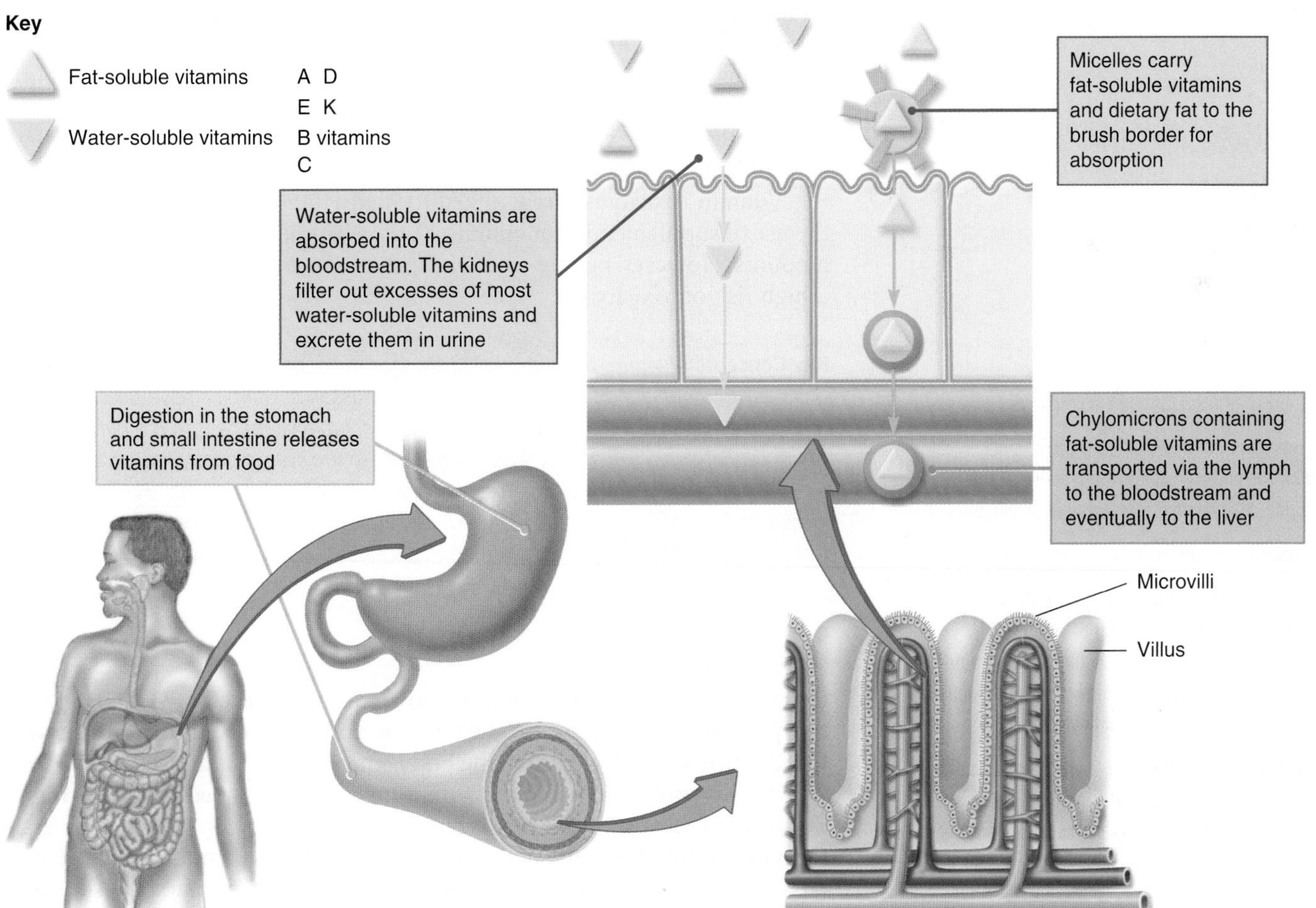
Key
Fat-soluble vitamins
A D
E K
Water-soluble vitamins
B vitamins
C
Water-soluble vitamins are absorbed into the bloodstream. The kidneys filter out excesses of most water-soluble vitamins and excrete them in urine
Micelles carry fat-soluble vitamins and dietary fat to the brush border for absorption
Digestion in the stomach and small intestine releases vitamins from food
Chylomicrons containing fat-soluble vitamins are transported via the lymph to the bloodstream and eventually to the liver
Microvilli
Villus

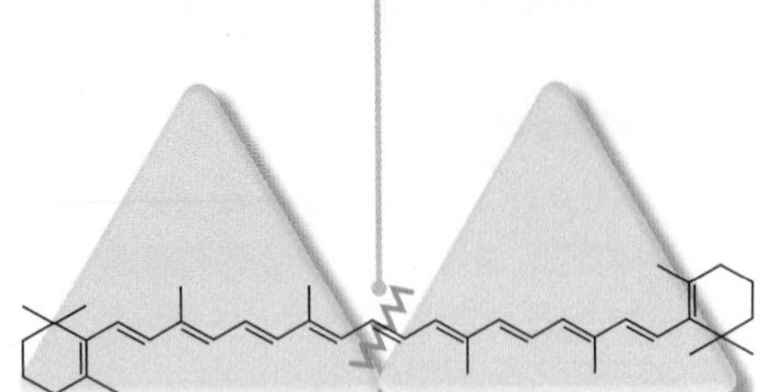

Figure 10.3 **Beta-carotene.** Beta-carotene may be cleaved at different locations, so it may yield fewer than two molecules of vitamin A. Other provitamin A carotenoids yield less vitamin A than beta-carotene.

of the triglycerides and leave behind chylomicron remnants that contain the fat-soluble vitamins. The liver picks up these remnants and either stores the vitamins for future use or repackages them for delivery via the bloodstream to other tissues.

Water-soluble vitamins are dissolved in the watery compartments of foods. Once absorbed, these nutrients travel directly into the bloodstream and then move independently in and around the cells of the body. Unlike fat-soluble vitamins, water-soluble vitamins do not need lipoprotein carriers. Their storage and excretion differ too. Whereas most fat-soluble vitamins accumulate and can be stored indefinitely, the kidneys filter out excess amounts of most water-soluble vitamins and excrete them in urine. Two vitamins are exceptions to this general rule: water-soluble vitamin B_{12} is stored more readily than the other water-soluble vitamins, and fat-soluble vitamin K is excreted more readily than the other fat-soluble vitamins.

Storage and Toxicity

Fat-soluble vitamins accumulate in the liver and adipose tissues, where they can be drawn upon in times of need. Once these vitamin stores are established, you can go for days, weeks, or even months without consuming more and suffer no ill effects. On the other hand, excessive intake of the fat-soluble vitamins A or D can exceed the body's storage capacity, with toxic effects.

Your body does not store most water-soluble vitamins in appreciable amounts, so they should be a part of your daily diet. Small variations in daily intake typically do not cause problems, however. For example, it takes 20 to 40 days of a diet deficient in the water-soluble vitamin C before deficiency symptoms emerge. Consuming excess water-soluble vitamins usually is harmless, since your body simply excretes the surplus. However, large amounts of some water-soluble vitamins—vitamin B_6, folate, niacin, even vitamin C—can be problematic, often seriously so.

Vitamin toxicity is rarely linked to high vitamin intakes from food or to the use of supplements that contain 100 to 150 percent of the recommended amounts. However, people who take megadoses of one or more vitamins run a high risk of toxicity.

Key Concepts *Vitamins are organic substances needed in minuscule amounts for various roles in regulation of body processes. Two classes of vitamins have been identified: fat-soluble vitamins (A, D, E, and K) and water-soluble vitamins (the B vitamins and vitamin C). Fat-soluble vitamins, which are stored in the liver and fatty tissues of the body, are generally excreted much more slowly than water-soluble vitamins. Because they are stored for long periods, fat-soluble vitamins generally pose a greater risk of toxicity than water-soluble vitamins when consumed in excess.*

Provitamins

Certain vitamins in foods are in inactive forms that the body cannot use directly. These substances are known as **provitamins**, or **vitamin precursors**. Once a provitamin is ingested, the body converts it to the active vitamin form. One familiar provitamin in many fruits and vegetables is beta-carotene (**Figure 10.3**). Once beta-carotene is absorbed, the body can convert it to the active form of vitamin A. In fact, beta-carotene is a major source of vitamin A in the diet. When experts calculate vitamin requirements or monitor consumption, they must take provitamins into account.

provitamins Inactive forms of vitamins that the body can convert into active usable forms. Also referred to as vitamin precursors.

vitamin precursors See *provitamins*.

retinoids Compounds in foods that have chemical structures similar to vitamin A. Retinoids include the active forms of vitamin A (retinol, retinal, and retinoic acid) and the main storage forms of retinol (retinyl esters).

retinol The alcohol form of vitamin A; one of the retinoids; thought to be the main physiologically active form of vitamin A; interconvertible with retinal.

Vitamins in Foods

THINK About It 2

What foods do you think of as good sources of vitamins? As mentioned, even very young children know that fruits and vegetables are important in the diet because "they give you vitamins." In fact, vitamins are found in every food group, including the fats and oils that most of us are trying to eat less of. One more reason to include variety in your diet is that no one food group, or one choice within a food group, is a good source of all vitamins.

The amounts of specific vitamins in a food depend on several factors. For plant foods—whether fruits, vegetables, or grains—sunlight, growing conditions, and the plant's maturity at harvest all affect the vitamin content. Although an animal's diet can have some impact on animal-derived food, its capacity for absorption and storage keeps the vitamin content fairly consistent.

Generally, the more a food is processed and cooked, the more vitamins it loses. Most food processing (e.g., cooking, milling grain, canning vegetables, and drying fruit) reduces vitamin content. For more information on how to preserve the vitamin content of your foods, see the FYI feature "Fresh, Frozen, or Canned? Raw or Cooked?" in Chapter 11, "Water-Soluble Vitamins."

Key Concepts *All types of foods contain vitamins. Provitamins are vitamin precursors that the body can convert to the active vitamin form. Growing conditions, storage, processing, and cooking all affect the amounts of vitamins in foods.*

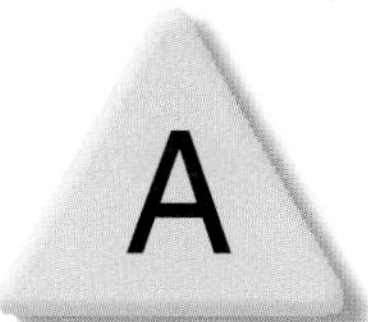

H
C—OH
H
Retinol

H
C=O
Retinal

O
C—OH
Retinoic acid

Figure 10.4 **Forms of vitamin A.** Retinol is the alcohol form of vitamin A, retinal is the aldehyde form, and retinoic acid is the acid form.

Vitamin A: The Retinoids

Vitamin A is best known for its role in vision, but it is also crucial for proper growth, reproduction, immunity, and cell differentiation. It helps maintain healthy bones as well as skin and mucous membranes. Vitamin A deficiency not only can destroy vision, but also disrupts numerous functions throughout the body.

Forms of Vitamin A

The body uses three active forms of vitamin A, known collectively as the **retinoids**. These compounds are **retinol**, the alcohol form of vitamin A; **retinal**, the aldehyde form of vitamin A; and **retinoic acid**, the acid form of vitamin A (see **Figure 10.4**). Although all three forms have essential functions, retinol is the key player in the vitamin A family. In fact, the standard unit for quantifying the biologic activity of the various forms of vitamin A and its precursors is known as a retinol activity equivalent (RAE).

Your body can easily convert retinol, which is required for reproduction and bone health, to retinal, the form of vitamin A essential for night and color vision. In turn, retinal can re-form retinol or it can irreversibly form retinoic acid, which is important for cell growth and differentiation. The interconvertible nature of retinol and retinal allows them to support all the activities of the vitamin A family.

Colorful plant pigments called **carotenoids** are precursors of vitamin A. The body converts some carotenoids, the **provitamin A** compounds, to vitamin A with varying degrees of efficiency. The yellow-orange pigment beta-carotene can be cleaved into two molecules of retinal and thus has the highest potential vitamin A activity of the provitamin A family. Of all the provitamin A carotenoids, beta-carotene yields the most vitamin A. **Figure 10.5** shows the interconversions of the three active forms of vitamin A.

retinal The aldehyde form of vitamin A; one of the retinoids; the active form of vitamin A in the photoreceptors of the retina; interconvertible with retinol.

retinoic acid The acid form of vitamin A; one of the retinoids; formed from retinal but not interconvertible; helps growth, cell differentiation, and the immune system; does not have a role in vision or reproduction.

carotenoids A group of yellow, orange, and red pigments in plants, including foods. Many of these compounds are precursors of vitamin A.

provitamin A Carotenoid precursors of vitamin A in foods of plant origin, primarily deeply colored fruits and vegetables.

Figure 10.5 **Vitamin A interconversions.** Whereas retinol and retinal are interconvertible, the reaction that forms retinoic acid is irreversible.

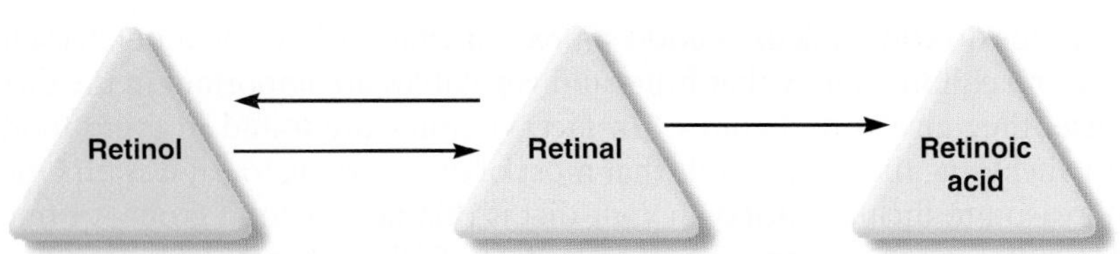

retinyl esters The main storage form of vitamin A; one of the retinoids. Retinyl esters are retinol combined with fatty acids, usually palmitic acid. Also known as preformed vitamin A.

retinol-binding protein (RBP) A carrier protein that binds to retinol and transports it in the bloodstream from the liver to destination cells.

cornea The transparent outer surface of the eye.

retina A paper-thin tissue that lines the back of the eye and contains cells called rods and cones.

rods Light-sensitive cells in the retina that react to dim light and transmit black-and-white images.

cones Light-sensitive cells in the retina that are sensitive to bright light and translate it into color images.

opsin A protein that combines with retinal to form rhodopsin in rod cells.

rhodopsin Found in rod cells, a light-sensitive pigment molecule that consists of a protein called opsin combined with retinal.

bleaching process A complex light-stimulated reaction in which rod cells lose color as rhodopsin is split into retinal and opsin.

Storage and Transport of Vitamin A

In well-nourished people, the liver stores more than 90 percent of the body's vitamin A; the remainder is deposited in adipose tissue, lungs, and kidneys.[1] The body stores vitamin A primarily as **retinyl esters**—retinol linked to a fatty acid, usually palmitic acid. Your liver gradually accumulates vitamin A reserves, which reach their peak in adulthood. The liver releases retinol in just the right amounts to maintain normal retinol blood levels. A healthy liver can store up to a year's supply of vitamin A, but taking large doses of vitamin A supplements can exceed this capacity and lead to toxicity.

Many fat-soluble vitamins need carrier proteins to ferry them in the blood to where the body needs them. For instance, **retinol-binding protein (RBP)** carries retinol released by the liver. Once the RBP drops off the retinol to a target cell, the cell can convert retinol to retinal or retinoic acid as needed. Continued production of RBP requires zinc and adequate intake of protein.

Key Concepts *Vitamin A occurs in three forms in the body: retinol, retinal, and retinoic acid. Each form of the vitamin has specific roles in the body. Most vitamin A is stored by the liver in the form of retinyl esters. Retinol-binding protein carries vitamin A in the bloodstream.*

Functions of Vitamin A

Vitamin A is crucial for vision, for maintaining healthy cells (particularly skin cells) for fighting infections and bolstering immune function, and for promoting growth and development. (See **Figure 10.6**.) In addition, the provitamin A carotenoids may play a role in prevention of cancer and other chronic diseases.

Vitamin A and Vision

When light enters the eye, it passes through the **cornea**, a transparent membrane, and hits the **retina**, the paper-thin tissues that line the back of the eye. The retina contains millions of light-sensitive cells called **rods** and **cones**. The rods react to dim light and process black-and-white images. The cones respond to bright light and translate it into color images. Within both rods and cones, a cascade of reactions converts light into a nerve signal the brain can process so we experience sight.

How does retinol become a functioning part of the retina? (See **Figure 10.7**.) Retinol is carried in the blood to the retina, where it is converted to retinal. Retinal in turn combines with the protein **opsin** to form a pigment known as **rhodopsin**. Rhodopsin is abundant in rod cells and makes it possible to see in dim light. When light strikes the retina, rod cells undergo a **bleaching process**, causing the color of the rod cells to fade. In this transformation, retinal separates from the opsin and undergoes a structural shift, from a "bent," or *cis*, configuration, to a "straightened," or *trans*, configuration. As

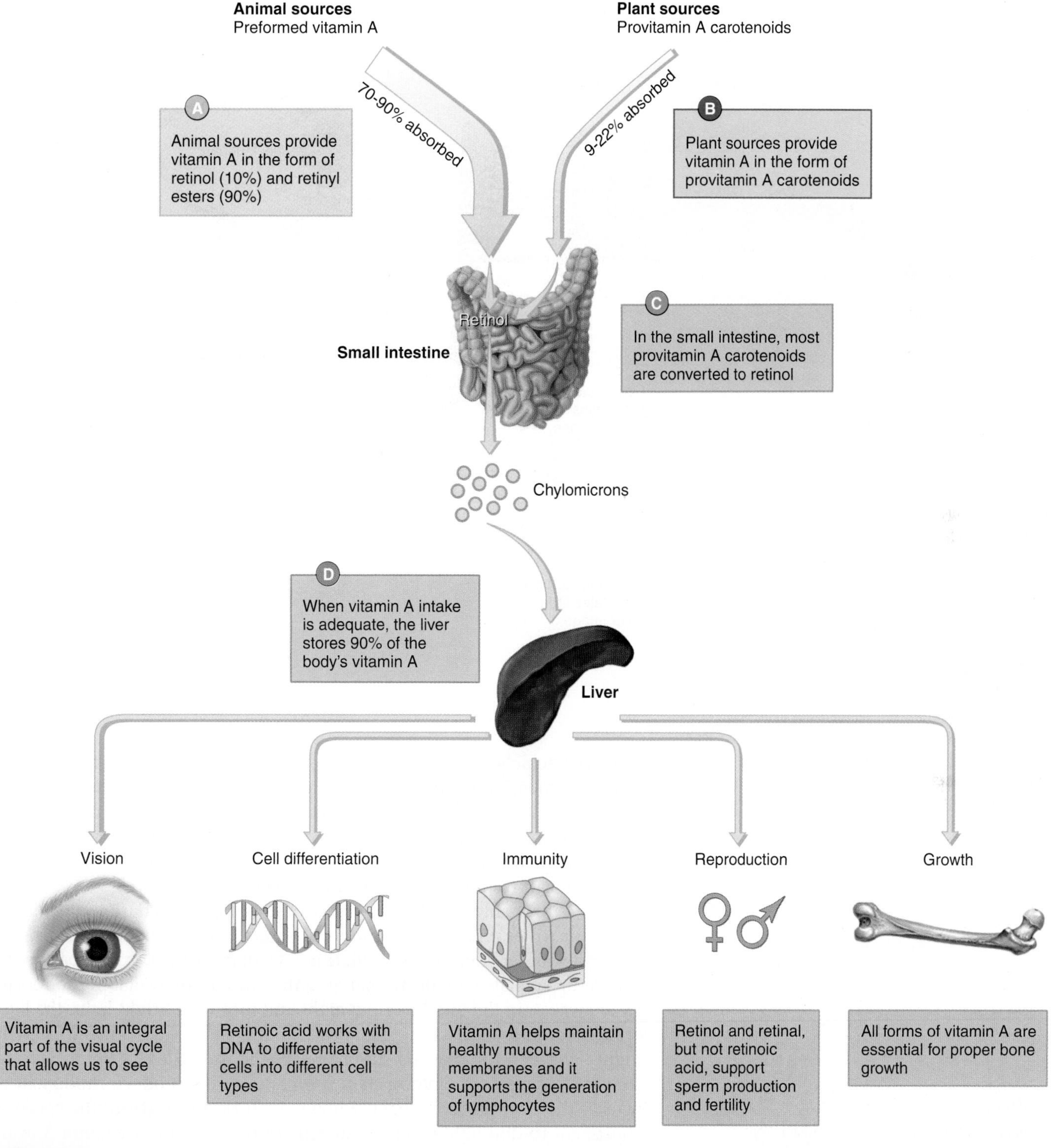
VITAMIN A: FROM SOURCE TO DESTINATION
Animal sources
Preformed vitamin A
Plant sources
Provitamin A carotenoids
70-90% absorbed
9-22% absorbed
A
Animal sources provide vitamin A in the form of retinol (10%) and retinyl esters (90%)
B
Plant sources provide vitamin A in the form of provitamin A carotenoids
Retinol
Small intestine
C
In the small intestine, most provitamin A carotenoids are converted to retinol
Chylomicrons
D
When vitamin A intake is adequate, the liver stores 90% of the body's vitamin A
Liver
Vision
Cell differentiation
Immunity
Reproduction
Growth
Vitamin A is an integral part of the visual cycle that allows us to see
Retinoic acid works with DNA to differentiate stem cells into different cell types
Vitamin A helps maintain healthy mucous membranes and it supports the generation of lymphocytes
Retinol and retinal, but not retinoic acid, support sperm production and fertility
All forms of vitamin A are essential for proper bone growth

Figure 10.6 **Vitamin A: from source to destination.** Retinoids from animal foods and carotenoids from plant foods are absorbed from the small intestine and carried by chylomicrons to the liver. Vitamin A plays a crucial role in vision and is essential for proper cell synthesis, reproduction, and bone growth.

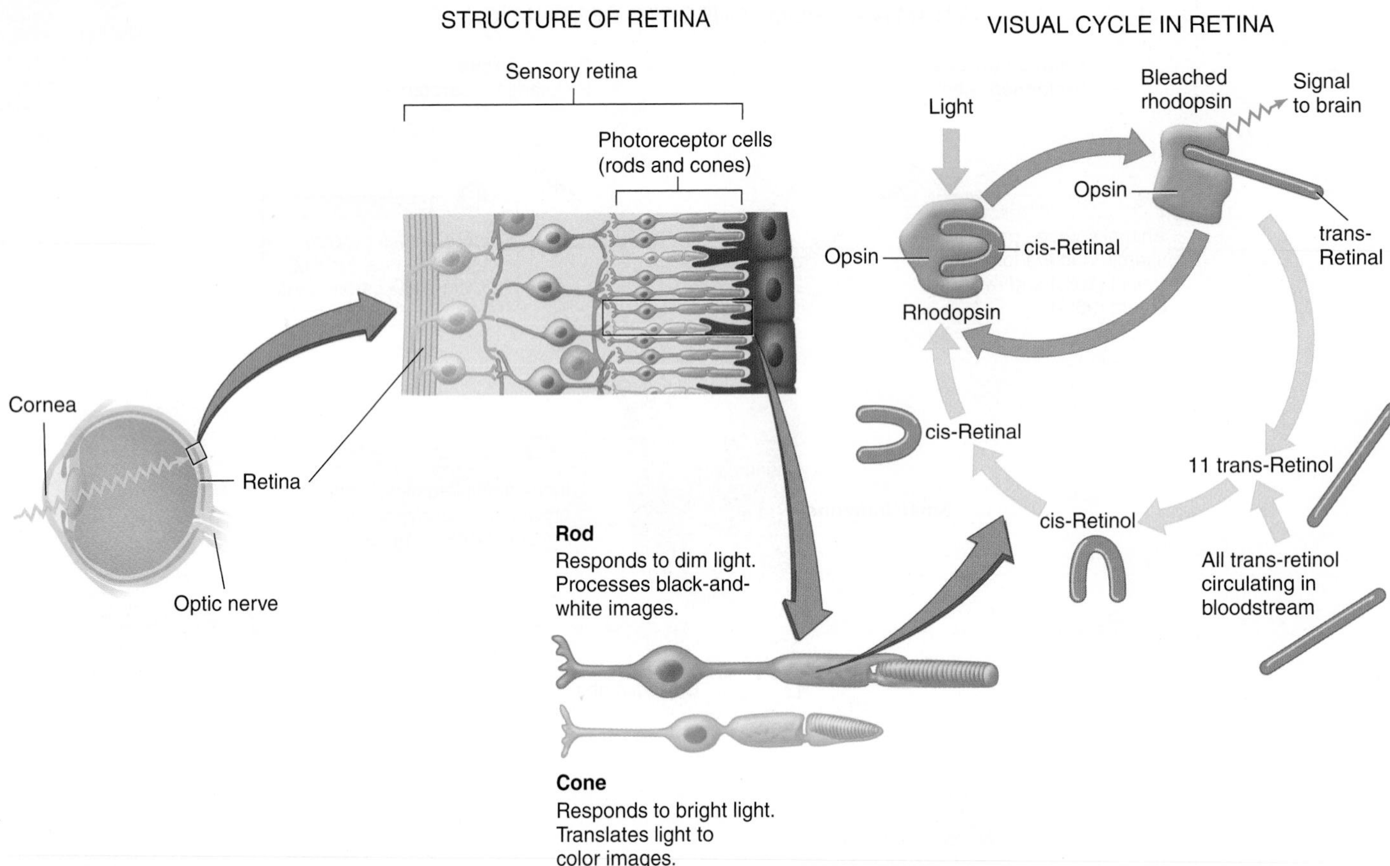

Figure 10.7 **Vitamin A and the visual cycle.** Rhodopsin is the combination of the protein opsin and vitamin A (retinal). When stimulated by light, opsin changes shape and vitamin A changes from its bent cis form to a straighter trans form. This sends a signal to the brain, and you see an image in black and white. A similar process using a different protein called iodopsin provides color.

the retinal detaches, the opsin changes shape as well, disrupting the activities in the cell membrane and generating an electrical impulse. This impulse is relayed to the brain, and you see a black-and-white image. Most of the retinal released in this process is quickly converted back to trans-retinol, and then to cis-retinal, which spontaneously recombines with opsin. The re-formed rhodopsin can respond to light again and begin another cycle.

You've probably had the experience of stepping into a dark room and being unable to see until your eyes adjust. The familiar explanation for this, that you must wait for your pupils to dilate and let in more light, is only part of the story. Your eyes also adapt by changing the amount of available rhodopsin. If you awaken in the middle of the night and turn on a bright light, the light level is blinding until your eyes adjust. Rhodopsin breaks down quickly in bright light, and the reduced supply makes the rod cells less light sensitive. Conversely, when you enter a dark room, your eyes produce rhodopsin to increase their sensitivity to light. Known as **dark adaptation**, the speed of adjustment to dim light is related directly to the amount of vitamin A available to regenerate rhodopsin. People with a vitamin A deficiency experience **night blindness**, the inability of the eyes to adjust to dim light or to regain vision quickly after exposure to a flash of bright light. Due to the lack of vitamin A, rhodopsin regeneration slows dramatically. Although the eyes contain only 0.01 percent of the body's vitamin A, they are so sensitive to vitamin A levels that one injection of the vitamin can relieve night blindness within minutes.[2]

THINK About It 3

dark adaptation The process that increases the rhodopsin concentration in your eyes, allowing them to detect images in the dark better.

night blindness The inability of the eyes to adjust to dim light or to regain vision quickly after exposure to a flash of bright light.

Vitamin A is also involved in color vision, as part of the pigment iodopsin in cone cells. During color vision, **iodopsin** undergoes a transformation cycle similar to that of rhodopsin. A lack of vitamin A affects rod cells before it affects cone cells, so as a vitamin A deficiency worsens, night blindness emerges before color blindness.

iodopsin Color-sensitive pigment molecules in cone cells that consist of opsin-like proteins combined with retinal.

Vitamin A in Cell Differentiation

Vitamin A's role in vision is crucial, but this function uses only a small fraction of the body's vitamin A supply. A much larger proportion, in the form of

A Short History of Vitamins

From roughly 1500 B.C.E. to 1900 C.E. there was an empirical understanding that some diseases (which we now call vitamin deficiency diseases) could be cured by eating certain foods. In about 400 B.C.E., the Greek physician Hippocrates, following the practice of Arab and Egyptian physicians, prescribed beef liver to people who were unable to see certain stars in the night sky. His maxim was "Let food be thy medicine," but he did not know that beef liver is a rich source of vitamin A, a fat-soluble vitamin necessary for vision.

Similarly, Native Americans knew empirically that extracts of pine needles could prevent or cure scurvy, a condition that includes bleeding gums and loss of energy. In 1753 James Lind, a Scottish surgeon, urged the British navy to include lemon juice in the diet of sailors to prevent scurvy. The navy finally adopted this practice 40 years later. In 1865 they substituted limes, which gave British sailors their nickname "limeys." We now know that the pine needles and citrus fruits provide vitamin C, a water-soluble vitamin whose deficiency causes scurvy.

Many scientists began systematically studying deficiency diseases in the late nineteenth century. They induced "deficiency states" in animals or humans by depriving them of certain foods. The subjects were restored to health when they ate the withheld food. In 1880 the Dutch scientist Christiaan Eijkman, for instance, produced beriberi in chickens by feeding them only polished (white) rice. When he restored their normal food of unpolished (brown) rice, the chickens quickly recovered. We now know that thiamin, which is removed during polishing, is essential for the health of both man and bird.

In the early twentieth century, scientists began to use chemistry to isolate and identify the critical factors in food that relieved "deficiency states." In 1912, for instance, Casimir Funk isolated a nitrogen-containing compound (an amine) in rice hulls. When given to thiamin-deprived chickens in its pure form, this amine restored the birds to health. Because this compound was required for life (*vita*) and was nitrogen-containing (*amine*), Funk coined the term *vitamines* to describe these essential growth factors. Other vitamines, or vitamins, as they later came to be called, continued to be discovered, purified, and eventually synthesized.

The discovery and naming of vitamins did not proceed without false starts. Some candidate substances did not meet the test of time, and thus we have no vitamins F, G, H, I, or J. On the other hand, vitamin B turned out to be a group of water-soluble vitamins rather than a single vitamin, so today we have eight "B vitamins." The last vitamin to be discovered was vitamin B_{12} and it was not completely synthesized until 1972.

As the vitamins were being isolated and characterized, it became clear that many Americans were not getting enough vitamins, so the National Academy of Sciences established recommended vitamin intakes. Many foods, especially flour and breads, are now fortified or enriched with vitamins.

Today we are exploring the health effects of vitamins beyond simply preventing deficiency diseases. This phase started in 1955, when large doses of niacin were found to lower cholesterol levels. Intense research is exploring the potential of the antioxidant vitamins C and E to slow aging and reduce risks for cancer, heart disease, and cataract formation. Several B vitamins are under investigation for their role in heart disease. Vitamins B_6, folate, and vitamin B_{12} affect the body's levels of the amino acid homocysteine, which was identified as an independent risk factor for coronary heart disease.

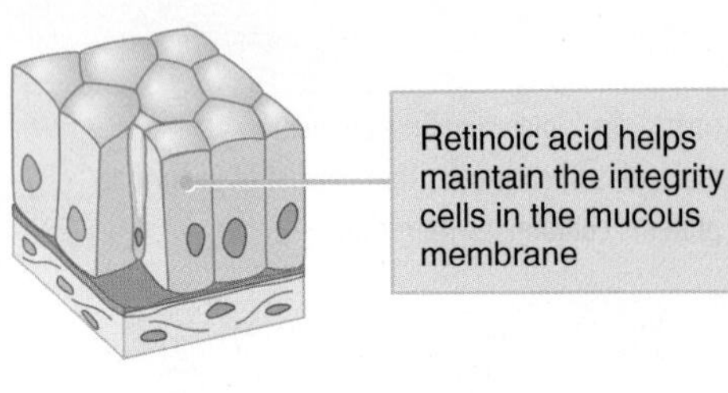

Retinoic acid helps maintain the integrity of cells in the mucous membrane

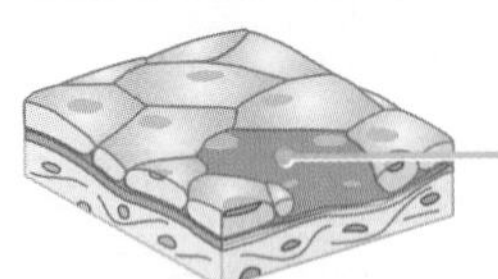

Figure 10.8 **Mucous membrane integrity.** Mucous membranes contain a higher percentage of goblet cells. Without retinoic acid, fewer stem cells become goblet cells, and these surfaces become hard and scaly.

retinoic acid, is put to work in normal cell differentiation, the process through which **stem cells** develop into highly specific types of cells with unique functions. Retinoic acid interacts with receptor sites on a cell's DNA—the genetic material that spurs production of particular proteins. When retinoic acid helps activate these receptors in the cell nucleus, stem cells begin transforming into mature differentiated cells.

This retinoic acid–dependent differentiation can be seen in **epithelial cells**, the millions of cells that cover and protect the external and internal surfaces of the body. (See **Figure 10.8**.) When epithelial cells differentiate, some develop into mucus-secreting cells (**goblet cells**), and others become different types of mature cells, such as skin cells.[3] Epithelial cells form **epithelial tissues**, which include skin and mucous membranes. Mucous membranes provide lubrication where needed—for example, along bronchial tubes and the digestive tract. Epithelial cells are on the front line protecting your body, and they are destroyed and replaced relatively quickly. Replacing these cells requires vitamin A. Because the turnover of skin cells is rapid, signs of vitamin A deficiency show up early in the skin and mucous membranes.

stem cells A formative cell whose daughter cells may differentiate into other cell types.

epithelial cells The millions of cells that line and protect the external and internal surfaces of the body. Epithelial cells form epithelial tissues such as skin and mucous membranes.

goblet cells One of the many types of specialized cells that produce and secrete mucus. These cells are found in the stomach, intestines, and portions of the respiratory tract.

epithelial tissues Closely packed layers of epithelial cells that cover the body and line its cavities.

Vitamin A and Immune Function

Vitamin A influences the immune system in important ways. It helps maintain the health of epithelial tissues, the first line of defense against bacterial, parasitic, and viral attack. Vitamin A also supports the generation of T lymphocytes, important immune cells, maintaining the body's ability to mount an immune response against infectious invaders.[4]

Vitamin A and Reproduction

Although the exact biochemical mechanism is unknown, vitamin A affects both male and female reproductive processes. Both retinol and retinal support reproduction, but retinoic acid does not. In men, vitamin A supports the production of sperm; in women, it helps maintain fertility, possibly by supporting the production of reproductive tract secretions.

Vitamin A and Bone Health

Vitamin A (retinol, retinal, and retinoic acid) is essential for bone growth.[5] As with the reproductive system, the exact mechanism is unclear, but a lack of vitamin A causes bones to weaken, although they also become thicker than normal. This may be due to a disruption of the bone remodeling process and the failure of immature bone cells to develop properly. Excessive vitamin A intake also has been linked to increased risk of bone loss and hip fracture.[6]

Key Concepts *Vitamin A plays a crucial role in vision as part of the compound rhodopsin in the rod cells of the retina. When light hits the retina, rhodopsin separates, changes shape, and sends a nerve impulse to the brain. When vitamin A is inadequate, the lack of rhodopsin makes it difficult to see in dim light. Vitamin A is also involved in cell differentiation, growth and development, immune function, reproduction, and bone health.*

Quick Bite

Vitamin A Isn't Just for Eyes

A study conducted in Nepal showed that women who took vitamin A supplements during pregnancy had a much lower risk of maternal mortality than those who took a placebo. The researchers concluded that regular and adequate intake of vitamin A or beta-carotene can reduce the risk of pregnancy-related death in areas where vitamin A deficiency is common.

Dietary Recommendations for Vitamin A

Similar amounts of dietary retinoids and carotenoids do not provide the same amount of vitamin A. To develop dietary recommendations, scientists reconciled this difference by creating a standardized measurement based on retinol, called **retinol activity equivalents (RAE)**. One retinol activity equivalent is the amount of a given form of vitamin A equal to the activity of 1 microgram (1/1,000,000 of a gram) of retinol. Using this standard, 12 micrograms (μg) of beta-carotene equals 1 RAE, and 24 micrograms of other carotenoids yields 1 RAE. (See **Figure 10.9**.)

You may also see the vitamin A content of dietary supplements expressed as **international units (IU)**. IU is an inexact, outdated measure of vitamin A that was derived using research that did not account for the poor bioavailability, or absorption efficiency, of carotenoids. One IU of vitamin A activity is equal to about 0.3 microgram of retinol from animal foods and 3.6 micrograms of beta-carotene from plant foods.

Most Americans take in adequate amounts of vitamin A and have large stores of the vitamin in their livers. The RDA for vitamin A for males aged 14 years and older is 900 micrograms RAE. For females aged 14 years and older, the vitamin A RDA is 700 micrograms RAE. Pregnant women should consume slightly more vitamin A (770 micrograms), while lactating women are advised to consume 1,300 micrograms RAE.[7]

1 retinol activity equivalent (RAE) = **1 μg retinol**
= **2 μg supplemental beta-carotene**
= **12 μg dietary beta-carotene**
= **24 mg dietary carotenoids**

Figure 10.9 **Retinol equivalents conversion.**

Sources of Vitamin A

About half the dietary vitamin A intake comes from animal food sources as **preformed vitamin A**, the retinoids (including retinyl esters, which are the main storage form of vitamin A). The other half of dietary vitamin A intake comes from fruits and vegetables in the form of provitamin A carotenoids, especially beta-carotene. **Figure 10.10** shows foods that are good sources of vitamin A.

Retinoids are found naturally only in animal foods. About 10 percent of vitamin A content is in the form of retinol, and the remaining 90 percent is retinyl esters. Liver and fish liver oils (e.g., cod liver oil) are among the top sources. Milk fat (as in whole milk, butter, and other dairy products) also contains vitamin A. Foods fortified with vitamin A (in the form of retinyl palmitate or retinyl acetate) include margarine, some breakfast cereals, and reduced-fat milks. Reduced-fat milks that are not fortified vary greatly in vitamin A content (e.g., unfortified nonfat milk contains no vitamin A). Products that are made from reduced-fat or skim milk, such as yogurt, are not generally fortified with vitamin A. The body absorbs about 75 percent of dietary retinol and retinyl esters.

The best sources of provitamin A carotenoids are dark-green and yellow-orange vegetables, such as carrots, spinach, broccoli, squash, sweet potatoes, and some orange-colored fruits such as cantaloupes, peaches, apricots, and mangos. In a varied diet, beta-carotene supplies about one-third the total vitamin A, even though the body absorbs this provitamin less efficiently than retinol or retinyl esters. For more information about carotenoids, see "The Carotenoids" section later in this chapter.

Key Concepts *Intake recommendations for vitamin A are expressed in RAEs (retinol activity equivalents) to account for the differences in bioavailability between retinoids and carotenoids. Current recommendations suggest that adult men consume 900 micrograms RAE each day; the recommendation for adult women is 700 micrograms RAE. Retinol is available from a few animal foods such as liver, fish liver oils, milk fat, and egg yolks. Vitamin A can also be formed from precursor compounds called carotenoids, which are found in some yellow-orange fruits and in dark-green and yellow-orange vegetables.*

retinol activity equivalents (RAE) A unit of measurement of the vitamin A content of a food. One RAE equals 1 μg of retinol.

international units (IU) An outdated system to measure vitamin activity. This measurement does not consider differences in bioavailability.

preformed vitamin A Retinyl esters, the main storage form of vitamin A. About 90 percent of dietary retinol is in the form of esters, mostly found in foods from animal sources.

Figure 10.10 **Food sources of vitamin A.** Vitamin A is found as retinol in animal foods and as beta-carotene and other carotenoids in plant foods. Some of the best sources are liver, orange and deep-yellow vegetables, and dark-green leafy vegetables. This figure, and others like it in the vitamin and mineral chapters, references the Daily Value standard used on food labels. By law, a food may be labeled a "Good Source" of a nutrient if it contains 10 to 19 percent of the Daily Value for that nutrient, and it is a "High Source" if it contains 20 percent or more of the Daily Value. Units are IU to be consistent with Daily Value definitions.

Source: US Department of Agriculture, Agricultural Research Service. USDA National Nutrient Database for Standard Reference, Release 22. 2009. Nutrient Data Laboratory Home Page, http://www.ars.usda.gov/ba/bhnrc/ndl.

Vitamin A

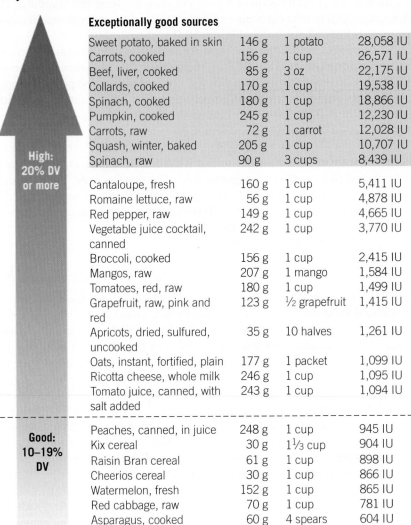

Daily Value = 5000 IU

	Food	Weight	Serving	Vitamin A
High: 20% DV or more	**Exceptionally good sources**			
	Sweet potato, baked in skin	146 g	1 potato	28,058 IU
	Carrots, cooked	156 g	1 cup	26,571 IU
	Beef, liver, cooked	85 g	3 oz	22,175 IU
	Collards, cooked	170 g	1 cup	19,538 IU
	Spinach, cooked	180 g	1 cup	18,866 IU
	Pumpkin, cooked	245 g	1 cup	12,230 IU
	Carrots, raw	72 g	1 carrot	12,028 IU
	Squash, winter, baked	205 g	1 cup	10,707 IU
	Spinach, raw	90 g	3 cups	8,439 IU
	Cantaloupe, fresh	160 g	1 cup	5,411 IU
	Romaine lettuce, raw	56 g	1 cup	4,878 IU
	Red pepper, raw	149 g	1 cup	4,665 IU
	Vegetable juice cocktail, canned	242 g	1 cup	3,770 IU
	Broccoli, cooked	156 g	1 cup	2,415 IU
	Mangos, raw	207 g	1 mango	1,584 IU
	Tomatoes, red, raw	180 g	1 cup	1,499 IU
	Grapefruit, raw, pink and red	123 g	½ grapefruit	1,415 IU
	Apricots, dried, sulfured, uncooked	35 g	10 halves	1,261 IU
	Oats, instant, fortified, plain	177 g	1 packet	1,099 IU
	Ricotta cheese, whole milk	246 g	1 cup	1,095 IU
	Tomato juice, canned, with salt added	243 g	1 cup	1,094 IU
Good: 10–19% DV	Peaches, canned, in juice	248 g	1 cup	945 IU
	Kix cereal	30 g	1⅓ cup	904 IU
	Raisin Bran cereal	61 g	1 cup	898 IU
	Cheerios cereal	30 g	1 cup	866 IU
	Watermelon, fresh	152 g	1 cup	865 IU
	Red cabbage, raw	70 g	1 cup	781 IU
	Asparagus, cooked	60 g	4 spears	604 IU
	Tangerines, raw	84 g	1 tangerine	572 IU
	Milk, nonfat, with added vitamin A	245 g	1 cup	500 IU

Vitamin A Deficiency

Although dietary deficiency of vitamin A is rare in North America and western Europe, it is the leading cause of childhood blindness worldwide, especially in Southeast Asia, parts of Africa, India, and Central and South America. In these regions, vitamin A deficiency typically results from general protein-energy malnutrition in infants and young children. It is estimated that 500,000 preschool-aged children worldwide become blind each year as a result of vitamin A deficiency. (See **Figure 10.11**.) Vitamin A deficiency retards growth and development and leads to bone deformities.

Although few Americans suffer from a vitamin A deficiency, certain groups are at risk. Newborns, especially premature infants, are at risk because their liver stores of vitamin A are low. Because their diets lack vitamin A–rich foods, impoverished people, particularly children and older adults, may suffer marginal vitamin A status. People with alcoholism or liver disease are at risk because their damaged livers may be incapable of storing much vitamin A. Medicines that alter lipid absorption inhibit vitamin A absorption too. People who have chronic diarrhea, celiac disease, Crohn's disease, cystic fibrosis, or pancreatic insufficiency and other fat-malabsorption conditions may develop vitamin A deficiency over time. In the United States, vitamin A deficiency occurs most often in people who suffer from fat-malabsorption syndromes or severely restricted diets as seen in anorexia nervosa. Inadequate intake of zinc also can cause symptoms of vitamin A deficiency because zinc is required for the body to use vitamin A efficiently.

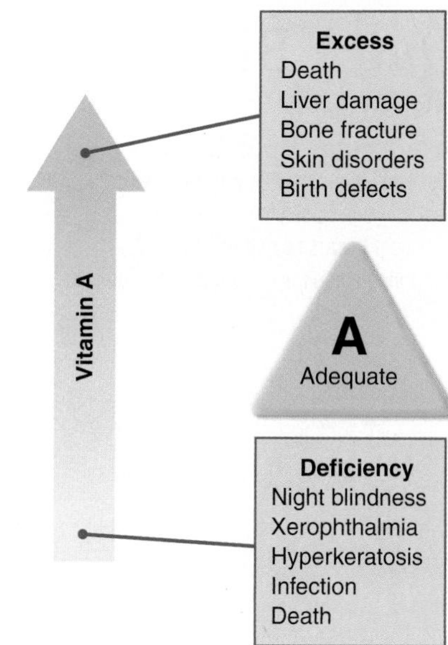

Figure 10.11 **Vitamin A intake.** A broad range of vitamin A intake is adequate and provides for normal function. Too much or too little vitamin A can have serious consequences.

Eyes

Night blindness is an early symptom of vitamin A deficiency, and can be corrected completely with early treatment. As the deficiency worsens, the lack of retinoic acid interferes with the normal differentiation of epithelial cells and reduces the formation of mucus-secreting goblet cells. As mucus production drops, the cornea and conjunctiva (the outer surface of the eye) and the mucous membrane lining the inner surface of the eyelid become extremely dry. The lack of mucus prevents the eye from washing away dirt and bacteria, thus increasing the likelihood of infection. As the cornea deteriorates, foamy, white triangular patches known as Bitot's spots develop. Eventually, irreversible scars form on the cornea, which also develops ulcers and sometimes liquefies during the final stages of deterioration. Collectively, these symptoms that progress toward total blindness are known as **xerophthalmia**. Unlike night blindness, which can be reversed with a single dose of vitamin A, corneal drying and scarring usually is permanent.

Skin

A lack of retinoic acid shifts the differentiation of epithelial cells toward the production of skin cells. This increased supply packs the skin with extra cells, increasing the density and making the skin hard and scaly. An early symptom of vitamin A deficiency is follicular **hyperkeratosis**, or "goose flesh." In this condition, the hair follicles on the skin become plugged with keratin, a protein normally present only on the outermost surface of the skin. As a result, the skin becomes rough and bumpy. Sweat glands lose their ability to secrete perspiration. Typically, hyperkeratosis causes thickening of the palms and soles, as well as attacking the flexure areas (elbows, knees, wrists, and ankles) of the skin. In advanced stages the entire body can be involved. Usually, the appearance of hyperkeratotic symptoms in the skin lags behind the development of other symptoms of vitamin A deficiency. When vitamin A is restored, the skin is slower to recover than other affected tissues.[8]

Other Epithelial Cells

Hyperkeratosis affects other types of epithelial cells and disrupts their ability to secrete mucus. This particularly affects the mouth, respiratory tract, urinary tract, female genital tract, seminal vesicles of the testes, and glands of the eyes, making them vulnerable to infection. In men, a vitamin A deficiency halts the production of sperm. Women can become infertile, possibly due to disruptions in the production of reproductive tract secretions.

Hyperkeratinization near sensory receptors causes a loss of taste and smell, which in turn can cause loss of appetite and weight.

xerophthalmia A condition caused by vitamin A deficiency that dries the cornea and mucous membranes of the eye.

hyperkeratosis Excessive accumulation of the protein keratin that produces rough and bumpy skin, most commonly affecting the palms and soles, as well as flexure areas (elbows, knees, wrists, ankles). It can affect moist epithelial tissues and impair their ability to secrete mucus. Also called hyperkeratinization.

Quick Bite

Avoid Polar Bear Liver

Liver and onions may be your favorite meal, but don't use polar bear liver. Polar bear liver is so rich in vitamin A that a single serving can be toxic for humans.

Immune Function

When lack of vitamin A leads to dry and dysfunctional epithelial tissues, microorganisms easily can breach the body's defenses. The respiratory tract, mucous membranes, and skin become especially vulnerable to infection. To make things worse, insufficient vitamin A reduces the number of T lymphocytes, which are important immune cells, and compromises their ability to mount an immune response. Vitamin A deficiency thus leaves a person highly susceptible to bacterial, parasitic, and viral infections. Children with mild vitamin A deficiencies run a high risk of diarrhea, respiratory tract infections, and measles. People with severe vitamin A deficiencies have such impaired immune systems that simple infections may be fatal.[9]

Vitamin A Toxicity

For adults, including adult women who are pregnant or breastfeeding, the Tolerable Upper Intake Level (UL) for vitamin A is 3,000 micrograms RAE as retinol. Vitamin A toxicity occurs infrequently, but as more people take megadoses of nutritional supplements, the potential for toxic overdoses increases. With the exception of a sustained diet of large amounts of liver or fish oils, food alone generally cannot supply massive amounts of vitamin A. Children are more vulnerable to toxicity, and overenthusiastic supplementation of vitamin A is dangerous and can be fatal.

Vitamin A toxicity has a wide range of symptoms, both subtle and overt, including fatigue, vomiting, abdominal pain, bone and joint pain, loss of appetite, skin disorders, headache, blurred or double vision, and liver damage, which in turn leads to jaundice. (See Figure 10.11.) The long-term Nurses' Health Study suggests that high intake of vitamin A (≥2,000 micrograms of retinol per day) is related to increased risk of hip fractures in older women.[10]

teratogen Any substance that causes birth defects.

Preformed vitamin A, taken in excess, is a known **teratogen**. Birth defects associated with vitamin A toxicity include cleft palate, heart abnormalities, and brain malfunction.[11] Excess vitamin A is most hazardous when taken during the two weeks prior to conception and the first two months of pregnancy. The embryo is undergoing a great deal of cell differentiation, and excess amounts of vitamin A appear to interfere with the vitamin's normal support of this process. An acute excess intake of vitamin A as retinol during pregnancy also can cause spontaneous abortions. Pregnant women should avoid prenatal supplements that contain retinol and instead use those that have beta-carotene as the vitamin A source. Pregnant women should get the approval of their doctor before taking retinol-containing supplements.

Although large doses of beta-carotene (provitamin A) may cause the harmless condition carotenodermia, they do not seem to cause any serious side effects. Conversion of beta-carotene to retinol occurs relatively slowly, and its absorption decreases as dietary intake increases.

Acne Treatment

Up to 90 percent of boys and up to 80 percent of girls experience acne during adolescence, making it the most common skin ailment seen by physicians. The disease has a wide spectrum, ranging from just a few transient pimples to large, chronic, painful nodules that scar when healing.[12]

Retinoic acid is the most commonly prescribed treatment to reduce the formation of blackheads and whiteheads. Retin-A (all-trans-retinoic acid) is available for topical use (applied to the skin). Accutane (13-cis-retinoic acid) is taken orally. Both Retin-A and Accutane increase one's sensitivity to the sun, so sun exposure must be limited to avoid sunburn. More important, these medications, like any large dose of vitamin A, cause birth defects, so any woman who may become pregnant should not take them. Since retinoids accumulate in fat stores, even from topical administration, these medications should be discontinued at least two years before becoming pregnant.

Key Concepts *Deficiency of vitamin A results in progressive vision loss from temporary night blindness, then reversible blindness, and finally permanent blindness. In addition, the lack of mucus secretions and reduced immune function make the person with vitamin A deficiency vulnerable to infections. Vitamin A toxicity can result from the use of supplements, even with dosages just a few times higher than the RDA. The consequences of vitamin A toxicity during pregnancy are potentially devastating, and pregnant women should avoid both retinol-containing supplements and medications made from retinoids, such as Accutane and Retin-A.*

The Carotenoids

Carotenoids are naturally occurring compounds that give the deep yellow, orange, and red colors to fruits and vegetables such as apricots, carrots, and tomatoes. Carotenoids also are abundant in dark-green vegetables, such as spinach, but the carotenoid colors are hidden by the plentiful green pigment chlorophyll. Although researchers have identified about 600 carotenoids, 50 of which are typically found in the U.S. diet, only 34 are found in blood samples and human milk.[13] The major carotenoids are alpha-carotene, beta-carotene, lutein, zeaxanthin, cryptoxanthin, and lycopene. The yellow-orange pigment beta-carotene, which lends its color to cantaloupe, carrots, and squash, is the most common carotenoid. The body can convert alpha-carotene, beta-carotene, and beta-cryptoxanthin to retinol, so they are called provitamin A carotenoids. Lycopene, lutein, and zeaxanthin have no vitamin A activity, so they are called nonprovitamin A carotenoids.

Functions of Carotenoids

Although carotenoids have diverse biological functions independent of their conversion to vitamin A, there is no evidence that carotenoids are essential nutrients in the technical sense. Because no other specific nutrient functions have been identified for any of the carotenoids, the Food and Nutrition Board has not established Dietary Reference Intakes (DRIs) for carotenoids.[14] Yet carotenoids have roles in fighting free radicals, bolstering immune function, enhancing vision, and preventing cancer.

Carotenoids as Antioxidants

Beta-carotene and other carotenoids function as potent antioxidants—substances that can interfere with the damaging effects of free radicals, which are highly unstable, reactive compounds. Free radicals can damage both the structure and function of cell membranes, nucleic acids, and electron-dense regions of proteins.[15] This damage may form the biological basis of several diseases associated with aging. Diets that emphasize antioxidant carotenoids are inversely associated with premature aging, cancer, atherosclerosis, cataracts, age-related macular degeneration, bone loss,[16] and an array of degenerative diseases.[17] For more information about free radicals and antioxidants, see the "Vitamin E" section later in this chapter.

Quick Bite

And They Called It Cantaloupe

The word *cantaloupe* comes from a papal garden in a small town near Rome named Cantaloupo. One-half of a medium cantaloupe has 466 RAE as beta-carotene.

Carotenoids and the Immune System

Dietary carotenoids can boost immunity by enhancing the body's immune responses. Carotenoids also can influence immune function through their antioxidant activity, regulation of membrane fluidity, and role in communication among cells.[18]

Carotenoids and Vision

Lutein and its close relative zeaxanthin are found in the macula, the central portion of the retina that is responsible for sharp and detailed vision. Scientists believe these carotenoids may protect the macula by filtering harmful blue light and by antioxidant activity.[19] Epidemiological studies suggest that increased intake of lutein lowers risk for age-related macular degeneration.[20] People with the highest intakes of lutein and zeaxanthin also have a decreased risk of cataracts.[21] However, beta-carotene supplementation seems to have no influence.[22]

Carotenoids and Cancer

In addition to providing antioxidant protection from free radical cell membrane and DNA damage, certain carotenoids, including lycopene and beta-carotene, can strengthen growth-regulatory signals between cells and help prevent damaged cells from reproducing and forming tumors. People with the highest intakes of carotenoid-rich fruits and vegetables and/or high blood levels of specific carotenoids usually have the lowest risk for certain types of cancer. Eating tomato products such as tomato sauce (yes, even ketchup), for example, is associated with reduced risk of prostate cancer.[23] Tomato products are excellent sources of the carotenoid lycopene, and research suggests that a diet rich in lycopene reduces the risk of heart disease, osteoporosis, and several cancers.[24]

Animal and human studies associate foods rich in specific carotenoids with reduced risks of specific cancers:[25]

- Lycopene may lower the risk of prostate cancer.
- Lutein, zeaxanthin, alpha-carotene, and lycopene may lower the risk of lung cancer.
- Alpha-carotene, beta-carotene, lutein, and zeaxanthin may lower the risk of breast cancer.
- Cryptoxanthin forms an antioxidant barrier in the human skin to protect against skin cancer and may also protect women from cervical cancer.

Generally, studies show stronger effects from fruits and vegetables in the diet than from isolated carotenoid supplementation.

Quick Bite

The Production Continues

Compared with freshly picked fruit, watermelon stored for 14 days at 70°F gained up to 40 percent more lycopene and 50 percent to 139 percent extra beta-carotene. Study findings showed that watermelons continue to produce these nutrients after they are picked and that chilling slows this process.

Absorption and Storage of Carotenoids

In foods, fibrous proteins tightly bind carotenoids, so your body absorbs only 20 to 40 percent of what you consume. (See **Figure 10.12**.) This proportion drops even further—to 10 percent or less—as the amount of carotenoids you eat increases. Olestra (a fat substitute in some snack foods) and dietary fiber also reduce carotenoid absorption. Conversely, dietary fat, protein, and vitamin E enhance carotenoid absorption. When dietary fat enters the small intestine, bile is secreted, which helps emulsify the fat and enhances the absorption of carotenoids. In fact, when there is a lack of bile, carotenoids are not absorbed.[26] Intestinal cells convert most absorbed carotenoids to

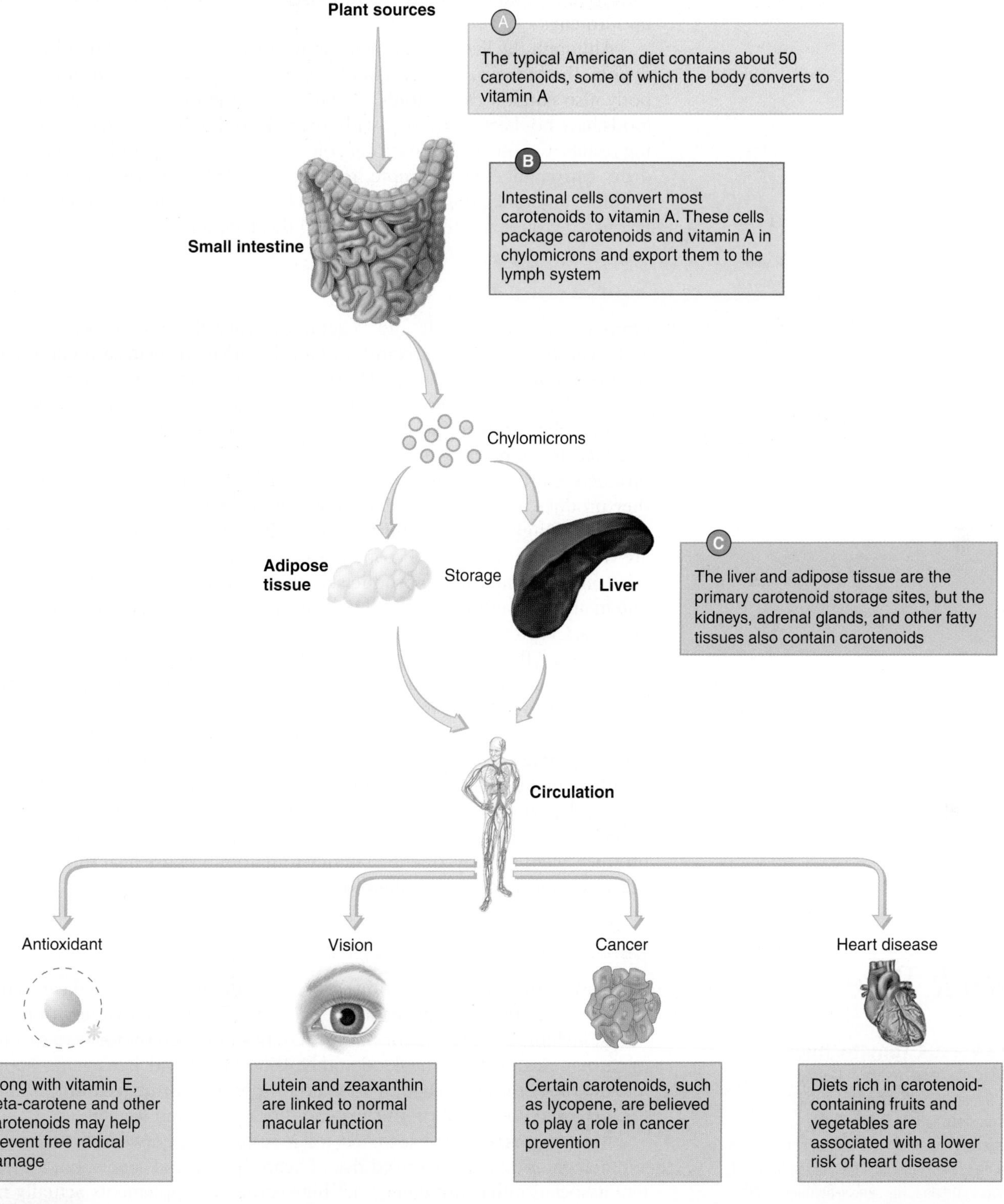
CAROTENOIDS: FROM SOURCE TO DESTINATION
Plant sources
A
The typical American diet contains about 50 carotenoids, some of which the body converts to vitamin A
Small intestine
B
Intestinal cells convert most carotenoids to vitamin A. These cells package carotenoids and vitamin A in chylomicrons and export them to the lymph system
Chylomicrons
Adipose tissue
Storage
Liver
C
The liver and adipose tissue are the primary carotenoid storage sites, but the kidneys, adrenal glands, and other fatty tissues also contain carotenoids
Circulation
Antioxidant
Vision
Cancer
Heart disease
Along with vitamin E, beta-carotene and other carotenoids may help prevent free radical damage
Lutein and zeaxanthin are linked to normal macular function
Certain carotenoids, such as lycopene, are believed to play a role in cancer prevention
Diets rich in carotenoid-containing fruits and vegetables are associated with a lower risk of heart disease

Figure 10.12 **Carotenoids: from source to destination.** In the body, the provitamin A carotenoids alpha-carotene, beta-carotene, and beta-cryptoxanthin can be converted to retinol. The nonprovitamin A carotenoids lycopene, lutein, and zeaxanthin have no vitamin A activity. Independent of vitamin A activity, carotenoids can function as antioxidants, and may be involved in normal macular function and reduced risk of heart disease and cancer.

vitamin A and deliver the remaining absorbed and unchanged carotenoids to the lymph and eventually the bloodstream, where they circulate bound to lipoproteins.

Although the liver and adipose tissue are the primary carotenoid storage depots, the kidneys, adrenal glands, and other fatty tissues throughout the body also contain carotenoids.[27] Extremely large intakes of carotenoid-rich foods have not been associated with toxic effects, but they can have disconcerting results. Carotenoids are strong coloring agents, and people who regularly drink carrot juice, for example, may suddenly discover that their skin has acquired an orange tinge! They have the harmless condition carotenodermia, just like the baby in the introduction to this chapter.

Sources of Carotenoids

Orange and yellow fruits and vegetables generally contain beta-carotene, alpha-carotene, and cryptoxanthin. Good sources of beta-carotene include carrots, pumpkins, winter squash, sweet potatoes, and some orange-colored fruits such as cantaloupes, apricots, and mangos. Carrots and pumpkins are rich in alpha-carotene too. Because of its yellow-orange color, beta-carotene is added to margarine, gelatin, soft drinks, cake mixes, cereals, and other products. Dark-green vegetables also contain abundant carotenoids; however, they produce less vitamin A than ripe orange-colored fruit.[28]

Surprisingly, oranges and tangerines have little beta-carotene, but they are rich in cryptoxanthin. Lycopene has a more reddish color; you will find it in tomatoes and tomato products, pink grapefruit, guava, and watermelon. Lutein and zeaxanthin are found in leafy green vegetables, pumpkins, and red peppers. Cryptoxanthin is found in mangos, nectarines, oranges, papaya, and tangerines.[29] Because it's hard to identify carotenoids in food just by looking, it's important to eat a wide variety of fruits and vegetables, and plenty of them, to ensure a good intake of all carotenoids.

A few minutes of cooking breaks some of the chemical bonds in food. This helps release carotenoids and makes them easier to absorb. In a study of healthy females, daily consumption of processed carrots and spinach over a four-week period tripled their beta-carotene blood levels compared with their blood levels when they consumed these vegetables raw.[30] Cooked tomato products yield more lycopene than raw tomatoes because heat ruptures plant cell walls, releasing the carotenoid.

Carotenoid Supplementation

More and more people are taking carotenoid supplements. Mixed carotenoid supplements derived from sea algae or palm oil contain a variety of carotenoids, including the six major ones. A UL has not been set for beta-carotene or carotenoids. Instead, the Food and Nutrition Board advises against supplementation for the general population and supports existing recommendations for increased consumption of carotenoid-rich fruits and vegetables.

Many scientists have searched for a connection between beta-carotene supplementation and a reduced risk of heart disease and cancer, but a consistent association has not emerged.[31]Beta-carotene supplements actually may cause harm to current smokers and people exposed to asbestos.[32] On the other hand, there is a strong link between eating fruits and vegetables rich in carotenoids and reduced disease rates.[33] In foods there may be beneficial interactions among naturally occurring beta-carotene, other carotenoids, and other phytochemicals. Additional carotenoids, such as lycopene, lutein, and cryptoxanthin, are now being studied. Although eating carotenoid-rich fruits

Quick Bite

Pizza Versus Tomato Juice

One U.S. study linked intake of tomato sauce, tomatoes, and pizza to lowered risk of prostate cancer. Tomato juice, however, was not protective. That's not surprising. According to John Erdman, Ph.D., of the University of Illinois in Urbana, the cancer-fighting carotenoid found in tomatoes (lycopene) is a fat-soluble substance, so it needs some fat like that found in pizza and most pasta sauces to be absorbed. The lycopene in tomato juice, however, seems to be especially poorly absorbed.

and vegetables is clearly linked to reduced disease rates, the use of carotenoid supplements is not recommended.

Vitamin D

Sometimes called the sunshine vitamin, vitamin D is unique because, given sufficient sunlight, your body can synthesize all it needs of this fat-soluble nutrient. In fact, it could be argued that vitamin D is technically not a nutrient—it is synthesized and functions like a hormone, and it is not always necessary in the diet. When the ultraviolet rays of the sun strike the skin, they alter a precursor derived from cholesterol, converting it into vitamin D. Although fortified milk and other foods supply vitamin D, your body can make plenty as long as it gets regular exposure to sunlight.

Vitamin D is essential for bone health and may help reduce cancer risk. In children, it promotes bone development and growth. In adults, it is necessary for bone maintenance. In the elderly, vitamin D helps prevent osteoporosis and fractures. In addition, supplemental vitamin D can reduce the risk of falls in the elderly.[34] Although severe vitamin D deficiency in children and adults is rare, groups at risk for vitamin D deficiency include exclusively breastfed infants, patients with fat malabsorption, obese people, individuals with limited sunlight exposure and those with dark skin, and older adults.[35]

Quick Bite

A Fishy Cure

Cod liver oil was well known in the early nineteenth century as a treatment for rickets, a bone disease common in children. It wasn't until the early 1900s, however, that vitamin D was identified as the "antirachitic" (antirickets) substance in cod liver oil.

Going Green

Resisting Oxidative Stress

Fossil fuel–burning power plants pump out a steady stream of essential energy, but they also produce reactive waste products that can damage the environment. Like coal-fired power plants that pollute the environment, cellular power plants (our mitochondria) produce reactive oxygen species (ROS) that slowly oxidize lipids and damage cell membranes, proteins, and DNA. Such oxidative stress has been implicated in diseases of aging (e.g., heart disease and cancer) and general age-related declines.

Because diets rich in antioxidants can reduce the incidence of age-related diseases, a dietary solution once seemed possible: simply add more antioxidants to our diet, and there should be fewer ROS to cause harm. However, large clinical trials of antioxidant supplementation not only failed to show clinically significant benefits but were actually harmful for some subgroups. This result was surprising. It illustrates that we still have a lot to learn about aging, and it sent scientists back to the drawing board.

How can we explain this seeming contradiction? Some scientists suggested that our cells are already stuffed to near capacity with antioxidant defenses; adding even more antioxidants may compromise intricate molecular machinery. Also, it might be that ROS can cause damage even before encountering the neutralizing antioxidants.

Instead of increasing antioxidants, perhaps we could make biomolecules intrinsically more resistant to oxidation? At a minimum, this radical approach should tell us something about antioxidants and aging. Retrotope, a Silicon Valley biotech company, is pursuing this approach using a stable isotope of hydrogen to construct variants of fatty acids and amino acids that are resistant to oxidative damage. (Tiny amounts of these varients already occur in nature.) Studies in yeast and mice show that when these oxidation-resistant variants replace oxidation-prone fatty acids critical to the maintenance of mitochondrial membranes, they do in fact provide protection from oxidative stress. It is hoped that when these fatty acids and amino acids are fed to mammals, similar resistance to oxidation will occur.

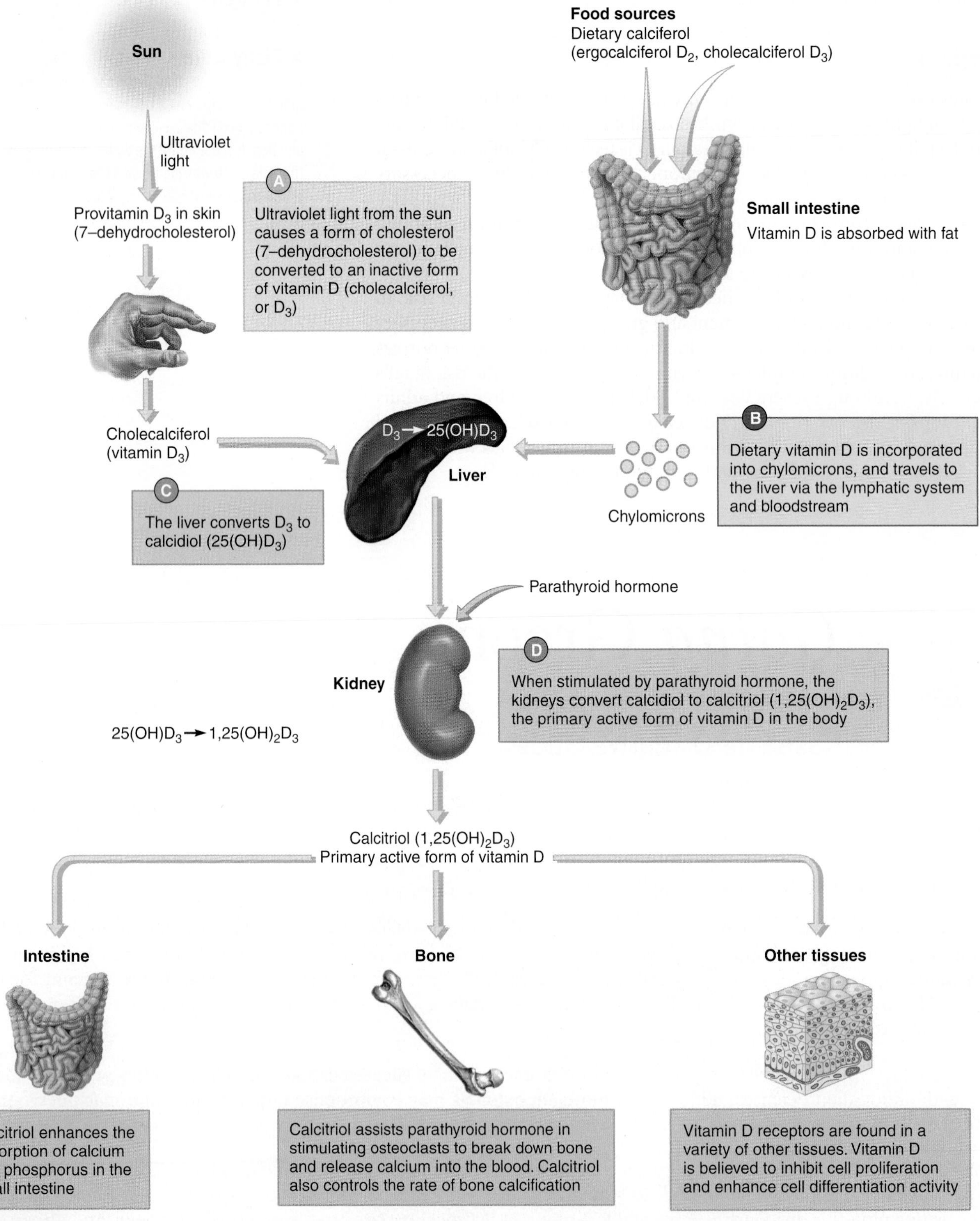
VITAMIN D: FROM SOURCE TO DESTINATION
Sun
Ultraviolet light
Provitamin D_3 in skin (7–dehydrocholesterol)
A
Ultraviolet light from the sun causes a form of cholesterol (7–dehydrocholesterol) to be converted to an inactive form of vitamin D (cholecalciferol, or D_3)
Food sources
Dietary calciferol (ergocalciferol D_2, cholecalciferol D_3)
Small intestine
Vitamin D is absorbed with fat
Cholecalciferol (vitamin D_3)
$D_3 \rightarrow 25(OH)D_3$
Liver
Chylomicrons
B
Dietary vitamin D is incorporated into chylomicrons, and travels to the liver via the lymphatic system and bloodstream
C
The liver converts D_3 to calcidiol ($25(OH)D_3$)
Parathyroid hormone
Kidney
$25(OH)D_3 \rightarrow 1,25(OH)_2D_3$
D
When stimulated by parathyroid hormone, the kidneys convert calcidiol to calcitriol ($1,25(OH)_2D_3$), the primary active form of vitamin D in the body
Calcitriol ($1,25(OH)_2D_3$)
Primary active form of vitamin D
Intestine
Bone
Other tissues
Calcitriol enhances the absorption of calcium and phosphorus in the small intestine
Calcitriol assists parathyroid hormone in stimulating osteoclasts to break down bone and release calcium into the blood. Calcitriol also controls the rate of bone calcification
Vitamin D receptors are found in a variety of other tissues. Vitamin D is believed to inhibit cell proliferation and enhance cell differentiation activity

Figure 10.13 **Vitamin D: from source to destination.** Vitamin D is unique because, given sufficient sunlight, your body can synthesize all it needs. Both dietary and endogenous vitamin D must be activated by reactions in the kidneys and liver. Active vitamin D [$1,25(OH)_2D_3$, or calcitriol] is important for calcium balance and bone health, and may have a role in cell differentiation.

Forms and Formation of Vitamin D

Vitamin D can be considered either a vitamin or a hormone. Like other vitamins, a lack of dietary vitamin D (coupled with minimal sun exposure) will cause a deficiency. The active form of vitamin D is like a hormone because it is made in one part of the body and regulates activities in other parts. (See **Figure 10.13**.)

Ten compounds, called vitamin D_1 through D_{10}, exhibit **antirachitic** properties; that is, they prevent a childhood bone disease called rickets. The most important of these compounds are D_2 (ergocalciferol) and D_3 (cholecalciferol). Ergocalciferol is found exclusively in plant foods. Cholecalciferol is found in animal foods (eggs and fish oils), but most is synthesized in the skin.

In the skin, UV radiation from the sun converts a cholesterol derivative (7-dehydrocholesterol) to cholecalciferol, which then enters the bloodstream and travels to the liver. The liver also receives dietary cholecalciferol and ergocalciferol from chylomicrons. In the liver, cholecalciferol and ergocalciferol are converted into calcidiol and then sent to the kidneys. The kidneys perform the final step—the formation of **1,25-dihydroxyvitamin D_3 [1,25$(OH)_2D_3$]**, also called **calcitriol**. 1,25$(OH)_2D_3$ is the active form of vitamin D, and the body derives about 90 percent of its 1,25$(OH)_2D^3$ from the cholecalciferol synthesized in the skin.[36]

> ## *Quick* Bite
>
> **"Children's Disease of the English"**
>
> In the seventeenth century, vitamin D deficiency was so common in British children that rickets was called the "children's disease of the English." Diets provided little vitamin D, and the lack of sun during many months of the year inhibited vitamin D synthesis in the skin.

Functions of Vitamin D

Vitamin D is a regulatory compound. Although its primary role is to regulate blood calcium levels,[37] it also is important for regulating cell differentiation and growth. Research shows that vitamin D may be protective against colorectal cancer.[38] (See the Nutrition Science in Action feature "Vitamin D and Colon Cancer.") Investigators also are looking for ways vitamin D and its derivatives might treat other conditions of abnormal cell growth, such as psoriasis and cancers of the blood, lung, and cervix. Vitamin D deficiency has been linked to increased risk for cardiovascular disease, multiple sclerosis, rheumatoid arthritis, and type 1 diabetes.[39]

Regulation of Blood Calcium Levels

The liver and adipose tissues store vitamin D. In times of need, the liver and kidneys convert stored vitamin D to 1,25$(OH)_2D_3$, the biologically active form in the body. 1,25$(OH)_2D_3$ helps maintain calcium and phosphorus blood levels within a normal range. 1,25$(OH)_2D_3$ acts directly and in concert with two other hormones: **parathyroid hormone** (parathormone) from the parathyroid gland, and **calcitonin** from the thyroid gland. (See Figure 11.21 in Chapter 11.) These hormones regulate activity in the bone, kidneys, and small intestine to adjust blood calcium levels. Much as a thermostat monitors temperature, receptors in the parathyroid gland monitor the blood levels of calcium.

When blood calcium levels drop, the parathyroid gland releases parathyroid hormone (PTH). PTH stimulates the activity of **osteoclasts** (bone cells that digest the bone matrix), releasing calcium ions from bone into the bloodstream. Parathyroid hormone also raises blood calcium levels by signaling the kidneys to slow calcium excretion. In addition, PTH stimulates the kidneys to activate vitamin D. 1,25$(OH)_2D_3$ is released by the kidneys and enhances the action of PTH on bone cells. 1,25$(OH)_2D_3$ then stimulates the intestinal cells to make more carrier proteins for calcium transport, enhancing

antirachitic Pertaining to activities of an agent used to treat rickets.

1,25-dihydroxyvitamin D_3 [1,25$(OH)_2D_3$] The active form of vitamin D. It is an important regulator of blood calcium levels.

calcitriol See *1,25-dihydroxyvitamin D_3*.

parathyroid hormone A hormone secreted by the parathyroid glands in response to low blood calcium. It stimulates calcium release from bone and calcium absorption by the intestines, while decreasing calcium excretion by the kidneys. It acts in conjunction with 1,25$(OH)_2D_3$ to raise blood calcium. Also called parathormone.

calcitonin A hormone secreted by the thyroid gland in response to elevated blood calcium. It stimulates calcium deposition in bone and calcium excretion by the kidneys, thus reducing blood calcium.

osteoclasts Bone cells that promote bone resorption and calcium mobilization.

Nutrition Science *in Action*

Vitamin D and Colon Cancer

Background: Studies of mice fed a diet rich in vitamin D have shown that vitamin D lowers the risk of colon cancer. Studies of humans link calcium and reduced colon cancer risk. Because vitamin D increases the absorption of calcium, high vitamin D intake may reduce colon cancer risk.

Hypothesis: People who have high vitamin D intakes will have a lower risk of colon cancer than people with low vitamin D intakes.

Experimental Plan: Recruit subjects aged 50 to 75 years from 13 Veterans Administration medical centers. Obtain complete medical histories and dietary information. Exclude subjects who are currently participating in other studies, have a history of colon disease, or have had prior colonic surgery or colonic examination. Follow and collect data for three years.

Results: The hypothesis is confirmed. Analyses of the data from 1,770 participants showed significant reductions in the relative risk of cancer with increased intake of vitamin D. Total calcium and total folate intake also showed significant risk reduction, but vitamin D dominated both. Participants who consumed more than 645 IU (16 micrograms) of vitamin D daily were 40 percent less likely to have advanced polyps.

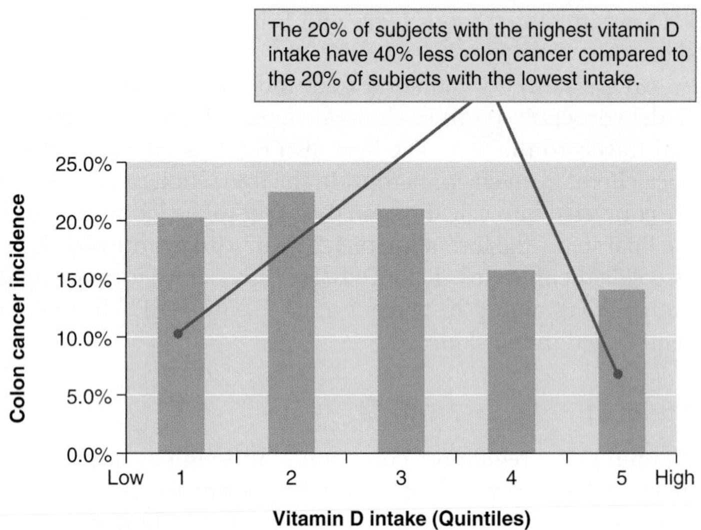

Conclusion and Discussion: Consuming vitamin D plus calcium may be a low-risk preventive strategy for colon cancer. This study also showed that smoking and moderate to heavy alcohol use increased the risk of colon cancer. Although men accounted for 96.8 percent of the study subjects, other studies confirmed these results in women. Scientists suggest that future studies will also compare the effects of vitamin D supplements with those obtained from diets rich in vitamin D.

Source: Based on Lieberman D, Prindiville S, Weiss D, Willett W, for VA Cooperative Study Group 380. Risk factors for advanced colonic neoplasia and hyperplastic polyps in asymptomatic individuals. *JAMA.* 2003;290(22):2959–2967.

the absorption of calcium from food and thereby helping to elevate blood levels of calcium.

When blood calcium levels are too high, the thyroid gland releases calcitonin and the parathyroid gland decreases its release of PTH. Calcitonin inhibits the activity of osteoclasts, shifting the balance toward the activity of **osteoblasts** (bone-building cells). This net bone-building activity removes calcium ions from the bloodstream and deposits them in new bone. Calcitonin promotes bone growth in children and helps maintain bone health during pregnancy and lactation. Because high levels of calcium in the blood inhibit release of parathyroid hormone, the kidneys continue to excrete calcium. In the absence of PTH, the kidneys activate little or no $1,25(OH)_2D_3$. In the small intestine, lower $1,25(OH)_2D_3$ levels reduce the production of protein carriers for calcium transport, thus reducing calcium absorption.

Even if calcium and phosphorus intakes are adequate, teeth and bones do not calcify normally without $1,25(OH)_2D_3$. Conversely, calcification progresses normally when $1,25(OH)_2D_3$ status is adequate even if calcium and phosphorus levels are low. $1,25(OH)_2D_3$ controls the rate of calcification independent of the absolute blood levels of calcium and phosphorus.

osteoblasts Bone cells that promote bone deposition and growth.

Key Concepts *The best-known function of vitamin D, in the active form of $1,25(OH)_2D_3$, is to help regulate blood calcium levels. $1,25(OH)_2D_3$ works with two other hormones, parathyroid hormone and calcitonin, to alter the amount of calcium in the bone, the amount excreted from the kidneys, and the amount absorbed from the intestine to keep blood levels in a normal range. It is known that $1,25(OH)_2D_3$ has effects on other tissues, but these functions have not been well studied.*

Dietary Recommendations for Vitamin D

Although the body can synthesize vitamin D, scientists still recognize vitamin D as an essential nutrient for most people. Because of the variability of sunlight throughout the year, and some people's limited sun exposure, intake recommendations have been developed. Dietary recommendations are given as Adequate Intake (AI) levels that assume no available vitamin D from skin synthesis.[40]

As people age, vitamin D synthesis decreases and intake recommendations increase. For men and women aged 19 through 50 years, the AI for vitamin D is 5 micrograms per day. For people aged 51 through 70, the AI increases to 10 micrograms per day, and for people older than 70, the AI rises to 15 micrograms per day. As is the case with vitamin A, International Units (IU) rather than micrograms (μg) will be found on supplement labels. The conversion works out to 1 μg = 40 IU. Therefore, 200 IU is the equivalent of the AI for ages 19 through 50.

Vitamin D has been evaluated in relation to bone mineral density, lower extremity function, dental health, and risk of falls, fractures, and colorectal cancer.[41] Most people do not reach optimal blood vitamin D levels with currently recommended intakes, and many nutritionists suggest that recommended vitamin D intakes should be increased for all adults.[42]

Infants are born with stores of vitamin D that last about nine months. Beyond that, they must obtain vitamin D via exposure to sunlight, formula, or a supplement administered under the guidance of a physician. Breast milk contains very little vitamin D and is unlikely to meet a baby's needs beyond infancy. Exclusively breastfed infants who receive little exposure to sunlight need supplemental vitamin D. Although the AI for infants and children from birth to 18 years is 5 micrograms per day, the American Academy of Pediatrics has issued updated guidelines that increase these recommendations.

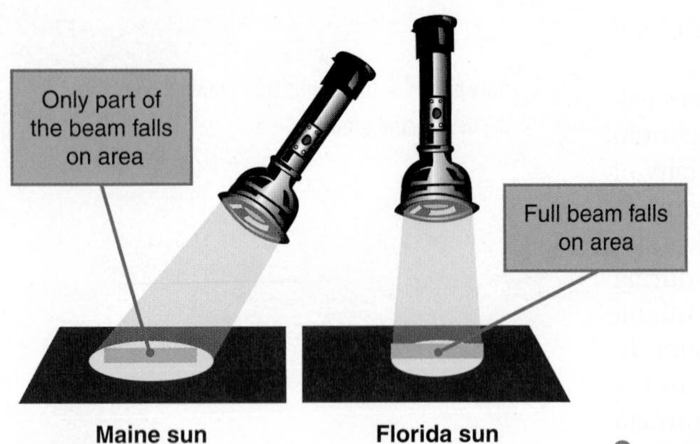

Figure 10.14 Sunlight in Maine and Florida.

For breastfed infants, the American Academy of Pediatrics (AAP) guidelines recommend (1) a minimum of 400 IU per day of supplemental vitamin D shortly after birth and continued until weaning and (2) consumption of 1,000 milliliters per day or more of vitamin D–fortified formula or whole milk. For older children and adolescents who do not obtain 400 IU per day through vitamin D–fortified milk and foods, the AAP recommends 400 IU of supplemental vitamin D daily. These recommendations are based on scientific evidence and the history of safe use of this amount of vitamin D in healthy infants, children, and adolescent populations.[43]

Sources of Vitamin D

In theory, all of our required vitamin D could be synthesized in the skin when it is exposed to UV light. In fact, the diet may supply only about 10 percent of our needs.[44]

Sunlight and Vitamin D Synthesis

How much exposure to the sun is needed for an adequate supply of vitamin D? It depends on several factors, including the following:

- *Time of day.* Exposure of arms and legs for 5 to 30 minutes between the hours of 10 A.M. and 3 P.M. twice per week generally is adequate.[45]
- *Season.* The sun is higher in the sky and delivers more radiation during the summer months.
- *Environment.* Eighty percent or more of the sun's UV rays penetrate clouds,[46] but ordinary window glass blocks UV radiation.
- *Location.* Sunlight is less intense in the northern and southern latitudes than near the equator. A sun worshipper in Florida receives 50 percent more radiation than one in Maine. (See **Figure 10.14**.)
- *Use of sunscreen.* Sunscreen protects the skin against sun damage, but it also almost entirely blocks the ultraviolet light necessary for vitamin D synthesis.
- *Skin type.* Light-skinned people absorb UV rays more quickly than dark-skinned people.

A rule of thumb is to expose your hands, face, and arms to the sun for about one-third to one-half the time it would take you to burn.[47] Repeat this exposure two to three times per week to get adequate vitamin D.

Dietary Sources of Vitamin D

Few foods naturally contain vitamin D, so the major dietary sources of the nutrient are fortified foods such as vitamin D–fortified milk. Other fortified foods, such as breakfast cereal, orange juice, margarine, yogurt, grains, and breads, are also available in the United States. Breads fortified with vitamin D successfully raised serum 25 (OH)D levels, improved bone mineral density, and produced no adverse effect in nursing home residents with limited sunlight exposure.[48]

Vitamin D is found in oily fish (e.g., herring, salmon, and sardines) as well as in cod liver oil and other fish oils. Egg yolk, butter, and liver supply various amounts of vitamin D depending on the vitamin D content of the

foods consumed by the source animals. Plants are a poor source, so strict vegetarians must get their vitamin D through exposure to sunlight. If sun exposure is not possible, nutritionists may recommend dietary supplements. **Figure 10.15** shows some foods that are sources of vitamin D.

Key Concepts *Intake recommendations for vitamin D are very small: only 5 micrograms per day for young adults. Needs from the diet increase with age as the ability of the skin to synthesize vitamin D declines. Few foods are naturally good sources of vitamin D, and so most of the dietary intake comes from fortified milk and other fortified foods.*

Quick Bite

Do You Know Vitamin D When You See It?

The general terms *vitamin D* and *calciferol* are used to refer to both vitamin D_2 (ergocalciferol) and vitamin D_3 (cholecalciferol), and to any combination of these two compounds.

Vitamin D Deficiency

Long-term deficiency of vitamin D takes a profound toll on the skeleton. When vitamin D is in short supply, the intestines absorb only about 10 to 15 percent of dietary calcium, so bones don't get enough of this bone-building mineral.

In a large, nationally representative sample, about 9 percent (7.6 million) of U.S. children and adolescents had vitamin D deficiency, which predisposes them to the development of rickets. In addition, they were more likely to have (1) elevated parathyroid hormone and hypertension and (2) lower calcium and HDL cholesterol levels. Those likely to have lower 25(OH)D levels were older children, girls, non-Hispanic blacks, Mexican Americans, other races, those born outside of the United States, those living in low-income households, obese children, and those who spent more time watching television, playing video games, or using computers. In contrast, children who drank milk daily or who took vitamin D supplements, or both, were less likely to be deficient.[49]

rickets A bone disease in children that results from vitamin D deficiency.

Rickets and Osteomalacia

In children with vitamin D deficiency, the bones weaken and the skeleton fails to harden. This condition, called **rickets**, is characterized by "bow legs,"

Vitamin D

Daily Value = 400 IU

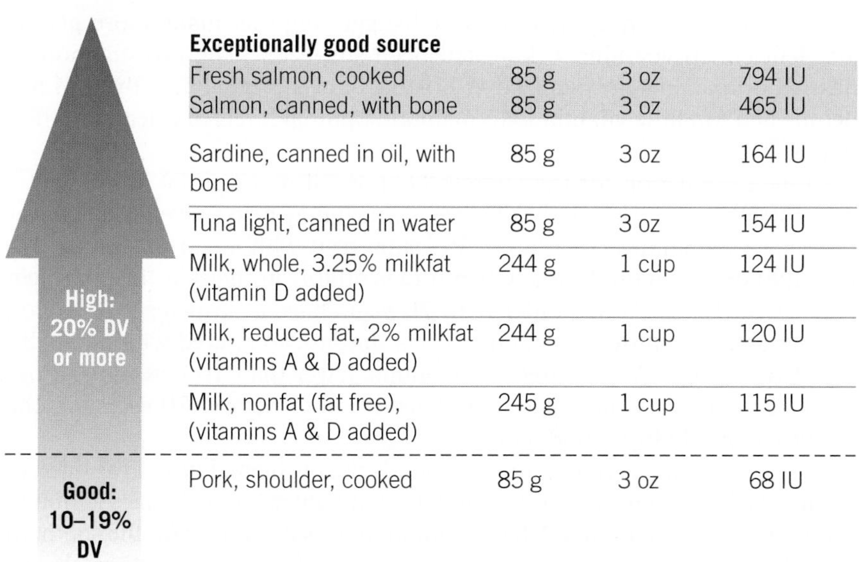

Exceptionally good source			
Fresh salmon, cooked	85 g	3 oz	794 IU
Salmon, canned, with bone	85 g	3 oz	465 IU
High: 20% DV or more			
Sardine, canned in oil, with bone	85 g	3 oz	164 IU
Tuna light, canned in water	85 g	3 oz	154 IU
Milk, whole, 3.25% milkfat (vitamin D added)	244 g	1 cup	124 IU
Milk, reduced fat, 2% milkfat (vitamins A & D added)	244 g	1 cup	120 IU
Milk, nonfat (fat free), (vitamins A & D added)	245 g	1 cup	115 IU
Good: 10–19% DV			
Pork, shoulder, cooked	85 g	3 oz	68 IU

Figure 10.15 Food sources of vitamin D. Only a few foods are naturally good sources of vitamin D. Therefore, fortified foods such as milk and ready-to-eat cereals are important, especially for people with limited exposure to the sun. Units are IU to be consistent with Daily Value definitions.

Source: US Department of Agriculture, Agricultural Research Service. USDA National Nutrient Database for Standard Reference, Release 22. 2009. Nutrient Data Laboratory Home Page, http://www.ars.usda.gov/ba/bhnrc/ndl.

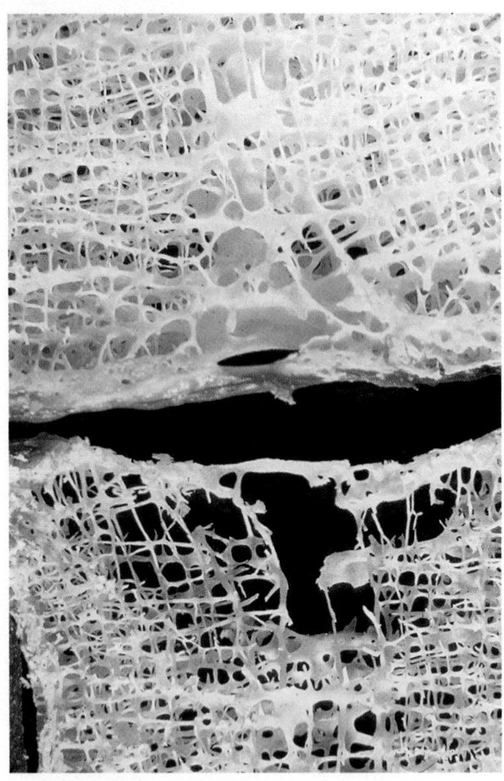

Figure 10.16 **Osteoporosis.** Normal (top) and osteoporotic bone (bottom). The osteoporotic bone is noticeably less dense.

osteomalacia A disease in adults that results from vitamin D deficiency; it is marked by softening of the bones, leading to bending of the spine, bowing of the legs, and increased risk for fractures.

osteoporosis A bone disease characterized by a decrease in bone mineral density and the appearance of small holes in bones due to loss of minerals.

Quick Bite

Too Much Cover
Many Arab women are clothed so that only their eyes are exposed to sunlight. Even though these women live in sunny climates near the equator, many suffer from osteomalacia.

"knock-knees," and other skeletal deformities. In the United States and Canada, nutritional rickets has been all but eliminated by vitamin D–fortified milk, infant vitamin supplements, and vitamin supplements for children with fat-malabsorption conditions. Scattered cases of rickets, however, have been seen in infants allergic to cow's milk and dark-skinned infants who were breastfed, drank nonfortified soy milk, or in some cases had metabolic disorders.[50] Worldwide, 30 to 50 percent of children and adults are at risk of vitamin D deficiency.[51]

In adults, vitamin D deficiency causes a similar skeletal problem called **osteomalacia**, or "soft bones." Osteomalacia increases the risk for fractures in the hip, spine, and other bones. In addition to preventing adequate calcium absorption, osteomalacia alters the function of the parathyroid gland, boosting calcium losses from the bones. Risk of osteomalacia is high in people who have diseases that affect the stomach, kidneys, gallbladder, liver, or intestine—organs that are involved with the absorption or activation of vitamin D.

Osteoporosis

Along with osteomalacia, vitamin D deficiency is associated with **osteoporosis**, increased bone turnover, and an increased risk of bone fractures. (See **Figure 10.16**.) Because vitamin D and calcium work together in bone remodeling, many supplement trials investigate both nutrients simultaneously. A review of evidence-based research found that vitamin D_3 (at 700–800 IU/day) and calcium (500–1,200 mg/day) supplements decreased the risk of falls, fractures, and bone loss in people aged 62 to 85 years.[52] For more information on osteoporosis, see Chapter 12, "Water and Major Minerals," and Chapter 15, "Diet and Health."

Vitamin D and Other Conditions

Emerging research currently is investigating vitamin D's role in the prevention of colorectal, prostate, and breast cancers.[53] Vitamin D might also play some role in the prevention and treatment of autoimmune diseases such as diabetes, multiple sclerosis, and rheumatoid arthritis, as well as hypertension and other medical conditions.[54]

Who Is Most at Risk for Vitamin D Deficiency?

In 1998 a pivotal study was published suggesting that many more people are deficient in vitamin D than had been suspected. The investigation of nearly 300 patients hospitalized in Boston showed that almost three of five people had too little vitamin D to maintain optimal levels of calcium in their bones.[55]

One explanation for the vitamin D shortfall may be that more people are protecting their skin with sunscreen, which may help prevent skin cancer but reduces vitamin D synthesis. Any sunscreen with a sun protection factor (SPF) of 8 or more blocks vitamin D synthesis in the skin. The problem worsens with age. Adults older than 70 years have a 75 percent reduction in their ability to produce vitamin D_3 via the sun, compared with adults 20 to 30 years old.[56] Among free-living adults, fewer than 10 percent of those aged 51 to 70 years and fewer than 2 percent of those over 70 years met the AI for vitamin D from food alone.[57]

Living in a northern region compounds the problem. During the dead of winter, daylight hours are so short and the sunlight is so weak that vitamin D synthesis halts. (See **Figure 10.17**.) Although the same is true for the southern latitudes, little of the world's population lives in this region. Fortunately, the skin of most people younger than 50 years can make sufficient amounts of vitamin D with just the amount of skin on the hands exposed for 10 to 15 minutes per day during warmer months. Most younger people make and store enough vitamin D during the summer to last through the winter months.

People over age 50 are advised to expose some skin to the sun for about 15 minutes each day during warm months. In the winter, many experts recommend a vitamin supplement. Most multivitamin/mineral supplements contain 10 micrograms (400 IU) of vitamin D. Healthy adults over age 70 should check with their physicians to determine whether more supplemental vitamin D is in order.

Despite lower levels of 25(OH)D, African Americans have fewer osteoporotic fractures than Caucasians due to greater bone density.[58] There is an inverse relationship between body mass index (BMI) and plasma 25(OH) D levels. Because vitamin D is fat soluble, the vitamin gets "trapped" in the subcutaneous fat tissue and is not as readily released into circulation.[59]

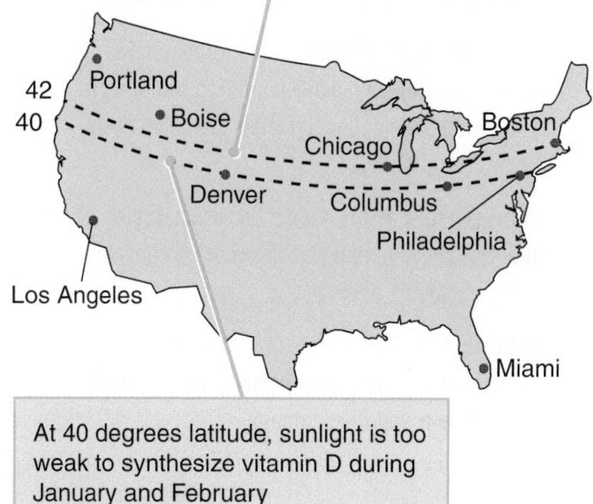
North of 42 degrees latitude, sunlight is too weak to synthesize vitamin D from late October through early March. The same effect occurs during the winter in the southern hemisphere south of 42 degrees latitude
42
40
Portland
Boise
Chicago
Boston
Denver
Columbus
Philadelphia
Los Angeles
Miami
At 40 degrees latitude, sunlight is too weak to synthesize vitamin D during January and February

Figure 10.17 **Mapping vitamin D synthesis.** Vitamin D synthesis halts for part of the winter if sunlight is too weak. In Los Angeles and Miami, the sunlight is strong enough to synthesize vitamin D year-round, even in January.

Vitamin D Toxicity

Sun exposure does not cause vitamin D toxicity, but high supplement doses can be highly toxic. The UL for adults older than 19 years is 50 micrograms (2,000 IU) per day. Before consuming supplements that contain more than the AI, people should consult a physician.

The hallmark of vitamin D toxicity is hypercalcemia—a high concentration of calcium in the blood. This condition affects numerous tissues in the body and can result in bone loss and kidney stones. Initially, it hampers the kidneys' ability to concentrate urine, causing excessive urination and thirst. Prolonged hypercalcemia can cause the excess calcium in the bloodstream to leave deposits in the soft tissues of the body, including the kidneys, blood vessels, heart, and lungs. Hypercalcemia also seems to affect the central nervous system, causing a severe depressive illness as well as nausea, vomiting, and loss of appetite. Because vitamin D toxicity is severe but unlikely in healthy people with intake levels lower than 10,000 IU per day, the current Tolerable Upper Limit (UL) for calcium is likely to be conservative.[60]

Key Concepts *Because vitamin D's primary function is to regulate the level of calcium in the blood, which affects storage of calcium in bone, a deficiency of the nutrient affects the skeletal system. In children, vitamin D deficiency leads to rickets; in adults, lack of the nutrient causes osteomalacia and contributes to osteoporosis. Vitamin D is toxic when consumed in excess, and large doses should be taken only under a physician's supervision. Exposure to sun does not cause vitamin D toxicity.*

Vitamin E

Consumers have long embraced the practice of taking large amounts of vitamin E, once touted as being able to boost sexual prowess and to prevent gray hair, wrinkles, and other signs of aging. Although many of these rumored benefits of vitamin E have never been supported by science, a growing body of research suggests that the nutrient may, in fact, be an important protector against chronic diseases associated with aging.

Forms of Vitamin E

In 1922 researchers discovered that an unknown substance in vegetable oils was necessary for reproduction in rats. It was given the chemical name

tocopherol The chemical name for vitamin E. There are four tocopherols (alpha, beta, gamma, delta), but only alpha-tocopherol is active in the body.

tocotrienols Four compounds (alpha, beta, gamma, delta) chemically related to tocopherols. The tocotrienols and tocopherols are collectively known as vitamin E.

lipid peroxidation Production of unstable, highly reactive lipid molecules that contain excess amounts of oxygen.

glutathione A tripeptide of glycine, cysteine, and glutamic acid that is involved in protection of cells from oxidative damage.

tocopherol, from the Greek word *tokos*, meaning "childbirth," added to the verb *phero*, meaning "to bring forth." The ending *ol* reflects the alcohol nature of the molecule. It was a full 40 years after discovery, however, before scientists gathered evidence showing that humans also need this substance, which they labeled vitamin E. In 1968 the Food and Nutrition Board of the National Academy of Sciences officially recognized vitamin E as an essential nutrient.

Vitamin E is not a single compound. It is actually two sets of four compounds each: the tocopherols (alpha, beta, gamma, and delta) and the chemically related **tocotrienols** (alpha, beta, gamma, and delta). Although all are absorbed, only alpha-tocopherol contributes toward meeting the human vitamin E requirement. Alpha-tocopherol is the most common form of vitamin E in food.

As with all fat-soluble vitamins, absorption of vitamin E requires adequate absorption of dietary fat. Like the other fat-soluble vitamins, it travels via chylomicrons and other lipoproteins for distribution throughout the body. (See **Figure 10.18**.) The GI tract absorbs 20 to 80 percent of dietary alpha-tocopherol, and the percentage declines as the amount of vitamin E consumed increases. Unabsorbed vitamin E is excreted in fecal matter.

Unlike the fat-soluble vitamins A and D, vitamin E does not accumulate in the liver. Adipose tissue contains about 90 percent of the vitamin E in the body. The remaining vitamin E is found in virtually every cell membrane in every tissue.

Functions of Vitamin E

Vitamin E is an antioxidant and its activity is enhanced by other nutrients involved in antioxidant pathways, such as vitamin C and selenium (a mineral). During normal metabolic processes, oxygen often reacts with other compounds to generate free radicals—highly unstable, toxic molecules that contain one unpaired electron. These unpaired electrons make free radicals highly reactive. Typically, a free radical attacks a nearby compound and steals an electron from it. Although that stabilizes the original free radical "thief," it turns the "robbed" molecule into a free radical, sparking a chain reaction capable of instantly producing a flood of free radicals.

Under normal circumstances, your body generates free radicals to help eliminate unwanted molecules. If various enzymes and antioxidants fail to control free radical activity, these highly reactive compounds attack cell membranes and cell constituents, including DNA. This unleashing of free radicals sets the stage for chronic diseases such as cancer and atherosclerosis.

A form of free radical damage that promotes atherosclerosis is **lipid peroxidation**—the production of unstable lipid molecules that contain an excess of oxygen. In this process, the cleavage of a carbon–carbon double bond in a fatty acid yields an intermediate compound that reacts with oxygen to form peroxides or free radicals. To stop lipid peroxidation, vitamin E acts as a potent antioxidant and interrupts the cascade of free radical formation. Vitamin E donates an electron to the electron-seeking free radical, thus preventing the free radical from finding an electron somewhere else and causing more damage. This makes vitamin E itself a free radical, but not a very reactive one. The body excretes some of this altered vitamin E and recycles the rest by adding an electron from another antioxidant, such as vitamin C. This vitamin C radical can regain its antioxidant form by swiping an electron from **glutathione**. The enzyme glutathione reductase restores glutathione to its antioxidant form and depends on the mineral selenium.

VITAMIN E: FROM SOURCE TO DESTINATION

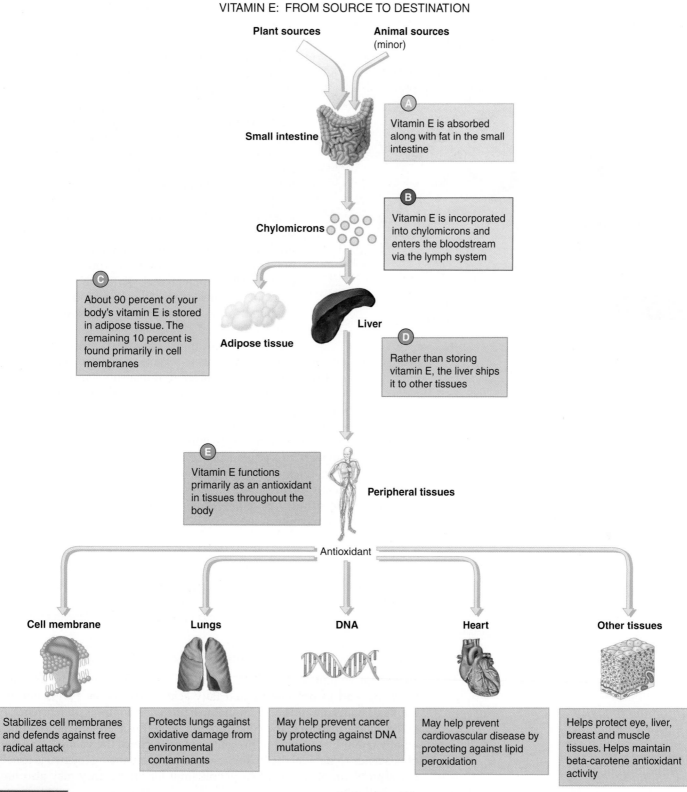

Plant sources

Animal sources (minor)

Small intestine

A Vitamin E is absorbed along with fat in the small intestine

Chylomicrons

B Vitamin E is incorporated into chylomicrons and enters the bloodstream via the lymph system

C About 90 percent of your body's vitamin E is stored in adipose tissue. The remaining 10 percent is found primarily in cell membranes

Adipose tissue

Liver

D Rather than storing vitamin E, the liver ships it to other tissues

E Vitamin E functions primarily as an antioxidant in tissues throughout the body

Peripheral tissues

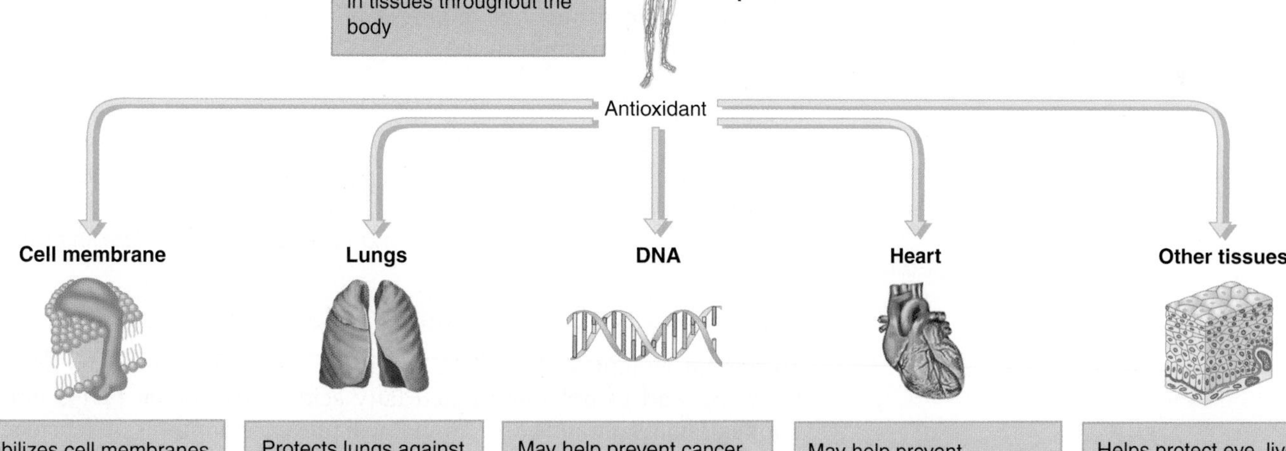

Figure 10.18 **Vitamin E: from source to destination.** Vitamin E is absorbed in the small intestine and carried to the liver by chylomicrons. The antioxidant activity of vitamin E helps stabilize cell membranes, protects tissues from oxidative damage, and reduces the risk of cancer and heart disease.

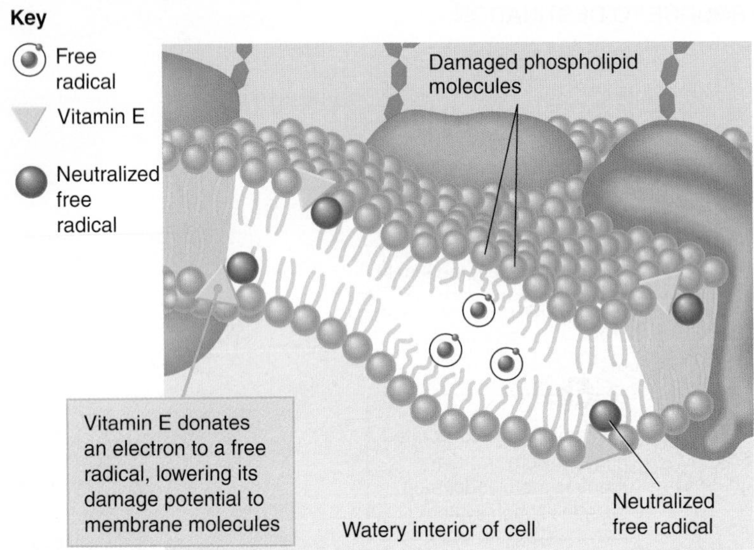

Figure 10.19 **Free radical damage.** Vitamin E helps prevent free radical damage to polyunsaturated fatty acids in cell membranes.

The polyunsaturated fatty acids (PUFAs) in cell membranes are especially vulnerable to assault by free radicals. Vitamin E resides in cell membranes and other phospholipid-rich tissues, where it serves as one of the body's chief defenses against damage by free radicals. (See **Figure 10.19**.)

Long-term intake of 15 milligrams (22 IU) per day of vitamin E decreases chronic disease risk; however 90 percent of Americans consume less than this amount, suggesting that supplementation may be beneficial.[61] Vitamin E supplementation may also reduce the risk of blood clots in women.[62] Observational studies have suggested that high intakes of antioxidant vitamins, including vitamin E, may lower the risk of some chronic diseases, especially heart disease.[63] However, randomized controlled and clinical trials have not supported these findings of protection from heart disease with supplemental vitamin E use. Currently, there are insufficient data to recommend supplemental vitamin E for prevention of heart disease in the general population.[64]

What about other age-related diseases? In some people, supplemental vitamin E appears to reverse age-related declines in immune function. Results of a clinical trial showed that supplemental vitamin E reduced the incidence and duration of respiratory infections in nursing home residents.[65] Although promising laboratory and animal studies suggest that vitamin E may slow the progression of Alzheimer's disease, a review of studies in humans failed to support these preliminary findings.[66] High dietary intake of vitamin E appears protective against cataracts and age-related macular degeneration, but research regarding vitamin E supplementation for these conditions remains inconsistent. Studies of vitamin E supplementation and cancer also have inconsistent findings, and supplemental vitamin E for cancer prevention is not recommended.

Key Concepts *Vitamin E is really a set of compounds called tocopherols and tocotrienols. Alpha-tocopherol is the only form of vitamin E that meets the vitamin E requirement. Vitamin E functions as an antioxidant, protecting cell membranes in all parts of the body from the damaging effects of oxidation. Vitamin E has been connected to reduction of risk for many degenerative diseases, such as heart disease and cancer.*

Dietary Recommendations for Vitamin E

To prevent vitamin E deficiency, the intake requirement must be related to body size and to polyunsaturated fatty acid intake. When PUFA intake is minimal, small amounts of vitamin E will prevent symptoms of deficiency. As PUFA intake increases, the concentration of PUFA in tissues also rises and more vitamin E is needed to prevent oxidation. Since the vitamin E content of oils tends to parallel the PUFA concentration, balancing the two is usually not a problem; however, when people limit fat intake, they may also limit vitamin E intake.

The RDA for vitamin E accommodates generous PUFA intake. It is set at 15 milligrams per day of alpha-tocopherol for adults (including pregnant women) and 19 milligrams per day for women who are breastfeeding. Supplement labels may still list vitamin E content in outdated International Units. If the vitamin E in the supplement is from natural sources, 1 IU equals 0.67

milligrams alpha-tocopherol. If synthetic vitamin E is used, the conversion is 1 IU equals 0.45 milligrams alpha-tocopherol.

Sources of Vitamin E

Vitamin E is found in many different foods from both plant and animal sources. Wheat germ oil contains the highest concentration of usable vitamin E. Vegetable and seed oils, such as safflower, cottonseed, and sunflower seed oils, are also rich sources. Although soybean and corn oils contain much vitamin E, only about 10 percent is alpha-tocopherol, the active form of vitamin E.[67] Foods made from vegetable oils, such as margarine and salad dressings, as well as nuts and seeds, also are good sources. Although substantial amounts of vitamin E are found in strawberries and some green leafy vegetables, most fruits and vegetables contribute only small amounts. Animal products are medium to poor sources of vitamin E and vary widely in their content depending on the fat composition of the given animal's diet. **Figure 10.20** shows foods that are good sources of vitamin E.

In the typical U.S. diet, about 20 percent of vitamin E intake comes from salad oils, margarine, and shortening. Vegetables supply about 15 percent, and more than 12 percent comes from meat, poultry, and fish. Breakfast cereal supplies about 10 percent and fruit contributes about 9 percent of the dietary vitamin E.[68] NHANES III data suggest that American adults consume 8 to 12 milligrams of vitamin E per day from foods. However, this value is likely to be less than actual consumption due to typical underreporting of total fat and energy intake.[69]

Cooking, processing, and storage can reduce the vitamin E content of foods substantially. (See Table 10.1.) During the milling of wheat to make white flour, for instance, vitamin E–rich wheat germ is removed, and if chloride dioxide is used for the bleaching process, all vitamin E is lost. Refining and

Vitamin E

Daily Value = 30 IU

	Food	Weight	Serving	Vitamin E
High: 20% DV or more	Total cereal	30 g	¾ cup	13.50 mg
	All-Bran Wheat Flakes	29 g	¾ cup	13.44 mg
	Tomato paste	262 g	1 cup	11.27 mg
	Sunflower seed kernels	32 g	¼ cup	8.35 mg
	Almonds	28 g	1 oz (24 nuts)	7.43 mg
	Spinach, frozen, cooked	190 g	1 cup	6.73 mg
	Sunflower oil	14 g	1 tbsp	5.59 mg
	Hazelnuts	28 g	1 oz	4.26 mg
Good: 10–19% DV	Tomato sauce, canned	245 g	1 cup	3.48 mg
	Pumpkin, canned	245 g	1 cup	2.60 mg
	Canola oil	14 g	1 tbsp	2.44 mg
	Broccoli, frozen, cooked	184 g	1 cup	2.43 mg
	Red peppers, raw	149 g	1 cup	2.35 mg
	Mangos, raw	207 g	1 mango	2.32 mg
	Peanuts, dry-roasted	28 g	1 oz (28 nuts)	2.21 mg

Figure 10.20 **Food sources of vitamin E.** Nuts and seeds, vegetable oil, and products made from vegetable oil, such as margarine, are among the best sources of vitamin E. Units are IU to be consistent with Daily Value definitions. *Note:* USDA tables list vitamin E in milligrams alpha-tocopherol equivalents (mg ATE). Conversion to IU was done using the formula 1 mg-ATE = 1.5 IU. The USDA Nutrient Database is not complete for vitamin E.

Source: US Department of Agriculture, Agricultural Research Service. USDA National Nutrient Database for Standard Reference, Release 21. 2008. http://www.ars.usda.gov/nutrientdata.

Table 10.1 **Reported Storage and Processing Losses of Vitamin E**

Food	Test Conditions	Vitamin E Loss
Peanut oil	Frying at 347°F (175°C) 30 minutes	32%
Safflower oil	Stored at room temperature, 3 months	55%
Tortillas	Stored at room temperature, 12 months	95%
Almonds	Roasting	80%
Wheat germ	Storage at 39°F (4°C) 6 months	10%
Wheat	Processing to white flour	92%
Bread	Baking	5–50%

Source: *Vitamin E Factbook.* LaGrange, IL: VERIS, 1999. Reprinted with the written consent of Veris Research Information Services.

purifying vegetable oils takes a substantial toll on their vitamin E content. In fact, the by-products of the refining process contain so much vitamin E that they are used to make supplements. Oxygen is the destructive culprit that attacks vitamin E, and both light and heat accelerate oxidation. Safflower oils stored at room temperature for three months lose more than half of their vitamin E. Roasting destroys 80 percent of the vitamin E in almonds.

Key Concepts *The RDA for vitamin E is 15 milligrams of alpha-tocopherol for both men and women. Vitamin E is found in wheat germ, vegetable and seed oils, and products made from these oils, such as salad dressing and margarine. Processing foods can reduce their vitamin E content.*

Vitamin E Deficiency

Because of the widespread use of vegetable oils and other sources in the food supply, vitamin E deficiency is rare in North America. Most deficiencies occur in people with fat-malabsorption syndromes such as cystic fibrosis. One feature of vitamin E deficiency is premature **hemolysis**—the breakdown of red blood cells. Without vitamin E to protect the cells against oxidation, destruction of cell membranes is rampant, causing red blood cells to burst. Hemolysis, and the associated anemia (called hemolytic anemia), is most often seen in infants born prematurely, before vitamin E has been transferred from mother to fetus in the last weeks of pregnancy. Special formulas and supplemental vitamin E are administered to premature babies to help correct the problem.

hemolysis The breakdown of red blood cells that usually occurs at the end of a red blood cell's normal life span. This process releases hemoglobin.

In children and adults, fat-malabsorption disorders and subsequent vitamin E deficiency usually cause neurological problems that affect the spinal cord and peripheral nerves. In adults, malabsorption must be prolonged, from 5 to 10 years, before signs of deficiency surface.

Vitamin E Toxicity

Vitamin E is relatively nontoxic, especially compared with fat-soluble vitamins A and D. It is difficult to consume too much vitamin E from food, but vitamin E supplements can cause problems.[70] One hazard of large doses of vitamin E is the potential to counter vitamin K's blood-clotting mechanism, described in the next section. People who take anticoagulant medications such as warfarin (Coumadin) or aspirin to prevent blood clots should confer with a physician before they self-prescribe large doses of vitamin E.

The antioxidant effects of vitamin E along with its inhibitory effects on platelet adhesion make it a logical choice for reducing heart disease risk. Observational studies support this theory, but results of clinical trials are limited and inconclusive.[71] It is not yet appropriate to recommend high vitamin E intake to reduce risk of chronic disease. For adults, the UL is 1,000 milligrams per day of any form of supplemental alpha-tocopherol.[72] Larger amounts can cause bleeding.[73] An analysis of 19 studies with more than 135,000 patients with chronic disease found that supplementation of 400 IU (approximately 270 milligrams) or more can increase mortality and should be avoided.[74] Healthy individuals given vitamin E supplements for primary disease prevention, however, showed no evidence of increased mortality.[75]

Key Concepts *Deficiencies of vitamin E are rare in adults, occurring primarily in people with fat-malabsorption syndromes. Preterm infants also run a high risk of vitamin E deficiency because they are delivered before the nutrient has a chance to move from the mother to the infant. Hemolysis is the hallmark of such a deficiency. Vitamin E is relatively nontoxic, although large doses interfere with blood clotting.*

Vitamin K

In 1929 Danish researcher Henrik Dam discovered a nutrient that plays a crucial role in blood clotting. He named it vitamin "K" for "koagulation." Although most people give little thought to consuming enough of this nutrient, vitamin K stands between life and death. Without vitamin K to promote blood clotting, a single cut would eventually lead to death by blood loss.

Vitamin K is a family of compounds known as quinones. It includes **phylloquinone** (K_1) from plant sources, **menaquinones** (collectively known as K_2) from animal sources and synthesized by our intestinal bacteria, and the synthetic substances **menadione**, Synkayvite, and Hykinone (collectively known as K_3). Phylloquinone is the major form in the diet and the most biologically active. Menaquinone is only 70 percent as active, and the synthetics drop to 20 percent. Phylloquinone, menaquinone, and the synthetic compound menadione are fat-soluble and primarily stored in the liver. These stores are relatively small and used up rapidly.

The synthetic compounds Synkayvite and Hykinone are water-soluble. These forms are well suited to the treatment of vitamin K deficiency caused by fat-malabsorption disorders. Menadione is considered an unsafe supplemental form of vitamin K.

phylloquinone The form of vitamin K that comes from plant sources. Also known as vitamin K_1.

menaquinones Forms of vitamin K that come from animal sources. Also produced by intestinal bacteria, they are collectively known as vitamin K_2.

menadione A medicinal form of vitamin K that can be toxic to infants. Also known as vitamin K_3.

Functions of Vitamin K

When you get a cut, small or large, and start to bleed, a series of reactions forms a clot that stops the flow of blood. This cascade of reactions involves the production of a series of proteins, and ultimately the protein fibrin. (See **Figure 10.21**.) Four of the procoagulation proteins in the cascade are vitamin K dependent, and all require calcium for activation. For example, vitamin K converts the precursor protein preprothrombin to prothrombin by adding carbon dioxide to glutamic acid (an amino acid) in the protein. This change imparts a calcium-binding capacity, which allows prothrombin to be changed to thrombin. These reactions are integral to the formation of a blood clot.

In addition to promoting the formation of blood clots, vitamin K assists bone formation.[76] The vitamin is thought to work by facilitating a process

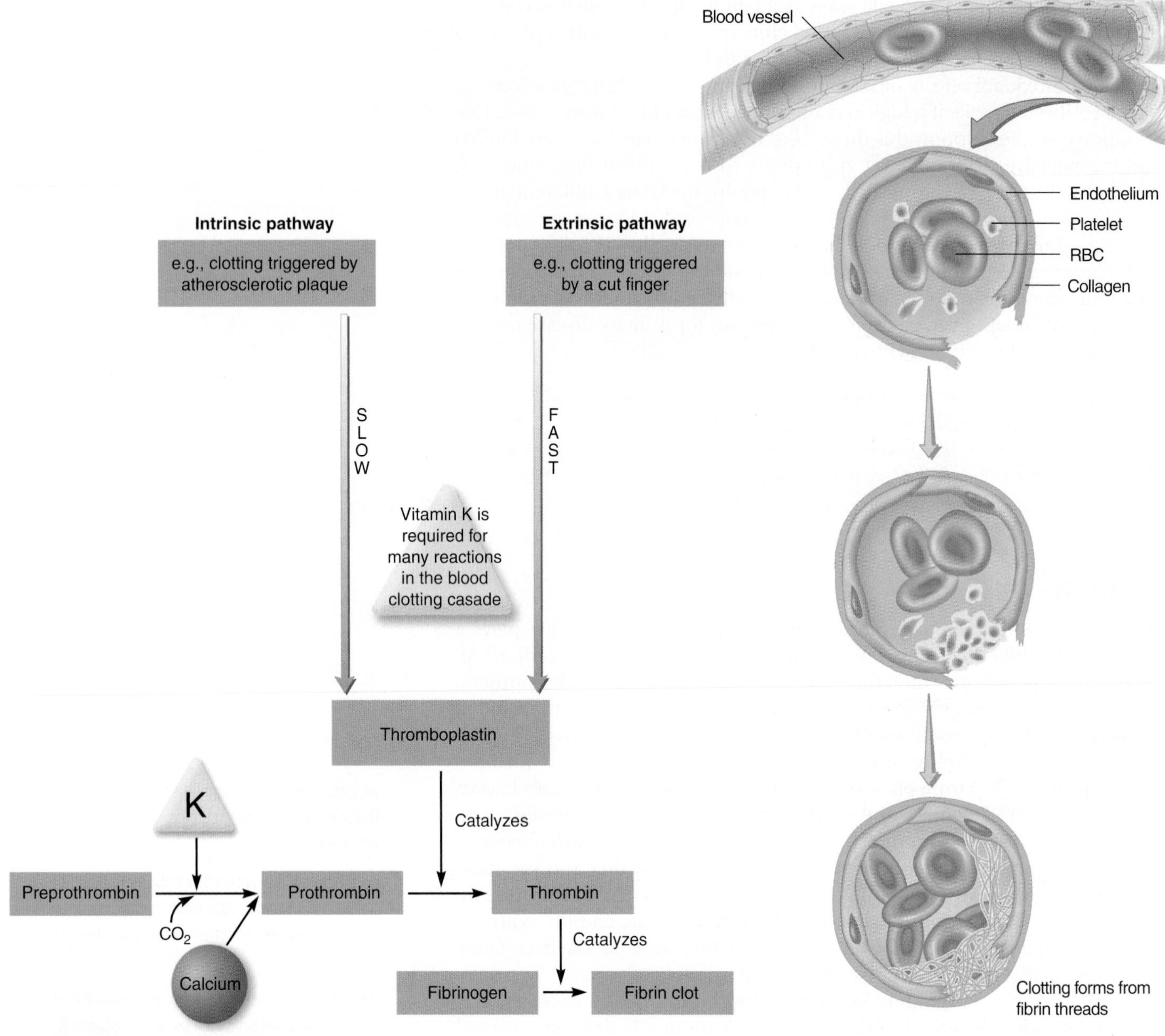

Figure 10.21 **Blood clotting and vitamin K.** The extrinsic and intrinsic pathways share the final steps in forming a clot. Vitamin K has a key role at several points—four of the procoagulation proteins in the cascade are vitamin K dependent.

needed to allow the protein osteocalcin to strengthen the skeleton. Vitamin K is important to the carboxylation of osteocalcin, which allows osteocalcin to become saturated with carboxyl groups (See **Figure 10.22**.). Low levels of vitamin K are associated with low bone mineral density. [77] Some research has shown a correlation between undercarboxylated osteocalcin and bone fractures; other evidence suggests an association between elevated risk of fractures and low levels of vitamin K in the blood.[78] At least two other vitamin K–dependent proteins have been isolated in bone, underscoring the vitamin's importance to bone health.

Key Concepts *Vitamin K was named for the Danish word "koagulation" because the nutrient works to promote the formation of blood clots. Vitamin K also is involved in bone health.*

Dietary Recommendations for Vitamin K

The AI for vitamin K for adult males is 120 micrograms. Recommendations for women are slightly lower: 90 micrograms per day. The AI doesn't change for pregnant and lactating women.

Dietary intake of vitamin K varies with age. In general, adults younger than 45 have intakes that range from 60 to 110 micrograms of phylloquinone per day. In contrast, intakes for adults older than 55 range from 80 to 210 micrograms of phylloquinone per day. Experts attribute this difference to the greater vegetable consumption of older adults compared with that of younger adults.[79]

As with other fat-soluble vitamins, vitamin K absorption depends on normal consumption and digestion of dietary fat. Absorption is poor in people with fat-malabsorption syndromes. Even under normal conditions, absorption of dietary vitamin K may be as low as 40 percent. (See **Figure 10.23**.)

Typical diets easily support vitamin K's role in blood clotting; however, vitamin K supplements may be necessary to support its role in bone health. Systematic review of studies has shown supplemental vitamin K to increase bone mineral density and reduce hip fractures by approximately 80 percent.[80]

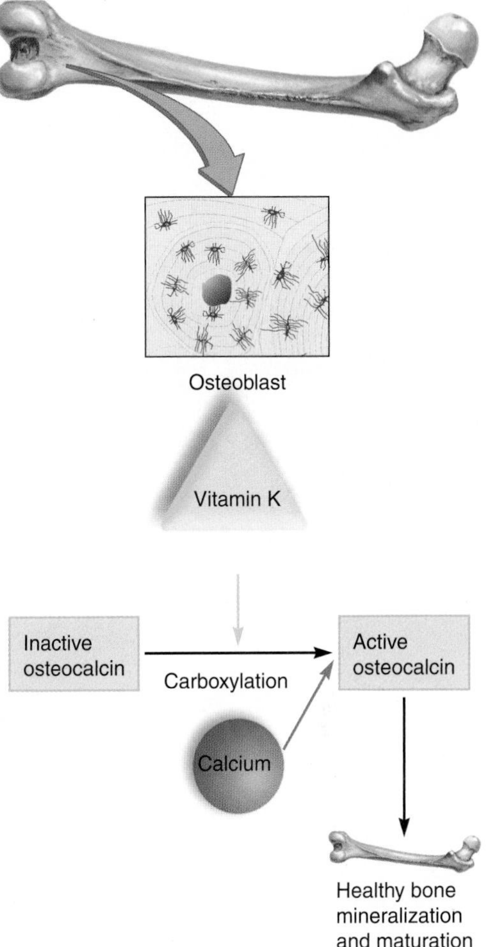

Figure 10.22 **Vitamin K and bone health.** Osteocalcin is an abundant bone protein that is required for bone mineralization and maturation. Vitamin K helps in the carboxylation of osteocalcin, greatly enhancing its calcium-binding properties.

Sources of Vitamin K

We obtain vitamin K from two sources: food (mostly plant food) and bacteria living in our colons. Dietary vitamin K is absorbed in the small intestine, and vitamin K produced by bacteria is absorbed in the colon.[81]

Phylloquinone is the primary form of dietary vitamin K. Green leafy vegetables, especially spinach, turnip greens, broccoli, and brussels sprouts, supply substantial amounts of phylloquinone. Certain vegetable oils (soybean, cottonseed, canola, and olive) also are good sources.[82] Exposure to light degrades vitamin K, so the phylloquinone content of oils varies not only with brand and batch but also with storage time if the oils are bottled in transparent containers. Therefore, vegetable oils may not be a reliable source of vitamin K.

In general, animal products contain limited amounts of vitamin K. Small amounts of menaquinones are found in egg yolks and butter, and various cheeses contain moderate amounts. Soybean products such as tofu contain substantial amounts of menaquinones. Liver contains moderate amounts of menaquinones, but because most people rarely eat liver, it is unlikely to contribute much to the general consumption of vitamin K. The concentrations of menaquinones in other animal organs, such as kidney, heart, and muscle, are low and nutritionally insignificant.[83] **Figure 10.24** shows foods that contain vitamin K.

Key Concepts *Dietary recommendations for vitamin K intake are small; the AI for adult men is 120 micrograms, and for adult women it is 90 micrograms. Vitamin K is found primarily in green vegetables and in some vegetable oils. Animal foods, in general, contain limited amounts of vitamin K.*

Vitamin K Deficiency

Although vitamin K has a crucial role in blood clotting, the body needs only small amounts. This makes vitamin K deficiency rare in healthy adults. On the other hand, preliminary research suggests that typical diets are supplying less than optimal amounts for bone health. Low dietary vitamin K intake is associated with reduced bone density in women[84] and also has been linked to increased fracture risk.[85]

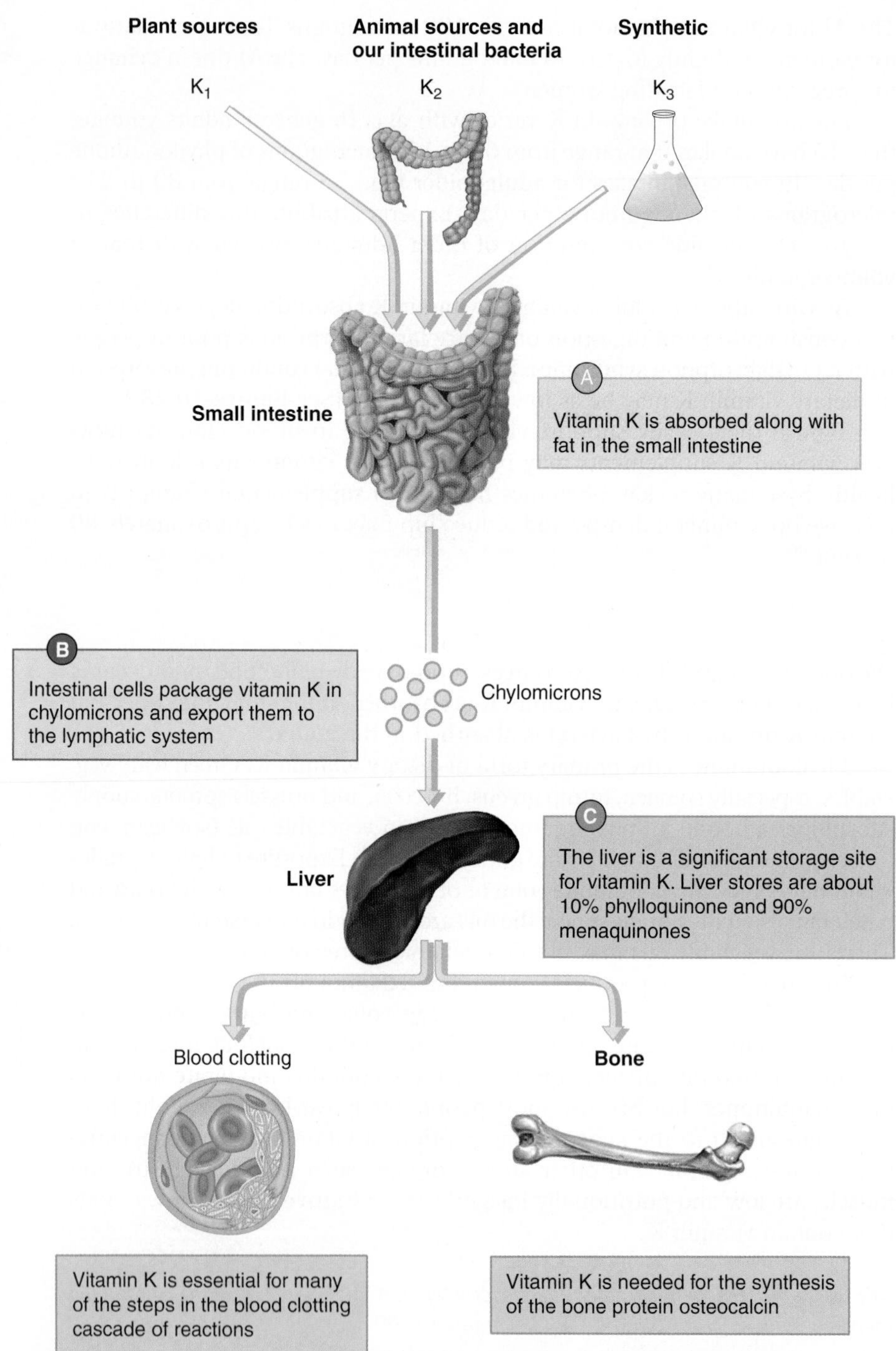

Figure 10.23 **Vitamin K: from source to destination.** Green leafy vegetables are rich sources of vitamin K. Intestinal bacteria produce 10 to 15 percent of our vitamin K, much less than previously believed. Vitamin K is important in both blood clotting and bone health.

Vitamin K

Daily Value = 80 μg

	Food	Weight	Serving	Vitamin K
	Exceptionally good sources			
High: 20% DV or more	Kale, frozen, cooked	130 g	1 cup	1,146.6 μg
	Spinach, cooked	180 g	1 cup	888.5 μg
	Collards, cooked	190 g	1 cup	836.0 μg
	Broccoli, cooked	156 g	1 cup	220.1 μg
	Brussels sprouts, cooked	156 g	1 cup	218.9 μg
	Okra, cooked	160 g	1 cup	64.0 μg
	Romaine lettuce, raw	56 g	1 cup	57.4 μg
	Cabbage, raw	70 g	1 cup	53.2 μg
	Blackeyed peas, cooked	165 g	1 cup	43.9 μg
	Soybeans, cooked	172 g	1 cup	33.0 μg
	Kiwifruit, fresh, raw	76 g	1 medium	30.6 μg
	Asparagus, cooked	60 g	4 spears	30.4 μg
	Blackberries, raw	144 g	1 cup	28.5 μg
	Pickles, cucumber, dill or kosher dill	65 g	1 pickle	25.4 μg
	Plums, dried (prunes)	42 g	5 prunes	25.0 μg
	Grapes, raw	160 g	1 cup	23.4 μg
	Cauliflower, cooked	124 g	1 cup	17.1 μg
Good: 10–19% DV	Margarine	14 g	1 tbsp	13.1 μg
	Green peppers, raw	149 g	1 cup	11.0 μg
	Kidney beans, canned	256 g	1 cup	11.0 μg
	Canola oil	14 g	1 tbsp	10.0 μg
	Cashew nuts, dry roasted	28 g	1 oz (18 nuts)	9.8 μg
	Tomatoes, red, raw	123 g	1 tomato	9.7 μg
	Mangos, raw	207 g	1 mango	8.7 μg

Figure 10.24 **Food sources of vitamin K.** The best sources of vitamin K are vegetables, especially leafy greens and those in the cabbage family.

Source: US Department of Agriculture, Agricultural Research Service. USDA National Nutrient Database for Standard Reference, Release 22. 2009. Nutrient Data Laboratory Home Page, http://www.ars.usda.gov/ba/bhnrc/ndl.

People who suffer fat-malabsorption syndromes, such as celiac disease, sprue, cystic fibrosis, ulcerative colitis, and Crohn's disease, however, can develop vitamin K deficiency. Prolonged use of antibiotics may cause a deficiency because the drugs can destroy the intestinal bacteria that produce vitamin K. Prior to surgery, a patient's vitamin K status is often tested to assess the risk for hemorrhaging because antibiotics are frequently part of the treatment regimen.

Megadoses of vitamins A and E counteract the actions of vitamin K. Vitamin A appears to hamper intestinal absorption of vitamin K, and excess vitamin E seems to decrease the vitamin K–dependent clotting factor, thus promoting bleeding. Physicians prescribe anticoagulant medications, such as warfarin (Coumadin) to reduce the risk of internal blood clotting that could block blood vessels leading to the heart or brain. People who take anticoagulants should maintain a consistent pattern of vitamin K consumption, because large fluctuations can interfere with the effectiveness of these drugs.[86]

Newborn babies, especially those who are breastfed, also run a risk of vitamin K deficiency because at birth they lack the intestinal bacteria that produce the nutrient, and they do not receive much vitamin K via the diet. To prevent hemorrhaging, infants typically receive an injection of vitamin K at birth. This dose usually meets their needs for several weeks, until the vitamin K–producing bacteria begin to flourish.

Vitamin K Toxicity

Vitamin K is stored primarily in the liver and is also found in bone. Because the body excretes vitamin K much more rapidly than the other fat-soluble vitamins, toxicity from food is rare and thus no UL has been set for vitamin K. A vitamin K overdose can cause hemolytic anemia. This condition has been seen in newborns who receive vitamin K in the form of menadione rather than the recommended form, phylloquinone.

Key Concepts *Vitamin K deficiencies are extremely rare. Because it takes several weeks before the intestinal bacteria that produce vitamin K begin to flourish in the intestine, newborns are routinely given injections of vitamin K at birth. Vitamin K toxicity is rare because the body excretes the nutrient more readily than the other fat-soluble vitamins.*

It is well known that milk is an excellent source of calcium, but did you know that milk also contains three of the four fat-soluble vitamins? Let's take a look at the Nutrition Facts from a carton of nonfat milk.

Nutrition Facts

Serving Size: 1 cup (240mL)
Servings Per Container about 8

Amount Per Serving

Calories 90 Calories from fat 0

	% Daily Value*
Total Fat 0g	0%
Saturated Fat 0g	0%
Fat 0g	
Cholesterol less than 5mg	1%
Sodium 130mg	5%
Total Carbohydrate 13g	4%
Dietary Fiber 0g	0%
Sugars 12g	
Protein 9g	18%

Vitamin A 10% · Vitamin C 4%
Calcium 30% · Iron 0%
Vitamin D 25%

* Percent Daily Values are based on a 2,000 calorie diet. Your daily values may be higher or lower depending on your calorie needs:

	Calories:	2,000	2,500
Total Fat	Less Than	65g	80g
Sat Fat	Less Than	20g	25g
Cholesterol	Less Than	300mg	300mg
Sodium	Less Than	2,400mg	2,400mg
Total Carbohydrate		300g	375g
Dietary Fiber		25g	30g
Protein		50g	65g

Calories per gram:
Fat 9 · Carbohydrate 4 · Protein 4

AMOUNTS PER 1 CUP SERVING:	FAT
WHOLE MILK	8g
FAT FREE MILK	0g

INGREDIENTS: GRADE A FAT FREE MILK, VITAMIN A PALMITATE, VITAMIN D_3.

Nonfat Milk	
Calories	90
Total Fat	0
Cholesterol	less than 5mg
Sodium	130mg
Total Carbohydrate	13g
Dietary Fiber	0g
Sugars	12g
Protein	9g
Vitamin A	10% DV
Vitamin C	4% DV
Calcium	30% DV
Iron	0% DV
Vitamin D	25% DV

Milk contains the fat-soluble vitamins A and D. Vitamin A is found naturally in whole milk and is added to reduced-fat milks. All milks are fortified with vitamin D. Although it is true that fat-soluble vitamins can be toxic in large doses because they are stored in the body, the amounts added to milk are not of concern. Vitamin K is not listed on the label, but milk is a good source of this fat-soluble vitamin as well. (Each cup of milk provides 10 micrograms, which is 12.5 percent of the Daily Value.)

A one-cup serving of fortified milk provides 10 percent of the 5,000 IU Daily Value of vitamin A. If you drank three cups of milk per day, you would get about one-third of your recommended amount of vitamin A. That's good news because dietary vitamin A is not always easy to obtain. One form, retinol, is found mainly in liver and fish liver oil, which are not always staples of the typical American diet. The provitamin forms of vitamin A, the carotenoids, are found in green leafy and dark-orange vegetables.

Vitamin D is important because it helps with the absorption of calcium and phosphorus, both important for bone health. Fish liver oil, sardines, and some fortified cereals are also good sources of vitamin D. As shown in the nutrition label, just one cup of milk gives you one-quarter of the vitamin D Daily Value. That's 25 percent of 10 micrograms, or 2.5 micrograms.

Keep in mind when selecting milk that nonfat (skim) milk contains vitamins A and D just like the higher-fat 2% and whole milk. Don't let the large banner "Vitamin A and D" printed on containers of whole milk trick you into thinking it contains more. It doesn't!

Learning Portfolio

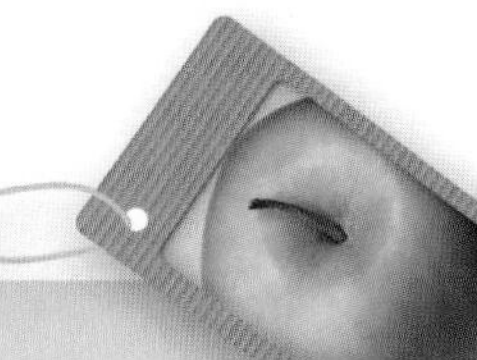

Key Terms

	page		page
antirachitic	407	osteomalacia	412
bleaching process	392	osteoporosis	412
calcitonin	407	parathyroid hormone	407
calcitriol	407	phylloquinone	419
carotenodermia	388	preformed vitamin A	397
carotenoids	391	provitamin A	391
cones	392	provitamins	390
cornea	392	retina	392
dark adaptation	394	retinal	391
epithelial cells	396	retinoic acid	391
epithelial tissues	396	retinoids	390
glutathione	414	retinol	390
goblet cells	396	retinol activity equivalents (RAE)	397
hemolysis	418	retinol-binding protein (RBP)	392
hyperkeratosis	399	retinyl esters	392
international units (IU)	397	rhodopsin	392
iodopsin	395	rickets	411
lipid peroxidation	414	rods	392
menadione	419	stem cells	396
menaquinones	419	teratogen	400
night blindness	394	tocopherol	414
1,25-dihydroxyvitamin D_3 [$1,25(OH)_2D_3$]	407	tocotrienols	414
opsin	392	vitamin precursors	390
osteoblasts	409	xerophthalmia	399
osteoclasts	407		

Study Points

- Vitamins are organic substances the body needs in minuscule amounts.
- Two classes of vitamins exist: fat-soluble vitamins (A, D, E, and K) and water-soluble vitamins (B vitamins and vitamin C).
- Vitamin A comes from preformed retinoids and the precursor carotenoids.
- Vitamin A functions in vision, cell differentiation, growth and development, and immune function.
- Sources of vitamin A include milk fat, liver, green leafy and yellow-orange vegetables, and yellow-orange fruits.
- Night blindness is an early symptom of vitamin A deficiency that, if not treated, can result in permanent blindness.
- Vitamin A is toxic when taken in large doses, causing liver damage and other problems.
- Vitamin D functions like a hormone and the body can synthesize it, but it is still considered a vitamin.
- A vitamin D precursor is produced from cholesterol when UV light hits the skin. Reactions in the liver and kidney are needed to produce a fully active vitamin D molecule.
- Vitamin D in foods is available mainly from fortified milk and other fortified products.
- The primary function of vitamin D is the regulation of blood levels of calcium.
- Vitamin D deficiency contributes to skeletal problems.
- Toxicity of vitamin D can develop with doses just a few times larger than the AI level.
- Vitamin E is an important antioxidant in the body and may help reduce the risk of chronic diseases such as heart disease and cancer.
- Vitamin E is found in vegetable oils and foods made from those oils.
- Deficiency and toxicity of vitamin E are relatively rare.
- Vitamin K is an important factor in blood coagulation.
- Although synthesized by intestinal bacteria, most of the vitamin K in the body comes from dietary sources, especially green vegetables.
- Vitamin K deficiency is rare, but newborns are susceptible if not given an injection of vitamin K at birth.
- Because the body excretes vitamin K easily, toxicity is unlikely.

Study Questions

1. List at least three characteristics of fat-soluble vitamins.
2. List the four fat-soluble vitamins by their general names and specific active forms.

3. What are the main roles of vitamin A in the body?
4. What vitamin deficiency is associated with night blindness?
5. What antioxidant is responsible for the yellow-orange color of cantaloupes?
6. Which fat-soluble vitamin is considered a hormone? What organs does this hormone affect?
7. From what precursor can vitamin D be synthesized?
8. What are the toxicity and deficiency symptoms of vitamin E?
9. How does a vitamin K deficiency lead to the inability to form a blood clot?
10. Which two fat-soluble vitamins are most toxic? Least toxic?

Try This

The PUFA Protection Challenge: Vitamin E Versus Oxygen

The object of this experiment is to see if vitamin E protects polyunsaturated fats (PUFAs) from oxidation. You'll need two glasses, one bottle of either safflower or corn oil, and some liquid vitamin E gel caps (which can be purchased at any pharmacy). Pour equal amounts of oil in each of the glasses. Bite a hole in 10 of the vitamin E gel caps and squeeze their contents into *one* of the glasses. Mark this glass with tape and write the letter E on it. Let the glasses sit uncovered on a countertop for several days or weeks. Check the freshness or rancidity of the oils by smelling them and noting whether they look clear or cloudy. Over time, one will become more rancid than the other. Which glass container won the challenge—the one with or without vitamin E? Why?

What About Bobbie?

Let's check out Bobbie's intake of vitamin A. Refresh yourself with her day of eating in Chapter 1. How do you think Bobbie did in terms of this fat-soluble vitamin? Her intake of 493 μg RAE is about 70 percent of the RDA of 700 μg RAE, so Bobbie is likely meeting her needs for vitamin A. Here are her best vitamin A sources:

Food	Vitamin A (μg RAE)
Carrot (2 Tbsp)	193
Cream cheese (3 Tbsp)	97
Spaghetti sauce (3 oz)	83
Cheese pizza (1 slice)	83
Salsa (½ cup)	43

Bobbie's best sources of vitamin A were both preformed vitamin A sources (animal-origin foods such as cream cheese and pizza cheese) and foods with vitamin A precursors (e.g., beta-carotene from carrots).

Here are some ways she could improve her vitamin A intake:

- Use spinach greens as the base of her salad instead of iceberg lettuce.
- Continue adding shredded carrots to her salad and consider adding them to her sandwich, too.
- Add a slice or two of tomato on top of the bagel with cream cheese.
- Alternate bagels (not high in vitamin A) and fortified cereals (high in vitamin A) for breakfast. This change would also add some milk to her diet, which would further increase her vitamin A intake (~140 μg RAE per cup).

References

1 Mahan KL, Escott-Stump S, eds. *Krause's Food, Nutrition, and Diet Therapy*. 12th ed. Philadelphia: WB Saunders, 2008.

2 Ibid.

3 McCollough FS, Northrop-Clewes CA, Thurnham DI. The effect of vitamin A on epithelial integrity. *Proc Nutr Soc.* 1999;58(2):289–293.

4 Semba RD. The role of vitamin A and related retinoids in immune function. *Nutr Rev.* 1998;56(1 pt 2):S38–S48.

5 Palacios C. The role of nutrients in bone health from A to Z. *Crit Rev Food Sci Nutr.* 2006;46(8):621–628.

6 National Institute of Musculoskeletal and Skin Diseases. Vitamin A and bone health. 2005. http://www.niams.nih.gov/Health_Info/Bone/Bone_Health/Nutrition/vitamin_a.pdf. Accessed 7/15/09.

7 Institute of Medicine, Food and Nutrition Board. *Dietary Reference Intakes for Vitamin A, Vitamin K, Arsenic, Boron, Chromium, Copper, Iron, Manganese, Molybdenum, Nickel, Silicon, Vanadium, and Zinc.* Washington, DC: National Academies Press, 2001.

8 McCollough, Northrop-Clewes, Thurnham. The effect of vitamin A on epithelial integrity.

9 Semba. The role of vitamin A and related retinoids in immune function.

10 Feskanich D, Singh V, Willett WC, Colditz GA. Vitamin A intake and hip fractures among postmenopausal women. *JAMA.* 2002;287:47–54; and Michaelsson K, Lithell H, Vessby B, Melhus H. Serum retinol levels and the risk of fracture. *N Engl J Med.* 2003;348:287–294.

11 Rothman KJ, Moore LL, Singer MR, et al. Teratogenicity of high vitamin A intake. *N Engl J Med.* 1995;333(21):1360–1373; and Oakley GP, Erickson JD. Vitamin A and birth defects. *N Engl J Med.* 1995;333(21):1414–1415.

12 Koo J. Acne: psychological effects are more than skin deep. *Skin Care Today.* 1998;4:4–5.

13 Institute of Medicine, Food and Nutrition Board. *Dietary Reference Intakes for Vitamin C, Vitamin E, Selenium, and Carotenoids.* Washington, DC: National Academies Press, 2000.

14 Ibid.

15 Jacob RA, Burri BJ. Oxidative damage and defense. *Am J Clin Nutr.* 1996;63:985S–990S.

16 Sahni S, Hannan MT, Blumberg J, et al. Inverse association of carotenoid intakes with 4-y change in bone mineral density in elderly men and women: the Framingham Osteoporosis Study. *Am J Clin Nutr.* 2009;89:416–424.

17 Krinsky NI, Johnson EJ. Carotenoid actions and their relation to health and disease. *Mol Aspects Med.* 2005;26(6):459–516; and Voutilainen S, Nurmi T, Mursu J, Rissanen TH. Carotenoids and cardiovascular health. *Am J Clin Nutr.* 2006;83(6):1265–1271.

18 Chew BP, Park JS. Carotenoid action on the immune response. *J Nutr.* 2004;134:257S–261S.

19 Trumbo PR, Ellwood KC. Lutein and zeanthin intakes and risk of age-related macular degeneration and cataracts: an evaluation using the Food and Drug Administration's evidence-based review system for health claims. *Am J Clin Nutr.* 2006;84(5):971–974.

20 Sies H, Stahl W. Non-nutritive bioactive constituents of plants: lycopene, lutein, and zeaxanthin. *Int J Vitam Nutr Res.* 2003:73(2):95–100.

21 Institute of Medicine, Food and Nutrition Board. *Dietary Reference Intakes for Vitamin C, Vitamin E, Selenium, and Carotenoids.*

22 Christen WG, Manson JE, Glynn RJ, et al. A randomized trial of beta carotene and age-related cataract in US physicians. *Arch Ophthalmol.* 2003;121(3):372–378.

23 Rao AV, Rao LG. Carotenoids and human health. *Pharmacol Res.* 2007;55:207–216.

24 Ibid.

25 Fairfield KM, Fletcher RH. Vitamins in chronic disease prevention in adults: scientific review. *JAMA.* 2002;287:3116–3126.

26 Rock CL, Jacob RA, Bowen PE. Update on the biological characteristics of the antioxidant micronutrients: vitamin C, vitamin E, and the carotenoids. *J Am Diet Assoc.* 1996;96:693–702.

27 Institute of Medicine, Food and Nutrition Board. *Dietary Reference Intakes for Vitamin C, Vitamin E, Selenium, and Carotenoids.*

28 Institute of Medicine, Food and Nutrition Board. *Dietary Reference Intakes for Vitamin A, Vitamin K.*

29 US Department of Agriculture, Agricultural Research Service. USDA Nutrient Database for Standard Reference, Release 21. 2008. http://www.nal.usda.gov/fnic/foodcomp/search/. Accessed 7/15/09.

30 Rock CL, Lovalo JL, Emenhiser C, et al. Bioavailability of beta-carotene is lower in raw than in processed carrots and spinach in women. *J Nutr.* 1998;128(5):913–916.

31 Hinds TS, West WL, Knight EM. Carotenoids and retinoids: a review of research, clinical, and public health applications. *J Clin Pharmacol.* 1997;37:551–558.

32 Institute of Medicine, Food and Nutrition Board. *Dietary Reference Intakes for Vitamin C, Vitamin E, Selenium, and Carotenoids.*

33 Fairfield, Fletcher. Vitamins in chronic disease prevention in adults; and Wright ME, Mayne ST, Swanson CA, et al. Dietary carotenoids, vegetables, and lung cancer risk in women: the Missouri Women's Health Study (United States). *Cancer Causes Control.* 2003;14(1):85–89.

34 Bischoff-Ferrari HA, Dawson-Hughes B, Willett WC, et al. Effect of vitamin D on falls: a meta-analysis. *JAMA.* 2004;291:1999–2006.

35 National Institutes of Health, Office of Dietary Supplements. Dietary supplement fact sheet: vitamin D. December 2008. http://ods.od.nih.gov/factsheets/vitamind.asp. Accessed 7/15/09.

36 Eastell R, Riggs BL. Vitamin D and osteoporosis. In: Feldman D, Glorieux FH, Pike JW, eds. *Vitamin D.* 2nd ed. San Diego: Academic Press, 2005:1101–1118.

37 Holick MF. Vitamin D: a millennium perspective. *J Cell Biochem.* 2003;88(2):296–307.

38 Lieberman D, Prindiville S, Weiss D, Willett W, for VA Cooperative Study Group 380. Risk factors for advanced colonic neoplasia and hyperplastic polyps in asymptomatic individuals. *JAMA.* 2003;290(22):2959–2967; and Bouillon R, Moody T, Sporn M, et al. NIH deltanoids meeting on vitamin D and cancer. Conclusion and strategic options. *J Steroid Biochem Mol Biol.* 2005;97:3–5.

39 Holick MF. Sunlight and vitamin D for bone health and prevention of autoimmune diseases, cancers, and cardiovascular disease. *Am J Clin Nutr.* 2004;80(suppl):1678S–1688S.

40 Institute of Medicine, Food and Nutrition Board. *Dietary Reference Intakes for Calcium, Phosphorus, Magnesium, Vitamin D, and Fluoride.* Washington, DC: National Academies Press, 1997.

41 Bischoff-Ferrari HA, Giovannucci E, Willett WC, et al. Estimation of optimal serum concentrations of 25-hydroxyvitamin D for multiple health outcomes. *Am J Clin Nutr.* 2006;84(1):18–28.

42 Holick MF, Chen TC. Vitamin D deficiency: a worldwide problem with health consequences. *Am J Clin Nutr.* 2008;87(4):1080S–1086S.

43 Wagner CL, Greer FR, and the Section on Breastfeeding and Committee on Nutrition. Prevention of rickets and vitamin D deficiency in infants, children, and adolescents. *Pediatrics.* 2008;122:1142–1152.

44 Vitamin D deficiency deemed widespread. *Tufts University Health & Nutrition Letter.* May 1998;16(3):1.

45 Holick MF. Vitamin D deficiency. *N Engl J Med.* 2007;357:266–281.

46 American Academy of Dermatology. The sun and your skin. http://www.aad.org/NR/exeres/B1BBACE1-A0D0-4565-AA74-63B7E6957239.htm?NRMODE5Published. Accessed 7/30/06.

47 Vitamin D deficiency: the silent epidemic. *Nutr Action.* 1997;24(8):4.

48 Mocanu V, Stitt PA, Costan AR, et al. Long-term effects of giving nursing home residents bread fortified with 125 μg (5000 IU) vitamin D_3 per daily serving. *Am J Clin Nutr.* 2009;89:1132–1137.

49 Kumar J, Muntner P, Kaskel FJ, et al. Prevalence and associations of 25-hydroxyvitamin D deficiency in US children: NHANES 2001–2004. *Pediatrics.* Published online August 3, 2009. DOI: 10.1542/peds.2009-0051. Accessed 8/8/09.

50 Holick MF. Resurrection of vitamin D deficiency and rickets. *J Clin Invest.* 2006;116:2062–2072; and Yu JW, Pekeles G, Legault L, et al. Milk allergy and vitamin D deficiency rickets: a common disorder associated with an uncommon disease. *Ann Allergy Asthma Immunol.* 2006;96(4):615–619.

51 Holick, Chen. Vitamin D deficiency.

52 Cranney C, Horsely T, O'Donnell S, et al. *Effectiveness and Safety of Vitamin D.* Evidence Report/Technology Assessment No. 158. Rockville, MD: Agency for Healthcare Research and Quality, 2007. AHRQ Publication No. 07-E013.

53 Davis CD, Hartmuller V, et al. Vitamin D and cancer: current dilemmas and future needs. *Nutr Rev.* 2007;65(8 pt 2):S71–S74.

54 Linus Pauling Institute Micronutrient Information Center. Vitamin D. November 2008. http://lpi.oregonstate.edu/infocenter/vitamins/vitaminD/index.html#lpi_recommend. Accessed 7/19/09.

55 Thomas MK, Lloyd-Jones DM, Thadhani RF, et al. Hypovitaminosis D in medical inpatients. *N Engl J Med.* 1998;338:777–783.

56 Need AG, Morris HA, Horowitz M, Nordin C. Effects of skin thickness, age, body fat, and sunlight on serum 25-hydroxy-vitamin D. *Am J Clin Nutr.* 1993;58:882–885; and Holick MF, Matsuoka LY, Wortsman J. Age, vitamin D, and solar ultra-violet [letter]. *Lancet.* 1989;2(8671):1104–1105.

57 Moore C. Vitamin D intake in the United States. *J Am Diet Assoc.* 2004;104:980–983.

58 National Institutes of Health, Office of Dietary Supplements. Dietary supplement fact sheet: vitamin D.

59 Ibid.

60 Hathcock JN, Shao A, Vieth R, Heaney R. Risk assessment for vitamin D. *Am J Clin Nutr.* 2007;85:6–18.

61 Traber MG, Frei B, Beckman JS. Vitamin E revisited: do new data validate benefits for chronic disease prevention? *Curr Opin Lipidol.* 2008;19(1):30–38.

62 Glynn RJ, Ridker PM, Goldhaber SZ, et al. Effects of random allocation to vitamin E supplementation on the occurrence of venous thromboembolism: report from the Women's Health Study. *Circulation.* 2007;116:1497–1503.

63 Jialal I, Traber M, Devaraj S. Is there a vitamin E paradox? *Curr Opin Lipidol.* 2001;12:49–53; and Kaul N, Devaraj S, Jialal I. Alpha-tocopherol and atherosclerosis. *Exp Biol Med.* 2001;226:5–12.

64 Institute of Medicine, Food and Nutrition Board. *Dietary Reference Intakes for Vitamin C, Vitamin E, Selenium, and Carotenoids.*

65 Meydani SN, Han SN, Hamer DH. Vitamin E and respiratory infection in the elderly. *Ann N Y Acad Sci.* 2004;1031:214–222.

66 Isaac MGEKN, Quinn R, Tabet N. Vitamin E for Alzheimer's disease and mild cognitive impairment (review). *Cochrane Database Syst Rev.* 2008;(3):CD002854.

67 Institute of Medicine, Food and Nutrition Board. *Dietary Reference Intakes for Vitamin C, Vitamin E, Selenium, and Carotenoids.*

68 Ibid.

69 Ibid.

70 Otten JJ, Hellwig JP, Meyers LD. Vitamin E. In: Institute of Medicine. *DRI, Dietary Reference Intakes: The Essential Guide to Nutrient Requirements.* Washington, DC: National Academies Press, 2006:234–244.

71 Fairfield, Fletcher. *Vitamins in chronic disease prevention in adults.*

72 Institute of Medicine, Food and Nutrition Board. *Dietary Reference Intakes for Vitamin C, Vitamin E, Selenium, and Carotenoids.*

73 Horwitt MK. Critique of the requirement for vitamin E. *Am J Clin Nutr.* 2001;73:1003–1005.

74 Miller ER III, Pastor-Barriuso R, Dalal D, et al. Meta-analysis: high-dosage vitamin E supplementation may increase all-cause mortality. *Ann Intern Med.* 2005;142:37–46.

75 Huang HY, Caballero B, Chang S, et al. *Multivitamin/Mineral Supplements and Prevention of Chronic Disease.* Evidence Report/Technology Assessment No. 139. Rockville, MD: Agency for Healthcare Research and Quality. http://www.ahrq.gov/downloads/pub/evidence/pdf/multivit/multivit.pdf. Accessed 7/20/09.

76 Pearson DA. Bone health and osteoporosis: the role of vitamin K and potential antagonism by anticoagulants. *Nutr Clin Pract.* 2007;22(5):517–544.

77 Vitamin K and bone health in adult humans. *Vitam Horm.* 2008;78:393–416.

78 Sokoll LJ, Booth SL, O'Brien ME, et al. Changes in serum osteocalcin, plasma phylloquinone, and urinary gamma-carboxyglutamic acid in response to altered intakes of dietary phylloquinone in human subjects. *Am J Clin Nutr.* 1997;65:779–784.

79 Booth SL, Suttle JW. Dietary intake and adequacy of vitamin K. *J Nutr.* 1998;128(5):785–788.

80 Cockayne S, Adamson J, Lanham-New S, et al. Vitamin K and the prevention of fractures: systematic review and meta-analysis of randomized controlled trials. *Arch Intern Med.* 2006;166:1256–1261.

81 Institute of Medicine, Food and Nutrition Board. *Dietary Reference Intakes for Vitamin C, Vitamin E, Selenium, and Carotenoids.*

82 US Department of Agriculture, Agricultural Research Service. USDA National Nutrient Database for Standard Reference, Release 21. http://www.ars.usda.gov/Services/docs.htm?docid=8964. Vitamin K list available at http://www.nal.usda.gov/fnic/foodcomp/Data/SR16/wtrank/sr16w430.pdf. Accessed 7/20/09.

83 Shearer MJ, Bach A, Kohlmeier M. Chemistry, nutritional sources, tissue distribution and metabolism of vitamin K with special reference to bone health. *J Nutr.* 1996;126(suppl):1181S–1186S.

84 Booth SL, Broe KE, Gagnon DR, et al. Vitamin K intake and bone mineral density in women and men. *Am J Clin Nutr.* 2003;77(2):512–516.

85 Feskanich D, Weber P, Willett, EC, et al. Vitamin K intake and hip fractures in women: a prospective study. *Am J Clin Nutr.* 1999;69(1):74–79.

86 Warren Grant Magnuson Clinical Center, National Institutes of Health Nutrient-Drug Interaction Task Force. Important information to know when you are taking Coumadin and vitamin K. Accessed 7/20/09.

CHAPTER 11

Water-Soluble Vitamins

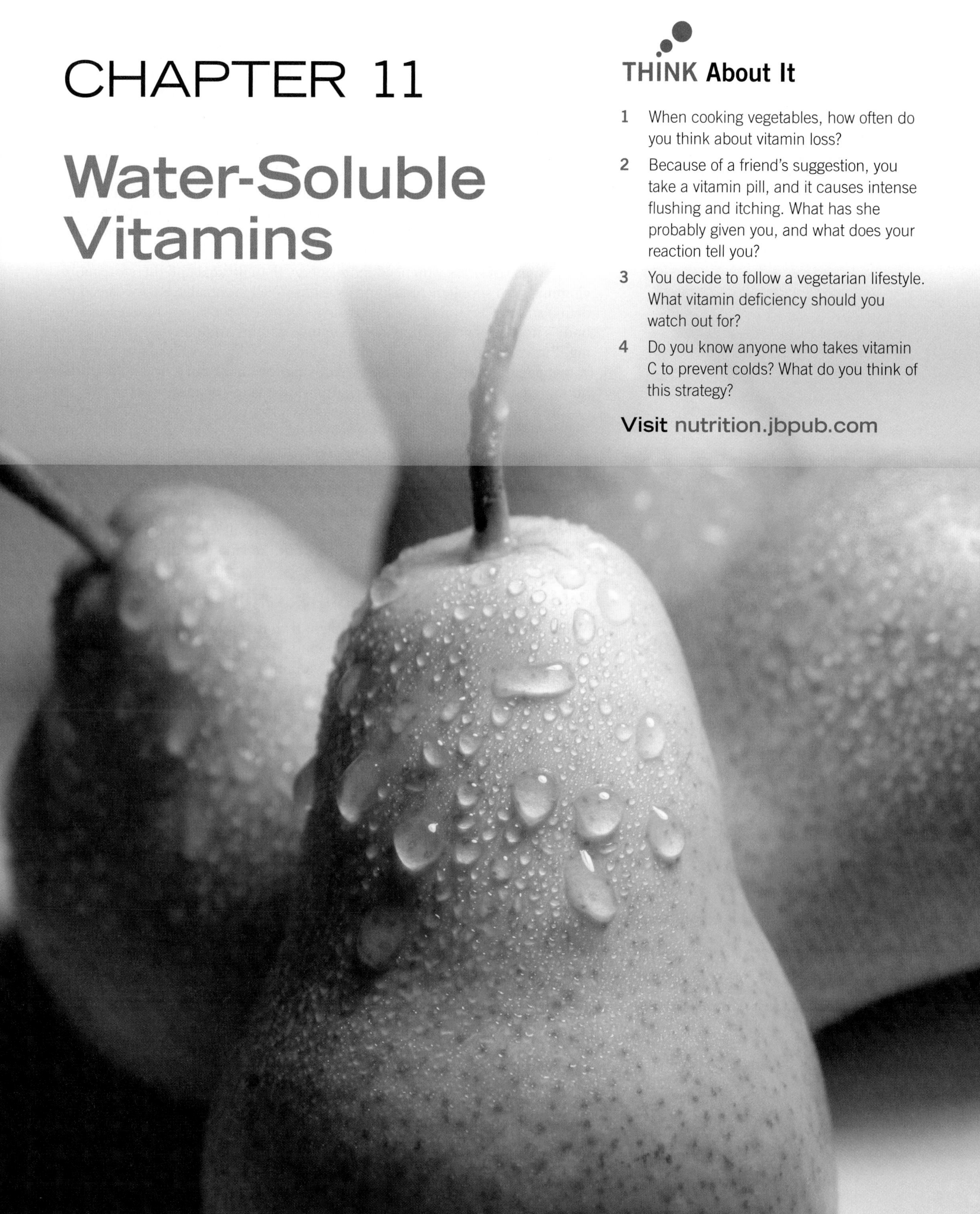

THINK About It

1 When cooking vegetables, how often do you think about vitamin loss?
2 Because of a friend's suggestion, you take a vitamin pill, and it causes intense flushing and itching. What has she probably given you, and what does your reaction tell you?
3 You decide to follow a vegetarian lifestyle. What vitamin deficiency should you watch out for?
4 Do you know anyone who takes vitamin C to prevent colds? What do you think of this strategy?

Visit nutrition.jbpub.com

Quick Bite

What Do You Believe?
Thirty-five percent of Americans surveyed in 1997 said that they believed vitamin supplements were necessary to ensure good health. Women were more likely than men to believe they needed supplements.

Feeling tired, run down, stressed out? Burning the candle at both ends? Too many workouts wearing you out? You've heard that vitamins give you energy. So a lack of energy must be a signal that you need more vitamins, right? Well, probably not.

First the facts: Although many people like to think of vitamins as energy boosters, in truth, vitamins do not supply calories for the body—a fact that distinguishes them from fat, carbohydrate, and protein. However, many B vitamins (water-soluble vitamins) facilitate the metabolic reactions that release energy. So in a sense, vitamins help you get energy by allowing carbohydrate, fat, and protein to become cellular fuel.

In times of stress, you need more energy than normal and therefore more vitamins, so a supplement is in order, right? Well, not really. First we need to define *stress*. Certainly physical stress (e.g., injury and illness) increases the body's need for energy, protein, and many vitamins and minerals to aid healing. But emotional stress (e.g., anxiety and fear) does not. It may seem that you expend a lot of mental energy studying for finals, but studying requires no more energy than sitting and chatting with your friends.

But surely if you do more physical exercise, you should take a vitamin, right? Again, not necessarily. Physical activity requires energy and therefore vitamins to help extract energy from food. But the food you consume to meet your energy needs for physical activity contains vitamins too, unless you meet your extra energy needs with chips and sodas! In most cases, healthful food choices—plenty of whole grains, fruits, vegetables, lean meats or meat alternatives, and low-fat dairy products—provide all the vitamins you need. So, check out your diet before you check out the vitamin supplements.

The Water-Soluble Vitamins: Eight Bs and a C

Water-soluble vitamins consist of the eight B vitamins and vitamin C. Scientists first viewed vitamin B as a single compound. However, after further study, they discovered that "it" was actually several vitamins. To differentiate the various B vitamins, scientists initially added numbers to the letter B—vitamins B_6 and B_{12}, for example. Today, with the exception of B_6 and B_{12}, we usually refer to the B vitamins by their names: thiamin (B_1), riboflavin (B_2), niacin (B_3), pantothenic acid, biotin, and folate.

Although fat-soluble vitamins tend to accumulate in the body, the kidneys generally remove and excrete excess water-soluble vitamins. The exception is vitamin B_{12}, which the liver stores in large amounts. Because your body does not store other water-soluble vitamins in appreciable amounts, they should be a part of your daily diet. Small variations in daily intake typically do not cause problems, however. For example, symptoms of vitamin C deficiency do not emerge until after 20 to 40 days of a diet deficient in this water-soluble vitamin.

Quick Bite

Is It a Fruit or a Vegetable?
In the eighteenth century, botanists defined fruits as the organ surrounding the seeds. This definition considers cucumbers, eggplants, peppers, pea pods, and corn kernels as fruits. Legally, though, they are all vegetables. In the late 1800s, the U.S. Supreme Court, while trying the case of a tomato importer, established a definition based on linguistic custom and usage. The importer had to pay the vegetable tax.

In general, water-soluble vitamins are more fragile than fat-soluble vitamins, and some cooking practices are particularly harmful. Vitamin C, thiamin, and riboflavin are especially vulnerable to heat and alkalinity, which can break chemical bonds. If you bake a vegetable casserole, you should know that water-soluble vitamins can be destroyed by prolonged heat. To reduce cooking time and intensify a vegetable's color, many cooks add baking soda, which also can destroy water-soluble vitamins. Water-soluble vitamins also are hydrophilic by nature, and water will leach them from vegetables during cooking. Cooking only partially destroys the vitamin content of a food, and some cooking methods are less destructive than others. The best cooking methods—steaming, stir-frying, and microwaving—use minimal amounts of water.

THINK About It 1

The B Vitamins

B vitamins act primarily as coenzymes, or as parts of coenzymes (compounds that enable specific enzymes to function). (See **Figure 11.1**.) The B vitamin part of a coenzyme helps catalyze the workings of metabolic pathways in cells. All B vitamins function in energy-producing metabolic reactions, and some also participate in other aspects of cellular metabolism.

Varied diets contain significant amounts of many vitamins, and vitamins often are added to foods such as cereals and other grain products. In the 1940s, the U.S. government mandated enrichment of bread and cereal products made from milled grains. Milling or refining grains removes the bran and germ to make white flour, white rice, refined cornmeal, flour for pasta, and most breakfast cereals. Processing grains also removes most B vitamins, vitamin E, and minerals such as iron, magnesium, and zinc. The loss of these nutrients from such staple foods could be devastating. In fact, during the nineteenth and early twentieth centuries, widespread adoption of these milling techniques left a wake of vitamin-deficiency diseases such as beriberi and pellagra. To prevent overt deficiencies, processors now return iron and three B vitamins to the grains they process. Replacing lost nutrients is called "enrichment." Most countries now require enriching staple grain products.

Food processors also "fortify" foods. Fortification is the process of adding extra nutrients to foods where they wouldn't be found naturally in consistently significant amounts. Iodized table salt (salt with added iodine) is a fortified food. Read the labels on some breakfast cereals: the ones with the long list of added vitamins and minerals are fortified foods. Because most breakfast cereals are fortified, they usually are good sources of vitamins and minerals. Fortification is sometimes required by law, as in the addition of vitamins A and D to milk and, most recently, the addition of folic acid to enriched cereal and grain products. Because of a 1998 FDA requirement, all enriched bread, flour, corn meal, pasta, rice, and other grain products must be fortified with folic acid.[1]

Enrichment and mandatory fortification programs helped eliminate most overt deficiency diseases in the United States and many other countries. However, mandatory enrichment replaces only some of the many nutrients lost in milling. Moreover, the American diet contains lots of highly refined foods that are not fortified or enriched—foods that have calories but almost no micronutrients.

During the production of highly refined grain products, processing also removes vitamin B_6, magnesium, and zinc. Enrichment does not replace these nutrients. To ensure a good balance of nutrients, experts recommend that people regularly eat whole-grain products such as whole-wheat bread, brown rice, and oatmeal.

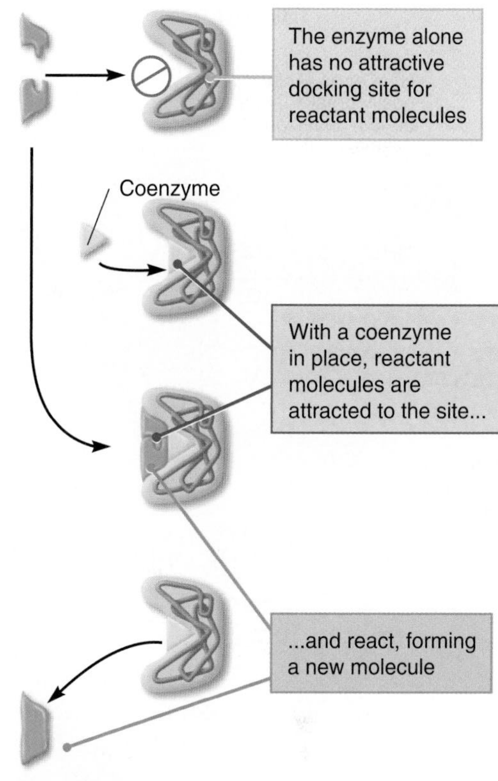
The enzyme alone has no attractive docking site for reactant molecules
Coenzyme
With a coenzyme in place, reactant molecules are attracted to the site...
...and react, forming a new molecule

Figure 11.1 **The coenzyme–enzyme partnership.** The B vitamins form coenzymes that enable specific enzymes to catalyze reactions.

Thiamin

Although mentioned in ancient Chinese writings from 2,600 B.C.E., the thiamin-deficiency disease **beriberi** remained largely unknown until the nineteenth century, when milling and refining grains became popular. In 1885 Dr. K. Takaki, Director General of the Japanese Naval Medical Services, demonstrated beriberi's dietary origins when he cured afflicted sailors by supplementing their diets with meat, milk, and whole grains.[2] Some years later, Christian Eijkman, a Dutch medical officer, induced beriberi in birds by feeding them only white rice, and then cured them by adding bran to their diet.[3] This led to the discovery of an "anti-beriberi" factor—thiamin.

beriberi Thiamin-deficiency disease. Symptoms include muscle weakness, loss of appetite, nerve degeneration, and edema in some cases.

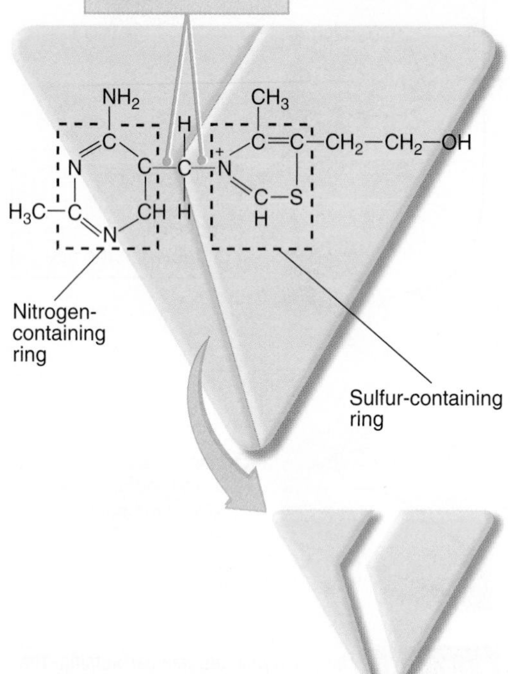

Figure 11.2 **Thiamin structure and vulnerability.** Water-soluble vitamins, especially thiamin, riboflavin, and vitamin C, are vulnerable to heat and alkalinity.

Isolated in 1926, thiamin (also known as vitamin B_1) gets its name from *thio*, meaning "sulfur," and *amine*, the nitrogen-containing group in the vitamin. As **Figure 11.2** shows, thiamin consists of a sulfur-containing ring and a nitrogen-containing ring attached to a carbon atom. Heat easily breaks the bonds between the two rings and the carbon atom, so cooking reduces a food's thiamin content. Alkaline solutions (those with a pH of 8 or higher) also break these bonds.

Functions of Thiamin

Like the other B vitamins, thiamin is an important participant in many energy-yielding reactions. Specifically, thiamin is the vitamin portion of the coenzyme **thiamin pyrophosphate (TPP)**, shown in **Figure 11.3**. TPP participates in a vital reaction known as **decarboxylation**, which removes a carboxyl group (–COOH) and releases it as carbon dioxide (CO_2). During glucose metabolism, for example, decarboxylation removes one carbon from the three-carbon substance pyruvate to form the two-carbon molecule acetyl CoA. (See **Figure 11.4**.) TPP is also involved in a decarboxylation step in the citric acid cycle.

Cells also use TPP in the pentose phosphate pathway, an alternative pathway to glycolysis. This series of reactions metabolizes glucose to make, among other products, the five-carbon monosaccharide deoxyribose for DNA synthesis, the five-carbon monosaccharide ribose for RNA synthesis, and the energy-rich molecule NADPH to help power biosynthesis.

Thiamin pyrophosphate also plays a role in nerve function, although the mechanism is still under investigation. Scientists suspect that TPP helps synthesize and regulate neurotransmitters—chemicals involved in the transmission of messages throughout the nervous system. TPP also may help produce energy to fuel nerve tissue.

Dietary Recommendations for Thiamin

The small difference in the RDA for adult men and women reflects the differences in their average size and energy use. The RDA for adult men aged 19 years and older is 1.2 milligrams; for adult women of the same age, the RDA is 1.1 milligrams per day. Pregnancy and lactation increase energy requirements, so thiamin requirements rise during these life stages. Thiamin intake recommendations are 1.4 milligrams per day during pregnancy and 1.5 milligrams per day during lactation. If a person's diet supplies adequate energy and includes thiamin-rich foods, it generally contains adequate amounts of thiamin.

thiamin pyrophosphate (TPP) A coenzyme of which the vitamin thiamin is a part. It plays a key role in decarboxylation and helps drive the reaction that forms acetyl CoA from pyruvate during metabolism.

decarboxylation Removal of a carboxyl group (–COOH) from a molecule. The carboxyl group is then released as carbon dioxide (CO_2).

Sources of Thiamin

Thiamin is found throughout the food supply, although most foods contain only small amounts. Pork is one of the richest food sources of thiamin. Legumes (mature beans and peas), some nuts and seeds, and some types of fish and seafood are good sources. Most thiamin in the U.S. diet, however, comes from enriched or whole-grain products such as bread, pasta, rice, and ready-to-eat cereals.[4] **Figure 11.5** shows some foods that provide thiamin.

Meat (except pork and organ meats), dairy products, seafood, and most fruits contain very little thiamin. Eating a wide variety of foods is the best way to ensure adequate thiamin consumption.

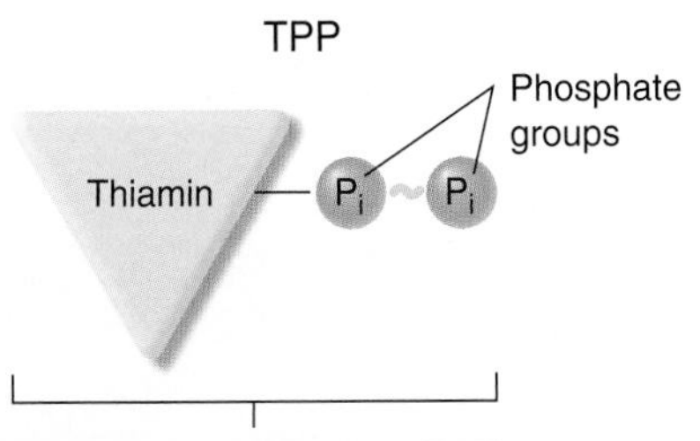

Figure 11.3 **Thiamin pyrophosphate (TPP).** Thiamin pyrophosphate contains the B vitamin thiamin and two phosphate groups.

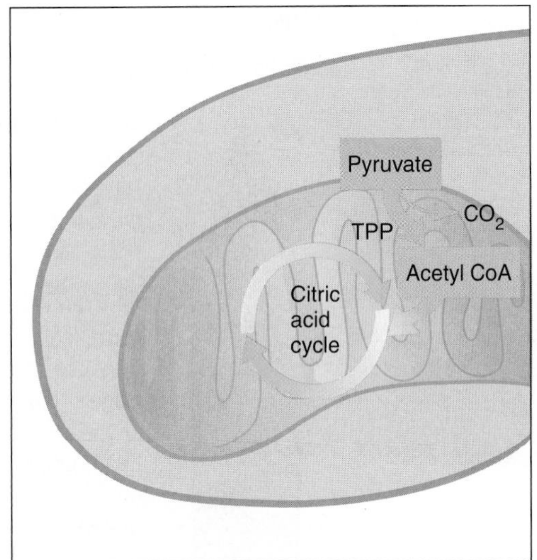

Figure 11.4 **TPP helps convert pyruvate to acetyl CoA.** In addition to coenzyme A and NAD^+, three other catalytic cofactors—TPP, α-lipoic acid, and FAD—help convert pyruvate to acetyl CoA.

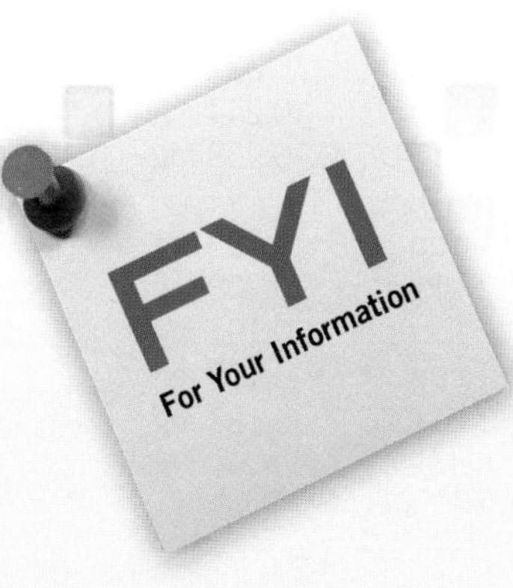

Fresh, Frozen, or Canned? Raw or Cooked?

Selecting and Preparing Foods to Maximize Vitamin Content

A food's vitamin content depends first on the original amount in the plant or animal while it is alive and growing. Although grazing materials and feed may have a minor impact on vitamin content, animal products tend to have fairly consistent levels. This reflects the animal's ability to concentrate and store vitamins. The vitamin content of plants, however, depends more on soil and growing conditions such as available moisture and sunlight. The maturity of a fruit or vegetable at the time it is harvested also influences its vitamin content.

Light, heat, air, acid, alkali, and cooking fluids can attack vitamins, so proper storage, processing, and cooking are important. Ideally, you should shop for produce as the Europeans do: choose fresh fruits and vegetables daily to minimize nutrient losses associated with prolonged storage. Barring that, choose clean, undamaged produce at each of your regular shopping trips. When storing foods, avoid temperature extremes, and minimize exposure to light and air with refrigeration or covered storage. It's best to eat fruits and vegetables soon after purchase; normal storage can decrease their vitamin content. The vitamin C content of fresh green beans, for example, drops by half after six days at home.

What about frozen and canned foods? The heat processing used in canning fruits and vegetables does deplete small amounts of vitamins but they end up in the liquid in which the food is packed. In addition, the vitamin content of canned foods is shelf stable and remains constant even after two years. The thiamin content of canned meats and beans is comparable to home-prepared versions. Vegetable sources of folate, such as spinach, retain most of their folate content when canned or frozen. The carotenes in vegetables and fruits are stable during the canning process. In fact, current research suggests the lycopene in tomatoes is a more effective antioxidant (it has been linked to reducing prostate cancer[1]) after tomatoes have been heated or canned.[2] Ready-to-drink orange juice loses about 2 percent of its vitamin C content each day once opened.[3]

Once fruits and vegetables are home and stored carefully, what is the best way to cook them? To maximize the vitamin content, think minimal—minimal amounts of heat, minimal amounts of cooking water, and minimal exposure to air. Try to minimize handling the food before and during cooking. Although dicing a food such as a potato reduces cooking time, it also exposes more surface area to vitamin-destroying influences. So, cut if you must, but not too small.

Steaming and microwaving are the best cooking methods for preserving vitamin content, because they minimize cooking time and water use. If you boil foods, try to use the cooking water for sauces, stews, or soups, because it contains many of the water-soluble vitamins lost from the food during cooking.

To retain the most vitamins in your food, be gentle with storage and handling, and kind with cooking. Minimize (heat, water, air exposure) to maximize!

1 Rao AV, Ray MR, Rao LG. Lycopene. *Adv Food Nutr Res.* 2006;51:99–164.

2 Ibid.

3 Johnston CS, Bowling DL. Stability of ascorbic acid in commercially available orange juice. *J Am Diet Assoc.* 2002;102:525–529.

Figure 11.5 **Food sources of thiamin.** Pork, whole and enriched grains, and fortified cereals are rich in thiamin. Most animal foods contain little thiamin.

Source: US Department of Agriculture, Agricultural Research Service. USDA National Nutrient Database for Standard Reference, Release 22. Nutrient Data Laboratory Home Page. http://www.ars.usda.gov/ba/bhnrc/ndl.

Thiamin

Daily Value = 1.5 mg

	Food	Amount (g)	Portion	Thiamin
Exceptionally good source	Total cereal, whole grain	30 g	¾ cup	1.5 mg
	Rice, white, long-grain, raw, enriched	185 g	1 cup	1.066 mg
	Pork, loin, cooked	85 g	3 oz	1.057 mg
High: 20% DV or more	All-Bran cereal	30 g	½ cup	0.681 mg
	Ham, lean, roasted	85 g	3 oz	0.587 mg
	Cheerios cereal	30 g	1 cup	0.580 mg
	Bagels, plain, enriched	89 g	4″ bagel	0.535 mg
	Soybeans, cooked	180 g	1 cup	0.468 mg
	Egg noodles, cooked, enriched	160 g	1 cup	0.462 mg
	Spaghetti, cooked, enriched	140 g	1 cup	0.384 mg
	Oat bran, cooked	219 g	1 cup	0.350 mg
Good: 10–19% DV	Salmon, cooked	155 g	½ fillet	0.333 mg
	Kidney beans, cooked	177 g	1 cup	0.283 mg
	English muffin, plain	52 g	1 muffin	0.281 mg
	Baked beans, canned	254 g	1 cup	0.244 mg
	Pistachio nuts, dry roasted	28 g	1 oz (47 nuts)	0.238 mg
	Orange juice	248 g	1 cup	0.223 mg
	Salami, cooked	57 g	2 slices	0.208 mg
	Ham, sliced, extra lean	57 g	2 slices	0.191 mg
	Chickpeas, cooked	164 g	1 cup	0.190 mg
	Pecans	28 g	1 oz (20 halves)	0.187 mg

There are few data from studies of humans on the bioavailability of thiamin from food.[5] See the section on thiamin toxicity for details about absorption of thiamin from supplements.

Thiamin Deficiency

In industrialized countries, thiamin deficiency usually is related to heavy alcohol consumption combined with limited food consumption. Alcoholics are at risk for thiamin deficiency for two reasons: (1) alcohol contributes calories without contributing nutrients, and (2) alcohol interferes with absorption of thiamin and many other vitamins. The poor and the elderly also may be at risk of deficiency due to inadequate energy intake or consumption of nutrient-poor foods. Eating mostly highly processed but unenriched foods and empty-calorie items such as alcohol, sugar, and fat can lead to a deficiency.

Beriberi

Beriberi is a term from the Singhalese language (spoken in Sri Lanka) that means "I can't, I can't." The phrase describes how doctors long ago diagnosed the disease: their patients were unable to rise from a squatting position. In fact, overall profound muscle weakness combined with nerve destruction ultimately leaves the victim of beriberi almost unable to move. This deficiency disease occurs in people whose major source of energy is polished rice, which is common in Southeast Asia. Polishing removes the rice hulls and thus their major source of thiamin.

An inadequate supply of this essential nutrient affects the cardiovascular, muscular, nervous, and gastrointestinal systems, which all rely on thiamin to help fuel their activities. The brain and nervous system rely on glucose for energy, and thiamin, as part of TPP, is crucial in glucose metabolism. The first signs of thiamin deficiency are weakness, irritability, headache, fatigue, and depression—functions associated with the brain and nervous system. These disturbances may appear after only 10 days on a thiamin-free diet.

As symptoms progress, "dry" beriberi (beriberi without edema) causes nerve degeneration, loss of nerve transmission leading to tingling sensations throughout the body, muscle wasting, poor arm and leg coordination, and deep pain in the calf muscles. "Wet" beriberi has additional symptoms, including an enlarged heart, heart failure, and severe edema (**Figure 11.6**). Because many B vitamins are in the same foods as thiamin, thiamin deficiency and other B vitamin deficiencies often go hand in hand.

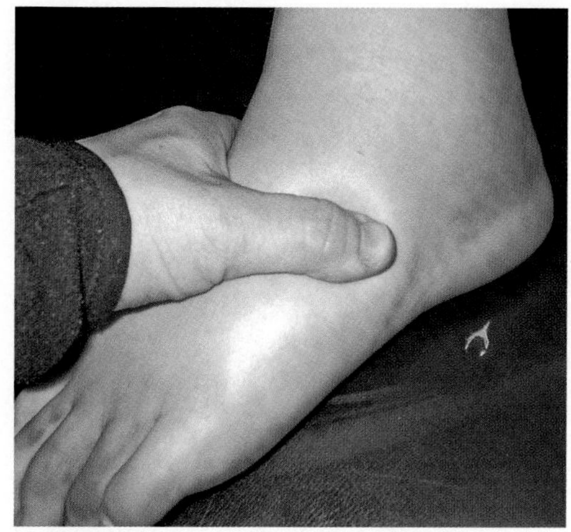

Figure 11.6 Edema, especially in the feet and legs, is a symptom of wet beriberi.

Wernicke-Korsakoff Syndrome

Alcohol-induced malnutrition is the most common cause of Wernicke-Korsakoff syndrome, another thiamin-deficiency disease. Symptoms include mental confusion, staggering, and constant rapid eye movements or paralysis of the eye muscles. Although the syndrome most often is associated with the stereotypical "Skid Row" alcoholic, it can occur in any heavy drinker, especially an aging alcoholic.

Thiamin Toxicity

To date, there are no reports of thiamin toxicity from either food or supplements. Supplements, which are cheap to produce, often include up to 200 times the Daily Value for thiamin. The Food and Nutrition Board has not set a Tolerable Upper Intake Level (UL) for this nutrient. Because thiamin absorption declines rapidly when a person consumes 5 or more milligrams at once, large doses of thiamin appear to be relatively innocuous. In addition, the kidneys rapidly excrete excess thiamin via urine.[6]

Riboflavin

At first, riboflavin and thiamin were considered the same vitamin. Scientists then discovered that heating the "anti-beriberi factor" destroyed its anti-beriberi properties but left its growth-promoting properties unscathed. The factor actually contained two active compounds: heat-vulnerable thiamin and a heat-stable component. In 1917, scientists identified the heat-stable component as another vitamin—called vitamin B_2 in England and vitamin G in the United States. This naming confusion ended when the new vitamin was finally dubbed riboflavin.

Riboflavin is named for its yellow color (*flavin* means "yellow" in Latin). In foods, though, it may give a green or bluish cast. You'll notice the color in uncooked egg whites and some brands of fat-free milk.

Functions of Riboflavin

The vitamin accepts and donates electrons with ease, so it participates in many oxidation-reduction reactions. Riboflavin is a part of two coenzymes: flavin mononucleotide (FMN) and flavin adenine dinucleotide (FAD). These

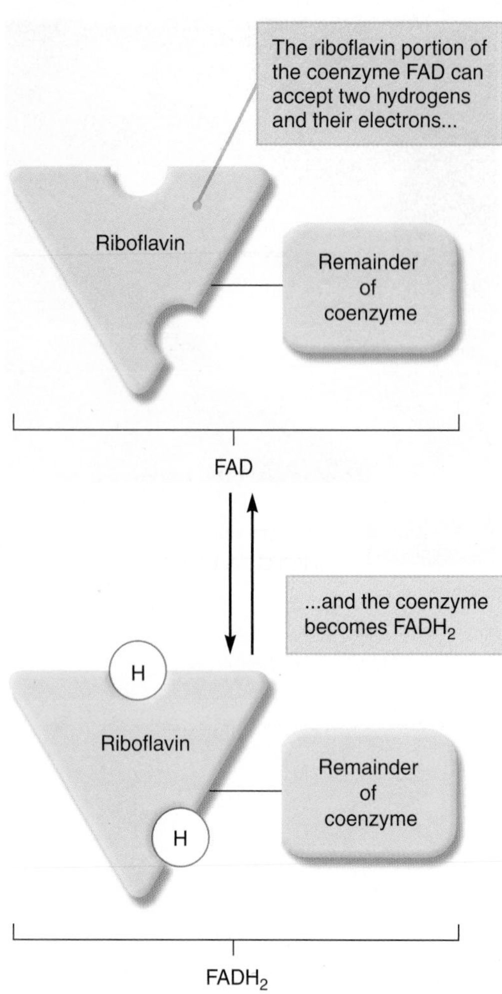

Figure 11.7 Riboflavin coenzymes easily transfer hydrogens. The riboflavin coenzyme flavin adenine dinucleotide (FAD) accepts hydrogens and electrons to become $FADH_2$.

glutathione peroxidase A selenium-containing enzyme that promotes the breakdown of fatty acids that have undergone peroxidation.

ariboflavinosis Riboflavin deficiency.

glossitis Inflammation of the tongue; a symptom of riboflavin deficiency.

angular stomatitis Inflammation and cracking of the skin at the corners of the mouth; a symptom of riboflavin deficiency.

cheilosis Inflammation and cracking of the lips; a symptom of riboflavin deficiency.

seborrheic dermatitis Disease of the oil-producing glands of the skin; a symptom of riboflavin deficiency.

coenzymes participate in numerous metabolic pathways, including the citric acid cycle and the beta-oxidation pathway that breaks down fatty acids. FMN and FAD act first as electron and hydrogen acceptors. In the citric acid cycle, for instance, FAD accepts hydrogen and electrons, forming the reduced form, $FADH_2$ (**Figure 11.7**). Later, this coenzyme delivers its high-energy electrons to the mitochondrial electron transport chain to produce ATP. Another riboflavin coenzyme, FMN, also accepts hydrogen and electrons, forming $FMNH_2$. FMN works in the electron transport chain to move electrons. Both coenzymes are crucial in energy metabolism.

Riboflavin-containing coenzymes also participate in reactions that remove ammonia during the deamination of some amino acids.[7] Riboflavin also is associated with the antioxidant activity of the glutathione reductase, **glutathione peroxidase**, and xanthine oxidase enzymes.

Dietary Recommendations for Riboflavin

For adults aged 19 and older, the RDA is 1.1 milligrams per day for women and 1.3 milligrams per day for men. Intake recommendations for riboflavin, like those for thiamin, reflect the higher energy needs of males. Pregnancy and lactation increase energy needs, so the RDA for women rises to 1.4 milligrams per day during pregnancy and to 1.6 milligrams per day during lactation.

Sources of Riboflavin

Although most plant and animal foods contain some riboflavin, milk, milk drinks, and yogurt supply about 15 percent of the riboflavin in the U.S. diet. Bread and bread products contribute approximately 10 percent, and ready-to-eat cereals add nearly as much.[8] Riboflavin is one of the four vitamins (thiamin, riboflavin, niacin, and folic acid) and one mineral (iron) that are added to enriched grain products. Organ meats such as liver and kidney are good sources of riboflavin, as are mushrooms and cottage cheese. **Figure 11.8** shows foods that provide riboflavin.

Riboflavin is more stable than thiamin and is resistant to acid, heat, and oxidation. On the other hand, light easily breaks it down. Riboflavin-rich foods should be stored in opaque packages. For example, packaging milk in paper or plastic cartons rather than clear glass better protects milk's riboflavin content.[9] (See **Figure 11.9**.)

Riboflavin absorption from food is good, and 60 to 65 percent of the riboflavins in milk and spinach is absorbed.[10]

Riboflavin Deficiency

Riboflavin deficiencies are rare. Several large surveys suggest that in the United States men take in about 2 milligrams of riboflavin per day, and women consume about 1.5 milligrams per day. Some people, however, consume only marginal amounts. Because people with alcoholism tend to have poor diets, for example, they risk riboflavin deficiency. Long-term use of barbiturate drugs such as phenobarbital also may lead to riboflavin deficiency. Repeated exposure to these drugs activates enzymes in the liver that accelerate the metabolism of riboflavin. Cancer, heart disease, and diabetes may also cause or worsen a riboflavin deficiency.[11]

Riboflavin deficiency (**ariboflavinosis**) shows up first around the mouth. The tongue gets shiny, smooth, and inflamed (**glossitis**); the mouth becomes painful and sore; the skin at the corners of the mouth cracks (**angular stomatitis**); and the lips become inflamed and split (**cheilosis**). The

Riboflavin

Daily Value = 1.7 mg

Level	Food	Weight	Serving	Riboflavin
	Exceptionally good sources			
	Beef, liver, cooked	85 g	3 oz	2.911 mg
	All-Bran flakes cereal	29 g	¾ cup	1.711 mg
	Total cereal, whole grain	30 g	¾ cup	1.701 mg
High: 20% DV or more	Yogurt, plain (skim milk)	227 g	8-oz container	0.531 mg
	Soybeans, cooked	172 g	1 cup	0.490 mg
	Cheerios cereal	30 g	1 cup	0.482 mg
	Mushrooms, cooked	156 g	1 cup	0.468 mg
	Milk (2% or 1% milkfat)	244 g	1 cup	0.451 mg
	Cottage cheese, low-fat	226 g	1 cup	0.447 mg
	Spinach, cooked	180 g	1 cup	0.425 mg
	Beet greens, cooked	144 g	1 cup	0.416 mg
	Buttermilk, low-fat	245 g	1 cup	0.377 mg
	Pork, spareribs, lean, cooked	85 g	3 oz	0.325 mg
Good: 10–19% DV	Ham, lean, cooked	85 g	3 oz	0.297 mg
	Almonds	28 g	1 oz (24 nuts)	0.287 mg
	Cream of Wheat cereal	142 g	1 packet	0.284 mg
	Salmon, cooked	55 g	½ fillet	0.265 mg
	Turkey, roasted	140 g	1 cup	0.255 mg
	Cheese, feta	28 g	1 oz	0.239 mg
	Lamb, loin, lean, cooked	85 g	3 oz	0.238 mg
	Bagels, plain	89 g	4″ bagel	0.231 mg
	Okra, frozen, cooked	184 g	1 cup	0.226 mg
	Kidney beans, canned	256 g	1 cup	0.220 mg
	Egg noodles, cooked, enriched	160 g	1 cup	0.218 mg

Figure 11.8 **Food sources of riboflavin.** The best sources of riboflavin include milk, liver, whole and enriched grains, and fortified cereals.

Source: US Department of Agriculture, Agricultural Research Service. USDA National Nutrient Database for Standard Reference, Release 22. Nutrient Data Laboratory Home Page. http://www.ars.usda.gov/ba/bhnrc/ndl.

Figure 11.9 **Packaging affects riboflavin content in milk.** Light breaks down riboflavin easily, so foods high in riboflavin (e.g., milk) are best stored in opaque containers.

oil-producing glands of the skin become clogged (**seborrheic dermatitis**). As the deficiency becomes severe, a characteristic anemia develops. Riboflavin deficiency usually exists along with other nutrient deficiencies. In fact, it may even make other deficiencies worse; for example, riboflavin deficiency disrupts vitamin B_6 metabolism and can lead to B_6 deficiency.[12]

Riboflavin Toxicity

No cases of riboflavin toxicity have been reported. Because the body readily excretes excess riboflavin, even large doses appear to pose no risk of harm. A UL has not been set for riboflavin.

Niacin

In 1867, scientists first produced a substance called nicotinic acid by oxidizing the nicotine from tobacco. Nicotinic acid is not, however, the same as or even closely related to the nicotine molecule. Seventy years later, Conrad Elvehjem

Quick Bite

Are You Smoking That Bread?

In the 1940s, anti-tobacco forces were confused about the differences between niacin and nicotine. They mistakenly warned that niacin-enriched bread could cause an addiction to cigarettes!

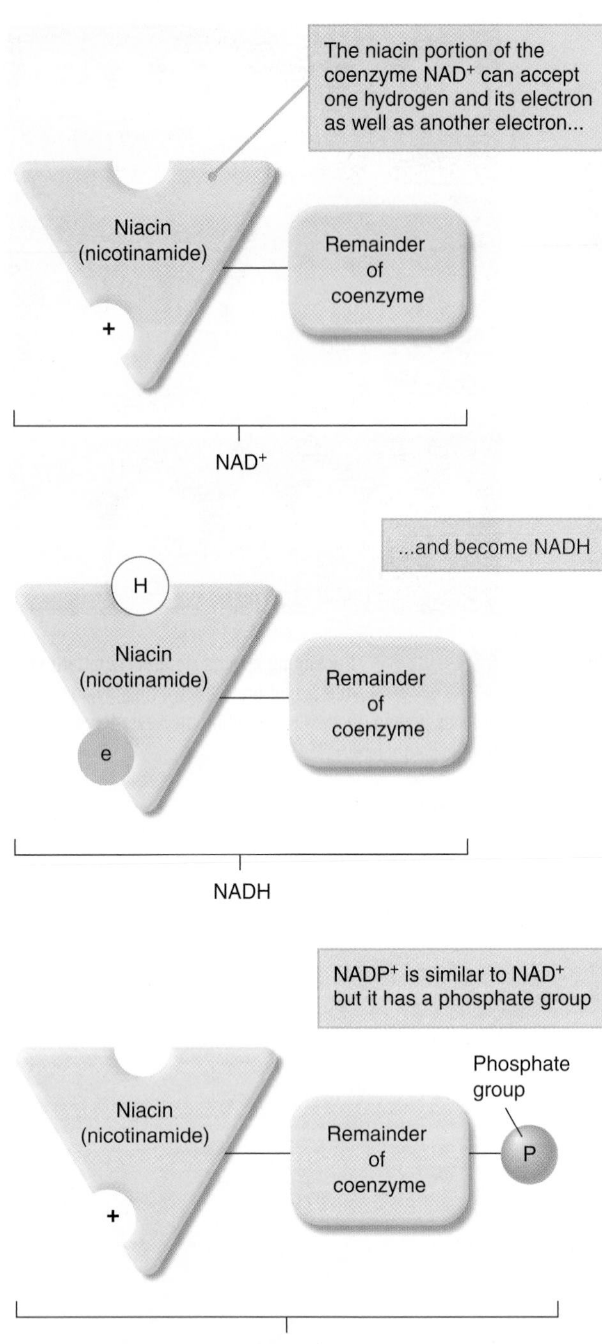
The niacin portion of the coenzyme NAD+ can accept one hydrogen and its electron as well as another electron...
Niacin (nicotinamide)
Remainder of coenzyme
+
NAD+
...and become NADH
H
Niacin (nicotinamide)
Remainder of coenzyme
e
NADH
NADP+ is similar to NAD+ but it has a phosphate group
Phosphate group
Niacin (nicotinamide)
Remainder of coenzyme
P
+
NADP+

Figure 11.10 **Niacin is part of the coenzymes NAD^+ and $NADP^+$.** Niacin, as nicotinamide, is an integral part of coenzymes critical to several metabolic reactions. NAD^+ is crucial to the formation of ATP, and $NADP^+$ is crucial to biosynthesis.

at the University of Wisconsin demonstrated that nicotinic acid cured dogs of a canine version of the human niacin-deficiency disease pellagra. In the early 1940s, the vitamin was renamed "niacin," an acronym of "nicotinic acid vitamin," so that people would not confuse it with nicotine.

Niacin actually is the name for two similarly functioning compounds: nicotinic acid and nicotinamide (also known as niacinamide). Like the other B vitamins, niacin is a coenzyme component (see **Figure 11.10**) and participates in at least 200 metabolic pathways.

Functions of Niacin

The niacin coenzymes, nicotinamide adenine dinucleotide (NAD^+) and nicotinamide adenine dinucleotide phosphate ($NADP^+$), play key roles in oxidation-reduction reactions. NAD^+ accepts electrons and hydrogen (i.e., is reduced) to form NADH. Under aerobic conditions, NADH carries high-energy electrons to the electron transport chain to help produce ATP. When you need energy in anaerobic conditions (say, during vigorous activity that pushes the body beyond its aerobic capacity), NADH powers the conversion of pyruvate to lactate as it loses electrons and a hydrogen (i.e., is oxidized) to become NAD^+. (See **Figure 11.11**.) This regenerated NAD^+ helps power the continued operation of glycolysis. Without it, glycolysis would halt, shutting off the supply of energy from glucose.

Many metabolic pathways that promote the synthesis of new compounds, such as fatty acids, rely on NADPH, the reduced form of $NADP^+$. NADPH is concentrated in cells (such as liver cells) that make large amounts of fatty acids.

Dietary Recommendations for Niacin

Niacin is unique among the B vitamins because your body can make it from the amino acid **tryptophan** as well as obtain it from foods. Intake recommendations are expressed as **niacin equivalents (NE)**, a measure that includes both preformed dietary niacin and niacin derived from tryptophan. The RDA for adult men of all ages is 16 milligrams of NE per day, and the RDA for adult women of all ages is 14 milligrams of NE. It increases to 18 milligrams of NE for pregnancy and 17 milligrams of NE for lactation.

Sources of Niacin

Most of the preformed niacin in the U.S. diet comes from meat, poultry, fish, enriched and whole-grain breads and grain products, and fortified ready-to-eat cereals. In a typical U.S. diet, beef and processed meats are substantial contributors.[13] Other good sources of niacin include mushrooms, peanuts, liver, and seafood. **Figure 11.12** shows foods that provide niacin. Because the vitamin is stable when heated, little niacin is lost during cooking.

The niacin precursor tryptophan is found in protein-rich animal foods, with the exception of gelatin. To convert tryptophan to niacin, your body needs other nutrients: riboflavin, vitamin B_6, and iron. Sixty milligrams of tryptophan yield about 1 milligram of niacin, or 1 niacin equivalent (NE).

To quickly determine the number of milligrams of niacin derived from tryptophan, divide the grams of high-quality dietary protein that exceed protein needs by 6. For instance, 30 grams of excess protein, divided by 6, yields 5 milligrams of niacin.

Because riboflavin, vitamin B_6, and iron affect the conversion of tryptophan to niacin, a deficiency of any one of these nutrients decreases tryptophan conversion. Certain rare metabolic disorders disrupt tryptophan conversion pathways. Pregnancy, on the other hand, increases the efficiency of converting tryptophan to niacin.

Tryptophan supplies about half of the average American's niacin intake. When estimating niacin consumption, remember that tables of food composition list only preformed niacin and therefore underestimate the amount of niacin some foods contribute via tryptophan.

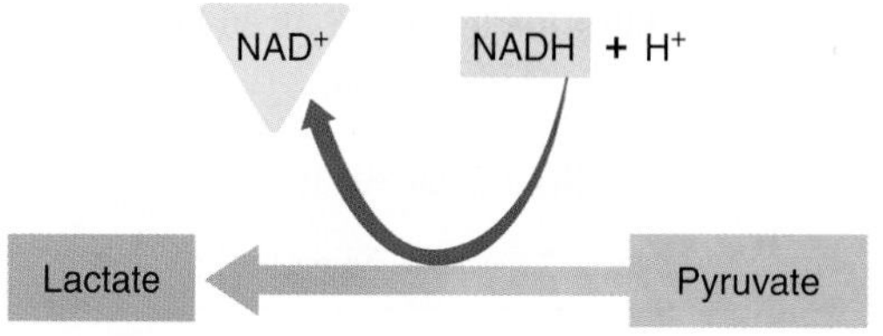

Figure 11.11 **Niacin helps convert pyruvate to lactate.** As a component of the coenzymes NAD^+ and NADH, niacin participates in many metabolic reactions.

tryptophan An amino acid that serves as a niacin precursor in the body. In the body, 60 milligrams of tryptophan yields about 1 milligram of niacin, or 1 niacin equivalent (NE).

niacin equivalents (NE) A measure that includes preformed dietary niacin as well as niacin derived from tryptophan; 60 milligrams of tryptophan yields about 1 milligram of niacin.

Niacin

Daily Value = 20 mg

	Food	Weight	Serving	Niacin
	Exceptionally good sources			
	Product 19 cereal	30 g	1 cup	20.010 mg
	All-Bran cereal	29 g	¾ cup	20.010 mg
High: 20% DV or more	Beef, liver, cooked	85 g	3 oz	14.854 mg
	Chicken, breast, roasted	86 g	½ breast	11.792 mg
	Tuna, light, canned in water	85 g	3 oz	11.288 mg
	Swordfish, cooked	85 g	3 oz	10.022 mg
	Pasta sauce	250 g	1 cup	9.793 mg
	Veal, leg, cooked	85 g	3 oz	8.976 mg
	Crispix cereal	29 g	1 cup	8.468 mg
	Kix cereal	30 g	1⅓ cup	7.275 mg
	Pork, loin, cooked	85 g	3 oz	7.212 mg
	Mushrooms, white, cooked	156 g	1 cup	6.958 mg
	Corn Flakes cereal	28 g	1 cup	6.832 mg
	Beef, sirloin, cooked	85 g	3 oz	6.100 mg
	Halibut, cooked	85 g	3 oz	6.055 mg
	Lamb, loin, cooked	85 g	3 oz	6.035 mg
	Turkey, light meat, roasted	84 g	3 oz	5.744 mg
	Cheerios cereal	30 g	1 cup	5.730 mg
	Salmon, cooked	85 g	3 oz	5.670 mg
	Beef, ground, 80% lean meat, cooked	85 g	3 oz	4.333 mg
Good: 10–19% DV	Haddock, cooked	85 g	3 oz	3.937 mg
	Peanuts	28 g	1 oz	3.919 mg
	Graham crackers	84 g	1 cup	3.462 mg
	Salami, cooked	57 g	2 slices	3.432 mg
	Barley, pearled, cooked	157 g	1 cup	3.239 mg
	Ham, sliced, extra lean	56 g	2 slices	3.230 mg
	Coffee, brewed	60 g	2 fl oz	3.124 mg
	Pretzels, hard, salted	60 g	10 pretzels	3.078 mg
	Shrimp, cooked	85 g	3 oz	2.610 mg
	Spaghetti, cooked, enriched	140 g	1 cup	2.365 mg
	White rice, cooked	158 g	1 cup	2.332 mg
	Sunflower seed kernels, dry roasted	32 g	¼ cup	2.253 mg
	Peanut butter	16 g	1 tbsp	2.144 mg

Figure 11.12 **Food sources of niacin.** Niacin is found mainly in meats and grains. Enrichment adds niacin as well as thiamin, riboflavin, folic acid, and iron to processed grains.

Source: US Department of Agriculture, Agricultural Research Service. USDA National Nutrient Database for Standard Reference, Release 22. Nutrient Data Laboratory Home Page. http://www.ars.usda.gov/ba/bhnrc/ndl.

CALCULATION OF NE FOR AN 80-KG (176-LB) MAN

His protein RDA is
80 kg × 0.8 g/kg = 64 g protein

Let us assume his diet contains 94 g of high-quality protein so that

94 g dietary protein
− 64 g protein (his protein RDA)
30 g protein in excess of needs

Tryptophan makes up about 1% of the protein so that

30 g protein × 0.01 = 0.3 g tryptophan (300 mg tryptophan)

60 mg tryptophan × 1 mg niacin (1 NE) so that

300 mg tryptophan ÷ 60 = 5 mg niacin (5 NE)

Shortcut Method
30 g excess protein ÷ 6 = 5 mg niacin (5 NE)

Figure 11.13 Soaking corn in a solution of lime (calcium hydroxide) releases bound niacin.

Niacin Deficiency

First documented in 1735 by a Spanish physician named Gaspar Casal, the niacin-deficiency disease pellagra was originally named *mal de la rosa*, or "red sickness," for the telltale redness that appears around the necks of people with the disease. Severely roughened skin is another hallmark, and the condition was later dubbed pellagra for the Italian *pelle*, or "skin," and *agra*, or "rough." Because the niacin coenzymes NAD^+ and $NADP^+$ are involved in just about every metabolic pathway, niacin deficiency wreaks havoc throughout the body. The primary symptoms of pellagra are known as the three Ds: dementia, diarrhea, and dermatitis. In severe cases, a fourth D—death—is the final outcome. Deficiencies of iron and vitamin B_6 may also contribute to pellagra.

During the early 1900s, as corn became a staple in the southwestern United States, pellagra emerged in epidemic proportions.[14] Because a protein in corn binds niacin tightly, it dramatically reduces niacin's bioavailability. We now know, however, that soaking corn in a solution of lime (calcium hydroxide) releases that bound niacin (see **Figure 11.13**). This disease also was common among the rural poor in the southeast, who subsisted on a diet of corn (maize), molasses, and salt pork, which is mostly fat. Between the end of World War I and the end of World War II, pellagra afflicted some 200,000 Americans. The incidence of pellagra started to decline during World War II because of the mandatory enrichment of bread flour and other cereal grains with niacin. After World War II, the enrichment program, combined with the postwar affluence that allowed people to purchase more protein-rich meat, poultry, and fish, finally curbed the disease. Sadly, pellagra continues to plague people living in Southeast Asia and Africa, whose diets lack sufficient niacin and protein.

Niacin Toxicity and Medicinal Uses of Niacin

Because megadoses of niacin (nicotinic acid) lower LDL cholesterol and raise HDL cholesterol, physicians may prescribe it. Although niacin has shown little severe toxicity, its side effects discourage widespread use.[15] The principal side effects are flushing (a feeling of prickly heat on the face and upper body), related itching, and tingling. Although serious liver toxicity has been reported, it is largely confined to the use of slow-release formulations taken as unregulated nutritional supplements.[16] Niacin's side effects usually are reversible with drug discontinuation or dose reduction. For adults, the UL for niacin is 35 milligrams per day from fortified foods, supplements, and medications. Niacin supplements containing more than the RDA should be taken only under medical supervision.

Researchers became interested in the potential of nicotinamide to prevent type 1 diabetes based on a study showing that nicotinamide protects insulin-secreting cells from inflammation and improves their function after the onset of diabetes.[17] However, a prospective clinical trial, the European Nicotinamide Diabetes Intervention Trial (ENDIT), showed that nicotinamide supplementation did not stop the development of diabetes.[18]

Key Concepts *Thiamin, riboflavin, and niacin are all incorporated into coenzymes that catalyze energy-yielding reactions. All three B vitamins participate in pathways that metabolize carbohydrate, protein, and fat. Enriched grains are a major source of these B vitamins, with pork ranking as a good source of thiamin, milk as a major source of riboflavin, and high-protein foods as sources of niacin. Deficiencies of these vitamins are rare in the United States. People with alcoholism have the highest risk of deficiencies. High doses of thiamin and riboflavin appear to be harmless, but megadoses of niacin should be taken only under medical supervision.*

Pantothenic Acid

In the 1930s a chemist named Roger J. Williams discovered that yeast requires a certain nutrient, which he called pantothenic acid. He suggested that if yeast needed this nutrient, humans might need it, too. First isolated in 1938, the chemical structure of pantothenic acid was identified by scientists in 1940.

The name pantothenic acid is derived from the Greek word *pantothen*, meaning "from every side." This B vitamin is widespread in the food supply, so it is well named. Although marketers have promoted pantothenic acid supplements as an "antistress" vitamin, there is no evidence from controlled studies to suggest it reduces feelings of anxiety or stress.[19]

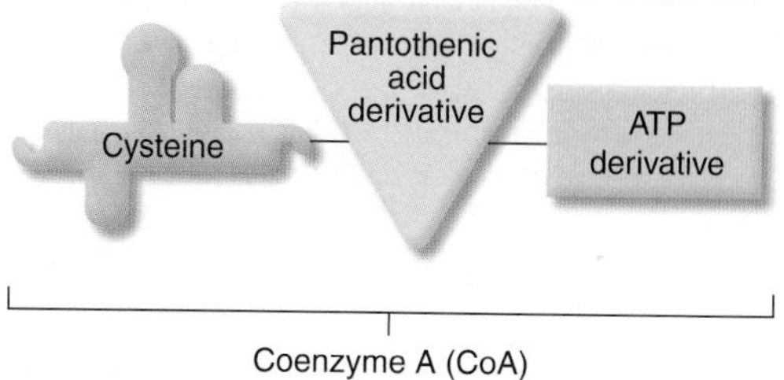

Figure 11.14 Pantothenic acid and coenzyme A. Pantothenic acid forms part of coenzyme A, which in turn is a component of acetyl CoA. Through coenzyme A, pantothenic acid is involved in many metabolic reactions.

Functions of Pantothenic Acid

Pantothenic acid is a component of coenzyme A (CoA), which in turn is a component of acetyl CoA. (See **Figure 11.14**.) Acetyl CoA sits at the crossroads of a number of metabolic pathways—both energy-generating pathways and biosynthetic pathways. It is formed from pyruvate (see **Figure 11.15**), starts the citric acid cycle, is a key building block of fatty acids, and is a precursor of ketone bodies.

Fatty acids also are known as acyl groups, and pantothenic acid is a component of the acyl carrier protein. During fatty acid synthesis, the acyl carrier protein binds fatty acids and carries them through a series of reactions that increases their chain length.

Dietary Recommendations for Pantothenic Acid

There are few data upon which to base dietary recommendations for pantothenic acid. As you learned in Chapter 2, when the data are insufficient to set an Estimated Average Requirement (EAR) for a nutrient, an RDA cannot be established. In these cases, and thus for pantothenic acid, an Adequate Intake (AI) level is set instead. For adults aged 19 to 50, the AI for pantothenic acid is 5 milligrams per day.

Sources of Pantothenic Acid

Pantothenic acid is widespread in the food supply. Although data on the specific pantothenic acid content of foods are sparse, food sources known to contain this vitamin include chicken, beef, potatoes, oats, tomato products, liver, kidney, yeast, egg yolk, broccoli, and whole grains.[20] **Figure 11.16** shows foods that are good sources of pantothenic acid.

Pantothenic acid is damaged easily. Freezing and canning appear to decrease the pantothenic acid content of vegetables, meat, fish, and dairy products. Processing and refining grains can reduce their pantothenic acid content by nearly 75 percent.[21]

Scientists do not have clear information about the bioavailability of pantothenic acid. It is assumed that the nutrient is well absorbed.

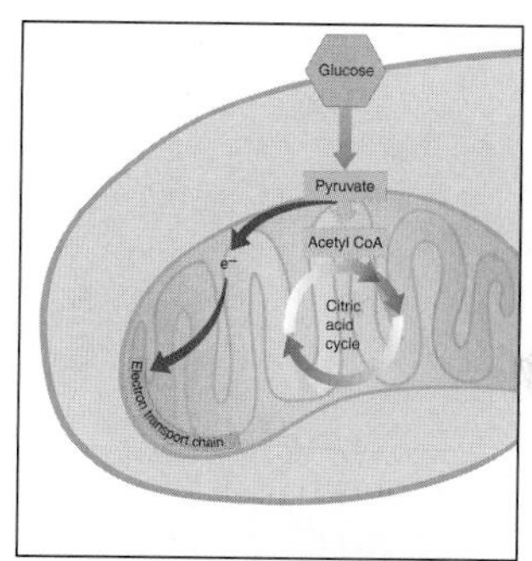

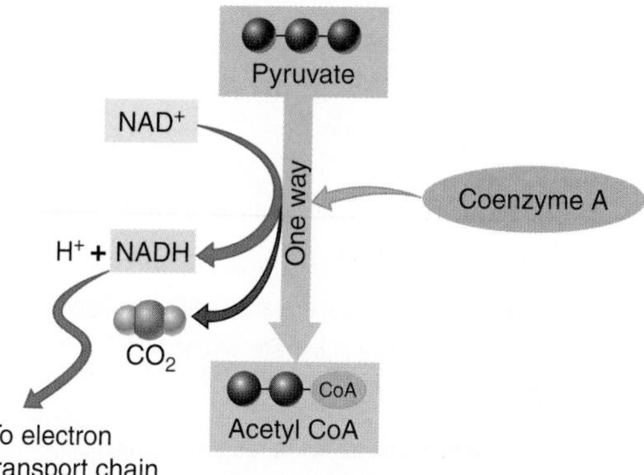

Figure 11.15 Pantothenic acid helps convert pyruvate to acetyl CoA. As part of coenzyme A, pantothenic acid helps form acetyl CoA from pyruvate. Niacin participates in this reaction as part of the coenzyme NAD^+.

Pantothenic Acid Deficiency

Pantothenic acid deficiencies are virtually nonexistent in the general population. The only observed cases of pantothenic acid deficiency are in people who were fed diets that completely lacked the nutrient or who were given a substance that prevents metabolism of pantothenic acid. These people suffered symptoms that included irritability, restlessness, fatigue, apathy, malaise, sleep

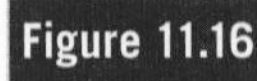

Figure 11.16 Food sources of pantothenic acid. Pantothenic acid is found widely in foods, but is abundant in only a few sources, such as liver.

Source: US Department of Agriculture, Agricultural Research Service. USDA National Nutrient Database for Standard Reference, Release 22. Nutrient Data Laboratory Home Page. http://www.ars.usda.gov/ba/bhnrc/ndl.

Pantothenic Acid

Daily Value = 10 mg

	Food	Weight	Portion	Pantothenic acid
High: 20% DV or more	Product 19 cereal	30 g	1 cup	10.080 mg
	All-Bran flakes cereal	29 g	¾ cup	10.005 mg
	Total cereal, whole grain	30 g	¾ cup	9.999 mg
	Beef liver, cooked	85 g	3 oz	5.902 mg
	Mushrooms, shiitake, cooked	145 g	1 cup	5.211 mg
Good: 10–19% DV	Sunflower seed kernels, dry roasted	32 g	¼ cup	2.253 mg
	Yogurt, plain, skim milk	227 g	8-oz container	1.455 mg
	Corn, canned	210 g	1 cup	1.418 mg
	Turkey, cooked	140 g	1 cup	1.320 mg
	Sweet potato, baked with skin	146 g	1 potato	1.291 mg
	Lentils, cooked	198 g	1 cup	1.263 mg
	Trout, cooked	85 g	3 oz	1.114 mg

disturbances, nausea, vomiting, numbness, tingling, muscle cramps, staggering gait, and hypoglycemia.

Pantothenic Acid Toxicity

High intakes of pantothenic acid have not caused adverse effects. Risk of toxicity appears to be extremely low, and therefore a UL has not been established.

Biotin

In 1924 three factors were identified as necessary for the growth of microorganisms. They were called "bios II," "vitamin H," and "coenzyme R." It soon became clear that all three were the same water-soluble, sulfur-containing vitamin—biotin.

In food, biotin is found both free and bound to protein. When proteins are digested, a biotin–lysine complex called **biocytin** is released.

biocytin A biotin–lysine complex released from digested protein.

carboxylation A reaction that adds a carboxyl group (–COOH) to a substrate, replacing a hydrogen atom.

biotinidase An enzyme in the small intestine that releases biotin from biocytin.

avidin A protein in raw egg whites that binds biotin, preventing its absorption. Avidin is destroyed by heat.

Functions of Biotin

Like the other B vitamins, biotin acts as a coenzyme in dozens of reactions. Among these reactions are amino acid metabolism, including the conversion of amino acids to glucose (gluconeogenesis); fatty acid synthesis; release of energy from fatty acids; and DNA synthesis.

Biotin-containing enzymes mainly catalyze **carboxylation** reactions, in which carbon dioxide is added to a substrate. (See **Figure 11.17**.) Some of the reactions that rely on biotin-containing enzymes include the following:

- Adding carbon dioxide to three-carbon pyruvate to yield four-carbon oxaloacetate. This process is one of the first steps in gluconeogenesis.

- Entry of three-carbon fatty acids into the citric acid cycle to yield energy
- Elongating fatty acid chains during fatty acid synthesis
- Breaking down leucine to the ketone body acetoacetate
- Breaking down isoleucine, methionine, threonine, and valine for entry into the citric acid cycle
- Synthesizing DNA

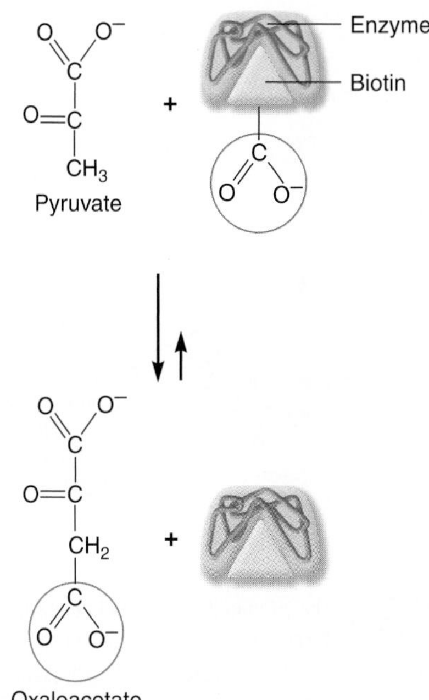

Figure 11.17 **Biotin aids carboxylation reactions.** Biotin is a coenzyme for several carboxylase enzymes. These enzymes transfer carboxyl groups, such as in the conversion of pyruvate to oxaloacetate.

Dietary Recommendations for Biotin

Just like pantothenic acid, there are not enough data on biotin to establish an EAR or an RDA. In fact, we know so little about human biotin requirements that the Adequate Intake value for adults is mathematically determined from the AI level for infants.[22] The infant value is based on the amount of biotin in human milk. The AI for biotin for adult men and women of all ages is 30 micrograms per day.

Sources of Biotin

Most tables of food composition do not list biotin content because it hasn't been determined for many foods. Good sources of biotin include cauliflower, liver, peanuts, and cheese. Most fruits and meats rank as poor sources. The enzyme **biotinidase** readily releases biotin from biocytin. Egg yolks are also a good source of biotin, but a protein called **avidin** in raw egg whites binds biotin and prevents its absorption from raw eggs. Heat destroys avidin, so it is unlikely to cause a biotin deficiency unless you eat a lot of raw eggs—at least a dozen daily. Of course, you should avoid eating anything that contains raw eggs because they might harbor *Salmonella* bacteria and cause foodborne illness.

Biotin Deficiency

Eating raw egg whites over a long period—months or years—can cause biotin deficiency. Because some anticonvulsant drugs break down biotin, people who take them for long periods also risk a deficiency. Infants born with biotinidase deficiency suffer from a rare genetic defect that leads to biotin depletion. Symptoms progress from initial hair loss and rash to convulsions and other neurological disorders. The deficiency also can delay growth and development. Early diagnosis and daily high doses of biotin (e.g., 10 milligrams per day) usually clear up symptoms. If not treated, biotin deficiency causes changes in blood pH that can lead to coma and death.

Biotin Toxicity

Biotin does not appear to be toxic at high doses. Children with biotinidase deficiency have been given as much as 200 milligrams of biotin daily without adverse side effects. A UL for biotin has not been established.

Quick Bite

Busy Bacteria

You may be aware that bacteria in the colon synthesize vitamin K, but did you know that colonic bacteria also make some biotin? Then again, when synthesizing this B vitamin these busy microbes may be pursuing a futile effort. Since the colon is downstream from the small intestine, the site of most biotin absorption, the bacteria's biotin may not be absorbed efficiently. Bacterial synthesis of biotin probably does not make an important contribution to your body's supply of biotin.

Vitamin B_6

Vitamin B_6 is a group of six compounds: pyridoxal (PL), pyridoxine (PN), pyridoxamine (PM), and their phosphorylated forms (PLP, PNP, and PMP), in which a phosphate group has been added (see **Figure 11.18**). Food contains the phosphorylated forms PLP, PNP, and PMP, but digestion strips off the phosphate groups. PL, PN, and PM then travel to the liver, which converts them to PLP (pyridoxal phosphate), the primary active coenzyme form.[23]

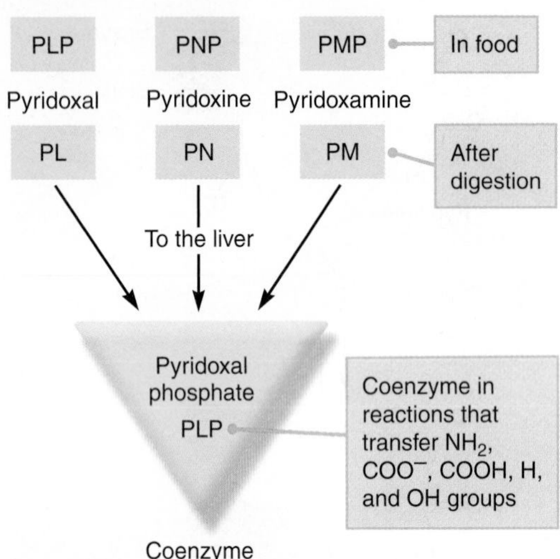

Figure 11.18 **The vitamin B_6 family and coenzyme form.** Vitamin B_6 is a group of six compounds: pyridoxal (PL), pyridoxine (PN), pyridoxamine (PM), and their phosphorylated forms PLP, PNP, and PMP. Digestion removes the phosphate groups and the liver converts PL, PN, and PM to PLP (pyridoxal phosphate), the active coenzyme form.

Functions of Vitamin B_6

The vitamin B_6 coenzyme PLP supports more than 100 different enzymes involved in reactions that include the transfer of amino groups (NH_2), carboxyl groups (COO– or COOH), or water (as H and OH). These enzymes support protein metabolism, blood cell synthesis, carbohydrate metabolism, and neurotransmitter synthesis.

Protein Metabolism

One of the primary tasks of PLP is to help metabolize amino acids and other nitrogen-containing compounds. As **Figure 11.19** shows, PLP plays a key role in transamination reactions, helping transfer an amino group from an amino acid to a keto acid and produce a new amino acid. Transamination, catalyzed by PLP, enables the body to make the 11 nonessential amino acids. Without adequate supplies of vitamin B_6, all amino acids become "indispensable," meaning the body cannot synthesize them and must obtain them from the diet (see the discussion of amino acids in Chapter 6, "Proteins and Amino Acids"). Over time, vitamin B_6 deficiency impairs protein synthesis and cell metabolism.

Blood Cell Synthesis

PLP supports the synthesis of the white blood cells of the immune system and is crucial for the synthesis of the red blood cells' hemoglobin rings, which carry oxygen. PLP also helps bind oxygen to hemoglobin. Inadequate vitamin B_6 disturbs this binding process, causing **microcytic hypochromic anemia**. In this type of **anemia**, red blood cells are smaller than normal and lack sufficient hemoglobin to carry oxygen. Iron deficiency also can cause microcytic hypochromic anemia.

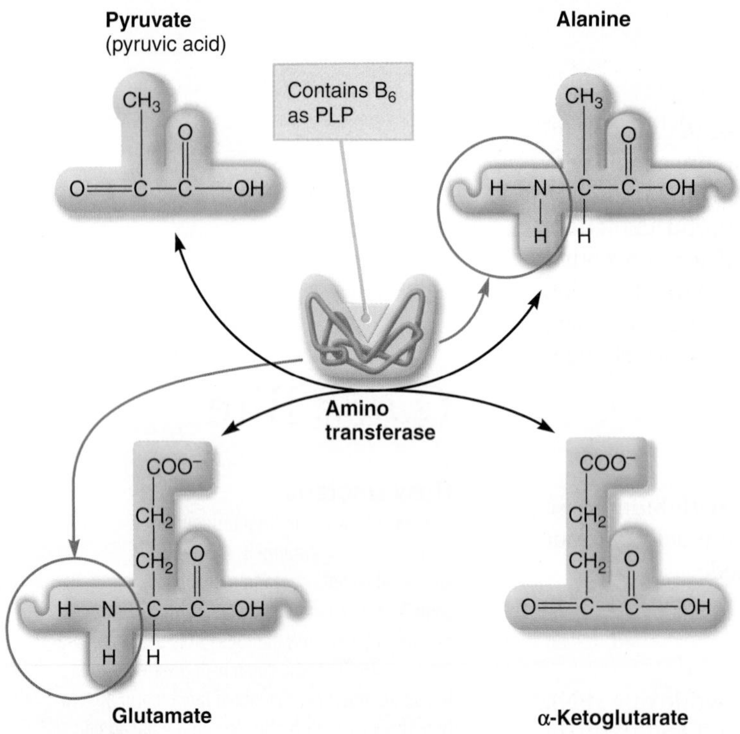

Figure 11.19 **Vitamin B_6 aids transamination reactions.** Vitamin B_6, as part of PLP, helps transfer an amino group from an amino acid to a ketoacid and produce a new amino acid.

Carbohydrate Metabolism

Through its role in transamination reactions, PLP participates in gluconeogenesis—producing glucose from amino acids. In addition, PLP facilitates glycogen breakdown.

Neurotransmitter Synthesis

PLP helps produce a number of neurotransmitters, including serotonin, gamma-amino butyric acid (GABA), dopamine, and norepinephrine. A vitamin B_6 deficiency can cause neurological symptoms—depression, headaches, confusion, and convulsions.

Vitamin B_6, Folate, and Heart Disease

Moderately high blood levels of the amino acid **homocysteine** are associated with fatal cardiovascular events. Homocysteine blood levels are influenced by dietary intake of vitamin B_6, folate, and vitamin B_{12}. Low intake of vitamin B_6 or folate can increase homocysteine levels, and high homocysteine levels may be a marker for heart disease.[24] Because the body accumulates large vitamin B_{12} stores to draw on when needed, variations in B_{12} intake seldom affect homocysteine levels. The body lowers homocysteine levels in one of two ways: (1) two PLP-dependent enzymes help convert homocysteine to cysteine, or (2) folate and vitamin B_{12}–dependent enzymes help convert homocysteine to methionine. An increase in fruit and vegetable intake also can affect homocysteine levels.Diets high in fruits and vegetables have been shown to increase levels of folate in the serum and red blood cells and also decrease plasma homocysteine.[25] Epidemiological evidence has shown that increased fruit and vegetable intake is associated with lower risk of cardiovascular disease.

microcytic hypochromic anemia Anemia characterized by small, pale red blood cells that lack adequate hemoglobin to carry oxygen; can be caused by deficiency of iron or vitamin B_6.

anemia Abnormally low concentration of hemoglobin in the bloodstream; can be caused by impaired synthesis of red blood cells, increased destruction of red cells, or significant loss of blood.

homocysteine An amino acid precursor of cysteine and a risk factor for heart disease.

Other Functions

As described earlier, the vitamin B_6 coenzyme also helps convert tryptophan to the B vitamin niacin.

Dietary Recommendations for Vitamin B_6

The RDA for vitamin B_6 for men and women aged 19 to 50 is 1.3 milligrams per day. For men 51 years and older, the RDA is 1.7 milligrams per day; for women 51 years and older, the RDA is 1.5 milligrams per day. Due to the role of vitamin B_6 in amino acid metabolism, people on very-high-protein diets may need higher intakes.[26]

Sources of Vitamin B_6

In the United States, the primary sources of vitamin B_6 are fortified, ready-to-eat cereals; mixed foods (including sandwiches) that contain primarily meat, fish, or poultry; white potatoes and other starchy vegetables; and noncitrus fruits.[27] Highly fortified cereals, beef liver and other organ meats, and fortified soy-based meat substitutes are especially rich sources. Other good sources of vitamin B_6 include bananas, potatoes, and sunflower seeds. Although whole grains contain vitamin B_6, refining removes B_6, and enrichment does not replace it. **Figure 11.20** shows foods that provide vitamin B_6.

Vitamin B_6 is not particularly stable and is especially sensitive to temperature. Heat can destroy as much as 50 percent of a food's vitamin B_6 content. About 75 percent of the vitamin B_6 in a varied diet is bioavailable, and vitamin B_6 taken without food is almost completely absorbed, even when taken in megadoses.[28]

Vitamin B_6 Deficiency

Vitamin B_6 deficiencies are rare. When one does occur, the deficiency leads to microcytic hypochromic anemia, seborrheic dermatitis, and neurological symptoms such as depression, confusion, and convulsions. Small deficits of vitamin B_6 can disrupt homocysteine metabolism, leading to increased blood levels of homocysteine.

Alcoholism boosts the risk of vitamin B_6 deficiency because alcohol decreases absorption of the nutrient and hampers synthesis of the coenzyme PLP. A breakdown product of alcohol metabolism also interferes with the functioning of vitamin B_6 coenzymes. In addition, two conditions frequently suffered by people with alcoholism—cirrhosis and hepatitis—damage liver tissue, preventing the liver from metabolizing vitamin B_6 to its coenzyme form.

Figure 11.20 **Food sources of vitamin B_6.** Meats are generally good sources of vitamin B_6 along with certain fruits (e.g., bananas) and vegetables (e.g., potatoes, carrots).

Source: US Department of Agriculture, Agricultural Research Service. USDA National Nutrient Database for Standard Reference, Release 22. Nutrient Data Laboratory Home Page. http://www.ars.usda.gov/ba/bhnrc/ndl.

Vitamin B_6

Daily Value = 2 mg

	Food	Weight	Serving	Vitamin B_6
	Exceptionally good sources			
	All-Bran cereal	30 g	½ cup	3.600 mg
	Product 19 cereal	30 g	1 cup	2.070 mg
	Total cereal, whole grain	30 g	¾ cup	2.000 mg
High: 20% DV or more	Chickpeas, canned	240 g	1 cup	1.135 mg
	Rice Krispies cereal	33 g	1¼ cup	0.990 mg
	Corn Flakes cereal	28 g	1 cup	0.963 mg
	Tuna, fresh, cooked	85 g	3 oz	0.882 mg
	Potato, baked, with skin	202 g	1 potato	0.628 mg
	Pork, loin, cooked	85 g	3 oz	0.596 mg
	Beef, sirloin, cooked	85 g	3 oz	0.536 mg
	Cheerios cereal	30 g	1 cup	0.533 mg
	Chicken, breast, cooked	86 g	½ breast	0.516 mg
	Turkey, light meat, cooked	84 g	3 oz	0.454 mg
	Brussels sprouts, frozen, cooked	155 g	1 cup	0.448 mg
	Red peppers, raw	149 g	1 cup	0.434 mg
	Bananas, raw	118 g	1 banana	0.433 mg
	Pork, ham, roasted	85 g	3 oz	0.400 mg
Good: 10–19% DV	Cod, cooked	85 g	3 oz	0.393 mg
	Pinto beans, cooked	171 g	1 cup	0.392 mg
	Plantains, cooked	154 g	1 cup	0.370 mg
	Pistachio nuts, dry roasted	28 g	1 oz (47 nuts)	0.361 mg
	Waffles, plain, frozen, toasted	33 g	1 waffle	0.345 mg
	Vegetable juice cocktail, canned	242 g	1 cup	0.339 mg
	Winter squash, cooked	205 g	1 cup	0.330 mg
	Beef, ground, 85% lean, cooked	85 g	3 oz	0.325 mg
	Broccoli, cooked	156 g	1 cup	0.312 mg
	Mangos, raw	207 g	1 mango	0.277 mg
	Salami, cooked	57 g	2 slices	0.260 mg
	Sweet potato, cooked	156 g	1 potato	0.257 mg
	Sunflower seed kernels, dry roasted	32 g	¼ cup	0.257 mg
	Carrots, cooked	156 g	1 cup	0.239 mg
	Cauliflower, cooked	124 g	1 cup	0.215 mg

Vitamin B_6 Toxicity and Medicinal Uses of Vitamin B_6

Megadoses of supplemental vitamin B_6—2,000 milligrams or more per day—can cause irreversible nerve damage that affects the ability to walk and causes numbness in the extremities.[29] Side effects have been noted at levels of 1,000 milligrams per day as well.

Some women self-prescribe large doses of vitamin B_6 to treat premenstrual syndrome (PMS)—the headache, bloating, irritability, and depression that may occur during the week or so before the onset of menstruation. Although vitamin B_6 has long been reputed to be an antidote for PMS, research has failed to prove its effectiveness.[30] Although women also have taken vitamin

B_6 to reduce symptoms of morning sickness during pregnancy, depression, and side effects of oral contraceptive medication, current scientific evidence is unclear on its benefit for this purpose.

Despite the risk of toxicity, some people have recommended high doses of vitamin B_6 as a treatment for carpal tunnel syndrome—a repetitive strain injury characterized by painful tingling in the wrist and fingers. Most well-designed scientific studies carried out in recent years, however, have failed to find a link between vitamin B_6 and improvement of carpal tunnel syndrome.[31] Physicians sometimes prescribe vitamin B_6 for children who experience seizures from no known cause.[32] Vitamin B_6 megadoses are not without risk, however, and can cause subtle neurological damage. Other side effects include upset stomach, headache, sleepiness, and a tingling, prickling, or burning sensation.

The reasons for the nerve damage associated with B_6 excess are unclear, but modification of proteins by PLP may be involved. The UL for vitamin B_6 intake is 100 milligrams per day, a common amount in over-the-counter vitamin supplements. Because of the potential hazards, vitamin B_6 megadoses should be taken only under medical supervision.

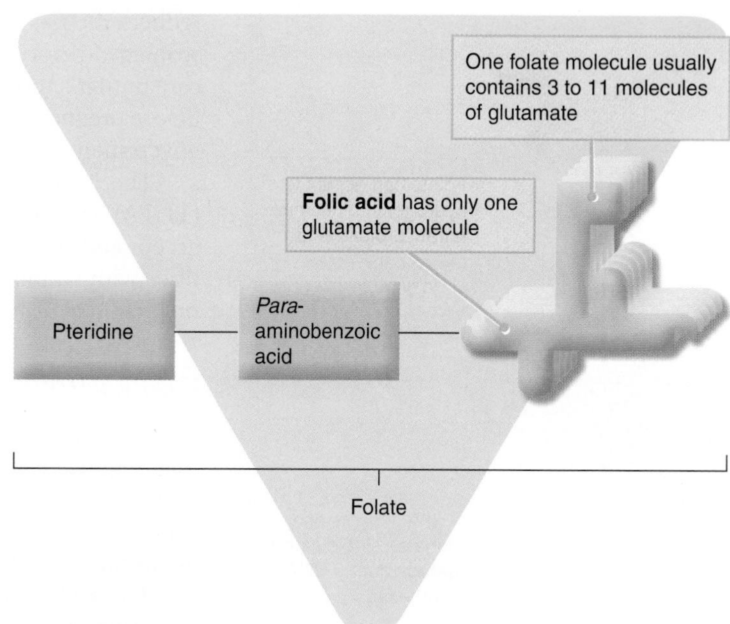
One folate molecule usually contains 3 to 11 molecules of glutamate
Folic acid has only one glutamate molecule
Pteridine
Para-aminobenzoic acid
Folate

Figure 11.21 **Folate and its major components.** Folate is made up of pteridine, *para*-aminobenzoic acid (PABA), and at least one molecule of glutamic acid (glutamate).

Key Concepts *Pantothenic acid and biotin are widespread in the food supply. Deficiencies of these B vitamins are rare because most people consume adequate amounts. Like the other B vitamins, pantothenic acid and biotin are parts of coenzymes involved in the metabolism of fat, carbohydrate, and protein. Vitamin B_6 is found in animal and plant foods and participates in protein metabolism, synthesis of neurotransmitters, and other metabolic pathways. Prolonged megadoses of vitamin B_6 can cause nerve damage.*

Folate

Eating raw liver, unappetizing though that may be, has long been known to cure a degenerative type of anemia. In 1945 a search for liver's curative component led to the discoveries of folate and vitamin B_{12}. Because folate and B_{12} work together to perform a number of biochemical functions, a deficiency of either one produces the same abnormalities in red blood cells.

Folate is named for its best natural source: green leafy vegetables (foliage). The term *folate* actually refers to a group of several closely related folate forms. As **Figure 11.21** shows, folate has three parts: pteridine, *para*-aminobenzoic acid (PABA), and at least one molecule of glutamic acid (glutamate). About 90 percent of the folate molecules found naturally in foods contain 3 to 11 glutamates. All but one of these glutamates is removed in the small intestine prior to absorption. The folic acid form of folate has only one glutamate. Folic acid is the most stable form of folate and is the form used for supplementation and fortification.

Functions of Folate

As a coenzyme, folate is crucial to DNA synthesis and cell division, amino acid metabolism, and the maturation of red blood cells and other cells. This involvement in basic cell reproduction and growth makes folate essential for healthy embryonic development. Good folate status in early pregnancy greatly

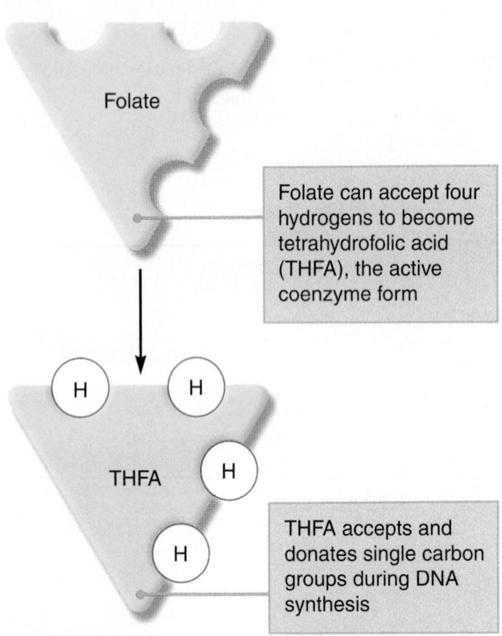
Folate
Folate can accept four hydrogens to become tetrahydrofolic acid (THFA), the active coenzyme form
H
H
THFA
H
H
THFA accepts and donates single carbon groups during DNA synthesis

Figure 11.22 **Folate, THFA, and DNA.** Five forms of tetrahydrofolic acid (THFA) are the active coenzyme forms of folate.

reduces the risk of birth defects called neural tube defects.[33] However, many women do not realize they have become pregnant or don't seek prenatal care until it's too late. That is why experts recommend folic acid supplements before pregnancy to all women who may become pregnant, and it is why the government mandated folic acid fortification.

The body converts folate to a coenzyme called tetrahydrofolic acid (THFA). (See **Figure 11.22.**) THFA has five active forms, all of which can accept and donate one-carbon units during metabolic reactions. Folate functions with vitamins B_6 and B_{12}. All three support red blood cell synthesis and help control homocysteine levels.

Dietary Recommendations for Folate

The bioavailability of folate varies depending on stomach contents and the folate source. The body absorbs nearly 100 percent of folic acid in supplements and fortified foods, but only about half to two-thirds of the folate naturally present in food.[34] To account for these differences, RDA values are expressed as **dietary folate equivalents (DFE)**.

dietary folate equivalents (DFE) A measure of folate intake used to account for the high bioavailability of folic acid taken as a supplement compared with the lower bioavailability of the folate found in foods.

The RDA for folate for males and females aged 19 years and older is 400 micrograms of DFE per day. The folate RDA for women increases significantly during pregnancy and lactation: 600 micrograms of DFE per day for pregnant women and 500 micrograms DFE per day while a woman is breastfeeding. To reduce the risk of bearing a child with certain birth defects, especially neural tube defects, the Institute of Medicine and the U.S. Public Health Service advise women of childbearing age to take in 400 micrograms of synthetic folic acid daily, from fortified foods or supplements, as well as to eat folate-containing foods.[35]

DRI Values and Bioavailability of Folate

1 μg DFE = 1 μg food folate

= 0.5 μg folic acid taken on an empty stomach

= 0.6 μg folic acid consumed with meals

Sources of Folate

Fortified breakfast cereals supply dietary folate. Some provide 400 micrograms in a moderate-size serving. Since 1998, folic acid fortification of enriched flour (including that used by commercial bakers) and enriched grain products has been mandatory in the United States and Canada.[36] This mandate calls for a fortification level of 1.4 milligrams of folic acid per kilogram of grain. A serving of enriched pasta, for example, typically provides 30 percent of the folate RDA. Dark-green leafy vegetables, asparagus, broccoli, orange juice, wheat germ, liver, sunflower seeds, and legumes are other good sources. Although vegetables other than dark-green leafy ones are less rich in folate, we eat foods such as green beans and vegetable soup so often that they make major contributions to our total folate intake.[37] **Figure 11.23** shows foods that provide folate.

Folate is extremely vulnerable to heat, ultraviolet light, and oxygen. Cooking and other food-processing and preparation techniques can destroy up to 90 percent of a food's folate. Experts recommend eating folate-rich fruits and vegetables raw or cooking them quickly in minimal amounts of water via steaming, stir-frying, or microwaving. Vitamin C in foods also helps protect folate from oxidation.

Folate status during the early stages of pregnancy is strongly linked with birth defects, specifically neural tube defects, and mandatory fortification is credited with preventing 50 to 75 percent of cases of neural tube defects.[38]

Scientists estimate that folate fortification increases folic acid intake by about 100 micrograms per day (an amount provided by slightly more than one-half cup of enriched pasta or one slice of bread), with the goal being to boost daily consumption by women of childbearing age to 400 micrograms

Folate

Daily Value = 400 DFE μg

	Food	Weight	Serving	Folate
	Exceptionally good sources			
	All-Bran Complete Wheat Flakes cereal	29 g	¾ cup	676 μg
	Total Corn Flakes cereal	30 g	1⅓ cup	676 μg
	Total cereal, whole grain	30 g	¾ cup	676 μg
High: 20% DV or more	Lentils, cooked	198 g	1 cup	358 μg
	Okra, frozen, cooked	184 g	1 cup	269 μg
	Spinach, cooked	180 g	1 cup	263 μg
	Black beans, cooked	172 g	1 cup	256 μg
	Egg noodles, cooked, enriched	160 g	1 cup	221 μg
	Bagels, plain, enriched	89 g	4″ bagel	201 μg
	Soybeans, cooked	180 g	1 cup	200 μg
	Collards, cooked	190 g	1 cup	177 μg
	Pretzels, hard, salted	60 g	10 pretzels	172 μg
	Macaroni, cooked, enriched	140 g	1 cup	167 μg
	Chickpeas, canned	240 g	1 cup	161 μg
	Broccoli, frozen, cooked	184 g	1 cup	103 μg
	Corn, canned	210 g	1 cup	103 μg
	Pita bread, white, enriched	60 g	6½″ pita	99 μg
Good: 10–19% DV	Romaine lettuce, raw	56 g	1 cup	76 μg
	Sunflower seeds	32 g	¼ cup	76 μg
	English muffin, plain, enriched	57 g	1 muffin	75 μg
	Red peppers, raw	149 g	1 cup	69 μg
	Bread, Italian	20 g	1 slice	61 μg
	Spinach, raw	30 g	1 cup	58 μg
	Potato, baked, with skin	202 g	1 potato	57 μg
	Tofu	120 g	1 piece	53 μg
	Tomato juice, canned	240 g	1 cup	49 μg
	Soymilk, original and vanilla, unfortified	245 g	1 cup	44 μg
	Crab, Alaska king, cooked	85 g	3 oz	43 μg

Figure 11.23 **Food sources of folate.** Good sources of folate are a diverse collection of foods: liver, legumes, leafy greens, and orange juice. Enriched grains and fortified cereals are other ways to include folic acid in the diet.

Source: US Department of Agriculture, Agricultural Research Service. USDA National Nutrient Database for Standard Reference, Release 22. Nutrient Data Laboratory Home Page. http://www.ars.usda.gov/ba/bhnrc/ndl.

of folic acid. However, the FDA's goal of 50 percent of women of childbearing age consuming at least 400 micrograms of folate daily has not yet been met for any ethnic or racial group.[39]

Folate Deficiency

Many scientists believe that folate deficiency is the most prevalent of all vitamin deficiencies. In developed countries, folate deficiency has been associated with those who have poor nutrition, such as the elderly or those with alcoholism. Others may have increased risk due to intestinal malabsorption, certain anemias, and the use of medications that interfere with folate absorption or activity.[40] Folate deficiency appears to play an important role in the development of anemia, atherosclerosis, neural tube defects, adverse pregnancy outcomes, and neuropsychiatric disorders.

When your folate reserves are good, your body normally can store enough folate to last two to four months without additional intake. Abnormal cell

Quick Bite

Can Folate Prevent Cancer?

When women took multivitamins containing folate for at least 15 years, they had a 75 percent reduction in colon cancer risk, according to the Harvard Nurses' Health Study. Folate intakes of more than 600 micrograms per day reduced breast cancer risk by 50 percent.

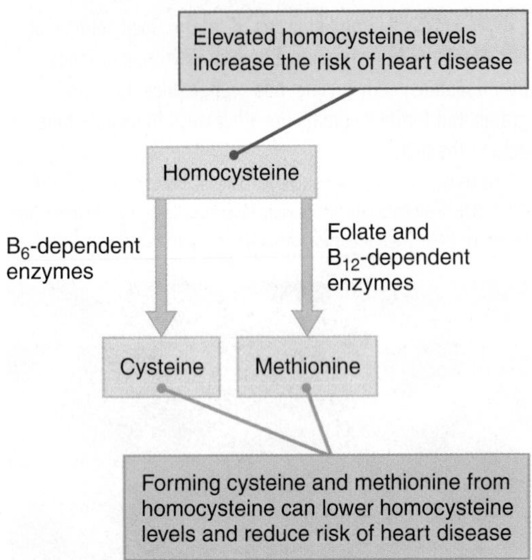

Figure 11.24 **Homocysteine and heart disease.** Elevated homocysteine levels are linked to an increased risk of heart disease. B_6-, B_{12}-, and folate-dependent enzymes help lower the amount of homocysteine by converting it to cysteine and methionine.

reproduction due to folate deficiency can be corrected within 24 hours by vitamin replacement. About 10 percent of the U.S. population may have insufficient folate stores. Deficiency may stem from the following conditions:

- *Inadequate folate consumption.* General malnutrition, often due to famine or poverty, causes folate deficiency. Cultural cooking methods that destroy folate, eating habits that avoid raw folate-rich vegetables, alcoholism, excessive dieting, and anorexia nervosa and bulimia nervosa can severely limit folate intake. The infirm or neglected elderly and institutionalized psychiatric patients also are at risk.
- *Inadequate folate absorption* due to abnormalities in the mucosal cells lining the GI tract.
- *Increased folate requirements* due to pregnancy and lactation, or other conditions. Certain diseases, such as blood disorders, leukemia, lymphoma, and psoriasis, can increase folate needs.
- *Impaired folate utilization*, typically associated with a vitamin B_6 deficiency.
- *Altered folate metabolism* arising from use of alcohol or certain prescription drugs such as barbiturates. Sulfa drugs and anticonvulsants probably impair folate absorption.
- *Excessive folate excretion* due to prolonged diarrhea.

Folate and Heart Disease

Research suggests that folate has an important role in preventing heart disease. Folate works with vitamin B_{12} and vitamin B_6 to reduce elevated homocysteine, which is a risk factor for cardiovascular disease.[41] (See **Figure 11.24.**) When folate intake is inadequate, homocysteine levels rise (during folate deficiency, homocysteine levels are markedly elevated). As folate intake increases, homocysteine levels drop. The Food and Nutrition Board used homocysteine levels as a primary factor in estimating the folate RDA, and the recommended folate intakes help maintain homocysteine at reduced levels. A daily intake of 400 micrograms of supplemental folic acid was adequate for reducing plasma homocysteine levels in older adults.[42] Since the FDA mandated folic acid fortification of the grain supply, blood folate levels have increased and homocysteine levels have decreased in the United States.[43] The role of folate supplementation for the prevention or treatment of cardiovascular disease, stroke, and all-cause mortality is currently under investigation.

Megaloblastic Anemia

Both folate and vitamin B_{12} are required for DNA synthesis and normal cell growth. A deficiency shows up soonest in cells that are reproducing the fastest. Red blood cells are rapidly dividing cells that must be replaced about every 120 days; they are among the first cells to be damaged by deficiency. The immature red blood cells cannot grow normally and cannot mature normally. Instead, these fragile blood cells grow into large, bizarre shapes and have greatly shortened life spans. (See **Figure 11.25**.) These large, fragile, immature cells, called **megaloblasts**, are a hallmark of **megaloblastic anemia**.

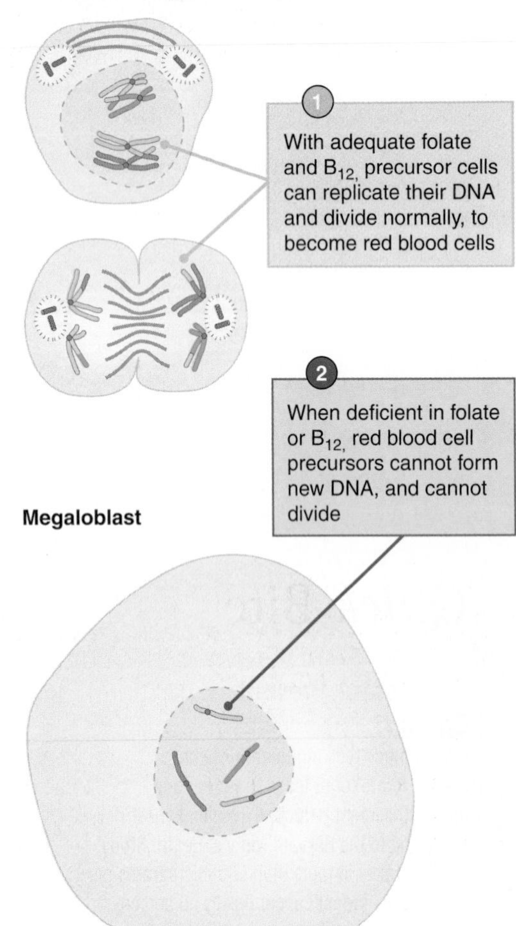

Figure 11.25 **Megaloblastic anemia.** When red blood cell precursors in the bone marrow cannot form new DNA, they cannot divide normally. These precursor cells continue to grow and become large, fragile, immature cells called megaloblasts. Megaloblasts displace red blood cells, resulting in megaloblastic anemia.

Megaloblasts may mature into **macrocytes**—abnormally large red blood cells with short life spans. As megaloblasts and macrocytes proliferate and the number of normal red blood cells decreases, the blood's ability to carry oxygen drops, causing weakness and fatigue. Folate-deficiency anemia commonly causes depression, irritability, forgetfulness, and disturbed sleep.

Impaired DNA synthesis caused by folate deficiency also affects the rapidly dividing cells lining the gastrointestinal tract. As a result, large, immature GI cells multiply and accumulate along the absorptive surface of the digestive tract, where they interfere with absorption, causing chronic diarrhea. In the mouth, these defective cells cause the tongue to appear beefy red. A lack of folate also impairs the synthesis of white blood cells, which are vital to the immune response.

megaloblasts Large, immature red blood cells produced when precursor cells fail to divide normally due to impaired DNA synthesis.

megaloblastic anemia Excess amounts of megaloblasts in the blood caused by deficiency of folate or vitamin B_{12}.

macrocytes Abnormally large red blood cells with short life spans.

neural tube defect (NTD) A birth defect resulting from failure of the neural tube to develop properly during early fetal development.

spina bifida A type of neural tube birth defect.

anencephaly A type of neural tube birth defect in which part or all of the brain is missing.

Neural Tube Defects

A large body of evidence links poor folate status during the early stages of pregnancy to an increased risk of a birth defect known as a **neural tube defect (NTD)**. In this type of birth defect, the neural tube fails to encase the spinal cord during early fetal development. This causes a number of disorders, including **spina bifida** and **anencephaly**. (See **Figure 11.26**.) These defects in the central nervous system occur within the first 30 days after conception.[44] Worldwide, NTDs afflict one to nine of every 1,000 infants born. The FDA's mandate to fortify enriched grains with folic acid has been estimated to have reduced the incidence of spina bifida by 26 percent.[45] Studies also show that women deficient in folate are more likely to have low-birth-weight babies[46] and premature deliveries.[47]

Folate and Cancer

Folate's role in the synthesis, repair, and function of DNA and RNA has led researchers to investigate DNA damage that may lead to cancer as a result of deficiency of this vitamin. Although not uniformly consistent, a large body of epidemiological studies generally indicates that low dietary intake and blood levels of folate increase risk of cancer and that high intake and blood levels reduce risk. However, the precise roles of folate deficiency in cancer and of folate supplementation in cancer prevention remain highly speculative.[48] A diet that contains at least five servings of fruits and vegetables daily has consistently been seen to reduce incidence of cancer and is currently the best protection.

Folate Toxicity

Because folate works so closely with vitamin B_{12}, it can mask a vitamin B_{12} deficiency. Older adults have increased risk of B_{12} deficiency, and consuming excess folate can prevent the formation of altered red blood cells that signals a lack of B_{12}. Some evidence also suggests that high intakes of folic acid may prompt or exacerbate the neurological problems associated with vitamin B_{12} deficiency. Concern regarding the masking of vitamin B_{12} deficiency has escalated following the mandatory fortification with folic acid.[49] Researchers estimate that 1 to 4 percent of adults over the age of 65 are at high risk for masking after fortification.[50]

Although rare, when hypersensitive people take folic acid supplements, they may suffer hives or respiratory distress. The UL for adults is 1,000 micrograms per day of folic acid from supplements and fortified foods. Researchers have found that folate intake in elders did not generally exceed the UL;

SPINE AFFECTED BY SPINA BIFIDA

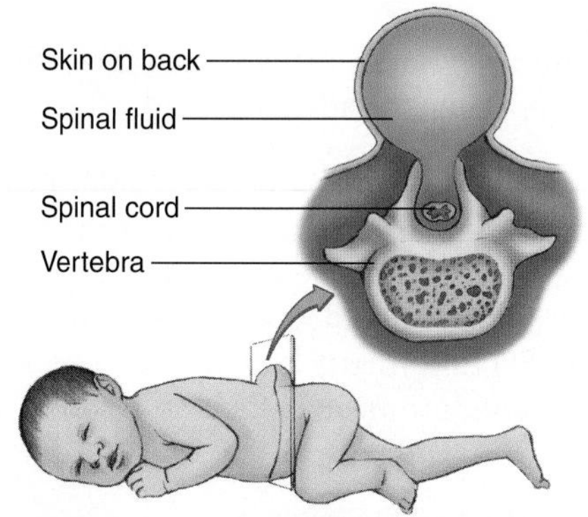

Figure 11.26 **Neural tube defects.** Poor folate status during the early stages of pregnancy, even before a woman may realize she is pregnant, increases the risk of a neural tube defect.

myelin sheath The protective coating that surrounds nerve fibers.

R-protein A protein produced by the salivary glands that may protect vitamin B_{12} as it travels through the stomach and into the small intestine.

atrophic gastritis An age-related condition in which the stomach loses its ability to secrete acid. In severe cases, ability to make intrinsic factor is also impaired.

however, 20 to 30 percent of children exceed the UL for their age groups (UL for ages 1–3 years = 300 μg/d; UL for ages 4–6 years = 400 μg/d).[51]

Vitamin B_{12}

Vitamin B_{12} is unlike other B vitamins. Plants do not provide it, and your body stores large amounts. Vitamin B_{12} is a group of cobalt-containing compounds, known collectively as cobalamin. In the United States, cyanocobalamin is the only form of vitamin B_{12} commercially available in supplements.

Functions of Vitamin B_{12}

Vitamin B_{12} plays a key role in folate metabolism by transferring a methyl group ($-CH_3$) from the folate coenzyme THFA, as **Figure 11.27** shows. Without vitamin B_{12}, THFA cannot change into its methylene form—the active form in many important metabolic pathways. For instance, a deficiency of the methylene form of THFA inhibits DNA synthesis. The partnership between

Going Green

Vitamin Buddies

When our early ancestors first moved from the rainforest onto the East African savannah they had to cope with an entirely new environment. The hot sun beat down mercilessly, forcing them back into the shade. To survive in the open they needed to develop a better way of fending off the sun—find something that would absorb or disperse ultraviolet light. The solution was melanin, the dark pigment in skin cells.

Biologists first thought that this pigmentation arose to protect against skin cancer. But skin cancers mostly develop after reproductive age and therefore could not have exerted the evolutionary pressure necessary to account for darker skin colors.

An alternative theory emerged when investigators showed that light-skinned people who had been exposed to strong sunlight had abnormally low levels of folate in their blood. In the laboratory, they found that subjecting human blood serum to simulated strong sunlight destroyed half its folate content within one hour. Scientists suggested that protection against the breakdown of folate was the evolutionary pressure selecting for dark skin.

Because folate status during the early stages of pregnancy is strongly linked with birth defects, adequate folate levels confer a reproductive advantage. So, why don't we all have dark skin? The answer lies in another vitamin—vitamin D.

As long as your skin gets regular exposure to sunlight, your body can make plenty of vitamin D. But as you move away from the equator, the intensity of the sunlight falls. Because light skin absorbs more UV sunlight than dark skin, light skin confers a reproductive advantage as you move toward the poles. Data from NASA on worldwide UV exposure levels on the earth's surface enabled scientists to map the world into three vitamin D zones, which correlated strongly to variations in skin color. Evolution struck a balance. Human populations evolved to have skin light enough to make sufficient vitamin D, yet dark enough to protect their stores of folate.

But What About the Inuits?

The Inuits are dark-skinned people who live in arctic regions where sunlight is poor. How can they have good vitamin D stores without good vitamin D synthesis in their dark skin? The answer lies in their diet, which is very high in fat from fish and whale blubber. Because vitamin D is found in oily fish (e.g., herring, salmon, and sardines) as well as in cod liver oil and other fish oils, the Inuits do not need sunlight to maintain good vitamin D status. Do you?

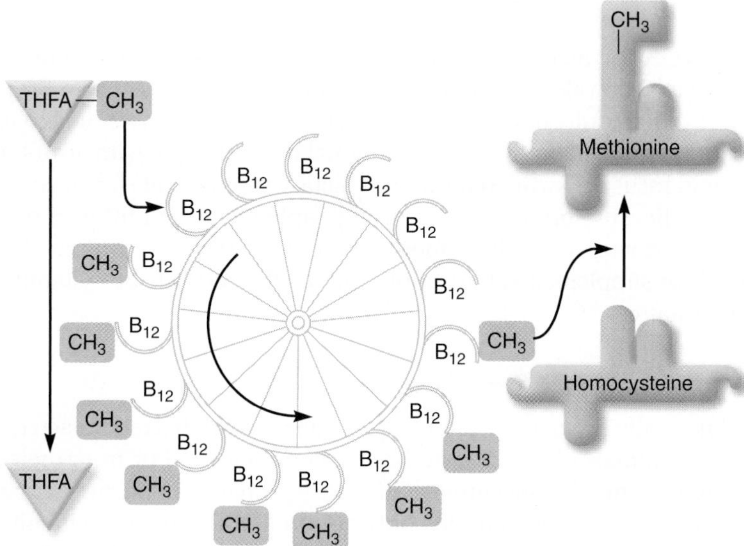
THFA — CH3
B12
CH3
Methionine
Homocysteine
THFA

Figure 11.27 **Vitamin B_{12} helps transfer methyl groups.** Vitamin B_{12} helps transfer a methyl group ($-CH_3$) from the folate coenzyme THFA. One destination for the methyl group is the reaction that converts homocysteine to methionine. This conversion reduces homocysteine blood levels, thereby lowering the risk of heart disease.

B_{12} and folate coenzyme THFA means that a vitamin B_{12} deficiency can lead to a folate deficiency, and a lack of either B_{12} or folate can precipitate megaloblastic anemia. Vitamin B_{12}–dependent enzymes also work with THFA to convert homocysteine to methionine, thereby reducing homocysteine blood levels and lowering the risk of heart disease.

Vitamin B_{12} also helps maintain the **myelin sheath**, the protective coating that surrounds nerve fibers. In addition, by helping to rearrange carbon atoms in fatty acid chains, vitamin B_{12} helps prepare them to enter the citric acid cycle.

Absorption of Vitamin B_{12}

Unless you're a vegan, it's easy to get enough vitamin B_{12} from your diet. But absorbing it is a complex process that requires several factors. (See **Figure 11.28**.) In the stomach, vitamin B_{12} binds with **R-protein**, a protein produced by the salivary glands that may protect vitamin B_{12} as it travels through the stomach and into the small intestine. Once there, pancreatic proteases such as trypsin cleave vitamin B_{12} from R-protein. Vitamin B_{12} then binds to intrinsic factor, a substance produced by the parietal cells of the stomach, the same cells that produce hydrochloric acid. Together, the two substances journey to the ileum of the small intestine and attach to receptor cells on the organ's brush border. The receptor cells absorb vitamin B_{12} and transfer it to transcobalamin II, a protein carrier in the blood. Transcobalamin II enters the bloodstream and delivers vitamin B_{12} to the liver, bone marrow, and developing blood cells.

A defect at any point in this process can cause a vitamin B_{12} deficiency. Factors that can impair vitamin B_{12} absorption include the following:

- Lack of R-protein, pancreatic enzymes, or intrinsic factor
- Absence or removal of the ileum or stomach
- Overgrowth of bacteria in the stomach
- Tapeworm
- Reduction of gastric acid production due to prolonged use of acid-inhibiting medications or an age-related condition called **atrophic gastritis**

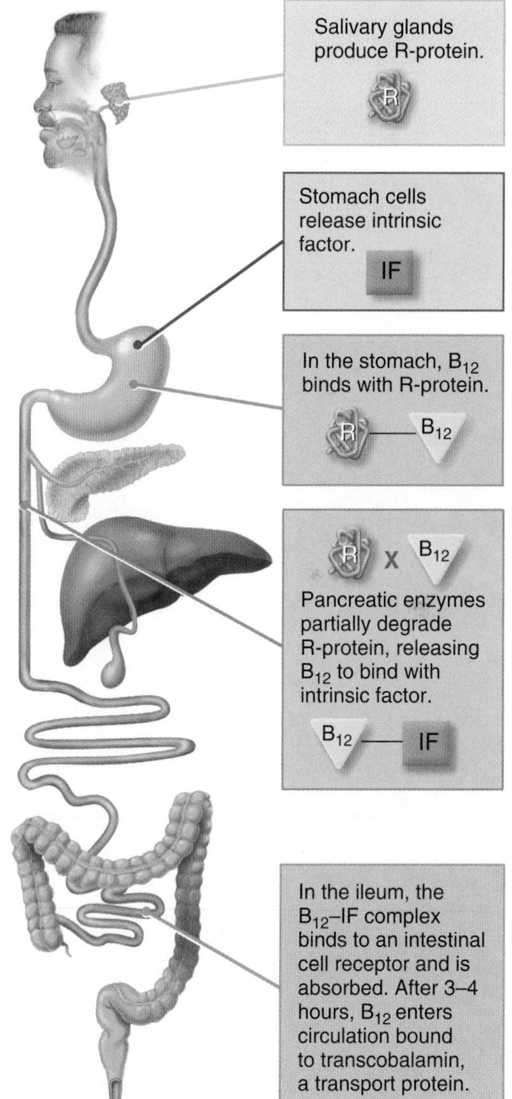
Salivary glands produce R-protein.
R
Stomach cells release intrinsic factor.
IF
In the stomach, B12 binds with R-protein.
R — B12
R x B12
Pancreatic enzymes partially degrade R-protein, releasing B12 to bind with intrinsic factor.
B12 — IF
In the ileum, the B12–IF complex binds to an intestinal cell receptor and is absorbed. After 3–4 hours, B12 enters circulation bound to transcobalamin, a transport protein.

Figure 11.28 **Absorption of vitamin B_{12}.** Absorption of B_{12} is a complex process that involves many factors and sites in the GI tract. Defects in this process, especially a lack of intrinsic factor, impair B_{12} absorption and can lead to B_{12} deficiency.

Dietary Recommendations for Vitamin B_{12}

The RDA for men and women aged 19 to 50 is 2.4 micrograms per day. Although the value for adults 51 and older is the same, up to 30 percent of these older adults have atrophic gastritis, which decreases the bioavailability of vitamin B_{12} naturally found in animal foods. People with atrophic gastritis should focus on fortified foods and dietary supplements for most of their B_{12} intake. Because up to 30 percent of people older than 50 may have trouble absorbing vitamin B_{12} from food, experts advise them to consume B_{12}-fortified foods or supplements. Our bodies more efficiently absorb vitamin B_{12} from these sources.[52]

Sources of Vitamin B_{12}

All naturally occurring vitamin B_{12} originates with bacteria. Bacteria produce it, and animals obtain it from bacteria on their food or from their intestinal bacteria. Animals concentrate and store B_{12}, mainly in the liver. Consequently animal-derived foods are our only good natural source of vitamin B_{12}, and liver is the richest source. Other sources are fortified foods, such as ready-to-eat cereals and some soy products.

Plants do not make vitamin B_{12}, but contaminating traces do exist on plant foods. Blue-green algae (cyanobacteria) are sometimes promoted as a B_{12} plant source, but their cobalamin is an inactive and biologically unavailable form. For vegans (vegetarians who avoid eggs and dairy, as well as meats), the most reliable food sources are fortified breakfast cereals, fortified soy products, and other foods fortified with B_{12}.

Mixed foods, including sandwiches whose main ingredient is meat, fish, or poultry, contribute most of our dietary B_{12}. The next most important sources are milk and milk products for women and beef for men. Although shellfish, liver and other organ meats, some game meat, and some kinds of fish are the richest sources of B_{12}, few people regularly eat these foods.[53] **Figure 11.29** shows foods that provide vitamin B_{12}.

Although definitive data are lacking, scientists conservatively estimate that about 50 percent of dietary B_{12} is bioavailable. That percentage may drop when a person consumes foods particularly high in vitamin B_{12}.

Vitamin B_{12} Deficiency

We can store enough vitamin B_{12} in the liver to last more than 2 years, and symptoms of deficiency may not appear for up to 12 years. Vegetarians who eat neither meat nor dairy products are at risk of vitamin B_{12} deficiency unless they take vitamin B_{12} supplements or regularly eat fortified cereals. Strict vegetarian (vegan) mothers who breastfeed may put their infants at risk of long-term neurological problems unless they include supplemental vitamin B_{12} in their diets.

THINK About It 3

Most vitamin B_{12} deficiency, especially in older people, is caused by inadequate intake or impaired absorption. To circumvent malabsorption, vitamin B_{12} injections deliver the vitamin directly to the bloodstream. Because the liver stores a substantial amount of B_{12}, monthly shots usually are sufficient. Other treatments include taking megadoses of vitamin B_{12} supplements (300 times the RDA) that overwhelm impaired absorption, and using a nasal gel containing vitamin B_{12}.

Symptoms of Vitamin B_{12} Deficiency

The major outcome of impaired vitamin B_{12} absorption is vitamin B_{12}–deficiency anemia. As in folate-deficiency anemia, lack of B_{12} causes the formation

Vitamin B_{12}

Daily Value = 6 µg

	Food	Weight	Portion	Vitamin B_{12}
	Exceptionally good sources			
High: 20% DV or more	Beef, liver, cooked	85 g	3 oz	70.66 µg
	Crab, Alaska king, cooked	85 g	3 oz	9.78 µg
	Special K cereal	31 g	1 cup	6.05 µg
	All-Bran cereal	30 g	½ cup	5.64 µg
	Salmon, cooked	85 g	3 oz	4.93 µg
	Rainbow trout, cooked	85 g	3 oz	4.22 µg
	Lobster, cooked	85 g	3 oz	2.64 µg
	Tuna, light, canned in water	85 g	3 oz	2.54 µg
	Beef, ground (75% lean), cooked	85 g	3 oz	2.39 µg
	Lamb, cooked	85 g	3 oz	2.25 µg
	Cheerios cereal	30 g	1 cup	1.86 µg
	Beef, sirloin, cooked	85 g	3 oz	1.43 µg
	Cheese, cottage, 1% milkfat	226 g	1 cup	1.42 µg
	Yogurt, plain, skim milk	227 g	8-oz container	1.38 µg
	Milk, 2% milkfat	244 g	1 cup	1.29 µg
	Halibut, cooked	85 g	3 oz	1.16 µg
Good: 10–19% DV	Swiss cheese	28 g	1 oz	0.95 µg
	Pork, spareribs, cooked	85 g	3 oz	0.92 µg
	Cod, cooked	85 g	3 oz	0.89 µg
	Salami, cooked	57 g	2 slices	0.86 µg
	Ricotta cheese, whole milk	246 g	1 cup	0.84 µg
	Frankfurter, beef	45 g	1 frank	0.77 µg

Figure 11.29 **Food sources of vitamin B_{12}.** Vitamin B_{12} is found naturally only in foods of animal origin such as liver, meats, and milk. Some cereals are fortified with vitamin B_{12}. *Note:* The DV for vitamin B_{12} is substantially higher than the current (1998) RDA of 2.4 micrograms for those age 14 and older.

Source: US Department of Agriculture, Agricultural Research Service. USDA National Nutrient Database for Standard Reference, Release 22. Nutrient Data Laboratory Home Page. http://www.ars.usda.gov/ba/bhnrc/ndl.

of megaloblasts and macrocytes rather than normal red blood cells. But there are important differences. Folate deficiency may lead to cognitive defects and depression, but B_{12} deficiency causes the myelin sheath to swell and break down, leading to brain abnormalities and spinal cord degeneration.

Neurological symptoms include tingling and numbness in the extremities, abnormal gait, and cognitive changes ranging from loss of concentration to memory loss, disorientation, and dementia.[54] If the megaloblastic anemia is inappropriately treated with folate, red blood cell production normalizes, but neurological damage worsens. Neurological effects may or may not be reversible, depending on their duration.

Pernicious Anemia

Pernicious anemia is the result of an autoimmune disorder in which the body destroys the parietal cells in the stomach.[55] Loss of parietal cells means a loss of intrinsic factor, which in turn reduces vitamin B_{12} absorption. Pernicious anemia is a major cause of vitamin B_{12} deficiency, although in the elderly, malabsorption of food-bound B_{12} causes the majority of B_{12} deficiency cases.[56] Pernicious anemia can affect people of all ages, races, and ethnic origins. Without treatment, nerve degeneration from vitamin B_{12} deficiency becomes irreversible and ultimately proves fatal. In fact, *pernicious* means "leading to death." Fortunately, timely vitamin B_{12} injections usually reverse the blood abnormalities and other signs of pernicious anemia within a matter of days. People with pernicious anemia are at a higher risk for stomach cancer.

pernicious anemia A form of anemia that results from an autoimmune disorder that damages cells lining the stomach and inhibits vitamin B_{12} absorption, leading to vitamin B_{12} deficiency.

Quick Bite

Chili Peppers Are Hot Stuff

An estimated one-quarter of the world's adults eat chili peppers every day. By weight, chili peppers are one of the richest sources of vitamins A and C. In addition, capsaicin, the substance that causes your mouth to burn, jump-starts the digestive process by stimulating salivation.

Vitamin B_{12} Toxicity

High levels of vitamin B_{12} from food or supplements have not been shown to cause harmful side effects in healthy people. Doses of 1 milligram are routinely used to treat pernicious anemia with no ill effects. A UL for vitamin B_{12} has not been determined.

Key Concepts *Folate and vitamin B_{12} work closely together. Fruits, vegetables, enriched grains, and fortified cereals contain folate, but only animal foods and fortified cereals contain bioavailable vitamin B_{12}. A deficiency of folate causes megaloblastic anemia and has been associated with neural tube defects. Deficiency of B_{12} causes a form of megaloblastic anemia and irreversible nerve damage. Vitamin B_{12} deficiency usually results from poor absorption, either due to pernicious anemia or other GI problems, such as atrophic gastritis. Because vitamin B_{12} is found only in animal foods, strict vegetarians must find an alternative source. Folate, vitamin B_{12}, and vitamin B_6 all play roles in the metabolism of the amino acid homocysteine, which has been implicated in heart disease.*

Vitamin C

For centuries, the insidious disease scurvy dogged humankind. Explorers and seafaring men especially feared this mysterious ailment that inflicted aching pain and made each journey a gamble with death. Writings that date back as far as 1500 B.C.E. describe their suffering in detail.

Although they did not know why, some travelers avoided this scourge. Unknowingly, they had eaten foods that contained vitamin C. The mystery began to be solved in 1746 by James Lind, a 30-year-old ship's surgeon in the British navy. In a controlled human nutrition clinical trial (see Figure 1.11 in Chapter 1, "Food Choices: Nutrients and Nourishment"), he carefully evaluated six different therapies for scurvy and showed that only those patients who received lemons or oranges recovered.[57] In the mid-1800s in Great Britain it was known that when potatoes were scarce, outbreaks of scurvy occurred.[58] When neither potatoes nor fruit were available, green vegetables were found to prevent scurvy. It was not until 1930 that scientists isolated the substance responsible for curing scurvy, the "antiascorbutic" factor, and named it vitamin C.

Vitamin C comes in two interchangeable, biologically active forms: a reduced form called ascorbic acid and an oxidized form called dehydroascorbic acid. Although most animals manufacture their own vitamin C, humans cannot, sharing this dubious distinction with fruit-eating bats, guinea pigs, and a few other isolated species. For some unknown reason, humans also appear to require much less vitamin C than most other animals.

reducing agent A compound that donates electrons or hydrogen atoms to another compound.

connective tissues Tissues composed primarily of fibrous proteins such as collagen, and which contain few cells. Their primary function is to bind together and support various body structures.

Functions of Vitamin C

Vitamin C is an antioxidant—it acts as a **reducing agent** and participates in many reactions by donating electrons or hydrogen ions. It also is essential to the activity of many enzymes. Unlike the B vitamins, however, it is not a coenzyme, and only indirectly activates enzymes.

Collagen Synthesis

Vitamin C plays an important role in the formation of collagen, a fibrous protein that helps reinforce the **connective tissues** that hold together the structures of the body. Collagen is made up of individual, linear proteins that wrap around one another like a cord of rope, forming a triple helix that imparts strength and flexibility. It is the most abundant protein in our bodies and the main fibrous component of skin, bone, tendons, cartilage, and teeth. It also is the major protein in connective tissue, which binds cells and tissues together, and in scar tissue.

Antioxidant Activity

Like vitamin E and beta-carotene (see Chapter 10), vitamin C works as an antioxidant and minimizes free radical damage in cells.[59] In addition to working independently as an antioxidant (**Figure 11.30**), vitamin C helps recycle oxidized vitamin E for reuse in the cells,[60] and vitamin C stabilizes the reduced form of the folate coenzyme. Eating foods rich in vitamin C may reduce the risk of chronic diseases such as heart disease, certain forms of cancer, and cataracts. It remains unclear whether the protective effects are due to vitamin C or to fruit and vegetable consumption in general. Study results for vitamin C supplements are contradictory.

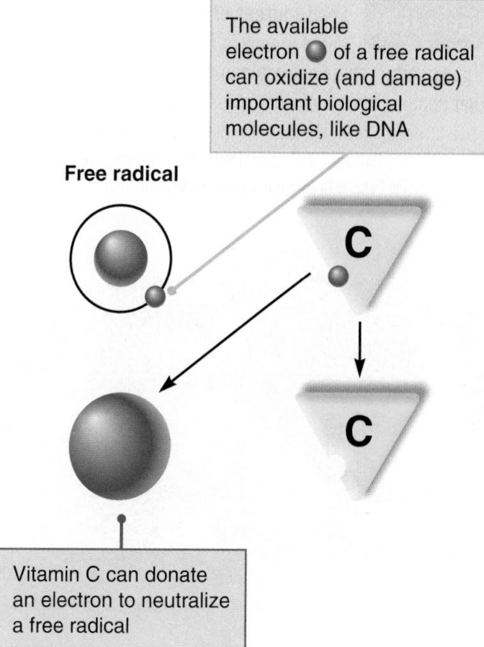
The available electron of a free radical can oxidize (and damage) important biological molecules, like DNA
Free radical
C
C
Vitamin C can donate an electron to neutralize a free radical

Figure 11.30 **Vitamin C is an antioxidant.** Vitamin C minimizes free radical damage by donating an electron. Vitamin C also indirectly activates many enzymes. Although essential to enzyme activity, unlike the B vitamins, vitamin C is not a coenzyme.

Iron Absorption

As a reducing agent, vitamin C enhances the absorption of nonheme iron, which comes mainly from plant foods (the small intestine absorbs nonheme iron better when it is reduced).

Synthesis of Vital Cell Compounds

Vitamin C helps synthesize carnitine, a compound that carries fatty acids from the cytosol to the mitochondria for energy production. Vitamin C also helps synthesize norepinephrine, epinephrine, the neurotransmitter serotonin, the thyroid hormone thyroxine, bile acids, steroid hormones, and purine bases used in DNA synthesis.

Immune Function

THINK About It 4

Vitamin C enables lymphocytes and other cells of the immune system to function properly. Based in part on the vitamin's importance to immunity, vitamin C has been reputed to prevent or cure the common cold. However, studies show that, at best, vitamin C may slightly reduce the duration of a cold in people exposed to brief periods of severe physical exercise or cold environments.[61]

Because vitamin C is used in cellular systems that break down and clear drugs from the body, drug use also can boost vitamin C requirements.

Dietary Recommendations for Vitamin C

For adults aged 19 and older, the RDA for vitamin C is 90 milligrams per day for men and 75 milligrams per day for women. For women, the RDA rises to 85 milligrams per day during pregnancy and 120 milligrams per day during lactation. Because smoking increases the metabolic turnover of vitamin C, the Food and Nutrition Board estimates that smokers require 35 milligrams per day more than nonsmokers.[62]

Sources of Vitamin C

Many, but not all, fruits and vegetables are high in vitamin C. Particularly good sources of vitamin C include potatoes, citrus fruits, tomatoes, fortified

Figure 11.31 **Food sources of vitamin C.** Vitamin C is found mainly in fruits and vegetables. Although citrus fruits are notoriously good sources, many other popular fruits and vegetables are rich in vitamin C.

Source: US Department of Agriculture, Agricultural Research Service. USDA National Nutrient Database for Standard Reference, Release 22. Nutrient Data Laboratory Home Page. http://www.ars.usda.gov/ba/bhnrc/ndl.

Vitamin C

Daily Value = 60 mg

Category	Food	Weight	Serving	Vitamin C
Exceptionally good sources				
	Red pepper, fresh	149 g	1 cup	190.3 mg
	Orange juice	248 g	1 cup	124.0 mg
	Cranberry juice cocktail	253 g	8 fl oz	107.0 mg
	Broccoli, cooked	156 g	1 cup	101.2 mg
High: 20% DV or more	Strawberries, fresh	166 g	1 cup	97.6 mg
	Brussels sprouts, cooked	156 g	1 cup	96.7 mg
	Grapefruit juice, pink	247 g	1 cup	93.9 mg
	Pineapple, raw	155 g	1 cup	74.1 mg
	Kiwifruit, fresh	76 g	1 medium	70.5 mg
	Oranges, raw	131 g	1 orange	69.7 mg
	Vegetable juice cocktail, canned	242 g	1 cup	67.0 mg
	Cantaloupe melon, raw	160 g	1 cup	58.7 mg
	Cauliflower, raw	100 g	1 cup	48.2 mg
	Mangos, raw	165 g	1 cup	45.7 mg
	Kale, frozen, cooked	130 g	1 cup	32.8 mg
	Raspberries, raw	123 g	1 cup	32.2 mg
	Honeydew melon, raw	170 g	1 cup	30.6 mg
	Soybeans, cooked	180 g	1 cup	30.6 mg
	Sweet potato, cooked, with skin	146 g	1 potato	28.6 mg
	Tomatoes, red, raw	180 g	1 cup	22.9 mg
	Spinach, cooked	180 g	1 cup	17.6 mg
	Grapes, red or green, raw	160 g	1 cup	17.3 mg
	Blueberries, raw	145 g	1 cup	14.1 mg
	Watermelon, raw	152 g	1 cup	12.3 mg
Good: 10–19% DV	Peaches, raw	170 g	1 cup	11.2 mg
	Prune juice, canned	256 g	1 cup	10.5 mg
	Lima beans, frozen, cooked	180 g	1 cup	10.4 mg
	Pumpkin, canned	245 g	1 cup	10.3 mg
	Bananas, raw	118 g	1 banana	10.3 mg
	Chickpeas, canned	240 g	1 cup	9.1 mg
	Cucumber, peeled, raw	280 g	1 large	9.0 mg
	Spinach, raw	30 g	1 cup	8.4 mg
	Nectarines, raw	136 g	1 nectarine	7.3 mg
	Pears, raw	166 g	1 pear	7.0 mg
	Carrots, raw	110 g	1 cup	6.5 mg
	Apples, raw, with skin	138 g	1 apple	6.3 mg
	Plums, raw	66 g	1 plum	6.3 mg

juice drinks, broccoli, strawberries, kiwifruit, cabbage, spinach and other leafy greens, and green peppers. Because vitamin C is highly vulnerable to heat and oxygen, fresh fruits and vegetables are the optimal sources. **Figure 11.31** shows some foods that provide vitamin C.

When people take in 30 milligrams to 120 milligrams daily, the intestine absorbs about 80 to 90 percent of vitamin C. However, when vitamin C consumption exceeds 6,000 milligrams daily, absorption drops to about 20 percent. Most of the residual vitamin C is excreted in the urine.

Vitamin C Deficiency

Scurvy is the well-known vitamin C–deficiency disease. Its first symptoms surface after about a month on a vitamin C–free diet. As the body loses its ability to synthesize collagen, connective tissue starts breaking down and gums and joints begin to bleed. Weakness develops, and small hemorrhages appear around the hair follicles on the arms and legs. As the disease progresses, previously healed wounds reopen, and bone pain, fractures, diarrhea, and psychological problems such as depression commonly emerge.

Scurvy is rare in developed countries, but possible among those who eat few fruits and vegetables, follow extremely restricted diets, or abuse alcohol or drugs.[63] Less severe vitamin C deficiency can impair cellular functions without causing overt scurvy. The most common symptoms are inflammation of the gums and fatigue. Although much of the past research on vitamin C has centered around the prevention of scurvy, this vitamin has also undergone speculation for its role in the prevention of chronic disease. The use of vitamin C for prevention of coronary heart disease, stroke, cancer, cataracts, and lead toxicity and in the treatment of cardiovascular disease, hypertension, cancer, diabetes mellitus, and the common cold require additional investigation.

Vitamin C Toxicity

Although megadoses of vitamin C do not appear to be acutely toxic to most healthy people, taking more than 2,000 milligrams daily for a prolonged period may lead to nausea, abdominal cramps, diarrhea, and nosebleeds.[64] The UL for vitamin C is 2,000 milligrams per day. In people with kidney disease, excess vitamin C also may contribute to oxalate-containing kidney stones. In healthy people, epidemiological studies do not support an association between excess vitamin C intake and kidney stones.[65] High vitamin C intakes also may bolster iron absorption—useful for some, but problematic for people with **hemochromatosis**, a metabolic disease that causes excess iron accumulation.

Finally, some experts suspect that large amounts of vitamin C may stimulate free radical damage by enhancing oxidation (a pro-oxidant effect), the opposite of its usual antioxidant activity.[66]

Key Concepts *Vitamin C, which is found in many fruits and vegetables, functions mainly in collagen synthesis. It also acts as an antioxidant. Vitamin C helps boost iron absorption and plays a part in hormone and neurotransmitter synthesis. A deficiency of vitamin C leads to scurvy, although this is rare today. Megadoses of vitamin C can cause gastrointestinal disturbances.*

Choline: A Vitamin-like Compound

Choline is a vitamin-like substance, but differs from a true vitamin. You can synthesize most, but probably not all, of the choline you need. Men who stay on a choline-free diet develop a deficiency over time. For this reason, dietary recommendations are now made for choline.

Unlike most vitamins, choline is more than a catalyst or coenzyme. Most choline in your body actually is a component of other substances, including acetylcholine (a neurotransmitter), lecithins, and bile (choline was named after the French word for bile, *chole*). Likewise, it is a source of methyl groups needed for DNA methylation. Metabolic pathways link choline, methionine,

hemochromatosis A metabolic disorder that results in excess iron deposits in the body.

folate, and vitamins B_6 and B_{12} in the metabolism of homocysteine. Low choline intake appears to increase folate requirements; conversely, low folate intake increases choline requirements.[67]

With the help of vitamin B_{12} and folate, the liver forms choline from the amino acids serine and methionine. If you eat enough protein to provide the essential amino acid methionine, your body can manufacture choline. Insufficient data are available to determine whether choline is truly essential in the human diet. The research that exists suggests that people on diets devoid of choline develop fatty liver and liver damage.

Because choline is widespread in the food supply, the risk of a deficiency is minimal in healthy people. Liver, eggs, beef, cauliflower, and peanuts are especially rich in choline. An AI for choline has been set at 550 milligrams per day for adult men, and 425 milligrams per day for adult women.

High doses of choline can cause hypotension (low blood pressure), sweating, diarrhea, and fishy body odor. The UL for adults is 3,500 milligrams of choline per day.

Conditional Nutrients

There are few substances we need for life that our bodies cannot make. These substances are nutrients such as vitamins that we must get from food. Our bodies routinely make countless other essential substances. However, under some circumstances—illnesses or inherited metabolic errors—we cannot make enough, so we must obtain them from our diets. These substances are *conditional nutrients*. Inositol, carnitine, taurine, and lipoic acid are examples of nutrients that are thought to be conditional.

Carnitine

Carnitine carries fatty acids from the cytosol into the mitochondria for entry into the citric acid cycle. In the mitochondria, carnitine also helps dispose of excess organic acids produced via metabolic pathways. The liver synthesizes carnitine from the amino acids lysine and methionine.

Meat and dairy products are the major dietary sources of carnitine. Carnitine does not appear to be an essential compound for healthy people, because strict vegetarians often eat diets virtually lacking carnitine without suffering ill effects. Low blood levels of carnitine have been observed in malnourished children and adults. Diets deficient in the amino acids needed to make carnitine may cause abnormal fatty acid metabolism.

Carnitine in large doses has been helpful in removing toxic compounds in people with certain inborn errors of metabolism. In addition, high doses of carnitine have been successful in treating progressive muscle disease, deterioration of the heart muscle, and, most recently, carnitine depletion in kidney dialysis patients.[68]

Inositol

Inositol is part of cell membrane phospholipids. Inositol phospholipids, a family of lipids containing inositol derivatives, are precursors of eicosanoids, substances that work like hormones in the body (for more on eicosanoids, see Chapter 5, "Lipids"). Inositol participates in a chain of reactions that ultimately increases the concentration of intracellular calcium, which in turn elicits a number of cell responses such as the relaying of messages by nerve cells. This may explain why inositol phospholipids are concentrated in brain tissue.

The body synthesizes inositol from glucose, and these two molecules have similar structures. Although there are nine forms of inositol, myo-inositol is the only one involved in human nutrition.

Although some plant foods contain inositol, animal-derived foods supply most dietary inositol. There is no reason to suspect inositol deficiency in the general population, and the Food and Nutrition Board has not set recommended intake levels. Inositol seems to become essential only for people with impaired inositol metabolism. Animal studies suggest that abnormal inositol metabolism may be associated with certain medical conditions such as diabetes, multiple sclerosis, kidney failure, and some cancers.

Taurine

Taurine has a well-documented role in bile salt formation, especially the bile salt that extracts cholesterol. Studies show that a decreased taurine content is associated with reduced cholesterol extraction and increased risk of atherosclerosis.[69] Taurine also acts as an antioxidant, has anti-inflammatory properties, and helps regulate the movement of fluid in and out of cells. In diabetes, taurine supplementation has shown promise in animal studies, but human studies have yielded mixed results.[70]

There is no evidence of taurine deficiency in the general population. Although it is found naturally only in foods from animal sources, strict vegetarians are not deficient. Apparently, people are able to synthesize all the taurine they need. Derived from the amino acids methionine and cysteine, taurine is one of the most abundant free amino acids in animals.

Taurine is one of several amino acids that have become popular additives to so-called smart drinks designed to assist in mental activities. However, no solid scientific evidence links taurine to improved mental abilities.

Lipoic Acid

Lipoic acid is a necessary cofactor in energy-producing reactions in mitochondria. For instance, lipoic acid helps convert pyruvate to acetyl CoA, the major linking step between glycolysis and the citric acid cycle. It is a potent antioxidant and is unique because it can neutralize both fat-soluble and water-soluble free radicals. Although health food stores sell lipoic acid supplements, no evidence supports their use by healthy people.

Bogus Vitamins

Many dietary supplements contain unnecessary substances. Yet hucksters often call these substances vitamins and tout their supposed benefits as health enhancers and disease treatments. The Internet is full of Web sites representing themselves as "nutrition sites" that endorse nutritional supplements that can prevent or cure almost anything. Despite ample scientific evidence to the contrary, quacks still hawk laetrile ("vitamin B_{12}") as a cancer cure. Some supplements contain hesperidin, *para*-aminobenzoic acid (PABA), pangamic acid, or rutin, even though these substances are not essential for human health. Consumers should be wary of anything that sounds "too good to be true" and investigate the claims using reputable Web sites and resources. Think twice before you pay a premium price for supplements that contain these bogus vitamins.

Key Concepts *The body contains a number of vitamin-like compounds synthesized from glucose and amino acids and found in the food supply. Although deficiencies of these substances are unlikely, some people with certain medical conditions may benefit from supplemental amounts of some of these compounds. Of course, supplements should be taken only with a physician's recommendation. Researchers are examining the needs for these substances and their effects on the body.*

The FDA requires all manufacturers to add folic acid to enriched grain products such as bread, flour, rice, and pasta. Folic acid, the synthetic form of folate, has been shown to decrease risk of neural tube defects. Folic acid or folate (its natural form) may also be important in reducing risk of heart disease and colon cancer. Prior to the fortification of enriched grains, it was difficult for some people to get enough of this B vitamin, in part because it is destroyed easily during cooking and storage. The purpose of folic acid fortification is to ensure that most people, especially women of childbearing age, can meet their needs for this B vitamin. Look at the Nutrition Facts label on a pasta package. Note how much folic acid is in a serving of pasta!

Calories	**200**
Total fat	2% (1 g)
Saturated fat	0%
Cholesterol	0%
Sodium	0%
Total carbohydrate	14%
Vitamin A	0%
Vitamin C	0%
Calcium	0%
Iron	10%
Folic acid	30%
Thiamin	35%
Niacin	20%
Riboflavin	15%

Some vegetables and legumes also contain folate, so combining pasta with vegetables, or enriched rice with black beans, would provide substantial amounts of folate. The next time you are at the grocery store, pay close attention to the food labels on grain products to see just how much folate you could consume from different grain products.

Looking again at this food label, what other water-soluble vitamins do you see? In addition to folic acid, this pasta contains substantial amounts of thiamin, niacin, and riboflavin. These are the "enrichment" vitamins, and one serving of pasta provides 15 to 35 percent of the Daily Value of each.

Nutrition Facts
Serving Size: 1/2 cup (56g)
Servings Per Container: 8
Amount Per Serving
Calories 200
Calories from fat 10
% Daily Value*
Total Fat 1g 2%
Saturated Fat 0g 0%
Trans Fat 0g
Cholesterol 0mg 0%
Sodium 0mg 0%
Total Carbohydrate 41g 14%
Dietary Fiber 2g 8%
Sugars 1g
Protein 7g
Vitamin A 0% • Vitamin C 0%
Calcium 0% • Iron 10%
Thiamin 35% • Riboflavin 15%
Niacin 20% • Folic acid 30%
* Percent Daily Values are based on a 2,000 calorie diet. Your daily values may be higher or lower depending on your calorie needs:
Calories: 2000 2,500
Total Fat Less Than 65g 80g
Sat Fat Less Than 20g 25g
Cholesterol Less Than 300mg 300mg
Sodium Less Than 2,400mg 2,400mg
Total Carbohydrate 300g 375g
Dietary Fiber 25g 30g
Calories per gram:
Fat 9 Carbohydrate 4 Protein 4

Learning Portfolio

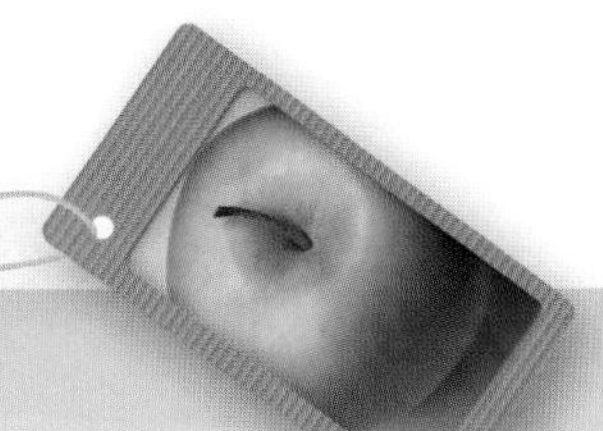

Key Terms

	page		page
anemia	445	hemochromatosis	459
anencephaly	451	homocysteine	445
angular stomatitis	436	macrocytes	451
ariboflavinosis	436	megaloblastic anemia	451
atrophic gastritis	452	megaloblasts	451
avidin	442	microcytic hypochromic anemia	445
beriberi	431	myelin sheath	452
biocytin	442	neural tube defect (NTD)	451
biotinidase	442	niacin equivalents (NE)	439
carboxylation	442	pernicious anemia	455
cheilosis	436	R-protein	452
connective tissues	456	reducing agent	456
decarboxylation	432	seborrheic dermatitis	436
dietary folate equivalents (DFE)	448	spina bifida	451
glossitis	436	thiamin pyrophosphate (TPP)	432
glutathione peroxidase	436	tryptophan	439

Study Points

- The water-soluble vitamins include the eight B vitamins and vitamin C.
- Thiamin (vitamin B_1) functions as the coenzyme thiamin pyrophosphate (TPP) in energy metabolism.
- Thiamin deficiency results in the classic disease beriberi. In industrialized countries, thiamin deficiency most often is associated with alcoholism. There is no known danger of toxicity related to high intakes of thiamin.
- Riboflavin (vitamin B_2) forms part of the coenzymes FAD and FMN, which function in energy metabolism as hydrogen and electron carriers.
- Ariboflavinosis (riboflavin deficiency) is characterized by inflammation of the mouth and tongue.
- Niacin (vitamin B_3) participates in energy metabolism as part of the coenzymes NAD^+ and $NADP^+$.
- Niacin deficiency results in pellagra, a disease characterized by diarrhea, dermatitis, dementia, and death.
- High doses of niacin, such as in the treatment of high blood cholesterol, can have toxic side effects, including liver damage.
- Pantothenic acid is a part of coenzyme A, a critical player in energy metabolism.
- Biotin-containing enzymes catalyze carboxylation reactions, which are important in many pathways involving energy-yielding nutrients.
- Biotin deficiency is rare, but may be induced by regularly consuming large quantities of raw egg whites.
- The coenzyme form of vitamin B_6 (pyridoxine) is called pyridoxal phosphate (PLP); it participates in a variety of reactions, primarily involving amino acid metabolism.
- Megadoses of vitamin B_6 can cause permanent nerve damage.
- Folate and vitamin B_{12} work closely together in a number of metabolic pathways, including reactions in cell division and DNA synthesis.
- Deficiency of either folate or vitamin B_{12} will result in megaloblastic anemia, but vitamin B_{12} deficiency also causes irreversible nerve damage.
- Poor folate status is associated with development of neural tube defects during pregnancy. Therefore, women of childbearing age are advised to take in 400 micrograms of folic acid each day from fortified foods or supplements in addition to other dietary folate.
- Vitamin C (ascorbic acid) functions in the synthesis of collagen and other vital compounds, and also works as an antioxidant.
- Vitamin C deficiency can cause scurvy, which is characterized by bleeding gums and small hemorrhages on the skin.
- A number of vitamin-like compounds have been identified, including choline, inositol, and taurine. These compounds are synthesized by the body and are not dietary essentials.

Study Questions

1. List the nine water-soluble vitamins and give one main function for each.
2. Which water-soluble vitamin can be made from an amino acid?
3. Name the diseases and/or characteristic symptoms of deficiency of each water-soluble vitamin.

4. A lack of which three B vitamins can cause anemia? Describe the differences among these anemias.
5. List the water-soluble vitamins demonstrated to be toxic in large doses. What signs indicate toxic levels of each vitamin?

Try This

The Antioxidant and the Apple

This experiment will help you see how vitamin C acts as an antioxidant. You will need an apple and a lemon. Slice the apple into eight pieces. Put four on one plate and four on another. Slice open the lemon and squeeze its juices over the apple slices on one plate. Leave the lemon on this plate to remind you which apple slices have been sprayed with lemon juice. Let both plates sit for 30 minutes. Do the apple slices look any different after 30 minutes? What is the difference? Why?

Supplemental Income

The object of this exercise is to critically review vitamin supplements. Go to the drug store and look at a few multivitamin supplements and "stress" formulas. Look at the %DV for the water-soluble vitamins. Do you see any that have more than 1,000% of the DV? Compare prices. Is it more expensive to buy supplements with more of these vitamins? Considering what you learned in this chapter, would it benefit you to take supplements that contain such a high amount of these vitamins? Why do you think supplements contain such large quantities of these vitamins?

What About Bobbie?

Let's take a look at Bobbie's intake of five water-soluble vitamins: thiamin, riboflavin, niacin, vitamin B_{12}, and vitamin C. Let's examine her day of eating (see Chapter 1) using the guidelines you've learned in this chapter. How did Bobbie do in terms of these water-soluble vitamins? She did well; she consumed ample amounts of most due to her varied food choices. Here is a summary of each of the vitamins.

Thiamin

Bobbie consumed 2.0 milligrams of thiamin, which is more than the RDA of 1.1 milligrams. Most of the foods Bobbie ate this day contributed to her thiamin intake, but the ones that contributed the most were the enriched grains from the bread, bagel, and spaghetti.

Riboflavin

Bobbie consumed 2.2 milligrams of riboflavin on this day, or more than the RDA of 1.1 milligrams. As with thiamin, a variety of foods contributed to her riboflavin intake, but the enriched grains (bread, bagel, and pasta) were among the best contributors. The meatballs Bobbie ate at dinner also contributed riboflavin.

Niacin

Bobbie's intake of niacin was also above her RDA. She consumed 27.5 milligrams this day compared to her RDA of 14 milligrams. If you remember from the protein chapter that Bobbie's intake of protein was quite high, it shouldn't surprise you that her niacin intake is high, too. Meat, poultry, fish, and other protein-containing foods, along with enriched grains, are some of the best sources of niacin. In this case, Bobbie's turkey sandwich, spaghetti with meatballs, and cheese pizza contributed niacin.

Vitamin B_{12}

Bobbie's intake of vitamin B_{12} (3.7 mg), like her intake of the other B vitamins, was above the RDA (2.4 mg). The foods that contributed to Bobbie's vitamin B_{12} intake were the animal products (turkey, egg, meatballs, Parmesan cheese, and cheese pizza).

Vitamin C

Although Bobbie enjoys tomato products such as salsa, spaghetti sauce, and pizza sauce, her intake of vitamin C (42 milligrams) was less than the RDA of 75 milligrams. Here are some other ways Bobbie could have included more vitamin C in her diet:

- Have some orange or grapefruit juice with breakfast.
- Choose spinach, broccoli, or Brussels sprouts instead of green beans for dinner.
- Use spinach as the base of her salad instead of iceberg lettuce.
- Add some sliced red pepper to her salad at lunch.
- Have an orange as a snack instead of the tortilla chips.

References

1 Junod SW. Folic acid fortification: fact and folly. 2001. http://www.fda.gov/AboutFDA/WhatWeDo/History/ProductRegulation/SelectionsFromFDLIUpdateSeriesonFDAHistory/ucm091883.htm.

2 Carpenter KJ. A short history of nutritional science: part 2 (1885–1912). *J Nutr*. 2003;133:975–984.

3 Ibid.

4 Institute of Medicine, Food and Nutrition Board. *Dietary Reference Intakes for Thiamin, Riboflavin, Niacin, Vitamin B_6, Folate, Vitamin B_{12}, Pantothenic Acid, Biotin, and Choline*. Washington, DC: National Academies Press, 1998.

5 Ibid.

6 Ibid.

7 Murray RK, Rodwell VW, Bender D, et al. *Harper's Illustrated Biochemistry*. 28th ed. New York: Lange Basic Science/McGraw-Hill Medical, 2009.

8 Institute of Medicine, Food and Nutrition Board. *Dietary Reference Intakes for Thiamin, Riboflavin*.

9 Mestdagh F, De Meulenaer B, De Clippeleer J, et al. Protective influence of several packaging materials on light oxidation of milk. *J Dairy Sci*. 2005;88:499–510.

10 Dainty JR, Bullock NR, Hart DJ, et al. Quantification of the bioavailability of riboflavin from foods by use of stable-isotope labels and kinetic modeling. *Am J Clin Nutr*. 2007;85:1557–1564.

11 Institute of Medicine, Food and Nutrition Board. *Dietary Reference Intakes for Thiamin, Riboflavin*.

12 Powers HJ. Riboflavin (vitamin B-2) and health. *Am J Clin Nutr*. 2003;77(6):1352–1360.

13 Institute of Medicine, Food and Nutrition Board. *Dietary Reference Intakes for Thiamin, Riboflavin*.

14 Park YK, Sempos CT, Barton CN, et al. Effectiveness of food fortification in the United States: the case of pellagra. *Am J Public Health*. 2000;90(5):727–738.

15 Brown BG. Expert commentary: niacin safety. *Am J Cardiol*. 2007;99(6A):32C–34C.

16 Guyton JR, Bayes HE. Safety considerations with niacin therapy. *Am J Cardiol*. 2007;99(6A):22C–31C.

17 Higdon J. *An Evidence-Based Approach to Vitamins and Minerals: Health Implications and Intake Recommendations*. New York: Thieme, 2003.

18 Gale EA, Bingley PJ, Emmett CL, et al. European Nicotinamide Diabetes Intervention Trial (ENDIT). *Lancet*. 2004;63(9413):910.

19 Sarubin-Fragakis A. *The Health Professional's Guide to Popular Dietary Supplements*. 3rd ed. Chicago: American Dietetic Association, 2007.

20 Trumbo PR. Pantothenic acid. In: Shils ME, Shike M, Ross AC, et al., eds. *Modern Nutrition in Health and Disease*. 10th ed. Philadelphia: Lippincott Williams & Wilkins, 2006:426–469.

21 Institute of Medicine, Food and Nutrition Board. *Dietary Reference Intakes for Thiamin, Riboflavin*.

22 Ibid.

23 Ibid.

24 Wierzbicki AS. Homocysteine and cardiovascular disease: a review of the evidence. *Diabetes Vasc Dis Res*. 2007;4(2):143–150.

25 Silaste M-L, Rantala M, Alfthan G, et al. Plasma homocysteine concentration is decreased by dietary intervention. *Br J Nutr*. 2003;89:295–301.

26 Institute of Medicine, Food and Nutrition Board. *Dietary Reference Intakes for Thiamin, Riboflavin*.

27 Ibid.

28 Gregory JF. Bioavailability of vitamin B6. *Eur J Clin Nutr*. 1997;51:S54–S59.

29 Schaumberg H, Kaplan J, Windebank A, et al. Sensory neuropathy from pyridoxine abuse. *N Engl J Med*. 1983;309:445–448.

30 National Institutes of Health, Office of Dietary Supplements. Dietary supplement fact sheet: vitamin B6. August 24, 2007. http://ods.od.nih.gov/factsheets/vitaminb6.asp. Accessed 7/23/09.

31 Aufiero E, Stitik TP, Foye PM, Chen B. Pyridoxine hydrochloride treatment of carpal tunnel syndrome: a review. *Nutr Rev*. 2004;62(3):96–104; and Ryan-Harshman M, Aldoori W. Carpal tunnel syndrome and vitamin B6. *Can Fam Physician*. 2007;53(7):1161–1162.

32 Clayton RT. B6-responsive disorders: a model of human dependency. *J Inherit Metab Dis*. 2006;29:317–326.

33 Pitkin RM. Folate and neural tube defects. *Am J Clin Nutr*. 2007;85(1):285S–288S.

34 Institute of Medicine, Food and Nutrition Board. *Dietary Reference Intakes for Thiamin, Riboflavin*; and Suitor CW, Bailey LB. Dietary folate equivalents: interpretation and application. *J Am Diet Assoc*. 2000;100:88–94.

35 Pitkin. Folate and neural tube defects.

36 Kim YI. Will mandatory folic acid fortification prevent or promote cancer? *Am J Clin Nutr*. 2004;80:1123–1128.

37 Institute of Medicine, Food and Nutrition Board. *Dietary Reference Intakes for Thiamin, Riboflavin*.

38 Ibid.; and Blom HJ, Shaw GM, den Heijer M, Finnell RH. Neural tube defects and folate: case far from closed. *Nat Rev Neurosci*. 2006;7(9):724–731.

39 Bentley TGK, Willett WC, Weinstein MC, Kuntz KM. Population-level changes in folate intake by age, gender, and race/ethnicity after folic acid fortification. *Am J Public Health*. 2006;96(11):2040–2047.

40 Khoury MJ, Ponka P. New insights into erythropoiesis: the roles of folate, vitamin B_{12}, and iron. *Annu Rev Nutr*. 2004;24:105–131.

41 Wierzbicki AS. Homocysteine and cardiovascular disease: a review of the evidence. *Diabetes Vasc Dis Res*. 2007;4(2):143–150.

42 Van Oort FV, Melse-Boonstra A, Brouwer IA, et al. Folic acid and reduction of plasma homocysteine concentrations in older adults: a dose-response study. *Am J Clin Nutr.* 2003;77(5):1318–1323.

43 Ganji V, Kafai MR. Demographic, lifestyle, and health characteristics and serum B vitamin status are determinants of plasma total homocysteine concentration in the post-folic acid fortification period, 1999–2004. *J Nutr*. 2009;139(2):345–352.

44 Pitkin. Folate and neural tube defects.

45 Centers for Disease Control and Prevention. Spina bifida and anencephaly before and after folic acid mandate—United States, 1995–1996 and 1999–2000. *MMWR Morb Mortal Wkly Rep*. 2004;53(17):362–365.

46 Relton CL, Pearce MS, Parker L. The influence of erythrocyte folate and serum vitamin B12 status on birth weight. *Br J Nutr*. 2005;93(5):593–599.

47 Siega-Riz AM, Savitz DA, Zeisel SH, et al. Second trimester folate status and preterm birth. *Am J Obstet Gynecol*. 2004;191(6):1851–1857.

48 Kim YI. Does a high folate intake increase the risk of breast cancer? *Nutr Rev*. 2006;64(10 pt 1):468–475.

49 Johnson MA. If high folic acid aggravates vitamin B12 deficiency what should be done about it? *Nutr Rev*. 2007;65(10):451–458.

50 Bentley, Willett, Weinstein, Kuntz. Population-level changes in folate intake.

51 Lewis CJ, Crane NT, Wilson DB, Yetley EA. Estimated folate intakes: data updated to reflect food fortification, increased bioavailability, and dietary supplement use. *Am J Clin Nutr*. 1999;70:198–207.

52 Watanabe F. Vitamin B12 sources and bioavailability. *Exp Biol Med*. 2007;232(10):1266–1274.

53 Institute of Medicine, Food and Nutrition Board. *Dietary Reference Intakes for Thiamin, Riboflavin*.

54 Ibid.

55 Ibid.

56 Dharmarajan TS, Adiga GU, Norkus EP. Vitamin B_{12} deficiency: recognizing subtle symptoms in older adults. *Geriatrics*. 2003;58(3):30–38.

57 Carpenter KJ. A short history of nutritional science: part 1 (1785–1885). *J Nutr*. 2003;133:638–645.

58 Ibid.

59 Li Y, Schellhorn HE. New developments and novel therapeutic perspectives for vitamin C. *J Nutr*. 2007;137(10):2171–2184.

60 Shils M, Shike M, Olson J, Ross AC, eds. *Modern Nutrition in Health and Disease*. 10th ed. Philadelphia: Lippincott Williams & Wilkins, 2005.

61 Douglas RM, Hemila H, Chalker E, Treacy B. Vitamin C for preventing and treating the common cold. *Cochrane Database Syst Rev*. 2007;(3):CD000980.

62 Institute of Medicine, Food and Nutrition Board. *Dietary Reference Intakes for Vitamin C, Vitamin E, Selenium, and Carotenoids*. Washington, DC: National Academies Press, 2000.

63 Ibid.

64 Institute of Medicine, Food and Nutrition Board. *Dietary Reference Intakes for Vitamin C, Vitamin E.*

65 Ibid.

66 Li Y, Schellhorn HE. New developments and novel therapeutic perspectives for vitamin C. *J Nutr*. 2007;137(10):2171–2184.

67 Niculescu MD, Zeisel SH. Diet, methyl donors and DNA methylation: interactions between dietary folate, methionine, and choline. *J Nutr*. 2002;132:2333S–2335S.

68 Bellinghieri G, Santoro D, Calvani M, et al. Carnitine and hemodialysis. *Am J Kidney Dis*. 2003;41(3 suppl 1):S116–S122.

69 Bouckenooghe T, Remacle C, Reusens B. Is taurine a functional nutrient? *Curr Opin Clin Nutr Metab Care*. 2006;9(6):728–733.

70 Schaffer SW, Azuma J, Mozaffari M. Role of antioxidant activity of taurine in diabetes. *Can J Physiol Pharmacol*. 2009;87(2):91–99.

CHAPTER 12

Water and Major Minerals

THINK About It

1 How much water does it usually take to quench your thirst?

2 Does drinking caffeinated beverages make you feel dehydrated?

3 How often do you salt your food before tasting it?

4 What's your primary source of calcium?

Visit nutrition.jbpub.com

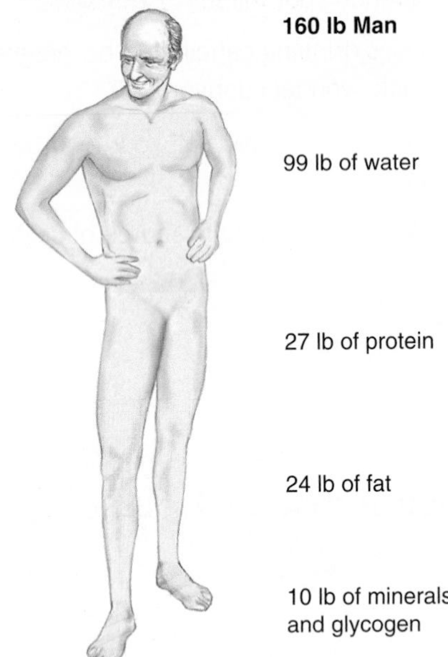

Figure 12.1 **Body composition.** The main constituent of the body is water. Adult males have more lean tissue and less fat than adult females, and therefore have more body water.

On your coast-to-coast flight with your father and your brother, you observe your father drink water frequently throughout the flight, whereas your brother alternates between Coke and beer. When you arrive at your destination, your brother complains of feeling utterly exhausted. In contrast, your father is lively and ready for a night on the town. How do you explain this?

First, it's important to know that the familiar beverage cart is not a random gesture of kindness by the airlines: regular fluid intake on flights is necessary for health! Although you are unaware of it, water evaporates from the skin at an accelerated rate in the low-humidity, high-altitude, pressurized cabin of an airplane. Thus, drinking fluids during the flight helps prevent dehydration. But you must choose the fluids carefully. Alcoholic and caffeinated beverages are diuretics. This means that they may increase fluid loss as urine, and therefore in the short term may not replace fluid losses as effectively as water, juice, and other caffeine-free beverages.

Your brother's lack of energy may be a symptom of mild dehydration. Although he has been drinking fluids, the diuretic effect of alcohol and caffeine may have limited fluid replacement. Dad, however, had the right idea—plenty of water along the way—and he's ready for action!

Water: The Essential Ingredient for Life

Water is absolutely essential. You could probably survive for weeks without food. But you can live only a few days without water. Humans have no capacity to store "spare" water, so we must quickly replace any that's lost.

Overall, water makes up between 45 and 75 percent of a person's weight. (See **Figure 12.1**.) Leaner people have proportionately more water because muscle tissue is nearly three-fourths water by weight, whereas adipose tissue is only about 10 percent water.

The one bit of chemistry that almost everyone can rattle off is the chemical formula for water: H_2O. Water is such a simple molecule (**Figure 12.2**) that people often do not appreciate its extraordinary physical and chemical properties. Water's strong surface tension, high heat capacity, and ability to dissolve many substances result from **hydrogen bonds** between a hydrogen atom of one water molecule and the oxygen atom of another water molecule.

Water in your body contains numerous dissolved minerals, called **electrolytes**, that are kept in constant balance. To live, each cell must have just the right mix of water and electrolytes. Although intracellular and extracellular fluids have different mixes, the proportions in each must stay within a narrow range. Despite a continuous flow of molecules between intracellular fluid, extracellular fluid, and the outside environment, the body maintains its electrolyte balance through the intake and excretion of water and the movement of ions.

Functions of Water

Water performs a wide variety of tasks in the body. (See **Figure 12.3**.) Water is the highway that moves nutrients and wastes between cells and organs. In the intestines, water solubilizes and moves nutrients to your cells and tissues, and it also carries waste out of your body in urine. What about nutrients and wastes that are not water-soluble? Your body either modifies them chemically so that they dissolve in water or packages them with proteins (e.g., lipoproteins). Your body's watery fluids, such as the bloodstream, can easily transport these protein packages throughout the body.

hydrogen bonds Noncovalent bonds between hydrogen and an atom, usually oxygen, in another molecule.

electrolytes [ih-LEK-tro-lites] Substances that dissociate into charged particles (ions) when dissolved in water or other solvents and thus become capable of conducting an electrical current. The terms *electrolyte* and *ion* often are used interchangeably.

heat capacity The amount of energy required to raise the temperature of a substance 1°C.

salts Compounds that result from the replacement of the hydrogen of an acid with a metal or a group that acts like a metal.

ions Atoms or groups of atoms with an electrical charge resulting from the loss or gain of one or more electrons.

cations Ions that carry a positive charge.

Heat Capacity

The **heat capacity** of a substance is the amount of energy required to raise its temperature 1 degree Celsius. Raising the temperature of a substance with a high heat capacity requires more energy than raising the temperature of a substance with a low one. Water, for instance, has about three times the heat capacity of iron. Warming or cooling a substance with a high heat capacity requires a relatively large amount of energy. You may have noticed this property when heating items in a microwave oven. Watery foods such as soup take much longer to heat than foods that contain little water, such as pizza and butter. Because of water's high heat capacity, it takes a lot of heat to change the temperature of the body; body water dampens the effects of extreme environmental temperatures on conditions in cells.

Cooling Ability

A rise in body temperature, whether due to exercise, environmental conditions, or illness, triggers the body's cooling system. If you get too warm, blood vessels dilate and you begin to sweat. The perspiration evaporates on the skin, thereby cooling your body. Moisture readily evaporates in dry air, so perspiring is most effective for cooling when the humidity is low. When the humidity is high, such as in humid, tropical environments, sweat does not evaporate readily, so even profuse sweating may not cool the body effectively.

Participation in Metabolism

Nearly all the chemical reactions of metabolism involve water. Water is the solvent for many biologically essential molecules (e.g., glucose, vitamins, minerals, and amino acids), and it is a product or reactant in many biochemical reactions.

pH Balance

Water is also an essential component of the body's mechanisms to maintain pH (acid–base) balance in the narrow range necessary for life. One of the major buffer systems involves carbonic acid and bicarbonate. Carbonic acid forms when dissolved carbon dioxide reacts with water ($CO_2 + H_2O \rightarrow H_2CO_3$). Carbonic acid can then dissociate to form H^+ and HCO_3^- (bicarbonate). The resulting H^+ helps increase acidity, lowering pH.

Body Fluids

Water is the major component of all body fluids. These fluids serve essential mechanical functions such as shock absorption, lubrication, cleansing, and protection. For example, amniotic fluid provides a gentle cushion that protects the fetus, synovial fluid allows joints to move smoothly, tears lubricate and cleanse the eyes, and saliva moistens food and makes swallowing possible.

Electrolytes and Water: A Delicate Equilibrium

Your body precisely controls and balances the concentration of electrolytes dissolved in its watery fluids. When **salts**, such as sodium chloride, dissolve in water (**Figure 12.4**), they come apart and form free **ions**, which are positively (e.g., Na^+) and negatively (e.g., Cl^-) charged particles. In an electrolyte solution, the number of positive charges always equals the number of negative charges. The main positively charged ions (**cations**) in the body are sodium

Water is a polar molecule. Although its net charge is zero, oxygen's strong attraction of the hydrogens' electrons makes it positive at one end and negative at the other

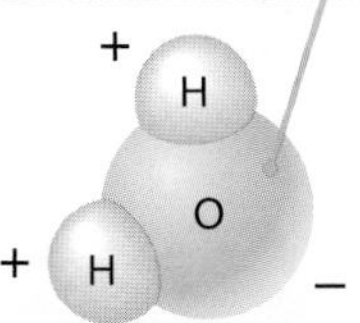

The more positive end of each water molecule is attracted to the more negative end of another – these weak attractions are called hydrogen bonds

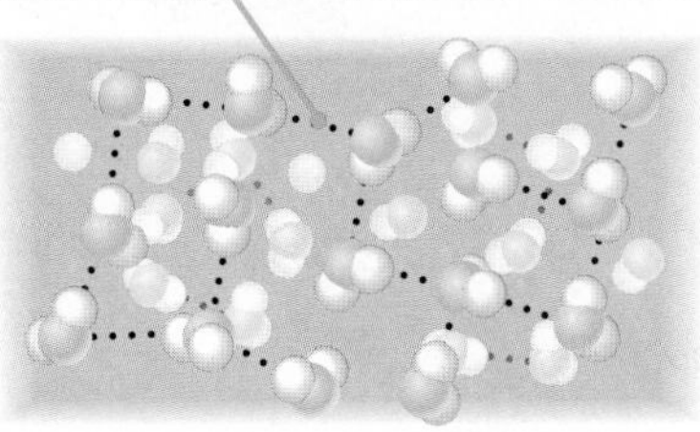

The millions of weak hydrogen bonds between water molecules are strong enough to support this water strider

Figure 12.2 **Water—a simple, yet powerful, molecule.** Water has a strong surface tension and high heat capacity. Because dissolved molecules are more likely to come together and react with one another, water's ability to dissolve substances makes chemical reactions more efficient.

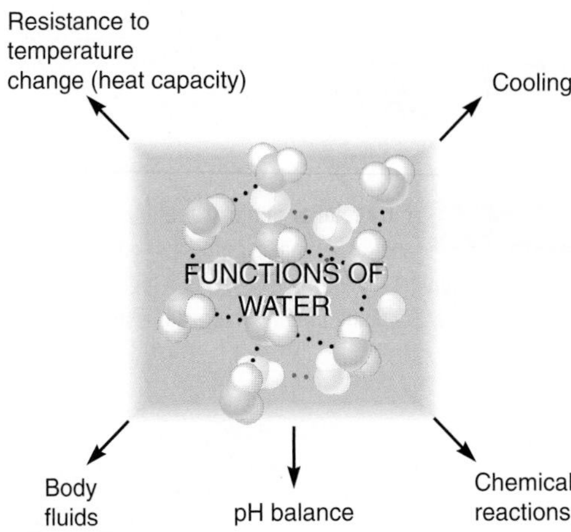

Figure 12.3 **Functions of water.** Water has many critical functions in the body.

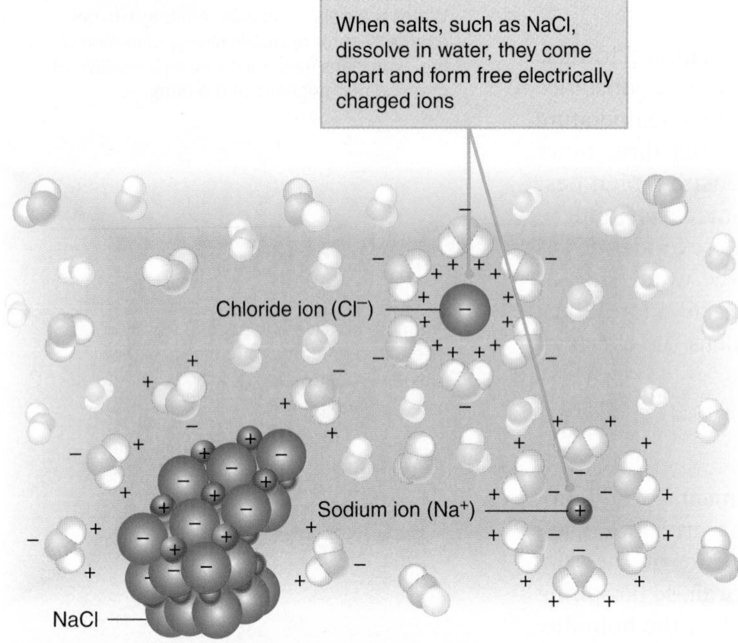

Figure 12.4 **Dissolving salt in water.** When dissolving salt, the oxygen atoms of the water molecules are attracted to the positively charged sodium ions. Water's hydrogen atoms are attracted to the negatively charged chloride ions.

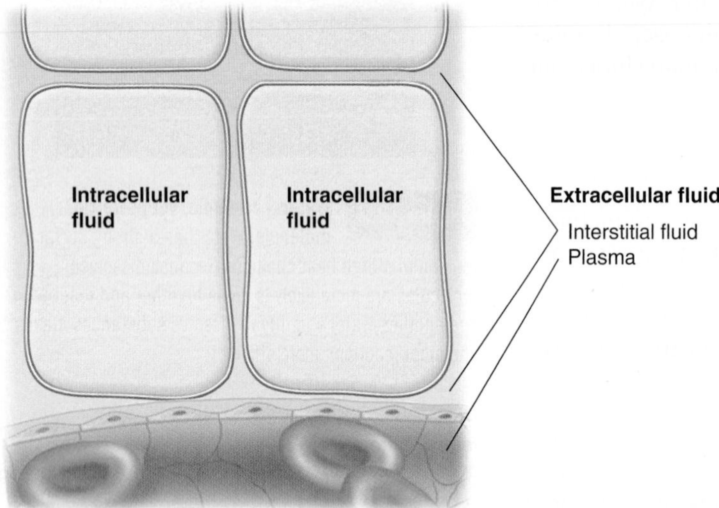

Figure 12.5 **Intracellular and extracellular fluid.** Extracellular fluids and their solutes (except for proteins) move across capillary membranes easily. Plasma (the fluid portion of the blood) has a higher concentration of proteins than interstitial fluid. Excluding protein, their compositions are roughly the same.

and potassium, and the main negatively charged ions (**anions**) are chloride and phosphate.

There are two major fluid compartments in the body. About two-thirds of body water is in intracellular fluid, and one-third is in extracellular fluid. The major components of extracellular fluid are interstitial fluid (the fluid between cells) and blood **plasma** (the fluid portion of blood). (See **Figure 12.5**.)

Sodium is the main cation in extracellular fluid, whereas potassium is the predominant cation in intracellular fluid. To maintain the balance of sodium and potassium, all cell membranes incorporate **sodium–potassium pumps** (**Figure 12.6**) that actively pump sodium out of the cell while allowing potassium back in. If **solutes** are more concentrated on one side of a **semipermeable membrane** (through which water, but not solutes, can pass easily), water flows to the side of higher concentration until the concentrations on both sides are the same. This movement is called **osmosis**; **osmotic pressure** is the force that causes water to flow across a membrane to the side with a higher concentration of ions. (See **Figure 12.7**.)

Key Concepts *Water is the most essential nutrient; we can survive much longer without food than without water. Water's functions in the body include temperature regulation, metabolism, acid–base regulation, lubrication, and protection. The balance of body fluids and the amount of electrolytes dissolved in the body's water are controlled precisely. Potassium is the main intracellular cation, and sodium is the main extracellular cation.*

Intake Recommendations: How Much Water Is Enough?

There is no one answer to the question of how much water is sufficient. We each need a different amount, depending on our size, body composition, and activity level, as well as the temperature and humidity of the environment. Over the course of a few hours, body water deficits can occur due to reduced intake or increased water losses from physical activity and environmental (e.g., heat) exposure. However, on a day-to-day basis, fluid intake, driven by the combination of thirst and the consumption of food and beverages at meals, allows maintenance of hydration status and total body water at normal levels.

The Adequate Intake (AI) for total water, including drinking water, beverages, and food, is 3.7 liters per day for men and 2.7 liters per day for women.[1] Intake recommendations are higher during pregnancy (3.0 liters per day) and lactation (3.8 liters per day). Activity and sweating increase water needs, so athletes and active people need much more water, especially if they work and train in warm, humid climates.

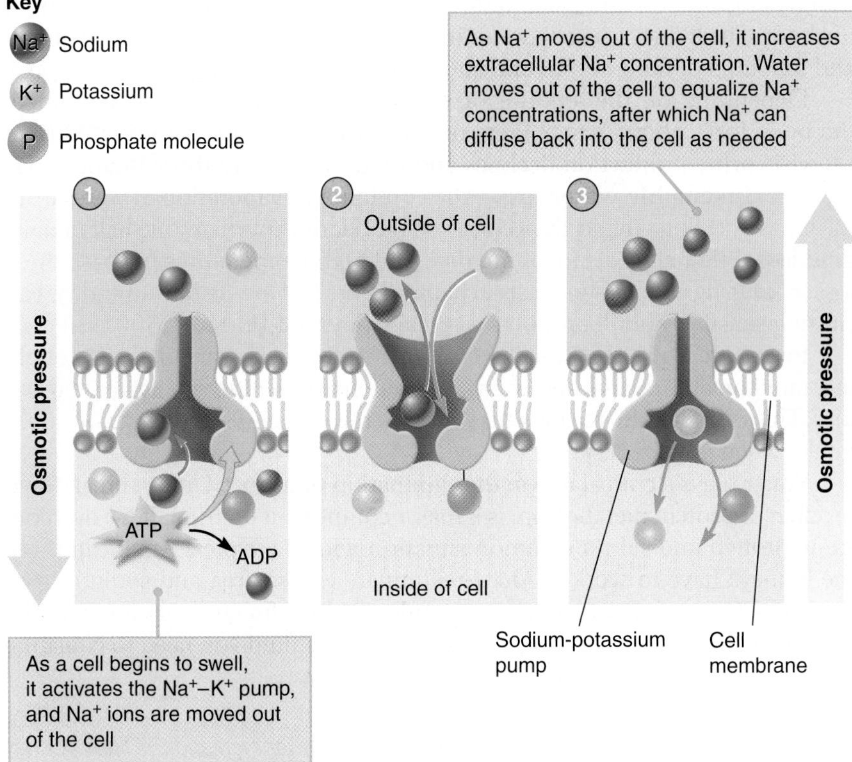
Key
Na+ Sodium
K+ Potassium
P Phosphate molecule
As Na+ moves out of the cell, it increases extracellular Na+ concentration. Water moves out of the cell to equalize Na+ concentrations, after which Na+ can diffuse back into the cell as needed
1
2
3
Outside of cell
Osmotic pressure
ATP
ADP
Inside of cell
Osmotic pressure
Sodium-potassium pump
Cell membrane
As a cell begins to swell, it activates the Na+–K+ pump, and Na+ ions are moved out of the cell

(1) Na^+ binds to a receptor site on the protein pump. Energy from ATP changes the shape of the protein, and it expels Na^+ to the outside, (2) while K^+ binds to a newly formed receptor site, causing another shape change that expels the K^+ to the cell's interior (3)

Figure 12.6 **Sodium–potassium pump.** The movement of sodium and potassium in and out of cells helps maintain the proper volume of fluid in the cell.

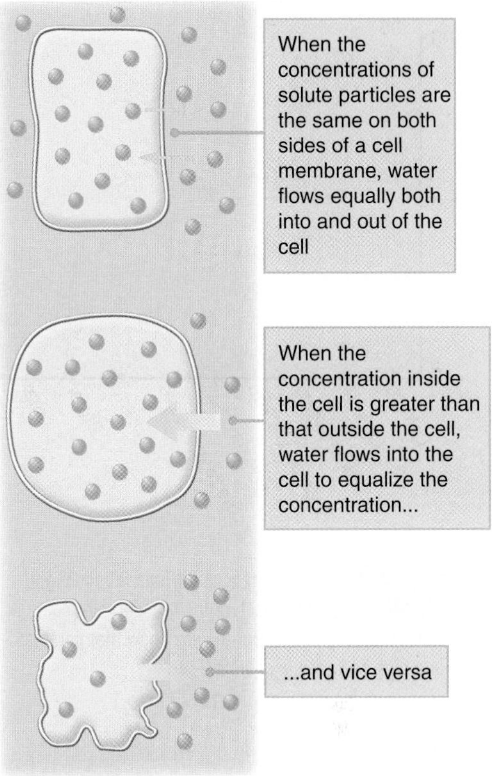

When the concentrations of solute particles are the same on both sides of a cell membrane, water flows equally both into and out of the cell

When the concentration inside the cell is greater than that outside the cell, water flows into the cell to equalize the concentration...

...and vice versa

Figure 12.7 **Osmosis.** Water moves across cell membranes to equalize concentrations of dissolved particles.

Water intake comes from a combination of drinking water, beverages, and the water in foods. Approximately 81 percent of our total daily water intake comes from beverages, with the remaining 19 percent from foods.[2] Some foods, such as fruits and vegetables, contain a substantial amount of water, whereas others—grain products, for example—provide very little. (See **Figure 12.8**.) Our bodies also produce a small amount of water (about 250 to 350 milliliters per day) in metabolic reactions. (See Chapter 7, "Metabolism.")

Sports Drinks and Water Absorption

Drinking plenty of plain water and eating a healthful diet easily replaces the fluid and electrolytes a person loses during moderate exercise in pleasant weather. But if you are involved in endurance activities or strenuous exercise in hot weather, consider using sports drinks instead of just plain water. Sports drinks contain glucose and electrolytes that improve the drink's taste, help maintain blood glucose levels, and enhance absorption.[3] (See Chapter 14, "Sports Nutrition.")

Water Excretion: Where Does the Water Go?

We continuously lose water from our bodies through various routes. In the lungs, water evaporates and exits in exhaled air. Water also departs through the

anions Ions that carry a negative charge.

plasma The fluid portion of the blood that contains blood cells and other components.

sodium–potassium pumps Mechanisms that pump sodium ions out of a cell, allowing potassium ions to enter the cell.

solutes Substances that are dissolved in a solvent.

semipermeable membrane Membrane that allows passage of some substances but blocks others.

osmosis The movement of a solvent, such as water, through a semipermeable membrane from the low-solute to the high-solute solution until the concentrations on both sides of the membrane are equal.

osmotic pressure The pressure exerted on a semipermeable membrane by a solvent, usually water, moving from the side of low-solute to the side of high-solute concentration.

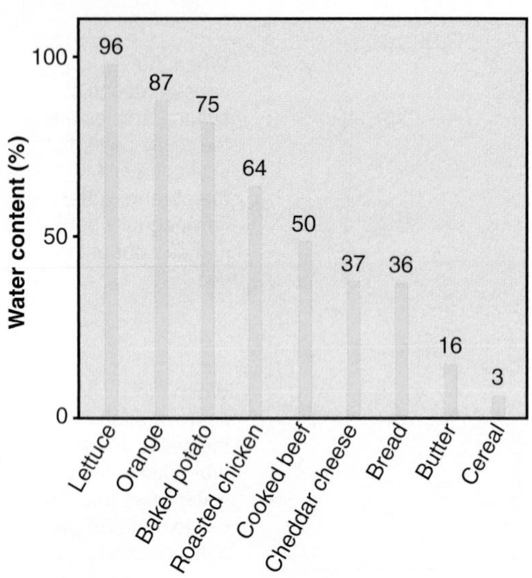

Figure 12.8 **Water content of various foods.** As you might expect, crunchy vegetables contain more water than dry cereal. But did you know that potatoes contain a high percentage of water?

skin by evaporation and perspiration. In the GI tract, feces carry water out of the body. The kidneys excrete water in urine. **Figure 12.9** summarizes sources and amounts of fluid output and shows how these balance with fluid intake.

Depending on the amount of water, protein, and sodium consumed, the body loses about 1 to 2 liters of water each day through urine. During exercise, urine production declines and fluid losses from the skin and lungs increase. **Insensible water loss**—the continuous evaporation of water from the lungs and skin—typically accounts for about one-fourth to one-half of daily fluid loss. High altitude, low humidity, and high temperatures increase these losses. During a coast-to-coast airplane flight, the low cabin humidity can cause insensible fluid losses of 4 to 6 cups (about 1,000 to 1,500 mL).[4]

Insensible losses rise, sometimes dramatically, during illness. Fever, coughing, rapid breathing, and watery nasal secretions all significantly increase water loss. This is one of the reasons that doctors recommend increasing your fluid intake when you are sick.

Water plays a critical role in the elimination of wastes. Urea, a breakdown product of protein metabolism, is a major component of urine. If we overconsume protein and salt (a common situation with the typical American diet), the kidneys have to work harder to eliminate excess urea and sodium from the body. This task requires water, so unless kidney function is impaired, the more protein and sodium you consume, the more fluid you need to consume and the more urine you are likely to produce.

Key Concepts *The AI for fluid intake is 3.7 liters per day for men and 2.7 liters per day for women. Water intake comes from a combination of foods, fluids, and water produced in normal metabolism. The main method of water excretion is in urine. In addition, fluid is lost through the skin and lungs, and in the feces. Losses are higher when a person perspires heavily or is ill. Water is critical in eliminating the body's waste products.*

insensible water loss The continual loss of body water by evaporation from the respiratory tract and diffusion through the skin.

osmoreceptors Neurons in the hypothalamus that detect changes in the fluid concentration in blood and regulate the release of antidiuretic hormone.

antidiuretic hormone (ADH) A peptide hormone secreted by the pituitary gland. It increases blood pressure and prevents fluid excretion by the kidneys. Also called vasopressin.

Water Balance

Our bodies maintain water balance by mechanisms that control water intake (e.g., thirst) and water excretion. Because of water's critical roles, the body works not only to balance fluid between compartments, but also to closely regulate total body water.

Regulation of Fluid Excretion

Our kidneys adjust the amount and concentration of urine in response to the body's hydration status. The kidneys can excrete a small volume of concentrated urine or a large volume of dilute urine while maintaining a relatively constant excretion of solutes such as sodium and potassium. This ability to regulate water excretion without major changes in solute excretion is an important survival mechanism, especially when water is in short supply.

When water intake is low, the kidneys conserve water. While continuing to excrete solutes, they reabsorb water, thus decreasing urine volume and concentrating the urine. When the body has an excess of water, the kidneys form and excrete a large volume of dilute urine.

How do the kidneys know when to conserve water? **Osmoreceptors**, special cells in the hypothalamus of the brain, are exquisitely sensitive to very small increases in extracellular sodium concentration and thus sense the body's need for water. If the sodium concentration rises, these receptors signal the pituitary gland to release **antidiuretic hormone (ADH)**. ADH decreases water loss by causing the kidneys to reabsorb water rather than excrete it in the urine. (See **Figure 12.10**.)

Quick Bite

Water, Water Everywhere and Not a Drop to Drink!

When shipwrecked sailors drink seawater, they quickly become severely dehydrated. This is because the concentration of salt in seawater is about double the maximum concentration of salt in urine. Thus, it takes 2 liters of urine to rid the body of the solutes ingested by drinking 1 liter of seawater.

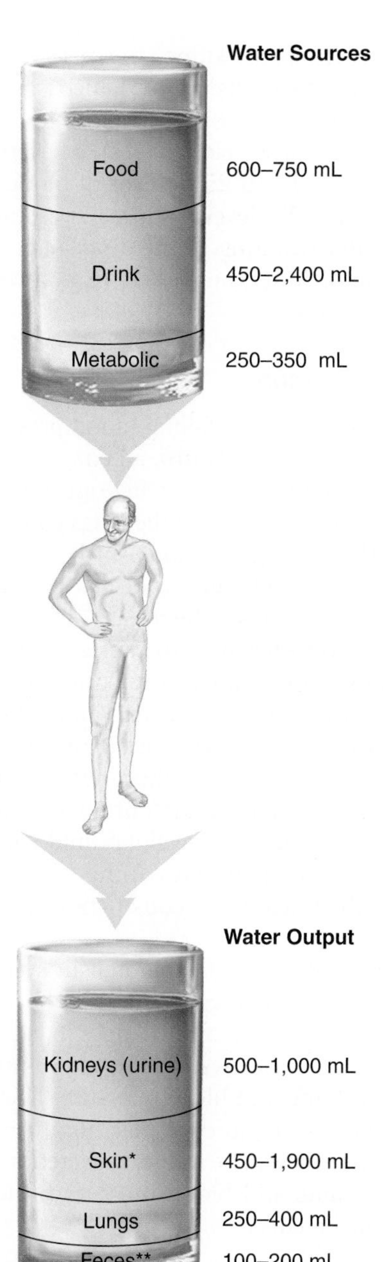

* (Insensible and perspiration)
The volume of perspiration is normally about 100 mL per day. In very hot weather or during heavy exercise, a person may lose 1 to 2 liters per hour.

** People with severe diarrhea can lose several liters of water per day in feces.

Figure 12.9 **Typical daily fluid intake and output.** To maintain fluid balance, your body regulates its fluid intake and output.

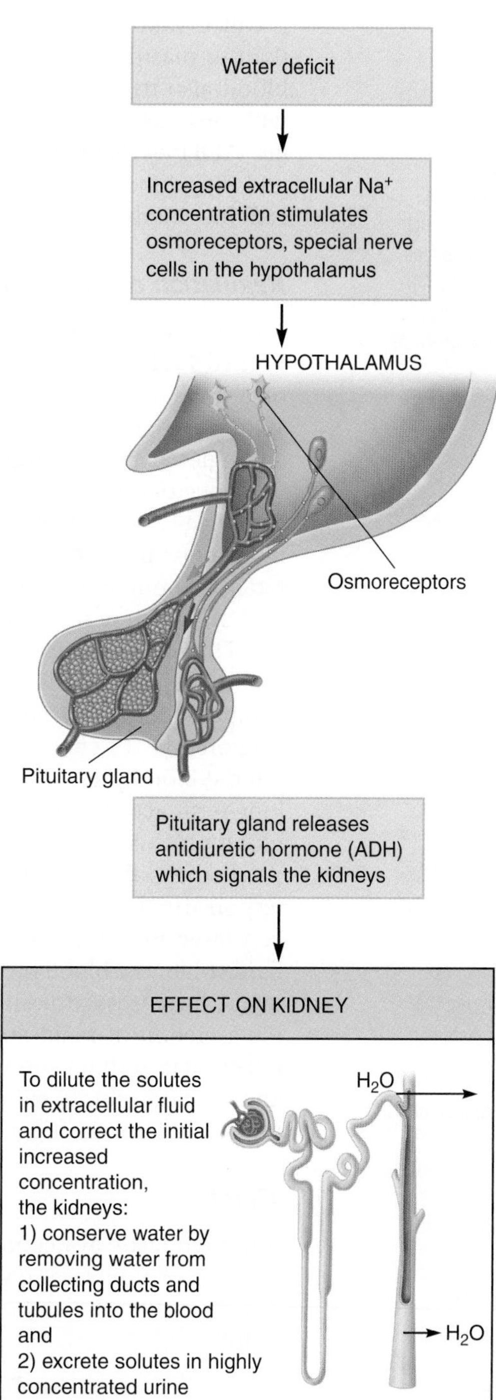

Figure 12.10 **Antidiuretic hormone regulates excretion.** In response to a water deficit, the osmoreceptor–ADH feedback system regulates solute concentrations in extracellular fluid.

Quick Bite

How Do Desert-Dwelling Animals Avoid Dehydration?

Some desert animals can concentrate their urine to nearly 100 times the maximum concentration of human urine. This allows such animals to survive on water obtained from food and their own metabolic reactions. Aquatic animals, on the other hand, minimally concentrate their urine. Beavers concentrate their urine to only about half that of humans.

In minute concentrations, ADH signals the kidney to conserve water. In higher concentrations ADH is a potent **vasoconstrictor**, which is why it also is called **vasopressin**. Although ADH is far less sensitive to blood volume than to plasma **osmolarity** (concentration of electrolytes), a severe loss of blood also triggers its release. A loss of 15 to 25 percent of blood volume will cause up to a 50-fold increase in ADH levels. Nausea is a potent trigger. ADH levels increase 100-fold after vomiting. Some drugs (e.g., nicotine and morphine) stimulate the release of ADH, but others (e.g., alcohol and caffeine) inhibit it.[5]

Regulation of Blood Volume and Pressure

The kidneys themselves have sensors that detect falling blood pressure. (See **Figure 12.11**.) In response, the kidneys release **renin**, an enzyme that splits off a small protein, **angiotensin I**, from the blood protein **angiotensinogen**. Within seconds, enzymes in the small blood vessels of the lungs convert nearly all angiotensin I to **angiotensin II**. Although angiotensin II is a powerful vasoconstrictor, it also acts directly on the kidneys to decrease excretion of sodium and water. In addition, this protein causes the release of **aldosterone**, a hormone from the adrenal glands. Aldosterone also causes the kidneys to retain sodium, and since water follows sodium, water retention increases as well. All of these processes work to restore blood pressure and volume.

The ability of angiotensin II to act as a vasoconstrictor and increase blood pressure is a life-saving measure. This acute short-term action helps compensate for a severe loss of blood, such as occurs during a hemorrhage. Angiotensin II's effect on the kidney increases extracellular fluid volume and arterial blood pressure over a period of hours or days. Although slower, this long-term action is more powerful than acute vasoconstriction in returning blood pressure to normal.

Perhaps the most important role of the renin-angiotensin system is its response to dietary sodium. It allows a person to consume either very small or very large amounts of sodium without causing major changes in extracellular fluid volume or blood pressure. Since water follows sodium, increased sodium intake increases extracellular fluid volume and blood pressure. This reduces the secretion of renin and production of angiotensin, leading to decreased retention of sodium and water by the kidneys. The resulting excretion of water and sodium returns extracellular volume and blood pressure to normal. A low sodium intake triggers the opposite effects.

Thirst

Although taste, availability, cultural patterns, and personal habits affect the amount of fluids we consume, thirst is our most important stimulus for drinking. Why do we become thirsty? The four major stimuli for thirst are as follows:[6]

1. Increased osmolarity of the fluid surrounding the osmoreceptors in the hypothalamus
2. Reduced blood volume and blood pressure
3. Increased angiotensin II
4. Dryness of the mouth and mucous membranes lining the esophagus

Drinking fluids temporarily alleviates thirst, so we stop our fluid intake and do not overhydrate. Remarkably, studies show that animals drink almost precisely the amount of water necessary to return their blood volume and electrolyte concentrations to normal.[7]

vasoconstrictor A substance that causes blood vessels to constrict.

vasopressin See *antidiuretic hormone*.

osmolarity The concentration of dissolved particles (e.g., electrolytes) in a solution expressed per unit of volume.

renin An enzyme, produced by the kidney, that affects blood pressure by catalyzing the conversion of angiotensinogen to angiotensin I.

angiotensin I [an-jee-oh-TEN-sin one] A 10-amino-acid peptide that is a precursor of angiotensin II.

angiotensinogen A circulating protein produced by the liver from which angiotensin I is cleaved by the action of renin.

angiotensin II In the lungs, the eight-amino-acid peptide angiotensin II is formed from angiotensin I. Angiotensin II is a powerful vasoconstrictor that rapidly raises blood pressure.

aldosterone [al-DOS-ter-own] A steroid hormone secreted from the adrenal glands that acts on the kidneys to regulate electrolyte and water balance. It raises blood pressure by promoting retention of sodium (and thus water) and excretion of potassium.

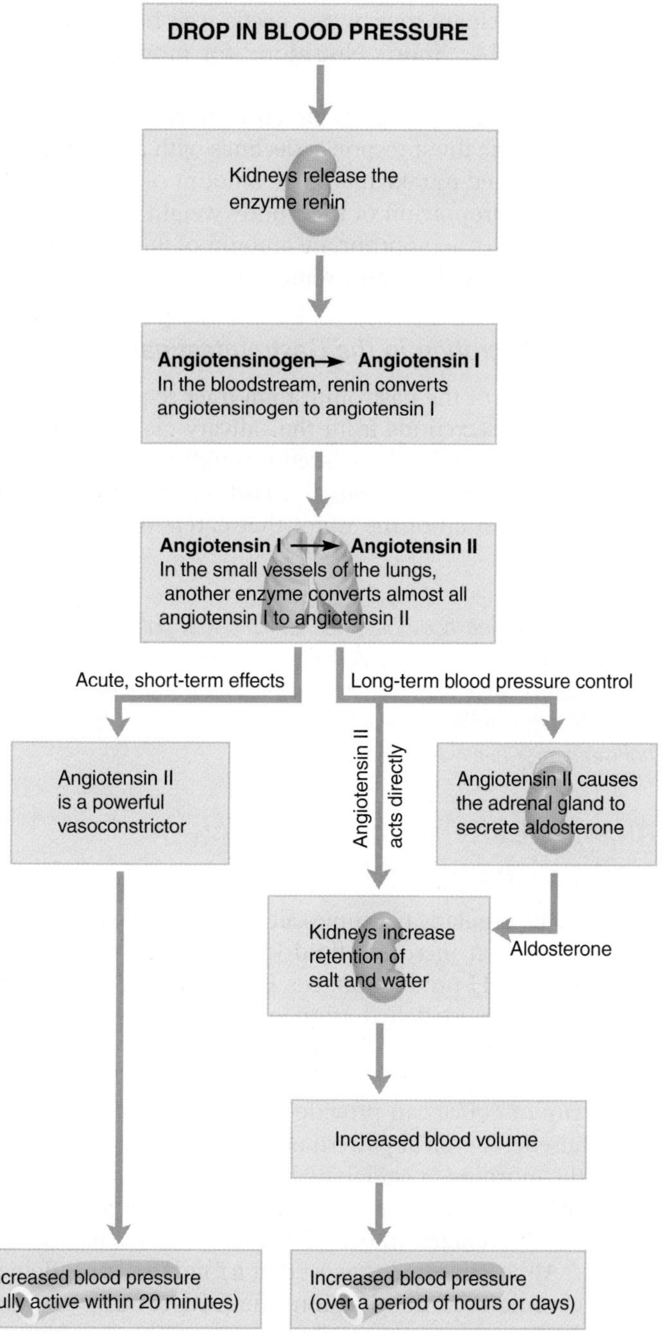
DROP IN BLOOD PRESSURE
Kidneys release the enzyme renin
Angiotensinogen → Angiotensin I
In the bloodstream, renin converts angiotensinogen to angiotensin I
Angiotensin I → Angiotensin II
In the small vessels of the lungs, another enzyme converts almost all angiotensin I to angiotensin II
Acute, short-term effects
Long-term blood pressure control
Angiotensin II is a powerful vasoconstrictor
Angiotensin II acts directly
Angiotensin II causes the adrenal gland to secrete aldosterone
Kidneys increase retention of salt and water
Aldosterone
Increased blood volume
Increased blood pressure (fully active within 20 minutes)
Increased blood pressure (over a period of hours or days)

Figure 12.11 **Regulating blood volume and pressure.** Within minutes after severe hemorrhage, the renin-angiotensin-vasoconstrictor mechanism is powerful enough to cause a life-saving rise in blood pressure. Malfunctions in the long-term blood pressure control mechanism can cause persistently high blood pressure (hypertension).

Nevertheless, thirst is not always a reliable guide to avoiding dehydration. Hot weather or heavy exercise can cause fluid losses of up to 1 to 2 liters per hour and deplete our fluids before we feel thirsty.[8] After you drink water, your body can take 30 to 60 minutes to absorb and distribute it throughout the body. For example, imagine you are roller blading in the hot sun and after an hour you pause momentarily to quench your thirst with a 0.5-liter bottle of water. That's not enough—you still have a deficit of 0.5 to 1.5 liters of water, and you'll continue to lose water while your body absorbs and distributes the water you just drank. To avoid dehydration in hot weather or when exercising, you need to drink fluids early and often.

THINK About It 1

Because heavy activity easily can cause dehydration, athletes also must be careful to drink adequate amounts of fluid. Athletic performance improves

Quick Bite

Why Do Salty Foods Make You Thirsty?

The thirst mechanism is highly sensitive to extracellular sodium concentration. Even a tiny rise in sodium crosses the thirst threshold and triggers the desire to drink.

Quick Bite

Is Airline Drinking Water Tainted?

About one-sixth of the drinking water samples taken in 2004 from airplane galley water taps were contaminated with bacteria. The findings prompted the Environmental Protection Agency to advise passengers with compromised immune systems or other health concerns to request canned or bottled beverages and avoid drinking coffee or tea made with tap water.

if athletes anticipate their water needs well before they begin to feel thirst. (See Chapter 14, "Sports Nutrition," for more on water recommendations for athletes.)

Older people and infants are particularly vulnerable to dehydration. The sensitivity of the thirst response declines with age, putting the elderly at high risk. Infants need to take in a large amount of water relative to their size because a large proportion of their body weight is water. Breast milk or infant formula provides an appropriate amount of fluid for infants. People who care for children and elders must remember to give them fluids often.

Water Reabsorption in the Gastrointestinal Tract

The operation of the gastrointestinal tract requires many liters of fluid each day. If all the secretions from the salivary glands, stomach, small intestine, pancreas, and gallbladder passed through the GI tract and out in the feces, we would dehydrate very rapidly! Fortunately, the small and large intestines reabsorb almost all of the water that enters them, so little water actually is lost in feces.

Key Concepts *The body has mechanisms that balance water among compartments and regulate total body water. Antidiuretic hormone (ADH) stimulates water reabsorption in the kidneys, whereas aldosterone stimulates the kidneys to reabsorb sodium. Thirst is not a reliable indicator to avoid dehydration when fluid losses are high, such as during hot weather or heavy exercise.*

Excess water intake and diuretics such as alcohol and caffeine decrease the secretion of antidiuretic hormone (ADH)

A fall in ADH levels signals the kidney to concentrate solutes in extracellular fluid by excreting water

EFFECT ON KIDNEY

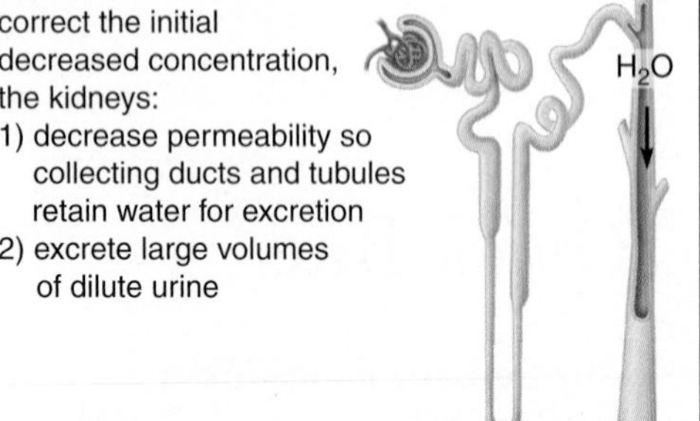

To concentrate solutes in extracellular fluid and correct the initial decreased concentration, the kidneys:
1) decrease permeability so collecting ducts and tubules retain water for excretion
2) excrete large volumes of dilute urine
H_2O

Figure 12.12 **Effects of decreased ADH level on kidney output.** Alcohol and caffeine increase water excretion by slowing the release of antidiuretic hormone (ADH).

Alcohol, Caffeine, and Common Medications Affect Fluid Balance

Anyone who regularly consumes alcohol probably realizes that it is a diuretic—a substance that increases fluid loss through increased urination. Alcohol suppresses ADH production (see **Figure 12.12**), and excessive alcohol consumption can cause dehydration, with symptoms of thirst, weakness, dryness of mucous membranes, dizziness, and light-headedness—all common side-effects of a hangover.

A cup of coffee can provide a morning pick-me-up, but the caffeine is a mild diuretic. A typical pattern of many busy Americans is a few cups of coffee in the morning, a caffeinated soda with lunch, another in the afternoon, and maybe a glass of wine or a beer with dinner. Studies of the effects of caffeinated beverages on overall hydration status have produced inconsistent results.[9] Although some suggest that a fondness for caffeinated beverages can cause chronic mild dehydration, the DRI committee examining water and electrolyte requirements concluded that caffeinated beverages contribute to the total water intake in a manner similar to noncaffeinated beverages.[10] Most Americans seem to consume a sufficient quantity and variety of beverages to maintain fluid balance.[11]

Doctors often prescribe diuretic medications to help lower blood pressure or decrease swelling caused by fluid retention. Because these medications can disrupt sodium and potassium balance, doctors typically monitor the patient's blood electrolyte levels and may prescribe potassium supplements to maintain a proper balance.

Dehydration

Dehydration, or too little water, is a major killer worldwide—infants and the frail elderly are especially vulnerable. Gastrointestinal infections are primarily responsible. These infections cause diarrhea and prolonged vomiting, leading to excessive water loss. Unless treated rapidly, a person who loses an amount of water equal to 20 percent of body weight is likely to become comatose and die. Burns also can cause deadly dehydration. Extensively damaged skin cannot protect the body and prevent excessive fluid loss.

Dehydration diminishes physical and mental performance. (See **Figure 12.13**.) Chronic mild dehydration—a fluid deficit of as little as 1 to 2 percent of body weight—can cause declines in alertness and the ability to concentrate while increasing feelings of tiredness and headache.[12] Such low levels of dehydration also impair decision making and reaction times. This may be important for tasks that involve judgment and skill, such as driving a car.

Early signs of dehydration include fatigue, dry mouth, headache, and dark urine with a strong odor. Change in urine color reflects the body's attempt to conserve water by increasing water reabsorption in the kidney. You probably have noticed that your urine becomes darker when you haven't had much to drink, whereas your urine is almost colorless when you've had plenty to drink. Low fluid intake increases the risk of kidney stones, and some experts believe it also increases the risk of urinary tract, breast, and colon cancers.[13]

Older adults and infants are particularly vulnerable to dehydration. The sense of thirst often diminishes with age, which can lead to decreased fluid intake. Older adults often take diuretic medications, which increases urine output. For a variety of reasons, older adults also may stop or reduce eating and drinking. The resulting physical and mental deterioration creates a vicious cycle, with food and fluid intake continuing to worsen.

Because infants can lose water rapidly through their skin, they need ample fluid relative to their size. Breast milk or infant formula generally provides all the fluid a baby needs. Severe diarrhea can cause swift and deadly dehydration, especially in older adults and infants. Normally, the intestines reabsorb

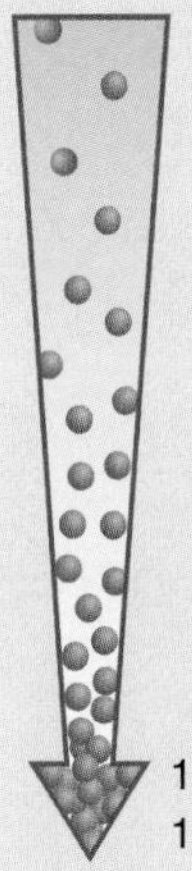

% Body weight loss	
0	
1	Thirst
2	Increased thirst, loss of appetite, discomfort
3	Impatience, decreased blood volume
4	Nausea, slowing of physical work
5	Difficulty concentrating, apathy, tingling extremities
6	Increasing body temperature, pulse and respiration rate
7	Stumbling, headache
8	Dizziness, labored breathing
9	Weakness, mental confusion
10	Muscle spasms, indistinct speech
11	Kidney failure, poor circulation due to decreased blood volume

Figure 12.13 **Effects of progressive dehydration.**

Going Green

The Thirst for Water Resources

The nets remained on deck and the boats stayed in the harbor. In one of the worst manmade fishery disasters in the nation, low levels of salmon stocks caused the closure of salmon fisheries in California for the first time ever.

Although several causes contributed to the decline, one of the most significant—and reversible—is the operation of the State Water Project (SWP) and Central Valley Project. These projects manage water for drinking, agriculture, urban, and ecosystem uses. The SWP provides a portion of the drinking water to 25 million Californians. Water has long been a contentious issue in California and the semi-arid West. Population growth and climate change promise to worsen the problem.

The most visible impacts of California's water projects are the dams that have been constructed to store and divert water. Dams in the Central Valley have entirely cut off access to more than 80 percent of historic salmon spawning grounds. Alterations in flow have increased water temperatures and reduced survival and reproductive success of salmon, which need cold water throughout their lifecycle.

California is working on a transition to a sustainable water system that restores healthy salmon runs while still meeting the water needs of the public. Fish-friendly strategies include water conservation, better efficiency, improved groundwater management, water recycling, and urban stormwater management.

nearly all the fluid secreted by digestive organs. But when intestinal disease causes diarrhea or prolonged vomiting, dehydration can occur. Worldwide, dehydration is a major killer of babies and young children, with infection the underlying culprit.

Water consumption, of course, is the primary treatment for dehydration. Oral rehydration solutions also can be used; typically these consist of simple ingredients including clean water, sugar, and table salt. Oral rehydration may be sufficient for mild dehydration, but intravenous fluids and hospitalization may be necessary for moderate to severe dehydration. Diarrhea and prolonged vomiting, which cause heavy fluid and electrolyte losses, can be fatal unless the person is rapidly rehydrated with electrolyte solutions.

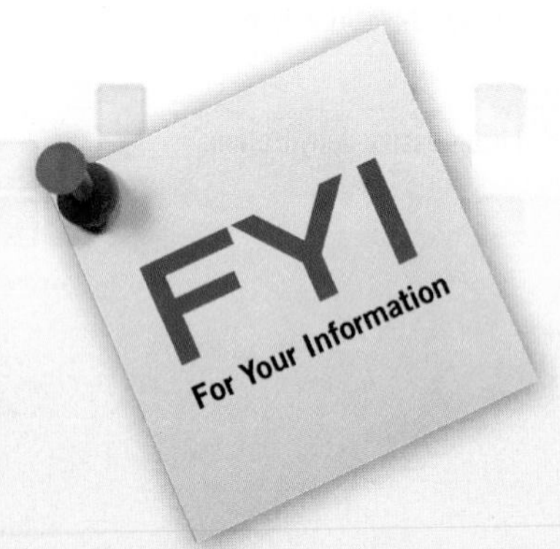

Tap, Filtered, or Bottled: Which Water Is Best?

Everywhere you look, it seems like more and more people are carrying and sipping on bottles of water. Theme parks even sell shoulder holsters for you to carry your bottle around with you. What's with the water craze? And what's wrong with the good old water fountain?

During the mid- to late 1980s, the growth in use of bottled water began. Initially, bottled mineral waters, such as Perrier, were associated with wealth and glamour. But like many trends adopted by the wealthy (white bread, for instance), bottled water soon became desirable to a wider range of people. It is estimated that Americans drink 8.8 billion gallons of bottled water each year.[1] In 2007, the U.S. per capita consumption of bottled water was 29.3 gallons.[2] Per capita consumption of bottled water has been growing by at least 1 gallon annually, more than doubling in a decade. U.S. residents now drink more bottled water annually than any other beverage except carbonated soft drinks. Soft drink consumption is roughly double that of bottled water consumption.[3] Major soft drink companies, such as Coca-Cola and PepsiCo, sell their own brands of bottled water.

Several factors are fueling the growth of the bottled-water industry. Baby boomers are seeking natural, low-calorie beverages, and fitness consciousness has reemphasized the importance of hydration. Media reports of contamination of tap water in major metropolitan areas sparked concerns about the safety and quality of tap water. Most Americans choose bottled water for what they think is *not* in it, rather than for what it contains.

From a nutritional perspective, it's important to drink plenty of fluids. Water is one of the best ways to replace lost fluids, and, at the simplest level, the source of the water doesn't really matter. Standards for municipal water systems are enforced by the Environmental Protection Agency (EPA), which requires regular testing and monitoring. Tap water can be considered a safe, clean source of water. Many municipal water systems add fluoride to tap water, an important weapon in the prevention of tooth decay. However, home-installed filtration systems for removing chlorine may also remove added fluoride, and most bottled waters do not contain fluoride. Some people don't like the taste of their local water supply and don't want to bother with maintaining a filtration system. In this case, or if you want your water "to go," bottled water may be the choice. The bottled-water industry offers

- high-volume, returnable containers from suppliers who stock the "water coolers" for offices or supermarkets;
- the familiar brands (e.g., Evian, Zephyrhills, Dasani, Aquafina) that are sold as alternatives to soft drinks; and
- bottled water in vending machines.

The bottled-water industry is regulated by the Food and Drug Administration (FDA), which, in 1995, published Standards of Identity for bottled water, set maximum allowable standards for contaminants, and established Current Good Manufacturing Practices (CGMP) for bottling plants. Keep in mind that the FDA regulates bottled waters that are sold interstate, and not those sold only in a particular area or state. Individual states may have their own quality standards for locally distributed waters.

Look beyond terms such as *artesian*, *mineral*, *spring*, or *purified* (see **Table 1**). The labels on most bottled water list the source of the water. Some consumers may be surprised to find that their favorite brand of water is really from a municipal source, not an underground spring! Nutrition Facts labels are required if the manufacturer makes a claim (e.g., sodium free) or adds minerals. These labels often do not show the natural mineral content of the water, which is really the only other nutritional aspect that could be expected.

The Academy of Nutrition and Dietetics (AND) suggests the following five factors be considered when choosing between bottled and tap water: the environment, safety, cost, taste, and fluoride.[4] The bottom line, according to the ADA, is that both tap and bottled water are

Water Intoxication

Because drinking fluids temporarily alleviates thirst, we rarely drink to the point of overhydration and dilution of body fluids. However, replacement of fluid losses following intensive or prolonged exercise with plain water (and no electrolytes) can result in overhydration and hyponatremia (low blood sodium) in athletes.[14] (See Chapter 14, "Sports Nutrition," for more on fluid balance for athletes.) Acute water toxicity has been reported due to rapid consumption of large quantities of fluids that greatly exceeded the kidney's maximal excretion rate of approximately 0.7 to 1.0 liters per hour.[15] A fraternity hazing ritual, for example, caused fatal water intoxication in a California

safe, and that bottled water offers no nutritional advantage unless it is fortified. Bottled water may encourage fluid consumption by making water more accessible; however, this may come at an environmental cost by contributing to additional waste.[5] Drinking sufficient water is the primary objective, especially when it replaces high-calorie, low-nutrient beverages.

Ultimately, the choice is up to the consumer—there is no clearly best choice of water.

1 Beverage Marketing Corporation. Bottled water: more than a story about sales growth. March 2008. http://www.bottledwater.org/public/2008_releases/2008-03-31_bw_stats.htm. Accessed 8/2/09.

2 Ibid.

3 Beverage Marketing Corporation. Beverage Marketing's 2008 findings: bottled water continues as number 2 in 2007. 2008. http://www.bottledwater.org/public/Stats_2007.doc. Accessed 8/2/09.

4 American Dietetic Association. Bottled water: is bottled water a better choice than tap water? May 2008. http://www.eatright.org/cps/rde/xchg/ada/hs.xsl/nutrition_17382_ENU_HTML.htm. Accessed 8/2/09.

5 Ibid.

Table 1 Definitions of Bottled Water Terms

- Mineral water must contain at least 250 parts per million (ppm) of dissolved minerals and come from a geologically and physically protected underground water source.
- Purified water is tap or ground water that has been treated by distillation, deionization, or reverse osmosis. This may be labeled "distilled water" if produced by steam distillation and condensation.
- Spring water comes from an underground formation from which water flows naturally to the surface; it is collected either at the spring or from a bore hole to the underground formation.
- Artesian water comes from tapping a confined underground aquifer that is below the natural water table. Generally the artesian well is located in a depression where the water table of the surrounding hills is higher. The "head" of pressure from the water table forces the water up through the tap line.
- Ground water comes from a subsurface saturated zone and is not under the direct influence of surface water.
- Well water comes from a drilled hole that taps the water of an aquifer, and is pumped to the surface.

Source: International Bottled Water Association. Frequently asked questions. http://www.bottledwater.org/public/BWFactsHome_main.htm. Accessed 8/2/09; and Food and Drug Administration. Ask the regulators: bottled water regulation and the FDA. February/March 2002. http://www.fda.gov/Food/FoodSafety/Product-SpecificInformation/BottledWaterCarbonatedSoftDrinks/ucm077079.htm. Accessed 8/2/09.

major mineral A major mineral is required in the diet and present in the body in large amounts compared with trace minerals.

State University student who was forced to drink large quantities of water while exercising vigorously.[16]

Overhydration can occur in people with untreated glandular disorders that cause excessive water retention. People with certain mental disorders have a compulsion to drink huge quantities of water. Usually, their kidneys can keep up because normal kidneys can excrete 15 to 20 liters of urine per day. In some psychiatric cases, however, overhydration has been fatal.[17] Several years ago, some dieters overenthusiastically followed a fad weight-reduction diet calling for massive water intake and suffered seizures from overhydration.

Key Concepts *Diuretic medications increase urinary fluid losses. Alcohol and caffeine have mild diuretic effects. Dehydration occurs when fluid loss exceeds fluid intake; it is a potential consequence of gastrointestinal disease, burns, and heavy sweating. Treatment involves replacing fluids, along with electrolytes if the condition is severe. Water intoxication is rare; normal kidneys can excrete many liters of fluid each day.*

Major Minerals

Unlike the nutrient molecules you have studied so far, minerals are inorganic elemental atoms or ions. Unlike carbohydrate, protein, and fat, minerals are not changed during digestion or when the body uses them. Unlike many vitamins, minerals are not destroyed by heat, light, or alkalinity. Calcium remains calcium, be it in seashells, milk, or bones. Iron remains iron, whether it is part of a cast-iron skillet or carried in the bloodstream as part of hemoglobin. This is true for all minerals.

Minerals play many essential roles in the body. Some minerals, such as magnesium, participate in the catalytic activity of enzymes. Others serve a structural function; for example, calcium and phosphorus are among the minerals that make our bones hard. Minerals are categorized as major or trace minerals based on the amount needed in the diet and the amount of the mineral in the body. The body requires more than 100 milligrams per day of each **major mineral**, whereas the dietary need for each trace mineral is less than 100 milligrams daily. **Figure 12.14** shows the relative amounts of the major and trace minerals in the body. This classification of minerals is unrelated to the mineral's biological importance. For example, iron is a trace

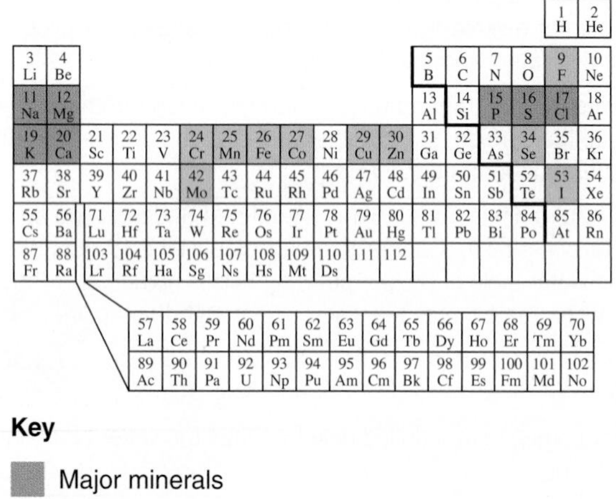

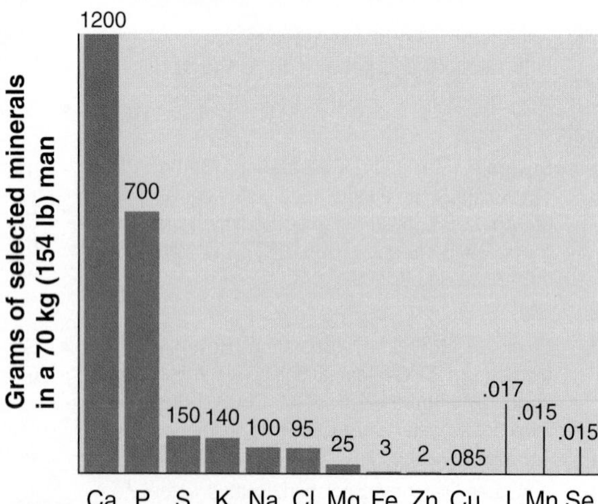

Figure 12.14 **Minerals in the human body.** Dietary minerals also are elements in the periodic table. Based on the amount of a mineral needed in the diet and the amount in the body, nutritionists categorize a mineral as major or trace.

Sources: Data from Gropper SS, Smith JS. *Advanced Nutrition and Human Metabolism.* 5th ed. Belmont, CA: Cengage Learning, 2008; and Stipanuk MH. *Biochemical and Physiological Aspects of Human Nutrition.* Philadelphia: WB Saunders, 2000.

mineral, but it plays a critical role in many major metabolic reactions. The trace minerals are discussed in Chapter 13.

Minerals in Foods

Foods from both plants and animals are sources of minerals. Generally speaking, animal tissue contains minerals in the proportion that the animal needs, so animal-derived foods are more reliable mineral sources.

Plant foods can be excellent sources of several minerals, but the mineral content of plants can vary dramatically depending on the minerals in the soil where the plants are found. Even the maturity of a vegetable, fruit, or grain can influence its mineral content. Because actual mineral content varies so much, the values published in food composition tables can be misleading. Often these values are omitted. Like plant foods, drinking water has variable mineral content. Nevertheless, it sometimes can be a significant source of minerals such as sodium, magnesium, and fluoride.

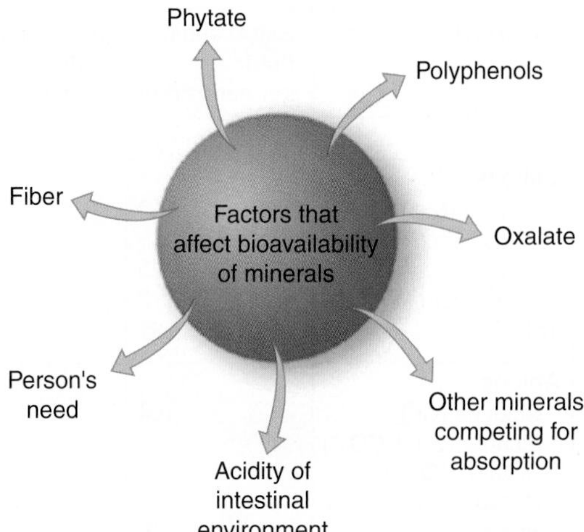

Figure 12.15 Factors that affect the bioavailability of minerals. A person's need and the dietary components of a meal can enhance or inhibit the absorption of a mineral.

Bioavailability

Your GI tract absorbs a much smaller proportion of minerals than vitamins—and probably for good reason. Once absorbed, excess minerals often are difficult for the body to flush out. In many cases, the body adjusts mineral absorption in relation to needs. For example, a calcium-deficient person absorbs calcium more readily than does a person with normal calcium status.

Megadosing with single mineral supplements can hamper the absorption of other minerals. Minerals such as calcium, iron, zinc, and magnesium, for example, all have similar chemical properties and compete for absorption.

Fiber and other components of food also affect mineral bioavailability. (See **Figure 12.15**.) High-fiber diets reduce absorption of iron, calcium, zinc, and magnesium. **Phytate** (a component of whole grains) binds minerals and carries them out of the intestine unabsorbed. **Oxalate** (found in spinach and rhubarb) binds calcium, markedly reducing calcium absorption.

Key Concepts *Minerals are essential inorganic elements. Those that we need and store in larger amounts are called major minerals, and those that we need in very small quantities are called trace minerals. A wide variety of foods contain minerals. Physiological needs, competition with minerals, and the fiber content of food all affect mineral bioavailability.*

Sodium

Many people do not realize that sodium (Na) is an essential nutrient. We know sodium best as a component of sodium chloride (table salt is about 40 percent sodium), and we have heard for years that we shouldn't eat too much salt. The *Dietary Guidelines* suggests that we "reduce daily sodium intake to less than 2,300 milligrams (mg) and further reduce intake to 1,500 mg among persons who are 51 and older and those of any age who are African American or have hypertension, diabetes, or chronic kidney disease. The 1,500 mg recommendation applies to about half of the U.S. population, including children, and the majority of adults."[18] Nevertheless, some sodium in the diet is essential for normal body function.

phytate (phytic acid) A phosphorus-containing compound in the outer husks of cereal grains that binds with minerals and inhibits their absorption.

oxalate (oxalic acid) An organic acid in some leafy green vegetables, such as spinach, that binds to calcium to form calcium oxalate, an insoluble compound the body cannot absorb.

Functions of Sodium

Sodium is the major cation in extracellular fluid and a critical electrolyte in the regulation of body fluids. It acts in concert with potassium, the major cation in intracellular fluid, and chloride, the major anion in extracellular fluid, to

Electrolytes	Extracellular* fluid concentration	Intracellular** fluid concentration
	meq/L	meq/L
Cations		
Sodium (Na^+)	140	13
Potassium (K^+)	5	140
Calcium (Ca^{2+})	5	Minimal
Magnesium (Mg^{2+})	2	7
Total	**151**	**160**
Anions		
Chloride (Cl^-)	104	3
Bicarbonate (HCO_3^-)	24	10
Sulfate (SO_4^{2-})	1	---
Phosphate (HPO_4^{2-})	2	107
Proteins	15	40
Organic anions	5	---
Total	**151**	**160**

* Values are for plasma. Interstitial fluid concentrations vary slightly (about 4 percent)

** Values are for cell water in muscle

Figure 12.16 **Cations and anions in intracellular and extracellular fluid.** Potassium, magnesium, phosphate, and proteins are the main solutes inside a cell. Sodium, chloride, and bicarbonate are the main solutes outside the cell.

Source: Reproduced from Oh MS, Uribarri J. Electrolytes, water, and acid–base balance. In: Shils ME, Shike M, Ross AC, et al., eds. *Modern Nutrition in Health and Disease.* 10th ed. Philadelphia: Lippincott Williams & Wilkins, 2006:149–193. Reprinted with permission.

maintain proper body water distribution and blood pressure. (See **Figure 12.16**.) Nerve transmission and muscle function require sodium. Sodium also helps control the body's acidity and aids the absorption of some nutrients, such as glucose.

Dietary Recommendations for Sodium

We rarely eat too little sodium; in fact, most of us eat substantially more than we need. Actual sodium *requirements* by the body are relatively small—only a few hundred milligrams daily. In order to make sure that the diet contains adequate amounts of all nutrients, however, the Food and Nutrition Board set the AI for sodium for adults at 1,500 milligrams per day.[19] The Tolerable Upper Intake Level (UL) for sodium is 2,300 milligrams per day. This suggested maximum level is echoed in the American Heart Association's Diet and Lifestyle Recommendations. The Daily Value on food labels is similar—2,400 milligrams per day. Just one teaspoon of table salt has 2,325 milligrams of sodium.

Sources of Sodium

The typical American diet contains 3,000 to 6,000 milligrams of sodium daily. Not only do Americans consume more than the recommended amounts of sodium, but they also are poor judges of the amount of sodium in their diets.[20] Surprisingly, processed foods—not table salt—contribute the most sodium. (See Table 12.1.) THINK About It 3

Figure 12.17 shows a breakdown of the sources of sodium in our diets. Seventy-seven percent of the sodium in the American diet comes from processed foods.[21] In addition to being higher in sodium, these foods are often lacking in many other nutrients such as fiber and antioxidants. Soy sauce and other sauces; pickled foods; salty or smoked meats, cheese, and fish; salted snack foods; bouillon cubes; and canned

Table 12.1 **Sodium Content of Various Foods**

Food	Serving Size	Sodium (mg)
Cucumber, with peel, raw	1 large (301 g)	6
Pickles, cucumber, dill	1 (65 g)	569
Pork, loin, roasted	3 oz (85 g)	39
Ham, cured	3 oz (85 g)	1,128
Whole-wheat bread	1 slice (28 g)	132
Biscuit from recipe	4″ biscuit (101 g)	586
Tomatoes, fresh	1 (123 g)	6
Spaghetti sauce, ready-to-serve	1 cup (250 g)	1,025
Milk, two-percent	1 cup (244 g)	115
American cheese	1 oz (28.35 g)	422
Baked potato	1 (202 g)	20
Potato chips	1 oz (28.35 g)	149

As food becomes more processed, the sodium content increases

Source: US Department of Agriculture, Agricultural Research Service. USDA National Nutrient Database for Standard Reference, Release 22. Nutrient Data Laboratory Home Page. http://www.ars.usda.gov/ba/bhnrc/ndl.

Dietary Guidelines for Americans, 2010
Key Recommendations

Foods and Food Components to Reduce

- Reduce daily sodium intake to less than 2,300 milligrams (mg) and further reduce intake to 1,500 mg among persons who are 51 and older and those of any age who are African American or have hypertension, diabetes, or chronic kidney disease. The 1,500 mg recommendation applies to about half of the U.S. population, including children, and the majority of adults.

and instant soups are all high-sodium foods. Seasonings based on salt (such as "lemon salt" and "seasoning salt") and those containing the flavor enhancer monosodium glutamate (MSG) also are high in sodium. If your diet is based on Asian foods that contain liberal amounts of soy sauce and MSG, you could be taking in 12,000 to 16,000 milligrams of sodium per day.

Your intestinal tract absorbs nearly all dietary sodium, which then travels throughout the body in the bloodstream. Your kidneys, those remarkable organs, retain the exact amount of sodium the body needs and excrete the excess sodium in the urine along with water.

Taking in too much sodium and not enough water can worsen dehydration. The old practice of giving athletes salt tablets before or after exercise is unnecessary and possibly harmful. On the other hand, radical sodium restriction is not a good idea either. Even though most Americans consume too much sodium, severe sodium restriction can limit the availability of other essential nutrients such as vitamin B_6, calcium, iron, and magnesium.[22]

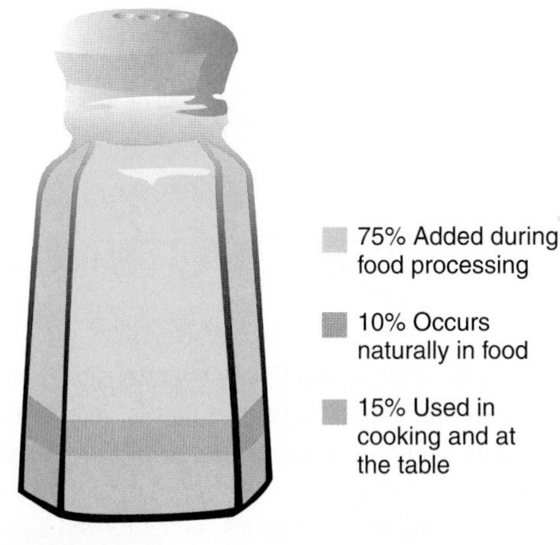

Figure 12.17 **Sources of dietary sodium.**

Hyponatremia

Blood sodium concentration sometimes can drop too low, usually as a result of severe diarrhea, vomiting, or intense prolonged sweating with replacement of water but not sodium. Consuming only water without food or other mineral sources also can depress blood sodium levels. The primary symptoms of low blood sodium, **hyponatremia**, resemble dehydration symptoms, and the treatment is similar—replacement of fluid and minerals through liquids and foods or through intravenous solutions if necessary. If severe hyponatremia is not treated, extracellular fluid moves into cells, causing them to swell. As brain cells swell and malfunction, the afflicted person can experience headache, confusion, seizures, or coma. Many illnesses, including cancer, kidney disease, and heart disease, can cause low blood sodium concentration. In these situations, treatment usually targets the underlying condition that caused the electrolyte imbalance.

Quick Bite

Sacred Salt

The physiological need for salt played an important role in shaping human history. Population groups tended to congregate where salt could be found, and civilizations in Africa, India, the Middle East, and China developed around rich salt deposits. At times, salt was traded at a value twice that of gold.

Hypernatremia

Rapid intake of large amounts of sodium (e.g., drinking seawater) can cause the retention of sodium and water in the blood. This causes **hypernatremia**, abnormally high concentration of sodium in the blood, and **hypervolemia**, an abnormal increase in blood volume. This leads to edema (swelling) and a rise in blood pressure. A healthy person with normal kidneys and ample water intake rapidly excretes excess sodium, so hypernatremia usually is seen only in patients with congestive heart failure or kidney disease. Eating too much sodium over a long period of time can contribute to high blood pressure (hypertension) in some people. For those with high blood pressure, lowering sodium intake is a useful dietary change that may lower blood pressure.[23] (See the Nutrition Science in Action feature "Exercise and Sodium Sensitivity.") Excess dietary sodium can also contribute to osteoporosis by increasing calcium loss in the urine.

hyponatremia Abnormally low sodium concentrations in the blood due to excessive excretion of sodium (by the kidney), prolonged vomiting, or diarrhea.

hypernatremia Abnormally high sodium concentrations in the blood due to increased kidney retention of sodium or rapid ingestion of large amounts of salt.

hypervolemia An abnormal increase in the circulating blood volume.

Hypertension

Hypertension, or persistent high blood pressure, affects nearly one-fourth of American adults and more than two-thirds of people older than 65.[24] It is a major risk factor for heart disease, kidney disease, and stroke. The good news is that hypertension can be treated and controlled. Many experts believe that a major cause of hypertension is a genetic predisposition combined with

Nutrition Science *in Action*

Exercise and Sodium Sensitivity

Observations: Most people with hypertension (persistent high blood pressure) are sodium sensitive; that is, increasing or reducing intake of sodium alters blood pressure. Some hypertensive people are sodium resistant; that is, changes in sodium intake do not affect blood pressure. In older adults, aerobic exercise training has been shown to lower blood pressure. The effect of aerobic exercise on blood pressure sensitivity to dietary sodium (Na^+) is unknown.

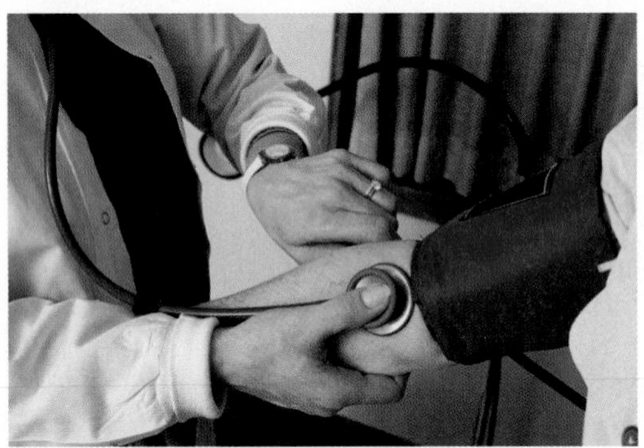

Hypothesis: Aerobic exercise training in older people with hypertension changes sodium sensitivity, with individuals switching from being sodium sensitive to sodium resistant.

Experimental Plan: Recruit 31 (12 male and 19 female) moderately overweight adults (ages 55–70 years) with mild hypertension but otherwise in good health. Design two diets—one high in sodium and the other low in sodium, but otherwise identical. Randomly have subjects consume one diet for eight days, eat regular food during a one-week washout, then consume the alternate diet for eight days. Measure blood pressure at baseline and on the eighth day of each sodium diet. Train subjects aerobically for six months with three 40-minute sessions per week of supervised treadmill walking. Measure subjects' blood pressures, repeat dietary crossover trial, and then measure blood pressures again.

Results: The hypothesis is confirmed. At baseline, 20 subjects (65 percent) were sodium sensitive and 11 (35 percent) were sodium resistant. After six months of aerobic training, 9 sodium-sensitive individuals became sodium resistant, and 1 sodium-resistant individual became sodium sensitive. The net post-exercise result was 12 (39 percent) sodium-sensitive and 19 (61 percent) sodium-resistant subjects.

Conclusion and Discussion: This study shows that aerobic training in older hypertensive people can alter blood pressure sensitivity to dietary sodium and increase the proportion of individuals who are sodium resistant. The precise mechanism responsible for this change is unknown. Future studies are needed to determine these underlying mechanisms and to examine the health implications of changing sodium sensitivity status.

Source: Dengel DR, Brown MD, Reynolds TH, Kuskowsk MA, Supiano MA. Effect of aerobic exercise training on blood pressure sensitivity to dietary sodium in older hypertensives. *J Hum Hypertens.* 2006;20:372–378.

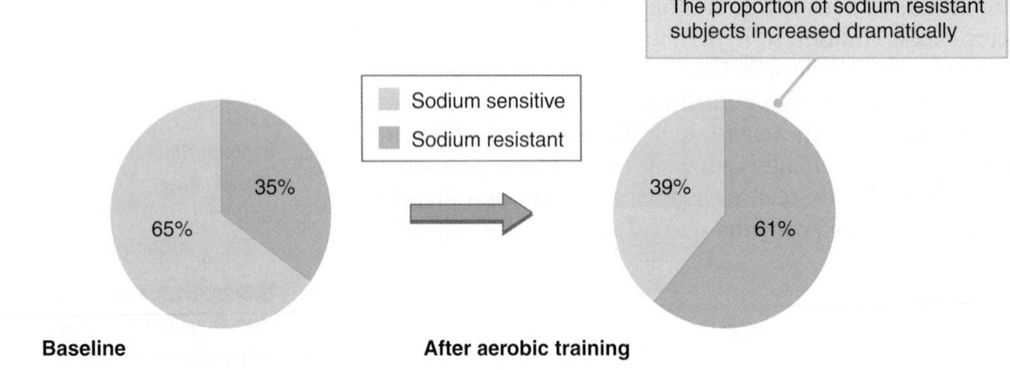

a high-sodium diet. Epidemiological studies show that people from high-sodium-consuming countries have a higher incidence of hypertension than people from countries with lower sodium intakes. Immigrants often adopt the "modern" lifestyle of their host country, a process called **acculturation**. This can have negative health consequences. For example, when Latino immigrants adopt the U.S. diet and lifestyle, sodium intake, blood pressure, and obesity tend to increase.

Sodium is not the only dietary factor associated with hypertension. Excess weight tends to raise blood pressure; regular exercise and weight loss help to reduce blood pressure. Reducing consumption of alcohol also tends to reduce blood pressure, and it improves the effectiveness of antihypertensive medications. Diets rich in calcium, magnesium, and potassium reduce blood pressure as well.[25]

Dietary survey data show low intakes of potassium, magnesium, and calcium in the southeastern United States, a region known as the "stroke belt" because of its high rates of hypertension and stroke.[26] The mechanism by which these minerals act on hypertension may be due in part to their interrelationship with sodium metabolism. For more on hypertension, see Chapter 15, "Diet and Health."

Quick Bite

Versatile Potassium

During the Middle Ages, saltpeter (potassium nitrate) was discovered to be a useful substance. It was used to extract other minerals from rock, as a fertilizer, and as an ingredient in gunpowder. It wasn't used to cure meat until the sixteenth or seventeenth century. Saltpeter was a major ingredient in the curing mixture until 1940, about the time that refrigeration emerged. Today, food manufacturers use small amounts of nitrites rather than saltpeter to preserve foods such as bacon, ham, and some sausages.

Key Concepts *Sodium is the major cation in the extracellular fluid; it plays a critical role in regulating proper water distribution and blood pressure. Nearly all of the sodium that people ingest is absorbed. Control of serum sodium is regulated by excretion. Our diets contain an overabundance of sodium, largely from processed foods. A typical American diet contains between 3,000 and 6,000 milligrams of sodium per day. The AI for sodium is 1,500 milligrams per day, and the UL is 2,300 milligrams. Abnormally low or high levels of sodium in the blood usually are associated with heart or kidney disease rather than dietary deficiency or excess. Hypertension is a risk factor for heart disease, kidney disease, and stroke. High sodium intake is a risk factor for hypertension. Some evidence suggests that low intake of potassium, calcium, and possibly magnesium may also contribute to the development of hypertension*

Potassium

Just as sodium is the major extracellular cation, potassium (K) is the key cation in cells. Potassium also can affect hypertension, but in a different way. If people with hypertension eat a diet rich in potassium-containing foods (such as fruits and vegetables), their blood pressure often improves.[27]

Functions of Potassium

Intracellular fluid contains about 95 percent of the body's potassium, with the highest amount in skeletal muscle cells. The flow of sodium and potassium in and out of cells is an important component of muscle contractions and the transmission of nerve impulses. The central nervous system (CNS) zealously protects its potassium—CNS potassium levels remain constant even in the face of falling levels in the muscle and blood. Potassium also helps regulate blood pressure.

Dietary Recommendations for Potassium

Although food manufacturers often add sodium to processed foods, they do not routinely add potassium. If a person's diet includes a lot of processed foods, it may fail to meet the potassium recommendations. Based on studies showing that potassium blunts the blood-pressure-raising effects of salt, the

acculturation The process of adopting the cultural traits and social behaviors of another group.

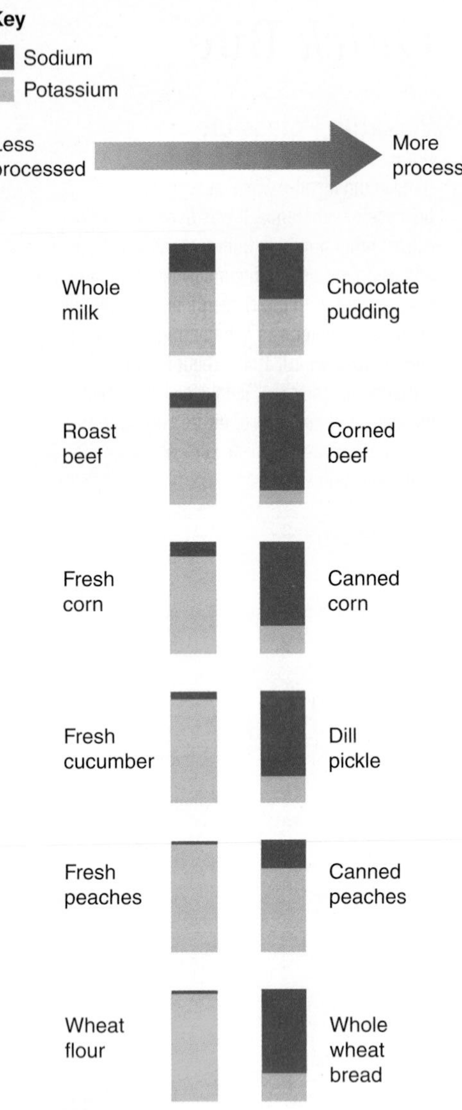

Figure 12.18 **Effects of food processing on sodium and potassium content.** Food processing tends to remove potassium and add sodium. Even when potassium is not removed, adding sodium reduces the ratio of potassium to sodium.

Quick Bite

Banana Facts

You may know that bananas are high in potassium, but did you also know that they have an unusually high carbohydrate content? Before ripening, a banana is almost entirely starch. After ripening, certain varieties are almost entirely sugar—as much as 20 percent by weight.

DRI Committee suggested a target intake level (AI) of 4,700 milligrams per day for adults.[28] This is higher than the current Daily Value of 3,500 milligrams and substantially more than most Americans eat (2,000 to 3,000 milligrams per day). **Figure 12.18** shows the effects that food processing has on the sodium and potassium levels in foods.

Sources of Potassium

Fresh vegetables and fruits, especially potatoes, spinach, melons, and bananas, are major dietary sources of potassium. Fresh meat, milk, coffee, and tea also contain significant potassium. (See **Figure 12.19**.) Many but not all salt

Potassium

Daily Value = 3,500 mg

	Food	Weight	Serving	Potassium
High: 20% DV or more	White beans, canned	262 g	1 cup	1,189 mg
	Dates	178 g	1 cup	1,168 mg
	Raisins, seedless	145 g	1 cup	1,086 mg
	Potato, baked, with skin	202 g	1 potato	1,081 mg
	Soybeans, cooked	180 g	1 cup	970 mg
	Spinach, cooked	180 g	1 cup	839 mg
	Tomato sauce	245 g	1 cup	811 mg
	Sweet potato, canned	255 g	1 cup	796 mg
	Lentils, cooked	198 g	1 cup	731 mg
Good: 10–19% DV	Yogurt, plain nonfat	227 g	8-oz container	579 mg
	Baked beans, canned	254 g	1 cup	569 mg
	Pumpkin, cooked	245 g	1 cup	564 mg
	Tomato juice, canned	243 g	1 cup	556 mg
	Mushrooms, cooked	156 g	1 cup	555 mg
	Bananas, raw	150 g	1 cup	537 mg
	Orange juice	248 g	1 cup	496 mg
	Brussels sprouts, cooked	156 g	1 cup	495 mg
	Potato chips, reduced fat	28 g	1 oz	494 mg
	Winter squash, cooked	205 g	1 cup	494 mg
	Halibut, cooked	85 g	3 oz	490 mg
	Tuna, yellowfin, fresh, cooked	85 g	3 oz	484 mg
	Artichokes, cooked	168 g	1 cup	480 mg
	Chickpeas, cooked	164 g	1 cup	477 mg
	Broccoli, cooked	156 g	1 cup	457 mg
	Cantaloupe melon, raw	160 g	1 cup	427 mg
	Apricots, dried	35 g	10 halves	407 mg
	Corn, canned	210 g	1 cup	391 mg
	Milk, nonfat	245 g	1 cup	382 mg
	Pork, loin, cooked	85 g	3 oz	382 mg
	Carrots, raw	110 g	1 cup	352 mg

Figure 12.19 **Food sources of potassium.** The best food sources of potassium are fresh fruits and vegetables, and certain dairy products and fish.

Source: US Department of Agriculture, Agricultural Research Service. USDA National Nutrient Database for Standard Reference, Release 22. 2009. Nutrient Data Laboratory Home Page, http://www.ars.usda.gov/ba/bhnrc/ndl.

substitutes contain potassium chloride—check the label to be sure. Generous intakes of fruits and vegetables, as recommended by the MyPlate food guidance system, will help increase potassium intake. African Americans may especially benefit from increased potassium intake—this population group typically has low intake of potassium and a high prevalence of hypertension and salt sensitivity.[29]

Hypokalemia

Hypokalemia, low blood potassium, results from potassium depletion. Moderate potassium deficiency is a likely factor in hypertension risk. Low potassium intake can also disrupt acid–base balance in the body and contribute to bone loss and kidney stones.[30] Severe potassium deficiency usually results from excessive losses. Prolonged vomiting, chronic diarrhea, laxative abuse, and use of diuretics are the most common causes of low blood potassium. Insufficient dietary potassium intake magnifies the effects of excess potassium loss. Symptoms include muscle weakness, loss of appetite, and confusion. Severe or rapid potassium depletion can disrupt heart rhythms—a potentially fatal problem.

People with poor diets, such as alcoholics and individuals who suffer from anorexia nervosa or bulimia nervosa, are at highest risk of potassium deficiency. Hypokalemia also is possible in people who overuse strong laxatives. Some diuretics prescribed for hypertension cause increased excretion of both water and potassium. People taking these diuretics are at increased risk for hypokalemia and must pay special attention to their potassium intake. Their doctors may prescribe potassium supplements to counter losses. Athletes and people doing physical labor in high temperatures have high water losses, so they also risk potassium deficiency.

Hyperkalemia

The kidneys effectively remove excess potassium, so the risk of toxicity from dietary intake is usually low. However, malfunctioning kidneys or an excess of intravenous potassium can cause **hyperkalemia**, or a high concentration of potassium in the blood. Because severe hyperkalemia can slow and eventually stop the heart, people who suffer from kidney failure must monitor their potassium intake carefully. The "cocktail" of drugs administered during execution by lethal injection sometimes includes potassium.

Key Concepts *Potassium is the major cation in the intracellular fluid. With sodium, it regulates muscle contractions and nerve impulse transmissions. For healthy adults, the AI for potassium is 4,700 milligrams per day, substantially more than most Americans consume. The major sources of dietary potassium are vegetables and fruits. The symptoms of hypokalemia are loss of appetite, muscle cramps, and confusion. Severe hyperkalemia can cause cardiac arrest and death.*

Chloride

Chloride (Cl^-) and chlorine (Cl_2) are not the same. Chloride is a negatively charged atom that people commonly eat as a component of table salt (NaCl). Chlorine, a highly reactive molecule composed of two atoms, is a poisonous gas. Water treatment facilities commonly use chlorine to kill bacteria and other germs.

hypokalemia Inadequate levels of potassium in the blood.

hyperkalemia Abnormally high potassium concentrations in the blood.

Functions of Chloride

Chloride is the major extracellular anion in the body. Although mostly found outside cells, chloride readily moves in and out of red blood cells. As these cells transport oxygen to body tissues or carbon dioxide to the lungs, the concentration of chloride ions shifts to sustain a neutral charge in the cell. This **chloride shift** maintains lower levels of chloride ions in arterial red blood cells than in venous red blood cells.

You have probably noticed the salty taste that sodium chloride (NaCl) imparts to blood, sweat, and tears. Both sodium and chloride help maintain the body's fluid balance. Chloride also readily combines with hydrogen ions (H^+) to form hydrochloric acid (HCl). In the stomach, hydrochloric acid kills many disease-causing bacteria that have been ingested and helps prepare protein for enzymatic digestion. In the large intestine, bacterial activity forms acid products. To neutralize these acid products, the cells lining the large intestine absorb chloride ions and secrete alkaline bicarbonate ions.[31] During an immune response, white blood cells use chloride ions to form a powerful chemical weapon to kill invading bacteria. In neurons, the coordinated movements of chloride and the cations sodium, potassium, and calcium help transmit nerve impulses.

Quick Bite

Discouraging Discoloration

Cutting or bruising causes discoloration of many fruits and vegetables, such as apples, bananas, pears, eggplants, avocados, and raw potatoes. Chloride ions inhibit the responsible enzyme, so salt will retard discoloration, although it also changes the flavor.

Dietary Recommendations for Chloride

Most of us consume much more chloride than the 2,300 milligrams per day that is the adult AI. Consumption of excess sodium and chloride may aggravate hypertension in salt-sensitive people. Since most chloride is consumed with sodium, limiting sodium to 2,300 milligrams as recommended by the American Heart Association would result in a chloride intake of about 3,450 milligrams. The Daily Value for chloride is 3,400 milligrams, just under the adult UL for chloride, which is 3,600 milligrams per day.

chloride shift The movement of chloride ions in and out of red blood cells to maintain a lower level of chloride in red blood cells in the arteries than in the veins.

metabolic alkalosis An abnormal pH of body fluids, usually caused by significant loss of acid from the body or increased levels of bicarbonate.

Sources of Chloride

Although some fruits and vegetables naturally contain chloride, most of our chloride intake comes from salt (for dietary sources of salt, see the "Sodium" section earlier in this chapter).

The average intake of chloride from salt is 4,500 milligrams per day (7.5 g of salt), which is much more than recommended. Reducing the use of salt, as recommended in the *Dietary Guidelines for Americans*, will reduce chloride intake. The kidneys excrete excess chloride, and some chloride also is lost in sweat. The only known cause of high blood chloride levels is severe dehydration.

Hypochloremia

Because vomiting removes hydrochloric acid along with other stomach contents, frequent vomiting can cause a chloride deficiency. People with bulimia nervosa often use self-induced vomiting as a way to compensate for binge eating, and thus may have low levels of chloride and other critical electrolytes, such as potassium. A person who combines repeated vomiting with inadequate consumption of fluid and minerals can suffer dehydration and **metabolic alkalosis** (high blood pH). Small variations in blood pH can have profound consequences—a 5 percent rise in pH can be fatal. Alkalosis can cause abnormal heart rhythm, a substantial drop in blood flow to the brain, decreased oxygen delivery to tissues, and abnormal metabolic activity. To treat this problem, doctors administer oral or intravenous fluids contain-

Quick Bite

Low-Calorie Chlorine?

Sucralose is a low-calorie sweetener made from sugar. During manufacture, a multistep process substitutes three chlorine atoms for three hydrogen–oxygen groups on the sugar molecule. This creates an exceptionally stable molecular structure that is 600 times sweeter than sugar. The sucralose molecule is chemically and biologically inert, so it passes through the body without being digested and is eliminated after consumption.

ing the deficient minerals. This replenishment of minerals and fluids restores pH balance.[32]

Key Concepts *Chloride is involved in many important metabolic functions. It is used to form the hydrochloric acid secreted in the stomach and is important in the generation of nerve impulses as well as in immune function. For healthy adults, the AI for chloride is 2,300 milligrams per day; average chloride intake from salt is 4,500 milligrams per day. People with bulimia nervosa may develop chloride deficiency as a result of self-induced vomiting.*

Calcium

Our bodies contain more calcium (Ca) than any other mineral, about 1.5 to 2 percent of our total weight. Adequate calcium intake over one's lifetime is essential for healthy bones and teeth that will remain strong into old age. Although we associate calcium primarily with bones, it plays many important roles in the body. Getting enough calcium in your diet not only maintains healthy bones but also may help prevent hypertension, decrease your odds of getting colon or breast cancer, improve weight control, and reduce the risk of developing kidney stones.

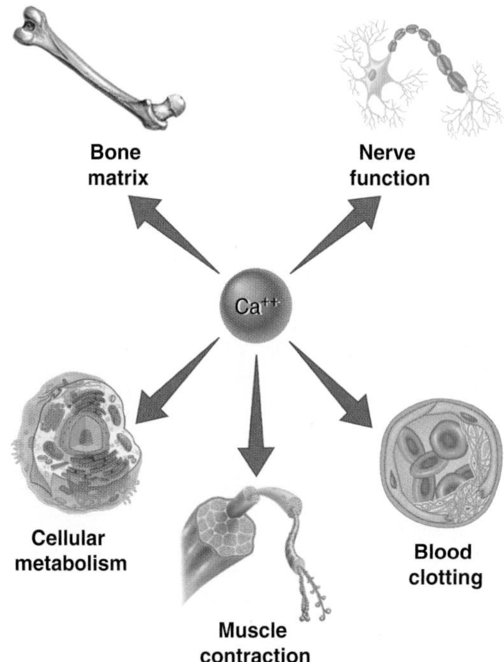

Figure 12.20 **Functions of calcium.** In addition to playing a key role in bone health, calcium in blood and soft tissues is essential for such diverse functions as blood clotting, muscle contractions, and nerve impulse transmission.

Functions of Calcium

Bones and teeth contain more than 99 percent of the body's calcium. This mineral makes bones hard and strong, able to withstand tremendous force without breaking—most of the time. The other 1 percent of body calcium is in blood and soft tissues, where it plays many equally crucial roles in such vital functions as muscle contraction, nerve impulse transmission, blood clotting, and cell metabolism. **Figure 12.20** shows the functions of calcium.

Bone Structure

Most of us think of bone as a simple structural framework for our bodies. We forget that bone is living tissue that changes in response to dietary intake and physical stresses. Bone also encases the marrow, the source of many types of blood and immune cells, and serves as the reserve site for minerals such as calcium and phosphorus.

Bone is made up of cells and an extracellular matrix. Two types of cells, osteoblasts and osteoclasts, continually remodel our bones—building them up and tearing them down. Osteoblasts are the construction team, and osteoclasts are the demolition team. Osteoblasts first secrete the collagen protein matrix that forms the initial framework for new bone. Then these bone builders help move minerals from the extracellular fluid to the bone surface, where the minerals become a hard crystalline material that surrounds the collagen fibers. Most of the calcium in bone is in the form of **hydroxyapatite**—a crystalline mineral complex of calcium and phosphorus. By weight, bone is two-thirds mineral and one-third water and protein, primarily collagen. While osteoblasts continually deposit bone, osteoclasts perform the opposite function by resorbing bone. As they break down bone, they release calcium and phosphate, which enter the bloodstream.

The activities of osteoblasts and osteoclasts determine how bones grow and change over time. Mineralization of bone is favored during **linear growth** (growth in height) and for 5 to 10 years thereafter. It is thought that we achieve peak bone mass sometime around age 30.

Throughout life, our bones change in response to our activities. The dynamic nature of bone allows it to be strengthened and rebuilt in areas under

hydroxyapatite A crystalline mineral compound of calcium and phosphorus that makes up bone.

linear growth Increase in body length/height.

Women and Calcium

Women should ask their physicians about how much calcium they need in their diets. Fat-free milk and low-fat dairy products are recommended. They're excellent sources of calcium.

Source: American Heart Association, Inc.

repeated stress—bone thickens when repeatedly subjected to loads. Even older adults can strengthen and rebuild their bones by performing weight-bearing exercise such as walking or weight lifting.[33]

The calcium in bones serves as a reservoir for calcium that is needed throughout the body. The body maintains a constant calcium blood level at all costs—at the expense of bone strength if necessary. Even if calcium intake is very low, the calcium concentration in the bloodstream remains steady because the body removes calcium from bone to sustain an adequate supply to other tissues. In the absence of kidney disease or hormonal abnormalities, your blood calcium level remains normal even if your diet is extremely deficient in calcium.

Nerve Function

Calcium is a key factor in normal transmission of nerve impulses. The movement of calcium into nerve cells triggers the release of neurotransmitters at the junction between nerves. The neuron releases neurotransmitters in direct proportion to the number of calcium ions that flow through the cell's calcium channels. Insufficient calcium can inhibit nerve transmissions.

Blood Clotting

Calcium is essential for the formation of **fibrin**, the fibrous protein that makes up the structure of blood clots. Calcium participates in nearly every step of the blood-clotting cascade. Blood will not clot in the absence of calcium, but calcium levels in the body seldom fall low enough to significantly impair blood clotting.

Muscle Contraction

Calcium has a central role in muscle contractions because the flow of calcium ions inside muscle cells is crucial for enabling muscles to contract and relax. Calcium sits at a critical location on the muscle fiber, facilitating the interaction of the muscle proteins myosin and actin. Stimulation of muscle fibers by nerve impulses, hormones, or stretch in the fiber increases the amount of calcium in the muscle cells and causes the muscle to contract. As the cells pump calcium ions back outside, the muscle relaxes. During exercise, one cause of muscle fatigue is the impaired activity of calcium in muscle cells.

Cellular Metabolism

Calcium is also a key player in regulation of cellular metabolism. When calcium enters a cell, it can bind to **calmodulin**, a regulatory protein. This binding activates calmodulin, which helps regulate a variety of enzymatic processes that affect cell secretions, **ciliary action**, cell division, and cell proliferation.

fibrin A stringy, insoluble protein that is the final product of the blood-clotting process.

calmodulin A calcium-binding protein that regulates a variety of cellular activities, such as cell division and proliferation.

ciliary action Wavelike motion of small hairlike projections on some cells.

Regulation of Blood Calcium

Circulating calcium performs a myriad of functions that are so critical that the body will demineralize bone to prevent even minor dips in blood calcium levels. Three hormones—calcitriol (the active form of vitamin D), parathyroid hormone, and calcitonin—regulate calcium status. They control intestinal absorption of calcium, bone calcium release, and calcium excretion by the kidneys. (See **Figure 12.21**.) The hormone estrogen also affects calcium balance. Lower estrogen production, as seen with menopause in women, causes both an increase in bone resorption and decrease in calcium absorption.[34]

LOW BLOOD CALCIUM		HIGH BLOOD CALCIUM	
Increase PTH secretion and calcitriol formation	**Thyroid/Parathyroid**	**Secrete calcitonin**	**Decrease PTH secretion and calcitriol formation**
Parathyroid gland secretes parathormone (PTH). Increased PTH levels stimulate calcitriol (vitamin D_3) production in the kidney	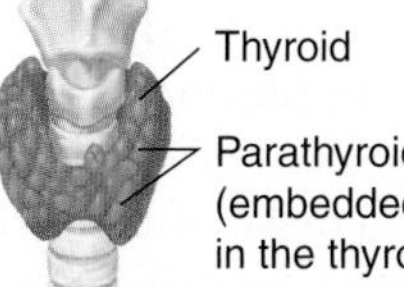	Thyroid gland secretes calcitonin	Parathormone formation slows and PTH levels drop. Decreased PTH levels slow calcitriol formation
Absorb more dietary calcium	**Small intestine**	**Absorb less dietary calcium**	
Calcitriol increases intestinal absorption of calcium and phosphorus	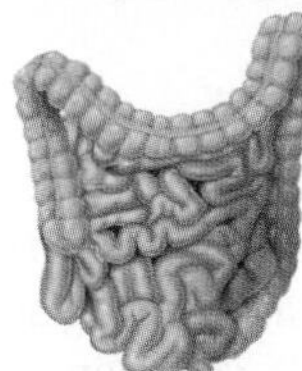	No major effect – calcitonin slightly inhibits calcium absorption	Decreased calcitriol slows intestinal absorption of calcium and phosphorus
Retain calcium	**Kidney**	**Excrete calcium**	
PTH and calcitriol increase calcium reabsorption in the kidney, thus decreasing calcium excretion	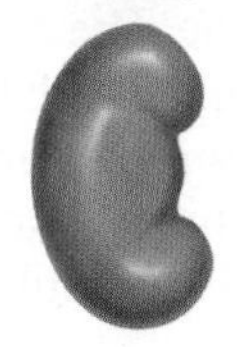	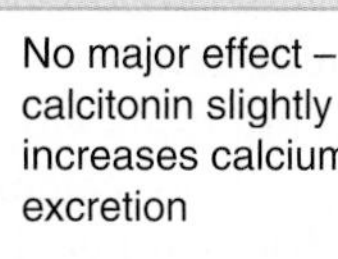 No major effect – calcitonin slightly increases calcium excretion	Decreased PTH and calcitriol levels increase calcium excretion
Move calcium from bone to bloodstream	**Bone**	**Move calcium from bloodstream to bone**	
PTH and calcitriol work together to stimulate osteoclast activity. The osteoclasts gobble up bone, releasing calcium into the bloodstream	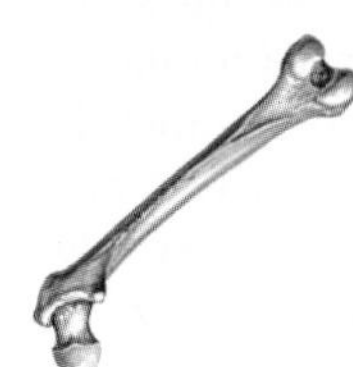	Calcitonin inhibits the activity of osteoclasts, shifting the balance toward the deposition of calcium in bone	Decreased PTH and calcitriol levels slow osteoclast activity and breakdown of bone
RAISE BLOOD CALCIUM		**LOWER BLOOD CALCIUM**	

Figure 12.21 **Regulating blood calcium levels.** Calcitonin has only a weak effect on calcium ion concentration. It is fast acting, but any decrease in calcium ion concentration triggers the release of PTH, which almost completely overrides the calcitonin effect. In prolonged calcium excess or deficiency, the parathyroid mechanism is the most powerful hormonal mechanism for maintaining normal blood calcium levels.

Vitamin D

Vitamin D increases calcium absorption by the intestine. Calcitriol, the active form of vitamin D, increases the production of calcium-binding proteins in the lining of the small intestine. The rate of calcium absorption seems to be directly proportional to the quantity of calcium-binding proteins.

Parathyroid Hormone

When plasma calcium levels are too low, the parathyroid gland secretes parathyroid hormone (PTH). PTH activates bone-resorbing osteoclasts that break down bone and release calcium and phosphorus into the blood. It also increases kidney reabsorption of calcium and stimulates calcitriol production, which then enhances intestinal calcium absorption. PTH greatly increases

Quick Bite

Paleolithic Calcium Intake

Hunter/gatherer populations during the late Paleolithic period did not drink milk or consume dairy products. Nonetheless, they do not appear to have suffered from calcium deficiency. Researchers estimate that the calcium intake by these populations was almost 1,600 milligrams per day, mostly from wild plants and nectars.

phosphorus excretion, so phosphorus blood levels actually drop in response to PTH despite an initial increase in supply from the breakdown of bone.

Calcitonin

When plasma calcium is too high, the thyroid gland secretes calcitonin. Calcitonin has weak effects on plasma calcium levels and acts in opposition to PTH. Although it has no major effects in the small intestine and kidney, it inhibits the formation and activity of osteoclasts. This shifts the osteoclast–osteoblast balance toward bone deposition. High concentrations of calcium in the blood decrease PTH production, and thus calcitriol production, slowing processes that move calcium into the bloodstream.

Dietary Recommendations for Calcium

Optimal calcium intake throughout life is extremely important. Bones become stronger and denser as children and young adults develop. Later in life, bones gradually become less dense. If children and young adults fail to take in enough calcium, they are more likely to develop osteoporosis (fragile, porous bones that easily break) later in life. The Adequate Intake level for calcium is 1,000 milligrams per day for adults aged 19 to 50, although calcium intake recommendations vary slightly among public health organizations. Adolescents need more calcium to maximize peak bone mass (the AI for ages 9 to 18 is 1,300 mg per day). The AI for adults aged 51 and older increases to 1,200 milligrams per day.

Unfortunately, many of us fall far short of these recommended calcium intakes. Although average calcium intake has increased slightly, most Americans still fail to meet current recommendations. Population surveys found that average calcium intakes were 1,081 and 793 milligrams per day for boys and girls aged 12 to 19 years, respectively; 1,025 and 797 milligrams per day for men and women aged 20 to 39 years; and 797 and 660 milligrams per day for men and women aged 60 years and older, which is well below recommended intake levels.[35] Many young women will attain a suboptimal peak bone mass and will be prone to osteoporosis as they age.

Sources of Calcium

Dairy products provide more than half of the calcium in the typical American diet. Of all the dairy products, nonfat milk is the most nutrient dense because of its high calcium content and low fat and calorie content. Nonfat yogurt is another excellent source of calcium. Cottage cheese has the least calcium of the dairy foods because processing removes much of its calcium. Ice cream and cheese are good sources of calcium, but they should be eaten only in moderation because of their high fat content.

Green leafy vegetables such as spinach have high levels of calcium, but most of the calcium is bound to oxalate and therefore cannot be absorbed. Chinese cabbage, kale, turnip greens, and calcium-processed tofu contain significant amounts of bioavailable calcium. Canned fish with bones, such as sardines, provides lots of calcium as long as you eat the bones. **Figure 12.22** shows food sources of calcium.

Some brands of orange juice, cereal, bread, and yogurt products are now fortified with calcium, making them good sources. Check labels carefully, because only a few of the many products on grocery shelves are fortified with calcium. **Figure 12.23** shows the variation in bioavailability among various sources of calcium.

Calcium

Daily Value = 1,000 mg

	Food	Weight	Serving	Calcium
	Exceptionally good sources			
	Whole-grain Total cereal	30 g	¾ cup	1,000 mg
	Cheese, ricotta, part skim milk	246 g	1 cup	669 mg
High: 20% DV or more	Yogurt, plain, nonfat	227 g	8-oz container	452 mg
	Collards, frozen, cooked	170 g	1 cup	357 mg
	Sardine, canned in oil, with bone	85 g	3 oz	325 mg
	Milk, low-fat, 1% milkfat	244 g	1 cup	305 mg
	Milk, nonfat, skim	245 g	1 cup	299 mg
	Milk, reduced fat, 2% milkfat	244 g	1 cup	293 mg
	Spinach, frozen, cooked*	190 g	1 cup	291 mg
	Milk, chocolate, low-fat	250 g	1 cup	290 mg
	Milk, buttermilk, low-fat	245 g	1 cup	284 mg
	Collards, cooked	190 g	1 cup	266 mg
	Soybeans, green, cooked	180 g	1 cup	261 mg
	Cheese, Swiss	28 g	1 oz	224 mg
	Cheese, provolone	28 g	1 oz	214 mg
	Cheese, mozzarella, part skim milk	28 g	1 oz	207 mg
	Cheese, cottage, low-fat	226 g	1 cup	206 mg
	Cheese, cheddar	28 g	1 oz	204 mg
	Cheese, muenster	28 g	1 oz	203 mg
Good: 10–19% DV	Salmon, pink, canned, with bones	85 g	3 oz	181 mg
	Kale, frozen, cooked	130 g	1 cup	179 mg
	Okra, frozen, cooked	184 g	1 cup	177 mg
	Kix cereal	30 g	1⅓ cup	171 mg
	Tofu	81 g	¼ block	163 mg
	Cheerios cereal	30 g	1 cup	122 mg
	Great northern beans, cooked	177 g	1 cup	120 mg
	Almonds	28 g	1 oz (24 nuts)	75 mg

*In spinach, oxalate binds calcium and prevents absorption of all by about 5 percent of the plant's calcium.

Figure 12.22 Food sources of calcium. Calcium is found in milk and dairy products, certain green leafy vegetables, and canned fish with bones.

Source: US Department of Agriculture, Agricultural Research Service. USDA National Nutrient Database for Standard Reference, Release 22. 2009. Nutrient Data Laboratory Home Page, http://www.ars.usda.gov/ba/bhnrc/ndl. http://www.ars.usda.gov/services/docs.htm?docid=8964.

Although eating a variety of healthful foods is always the best way to obtain nutrients, some people, especially those with limited dairy intake, may need to take supplements to ensure adequate calcium intake. Flavored, chewable, calcium-containing antacids are an inexpensive and easy-to-take source of extra calcium. For more information, see the FYI feature "Calcium Supplements: Are They Right for You?"

Calcium Absorption

Calcium absorption is relatively inefficient, and we usually absorb only 25 to 35 percent of the calcium we eat.[36] Calcium absorption can vary due to a number of factors, including age, presence of adequate vitamin D, the body's need for calcium, and calcium intake. For example, if a child and a healthy elderly person eat the same meal, the child may absorb 60 percent of the calcium in the food, whereas the elderly person might absorb only 15 percent.

Calcium absorption is particularly high during pregnancy and infancy and is at its lowest in old age.

Calcium absorption is inversely related to calcium intake. The body adjusts the percentage it absorbs based on the amount in the diet: an increase in dietary calcium reduces absorption, and a decrease in dietary calcium enhances absorption.[37] In the absence of vitamin D, calcium absorption can drop to

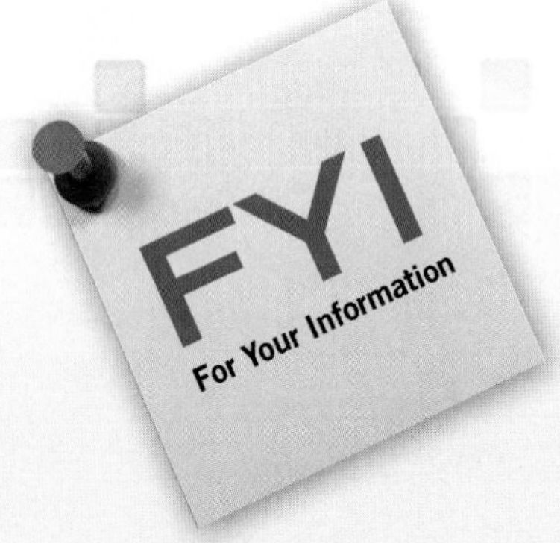

Calcium Supplements: Are They Right for You?

After reading the section on calcium, you may be wondering whether you need a calcium supplement. After all, calcium is critical for so many bodily functions, and getting enough calcium reduces the risk of osteoporosis later in life.

Before you head to the supplement aisle at the grocery store, take a critical look at your diet, especially your intake of milk and other dairy products. In the United States and Canada, dairy foods are the major sources of dietary calcium; without them, it may be difficult to reach the AI for calcium. People who exclude dairy products, such as vegans and those with milk allergy, must choose foods carefully to find rich calcium sources.

Calcium sources vary widely in their bioavailability. Although labels are required to list the %DV for calcium, they don't indicate how much of that calcium the body will absorb. For example, ½ cup of spinach contains about 120 milligrams of calcium, but the body will absorb only 5 percent of that calcium! Intake recommendations are based on the mix of sources in the typical American diet. Other cultures manage on much lower intakes in part because they do not consume the many food constituents that deplete calcium or reduce its absorption. Vegetarians may, in fact, need less calcium than meat-eaters. If you are considering spinach as your sole source of calcium, however, check out **Table 1**. It shows the amount of certain foods needed to equal the calcium available from 1 cup of milk (about 30 percent of the 300 milligrams of calcium in 1 cup of milk is bioavailable).

You can see from Table 1 that the amount of bioavailable calcium varies quite a bit among green leafy vegetables! If your diet is low in calcium, try adding some of the higher-calcium foods. Incorporating calcium-rich foods into the diet adds other important vitamins and minerals.

Even armed with more information about calcium in the diet, you may still decide to investigate the supplement market. Again, there are a variety of choices: calcium carbonate, calcium citrate, calcium lactate, calcium phosphate, coral calcium . . . how to decide? First, it's important to know that the absorption of calcium from most supplements is about equal—roughly 30 percent. The calcium citrate malate that is used in some brands of fortified juice and a limited number of supplements, is absorbed a little better—35 percent. However, a typical calcium citrate malate tablet has less calcium than a tablet of another type, such as calcium carbonate. Calcium carbonate is usually the most concentrated per tablet, so taking fewer pills per day will supply enough; also, this type of supplement tends to be less expensive. Chelated calcium supplements can improve absorption a bit, but the extra expense is probably not worth it.

Other factors to consider are that calcium supplements may be absorbed better if taken between meals. Also, you need to get plenty of vitamin D, either through casual exposure to the sun, in fortified milk, or as part of a supplement (many calcium supplements have added vitamin D). Vitamin D is important for the absorption of calcium. In addition, bones get stronger with regular, weight-bearing exercise, so make sure to include that in your healthful lifestyle.

Table 1 Foods That Provide the Calcium Equivalent of 1 Cup (8 fl oz) of Milk

Food	Amount	Food	Amount
Almonds, dry roasted	6 oz	Mustard greens	1⅓ C
Beans, pinto	6⅓ C	Radish	4½ C
Beans, red	7 C	Rutabaga	2¼ C
Beans, white	2½ C	Sesame seeds, no hulls	12 oz
Broccoli	2½ C	Soy milk, unfortified	30 C
Brussels sprouts	4 C	Spinach	7¾ C
Cabbage, Chinese	1 C	Tofu, calcium set	½ C
Cabbage, green	3 C	Turnip greens	1 C
Calcium-fortified juices*	5 fl oz	Watercress	3½ C
Cauliflower	4 C		
Kale	1¾ C		
Kohlrabi	3½ C		

*Fortified with calcium as calcium citrate malate.

Source: Adapted from Weaver CM, Plawecki KL. Dietary calcium: adequacy of a vegetarian diet. *Am J Clin Nutr.* 1994;59(suppl):1238S–1241S.

less than 10 percent of dietary calcium.[38] Phytates (in nuts, seeds, and grains) depress calcium absorption, as do oxalates and high levels of phosphorus and magnesium from supplements.

Dietary fiber, except for wheat bran, has little effect on calcium absorption. High intakes of wheat bran have been found to depress calcium absorption from milk. Low estrogen levels, as seen in postmenopausal women, can lower calcium absorption to about 20 percent. Many women take estrogen supplements after menopause to maintain calcium absorption and lower the risk of osteoporosis. Calcium from supplements is absorbed most efficiently when taken between meals at individual doses of 500 milligrams or less.[39]

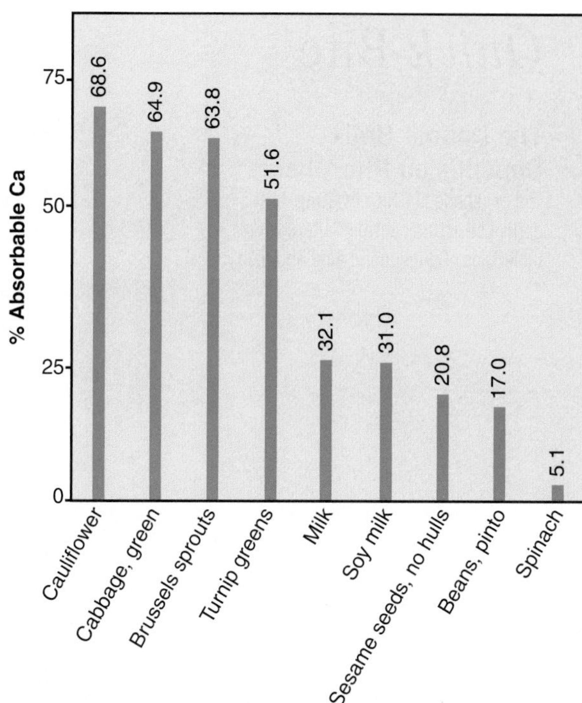

Figure 12.23 **Bioavailability of calcium from different sources.** Your body can absorb more than two-thirds of the calcium in cauliflower, but only about 5 percent of the calcium in spinach. Oxalate in spinach binds calcium and inhibits its bioavailability.

Source: Adapted from Weaver CM, Plawecki KL. Dietary calcium: adequacy of a vegetarian diet. *Am J Clin Nutr.* 1994;59(suppl):1238S–1241S.

Hypocalcemia

A lower than normal level of calcium in the blood is called **hypocalcemia**. Because the body uses bone calcium to maintain normal blood calcium levels, hypocalcemia is relatively uncommon. The causes of hypocalcemia include kidney failure, parathyroid disorders, and vitamin D deficiency. Significant hypocalcemia can cause muscle spasms, facial grimacing, and convulsions.

A chronic dietary calcium deficiency can result in osteoporosis either by suboptimal bone growth in childhood and adolescence or increased rate of bone loss after menopause. Studies also link low calcium intake to an increased risk of hypertension, colon cancer, and preeclampsia (a complication of pregnancy marked by high blood pressure, edema, and protein in the urine).[40]

Hypercalcemia

The two major causes of **hypercalcemia** are cancer and the overproduction of PTH by the parathyroid gland. Hypercalcemia can result in fatigue, confusion, loss of appetite, and constipation. Calcium may be deposited in the soft tissues, where it can impair organ function. Very high levels of blood calcium can lead to coma and cardiac arrest.

Excess calcium supplementation usually does not result in hypercalcemia, but may cause mineral imbalances by interfering with the absorption of other minerals, such as iron, magnesium, and zinc. Calcium supplements that contain citrate and ascorbic acid enhance iron absorption, but other forms can cut iron absorption in half. Calcium also may interfere with absorption of some medications, such as tetracycline.[41] The Food and Nutrition Board has established a UL for calcium of 2,500 milligrams per day.

Osteoporosis

Osteoporosis means "porous bone." It's a good description. In osteoporosis, bone mass or density declines and bone quality deteriorates, leaving the bones fragile and vulnerable to fractures. Osteoporosis is the major cause of bone fractures in older adults, primarily postmenopausal women. Ten million individuals in the United States have osteoporosis, and 34 million more are at increased risk because of low bone mass.[42]

Calcium is an important factor in bone health, but it is not the only nutritive factor. Normal development and mineralization of bone requires calcium, phosphorus, fluoride, magnesium, vitamin D, vitamin A, vitamin K, and protein. A study of postmenopausal women found significant relationships between bone mineral density and intake of energy, protein, calcium,

hypocalcemia A deficiency of calcium in the blood.

hypercalcemia Abnormally high concentrations of calcium in the blood.

Quick Bite

The Double Helix Depends on Phosphorus
The backbone of DNA's twisting, ladderlike structure contains alternating molecules of phosphoric acid and deoxyribose.

magnesium, zinc, and vitamin C.[43] For more on osteoporosis and its risk factors, see Chapter 15, "Diet and Health."

Key Concepts *Calcium is a major component of bones and teeth. In addition, calcium is required for muscle contraction, nerve impulse transmission, blood clotting, and regulation of cell metabolism. For adults, 1,000 milligrams per day is recommended; a greater amount is suggested for adolescents and older adults. Dairy foods and fortified foods are major dietary sources of calcium. Calcium status is regulated by three hormones that control intestinal absorption, bone calcium release, and kidney excretion: calcitriol, parathyroid hormone, and calcitonin. Lack of dietary calcium contributes to the development of osteoporosis. Osteoporosis is a progressive loss of bone mass, resulting in fragile bones that are susceptible to fracture. Several minerals, including calcium, phosphorus, magnesium, and fluoride, are important for bone health.*

Phosphorus

Phosphorus (P), like calcium, serves many roles in the biochemical reactions of cells and has a critical role in bone as part of the mineral complex hydroxyapatite. Phosphorus intake typically exceeds that of calcium because it is so widespread in the food supply. Most phosphorus in the body is in the form of the phosphate ion (PO_4^{3-}). In fact, phosphate is the most abundant intracellular anion.

Functions of Phosphorus

Bones are the major storehouse of phosphorus, holding nearly 85 percent of the body's supply. The remaining phosphorus is found in cells of soft tissues (approximately 15 percent) and extracellular fluid (approximately 0.1 percent). It helps activate and deactivate enzymes in a process called **phosphorylation**. Phosphorus is an essential component of ATP, the universal energy source for all cells. Phosphorus also is a component of DNA, RNA, and phospholipids in cell membranes and lipoproteins.

Dietary Recommendations for Phosphorus

The phosphorus RDA for adults is 700 milligrams per day. Adolescents need more, about 1,250 milligrams per day, to support growth. The average adult intake is between 1,000 and 1,500 milligrams per day, so phosphorus deficiencies due to dietary insufficiency are rarely seen.

Sources of Phosphorus

Phosphorus is abundant in our food supply. In general, foods rich in protein (milk, meat, and eggs) also are rich in phosphorus. Food additives, especially those in processed meat and soft drinks, supply up to 30 percent of our phosphorus. **Figure 12.24** shows selected food sources of phosphorus. Food manufacturers often add phosphate salts to processed foods to improve moisture retention and smoothness.

Because phosphorus density is higher in cow's milk than in most other foods, people with high dairy-product intakes have high-phosphorus diets. Soft drinks often contain phosphoric acid, although the phosphorus level is not high—about 50 milligrams in a 12-ounce cola, compared with 370 milligrams in 12 ounces of fat-free milk. However, among heavy cola drinkers who consume five or more per day, soda is an important contributor to phosphorus intake.[44] Dairy products have phosphorus plus calcium (460 milligrams in

phosphorylation The addition of phosphate to an organic (carbon-containing) compound. Oxidative phosphorylation is the formation of high-energy phosphate bonds (ADP + Pi $\rightarrow$ ATP) from the energy released by oxidation of energy-yielding nutrients.

Phosphorus

Daily Value = 1,000 mg

	Food	Weight	Serving	Phosphorus
High: 20% DV or more	Cheese, ricotta, part skim milk	246 g	1 cup	450 mg
	Beef, liver, cooked	85 g	3 oz	412 mg
	Pollock, cooked	85 g	3 oz	410 mg
	Sunflower seed kernels, dry roasted	32 g	¼ cup	370 mg
	Cottage cheese, low-fat	226 g	1 cup	368 mg
	Lentils, cooked	198 g	1 cup	356 mg
	Turkey cooked	140 g	1 cup	298 mg
	Swordfish, cooked	85 g	3 oz	286 mg
	Chickpeas, cooked	164 g	1 cup	276 mg
	Yogurt, fruit, low-fat	227 g	8-oz container	270 mg
	Oat bran, cooked	219 g	1 cup	261 mg
	Milk, nonfat	245 g	1 cup	247 mg
	Black beans, cooked	172 g	1 cup	241 mg
Good: 10–19% DV	Beef, top sirloin, cooked	85 g	3 oz	198 mg
	Lamb, cooked	85 g	3 oz	197 mg
	Chicken, breast, cooked	86 g	½ breast	196 mg
	Tuna, white, canned in water	85 g	3 oz	184 mg
	Ground beef, 85% lean, cooked	85 g	3 oz	168 mg
	Ham, sliced, extra lean	57 g	2 slices	163 mg
	Brown rice, cooked	195 g	1 cup	162 mg
	Swiss cheese	28 g	1 oz	161 mg
	Lobster, cooked	85 g	3 oz	157 mg
	Cashew nuts, oil roasted	28 g	1 oz (18 nuts)	151 mg
	Mozzarella cheese, part skim milk	28 g	1 oz	149 mg
	Raisins, seedless	145 g	1 cup	146 mg
	Soymilk, original and vanilla, unfortified	245 g	1 cup	127 mg
	Tofu	120 g	1 piece	110 mg

Figure 12.24 **Food sources of phosphorus.** Phosphorus is abundant in the food supply. Meats, legumes, nuts, dairy products, and grains tend to have more phosphorus than fruits and vegetables.

Source: US Department of Agriculture, Agricultural Research Service. USDA National Nutrient Database for Standard Reference, Release 22. 2009. Nutrient Data Laboratory Home Page, http://www.ars.usda.gov/ba/bhnrc/ndl.

12 ounces), whereas sodas have phosphorus but virtually no calcium (10 milligrams or less in a 12-ounce can)—an important distinction.

Our bodies directly absorb phosphorus from most food sources, with one major exception—plant seeds. All plant seeds (beans, peas, cereals, and nuts) contain phosphorus in a storage form, phytic acid. Our bodies do not produce the enzymes necessary to break down phytic acid. Still, we can absorb up to 50 percent of this phosphorus because other foods and bacteria in our large intestines contain the necessary enzymes. Yeasts also can break down phytic acid, so our bodies absorb more phosphorus from whole grains when they are part of leavened bread, for example, than from grains in unleavened bread and breakfast cereals. Although excess calcium interferes with phosphorus absorption—possibly because unabsorbed calcium binds with phytic acid and prevents bacterial breakdown—typical dietary calcium levels have no effect.

Generally, we absorb between 55 and 70 percent of dietary phosphorus, and the kidneys excrete any excess in the urine. Unlike calcium absorption, phosphorus absorption does not increase as dietary intake decreases.[45] On the other hand, the body's phosphorus needs can drive phosphorus absorption efficiency. Although the efficiency of phosphorus absorption, unlike calcium absorption, does not vary with increased dietary intake, it rises dramatically when the body has low phosphorus levels.

In the intestines, calcitriol enhances both calcium and phosphorus absorption. Parathyroid hormone, on the other hand, has opposite effects on calcium and phosphorus levels. PTH not only maintains calcium levels by stimulating the kidneys to reabsorb calcium, but also causes rapid loss of phosphorus in the urine. The two most important regulators of urinary phosphorus excretion are PTH and the amount of phosphorus in the diet.[46]

Hypophosphatemia

hypophosphatemia Abnormally low phosphate concentration in the blood.

hyperparathyroidism Excessive secretion of parathyroid hormone, which alters calcium metabolism.

hyperphosphatemia Abnormally high phosphate concentration in the blood.

Phosphorus is so common in foods that only near-total starvation will cause a dietary phosphorus deficiency. Rather, an underlying disorder typically causes **hypophosphatemia**, low blood phosphate, either by restricting absorption or enhancing excretion. Physicians commonly encounter hypophosphatemia, and about 2 percent of patients admitted to general hospitals suffer from it.[47] Some of its more common causes include **hyperparathyroidism** (excessive secretion of PTH, often because of a parathyroid tumor), vitamin D deficiency, and overuse of aluminum-, magnesium-, or calcium-containing antacids that bind phosphate. Common symptoms of hypophosphatemia include anorexia, dizziness, bone pain, muscle weakness, and a waddling gait. Chronic hypophosphatemia affects primarily the musculoskeletal system, causing muscle weakness and damage, including respiratory problems due to poor diaphragm function. Long-standing hypophosphatemia can cause rickets and osteomalacia.

Hyperphosphatemia

Physicians also frequently see **hyperphosphatemia**, high blood phosphate, which most commonly is a consequence of kidney disease. Other causes include an underactive parathyroid gland, taking too many vitamin D supplements, and overuse of phosphate-containing laxatives. Excess phosphorus can bind calcium, and since low calcium concentrations can cause nerve fibers to discharge repeatedly without provocation, this can lead to severe muscle spasms and convulsions.

If your diet contains excessive phosphorus and not enough calcium, you may be at risk for increased bone loss. However, a high phosphorus intake alone is unlikely to have an adverse affect on bone health.[48] Replacing milk as a beverage with cola, a common practice among adolescents and Americans of all ages, increases phosphates in the diet (from cola) while reducing calcium intake. Some experts believe that this practice may be a significant factor in the development of osteoporosis later in life. The UL for phosphorus is 4,000 milligrams per day for people aged 9 to 70.

Key Concepts *Phosphorus is common in many crucial metabolic systems. It is used to activate and deactivate enzymes and is an essential component of ATP, the energy source of the cell. Phosphorus is found in the phospholipids of cell membranes and is part of the hydroxyapatite in bone. About 85 percent of phosphorus is found in bone. Milk and meat are major sources of dietary phosphorus, and up to 30 percent of dietary intake comes from food additives. The RDA for adults is 700 milligrams per day, increasing to 1,250 milligrams per day for teens. Diets high in phosphorus and low in calcium can contribute to bone loss.*

Magnesium

Magnesium (Mg) is the fourth most abundant cation in the body and is about one-sixth as plentiful in cells as potassium. About 50 to 60 percent of the body's magnesium is in bone, with the remainder distributed equally between muscle and other soft tissue. The magnesium in bone provides a large reservoir in case deficiencies in soft tissue magnesium occur. Most magnesium resides in cells, with only 1 percent in extracellular fluid.

Functions of Magnesium

Magnesium participates in more than 300 types of enzyme-mediated reactions in the body, including those in DNA and protein synthesis. In the mitochondria, magnesium is essential for the production of ATP via the electron transport chain. Since ATP is the universal energy source for all cells, an absence of magnesium would quickly halt cellular activity. In the glycolysis pathway alone, seven key enzymes require magnesium. Magnesium also participates in muscle contraction and blood clotting.

Dietary Recommendations for Magnesium

Because of the large amount of magnesium in bone, blood magnesium levels may not be indicative of total body status. Therefore, assessing deficiency and setting intake recommendations are difficult. The RDA for magnesium in adults aged 19 to 30 years is 400 milligrams per day for men and 310 milligrams per day for women. This value rises slightly in adults aged 31 to 70, to 420 milligrams for men and 320 milligrams for women. The average adult diet in the United States contains only about three-fourths of the magnesium RDA, and slightly less than the Estimated Average Requirement (EAR) for magnesium. However, overt symptoms of low magnesium are relatively uncommon in healthy people.[49] This is because so much magnesium is stored in bone that levels in cells and body fluids remain constant even if intake is somewhat less than optimal.

Sources of Magnesium

Magnesium is ubiquitous in foods, but the amount varies widely depending on the food source. This mineral enters our diet mostly from plants. Whole grains and vegetables such as spinach and potatoes are good sources of magnesium, as are legumes, tofu, and some types of seafood. **Figure 12.25** shows food sources of magnesium.

Refined foods are low in magnesium content. Processed grains lose up to 80 percent of their magnesium, and enrichment does not replace it. Chocolate contains modest amounts of magnesium, but unfortunately not enough to compensate for its high fat and calorie content. Tap water can also be a significant source of the mineral in some communities with "hard" water. Total magnesium intake usually is proportional to calorie intake, so young people and adult men have higher intakes than women and older adults.

We generally absorb about 50 percent of dietary magnesium. Although high-fiber diets often have a negative effect on mineral absorption, high-fiber foods containing fermentable carbohydrates (e.g., resistant starch, oligosaccharides, and pectin) actually improve magnesium absorption. High calcium intake, usually in the form of supplements, can interfere with magnesium absorption. This is another reason why food is a better source of nutrients than supplements. People who must take calcium supplements should be sure to regularly eat foods with high magnesium content.

Quick Bite

Magnesium Says: "Let the Competition Begin!"

The pigment chlorophyll, which is responsible for the deep green color of vegetables, contains a magnesium atom at its molecular center. Heat easily displaces this magnesium, and in acidic cooking water, hydrogen ions rush in to replace it. The altered chlorophyll is grayish-green. This replacement of magnesium by hydrogen is the most common cause of the dull, olive-green color of many cooked vegetables. On the other hand, if the acidic cooking water also contains zinc or copper ions, these minerals beat out hydrogen in the race for the central spot in the chlorophyll. This combination makes cooked vegetables bright green.

Figure 12.25 **Food sources of magnesium.** Most of the magnesium in the diet comes from plant foods such as grains, vegetables, and legumes.

Source: US Department of Agriculture, Agricultural Research Service. USDA National Nutrient Database for Standard Reference, Release 22. 2009. Nutrient Data Laboratory Home Page, http://www.ars.usda.gov/ba/bhnrc/ndl.

Magnesium

Daily Value = 400 mg

	Food	Weight	Serving	Magnesium
High: 20% DV or more	Semisweet chocolate	168 g	1 cup	193 mg
	Spinach, cooked	180 g	1 cup	157 mg
	Soybeans, cooked	172 g	1 cup	148 mg
	Black beans, cooked	172 g	1 cup	120 mg
	Halibut, cooked	85 g	3 oz	91 mg
	Oat bran, cooked	219 g	1 cup	88 mg
	Brown rice, cooked	195 g	1 cup	84 mg
	Kidney beans, cooked	177 g	1 cup	80 mg
Good: 10–19% DV	Almonds	28 g	1 oz (24 nuts)	76 mg
	Cashew nuts, dry roasted	28 g	1 oz	74 mg
	Lentils, cooked	198 g	1 cup	71 mg
	Soymilk, original and vanilla, unfortified	245 g	1 cup	61 mg
	Potato, baked, with skin	202 g	1 potato	57 mg
	Tuna, yellowfin, fresh, cooked	85 g	3 oz	54 mg
	Crab, Alaska king, cooked	85 g	3 oz	54 mg
	Artichokes, cooked	120 g	1 medium	50 mg
	Peanuts, dry roasted	28 g	1 oz (28 nuts)	50 mg
	Raisins, seedless	145 g	1 cup	46 mg

hypomagnesemia An abnormally low concentration of magnesium in the blood.

hypermagnesemia An abnormally high concentration of magnesium in the blood.

Hypomagnesemia

Poor magnesium intake typically goes hand in hand with poor intake of other nutrients, and magnesium deficiency by itself is unusual.[50] It is uncommon to see an isolated deficiency of any of the intracellular minerals.[51]

Hypomagnesemia, or magnesium deficiency, occurs with a variety of diseases, including kidney disease, and is associated with alcoholism and some types of diuretic drugs. People who have prolonged diarrhea can be at risk for magnesium deficiency. People who have chronically poor diets are also at risk, especially if they abuse alcohol. Nearly all chronic alcoholics have symptoms of hypomagnesemia because they often have poor diets and because alcohol increases urinary excretion of magnesium.

In research studies, healthy people whose diets are deficient in magnesium usually have no symptoms for a few weeks because of the large supply of magnesium stored in bone. Gradually, loss of appetite, nausea, and weakness develop. After more time, muscle cramps, irritability, and confusion occur. The heart rhythm may become disturbed. If hypomagnesemia becomes extreme, death can result, usually due to heart rhythm problems. Studies have shown that people living in areas with high magnesium content in the water have a lower incidence of sudden death from heart attacks.[52]

Quick Bite

Do Onions Make You Cry?

The cabbage and onion families have sulfur-based compounds that are transformed into odiferous compounds when their tissues are broken. Cutting into a raw onion mixes the contents of its cells, bringing enzymes into contact with an odorless precursor substance apparently derived from the sulfur-containing amino acid cysteine. The volatile result, a powerful sulfur-containing irritant, causes most people's eyes to water, apparently by dissolving in fluids that surround the eye and forming sulfuric acid.

Hypermagnesemia

Hypermagnesemia, an abnormally high concentration of magnesium in the blood, is uncommon in the absence of kidney disease. People with kidney failure, especially if they use magnesium-containing antacids or laxatives, are most likely to suffer hypermagnesemia. High blood magnesium leads to nausea and general weakness. The UL established by the Food and Nutrition Board recommends that healthy people not take more than 350 milligrams of magnesium per day as a supplement or in medicines. Physicians sometimes intentionally administer high doses of magnesium during pregnancy to stop premature labor. This requires frequent monitoring to avoid toxicity that can lead to respiratory paralysis and death.

Key Concepts *Magnesium is a cofactor for more than 300 enzymes. Magnesium is required for cardiac and nerve function, and it helps form ATP. Sixty percent of magnesium is stored in bone. The RDA for magnesium in adults is 400 milligrams per day for men and 310 milligrams per day for women. Whole grains and vegetables are good sources of magnesium. People who suffer from chronic diarrhea or vomiting can be at risk for magnesium deficiency. Alcoholism is associated with magnesium deficiency because alcoholics are often malnourished and because alcohol stimulates urinary loss of magnesium.*

After reading this chapter you should have a greater appreciation of the importance of calcium in your diet. If you don't consume dairy products, or consume them infrequently, getting enough calcium can be difficult. Today, soft drinks have become more popular than milk. To combat your potential lack of calcium, more and more food products are being fortified with this mineral. Did you know that many brands of orange juice now provide as much calcium per serving as a glass of milk? Check out the following Nutrition Facts label from a calcium-fortified orange juice.

This orange juice contains 35% of the Daily Value for calcium (1,000 mg). That's 350 milligrams of the 1,000 milligrams you need. That's a pretty good hit of calcium for just one 8-ounce glass of OJ. Surprisingly, it's slightly more calcium than an 8-ounce cup of milk. You can see from the comparison at the bottom of the label that this fortified juice increases the calcium %DV from 2% (in regular orange juice) to 35%.

Look at the label again. How much fiber can you get from this juice? That's right; fiber isn't listed on the label, because most juices don't contain fiber. Since the majority of Americans need more fiber in their diets, it's a good idea not to go overboard on juices and choose whole pieces of fruit as well.

In addition to being a great source of calcium, this orange juice contains folate (another nutrient often insufficient in diets), lots of vitamin C, other B vitamins, and potassium. As part of a breakfast or even with a snack, this juice packs a lot of nutrients in its 110 calories.

Nutrition Facts
Serving Size: 8 fl oz (240 mL)
Servings Per Container: 8
Amount Per Serving
Calories 110 Calories from fat 0

	% Daily Value*
Total Fat 0g	0%
Sodium 0mg	0%
Potassium 450mg	13%
Total Carbohydrate 26g	9%
Sugars 22g	
Protein 2g	

Vitamin C 180% · Calcium 35%
Thiamin 10% · Niacin 4%
Vitamin B 6% · Folate 15%

Not a significant source of saturated fat, trans fat, cholesterol, dietary fiber, vitamin A, and iron.

* Percent Daily Values are based on a 2,000 calorie diet.

% of Daily Value of Calcium:	
Calcium-Fortified Orange Juice	35%
Regular Orange Juice	2%
% of Daily Value of Viatmin C	
Calcium-Fortified Orange Juice	180%
Regular Orange Juice	120%

Sulfur

Sulfur (S) is different from the other minerals discussed in this chapter because it is not used alone as a nutrient. In the body, sulfur primarily is a component of organic compounds, such as the vitamins biotin and thiamin and the amino acids methionine and cysteine. Sulfur in these amino acids is especially important to protein structure. Disulfide bridges that form when sulfur atoms bind to each other cause proteins to fold in specific ways as sulfur atoms along the protein are pulled together. A protein's folding and shape are critical for its function. Sulfur is also important in some of the liver's drug-detoxifying pathways. In its ionic form, sulfate (SO_4^{2-}), sulfur helps maintain acid–base balance.

Sulfur-containing amino acids provide ample sulfur for anyone who consumes adequate amounts of protein. Deficiency of sulfur is unknown in humans.

Key Concepts *Sulfur is a component of the amino acids methionine and cysteine, as well as of the vitamins biotin and thiamin. Sulfur is important in drug detoxification and in maintaining acid–base balance. Because sulfur is a component of all proteins, a diet sufficient in protein contains adequate sulfur.*

Learning Portfolio

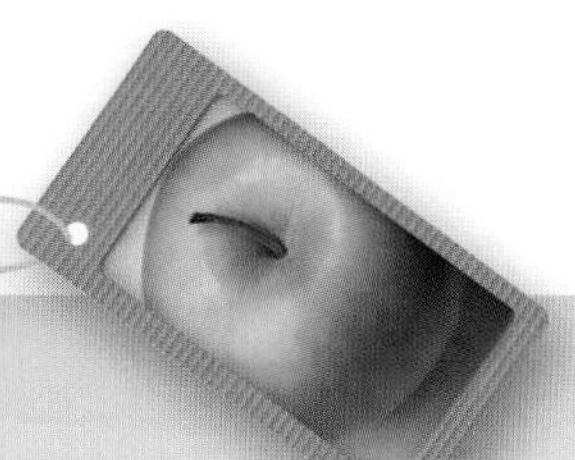

Key Terms

	page		page
acculturation	485	hypokalemia	487
aldosterone [al-DOS-ter-own]	474	hypomagnesemia	500
angiotensin I [an-jee-oh-TEN-sin one]	474	hyponatremia	483
angiotensin II	474	hypophosphatemia	498
angiotensinogen	474	insensible water loss	472
anions	471	ions	468
antidiuretic hormone (ADH)	472	linear growth	489
calmodulin	490	major mineral	480
cations	468	metabolic alkalosis	488
chloride shift	488	osmolarity	474
ciliary action	490	osmoreceptors	472
electrolytes [ih-LEK-tro-lites]	468	osmosis	471
fibrin	490	osmotic pressure	471
heat capacity	468	oxalate (oxalic acid)	481
hydrogen bonds	468	phosphorylation	496
hydroxyapatite	489	phytate (phytic acid)	481
hypercalcemia	495	plasma	471
hyperkalemia	487	renin	474
hypermagnesemia	500	salts	468
hypernatremia	483	semipermeable membrane	471
hyperparathyroidism	498	sodium–potassium pumps	471
hyperphosphatemia	498	solutes	471
hypervolemia	483	vasoconstrictor	474
hypocalcemia	495	vasopressin	474

Study Points

- Water is the most essential nutrient; we can live much longer without food than without water. The AI for water is 3.7 liters per day for men and 2.7 liters per day for women.
- Water is important for the movement of nutrients and waste, cellular reactions, temperature regulation, and acid–base balance. Moreover, fluids in the body lubricate and cushion joints, cleanse the eyes, and moisten the food we eat.
- Dissolved ions, or electrolytes, help to maintain normal fluid balance.
- Fluid is lost from the body via the urine, skin, feces, and lungs. The hormones ADH and aldosterone regulate fluid excretion from the kidneys.
- The thirst response stimulates fluid intake. Caffeine, alcohol, and diuretic medications increase fluid excretion. Dehydration results when fluid intake is less than losses; it can seriously impair physical and mental performance.
- Minerals are inorganic elements and are categorized as major or trace depending on the amount in the body and the amount needed in the diet.
- The bioavailability of minerals may be affected by excess intake of single-mineral supplements, phytate, oxalate, and fiber in plant foods, and mineral status in the body.
- Sodium, the major extracellular cation, helps regulate water distribution and blood pressure. The adult AI for sodium is 1,500 milligrams per day, and the UL is 2,300 milligrams—less than average intakes (3,000 milligrams to 6,000 milligrams per day).
- Hypertension increases risk for heart disease, stroke, and kidney disease. Sodium has long been linked to hypertension, but only some individuals are salt sensitive. Other dietary factors linked to hypertension include high chloride intake and low potassium, calcium, and magnesium intake.
- Potassium, the major cation in the intracellular fluid, is necessary for nerve and muscle function. It is provided in the diet mainly from unprocessed foods, including fruits and vegetables. The adult AI for potassium is 4,700 milligrams per day, substantially more than what most Americans eat (2,000 to 3,000 milligrams per day).
- Chloride is the major extracellular anion and a component of stomach acid. Chloride deficiency is most often associated with prolonged vomiting. Most Americans consume much more chloride than the AI, which is 2,300 milligrams per day.
- Calcium, the most abundant mineral in the body, is found in bones. It also functions in blood clotting, nerve and muscle function, and cellular metabolism. Major dietary sources of calcium are dairy products, calcium-fortified foods, and certain vegetables.
- Osteoporosis results from excessive bone loss. Postmenopausal women are at highest risk for osteoporosis. Adequate dietary calcium, vitamin D, and physical activity throughout the life span reduce the risk for osteoporosis.

- Phosphorus is a key component of ATP, DNA, RNA, phospholipids, and lipoproteins. Because phosphorus is widespread in foods, dietary phosphorus intake is rarely inadequate.
- Plant foods such as whole grains and vegetables are important sources of magnesium, which is a cofactor for hundreds of enzymes. Low levels of magnesium are associated with kidney disease, alcoholism, and use of diuretics.
- Sulfur does not function alone as a nutrient, but as a component of certain amino acids and the vitamins biotin and thiamin.

Study Questions

1. What are the two main factors that affect absorption of a mineral?
2. What functions does chloride perform in the human body?
3. What is the role of aldosterone in the body, and how is it released?
4. Name four of the main biological functions of water.
5. What is the recommended intake level for sodium?
6. What three major minerals affect bone health?
7. What are the major functions of calcium, other than its relation to bone health?
8. How does the body compensate for low calcium intake?
9. Which people have a high risk of hypomagnesemia?
10. How does the body use sulfur? What is its role in protein function?

Try This

Calcium Food Diary

The purpose of this exercise is to see how much calcium you consume in a typical day. Start by keeping a food diary for three days (two weekdays and one weekend day). While keeping the diary, try not to change your eating habits. (Altering the way you eat would reduce the accuracy of your project.) After completing the diary, add up the amounts of calcium you consume using Appendix A in the back of your textbook or using the EatRight Analysis or Nutritionist Pro software. The calcium AI value for adults between the ages of 19 and 50 is 1,000 milligrams. How does your average calcium intake compare? If your calcium intake is not meeting the AI, how can you include more calcium in your diet?

Osmosis Experiment

Purchase some celery and let it sit for a week or two until it becomes limp. When the celery looks limp and lifeless, fill your sink with cold water and soak the celery. When it has soaked for several hours, take the celery out and examine its appearance. Notice anything different? Because the crispness of celery is due to osmotic pressure, when you soaked the limp celery, it absorbed water into its cells and became crisp again.

What About Bobbie?

Let's take a look at Bobbie's intake of the major minerals calcium, magnesium, and sodium. Refer to Chapter 1 to refresh yourself with Bobbie's one-day intake. How do you think she did?

Calcium

Bobbie's calcium intake was low on the day she recorded her food intake. She consumed 710 milligrams, but the Adequate Intake (AI) for a 20-year-old woman is 1,000 milligrams. If this day reflects her usual intake, then she is at risk of poor bone mineralization and a lower than average peak bone mass. This increases her risk of osteoporosis.

Magnesium

Bobbie's intake of magnesium was 310 milligrams, and the Recommended Dietary Allowance (RDA) for a woman her age is 320 milligrams. If this one-day record reflects her usual eating, she probably is consuming an adequate amount of magnesium and does not need to increase her intake of this mineral. Some of the best sources of magnesium in her diet were the banana, tortilla chips, and spaghetti noodles.

Sodium

Bobbie's intake of 4,820 milligrams of sodium was much higher than the AI of 1,500 milligrams and twice the UL of 2,300 milligrams per day! This should not be a surprise because most of Bobbie's meals are either convenience items or prepared by someone else (e.g., the school's cafeteria), which makes it hard to control sodium content. The biggest contributors to her high intake of sodium were the sourdough bread, salad dressing, salsa, spaghetti sauce, and pizza. Bobbie should try to eat fewer convenience foods and more fresh foods. She would also benefit from drinking extra water because her intake of sodium is so high.

References

1 Institute of Medicine, Food and Nutrition Board. *Dietary Reference Intakes for Water, Potassium, Sodium, Chloride, and Sulfate*. Washington, DC: National Academies Press, 2004.

2 Campbell SM. Hydration needs throughout the lifespan. *J Am Coll Nutr*. 2007;26:585S–587S.

3 Sawka MN, Burke LM, Eichner ER, et al. American College of Sports Medicine position stand: exercise and fluid replacement. *Med Sci Sports Exerc*. 2007;39:377–390.

4 Johnson R, Tulin B. *Travel Fitness*. Champaign, IL: Human Kinetics, 1995.

5 Guyton AC, Hall JE. *Textbook of Medical Physiology*. 11th ed. Philadelphia: Elsevier Saunders, 2006.

6 Ibid.

7 Ibid.

8 Ibid.

9 Institute of Medicine, Food and Nutrition Board. *Dietary Reference Intakes for Water, Potassium*.

10 Ibid.

11 Kleiner SM. Water: an essential but overlooked nutrient. *J Am Diet Assoc*. 1999;2:200–206.

12 Maughan RJ. Impact of mild dehydration on wellness and on exercise performance. *Eur J Clin Nutr*. 2003;57(suppl 2):S19–S23.

13 Kleiner. Water.

14 Murray B, Stofan J, Eichner ER. Hyponatremia in athletes. *Sports Sci Exchange*. 2003;16(1):1–6.

15 Institute of Medicine, Food and Nutrition Board. *Dietary Reference Intakes for Water, Potassium*.

16 Nevius CW. In hazing, dumb stunts can be fatal. *San Francisco Chronicle*. February 8, 2005. http://www.sfgate.com/cgi-in/article.cgi?f=/c/a/2005/02/08/BAG61B7D341.DTL. Accessed 7/30/09.

17 Loas G, Mercier-Guidez E. Fatal self-induced water intoxication among schizophrenic inpatients. *Eur Psychiatry*. 2002;17:307–310.

18 US Department of Agriculture and US Department of Health and Human Services. *Dietary Guidelines for Americans, 2010*. 7th ed. Washington, DC: US Government Printing Office, December 2010.

19 Institute of Medicine, Food and Nutrition Board. *Dietary Reference Intakes for Water, Potassium*.

20 Loria CM, Obarzanek E, Ernst ND. Choose and prepare foods with less salt: dietary advice for all Americans. *J Nutr*. 2001;131(2S-1):536S–551S.

21 Mayo Clinic. Sodium: are you getting too much? http://www.mayoclinic.com/health/sodium/NU00284. Accessed 8/1/09.

22 Morris CD. Effect of dietary sodium restriction on overall nutrient intake. *Am J Clin Nutr*. 1997;65(2 suppl):687S–691S.

23 Jürgens G, Graudal NA. Effects of low sodium diet versus high sodium diet on blood pressure, renin, aldosterone, catecholamines, cholesterols, and triglyceride. Cochrane Database Syst Rev. 2004;1:CD004022.

24 The Seventh Report of the Joint National Committee on Prevention, Detection, Evaluation, and Treatment of High Blood Pressure: the JNC 7 report. *JAMA*. 2003;289(19):2560–2572.

25 American Heart Association. Your high blood pressure questions answered: potassium. http://www.americanheart.org/presenter.jhtml?identifier=3025146. Accessed 7/31/09.

26 Hajjar I, Kotchen T. Regional variations of blood pressure in the United States are associated with regional variations in dietary intakes: the NHANES-III data. *J Nutr*. 2003;133:211–214.

27 Karppanen H, Karppanen P, Mervaala E. Why and how to implement sodium, potassium, calcium, and magnesium changes in food items and diets? *J Hum Hypertens*. 2005;19(suppl 3):S10–S19.

28 Institute of Medicine, Food and Nutrition Board. *Dietary Reference Intakes for Water, Potassium*.

29 US Departments of Agriculture and Health and Human Services. *Dietary Guidelines for Americans, 2010*.

30 Institute of Medicine, Food and Nutrition Board. *Dietary Reference Intakes for Water, Potassium*.

31 Guyton, Hall. *Textbook of Medical Physiology*.

32 Fauci AS, Braunwald E, Kasper DL, et al. *Harrison's Principles of Internal Medicine*. 17th ed. New York: McGraw-Hill, 2008.

33 Fiatarone Singh MA, Bernstein MA. Exercise for the older adult: nutrition implications. In: Bernstein MA, Luggen AS, eds. *Nutrition for the Older Adult*. Sudbury, MA: Jones & Bartlett, 2009.

34 National Institutes of Health, Office of Dietary Supplements. Dietary supplement fact sheet: calcium. http://ods.od.nih.gov/factsheets/calcium.asp. Accessed 8/1/09.

35 Ervin RB, Wang C-Y, Wright JD, Kennedy-Stephenson J. *Dietary Intake of Selected Minerals for the United States Population: 1999–2000*. Hyattsville, MD: National Center for Health Statistics, 2004. Advance Data from Vital and Health Statistics, No. 341.

36 Rafferty K, Heaney RP. Nutrient effects on the calcium economy: emphasizing the potassium controversy. *J Nutr*. 2008;138(1 suppl):166S–171S.

37 Institute of Medicine, Food and Nutrition Board. *Dietary Reference Intakes for Calcium, Phosphorus, Magnesium, Vitamin D, and Fluoride*. Washington, DC: National Academies Press, 1997.

38 National Institutes of Health. Optimal calcium intake. *NIH Consensus Statement* 1994;12(4):1–31.

39 National Institutes of Health, Office of Dietary Supplements. Dietary supplement fact sheet: calcium.

40 Ibid.

41 Ibid.

42 National Institute of Arthritis and Musculoskeletal and Skin Diseases. Osteoporosis: facts and figures. http://www.niams.nih.gov/Health_Info/Bone/Osteoporosis/. Accessed 7/31/09.

43 Ilich JZ, Brownbill RA, Tamborini L. Bone and nutrition in elderly women: protein, energy, and calcium as major determinants of bone mineral density. *Eur J Clin Nutr*. 2003;57(4):554–565.

44 Institute of Medicine, Food and Nutrition Board. *Dietary Reference Intakes for Calcium, Phosphorus*.

45 Ibid.

46 Ibid.

47 Stein JH, Sande MA, Zvaifler NJ, et al. *Internal Medicine*. 5th ed. St. Louis: Mosby, 1998; and Lederer E, Ouseph R, Mittal D, et al. Hypophosphatemia: treatment and medication. eMedicine. http://emedicine.medscape.com/article/242280-treatment. Accessed 8/6/09.

48 Institute of Medicine, Food and Nutrition Board. *Dietary Reference Intakes for Calcium, Phosphorus*.

49 Ibid.

50 Fauci, Braunwald, Kasper, et al. *Harrison's Principles of Internal Medicine*.

51 Ibid.

52 Klevay LM, Milne DB. Low dietary magnesium increases supraventricular ectopy. *Am J Clin Nutr*. 2002;75(3):550–554.

CHAPTER 13

Trace Minerals

THINK About It

1 Do you think a person with an infection should take iron supplements?
2 You disclose to a friend that you tend to be low in iron. She knows you are vegetarian and suggests you drink milk. What false assumption might she be making?
3 You know that a number of people in your family have had goiter or take thyroxine. You also notice that none of these people like fish. Any relationship?
4 Some people argue that fluoridation is overdone. What is your position? Would you vote for fluoridating all water supplies?

Visit nutrition.jbpub.com

Figure 13.1 **Mineral content of soil influences the nutrient value of plants.** The mineral content of plants reflects the mineral content of the soil in which they are grown.

One of your "meat-and-potatoes" friends argues that animal foods are the best sources of minerals because animals concentrate the minerals they eat from plants. Your vegetarian friend disagrees, saying that minerals are plentiful in plant foods, but processing removes them. Another friend contends that American agricultural practices have stripped the mineral content from the soil, so supplements are really the only way to get adequate mineral intake. Who's right?

As you saw in Chapter 12, protein-rich animal foods are good sources of some minerals such as calcium, phosphorus, and sulfur. Other major minerals (e.g., potassium and magnesium) are plentiful in plant foods. This chapter focuses on trace minerals—that is, minerals present in the body in small quantities, and therefore needed by the body in small amounts. Meats are the best food sources for some of these minerals—iron and zinc, for instance. Whole grains are also good sources of several minerals, including iron, copper, selenium, and manganese. Water is a major source of fluoride, a mineral that often occurs naturally in water or is added during municipal water treatment.

But what about the mineral content of soil? (See **Figure 13.1**.) The mineral content of soil certainly influences the nutrient value of the plants that grow in it. This is especially true for the trace minerals selenium and iodine. How important is this to our dietary intake? Is the soil's mineral content depleted, as some supplement suppliers claim? Adequate nutrition is as important for healthy plants as it is for healthy livestock and people. If soil lacks a nutrient the plant needs, the plant will not grow. Fertilization adds nutrients to the soil, and so does the natural degradation of rocks, plants, and animals. There is little evidence for specific nutritional claims based on the mineral content of the soil. In addition, few people consume only foods grown locally. A varied diet typically includes foods from many different locales and thus from a wide variety of soils.

What Are Trace Elements?

Trace elements are essential minerals found in a large variety of animal and plant foods; these nutrients have both regulatory and structural functions in the body. Trace elements differ from the major minerals (e.g., calcium, phosphorus, magnesium) in two ways. First, the dietary requirements for each of the trace elements are less than 100 milligrams per day. For example, iron and zinc intake recommendations for adults range from 8 milligrams to 18 milligrams per day, whereas the adult daily calcium recommendation is 1,000 milligrams per day. Second, the total amount of each trace element found in the body is small, less than 5 grams. For example, the total amount of iron in the body is 2 to 4 grams, or about the amount of iron in a small nail. In contrast, a typical adult body contains more than 1,000 grams of calcium. **Figure 13.2** shows the trace elements on the periodic table.

Why Are Trace Elements Important?

Despite the minuscule amounts in the body, trace elements are crucial to many body functions, including metabolic pathways. Trace elements serve as cofactors for enzymes, components of hormones, and participants in oxidation-reduction reactions. They are essential for growth and for normal functioning of the immune system. Deficiencies may cause delayed sexual maturation, poor growth, mediocre work performance, faulty immune function, tooth decay, and altered hormonal function.

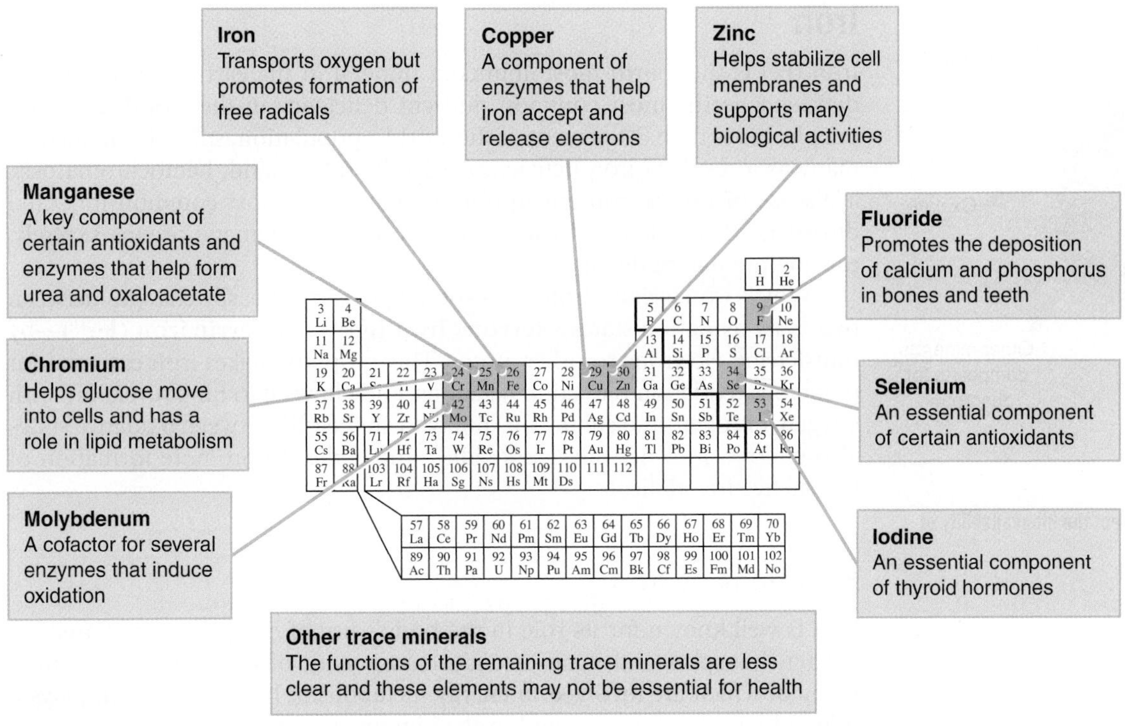

Iron
Transports oxygen but promotes formation of free radicals
Copper
A component of enzymes that help iron accept and release electrons
Zinc
Helps stabilize cell membranes and supports many biological activities
Manganese
A key component of certain antioxidants and enzymes that help form urea and oxaloacetate
Fluoride
Promotes the deposition of calcium and phosphorus in bones and teeth
Chromium
Helps glucose move into cells and has a role in lipid metabolism
Selenium
An essential component of certain antioxidants
Molybdenum
A cofactor for several enzymes that induce oxidation
Iodine
An essential component of thyroid hormones
Other trace minerals
The functions of the remaining trace minerals are less clear and these elements may not be essential for health

Figure 13.2 **Trace elements on the periodic table.** Trace minerals are found in the body and required in the diet in small amounts, but they play important roles in the body.

Technological advances in recent years have triggered an explosion of exciting new research because scientists can now track trace elements throughout the body more effectively. Working together, nutritionists, biochemists, biologists, immunologists, geneticists, and epidemiologists are uncovering the mysteries behind many of these fascinating elements and finding new links between trace elements and a variety of diseases and genetic disorders.

Other Characteristics of Trace Elements

Foods from animal sources, particularly liver, are good sources of many trace minerals. Amounts in plant foods can differ dramatically from region to region, depending on the soil's mineral content. Even the maturity of a vegetable, fruit, or grain can influence its mineral content. Since actual mineral content is so variable, the values published in food composition tables can be misleading. Food tables, even many of the popular computerized nutrient databases, often have incomplete information about trace mineral content.

Even if we are fairly sure of the amount of a particular mineral in a food, other components of the diet can affect the mineral's bioavailability. Trace minerals are affected by the same factors that affect bioavailability of the major minerals (see **Figure 13.3**), including fiber, phytate, polyphenols, oxalate, the acidity of the intestinal environment, and the person's need for that mineral. High doses of other minerals can compete with trace minerals and inhibit their absorption. Treatment for mineral toxicity sometimes exploits these antagonistic interactions between minerals. For example, high doses of zinc may be given to patients with a genetic disorder of copper overload (Wilson's disease) because zinc inhibits copper absorption.

Quick Bite

Hair Analysis Is a Misguided Measure

Although discredited as a measure of trace mineral status in individuals, hair analysis is promoted with the claim that it can reveal mineral deficiencies. This measure lacks sensitivity and is unreliable. The color, diameter, and rate of growth of a person's hair, the season of the year, the geographic location, and the person's age and sex can affect the levels of minerals in hair. It is possible for hair concentration of an element (zinc, for example) to be high even though deficiency exists in the body. Hair dyes, perming agents, and certain shampoos also alter the mineral content of hair.

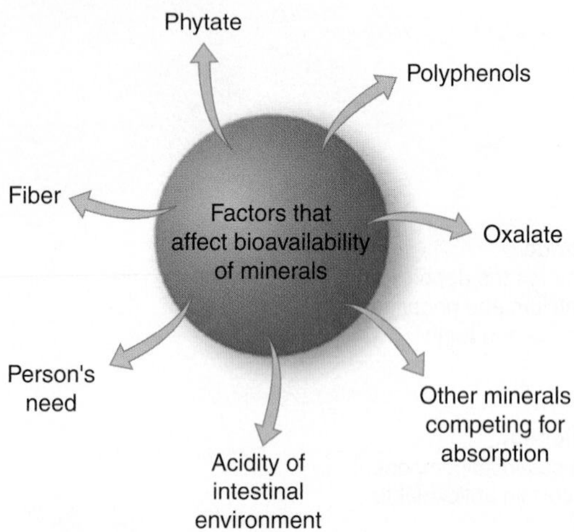

Figure 13.3 **Factors that affect the bioavailability of minerals.**

Iron

Iron (Fe) is the fourth most abundant mineral in the earth's crust, yet iron deficiency is the most common nutrient deficiency in the world; 2 billion people, more than 30 percent of the world's population, suffer from anemia, many as a result of iron deficiency.[1] On the other hand, hemochromatosis, a disease of excess iron absorption, is one of the most common inherited disorders. If not detected early, this disorder can damage organs severely, causing premature death.

Why is iron useful? Iron has a special property. It easily changes between two of its oxidation states—**ferrous iron (Fe^{2+})** and **ferric iron (Fe^{3+})**—by transferring electrons to other atoms. This property makes iron essential for numerous oxidation-reduction reactions, and allows it to bind reversibly with oxygen, nitrogen, and sulfur. The ability to shift easily between oxidative states also endows iron with its "dark side"—the ability to promote formation of destructive free radicals.

Functions of Iron

Iron is well known for its role in the body's use of energy; it is required for oxygen transport and is an essential component of hundreds of enzymes, many of which are involved in energy metabolism. In addition, iron plays a role in brain development and in the immune system.

Oxygen Transport

Iron's ability to carry oxygen is crucial. As a component of two **heme** proteins—hemoglobin and **myoglobin**—iron transports oxygen in the body. **Figure 13.4** shows the structures of heme and hemoglobin. With iron at the center, heme proteins have the unique chemical property of easily loading and unloading oxygen, and they give blood its red color. Hemoglobin in red blood cells transports oxygen in the blood, delivering it through the capillary beds to the tissues. Myoglobin in muscle facilitates the movement of oxygen into muscle cells.

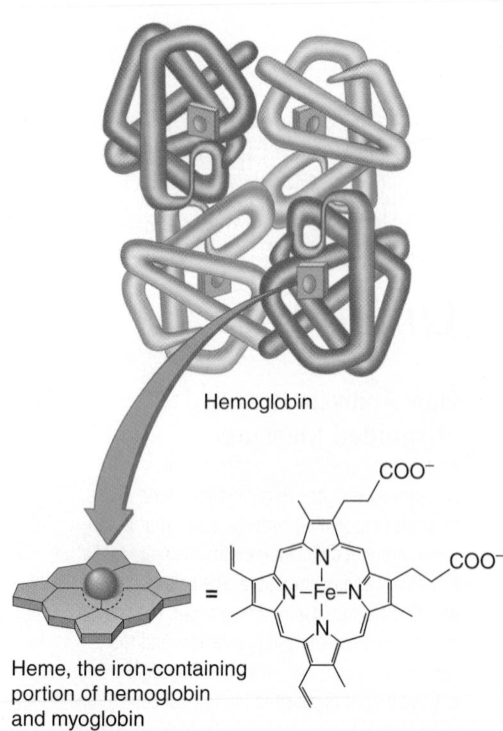

Figure 13.4 **Heme in hemoglobin.** Iron in the heme portion of hemoglobin and myoglobin binds and releases oxygen easily. Hemoglobin in red blood cells transports oxygen in the blood and gives blood its red color.

Enzymes

Hundreds of enzymes have iron as a constituent or need it as a cofactor in reactions. One of iron's best-known roles is as a component of enzymes involved in energy metabolism. **Cytochromes**, for example, are heme-containing compounds critical to the electron transport chain.

The rate-limiting enzyme in gluconeogenesis requires iron. Iron also is a cofactor for antioxidant enzymes that protect against damaging free radicals. Interestingly, excess iron can also catalyze the formation of these highly reactive and potentially destructive substances.

Immune Function

Optimal immune function requires iron, which creates a treatment dilemma in areas of the world with rampant disease and iron deficiency. Because iron nourishes certain bacteria, iron supplementation can worsen an infection, particularly malaria.[2] In the absence of an infection, iron supplementation is appropriate for treating iron deficiency.

Brain Function

Iron is essential for optimal brain and nervous system development and function. In children, iron-deficiency anemia can lead to learning and behavior problems.[3] Evidence also supports a role for iron in **myelinization**—the development of the myelin sheath around nerve fibers.[4] Iron's participation in brain development is an active area of research. Iron also is involved in producing neurotransmitters, chemicals that carry messages between nerve cells. **Figure 13.5** summarizes the functions of iron.

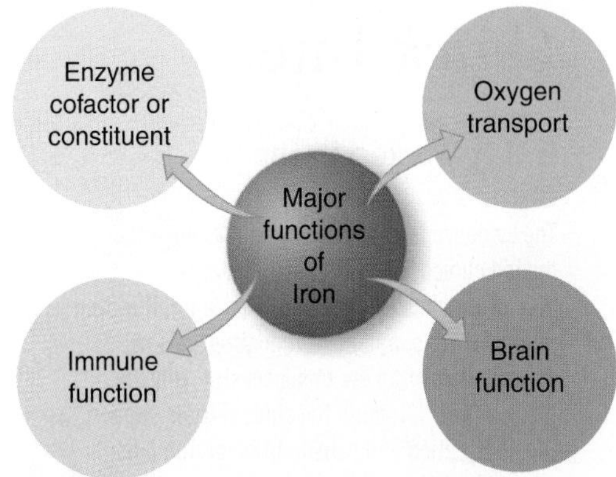

Figure 13.5 **Major functions of iron.** Well known for its role in transporting oxygen in the blood, iron also is essential for optimal immune function and nerve health. In addition, it is a cofactor in numerous reactions.

Regulation of Iron in the Body

Total body iron averages about 4 grams in men and a little more than 2 grams in women.[5] When the body has sufficient iron to meet its needs, most iron (greater than 70 percent) can be classified as functional iron; the remainder is storage or transport iron. The majority of the iron in the body, more than two-thirds, can be found in hemoglobin, and the rest is found in myoglobin and enzymes (e.g., cytochromes).[6] The body regulates its iron status by balancing absorption, transport, storage, and losses.[7]

Iron Absorption

The body controls its iron levels by regulating intestinal absorption.[8] When the absorptive mechanism operates normally, a person maintains functional iron and tends to establish iron stores. The body's capacity to absorb dietary iron depends on the body's iron status and need, normal GI function, the amount and type of iron in the diet, and dietary factors that enhance or inhibit iron absorption.

Process of Iron Absorption To avoid iron toxicity, the body regulates its absorption of iron. (See **Figure 13.6**.) Intestinal cells act as gatekeepers, forming an initial barrier that turns away excess (and potentially harmful) iron. Once admitted into the intestinal cell, iron has three potential fates:

- It can be used by the cell itself.
- It can be released into the blood and carried to other tissues by **transferrin**, the major iron-transporting protein in the body.
- It can be stored as **ferritin**.

The body's need for iron determines its fate: the greater the need, particularly for synthesis of red blood cells, the more transferrin binds iron and transports it to bone marrow and other tissues. If iron stores are high, the extra iron remains in the cell and is excreted along with mucosal cells that are sloughed off at the end of their life cycle. Some scientists propose that intestinal ferritin acts as an "iron sink," which prevents the accumulation of iron to toxic levels.[9]

Effect of the Body's Iron Status on Iron Absorption Depending on the size of the body's iron stores, absorption of dietary iron (i.e., iron bioavailability) can vary from less than 1 percent to greater than 50 percent. The GI tract increases iron absorption when the body's iron stores are low and decreases absorption when stores are sufficient. The body also gives priority to red blood cell production; an increased production rate, such as during pregnancy or after blood loss, can trigger a several-fold increase in iron uptake.[10]

Among adults, men absorb approximately 6 percent of dietary iron, and nonpregnant women of childbearing age absorb approximately 13 percent. Women's higher absorption rate primarily reflects their lower iron intake and

ferrous iron (Fe^{2+}) The reduced form of iron most commonly found in food.

ferric iron (Fe^{3+}) The oxidized form of iron able to be bound to transferrin for transport.

heme A chemical complex with a central iron atom (ferric iron Fe^{3+}) that forms the oxygen-binding part of hemoglobin and myoglobin.

myoglobin The oxygen-transporting protein of muscle that resembles blood hemoglobin in function.

cytochromes Heme proteins that transfer electrons in the electron transport chain through the alternate oxidation and reduction of iron.

myelinization Development of the myelin sheath, a substance that surrounds nerve fibers.

transferrin A protein synthesized in the liver that transports iron in the blood to the erythroblasts for use in heme synthesis.

ferritin A complex of iron and apoferritin that is a major storage form of iron.

Quick Bite

But It Worked in the Lab . . .

The evidence is clear from carefully conducted clinical trials that supplements reduce iron deficiency during pregnancy. However, public health supplementation programs in communities often are unsuccessful. Why the discrepancy? Although the clinical trials support the distribution and consumption of iron pills, programs in the "real world" have several limiting factors: inadequate supply of iron tablets, limited access to care, poor or nonexistent nutrition counseling, lack of knowledge, and the uncomfortable side effects experienced by some women. These factors are important causes of noncompliance.

higher iron losses as a result of menstruation. Iron absorption also is high among iron-deficient persons.

Effect of GI Function on Iron Absorption Although most iron absorption occurs in the duodenum and jejunum of the small intestine, the stomach also has an important role. Gastric acid facilitates the solubilization of iron and promotes the conversion of ferric iron (Fe^{3+}) to ferrous iron (Fe^{2+}), the form that most easily enters the absorptive intestinal cells. The stomach's retention and mechanical mixing of food also maximize iron's bioavailability. Gastric acid production generally declines with aging, reducing iron absorption in the older adults.

Effect of the Amount and Form of Iron in Food Food contains two types of iron—**heme iron** and **nonheme iron**. Heme iron is a part of hemoglobin and myoglobin, so it is found only in animal tissue. Heme iron is much more absorbable than nonheme iron. Although meat, fish, and poultry contain various amounts of heme iron and nonheme iron, the mix averages about 50 percent heme iron and 50 percent nonheme iron.[11] In contrast, plant-based and iron-fortified foods contain only nonheme iron. (See **Figure 13.7**.) Vegetarian diets, by definition, contain little to no heme iron.

Heme iron is much more bioavailable than nonheme iron.[12] Depending on the body's iron stores, heme iron absorption ranges from 15 to 35 percent of the amount ingested.[13] As the amount of iron ingested increases, the proportion absorbed decreases.

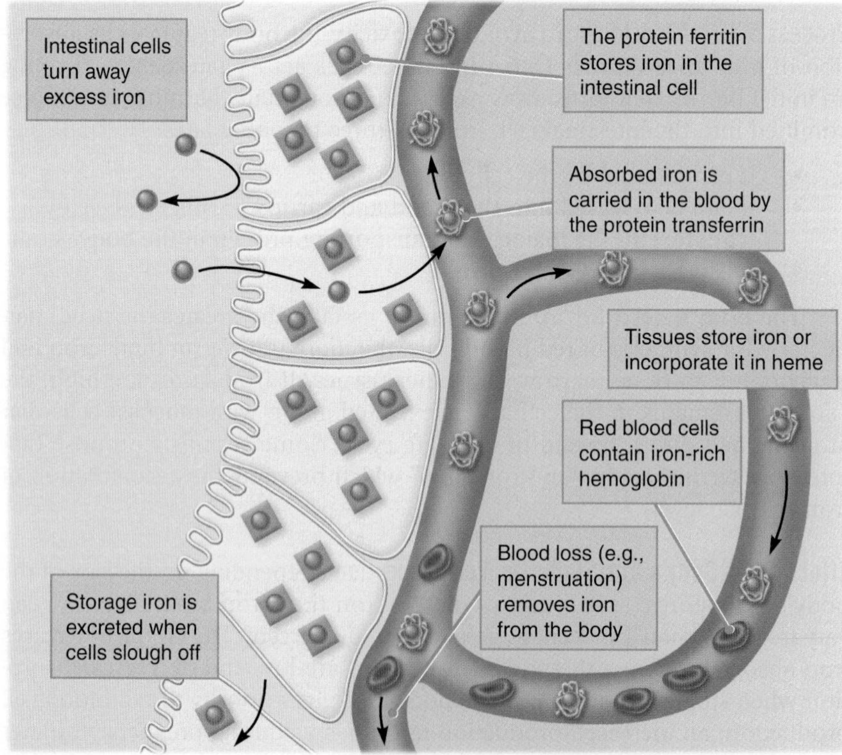

Figure 13.6 **Iron absorption.** The amount of iron absorbed depends on several factors: normal GI function, need for iron, the amount and kind of iron consumed, and dietary factors that enhance or inhibit iron absorption.

heme iron The iron found in the hemoglobin and myoglobin of animal foods.

nonheme iron The iron in plants and the iron in animal foods that is not part of hemoglobin or myoglobin.

polyphenols Organic compounds that include an unsaturated ring containing more than one –OH group as part of their chemical structures; may produce bitterness in coffee and tea.

Dietary Factors That Enhance Iron Absorption Heme iron absorption is relatively independent of meal composition. On the other hand, meal composition strongly influences nonheme iron absorption. Table 13.1 lists factors that inhibit or enhance absorption of iron. The two most important dietary factors that boost absorption of nonheme iron are organic acids, especially vitamin C (ascorbic acid), and meat, including fish and poultry. Organic acids maintain the iron in a soluble, bioavailable form as the stomach contents enter the duodenum. To exert this effect, ascorbic acid must be present in the same meal as the nonheme iron. Other organic acids (e.g., citric, malic, and tartaric acids) appear to have effects comparable to those of ascorbic acid. It is unclear exactly how meat enhances absorption of nonheme iron, but the presence of meat, fish, or poultry increases absorption efficiency.

Dietary Factors That Inhibit Iron Absorption The most significant inhibitors of iron absorption are phytic acid (phytate), which is found in whole grains, and **polyphenols**, which are found in tea, coffee, other beverages, and many plants. (See **Figure 13.8**.) Even though minute amounts of these substances can reduce iron absorption, eating foods rich in vitamin C at the same meal counteracts this effect. The benefits of eating whole grains, which are nutrient dense and rich in fiber, outweigh the negative impact on iron absorption. Rather than cut back on whole grains, include small amounts of meat and/or generous amounts of vitamin C–rich fruits and vegetables with meals to improve iron absorption.

Other inhibitors of nonheme iron absorption include soy, calcium, zinc, oxalates, tannins (found in tea), polyphenols, phytates (found in whole grains and legumes), and fiber. The long-term significance of these inhibitory factors on iron status is unclear. Calcium, zinc, and iron compete for absorption, and each can inhibit absorption of another.[14] Many women take calcium supplements to reduce their risk of osteoporosis. To minimize interference with iron absorption, calcium supplements should be taken alone at bedtime rather than with meals.

Iron Absorption and Vegetarianism

When evaluating the nutritional value of a vegetarian diet, iron and zinc are key concerns. With elimination of meat and increased intake of phytate-containing legumes and whole grains, vegetarians absorb less dietary iron and zinc than nonvegetarians. Thus, vegetarians may need more dietary iron than those who eat animal products.[15] In developed countries with ample and varied food supplies, vegetarians generally consume sufficient iron. Although vegetarians tend to have lower iron stores than nonvegetarians, they appear to have no greater incidence of iron deficiency.

Table 13.1 **Factors That Affect Iron Absorption**

Inhibitors	Enhancers
Fiber and phytate	Vitamin C (ascorbic acid)
Calcium and phosphorus (milk/dairy)	Factor in meat, poultry, and fish
Tannins, found in tea	HCl secreted in the stomach
Polyphenols	Citric, malic, and tartaric acid
Oxalate	

MEAT

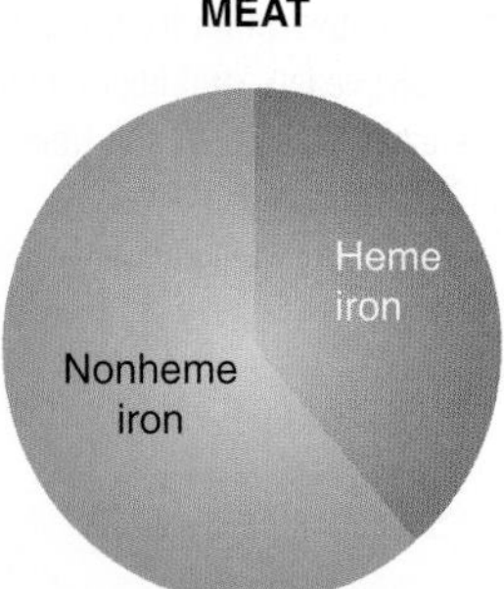

Beef, chicken, and fish contain about 40% heme and 60% nonheme iron. Eggs and dairy products contain no hemoglobin or myoglobin, so they contain only nonheme iron.

LEGUMES AND VEGETABLES

Beans, fortified cereals, soybeans, and green leafy vegetables are sources of nonheme iron.

AVERAGE DAILY DIET

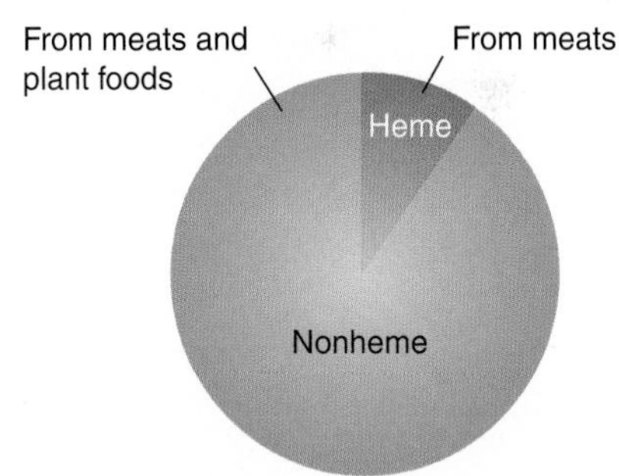

The average diet contains much more nonheme iron than heme iron.

Figure 13.7 **Sources of heme and nonheme iron.** Heme iron is found only in meats. Nonheme iron is found in both plant and animal foods. Eggs and dairy products contain small amounts of nonheme iron only.

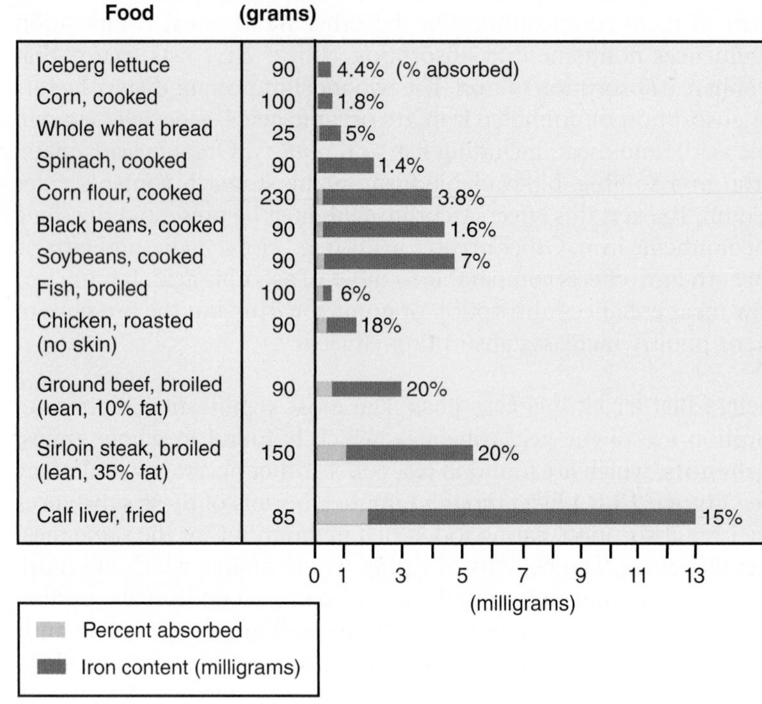

Figure 13.8 **Iron absorption from foods.** Phytates, polyphenols, and fiber inhibit iron absorption, so the bioavailability of iron from plant foods is much lower than that from animal foods.

Source: Modified from a figure by Laurie Grace from Scrimshaw NS. Iron deficiency. *Scientific American.* October 1991:48. Reprinted by permission of Laurie Grace.

Iron Transport and Storage

Transferrin delivers iron from the intestines to the tissues and redistributes iron from storage sites to various body compartments. Individual cells take up the iron transported on transferrin via **transferrin receptors** on the cell membranes.[16] The number of transferrin receptors varies with the cell's need for iron; tissues with the highest iron need (e.g., bone marrow, liver, and placenta) have the highest concentration of transferrin receptors. (See **Figure 13.9**.)

The body stores surplus iron either as part of the soluble protein complex ferritin or as the insoluble protein complex **hemosiderin**. The liver, bone marrow, spleen, and skeletal muscle harbor most of the body's ferritin and hemosiderin, and small amounts of ferritin circulate in the bloodstream. In healthy people, ferritin contains most of the stored iron. When long-term negative iron balance depletes iron stores, iron deficiency begins.

Iron Turnover and Loss

The body tightly regulates its iron content to ensure adequate stores while protecting against toxicity. It recycles iron, and adjusts absorption and excretion as needed.

Red blood cell formation and destruction are responsible for most iron turnover. In adult men, for example, the breakdown of older red blood cells supplies approximately 95 percent of the iron required to produce new red blood cells. Dietary sources supply only 5 percent. In contrast, this balance is 70/30 in infants, whose growth needs tend to outstrip the recycled supply.

Adults lose about 1 milligram of iron daily in feces and sloughed-off mucosal and skin cells. Women of childbearing age require additional iron (an average of 0.3 to 0.5 mg of iron absorbed daily) to compensate for blood loss during menstruation. Pregnancy increases iron needs markedly to support growth of the fetus and expansion of the maternal blood supply. During

transferrin receptors Specialized receptors on the cell membrane that bind transferrin.

hemosiderin An insoluble form of storage iron.

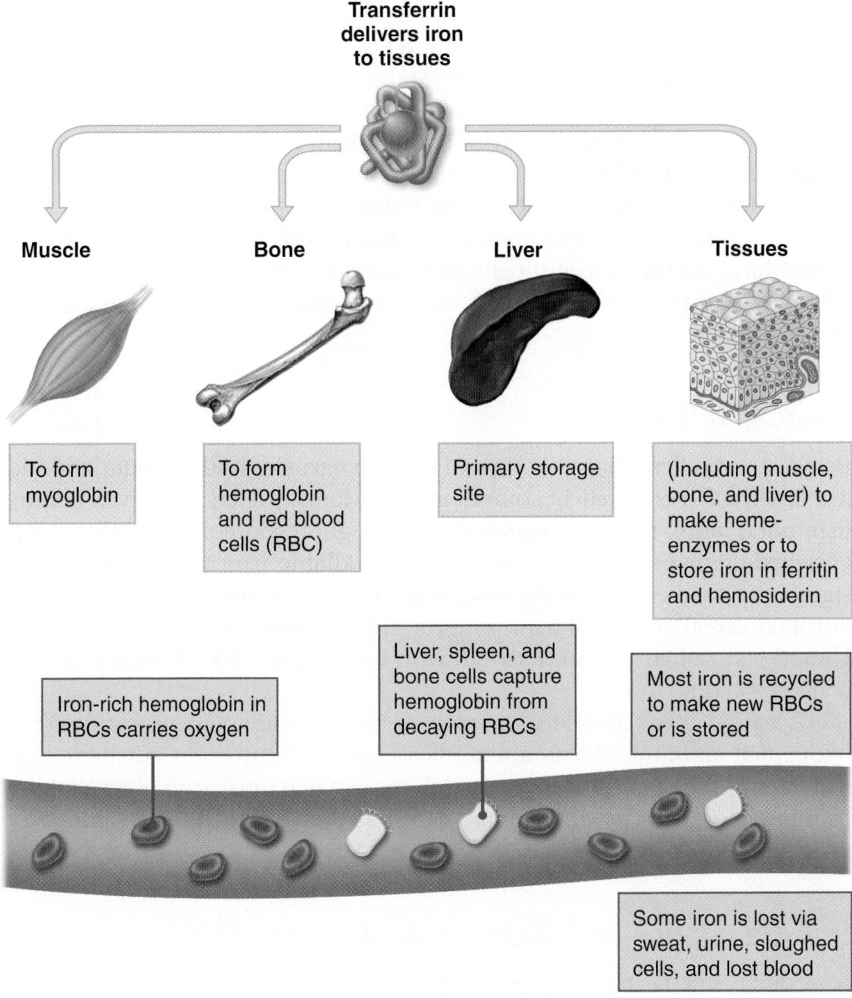
Transferrin delivers iron to tissues
Muscle
Bone
Liver
Tissues
To form myoglobin
To form hemoglobin and red blood cells (RBC)
Primary storage site
(Including muscle, bone, and liver) to make heme-enzymes or to store iron in ferritin and hemosiderin
Iron-rich hemoglobin in RBCs carries oxygen
Liver, spleen, and bone cells capture hemoglobin from decaying RBCs
Most iron is recycled to make new RBCs or is stored
Some iron is lost via sweat, urine, sloughed cells, and lost blood

Figure 13.9 **Iron in the body.** Transferrin transports iron to tissues for the synthesis of heme or storage in ferritin and hemosiderin.

pregnancy, a woman requires an absorption of an average of 4 milligrams of additional iron daily over the 280 days of gestation. Blood loss with childbirth depletes iron; thus, women with repeated pregnancies close together are likely to have poor iron status and need extra iron.

All people lose tiny amounts of iron daily in normal gastrointestinal blood loss, but gastrointestinal problems can cause significant iron loss. Peptic ulcer, inflammatory bowel disease, and bowel cancer can cause gastrointestinal bleeding. Hookworm infections, although uncommon in the United States and Canada, are a major cause of chronic blood loss leading to iron deficiency in endemic areas.[17]

Dietary Recommendations for Iron

Scientists base recommendations for iron intake on the replacement of daily iron losses and the bioavailability of dietary iron. The primary routes of loss are bleeding, gastrointestinal losses (mainly exfoliation of the intestinal mucosa), sloughing of skin, and sweat. The RDA for iron is based on average losses of 1 milligram per day for adult men and 1.4 milligrams per day for premenopausal women, combined with an absorption percentage of 18 percent from a mixed diet. The RDAs for adults are 8 milligrams per day for men and postmenopausal women and 18 milligrams per day for women of childbearing age.

Dietary iron intakes of most men may exceed their RDA, whereas women's intakes often are well below the RDA. Lower iron intake for women usually is attributed to lower energy intake.

The iron needs of infants are a special concern. During the final weeks of pregnancy, babies ideally store enough iron in the liver, bone marrow, spleen, and hemoglobin-rich blood to see them through their first six months of life. However, if the mother's iron nutrition is poor or the baby is born early, the baby's iron stores are smaller and do not last. To help ensure that babies have adequate iron, pregnant women are urged to meet the RDA of 27 milligrams per day. Infant baby cereal and many infant formulas are fortified with iron.

Sources of Iron

Beef is an excellent dietary source of iron, in terms of both amount and bioavailability. Other excellent sources include clams, oysters, and liver. Poultry, fish, pork, lamb, tofu, and legumes are also good sources. Whole-grain and enriched-grain products contain less bioavailable iron than meat but are significant sources of iron because they constitute a major part of our diets. Fortified cereals also make an important contribution to iron intake in the United States. Dairy products are low in iron. **Figure 13.10** shows the iron content of some foods.

A varied diet (adequate in calories, rich in fruits and vegetables, and with small amounts of lean animal flesh) generally provides adequate iron. Vegetarians who consume no animal tissue can maximize iron bioavailability from other sources by consuming vitamin C–rich fruits and vegetables with every meal.

Iron Deficiency and Measurement of Iron Status

Iron deficiency is the most common nutritional deficiency worldwide. Although significantly more prevalent in developing countries than in the rest of the world, it remains a public health concern in the United States. Infants and toddlers, adolescent girls, women of childbearing age, and pregnant women are particularly vulnerable.

Iron deficiency is most prevalent in 6- to 24-month-old children, who are in a period of rapid brain growth and development of cognitive and motor skills. Iron stores from fetal development have been depleted, and a major source of energy in the young child's diet is milk, a poor source of iron. If iron stores are not replaced before the child passes critical developmental milestones, developmental deficits from iron deficiency may be irreversible.

Significant and potentially irreversible alterations in brain and central nervous system development can occur in infants who experience iron deficiency during the early stages of life.[18] Children with low iron levels also are more likely to have sleep disturbance and attention-deficit/hyperactivity disorder.[19] Research in this area is still evolving and complicated by the difficulty of separating the roles of iron deficiency and other environmental factors (e.g., generalized malnutrition, poverty, and low parental education) that also impair psychomotor and mental development.

Progression of Iron Deficiency

Iron deficiency progresses through three distinct stages, shown in Table 13.2. The third stage is iron-deficiency anemia, a severe form of iron deficiency that is defined by low hemoglobin levels.

Quick Bite

Grandma's Cast-Iron Skillet Helped Her Avoid Iron Deficiency

Iron deficiency is the most common form of malnutrition in the United States. However, this is a relatively recent phenomenon. Americans used to cook using cast-iron pots and pans. A study showed that using these utensils to cook acidic foods like spaghetti sauce and apple butter increases the iron content of such foods by a factor of 30- to 100-fold. Our preference for stainless steel, aluminum, and enamelware does not allow this fortification.

Iron

Daily Value = 18 mg

DV level	Food	Weight	Serving	Iron
	Exceptionally good sources			
	Product 19 cereal	30 g	1 cup	18.09 mg
	Whole-grain Total	30 g	¾ cup	18.00 mg
	Total Corn Flakes cereal	30 g	1⅓ cup	18.00 mg
High: 20% DV or more	Clams, raw	85 g	3 oz	11.88 mg
	Rice Krispies cereals	33 g	1¼ cup	11.35 mg
	Cheerios cereal	30 g	1 cup	9.53 mg
	Cream of Wheat cereal, cooked	251 g	1 cup	9.39 mg
	Lentils, cooked	198 g	1 cup	6.59 mg
	Spinach, cooked	180 g	1 cup	6.43 mg
	Bagels, plain	89 g	4″ bagel	5.38 mg
	Semisweet chocolate	168 g	1 cup	5.26 mg
	Beef liver, cooked	85 g	3 oz	5.24 mg
	Kidney beans, cooked	177 g	1 cup	5.20 mg
	Chickpeas, cooked	164 g	1 cup	4.74 mg
Good: 10–19% DV	Beets, canned	170 g	1 cup	3.09 mg
	Baked beans	254 g	1 cup	3.02 mg
	Prune juice, canned	256 g	1 cup	3.02 mg
	Raisins, seedless	145 g	1 cup	2.73 mg
	Tomato sauce, canned	245 g	1 cup	2.50 mg
	Turkey, cooked	140 g	1 cup	2.49 mg
	Beef, steak, cooked	85 g	3 oz	2.44 mg
	Peas, green, frozen, cooked	160 g	1 cup	2.43 mg
	Lamb, cooked	85 g	3 oz	2.30 mg
	Chicken liver, cooked	20 g	1 liver	2.28 mg
	Beef, ground (85% lean), cooked	85 g	3 oz	2.21 mg
	Collards, cooked	190 g	1 cup	2.20 mg
	Potato, baked, with skin	202 g	1 potato	2.18 mg
	Barley, cooked	157 g	1 cup	2.09 mg

Figure 13.10 **Food sources of iron.** Iron is found in red meats, certain seafoods, vegetables, and legumes, and is added to enriched grains and breakfast cereals.

Source: US Department of Agriculture, Agricultural Research Service. USDA National Nutrient Database for Standard Reference, Release 22. 2009. Nutrient Data Laboratory Home Page, http://www.ars.usda.gov/ba/bhnrc/ndl.

Table 13.2 Stages of Iron Deficiency

Stage	Biochemical Sign	Functional Implications
Depletion of iron stores	Decreased ferritin	None
Depletion of functional iron	Decreased transferrin saturation	Decreased physical performance
	Increased erythrocyte protoporphyrin	
Iron-deficiency anemia	Decreased hemoglobin	Cognitive impairment, poor growth, decreased
	Decreased hematocrit	performance, and decreased exercise tolerance
	Decreased red cell size	

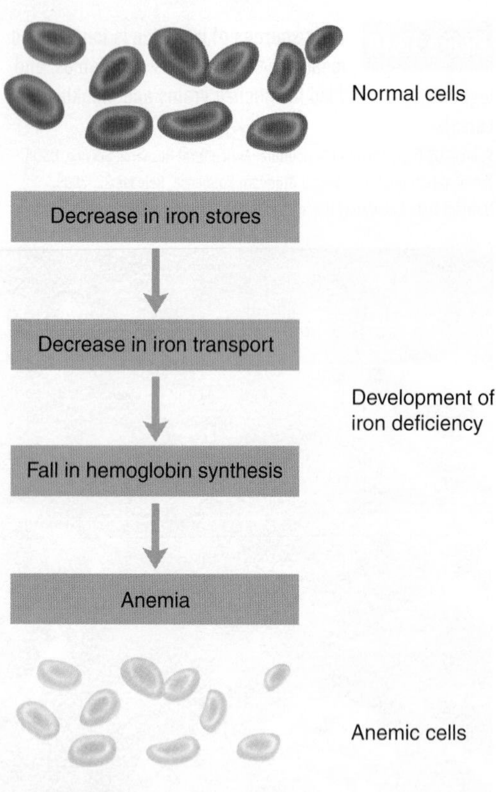

Figure 13.11 **Normal and anemic red blood cells.** Iron deficiency can progress to iron-deficiency anemia, a severe form of iron deficiency that is accompanied by low hemoglobin levels.

Depletion of iron stores is the first stage of iron deficiency, which causes no physiological impairments. Because serum ferritin is proportional to the body's total iron stores, a test of serum ferritin is a good way to assess iron deficiency.

Depletion of functional and transport iron is the second stage of iron deficiency—the stage between iron depletion and actual anemia. The newest and most sensitive measure of this intermediate stage is the serum level of transferrin receptors (TfRs). As the body's iron status falls, TfR levels increase in proportion to the iron deficit. Other blood values used to detect this stage are **transferrin saturation** and **protoporphyrin** levels. Transferrin saturation is a measure of the residual binding capacity for iron, which increases when a lack of iron does not saturate transferrin. Protoporphyrin and iron combine to make heme, the iron-containing portion of hemoglobin. When the supply of iron is inadequate for heme synthesis, blood levels of protoporphyrin rise.

Because second-stage iron depletion impairs the function of iron-requiring enzymes needed for aerobic energy production, an iron-depleted person may be unable to work at full capacity. The impact of mental and physical performance impairments in women with iron deficiency even without anemia is a cause for concern for women in roles such as the military. Prevalence rates of almost 30 percent for iron deficiency and 13 percent for iron-deficiency anemia have been found among active female recruits.[20] More human studies are required to determine whether iron depletion affects other physiological processes.

The third and most severe stage of iron deficiency is anemia—a disease characterized by insufficient or defective red blood cells, or both. A lack of iron inhibits production of normal red blood cells, while normal cell turnover continues to deplete the red blood cell population. Red blood cell production falters, producing red blood cells that are pale and smaller than normal. Hemoglobin and **hematocrit** (concentration of red blood cells in the blood) levels also are low. This type of anemia, known for its small, pale red blood cells, is called microcytic hypochromic anemia. Inadequate vitamin B_6 also can cause microcytic hypochromic anemia. Another type of anemia, megaloblastic anemia, is known for its abnormally large, immature red blood cells and is caused by inadequate folate or vitamin B_{12}. (See Chapter 11, "Water-Soluble Vitamins," for more details.) **Figure 13.11** shows normal and anemic blood cells.

The symptoms of microcytic hypochromic anemia vary according to its severity and the speed of its development. They include fatigue, pallor, breathlessness with exertion, decreased tolerance of cold, behavioral changes, deficits in immune function, cognitive impairment, decreased work performance, and impaired growth. In children, iron deficiency is associated with apathy, short attention span, irritability, and reduced ability to learn.[21]

transferrin saturation The extent to which transferrin has vacant iron-binding sites (e.g., low transferrin saturation indicates a high proportion of vacant iron-binding sites).

protoporphyrin A chemical complex that combines with iron to form heme.

hematocrit Percentage volume occupied by packed red blood cells in a centrifuged sample of whole blood.

Iron Toxicity

The Tolerable Upper Intake Level (UL) for iron is based on the level that causes gastrointestinal distress. For adults, the UL for iron is 45 milligrams per day.

Iron Poisoning in Children

Accidental iron overdose is a leading cause of poisoning deaths in young children in the United States.[22] The iron products involved range from nonprescription daily multivitamin/mineral supplements for children to high-potency prescription iron supplements for pregnant women. Parents who are cautious about keeping other medications out of reach often do not realize that over-the-counter iron tablets and iron-containing multivitamin/mineral supplements can be toxic to children. Even a few pills can cause the death of a small child. Symptoms of iron intoxication include nausea, vomiting, diarrhea, rapid heartbeat, dizziness, and confusion. Death can occur within hours of ingestion. If iron poisoning is suspected, the child should receive immediate emergency medical care.

Hereditary Hemochromatosis

Hereditary hemochromatosis is a form of chronic **iron overload**. Although it was once believed to be rare, scientists now know that mild forms are quite common.[23] A genetic defect causes excessive iron absorption. Over the years, iron can build up in many parts of the body, leading to severe organ damage and even death. Diabetes, heart disease, cirrhosis, liver cancer, and arthritis can all be consequences of hemochromatosis.

Serious complications of hemochromatosis are five to ten times more common in men than women, primarily because of women's blood loss associated with menstruation and pregnancy. Treatment of hemochromatosis includes minimizing iron intake and frequent phlebotomy (removal of blood) to withdraw some of the iron that blood carries in cells. With early diagnosis and treatment, a person with hemochromatosis can avoid organ damage and other complications and have a normal life span.

Iron overload is highly prevalent in some African communities. Researchers originally thought the custom of consuming beer brewed in steel drums was entirely responsible. These beverages have a large amount of highly bioavailable iron, and alcohol enhances the absorption of iron. However, researchers have found strong evidence for a gene, distinct from the hemochromatosis gene in Caucasians, that may predispose individuals to this disorder.[24]

Key Concepts *Iron is essential for life but highly toxic in excess. Iron is a key component of the oxygen transporters hemoglobin and myoglobin, and of many enzymes involved in energy metabolism. Heme iron is absorbed more efficiently than nonheme iron. The body carefully regulates iron absorption; iron can be bound to transferrin for transport, or stored as ferritin or hemosiderin. The best dietary source of iron is red meat. Iron deficiency develops gradually, with anemia being the most severe manifestation of deficiency. Iron poisoning is potentially deadly, especially for young children. Hereditary hemochromatosis is a common genetic disease that causes iron overload.*

iron overload Toxicity from excess iron.

Going Green

Could Iron Help Cool Global Warming?

Recent experimentation as well as geological records suggest that iron deficiency is limiting phytoplankton production.

Researchers studying ocean sediment cores suggest that ice ages were preceded by high levels of ocean iron. They inferred that this iron, derived from terrestrial environments, balanced the natural oceanic iron deficit, and resulted in the eruption of plant and phytoplankton life. From the surface waters phytoplankton then drew down carbon dioxide from the atmosphere. Scientists believe that this drawdown of the greenhouse gas led to global cooling and ice ages.

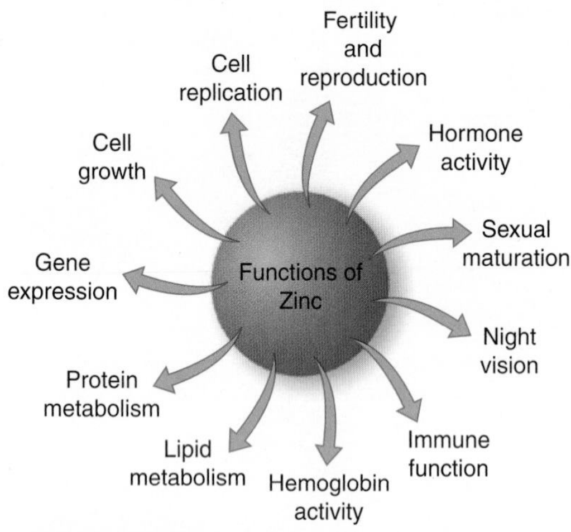

Figure 13.12 **Functions of zinc in the body.** Because zinc is involved in so many different functions, it is fortunate that overt zinc deficiency is rare.

Zinc

It's hard to believe that a nutrient so important to health could go unnoticed until as recently as 50 years ago, but that is the case with zinc (Zn). Some people may think of zinc only in connection with the "zinc oxide" cream used topically as a sunscreen or with zinc lozenges promoted as a treatment for colds; few consumers realize that dietary zinc is absolutely essential for health.

Scientists first recognized human zinc deficiency in 1961.[25] They found severe zinc deficiencies in young, severely growth-retarded Iranian men. In addition to suffering from dwarfism, these men were anemic and extremely lethargic and had **hypogonadism** (poorly developed genitals), and some couldn't see well in the dark. Their diets consisted mainly of wheat bread and were almost devoid of animal protein. These men also were known to eat clay (**geophagia**). Scientists hypothesized that the high phytate content of their diet, along with the geophagia, impaired absorption of both zinc and iron. Six years later, a study in Egypt confirmed zinc's role; zinc supplementation improved growth and genital development.[26]

Functions of Zinc

The body contains a small amount of zinc—between 1.5 and 2.5 grams, or about the same amount of zinc as is in a **galvanized** nail, which has a thin layer of zinc to protect it from corrosion. Zinc is a component of every living cell. The functions of zinc fall into three categories: catalytic, structural, and regulatory. Zinc is best known for its participation in enzyme structure and function, but it also supports many other diverse biological activities through a role in controlling gene regulation. **Figure 13.12** illustrates the functions of zinc in the body.

Zinc and Enzymes

Zinc is critical to the proper function of more than 70 and possibly over 200 enzymes.[27] As a component of **metalloproteins**, which are proteins that have a mineral as an essential part of their structures, zinc is essential for their structural integrity and function, regulation of their activities, and their ability to catalyze reactions. In the cytoplasm, zinc and copper are key components of superoxide dismutase, an enzyme that speeds antioxidant reactions and helps protect cells from free radical damage.

Zinc's Role in Nucleic Acid Metabolism

Zinc also is inextricably linked to gene expression. In severe zinc deficiency, cells fail to replicate. This may be why zinc is so important for the normal growth of children and the sexual maturation of adolescents. Furthermore, certain tissues with high turnover rates, such as cells lining the GI tract, skin cells, immune cells, and blood cells, are particularly vulnerable to a zinc deficiency. As a result, zinc-deficient people often have diarrhea, dermatitis, and depressed immunity.

Zinc and the Immune System

Zinc is vital to a vigorous immune response and is essential to the proper development and maintenance of the immune system. Without zinc, your body could not fight off invading viruses, bacteria, and fungi. Even mild deficiency may increase the risk of infection.

hypogonadism Decreased functional activity of the gonads (ovaries or testes) with retardation of growth and sexual development.

geophagia Ingestion of clay or dirt.

galvanized Iron or steel with a thin layer of zinc plated onto it to protect against corrosion.

metalloproteins Proteins with a mineral element as an essential part of their structure.

Zinc and Vision

Zinc-deficient people may show signs of night blindness or other classic signs of vitamin A deficiency. Zinc is a key component of the enzyme that activates vitamin A in the retina. Thus, a lack of zinc interferes with vitamin A activity in the eye.

Zinc and Gene Regulation

Zinc enables certain small proteins to fold and form a stable "zinc-finger" structure. This structure interacts with a region of DNA. Without zinc, that area of a gene won't function.[28] This function of zinc may explain how it influences the immune system. Discovery and characterization of zinc-finger protein families is an active area of nutrition research.

Other Zinc Functions

Zinc is essential for a number of other diverse biological functions:

- *Hormonal.* Zinc interacts with a number of hormones, including insulin and its influence on carbohydrate metabolism.
- *Growth and reproduction.* Zinc plays an important role in pregnancy outcome, fetal development, and bone health.
- *Hemoglobin activity.* Zinc increases the affinity of hemoglobin for oxygen and indirectly influences hemoglobin synthesis.
- *Taste.* Some studies show that zinc participates in taste perception and appetite regulation.
- *Cell death.* Zinc can induce as well as inhibit the process of apoptosis, also known as programmed cell death.[29]
- *Wound healing.* Since ancient Egyptian times, zinc has been used to enhance wound healing.[30] Zinc participates in the maintenance of skin and mucosal membrane integrity.[31] Skin ulcers are frequently treated with zinc supplementation.

Quick Bite

Bizarre Behavior or Nutritional Deficiency?

In all cultures, races, and geographic regions, certain people have strange cravings for nonfood items. These cravings include ice (pagophagia), clay and dirt (geophagia), cornstarch (amylophagia), stone (lithophagia), paper, toilet tissue, soap, and foam. Pica, the compulsive consumption of nonfood items, often is associated with either iron or zinc deficiency, but it may also be the result of cultural beliefs or a response to family stresses. Whatever the cause, the behavior is not benign. It can injure teeth as well as cause constipation, intestinal obstruction or perforation, lead poisoning, pregnancy complications, poor growth in children, and mineral deficiencies.

Regulation of Zinc in the Body

Zinc Absorption

The body absorbs small amounts of zinc more effectively than large doses, and absorption ranges between 10 and 35 percent—a range similar to heme iron absorption. The degree of zinc absorption depends on the person's zinc status and zinc needs, the zinc content of the meal, and the presence of competing minerals. People with zinc deficiency absorb zinc more thoroughly than those with optimal zinc status. Absorption increases during times of increased need, such as growth spurts, pregnancy, and lactation. On the other hand, certain dietary factors, such as phytate and fiber, can impair absorption of zinc. **Figure 13.13** shows the zinc absorption process.

Dietary Factors That Inhibit Zinc Absorption

Phytate, which is present in plant products such as cereals and legumes, can bind zinc in insoluble complexes, thus inhibiting zinc's absorption. Although dietary fiber often is implicated in reduced zinc absorption, this effect more likely is due to the high phytate content of high-fiber foods.[32] Calcium in a meal does not appear to affect zinc absorption, but supplemental calcium taken with meals high in phytate may increase phytate's ability to bind zinc and may decrease zinc's bioavailability. Although some vegetarian diets

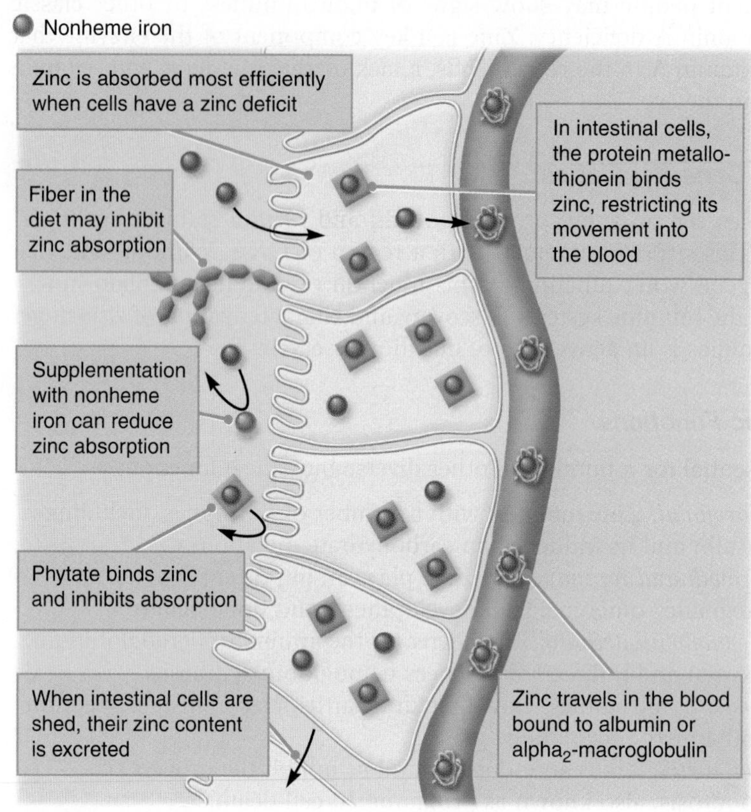
Key
Zinc
Nonheme iron
Zinc is absorbed most efficiently when cells have a zinc deficit
Fiber in the diet may inhibit zinc absorption
Supplementation with nonheme iron can reduce zinc absorption
Phytate binds zinc and inhibits absorption
When intestinal cells are shed, their zinc content is excreted
In intestinal cells, the protein metallothionein binds zinc, restricting its movement into the blood
Zinc travels in the blood bound to albumin or alpha$_2$-macroglobulin

Figure 13.13 **Zinc absorption.** Intestinal cells act as temporary buffers that help regulate zinc absorption.

contain enough phytate and fiber to depress zinc absorption significantly, most American diets do not.[33] For vegetarians whose diets consist mainly of phytate-rich unrefined grains and legumes, zinc requirements may exceed the RDAs.[34]

The negative effect of high-dose nonheme iron supplementation (such as during pregnancy) on zinc absorption is well documented.[35] On the other hand, your body absorbs heme iron (from meat) differently, so heme iron has no effect on zinc absorption. Eating iron-fortified foods is unlikely to inhibit zinc absorption.

Zinc Transport and Distribution

Zinc circulates in the bloodstream loosely bound to albumin and more tightly bound to another protein, alpha$_2$-macroglobulin. Zinc travels to the liver and to the tissues where it is most needed. Muscle and bone contain 90 percent of the body's zinc; the remainder is divided primarily among the liver, kidney, pancreas, brain, skin, and prostate. **Figure 13.14** shows zinc in the body.

Zinc Homeostasis and Excretion

The body has no long-term storehouse of zinc to draw upon when dietary zinc is low. Despite the lack of zinc storage, the body balances zinc absorption and excretion, thus maintaining zinc homeostasis even when confronted with varying needs and dietary conditions.

Intestinal cells act as temporary buffers that help regulate zinc absorption. The protein **metallothionein** binds zinc in the intestinal mucosal cells and

metallothionein An abundant, nonenzymatic, zinc-containing protein.

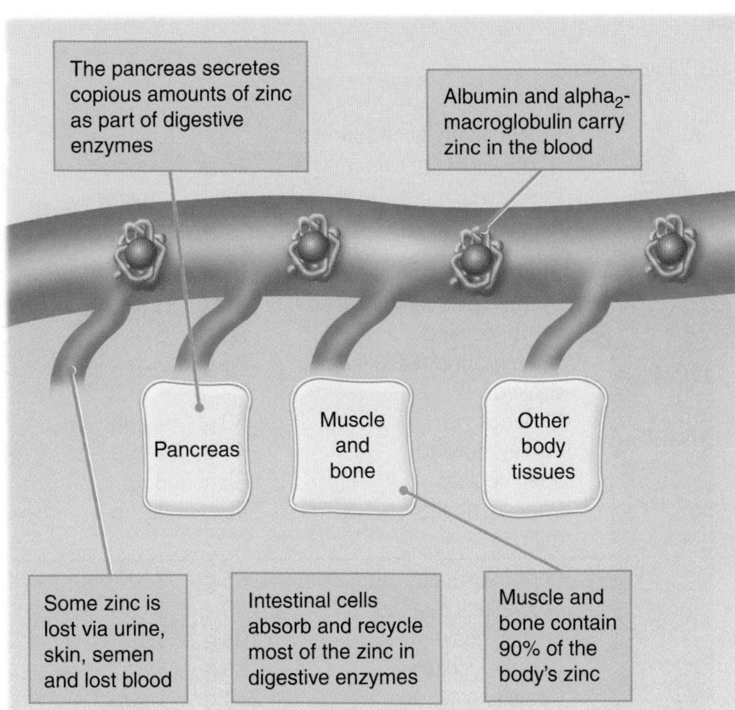
The pancreas secretes copious amounts of zinc as part of digestive enzymes
Albumin and alpha2-macroglobulin carry zinc in the blood
Pancreas
Muscle and bone
Other body tissues
Some zinc is lost via urine, skin, semen and lost blood
Intestinal cells absorb and recycle most of the zinc in digestive enzymes
Muscle and bone contain 90% of the body's zinc

Figure 13.14 **Zinc in the body.** Zinc is a component of every living cell and helps stabilize cell membranes. More than 80 enzymes contain zinc.

impedes its movement into the bloodstream. When zinc intake is high, the body makes more metallothionein to retain more zinc in the intestinal cells. Intestinal cells and other cells produce zinc transporter proteins, which help to maintain body homeostasis.[36]

During digestion, the pancreas secretes as much as 4.0 milligrams of zinc per day in the pancreatic juice. When the body needs zinc, intestinal cells reabsorb most of this secreted zinc. Otherwise, the body excretes it in the feces along with unabsorbed dietary zinc and sloughed, zinc-containing intestinal cells. The body also excretes zinc in minor amounts via urine, sweat, skin, hair, semen, and menstrual fluids.

Dietary Recommendations for Zinc

The RDA for adult males is 11 milligrams per day, and for females it is 8 milligrams per day. Experts recommend increasing zinc intake to 11 milligrams per day during pregnancy to provide for the growing fetus, and to 12 milligrams per day during lactation.

Although most children and adults in the United States and Canada consume more than the RDA, a significant number of older adults eat less than recommended levels. Estimates from the NHANES III data found that as many as 45 percent of adults ages 60 years and older do not meet the EAR for zinc.[37]

Sources of Zinc

Zinc usually is abundant in foods that are good sources of protein, especially red meat and seafood such as oysters and clams. For poultry, dark meat is a richer source than white meat. The zinc in animal foods is generally well absorbed. Conversely, whole grains have a relatively high amount of zinc, but it is poorly absorbed. Fruits and vegetables generally are poor zinc sources.

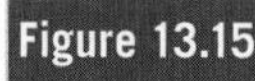

Figure 13.15 Food sources of zinc. Meats, organ meats, and seafoods are the best sources of zinc.

Source: US Department of Agriculture, Agricultural Research Service. USDA National Nutrient Database for Standard Reference, Release 22. 2009. Nutrient Data Laboratory Home Page, http://www.ars.usda.gov/ba/bhnrc/ndl.

Zinc

Daily Value = 15 mg

Category	Food	Weight	Serving	Zinc
Exceptionally good sources	Oyster, cooked	85 g	3 oz	74.06 mg
	All-Bran Complete Wheat Flakes cereal	29 g	¾ cup	15.08 mg
High: 20% DV or more	Beef, chuck, cooked	85 g	3 oz	7.00 mg
	Crab, Alaska king, cooked	85 g	3 oz	6.48 mg
	Lamb, cooked	85 g	3 oz	6.21 mg
	Beef, ground (85% lean), cooked	85 g	3 oz	5.36 mg
	Cheerios	30 g	1 cup	4.76 mg
	Turkey, cooked	140 g	1 cup	4.34 mg
	Veal, cooked	85 g	3 oz	3.48 mg
	Cheese, ricotta, part skim milk	246 g	1 cup	3.30 mg
Good: 10–19% DV	Pork (ham), cooked	85 g	3 oz	2.77 mg
	Chickpeas, canned	240 g	1 cup	2.54 mg
	Lentils, cooked	198 g	1 cup	2.51 mg
	Lobster, cooked	85 g	3 oz	2.48 mg
	Cereals, oats, regular, instant	234 g	1 cup	2.34 mg
	Clams, canned	85 g	3 oz	2.32 mg
	Wild rice, cooked	164 g	1 cup	2.20 mg
	Beans, black, cooked	172 g	1 cup	1.93 mg
	Pine nuts, dried	28 g	1 oz	1.83 mg
	Turkey, light meat, cooked	84 g	3 oz	1.71 mg
	Yogurt, fruit, low-fat	227 g	8-oz container	1.68 mg

Adequate zinc intake is of special concern for vegetarians because they do not eat many of the foods that are the best sources of this mineral. **Figure 13.15** shows the zinc content of some foods.

Zinc Deficiency

In the United States and Canada, zinc deficiency is uncommon and usually occurs in people with illnesses that impair absorption. In other parts of the world, zinc deficiency is most prevalent in populations that subsist on cereals and little else. Diarrhea and chronic infections such as pneumonia can cause excessive zinc excretion. These diseases are commonplace in developing countries, where zinc deficiency may be widespread. In some of these areas, zinc supplementation has decreased the incidence of acute lower respiratory infection, diarrhea, and attacks of malaria in children.

As Table 13.3 shows, the primary culprits in marginal zinc deficiency are increased needs, poor intake, poor absorption, and excessive losses. During pregnancy, zinc deficiency may contribute to complications and low birth weight.[38] Malabsorption syndromes such as cystic fibrosis and **Crohn's disease** impair zinc absorption. Symptoms of moderate to severe zinc deficiency include poor growth, delayed or abnormal sexual development, diarrhea, severe skin rash and hair loss, impaired immune response, and impaired taste acuity. (See Table 13.4.)

Crohn's disease A disease that causes inflammation and ulceration along sections of the intestinal tract.

Zinc Toxicity

Because the body efficiently rids itself of excess zinc, toxicity from high dietary zinc intake is rare. Yet there have been isolated accounts of acute zinc toxicity in people who consumed large amounts of acidic foods or beverages that had been stored in galvanized containers. High doses of zinc may cause acute gastrointestinal distress, nausea, vomiting, and cramping.

Zinc and the Common Cold

The common cold, one of our most common illnesses, affects American adults two to four times per year and children six to ten times per year.[1] Colds are even more frequent in young children in day care settings and preschools. Because of missed work and decreased productivity, colds can be an economic stressor as well as a physical nuisance. A cure for the common cold would be of great benefit, and scientists have long pursued this goal.

Because of zinc's role in immune function, 11 placebo-controlled studies between 1984 and 1998 investigated the effect of zinc lozenges on the common cold. Roughly half of the studies produced positive results and the other half had negative findings.

One study with positive results gained considerable attention from the press. As a result, zinc lozenges are on nearly every pharmacy shelf in the United States. This study recruited 100 people during the winter of 1994. Researchers enrolled subjects within 24 hours of the onset of their common cold symptoms. Every 2 hours while awake, half the subjects took placebo lozenges and half took lozenges containing 13 milligrams of zinc, an average of six lozenges per day. They could take acetaminophen, but they were asked to refrain from taking other cold medicines or antibiotics during the trial. In the zinc group, colds resolved in an average of 4 days. In comparison, cold symptoms in the placebo group persisted for 7 days.[2]

Although scientists have suggested several hypotheses, the mechanism for the effect is unclear. Zinc deficiency is known to impair immune function, but could all these people have been zinc deficient? This is doubtful. Some speculate that zinc may inhibit viral replication.

During the trial, many of the experimental subjects experienced side effects, including nausea, bad taste, and sore mouths. In addition to the mild side effects and the cost of the lozenges, such high doses of zinc could have harmful effects. Long-term use of high doses of zinc induces copper deficiency. On average, those in the experimental group took close to 480 milligrams of zinc during the week of their cold. If children have eight colds per year and take nearly 500 milligrams of zinc per cold, could that be enough to induce widespread copper deficiency?

The same research group studied 249 randomly selected children in a double-blind, placebo-controlled trial. The experimental group took zinc gluconate lozenges at the first sign of cold symptoms. Depending on age, each child received 50 to 60 milligrams of zinc per day. There was no difference between groups in the time for all cold symptoms to resolve—a median of 9 days. Although the researchers noted several limitations of their study, they concluded that we still need additional studies to determine what role, if any, zinc has in treatment of the common cold.[3]

Research continues to provide conflicting results, with some studies finding a benefit of lozenges[4] and others finding no effect of zinc supplementation.[5] Review studies have also reported inconclusive findings.[6]

Research to determine the effects of zinc for the treatment of the common cold and which formulation is most effective is ongoing. Because of current inconclusive findings and the potential side effects of excess zinc intake, we should think twice before routinely giving children (and ourselves) zinc lozenges every time a cold strikes.

1 National Institute of Allergy and Infectious Diseases. Common cold. http://www3.niaid.nih.gov/healthscience/healthtopics/colds. Accessed 8/6/09.

2 Mossad SB, Macknin ML, Medendorp SV, Mason P. Zinc gluconate lozenges for treating the common cold: a randomized, double-blind placebo-controlled study. *Ann Intern Med.* 1996;125:81–88.

3 Macknin ML, Piedmonte M, Calendine C, et al. Zinc gluconate lozenges for treating the common cold in children: a randomized controlled trial. *JAMA.* 1998;279:1962–1967.

4 Prasad AS, Beck FW, Bao B, et al. Duration and severity of symptoms and levels of plasma interleukin-1 receptor antagonist, soluble tumor necrosis factor receptor, and adhesion molecules in patients with common cold treated with zinc acetate. *J Infect Dis.* 2008;197:795–802.

5 Turner RB, Cetnarowski WE. Effect of treatment with zinc gluconate or zinc acetate on experimental and natural colds. *Clin Infect Dis.* 2000;31:1202–1208.

6 Caruso TJ, Prober CG, Gwaltney JM Jr. Treatment of naturally acquired common colds with zinc: a structured review. *Clin Infect Dis.* 2007;45:569–574; and Marshall I. Zinc for the common cold. *Cochrane Database Syst Rev.* 2000;(2):CD001364.

Table 13.3 Risk Factors for Zinc Deficiency

Dietary Deficiency	Protein-energy malnutrition	Vegan diets
	Poor food choices	IV feeding without zinc
Increased Requirements	Burn patients	Pregnancy and lactation
	Growth spurts	Chronic infection
Malabsorption	Acrodermatitis enteropathica	Geophagia or pica
	Celiac disease, Crohn's disease	High-phytate diets
	Cystic fibrosis	Chronic iron supplementation
Increased Losses	Sickle cell disease	Burns and surgery
	Diabetes	Chronic diarrhea
	Renal disease	

Chronic intake of moderately elevated amounts of zinc is a more common cause of zinc toxicity. Usually, excessive zinc supplementation is at fault. Doses as low as 50 milligrams per day can cause vomiting.[39] Prolonged zinc supplementation interferes with copper metabolism and can cause low blood copper levels.[40] Excess zinc intake also adversely affects blood lipids by elevating LDL and depressing HDL levels.[41] Doses of 80 milligrams per day of zinc for an average of six years have been associated with an increase in hospitalizations for urinary tract infections and kidney stones.[42] The UL for zinc is set at 40 milligrams per day.

Table 13.4 Effects of Zinc Deficiency

Severe Deficiency	Moderate Deficiency
Hypogonadism	Delayed sexual maturation
Cessation of growth	Growth retardation
Patchy loss of hair	Pregnancy complications
Skin lesions and rashes	Acne
Impaired taste (hypogeusia)	Increased infections
Loss of appetite/anorexia	
Diarrhea	
Decreased thyroid hormone synthesis	
Night blindness	
Recurrent infections	

Chronic high intakes of zinc relative to copper can inhibit copper absorption and with time may induce a copper deficiency. Doctors use the interaction of zinc and copper to treat patients with **Wilson's disease**, a genetic disorder of hyperabsorption and accumulation of copper. Zinc works by blocking copper absorption and increasing its excretion, thus preventing its accumulation in the body.

Key Concepts *Zinc is important for normal growth and development, immune function, and the function of many enzymes. Zinc homeostasis is maintained by regulating intestinal absorption. Iron, zinc, and copper all compete for absorption, but problems don't usually occur if these minerals are coming from balanced dietary rather than supplemental sources. The best food sources for zinc are beef, oysters, crab, legumes, and unrefined whole grains. Zinc deficiency is most prevalent in populations that subsist on cereal protein.*

Quick Bite

On Your Next Moonlit Stroll, Think Selenium!

Selenium takes its name from the Greek word *Selênê*, "moon," because it has a pasty white color. In mythology, Selene is the Greek goddess of the moon. Ancient Greeks often blamed Selene and her brother Helios (god of the sun) for pestilent diseases and death.

Selenium

The story of selenium (Se) is a recent one and becomes more complex as scientists explore its role at the molecular level. Historically, because animals grazing on selenium-rich soils suffered selenium poisoning, scientists focused on its toxicity. This changed in 1957, when researchers first demonstrated selenium's nutritional benefits in vitamin E–deficient animals. But not until 1979 did evidence emerge that selenium is essential for humans. Chinese scientists reported an association between low selenium status and **Keshan disease**, a heart disorder that strikes children in the Keshan province of China. The Chinese scientists demonstrated that selenium supplements could prevent the disease. Although selenium deficiency does not cause the disease, it predisposes a child to heart damage after a particular type of viral infection. When selenium intake is adequate, the virus apparently does not cause Keshan disease.

Functions of Selenium

Although scientists have identified nearly 50 selenium-containing proteins, two amino acid derivatives—**selenomethionine**, a methionine derivative, and **selenocysteine**, a cysteine derivative—contain most of the body's selenium. Selenomethionine is a selenium "storage compartment," and selenocysteine is selenium's biologically active form. As selenocysteine, selenium is a component of enzymes involved in antioxidant protection and thyroid hormone metabolism.

Selenium is best known as a component of glutathione peroxidases, a family of antioxidant enzymes. The discovery of these enzymes resolved a puzzling overlap in the functions of selenium and vitamin E. Both nutrients play a role in preventing lipid peroxidation and membrane damage. Glutathione peroxidases promote the breakdown of fatty acids that have undergone peroxidation, thus eliminating highly reactive free radicals. (See **Figure 13.16a**.) This reduction in free radicals spares vitamin E, making it available to stop other chain reactions of free radicals. (See **Figure 13.16b**.) Since glutathione peroxidases require selenium, dietary selenium indirectly spares vitamin E.

In recent years, scientists have identified selenium as a component of enzymes involved in the metabolism of iodine and thyroid hormone. Iodine deficiency alone causes **hypothyroidism**, and a combined deficiency of selenium and iodine increases the severity of the disease. There also is some

Wilson's disease Genetic disorder of increased copper absorption, which leads to toxic levels in the liver and heart.

Keshan disease Selenium-deficiency disease that impairs the structure and function of the heart.

selenomethionine A selenium-containing amino acid derived from methionine that is the storage form of selenium.

selenocysteine A selenium-containing amino acid that is the biologically active form of selenium.

hypothyroidism The result of a lowered level of circulating thyroid hormone, with slowing of mental and physical functions.

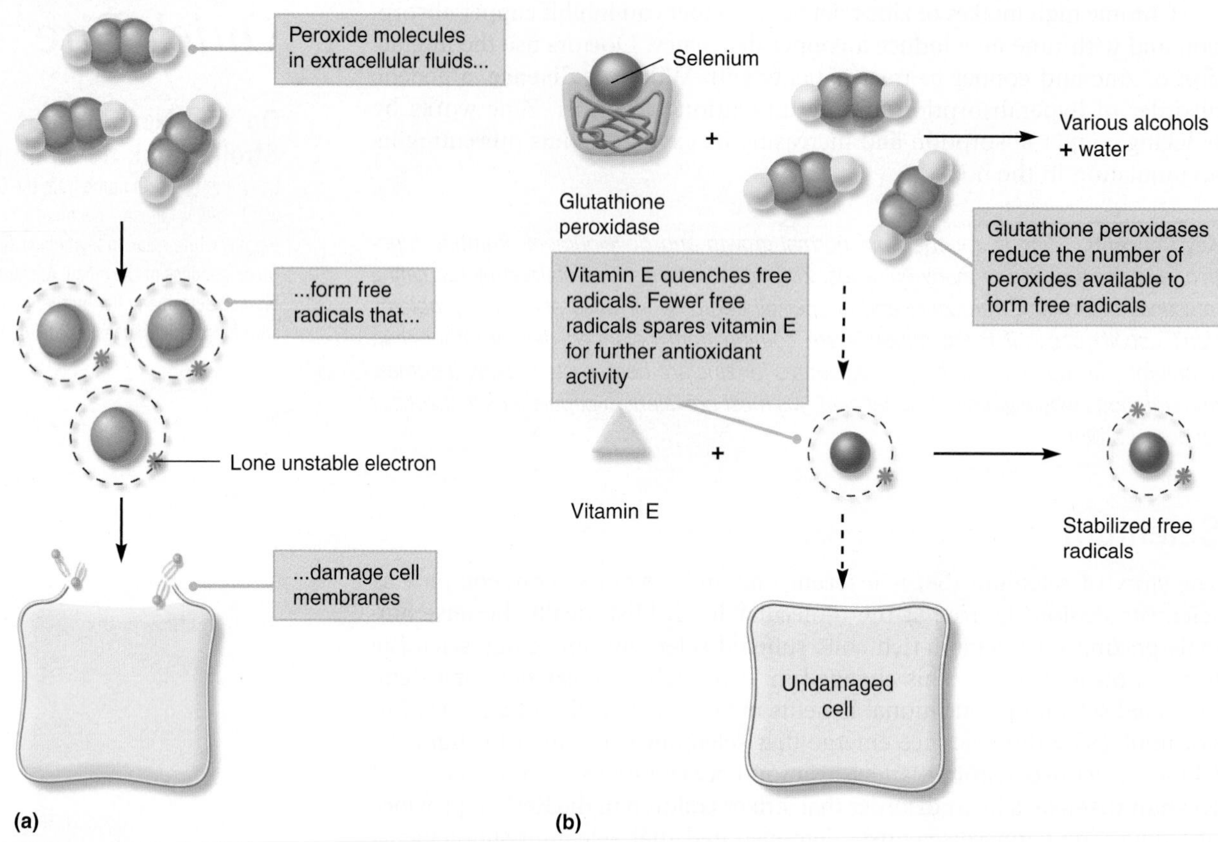
Peroxide molecules
in extracellular fluids...
...form free
radicals that...
Lone unstable electron
...damage cell
membranes
(a)
Selenium
Glutathione
peroxidase
+
Various alcohols
+ water
Glutathione peroxidases
reduce the number of
peroxides available to
form free radicals
Vitamin E quenches free
radicals. Fewer free
radicals spares vitamin E
for further antioxidant
activity
+
Vitamin E
Stabilized free
radicals
Undamaged
cell
(b)

Figure 13.16 **Free radicals.** (a) Peroxides form free radicals that damage cell membranes and have been implicated in heart disease. (b) Selenium and vitamin E help combat free radicals. Since glutathione peroxidases require selenium, dietary selenium indirectly spares vitamin E.

evidence that a combined deficiency of both minerals during pregnancy is involved in some forms of **cretinism** in newborns.

Selenium is important in the immune system and its response to infections. Research suggests that selenium may have some anticancer benefits, but more investigation is needed.[43] Ongoing population research and large-scale trials are working to determine selenium's relationship to cancer. Small increases in selenium intake can be toxic, and selenium supplements for cancer prevention are not recommended.

Regulation of Selenium in the Body

Selenomethionine and selenocysteine are the principal dietary forms of selenium. The body efficiently absorbs these selenoamino acids, with estimates ranging from 50 to 90 percent.[44] The presence of vitamins A, C, and E and reduced glutathione enhance selenium absorption, but phytates and heavy metals such as mercury interfere with its bioavailability.

The selenium regulatory process maintains a low concentration of highly reactive free selenocysteine, and achieves homeostasis through excretion of excess mineral. The major routes of selenium excretion are the urine and the feces. When intake is excessive, the skin and lungs serve as additional excretory routes.

cretinism A congenital condition often caused by severe iodine deficiency during gestation, which is characterized by arrested physical and mental development.

Selenium

Daily Value = 70 µg

	Food	Weight	Serving	Selenium
	Exceptionally good source			
	Brazil nuts	28.35 g	1 oz (6–8 nuts)	543.5 µg
High: 20% DV or more	Tuna, canned in water	85 g	3 oz	68.3 µg
	Oysters, cooked	85 g	3 oz	56.5 µg
	Swordfish, cooked	85 g	3 oz	52.4 µg
	Turkey, cooked	140 g	1 cup	51.5 µg
	Couscous, cooked	157 g	1 cup	43.2 µg
	Cheese, ricotta, part skim milk	246 g	1 cup	41.1 µg
	Spaghetti, cooked, enriched	140 g	1 cup	37.0 µg
	Pork, loin, cooked	85 g	3 oz	36.7 µg
	Lobster, cooked	85 g	3 oz	36.3 µg
	Crab, Alaska king, cooked	85 g	3 oz	34.0 µg
	Cream of Wheat cereal, cooked	239 g	1 cup	30.6 µg
	Sunflower seed kernels, dry roasted	32 g	1/4 cup	25.4 µg
	Cottage cheese, low-fat (2% milkfat)	226 g	1 cup	22.4 µg
	Bagels, plain, enriched	89 g	4″ bagel	20.3 µg
	Brown rice, cooked	195 g	1 cup	19.1 µg
	Beef, ground (85% lean), cooked	85 g	3 oz	18.4 µg
	Ham, sliced, extra lean	57 g	2 slices	17.9 µg
	Salami	57 g	2 slices	17.7 µg
	Pita, white, enriched	60 g	6 1/2″ pita	16.3 µg
Good: 10–19% DV	Trout, rainbow, cooked	85 g	3 oz	12.8 µg
	Baked beans, canned	254 g	1 cup	12.7 µg
	Oatmeal, cooked, unenriched	234 g	1 cup	12.6 µg
	Soybeans, cooked, boiled	172 g	1 cup	12.6 µg
	Tofu	120 g	1 piece	10.7 µg
	Spinach, frozen, cooked	190 g	1 cup	10.5 µg
	Bread, rye	32 g	1 slice	9.9 µg
	Milk, whole	244 g	1 cup	9.0 µg
	Bread, pumpernickel	32 g	1 slice	7.8 µg

Figure 13.17 **Food sources of selenium.** Selenium is found mainly in meats, organ meats, seafood, and grains. Brazil nuts are exceptionally high in selenium.

Source: US Department of Agriculture, Agricultural Research Service. USDA National Nutrient Database for Standard Reference, Release 22. 2009. Nutrient Data Laboratory Home Page, http://www.ars.usda.gov/ba/bhnrc/ndl.

Selenium status, like the status of many trace minerals, is difficult to evaluate. There are no sensitive tests that can readily distinguish between adequate and suboptimal levels of selenium.

Dietary Recommendations for Selenium

Selenium is one of the "youngest" nutrients for which an RDA exists. The first RDA for selenium was established in 1989. The RDA was based on data from Chinese scientists who conducted repletion experiments in selenium-depleted subjects living in areas where Keshan disease was endemic. The RDA for selenium was revised in 2000. For both men and women, the selenium RDA is 55 micrograms per day.[45]

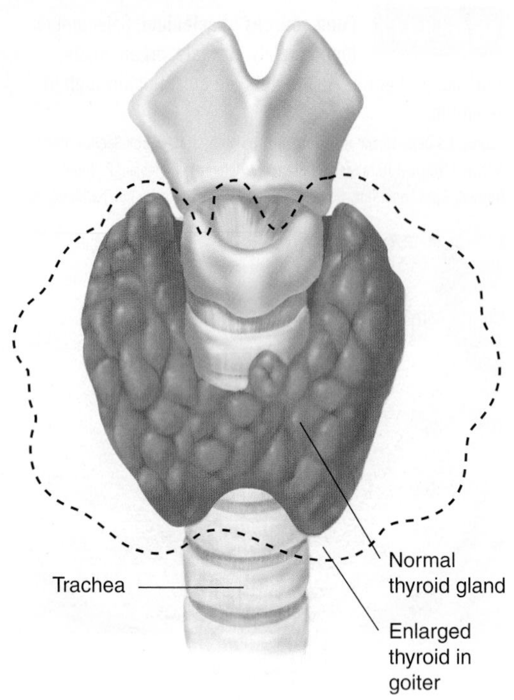

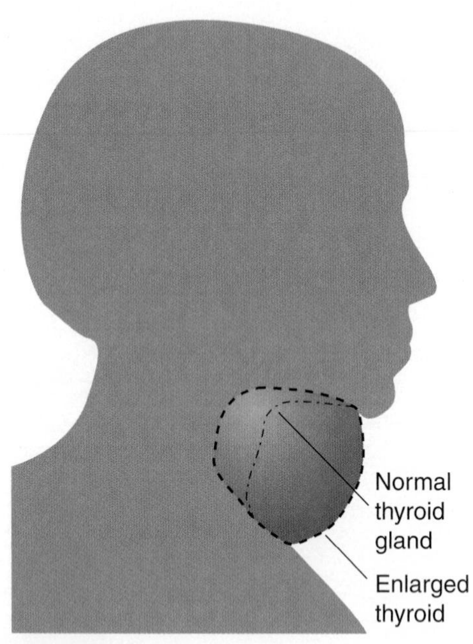

Figure 13.18 **Enlargement of the thyroid gland in goiter.** Iodine deficiency results in goiter. Use of iodized salt dramatically reduces goiter rates. This finding led to the widespread fortification of table salt with iodine.

Sources of Selenium

Selenium levels are quite variable in plant foods and generally reflect the selenium content of the soil in which the plant was grown. Because animals accumulate selenium in their tissues, the selenium content of food from animal sources generally is more consistent than the selenium content of plants. Organ meats and seafood are consistently good selenium sources. Other meats contain somewhat lower amounts of the mineral. The typical American diet provides adequate selenium. **Figure 13.17** shows some food sources of selenium.

Selenium Deficiency

Chronic selenium deficiency predisposes a person to Keshan disease. Until recently, this disease was a major public health problem in China's Keshan province. Borderline deficiency appears to limit the ability to fight viral infections and may predispose a person to some kinds of cancer.[46] Doctors have found selenium deficiency in people who receive long-term **total parenteral nutrition (TPN)**. Although after several years of TPN these patients may suffer heart problems and muscle weakness, no specific visible symptoms have been defined for selenium deficiency.

Selenium Toxicity

Chronic consumption of excess selenium can cause brittle hair and nails, and their eventual loss. Although typical dietary intakes are unlikely to exceed safe amounts, selenium supplements can cause problems. Overenthusiastic media reports of research on selenium and cancer, coupled with easy access to selenium supplements, may cause some people to consume unhealthful quantities. The UL is set at 400 micrograms per day for adults.[47]

Key Concepts *Selenium is best known for its role as an essential component of the antioxidant enzymes glutathione peroxidases. Selenium interacts with vitamin E in antioxidant systems and with iodine in thyroid hormone metabolism. It also is important for good immune function. Good dietary sources for selenium are organ meats and seafood. A deficiency of selenium may predispose a child to Keshan disease, a rare heart disease caused by a virus. New research also links marginal selenium status to cancer risk.*

Iodine

Ancient Chinese writings first recorded descriptions of what we now know to be the iodine-deficiency diseases cretinism and **goiter** (see **Figure 13.18**). Cretins were described as feeble-minded dwarfs with puffy facial features and a stumbling gait. In the Middle Ages, European paintings commonly depicted cretins as angels or demons. As late as the early 1900s, goiter was common in certain parts of the United States, particularly the upper Midwest. In 1922, scientists demonstrated that the use of iodized salt by 50,000 school children dramatically reduced goiter rates. In the United States, these findings led to the widespread fortification of table salt with iodine (I). Since the 1980s, the World Health Organization has been at the forefront of a worldwide public health drive to eliminate iodine deficiency by encouraging universal salt iodization. This strategy has been implemented in most countries where iodine deficiency is a public health problem, and UNICEF estimates that 66 percent of households worldwide now have access to iodized salt.[48]

Functions of Iodine

Iodine is an essential component of the two thyroid hormones: **triiodothyronine (T3)** and **thyroxine (T4)**. Thyroid hormones control the regulation of body temperature, basal metabolic rate, reproduction, and growth. Although the thyroid hormones released by the thyroid gland are about 93 percent thyroxine and only 7 percent triiodothyronine, triiodothyronine is about four times more potent than thyroxine.[49] Within a few days of secretion, the body converts most of the thyroxine to the more active triiodothyronine.

total parenteral nutrition (TPN) Feeding a person by giving all essential nutrients intravenously.

goiter A chronic enlargement of the thyroid gland, visible as a swelling at the front of the neck; usually associated with iodine deficiency.

triiodothyronine (T3) An iodine-containing thyroid hormone with several times the biologic activity of thyroxine (T4).

thyroxine (T4) An iodine-containing hormone secreted by the thyroid gland to regulate the rate of cell metabolism; known chemically as tetraiodothyronine.

thyroglobulin The storage form of thyroid hormone in the thyroid gland.

thyroid-stimulating hormone (TSH) Secreted from the pituitary gland at the base of the brain, a hormone that regulates synthesis of thyroid hormones.

Iodine Absorption and Metabolism

Much of the iodine in foods is in the form of iodide (the reduced form) and iodates. The intestine absorbs nearly all of it, from 95 to 100 percent. The entire body contains between 15 and 20 milligrams, 70 to 80 percent of which resides in the thyroid gland. Each day the thyroid gland "traps" between 60 and 120 micrograms of iodide for eventual incorporation into the thyroid hormones. Enzymes oxidize the iodide, and then other enzymes bind it to **thyroglobulin**, the storage form of thyroid hormones.

Thyroid stimulating hormone (TSH) signals the thyroid gland to cleave T3 and T4 from thyroglobulin and release them into the bloodstream. In various body organs, three different enzymes convert most of the T4 to T3. Research reveals that all three of these converting enzymes are selenium dependent. Therefore, a deficiency in selenium may lead to inefficient use of iodine in thyroid hormones.

The kidneys excrete most excess iodine in urine, but some is lost in sweat, especially in hot, humid climates.

Dietary Recommendations for Iodine

To replace losses and prevent deficiency of iodine, the thyroid gland needs at least 60 micrograms daily. Because iodine absorption is very efficient, intakes of 75 micrograms per day should be sufficient for adults. To provide a margin of safety, however, the RDA is set at 150 micrograms per day for both men and women.

Sources of Iodine

Because the ocean is the best source of iodine, the best food sources are seafoods. Saltwater fish have higher concentrations of iodine than fresh water fish. The dairy industry adds iodide to cattle feed and uses sanitizing solutions that contain iodine. These measures add substantial amounts of iodine to milk and dairy products. Natural iodine levels in plants reflect soil levels. For many people, iodized salt used in cooking and at the table is their primary source of iodine. In the United States, iodized salt contains an average of 76 micrograms of iodine per gram of salt.

Excluding iodized salt, the average U.S. diet contains between 230 and 400 micrograms of iodine per day. After salt, dairy products supply most of our dietary iodine, followed by 10 to 15 percent from meat, fish, and poultry and 5 to 15 percent from grains and cereals. Salt added during cooking and at the table contributes 35 to 70 micrograms of iodide to the average adult's daily diet. **Figure 13.19** shows the iodine content of some foods.

Figure 13.19 **Food sources of iodine.** Few foods are rich in iodine; it is found mainly in milk, seafood, and some grain products.

Source: Data from Pennington, JAT. *Bowes and Church's Food Values of Portions Commonly Used.* 17th ed. Philadelphia, PA: Lippincott-Raven Publishers, 1998.

Iodine

Daily Value = 150 μg

	Food	Amount	Portion	Iodine
Exceptionally good source	Salt (iodized)	1 g		77 μg
High: 20% DV or more	Cod, cooked	85 g	(3 oz)	99 μg
	Corn grits, enriched, cooked		1 cup	68 μg
	Milk, 2% milkfat	240 mL	(1 cup)	56 μg
	Milk, nonfat	240 mL	(1 cup)	51 μg
	White bread	50 g	(2 slices)	46 μg
	Tortilla, flour	55 g		41 μg
	Beef liver, cooked	85 g	(3 oz)	36 μg
	Navy beans, cooked	90 g	(½ cup)	35 μg
	Shrimp, cooked	85 g	(3 oz)	35 μg
	Potato, baked	110 g	(1 small)	34 μg
	Turkey breast, cooked	85 g	(3 oz)	34 μg
	Whole-wheat bread	50 g	(2 slices)	32 μg
Good: 10–19% DV	Egg, cooked	50 g	(1 large)	24 μg
	Oatmeal, cooked		1 cup	16 μg

Iodine Deficiency

As early as 1830, iodine deficiency was linked to the presence of goiter. We now understand that a deficiency of iodine inhibits the synthesis of thyroid hormones. As the body senses the lack of thyroid hormones, it produces more and more TSH. TSH causes the thyroid gland to grow, eventually resulting in a goiter. Goiter causes the usual symptoms of hypothyroidism—cold intolerance, weight gain, sluggishness, and a decreased body temperature. Mild or moderate iodine deficiency also has been shown to decrease IQ scores by about 10 to 15 points.[50]

Severe iodine deficiency during early pregnancy causes cretinism. Most cretins have stunted growth and are deaf, mute, and mentally retarded. A selenium deficiency may be partly responsible for a form of cretinism commonly seen in Africa.

Raw cabbage, turnips, rutabagas, and cassava contain compounds known as **goitrogens**, which are compounds that block the body's absorption and use of iodine. Consuming large amounts of these foods in their raw form can cause problems; cooking inactivates the goitrogens. Iodine-deficiency disorders are common in developing countries where iodine consumption is low and raw cassava and similar vegetables are a major part of the diet.

Quick Bite

Iodine or Iodide: What's in a Name?

Iodine (I_2) is a bluish-black solid that gives off a purple vapor, which gives the element its name. The word *iodine* stems from the Greek word *iôdêdes*, meaning "violet-colored."

Iodide (I^-) is the colorless negative ion of iodine. Iodine circulates in the body bound either to protein or as free iodide ions. Sodium iodide and potassium iodide are iodide salts commonly used in medicines.

goitrogens Compounds that can induce goiter.

Iodine Toxicity

Because high amounts of iodine inhibit synthesis of thyroid hormones and stimulate growth of the thyroid gland, iodine toxicity also can cause goiter. Overzealous supplementation is the most common cause of iodine toxicity. A successful program of iodine fortification must be balanced against the risk of iodine-induced hyperthyroidism, especially in areas of severe iodine deficiency. The UL for iodine is 1,100 micrograms per day.

Key Concepts *Iodine is an essential component of thyroid hormones. Iodine deficiency causes overstimulation of the thyroid gland and eventual goiter. The best food source of* *iodine is seafood. Many people around the world are still at risk for iodine deficiency, but iodization of salt is a powerful preventive measure.*

Copper

Researchers first recognized the essential nature of copper (Cu) for experimental animals in 1928, but not until the 1960s did evidence emerge that copper deficiency occurs in humans. Cloning of the genes for two genetic disorders of copper metabolism—Wilson's disease (copper toxicity) and **Menkes' syndrome** (copper deficiency)—has fueled interest in copper and led to exciting new discoveries about its metabolism and physiological role. Although simple dietary copper deficiency is not a significant public health concern, excessive supplementation with other trace minerals can cause a secondary copper deficiency.

Functions of Copper

Copper-containing enzymes have many functions, including acting as an antioxidant, participating in the electron transport chain, and aiding the biosynthesis of the pigment melanin and the connective tissue proteins collagen and elastin. Perhaps the most important function of copper is as a component of **ceruloplasmin**, the enzyme that catalyzes the oxidation of ferrous (Fe^{2+}) to ferric (Fe^{3+}) iron for incorporation into transferrin. The absence of ceruloplasmin leads to accumulation of iron in the liver, similar to what is seen in iron overload or hemochromatosis. Copper is an important component of the superoxide dismutases, enzymes involved in antioxidant reactions. Copper also plays a role in various other activities, including myelinization of nervous tissue, immune function, and cardiovascular function.

Copper Absorption, Use, and Metabolism

Depending on the amount of copper in the meal and other dietary factors, the intestine absorbs approximately 50 percent of dietary copper. Amino acids, particularly histidine, enhance copper absorption. On the other hand, a number of minerals, most notably iron and zinc, may interfere with copper absorption. Because high-dose iron supplementation is more common than zinc supplementation, the iron–copper interaction is of greater concern. Dietary phytates do not appear to inhibit copper absorption. Because copper is best absorbed in an acidic environment, antacids can reduce copper absorption.

Albumin transports copper from the intestinal cells to the liver, where about two-thirds is incorporated into ceruloplasmin. The average healthy adult body contains approximately 100 milligrams of copper at any time, mainly distributed among the liver, brain, blood, and bone marrow. The body stores relatively little copper, and excretes nearly all excess copper in feces and a minor amount in the urine. Copper excreted in the feces includes unabsorbed dietary copper, copper released in bile, and copper in cells sloughed from the intestinal wall.

Dietary Recommendations and Food Sources for Copper

There is no single reliable index of copper status. Balance studies have been previously used to estimate copper needs. However, balance studies in humans are problematic, so a combination of plasma, serum, and blood cell measures were used to develop the copper RDA.[51] The RDA for both men and women is 900 micrograms per day.

Quick Bite

A Penny for Your . . .

How do the amounts of zinc and copper in a U.S. penny compare to the amounts in your body? Today's penny is mostly zinc (2.4 grams), covered with some copper plating (62.5 mg). A penny's zinc is in the upper range of the body's zinc content, but the amount of copper falls short. It takes the copper in about 1½ pennies to equal the amount of copper in your body.

Menkes' syndrome A genetic disorder that results in copper deficiency.

ceruloplasmin A copper-dependent enzyme responsible for the oxidation of ferrous ion (Fe^{2+}) to ferric ion (Fe^{3+}), enabling iron to bind to transferrin. Also known as ferroxidase I.

Figure 13.20 **Food sources of copper.** Copper is found in a limited variety of foods. The best sources are beef, seafood, legumes, and nuts.

Source: US Department of Agriculture, Agricultural Research Service. USDA National Nutrient Database for Standard Reference, Release 22. 2009. Nutrient Data Laboratory Home Page, http://www.ars.usda.gov/ba/bhnrc/ndl.

Copper

Daily Value = 2 mg

	Food	Weight	Serving	Copper
	Exceptionally good sources			
	Beef liver, cooked	85 g	3 oz	12.40 mg
	Oyster, cooked	85 g	3 oz	3.65 mg
High: 20% DV or more	Lobster, cooked	85 g	3 oz	1.649 mg
	Shiitake mushrooms, cooked	145 g	1 cup	1.299 mg
	Chocolate, semisweet	168 g	1 cup	1.176 mg
	Crab, Alaska king, cooked	85 g	3 oz	1.005 mg
	Cashew nuts, dry roasted	28 g	1 oz	0.629 mg
	Sunflower seed kernels, dry roasted	32 g	¼ cup	0.586 mg
	Lentils, cooked	198 g	1 cup	0.497 mg
	Walnuts	28 g	1 oz (14 halves)	0.450 mg
Good: 10–19% DV	Pistachio nuts, dry roasted	28 g	1 oz (47 nuts)	0.376 mg
	Black beans, cooked	172 g	1 cup	0.359 mg
	Pecans	28 g	1 oz (20 halves)	0.340 mg
	Soymilk, original and vanilla, unfortified	245 g	1 cup	0.314 mg
	Spinach, cooked	180 g	1 cup	0.313 mg
	Almonds	28 g	1 oz (24 nuts)	0.282 mg
	Ham, sliced, extra lean	57 g	2 slices	0.276 mg
	Potato, baked, with skin	202 g	1 potato	0.238 mg
	Blackberries, raw	144 g	1 cup	0.238 mg

Copper is widely distributed in foods. The richest food sources include organ meats (e.g., liver), shellfish, nuts and seeds, legumes, peanut butter, and chocolate. (See **Figure 13.20**.) Although information about the copper content of foods is incomplete, dietary surveys in the United States suggest that adults consume an average of about 1.2 milligrams of copper per day.[52]

Quick Bite

Egg Whites? Please Stand Up!

Although cooking food in a copper pot is inadvisable, copper mixing bowls can be a plus. Meringues made in ceramic or steel bowls tend to be snowy white and drier than those made in copper bowls. Making meringue in a copper bowl leads to a creamier, yellowish foam that is harder to overbeat into a lumpy liquid. The copper bowl contributes copper ions to conalbumin, a metal-binding egg protein, thus stabilizing the whipped egg whites.

Copper Deficiency

Overt copper deficiency is relatively rare in humans. Copper deficiency occurs most commonly in preterm infants. These babies have low copper stores at birth and a rapid growth rate, which elevates needs. Because cow's milk has little copper and it is poorly bioavailable, infants who are inappropriately fed unmodified cow's milk are more likely to develop a deficiency than breastfed infants.

Copper deficiency most commonly causes anemia, hypercholesterolemia, and bone abnormalities.[53] In copper-deficiency anemia, low ceruloplasmin activity causes defective iron mobilization. Copper-deficient young children often suffer bone abnormalities. Probably caused by poor synthesis of connective tissue, these abnormalities mimic the changes observed in scurvy. In experimental settings, copper deficiency causes elevated blood cholesterol, impaired glucose tolerance, and heart-related abnormalities. Copper deficiency during pregnancy may have adverse consequences for fetal growth and development.[54]

Menkes' syndrome is an extremely rare (approximately 1 in 100,000 live births) genetic copper disorder in which there is a failure to absorb copper into the bloodstream and therefore a lack of functional copper-containing proteins such as ceruloplasmin. Serum copper and ceruloplasmin levels are low, but copper accumulates in the intestinal mucosal cells and in the muscle, spleen, and kidney.[55] Menkes' syndrome causes neurological degeneration, peculiar kinky hair, abnormal connective tissue development, osteoporosis, and poor growth. Although this syndrome is usually fatal in infancy or early childhood, copper-histidine treatment within the first few days of life may prevent irreversible damage.

Quick Bite

Cooking in Copper
Because the copper imparted a bright green color to cooked green vegetables, cooking vegetables in uncoated copper pans was once encouraged. This practice often led to decreased liver and brain function. The Swedish military recognized copper toxicity and banned copper cooking utensils in 1753.

Copper Toxicity

Compared with other trace elements, copper is relatively nontoxic. The UL for copper is 10,000 micrograms per day. Wilson's disease is a rare (1 in 200,000) genetic copper toxicity disorder that impairs copper excretion in bile, causing toxic accumulation in the liver, brain, kidney, and eye. As copper accumulates in red blood cells, it causes anemia. People with Wilson's disease frequently appear healthy until adolescence or early adulthood. Without treatment, they develop serious liver and neurological problems. Copper toxicity may be treated either by **chelation therapy** to bind and remove copper or with zinc supplementation to decrease copper absorption. Lifelong treatment can prevent many complications of Wilson's disease.

chelation therapy Use of a chelator (e.g., EDTA) to bind metal ions to remove them from the body.

Key Concepts *The most important function of copper is as a component of ceruloplasmin, the enzyme that catalyzes the oxidation of iron for transport in transferrin. Food sources for copper include organ meats, shellfish, nuts and seeds, legumes, peanut butter, chocolate, and dried fruits. Copper deficiency is relatively rare in humans. Usual copper intakes fall below the current safe and adequate level.*

Manganese

Recognized for centuries, manganese (Mn) derives its name from a Greek term for magic. Although its many functions are not magical, they are unique. Manganese is essential not only in biological systems but also in iron and steel production. It has many industrial uses in such diverse products as dry-cell batteries, glass, ceramics, paints, varnishes, inks, dyes, and fertilizers. Industrial exposure, rather than excessive intake, is the more frequent cause of manganese toxicity.

Functions of Manganese

The body contains between 10 and 20 milligrams of manganese, which is concentrated primarily in the bone, liver, pancreas, and brain. Despite this limited quantity, manganese is a key component of several enzymes:

- *Mn-superoxide dismutase*, located in the mitochondria of cells, is an antioxidant that prevents tissue damage due to lipid oxidation.
- *Arginase* helps form urea in the urea cycle.
- *Pyruvate carboxylase* helps convert pyruvate to oxaloacetate.

Manganese also activates numerous enzymes involved in the formation of cartilage in bone and skin.

Quick Bite

Highway Harvest
Oil companies often add a type of manganese to modern gasoline as an antiknock compound to increase the octane rating for high-compression engines. It is now evident that plants along highways accumulate manganese from passing cars.

Manganese Absorption, Use, and Homeostasis

Absorption of manganese is poor, only 1 to 15 percent. This low absorption rate may protect against toxicity. Some research suggests that high levels of iron, calcium, and phosphorus may inhibit absorption. Fiber and phytate also may limit manganese absorption, but to a lesser degree than they affect the absorption of most other trace minerals. Following absorption, transferrin binds manganese and transports it in the bloodstream.

Excretion, rather than absorption, regulates the body's manganese. Bile is the main excretory route. Should the intestine absorb excess manganese, the body may quickly dump this excess back into the intestine as part of bile. There is no storage form of manganese. As with zinc, there does not appear to be a reliable indicator of manganese status in adults.

Dietary Recommendations and Food Sources for Manganese

The AI for manganese is 2.3 milligrams per day for men and 1.8 milligrams per day for women. Tea, nuts, cereals, and some fruits are the best food sources of manganese. Some estimates suggest that coffee or tea supplies as much as 20 to 30 percent of our daily manganese intake. Meat, dairy products, poultry, fish, and refined foods are poor sources; they contain little manganese. **Figure 13.21** shows the manganese content of some foods.

Manganese Deficiency

Although people who consume normal varied diets do not appear to be at risk for manganese deficiency, certain disorders may cause suboptimal status. Manganese deficiency has been shown to lead to bone demineralization and impaired growth in children, decreased serum cholesterol levels and a transient skin rash in young men, and mildly abnormal glucose tolerance in young women.[56] In animal studies, manganese deficiency has dramatic effects: impaired growth, skeletal abnormalities, impaired glucose tolerance, impaired reproductive system, and altered carbohydrate and fat metabolism.[57]

Manganese Toxicity

Manganese toxicity is a greater threat than manganese deficiency. Foundry workers exposed to airborne manganese dust have experienced severe manganese toxicity. Their symptoms included irritability, hallucinations, and severe lack of coordination. Lower doses of airborne manganese can impair memory and cause impaired motor coordination similar to that experienced in Parkinson's disease. The UL for manganese is 11 milligrams per day.

Key Concepts *Manganese is important to the functioning of several enzymes in the human body. Our usual intake of manganese falls within the currently recommended intake range. Food sources for manganese are tea, coffee, cereals, and some fruits. Toxicity is more a threat than deficiency is, primarily to people who are exposed industrially to high levels of manganese dust.*

Quick Bite

Accidental Discovery

In the early 1900s, people noticed that inhabitants of towns with naturally high levels of fluoride in their water had healthier teeth. To test the correlation between fluoride and tooth decay, in 1945 four cities in the United States and one in Canada took part in a controlled study of water fluoridation. The results were impressive, establishing that fluoride helps to prevent tooth decay.

Fluoride

Fluoride (F), the ionized form of fluorine, has the unique ability to prevent dental caries. Although people first observed this beneficial effect in the early 1800s, scientific proof did not emerge until the time of World War II. In 1945

Manganese

Daily Value = 2 mg

	Food	Weight	Serving	Manganese
	Exceptionally good sources			
	Pineapple, canned in juice	249 g	1 cup	2.791 mg
	Pine nuts	28 g	1 oz	2.495 mg
	All-Bran cereal	30 g	½ cup	2.223 mg
	Oat bran, cooked	219 g	1 cup	2.111 mg
High: 20% DV or more	Spaghetti, whole-wheat, cooked	140 g	1 cup	1.931 mg
	Okra, frozen, cooked	184 g	1 cup	1.879 mg
	Brown rice, cooked	195 g	1 cup	1.765 mg
	Raisin Bran cereal	61 g	1 cup	1.734 mg
	Spinach, cooked	180 g	1 cup	1.683 mg
	White beans, canned	262 g	1 cup	1.349 mg
	Pecans	28 g	1 oz (20 halves)	1.276 mg
	Lentils, cooked	198 g	1 cup	0.978 mg
	Walnuts	28 g	1 oz (14 halves)	0.968 mg
	Raspberries, raw	123 g	1 cup	0.824 mg
	Sweet potato, baked, with skin	146 g	1 potato	0.726 mg
	Maple syrup	20 g	1 tbsp	0.660 mg
	Almonds	28 g	1 oz (24 nuts)	0.648 mg
	Strawberries, raw	166 g	1 cup	0.641 mg
	Blueberries, raw	145 g	1 cup	0.487 mg
Good: 10–19% DV	Pumpkin, canned	245 g	1 cup	0.365 mg
	Bananas, raw	118 g	1 banana	0.319 mg
	Ham, sliced	57 g	2 slices	0.316 mg
	Broccoli, cooked	156 g	1 cup	0.303 mg
	Peanut butter	16 g	1 tbsp	0.288 mg
	Cauliflower, frozen, cooked	180 g	1 cup	0.270 mg
	Cucumber, with peel, raw	301 g	1 large	0.238 mg
	Cocoa, dry powder	5 g	1 tbsp	0.207 mg

Figure 13.21 **Food sources of manganese.** Manganese is found mainly in plant foods such as grains, legumes, vegetables, and some fruits.

Source: US Department of Agriculture, Agricultural Research Service. USDA National Nutrient Database for Standard Reference, Release 22. 2009. Nutrient Data Laboratory Home Page, http://www.ars.usda.gov/ba/bhnrc/ndl.

many U.S. water suppliers began voluntarily fluoridating water to improve the dental health of children. Now that use of fluoridated toothpaste and mouthwash is widespread, some experts are raising concerns about potential harm from excessive fluoride intake.

Functions of Fluoride

Bones and teeth contain nearly 99 percent of the body's fluoride. Fluoride supports the **mineralization** of bones and teeth by promoting the deposition of calcium and phosphorus.

mineralization The addition of minerals, such as calcium and phosphorus, to bones and teeth.

Fluoride's cavity-prevention activity is an effect localized in the mouth. Bacteria in the mouth cause dental caries, an infectious disease. When a person eats food, especially carbohydrate foods, these oral bacteria multiply and produce organic acids that eat away tooth enamel, especially beneath plaque. When food leaves the mouth, remineralization begins. If remineralization does not keep pace with demineralization, your teeth become pitted with dental caries. Fluoride decreases the demineralization of tooth enamel and accelerates the subsequent remineralization process. It also inhibits bacterial

Academy of Nutrition and Dietetics

The Impact of Fluoride on Health

The Academy of Nutrition and Dietetics reaffirms that fluoride is an important element for all mineralized tissues in the body. Appropriate fluoride exposure and usage is beneficial to bone and tooth integrity and, as such, has an important, positive impact on health throughout life.

Reproduced from *J Am Diet Assoc.* 2005;105:1620–1628. Reprinted with permission from Elsevier.

activity in dental plaques. These cavity-fighting actions can help make your next trip to the dentist a pleasant one.

Regular ingestion of fluoride is especially important during the eruption of new teeth in children. When administered topically, fluoride's support of tooth enamel remineralization can benefit people of all ages.

Fluoride Absorption and Excretion

Your body absorbs almost all the fluoride in water and other liquid beverages. The bioavailability of fluoride in food ranges between 50 and 80 percent. After absorption, the body distributes fluoride in "hard" tissues, mainly the bones and teeth. Excess fluoride is excreted mainly in the urine.

Dietary Recommendations for Fluoride

The AI for fluoride is 4 milligrams per day for adult men, and 3 milligrams per day for women. As of 1995, the American Dental Association and American Academy of Pediatrics no longer recommend fluoride supplementation from birth, and recommend that nonfluoridated water be used to mix infant formula. Children can begin to drink fluoridated tap water after their first birthday. For children living in areas without a fluoridated water supply, fluoride supplements should be used only by prescription from a pediatrician or dentist.[58] The AI for fluoride for infants is 0.01 milligram per day for ages 0 to 5 months and 0.5 milligram per day for ages 6 to 11 months.

Sources of Fluoride

Water is the main source of fluoride, whether the fluoride is naturally present or added. To reduce the incidence of dental caries, the CDC recommends that water fluoridation be extended to additional communities and that fluoride toothpaste be used widely.[59] According to the American Dental Association, the optimal fluoride level in drinking water that has been proven beneficial in reducing tooth decay is 0.7 to 1.2 parts per million.[60] Artificially fluoridated water contains 0.7 to 1.2 milligrams per liter. Fluoride naturally present in drinking water may vary from less than 0.1 milligram to more than 10 milligrams per liter. The Environmental Protection Agency's regulations require public drinking water systems to remove excess fluoride so that it does not exceed 4.0 milligrams per liter.[61] Almost two-thirds of the U.S. population receive optimally fluoridated water;[62] most other developed countries do not fluoridate their water.

The balance between the positive effects of just enough fluoride and the negative effects of too much fluoride has become the subject of debate. Some scientists argue that artificial fluoridation is an outdated practice. Fluoridation was instituted 50 years ago, when it served as the exclusive source of fluoride for children. Now, however, there are other fluoride sources, including ready-to-feed infant formulas, fluoride supplements, mouthwash, toothpaste, and some beverages. The combination of all of these sources may put children at increased risk for excessive fluoride intake and **fluorosis**.

fluorosis Mottled discoloration and pitting of tooth enamel caused by prolonged ingestion of excessive fluoride.

Because there are so many sources of fluoride, it is difficult to determine the current effectiveness of artificial fluoridation of the water supply. Some opponents argue that artificial fluoridation is inappropriate and is "mass medication of the public water supply."[63] However, the dramatic decline in dental carries since fluoridation was initiated is undeniable. To retain the benefits yet avoid overconsumption, the American Dental Association recommends the fluoridation of all water supplies and regulation of other fluoride sources.

THINK About It 4

Fluoride Deficiency, Toxicity, and Pharmacological Applications

Low fluoride intake increases the risk for dental caries and may hamper the integrity of bone. Adequate fluoride intake in childhood can decrease the incidence of tooth decay by 30 to 60 percent. During tooth development, prolonged excessive fluoride intake can cause fluorosis. (See **Figure 13.22**.) In mild fluorosis, white specks form on the teeth. Severe fluorosis can cause permanent brownish stains and weakened teeth. Consumption of water naturally high in fluoride is the main cause of fluorosis, but children who chronically swallow large amounts of fluoridated toothpaste are also at risk. For children under 6 years old, parents should supervise the use of fluoride-containing products to prevent consumption. The UL for fluoride is 10 milligrams per day.

Hemodialysis patients who have been given too much fluoride can suffer acute fluoride toxicity with symptoms that include headaches, nausea, and abnormal heart rhythms. Other observed effects of fluorosis include hip fractures, chronic gastritis, and weak, stiff joints.

Researchers have studied fluoride for the treatment of osteoporosis in postmenopausal women. Although fluoride treatment appears to increase bone density, it also seems to make them more brittle and susceptible to fracture despite their higher density.[64] Fluoride is not an approved treatment for osteoporosis.

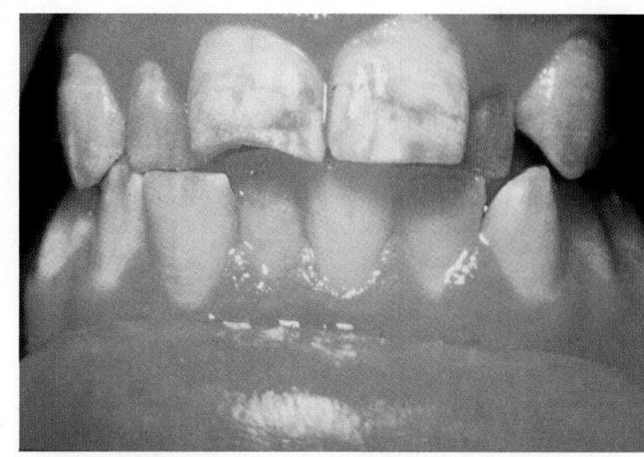

Figure 13.22 **Tooth mottling in fluorosis.** During tooth development, prolonged excessive fluoride intake can cause fluorosis, which discolors and damages teeth.

Key Concepts *Bones and teeth contain 99 percent of body fluoride. Fluoride supports remineralization, and its major function is the prevention of dental caries. Fluoride is unique in that the main dietary source is water, not food. The majority of our nation's municipal water supplies are artificially fluoridated. Excess fluoride can cause fluorosis. Mild fluorosis with mottling of the teeth is primarily a cosmetic problem; severe fluorosis can weaken teeth.*

Chromium

Chromium (Cr) plays an important but poorly understood role in moving glucose into cells, and in lipid metabolism. Although researchers established chromium's essential role in glucose tolerance during the late 1950s and early 1960s, the development of reliable analytical methods took another 20 years. As with many trace minerals, low levels in biological tissues, the requirement for specialized instruments, and the potential for sample contamination make chromium assessment particularly challenging.[65]

Functions of Chromium

Chromium enhances the effects of insulin and is important for proper metabolism of carbohydrates and lipids. It also may play a role in metabolism of nucleic acids and in immune function and growth. Athletes are especially interested in chromium because of its purported effects on body composition.

Chromium Absorption, Transport, and Excretion

Little is known about chromium absorption. Uptake of the inorganic form is thought to be low (about 1 to 2 percent); absorption of organic chromium (a combination of chromium and an organic acid such as chromium picolinate) may be higher (10 to 25 percent). Absorption increases with need and decreases with higher amounts in the diet. Other dietary factors also can influ-

Quick Bite

Conspiracy Theory

Although the U.S. Public Health Service and the World Health Organization officially endorsed the fluoridation of water in the 1950s, some groups continue to oppose the practice. Objectors claim that water fluoridation violates civil rights, that fluoride is a "nerve poison," and that fluoride is unwanted compulsory medication that can have dangerous side effects. Some groups even claim that fluoridation is a component of a conspiracy for national destruction. So far, objectors have been unable to substantiate their claims, and the courts have upheld the constitutionality of fluoridation.

albumin A protein that circulates in the blood and functions in the transport of many minerals and some drugs.

ence chromium absorption. Vitamin C and niacin, for example, can increase chromium absorption, and diets high in sugar decrease it.[66]

Transferrin and **albumin** transport chromium in the bloodstream. The body contains approximately 4 to 6 milligrams of chromium, mostly in the liver, spleen, and bone; the remainder is widely dispersed at very low concentrations. The body excretes excess chromium in the urine.

Dietary Recommendations and Food Sources for Chromium

For adults aged 19 to 50 years, the AI for chromium is 35 micrograms per day for men and 25 micrograms per day for women. The AI for older adults is 5 micrograms less. More data on actual requirements for chromium and the chromium content of foods are needed for more specific dietary recommendations.

The chromium content of foods varies widely. Good sources include brewer's yeast, processed meats, whole grains, green beans, broccoli, and spices. Cooking acidic foods in stainless steel containers leaches some chromium into the food.

Chromium Deficiency

The difficulty of assessing chromium status makes it hard to determine the effects of deficiency. Nevertheless, studies in animals and humans point to the following signs of chromium deficiency: decreased insulin-mediated glucose uptake by cells, decreased insulin sensitivity, elevated blood glucose and insulin levels, and blood lipid abnormalities. Patients who subsist on long-term intravenous feedings inadequate in chromium may suffer brain and nerve disorders.[67]

Chromium Toxicity

The only known cases of chromium toxicity occurred in people exposed to airborne chromium compounds in industrial settings. Because inorganic chromium is so poorly absorbed, extremely high oral intakes would be necessary to attain toxic levels. Numerous experiments show 200 micrograms of inorganic chromium to be a safe dose for supplementation. Studies of chromium picolinate supplements show DNA damage in animal cells and have raised safety concerns about this supplemental form (see the FYI feature "Chromium, Exercise, and Body Composition"). To date, no UL has been set for chromium.

The role of chromium supplements remains controversial. Recommendations from the American Diabetes Association state that "at the present, benefit from chromium supplementation in individuals with diabetes or obesity has not been clearly demonstrated and therefore [supplementation] can not be recommended."[68] This statement is based on an evaluation of chromium studies.

However, supplementation with chromium picolinate, a highly bioavailable form of chromium, has been shown to reduce insulin resistance and the risk of type 2 diabetes and cardiovascular disease. Furthermore, the FDA published the following qualified health claim: "One small study suggests that chromium picolinate may reduce the risk of insulin resistance, and therefore possibly may reduce the risk of type 2 diabetes. FDA concludes, however, that the existence of such a relationship between chromium picolinate and either insulin resistance or type 2 diabetes is highly uncertain."[69]

Quick Bite

Chrome-Plated Cars

The cars of the 1950s sported fins and loads of chrome. The chromium in your body is the same metal used for electroplating hard chrome. Using electric current, chromium ions bond with the original surface, creating a bond between the metals so hard it will remain intact even when subjected to extreme force.

Based on perceived but unfounded beneficial effects on body composition, chromium supplements are popular among many athletes and bodybuilders. However, there is little evidence from well-designed studies that chromium increases lean body mass or decreases body fat.[70]

Key Concepts *The primary function of chromium in the body is to potentiate the effects of insulin. Sources of chromium include mushrooms, dark chocolate, prunes, nuts, asparagus, whole grains, wine, brewer's yeast, and some beers. Reliable assessment of chromium status is difficult.*

Molybdenum

Molybdenum (Mo) is essential to both plants and animals. In humans, molybdenum functions as a cofactor for several enzymes that induce oxidation.

Molybdenum Absorption, Use, and Metabolism

The intestine absorbs molybdenum efficiently—some studies suggest up to 80 to 90 percent of the amount consumed. However, the body excretes it rapidly in urine and in bile. Fiber and phytate have no effect on its absorption.

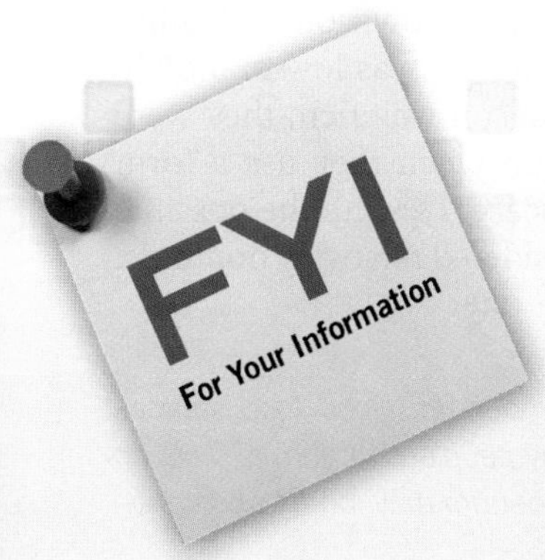

Chromium, Exercise, and Body Composition

Because chromium supplements are purported to increase lean body mass (LBM) and decrease body fat during resistance training, they have generated a great deal of popular interest. Yet study results are contradictory, and chromium's influence on body composition is controversial. The USDA's Human Nutrition Research Center in Beltsville, Maryland, reviewed numerous studies of chromium and body composition.[1] Although several of the studies show that chromium supplementation positively affects gains achieved with resistance training, a number of other experiments show no effect.[2] A literature review examined the effects of 200 to 1,000 micrograms per day of chromium (in the form of chromium picolinate) and found no significant benefit on body mass or body composition.[3] Although some studies found that chromium supplements may help with weight loss, the benefit was negligible.[4]

What are the issues raised by these studies and how are we to understand the contradictory results? After researchers reported the initial positive results, the press and supplement advertisers overstated the benefits of chromium supplementation, thereby creating unrealistic expectations. Back in 1996, the Federal Trade Commission (FTC) ordered the maker of chromium picolinate supplements to stop making unsubstantiated claims of weight loss and health benefits. Despite the FTC's intervention, sales of chromium supplements continue to grow.[5]

Differences in experimental design explain many of these inconsistent results. In some studies the dosage may have been too low and the time period may have been too short to show any effect. One of the limitations of any chromium study is the inability to assess the initial status of the subjects.

There is no evidence that chromium supplements provide a "quick fix" for athletes, and long-term chromium intake probably has a minimal effect on body composition and body weight. Because chromium can interact with iron and zinc, chromium supplementation raises concern about adverse effects. As is the case with many trace minerals, only further investigation will clarify the role of chromium in human health.

The best advice for achieving a healthy, fit body? A varied diet, and regular exercise—not reliance on supplements.

1 Anderson RA. Effects of chromium on body composition and weight loss. *Nutr Rev.* 1998;56:266–270.

2 Evans GW. The effect of chromium picolinate on insulin controlled parameters in humans. *Int J Biosoc Med Res.* 1989;11:163–180.

3 Vincent JB. The potential value and toxicity of chromium picolinate as a nutritional supplement, weight loss agent and muscle development agent. *Sports Med.* 2003;33:213–230.

4 Pittler MH, Stevinson C, Ernst E. Chromium picolinate for reducing body weight: meta-analysis of randomized trials. *Int J Obes Relat Metab Disord.* 2003;27:522–529.

5 Vincent JB. *The Nutritional Biochemistry of Chromium* (III). Amsterdam: Elsevier, 2007.

Quick Bite

Molybdenum Takes a Stand Against the Elements

Molybdenum is a silvery-gray metal that is not found free in nature. It has properties similar to tungsten and is used as an alloy to strengthen and protect metal from corrosion.

Dietary copper is the only significant inhibitor of molybdenum absorption. The body contains about 2 milligrams of molybdenum, 90 percent of which is located in the liver.

Dietary Recommendations and Food Sources for Molybdenum

For adults, the molybdenum RDA is 45 micrograms per day. Although data are limited, typical intakes in the United States exceed the RDA. Peas, beans, and some breakfast cereals are the richest food sources for molybdenum. Organ meats such as liver and kidney also are fairly rich sources, but other meats tend to be poor sources.

Molybdenum Deficiency and Toxicity

Molybdenum deficiency does not occur in people who eat a normal diet. People on total parenteral nutrition who do not receive molybdenum can suffer weakness, mental confusion, and night blindness. People with a rare congenital disorder have deficient amounts of sulfite oxidase, a molybdenum-dependent enzyme. These people suffer from neurological problems similar to those of severe molybdenum deficiency.

Scientists first recognized the interaction between dietary copper and molybdenum in sheep and cattle that grazed on grass grown on soil either very poor or very rich in molybdenum. If the soil content was low in molybdenum, the animals suffered copper toxicity; if the soil was rich, they were deficient in copper. Doctors exploit this interaction when they use a form of molybdenum to treat patients with Wilson's disease. Despite the possible interaction with copper, molybdenum salts are considered relatively nontoxic. The UL for molybdenum is 2,000 micrograms per day.

Key Concepts *Several important enzymes require molybdenum. Good food sources include peas, beans, and some breakfast cereals. Healthy people with normal diets do not suffer molybdenum deficiency. High intakes of molybdenum may inhibit absorption of copper.*

Other Trace Elements and Ultratrace Elements

The body contains minuscule amounts of "ultratrace" minerals and may require less than 1 milligram per day of each one. At least 18 minerals could be considered ultratrace: aluminum, arsenic, boron, bromide, cadmium, chromium, fluoride, germanium, iodine, lead, lithium, molybdenum, nickel, rubidium, selenium, silicon, tin, and vanadium. Dietary recommendations are fairly clear and there is substantial research on five of these minerals: iodine, fluoride, manganese, molybdenum, and selenium (all discussed previously). The functions of the remaining minerals are less clear. Although new evidence and media coverage have focused on arsenic, boron, nickel, silicon, and vanadium, data do not exist for the establishment of AIs or RDAs for these minerals. ULs have been set for boron, nickel, and vanadium. (See Table 13.5.)

Arsenic

Although arsenic (As) has been an infamous poison for centuries, inorganic arsenic may actually be an essential ultratrace element.[71] As a colorless, tasteless toxin, arsenic trioxide can be fatal in a dose as low as 2 milligrams.

Table 13.5 Tolerable Upper Intake Levels (UL) for Ultratrace Elements

Arsenic	No UL set
Boron	20 mg/day
Nickel	1 mg/day
Silicon	No UL set
Vanadium	1.8 mg/day

On the other hand, arsenic-deprived laboratory animals have poor growth and abnormal reproduction. Arsenic may also participate in methionine metabolism. The mean childhood dietary intake for inorganic arsenic has been estimated at 3.2 micrograms per day, with a range of 1.6 to 6.2 micrograms per day.[72] For adults, median intake of arsenic was 2.0 to 2.9 micrograms per day in men and 1.7 to 2.1 micrograms per day in women.[73] The most concentrated food sources are oysters, mussels, fish, and drinking water. In a typical diet, dairy products provide 31 percent of arsenic in the diet, and meat, poultry, fish, grains, and cereals together provide 56 percent. A UL has not been established for arsenic. Given arsenic's highly poisonous nature, much more careful research is required to establish recommended intake and UL levels.

Boron

Boron (B) appears to play an important role in bone metabolism, probably in conjunction with other nutrients such as calcium, magnesium, and vitamin D. Studies indicate that boron also plays a role in promoting brain health and immunity.[74] Boron deficiency depresses growth and is worsened by a vitamin D deficiency. Conversely, boron supplementation lessens the bone abnormalities observed in vitamin D deficiency.

Fruits, nuts, vegetables, legumes, and, depending on geographic location, water are the main sources of boron. The body absorbs close to 90 percent of the amount consumed and then promptly excretes most of it in the urine. The usual dietary intake of boron is between 0.87 and 1.35 milligrams per day for adults.[75] Based on average consumption as well as supplementation studies, scientists estimate that the daily boron requirement is 1 milligram per day. Chronic boron toxicity symptoms include poor appetite, nausea, weight loss, and decreased sexual activity, seminal volume, and sperm count.[76] More research is needed to set safe lower limits for dietary intake. The UL for boron is 20 milligrams per day.

Nickel

Nickel (Ni) is widely distributed throughout the body in very low concentrations that add up to a total body content of approximately 10 milligrams. Most of the research on nickel has been conducted in animals; by extrapolation, scientists assume nickel is essential in humans.

A few nickel-containing enzymes have been identified, and nickel can activate or inhibit a number of enzymes that usually contain other elements. Nickel alters the properties of cell membranes and affects oxidation-reduction systems in cells. Nickel also may function in vitamin B_{12} and folate metabolism.[77]

Nuts, legumes, grains, and vegetables are the best sources of nickel. Depending on the amount of plant foods consumed, dietary intake of nickel varies widely. Adults consume approximately 79 to 105 micrograms of nickel per day from dietary sources and supplements.[78] There is no known nickel deficiency in humans. Toxicity has occurred only in workers exposed to nickel dust or nickel carbonyl in industrial settings. The UL for nickel is 1 milligram per day.

Silicon

Silicon (Si) is the most common element in the earth's crust. The human body contains roughly 1.5 grams of silicon—less than the amount of magnesium, but about the same as iron and zinc. Connective tissues such as the aorta, trachea, tendons, bones, and skin contain much of the body's silicon. From animal studies, scientists hypothesize that silicon helps strengthen collagen and elastin. Experimental diets lacking silicon caused poor growth and skeletal abnormalities in baby chickens. However, there are no known symptoms of silicon deficiency in humans. Studies suggest that silicon may help prevent atherosclerosis in the elderly. This element is relatively nontoxic when ingested orally, and no UL has been set for it. However, breathing airborne silicon particles may cause **silicosis**, a type of silicon toxicity.

silicosis A disease that results from excess silicon exposure.

Unrefined grains, cereals, vegetables, and fruits supply most of our dietary silicon. Animal foods are poor sources. Determining a dietary recommendation is difficult because of the lack of human studies showing signs of deficiency. Silicon intakes were found to be between 23 and 28 milligrams per day in the Framingham Offspring Cohort.[79] This study determined that increased silicon intake is associated with increased bone mineral density in this population.[80]

Vanadium

In the body, vanadium (V) can exist in a form that is structurally similar to phosphate. Interestingly, in the late 1970s it was noted that *in vitro* vanadium inhibits ATP synthase, an enzyme required for ATP production. Presumably, vanadium replaces phosphate and blocks the reaction. In rats with experimentally induced diabetes, vanadium has also been shown to mimic insulin. However, a precise function for vanadium in humans has not been found, and given the tiny amounts that we consume, deficiencies have not been observed. The UL for vanadium is 1.8 milligrams per day.

Key Concepts *Ultratrace minerals are elements with very low estimated requirements. Although specific biochemical functions have not been defined for the minerals arsenic, boron, nickel, silicon, and vanadium, they are thought to be essential for humans.*

If you looked at a list of minerals, could you pick out the trace minerals? Let's see how well you do! Look at the accompanying Nutrition Facts label from a breakfast cereal and guess how many trace minerals are listed.

You should be able to spot three trace minerals on the label: iron, zinc, and copper. Looking at the "ingredients" and "vitamins and minerals" lists, you can see that the iron and zinc were added, but the copper appears to come naturally from the cereal. Why do you think these trace minerals are added to this cereal? Many people (especially children) eat marginal amounts of iron and zinc. The best sources of these minerals are meats, liver, and shellfish. Most children don't eat much shellfish or liver, so adding the minerals to cereals, which they do eat, is an easy way to make sure they get 45 percent and 25 percent of the Daily Values for iron and zinc, respectively.

The last mineral you see listed is copper. There is 2 percent of the Daily Value for copper in one serving of this cereal. That's 0.04 milligram (2% of 2 mg).

Nutrition Facts
Serving Size: 1 cup (30g)
Servings Per Container about 9

Amount Per Serving	Cheerios	with 1/2 cup skim milk
Calories	110	150
Calories from Fat	15	20
% Daily Value**		
Total Fat 2g*	3%	3%
Saturated Fat 0g	0%	3%
Trans Fat 0g		
Polyunsaturated Fat 0.5g		
Monounsaturated Fat 0.5g		
Cholesterol 0mg	0%	1%
Sodium 280mg	12%	15%
Total Carbohydrate 22g	7%	9%
Dietary Fiber 3g	11%	11%
Soluble Fiber 1g	11%	11%
Sugars 1g		
Other carbohydrates 1g		
Protein 3g		
Vitamin A	10%	15%
Vitamin C	10%	10%
Calcium	4%	20%
Iron	45%	45%
Vitamin D	10%	25%
Thiamin	25%	30%
Riboflavin	25%	35%
Niacin	25%	25%
Vitamin B6	25%	25%
Folic Acid	50%	50%
Vitamin B12	25%	35%
Phosphorus	10%	25%
Magnesium	8%	10%
Zinc	25%	30%
Copper	2%	2%

*Amount in Cereal. A serving of cereal plus skim milk provides 2g total fat (0.5g saturated fat, 1g monosaturated fat). less than 5mg cholesterol, 350mg sodium, 300mg potassium, 28g total carbohydrate (7g sugars) and 7g protein.

**Percent Daily Values are based on a 2,000 calorie diet. Your daily values may be higher or lower depending on your calorie needs:

	Calories:	2,000	2,500
Total Fat	Less Than	65g	80g
Sat Fat	Less Than	20g	25g
Cholesterol	Less Than	300mg	300mg
Sodium	Less Than	2,400mg	2,400mg
Potassium		3,500mg	3,500mg
Total Carbohydrate		300g	375g
Dietary Fiber		25g	30g

INGREDIENTS: WHOLE GRAIN OATS (INCLUDES THE OAT BRAN), MODIFIED FOOD STARCH, SUGAR, SALT, OAT FIBER, TRISODIUM PHOSPHATE, CALCIUM CARBONATE, VITAMIN E (MIXED TOCOPHEROLS) ADDED TO PRESERVE FRESHNESS.

VITAMINS AND MINERALS: IRON AND ZINC (MINERAL NUTRIENTS), VITAMIN C (SODIUM ASCORBATE), A B VITAMIN (NIACINAMIDE), VITAMIN B6 (PYRIDOXINE HYDROCHLORIDE), VITAMIN B2 (RIBOFLAVIN), VITAMIN B1 (THIAMIN MONONITRATE), VITAMIN A (PALMITATE), A B VITAMIN (FOLIC ACID), VITAMIN B12, VITAMIN D.

Learning Portfolio

Key Terms

	page		page
albumin	540	Menkes' syndrome	533
ceruloplasmin	533	metalloproteins	520
chelation therapy	535	metallothionein	522
cretinism	528	mineralization	537
Crohn's disease	524	myelinization	511
cytochromes	511	myoglobin	511
ferric iron (Fe^{3+})	511	nonheme iron	512
ferritin	511	polyphenols	512
ferrous iron (Fe^{2+})	511	protoporphyrin	518
fluorosis	538	selenocysteine	527
galvanized	520	selenomethionine	527
geophagia	520	silicosis	544
goiter	531	thyroglobulin	531
goitrogens	532	thyroid-stimulating hormone (TSH)	531
hematocrit	518	thyroxine (T4)	531
heme	511	total parenteral nutrition (TPN)	531
heme iron	512	transferrin	511
hemosiderin	514	transferrin receptors	514
hypogonadism	520	transferrin saturation	518
hypothyroidism	527	triiodothyronine (T3)	531
iron overload	519	Wilson's disease	527
Keshan disease	527		

Study Points

- Trace elements are minerals that the body needs in small amounts. They are involved in a variety of structural and regulatory functions and are found in both animal and plant foods.
- Iron functions in oxygen transport as part of hemoglobin and myoglobin. It is also an enzyme cofactor, important for immune function, and involved in normal brain function.
- Iron balance is regulated through absorption; absorption increases when body status is low, and decreases when stores are normal. Meat, vitamin C, and stomach acid tend to increase nonheme iron absorption. Phytate, phenolic compounds, and high doses of other minerals tend to decrease iron absorption.
- Recommendations for iron intake consider the amount needed to replace daily losses and the bioavailability of iron from a typical mixed diet. Due to regular iron losses via menstrual bleeding, women of childbearing age need more iron than adult men do.
- The best sources of iron are meats. Enriched and whole grains are significant sources in the American diet.
- Iron deficiency is the most common nutritional deficiency worldwide. The most severe stage of deficiency, following reduction of iron stores and transport iron, results in anemia.
- Iron toxicity can result from acute ingestion of high doses or chronic excessive iron absorption. Accidental iron overdose is a leading cause of poisoning deaths of children younger than age 6 in the United States.
- Zinc is a cofactor for numerous enzymes and is crucial for normal growth, development, and immune function. It is found in protein-rich foods, particularly red meats.
- Zinc deficiency results in poor growth, impaired taste, delayed wound healing, and impaired immune response.
- Selenium functions as part of the glutathione peroxidases, important antioxidant enzymes. Good sources of selenium are organ meats and seafood. Deficiency of selenium appears to be rare, but has been described in an area of China called the Keshan region.
- Iodine is necessary for the formation of thyroid hormones, which regulate metabolic rate and body temperature. Much of the iodide in the American diet comes from iodized salt. Iodine deficiency results in goiter. If severe deficiency occurs during pregnancy, the child may be born with cretinism.
- Copper functions in many enzyme systems, including those involved with antioxidant mechanisms, iron utilization, and immune function. The richest food sources of copper include organ meats, shellfish, nuts and seeds, peanut butter, and chocolate.
- Copper deficiency results in anemia, decreased numbers of white blood cells, and bone abnormalities.
- Manganese functions in conjunction with several enzyme systems. The best food sources include tea, coffee, nuts, cereals, and some fruits. Manganese deficiency and toxicity are uncommon; toxicity is usually associated with exposure through manganese mines.
- Fluoride promotes mineralization of bones and teeth and protects the teeth from caries. Water is a major

source of fluoride, due to either naturally high content or added fluoride. Fluorosis is the result of excessive fluoride intake and results in mottling of the teeth.

- Chromium functions in the normal use of insulin to promote glucose use. Rich sources of chromium are mushrooms, dark chocolate, prunes, nuts, asparagus, whole grains, wine, brewer's yeast, and some beers. Chromium deficiency in humans is difficult to assess, and toxicity of inorganic chromium is unlikely.
- Although the body contains only about 2 milligrams of molybdenum, it is an important enzyme cofactor. Good food sources are peas, beans, and some breakfast cereals. Molybdenum deficiency and toxicity are both rare.
- Ultratrace minerals are those required in extremely small amounts; the specific function of many of these nutrients is unknown. Some ultratrace minerals are arsenic, boron, nickel, silicon, and vanadium.

Study Questions

1. In what two ways do trace minerals differ from major minerals?
2. Name two ways that minerals differ from most vitamins.
3. List five factors that can affect a mineral's bioavailability.
4. Explain the differences between "heme" and "nonheme" iron. Which is absorbed better?
5. List the three stages of iron deficiency and the effects of each.
6. What are some of the main functions of zinc?
7. Describe the common causes of zinc deficiency.
8. What are the main functions of selenium?
9. Iodine is a component of which hormones? What are the functions of these hormones? How is selenium linked to these hormones?
10. What are goitrogens and how are they related to goiter?
11. Define Wilson's disease and Menkes' syndrome.
12. What are the functions of manganese in the body?
13. How does fluoride prevent dental caries?
14. Which foods contain chromium, and why is chromium important?

Try This

A Simple Check on Your Zinc

Reported in the *Lancet* in the early 1980s, this simple test can provide a rough signal of your zinc status. Buy some zinc sulfate at a health food store. Dissolve it in distilled water to make a 0.1 percent zinc sulfate solution. Refrain from eating, drinking, and smoking for at least an hour before the test. Then swish a teaspoon of the solution around your mouth for 10 seconds. If it tastes unpleasant or metallic, your level of zinc is probably adequate. However, if the solution tastes like water, you may be consuming less zinc than you need.

What About Bobbie?

Let's take a look at Bobbie's intake of the trace minerals iron, zinc, and selenium. Refer to Chapter 1 to review Bobbie's complete food record. Bobbie's intakes of iron, zinc, and selenium exceeded the Recommended Dietary Allowances for her age. This reflects the fact that Bobbie's calorie intake is high enough to satisfy her needs and she selected a wide variety of foods. Below you'll see the foods she ate that contributed the most to her trace mineral intake.

Iron	
Bobbie's intake	20 mg
Bobbie's RDA	18 mg

Most of Bobbie's iron came from enriched grains and red meat. Here are her top four iron sources and the amount each provided:

Spaghetti pasta	2.9 mg
Bagel	2.7 mg
Meatballs	2.3 mg
Pizza	1.5 mg

Zinc	
Bobbie's intake	14 mg
Bobbie's RDA	8 mg

Bobbie's best source of zinc is red meat—the meatballs she had on her spaghetti. Here are her top four zinc sources and the amount each provided:

Meatballs	4.9 mg
Pizza (cheese)	2.2 mg
Spaghetti pasta	1.1 mg
Bagel	0.8 mg

Selenium	
Bobbie's intake	126 μg
Bobbie's RDA	55 μg

Bobbie's best sources of selenium are grain products and meats. Here are her top four selenium sources and the amount each provided:

Spaghetti	44 μg
Bagel	22 μg
Meatballs	18 μg
Turkey	18 μg

References

1 World Health Organization. Micronutrient deficiencies: iron deficiency anemia. http://www.who.int/nutrition/topics/ida/en/. Accessed 8/2/09.

2 Gleason G, Scrimshaw NS. An overview of the functional significance of iron deficiency. In: Kraemer K, Zimmermann MB. *Nutritional Anemia*. Basel, Switzerland: Sight and Life Press, 2007:45–58.

3 Ibid.

4 De Andraca I, Castillo M, Walter T. Psychomotor development and behavior in iron-deficient anemic infants. *Nutr Rev*. 1997;55(4):125–132.

5 Institute of Medicine, Food and Nutrition Board. *Dietary Reference Intakes for Vitamin A, Vitamin K, Arsenic, Boron, Chromium, Copper, Iodine, Iron, Manganese, Molybdenum, Nickel, Silicon, Vanadium, and Zinc*. Washington, DC: National Academies Press, 2001.

6 National Institutes of Health, Office of Dietary Supplements. Dietary supplement fact sheet: iron. August 2007. http://ods.od.nih.gov/factsheets/iron.asp. Accessed 8/2/09.

7 Institute of Medicine, Food and Nutrition Board. *Dietary Reference Intakes for Vitamin A, Vitamin K*.

8 Miret S, Simpson RJ, McKie AT. Physiology and molecular biology of dietary iron absorption. *Annu Rev Nutr*. 2003;23:283–301.

9 Beard JL, Dawson BS, Pinero DJ. Iron metabolism: a comprehensive review. *Nutr Rev*. 1996;54(10):295–317.

10 Institute of Medicine, Food and Nutrition Board. *Dietary Reference Intakes for Vitamin A, Vitamin K*.

11 Otten JJ, Hellwig JP, Meyers JD, eds. *Dietary Reference Intakes: The Essential Guide to Nutrient Requirements*. Washington, DC: National Academies Press, 2006.

12 Lynch S. Iron metabolism. In: Kraemer K, Zimmermann MB. *Nutritional Anemia*. Basel, Switzerland: Sight and Life Press, 2007:59–76.

13 Gropper SS, Smith JL, Groff JL. *Advanced Nutrition and Human Metabolism*. 5th ed. Australia: Wadsworth/Cengage Learning, 2009.

14 Mendoza C, Peerson JM, Brown KH, Lönnerdal B. Effect of a micronutrient fortificant mixture and two amounts of calcium on iron and zinc absorption from a processed food supplement. *Am J Clin Nutr*. 2004;79(2):244–250.

15 Hunt JR. Bioavailability of iron, zinc, and other trace minerals from vegetarian diets. *Am J Clin Nutr*. 2003;78:633S–639S.

16 Gropper, Smith, Groff. *Advanced Nutrition and Human Metabolism*.

17 Hookworm infection (ancylostomiasis). In: Porter RS, Kaplan JL, eds. *The Merck Manual for Healthcare Professionals* [Online]. http://www.merck.com/mmpe/sec14/ch182/ch182f.html. Accessed 8/4/09.

18 Beard J. Why iron deficiency is important in infant development. *J Nutr*. 2008;138(12):2534–2536.

19 Cortese S, Konofal E, Bernardina BD, et al. Sleep disturbances and serum ferritin levels in children with attention-deficit/hyperactivity disorder. *Eur Child Adolesc Psychiatry*. 2009;18(7):393–399.

20 Israeli E, Merkel D, Constantini N, et al. Iron deficiency and the role of nutrition among female military recruits. *Med Sci Sports Exerc*. 2008;40(11 suppl):S685–690.

21 Institute of Medicine, Food and Nutrition Board. *Dietary Reference Intakes for Vitamin A, Vitamin K*.

22 Morris CC. Pediatric iron poisonings in the United States. *South Med J*. 2000;93(4):352–358.

23 Bulaj ZJ, Ajioka RS, Phillips JD, et al. Disease-related conditions in relatives of patients with hemochromatosis. *N Engl J Med*. 2000;343:1529–1535.

24 Gordeuk V, Mukiibi J, Hasstedt SJ, et al. Iron overload in Africa: interaction between a gene and dietary iron content. *N Engl J Med*. 1992;326(12):95–100.

25 Prasad AS, Helstead JA, Nadami M. Syndrome of iron deficiency anemia, hepatosplenomegaly, hypogonadism, dwarfism and geophagia. *Am J Med*. 1961;31:532–546.

26 Sandstead HH, Prasad AS, Schubert AR, et al. Human zinc deficiency endocrine manifestations and response to treatment. *Am J Clin Nutr*. 1967;20;422–442.

27 Gropper, Smith, Groff. *Advanced Nutrition and Human Metabolism*.

28 King JC, Cousins RJ. Zinc. In: Shils ME, Shike M, Ross AC, et al., eds. *Modern Nutrition in Health and Disease*. 10th ed. Philadelphia: Lippincott Williams & Wilkins, 2006:271–285.

29 Ibid.

30 Medline Plus. Zinc. http://www.nlm.nih.gov/medlineplus/druginfo/natural/patient-zinc.html. Accessed 8/6/09.

31 Wintergerst ES, Maggini S, Hornig DH. Contribution of selected vitamins and trace elements to immune function. *Ann Nutr Metab*. 2007;51:301–323.

32 King, Cousins. Zinc.

33 Hunt JR. Bioavailability of iron, zinc, and trace elements from vegetarian diets. *Am J Clin Nutr*. 2003;78(suppl):633S–639S.

34 Craig WJ, Mangels AR, American Dietetic Association. Position of the American Dietetic Association: vegetarian diets. *J Am Diet Assoc*. 2009;109(7):1266–1282.

35 Krebs NF. Overview of zinc absorption and excretion in the human gastrointestinal tract. *J Nutr*. 2000;130:1374S–1377S.

36 King, Cousins. Zinc.

37 Ervin RB, Kennedy-Stephenson J. Mineral intakes of elderly adult supplement and non-supplement users in the third National Health and Nutrition Examination Survey. *J Nutr*. 2002;132:3422–3427.

38 Zinc. In: Porter RS, Kaplan JL, eds. *The Merck Manual for Healthcare Professionals* [Online]. http://www.merck.com/mmpe/sec01/ch005/ch005j.html. Accessed 8/4/09.

39 Prasad AS. Zinc: an overview. *Nutrition*. 1995;11:93.

40 Zinc. *Merck Manual for Healthcare Professionals* [Online].

41 Institute of Medicine, Food and Nutrition Board. *Dietary Reference Intakes for Vitamin A, Vitamin K*.

42 Johnson AR, Munoz A, Gottlieb JL, Jarrard DF. High dose zinc increases hospital admissions due to genitourinary complications. *J Urol*. 2007;177:639–643.

43 Institute of Medicine, Food and Nutrition Board. *Dietary Reference Intakes for Vitamin C, Vitamin E, Selenium, and Beta-Carotene, and Other Carotenoids*. Washington, DC: National Academies Press, 2000.

44 Ibid.

45 Ibid.

46 Combs GF Jr. Selenium in global food systems. *B J Nutr*. 2001;85:517–547.

47 Institute of Medicine, Food and Nutrition Board. *Dietary Reference Intakes for Vitamin C, Vitamin E*.

48 World Health Organization. Micronutrient deficiencies: iodine deficiency disorders. http://www.who.int/nutrition/topics/idd/en/index.html. Accessed 9/6/09.

49 Guyton AC, Hall JE. *Medical Textbook of Physiology*. 10th ed. Philadelphia: WB Saunders, 2000.

50 Iodine. In: Porter RS, Kaplan JL, eds. *The Merck Manual for Healthcare Professionals* [Online]. http://www.merck.com/mmpe/sec01/ch005/ch005e.html. Accessed 8/4/09.

51 Institute of Medicine, Food and Nutrition Board. *Dietary Reference Intakes for Vitamin A, Vitamin K*.

52 US Department of Agriculture. *Continuing Survey of Food Intakes by Individuals and the Diet and Health Knowledge Survey 1994–1996*. Beltsville, MD: Beltsville Human Nutrition Research Center/ARS, 1998.

53 Harvey LJ, McArdle HJ. Biomarkers of copper status: a brief update. *Br J Nutr*. 2008;99(suppl 3):S10–S13.

54 Gambling L, Andersen HS, McArdle HJ. Iron and copper, and their interactions during development. *Biochem Soc Trans*. 2008;36(pt 6):1258–1261.

55 Turnland JR. Copper. In: Shils ME, Shike M, Ross AC, et al., eds. *Modern Nutrition in Health and Disease*. 10th ed. Philadelphia: Lippincott Williams & Wilkins, 2006:286–299.

56 Linus Pauling Institute. Micronutrient research for optimum health: manganese. http://lpi.oregonstate.edu/infocenter/minerals/manganese/. Accessed 8/5/09.

57 Ibid.

58 American Dental Association. Fluoride and fluoridation. http://www.ada.org/public/topics/fluoride/infantsformula_faq.asp. Accessed 8/5/09.

59 Centers for Disease Control and Prevention. Recommendations for using fluoride to prevent and control dental caries in the United States. *MMWR* 2001;50(RR-14):1–42.

60 American Dental Association. ADA positions and statements: interim guidance on fluoride intake for infants and young children. November 8, 2006. http://www.ada.org/prof/resources/positions/statements/fluoride_infants.asp. Accessed 8/5/09.

61 Centers for Disease Control and Prevention. Recommendations for using fluoride to prevent and control dental caries in the United States.

62 Centers for Disease Control and Prevention. Populations receiving optimally fluoridated public drinking water—United States, 2000. *MMWR*. 2002;51(7):144–147.

63 DeLong J. Fluoride in Washoe water up for debate again. *Reno Gazette Journal*. April 18, 2009. http://www2.fluoridealert.org/Alert/United-States/Nevada/Fluoride-in-Washoe-water-up-for-debate-again. Accessed 9/6/09.

64 Licata A. Bone density vs bone quality: what's a clinician to do? *Cleveland Clin J Med*. 2009;76(6):331–336.

65 DiSilvestro RA. *Handbook of Minerals as Nutritional Supplements*. Boca Raton, FL: CRC Press, 2005.

66 National Institutes of Health, Office of Dietary Supplements. Dietary supplement fact sheet: chromium. http://ods.od.nih.gov/factsheets/chromium.asp. Accessed 8/5/09.

67 Hummel M, Standt E, Schnell O. Chromium in metabolic and cardiovascular disorders. *Horm Metab Res*. 2007;39:743–751.

68 American Diabetes Association. Standards of medical care in diabetes (position statement). *Diabetes Care*. 2006;29(suppl 1):14.

69 Trumbo PR, Ellwood KC. Chromium picolinate intake and risk of type 2 diabetes: an evidence-based review by the United States Food and Drug Administration. *Nutr Rev*. 2006;64(8):357–363.

70 Sarubin-Fragakis A, Thomson C. *The Health Professional's Guide to Popular Dietary Supplements*. 3rd ed. Chicago: American Dietetics Association, 2007.

71 Eckhert CD. Other trace elements. In: Shils ME, Shike M, Ross AC, et al., eds. *Modern Nutrition in Health and Disease*. 10th ed. Philadelphia: Lippincott Williams & Wilkins, 2006:338–350.

72 Yost LJ, Tao S-H, Egan SK, et al. Estimation of dietary intake of inorganic arsenic in U.S. children. *Hum Ecol Risk Assess*. 2004;10(3):473–483.

73 Institute of Medicine, Food and Nutrition Board. *Dietary Reference Intakes for Vitamin A, Vitamin K*.

74 Nielsen FH. Is boron nutritionally relevant? *Nutr Rev*. 2008;66(4):183–191.

75 Institute of Medicine, Food and Nutrition Board. *Dietary Reference Intakes for Vitamin A, Vitamin K*.

76 Eckhert. Other trace elements.

77 Uthus EO, Poellot RA. Dietary folate affects the response of rats to nickel deprivation. *Biol Trace Elem Res*. 1996;52:23–35.

78 Institute of Medicine, Food and Nutrition Board. *Dietary Reference Intakes for Vitamin A, Vitamin K*.

79 Jugdaohsingh R, Tucker KL, Qiao N, et al. Dietary silicon intake is positively associated with bone mineral density in men and premenopausal women of the Framingham Offspring Cohort. *J Bone Miner Res*. 2004;19(2):297–307.

80 Ibid.

CHAPTER 14

Sports Nutrition

Eating for Peak Performance

THINK About It

1 How much importance do you place on being physically active?

2 How often do you suffer from muscle fatigue? What do you think causes it?

3 How often do you think about food choices when you're planning a physical activity?

4 What kind of protein do you emphasize in your diet?

Visit nutrition.jbpub.com

Dietary Guidelines for Americans, 2010
Key Recommendations

Balancing Calories to Manage Weight
- Prevent and/or reduce overweight and obesity through improved eating and physical activity behaviors.
- Increase physical activity and reduce time spent in sedentary behaviors.

Today is the big 10,000-meter race. You've trained for months. Fans in the crowd shade their eyes as they watch you and your competitors walk onto the track. "Ready," shouts the starter. "Get set." You toe the starting line and adrenaline increases your heart rate, diverting blood to your muscles and mobilizing energy stores in your liver, muscles, and fat. "Go!" Within a fraction of a second, a torrent of calcium flows into your muscle cells, causing your muscles to contract and launching you from the starting line.

How will you perform in this race? Will your breakfast help or hinder your performance? Will what you ate yesterday and the day before affect your stamina? Does it matter what you eat after you finish the race? Find the answers to these questions and learn about the links between nutrition and sports performance in this chapter.

Nutrition and Physical Performance

Just how physically active do you need to be? (See **Figure 14.1**.) Both the National Institutes of Health (NIH) and Health Canada have found that just small to moderate amounts of physical activity can produce substantial health benefits. Physically active people have a lower risk of developing many chronic diseases, such as coronary heart disease, diabetes, hypertension, osteoporosis, and obesity. Active people also experience an increased sense of well-being and are much better equipped to cope with stress. Health Canada recommends choosing a variety of activities from three types of exercise: endurance, flexibility, and strength. (See **Figure 14.2**.) See Appendix D for *Canada's Physical Activity Guide to Healthy Active Living*.

THINK About It 1

The American College of Sports Medicine (ACSM) and the American Medical Association launched a program called *Exercise is Medicine* in 2007.[1] This program's vision is to make physical activity and exercise a standard part of disease prevention and treatment in the United States. The goals of this program include raising public awareness of the need for a physically active lifestyle, emphasizing the medical importance of exercise to physicians and other health care workers, and instructing physicians in writing prescriptions for exercise. The ACSM notes an important distinction between physical activity as it relates to health and exercise for physical fitness. [2] According to the ACSM, the level of physical activity that may reduce the risk of various chronic diseases may not be enough—in quantity or quality—to improve physical fitness. According to the U.S. Department of Agriculture (USDA) and MyPlate, a minimum of 30 minutes of moderate-intensity physical activity on most days of the week will result in some health benefits. However, 60 minutes of daily physical activity is needed to prevent weight gain and fully achieve health benefits.[3]

What is physical fitness? Measures of fitness may include such factors as strength, endurance, flexibility, and breathing capacity. The ACSM defines physical fitness as "the ability to perform moderate to vigorous levels of physical activity without undue fatigue and the capability of maintaining this level of activity throughout life."[4] In other words, it is more than being able to run a long distance or lift a lot of weight at the gym. Being fit is not defined only by what kind of activity you do, how long you do it, or at what level of intensity. Although these are important measures of fitness, they only address single areas. Overall fitness is made up of five main components:

1. *Cardiorespiratory fitness:* The ability of the body's circulatory and respiratory systems to supply fuel during sustained physical activity.

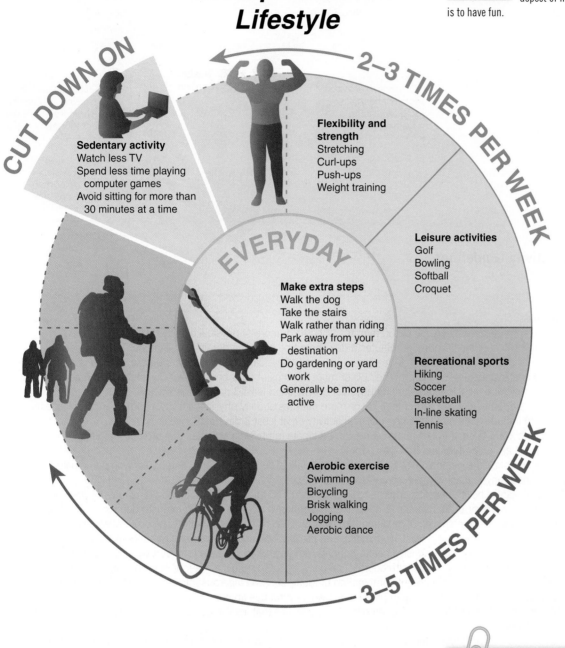

Develop an Active Lifestyle

CUT DOWN ON

Sedentary activity
Watch less TV
Spend less time playing computer games
Avoid sitting for more than 30 minutes at a time

2–3 TIMES PER WEEK

Flexibility and strength
Stretching
Curl-ups
Push-ups
Weight training

Leisure activities
Golf
Bowling
Softball
Croquet

EVERYDAY

Make extra steps
Walk the dog
Take the stairs
Walk rather than riding
Park away from your destination
Do gardening or yard work
Generally be more active

3–5 TIMES PER WEEK

Recreational sports
Hiking
Soccer
Basketball
In-line skating
Tennis

Aerobic exercise
Swimming
Bicycling
Brisk walking
Jogging
Aerobic dance

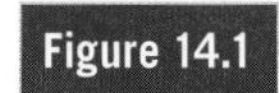

Be active. Perhaps the most important aspect of increasing physical activity is to have fun.

2. *Muscular strength:* The ability of the muscle to exert force during an activity.
3. *Muscular endurance:* The ability of the muscle to continue to perform without fatigue.
4. *Body composition:* The relative amounts of fat and lean body mass. Body composition is an important component to consider for health and weight management.
5. *Flexibility:* The range of motion around a joint. Good flexibility in the joints can help prevent injuries through all stages of life.

Table 14.1 shows guidelines for levels of physical activity to promote health and to achieve and maintain fitness.

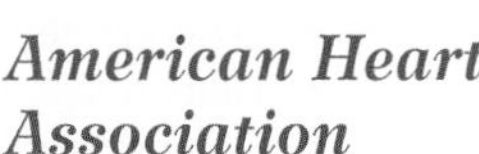

Physical Activity

Physical inactivity is a major risk factor for developing coronary artery disease. Even moderately intense physical activity such as brisk walking is beneficial when done regularly for a total of 30 minutes or longer on most days.

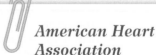

Source: © American Heart Association, Inc.

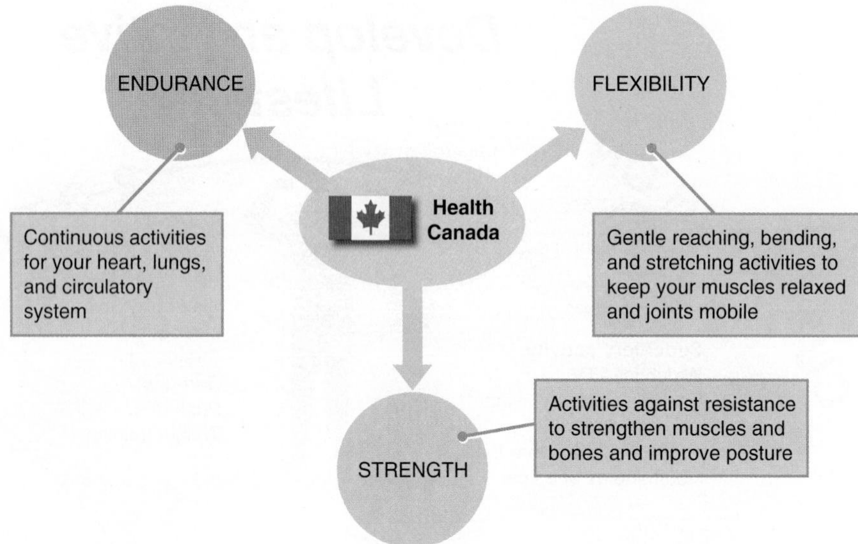
ENDURANCE
FLEXIBILITY
Health Canada
Continuous activities for your heart, lungs, and circulatory system
Gentle reaching, bending, and stretching activities to keep your muscles relaxed and joints mobile
Activities against resistance to strengthen muscles and bones and improve posture
STRENGTH

Figure 14.2 **Variety is the spice of life.** Health Canada recommends that you do a variety of activities from each group—endurance, flexibility, and strength—to receive the most health benefits.

Source: Adapted from *Canada's Physical Activity Guide to Healthy Active Living.*

Table 14.1 **Physical Activity Guidelines**

Age Group	Guidelines
6 to 17 years	Children and adolescents should do 60 minutes (1 hour) or more of physical activity daily. • Aerobic: Most of the 60 or more minutes a day should be either moderate[a]- or vigorous[b]-intensity aerobic physical activity, and should include vigorous-intensity physical activity at least 3 days a week. • Muscle-strengthening:[c] As part of their 60 or more minutes of daily physical activity, children and adolescents should include muscle-strengthening physical activity on at least 3 days of the week. • Bone-strengthening:[d] As part of their 60 or more minutes of daily physical activity, children and adolescents should include bone-strengthening physical activity on at least 3 days of the week. • It is important to encourage young people to participate in physical activities that are appropriate for their age, that are enjoyable, and that offer variety.
16 to 64 years	• All adults should avoid inactivity. Some physical activity is better than none, and adults who participate in any amount of physical activity gain some health benefits. • For substantial health benefits, adults should do at least 150 minutes (2 hours and 30 minutes) a week of moderate-intensity, or 75 minutes (1 hour and 15 minutes) a week of vigorous-intensity aerobic physical activity, or an equivalent combination of moderate- and vigorous-intensity aerobic activity. Aerobic activity should be performed in episodes of at least 10 minutes, and preferably, it should be spread throughout the week. • For additional and more extensive health benefits, adults should increase their aerobic physical activity to 300 minutes (5 hours) a week of moderate-intensity, or 150 minutes a week of vigorous-intensity aerobic physical activity, or an equivalent combination of moderate- and vigorous-intensity activity. Additional health benefits are gained by engaging in physical activity beyond this amount. • Adults should also include muscle-strengthening activities that involve all major muscle groups on 2 or more days a week.
65 years and older	• Older adults should follow the adult guidelines. When older adults cannot meet the adult guidelines, they should be as physically active as their abilities and conditions will allow. • Older adults should do exercises that maintain or improve balance if they are at risk of falling. • Older adults should determine their level of effort for physical activity relative to their level of fitness. • Older adults with chronic conditions should understand whether and how their conditions affect their ability to do regular physical activity safely.

[a]Moderate-intensity physical activity: Aerobic activity that increases a person's heart rate and breathing to some extent. On a scale relative to a person's capacity, moderate-intensity activity is usually a 5 or 6 on a 0-to-10 scale. Brisk walking, dancing, swimming, or bicycling on a level terrain are examples.

[b]Vigorous-intensity physical activity: Aerobic activity that greatly increases a person's heart rate and breathing. On a scale relative to a person's capacity, vigorous-intensity activity is usually a 7 or 8 on a 0-to-10 scale. Jogging, singles tennis, swimming continuous laps, or bicycling uphill are examples.

[c]Muscle-strengthening activity: Physical activity, including exercise, that increases skeletal muscle strength, power, endurance, and mass. It includes strength training, resistance training, and muscular strength and endurance exercises.

[d]Bone-strengthening activity: Physical activity that produces an impact or tension force on bones, which promotes bone growth and strength. Running, jumping rope, and lifting weights are examples.

Source: Reproduced from *Dietary Guidelines for Americans 2010,* 7th ed., US Government Printing Office, 2010. Courtesy of US Department of Agriculture and US Department of Health and Human Services.

Nutrition has taken its rightful place as a vital component of any program that seeks to enhance health, fitness, and athletic performance. In a joint position paper, the Academy of Nutrition and Dietetics, the Dietitians of Canada, and the ACSM state that "physical activity, athletic performance, and recovery from exercise are enhanced by optimal nutrition."[5] But just what is "optimal nutrition"? Is it the same for a child who plays recreational softball and for a senior citizen who takes daily walks to reduce the risk of type 2 diabetes? What about the competitive athlete who strives to maximize athletic performance and uses nutrition to gain a competitive edge? To understand the relationship between physical activity and nutrition, you first need to appreciate how we use energy during exercise.

Key Concepts *Exercise provides numerous health benefits, including reduced risk of chronic disease. Physical fitness includes strength, endurance, and flexibility. For optimal physical performance, nutrition is an essential part of all athletic training programs.*

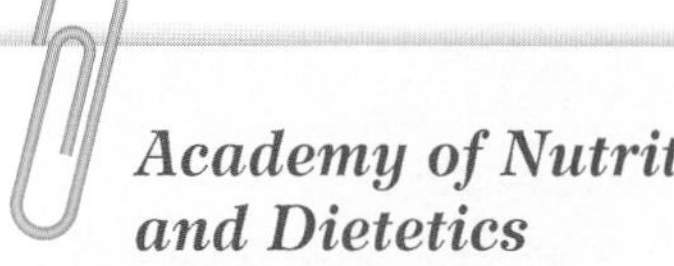

Academy of Nutrition and Dietetics

Nutrition and Athletic Performance

It is the position of the Academy of Nutrition and Dietetics, Dietitians of Canada, and the American College of Sports Medicine that physical activity, athletic performance, and recovery from exercise are enhanced by optimal nutrition. These organizations recommend appropriate selection of food and fluids, timing of intake, and supplement choices for optimal health and exercise performance.

Source: Position of the American Dietetic Association, Dietitians of Canada, and the American College of Sports Medicine: nutrition and athletic performance. *J Am Diet Assoc.* 2009;109:509–527.

Energy Systems, Muscles, and Physical Performance

Let's return to your race. As you leave the starting line, your body immediately ramps up energy production to meet the increased demand. Just as a rocket uses different fuel systems and stages to power its leap into space, your body uses three different energy systems to launch, accelerate, and maintain the exercise you are performing (endurance).

ATP–CP Energy System

As you launch yourself from the starting line, it takes less than a second for your contracting muscles to burn their entire reserve of adenosine triphosphate (ATP), the immediate energy source for cells. Luckily, your body has a small reservoir of **creatine phosphate** (also called **phosphocreatine**) that your muscles can convert quickly to ATP. (See **Figure 14.3**.) Muscle cells contain

creatine phosphate An energy-rich compound that supplies energy and a phosphate group for the formation of ATP. Also called phosphocreatine.

phosphocreatine See *creatine phosphate*.

creatine phosphate + ADP + H+ = ATP + creatine

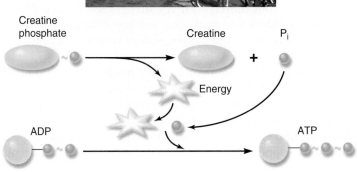

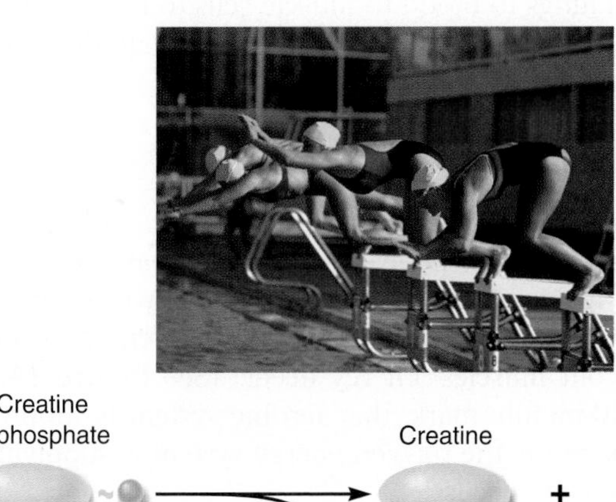

Figure 14.3 **ATP–CP energy system.** To maintain relatively constant ATP levels during an initial explosive burst of high-intensity activity, your body uses its ATP–CP energy system to generate ATP from creatine phosphate.

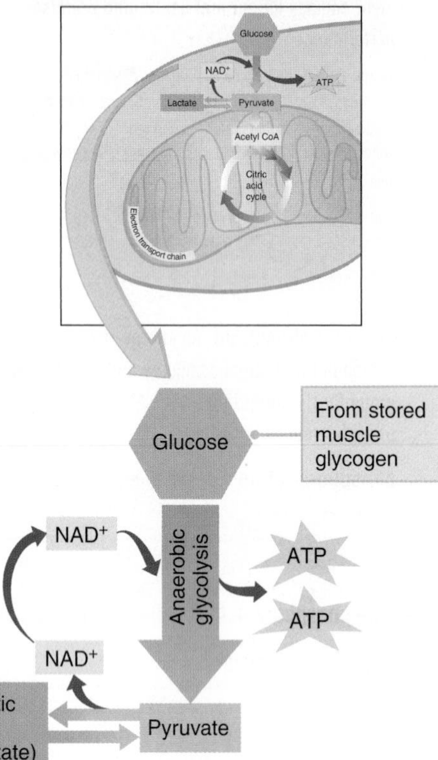

Figure 14.4 **Lactic acid energy system.** During short events requiring power and speed, the lactic acid energy system supplies much of the energy. Because the lactic acid system does not require oxygen, these events are anaerobic activities.

ATP–CP energy system A simple and immediate anaerobic energy system that maintains ATP levels. Creatine phosphate is broken down, releasing energy and a phosphate group, which is used to form ATP.

lactic acid energy system Anaerobic energy system; using glycolysis, it rapidly produces energy (ATP) and lactate. Also called anaerobic glycolysis.

four to six times as much creatine phosphate as ATP.[6] Together, your available ATP and creatine phosphate, the **ATP–CP energy system**, can power an all-out effort for only 3 to 15 seconds.[7] To continue the race, you must enlist carbohydrate stored as glycogen in your muscles and liver. Your cells rapidly disassemble glycogen to glucose, from which they can extract ATP.

Lactic Acid Energy System

For the next minute or two, the acceleration stage, your body uses the simplest and speediest chemical pathways to produce ATP from glucose: the **lactic acid energy system**. (See **Figure 14.4**.) Like the ATP–CP energy system, these pathways are anaerobic—they do not require oxygen. The raw material, glucose, is much more plentiful than creatine phosphate, but its breakdown also produces a by-product: lactate (lactic acid). Although research shows that cells can extract some energy from lactic acid aerobically,[8] most lactic acid accumulates in cells, making them more acidic. A rise in acidity impairs the breakdown of glucose and inhibits calcium binding. Without calcium, muscles cannot contract. For years, coaches and athletes have blamed lactic acid for muscle fatigue. But it's the change in pH, rather than the lactic acid substance itself, that is the primary culprit.[9]

To continue running beyond the first few minutes, your body employs a sophisticated, oxygen-based system to process lactic acid and squeeze out much more ATP from glucose.

Oxygen Energy System

For the endurance stage, cells can use lengthy, complex chemical pathways in their mitochondria—small units within cells that function as power-generating plants—to convert food and oxygen to ATP. (See **Figure 14.5**.) These reactions are aerobic—they require abundant oxygen. In contracting muscle, blood vessels dilate and deliver a 20-fold increase in oxygen-rich blood to muscle cells,[10] a sufficient supply for mitochondria to produce ATP. In contrast to the two anaerobic systems (the ATP–CP system and lactic acid system), the **oxygen energy system** can produce a tremendous amount of ATP. Another advantage is that the oxygen energy system can extract energy from fat as well as glucose. However, because the required oxygen must travel a long distance—from lungs to blood to muscle cells to mitochondria—the oxygen energy system produces ATP at a much slower rate than the anaerobic systems do.

Teamwork in Energy Production

The energy systems work together to fuel athletic performance. (See **Figure 14.6**.) Although all three energy systems are always active, one system may be the primary fuel source for a particular activity or exercise intensity. During the first 2 minutes of your race, the oxygen energy system is supplying about half of your muscles' energy needs. (See **Figure 14.7**.) By the time you pass the 30-minute mark, this aerobic system is supplying 95 percent; at two hours or more, the oxygen energy system is supplying 98 percent of your muscles' energy needs.[11]

As long as ATP production by the mitochondria meets energy needs, you are exercising aerobically; highly trained athletes can sustain such exercise for hours. If the exercise rate exceeds your body's ability to supply oxygen to your muscles, you are exercising anaerobically, rapidly depleting your creatine phosphate and glycogen reserves. Once these are exhausted, if available oxygen cannot support the oxygen energy system, performance plummets.

Carbohydrate stores are limited. A 68-kilogram (150-pound) man with 10 to 20 percent body fat, for example, has carbohydrate stores of 1,800 to 2,000 kilocalories in muscle glycogen, liver glycogen, and blood glucose. Compare this with the energy he stores in fat. His fat tissue holds roughly 63,000 to 120,000 kilocalories.[12] Although the body can burn protein for energy, in well-fed people protein probably provides no more than 5 percent of energy expended in exercise.[13]

Glycogen Depletion

At the beginning of the race, your body rapidly uses muscle glycogen. But as the race grinds on, the rate of glycogen use markedly slows. During the first 1.5 hours, glycogen stores drop steadily to about one-third their starting levels. About 3 hours into the run, as glycogen stores become almost entirely depleted, you may "hit the wall." Your muscles become weak and heavy, your legs shake, and you become confused. Marathon runners commonly experience a sudden onset of exhaustive fatigue around the 18- to 20-mile mark. Drinking fluids that contain glucose can partially compensate for glycogen depletion and soften its effects. Dehydration can cause an even faster onset of fatigue, so drinking plenty of fluids is essential during endurance events.

As exercise intensity increases, glycogen depletion accelerates. Sprinting, for example, uses muscle glycogen 35 to 40 times faster than walking.[14] **Figure 14.8** illustrates how the sensation of fatigue relates to the depletion of muscle glycogen.

Endurance Training

In untrained people, endurance training can increase endurance by as much as 500 percent.[15] To increase endurance, training enhances aerobic capacity by increasing the number of mitochondria and improving the body's ability to deliver oxygen to them. This decreases the reliance on anaerobic energy systems, extending the availability of glycogen reserves and delaying fatigue.

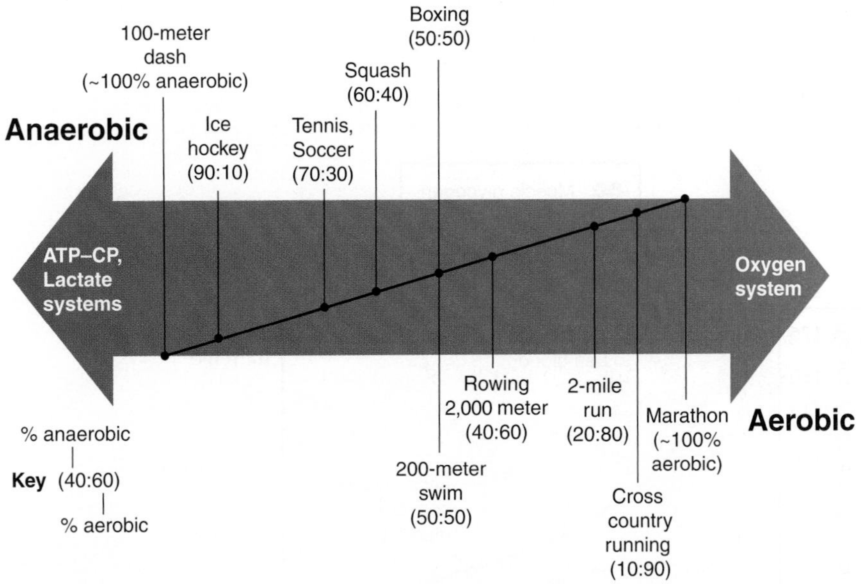

Figure 14.6 **The anaerobic–aerobic continuum.** Most activities use ATP from both anaerobic and aerobic energy systems. However, the 100-meter dash is considered completely anaerobic, and the marathon is considered completely aerobic.

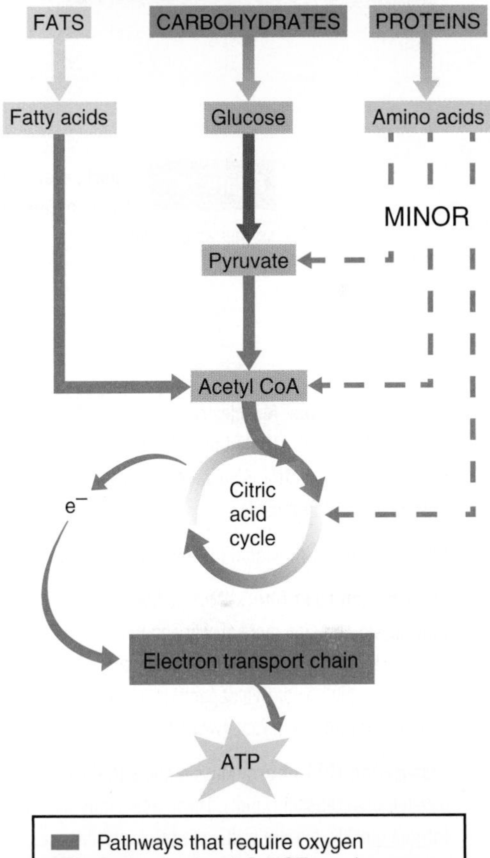

Figure 14.5 **Oxygen energy system.** During longer endurance events (aerobic events), the oxygen energy system supplies most of the energy. This energy system requires oxygen and primarily relies on carbohydrate and fat as fuels.

oxygen energy system A complex energy system that requires oxygen. To release ATP, it completes the breakdown of carbohydrate and fatty acids via the citric acid cycle and electron transport chain.

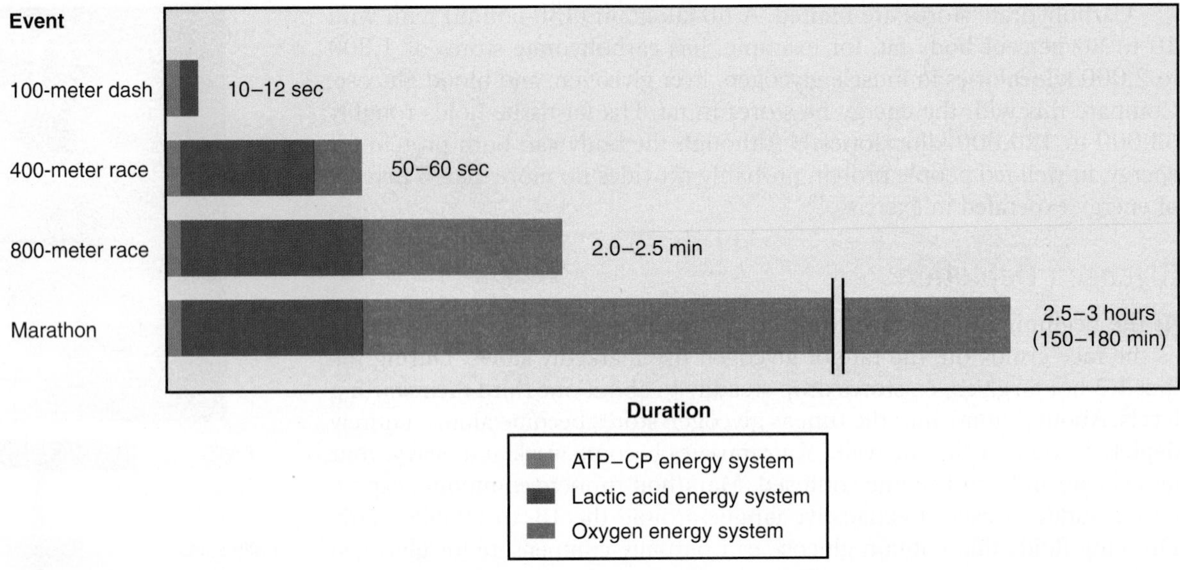

Figure 14.7 **Sports events and energy systems.** Short-term, explosive events rely upon the ATP–CP and lactic acid energy systems. For longer events, your body turns to the oxygen energy system. During endurance events, your body uses this system to burn fat as well as glucose.

Key Concepts *Muscle cells use three different energy systems to produce ATP: the ATP–CP energy system, the lactic acid energy system, and the oxygen aerobic system. The ATP–CP and lactic acid energy systems rely on carbohydrate and do not require oxygen. The oxygen energy system requires oxygen and relies on carbohydrates and fats. During the early minutes of high-intensity exercise, the anaerobic systems are the predominant source of ATP. During lower-intensity endurance events, the aerobic system supplies ATP, although at a much slower rate. Dehydration and depletion of glycogen stores are major factors in fatigue. Training increases the efficiency of oxygen delivery to muscle and increases the number of muscle mitochondria available for aerobic metabolism.*

skeletal muscles Muscles composed of bundles of parallel, striated muscle fibers under voluntary control. Also called voluntary muscle or striated muscle.

muscle fibers Individual muscle cells.

slow-twitch (ST) fibers Muscle fibers that develop tension more slowly and to a lesser extent than fast-twitch muscle fibers. ST fibers have high oxidative capacities and are slower to fatigue than fast-twitch fibers.

fast-twitch (FT) fibers Muscle fibers that can develop high tension rapidly. These fibers can fatigue quickly, but are well suited to explosive movements in sprinting, jumping, and weight lifting.

aerobic endurance The ability of skeletal muscle to obtain a sufficient supply of oxygen from the heart and lungs to maintain muscular activity for a prolonged time.

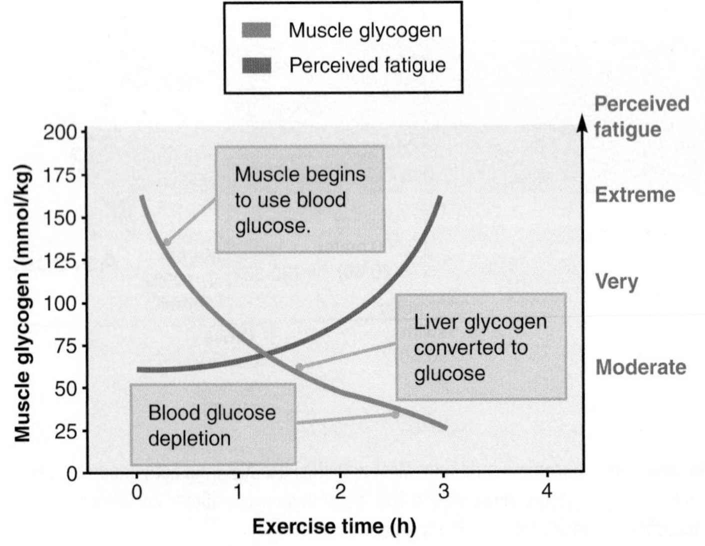

Figure 14.8 **Glycogen depletion and the sensation of fatigue.** As muscle glycogen levels decline, fatigue and eventually exhaustion set in.

Muscles and Muscle Fibers

Your body contains hundreds of muscles that help control a myriad of functions, from regulating blood pressure to climbing stairs. **Skeletal muscles** are bundles of parallel, striated fibers attached to your skeleton. (See **Figure 14.9**.) These muscles are responsible for your physical movement and are under your conscious control. If you decide to bend your arm, for example, you consciously contract your biceps. Your body contains more than 600 skeletal muscles and uses 9 of them just to control your thumb!

Individual muscle cells are called **muscle fibers**; skeletal muscle has two primary types:

- **Slow-twitch (ST) fibers**
- **Fast-twitch (FT) fibers**

They derive their names from the difference in their speed of action. One type of fast-twitch fiber can contract 10 times faster than slow-twitch fibers.[16]

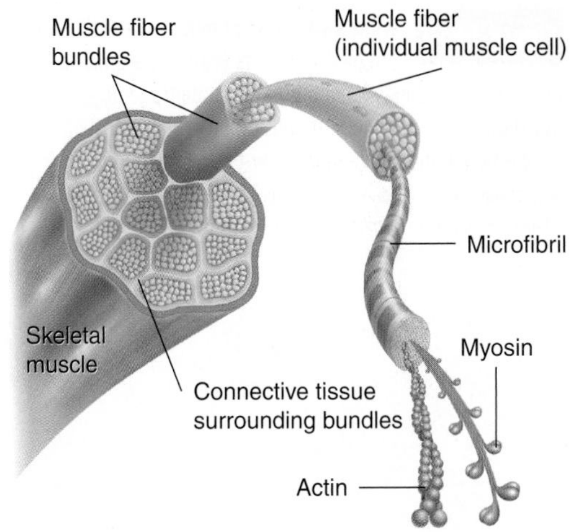

Figure 14.9 **Basic structure of skeletal muscle.** A muscle fiber is an individual muscle cell that usually extends the entire length of the muscle. Each muscle fiber contains hundreds to thousands of microfibrils. Each microfibril contains thousands of actin and myosin filaments, large protein molecules responsible for muscle contractions.

Slow-Twitch Fibers

To power their activity, slow-twitch fibers efficiently produce energy by breaking down carbohydrate and fat via aerobic pathways—metabolic reactions that require oxygen. As long as the aerobic pathways are active, ST fibers can produce energy to sustain their movement. With a sufficient supply of oxygen, ST fibers can maintain muscular activity for a prolonged time. This ability is known as **aerobic endurance**.

Because ST fibers have high aerobic endurance, your body predominantly relies on them during low-intensity endurance events, such as a marathon, and during everyday activities, such as walking.

Fast-Twitch Fibers

Compared with ST fibers, fast-twitch fibers have poor aerobic endurance. They are optimized to perform anaerobically (when the oxygen supply is limited). FT fibers can efficiently produce energy for their use via metabolic pathways that do not require oxygen. Bundles of FT fibers exert considerably more force than bundles of ST fibers; due to their limited endurance, however, FT fibers tire quickly.

The body recruits both ST and FT fibers during shorter, higher-intensity endurance events, such as the mile run or the 400-meter swim. During highly explosive events, such as the 100-meter dash and the 50-meter sprint swim, the body still recruits both types, but FT fibers contribute most of the muscle power.

Fiber Type and the Athlete

Genes determine the relative proportion of muscle fiber types in athletes. Although distance runners who have a high percentage of ST fibers are well suited for endurance events, they will not succeed as elite sprinters. Conversely, sprinters who have predominantly FT fibers are better equipped for explosive events, but they will not become competitive marathon runners. (See **Figure 14.10**.)

Key Concepts *A muscle cell is called a muscle fiber. The two main types of skeletal muscle fibers are slow-twitch and fast-twitch fibers. Slow-twitch fibers generate fuel through aerobic pathways, whereas fast-twitch fibers produce energy using anaerobic pathways. Fast-twitch fibers can exert more force, but have limited endurance.*

Quick Bite

Use It or Lose It!

The benefits of training begin to disappear after only two weeks of inactivity. Muscular endurance (the ability of a muscle to avoid fatigue) declines, and activities of certain oxidative enzymes drop by as much as 40 percent. By the fourth week, muscle glycogen levels also may drop by 40 percent. Flexibility is quickly lost, and inactivity can substantially decondition the heart muscle and cardiovascular system.

Quick Bite

Pound for Pound?

Women's muscles have smaller muscle fiber cross sections and less muscle mass than men. For a given amount of muscle, however, there is no difference in strength between men and women.

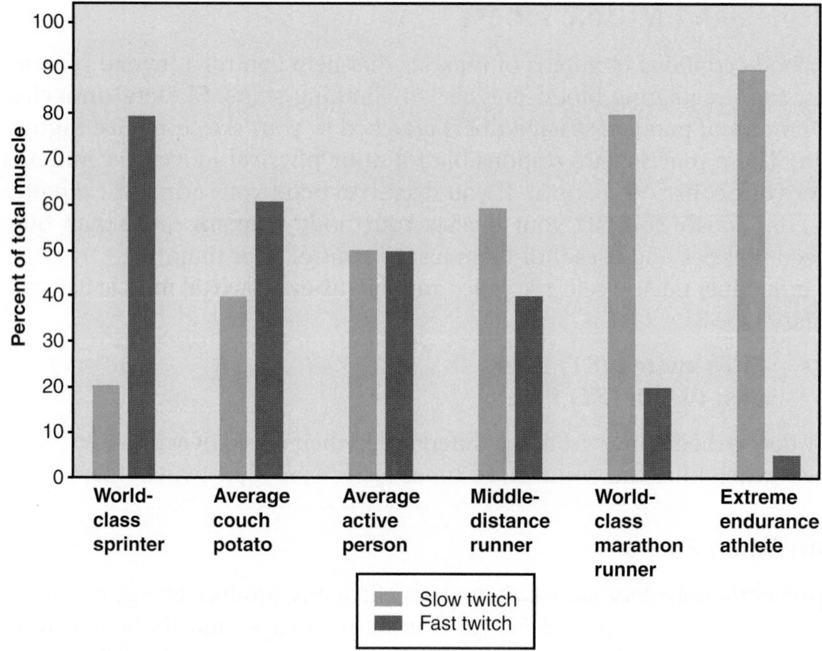

Figure 14.10 **What's your mix of muscle fibers?** If you are best at events requiring explosive movements, you may have a greater percentage of fast-twitch muscle fibers. If endurance events are your specialty, you may have more slow-twitch fibers.

Source: Adapted from Andersen JL, Scherling P, Saltin B. Muscle, genes and athletic performance. *Scientific American.* 2000;283(3):49.

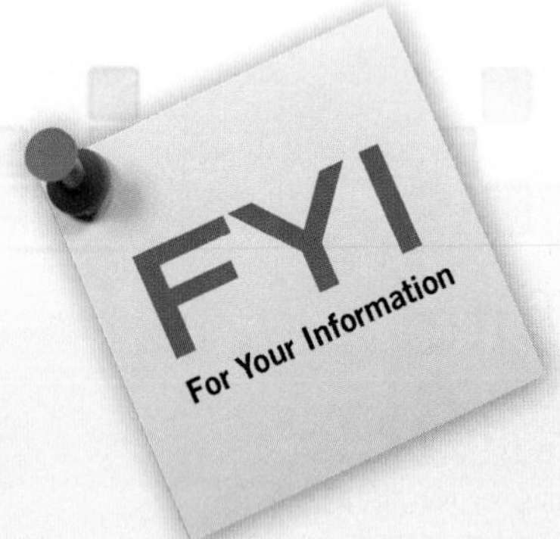

Lactate Is Not a Metabolic Dead End

Today's race is 200 meters, and you are in the lead. The crowd roars with excitement and your coach screams as your feet slam over and over on the hard gray cinder track. Other runners are close behind, and you can feel them breathing and pounding at your heels. Air whistles in and out of your wheezing lungs as you doggedly push to stay ahead. Your muscles are screaming, but they carry you across the finish line. A winner!

As you slump in exhaustion, you wonder how your limp muscles carried you through to the end. Each leg seemed to weigh a thousand pounds. As your muscles tire, lactate levels rise and the pH in your muscle cells drops. Scientists, coaches, and athletes have long believed that lactate was a useless, even toxic, dead-end substance. Research proves otherwise. It is the overall acidification of the muscle tissue, rather than a buildup of lactate, that primarily causes muscle fatigue. Also, lactate is now recognized as a fuel in its own right. In addition to acting as a metabolic shunt, lactate is a useful fuel produced and consumed under all conditions of oxygen availability, while exercising or at rest.

Without the energy supplied by the lactic acid energy system, you would never have crossed the finish line. While your body anaerobically burned muscle glycogen, it produced large amounts of lactate. Where does this lactate come from, and how does your body handle it?

Cori Cycle

During vigorous exercise, your contracting muscle cells quickly extract small amounts of ATP from glucose. This simple pathway, called glycolysis, splits glucose into pyruvate molecules faster than the oxygen energy system can accept them for further processing. Cells divert excess pyruvate to lactate to help alleviate the backup.

Lactate accumulates rapidly in muscle cells, which receive a boost of energy by burning some lactate with oxygen—a strategy that yields far more energy than glycolysis alone.[1] Most lactate easily diffuses through muscle cell membranes into the bloodstream. The liver picks up the circulating lactate and converts it back to pyruvate. Using energy-demanding reactions, the liver transforms pyruvate to glucose. Glucose enters the bloodstream and travels back to the skeletal muscle cells, where it reenters energy-producing pathways.

This recurring circular pathway is called the *Cori cycle*. When pyruvate is backed up in muscle cells, the Cori cycle buys time with a detour through the liver. When oxygen becomes readily available, the oxygen energy system becomes the main pathway.

Lactate Shuttle

The pathways of the Cori cycle are an important, but incomplete, part of the lactate picture. The use of the Cori cycle as a holding pattern led to the mistaken belief that lactate was simply a metabolic dead end. More recent studies described a more extensive role for this long-maligned substance.

Researchers now recognize lactate as an important means of distributing carbohydrate

Optimal Nutrition for Athletic Performance

THINK About It 3

The optimal diet for most physically active people—from the college student who plays intramural basketball to the 50-year-old woman who enjoys walking during her lunch break—includes a variety of nutrient-dense foods. (See Chapter 2, "Nutrition Guidelines and Assessment.") Food choices should be high in carbohydrate (more than 60 percent of calories), low in fat (less than 30 percent of calories), and moderate in protein. When energy needs are met by eating a variety of foods from each of the MyPlate food groups, micronutrient (vitamin and mineral) needs are often met as well.

Athletes, coaches, and scientists have long recognized that training and good nutrition go hand in hand when it comes to improving performance. An accumulating body of scientific evidence now confirms that nutrition can profoundly influence the molecular and cellular processes that occur in muscle during exercise and recovery.[17]

Optimal nutrition is an essential part of every athlete's training program and can make a difference when winning is measured in fractions of seconds

Quick Bite

Fast-Twitch Fish

A large percentage (40 to 60 percent) of a fish's body weight is muscle tissue. Although it spends much of its life slowly cruising, a fish must be able to execute occasional quick bursts of high speed to escape predators or catch a meal. Thus, fish muscle is composed of approximately 75 to 90 percent fast-twitch fibers, and fish flesh often is white. The slow-twitch fibers generally are concentrated just under the skin or near fins that are used during slow or high speeds. This arrangement is possible only because fish are buoyant. Land animals could not survive dragging around a large mass of muscle that they used only occasionally in extreme situations.

energy sources after a meal and during sustained physical exercise. Lactate's advantage is its ability to move rapidly between cells. It is a small molecule and, unlike glucose, does not need insulin to cross a cell membrane.

Under resting conditions of plentiful carbohydrate and oxygen, diverse tissues such as skeletal muscle, liver, and skin produce lactate.[2] In these conditions, the supply of raw materials, rather than limited oxygen, drives the formation of lactate.

According to the lactate shuttle hypothesis, lactate formed in muscle cells becomes an energy source at other sites, either adjacent or remote. Skeletal muscle, once thought simply to produce lactate, also directly uses lactate as a fuel. At times, skeletal muscle actually removes more lactate than it produces. The heart muscle is fully aerobic, but it both produces and consumes lactate. Studies suggest that during exercise lactate is the major fuel for the heart and the preferred fuel for certain muscle fibers.[3]

The next time you complain about sore, tired muscles, don't blame lactate. Instead, think about the daily usefulness of lactate and how this little-respected substance helped power you to the finish.

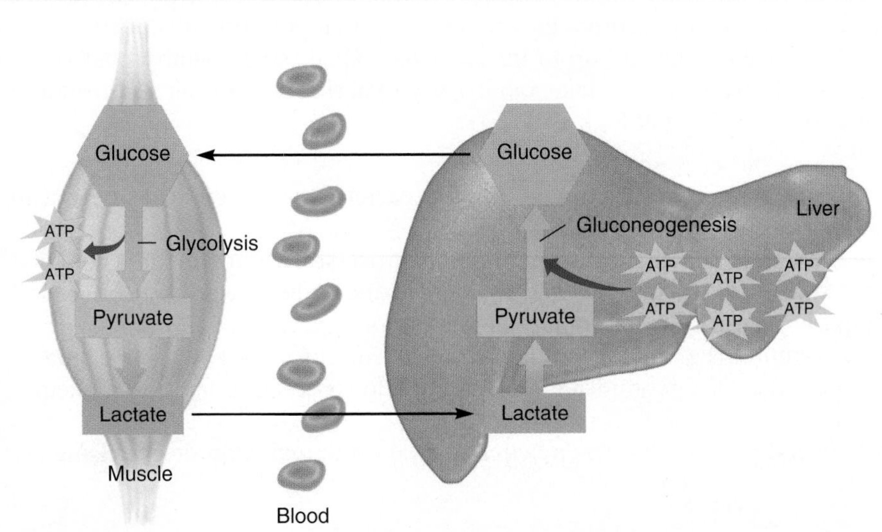

The Cori cycle. The Cori cycle shifts some of the metabolic burden of contracting muscle to the liver. Lactate formed in contracting muscle travels to the liver, which uses it to form glucose. This glucose returns to the muscle to fuel further contractions.

1 Hashimoto T, Hussien R, Brooks GA. Colocalization of MCT1, CD147, and LDH in mitochondrial inner membrane of L6 muscle cells: evidence of a mitochondrial lactate oxidation complex. *Am J Physiol Endocrinol Metab.* 2006;290(6):E1237–E1244.

2 Brooks GA. Mammalian fuel utilization during sustained exercise. *Comp Biochem Physiol.* 1998;120:89–107.

3 Myers J, Ashley E. Dangerous curves: a perspective on exercise, lactate, and the anaerobic threshold. *Chest.* 1997;111:787–795.

Quick Bite

The Weaker Sex?

Prior to the 1960s, women were banned from running any race longer than 800 meters, and they could not officially participate in marathon competitions until 1970. The race authorities mistakenly believed that women could harm themselves and were unsuitable for distance running. Imagine their amazement during the 1984 Olympic Games when Joan Benoit won the gold medal for the women's marathon with a time of 02:24:52—a time that would have won 11 of the previous 20 men's Olympic marathons!

or inches. General recommendations for competitive athletes include the following:[18]

- Consume adequate energy (calories) and nutrients to support health and performance.
- Maintain appropriate sports-specific ranges for percent body fat and fat-free body mass.
- Promote optimal recovery from training.
- Maintain hydration status.

The underlying foundations of a training diet are similar to the basic principles incorporated in the *Dietary Guidelines for Americans* and Canada's Guidelines for Healthy Eating. The primary differences are increased fluid needs to cover an athlete's sweat losses, and increased energy needs to fuel physical activity. Studies indicate that athletes often are confused about nutrition and may not follow the dietary recommendations for peak sports performance.[19] Let's take a closer look at the nutritional needs of athletes.

Energy Intake and Exercise

Adequate energy intake is the first nutrition priority for athletes. Meeting energy needs is critical for athletic performance and for maintaining or increas-

Going Green

Exercise High

You and your friend are off to Denver, Colorado, a mile-high city surrounded by beautiful mountains and tons of greenery. Like other outdoor athletes, you are environmentally conscious, vocal, and passionate about maintaining a pristine environment. You can't wait for that invigorating 5-mile run in the fresh mountain air as you try out your new running shoes. Your friend, however, warns that what you easily can do at home is more difficult at 5,000 feet and suggests a less strenuous hike for that first day in Denver. Although you recognize that your friend is offering sound advice, your immediate exuberance makes you feel invulnerable and up to the challenge. Then you remember that you got sick running in the mountains several years ago, and instead agree to take another day to acclimate yourself and read about exercising at high altitudes. Here are some tips about exercising at high altitudes.

- *Acclimate.* Allow time for your body to acclimate: thin air at high altitudes makes exercising more difficult by reducing the oxygen available to your lungs. Your body adjusts within a day or two.
- *Hydrate.* Another difficulty in high-altitude exertion is dehydration stopping body processes. Mountain air is cool and dry, so drink lots of water to keep hydrated. At least for the first few days, avoid caffeine and don't drink alcohol. Both caffeine and alcohol are diuretics and can quickly cause dehydration and hinder performance.
- *Attend to physical symptoms.* Be aware of the symptoms of acute mountain sickness, such as nausea, dizziness, and headache. If you experience any of these symptoms, it's a good idea to descend to a lower level. If that doesn't help, you should seek medical attention.
- *Eat appropriately.* A diet high in carbohydrate and low in salt offers a better adaptation in high-altitude exercising and reduces the risk of acute mountain sickness.

Greening Your Exercise Routine

In addition to practicing good nutrition, sports enthusiasts and athletes can contribute to a green planet by using reusable water bottles or a hydration system instead of single-use disposable plastic bottles, and by picking up bottles, cans, and paper along the running and walking trails.

ing lean body mass. Sports nutritionists recommend eating small, frequent meals to maintain energy metabolism, improve nutrient intake, achieve desired body composition, support a training schedule, and reduce injuries.[20] During times of high physical activity, energy and macronutrient needs—especially carbohydrate and protein intake—must be met in order to maintain body weight, replenish glycogen stores, and provide adequate protein for building and repairing tissues.[21]

World-class athletes who train strenuously three to four hours each day can almost double their energy needs. The energy demand can be so high that some athletes have trouble consuming enough calories.[22] In contrast, athletes who compete in sports where they are judged by build and in sports with weight classifications often restrict energy intake to avoid weight gain. Energy intakes that are too low can lead to a loss of muscle mass, menstrual dysfunction, lower bone density, and increased risk of fatigue, injury, and illness.[23]

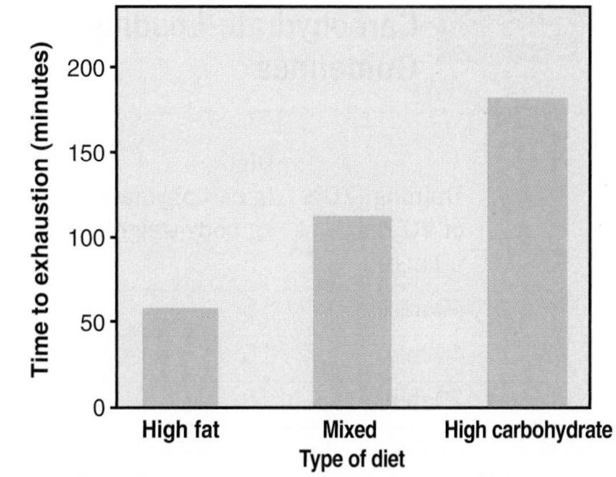

Figure 14.11 **Diet composition and endurance.** Athletes can exercise longer when eating a high-carbohydrate diet.

Carbohydrate and Exercise

Guidelines for athletes recommend high carbohydrate intakes during training.[24] A high-carbohydrate diet helps increase glycogen stores and extend endurance. (See **Figure 14.11**.) For endurance athletes, research studies suggest that carbohydrate should supply a minimum of 60 percent of total calories.[25] A high-carbohydrate diet also may prevent mental as well as physical fatigue and is important for stop-and-go sports such as basketball, football, and soccer.[26]

For all athletes, dietary carbohydrates should come mainly from complex carbohydrates, which provide many of the B vitamins necessary for energy metabolism, along with iron (if enriched) and fiber (if whole grain). Although added sugars should be minimized, some athletes may need to include more simple sugars to meet energy requirements.

carbohydrate loading Changes in dietary carbohydrate intake and exercise regimen before competition to maximize glycogen stores in the muscles. It is appropriate for endurance events lasting 60 to 90 consecutive minutes or longer. Also known as glycogen loading.

glycogen loading See *carbohydrate loading.*

Carbohydrate Loading

Just as you might top off the gas tank in a car before a long trip, athletes can fill their glycogen stores prior to training or competition. In a process called **carbohydrate loading**, or **glycogen loading**, athletes manipulate their carbohydrate intake and exercise regimen to maximize muscle glycogen stores. (See **Figure 14.12**.)

Current recommendations for carbohydrate loading include an intake of 60 to 70 percent of total calories from carbohydrate, along with a decrease in exercise intensity and duration prior to competition.[27] Table 14.2 is a training plan for endurance athletes that includes carbohydrate loading and exercise for the week before an event. The glycogen content of exercised muscles more than doubles in athletes who follow these recommendations, and this extends the duration of higher-intensity activity. For example, distance runners who carbohydrate-load may be able to keep a faster pace for a longer time and finish a race sooner.[28]

Even though "extra" glycogen prior to competition sounds like a perfect plan, there is a downside to carbohydrate loading. For each gram of glycogen stored in muscle tissue, the body also stores about 3 grams of water. Many athletes who carbohydrate-load complain about this weight gain and sub-

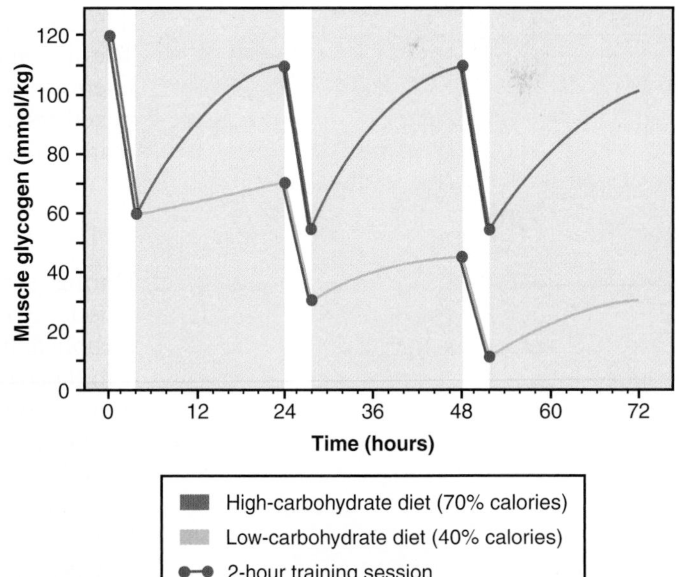

Figure 14.12 **Diet composition, training, and muscle glycogen.** A high-carbohydrate diet replenishes glycogen stores better than a low-carbohydrate diet.

Source: Adapted from Costill DL, Miller JM. Nutrition for endurance sport: carbohydrate and fluid balance. *Int J Sport Nutr.* 1980;1:2–14.

Table 14.2 **Carbohydrate-Loading Guidelines**

Day	Training (70% of VO_2max)	Diet (g carbohydrate/kg body weight)
1	90 min.	5
2	40 min.	5
3	40 min.	5
4	20 min.	10
5	20 min.	10
6	Rest	10
7	Competition	

Source: Dunford M, ed. Carbohydrate and exercise. In: *Sports and Nutrition.* 4th ed. © 2006 American Dietetic Association, American Diabetes Association. Reprinted with permission.

sequent sluggishness. Some opt to train and compete without carbohydrate loading because, for them, the risk of physical discomfort outweighs the benefit of a greater carbohydrate store.

If you participate in an aerobic activity for fewer than 60 to 90 consecutive minutes, carbohydrate loading probably will provide no benefit. Instead, experts recommend that you taper your training program a few days before competition and eat a diet that provides 70 percent of its calories from carbohydrate for one or two days before the event.[29]

Carbohydrate Intake Before Exercise

Eating carbohydrate two to four hours before morning exercise helps replenish glycogen stores and improve endurance. To minimize problems with gastrointestinal (GI) distress, the carbohydrate and caloric content of the meal should be smaller when eaten closer to a workout. Although some athletes can tolerate solid foods, others prefer liquids to avoid GI distress. Because protein and fat take longer to digest and absorb, preexercise meals should contain no more than 10 to 15 percent of the total calories as protein and less than 20 percent of calories from fat. Table 14.3 offers guidelines for timing of meals before an event.

Many athletes are confused about whether to eat less than an hour before exercise. To decrease hunger, delay fatigue, and improve performance, athletes who cannot fully refuel several hours prior to a workout must rely on "last-minute" carbohydrate intake. Although early research suggested that consuming carbohydrate within one hour before activity could cause low blood glucose levels and early fatigue, later studies report no effect or no improved performance.[30]

Preexercise Meals and the Glycemic Index

As you may recall from Chapter 4, "Carbohydrates," individual foods have different effects on blood glucose levels independent of carbohydrate content. The glycemic index of foods is a measure of this effect and has attracted recent interest in relation to the diets of athletes. Current studies have produced mixed results, so it remains unclear whether the glycemic index of carbohydrate in pre-exercise meals affects performance.[31]

Carbohydrate Intake During Exercise

During exercise, athletes can maintain their carbohydrate supply to exercising muscle by consuming beverages with low to moderate amounts of simple carbohydrate.[32] When an event lasts at least one hour, drinking fluids with 4 to 8 percent carbohydrate, the amount in sports drinks, enables athletes to exercise longer and sprint harder at the finish. (See the Nutrition Science in Action feature "Fourth-Quarter Performance.") Although sports drinks also are suitable during events lasting less than one hour, plain water is adequate for maintaining hydration during these shorter events.[33] Consuming carbohydrate before and during an event improves performance more than either strategy alone.

Carbohydrate Intake Following Exercise

It can take 24 to 48 hours after an event to replenish glycogen stores, and the timing and type of carbohydrates are important factors in the refueling

Table 14.3 Timing Meals Before Events

Time:	8:00 A.M. event, such as a road race, swim meet, or stationary cycling class
Meals:	Eat a carbohydrate-rich dinner, and drink extra water the day before. On the morning of the event, about 6:00 or 6:30, have a light 200- to 400-calorie meal (depending on your tolerance), such as yogurt and a banana or one or two energy bars, tea or coffee if you like, and extra water. Eat familiar foods. If you want a larger meal, consider getting up to eat between 5:00 and 6:00. If your body cannot handle any breakfast before early-morning exercise, eat your breakfast before going to bed the night before. The bowl of cereal, bagel with peanut butter, or packets of oatmeal will help boost liver glycogen stores and prevent low blood sugar the next morning.
Time:	10:00 A.M. event, such as a bike race or soccer game
Meals:	Eat a high-carbohydrate dinner, and drink extra water the day before. On the morning of the event, eat a familiar breakfast by 7:00 to allow three hours for the food to digest. This meal will prevent the fatigue that results from low blood sugar. Popular choices include oatmeal, a bagel, and yogurt.
Time:	11:00 A.M. lightweight crew race, wrestling match, or other weight-class sport that requires a weigh-in one to two hours beforehand
Meals:	Athletes who have crash dieted and dehydrated themselves to reach a specific weight for their sport have only a few hours after weigh-in to prepare for the competition. They need to replace water, carbohydrate, and sodium. An ideal target for a 150-pound (68 kg) depleted athlete would be 700 calories (primarily from carbohydrate), 2,200 milligrams of sodium, and 2 quarts (2 L) of water. The intake will vary greatly depending on the individual athlete's tolerance for food. Too many wrestlers end up vomiting on the mat after having pigged out after the weigh-in. Food choices might include the following: Chicken noodle soup, bread, and lots of water V8 juice, pretzels, and water Ginger ale or cola, a ham with mustard sandwich, and water Gatorade Endurance plus baked potato chips
Time:	2:00 P.M. event, such as a football or lacrosse game
Meals:	An afternoon game allows time for you to have either a big high-carbohydrate breakfast and a light lunch or a substantial brunch by 10:00, allowing four hours for digestion time. As always, eat a high-carbohydrate dinner the night before, and drink extra fluids the day before and up to noon. Popular brunch choices include French toast, pancakes, or cereal and poached eggs on toast.
Time:	8:00 P.M. event, such as a basketball game
Meals:	You can thoroughly digest a hefty high-carbohydrate breakfast and lunch by evening. Plan for dinner, as tolerated, by 5:00, or have a lighter meal between 6:00 and 7:00. Drink extra fluids all day. Two popular dinner choices include pasta with tomato sauce and chicken with a large serving of rice or potato.
Time:	All-day event, such as a hard hike,100-mile (160 km) bike ride, or a day of cross-country skiing
Meals:	Two days before the event, cut back on your exercise. Take a rest day the day before to allow your muscles the chance to replace depleted glycogen stores. Eat carbohydrate-rich meals at breakfast, lunch, and dinner. Drink extra fluids. On the day of the event, eat a tried-and-true breakfast depending on your tolerance. Bagels with a little peanut butter are a favorite. While exercising, plan to eat carbohydrate-based foods (energy bars, dried fruit, sports drinks, gels) every 60 to 90 minutes to maintain normal blood sugar. If you stop at lunchtime, eat a comfortable-sized meal, but in general try to distribute your calories evenly throughout the day. Foods with fat, such as peanut butter, nuts, and cheese, can offer sustained energy; dietary fat takes a few hours to be converted into fat used for fuel. Drink fluids before you get thirsty; you should need to urinate at least three times throughout the day.

Source: Clark N. *Nancy Clark's Sports Nutrition Guidebook.* 4th ed. Champaign, IL: Human Kinetics, 2008:173–175. Reprinted with permission.

Nutrition Science *in Action*

Fourth-Quarter Performance

Background: Consuming drinks containing carbohydrates during prolonged endurance exercise previously has been demonstrated to improve athletes' exercise outcomes, including endurance and speed, as well as measures of mood. Much less is known about the effects of carbohydrate feedings during intermittent high-intensity exercise, such as playing competitive basketball and soccer.

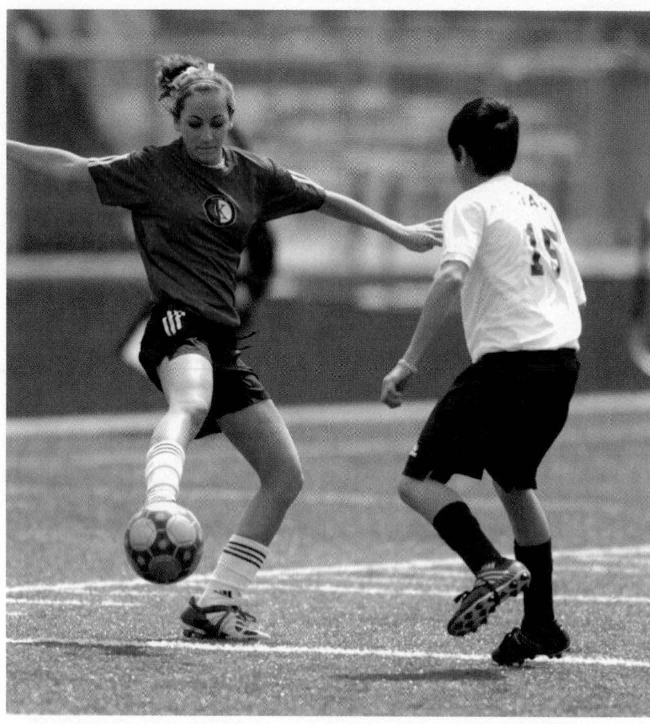

Hypothesis: Carbohydrate feedings during intermittent high-intensity exercise will result in faster sprint times.

Experimental Plan: Twenty active men ($N = 10$) and women ($N = 10$) who participate in intermittent high-intensity team sports performed two experimental trials during which they were fed either a carbohydrate solution (CHO) or a flavored placebo (PBO). Experimental trials consisted of four 15-minute quarters of shuttle running with variable intensities ranging from walking to running to maximal sprinting and performing 40 jumps at a target hanging at 80 percent of their maximum vertical jump height. The first and third quarters were followed by 5-minute breaks, and the second quarter by a 20-minute halftime break.

Results: The hypothesis is confirmed. Compared with the placebo, CHO feedings during exercise resulted in faster 20-meter sprint times, especially during the fourth quarter.

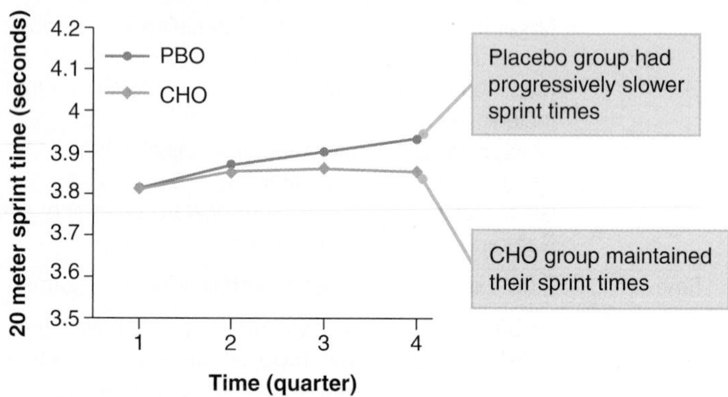

Conclusion and Discussion: These results combined with other measures collected during this experiment show that compared to the placebo, CHO feedings during intermittent high-intensity exercise improved sprinting and jumping performance, speed and agility, and overall mood late in exercise. The results suggest that CHO feedings during team sporting events, such as basketball, can contribute to athletes' ability to perform their best. Future studies of CHO feedings on exercise and cognitive function will be an important contribution to the sports nutrition literature.

Source: Based on Winnick JJ, Davis JM, Welsh RS, et al. Carbohydrate feedings during team sport exercise preserve physical and CNS function. *Med Sci Sports Exerc.* 2005;37(2):306–315.

process. Athletes who ingest 1.5 grams of carbohydrate per kilogram body weight within 30 minutes after exercise have been shown to experience a greater rate of muscle glycogen resynthesis than when supplementation is delayed by two hours, largely due to a greater sensitivity of muscle to insulin.[34] Some research shows that the first 15 minutes are critical.[35]

The best way to replenish glycogen stores after intense exercise is to consume 1 to 1.5 grams of carbohydrate per kilogram of body weight within 30 minutes after a workout, followed by an additional 1 to 1.5 grams per kilogram two hours later.[36] A 70-kilogram (154-pound) athlete who exercises vigorously for 90 minutes or more, for example, would consume 70 to 100 grams of carbohydrate immediately after exercise, followed by another 70 to 100 grams two hours later. Consuming high-glycemic-index foods enhances glycogen synthesis.[37] Among simple sugars, glucose and sucrose appear equally effective in replenishing glycogen, but fructose alone is not as effective.[38]

Carbohydrate intake after exercise also benefits protein metabolism. Several researchers have shown that these levels of carbohydrates taken immediately or one hour after resistance exercise decrease protein breakdown and enhance protein retention.[39]

Key Concepts *Energy intake is the most important element of the athlete's diet, and the major source of energy should be carbohydrates. Foods rich in complex carbohydrates, which also can provide fiber, iron, and B vitamins, are best. A high-carbohydrate diet prior to competition helps maximize glycogen stores and endurance. Carbohydrate loading is a process of adjusting carbohydrate intake and training intensity to maximize glycogen stores just before an event. Consuming carbohydrates soon after exercise enhances the rebuilding of glycogen stores.*

Dietary Fat and Exercise

During exercise, carbohydrates and fats are the two main fuel sources. Endurance (aerobic) training increases the capacity of your oxygen energy system, enhancing your body's ability to use fat as a fuel. Exercise intensity also affects fuel use. During low- to moderate-intensity exercise, fatty acids are the major fuel source. During high-intensity exercise, the predominant energy source is glucose.

This does not mean that endurance athletes should consume diets high in fat. High-fat diets usually are lower in carbohydrate, thus limiting muscles' ability to replenish glycogen stores. High-fat diets often are high in calories, saturated fat, and cholesterol; your body also digests fat more slowly than carbohydrate.

Fat Intake and the Athlete

Fat intake should not be overly restricted. There is no performance benefit in consuming a diet with less than 15 percent of energy from fat.[40] Extreme fat restriction limits food choices, especially sources of protein, iron, zinc, and essential fatty acids. In addition, athletes with high caloric needs (greater than 5,000 kilocalories per day) may find it difficult to eat enough food without consuming more than 20 to 35 percent of their calories from fat, the range recommended for the general population. Sports nutritionists recommend that any extra fat calories come from monounsaturated and polyunsaturated sources. Saturated fat intake should be limited to less than 10 percent of energy, and trans fats should be avoided as much as possible.

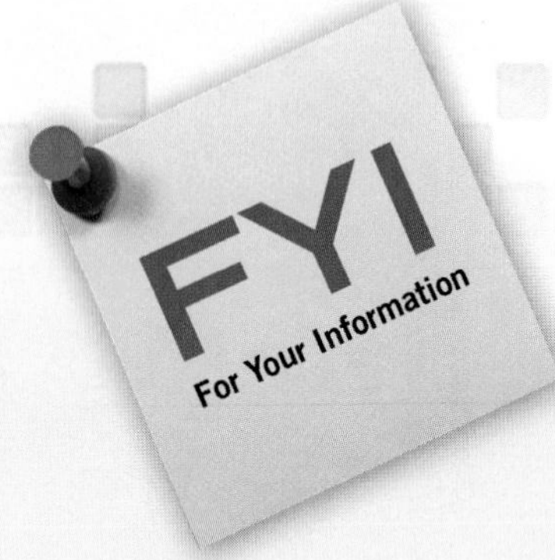

Nutrition Periodization: Tailoring Nutrition Intake to Exercise Goals

Athletes, competitive as well as recreational, adjust their training schedules based on desired performance outcomes. Athletes are not constantly "in season," and their training during a 12-month period can be broken down into three phases: preparation, competition, and transition. This concept is referred to as exercise periodization.[1]

Let's take a look at each training phase more closely:

- *Preparation.* Also called the macrocycle, this phase leads up to the competition phase. Training is both general and specific, with goals to improve aerobic endurance, strength, and flexibility.
- *Competition.* Also called the mesocycle, the performance goals during this phase are to improve strength and speed.
- *Transition.* Also called the microcycle, this phase is the time spent between competition and the next preparation cycle. Workouts in this phase, also referred to as the "off-season" or "active recovery," are generally less structured and are intended for the athlete to improve on his or her weaknesses.

During exercise periodization, an athlete's nutrition needs will change. Adjusting macronutrient (carbohydrate, fat, and protein) intake to enhance the training cycle enables athletes to provide the best combination of fuel for their bodies all year long.[2] This process is referred to as nutrition periodization, and it goes hand in hand with exercise periodization:

- *Preparation.* This is the one phase where, if needed, athletes should focus on changing their weight or body fat percentage, or on building muscle. This is a time when habits regarding diet can be changed and an in-depth evaluation of regular dietary habits can occur. Adjustments are made within the diet to work toward a desired competition weight or body composition.
- *Competition.* During this phase, a routine for eating during the competition season should be well established. The focus should not be on changing weight or experimenting with different food choices. Recovery after exercise is an important focus.
- *Transition.* This is a time to focus on calorie control and good nutrition. It is a time to experiment with and enjoy different types of foods.

Use the information in the accompanying tables as guidelines for successful nutrition periodization.[3]

Daily Needs (No Weight Loss)[1]

Training Phase	*Carbohydrate*	*Protein*	*Fat*	*Hydration (color of urine)*
Preparation	5–12+ g/kg	1.2–1.7 g/kg	0.8–1.0 g/kg	Lemonade
Pre-Race	7–13 g/kg	1.4–2.0 g/kg	0.8–2.0 g/kg	Lemonade
Race	7–19 g/kg	1.4–2.0 g/kg	0.8–3.0 g/kg	Diluted lemonade
Transition	5–6 g/kg	1.2–1.4 g/kg	0.8–1.0 g/kg	Lemonade

Daily Needs: Summary[1]

Training Phase	*Daily Kcalorie Difference*
Preparation	—
Pre-Race	+ 620–1,007
Race	+ 0–2,322
Transition	– 620–5,101

Example: 155-pound Male[1]

Training Phase	*Carbohydrate (g)/Kcalories*	*Protein (g)/Kcalories*	*Fat (g)/Kcalories*	*Total Daily Kcalories*
Preparation	352–845+/1,408–3,380	85–120/340–480	56–70/504–630	2,252–4,490+
Pre-Race	493–916/1,972–3,664	99–141/396–564	56–141/504–1,269	2,872–5,497
Race	493–1,339/1,972–5,356	99–151/396–564	56–211/504–1,899	2,872–7,819
Transition	352–453/340–396	85–99/340–396	56–70/504–630	2,252–2,718

1 Seebohar B. *Nutrition Periodization for Endurance Athletes.* Boulder, CO: Bull, 2004.
2 Block O, Kravitz L. Tailoring nutrient intake to exercise goals. *IDEA Fitness Journal.* 2006;3:48–55.
3 Seebohar, B. *Nutrition Periodization for Endurance Athletes.* Reprinted with permission of Bull Publishing.

Protein and Exercise

Historically, many athletes believed they could become stronger by eating muscle from animals. Many bodybuilders and weightlifters still believe a meal of steak and eggs is their most important source of calories.[41] Current research suggests that athletes require only slightly higher protein intakes than sedentary people.[42]

Some popular books with unscientific premises may recommend alternative amounts of macronutrients, such as 40 percent carbohydrate, 30 percent fat, and 30 percent protein. With its popularity, athletes' interest in optimal protein intake surged. Athletes—from endurance runners to football players to weekend warriors—are asking the question, "Do I need to eat more protein and less carbohydrate for optimal performance?"

Figure 14.13 Optimal nutrition was an important part of Lance Armstrong's training regimen, allowing him to win the Tour de France a record seven times.

Protein Recommendations for Athletes

The adult Recommended Dietary Allowance (RDA) for protein is 0.8 gram of protein per kilogram of body weight per day,[43] and people who regularly engage in low-intensity exercise do not need additional protein.[44]

The Food and Nutrition Board does not recommend a specific RDA for endurance or strength athletes; however, based on a position statement from the ACSM and the Academy of Nutrition and Dietetics, an upper limit of 1.7 grams of protein per kilogram per day will meet the needs of even the hardest-trained athletes.[45] Some studies suggest that endurance athletes involved in heavy training require 1.2 to 1.4 grams of protein per kilogram of body weight per day,[46] and resistance-trained athletes may need as much as 1.6 to 1.7 grams per kg (0.55 to 0.77 grams per pound) body weight.[47] Ultra-endurance athletes who are training for extreme events, such as the Tour de France (**Figure 14.13**), need up to 2 grams per kilogram.[48] Some studies show that protein intake of 1.4 to 2.0 grams per kilogram per day for physically active individuals is not only safe, but also may improve adaptations to exercise training.[49] In addition, preexercise ingestion of protein plus carbohydrates has been shown to produce significantly greater levels of muscle protein synthesis.[50] These requirements can easily be met through diet and without the use of supplements, provided that sound nutrition principles are followed and energy intake is adequate to maintain body weight.[51]

Increased protein synthesis during training is an indicator of muscle growth. Strength athletes consuming 1.4 grams of protein per kilogram of body weight per day synthesize more body protein than athletes consuming 0.9 gram. However, when protein intake was increased to 2.4 grams per kilogram, protein synthesis did not increase further.[52] After adjusting for higher levels of protein oxidation with higher intakes, researchers recommend that strength athletes consume 1.6 to 1.7 grams of protein per kilogram per day.[53] A 91-kilogram (200-pound) strength athlete who wants to build muscle mass would consume about 150 grams of protein. Table 14.4 shows the protein requirements of various levels of physical activity.

Quick Bite

The First Sports Trainers

During the time of the ancient Olympic games, sports trainers demanded that their athletes follow strict training regimens: 10 months of regulated diet, bathing, exercise, rest, and massage. Until 480 B.C.E., Olympic athletes consumed a mostly vegetarian diet of cheese, porridge, figs, wine, and meal cakes. After twice winning the Olympic long race, however, Dromeus of Stymphalus revolutionized the ancient training diet by advocating mammoth amounts of meat and exercise.

Table 14.4 Protein Requirements of Sedentary and Active People

Activity Level	Protein Requirements (g protein/kg body weight)
Sedentary	0.8
Strength athlete	1.6–1.7
Endurance athlete	1.2–1.4
Maximum usable amount for adults	2.0

Source: Adapted from Snyder AC, Naik J. Protein requirements of athletes. In: Berning JR, Steen SN, eds. *Nutrition for Sport and Exercise.* 2nd ed. Sudbury, MA: Jones & Bartlett, 1998.

Protein Intake and the Athlete

THINK About It 4

Athletes don't need protein powders or amino acid supplements to meet the protein demands of athletic performance.[54] Their best protein sources are high-quality protein foods, including legumes, low-fat dairy products, egg whites, lean beef and pork, chicken, turkey, and fish. (See Chapter 6, "Proteins and Amino Acids," for more on protein sources.)

Vegetarian athletes can achieve adequate protein intake and meet their energy needs by eating a variety of protein-rich foods from plant sources such as grains, nuts, beans, and seeds. Because plant proteins are less digestible than animal foods, the total amount of protein consumed may need to be higher.

Quick Bite

Lost in Space
Vigorous weight training can double or triple a muscle's size, whereas the lack of use during space travel can shrink it by 20 percent in two weeks.

Protein Intake After Exercise

Protein combined with carbohydrate in a postexercise meal increases glycogen synthesis more than carbohydrate alone[55] and stimulates more protein synthesis.[56] Researchers suggest athletes consume 4 grams of protein for every 10 grams of carbohydrate (grams protein = 40% grams carbohydrate).[57] For example, using postexercise recommendations of 1.5 grams of carbohydrate per kilogram of body weight, a 55-kilogram female athlete would need 82.5 grams of carbohydrate ($55 \times 1.5 = 82.5$ g) and 33 grams of protein ($82.5 \times 0.40 = 33$ g). How does this translate to food? A small bagel, 2 ounces of string cheese, and 8 ounces of low-fat yogurt would be a portable snack to enjoy after a hard workout (provides 86 grams of carbohydrate and 33 grams of protein). Another food that provides ample amounts of carbohydrate and protein is low-fat milk. Low-fat milk has been shown to be at least as effective as commercially available sports drinks as a rehydration beverage, if not more effective.[58] Milk is more nutrient dense than traditional sports drinks and thus can be a better beverage choice for individuals who partake in strength and endurance activities.

Dangers of High Protein Intake

diuresis The formation and secretion of urine.

Excessive protein intake from food or supplements enhances **diuresis** (loss of body water) as the body attempts to excrete excess nitrogen through the urine. This increases the risk for dehydration and may contribute to mineral losses. High-protein diets often are high in saturated and total fat and may contribute to obesity, osteoporosis, heart disease, and certain types of cancer. (See Chapter 6, "Proteins and Amino Acids.")

High intakes of single-amino-acid supplements may impair absorption of other amino acids. Further, the amount of amino acids contained in supplements is very small compared with the amount in food. For example, one pill may contain 500 milligrams of an amino acid, but 1 ounce of meat, poultry, or fish provides more than 7,000 milligrams of indispensable and dispensable amino acids! And, the cost of supplements is higher.

Key Concepts *Although fat is an important fuel for exercise, a high-fat diet is not necessary. General recommendations that fat not exceed 20 to 35 percent of total energy intake are appropriate for athletes. Dietary protein is a source of energy and also a source of amino acids for body protein synthesis. The protein requirements of athletes are slightly higher than those of sedentary adults, but still within the normal range of protein consumption. High-protein diets are neither recommended nor necessary. Low-fat dairy products, egg whites, lean beef and pork, chicken, turkey, fish, and legumes are good sources of protein.*

Vitamins, Minerals, and Athletic Performance

Many reactions that support exercise and physical activity require vitamins and minerals. They help extract energy from nutrients, transport oxygen, and repair tissues. Researchers have long debated whether physically active people have greater vitamin and mineral needs than sedentary people.

B Vitamins

Because B vitamins are essential for energy metabolism (see Chapter 11, "Water-Soluble Vitamins"), wouldn't athletes, with their high energy needs, require more B vitamins? Not necessarily. B vitamins are needed for chemical reactions that release energy. But if athletes consume adequate calories and ample complex carbohydrates, fruits, and vegetables, they eat plenty of B vitamins. However, if athletes consume too few calories or eat mostly refined sugars in lieu of complex carbohydrates, they can compromise their B vitamin intake.

Vegan athletes who do not include fortified foods, such as some soy products and ready-to-eat cereals, may have a problem with vitamin B_{12} intake. They should consult a medical advisor or registered dietitian to determine whether they need B_{12} supplements.

Calcium

Calcium is essential for normal muscle function and strong bones. Adequate calcium intake coupled with regular exercise slows the deterioration of the skeleton with age and can reduce the risk of osteoporosis.

Inadequate calcium may increase the risk of stress fractures in athletes. This is of particular concern for the amenorrheic athlete (discussed in the "Female Athlete Triad" section later in this chapter). Athletes should strive to meet the Adequate Intake (AI) for calcium from a variety of low-fat dairy products and other calcium-rich foods. This is especially true for teens, whose calcium needs (1,300 mg/day) are higher than those of adults (1,000 mg/day).

Iron

Iron is vital to oxygen delivery for aerobic energy production during endurance exercise and may be the most critical mineral with implications for sports performance. As an essential part of hemoglobin and myoglobin, iron helps deliver oxygen to active muscle cells. It is also a key component of several enzymes vital to the production of ATP by the oxygen energy system. (For more details about iron's functional roles, see Chapter 12, "Water and Major Minerals.")

Because of menstrual losses and lower dietary iron intakes, female athletes have a greater risk of iron deficiency than male athletes. In endurance athletes, the impact of running can cause mechanical trauma to capillaries in the feet and increase the breakdown of red blood cells. The increased breakdown may contribute to low iron status.[59] Some studies suggest that athletes involved in heavy training may need 30 to 70 percent more iron than nonathletes.[60]

Endurance training also increases the volume of plasma in the blood without initially changing the amount of hemoglobin. This dilutes the hemoglobin, even though training typically maintains or increases the amount of total hemoglobin. This condition, called **sports anemia**, is a false anemia for most athletes and can be remedied with a few days of rest.

Although many elite athletes, especially endurance athletes, have mild iron deficiency, few are anemic.[61] Although anemia can seriously impair a person's capacity to perform activities in the first stage of iron deficiency, there appears to be little effect on performance.[62]

sports anemia A lowered concentration of hemoglobin in the blood due to dilution. The increased plasma volume that dilutes the hemoglobin is a normal consequence of aerobic training.

Other Trace Minerals

Strenuous exercise taxes the body's reserves of copper (essential for red blood cell synthesis) and zinc (vital to the work of many enzymes involved in energy

Quick Bite

Sweating a World Record

When Alberto Salazar ran the Olympic marathon in 1984, he went down in the record books for sweat production. He lost 12 pounds during the 26.2-mile race, despite drinking about 2 liters. His sweat rate was approximately 3.7 liters per hour.

production). During endurance events, increased fluid loss increases mineral losses—zinc in urine and relatively high amounts of both zinc and copper in sweat.

Although these losses may cause marginal deficiencies, supplementation is not necessarily recommended. High-dose supplements of iron, copper, or zinc can interfere with the normal absorption of these and other minerals, so an excess of one can cause a deficiency of the others. Table 14.5 is an example of a training diet that would meet an athlete's needs for vitamins and minerals through food, which is preferable to taking supplements.

Key Concepts *Vitamins and minerals are important components of athletes' diets. B vitamins are necessary for normal energy metabolism. Adequate calcium intake can help protect against stress fractures and, coupled with exercise, delays the onset of osteoporosis. Iron is needed to carry oxygen. Strenuous exercise can tax the body's reserves of both copper and zinc.*

Fluid Needs During Exercise

Exercise generates heat, and heavy exercise can increase heat production 15- to 20-fold. (See **Figure 14.14**.) The increase in body heat triggers sweating, and sweat cools your body as it evaporates on your skin. The body of a well-

Table 14.5 A Sample Training Diet

Athlete performs prolonged daily training
Body weight = 70 kilograms
Energy intake = 3,400 kilocalories

Macronutrients

Carbohydrate	*Protein*	*Fat*
535 g	128 g	83 g
63% kcal	15% kcal	22% kcal
7.5 g/kg body weight*	1.8 g/kg body weight**	

Breakfast
8 oz orange juice
2 C Cheerios cereal
8 oz 1% milk
1 large bran muffin

Lunch
2 slices whole-wheat bread
2 oz turkey
2 slices tomato
Lettuce leaf
2 tsp mayonnaise
1 med apple
12 oz cranberry juice

Pre-exercise
8 oz Gatorade
1 cereal bar

Postexercise
1 bagel
2 oz string cheese
16 oz apple juice

Dinner
3 oz chicken breast
1 lg baked potato with
2 Tbsp low-fat sour cream
2 whole wheat dinner rolls
1 tsp margarine
1 C cooked broccoli
1 C salad greens with
2 Tbsp Italian salad dressing
8 oz 1% milk
1 C low-fat frozen yogurt

* Recommended carbohydrate intake goals for prolonged daily training
** Recommended protein intake goals up to 2 g/kg body weight for extreme training loads

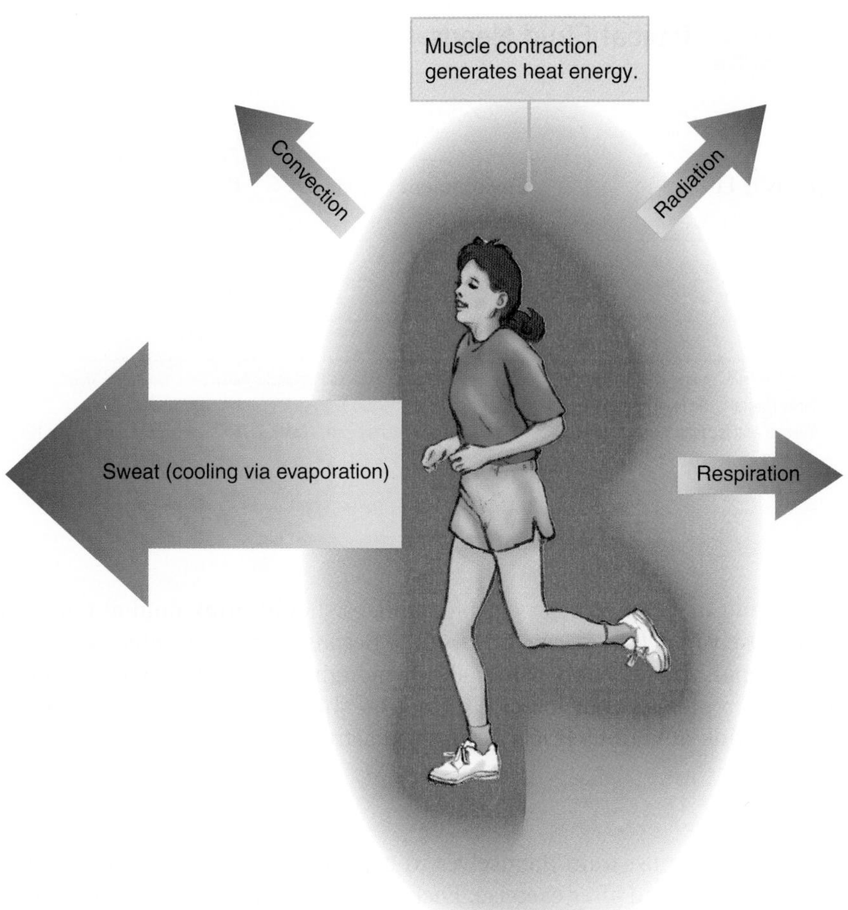

Figure 14.14 **Dissipation of heat during exercise.** During exercise, radiation, convection, and respiration are responsible for some heat loss, but evaporation of sweat dissipates more than 80 percent of the heat generated by increased physical activity.

trained athlete begins to cool itself soon after exercise begins. Even before core body temperature rises, the athlete's body starts to produce sweat. Sweat rate is affected by environmental temperature (extreme heat or extreme cold), humidity (higher humidity increases the rate of sweat production but reduces the efficiency of evaporation), type of clothing, fitness level, and initial fluid balance. During exercise in hot weather, sweat losses of endurance athletes can easily exceed 1 liter per hour.[63]

To keep the body from overheating, blood must flow to the skin, where evaporating sweat can dissipate heat. During exercise, the cooling demand for blood flow to the skin may compete with the cardiovascular demand for blood to deliver "fuel" to working muscles. Dehydration stresses both systems, making each less efficient. Without fluid replacement during heavy exercise, athletes can become dehydrated quickly, and a water deficit of 2 percent of body weight degrades athletic performance.[64] Signs of dehydration include the following:

- Elevated heart rate at a given exercise intensity
- Increased rate of **perceived exertion** during activity
- Decreased performance
- Lethargy
- Concentrated urine
- Infrequent urination
- Loss of appetite

perceived exertion The subjective experience of how difficult an effort is.

Drinking fluid during exercise helps offset fluid loss, minimize cardiovascular changes, reduce perception of effort, and maintain a supply of fuel

Table 14.6 **Typical Fluid Needs**

Activity Level	Environment	Fluid Requirements (liters per day)
Sedentary	Cool	2–3
Active	Cool	3–6
Sedentary	Warm	3–5
Active	Warm	5–10+

Note that fluid requirements include fluid from all sources—liquids, food, and metabolic water. See Chapter 12, "Water and Major Minerals," for more information.

Source: Adapted from Murray R. Drink more! Advice from a world class expert. *ACSM's Health and Fitness Journal.* 1997;1:19–23, 50.

to working muscles. When possible, athletes should drink fluid at rates that most closely match their sweating rates.[65] Because exercise inhibits the body's thirst signal, you probably won't take in enough fluid if you wait until you are thirsty to replenish your losses. Table 14.6 shows how much fluid a person should drink at various levels of physical activity.

Hydration

Active people must train themselves to consume adequate amounts of fluid before, during, and after exercise. Each person will have different water electrolyte losses based on factors such as body weight, genetic makeup, and metabolism, so each person should customize his or her hydration strategies.[66] Specific formulas and calculations are available to guide individuals in assessing these factors.[67]

The goal of hydrating before exercise is to start the physical activity with normal plasma electrolyte levels.[68] When hydrating before exercise, individuals should slowly drink beverages at least four hours before the exercise task.[69] Consuming beverages with sodium can help to stimulate thirst and retain needed fluids.[70] Because even partial dehydration can compromise performance (see Table 14.7), athletes should maintain fluid balance during the event.

The goal of drinking during exercise is to prevent excessive dehydration (> 2 percent body weight loss) and excessive changes in electrolyte balance.[71] It is difficult to recommend a specific fluid and electrolyte replacement schedule because of the nature of different exercise tasks, weather conditions, and other factors. Individuals should develop customized fluid-replacement programs that prevent excessive dehydration. If time permits, consumption of normal meals and beverages will restore hydration status. Individuals who require rapid recovery from excessive dehydration can drink approximately 1.5 liters of fluid for each kilogram of body weight lost.[72] Consuming beverages and snacks that contain sodium will help expedite rapid and complete recovery by stimulating thirst and fluid retention.[73]

Should athletes choose water, sports drinks, or other beverages? During activities that last fewer than 60 continuous minutes, water can replace fluid lost in sweat and help offset the rise in core temperature. During exercise that lasts longer than 60 continuous minutes, muscle and liver glycogen stores become depleted. Consuming fluids that contain carbohydrate and sodium

Table 14.7 Adverse Effects of Dehydration on Exercise and Performance

Percent Body Weight Loss	Adverse Effects on Performance
1	The thirst threshold. Leads to decrease in physical work capacity.
2	Stronger thirst, vague discomfort, loss of appetite.
3	Dry mouth, increasing hemoconcentration, reduction in urine output.
4	Decrease of 20 to 30% in physical work capacity.
5	Difficulty concentrating, headache, sleepiness.
6	Severe impairment in ability to regulate body temperature during exercise; increased respiratory rate, leading to tingling and numbness of extremities.
7	Collapse is likely if combined with heat and exercise.

can delay fatigue (see **Figure 14.15**), enhance palatability of fluids, and promote fluid retention.[74]

Optimal sports drinks provide energy (from glucose, glucose polymers, or sucrose) and electrolytes in a **palatable** solution that promotes rapid absorption (less than 10 percent carbohydrate concentration). (See Table 14.8.) The palatability of beverages containing electrolytes and 4 to 8 percent carbohydrate may increase the voluntary intake of fluid.[75] Beverages such as fruit juices and soft drinks are concentrated sources of carbohydrates (more than 10 percent) and may slow gastric emptying. In juices and many soft drinks, the main carbohydrate is fructose, which is associated with slower stomach

palatable Pleasant tasting.

Table 14.8 Desirable Composition of Sports Beverages

Characteristic	Comment
Fuel source	Contains carbohydrate: glucose, sucrose, and glucose polymers (maltodextrin). Goal intake is 60–70 g/hr (approximately 1 liter of a 6–8 percent carbohydrate drink).
Electrolytes	Contains sodium (70–165 mg per 240 mL) and potassium (30–75 mg per 240 mL) to replace sweat electrolyte loss when exercise is longer than 3–4 hours. Electrolytes also enhance palatability.
Rapid absorption	Contains 6–8 percent carbohydrate. Higher carbohydrate concentration slows gastric emptying and intestinal absorption.
Palatability	Flavored beverages enhance consumption. Electrolytes enhance flavor. Carbonation may decrease amount of fluid consumed.

Source: Fink HH, Burgoon LA, Mikesky AE. *Practical Applications in Sports Nutrition.* 2nd ed. Sudbury, MA: Jones & Bartlett, 2009.

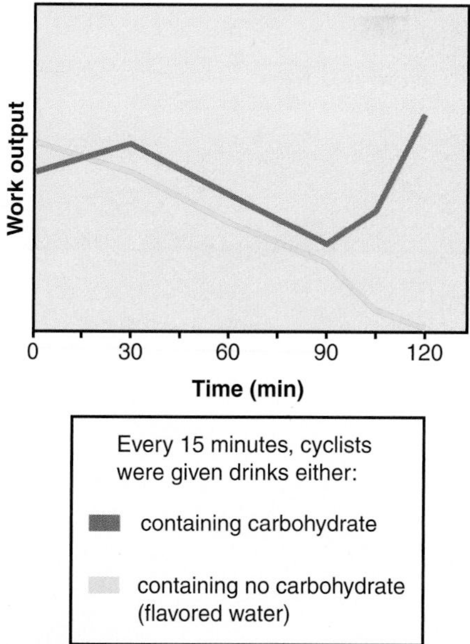

Figure 14.15 **Sports drinks and performance.** Consuming carbohydrate drinks dramatically increases power output after 90 minutes.

Quick Bite

Training: Young at Heart or Skeletal Old Age?

With endurance training, younger athletes largely achieve improvements as a result of increased cardiac output. Older athletes show greater improvement in the activities of the oxidative enzymes in their skeletal muscles.

emptying and abdominal cramps. Carbonated soft drinks may decrease the volume of fluid consumed and delay stomach emptying.

Athletes should avoid beverages that contain alcohol. Some athletes use alcohol for psychological benefits—calming nerves, improving self-confidence, and reducing anxiety, pain, and muscle tremor. This misguided effort fails to recognize alcohol's negative influence on physical performance. Alcohol slows reaction time, impairs coordination, and upsets balance. Its diuretic action contributes to dehydration and may impair regulation of body temperature.

For endurance events that last longer than four to five hours (or shorter events in high heat and humidity), athletes who do not replace electrolytes put themselves at risk for abnormally low levels of blood sodium. This life-threatening condition is associated with an excessive loss of electrolytes in sweat and with the excessive consumption of fluid, such as plain water, that does not replace electrolytes. See Table 14.9 for a summary of the American College of Sports Medicine's position on the amount and type of fluid to consume before, during, and after activity.

Table 14.9 American College of Sports Medicine Position on Fluid Replacement

Before Activity or Competition

- Drink adequate fluids during the 24 hours before an event, especially during the meal before exercise, to promote proper hydration before exercise or competition.
- Drink about 500 milliliters (~17 ounces) of fluid about two hours before exercise to promote adequate hydration and allow time for excretion of excess ingested water.

During Activity or Competition

- Start drinking early and at regular intervals to consume fluids at a rate sufficient to replace all the water lost through sweating or consume the maximal amount that can be tolerated.
- Fluids should be cooler than ambient temperature and flavored to enhance palatability and promote fluid replacement.

During Competition That Lasts More Than One Hour

- To maintain blood glucose concentration and delay the onset of fatigue, the fluid replacement should contain 4 to 8 percent carbohydrate. Electrolytes (primarily salt) are added to make the solution taste better and reduce the risk of low blood levels of sodium. About 0.5 to 0.7 grams of sodium per liter of water replaces sodium lost by sweating.

Following Activity or Competition

- Complete restoration of the extracellular fluid compartment cannot be sustained without replacement of lost sodium.
- For each pound (0.45 kilograms) of body weight lost, consume at least 2 cups (0.47 liters) of fluid.
- Thirst sensation is not an adequate gauge of dehydration, and postexercise consumption stimulates obligatory urine losses. Research shows that drinking an amount of liquid that is 125 to 150 percent of fluid loss is usually enough to promote complete rehydration.

Source: Modified from American College of Sports Medicine. Position stand: exercise and fluid replacement. *Med Sci Sports Exerc.* 2007;39:377–390. Reprinted by permission of Lippincott Williams & Wilkins, http://lww.com.

Nutrition Needs of Young Athletes

Young athletes (younger than 19 years) should place a higher priority on nutritional needs for growth and development than on athletic performance.[76] Studies indicate that diets in young athletes are often marginal or inadequate in energy intake.[77] The consequences of chronic low energy intake include the following:[78]

- Short stature and delayed puberty
- Nutrient deficiencies and dehydration
- Menstrual irregularities
- Poor bone health
- Increased incidence of injuries
- Increased risk of developing eating disorders

Parents and youth need to understand the energy and nutrient demands of growth and training, and many need help in planning meals and snacks to meet those needs. Many sport activities for this age group take place after school, and some schools serve lunch as early as 10:45 A.M. To provide energy for the activity and nutrients for recovery, young people should have meals and snacks before and after exercise. Easily portable snacks include fruit, pretzels, dry cereal, cereal bars, yogurt, sports drinks, sandwiches, and milk. Young athletes must drink adequate fluids during the day as well as at practice and competition. This is especially important because youths have a high tolerance for exercising in heat, which puts them at increased risk for heat exhaustion and heatstroke.

Quick Bite

Climbing with Age

Aging does not seem to impair a healthy person's ability to perform activities at a high altitude. However, aging reduces our ability to sweat. Our ability to regulate body temperature declines, thus reducing our ability to exercise safely in hot environments.

Key Concepts *Exercise of any type increases fluid losses through sweat. Evaporation of sweat from the skin allows the body to cool itself. Fluid losses must be replaced to avoid dehydration. Athletes need to drink plenty of fluid before, during, and after exercise. Fluid choices depend on the duration of activity and the preferences of the athlete. Optimal sports drinks provide energy and electrolytes in a solution that promotes rapid absorption. Nutrient intakes by young athletes must support both competition and continued growth.*

Nutrition Supplements and Ergogenic Aids

The pressure to win contributes to athletes' search for a competitive edge. Supplement use (i.e., for the purpose of enhancing athletic performance) is increasing among adolescent and collegiate athletes, and the average age of initiation of use is decreasing.[79] In the adolescent population, use is estimated at 24 to 29 percent, and the likelihood of use increases with increasing physical activity.[80] One large study found that about two-thirds of supplement use starts before college, and 9.2 percent begins before high school.[81] More than 75 percent of recreational and elite athletes use nutritional supplements and **ergogenic aids** with the expectation of improved performance.[82] More than 30 percent of American male and female adolescents are reported to use high-energy drinks and capsules on a regular basis.[83] Nutrition supplements and ergogenic aids include products and practices that

- Provide calories (e.g., liquid supplements and energy bars)
- Provide vitamins and minerals (including multivitamin supplements)
- Contribute to performance during exercise and enhance recovery after exercise (e.g., sports drinks and carbohydrate supplements)

ergogenic aids Substances that can enhance athletic performance.

Table 14.10 Types of Ergogenic Aids

Type of Ergogenic Aid	Description	Examples
Nutritional	Any supplement, food product, or dietary manipulation that enhances work capacity or athletic performance.	Carbohydrate loading; amino acid or vitamin supplements
Physiological	Any practice or substance that enhances the functioning of the body's various systems (e.g., cardiovascular, muscular) and thus improves athletic performance.	Any type of physical training (e.g., endurance, strength), blood doping via transfusions, warming up and/or stretching
Psychological	Any practice or treatment that changes mental state and thereby enhances sport performance.	Visualization, hypnosis, pep talks, relaxation techniques
Biomechanical	Any device, piece of equipment, or external product that can be used to improve athletic performance during practice or competition.	Weight belts, knee wraps, oversize tennis rackets, body suits (swimming/track)
Pharmacological	Any substance or compound classified as a drug or hormonal agent that is used to improve work output and/or sport performance.	Hormones (e.g., growth hormones, anabolic steroids), caffeine

- Are believed to stimulate and maintain muscle growth (e.g., purified amino acids)[84]
- Contain micronutrients, herbal, and/or cellular components that are promoted as ergogenic aids to enhance performance (e.g., caffeine, chromium picolinate, and creatine)[85]
- Are used for nutritional, physiological, psychological, biomechanical, or pharmacological reasons (see Table 14.10)

Most nutritional supplements are unnecessary for athletes who select a variety of foods and meet their energy needs. However, iron and calcium supplements may be recommended for female athletes if their diets are low in these nutrients. Liquid supplements and sports bars that contain carbohydrates, proteins, and fats can provide an easy way to increase energy intake. Sports drinks, gels, and recovery drinks also can contribute to needed fluids and carbohydrates before, during, and after exercise.

Dietary supplements marketed as performance enhancers are another matter. Herbals, glandulars, enzymes, hormones, and other compounds aimed at athletes carry many attractive claims. Although some products have been well researched, most lack vigorous clinical trials to evaluate efficacy, apply to only one gender (usually males), or are relevant to only one sport (e.g., weight lifting).

Regulation and Concerns About Dietary and Herbal Supplements

All prescription and over-the-counter drugs and food additives must meet the Food and Drug Administration's safety and effectiveness requirements; however, dietary supplements bypass these regulations. Before 1994, when the Dietary Supplement Health and Education Act (DSHEA) was signed into law, dietary supplements were regulated in the same manner as other foods. Prior to the DSHEA, many people felt that the FDA was too restrictive in regulating dietary supplements. As a result, the DSHEA was passed and dietary supplements were placed in a special category of "foods."[86] Currently, dietary supplement manufacturers must adhere to a number of federal regulations before a product can go on the market, they must have evidence that the ingredients sold in their supplements are generally safe if required to do so by the FDA, and they must follow Good Manufacturing Practice Guidelines.

Manufacturers themselves have the responsibility to determine and communicate product safety, as well as defend any representations or claims made about the product and show that the claims are not false or misleading.[87] DSHEA requires supplement manufacturers to include the following information on the label: "This statement has not been evaluated by the FDA. This product is not intended to diagnose, treat, cure, or prevent any disease."[88] Over the last 10 to 15 years, in an effort to abide by the DSHEA requirements and to follow the Good Manufacturing Practice Guidelines, a number of supplement companies have employed teams of researchers (many of whom are MS- or PhD-prepared exercise physiologists or sports nutrition specialists) who help educate the public about nutrition and exercise, provide input on product development, conduct preliminary research on products, or assist in coordinating research trials conducted by independent research teams.[89]

Although laws exist to ensure product safety and reliability, there is still room for discrepancy between the actual content of supplements and what is reported on the label. Results of an extensive survey conducted in a laboratory in Germany looked at the prevalence of supplements contaminated with products not listed on their product labels. A total of 634 different product samples were purchased from 13 countries around the world. These were analyzed for the presence of steroid hormones and their precursors. Ninety-four supplements (14.8 percent of the total) were shown to contain prohibited substances. For another 10 percent, the analysis was not conclusive, but steroids may have been present. That is close to a one-in-four risk! Substantial numbers of positive tests were obtained from products bought in the Netherlands (26 percent), the United States (19 percent), United Kingdom (19 percent), and elsewhere. The names of the prohibited supplements have not been published, but they included vitamins and minerals, protein supplements, creatine, and many others.[90]

Two important conclusions can be drawn from the above information: (1) many supplements that people purchase online or in health food stores are produced in countries where product contamination has been found and where industry quality control points are often minimal, and (2) dietary supplements may contain substances not shown on the package label that may be harmful or can lead to a positive doping test in sport competitions.

Given the documented widespread contamination of nutritional supplements,[91] high-performing athletes are generally advised to stay away from supplements because their purity and safety are not guaranteed. This recommendation should not, however, be confused with responsible and educated use of supplements, if and when indicated. In fact, the Academy of Nutrition

Quick Bite

Placebo Power!

Athletes involved in a heavy weight-lifting program volunteered to participate in a study in which they would take what they thought were anabolic steroids. The results were dramatic: during four weeks of treatment, these experienced weightlifters had a nearly 7.5-fold increase in the rate of their strength gain. However, they were taking a placebo—an inactive substance identical in appearance to the genuine drug. Because there was no pharmacological effect, gains were solely due to their belief in the treatment.

and Dietetics, the Dieticians of Canada, and the American College of Sports Medicine issued a joint position statement, published in 2009, regarding nutrition and athletic performance.[92] This position indicates that physical performance and recovery are enhanced by optimal nutrition and that although supplementation is normally not necessary by athletes with an adequate diet, it may be needed if energy intake is restricted or groups of food are eliminated from their diet.

A federal report addressing growing concerns about the supplement industry and how adverse events resulting from supplement use are largely underreported was released in 2009.[93] As a result, just as changes were made to the regulation of supplements back in 1994, changes to the industry's self-regulation may be on the horizon.

Convenience Supplements

Convenience supplements are meal replacement powders, ready-to-drink supplements, energy bars, and energy gels. They represent the largest segment of the nutrition industry, claiming 50 to 75 percent of most company's sales.[94] They are typically fortified with 33 to 50 percent of the RDA for vitamins and minerals and generally differ on the amount of carbohydrate, protein, and fat they contain.[95] For use in sports nutrition, convenience supplements are best suited to provide carbohydrate, protein, and other nutrients prior to or following exercise in situations in which the athlete does not have time to choose, prepare, and eat a regular meal. They are most appropriately used to improve availability of macronutrients, not as a replacement for a day of good eating.

Weight-Gain Powders

One common way athletes try to increase muscle mass is to add extra calories from protein to their diet. Studies have consistently shown that adding an extra 500 to 1,000 calories per day to your diet will promote significant weight gain,[96] and protein powders are a relatively easy way to do just that. However, only about 30 to 50 percent of the weight gained on high-calorie diets is muscle, while the remaining amount of weight gained is fat.[97] There is no evidence that increasing protein intake above recommended levels improves muscle growth; however, protein supplements may be useful to meet body needs for athletes whose protein intake is inadequate in their overall diet.[98] Remember, it is adequate resistance training fueled by sufficient calorie intake, along with adequate rest between training sessions, that contributes to muscle formation, not protein intake alone. Caution should be used with this type of weight-gain approach because the extra calories ingested may increase body fat rather than muscle mass.

Amino Acids

Researchers have studied the use of individual amino acids to enhance performance and have not found obvious benefits.

Branched-chain amino acids (BCAAs) are often used as an anticatabolic compound in an effort to decrease the breakdown of body tissue. The BCAAs leucine, isoleucine, and valine are reported to aid in endurance exercise by counteracting central fatigue, possibly by interfering with tryptophan kinetics or other mechanisms, thus improving performance.[99] Supplements containing BCAAs may prove to be helpful for sports such as tennis, soccer, distance running, cycling, and swimming. The research has been conflicting, and further study is needed.[100] Because safety and effectiveness have not been established, BCAA supplements are not recommended.

HMB, also known as hydroxymethylbutyrate, beta-hydroxyisovalerate, and 3-hydroxyisovalerate, is a metabolite of the essential branched-chain amino acid leucine. It is found in foods such as catfish, citrus fruits, and breast milk.[101] HMB is promoted as an "anticatabolic" agent that exerts an anabolic effect by suppressing protein breakdown and cellular damage after intense exercise, thereby allowing quicker recovery and increased lean body mass and strength.[102] HMB also is a cholesterol precursor, and its promotion of muscle growth may be due to its provision of a larger supply of cholesterol for cell membrane synthesis to "patch up" local deficiencies of membrane cholesterol that are believed to occur with muscular hypertrophy.[103]

Glutamine, the dispensable amino acid, is a popular supplement for strength athletes. Proponents of glutamine supplements suggest that intense weight training produces catabolic effects on muscle protein and therefore would increase glutamine requirements. However, supplementation studies have not supported an ergogenic effect of glutamine supplementation.[104] Glutamine is also known to be used by immune cells, and some athletes use supplements enriched with glutamine in an attempt to optimize immune function.[105]

Creatine

Creatine, a nitrogenous compound in meats and fish, is synthesized by the liver, pancreas, and kidney. Muscles store creatine mainly as creatine phosphate, which functions as part of the ATP–CP energy system. Creatine has become a popular supplement based on the theory that increasing muscle creatine would prolong short-term energy availability and thus improve performance in short-term, high-intensity activities (such as weight lifting).[106] Several well-controlled studies have shown improvements in muscle strength when creatine supplementation was added to a strength training regimen.[107] Creatine supplements also may improve the explosive power needed for sprints.[108] However, creatine supplements appear to have no benefit for aerobic training.

creatine An important nitrogenous compound found in meats and fish, and synthesized in the body from amino acids (glycine, arginine, and methionine).

The main side effect seems to be immediate weight gain attributable to water retention. Frequently, gastrointestinal side effects are reported anecdotally, including nausea, diarrhea, dyspepsia, and abdominal pain, possibly due to malabsorption of high doses of creatine.[109] Other adverse effects that have been reported include rash, dyspnea, anxiety, headache, and fatigue.[110] The *Physician's Desk Reference* states that contraindications to creatine use include renal failure and other renal disorders, including nephrotic syndrome, and that creatine should be avoided in children, adolescents, pregnant women, nursing mothers, diabetics, and other persons at risk for renal disease.[111]

Increases in muscle mass are probably a response to the increased stress that an athlete can put on muscle tissue by maximal exercise bursts—the supplement without weight training will have no effect. Also, the ability to store more CP may vary widely among people, so supplements may not be effective for everyone.

With the increasing popularity of creatine supplementation comes questions about its long-term safety. Anecdotal reports of muscle cramps, muscle strains, kidney dysfunction, and GI distress have raised concerns. However, college football players who have used creatine for as long as five years have not shown any negative health effects, including no detrimental effects on liver or kidney function.[112] In another study of college football players, creatine supplementation during training did not increase the risk of muscle cramping or injury.[113] Nevertheless, the FDA has advised consumers to consult a physician before they use creatine.

Antioxidants

As we exercise, our muscles consume more oxygen than when we are at rest. Increased oxygen consumption leads to increased production of free radicals. Free radicals can damage cell membranes and DNA, leading to conditions such as cancer, aging, and a number of degenerative diseases. So, exercise promotes health, but it may also increase cell damage.

Antioxidants, which are compounds that seek out and neutralize free radicals, may protect muscles and cells from the damage that can result from exercise.[114] Antioxidants come in different forms, such as vitamins, minerals, enzyme complexes, and herbs. Vitamin C, vitamin E, and beta-carotene are well-known antioxidants. Antioxidants can be obtained via food or supplements. Examples of good food sources of antioxidants include deep orange- and green-colored vegetables, citrus fruits, whole grains, and green tea.

People who exercise infrequently or sporadically, as well as those who exercise intensely and for long periods of time, have higher risk for damage than those who exercise regularly and on a more moderate schedule. Studies show that regular, moderate exercise enhances the antioxidant defense system and protects against exercise-induced free radical damage. In contrast, intense exercise in untrained individuals overwhelms the body's defenses, resulting in increased free radical damage.

Does supplementing with antioxidants or eating foods rich in antioxidants repair free radical damage after exercise? The answer is a bit complex. Nutrition deficiencies can create difficulties in training and recovery (possibly due to free radical damage); however, the role of antioxidant supplementation in a well-nourished athlete is controversial. It is not necessary, or advisable, for a well-nourished athlete to take antioxidant supplements.[115]

Regarding antioxidants and exercise, the best recommendation goes back to the basics: follow a balanced training program that emphasizes regular exercise, and eat five servings of fruits or vegetables each day. These practices will ensure that you are developing your antioxidant systems and that your diet is providing the necessary components.

Caffeine

Caffeine is a natural stimulant. Research suggests that caffeine may affect athletic performance by facilitating signals between the nervous system and the muscles, as well as by decreasing an athlete's perceived effort during exercise. Caffeine may also increase the body's ability to break down fat for energy. Evidence suggests that caffeine enhances endurance and provides a small, but worthwhile, enhancement of performance over a range of exercise protocols, from short-duration, high-intensity events to ultra-endurance events.[116] In studies that examined prolonged exercise lasting 60 minutes or longer, the beneficial effects from caffeine intake occurred at small to moderate levels of intake (1–3 mg/kg body weight or total of 70–150 mg caffeine) and when caffeine was ingested at a variety of times (before and/or throughout exercise or toward the end of exercise when the athlete was becoming fatigued).[117]

Caffeine may produce ergogenic effects at doses as low as 250 milligrams (3.0–3.5 mg/kg body weight).[118] Most studies showing benefit used doses of around 400 to 600 milligrams,[119] and on a body-weight basis, a reasonable dose would be 5 milligrams per kilogram.[120] In the past, caffeine was banned by the World Anti-Doping Agency (WADA) above a threshold urinary concentration, but in 2007, WADA declared it legal at any level.[121] However, the National Collegiate Athletic Association (NCAA) has set an upper legal limit of 15 micrograms per milliliter (μg/mL) in urine.[122] A 100-milligram dose of caffeine increases urine levels by approximately 1.5 μg/mL; therefore, 800 to 1,000 mg would need to be ingested to approach the legal limit.[123] The ergogenic benefits of caffeine use may depend on abstinence for several days before,[124] and its effect is more pronounced in relative nonusers (<50 mg per day) than in regular users (>300 mg per day).[125]

Caution should be taken when consuming beverages that contain caffeine. At high levels of intake, caffeine has the potential to increase heart rate, impair or alter fine-motor control and technique, interfere with sleep patterns, and affect recovery between training sessions. It is important to find the lowest effective dose of caffeine that can be used to achieve performance enhancement.[126] No evidence suggests that performance increases with increases in caffeine intake, and long-term intake of large amounts of caffeine (>500 mg per day) is generally discouraged.[127]

Ephedrine

Ephedrine was a popular ergogenic supplement until its sale in the United States was prohibited by the FDA.[128] Despite its previous ban by the NFL, NCAA, and IOC, athletes continued to use ephedrine, either as a weight-loss aid or to gain a performance edge. Ephedrine stimulates the central nervous system and is an effective bronchodilator. In addition, it raises both heart rate and blood pressure. Athletes hoped its stimulatory effects would improve performance, suppress appetite, and promote weight loss. Some studies support these purported benefits, especially when ephedrine is combined with caffeine.[129]

Ephedrine became one of the most controversial supplements on the market. Found in many products as either the herbal ma huang (ephedra) or the synthetic ephedrine, serious side effects such as hypertension, insomnia, anxiety, tremors, headache, dependence, psychosis, nephrolithiasis, seizures, arrhythmias, strokes, myocardial infarction, and even death have been attributed to this supplement.[130] When the 2003 heatstroke-related death of Major League Baseball pitcher Steve Bechler was linked to ephedra use, sports organizations and other groups began to pay more attention. A government-sponsored review of safety and efficacy concluded that the use of ephedrine, ephedra-containing dietary supplements, or ephedrine plus caffeine is associated with two to three times the risk of nausea, vomiting, psychiatric symptoms such as anxiety and change in mood, autonomic hyperactivity, and palpitations.[131] Studies such as this led to the FDA's conclusion that ephedrine posed an unreasonable risk of illness and injury. Although prohibited by the FDA, ephedrine is still available to athletes via the Internet. Ephedra's risks clearly outweigh its benefits, however.

Sodium Bicarbonate

Some athletes consume sodium bicarbonate (baking soda) in the belief that it will help neutralize the buildup of lactic acid in muscles. Whether **soda loading** actually produces an ergogenic effect is controversial. Sodium bicarbonate ingestion has been shown to improve performance in single-bout, high-intensity events, probably due to an increase in buffering capacity.[132] Likewise, studies that evaluate events lasting from 2 to 10 minutes, where lactic acid buildup is most likely, have shown some positive results related to interval training performance.[133]

soda loading Consumption of bicarbonate (baking soda) to raise blood pH. The intent is to increase the capacity to buffer acids, thus delaying fatigue. Also known as bicarbonate loading.

Bicarbonate loading can also produce negative effects. Athletes who follow this regimen report side effects such as intestinal discomfort, stomach distress, nausea, cramping, diarrhea, and water retention. Although bicarbonate loading is not banned, it does have serious health-related consequences. Bicarbonate loading increases blood alkalinity and influences blood pressure. Anyone with high blood pressure (hypertension) should not bicarbonate-load.

Chromium

The trace mineral chromium is vital to the movement of glucose into cells. Because of the link between chromium, glucose use, and insulin, chromium has become a popular supplement (typically in the form of chromium picolinate) for both weight loss and athletic performance. The theory is that by enhancing insulin action, chromium increases amino acid uptake, which then increases protein synthesis and promotes a gain in muscle mass.

Although the developers of the chromium picolinate supplements had promising results in several studies, a review of 24 studies found no significant reduction in body fat or increase in lean muscle mass.[134] Chromium supplementation does not appear to enhance body composition or performance in well-trained individuals.[135] Given these results and the potential risks from chromium picolinate supplementation (see Chapter 13, "Trace Minerals"), this supplement cannot be recommended.

Iron

Iron supplements are used commonly by athletes for performance enhancement, a practice that can be helpful or harmful. In the presence of iron-deficiency anemia, which is more common in young athletes than in the general population, supplementation is clearly beneficial for performance;[136] however, the diagnosis can be difficult to establish in athletes. The reason is that in response to training, hemoglobin concentration decreases as the plasma volume expands to a greater degree than does red cell mass, resulting in sports anemia. An elevated serum transferrin receptor level is an indicator of iron deficiency in athletes. Studies of iron supplementation showed objective performance improvement only in athletes who had iron-deficiency anemia or untrained individuals with low ferritin levels.[137] Athletes with normal or low ferritin levels do not benefit from supplementation.[138] Iron supplementation does not come without risks. Complications of iron overload include hemochromatosis.[139]

Key Concepts *Numerous dietary supplements, such as caffeine, chromium, creatine, and antioxidants, are marketed for performance-enhancing effects. However, few have been subjected to rigorous clinical trials or long-term safety evaluation. Athletes should consult a physician before adding dietary supplements to their training regimen.*

Quick Bite

The Burn to the Finish

The pain a runner feels when approaching the finish line and immediately after the event is called acute muscle soreness. The culprits include a buildup of metabolic by-products, and tissue edema caused by fluid seeping from the bloodstream into surrounding tissues. The pain and soreness usually disappear within minutes or hours.

Weight and Body Composition

Pete, a bodybuilder, wants to bulk up by gaining 15 pounds of muscle and not fat. Sarah, on the other hand, wants to compete as a lightweight rower and needs to lose 7 pounds. Some athletes struggle to lose weight, but others find it nearly impossible to gain weight and muscle mass. Whether intentionally gaining or losing weight, weight change should be accomplished slowly—during the off-season or at the beginning of the season before competition starts.

Body composition and body weight are just two of many factors that affect exercise performance. Body composition can affect strength, agility, and appearance. Body weight can influence speed, endurance, and power. Because body fat adds weight without adding strength, many sports emphasize low body fat percentages. Yet, by themselves, body composition and body weight do not accurately predict athletic performance.[140]

Weight Gain: Build Muscle, Lose Fat

Weight gain is influenced by genetics, stage of adolescent development, gender, body mass, diet, training program, prior resistance training, motivation, and use of supplements and anabolic steroids, among other factors. Complex interactions among these factors make it difficult to predict an athlete's ability to meet a weight goal. However, experience tells us the following:

- Untrained male athletes can gain approximately 3 to 4 pounds of lean body mass per month in the early stages of a rigorous resistance-training program.[141] Because of their smaller muscle mass and lean tissue, young women can achieve only 50 to 75 percent of the gains seen in male counterparts, but with the same relative strength.
- Approximately 20 percent of the increase in lean body mass occurs in the first year of resistance training, tapering to 1 to 3 percent in subsequent years. Scientists believe that the rate declines as muscle mass approaches the maximum potential amount determined by genetics.
- Some male athletes of high school age have difficulty gaining muscle mass. These athletes may be in the early stages of the adolescent growth spurt and may lack sufficient levels of the male hormones to stimulate muscle development.

Nutrition plays an important role in increasing lean body mass. Athletes must consume enough calories, along with adequate carbohydrate and protein, to gain the desired muscle mass.[142]

Key Concepts *Athletes often seek to improve their power and strength by increasing muscle mass. Weight gain as muscle requires increased dietary calories, primarily as carbohydrate, combined with strength training.*

Weight Loss: The Panacea for Optimal Performance?

As the pressure to win increases, many coaches and athletes come to believe that weight loss and lower body fat composition will provide that competitive edge. Athletes strive for lower body weight and lower body fat for three reasons: (1) to improve appearance, especially in aesthetic sports (e.g., diving, figure skating, gymnastics), (2) to enhance performance where lower body weight may increase speed (e.g., race walking, running, pole vaulting, jumping, cross-country skiing), or (3) to qualify in a lower weight category (e.g., wrestling, boxing, and rowing).[143] **Figure 14.16** illustrates the key factors in a successful weight-loss program.

As healthy young adults, men average 15 percent body fat, and women average 25 percent.[144] Although these averages provide starting points, recommendations for individual athletes must account for genetic background, age, gender, sport, health, and weight history. Male athletes should not go below 5 to 7 percent body fat. For female athletes, current research data suggest a minimum of 13 to 17 percent body fat to maintain normal menstrual function, which in turn is important for maintaining bone health.[145]

Quick Bite

What's the Best "Fat-Burning" Exercise?

It's a common misconception that low-intensity exercise is superior for "fat burning." Aerobic activities do use a greater percentage of fat as fuel, but it is the total amount of calories expended during exercise that supports increased mobilization of fat in response to a caloric deficit. In terms of actual energy expenditure, higher-intensity exercise requires more calories for a given time period than exercise at a lower intensity. Thus, to lose body fat, the fuel (source of calories) is not as important as the amount of energy expended.

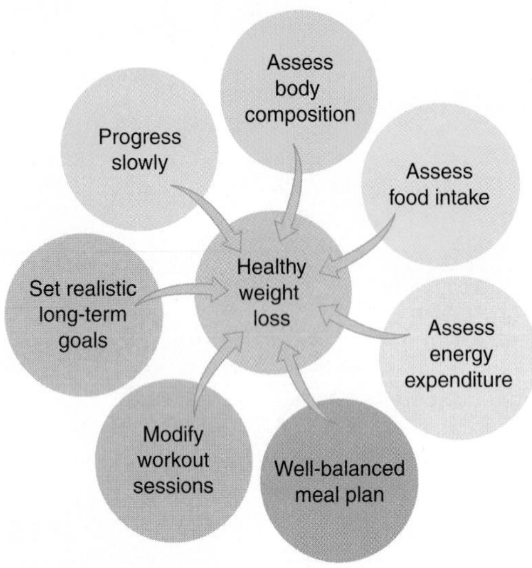

Figure 14.16 **Keys to successful weight loss.** Just as athletes focus on proper training techniques to avoid injury and improve performance, they should focus on proper weight-loss strategies to lose weight and maintain health.

Keeping accurate food and training records provides information on energy intake and expenditure. The best way for athletes to sustain a safe and sensible loss of body fat is to reduce calorie intake moderately and modify their training program. A combination of resistance training and aerobic activity is best for weight loss, because it helps maintain or even increase lean body mass while simultaneously decreasing fat mass.

Beware of fad weight-loss methods such as ketogenic diets, high-protein diets, and semistarvation diets. These practices can compromise energy reserves, body composition, and psychological well-being, leading to decreased performance and increased health risks. Athletes often are alert to the latest supplements to hit the market. Many claim to accelerate the burning of body fat and augment weight loss. In reality, studies show that most "fat burners" are ineffective or associated with only very modest weight loss in obese subjects.[146]

Key Concepts *Before embarking on a weight-loss program, athletes should carefully evaluate their goals and set a realistic plan for weight loss and maintenance. Safe weight-loss practices include modest changes in food intake accompanied by gradual increases in aerobic activity.*

Weight Loss: Negative Consequences for the Competitive Athlete?

Changing body size and shape can have detrimental effects. An unrealistic perception of optimal body weight and a belief that weight loss is necessary for improved performance can contribute to unhealthy weight-loss practices.[147] Athletes risk medical problems when dieting goes awry.

Making Weight

Wrestlers, weight lifters, boxers, jockeys, rowers, and coxswains face competitive pressures to "make weight" to compete or to be certified in a lower weight classification. Such athletes often resort to the **pathogenic** weight-control behaviors summarized in Table 14.11. Repeated cycles of rapid weight loss and subsequent regain increase the risk of disordered eating, fatigue, psychological distress (anger, anxiety, depression), dehydration, and sudden death.

Studies show that wrestlers, in attempts to gain a competitive advantage, will try to reduce weight a few days before or on the day of competition.[148] Often, extreme measures are taken to lose a significant amount of weight. In the process, body water loss may be extensive and dangerous. A fluid loss of only 2 percent of initial body weight (3 pounds for a 150-pound individual) can decrease athletic performance by elevating heart rate and lowering **cardiac output**. Moderate to severe dehydration (more than 3 to 5 percent of body weight) can be dangerous because of increased core body temperature, electrolyte imbalances, and cardiac and kidney changes. These conditions may result in heat illness, including heat cramps, heat exhaustion, or heatstroke.

Rapid weight loss can have serious health consequences. During one month in 1998, three previously healthy collegiate wrestlers died trying to make weight.[149] These athletes had not only dropped significant weight preseason—more than 20 pounds (9 kilograms)—but also lost between 3.5 to 9 pounds (1.6 to 4 kilograms) in the one to nine hours before their deaths. The wrestlers restricted food and fluid intake. To maximize sweat losses, they wore vapor-impermeable suits under cotton warm-up suits and exercised vigorously in hot environments. Dehydration and **hyperthermia** (elevated

pathogenic Capable of causing disease.

cardiac output The amount of blood expelled by the heart.

hyperthermia A much higher than normal body temperature.

Table 14.11 **Pathogenic Weight-Loss Practices**

Behavior	Consequence
Fasting	Loss of lean body mass and decreased metabolic rate
Diet pills	Medical side effects and weight regained when discontinued
Fat-free diets	Deficient in macronutrients and micronutrients; difficult to maintain
Diuretics	Dehydration and electrolyte imbalance; no fat loss
Laxatives	Dehydration; no fat loss; may be addicting
Sweating	Dehydration; heat injury; no fat loss
Excessive exercise	Risk of injury and overtraining; no fat loss
Enemas	Dehydration and GI problems; no fat loss
Fluid restriction	Dehydration; heat injury; no fat loss
Self-induced vomiting	Dehydration; acid–base and electrolyte imbalances; esophageal tears and GI bleeding; erosion of dental enamel and swollen parotid glands

Source: Modified from Otis CL. Too slim, amenorrheic, fracture-prone: the female athlete triad. *ACSM's Health and Fitness.* 1998;2:2–25. Reprinted by permission of Lippincott Williams & Wilkins, http://lww.com.

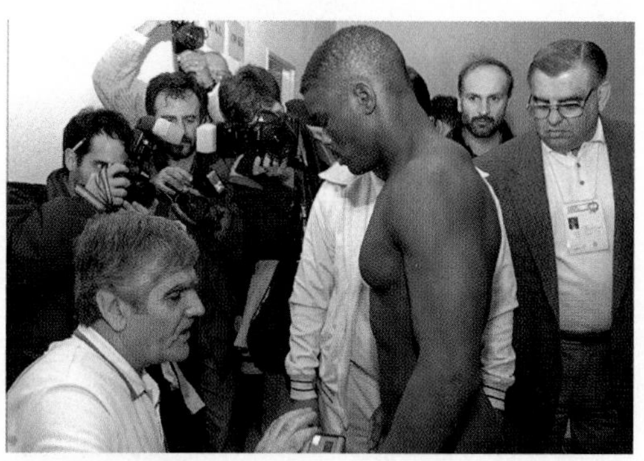

Figure 14.17 **Weighing in.** The NCAA discourages athletes from reducing their weight through intentional dehydration, a dangerous and potentially deadly practice.

body temperature) led to their demise. Since 1998, the NCAA has revised the guidelines for monitoring weight-loss practices and weigh-in procedures. (See **Figure 14.17**.) This includes educating coaches and athletic trainers about healthy weight-control strategies and limiting the amount of preseason and precompetition weight loss.[150] More recently, the NCAA has adopted a new weigh-in format that requires athletes to have a season minimum weight, established at the start of the year. This format attempts to prevent the use of techniques and tools that have been used in the past for rapid dehydration that results in rapid weight loss.[151]

Female Athlete Triad

Although the majority of female athletes benefit from increased physical activity, there are those who go too far and risk developing a trio of medical problems. (See "Spotlight on Eating Disorders.") In 1991, the American College of Sports Medicine coined the term **female athlete triad** to describe the interaction of disordered eating, amenorrhea, and premature osteoporosis.[152] Female athletes who compete in endurance sports, such as long-distance running; aesthetic sports, such as gymnastics; antigravitational sports, such as indoor rock climbing; and sports with weight classifications, such as karate, are at the greatest risk.[153]

female athlete triad A syndrome in young female athletes that involves disordered eating, amenorrhea, and lowered bone density.

Disordered Eating

Female athletes who compete in endurance events, such as long-distance running, or in sports where appearance is important (e.g., gymnastics, figure skating, diving) are at higher risk for disordered eating behaviors. In some cases, disordered eating can progress to an eating disorder. Anorexia nervosa

Quick Bite

Ouch! But I Felt Fine Yesterday . . .

After a bout of heavy exercise, a person may not feel muscle soreness for a day or two. We do not fully understand this painful phenomenon, which is called delayed-onset muscle soreness. Activities that lengthen muscles seem to be the primary cause. The muscles suffer damage, with micro-tears in their structure. This leads to an inflammatory response, causing localized muscle pain, swelling, and tenderness.

appears to be no more prevalent among female athletes than among nonathletes. However, the prevalence of bulimia nervosa and subclinical eating disorders is higher in athletes.[154] Data suggest that lean-sport athletes are at greater risk for disordered eating than athletes in nonlean sports.[155] For more on disordered eating and eating disorders, see the "Spotlight on Eating Disorders."

Amenorrhea

In the general population, 2 to 5 percent of women have **amenorrhea**. However, the prevalence is much higher in athletes.[156] Research indicates that amenorrhea in athletic women is related to the combined effects of increased physical activity, weight loss, low body fat levels, and insufficient energy intake.

amenorrhea [A-men-or-Ee-a] Absence or abnormal stoppage of menses in a female; commonly indicated by the absence of three to six consecutive menstrual cycles.

Premature Osteoporosis

Health consequences of amenorrhea include premature osteoporosis. Research shows that amenorrheic athletes experience rapid loss of bone mineral density in the spine, which can spread to other parts of the skeleton if amenorrhea continues for a long time.

Treatment involves replacing estrogen, which is low in amenorrheic females. Oral contraceptives are the most common method of estrogen replacement and can also serve as a reliable form of birth control. Calcium supplementation is also recommended. Although bone mineralization may never return to normal in amenorrheic athletes, studies indicate that reducing the intensity of training, improving dietary intake, and increasing body weight can help restore menstruation and increase bone density.[157]

Breaking the Triad

Female athletes at risk are perfectionists, driven to excel in a given sport, who believe that a specific athletic body image is required to excel as an athlete.

Table 14.12 Combating Disordered Eating in Athletes

De-emphasize body weight. Do not view the athlete's weight as the primary contributor to, or detractor from, athletic performance. Research indicates that athletes can achieve appropriate weight and fitness when the focus is on physical conditioning and strength development, as well as the cognitive and emotional aspects of performance.

Eliminate group weigh-ins. Often viewed as a way to motivate the team, the practice of group weigh-ins can be destructive to people who are struggling with their body image and disordered eating. If there is a legitimate reason for weighing an athlete, explain the reason and weigh the athlete privately.

Treat each athlete individually. Many athletes have an unrealistic perception of what an ideal body weight is, especially in sports for which leanness is considered important. Additionally, athletes may strive for weight and body composition that may be realistic in only a few genetically endowed people. It is important to understand that genetic and biological processes, rather than one's willpower to control food intake, affect a person's weight.

Facilitate healthy weight management. Be sensitive to issues related to weight control and dieting. Because many athletes have limited knowledge of sports nutrition, they resort to pathogenic weight-loss practices. Athletes can benefit from nutrition counseling by a sports nutritionist or a registered dietitian who has experience in working with athletes and disordered eating.

Source: Modified from Thompson RA, Sherman RT. Reducing the risk of eating disorders in athletics. *Eating Disorders: J Treatment Prevent.* 1993;1:65–78. Reproduced by permission of Taylor & Francis Group, LLC, http://www.taylorandfrancis.com.

Some reports estimate as many as 60 percent of female athletes in aesthetic sports (e.g., dance, skating, diving, gymnastics) and weight-dependent sports (e.g., rowing, martial arts, horse racing) may be at risk.[158]

Screening, referral, and education are keys to preventing the female athlete triad. Prevention and treatment are most successful when they are multidisciplinary efforts carried out by a team of medical, athletic, nutrition, and mental health experts. Proactive sports education includes reducing the emphasis on body weight, eliminating group weigh-ins, treating each athlete individually, and facilitating healthy weight management. (See Table 14.12.)

Key Concepts *Pathogenic weight-control practices increase the risk of dehydration and compromise performance; they may have long-term serious consequences for athletes. The female athlete triad—disordered eating, amenorrhea, and premature osteoporosis—results from excessive weight loss. Often weight loss is driven by unrealistic ideas of appropriate body weight and shape for competition. Education of coaches and athletes is essential to prevent the female athlete triad.*

Sports drinks are often recommended instead of plain water for those who engage in vigorous physical activity. Their proponents claim that they quickly replenish the body's supply of nutrients, particularly electrolytes. Let's take a look at the Nutrition Facts panel from a popular sports drink, Gatorade.

First, look closely at the serving size—it's not the whole container. This is worth noting because many people might drink the whole container and assume they were getting 50 calories. Not true! The whole container has 200 calories (50 × 4 servings). It's always a good idea to look at the serving size when you are studying a nutrition label.

So what makes this sports drink different from plain (and inexpensive) water? This one has added carbohydrate, sodium, and potassium. Replacing carbohydrate during long workouts prevents complete depletion of glycogen stores. Most sports drinks have between 6 and 8 percent simple sugar. Higher amounts would limit water absorption, and replacement of water is more critical than replacement of glucose.

Sodium and potassium are added to sports drinks to improve taste and help replace electrolytes that are lost during exercise. Gatorade contains 110 milligrams of sodium and 30 milligrams of potassium. For many athletes, and certainly for recreational exercisers, water really is the best fluid replacer. Although both sodium and potassium are lost in sweat, water is lost in greater quantities. Sports drinks have been shown to benefit only athletes who are strenuously exercising for longer than an hour. With prolonged exercise and sweat losses, large losses of electrolytes can make a person dizzy and weak, and may even lead to heat exhaustion or heatstroke.

The next time you head out for a bike ride, consider how long you'll be gone and how strenuous your ride will be, and then consider whether you'll need a sports drink. Also consider your personal taste—if a flavored sports drink will encourage you to replace fluids more than plain water will, that may be an important advantage. Just don't forget to read the label!

Nutrition Facts
Serving Size 8 fl oz (240mL)
Servings Per Container 4
Amount Per Serving
Calories 50
% Daily Value*
Total Fat 0g 0%
Trans Fat 0g
Sodium 110mg 5%
Potassium 30mg 1%
Total Carbohydrate 14g 5%
Sugars 14g
Protein 0g
Not a significant source of Calories from Fat, Saturated Fat, Trans Fat, Cholesterol, Dietary Fiber, Vitamin A, Vitamin C, Calcium, Iron.
* Percent Daily Values are based on a 2,000 calorie diet.

Learning Portfolio

Key Terms

	page		page
aerobic endurance	558	hyperthermia	586
amenorrhea [A-men-or-Ee-a]	588	lactic acid energy system	556
ATP–CP energy system	556	muscle fibers	558
carbohydrate loading	563	oxygen energy system	557
cardiac output	586	palatable	575
creatine	581	pathogenic	586
creatine phosphate	555	perceived exertion	573
diuresis	570	phosphocreatine	555
ergogenic aids	577	skeletal muscles	558
fast-twitch (FT) fibers	558	slow-twitch (ST) fibers	558
female athlete triad	587	soda loading	583
glycogen loading	563	sports anemia	571

Study Points

- Exercise promotes health and reduces risk of chronic diseases.
- The ACSM defines physical fitness as "the ability to perform moderate to vigorous levels of physical activity without undue fatigue and the capability of maintaining this level of activity throughout life."
- The muscular system contains three types of muscles: smooth, cardiac, and skeletal. There are two types of muscle fibers: slow-twitch (ST) and fast-twitch (FT). ST fibers have high aerobic endurance; FT fibers are optimized to perform anaerobically. Your body depends predominantly on ST fibers for low-intensity events and on FT fibers for highly explosive events.
- The body uses three systems to produce energy for physical activity: (1) the ATP–CP energy system (anaerobic), (2) the lactic acid energy system (anaerobic), and (3) the oxygen energy system (aerobic).
- Anaerobic and aerobic metabolism work together to fuel all types of exercise. During the early minutes of high-intensity exercise, the ATP–CP energy system and the lactic acid energy system provide most of the energy. Endurance activities are fueled primarily by the metabolism of glucose and fatty acids in the oxygen energy system.
- Training improves use of fat as a fuel by enhancing oxygen delivery and increasing the number of mitochondria in muscle.
- Carbohydrates should be the major source of energy in the athlete's diet and should come from complex carbohydrates, which can provide fiber, iron, and B vitamins. Athletes need carbohydrates so that muscle glycogen stores and blood glucose concentrations will be adequate for training and competitive events. Likewise, carbohydrates are necessary to replenish glycogen stores after intense exercise.
- Carbohydrate loading is a process of reducing activity while increasing carbohydrate intake to maximize glycogen stores.
- Fat is a major fuel source for exercise, but high fat intake is neither required nor recommended.
- The protein needs of athletes are higher than for sedentary individuals, but generally athletes who consume adequate amounts of energy get enough protein. High-protein foods include low-fat dairy products, egg whites, lean beef and pork, chicken, turkey, fish, and legumes.
- Other nutrients important to the athlete's diet include B vitamins, iron, zinc, and calcium.
- Water is the most essential nutrient and is easily lost from the body with heavy sweating. Replacing fluid with water or sports drinks is important to prevent dehydration. Optimal sports drinks provide energy and electrolytes in a palatable solution that is rapidly absorbed.
- Athletes who are still growing have even higher energy and nutrient needs to support both physical activity and normal growth.
- Many dietary supplements are promoted as ergogenic aids—substances that enhance performance. Few well-controlled studies on their efficacy and safety have been done, however.
- Many athletes strive to either gain or lose weight so as to improve performance. In both cases, realistic goals and gradual changes are necessary for long-term success. Gains in muscle mass require increased calorie intake and weight training. Successful weight loss requires modest reductions in energy intake and increases in aerobic activity.
- Weight-control efforts that involve fasting, excessive sweating, purging, diuretics, or laxatives are detrimental to health.
- Disordered eating accompanied by amenorrhea and premature osteoporosis is known as the female athlete triad.

Study Questions

1. List the three different energy systems that your body uses to generate energy during exercise. When is each active during exercise?
2. What are muscle fibers, and what are the two major types?
3. What are the general recommendations for the balance of carbohydrate, fat, and protein in an athlete's diet?
4. What is carbohydrate loading?
5. How do protein recommendations for athletes vary from those for nonathletes?
6. Name three minerals that are of concern for athletes because they may not consume enough.
7. What is sports anemia and why does it happen? How does it compare with other anemias?
8. Define the term *ergogenic aid*. Is there a clear, research-based answer to whether ergogenic supplements work?
9. List the three components of the female athlete triad.

Try This

The Popularity of Ergogenic Aids

Take a trip to a health food store to see just how popular (and expensive!) ergogenic aids are. Try to locate each of the supplements listed in this chapter. Are they all available? What are their prices? Ask a salesperson what he or she knows about each of them. Do the answers match what you read in the text?

Commit to Get Fit

Do you meet the American College of Sports Medicine's definition of fitness? Answer the following questions with a yes or no.

1. Do you exercise consistently three to five days per week?
2. When you exercise, does it include 20 to 60 minutes (20 minutes for intense activity and 60 minutes for less intense activity) of continuous aerobic activity?
3. Does your type of exercise use large muscle groups? Can you maintain it? Is it rhythmical and aerobic?
4. Does part of your activity include strength training of a moderate intensity (a minimum of one set of 8 to 12 repetitions of 8 to 10 exercises) at least two days per week?

If you answered no to any of these questions, you are not following the ACSM's suggestions to develop and maintain cardiorespiratory and muscular fitness. Choose a question to which you answered no and set a specific goal to include that factor in your exercise routine.

What About Bobbie?

Imagine that Bobbie is training to compete in a marathon at the end of the semester. She has been exercising consistently and increasing her endurance and mileage times. She hasn't spent much time focusing on her diet, though, and wants to know what changes she could make to improve her nutrition and therefore her performance. Assume that her current diet meets her calorie needs. How would you compare Bobbie's diet to the guidelines you read about in this chapter?

Macronutrient Contributions

Start with her overall contribution of carbohydrates, proteins, and fats. Compare Bobbie's macronutrient intake to the general sports nutrition recommendations.

	Bobbie's	**Recommendations**
Carbohydrates	51%	60 to 70%
Proteins	17%	≈ 15%
Fats	34%	≈ 20%

As you can see, Bobbie's diet is higher in fat and lower in carbohydrates than is recommended for an athlete. If she were to reduce her intake of cream cheese, mayonnaise, cookies, and salad dressing and increase her fruits, vegetables, and whole grains, her diet would come closer to the recommendations for sports nutrition.

Protein

Now let's calculate her protein need based on the athlete's guideline and see whether she's consuming enough to maintain lean muscle mass and recover well from exercise.

The protein recommendation for an athlete is approximately 1.2 to 1.4 grams per kilogram of body weight. Bobbie weighs 155 pounds, so her recommended intake is as follows:

$$155 \text{ lb} \div 2.2 \text{ kg per lb} = 70.45 \text{ kg}$$

$$70.45 \text{ kg} \times 1.3 \text{ g/kg} = 91.6 \text{ g protein}$$

Bobbie's protein intake was 96 grams, which makes her protein intake a near-perfect match for her needs.

Minerals

Look at the two primary minerals that might be inadequate in the diets of athletes, especially female athletes. Below is a comparison of Bobbie's calcium and iron intake and her daily recommendations.

	Bobbie's	Recommendations
Calcium	710 mg	1,000 mg
Iron	20 mg	8 mg

As you can see, Bobbie did a very good job of consuming iron, but she is short of her calcium need. If she were to replace the diet soda she had at lunch with 1 cup of nonfat or 1 percent milk, her intake of calcium would rise to just about 1,000 milligrams. Or she could change her afternoon snack of chips and salsa to a cup of yogurt to accomplish the same thing.

Hydration

Check out Bobbie's intake of fluids in Chapter 1. Although her overall fluid intake is consistent with the AI, how many ounces of plain water did she consume? That's right, she had only 16 ounces! Bobbie is making the same mistake that many athletes do—she's not drinking enough water. Poor hydration status will probably affect her performance adversely. Bobbie's biggest change should be to increase her fluid intake. She'd be smart to drink at least 12 to 16 ounces of caffeine-free fluids at all of her meals and snacks. That way she'll stay hydrated and be able to perform at an optimal level!

References

1 American College of Sports Medicine, American Medical Association. ACSM and AMA launch "Exercise is Medicine" program. ACSM press release; November 7, 2007. http://www.acsm.org/AM/Template.cfm?Section=Home_Page&TEMPLATE=/CM/ContentDisplay.cfm&CONTENTID=859. Accessed 1/31/09.

2 Jonas S, Phillips E. *ACSM'S Exercise Is Medicine: A Clinician's Guide to Exercise Prescription*. Philadelphia: Lippincott Williams & Wilkins, 2009.

3 Institute of Medicine, Food and Nutrition Board. *Dietary Reference Intakes for Energy, Carbohydrate, Fiber, Fat, Fatty Acids, Cholesterol, Protein, and Amino Acids*. Washington, DC: National Academies Press, 2005.

4 American College of Sports Medicine. Position stand: the recommended quantity and quality of exercise for developing and maintaining cardiorespiratory and muscular fitness and flexibility in healthy adults. *Med Sci Sports Exerc*. 1998;30:975–991.

5 American Dietetic Association, Dietitians of Canada, American College of Sports Medicine. Position statement: nutrition and athletic performance. *J Am Diet Assoc*. 2009;109(3):509–527.

6 Connolly-Schoonen J. Physiology of anaerobic and aerobic exercise. In: Dunford M, ed. *Sports Nutrition: A Practice Manual for Professionals*. 4th ed. Chicago: American Dietetic Association, 2006.

7 Wilmore JH, Costill DL. *Physiology of Sport and Exercise*. 3rd ed. Champaign, IL: Human Kinetics, 2004.

8 Hashimoto T, Hussien R, Brooks GA. Colocalization of MCT1, CD147, and LDH in mitochondrial inner membrane of L6 muscle cells: evidence of a mitochondrial lactate oxidation complex. *Am J Physiol Endocrinol Metab*. 2006;290(6):E1237–E1244.

9 Brooks GA, Fahey TD, White T. *Exercise Physiology*. Mountain View, CA: Mayfield, 1996:705; and Cairns SP. Lactic acid and exercise performance: culprit or friend? *Sports Med*. 2006;36:279–291.

10 Brown GC. Speed limits. *The Sciences*. 2000;40(5):32–37.

11 McArdle WD, Katch FI, Katch VL. *Essentials of Exercise Physiology*. 3rd ed. Baltimore, MD: Lippincott Williams & Wilkins, 2005.

12 Ibid.

13 American Dietetic Association, Dietitians of Canada, American College of Sports Medicine. Nutrition and athletic performance.

14 Wilmore, Costill. *Physiology of Sport and Exercise*.

15 Brown GC. *The Energy of Life*. New York: Simon & Schuster, 1999.

16 Andersen JL, Scherling P, Saltin B. Muscle, genes and athletic performance. *Scientific American*. 2000;283(3):48–55.

17 Hawley, JA, Tipton, KD, Millard-Stafford, ML. Promoting training adaptations through nutritional manipulations. *J Sports Sci*. 2006;24:709–721.

18 Berning JR, Steen SN. *Nutrition for Sport and Exercise*. 2nd ed. Sudbury, MA: Jones & Bartlett, 1998.

19 Hawley J, Dennis SC, Lindsay FH, Noakes TD. Nutritional practices of athletes: are they sub-optimal? *J Sports Sci*. 1995;13(suppl):S75–S87.

20 Benardot D, Thompson WR. Energy from food for physical activity: enough and on time. *ACSM's Health & Fitness*. 1999;3:14–18.

21 American Dietetic Association, Dietitians of Canada, American College of Sports Medicine. Nutrition and athletic performance.

22 Vinci DM. Effective nutrition support programs for college athletes. *Int J Sports Nutr*. 1998;8:308–320.

23 American Dietetic Association, Dietitians of Canada, American College of Sports Medicine. Nutrition and athletic performance.

24 Kerksick C, Harvey T, Stout J, et al. International Society of Sports Nutrition position stand: nutrient timing. *J Int Soc Sports Nutr*. 2008;5:17.

25 Coleman EJ. Carbohydrate and exercise. In: Dunford M, ed. *Sports Nutrition: A Practice Manual for Professionals*. 4th ed. Chicago: American Dietetic Association, 2006.

26 Meeusen R, Watson P, Dvorak J. The brain and fatigue: new opportunities for nutritional interventions? *J Sports Sci*. 2006;24(7):773–782.

27 Coleman. Carbohydrate and exercise.

28 Ibid.

29 Sedlock DA. The latest on carbohydrate loading: a practical approach. *Curr Sports Med Rep*. 2008;7(4):209–213.

30 American Dietetic Association, Dietitians of Canada, American College of Sports Medicine. Nutrition and athletic performance.

31 Ibid.

32 Kerksick, Harvey, Stout, et al. Nutrient timing.

33 American Dietetic Association, Dietitians of Canada, American College of Sports Medicine. Nutrition and athletic performance.

34 Kerksick, Harvey, Stout, et al. Nutrient timing.

35 Coleman. Carbohydrate and exercise.

36 Ibid.

37 Tarnopolsky MA, Gibala M, Jeukendrup AE, Phillips SM. Nutrition needs of elite athletes. Part I: carbohydrate and fluid requirements. *Eur J Sport Sci.* 2005;5:3–14.

38 American Dietetic Association, Dietitians of Canada, American College of Sports Medicine. Nutrition and athletic performance.

39 Roy B, Tarnopolosky M, MacDougall J, et al. Effect of glucose supplement timing on protein metabolism after resistance training. *J Appl Physiol.* 1997;82:1882–1888.

40 Ibid.

41 Institute of Medicine, Food and Nutrition Board. *Dietary Reference Intakes for Energy, Carbohydrate.*

42 Campbell B, Kreider RB, Ziegenfuss T, et al. International Society of Sports Nutrition position stand: protein and exercise. *J Int Soc Sports Nutr.* 2007:4:8.

43 Institute of Medicine, Food and Nutrition Board. *Dietary Reference Intakes for Energy, Carbohydrate.*

44 Carroll C. Protein and exercise. In: Dunford M, ed. *Sports Nutrition: A Practice Manual for Professionals.* 4th ed. Chicago: American Dietetic Association, 2006.

45 Phillips SM. Dietary protein for athletes: from requirements to metabolic advantages. *Appl Physiol Nutr Metab.* 2006;31:647–654.

46 Ibid.

47 Gibala MJ. Dietary protein, amino acid supplements, and recovery from exercise. *GSSI Sports Sci Exchange.* 2002;15(4):1–4.

48 Hawley J, Burke L. *Peak Performance: Training and Nutritional Strategies for Sport.* Leonards, Australia: Allen & Unwin, 1998.

49 Gibala. Dietary protein, amino acid supplements, and recovery from exercise.

50 Tipton KD, Elliott TA, Cree MG, et al. Ingestion of casein and whey protein results in muscle anabolism after resistance exercise. *Med Sci Sports Exerc.* 2004;36:2073–2081.

51 Gibala. Dietary protein, amino acid supplements, and recovery from exercise.

52 Tarnopolosky MA, Atkinson SA, MacDougall JD, et al. Evaluation of protein requirements for trained strength athletes. *J Appl Physiol.* 1992;73:1986.

53 Gibala. Dietary protein, amino acid supplements, and recovery from exercise.

54 Ibid.

55 Stellingwerff T, Boit MK, Res PT. Nutritional strategies to optimize training and racing in middle-distance athletes. *J Sports Sci.* 2007;25(suppl 1):S17–S28.

56 Miller SL, Tipton KD, Chinkes DL, et al. Independent and combined effects of amino acids and glucose after resistance exercise. *Med Sci Sports Exerc.* 2003;35:449–455.

57 Storlie J. From fork to muscle. *Training & Conditioning.* 1998;8:26, 28–29, 32–33.

58 Roy B. Milk: the new sports drink? A review. *J Int Soc Sports Nutr.* 2008,5:15.

59 Telford RD, Sly GJ, Hahn RB, et al. Footstrike is the major cause of hemolysis during running. *J Appl Physiol.* 2003;94:38–42.

60 Institute of Medicine, Food and Nutrition Board. *Dietary Reference Intakes for Vitamin A, Vitamin K, Arsenic, Boron, Chromium, Copper, Iodine, Iron, Manganese, Molybdenum, Nickel, Silicon, Vanadium, and Zinc.* Washington, DC: National Academies Press, 2001.

61 Fallon K. Utility of hematological and iron-related screening in elite athletes. *Clin J Sport Med.* 2004;14:145–152.

62 Zhu YI, Haas JD. Iron depletion without anemia and physical performance in young women. *Am J Clin Nutr.* 1997;66:334–341.

63 Institute of Medicine, Food and Nutrition Board. *Dietary Reference Intakes for Water, Potassium, Sodium, Chloride, and Sulfate.* Washington, DC: National Academies Press, 2004.

64 Ibid.

65 Coyle EF. Fluid and fuel intake during exercise. *J Sports Sci.* 2004;22:39–55.

66 American College of Sports Medicine, Sawka MN, Burke LM, et al. American College of Sports Medicine position stand: exercise and fluid replacement. *Med Sci Sports Exerc.* 2007;39:377–390.

67 Ibid.

68 Ibid.

69 Ibid.

70 Ibid.

71 Ibid.

72 Ibid.

73 Ibid.

74 Ibid.

75 Passe DH, Stofan JR, Rowe CL, et al. Exercise condition affects hedonic response to sodium in a sports drink. *Appetite.* 2009;52(3):561–567.

76 American Academy of Pediatrics Committee on Sports Medicine and Fitness. Promotion of healthy weight-control practices in young athletes. *Pediatrics.* 2005;116(6):1557–1564.

77 Cotunga N, Vickery CE, McBee S. Sports nutrition for young athletes. *J School Nurs.* 2005;21(6):323–328.

78 Ibid.

79 National Collegiate Athletic Association. *NCAA Study of Substance Use of College Student-Athletes.* http://www.ncaa.org/library/research/substance_use_habits/2006/2006_substance_use_report.pdf. Accessed 7/2/09.

80 Dorsch KD, Bell A. Dietary supplement use in adolescents. *Curr Opin Pediatr.* 2005;17(5):653–657.

81 National Collegiate Athletic Association. *NCAA Study of Substance Use of College Student-Athletes.*

82 Petroczi A, Naughton D, Mazanov J, et al. Performance enhancement with supplements: incongruence between rationale and practice. *Int Soc Sports Nutr.* 2007;4:19.

83 Hoffman J, Kang J, Ratamess N, et al. Examination of a pre-exercise, high energy supplement on exercise performance. *J Int Soc Sports Nutr.* 2009;6:2.

84 Dunford M, Smith M. Dietary supplements and ergogenic aids. In: Dunford M, ed. *Sports Nutrition: A Practice Manual for Professionals.* 4th ed. Chicago: American Dietetic Association, 2006.

85 Ibid.

86 Kreider RB, Almada AL, Antonio J, et al. ISSN exercise and sport nutrition review: research and recommendations. *J Int Soc Sports Nutr.* 2004;1:1–44.

87 US Food and Drug Administration. Overview of dietary supplements: what is a dietary supplement? http://www.fda.gov/Food/DietarySupplements/ConsumerInformation/ucm110417.htm#regulate. Accessed 6/22/09.

88 Ibid.

89 Ibid.

90 Maughan R. Supplement contamination: is the risk real? Gatorade Sport Science Library. 2008. http://www.gssiweb.com/Article_Detail.aspx?articleid=613. Accessed 6/24/09.

91 Baume N, Mahler N, Kamber M, et al. Research of stimulants and anabolic steroids in dietary supplements. *Scand J Med Sci Sports.* 2006;16:41–48.

92 American Dietetic Association, Dietitians of Canada, American College of Sports Medicine. Nutrition and athletic performance.

93 Sullivan M. FDA urged to step up regulation of supplements: adverse events are largely underreported. *Family Practice News.* 2009;29(6):1–2.

94 Kreider, Almada, Antonio, et al. ISSN exercise and sport nutrition review.

95 Ibid.

96 Ibid.

97 Ibid.

98 Ciocca M. Medication and supplement use by athletes. *Clin Sports Med.* 2005;24:719–738.

99 Newsholme EA, Blomstrand E. Branched-chain amino acids and central fatigue. *J Nutr.* 2006;136:274S–276S.

100 Ibid.

101 Armsey TD, Hosey RG. Medical aspects of sports: epidemiology of injuries, preparticipation physical examination, and drugs in sports. *Clin Sports Med.* 2004;23(2):255–279.

102 Tokish JM, Kocher MS, Hawkins RJ. Ergogenic aids: a review of basic science, performance, side effects, and status in sports. *Am J Sports Med.* 2004;32(6):1543–1553.

103 Palisin T, Stacy JJ. Beta-hydroxy-beta-methylbutyrate and its use in athletics. *Curr Sports Med Rep.* 2005;4(4):220–223.

104 Antonio J, Sanders MS, Kalman D, et al. The effects of high-dose glutamine ingestion on weightlifting performance. *J Strength Cond Res.* 2002;16:157–160; and Haub MD, Potteiger JA, Nau KL, et al. Acute l-glutamine ingestion does not improve maximal effort exercise. *J Sports Med Phys Fitness.* 1998;38:240–244.

105 Ciocca. Medication and supplement use by athletes.

106 Buford T, Kreider R, Stout J, et al. International Society of Sports Nutrition position stand: creatine supplementation and exercise. *J Int Soc Sports Nutr.* 2007;4:6.

107 Cribb PJ, Williams AD, Hayes A. A creatine-protein-carbohydrate supplement enhances responses to resistance training. *Med Sci Sports Exerc.* 2007;39:1960–1968.

108 Skare OC, Skalberg AR. Creatine supplementation improves sprint performance in male sprinters. *Scand J Med Sci Sports.* 2001;11:96–102.

109 Lattavo A, Kopperud A, Rogers P. Creatine and other supplements. *Pediatr Clin North Am.* 2007;54(4):735–760.

110 PDR Health. Creatine. http://www.pdrhealth.com/durg_info/nmdrugprofiles/cre_0086.shtml. Accessed 7/2/09.

111 Buford, Kreider, Stout, et al. Creatine supplementation and exercise.

112 Kreider RB, Melton C, Rasmussen CJ, et al. Long-term creatine supplementation does not significantly affect clinical markers of health in athletes. *Mol Cell Biochem.* 2003;244:95–104; and Mayhew DL, Mayhew JL, Ware JS. Effects of long-term creatine supplementation on liver and kidney functions in American college football players. *Int J Sport Nutr Exerc Metab.* 2003;12:453–460.

113 Greenwood M, Kreider RB, Melton C, et al. Creatine supplementation during college football training does not increase the incidence of cramping or injury. *Mol Cell Biochem.* 2003;244:83–88.

114 Morillas-Ruiz JM, Garcia JA, Lopez FJ, et al. Effects of polyphenolic antioxidants on exercise-induced oxidative stress. *Clin Nutr.* 2006;25(3):444–453.

115 Jenkins RR. Exercise and oxidative stress methodology: a critique. *Am J Clin Nutr.* 2000;72(suppl):670S–674S.

116 Australian Sports Commission, Australian Institute of Sport. Fact sheet: caffeine. http://www.ausport.gov.au/ais/nutrition/supplements/supplement_fact_sheets/group_a_supplements/caffeine. Accessed 7/17/08.

117 Ibid.

118 Lattavo, Kopperud, Rogers. Creatine and other supplements.

119 Keisler BD, Armsey TD. Caffeine as an ergogenic aid. *Curr Sports Med Rep.* 2006;5(4):215–219.

120 Lattavo, Kopperud, Rogers. Creatine and other supplements.

121 World Anti-Doping Agency. The 2007 prohibited list: international standard. http://www.wada-ama.org/rtecontent/document/2007_List_En.pdf. Accessed 7/2/09.

122 National Collegiate Athletic Association. NCAA banned-drug classes 2006–2007. http://www1.ncaa.org/membership/ed_outreach/health-safety/drug_testing/banned_drug_classes.pdf. Accessed 7/2/09.

123 World Anti-Doping Agency. The 2007 prohibited list.

124 Lattavo, Kopperud, Rogers. Creatine and other supplements.

125 Keisler, Armsey. Caffeine as an ergogenic aid.

126 Ibid.

127 Ibid.

128 US Food and Drug Administration. FDA issues regulation prohibiting sale of dietary supplements containing ephedrine alkaloids and reiterates its advice that consumers stop using these products. *FDA News.* February 6, 2004. http://www.cfsan.fda.gov/~lrd/fpephed6.html. Accessed 1/31/09.

129 Bell DG, McLellan TM, Sabiston CM. Effect of ingesting caffeine and ephedrine on 10-km run performance. *Med Sci Sports Exerc.* 2002;34:344–349; Jacobs I, Pasternak H, Bell DG. Effects of ephedrine, caffeine, and their combination on muscular endurance. *Med Sci Sports Exerc.* 2003;35:987–994; and Shekelle PG, Hardy ML, Morton SG, et al. Efficacy and safety of ephedra and ephedrine for weight loss and athletic performance: a meta-analysis. *JAMA.* 2003;289:1537–1545.

130 Lattavo, Kopperud, Rogers. Creatine and other supplements.

131 Shekelle, Hardy, Morton, et al. Efficacy and safety of ephedra and ephedrine for weight loss and athletic performance.

132 Lattavo, Kopperud, Rogers. Creatine and other supplements.

133 Horswill CA. Effects of bicarbonate, citrate, and phosphate loading on performance. *Int J Sport Nutr.* 1995;5(suppl):S111–S119.

134 Vincent JB. The potential value and toxicity of chromium picolinate as a nutritional supplement, weight loss agent and muscle development agent. *Sports Med.* 2003;33:213–230.

135 Williams M. Dietary supplements and sports performance: minerals. *J Int Soc Sports Nutr.* 2005,2:43–49.

136 Ciocca M. Medication and supplement use by athletes. *Clin Sports Med.* 2005;24:719–738.

137 Lattavo, Kopperud, Rogers. Creatine and other supplements.

138 Ibid.

139 Zoller H, Vogel W. Iron supplementation in athletes: first do no harm. *Nutrition.* 2004;20:615–619.

140 Houtkooper LB. Body composition. In: Manore MM, Thompson JL. *Sport Nutrition for Health and Performance.* Champaign, IL: Human Kinetics, 2000:199–219.

141 Rozenek R, Ward P, Long S, Garhammer J. Effects of high-calorie supplements on body composition and muscular strength following resistance training. *J Sports Med Phys Fitness.* 2002;42:340–347.

142 Storlie. From fork to muscle.

143 McArdle, Katch, Katch. *Essentials of Exercise Physiology.*

144 Ibid.

145 Ibid.

146 Clarkson PM. The skinny on weight loss supplements and drugs. *ACSM's Health & Fitness.* 1998;2:18–26, 55.

147 Thompson JL. Energy balance in young athletes. *Int J Sports Nutr.* 1998;8:160–174.

148 Metz G. The NCAA weighs in. *Training & Conditioning.* 1998;8:16–17, 19, 21–23.

149 Centers for Disease Control and Prevention. Rapid weight loss in wrestlers results in death. *MMWR.* 1998;47(6):105–108.

150 Metz. The NCAA weighs in.

151 Center for Nutrition in Sport and Human Performance. *Taking It to the Mat: The Wrestler's Guide to Optimal Performance.* http://www.ncaa.org/wps/wcm/connect/resources/file/eba9744a11a4f35/mat.pdf. Accessed 1/31/09.

152 Manore MM, Kam LC, Loucks AB. The female athlete triad: components, nutrition issues, and health consequences. *J Sports Sci.* 2007;25(suppl 1):61–71.

153 Torstveit MK, Sundgot-Borgen J. The female athlete triad: are elite athletes at increased risk? *Med Sci Sports Exerc.* 2005;37:184–193.

154 Sundgot-Borgen J. Risk and trigger factors for the developing of eating disorders in female elite athletes. *Med Sci Sports Exerc.* 1994;4:414–419.

155 Reinking MF, Alexander LE. Prevalence of disordered-eating behaviors in undergraduate female collegiate athletes and nonathletes. *J Athl Train.* 2005;40:47–51.

156 Smith AD. The female athlete triad: causes, diagnosis, and treatment. *Physician Sportsmed.* 1996;24:67–70, 75–76, 86.

157 Dueck CA, Manore MM, Matt KS. Role of energy balance in athletic menstrual dysfunction. *Int J Sport Nutr.* 1996;6:165–190.

158 Otis CL, Drinkwater B, Johnson M, et al. American College of Sports Medicine position stand: the female athlete triad. *Med Sci Sports Exerc.* 1997;29:i–ix.

Spotlight on Eating Disorders

THINK About It

1 What's your view of the ideal female body?

2 When should you be concerned that you—or someone you know—is dieting obsessively?

3 Given the right situation, what foods are you likely to binge on?

4 How many magazines do you read that promote dieting or encourage thinness?

Visit nutrition.jbpub.com

Figure SED.1 **Can you spot the person with the eating disorder?** Some people with eating disorders have normal body weights and are difficult to spot.

A gaunt, hollow-cheeked college freshman confides to her roommate that she feels chubby. After an enormous lunch, a secretary works her way through a bag of cookies and polishes off a box of chocolates. A swimming champion who obsesses over every calorie becomes concerned that she hasn't had a period in two months. Disordered eating? Very likely! Eating disorder? Possibly!

Eating disorders and **disordered eating** are not the same. An eating disorder such as anorexia nervosa or bulimia nervosa is an illness that can seriously interfere with daily activities. Disordered eating is usually a temporary or mild change in eating patterns, often accompanied by a desire to avoid or stop the pattern. Although the behavior can occur after an illness or stressful event, it often is related to a dietary change intended to improve one's health or appearance. Unless disordered eating persists, it rarely requires professional intervention. Disordered eating, however, can lead to an eating disorder.

For most of us, eating is a pleasure. For people with an eating disorder, however, food is a source of continual stress and anxiety. (See **Figure SED.1**.) Eating disorders require professional intervention. They include a spectrum of emotional illnesses ranging from self-imposed starvation to chronic binge eating. These illnesses stem from severe mental and physical distortions of the eating process and produce physical consequences that are often life threatening.[1]

Most of us have eaten to the point of discomfort on occasion. (Thanksgiving dinner comes to mind.) And many of us have cut out desserts at one time or another, hoping to fit into a special outfit or to lose weight for an athletic event or job interview. But stuffing yourself at a holiday meal or going on an occasional diet does not constitute an eating disorder. Persistent inability to eat in moderation is often a defining characteristic of an eating disorder.[2]

eating disorders A spectrum of abnormal eating patterns that eventually may endanger a person's health or increase the risk for other diseases. Generally, psychological factors play a key role.

disordered eating An abnormal change in eating pattern related to an illness, a stressful event, or a desire to improve one's health or appearance. If it persists it may lead to an eating disorder.

anorexia nervosa [an-or-EX-ee-uh ner-VOH-sah] An eating disorder marked by prolonged decrease of appetite and refusal to eat, leading to self-starvation and excessive weight loss. It results in part from a distorted body image and intense fear of becoming fat, often linked to social pressures.

body image A person's mental concept of his or her physical appearance, constructed from many different influences.

binge-eating disorder An eating disorder marked by repeated episodes of binge eating and a feeling of loss of control. The diagnosis is based on a person's having an average of at least two binge-eating episodes per week for six months.

The Eating Disorder Continuum

The American Psychiatric Association's *Diagnostic and Statistical Manual of Mental Disorders* (DSM-IV) categorizes three types of eating disorders, with small but significant areas of overlap. These categories form a continuum, ranging from self-starvation at one end to compulsive overeating at the other. (See **Figure SED.2**.) **Anorexia nervosa** occurs at the self-starvation end of the continuum. Anorexia is a self-imposed starvation syndrome that is triggered by a severely distorted **body image**.

Attributes perceived as beautiful vary with the eye of the beholder and are subject to cultural and individual preferences. Fashion designers, for example, sell their ideals of beauty via waiflike models. These sinewy women who line the fashion catwalks and appear in fashion magazines stand in stark contrast to the majority of U.S. women, whose average dress size has grown to size 14.

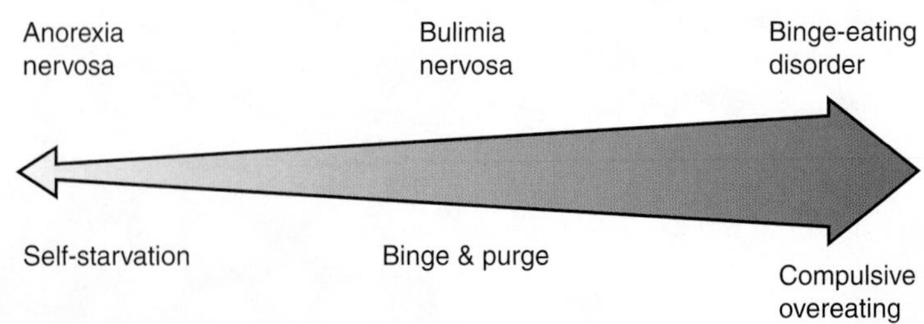

Figure SED.2 **The eating disorder continuum.**

In contrast to the Western preference for bony beauty, some cultures have traditionally prized heavy bodies and do not have a negative view of obesity.

People with anorexia are at war with their bodies. Even when they are dangerously underweight, people with anorexia typically see themselves as fat. Severely restricting food intake is another symptom of anorexia nervosa. It may also involve purging (self-induced vomiting) and exercising excessively. Anorexia is most prevalent among adolescent females.

At the opposite end of the continuum is **binge-eating disorder**, formerly known as **compulsive overeating**. People with binge-eating disorder chronically consume massive quantities of food. Diagnosis of binge-eating disorder, which often coexists with obesity, is based on a person engaging in an average of two binge-eating episodes per week for six months. Such episodes often are triggered by emotions such as frustration, anger, depression, and anxiety.[3]

Like those with binge-eating disorder, people with **bulimia nervosa** compulsively gorge themselves. Like those with anorexia, people with bulimia desperately want to be thin and resort to purging to reach this goal. After gorging, people with bulimia often become disgusted with themselves and terrified of getting fat. To compensate, bulimic people make themselves vomit, use laxatives, exercise excessively, and take other action to avoid gaining weight.

It is important to realize that few people who suffer from eating disorders are purely anorexic, bulimic, or binge eaters. Many swing from one disordered eating pattern to another, alternately starving and gorging themselves. People may suffer from binge-eating disorder at one point in their lives, and anorexia or bulimia at another.[4] Table SED.1 shows the diagnostic criteria for these eating disorders.

Table SED.1 **Diagnostic Criteria for Eating Disorders**

Anorexia nervosa

- Body weight < 85% of expected weight (or BMI $\leq$ 17.5 kg/m^2)
- Intense fear of weight gain
- Inaccurate perception of own body size, weight, or shape
- Amenorrhea (in females after menarche)

Bulimia nervosa

- Recurrent binge eating (at least two times per week for three months)
- Recurrent purging, excessive exercise, or fasting (at least two times per week for three months)
- Excessive concern about body weight or shape
- Absence of anorexia nervosa

Binge-eating disorder

- Recurrent binge eating (at least two times per week for six months)
- Marked distress with at least three of the following:
  - Eating very rapidly
  - Eating until uncomfortably full
  - Eating when not hungry
  - Eating alone
  - Feeling disgusted or guilty after a binge
- No recurrent purging, no excessive exercising, and no fasting
- Absence of anorexia nervosa

Source: American Psychiatric Association. *Diagnostic and Statistical Manual of Mental Disorders.* 4th ed. Text revision (DSM-IV-TR). Washington, DC: American Psychiatric Association, 2000. Reprinted with permission.

History of a Modern Malady

Contrary to public perception, eating disorders are not new diseases. In fact, the first formal report of anorexia nervosa appeared in the medical literature in the 1870s.[5] Informal reports of a "voluntary starvation syndrome" were published as early as 1694.[6] Some nutritional anthropologists argue that eating disorders can be traced to even more ancient times. During the Middle Ages, for instance, early Christian ascetics, who led lives of contemplation and rigorous self-denial, shunned worldly pleasures, including food, to show obedience and become closer to God. These people alternated periods of semistarvation with frequent fasts. Was this anorexia disguised as religious devotion? Some scholars think so.[7]

Early Greeks and Romans, in contrast, exhibited exaggerated bingeing and purging behavior at banquets that lasted for days. Guests gorged to the point of physical pain, then tickled their throats with feathers to induce vomiting. Once their stomachs were empty, they returned to the table. Rather than finding this behavior repulsive or shameful, the ancient Romans glorified it. They even built areas known as vomitoriums into their banquet halls.[8]

Some scholars contend these ancient Romans had bulimia. Others disagree, arguing that the Roman men ate for pleasure in the company of others and purged only so they could rejoin the feast. In contrast, modern bulimia sufferers are usually females who gorge and purge in isolation—and in hopes of achieving an unrealistic cultural standard of beauty. Furthermore, today's bulimia sufferers invariably feel shame, low self-esteem, and even self-hate connected with their eating habits.

Although eating disorders are not an exclusively modern malady, it's clear that eating disorders have become increasingly common in the past four decades. A British model named Twiggy, nicknamed for her sticklike appearance,

compulsive overeating See *binge-eating disorder.*

bulimia nervosa [bull-EEM-ee-uh] An eating disorder marked by consumption of large amounts of food at one time (binge eating) followed by a behavior such as self-induced vomiting, use of laxatives, excessive exercise, fasting, or other practices to avoid weight gain.

Figure SED.3 **Eye of the beholder.** In the 1960s, Twiggy became the role model for young women who wanted to be thin and glamorous.

ushered in the epidemic in the early 1960s. Fashion magazine stories reported that she subsisted on water, lettuce, and a single daily serving of steak and that she had learned to suppress her hunger pangs. Rather than condemn these clearly dangerous eating habits, the magazines held Twiggy up as a model of self-control for girls and young women. (See **Figure SED.3**.)

Our national denial regarding the dangers of semistarvation ended abruptly and dramatically in 1983 with the highly publicized death of 32-year-old pop singer Karen Carpenter from complications of anorexia. Widespread media coverage of her death highlighted the lethal potential of eating disorders and made the terms *anorexia* and *bulimia* household words. Other stars of film, TV, sports, and the fashion world—Princess Diana, Jane Fonda, Janet Jackson, Ally Sheedy, Calista Flockhart, Cathy Rigby, Zina Garrison, Felicity Huffman, Lindsay Lohan, Mary-Kate Olsen, and Kate Beckinsale, to mention a few—have spoken about their eating disorders. Some have described the physical, emotional, and social damage these diseases caused in their own lives. But, ironically, increased visibility and knowledge have not stemmed the tide of eating disorders. To the contrary, the prevalence of eating disorders and disordered eating continues to increase.[9]

Key Concepts *Eating disorders are unhealthy conditions known to exist from ancient times. Today, they have become alarmingly common in industrialized countries, particularly the United States. Eating disorders range from the self-starvation of anorexia nervosa to the compulsive overeating of binge-eating disorder.*

Figure SED.4 **Thin is in.** In 1998, Mattel overhauled Barbie's look for the millennium, giving her slimmer hips, a wider waist, and smaller breasts. Barbie's periodic overhauls are meant to fit the fashion of the times. Does the new Barbie (right) represent a realistic role model for today's young girls?

No Simple Causes

Certain people appear to have a predisposition to eating disorders that may be rooted in psychological, biological, or cultural causes. A person who suffers from depression or **obsessive-compulsive disorder**, for example, may have an increased risk of developing an eating disorder. The vulnerability also may be biological. Indeed, there is evidence that genetic factors may create an increased risk for eating disorders. Another important factor in the development of eating disorders is society's emphasis on extreme thinness. It is clear that eating disorders are complex problems, with multiple causes. Social, psychological, and biological factors all play roles.

Eating disorders can develop when people, especially women, feel social pressure to achieve an unrealistic standard of thinness. Modern Western culture encourages women to weigh less than what is considered healthy. This means that most women cannot attain what society considers the "ideal" female form without significant food deprivation. These pressures affect even very young girls, starting with their first Barbie doll and her unnatural shape (see **Figure SED.4**), if not before.[10]

Psychological factors are important as well. These encompass everything from peer relationships to relationships with parents. Studies have shown that adolescent girls who were teased about their weight by peers had a more negative image of their bodies and lower self-esteem regardless of a girl's actual weight.[11] Findings were similar for adolescent boys and for teens of varied racial and ethnic backgrounds. Studies also have linked more severe forms of emotional trauma to disordered eating. For example, researchers at Texas A&M University detected symptoms of **post-traumatic stress disorder (PTSD)** in more than half of the anorexia and bulimia patients they studied.[12] PTSD occurs in people who have endured a significant trauma, such as child abuse or rape. Eating disorders also may be associated with dysfunctional family relationships. Some psychologists believe that people with anorexia and bulimia are trying to fulfill unrealistic parental expectations of perfection, in part by succumbing to societal pressure to be very thin.

In recent years, scientists have made major advances in understanding the biological foundation of eating disorders, and studies have linked abnormal levels of neurotransmitters, especially serotonin, to eating disorders.[13] Researchers, for example, have shown that bulimia patients experience spontaneous improvement in eating habits when they take antidepressant medication that increases brain levels of serotonin.[14] Many antiobesity drugs also affect serotonin levels.[15]

Neurotransmitters are just one focus of research into the biology of eating disorders. Another line of investigation focuses on genes. Recently, researchers have confirmed that eating disorders run in families. For some women, social characteristics within the family—such as having highly educated parents and maternal grandparents, as well as achieving higher grades in school themselves—have been found to confer a higher risk.[16] In addition, eating disorders occur most frequently in families with a history of obsessive-compulsive disorders, anxiety disorders, and depression.[17] Both depression and obsessive-compulsive behavior have been linked to atypical levels of serotonin and norepinephrine in the brain.[18]

It's likely that many genes are involved in the development of eating disorders. Two recently discovered genes are involved in the synthesis and release of the hormones leptin and **orexin**.[19] The leptin gene regulates the body's production of leptin, a hormone that causes rapid weight loss in genetically obese mice. (Unfortunately, leptin has not stimulated the same reaction in humans.) The orexin gene regulates production of two appetite-stimulating hormones, orexin A and orexin B (after the Greek word *orexis*, meaning "appetite"). In experiments, rodents injected with either hormone increased their food consumption 8- to 10-fold.[20]

The discoveries of the leptin and orexin genes significantly advance our understanding of brain chemistry and eating disorders and may eventually lead to new classes of more effective drugs. Drugs that mimic orexins, for example, might help patients with anorexia or other wasting syndromes by increasing their appetites. Conversely, drugs that block orexins might help patients struggling with obesity and binge eating, or a leptinlike drug may eventually be used to stimulate weight loss. At the very least, discovery of these genes supports the idea that biological factors probably contribute to the development of eating disorders in vulnerable people.

Key Concepts *The precise causes of eating disorders remain obscure. Researchers have debated whether eating disorders are primarily psychological or genetic in origin. The current view is that eating disorders are a result of the complex interaction of social, biological, and psychological factors. In other words, eating disorders occur in biologically susceptible individuals exposed to particular types of environmental stimuli.*

Anorexia Nervosa

Until the 1960s, few doctors ever saw a case of anorexia nervosa in their own practices, although they learned about the condition in medical school. By the mid-1970s, however, physicians were reporting many cases of anorexia, particularly among young women. Today this serious disorder occurs in an estimated 1 in 200 women, usually starting in adolescence. More than 90 percent of cases occur in women, and the death rate from anorexia nervosa is about 10 times the death rate of women without anorexia.[21]

The term *anorexia nervosa*, which translates to "nervous loss of appetite," is misleading. People diagnosed with anorexia don't lose their appetite except

Quick Bite

Magazine Manipulations

When researchers studied fifth- through twelfth-grade girls in a working-class suburb in the Northeast, nearly 50 percent reported that they wanted to lose weight because of pictures in magazines. Frequent readers of fashion magazines were two to three times more likely to be influenced to diet or exercise to lose weight. Seventy percent of the girls reported that magazine pictures influenced their conception of the perfect body.

obsessive-compulsive disorder A disorder in which a person attempts to relieve anxiety by ritualistic behavior and continuous repetition of certain acts.

post-traumatic stress disorder (PTSD) An anxiety disorder characterized by an emotional response to a traumatic event or situation involving severe external stress.

orexin A type of hormone in the brain that might affect food consumption.

Quick Bite

A Skinny Trend

In 1970, the average Playboy Playmate weighed 11 percent below the national average. Only 8 years later, in 1978, the average weight of Playboy Playmates was 17 percent below average. Today, the average model is 22 to 23 percent leaner than the average American woman.

emetics Agents that induce vomiting.

enemas Infusions of fluid into the rectum, usually for cleansing or other therapeutic purposes.

diuretics [dye-u-RET-iks] Drugs or other substances that promote the formation and release of urine. Diuretics are given to reduce body fluid volume in treating such disorders as high blood pressure, congestive heart disease, and edema. Both alcohol and caffeine act as diuretics.

laxatives Substances that promote evacuation of the bowel by increasing the bulk of the feces, lubricating the intestinal wall, or softening the stool.

in the final stages of the disorder. Instead, they are obsessed with food. But their obsession with thinness is even greater. The German term for the disorder, *pubertätsmagersucht*, or "mania for leanness," more accurately reflects the nature of the disease. The hallmark of anorexia nervosa is dramatic loss of weight, usually to less than 85 percent of the expected weight for height or a body mass index (BMI) of less than or equal to 17.5 kg/m^2. (See **Figure SED.5**.)

Anorexia is more prevalent in industrialized societies that share an abundance of food and an attitude that equates beauty, particularly feminine beauty, with thinness. Nine of 10 anorexia sufferers are female—probably because Western society emphasizes thinness more for women than for men.[22] Studies show that the peak age of onset is between 15 and 19 years old,[23] and the typical anorexia sufferer has been an upper-class Caucasian female adolescent. Unfortunately, during the past decade, anorexia has become more of an equal-opportunity disorder. Physicians have reported cases of the disorder in young women from all social and ethnic backgrounds; it is especially prevalent in women who participate in activities that emphasize leanness, including modeling, ballet, and gymnastics. In addition, anorexia has increased significantly among African American women.[24]

Causes of Anorexia Nervosa

On the surface, anorexia nervosa usually seems to result from a weight-loss program gone awry. A high school freshman may go on a diet after her boyfriend or gymnastics coach tells her she is too heavy. An eighth-grader may want to lose weight to be more popular at a new school. The diet may start out just fine, but it never stops.

Beneath the surface, psychological issues are typically at work. Because most cases of anorexia begin around the age of puberty, some psychologists theorize that anorexic behavior is an attempt to prevent or delay sexual

Quick Bite

Fashion Designers and Weight Guidelines for Models

The fashion industry sells women an ideal of beauty embodied in the models who walk the runways and appear in fashion magazines. Spurred by the deaths of several South American models—one reportedly trying to live on lettuce and Diet Coke—fashion designers in Spain and Italy issued regulations in late 2006 to raise weight limits for fashion models. They require a BMI of at least 18, which means that models must weigh at least 56 kilograms (123 pounds) if their height is 1.75 meters (5 feet, 9 inches) or more. These figures are in sync with World Health Organization (WHO) standards of the minimum healthy weight. Designers excluded super-skinny models who did not meet the minimum requirements from performing in a Madrid fashion show.

The U.S. fashion industry has not followed suit. It has no plans to require models to achieve an objective measure of health, such as a height-to-weight ratio, despite a poll on *Elle* magazine's Web site in which two-thirds of respondents indicated they wished that American designers would follow the examples of fashion show organizers in Milan and Madrid in banning overly skinny models. However, at a meeting of the Council of Fashion Designers of America, the industry introduced guidelines for designers, aimed at promoting healthier behavior among its models and at educating designers on how to recognize disorders.

Figure SED.5 **BMI and underweight.** When managing eating disorders, BMI can help guide decisions about nutrition, medications, and psychotherapy.

Source: Data from American Psychiatric Association. *Diagnostic and Statistical Manual of Mental Disorders.* 4th ed. Text revision (DSM-IV-TR). Washington, DC: American Psychiatric Association, 2000.

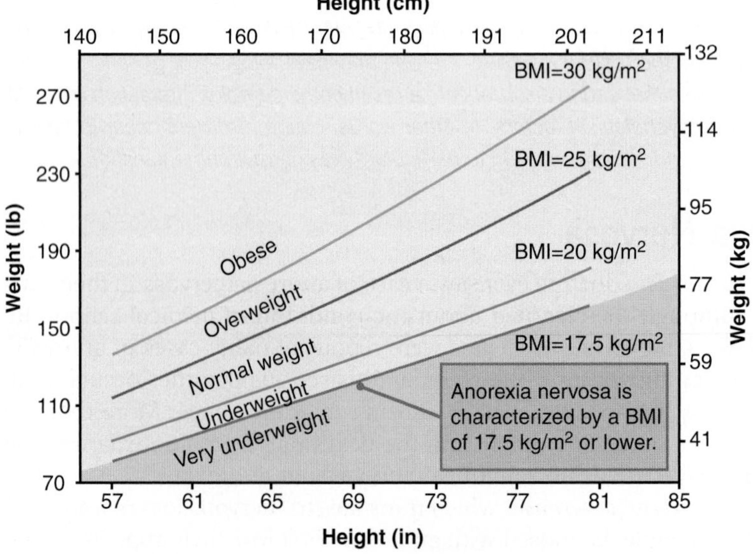

maturation. By retaining a child's body, a young girl may hope to avoid the pressures of the teen years and the responsibilities of adulthood. In addition, psychologists report that anorexia sufferers tend to be rigid, perfectionistic, all-or-nothing thinkers. Sufferers tend to lack a sense of independence and control over their own destiny. They may attempt to compensate for this through acts of intense self-discipline. Parents may facilitate this syndrome by being overly protective or rigid or by holding a child to excessively high standards of achievement.[25] Additional risk factors commonly associated with onset of anorexia include extremely high levels of exercise, distorted body image, obsessive-compulsive disorders, and negative self-esteem.[26]

Warning Signs

Parents and friends of people with anorexia often miss early signs of the disease. It can be easy to mistake a loved one's obsession with dieting, avoidance of particular foods, or rigorous exercise schedule for a reasonable desire to lose weight.[27] When asked about a child who has been diagnosed with anorexia, most parents will describe a "wonderful" daughter—one who has always been cooperative, obedient, an exceptional student, and unusually neat and organized. When she started to diet, she did so with the same zeal and dedication she exhibited in other areas of her life.[28]

Initially, someone with anorexia has a feeling of power. Sufferers enjoy a feeling of control as they learn to deny their hunger and limit their food intake. Early warning signs include obsessively counting calories; developing lists of "safe" foods and foods to avoid; cutting foods, even peas, into small pieces; and spending a great deal of time rearranging food on a plate. To suppress
THINK About It 2 hunger, a person with anorexia may drink up to 30 cups of water or diet soda a day. Anorexia sufferers also may channel their obsessions with food into the preparation of elaborate meals for others without eating any of the food themselves.[29] Table SED.2 shows the warning signs of anorexia.

As the disease progresses, anorexia sufferers become increasingly disillusioned, withdrawn, and hostile. Success always seems beyond their grasp. No matter how thin they are, they see themselves as overweight. (See **Figure SED.6**.) When they eat more than they think they should, they may induce vomiting or use **emetics**, **enemas**, **diuretics**, or **laxatives**. Or they may exercise relentlessly. Eventually, their efforts to avoid obesity take over their lives. They start to avoid social situations that may expose their behaviors and so withdraw more and more from friends and family. Groggy and irritable from food deprivation and sleep disturbances, people with advanced anorexia spend so little time on their schoolwork or jobs that their performance deteriorates. Yet when confronted with their obsessive dieting or deteriorating behavior, they will deny that anything is unusual.[30]

Treatment

Just as there is no one cause for anorexia nervosa, there is no single way to cure it. In fact, most experts doubt that patients with anorexia can ever be cured. Research suggests that with intensive therapy, most patients can achieve normal weight. However, they may struggle all their lives with a moderate to severe preoccupation with food and body weight, poor social relationships, and depression. The earlier a patient begins treatment, the better the prognosis.

The course of anorexia varies greatly. In rare instances, a sufferer recovers spontaneously without treatment. More typically, a patient recovers only after a variety of treatments or enters a cyclical pattern of weight gain and

Table SED.2 Warning Signs of Anorexia

Anorexia nervosa is a disorder in which preoccupation with dieting and thinness leads to excessive weight loss. The person with anorexia may not acknowledge that weight loss and restricted eating are problems. Family and friends can help by recognizing that the following are warning signs:

- Loss of a significant amount of weight
- Continuing to diet, although thin
- Feeling fat, even after losing weight
- Fear of weight gain
- Cessation of monthly menstrual periods
- Preoccupation with food, calories, nutrition, and/or cooking
- Preferring to eat in isolation
- Exercising compulsively
- Bingeing and purging

Figure SED.6 Distorted body image.

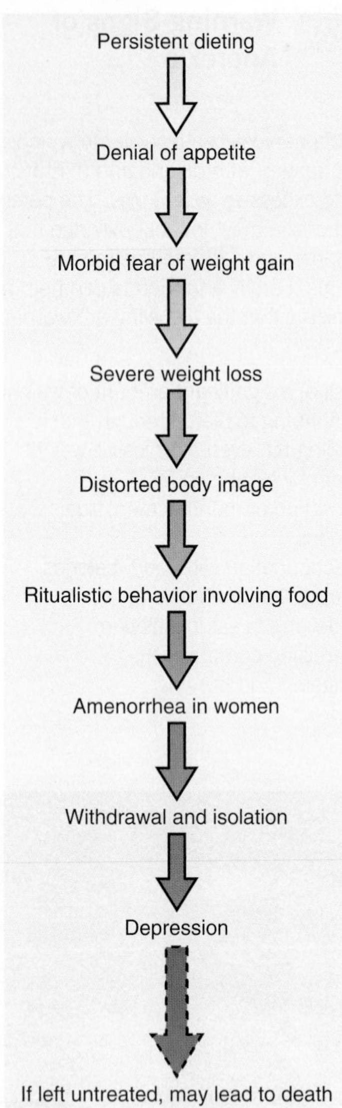

Figure SED.7 The progression of anorexia.

relapse. From 30 to 50 percent of anorexia patients also have symptoms of bulimia, which can complicate diagnosis and treatment.[31] Tragically, in 6 to 18 percent of cases, the disease proves fatal. (See **Figure SED.7**.) Patients who have other emotional disorders, such as major depression or substance abuse, are the most likely to die from complications of the disease. Potentially fatal complications of anorexia include starvation and suicide.[32]

As with many other behavioral disorders, people with anorexia usually deny the danger of their situation. And so family and friends must intervene to get sufferers to treatment—often by getting together and supportively confronting the person with evidence that something is seriously wrong. This common technique helps people accept the need for at least an initial medical screening. The complex and multifaceted nature of anorexia requires a team of experienced health care professionals, including physicians, clinical dietitians, and psychotherapists, so that both the physical and psychological aspects of the disorder can be addressed. One of the best places to find an experienced team of therapists is at an eating disorder clinic associated with a major medical facility.[33]

The first goal of treatment is to stabilize a patient's physical condition. The second is to convert the patient, who is typically reluctant, into a willing participant in the treatment plan. A combination of hospitalization, psychotherapy, and pharmacotherapy is often necessary.

Restoring the patient's nutritional status is of prime importance. Otherwise, dehydration, starvation, and electrolyte imbalances can lead to serious health problems and even death. (See Table SED.3.) If a patient has lost more than 30 percent of body weight over a three-month period or weighs 70 percent or less of the standard weight considered healthy for height, hospitalization is essential. (See Table SED.4.) Restoration of body weight and return of menses are primary therapeutic goals for the treatment of eating disorders.[34] Once the patient's physical condition has stabilized and some physical symptoms of starvation have disappeared, psychotherapy can begin in earnest. Many therapists use a cognitive–behavioral approach to help the patient challenge irrational beliefs and establish healthy attitudes and behaviors for gaining and maintaining weight.

The early phases of weight gain are filled with challenges for both patient and clinician. Patients must gain a certain amount of weight to prevent death or permanent damage while the psychotherapeutic portion of their treatment is still in the very early phases. At first, the patient is encouraged to simply eat enough food to minimize or stop weight loss. Next, the patient is started on a very slow process of weight gain, all the while receiving intensive psychotherapy. The first sign of weight gain can precipitate a crisis. Phobia of obesity may return with renewed vengeance. Many patients refuse to eat. Others resist treatment in covert ways. If not restricted to bed and closely supervised, they may try to burn off calories through relentless exercise or by purging. To avoid detection, they adopt a series of behaviors to conceal their lack of weight gain. These include wearing concealing clothes or "bulking up" before weigh-ins by filling their pockets with coins or drinking large amounts of water or diet soda.[35]

Psychologists use a variety of psychotherapeutic techniques to help the patient deal with underlying emotional issues such as depression. Treatment programs generally use a combination of behavioral therapy, individual psychotherapy, patient education, family education, and family therapy. Frequently, therapists find family conflicts at the heart of the eating disorder. Ongoing therapy for the patient and family is key to successful recovery. As the patient's symptoms resolve, she or he must find new ways to relate to and communi-

Table SED.3 Side Effects of Excessive Weight Loss in Anorexia Nervosa

Emaciation
- Loss of fat stores and muscle mass
- Reduced thyroid metabolism
- Cold intolerance
- Difficulty maintaining core body temperature

Hematological
- Leukopenia (abnormal decrease of white blood cells)
- Iron-deficiency anemia

Other
- Growth of lanugo (fine, babylike hairs) over the trunk
- Osteopenia (mineral depletion in bone)
- Premature osteoporosis

Neuropsychiatric
- Abnormal taste sensation
- Depression
- Impaired thought processes

Cardiac
- Loss of cardiac muscle, resulting in a smaller heart
- Abnormal heart rhythm
- Increased risk of sudden death

Gastrointestinal
- Delayed gastric emptying
- Bloating
- Constipation
- Abdominal pain

Table SED.4 When Hospitalization Is Needed

Suggested criteria for hospitalization for individuals with anorexia nervosa include:

- Weight loss of greater than 30 percent over three months
- Severe metabolic disturbance
- Severe depression or suicide risk
- Severe bingeing and purging
- Failure to maintain outpatient weight contract
- Psychosis
- Family crisis

Source: Data from American Psychiatric Association. *Diagnostic and Statistical Manual of Mental Disorders.* 4th ed. Text revision (DSM-IV-TR). Washington, DC: American Psychiatric Association, 2000.

cate with family members. Family members must remain open and willing to change their behavior toward the person with the eating disorder.

Dietitians work closely with the psychotherapist to help patients develop a realistic view of food and to reshape their food selection and eating behaviors. Although no pharmaceutical agent has been developed specifically to treat anorexia, some antidepressants have proved useful.[36]

Most patients with anorexia nervosa require continued intervention after discharge from the hospital or treatment program. Support groups for people with eating disorders and their families can be an important link in the recovery process. Support groups also can be a useful technique for easing a resistant patient into treatment. With expert help and ongoing therapy, patients with anorexia can develop new mechanisms for coping with life's stresses, eventually replacing their disordered relationship to food with new, healthier interpersonal relationships.

Key Concepts *The hallmark symptoms of anorexia nervosa are a mania for thinness and self-imposed starvation. Sufferers manifest a body weight as much as 15 percent below normal, a severely distorted body image, withdrawal from family and friends, and various physical and psychological changes related to starvation. Treatment for anorexia nervosa often focuses on family relationships, and although it may not cure, psychotherapy can facilitate healthier attitudes toward food, body image, and personal relationships.*

Bulimia Nervosa

Although the behavior we now call bulimia was practiced in Greek and Roman times, it has been recognized as a psychiatric illness for only 30 years. Gerald Russell, a British psychiatrist, first coined the term *bulimia nervosa* in 1979 to describe a syndrome of bingeing and purging in young Caucasian women. The average patient with bulimia is an unmarried Caucasian woman

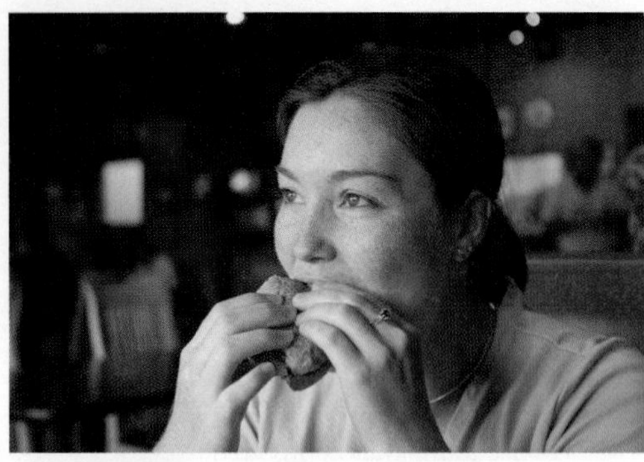

Figure SED.8 The typical person suffering from bulimia is an unmarried Caucasian woman in her twenties or thirties.

in her twenties or thirties with a normal or near-normal body weight. (See **Figure SED.8**.) Patients with bulimia are more likely to be sexually active than are those with anorexia and often are involved in destructive relationships. Almost anyone can be affected, however.

The relationships among dieting, bingeing severity, and alcohol use were studied in a sample of women in their first year of college. A positive relationship was found between dieting and bingeing severity and the frequency, intensity, and negative consequences of alcohol use in young women.[37]

People with bulimia nervosa tend to feel very disorganized. They report suffering from depression and low self-esteem. Many were sexually abused as children. Food was often a source of comfort, and eating gradually evolved into a tool for dealing with every unpleasant event, from boredom to major life crises.

It is estimated that between 1 percent and 3 percent of American adolescent and young adult females have bulimia. But bulimia, particularly in its milder forms, often goes undetected. This is because people with bulimia are very secretive about their behaviors, typically limiting their binge-and-purge episodes to the middle of the night or times when they are assured of privacy. Also, unlike patients with anorexia or binge-eating disorder, whose body weights may hint at their underlying psychiatric disorder, the body weight of a patient with bulimia is usually average or only slightly above average. Several studies have found that as many as 40 percent of college-aged women occasionally binge and purge—often enough to raise concern but too infrequently for an official diagnosis of bulimia.[38] Table SED.5 lists the warning signs of bulimia.

Quick Bite

I'm So Hungry I Could Eat an Ox!

The term *bulimia* is derived from the Greek words *bous*, meaning "ox," and *limos*, meaning "hunger."

Causes of Bulimia

Bulimia seems to occur most often in people who have an intense desire to nurture themselves with food but who are also strongly influenced by our societal obsession with thinness. One description of people with bulimia characterizes them as being obsessed with food but repulsed by fat. In contrast to people with anorexia, people with bulimia focus more on food than on thinness.

Psychologists who have treated patients with bulimia have found that they typically did not receive sufficient nurturing during their formative years.

Academy of Nutrition and Dietetics

Nutrition Intervention in the Treatment of Anorexia Nervosa, Bulimia Nervosa, and Other Eating Disorders

It is the position of the Academy of Nutrition and Dietetics (AND) that nutrition intervention, including nutritional counseling by a registered dietitian, is an essential component of the team treatment of patients with anorexia nervosa, bulimia nervosa, and other eating disorders during assessment and treatment across the continuum of care.

Source: Position of the American Dietetic Association: nutrition intervention in the treatment of anorexia nervosa, bulimia nervosa, and other eating disorders. *J Am Diet Assoc.* 2006;106:(12):2073–2082. Copyright 2006. Reprinted with permission from Elsevier.

Table SED.5 Warning Signs of Bulimia

Bulimia nervosa involves frequent episodes of binge eating, almost always followed by purging and intense feelings of guilt or shame. The sufferer feels out of control and recognizes that the behavior is not normal. The signs that a person may have bulimia include:

- Bingeing, or eating uncontrollably
- Compensating for binges by strict dieting, fasting, vigorous exercise, vomiting, or abusing laxatives or diuretics in an attempt to lose weight
- Using the bathroom frequently after meals
- Preoccupation with body weight
- Depression or mood swings
- Irregular menstrual periods
- Dental problems, swollen cheeks or glands, heartburn, or bloating
- Personal or family problems with drugs or alcohol

Whereas families of anorexic patients tend to have a lot of rigidly defined roles and rules, families of bulimic patients tend to lack structure. Roles may be loosely defined. Parents are often described as distant and judgmental. Significant family conflict usually exists. Patients often feel that their families failed to provide an adequate sense of security and protection.[39]

binge Consumption of a very large amount of food in a brief time (e.g., two hours) accompanied by a loss of control over how much and what is eaten.

purge Emptying of the GI tract by self-induced vomiting and/or misuse of laxatives, diuretics, or enemas.

Obsessed by Thoughts of Food

A person with bulimia chronically **binges** and **purges**. To meet the official definition of the disorder, bingeing and purging must occur at least twice a week for at least three months. Purging may be accompanied or replaced by fasting, excessive exercise, or other behaviors that compensate for the binge episode. Between binges, people with bulimia typically restrict their dietary intake to a limited number of low-calorie foods they consider "safe." This dietary control is an illusion, however. The average bulimic sufferer is obsessed by thoughts of food and spends a great deal of time both planning the next

Diary of an Eating Disorder

Every time I leave one of my sessions I feel better. We talk about stuff; I feel, express, and even cry. Today was the third time since I left her office to come home and throw up. I think things are getting better despite the fact that my mind focuses 80 percent of the time on food during the 55 minutes. But it's like the kitchen is a refuge for my mind. I always know it will be there, waiting to embrace me when I get home.

Alone is how I hope to find it. I have been thinking of what I will sink my teeth into first. Usually I go for the fat-free chocolate cake, then to the frozen yogurt (which makes it all come up much smoother). I don't think this is normal, though I am not really concerned. I feel like a million-pound weight has been swept away by the effortless flush of the toilet. The hardest thing is to look in the mirror after I have thrown up. Sometimes I wipe my face before I look. Other times I leave the spit, bile, and food on my mouth and hands. I just stand there holding my hands up, with my shoulders slumped over. I produce this expression of absolute helplessness—then I laugh. I guess I am amazed by the act I've just committed. I can't explain why, I can't believe that it is really me doing this. Why would I do something like throw up? I really have no reason to torture myself. Bulimia was always them—I can't possibly be like that. I throw up, but I am not a bulimic. I sure as hell don't have an eating disorder.

I am totally for this whole counseling thing because I feel sad a lot and I want to feel better. But I can't leave there and not feel that I have to get this crap out. All this stuff that we talk about.

Today, Dr. Tant asked me when this all began. My first thought was, "Oh this throwing up thing? I can't remember." But I do recall one time when my ex-boyfriend Matt and I had gone to a really nice dinner. My recollection of the evening was that it was perfect. I remember thinking about how this food was really fattening, though, and how it would make me fat if I kept it down. I didn't know or have the willpower to just not eat it. Over and over I tortured and berated myself about the effects this dinner would have on my body. I couldn't bear it. This dinner was no longer one meal; it was going to ruin my body and make me fat. I couldn't stand that food being inside me another moment. Looking back I can't imagine how I could have thrown up right there on the side of the road. It was like I had no couth. I told Matt to pull over, and I just stuck my hand down my throat. Rationalizing the act while engaging in it, I then jumped back in the truck to carry on with the night. We never discussed my vile act other than Matt saying, "I can't believe you just did that."

"I know," I responded, "but it just was making me feel so sick. I mean, my stomach was really nauseous [sic]." Basically I don't know when I began this war with myself, but I know it caused me to fear myself. The rest is a blur—its beginning, its incentive. I heard Dr. Tant's question. I just didn't have the answer.

Chelsea Browning Smith

Source: Smith CB. *Diary of an Eating Disorder*. Dallas, TX: Taylor Publishing Company, 1998. Reprinted by permission of Taylor Trade Publishing, an imprint of Rowman & Littlefield Publishing Group.

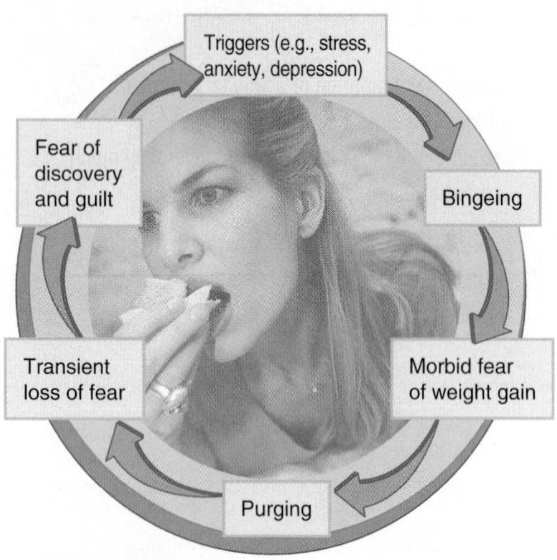

Figure SED.9 The binge-and-purge cycle of bulimia.

binge and trying to resist the urge to binge.[40] **Figure SED.9** illustrates the binge-and-purge pattern of bulimia.

Just what triggers a binge is not clear. People with bulimia tend to be all-or-nothing thinkers. If they eat a single piece of food from their forbidden list, such as a cookie, they feel driven to consume the entire box. Some researchers believe that hunger caused by very restrictive dieting, combined with a buildup of everyday stresses, overwhelms the person's resolve and precipitates a binge.

During a binge, individuals with bulimia typically consume massive quantities of highly palatable "forbidden" foods such as pastry, ice cream, and candy. This gorging takes place over a relatively short time span—say, an hour or two. Binges may contain up to 10,000 kilocalories. Afterward, feeling physically ill from overingesting, sufferers use a variety of purging techniques, such as self-induced vomiting or excessive quantities of laxatives, to rid themselves of the food. Or they may follow a binge with a period of very strict fasting and heightened exercise.

Purging leads to a variety of physical symptoms. Over time, gastric acid in vomit burns the lining of the pharynx, esophagus, and mouth, erodes tooth enamel, and may even result in loss of teeth. Repeated vomiting also can enlarge the salivary glands and erode the lining of the stomach and esophagus.

Excessive self-induced vomiting and diarrhea can upset the body's delicate biochemical balance through loss of electrolytes and body water. Among other dangers, changes in electrolyte balance can trigger an irregular heartbeat and precipitate a life-threatening medical crisis. In 2005, intense media attention focused on Terri Schiavo, who suffered from bulimia and collapsed when her potassium levels dipped frighteningly low. Her heart stopped, which likely caused decreased blood flow to her brain, leading to brain damage.

Excessive use of emetics (drugs to induce vomiting) and laxatives carries its own risks. Repeated use of emetics is toxic to the liver and kidneys, and abuse of laxatives can damage the lining of the large intestine. Table SED.6 shows the side effects of bulimic purging.

Table SED.6 Side Effects of Purging in Bulimia Nervosa

Metabolic effects
- Electrolyte abnormalities
- Low blood magnesium

Gastrointestinal
- Inflammation of the salivary glands
- Pancreatic inflammation and enlargement
- Esophageal inflammation or ulcers
- Gastric erosion
- Dysfunctional bowel

Dental
- Erosion of dental enamel, particularly of front teeth, with corresponding decay

Neuropsychiatric
- Fatigue
- Weakness
- Impaired thought processes
- Seizures (related to large fluid shifts and electrolyte disturbances)
- Mild inflammation of peripheral nerves

Treatment

Little research has been done on the long-term course of bulimia. It appears, however, that bulimia is easier to treat than anorexia, perhaps because bulimic patients tend to recognize that their behavior is abnormal. Following treatment, more than half of patients report an improvement in their binge-eating and coping behaviors. About 30 percent of patients eventually become symptom-free. The rest, however, struggle with the disorder to some degree throughout their lives. To reduce the risk of relapse, therapists encourage patients to stay involved in support groups after completing formal therapy.

Cognitive behavior therapy is key to helping patients reshape their attitudes about food and identify situations that trigger bingeing. The therapist's goal is to help patients let go of their need to categorize foods as safe or dangerous, good or bad. Patients must learn techniques for dealing with stress and uncomfortable or painful memories and feelings. Depression, which typically accompanies this disorder, must be treated as well. Many patients with bulimia also require treatment for substance abuse. A patient is hospitalized only when severely depressed or when purging is so frequent that physical damage has occurred or is imminent.

Medication can be an effective adjunct to psychotherapy. Serotonin-enhancing antidepressants have been used successfully to treat bulimia.

Key Concepts *Key symptoms of bulimia nervosa are binge-eating episodes at least twice a week for three months, followed by behaviors that compensate for the binges, such as severe dieting, purging, or a combination of dieting and purging. The body weights of people with bulimia are typically close to or slightly above that considered healthy for their heights. Treatment emphasizes reshaping a person's attitudes toward food and recognizing contexts that trigger bingeing.*

Binge-Eating Disorder

Binge eating is the most common eating disorder in industrialized nations, and differs from bulimia in that the person with this disorder does not attempt to compensate by purging or other means. Overeating has been reported in the medical literature since scribes first put stylus to tablet. And over the generations, many societies have considered obesity a sign of good health, wealth, and even fertility. But modern Western society is not among these. Binge eating is now recognized as an eating disorder not otherwise specified (EDNOS). This term is used to describe those conditions that meet the definition for eating disorders, but not the criteria for anorexia or bulimia.[41] EDNOS was described by Bruch in 1973 as an atypical form of eating disorder seen in her patients.[42] EDNOS comprises the largest category of eating disorders. Binge eating has gained increased attention since it became categorized as an EDNOS. It occurs only in societies where people have access to an abundant supply of food. Its precise causes are unclear. However, the condition seems to be related to an intense desire to nurture oneself with food or to reduce stress by eating.[43] In 1994, the American Psychiatric Association recognized binge-eating disorder as an emotional illness.

Stress and Conflict Often Trigger Binge Eating

A person with binge-eating disorder consumes excessive quantities of food in a relatively short period of time at least twice a week. In some instances, binge eaters adopt a grazing pattern. "Grazers" eat constantly for extended periods of time, eventually consuming an exceptionally large quantity of food. This pattern of overindulgence may be seen in people who restrict their food intake at work or school but seek solace in food at home.

Not all people who binge are obese, but bingeing is common among the severely obese and people with a history of weight cycling. In the United States, at least 30 percent of the people enrolled in weight-management programs report behaviors consistent with a diagnosis of binge-eating disorder, compared with only 3 to 5 percent of the general population.[44] (See Table SED.7.)

Many binge eaters begin dieting in grade school and start bingeing during adolescence or in their early twenties. Typically, they try numerous weight-loss programs without long-term success. Binge eaters exhibit many of the same characteristics as bulimic patients. More than 50 percent have clinical depression. Feelings of depression, loneliness, anxiety, or stress can precipitate a binge. Like other patients with eating disorders, those with binge-eating disorder are all-or-nothing thinkers. They tend to categorize foods as safe or dangerous. Eating even a small serving of a forbidden food can trigger a binge. Typical binge foods include sweets, pastries, ice cream, and high-fat snacks such as nuts and chips. However, if junk foods aren't handy, binge eaters may eat large quantities of starchy foods such as potatoes, bread, and pasta. **Figure SED.10** illustrates some factors that trigger binge eating.

Most binge eaters are people who have not learned to express or even acknowledge their feelings. During therapy sessions, many binge eaters report

Quick Bite

When Plumpness Was Valued

In centuries past, extra pounds displayed one's wealth and prosperity. The wealthy could afford abundant food and didn't perform physical labor.

Table SED.7 Warning Signs of Binge-Eating Disorder

Binge eaters, like bulimia sufferers, experience periods of uncontrolled eating that they usually keep secret. Binge eaters often are depressed and sometimes have other psychological problems. Signs that a person may have a binge-eating disorder include:

- Episodes of binge eating
- Eating when not physically hungry
- Frequent dieting
- Feeling unable to stop eating voluntarily
- Awareness that eating patterns are abnormal
- Weight fluctuations
- Depressed mood
- Attribution of social and professional successes and failures to weight

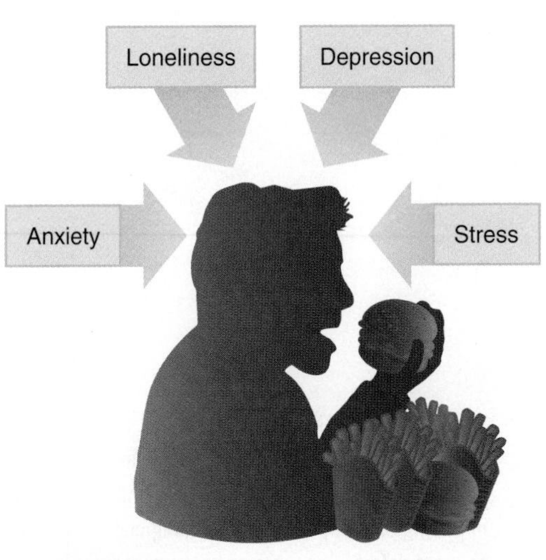

Figure SED.10 Feelings of loneliness, depression, anxiety, or stress can trigger a binge-eating episode.

Figure SED.11 **The vicious cycle of binge eating.** Binge-eating disorder is the most common eating disorder.

feeling helpless to change the course of events or behaviors of others around them. Rather than acknowledge their feelings, they swallow them—aided by large quantities of food. They become addicted to the behavior itself because it is the only way they can get relief from stress. (See **Figure SED.11**.)

Binge eating often is a learned response to stress or conflict, passed down from one generation to the next. Parents may use food rather than affection and discussion to shape their children's behavior. Food is used for celebration and consolation, for reward and punishment. Children growing up in such environments learn to eat in response to emotions rather than to hunger. As adults, they turn to food to satisfy their emotional needs.

Treatment

Little is known about the course and prognosis of binge-eating disorder. However, people who become obese as a result of this disorder are at risk of developing weight-related health problems, including type 2 diabetes, hypertension, degenerative joint disease, heart disease, and even certain cancers.

People who have binge-eating disorder are rarely able to control the condition themselves. They usually require therapy to help them identify their long-buried emotions and learn techniques for giving voice to their feelings. Therapists experienced in treating this disorder discourage patients from trying to lose weight initially. Any attempts to restrict food intake can backfire by creating anxiety and provoking a binge. The major focus of therapy is to help patients identify their emotions and separate true biological hunger from emotional hunger. Once significant progress is made in these areas, the patient is better equipped psychologically to address weight issues.

Long-term support is key to keeping binge eaters from relapsing. Self-help groups such as Overeaters Anonymous are one source of support. These groups are organized according to the 12-step philosophy of Alcoholics Anonymous. In addition, many hospitals in large urban areas have support groups led by trained therapists. Hospitals and clinics that provide medically supervised fasting programs such as Optifast often supply this type of service as well.

Many patients with binge-eating disorder benefit from antidepressant medications. These drugs reduce the urge to binge, most likely by altering the brain's serotonin level. Various weight-management medications are now in development. These also may curb the urge to binge.

Key Concepts *Binge-eating disorder is the most common eating disorder seen in people of all ages and backgrounds. Like people with bulimia, those with binge-eating disorder consume significantly more food than is typically eaten in a given period of time. Unlike bulimia, those with binge-eating disorder do not purge or fast. Not all binge eaters are obese, although many obese people binge. Therapy aims to help patients identify their emotions and separate true biological hunger from emotional hunger.*

Body Dysmorphic Disorder

body dysmorphic disorder (BDD) An eating disorder in which a distressing and impairing preoccupation with an imagined or slight defect in appearance is the primary symptom.

People with **body dysmorphic disorder (BDD)** are preoccupied with an imagined or slight defect in appearance, worrying, for example, that their skin is scarred, that they are balding, or their nose is too big. Patients may engage in long rituals of grooming, repeatedly combing hair, applying makeup, or picking at their skin. The condition's severity varies. Whereas some people can manage it, for others the preoccupation causes significant distress and impairment: they may have few friends, avoid dating, miss school or work, and feel very self-conscious in social situations.

Many patients affected with BDD have coexisting conditions, such as obsessive-compulsive disorder (OCD), major depression, delusions, or social phobia. Approximately 2 to 7 percent of patients who undergo plastic surgery have BDD and are generally unhappy with the results.

BDD affects 1 to 2 percent of the general population; however, BDD frequently goes undiagnosed. Patients are ashamed of their problem and fail to report it to their physicians. Even though it is a serious and distressing condition, it is easily trivialized. In addition, even many health professionals are unaware that BDD is a psychiatric disorder that often responds to psychiatric treatment. Many people seek treatment from dermatologists, plastic surgeons, and other physicians, but these professionals often are unaware of this disorder and thus are unhelpful.

Psychiatric treatment, including medication and cognitive behavior therapy, can effectively decrease symptoms and suffering. The therapist helps the person with BDD resist compulsive BDD behaviors (for example, mirror checking), face avoided situations (for example, social situations), and develop a more realistic view of his or her appearance. Medications, including selective serotonin reuptake inhibitors (SSRIs), can relieve obsession and decrease distress and depression.[45]

Night-Eating Syndrome

When a person grazes through the evening, finds herself plotting midnight refrigerator raids, and wakes at night to eat, she may have **night-eating syndrome (NES)**. A person with this disorder

- Eats more than half of daily calories during and after the evening meal
- Wakes up at least once a night to eat, especially high-carbohydrate snacks
- Feels tense, anxious, worried, or guilty while eating
- Lacks appetite for breakfast and postpones it for hours
- Persists in this behavior for at least three months

Although a quarter of obese people suffer from it, NES is a fairly uncommon eating disorder in the general population, affecting only 1 to 1.5 percent of adults in the general population, 6 to 16 percent of patients in weight-reduction programs, and 8 to 42 percent of candidates for bariatric surgery.[46] Although underlying causes are not fully understood, the disorder may result from a combination of biological, genetic, and emotional factors. Researchers have noted several hormonal imbalances among NES sufferers: levels of both melatonin (a sleep-inducing hormone) and leptin (an appetite-suppressing hormone) were significantly reduced from normal levels. Cortisol—the so-called stress hormone that kicks in when we feel tense—appears higher at night in night eaters, perhaps arousing them to wake up and head for the kitchen. Stress, depression, and anxiety commonly affect mood among those with the condition.

NES involves a disturbed food intake circadian rhythm, which may be out of sync by as much as four to five hours with a person's normal sleep rhythm. It is possibly the first clinical disorder to manifest differing circadian rhythms of two biological systems.

night-eating syndrome (NES) An eating disorder in which a habitual pattern of interrupting sleep to eat is the primary symptom.

The heavy preference for carbohydrates, which trigger the brain to produce "feel-good" neurochemicals, suggests that night eating may be an attempt to

Quick Bite

When Men Starve

During World War II, researchers at the University of Minnesota conducted a starvation study on 36 male volunteers, all conscientious objectors. Their typical food intake was cut in half, and they lost about 25 percent of their body weight. Researchers noted significant psychological changes as well. The subjects began obsessing about food, collecting recipes and cookbooks, and hoarding food-related objects. They became apathetic, chronically exhausted, and lost all interest in sex. Most were afraid to leave the experimental conditions for fear of losing control in the outside world.

self-medicate mood problems. A dietitian can help develop meal plans that distribute intake more evenly throughout the day so that a person is not as vulnerable to caloric loading in the evening. Stress-reduction programs, including psychological therapy, can be helpful.[47]

Key Concepts *Body dysmorphic disorder is often seen with coexisting conditions such as obsessive-compulsive disorder, major depression, delusions, or social phobia. Patients with BDD magnify slight defects and are preoccupied with their appearance.*

Night-eating syndrome, though uncommon, affects up to a quarter of obese people. People with NES interrupt normal sleep to eat and often feel stressed, anxious, and depressed. They typically have hormonal imbalances. Psychotherapy and stress reduction therapy can be helpful.

Males: An Overlooked Population

An estimated 5 to 15 percent of people with anorexia or bulimia and an estimated 35 percent of those with binge-eating disorder are male.[48] As many as a million boys and men in the United States struggle with eating disorders.[49] Yet males with eating disorders have been "ignored, neglected or dismissed because of statistical infrequency of the disease, combined with the pervasive myth that eating disorders are a female disease," according to Arnold E. Andersen, former director of the Eating and Weight Disorders Clinic at Johns Hopkins University and scientific editor of the book *Males with Eating Disorders*.[50]

Women who develop eating disorders may feel fat, but they typically are near average weight. In contrast, most men who develop these diseases are overweight. Many were seriously teased about their weight as children. Whereas women are concerned primarily with weight, men are concerned with shape and muscle definition. Indeed, men often develop disordered eating habits while trying to improve their athletic performance. Finally, more men than women diet to prevent medical consequences associated with being overweight.

Why do fewer males than females develop full-blown eating disorders? Andersen contends that there is a "dose-response" relationship between the amount of sociocultural pressure to be thin and the probability of developing an eating disorder. Consider that articles and advertisements that promote dieting usually target young women rather than young men. When men are exposed to activities that require leanness, such as wrestling, swimming, running, and horse racing, they exhibit a substantial increase in anorexic behavior. It seems clear that cultural conditioning, not gender, contributes to the incidence of eating disorders.[51]

Furthermore, the degree of thinness held up as desirable for women is 15 percent below a healthy body weight, whereas the degree of thinness held up as desirable for men is well within the healthy limits of normal weight. Thus, women are more likely than men to alter their eating habits to achieve the desired appearance.

An Unrecognized Disorder

anorexia athletica Eating disorder associated with competitive participation in athletic activity.

Like women, most men develop eating disorders during adolescence. But males can develop eating disorders during preadolescence and young adulthood as well. The diagnostic criteria for anorexia and bulimia in men and women are similar. But doctors are so conditioned to viewing eating disorders as a female phenomenon that they often miss eating disorders in males. Likewise, the patient, his family, and friends may not recognize disordered eating patterns. (See Table SED.8.) Because our culture accepts overeating among men more readily than in women, binge eating in particular may go unrecognized in men. In addition, anorexia may elude diagnosis in men more often than in women because malnourished men don't experience definitive symptoms, such as a woman's loss of menstrual periods, that can alert professionals and others to the problem. Men also tend to view an eating disorder as a "woman's disease," so they often are hesitant to seek medical attention.[52]

Key Concepts *Men also suffer from eating disorders, although at rates much lower than those of women. Like women, men typically develop eating disorders during adolescence and young adulthood, but they are more often overweight and striving for a particular body shape and muscularity. Although the diagnostic criteria are the same, with the exception of amenorrhea, eating disorders in men are often undiagnosed due to societal conditioning that views eating disorders as "female" diseases.*

Anorexia Athletica

Participation in competitive athletics seems to be a common link in the development of eating disorders among males and females, regardless of their social or ethnic backgrounds. Sports-related eating disorders are known as **anorexia athletica.**[53] Although recent studies have not found higher rates of disordered eating in athletes as compared to nonathletes, those athletes who compete in lean sports are at higher risk.[54] Lean sports—those that emphasize leanness or body image—include distant running and swimming, gymnastics, dance, and diving **(Figure SED.12)**. Athletes who have anorexia athletica seek to achieve an unrealistic body size that they consider desirable for purposes of competition. In many cases, athletes with mild eating disorders are able to disguise their disease as attention to fitness. People who seem to be addicted to their exercise routine are at greater risk of developing eating disorders.[55]

Coaches and trainers play a significant role in the development of eating disorders among athletes.[56] The attitude that leanness equals performance, exemplified by sayings such as "get down to your fighting weight," still prevails.[57]

The Female Athlete Triad

Female athletes who fall prey to the "thin-at-any-cost" philosophy are at risk of developing a condition known as the female athlete triad. (See **Figure SED.13.**) This syndrome is characterized by disordered eating, amenorrhea (absence of menstruation), and abnormally low bone density. This triad occurs especially in young women involved in sports that involve appearance (e.g., gymnastics) and endurance (e.g., long-distance running).

Once body fat falls below 20 percent, a woman's estrogen levels often drop significantly. As a result, women's bodies enter a menopause-like state years ahead of time. Their periods become irregular or cease altogether. Bone loss accelerates, just as it would after natural menopause. Many female athletes who suffer from this triad have the bone density of women in their fifties and sixties. Weakened bones are more likely to fracture during exercise or daily activities. Stress fractures can be a red flag for female athlete triad. Because much of this bone loss is irreversible, women who suffer from the female athlete triad are at increased risk of developing osteoporosis.[58]

To help combat this alarming trend, the American College of Sports Medicine and the National Collegiate Athletic Association (NCAA) have established an eating disorders awareness campaign aimed at coaches and

Table SED.8 Signs of an Undisclosed Eating Disorder

People with eating disorders usually exhibit several of the following signs.

Physical

- Arrested growth
- Marked change or frequent fluctuations in weight
- Inability to gain weight
- Fatigue
- Constipation or diarrhea
- Susceptibility to fractures
- Delayed menarche
- Calcium or phosphorus imbalances, abnormal blood pH, or high serum amylase levels

Behavioral

- Change in eating habits
- Difficulty in social settings
- Reluctance to be weighed
- Depression
- Social withdrawal
- Repeated absence from school or work
- Deceptive or secretive behavior
- Stealing (e.g., to obtain food)
- Substance abuse
- Excessive exercise

Source: Reproduced from Becker AE, Grinspoon SK, Klibanski A, Herzog DB. Eating disorders. *N Engl J Med.* 1999;340(14):1092–1098.

Figure SED.12 Christy Henrich, a top Olympic gymnast, weighed less than 60 pounds when she died in 1994 at age 22 of multiple organ failure, a complication resulting from anorexia and bulimia.

trainers.[59] The NCAA also has a three-part video series, *Nutrition and Eating Disorders*, to acquaint coaches and trainers with the causes and effects of eating disorders as well as the steps to take when they suspect an athlete has an eating disorder.

Key Concepts *Athletics can be a gateway to eating disorders. Female athletes who develop restrictive eating habits are at risk for developing a more severe syndrome known as the female athlete triad. Disordered eating, amenorrhea, and abnormally low bone density characterize this syndrome. If not corrected, the female athlete triad can hinder athletic performance and set the stage for lifelong health problems.*

Vegetarianism and Eating Disorders

Some researchers have found a strong correlation between vegetarianism and eating disorders in teenagers. A study conducted in Minnesota schools found that 81 percent of students who classified themselves as vegetarians were female. Compared with nonvegetarian peers, these self-described vegetarians were twice as likely to participate in frequent diets, four times as likely to report intentional vomiting, and eight times as likely to report laxative use.[60] Some people with eating disorders try to disguise a change in eating habits by adopting a strict vegetarian diet.[61]

Smoking and Eating Disorders

British medical researcher Arthur Crisp described a variation on eating disorders. His previous studies showed that smoking is more common among teens with eating disorders than in the general teenage population. (See **Figure SED.14**.) His later research indicates that despite ample knowledge of the health risks of smoking, girls of average or slightly above average weight are taking up smoking in record numbers to curb their appetites. Though not frankly anorexic or bulimic, many young subjects report they periodically combine smoking with self-induced vomiting to enhance weight-control efforts.[62] This combined behavior is of particular interest and concern to researchers.

Diabulimia

Although not a new practice, **diabulimia** has gained recent media attention and recognition by health care professionals.[63] Diabulimia is the deliberate injection, by those with type 1 diabetes, of less insulin than prescribed, for the purpose of losing weight. Taking less insulin than prescribed prevents the body from using glucose. Similar to other eating disorders, diabulimia, although not a formal medical condition, is seen most often in teenage girls and young women.[64] Although features in each case may differ, diabulimics often display characteristics of nondiabetics with eating disorders, such as distorted body image, perfectionism, and obsessive behaviors. Women who take less insulin than prescribed had higher rates of developing diabetes-related complications such as eye disease, kidney disease, nerve damage to the feet and hands, heart attacks, and strokes and a three-times increased risk of death.[65]

Baryophobia

Baryophobia, a disorder characterized by fear of fat, was virtually unheard of until the late 1970s, when pediatricians began reporting a surprising number of young patients from affluent backgrounds whose growth appeared to

Quick Bite

Orthorexia

Orthorexia, meaning "fixation on righteous eating," is an informal term used to describe those who become obsessed with a perfect diet. Orthorexics are sometimes referred to as "health food junkies."

diabulimia The deliberate injection by those with type 1 diabetes of less insulin than prescribed for the purpose of losing weight.

baryophobia [barry-oh-FO-bee-ah] An uncommon eating disorder that stunts growth in children and young adults as a result of underfeeding.

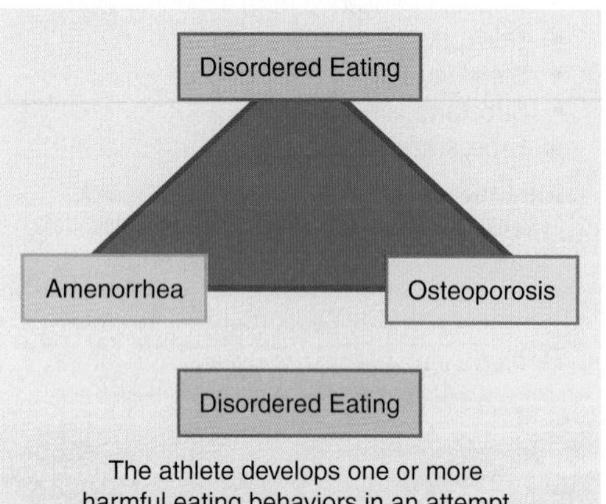

Disordered Eating

The athlete develops one or more harmful eating behaviors in an attempt to lose weight. The result is an energy deficit.

Amenorrhea

An energy deficit leads to a reduction in body fat. Once body fat falls below about 20 percent, the athlete's body often stops producing the hormones needed to make estrogen, resulting in menstrual cycle irregularities.

Osteoporosis

The lack of estrogen decreases calcium absorption and retention. Dietary deficiency of calcium also is common. Left untreated, this lack of calcium leads to bone loss, stress fractures, and osteoporosis.

Figure SED.13 **Female athlete triad.** Disordered-eating that results in excessive weight loss can lead to amenorrhea, which in turn leads to osteoporosis.

be stunted because of poor nutrition. In some instances, the stunting occurs when a child secretly starts to diet in order to fit in better with his or her trimmer classmates. More often, however, the child's parents are at the root of the problem.

Many well-intentioned parents underfeed their children in an attempt to "protect" them from inheriting their family's tendency toward obesity, heart disease, or diabetes. But the low-fat, high-carbohydrate diet beneficial to many adults may supply too few calories to meet the energy demands of active, growing children. In such instances, the entire family needs nutritional counseling to help them understand what constitutes a healthful diet and realistic body weight for a growing child.[66]

Figure SED.14 **A dangerous habit.** Smoking among young women has failed to decline, and in some cases has been linked to eating disorders.

Infantile Anorexia

Unwitting parents can even create disordered eating in infants, perhaps setting the stage for eating disorders later in life.[67] Childhood nutrition specialist Ellyn Satter has analyzed videotapes of infant feedings. Satter examined whether parents responded to—or ignored—their babies' nonverbal eating readiness cues. She concluded that many parents fail to recognize their babies' body language: they feed their babies too rapidly or too slowly, they offer foods the baby doesn't care for, or they persist in trying to feed a clearly full baby who is turning away from food. These well-meaning parents may inadvertently teach their babies to ignore hunger and satiety (fullness) cues and, instead, to eat in response to outside influences.[68]

Reports of a disorder called **infantile anorexia** lend support to Satter's observations. A team of child psychiatrists at the Children's National Medical Center in Washington, D.C., described this disorder, in which severe feeding difficulties begin as an infant is introduced to solid foods.[69] Symptoms include persistent food refusal for more than a month, malnutrition, parental concern about the child's poor food intake, and significant caregiver–infant conflict during feeding. The disorder typically starts or worsens during the transition from nursing to spoon-feeding and self-feeding, between ages 6 months and 3 years.

Babies with infantile anorexia should not be confused with picky eaters. Picky eaters may initially refuse all foods but allow themselves to be coaxed into eating. Picky eaters have strong food likes and dislikes but are not malnourished. And the relationship between the picky eaters and their parents or caregivers lacks the element of frustration and conflict seen in infantile anorexia.

Infantile anorexia has many serious consequences. Malnutrition can impair the developing brain and adds special stress to the parent–infant relationship. Furthermore, early conflict around meals may herald a lifelong unhealthy relationship with food.

Key Concepts *Researchers are continuously recognizing associations between eating disorders and behaviors such as vegetarianism and smoking. Even diabetics, babies, and young children may suffer from disordered eating patterns.*

Quick Bite

Pregorexia

Pregorexia is a term used to describe pregnant women who reduce calories and exercise in excess in an effort to control weight gain during pregnancy.

infantile anorexia Severe feeding difficulties that begin with the introduction of solid foods to infants. Symptoms include persistent food refusal for more than one month, malnutrition, parental concern about the child's poor food intake, and significant caregiver–infant conflict during feeding.

Combating Eating Disorders

Eating disorders are extremely difficult to treat, although advances in neurochemistry and scientific understanding of the mind–body connection may provide new avenues of treatment. Most experts agree that emphasis should be placed on preventing eating disorders.

Table SED.9 Intuitive Eating

The first six principles are positive steps to better nutrition and health. They are followed by your steps to rid yourself of false diet principles that we have been misled to believe and that have promoted eating disorders.

1. **Honor your hunger.** Feed your body with adequate energy and carbohydrates. Excessive hunger can trigger a primal drive to overeat. Intentions of moderate, conscious eating are fleeting and irrelevant. Learning to honor this first biological signal sets the stage for rebuilding trust with yourself and food.
2. **Respect your body signals.** Your body will tell you that you are no longer hungry. Pause in the middle of a meal or food and ask yourself how the food tastes and what your current fullness level is.
3. **Discover the satisfaction factor.** When you eat what you really want, in an environment that is inviting and conducive, the pleasure you derive will be a powerful force in helping you feel satisfied and content. By providing this experience for yourself, you will find that it takes less food to decide you've had "enough."
4. **Respect your body.** You have a genetic blueprint. Just as a size 8 foot does not squeeze into a size 6 shoe, it is equally futile (and uncomfortable) to aim for a body size unrelated to your genes. But mostly, respect your body, so you can feel better about who you are. It's hard to reject the diet mentality if you are unrealistic and overly critical about your body shape.
5. **Exercise—feel the difference.** Mobilize yourself, but forget militant exercise. Shift your focus to how it feels to move your body, rather than the calorie-burning effect of exercise. If you focus on how you feel from working out, such as energized, it can make the difference between rolling out of bed for a brisk morning walk or hitting the snooze alarm.
6. **Honor your health—gentle nutrition.** Make food choices that honor your health and tastebuds while making you feel well. Remember that you don't have to eat a perfect diet to be healthy. You will not suddenly get a nutrient deficiency or gain weight from one snack, one meal, or one day of eating. It's what you eat consistently over time that matters—progress, not perfection, is what counts.
7. **Honor your feelings without using food.** Find ways to comfort, nurture, distract, and resolve your issues without using food. Anxiety, loneliness, boredom, and anger are emotions. Each has its own trigger, and each has its own appeasement. Food won't fix any of these feelings, although it may temporarily comfort, distract from pain, or even numb you into a food hangover. If anything, eating for an emotional hunger will complicate your problems.
8. **Reject the diet mentality.** Disregard diets that offer you false hopes of losing weight quickly, easily, and permanently. Reject lies that lead you to feel like a failure when each new diet stops working and you gain back the weight.
9. **Make peace with food.** Call a truce, stop the food fight! Give yourself unconditional permission to eat. Denying yourself a particular food can lead to feelings of deprivation that build into uncontrollable cravings, and often bingeing. No "last supper" overeating, and no overwhelming guilt.
10. **Challenge the food police.** Shout "no" to wrongheaded thoughts that declare you're "good" for eating less than 1,000 calories or "bad" because you're eating chocolate cake. The food police monitor the unreasonable rules that dieting has created. The police station is housed deep in your psyche, and its loudspeaker shouts negative barbs, hopeless phrases, and guilt-provoking indictments. Chasing the food police away is a critical step in returning to intuitive eating.

Source: Courtesy of Evelyn Tribole and Elyse Resch, *Intuitive Eating*, St. Martin's Press, New York, 1995, 2003.

Quick Bite

Advice from the Father of Medicine

Do not allow the body to attain extreme thinness for that too is treacherous, but bring it only to a condition which will naturally continue unchanged, whatever that may be.

—Hippocrates, 400 B.C.E

Preventing eating disorders depends on establishing appropriate mind–body–food relationships. Eating intuitively, an alternative approach to the diet mentality of our culture, suggests that we should trust ourselves and follow the body's signals. This approach might entail reframing our relationships to our body—for example, learning to distinguish physical from emotional feelings and gaining a sense of body wisdom. It's also a process of making peace with food and expunging constant "food worry" thoughts. One plan for learning to eat intuitively is presented in Table SED.9.

Although intuitive eating appears simple, it entails complex processes. For example, one basic principle of intuitive eating is the ability to respond to inner body cues. "Eat when you're hungry and stop when you're full" may sound like a no-brainer, but it requires developing sensitivity to your body's signals.

The NIH believes that health care professionals should lead the eating disorder prevention effort by learning to promote self-esteem in their patients and teaching patients that people can be healthy at every size. Ideally, this

Table SED.10 Preventing Eating Disorders

To join the effort to prevent eating disorders, follow these tips:

- Celebrate the diversity of human body shapes and sizes.
- Present accurate information about nutrition, weight management, and health.
- Discourage restrictive eating practices, including skipping meals.
- Encourage people to eat in response to hunger, not emotions.
- Reinforce messages about good eating and activity patterns at school and at home.
- Carefully phrase comments about a person's weight, body, or fitness level.
- Teach children and young people how to constructively express negative emotions.
- Encourage parents, teachers, coaches, and other professionals who work with children to do likewise.
- Encourage people of all ages to focus on personal qualities rather than physical appearance, of themselves and others.
- Find and promote images of fit people of all sizes and shapes.

approach would have a ripple effect: patients would transmit these beliefs to others. A variety of public information campaigns aimed at parents and people who work with children and adolescents have evolved over the past decade to help promote eating disorder awareness. A prominent example is the Body Size Acceptance campaign coordinated through the University of California, Berkeley, under the direction of Joanne Ikeda. (See Table SED.10.)

Quick Bite

Scary Statistics

About 5 million Americans have anorexia nervosa, bulimia, or binge-eating disorders. Researchers estimate that 15 percent of young women have disordered eating attitudes and behaviors. Every year an estimated 1,000 people die from anorexia nervosa.

Learning Portfolio

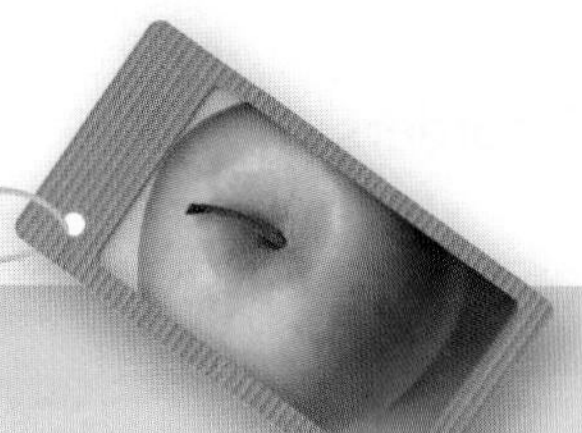

Key Terms

	page
anorexia atheletica	610
anorexia nervosa [an-or-EX-ee-uh ner-VOH-sah]	596
baryophobia [barry-oh-FO-bee-ah]	612
binge	605
binge-eating disorder	596
body dysmorphic disorder (BDD)	608
body image	596
bulimia nervosa [bull-EEM-ee-uh]	597
compulsive overeating	597
diabulimia	612
disordered eating	596
diuretics [dye-u-RET-iks]	600
eating disorders	596
emetics	600
enemas	600
infantile anorexia	613
laxatives	600
night-eating syndrome (NES)	609
obsessive-compulsive disorder	599
orexin	599
post-traumatic stress disorder (PTSD)	599
purge	605

Study Points

- An eating disorder is a complex emotional illness, the primary symptom of which is significantly altered eating habits. Eating disorders occur in biologically susceptible people exposed to particular types of environmental stimuli.
- Although eating disorders existed even in ancient times, they have become alarmingly common in industrialized countries.
- Eating disorders involve highly restrictive eating patterns (seen in anorexia nervosa), a combination of compulsive overeating and purging (seen in bulimia nervosa), or unrestricted binge eating.
- Eating disorders are common in people who participate in body-conscious activities such as dance, wrestling, gymnastics, and bodybuilding.
- From 1 to 5 percent of people with eating disorders are male.
- Anorexia nervosa is an obsession for thinness manifested in self-imposed starvation.
- The typical person with anorexia nervosa is a young Caucasian woman from an upper-class, achievement-oriented family.
- Victims of anorexia nervosa have a body weight at least 15 percent below normal, a distorted body image, and physical and psychological symptoms related to starvation.
- The body weight of people with bulimia nervosa is close to or even slightly above that considered healthy for their height.
- Key symptoms of bulimia nervosa are binge-eating episodes occurring at least twice a week for three months, followed by severe dieting, purging, or a combination of dieting and purging.
- Binge-eating disorder is the most common eating disorder.
- Like those with bulimia, people with binge-eating disorder consume more food than is typically eaten in a given period of time.
- People with body dysmorphic disorder (BDD) are preoccupied with an imagined or slight defect in appearance.
- In night-eating syndrome, the food intake rhythm may be out of sync with a person's normal sleep rhythm by as much as four to five hours.
- Many competitive athletes, both male and female, have disordered eating behaviors.
- Disordered eating, amenorrhea, and abnormally low bone density characterize the female athlete triad.
- The best treatment for eating disorders is prevention. Once an eating disorder has become entrenched, intensive and prolonged treatment is typically required. Many people require lifelong support to maintain healthful eating and lifestyle habits.

Study Questions

1. List the diagnostic criteria for anorexia nervosa, bulimia nervosa, and binge-eating disorder.
2. What are the warning signs of anorexia nervosa?
3. What is the usual treatment for people with anorexia nervosa, and what do most experts say about their recovery?
4. What is the typical profile of a person with bulimia nervosa?

5. Describe an eating binge and all the behaviors that constitute purging.
6. How does binge-eating disorder differ from bulimia?

Try This

Is There Any Help Out There?

How much help is available in your community for people with eating disorders? Scan the telephone directory (Yellow Pages) or the Web for eating disorder clinics, programs, and centers. Call them or visit their Web sites to inquire about their services. Do they have a psychologist, medical doctor, dietitian, nurse, and/or social worker on staff? Is it an inpatient or outpatient program? What is their philosophy of therapy? What is their success rate? What are their payment plans?

What About Bobbie?

Bobbie's friend Janet has been struggling with anorexia nervosa for some time. Bobbie recently expressed concern again and asked Janet about her eating habits. Janet told Bobbie she eats the following foods in a typical day:

"Breakfast"
1 head of iceberg lettuce, with salt and pepper but no dressing (If she wakes up really hungry, she'll have another with vinegar on it.)

"Snack"
6 to 8 white mushrooms

"Lunch"
3 or 4 dill pickles

"Dinner"
1 12-ounce can artichoke hearts (rinsed)
Fluids include mineral water, diet cola, and/or caffeinated tea.

Let's compare this intake with Bobbie's (see Chapter 1 to review Bobbie's one-day diet). First, Janet's daily intake is just under 300 kilocalories, compared with Bobbie's 2,440. Not only is Janet at risk due to her lack of calories, but also her intake of protein is approximately 0 grams. Her body has already used any glycogen it had as reserve fuel. In addition, at 5 feet 3 inches and 98 pounds, she has very little reserve fat tissue for future energy needs. Without intake of dietary protein, her organ and muscle tissues have become prime targets for degradation. Even though Janet takes a multivitamin and a mineral supplement, if she doesn't seek help soon, she may suffer the typical symptoms and effects of starvation and malnutrition.

References

1 American Dietetic Association. Position of the American Dietetic Association: nutrition intervention in the treatment of anorexia nervosa, bulimia nervosa, and other eating disorders. *J Am Diet Assoc*. 2006;109:2073–2082.

2 Ibid.

3 Crowther JH, Sanftner J, Bonifazi DZ, Sheperd KL. The role of daily hassles in binge eating. *Int J Eat Disord*. 2001;29:449–454.

4 Johnson JG, Cohen P, Kasen S, Brook JS. Eating disorders during adolescence and the risk for physical and mental disorders during early adulthood. *Arch Gen Psych*. 2002;59:545–552.

5 Pearce JM. Richard Morton: origins of anorexia nervosa. *Eur Neurol*. 2004;52:191–192.

6 Ibid.

7 Suraf M. Holy anorexia and anorexia nervosa: society and the concept of disease. *Pharo*. 1998;61(4):2–4.

8 Reid TR. The world according to Rome. *National Geographic*. 1997;8:54–83.

9 Norris ML, Boydell KM, Pinhas L, Katzman DK. Ana and the Internet: a review of pro-anorexia websites. *Int J Eat Disord*. 2006;39 (6):443–447; and Harshbarger J, Ahlers-Schmidt C, Mayans L, et al. Pro-anorexia websites: what a clinician should know. *Int J Eat Disord*. 2008;42(4):367–370.

10 Neumark-Sztainer D, Story M, Hannan PJ, et al. Weight-related concerns and behaviors among overweight and nonoverweight adolescents: implications for preventing weight-related disorders. *Arch Pediatr Adolesc Med*. 2002;156:171–178.

11 Eisenberg ME, Neumark-Sztainer D, Story M. Associations of weight-based teasing and emotional well-being among adolescents. *Arch Pediatr Adolesc Med*. 2003;157:733–738.

12 Gleaves DH. Scope and significance of posttraumatic symptomatology among women hospitalized for an eating disorder. *Int J Eat Disord*. 1998;2:147–156.

13 Kaye WH, Frank GK, Bailer UF, Henry SE. Neurobiology of anorexia nervosa: clinical implications of alterations in the function of serotonin and other neuronal systems. *Int J Eat Disord*. 2005;37(suppl):S15–S19.

14 Mayer LE, Walsh BT. The use of selective serotonin reuptake inhibitors in eating disorders. *J Clin Psychiatry*. 1998;59(suppl 15):28–34.

15 Kaye W, Gendall K, Strober M. Serotonin neuronal function and selective serotonin reuptake inhibitor treatment in anorexia and bulimia nervosa. *Biol Psychiatry*. 1998;44:825–838.

16 Ahrén-Moonga J, Silverwood R, Af Klinteberg B, Koupil I. Association of higher parental and grandparental education and higher school grades with risk of hospitalization for eating disorders in females: the Uppsala Birth Cohort Multigenerational Study. *Am J Epidemiol*. Published online July 9, 2009. doi:10.1093/aje/kwp166.

17 Lilenfeld LR, Kaye WH, Greeno CG, et al. A controlled family study of anorexia nervosa and bulimia nervosa: psychiatric disorders in first-degree relatives and effects of proband comorbidity. *Arch Gen Psychiatry*. 1998;55:603–610.

18 Aragona M, Vella G. Psychopathological considerations on the relationship between bulimia and obsessive-compulsive disorder. *Psychopathology*. 1998;31:197–205.

19 Shirasaka T, Takasaki M, Kannan H. Cardiovascular effects of leptin and orexins. *Am J Physiol Regul Integr Comp Physiol*. 2003;284(3):R639–R651.

20 Sakurai T, Amemiya A, Ishii M, et al. Orexins and orexin receptors: a family of hypothalamic neuropeptides and G protein-coupled receptors that regulate feeding behavior. *Cell*. 1998;92:573–585.

21 American Medical Association. JAMA patient page: anorexia nervosa. *JAMA*. 2006;295(22):2684.

22 American Psychiatric Association. *Diagnostic and Statistical Manual of Mental Disorders*. 4th ed., text revision (DSM-IV-TR). Washington, DC: American Psychiatric Association, 2000.

23 Bulik CM, Reba L, Siega-Riz AM. Anorexia nervosa: definition, epidemiology, and cycle of risk. *Int J Eat Disord*. 2005;37(suppl):S2–S9.

24 Mulholland AM, Mintz LB. Prevalence of eating disorders among African American women. *J Counsel Psychol*. 2001;48(1):111–116.

25 Sim LA, Sadowski CM, Whiteside SP, Wells LA. Family-based therapy for adolescents with anorexia nervosa. *Mayo Clin Proc*. 2004;79:1305–1308.

26 American Dietetic Association. Nutrition intervention in the treatment of anorexia nervosa, bulimia nervosa, and other eating disorders.

27 Keel PK, Dorer DJ, Eddy KT, et al. Predictors of mortality in eating disorders. *Arch Gen Psych*. 2003;60:179–183.

28 Neumark-Sztainer, Story, Hannan, et al. Weight-related concerns and behaviors among overweight and nonoverweight adolescents.

29 Keel, Dorer, Eddy, et al. Predictors of mortality in eating disorders.

30 American Dietetic Association. Nutrition intervention in the treatment of anorexia nervosa, bulimia nervosa, and other eating disorders.

31 National Institutes of Health. National Center for Health Statistics. http://www.nih.gov.

32 American Psychiatric Association. DSM-IV-TR.

33 Brownell K, Fairburn M. *Eating Disorders and Obesity: A Comprehensive Handbook*. 2nd ed. New York: Guilford Press, 2002.

34 American Dietetic Association. Nutrition intervention in the treatment of anorexia nervosa, bulimia nervosa, and other eating disorders.

35 Keel, Dorer, Eddy, et al. Predictors of mortality in eating disorders.

36 Mitchell JE, Crow S. Medical complications of anorexia nervosa and bulimia nervosa. *Curr Opin Psychiatry*. 2006;19(4):438–443.

37 Krahn DD, Kurth CL, Gomberg E, Drewnowski A. Pathological dieting and alcohol use in college women—a continuum of behaviors. *Eat Behav*. 2005;6(1):43–52.

38 Keel, Dorer, Eddy, et al. Predictors of mortality in eating disorders.

39 American Dietetic Association. Nutrition intervention in the treatment of anorexia nervosa, bulimia nervosa, and other eating disorders.

40 French SA, Leffert N, Story M, et al. Adolescent binge/purge and weight loss behaviors: associations with developmental assets. *J Adolesc Health*. 2001;28:211–221.

41 Bisaga K, Waltsh BT. History of classification of eating disorders. In: Norring C, Palmer RL, eds. *EDNOS, Eating Disorders Not Otherwise Specified: Scientific and Clinical Perspectives on the Other Eating Disorders*. New York: Routledge, 2005.

42 Bruch H. Thin fat people. *J Am Med Womens Assoc*. 1973;28(4):187–188.

43 American Psychiatric Association. DSM-IV-TR.

44 Ibid.; and Spear BA. Does dieting increase the risk for obesity and eating disorders? *J Am Diet Assoc*. 2006:106(4):523–525.

45 Veale D. Body dysmorphic disorder. *Postgrad Med J*. 2004:80:67–71.

46 Stunkard A, Allison K, Lundgren J. Issues for DSM-V: night eating syndrome. *Am J Psychiatry*. 2008;165:424.

47 Allison KC, Lundgren JD, O'Reardon JP, et al. Proposed diagnostic criteria for night eating syndrome. *Int J Eat Disord*. Published online April 17, 2009. doi:10.1002/eat.20693.

48 National Institutes of Mental Health. The numbers count: mental disorders in America. 2008. http://nimh.nih.gov/health/publications/the-numbers-count-mental-disorders-in-america/index.shtml#Eating. Accessed 7/29/09.

49 Andersen AE, Cohn L, Holbrook T. *Making Weight: Men's Conflicts with Food, Weight, Shape, and Appearance*. Carlsbad, CA: Gurze Books, 2000.

50 Andersen EA. *Males with Eating Disorders*. New York: Brunner Mazel, 1990.

51 Strober M, Freeman R, Lampert C, et al. Males with anorexia nervosa: a controlled study of eating disorders in first-degree relatives. *Int J Eat Disord*. 2001;29:263–269.

52 Bryant-Jefferies R. *Counselling for Eating Disorders In Men: Person-Centered Dialogues*. Oxford, England: Radcliffe, 2005.

53 Sudi K, Öttl K, Payerl D, et al. Anorexia athletica. *Nutrition*. 2004;20:657–661.

54 Reinking MF, Alexander LE. Prevalence of disordered-eating behaviors in undergraduate females, collegiate athletes, and nonathletes. *J Athl Train*. 2005;40:47–51.

55 Benyo R. *The Exercise Fix*. Berkeley, CA: Leisure Press, 1991.

56 American Academy of Pediatrics Committee on Sports Medicine and Fitness. Promotion of healthy weight-control practices in young athletes [published errata in *Pediatrics* 2006;117(4):1467]. *Pediatrics*. 2005;116(6):1557–1564.

57 Otis CI, Drinkwater B, Johnson M, et al. American College of Sports Medicine position stand: the female athlete triad. *Med Sci Sports Exerc*. 2005:37(2):184–193.

58 Ruud JS, Woolsy MN, Dorfman L. Eating disorders in athletes. In: Rosenbloom CA, ed. *Sports Nutrition*. 3rd ed. Chicago: American Dietetic Association, 2000.

59 Sherman R, Thompson R. *Managing the Female Athlete Triad: NCAA Coaches Handbook*. Indianapolis, IN: National Collegiate Athletic Association, 2005. http://www.ncaa.org/wps/wcm/connect/2db7d8004e0db26bac18fc1ad6fc8b25/female_athlete_triad.pdf?MOD=AJPERES&CACHEID=2db7d8004e0db26bac18fc1ad6fc8b25. Accessed 7/29/09.

60 Perry CL, McGuire MT, Neumark-Sztainer D, Story M. Characteristics of vegetarian adolescents in a multiethnic urban population. *J Adolesc Health*. 2001;29(6):406–416.

61 Klopp SA, Heiss CJ, Smith HS. Self-reported vegetarianism may be a marker for college women at risk for disordered eating. *J Am Diet Assoc*. 2003;103:745–747.

62 Crisp AH, Halek C, Sedgewick P, et al. Smoking and pursuit of thinness in schoolgirls in London and Ottawa. *Postgrad Med J*. 1998;74:473–479.

63 Ruth-Sahd LA, Schneider M, Haagen B. Diabulimia: what it is and how to recognize it in critical care. *Dimens Crit Care Nurs*. 2009;28(4):147–153.

64 Mathieu J. What is diabulimia? *J Am Diet Assoc*. 2008;108(5):769–770.

65 Goebel-Fabbri AE, Fikkan J, Franko DL, et al. Insulin restriction and associated morbidity and mortality in women with type 1 diabetes. *Diabetes Care*. 2008;31:415–419.

66 Ganley T, Sherman C. Exercise and children's health. *Physician Sportsmed*. 2000;28(2):85–93.

67 Ibid.

68 Satter E. *Child of Mine*. Denver, CO: Bull Publishing, 2000.

69 Chatoor I. Feeding disorders in infants and toddlers: diagnosis and treatment. *Child Adolesc Psychiatr Clin North Am*. 2002;11:163–183.

CHAPTER 15

Diet and Health

THINK About It

1 Is there a history of heart disease in your family?

2 Do you know your blood pressure?

3 How often do you salt your food before tasting it?

4 How often do you worry about your personal risk of cancer?

Visit nutrition.jbpub.com

What caused Joel Smith to have a heart attack at age 48? Not his age. Few men suffer heart attacks before age 50. What about his cholesterol? Possibly. Joel inherited the tendency to have high levels of both LDL cholesterol and homocysteine, an amino acid that is a risk factor for heart disease. Could his diet have been a contributing factor? Over his lifetime, Joel has enjoyed plenty of hearty meals with lots of meat, gravy, pie, and ice cream. He never developed the habit or pleasure of eating many fruits or vegetables.

Joel was an athlete in high school, wasn't he? Just prior to his heart attack, Joel was playing a spirited game of basketball with his kids. Yet despite his enjoyment of sports, he limited his physical activity to an occasional weekend basketball game. Some time before his heart attack, Joel developed a respiratory infection from bacteria called *Chlamydia pneumoniae* (thought by some experts to be a cause of arterial damage and atherosclerosis).

All these factors, including the unaccustomed vigorous activity, contributed to Joel's heart attack. It is difficult to separate out the relative importance of each factor, but taken collectively they culminated in a potentially fatal event. With some changes in his lifestyle, Joel might have avoided his heart attack. Eating more fruits and vegetables and limiting intake of fat would have helped, as would shooting hoops on a more regular basis or taking a brisk, 60-minute walk each day. You cannot change the inherited tendency to develop a disease, but you almost always can reduce your risk by modifying your lifestyle.

Nutrition and Chronic Disease

What does it mean to be healthy? The World Health Organization (WHO) defines health as "a state of complete physical, mental, and social well-being and not merely the absence of disease or infirmity."[1] Although most of us focus on the last part of that definition, "the absence of disease or infirmity," the first part is equally important. As you have learned, nutrition is an important part of physical, mental, and social well-being. It also is important for preventing disease.

Disease can be defined as "an impairment of the normal state of a living animal or one of its parts" and can arise from environmental factors or specific infectious agents, such as bacteria or viruses.[2] Diseases may be acute (short-lived illnesses that arise and resolve quickly) or chronic (diseases with a slow onset and long duration). Although nutrition can affect our susceptibility to acute diseases—and contaminated food is certainly a source of acute disease—our food choices are more likely to affect our risk for developing chronic diseases such as heart disease or cancer. In its report *Diet, Nutrition and the Prevention of Chronic Diseases*, the WHO states that "the diets people eat, in all their cultural variety, define to a large extent people's health, growth, and development."[3] Other lifestyle factors, such as smoking and exercise, in addition to genetic factors, may also determine who gets sick and who remains healthy.

Healthy People 2010

In 2000, the U.S. Department of Health and Human Services published *Healthy People 2010*, a comprehensive set of disease prevention and health promotion objectives for the nation.[4] The Healthy People 2010 initiative includes two overarching goals: (1) increase the quality and years of healthy life and (2) eliminate health disparities. These two goals are supported by specific objectives in 28 focus areas (see **Figure 15.1**). "Nutrition and Over-

Healthy People 2010

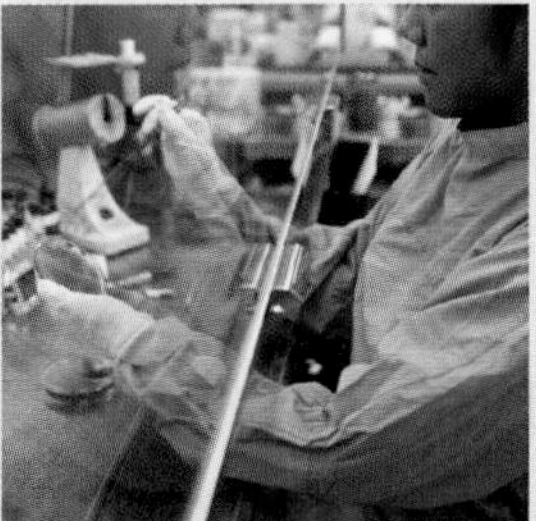

Access to Quality Health Services
Arthritis, Osteoporosis, and Chronic Back Conditions
Cancer
Chronic Kidney Disease
Diabetes
Disability and Secondary Conditions
Educational and Community-Based Programs
Environmental Health
Family Planning
Food Safety
Health Communication
Heart Disease and Stroke

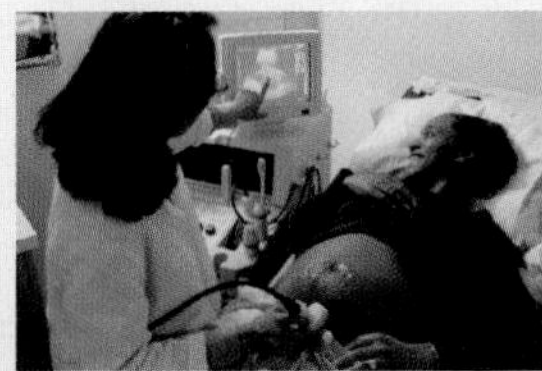

HIV
Immunization and Infectious Diseases
Injury and Violence Prevention
Maternal, Infant, and Child Health
Medical Product Safety
Mental Health and Mental Disorders
Nutrition and Overweight
Occupational Health and Safety
Oral Health
Physical Activity and Fitness
Public Health Infrastructure
Respiratory Diseases

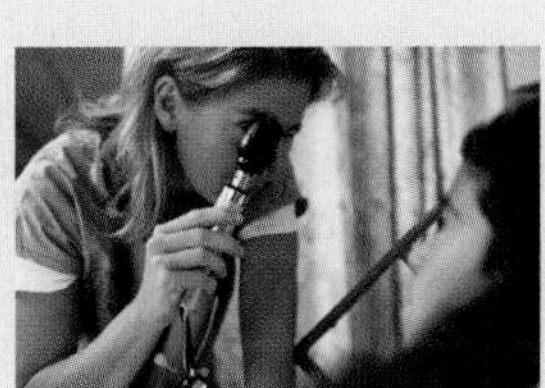

Sexually Transmitted Diseases
Substance Abuse
Tobacco Use
Vision and Hearing

Figure 15.1 **Healthy People 2010.** Healthy People 2010 is a comprehensive set of disease prevention and health promotion objectives for the United States to achieve over the first decade of this century. Specific objectives in each of these 28 focus areas support the overarching objectives of increasing quality and years of healthy life, and eliminating health disparities. For more on Healthy People 2010, visit http://www.healthypeople.gov.

weight" is one of the focus areas; its objectives include increasing intake of fruits, vegetables, and whole grains while decreasing intake of fat, saturated fat, and sodium. These ideas probably sound familiar; they are the same concepts found in the *Dietary Guidelines for Americans*.

Obesity and Chronic Disease

Once considered merely an aesthetic issue, obesity is now widely recognized as a major public health problem. It is a risk factor for the major chronic diseases of public health significance in the United States and Canada: coronary heart disease, cancer, diabetes, hypertension, and metabolic syndrome. Good health habits and proper weight management are key components of a healthy lifestyle that avoids or at least delays the onset of these diseases. Often, weight loss—or, at a minimum, no further weight gain—can improve health outcomes dramatically.

As you learned in Chapter 9, "Energy Balance, Body Composition, and Weight Management," overweight and obesity are defined in terms of body mass index (BMI) values. Ideally, measuring body fatness would be a better indicator of chronic disease risk, because it is excess body fatness rather than

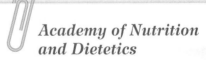

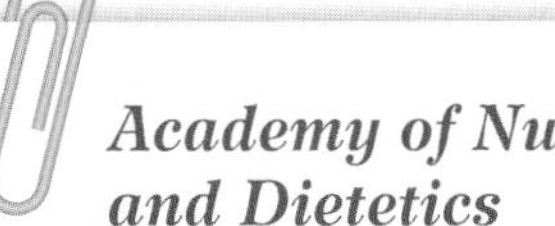

Academy of Nutrition and Dietetics

The Role of Dietetics Professionals in Health Promotion and Disease Prevention

It is the position of the Academy of Nutrition and Dietetics that primary prevention is the most effective, affordable course of action for preventing and reducing risk for chronic disease. Registered dietitians and dietetic technicians . . . are leaders in delivering preventive services in both clinical and community settings, including advocating for funding and inclusion of these services in programs and policy initiatives at local, state, and federal levels. In addition, registered dietitians are leaders in facilitating and participating in research in chronic disease prevention and health promotion.

Source: Position of the American Dietetic Association: The Roles of Registered Dietitians and Dietetic Technicians, Registered in Health Promotion and Disease Prevention. *J Am Diet Assoc.* 2006;106: 1875–1884. Copyright 2006. Reprinted with permission from Elsevier.

excess body weight that is linked to increased risks. Waist circumference, for example, can be a valuable screening tool for identifying excess abdominal fatness. Public health objectives, such as those in Healthy People 2010, emphasize the need for healthful eating behaviors, beginning in childhood, that help us achieve and maintain a healthy weight.

Physical Inactivity and Chronic Disease

A sedentary lifestyle is also a significant risk factor for chronic disease. Physically active people generally outlive those who are inactive, and inactivity is

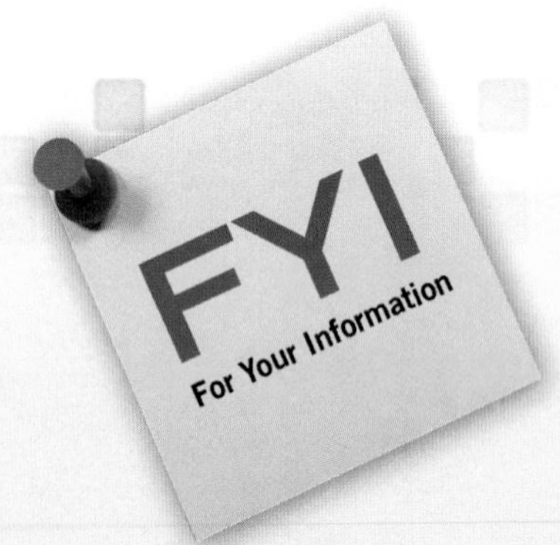

Overweight and Obesity: Health Consequences

Health problems resulting from overweight and obesity could reverse many health gains achieved in the United States in recent decades. Overweight and obesity may soon cause as much preventable disease and death as cigarette smoking. The primary concern of overweight and obesity is one of health, not appearance.

Potential consequences of overweight and obesity are summarized here. In many cases, a small amount of weight loss can reverse chronic disease risks. (See Chapter 9, "Energy Balance, Body Composition, and Weight Management.")

Premature Death

- An estimated 300,000 deaths per year may be attributable to obesity.
- The risk of death rises with increasing weight.
- Even moderate weight excess (10 to 20 pounds for a person of average height) increases the risk of death, particularly among adults aged 30 to 64 years.
- Individuals who are obese (BMI > 30 kg/m^2) have a 50 to 100 percent increased risk of premature death from all causes, compared with individuals with a healthy weight.

Heart Disease

- The incidence of heart disease (heart attack, congestive heart failure, sudden cardiac death, angina or chest pain, and abnormal heart rhythm) is increased in persons who are overweight or obese (BMI > 25 kg/m^2).
- High blood pressure is twice as common in adults who are obese than in those who are at a healthy weight.
- Obesity is associated with elevated triglycerides (blood fat) and decreased HDL cholesterol ("good cholesterol").

Diabetes

- A weight gain of 11 to 18 pounds increases a person's risk of developing type 2 diabetes to twice that of individuals who have not gained weight.
- Over 80 percent of people with diabetes are overweight or obese.

Cancer

- Overweight and obesity are associated with an increased risk for some types of cancer, including endometrial (cancer of the lining of the uterus), colon, gallbladder, prostate, kidney, and postmenopausal breast cancer.
- Women who gain more than 20 pounds from age 18 to midlife double their risk of postmenopausal breast cancer compared with women whose weight remains stable.

Breathing Problems

- Sleep apnea (interrupted breathing while sleeping) is more common in obese persons.
- Obesity is associated with a higher prevalence of asthma.

Arthritis

- For every 2-pound increase in weight, the risk of developing arthritis is increased by 9 to 13 percent.
- Symptoms of arthritis can improve with weight loss.

Reproductive Complications

- Obesity in premenopausal women is associated with irregular menstrual cycles and infertility.
- Complications of pregnancy
  - Obesity during pregnancy is associated with increased risk of death in both the baby and the mother, and increases the risk of maternal high blood pressure by 10 times.

almost as significant a risk factor for heart disease as high blood pressure, smoking, or high blood cholesterol. Physical activity also plays a significant role in long-term weight management. The 2008 *Physical Activity Guidelines for Americans* states that "Physical activity is safe for almost everyone and the health benefits of physical activity far outweigh the risks. . . . For all individuals, some activity is better than none."[5] Including at least 30 minutes per day of moderate physical activity such as brisk walking or cycling will help reduce chronic disease risk; weight-management efforts are enhanced by higher amounts of exercise—at least 60 minutes per day. See Chapter 14, "Sports Nutrition," for more recommendations on physical activity.

- In addition to many other complications, women who are obese during pregnancy are more likely to have gestational diabetes and problems with labor and delivery.
- Infants born to women who are obese during pregnancy are more likely to be high birth weight, and therefore the need for cesarean section delivery increases as well as the infant's risk of low blood sugar (which can be associated with brain damage and seizures).
- Obesity during pregnancy is associated with an increased risk of birth defects, particularly neural tube defects such as spina bifida.

Additional Health Consequences

- Overweight and obesity are associated with increased risks of gallbladder disease, incontinence, and depression as well as increased risk for surgical intervention.
- Obesity can affect the quality of life through limited mobility and decreased physical endurance as well as through social, academic, and job discrimination.

Children and Adolescents

- Risk factors for heart disease, such as high cholesterol and high blood pressure, occur with increased frequency in overweight children and adolescents compared with those with a healthy weight.
- Type 2 diabetes, previously considered an adult disease, has increased dramatically in children and adolescents. Overweight is closely linked to type 2 diabetes.
- Overweight adolescents have a 70 percent chance of becoming overweight or obese adults. This increases to 80 percent if one or more parent is overweight or obese.
- The most immediate consequence of overweight, as perceived by children themselves, is social discrimination.

Benefits of Weight Loss

- Weight loss as modest as 5 to 15 percent of total body weight in a person who is overweight or obese reduces the risk factors for some diseases, particularly heart disease.
- Weight loss can result in lower blood pressure, lower blood sugar, and improved cholesterol levels.
- A person with a BMI above the healthy weight range may benefit from weight loss, especially if he or she has other health risk factors, such as high blood pressure, high cholesterol, smoking, diabetes, a sedentary lifestyle, and a personal and/or family history of heart disease.

People tend to think of overweight and obesity as strictly a personal matter, but there is much that local communities can and should do to address these problems and improve the health of the population in general.

Actions for Communities

- Ensure daily, quality physical education in all school grades.
- Build physical activity into regular routines and playtime for children and their families.
- Create more opportunities for physical activity at worksites.
- Make community facilities available and accessible for physical activity for all people, including the elderly.
- Promote healthier food choices, including at least five servings of fruits and vegetables each day, and reasonable portion sizes at home, in schools, at worksites, and in communities.
- Ensure that schools provide healthful foods and beverages on school campuses and at school events.

Source: US Department of Health and Human Services. *The Surgeon General's Call to Action to Prevent and Decrease Overweight and Obesity.* 2001. http://www.surgeongeneral.gov/topics/obesity. Accessed 8/31/09.

Quick Bite

Biological Blueprint

Nearly all 100 trillion cells in the human body contain a copy of the entire human genome, the complete set of genetic instructions necessary to build a human being.

genes Sections of DNA that contain hereditary information. Most genes contain information for making proteins.

Human Genome Project An effort coordinated by the Department of Energy and the National Institutes of Health to map the genes in human DNA.

Genetics and Disease

In the last several years, knowledge has exploded regarding the relationship between our genetic makeup and disease. We now recognize that nearly all diseases have some genetic component. Most human illnesses occur because of the interaction of many genetic, environmental, nutritional, and lifestyle factors. (See **Figure 15.2**.) As the number one killer in the United States, cardiovascular disease is a good example of how genetic influences affect the development of disease.[6] A family history of heart disease is an important risk factor for developing the disease.

THINK About It 1

Although some cancers, for example, breast cancer, have a genetic basis and affect many members of a given family, most cancers seem to be caused by a variety of factors. Because identical twins have the same genetic makeup, they serve as an ideal population for examining the effects of environmental exposure on cancer incidence. Although genetic factors exert a varied effect on whether someone gets cancer, examination of twin studies supports the role of environmental agents in the incidence of cancer.[7]

Understanding how our **genes** influence our risk for disease has been a major goal of the **Human Genome Project**, an international effort spearheaded by the U.S. National Institutes of Health (NIH). The Human Genome Project is providing scientists with clues to the genetic variations that are

Chronic diseases	Dietary risk factors: High-fat diet	Excessive alcohol intake	Low complex carbohydrate/fiber	Low vitamin and/or mineral intake	High sugar intake	High intake of salty or pickled foods	Nondietary risk factors: Genetics	Age	Sedentary lifestyle	Smoking and tobacco use	Stress	Environmental contaminants
Cancers	?*	X	X	X		X	X	X	X	X		X
Hypertension	X	X		X		in salt sensitive people	X	X	X	X	X	
Diabetes (type 2)	X		X				X	X	X			
Osteoporosis		X		X			X	X	X	X		
Atherosclerosis	X		X	X			X	X	X	X	X	
Obesity	X	X	X		X		X		X			
Stroke	X		X				X	X	X	X	X	
Diverticulosis	X		X	X				X	X			
Dental and oral diseases				X	X		X			X		

*The Nurses' Health Study, a large prospective study, found no evidence linking higher total fat intake with increased risk of breast cancer. These results call into question theories that link dietary fat to other cancers.

Figure 15.2 **Risk factors for chronic diseases.** Diet, lifestyle choices, and genetics interact to shape a person's risk profile.

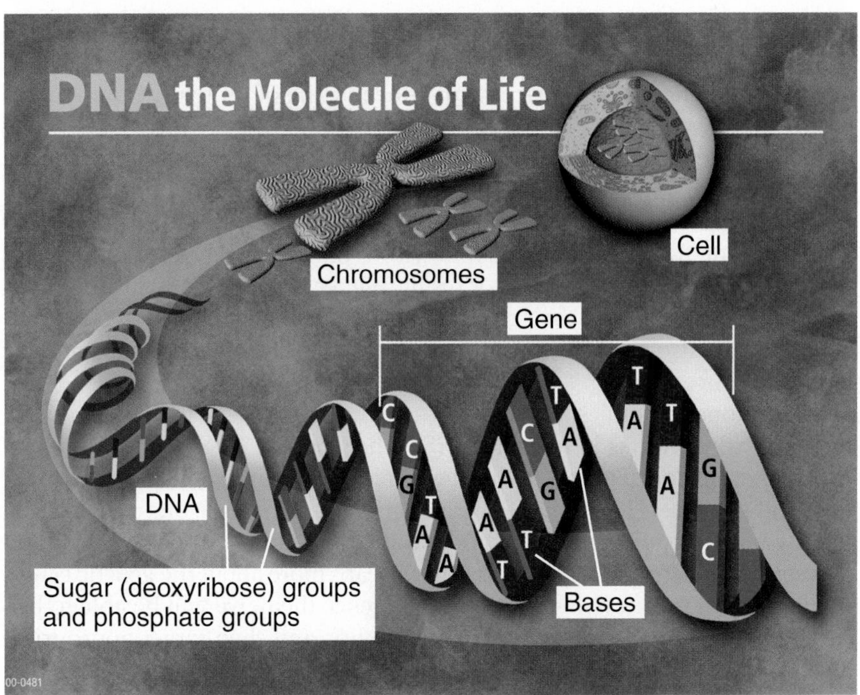

Figure 15.3 **Structure of DNA.** All the instructions needed to direct cellular activities are contained within the chemical DNA (deoxyribonucleic acid). The DNA sequence is the particular side-by-side arrangement of bases along the DNA strand (e.g., ATTCCGGA). This order spells out the exact instructions required to build proteins and create a unique person.
Source: Reproduced from US Department of Energy, Human Genome Program. http://www.ornl.gov/hgmis.

responsible for common illnesses. Understanding the genetics of diseases will allow researchers to develop more effective medications and may lead to routine gene-based treatments.[8]

The Workings of DNA and Genes

Our genetic instructions are carried by deoxyribonucleic acid (DNA), a molecule that can be visualized as an immensely long, corkscrew-shaped ladder—a double helix. (See **Figure 15.3**.) DNA is made of subunits called **nucleotides**. Each nucleotide contains one sugar molecule (deoxyribose—a five-carbon sugar), one phosphate molecule, and one base. The sugar and phosphate molecules make up the "side rails" of a DNA molecule, and the bases form the "rungs." That is, the base in each nucleotide of one "side rail" joins with a base in a nucleotide on the opposite "side rail." DNA has only four bases—adenine (A), thymine (T), guanine (G), and cytosine (C)—and each base is picky about its partner. To form a **base pair**, A always joins with T, and G always joins with C. Thus, the sequence of bases on one side of the ladder (for example, AGCGT) determines the **complementary sequence** on the other side (TCGCA). Using this "genetic alphabet," an enormous number of messages can be written.

Genes are sequences of DNA that carry the **genetic code** for making proteins. The genetic code combines the four "letters" of the genetic alphabet in various ways to spell out three-letter "words" that specify which amino acid is needed at each step in making a protein. Errors in the code may be harmless, or they may lead to serious disease. For example, people with sickle cell anemia have a mistake (called a **mutation**) in their genetic code for the amino acids making up the protein beta-globin. Beta-globin is part of the oxygen-carrying protein hemoglobin found in red blood cells. This mutated section of the genetic code in sickle cell anemia patients contains the sequence GTG (the code for valine) instead of GAG (the code for glutamate), so their cells manufacture beta-globin proteins with the wrong amino acid. Hemoglobin

nucleotides Subunits of DNA or RNA consisting of a nitrogenous base (adenine, guanine, thymine, or cytosine in DNA; adenine, guanine, uracil, or cytosine in RNA), a phosphate molecule, and a sugar molecule (deoxyribose in DNA and ribose in RNA). Thousands of nucleotides are linked to form a DNA or RNA molecule.

base pair Two nitrogenous bases (adenine and thymine or guanine and cytosine), held together by weak bonds, that form a "rung" of the "DNA ladder." The bonds between base pairs hold the DNA molecule together in the shape of a double helix.

complementary sequence Nucleic acid base sequence that can form a double-stranded structure with another DNA fragment by following base-pairing rules (A pairs with T, and C pairs with G). The complementary sequence to GTAC, for example, is CATG.

genetic code The instructions in a gene that tell the cell how to make a specific protein. A, T, G, and C are the "letters" of the DNA code; they stand for the chemicals adenine, thymine, guanine, and cytosine, respectively, which make up the nucleotide bases of DNA. Each gene's code combines the four chemicals in various ways to spell out three-letter "words" that specify which amino acid is needed at every step in making a protein.

mutation A permanent structural alteration in DNA. In most cases, DNA changes either have no effect or cause harm. Occasionally, a mutation can improve an organism's chance of surviving and passing the beneficial change on to its descendants. Certain mutations may lead to cancer or other diseases.

Quick Bite

Who Am I?

Our entire collection of genes, the human genome, contains about 25,000 genes. These genes consist of building blocks called base pairs. The human genome contains about 3 billion base pairs. Your mother supplied half of your genes and your father supplied the other half to create your unique combination. Unless you are an identical twin, no other person has your exact combination of genes.

containing this faulty protein cannot carry a full load of oxygen and causes red blood cells to form a sickle shape.

Diet influences **gene expression**—the making of proteins. Components in the diet can enhance or inhibit gene expression, thereby increasing or decreasing protein synthesis. Folate status, for example, influences the genetic instructions for the production of an enzyme called MTHFR (methylenetetrahydrofolate reductase). This enzyme works in folate metabolism to convert homocysteine to methionine. People with a particular DNA mutation have reduced enzyme activity and, as a result, higher homocysteine levels. When their folate status is low, their risk for heart disease is significantly elevated.[9] Scientists are also studying how folate status and this genetic mutation may influence cancer risk.

Nutritional genomics, which focuses on the influences of food components on gene expression, is in its infancy. (See the Chapter 1 FYI feature "Are Nutrigenomics in Your Future?") Nutrigenomics is the junction between health, diet, and genetics. The study of nutrigenomics will increase our understating of how nutrition affects normal body functioning and the development and prevention of diet-related diseases.[10] As we learn more about the genetic causes of disease and the lifestyle factors that influence them, we will be able to better screen individuals for disease susceptibility, and then target appropriate lifestyle interventions to reduce their risk.[11]

Key Concepts *Diseases can be acute or chronic. Nutrition and other lifestyle factors such as obesity and physical inactivity strongly influence the risk of developing chronic diseases. Our genetic makeup also influences disease risk. Genes are segments of DNA that contain the code for making proteins. Gene expression can be modified by diet. Understanding how our genes can affect the course of a disease may influence future population screening and produce targeted interventions to reduce disease risk.*

gene expression The process by which proteins are made from the instructions encoded in DNA.

cardiovascular disease (CVD) Any abnormal condition characterized by dysfunction of the heart and blood vessels. CVD includes atherosclerosis (especially coronary heart disease, which can lead to heart attacks), cerebrovascular disease (e.g., stroke), and hypertension (high blood pressure).

Cardiovascular Disease

Cardiovascular disease (CVD) is the leading cause of death in the United States and Canada, claiming one life every minute. Nearly half of all Americans alive today will die from CVD. Although CVD primarily affects men and older adults, heart attack is the number one killer of American women older than 65, and a leading cause of death in women older than 25 years.[12] In addition, 45 percent of heart attacks occur in people younger than 65.[13] But not all the news is bad: in the past 50 years, lifestyle changes and medical advances have led to significant progress in the fight against CVD.

CVD is significantly related to the so-called American way of life. Too many Americans eat a high-fat diet, are overweight and sedentary, smoke cigarettes, manage stress ineffectively, do not manage their high blood pressure or high blood cholesterol levels, and do not know the signs of CVD. Of course, not all the risk factors for CVD are controllable—some people inherit a tendency toward persistent high blood pressure. But many factors can be changed, treated, or modified, so you have the power to significantly reduce your risk.

Quick Bite

Hardy Hearts

By the end of a normal life span, the human heart has pumped more than 3 billion times. Despite this heavy use, heart failures are usually caused by heart attacks or problems with blood vessels and valves; heart muscle itself rarely wears out.

The Cardiovascular System and Cardiovascular Disease

The cardiovascular system consists of the heart and blood vessels (veins, arteries, and capillaries). (See **Figure 15.4**.) Together, they pump and circulate blood throughout the body. A person weighing 150 pounds has about 5 quarts of blood, which circulates about once every minute.

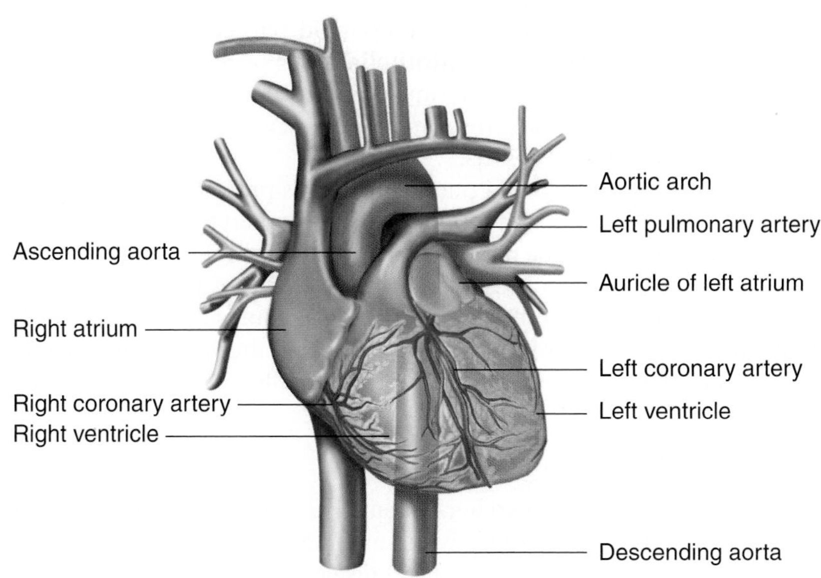

Figure 15.4 **The heart and major arteries.** Oxygenated blood is pumped through the arteries (red), and oxygen-depleted blood is returned to the heart via the veins (blue).

What Is Atherosclerosis?

When we talk about diet and heart disease, we are usually referring to **coronary heart disease (CHD)**. CHD is caused by **atherosclerosis**, a slow, progressive hardening and narrowing of the arteries by deposits of fat, cholesterol, and other substances. (See **Figure 15.5**.) When serious, atherosclerosis may result in angina pectoris (chest pain) or myocardial infarction (heart attack). Atherosclerosis of the cerebral arteries leading to the brain can cause a stroke.

Atherosclerosis is one type of arteriosclerosis, which literally means "hardening of the arteries." As deposits, called **plaque**, accumulate along the artery walls, the arteries lose their elasticity and their ability to expand and contract, thereby restricting blood flow. Once narrowed in this way, an artery is vulnerable to plaque rupture and blockage by blood clots.

coronary heart disease (CHD) A type of heart disease caused by narrowing of the coronary arteries that feed the heart, which needs a constant supply of oxygen and nutrients carried by the blood in the coronary arteries. When the coronary arteries become narrowed or clogged by fat and cholesterol deposits and cannot supply enough blood to the heart, CHD results.

atherosclerosis A type of "hardening of the arteries" in which cholesterol and other substances in the blood build up in the walls of arteries. As the process continues, the arteries to the heart may narrow, cutting down the flow of oxygen-rich blood and nutrients to the heart.

plaque A buildup of substances that circulate in the blood (e.g., calcium, fat, cholesterol, cellular waste, and fibrin) on a blood vessel wall, making it vulnerable to blockage from blood clots.

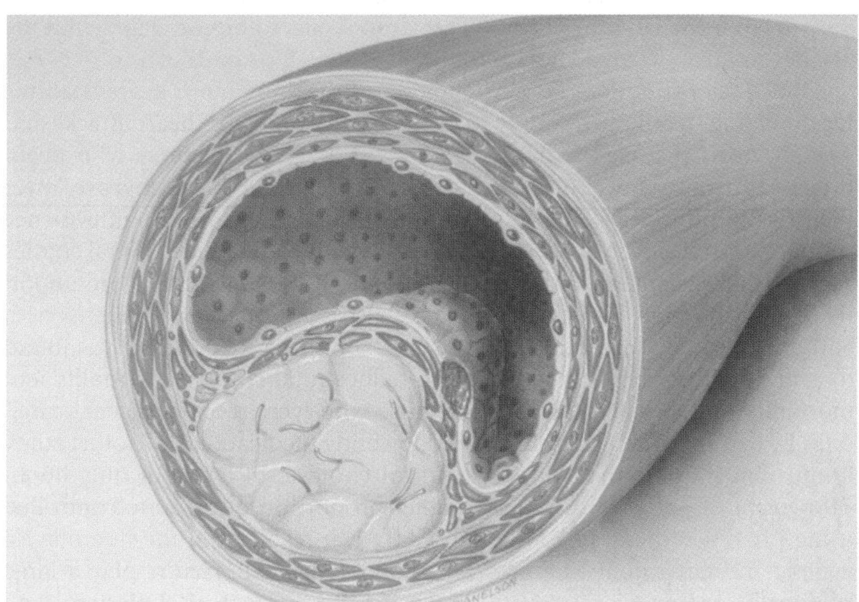

Figure 15.5 **Development of atherosclerosis.** Atherosclerotic plaque is formed by a buildup of fatty material in the wall of an artery. An artery narrowed by plaque is vulnerable to blockage by a blood clot, causing a heart attack or stroke.

Quick Bite

Who Discovered Atherosclerosis?
Leonardo da Vinci offered the first detailed analysis of diseased blood vessels and was also the first to attribute this pathology to diet.

Plaque buildup begins when excess lipid particles collect beneath the cells that line an artery, called **endothelial cells** or the **endothelium**. High cholesterol, high blood pressure, smoking, and diabetes can all damage the endothelium and initiate atherosclerosis. Certain viral and bacterial infections also may damage blood vessels.[14]

Platelets, components of one of the body's protective mechanisms, collect at the damaged area and form a cap of cells, thereby isolating the plaque within the artery wall. The narrowed artery is vulnerable to blockage by clots that can form if the cap breaks and the fatty core of the plaque combines again with platelets and other clot-producing factors in the blood. If the heart, brain, or other organs are deprived of blood, and the vital oxygen that blood carries, the effects of atherosclerosis can be deadly.

Cholesterol and Atherosclerosis

In the early 1960s researchers identified high blood cholesterol, or **hypercholesterolemia**, along with smoking and high blood pressure, as principal risk factors for coronary heart disease. They understood that a high-fat, high-cholesterol diet tends to raise blood cholesterol, and high blood cholesterol levels promote atherosclerosis. Atherosclerosis leads to artery disease and often causes heart attacks or strokes.

Total cholesterol levels do not tell the entire story. The levels of LDL and HDL cholesterol predict a person's risk for developing atherosclerosis more accurately than the individual's total cholesterol levels. High LDL cholesterol is a greater risk than high total cholesterol, with some kinds of LDL being more dangerous than others. For example, high levels of **lipoprotein a [Lp(a)]**, a low-density lipoprotein, seem especially harmful. High levels of Lp(a) prevent the normal breakup of blood clots that cause heart attack or stroke. Although Lp(a) is associated with heart disease, it was previously thought to be uninfluenced by diet. However, Lp(a) concentrations do appear to be affected by the composition of dietary fats, especially trans and saturated fats.[15] Additional research is needed on other dietary components. Low HDL cholesterol levels increase the risk of cardiovascular disease, as do high levels of triglycerides and other blood lipids. See Chapter 5, "Lipids," for more on cholesterol and lipoproteins.

Deaths from coronary heart disease have fallen dramatically, by almost 35 percent from 1995 to 2005.[16] That drop seems to be correlated with the 10 percent drop in total cholesterol levels.[17] (See **Figure 15.6**.)

But does eating less fat and cholesterol make us more heart healthy? Or do falling death rates simply reflect better treatment of heart attacks and existing heart disease? Experts recommend that even patients who begin drug treatments to lower their cholesterol also make lifestyle changes to lower their risk in other ways and minimize medication use.[18] Although evidence supports the effectiveness of preventive efforts, including diet, several studies suggest that treatment, rather than prevention, has been the more important factor in reducing deaths from heart disease.[19] In 16,000 patients with coronary heart disease, use of plasma LDL-lowering medication was found to achieve target cholesterol levels and reduce total coronary mortality and morbidity and stroke more than for those who were receiving "usual care," only 14 percent of whom were on lipid-lowering medication.[20] Another study found that lifestyle interventions control cholesterol levels in only about 10 percent of patients and that a higher proportion of men are controlled using pharmacotherapy.[21] Although CHD can result from the interplay of genetic and environmental factors, modifiable lifestyle factors play a large role in the risk of disease. Multidimensional treatment of cholesterol and

endothelial cells Thin, flattened cells that line internal body cavities in a single layer.

endothelium See *endothelial cells.*

platelets Tiny disk-shaped components of blood that are essential for blood clotting.

hypercholesterolemia The presence of greater than normal amounts of cholesterol in the blood.

lipoprotein a [Lp(a)] A substance that consists of an LDL "bad cholesterol" part plus a protein (apoprotein a), whose exact function is currently unknown.

C-reactive protein (CRP) A protein released by the body in response to acute injury, infection, or other inflammatory stimuli. CRP is associated with future cardiovascular events.

risk factors Anything that increases a person's chance of developing a disease, including substances, agents, genetic alterations, traits, habits, or conditions.

other heart disease risk factors that includes both lifestyle modifications and pharmacotherapy is likely the most beneficial way to prevent the vast majority of CHD events.[22]

Inflammation and Atherosclerosis

The idea that chronic infection can lead to unsuspected disease is not new. Bacterial infection, for example, is known to cause stomach ulcers. Infection caused by bacteria or viruses is suspected to be a factor in heart disease as well. *Chlamydia pneumoniae* bacteria have been shown to have a significant association with atherosclerotic plaque, and the herpes simplex virus has also been proposed as an infectious agent leading to inflammatory atherosclerosis.[23]

C-reactive protein (CRP), a protein released in response to acute injury, infection, or other inflammatory stimuli, may offer a new assessment tool for CVD risk.[24] Independent of other risk factors, researchers found that the higher the levels of CRP in humans, the higher the risk of heart attack.[25] An eight-year follow-up study of more than 14,000 initially healthy women found that elevated levels of CRP help in predicting future cardiovascular events, such as heart attack.[26]

Scientists hypothesize that inflammation (indicated by an elevated CRP level) makes the cap over a plaque more likely to rupture. Elevated CRP levels have been associated with smoking and obesity, and lower CRP levels are found in people who are physically active.

Key Concepts *Cardiovascular disease is the leading cause of death in the United States and Canada. CVD is significantly related to unhealthy aspects of the American lifestyle, such as smoking, overeating, lack of exercise, high cholesterol levels, and uncontrolled blood pressure. An infection caused by bacteria or viruses may also lead to heart disease. The body releases C-reactive protein (CRP) in response to acute injury, infection, or other inflammatory stimuli; CRP levels may be predictive of heart disease risk.*

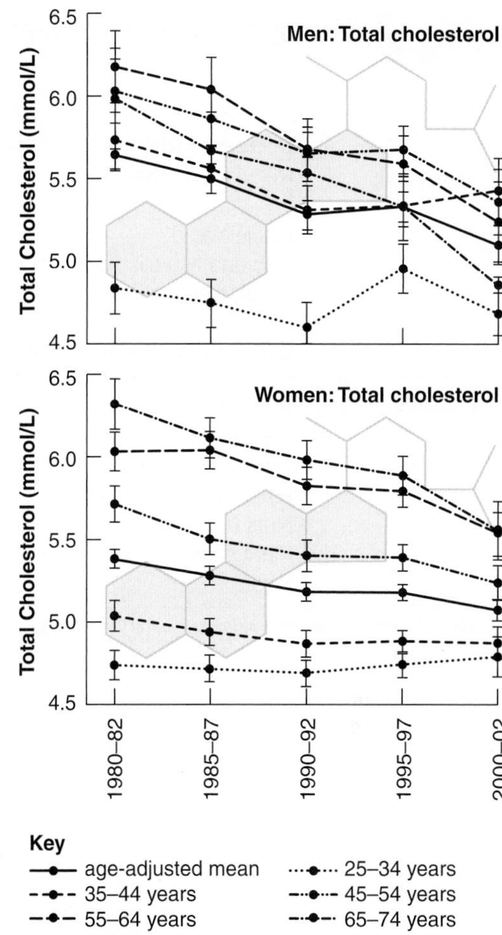

Figure 15.6 **Trends in age-adjusted mean serum cholesterol.** Since the 1960s, mean serum cholesterol levels have steadily declined, along with a decline in death rates from coronary heart disease.

Source: Reproduced from Arnett, DK, et al. Twenty-year trends in serum cholesterol, hypercholesterolemia, and cholesterol medication use: the Minnesota heart survey, 1980–1982 to 2000–2002. *Circulation* 2005;112:3884–3891. Reprinted with permission from Wolters Kluwer Health.

Risk Factors for Atherosclerosis

Risk factors are conditions or behaviors that increase your likelihood of developing a disease. When you have more than one risk factor for atherosclerosis, your chance of having a heart attack or stroke greatly multiplies. Fortunately, most heart disease risk factors are largely within your control. Risk factors for atherosclerosis that are under your control include

- High blood pressure
- High blood cholesterol
- Cigarette smoking
- Diabetes
- Overweight
- Physical inactivity

Risk factors beyond your control include

- Age (45 or older for men; 55 or older for women)
- Family history of early heart disease (having a mother or sister who has been diagnosed with heart disease before age 65, or a father or brother diagnosed before age 55)

Table 15.1 shows not only factors associated with increased risk of cardiovascular disease, but also factors that may decrease risk. Focusing on risk reduction factors is an important public health strategy for reducing the burden of atherosclerosis in the United States and Canada.

Quick Bite

How Do Cholesterol-Lowering Medications Work?

One class of cholesterol-lowering medications, the bile acid sequestrants, works by combining bile acid and cholesterol in the intestine to form compounds that the body cannot absorb. Because this cholesterol is then lost in feces, cholesterol must be taken from the blood to make more bile, thus lowering the blood cholesterol level. Another popular type of medication, the statins, interferes with cholesterol synthesis in the liver.

Table 15.1 **Strength of Evidence Regarding Lifestyle Factors and Risk of Cardiovascular Disease**

	Decreased Risk	No Relationship	Increased Risk
Convincing	Regular exercise	Vitamin E supplements	Myristic and palmitic acid (saturated fatty acids)
	Linoleic acid		Trans fatty acids
	Fish and fish oils (EPA, DHA)		High sodium intake
	Vegetables and fruits		Overweight
	Potassium		High alcohol intake (for stroke)
	Low to moderate alcohol intake (for CHD)		Smoking
Probable	α-linolenic acid	Stearic acid	Dietary cholesterol
	Oleic acid		Unfiltered boiled coffee
	Nonstarch polysaccharides (fiber)		
	Whole-grain cereals		
	Nuts (unsalted)		
	Plant sterols/stanols		
	Folate		

Source: Data from *Diet, Nutrition and the Prevention of Chronic Diseases: A Report of a Joint WHO/FAO Expert Consultation.* Geneva, Switzerland: World Health Organization, 2003. WHO Technical Report Series 916.

Dietary and Lifestyle Factors for Reducing Atherosclerosis Risk

The diet and lifestyle recommendations of the American Heart Association (AHA) are part of a comprehensive plan to reduce the incidence of atherosclerosis and are appropriate for anyone over the age of 2 years.[27] Major diet and lifestyle goals are (1) consuming an overall healthy diet, (2) aiming for a healthy body weight (defined as a BMI of 18.5 to 24.9 kg/m^2), (3) aiming for a desirable lipid profile as defined by the National Cholesterol Education Program (NCEP) of the National Heart, Lung, and Blood Institute (NHLBI) (see Table 15.2), (4) aiming for a normal blood pressure, (5) aiming for a normal blood glucose level, (6) being physically active, and (7) avoiding use

Table 15.2 **Adult Blood Cholesterol and Triglyceride Levels**

Total Cholesterol		LDL Cholesterol	
Desirable	< 200	Optimal	< 100
Borderline high	200–239	Near or above optimal	100–129
High	≥ 240	Borderline high	130–159
		High	160–189
		Very high	≥ 190
Triglyceride		**HDL Cholesterol**	
Normal	< 150	Low	< 40
Borderline high	150–199	High	≥ 60
High	200–499		
Very high	≥ 500		

Note: All units are mg/dL.

Source: Data from National Cholesterol Education Program. *Third Report of the Expert Panel on Detection, Evaluation, and Treatment of High Blood Cholesterol in Adults (Adult Treatment Panel III), Final Report.* Washington, DC: US Department of Health and Human Services, 2003. NIH publication 02-5215.

of and exposure to tobacco products. Specific AHA recommendations, along with other diet and lifestyle factors related to cardiovascular disease risk reduction, are summarized in the following subsections.

Balance Calorie Intake and Physical Activity to Achieve or Maintain a Healthy Body Weight

Obesity is an independent risk factor for cardiovascular disease, and weight gain during the teen years and in adulthood is associated with increased risk of heart disease.[28] To avoid weight gain, calorie intake needs to match calorie output. Awareness of the calorie content of foods and beverages and control of portion sizes are major steps toward calorie control.

Physical activity helps reduce cardiovascular disease.[29] Current recommendations suggest engaging in a minimum of 30 minutes of moderate-intensity activity on most days of the week; more activity would reduce heart disease risk further. In a study of postmenopausal women, brisk walking and more vigorous exercise (e.g., aerobics, tennis) were equally beneficial in reducing cardiovascular events.[30]

Consume a Diet Rich in Fruits and Vegetables

Fruits and vegetables are rich in nutrients and fiber and also low in calories. Eating more fruits and vegetables helps meet nutrient intake requirements without overindulging in calories. In addition, diets that emphasize fruits and vegetables have consistently been shown to lower cardiovascular disease risk factors. (See the Nutrition Science in Action feature "Coronary Heart Disease.") A variety of vegetables and fruits, with an emphasis on whole, unprocessed sources, is recommended. Also recommended are preparation methods that do not add calories, saturated or trans fat, sugar, or salt.

Brightly colored vegetables and fruits are not only nutrient-rich but also are good sources of phytochemicals, including antioxidants. In the blood, oxygen free radicals can attack and oxidize low-density lipoproteins; as these oxidized LDLs are deposited in blood vessel walls, the process of building up plaque begins.[31] Although some studies suggest that antioxidant supplements may provide a beneficial effect against heart disease, collectively, research has not demonstrated a beneficial effect of antioxidant supplement use on the incidence of CVD or death from it.[32] In some cases antioxidant supplements may even increase mortality,[33] however, reducing heart disease risk by eating more fruits and vegetables is still highly recommended.[34] For example, higher fruit and vegetable intake, especially leafy green vegetables, lowers risk of heart disease.[35] Because fruits and vegetables contain so many vitamins, minerals, and phytochemicals that could be working alone or in combination, diets rich in a variety of fruits and vegetables—sources of antioxidant vitamins and other antioxidant compounds—continue to constitute a cornerstone of dietary recommendations.[36]

Choose Whole-Grain, High-Fiber Foods

Diets that emphasize whole grains and other foods rich in fiber have been linked to improved overall diet quality and reduced cardiovascular disease risk.[37] As described in Chapter 4, "Carbohydrates," certain types of fiber can bind to bile acids in the gastrointestinal tract. These bile acids are excreted via the feces rather than recycled and reused. Additional bile acids must then be made from cholesterol, lowering the total amount in the body. In the large intestine, intestinal bacteria partially digest fiber and then produce short-chain fatty acids, some of which are linked to reduced cholesterol synthesis.[38] The

Nutrition Science *in Action*

Coronary Heart Disease

Background: A number of studies have shown that components of fruits and vegetables may reduce the risk of coronary heart disease (CHD). Few studies, however, have examined the relationship between fruit and vegetable consumption and the risk for CHD.

Hypothesis: People with high intakes of fruits and vegetables will have a lower risk of CHD events (heart attacks) than people with low intakes.

Experimental Plan: Using food-frequency questionnaires, follow participants in the Nurses' Health Study and the Health Professionals' Follow-up Study for 14 years. Select men and women free of diagnosed cardiovascular disease, cancer, and diabetes. Control for standard CHD risk factors and compare the lowest and highest intake of fruit and vegetables with the incidence of CHD events.

Results: The hypothesis is confirmed. After controlling for other risk factors, people in the highest fruit and vegetable intake group (top 20 percent, who averaged 9 to 10 servings per day) had significantly fewer CHD events compared with those in the lowest fruit and vegetable intake group (lowest 20 percent, who averaged fewer than 3 servings per day).

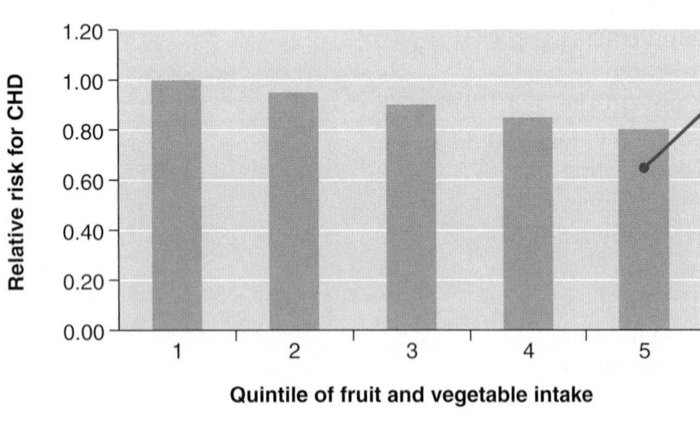

Conclusion and Discussion: People with high intakes of fruits and vegetables were older, smoked less, and generally had healthier living habits than those with low intakes. Although the lower incidence of heart attacks in the high-intake group is partially explained by health factors other than diet, it also was associated independently with high fruit and vegetable intake. This study suggests that consumption of fruits and vegetables, particularly green leafy vegetables and vitamin C–rich fruits and vegetables, reduces the risk of CHD. Future studies might look at the effects of taking certain supplements to enhance the effects of consuming green leafy vegetables and vitamin C–rich fruits.

Source: Based on Joshipura KJ, Hu FB, Manson JE, Stampfer MJ, et al. The effect of fruit and vegetable intake on risk for coronary heart disease. *Ann Intern Med.* 2001;134(12):1106–1114.

Adequate Intake (AI) level for fiber (14 grams per 1,000 kilocalories) is based on the amount of fiber that has been shown to reduce CVD risk.[39] People who eat more whole grains (2 and a half servings each day) are 21 percent less likely to have heart disease than those who eat less than 2 servings a week.[40] The American Heart Association and the *Dietary Guidelines for Americans* recommend that at least half of grain intake come from whole grains.

Consume Fish, Especially Oily Fish, at Least Twice a Week

In the 1970s a study of the Inuits (Greenland Eskimos) focused attention on the beneficial effects of EPA and DHA, the omega-3 fatty acids in fish fats.[41] Researchers were puzzled: this group of people had a high intake of fat, saturated fat, and cholesterol from marine mammals and fish, yet they showed little evidence of atherosclerosis. The Inuits were compared with the Danes, among whom atherosclerosis was common and whose diet was similarly high in fat, but from meats and dairy products. It became clear that the high EPA and DHA content of fish in the Inuit diet protects against heart disease by discouraging blood cells from clotting and from sticking to artery walls, and by reducing inflammation. Studies of other groups have since shown similar results. The Japanese, for example, with their generous fish intake, have low rates of atherosclerosis. Many other studies point in the same direction; some show that as few as two or three servings of fish weekly can be protective. Not only does fish provide EPA and DHA, but also it can displace other foods higher in saturated and trans fatty acids from the diet.

Omega-3 fatty acids have been shown to decrease arrhythmias, triglyceride levels, and rate of atherosclerotic plaque, as well as to slightly lower blood pressure and reduce the incidence of CVD.[42] A review of large studies, some dating back even 20 to 30 years, demonstrates benefits of omega-3 fish oils for protection against multiple aspects of CVD in healthy individuals, especially for those with existing CVD.[43] Studies support the idea that consuming omega-3s from fish and fish oils protects against heart disease and its many complications.[44] The Nurses' Health Study shows that higher consumption of fish or omega-3 fatty acids also reduces the risk of stroke caused by blood clots.[45] Scientists are also investigating whether omega-3s may help some chronic inflammatory conditions such as rheumatoid arthritis, asthma, inflammatory bowel disease, as well as renal disease, bone density, cognitive function, metabolic syndrome, and diabetes, although research in these areas is still inconclusive.[46] All in all, there are certainly enough positive results to encourage further study and recommend regular consumption of cold-water fish (e.g., salmon, cod) for EPA and DHA, as well as plant foods with alpha-linolenic acid.[47]

Limit Your Intake of Saturated and Trans Fat and Cholesterol

Saturated and trans fatty acids raise total and LDL cholesterol and should be minimized in a heart-healthy diet. One important difference: whereas saturated fats also raise HDL cholesterol, trans fats have been shown to lower HDL cholesterol, making them twice as troublesome. The American Heart Association recommends limiting saturated fat intake to less than 7 percent of total calories, and trans fat intake to less than 1 percent (the 2010 *Dietary Guidelines* recommends keeping trans fat intake "as low as possible"). This is a significant reduction from the typical U.S. consumption. Cross-sectional dietary evaluation suggests that only 7 percent of people meet recommendations for total fat, and 15 percent for saturated fat.[48] In addition, Americans still consume twice the daily recommendation for trans fats.[49] Replacing saturated fats with monounsaturated or omega-6 polyunsaturated fatty acids lowers both total and LDL cholesterol. Research also shows that consuming monounsaturated fats, such as olive oil, lowers total and LDL cholesterol without lowering HDL.[50]

This positive effect of olive oil may explain why Greeks, Turks, Italians, and others around the Mediterranean who eat a diet high in fat still have low rates of heart disease. Their overall diet pattern seems to model AHA recommendations: ample fresh fruits, vegetables, pasta, and whole grains; small amounts of meat and poultry; and generous use of olive oil. Favorable results from both epidemiological and intervention studies have made the Mediterranean diet popular.[51]

Does the total amount of fat consumed make a difference? The AHA supports recommendations of the Institute of Medicine (the DRI values) and the NCEP for a total fat intake of 25 to 35 percent of energy intake. However, composition of total fat intake does seem to influence risk. When researchers compared replacement of saturated fat calories with either protein or monounsaturated fat, they found that a high-protein diet (25 percent of calories from protein, 48 percent from carbohydrate, and 27 percent from fat) reduced blood pressure and lowered LDL cholesterol, but also lowered HDL cholesterol.[52] The higher-fat diet (37 percent of calories from fat, 48 percent from carbohydrate, and 15 percent from protein) resulted in lower blood pressure, no change in LDL cholesterol, and increased HDL cholesterol. In this diet, 21 percent of the calories came from monounsaturated fat, mostly olive and canola oils. Another study, in which saturated fat was replaced by a concomitant intake from polyunsaturated fatty acids, found a more significant reduction in CHD as compared with replacement by monounsaturated fatty acids or carbohydrates.[53]

What about cholesterol intake? Some evidence links cholesterol intake to blood cholesterol levels, and because cholesterol is not essential in the diet, it should be limited. When people reduce their saturated fat intake by limiting fat from dairy products and meats, cholesterol intake usually goes down. The AHA recommends limiting cholesterol intake to less than 300 milligrams per day.

Minimize Your Intake of Beverages and Foods That Contain Added Sugars

As discussed in Chapter 4, "Carbohydrates," added sugar intake in the United States has risen dramatically in the last 20 years. Reducing consumption of added sugars helps to improve the nutrient quality of the diet and also reduces calorie intake. Paying attention to sources of added sugars will help individuals achieve weight goals.

Choose and Prepare Foods with Little or No Salt

Hypertension is a major risk factor for cardiovascular disease, and generally, blood pressure rises as salt intake rises. Further discussion of salt, sodium, other minerals, and blood pressure follows in the section "Hypertension" later in this chapter. The AHA suggests that reducing sodium intake to 2,300 milligrams (about 1 teaspoon of salt) per day or less is an achievable goal.

If You Consume Alcohol, Do So in Moderation

Numerous studies associate moderate alcohol consumption with a substantial decrease in heart disease risk.[54] Although the positive effects of alcohol are generally associated with wine, and particularly red wine consumption, the benefits are found with other forms of alcohol.[55] However, alcohol is addictive, and high intake can have adverse effects on the body. So, the AHA recommends limiting alcohol intake to no more than one drink per day for women and two drinks per day for men, ideally with meals.

The positive effects of alcohol on heart disease risk provide at least a partial explanation for the "French paradox," the fact that the French eat rich cheeses and fatty meats, yet still have low rates of heart disease. They also have relatively high intakes of fruits, vegetables, and red wine—all rich sources of antioxidant phytochemicals. The active compound of the French paradox was recently identified to be a compound called resveratrol. In addition to its heart-protective effects, resveratrol may also have anticancer, anti-inflammatory, antiaging benefits.

When You Eat Food That Is Prepared Outside of the Home, Follow the AHA's 2006 Diet and Lifestyle Recommendations

More and more of our meals are either eaten away from home or brought home as takeout food. All too often, our choices away from home are high in saturated and trans fat, cholesterol, added sugars, and sodium and low in fiber, fruits, and vegetables. Also, portion sizes at restaurants are typically more than those recommended by MyPlate. Consumers need to make wise choices both at home and away from home. Splitting entrée portions with a companion, choosing steamed vegetables instead of a loaded baked potato, or substituting a salad with low-fat dressing for french fries will help individuals follow the AHA guidelines. For more tips for heart-healthy choices when dining out, see Table 15.3.

Other Dietary Factors

B Vitamins Folate and vitamins B_6 and B_{12} are involved in pathways that convert one amino acid, homocysteine, to another amino acid, methionine. As

Table 15.3 **Tips for Dining Out**

Are you able to stick to your low-saturated-fat, low-cholesterol diet when eating out? If not, you will be able to if you follow these tips:

- Choose restaurants that have low-saturated-fat, low-cholesterol menu choices. Don't be afraid to make special requests—it's your right as a paying customer.
- Control serving sizes by asking for a side-dish or appetizer-size serving, sharing a dish with a companion, or taking some home.
- Ask that gravy, butter, rich sauces, and salad dressing be served on the side. That way, you can control the amount of saturated fat and cholesterol that you eat.
- Ask to substitute a salad or baked potato for chips, fries, coleslaw, or other extras—or just ask that the extras be left off your plate.
- When ordering pizza, order vegetable toppings such as green pepper, onions, and mushrooms instead of meat or extra cheese. To make your pizza even lower in saturated fat and cholesterol, order it with half the cheese or no cheese.
- At fast food restaurants, go for salads, grilled (not fried or breaded) skinless chicken sandwiches, regular-sized hamburgers, or roast beef sandwiches. Go easy on the regular salad dressings and fatty sauces. Limit your consumption of jumbo or deluxe burgers, sandwiches, french fries, and other foods.

Reading the Menu

- Choose low-saturated-fat, low-cholesterol cooking methods. Look for terms such as the following: steamed, in its own juice (au jus), garden fresh, broiled, baked, roasted, poached, tomato juice, dry boiled (in wine or lemon juice), and lightly sautéed or lightly stir-fried.
- Be aware of dishes that are high in saturated fat and cholesterol. Watch out for terms such as the following: butter sauce, fried, crispy, creamed, in cream or cheese sauce, au gratin, au fromage, escalloped, Parmesan, hollandaise, bernaise, marinated (in oil), stewed, basted, sautéed, stir-fried, casserole, hash, prime, pot pie, pastry crust.

Source: Data from National Heart, Lung and Blood Institute. Dining out on the TLC diet. http://www.nhlbi.nih.gov/chd/Tipsheets/diningout.htm. Accessed 8/31/09.

noted earlier, high levels of homocysteine may contribute to heart disease by promoting atherosclerosis, excessive blood clotting, or blood vessel rigidity. Folate and vitamins B_6 and B_{12} can help reduce destructive levels of homocysteine. Scientists believe that consuming a diet rich in fruits, vegetables, and low-fat dairy products—such as the DASH diet, which is also rich in these vitamins—helps lower blood homocysteine and therefore reduce risk of heart disease.[56] For more information, see the FYI feature "The B Vitamins and Heart Disease" in Chapter 11, "Water-Soluble Vitamins."

Soy Soy-based foods, such as soy milks, soy burgers, tofu, and tempeh, have become popular items in grocery stores. In October 1999, the U.S. Food and Drug Administration (FDA) approved labeling for foods containing soy protein as protective against coronary heart disease. Since then, many well-controlled studies on soy protein substantially added to our scientific knowledge base. The American Heart Association Nutrition Committee reevaluated the evidence on soy protein and found that the direct cardiovascular health benefit of soy protein is minimal at best.[57] In their assessment of 22 randomized trials conducted since 1999, the AHA Nutrition Committee found that isolated soy protein with isoflavones (ISF) constantly lowered LDL cholesterol in hyperlipidemic people but had no effect on HDL cholesterol, triglycerides, lipoprotein a, or blood pressure.[58]

Other components in soybeans may provide favorable effects. Because many soy products have a high content of protein, polyunsaturated fats, fiber, vitamins, and minerals and low content of saturated fat, using these foods to replace foods high in animal protein, fat, and cholesterol may confer benefits to cardiovascular health.

Soy also contains isoflavones, a group of compounds often referred to as phytoestrogens because of their hormonelike effects. Phytoestrogens are also found in lignins from flax seed, whole grains, and some fruits.

Putting It All Together

Healthy People 2010 objectives target reducing deaths from heart disease and stroke as well as reducing the number of adults with high blood cholesterol levels. To accomplish these goals, dietitians recommend lowering total fat intake, lowering saturated and trans fat intake, maintaining a healthy body weight, and exercising on a regular basis. Eating fruits, vegetables, legumes, and grains that contain fiber helps lower cholesterol levels too. These foods contain antioxidants and B vitamins, such as B_6 and folate, that may also reduce the risk of heart disease. Substituting fish or soy foods for high-fat meats and cheeses can be beneficial as well.

Key Concepts *To reduce your risk of heart disease, get regular exercise, control your weight, and don't smoke. Dietary changes you can make to reduce your heart disease risk include eating less fat, saturated and trans fat, and cholesterol while increasing intake of fruits, vegetables, and whole grains. Look for sources of omega-3 fatty acids and fiber in your food choices.*

Hypertension

Persistent high blood pressure (**hypertension**) often is called a "silent killer," because although it usually has no specific symptoms or early warning signs and appears as no threat, it can kill you. You can be hypertensive for years without realizing it. During those years, untreated hypertension may cause

hypertension When resting blood pressure persistently exceeds 140 mm Hg systolic or 90 mm Hg diastolic.

blood pressure The pressure of blood against the walls of a blood vessel or heart chamber. Unless there is reference to another location, such as the pulmonary artery or one of the heart chambers, this term refers to the pressure in the systemic arteries, as measured, for example, in the forearm.

sphygmomanometer [sfig-mo-ma-NOM-eh-ter] An instrument for measuring blood pressure and especially arterial blood pressure.

systolic Pertaining to a heart contraction. Systolic blood pressure is measured during a heart contraction, a time period known as systole.

diastolic Pertaining to the time between heart contractions, a period known as diastole. Diastolic blood pressure is measured at the point of maximum cardiac relaxation.

essential hypertension Hypertension for which no specific cause can be identified. Ninety to 95 percent of people with hypertension have essential hypertension.

secondary hypertension Hypertension caused by an underlying condition such as a kidney disorder. Once the underlying condition is treated, the blood pressure usually returns to normal.

damage to vital organs, particularly the heart, the brain, the kidneys, and the eyes. It increases the risk of heart attack, congestive heart failure, stroke, and kidney failure. The good news is that hypertension can be treated and controlled. In 2005–2006, nearly 20 percent of U.S. adults were hypertensive and almost 30 percent more were prehypertensive; for those over the age of 60, the prevalence of hypertension is 67 percent.[59]

What Is Blood Pressure?

Blood pressure is the force exerted by the blood on the walls of the blood vessels, especially the arteries. This force is created by the pumping action of the heart. Every time the heart contracts, or beats (systole), blood pressure increases. When the heart relaxes between beats (diastole), the pressure decreases. Blood pressure can fluctuate considerably, depending on various factors. When you are excited, afraid, or exercising, for example, your heart pumps more blood into your arteries and your blood pressure rises. Blood pressure rises and falls during the day. When it stays elevated over time, it's called hypertension.

Blood pressure is measured using a **sphygmomanometer** (blood pressure cuff) (see **Figure 15.7**), and is expressed as two numbers. The **systolic** pressure is the higher number and represents pressure during the heart's contraction. The **diastolic** pressure is the lower number, measured during the heart's resting phase. Normal blood pressure is defined as a systolic pressure less than 120 mm Hg (millimeters mercury) and a diastolic pressure less than 80 mm Hg.

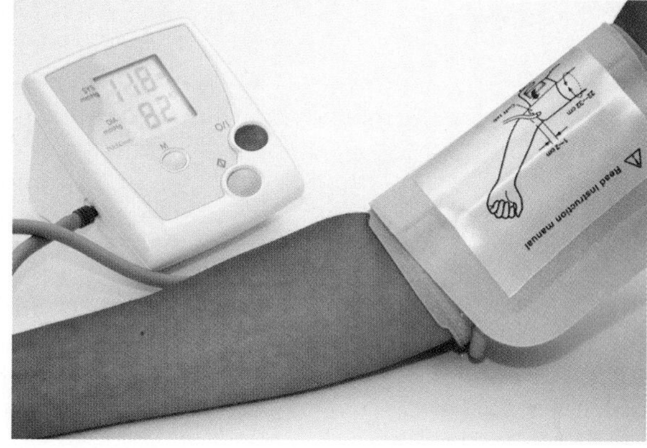

(a)

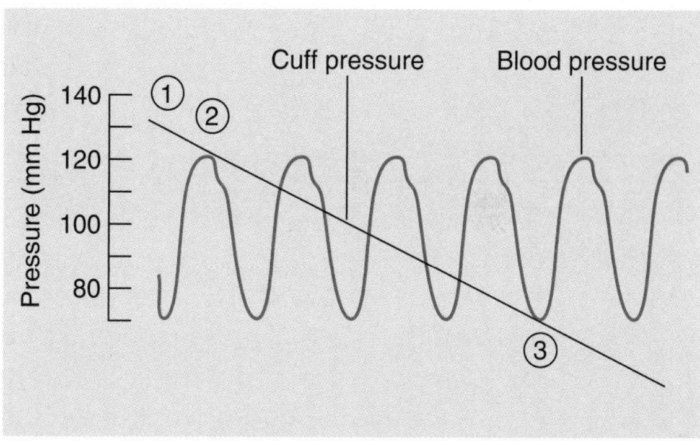

(b)

Figure 15.7 **Blood pressure reading.** (a) A sphygmomanometer (blood pressure cuff) is used to determine blood pressure. (b) As shown, the blood pressure rises and falls with each contraction of the heart.

1. When the pressure in the cuff exceeds the arterial peak pressure, blood flow stops. No sound is heard.
2. As cuff pressure is gradually released, a sound can be heard when pressure in the cuff falls below the peak arterial pressure. At this point, called systolic pressure, blood begins flowing through the artery again.
3. As cuff pressure continues to drop, the sound stops when the cuff pressure is equal to the lowest pressure in the artery. At this point, called the diastolic pressure, the artery is fully open.

What Is Hypertension?

The Joint National Committee on Prevention, Detection, Evaluation, and Treatment of High Blood Pressure (JNC) released new classifications for hypertension in 2003.[60] (See Table 15.4.) The JNC 7 report added a new category of "prehypertension," recognizing that individuals with blood pressure between 130/80 and 139/89 mm Hg are twice as likely to develop hypertension as those with lower values.

Persistent high blood pressure of unknown cause (90 percent of cases) is called **essential hypertension**. Essential hypertension most likely has many contributing factors, including diet, obesity, alcohol abuse, lack of exercise, physical and emotional stress, and psychological and genetic factors. When the condition results from another problem, such as a kidney defect, it is called **secondary hypertension**. In secondary hypertension, blood pressure usually returns to normal when the underlying defect is corrected.

Renin and Hypertension

The enzyme renin is associated with some cases of essential hypertension. This enzyme promotes the formation of angiotensin proteins, which cause the arteries to constrict. Some people with essential hypertension have higher than normal levels of renin in their blood. People with high renin levels have an increased incidence of heart attacks, strokes, and kidney failure.

Other people with essential hypertension have lower than normal levels of renin in their blood. Their hypertension may be caused primarily by increased blood volume. This condition could result either from decreased sodium excretion by the kidneys or from increased

Table 15.4 **Blood Pressure Classifications for Adults**[a]

Category	Systolic (mm Hg)[b]		Diastolic (mm Hg)[b]
Normal	Less than 120	*and*	Less than 80
Prehypertension	120–139	*or*	80–89
Stage 1 Hypertension	140–159	*or*	90–99
Stage 2 Hypertension	160 or higher	*or*	100 or higher

[a]For adults 18 and older who are not on medicine for high blood pressure and do not have a short-term serious illness.
[b]Millimeters of mercury

Source: Data from Chobanian AV, Bakris GL, Black HR, et al. The Seventh Report of the Joint National Committee on Prevention, Detection, Evaluation, and Treatment of High Blood Pressure: the JNC 7 report. *JAMA.* 2003;289(19):2560–2572. Reprinted with permission.

secretion of aldosterone, a hormone that causes the kidneys to retain sodium and water.

Stress and Hypertension

Stress may contribute to sustained high blood pressure. When stressors, either internal or external, activate the sympathetic nervous system, heart rate increases, arteries constrict, and the blood exerts greater force on the artery walls. Chronic stress has been implicated in heart disease.

Risk Factors for Hypertension

Even though the cause for most cases of hypertension is unknown, several factors clearly contribute to hypertension. As with heart disease risk, some hypertension risk factors are controllable and others are uncontrollable. Risk factors for hypertension under your control include the following:

- *Obesity.* People with a BMI of 30 kg/m^2 or higher are more likely to develop high blood pressure.
- *Eating too much salt.* High sodium intake increases blood pressure in some people.
- *Lack of physical activity.* A sedentary lifestyle is associated with overweight and increased blood pressure.
- *Drinking too much alcohol.* Heavy and regular use of alcohol increases blood pressure.

Risk factors for hypertension that are beyond your control include the following:

- *Race.* African Americans develop high blood pressure more often, at earlier ages, and with more severity than Caucasians.[61]
- *Age.* Blood pressure risk rises with age; people with normal blood pressure at age 55 have a 90 percent lifetime risk of developing hypertension.[62]
- *Heredity.* Family history of hypertension is a strong predictive factor.

Dietary and Lifestyle Factors for Reducing Hypertension

The National High Blood Pressure Education Program (NHBPEP) has updated its recommendations for preventing hypertension.[63] These recommendations are very similar to the AHA recommendations for reducing heart disease risk, which include following a healthy eating plan. They also direct you to do the following:

- Maintain normal body weight for adults (BMI 18.5–24.9 kg/m^2).
- Reduce dietary sodium intake to no more than 6,000 milligrams of sodium chloride or 2,400 milligrams of sodium per day.
- Engage in regular aerobic physical activity, such as brisk walking, at least 30 minutes per day most days of the week.
- Limit alcohol consumption to no more than 1 ounce of ethanol per day for most men and no more than 0.5 ounce for most women.
- Consume a diet rich in fruits and vegetables, low-fat dairy products, and foods with a reduced content of saturated and total fat (DASH eating plan).

Sodium

Excess sodium can hold excessive fluid in the body, at least temporarily. These excesses can be burdensome on the kidneys, heart, and blood vessels. The consensus among heart disease experts is that too much sodium, ingested routinely over the years, plays a role in the underlying causes of hypertension in genetically predisposed or "salt-sensitive" people. The more salt they eat, the higher their blood pressure.

Population studies appear to confirm this conclusion. Rates of hypertension are higher in countries with high sodium intakes. On the other hand, primitive people, whose diets contain very little sodium, seldom have hypertension. If they continue to eat their traditional diet, their blood pressure does not rise with age. If they adopt a "modern" (higher-sodium) diet, however, their blood pressure tends to rise, and they are more likely to become hypertensive. In a multiethnic sample, for those born outside the United States, each 10 years of living in the United States has been associated with a higher prevalence of hypertension.[64]

Other Dietary Factors

Sodium is not the only dietary factor associated with hypertension. Excess weight tends to raise blood pressure; regular exercise and weight loss help to reduce blood pressure. Reducing consumption of alcohol also tends to reduce blood pressure and improves the effectiveness of antihypertensive medications. Eating a diet rich in calcium, magnesium, and potassium reduces blood pressure as well.[65] The mechanism by which these minerals act on hypertension may in part reflect their interrelationship with sodium metabolism.

The DASH Diet

The original **DASH (Dietary Approaches to Stop Hypertension)** study, a multicenter NHLBI-sponsored trial, tested the effects of different dietary patterns on blood pressure. After a control period, the 459 subjects in this study received one of three diets for an eight-week period:[66]

1. *Control diet:* Macronutrient and fiber content equal to U.S. average; 4 servings of fruits and vegetables per day; 0.5 serving of dairy products per day; potassium, magnesium, and calcium levels close to the 25th percentile of U.S. consumption
2. *Fruit and vegetable diet:* 8.5 servings of fruits and vegetables per day; potassium and magnesium levels at the 75th percentile of U.S. consumption; other nutrients similar to control diet

Quick Bite

The Salt Wars

Salt was so precious historically that battles were fought over access to it. Of warring German tribes the Roman historian Tacitus wrote, "These Chatti and Hermanduri! They fight bloody wars over who shall possess a salt 'stream.'" In Roman times, soldiers were paid a special allowance to buy salt. The allowance was called *salarium*, which gives us the word *salary*.

DASH (Dietary Approaches to Stop Hypertension) An eating plan low in total fat, saturated fat, and cholesterol and rich in fruits, vegetables, and low-fat dairy products that has been shown to reduce elevated blood pressure.

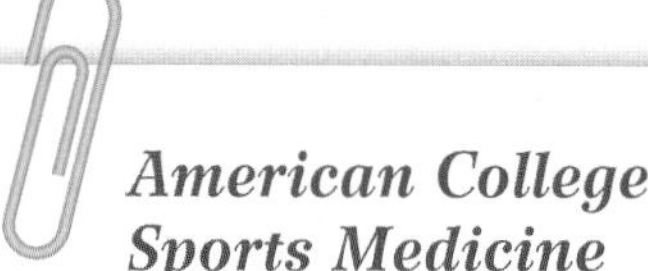

American College of Sports Medicine

Exercise and Hypertension

Exercise remains a cornerstone therapy for the primary prevention, treatment, and control of hypertension. The optimal training frequency, intensity, time, and type (FITT) needs to be more precisely defined in order to optimize the blood pressure-lowering capacities of exercise, particularly in children, women, older adults, and certain ethnic groups. Based upon the current evidence, the following exercise prescription is recommended for those with high blood pressure:

- Frequency: on most, preferably all, days of the week
- Intensity: moderate intensity
- Time: at least 30 minutes of continuous or accumulated physical activity per day
- Type: primarily endurance physical activity supplemented by resistance exercise

Source: Pescatello LS, Franklin BA, Fagard R, et al. American College of Sports Medicine position stand. Exercise and hypertension. *Med Sci Sports Exerc.* 2004;36:533–553. Reprinted with permission from Wolters Kluwer Health.

Table 15.5 Sample Menus from the DASH Study

Meal	Control Diet	Fruit and Vegetable Diet	DASH Combination Diet
Breakfast	Apple juice Sugar-frosted flakes White toast Butter Jelly Whole milk	Orange juice Oat bran muffin Raisins Dried apricots Butter	Orange juice Granola bar Fat-free yogurt 1% low-fat milk Banana
Lunch	Ham-and-chicken sandwich on white bread, with lettuce, pickles, mustard, and mayonnaise Fruit cocktail	Ham-and-Swiss cheese sandwich on whole-wheat bread Banana	Smoked turkey sandwich on whole-wheat bread with lettuce and mayonnaise Fresh orange
Dinner	Spiced cod Scallion rice Carrots Butter French rolls	Spiced cod Scallion rice Lima beans Butter Dinner rolls Melon balls	Spiced cod Scallion rice Spinach Margarine Dinner rolls Melon balls 1% low-fat milk
Snack	Graham crackers Vanilla frosting Tropical fruit punch	Peanuts	Peanuts Dried apricots Melon balls

Source: Karanja NM, Obarzanek E, Lin P-H, et al. Descriptive characteristics of the dietary patterns used in the Dietary Approaches to Stop Hypertension trial. *J Am Diet Assoc.* 1999;99(suppl 8):S19–S27. Copyright © 1999. Reprinted with permission from Elsevier.

3. *Combination diet:* 10 servings of fruits and vegetables per day; 2.7 servings of low-fat dairy products per day; less fat, saturated fat, and cholesterol than control diet; potassium, magnesium, and calcium levels at the 75th percentile of U.S. consumption

The sodium content of the diets averaged about 3,000 milligrams per day. The study excluded subjects who were taking antihypertensive medications, unless their physicians had given them permission to discontinue their medication for the course of the study.[67]

Both the fruit and vegetable diet and the combination diet significantly lowered the systolic and diastolic blood pressure in all subjects and in subgroups analyzed by sex, ethnicity, and hypertensive/normotensive status. For hypertensive individuals, the DASH combination diet lowered blood pressure as much as antihypertensive drugs. Widespread adoption of the DASH eating plan could lead to a downward shift in the incidence and severity of the disease. Because recent data indicate a slight rise in the incidence of stroke, kidney disease, and heart failure and a leveling of the heart disease death rate among U.S. adults, the NHLBI recommends that all Americans—not just those with hypertension—follow the DASH eating plan.[68] Table 15.5 shows sample meals from the three DASH diets used in the study.

Results from a follow-up study, the DASH-Sodium trial, support both the DASH-style dietary changes and lower sodium intake. This study used different levels of daily sodium restriction (3,300 mg, 2,400 mg, and 1,500 mg) and two diet plans (a "typical" American diet and the DASH diet). Approximately 41 percent of the participants had hypertension. Reducing sodium intake lowered blood pressure for participants in both dietary treatment arms, but the DASH diet in combination with sodium restriction was more effective than the low-sodium control diet alone.[69]

To help keep blood pressure at healthy levels, the DASH eating plan is rich in potassium. A potassium-rich diet may help to reduce elevated or high blood pressure, but be sure to get your potassium from food sources, not from supplements. Many fruits and vegetables, some milk products, and fish are rich sources of potassium. (See Chapter 12, "Water and Major Minerals.") Because of the additional fruits and vegetables and therefore the antioxidant nutrients, phytochemicals, and fiber that people consume while following the DASH diet, the eating plan has the potential to extend beyond cardiovascular benefits. Adherence to the DASH eating plan has been shown to be inversely associated with the incidence of type 2 diabetes[70] and to lower rates of heart failure,[71] and may reduce risk of cancer and osteoporosis.[72]

Putting It All Together

High blood pressure can be controlled and even prevented by making modifications in diet and lifestyle, as described previously. The PREMIER clinical trial was designed to assess the effects of behavioral lifestyle interventions on blood pressure over a six-month period.[73] The behavioral interventions included weight loss of at least 15 pounds for individuals with a BMI greater than or equal to 25 kg/m^2, at least 180 minutes per week of moderate-intensity physical activity, and restricted intake of sodium (2,400 mg/day or less) and alcohol (1 ounce or less for men and 0.5 ounce or less for women). One study group received general advice on factors that affect blood pressure, while two other groups received regular group and individual counseling. One group receiving behavioral counseling was also instructed on the DASH diet.

Weight loss occurred in all three groups, but only the behavioral intervention groups showed improvements in fitness. Blood pressure was significantly reduced in the groups making lifestyle changes. Control of existing hypertension was most successful in the group following the DASH diet.[74]

These findings were supported by another PREMIER intervention designed to help participants follow the DASH eating plan and the current DRIs. Participants were divided into an advice-only control group, an established intervention group, or a group following the established intervention plus the DASH plan. Although participants in both established intervention groups reduced their energy, total fat, saturated fat, and sodium intake, only those in the established intervention plus DASH plan group also increased their intakes of fruits, vegetables, dairy, protein, fiber, calcium, potassium, and magnesium as well as other vitamins and minerals.[75]

These results support the advice of the NHBPEP described earlier and provide a mechanism to achieve the Healthy People 2010 objective of reducing the proportion of adults with hypertension. Blood pressure can be unhealthy even if it stays only slightly above the cutoff level of 120/80 mm Hg. The higher blood pressure rises above normal, the greater the health risk. Recognition and control of high blood pressure are essential for avoiding damage to vital organs. Checking your blood pressure on a regular basis is the key to detecting this silent killer. Following diet and lifestyle recommendations as suggested by the NHBPEP, which includes the DASH eating plan, may be the key to prevention.

Key Concepts *Hypertension is a risk factor for atherosclerosis, kidney disease, and stroke. Blood pressure tends to rise with age, and rates of hypertension are higher among African Americans. Sodium intake affects blood pressure, especially in those individuals who are salt sensitive. Low intake of potassium, calcium, and possibly magnesium also may contribute to the development of hypertension. Eating a diet replete with fresh foods and avoiding processed foods will not only improve the balance of minerals in our diet but may also reduce risk of disease.*

Cancer

Cancer is the second leading cause of death in the United States.[76] In fact, one in every four deaths in this country is attributable to cancer. Reducing both the number of new cancer cases and the death rates from cancer are key objectives of Healthy People 2010. Cancer comprises a group of more than 100 diseases that involve the uncontrolled division of the body's cells. Although it can develop in virtually any of the body's tissues, and each type of cancer has its unique features, the basic processes that produce cancer are quite similar in all forms of the disease. To understand cancer, it is helpful to know what happens when normal cells become cancerous.

What Is Cancer?

The body consists of many types of cells. Normally, cells grow and divide to produce more cells only when the body needs them. This orderly process helps keep the body healthy. Sometimes, however, cells keep dividing when new cells are not needed. These extra cells form a mass of **tissue**, called a growth or **tumor**.

Tumors can be **benign** or **malignant**. Benign tumors are not cancer. They can often be removed and, in most cases, they do not regrow. Cells from benign tumors do not spread to other parts of the body. Most important, benign tumors rarely pose a threat to life. In contrast, malignant tumors are cancer. Cells in these tumors are abnormal and divide without control or order. As a result, they can invade and damage nearby tissues and organs. Also, cancer cells can break away from a malignant tumor and enter the bloodstream or the lymphatic system. In this way, cancer can spread from the original cancer site to form new tumors in other organs. The spread of cancer is called **metastasis**.

Most cancers are named for the organ or type of cell in which they originate. Cancer that begins in the colon is colon cancer, for example, and cancer that begins in skin cells known as **melanocytes** is called **melanoma**. **Leukemia** and **lymphoma** are cancers that arise in blood-forming cells. The abnormal blood cells circulate in the bloodstream and lymphatic system. They may also invade (infiltrate) body organs and form tumors.

Cancer develops in a multistage process that can take many years. There are typically three phases of development.

1. *Initiation* occurs when something alters a cell's genetic structure and prepares it to act abnormally during later stages.
2. *Promotion*, a reversible stage, occurs when a chemical or other factor encourages initiated cells to become active.
3. *Progression* occurs when promoted cells multiply and perhaps invade surrounding healthy tissue.

cancer A term for diseases in which abnormal cells divide without control. Cancer cells can invade nearby tissues and can spread through the bloodstream and lymphatic system to other parts of the body.

tissue A group or layer of cells that are alike and that work together to perform a specific function.

tumor An abnormal mass of tissue that results from excessive cell division. Tumors perform no useful body function. They may be benign (not cancerous) or malignant (cancerous).

benign [beh-NINE] Not cancerous; does not invade nearby tissue or spread to other parts of the body.

malignant [ma-LIG-nant] Cancerous; a growth with a tendency to invade and destroy nearby tissue and spread to other parts of the body.

metastasis [meh-TAS-ta-sis] The spread of cancer from one part of the body to another. Tumors formed from cells that have spread are called "secondary tumors" and contain cells that are like those in the original (primary) tumor. The plural is *metastases*.

melanocytes [mel-AN-o-sites] Cells in the skin that produce and contain the pigment called melanin.

melanoma A form of skin cancer that arises in melanocytes, the cells that produce pigment. Melanoma usually begins in a mole.

leukemia [loo-KEE-mee-a] Cancer of blood-forming tissue.

lymphoma [lim-FO-ma] Cancer that arises in cells of the lymphatic system.

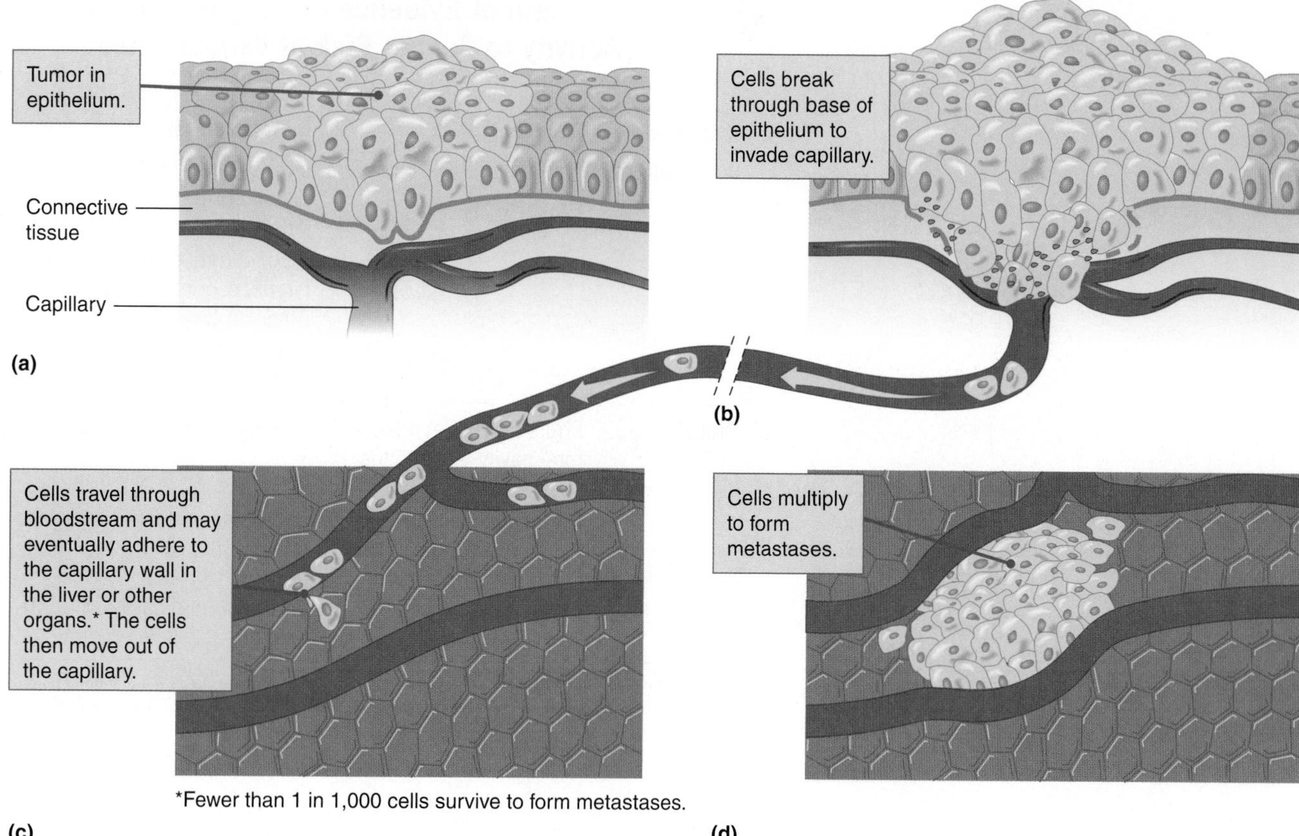
Tumor in epithelium.
Connective tissue
Capillary
(a)
Cells break through base of epithelium to invade capillary.
(b)
Cells travel through bloodstream and may eventually adhere to the capillary wall in the liver or other organs.* The cells then move out of the capillary.
*Fewer than 1 in 1,000 cells survive to form metastases.
(c)
Cells multiply to form metastases.
(d)

Figure 15.8 **How cancer cells multiply and spread.** Cancer cells can break away from a malignant tumor, enter the bloodstream or the lymphatic system, and travel to new sites to form new tumors in other organs.

When cancer spreads (metastasizes), cancer cells are often found in nearby or regional **lymph nodes** (sometimes called lymph glands). If the cancer has reached these nodes, it means that cancer cells may have spread to other organs, such as the liver, bones, or brain. (See **Figure 15.8**.) When cancer spreads from its original location to another part of the body, the new tumor has the same kind of abnormal cells and the same name as the primary tumor. If lung cancer spreads to the brain, for example, the cancer cells in the brain are actually lung cancer cells. The disease is called metastatic lung cancer (it is not brain cancer).

Risk Factors for Cancer

The more we can learn about what causes cancer, the more likely we are to find ways to prevent it. Although doctors can seldom explain why one person gets cancer and another does not, they know that cancer is not caused by an injury, such as a bump or bruise. Also, although being infected with certain viruses may increase the risk of some types of cancer, cancer is not contagious; no one can "catch" cancer from another person.

THINK About It 4

Cancer usually develops over time. It results from a complex mix of factors related to lifestyle, heredity, and environment. Researchers have identified a number of factors that increase a person's chance of developing cancer. Many types of cancer are related to the use of tobacco, items that people eat and drink, exposure to ultraviolet (UV) radiation from the sun, and exposure to cancer-causing agents (**carcinogens**) in the environment and the workplace. Some people are more sensitive than others to factors that cause cancer.

lymph nodes [limf nodes] Rounded masses of lymphatic tissue that are surrounded by a capsule of connective tissue. Lymph nodes filter lymph (lymphatic fluid), and they store lymphocytes (white blood cells). They are located along lymphatic vessels. Also called lymph glands.

carcinogens [kar-SIN-o-jins] Any substances that cause cancer.

Table 15.6 Strength of Evidence Linking Diet and Physical Activity to Cancer Risk at Various Sites

Evidence	Decreased Risk	Increased Risk
Convincing	Physical activity (colon)	Overweight/obesity (esophagus, colorectum, breast, endometrium, kidney)
		Alcohol (oral cavity, pharynx, larynx, esophagus, liver, breast)
		Aflatoxin (liver)
		Chinese-style salted fish (nasopharynx)
Probable	Fruits and vegetables (oral cavity, esophagus, stomach, colorectal)	Preserved meat (colorectal)
	Physical activity (breast)	Salt-preserved foods and salt (stomach)
		Very hot (thermally) drinks and food (oral cavity, pharynx, esophagus)

Source: Reproduced from *Diet, Nutrition and the Prevention of Chronic Diseases: A Report of a Joint WHO/FAO Expert Consultation.* Geneva, Switzerland: World Health Organization, 2003. WHO Technical Report Series 916. Reprinted with permission.

Nevertheless, some people who develop cancer have none of the known risk factors. And some people who do have risk factors do not develop the disease. Researchers have learned that cancer is caused by changes (called mutations or alterations) in genes that control normal cell growth and cell death. Most cancer-causing gene changes are generated by factors in a person's lifestyle or the environment. However, some alterations that may lead to cancer are inherited; that is, they are passed from parent to child. Having such an inherited gene alteration increases the risk of cancer, but it does not mean that the person is certain to develop cancer.

The Diet–Cancer Link

Although evidence suggests that between 20 and 30 percent of cancers are due to poor food choices and physical inactivity, the role played by nutrition and diet in cancer development is complex.[77] Some dietary factors may act as promoters; many others may have protective roles, blocking the cellular changes in one of the developmental stages. Table 15.6 summarizes the evidence regarding diet–cancer links.

Food choices interact with other lifestyle factors and also with genetics to affect cancer risk.[78] As the field of nutritional genomics evolves, it will enhance our ability to target dietary interventions for cancer prevention and treatment.[79] Until that time, the general dietary guidelines from the American Cancer Society (ACS) can be used.

Dietary and Lifestyle Factors for Reducing Cancer Risk

In 2006, the American Cancer Society updated its *Nutrition and Physical Activity Guidelines for Cancer Prevention.*[80] These guidelines emphasize physical activity and weight control and also suggest how communities can provide opportunities for Americans to be physically active. Note that the four major recommendations for individual choices are similar to the guidelines for reducing the risk of heart disease.

Recommendations for community action connect directly to the recommendations for individual choices and include the integration of social, economic, and cultural factors that have the ability to influence an individual's choice regarding diet and physical activity. The ACS recommends that community organizations work to create social and physical environments that are supportive of healthy nutrition and physical activity so that all people have the opportunity to make choices that can reduce their cancer risk.

Recommendations for Individual Lifestyle Choices

1. Maintain a healthful weight throughout life.
   - Balance caloric intake with physical activity.
   - Avoid excessive weight gain throughout the life cycle.
   - Achieve and maintain a healthy weight if currently overweight or obese.
2. Adopt a physically active lifestyle.
   - *Adults:* Engage in at least 30 minutes of moderate to vigorous physical activity, above usual activities, on five or more days of the week. Forty-five to 60 minutes of intentional physical activity is preferable.
   - *Children and adolescents:* Engage in at least 60 minutes per day of moderate to vigorous physical activity at least five days per week.
3. Eat a healthy diet, with an emphasis on plant sources.
   - Choose foods and beverages in amounts that help achieve and maintain a healthy weight.
   - Eat five or more servings of vegetables and fruits each day.

Going Green

What Do Smokers Eat?

Is smoking bad for you? What about the health of the planet? We all know the answer: a loud and resounding *yes*. Smoking dramatically increases the risk for many diseases, including cancer and cardiovascular disease. But what about the dietary habits of smokers? Are they any different from nonsmokers?

Researchers analyzed 51 published nutritional studies from 15 different countries comparing 47,250 nonsmokers with 35,870 smokers. Studies show that smokers have higher intakes of total fat, saturated fat, cholesterol, and alcohol. Compared with nonsmokers, smokers also have lower intakes of antioxidant vitamins and fiber. The researchers concluded that "the nutrient intakes of smokers differ substantially from those of nonsmokers." They also suggested that these differences may contribute to the already harmful effects of smoking on cancer and coronary heart disease.

Not only is smoking a serious health problem, but also the way in which smokers dispose of unsmoked remnants is a serious problem for the planet. Cigarette butt litter may be the world's greatest environmental litter problem, with about 4.3 trillion cigarette butts tossed onto roads, pavements, beaches, parks, forests, and waterways each year.

What can we do with this information? Perhaps public health prevention programs aimed at smokers as well as potential smokers should include promoting better nutritional habits as well as effective cigarette butt disposal.

- Choose whole grains in preferences to processed (refined) grains and sugars.
- Limit consumption of processed meats and red meats.

4. If you drink alcoholic beverages, limit consumption.
   - People who drink alcohol should limit their intake: not more than two drinks per day for men and one drink a day for women.

The WHO report *Diet, Nutrition and the Prevention of Chronic Diseases* supports these recommendations and adds four others: (1) reduce consumption of Chinese-style fermented salted fish, salt-preserved foods, and salt; (2) minimize exposure to **aflatoxin** in foods (e.g., in cereals, oilseeds [peanut, soybean, sunflowers], spices, and tree nuts); (3) reduce consumption of preserved meat (e.g., sausages, salami, bacon, ham); and (4) avoid consuming foods or drinks when they are at a scalding hot temperature.[81]

aflatoxin A toxin produced by a mold that grows on crops, such as peanuts, tree nuts, corn, wheat, and oil seeds (like cottonseed).

Fat

High-fat diets have been associated with an increase in the risk of cancers of the colon and rectum, prostate, and endometrium. The association between high-fat diets and breast cancer appears to be much weaker. The Nurses' Health Study followed more than 121,000 women for 14 years and found no evidence that higher total fat intake was associated with an increased risk of breast cancer.[82] These results call into question theories that link dietary fat with other cancers. Others, however, have questioned the dietary assessment methodology of the Nurses' Health Study, suggesting that the food frequency questionnaires used may not be a sensitive enough measure of fat intake.[83] Prospective investigations from Europe suggest there may be a weak association between saturated fat and breast cancer in women.[84]

High intake of red meat (beef, pork, lamb) and processed meat (bacon, sausage, hot dogs, lunch meat) is associated with some types of colorectal cancer; long-term consumption of poultry and fish is associated with reduced risk.[85] High intake of red meat, total fat, and animal fat has been linked to prostate cancer.[86] Overall, calorie intake (and the resulting obesity from excess calories) may be a more important factor than fat intake.[87]

Vegetables and Fruits

Evidence that vegetable and fruit consumption reduces cancer risk has led to attempts to isolate specific nutrients and to administer these in pharmacological doses to high-risk populations. Most of these attempts have failed to prevent cancer and, in some cases, have produced adverse effects. Notable examples include the three randomized trials of beta-carotene for the prevention of lung cancer, undertaken because many observational epidemiological studies showed that people eating foods high in beta-carotene had a lower risk of lung cancer. Two of the clinical trials showed that smokers taking high-dose beta-carotene supplements developed lung cancer at higher rates than those taking a placebo,[88] and a third study showed no effect.[89] These findings support the idea that beta-carotene may be only a proxy for other single nutrients or combinations of nutrients found in whole foods and that taking a single nutrient in large amounts may be harmful.

It remains unclear which components of vegetables and fruits are most protective against cancer. Vegetables and fruits are complex foods, with each containing more than 100 potentially beneficial substances, including vitamins, minerals, and fiber. Specific phytochemicals, such as carotenoids, flavonoids, terpenes, sterols, indoles, and phenols, show benefit against certain cancers in experimental studies. (For more on phytochemicals, see "Spotlight on Complementary Nutrition.") In addition to having antioxidant effects, nutrients and other phytochemicals may inhibit multiplication of cancer cells, alter enzymes, inhibit the conversion of chemicals into toxins, and alter hormone metabolism. Until more is known about specific food components, however, the best advice is to eat five or more servings of a variety of vegetables and fruits in their various forms: fresh, frozen, canned, dried, and juiced.

Despite strong encouragement from numerous health agencies to eat at least five servings of vegetables and fruits each day, intake of these foods remains below recommended levels among both adults and children.[90] In 1991, concern about low intake levels prompted a nationwide initiative—the National 5 A Day for Better Health program—to help ensure that vegetables and fruits are available and accessible to all population groups and to increase vegetable and fruit consumption to five to nine servings per day.[91] Fruit & Veggies—More Matters is the newest public health campaign to encourage people to eat more fruits and vegetables. Recommended intake is based on individual calorie needs, ranging from four to thirteen servings daily.[92]

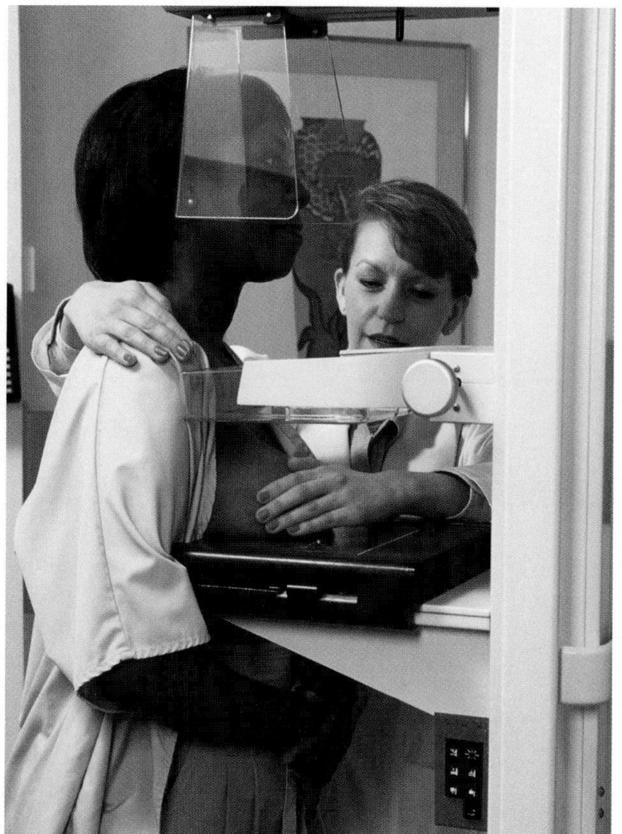

Figure 15.9 **Cancer screening tests.** Mammograms can detect breast cancer at an early stage and improve chances for successful treatment.

Whole Grains and Legumes

Whole grains are an important source of many vitamins and minerals, such as folate, vitamin E, and selenium, all of which have been associated with lower risk of colon cancer.[93] Whole grains are higher in fiber, certain vitamins, and minerals than are processed (refined) flour products. The Black Women's Health Study, a prospective study of over 50,000 women, suggests that a diet containing more whole grains, vegetables, fruit, and fish (the "prudent diet") is associated with lower risk of breast cancer when compared with a Western diet containing refined grains, processed meats, and sweets.[94] In another study, adherence to a Mediterranean diet and dietary patterns characterized by low intake of meat and starches and high intake of legumes was found to reduce risk of breast cancer in Asian American women.[95]

Although evidence for the association between fiber and cancer risk is inconclusive,[96] consumption of high-fiber foods is still recommended. Because the benefits that grain-based foods impart may derive from their other nutrients and phytochemicals, as well as from fiber, it is best to obtain fiber from whole grains—and vegetables and fruits—rather than from fiber supplements.

Beans and other legumes are excellent sources of many vitamins and minerals, protein, and fiber. Legumes and, in particular, soy are especially rich in nutrients and phytochemicals that may protect against prostate cancer[97] and possibly breast cancer,[98] and can be a useful low-fat, high-protein alternative to meat.

Putting It All Together

Some cancer risk factors can be avoided. Others, such as inherited factors, are unavoidable, but it may be helpful to be aware of them. People can help protect themselves by avoiding known risk factors whenever possible. They can also talk with their doctors about regular checkups and the value of cancer screening tests (see **Figure 15.9**). Reducing both the number of new cancer cases and the death rates from cancer are key objectives of Healthy People 2010.

To reduce your cancer risk, eat a moderately low-fat diet and increase your consumption of fruits, vegetables, and whole grains. Maintain a healthy weight, exercise regularly, don't smoke, and don't use alcohol excessively. If these recommendations are beginning to sound like a broken record, you're right—the same lifestyle changes that reduce risk of atherosclerosis and hypertension can reduce risk of cancer.

Key Concepts *Cancer develops when something alters cellular DNA so that cells divide and multiply uncontrollably. Both genetic factors and environmental factors, including diet, influence cancer risk. Although the evidence linking dietary fats with cancer is contradictory, many other dietary factors play key roles in reducing risk. Strategies for reducing cancer risk include eating more fruits, vegetables, and whole grains; increasing physical activity; maintaining a healthy weight; and limiting alcohol consumption.*

Diabetes Mellitus

Almost everyone knows someone who has diabetes. An estimated 23.6 million people—7.8 percent of the population—in the United States have diabetes mellitus.[99] Although an estimated 17.9 million have been diagnosed, unfortunately 5.7 million people do not realize that they have this serious, lifelong condition.[100] **Figure 15.10** shows the prevalence of obesity and diagnosed diabetes among U.S. adults.

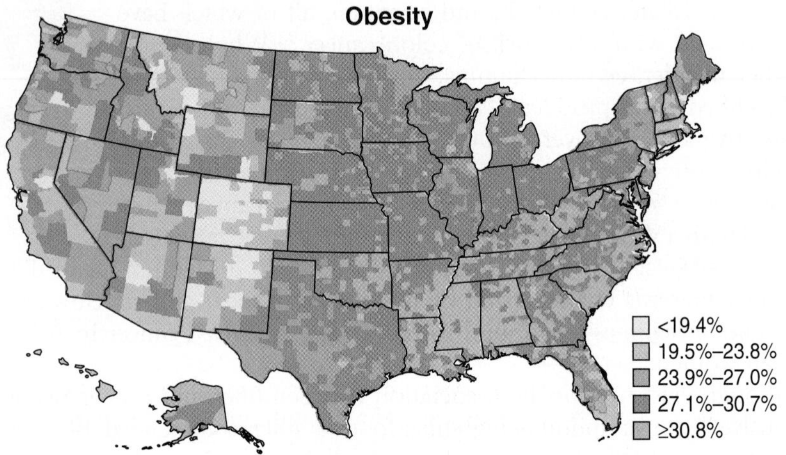

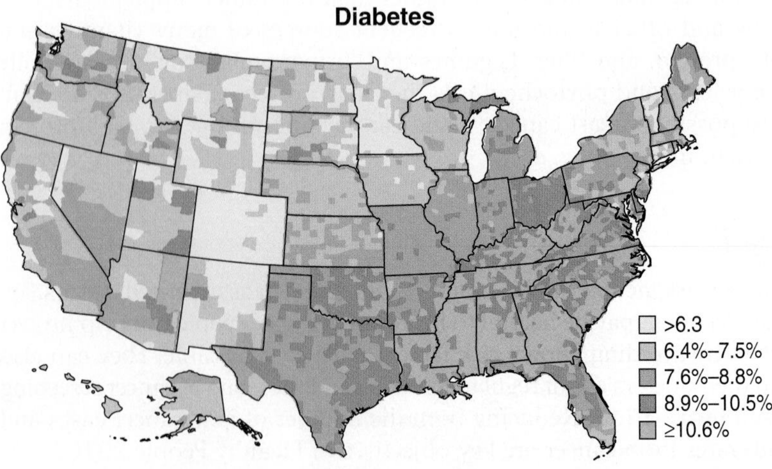

Figure 15.10 Prevalence of obesity and diagnosed diabetes among U.S. adults, 2007.

Source: Centers for Disease Control and Prevention: National Diabetes Surveillance System. Available online at: http://www.cdc.gov/diabetes/statistics/index.htm. Accessed 3/9/2010.

What Is Diabetes?

Diabetes is a disorder of carbohydrate metabolism—the way our bodies use digested carbohydrates for growth and energy. Recall from Chapter 4, "Carbohydrates," that carbohydrates in food are digested and absorbed, and end up as glucose in the blood. Glucose is a major source of fuel for the body. After digestion, glucose passes into the bloodstream and into cells, where it is used for growth and energy. For glucose to enter into most types of cells, insulin must be present. Insulin is a hormone produced by the pancreas.

When we eat carbohydrates, the pancreas should automatically produce the right amount of insulin to move glucose from blood into our cells. In people with diabetes, however, the pancreas either produces little or no insulin, or the cells do not respond appropriately to the insulin that is produced. As a result, glucose builds up in the blood, causing **hyperglycemia**—an abnormally high blood glucose level that is the hallmark of diabetes mellitus.

hyperglycemia [HIGH-per-gly-SEE-me-uh] Abnormally high concentration of glucose in the blood.

Even though glucose in the blood is overabundant, it is unable to enter starving cells to fuel their needs. For this reason diabetes often is called a disease of "starvation in the midst of plenty." In an ironic twist of fate, these starving cells signal the liver to make more glucose, worsening the hyperglycemia. The kidneys are taxed beyond their capacities to reabsorb glucose, and the excess spills into the urine, where it can be detected by urine glucose tests. Thus, even though the blood contains large amounts of glucose, the body loses access to its main source of fuel.

Unable to use glucose, cells turn to other energy sources—fat and protein. But these options can lead to other problems. Excessive use of fat as an energy source, without available glucose in the cell, causes ketosis and acidosis, dangerously high acidity levels in the blood. Breaking down muscle proteins to fuel the cells causes muscle wasting and weakness. Alterations in fat and protein metabolism often accompany hyperglycemia.[101]

Over time, abnormally high blood glucose levels increase risk of high blood pressure, heart disease, and kidney disease. Excess glucose in the blood reacts with and damages body proteins and tissues, especially in the eyes, kidneys, nerves, and blood vessels. Complications of diabetes can contribute to degenerative conditions such as peripheral vascular disease (disease of blood vessels that supply the feet and legs), deterioration of the eye and eventual blindness, kidney disease, and progressive nerve damage. Diabetes is responsible for more than 60 percent of all nontraumatic amputations of the lower extremities and 44 percent of all new cases of kidney failure in adults.[102] Diabetes is also the leading cause of blindness in adults.[103] Diabetics are forty times more likely to develop glaucoma.[104] Sixty percent of people with diabetes have high blood pressure, and nearly all have one or more lipid abnormality.[105] People with diabetes are two to four times more likely to develop heart disease than people without diabetes. In the United States and Canada, diabetes is one of the leading contributors to death and disability.

Diagnosis of Diabetes Mellitus

A diagnosis of diabetes mellitus is usually made by measuring plasma glucose concentration either after an overnight fast, as part of an oral glucose tolerance test (OGTT) (see **Figure 15.11**), or any time of the day if a patient presents with symptoms of diabetes. The classic symptoms of diabetes mellitus are polyuria (excessive urination), polydipsia (excessive thirst), and unexplained weight loss, sometimes with polyphagia (excessive eating). The diagnostic criteria for diabetes mellitus are shown in Table 15.7.

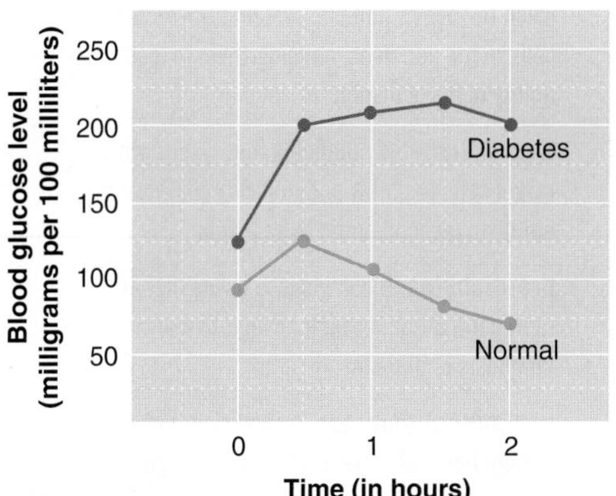

Figure 15.11 **Glucose tolerance test.** A glucose tolerance test measures the level of glucose in the blood following consumption of a standard dose of glucose. Glucose tolerance tests are used to diagnose diabetes.

Table 15.7 **Diagnostic Criteria for Diabetes Mellitus**

Symptoms of diabetes plus casual plasma glucose concentration ≥ 200 mg/dL (11.1 mmol/L)

or

Fasting plasma glucose ≥ 126 mg/dL (7.0 mmol/L)

or

Two-hour postload glucose ≥ 200 mg/dL (11.1 mmol/L) during an oral glucose tolerance test

Source: Reproduced from American Diabetes Association. Diagnosis and classification of diabetes mellitus. *Diabetes Care.* 2007;30(suppl 1):S42–S47. Reprinted by permission.

Three major types of diabetes exist:

1. ***Type 1 diabetes.*** Type 1 diabetes usually is diagnosed in children and young adults and was previously known as insulin-dependent diabetes (IDDM) or juvenile diabetes. In type 1 diabetes, the body fails to produce insulin, the hormone that "unlocks" cells, allowing glucose to enter and fuel them. Roughly 5 to 10 percent of Americans who are diagnosed with diabetes have type 1 diabetes.[106]
2. ***Type 2 diabetes.*** In type 2 diabetes, either the body does not produce enough insulin or cells ignore the insulin. Type 2 diabetes was previously known as non-insulin-dependent diabetes (NIDDM) or adult-onset diabetes. Approximately 90 to 95 percent of all Americans with diabetes mellitus have type 2 diabetes.[107]
   - ***Pre-diabetes** (impaired glucose tolerance or impaired fasting glucose)*. Pre-diabetes is a condition in which a person's blood glucose levels are higher than normal but not high enough to warrant a diagnosis of type 2 diabetes. Almost 26 percent of American adults (57 million people) had pre-diabetes in 2007.[108]
3. ***Gestational diabetes.*** Gestational diabetes occurs in a pregnant woman who has never had diabetes, but who develops hyperglycemia during pregnancy. It affects approximately 4 percent of all pregnant women—about 135,000 cases in the United States each year.

Type 1 Diabetes Mellitus

Type 1 diabetes usually occurs in people younger than 30 and often develops suddenly. People with type 1 diabetes lack insulin, usually because an autoimmune response has destroyed insulin-producing cells of the pancreas. Symptoms include excessive thirst, frequent urination, rapid weight loss, and blurred vision.[109] When blood glucose levels rise, glucose spills into the urine, taking water with it and causing frequent urination and increased thirst. Although blood glucose levels are high, the lack of insulin prevents glucose from entering cells to be burned for energy. The result is weight loss and feelings of hunger.

People with type 1 diabetes require lifelong, daily insulin injections balanced with a healthful diet and regular exercise to maintain blood glucose levels in the normal range. Because exercise lowers blood glucose levels, individuals must consider the timing of exercise in addition to food intake and insulin injections to avoid lowering blood glucose levels excessively.

type 1 diabetes Diabetes that occurs when the body's immune system attacks beta cells in the pancreas, causing them to lose their ability to make insulin.

type 2 diabetes Diabetes that occurs when target cells (e.g., fat and muscle cells) lose the ability to respond normally to insulin.

pre-diabetes Blood glucose levels higher than normal but not high enough to warrant a diagnosis of diabetes.

gestational diabetes A condition that results in high blood glucose levels during pregnancy.

insulin resistance State in which enough insulin is produced but cells do not respond to the action of insulin. Also called insulin insensitivity.

Type 2 Diabetes Mellitus

In type 2 diabetes, glucose has trouble entering body cells because either the pancreas cannot produce enough insulin or cells in the body become resistant to the action of insulin. Although obesity contributes to **insulin resistance** in many people with type 2 diabetes, genetic factors may play a role. Type 2 diabetes usually develops in overweight individuals aged 45 and older. However, with the rising prevalence of obesity, type 2 diabetes is occurring more frequently in adolescents.

The result is the same as for type 1 diabetes—glucose builds up in the blood, and the body cannot use its main source of fuel efficiently. Type 2 diabetes is often part of a metabolic syndrome that includes obesity, elevated blood pressure, and high levels of blood triglycerides. (See the "Metabolic Syndrome" section later in this chapter.)

In contrast to the sudden onset of type 1 diabetes, the symptoms of type 2 diabetes develop gradually, and some people may not show symptoms for many years. Symptoms of type 2 diabetes may eventually include fatigue or nausea, frequent urination, unusual thirst, weight loss, blurred vision, frequent infections, and slow healing of wounds or sores.

Pre-diabetes

Before people develop type 2 diabetes, they usually have pre-diabetes—impaired glucose tolerance that results in a blood glucose level that is higher than normal yet not high enough to be diagnosed as diabetes. Some long-term damage to the body, especially to the heart and circulatory system, may already be occurring during the pre-diabetes stage.

People who have pre-diabetes are at increased risk for developing both type 2 diabetes and heart disease. Unless they take steps towards prevention, such as dietary changes, moderate weight loss, and regular exercise, many will develop type 2 diabetes within 10 years.

Gestational Diabetes Mellitus

Pregnant women who have never had diabetes before but who develop impaired glucose tolerance during pregnancy are said to have gestational diabetes. Although the cause of gestational diabetes remains unknown, researchers have uncovered certain clues. The placenta produces hormones that help the baby develop. Unfortunately, these hormones also block the action of the mother's insulin in her body. This insulin resistance makes it difficult for the mother's body to use insulin and can triple the amount of insulin needed to get sufficient glucose into her cells. Gestational diabetes occurs more often in African Americans, Native Americans, and Hispanic Americans, and is more common among obese women and women with a family history of diabetes.

In women with gestational diabetes, blood glucose levels usually decrease after pregnancy. Once a woman has had gestational diabetes, however, her chances are 2 in 3 that it will return in future pregnancies. In a few women, pregnancy reveals preexisting type 1 or type 2 diabetes that requires ongoing treatment after pregnancy. Forty to 60 percent of women who had gestational diabetes will develop type 2 diabetes later in life.[110] Both forms of diabetes involve insulin resistance.

Low Blood Glucose Levels: Hypoglycemia

Excess insulin results in low blood sugar, or **hypoglycemia**. Too much glucose enters cells, lowering blood glucose levels too far. When blood glucose levels drop too low, nervousness, irritability, hunger, headache, shakiness, rapid heartbeat, and weakness can develop. A further drop in blood glucose levels can cause coma and death.

A person with diabetes can develop hypoglycemia in response to an overdose of insulin or vigorous exercise. In nondiabetic individuals, two types of hypoglycemia occur. **Reactive hypoglycemia** occurs about one hour after eating carbohydrate-rich food. The body overreacts and produces too much insulin in response to the food. Individuals can prevent reactive hypoglycemia by eating frequent, smaller meals to smooth out blood glucose responses to food. **Fasting hypoglycemia** occurs because the body produces too much insulin even when no food is eaten. Pancreatic tumors can cause fasting hypoglycemia.

hypoglycemia [HIGH-po-gly-SEE-mee-uh] Abnormally low concentration of glucose in the blood; any blood glucose value below 40 to 50 mg/dL of blood.

reactive hypoglycemia A type of hypoglycemia that occurs about one hour after eating carbohydrate-rich food. The body overreacts and produces too much insulin in response to food, rapidly decreasing blood glucose.

fasting hypoglycemia A type of hypoglycemia that occurs because the body produces too much insulin even when no food is eaten.

Key Concepts *Approximately 23.6 million people in the United States have diabetes mellitus, a leading cause of death and disability. Unfortunately, 5.7 million of these people (about one-fourth) are unaware that they have the disease. Three major types of diabetes have been identified: type 1, type 2, and gestational diabetes. Type 1, the most severe form, requires a daily regimen of insulin, careful diet control, and physical activity. In type 2 diabetes, the treatment focuses on diet and weight loss. Gestational diabetes occurs during pregnancy and usually goes away after delivery.*

Risk Factors for Diabetes

Some people are at higher risk than others for developing diabetes. Table 15.8 lists the risk factors for type 1 and type 2 diabetes. Anyone with a family history of diabetes has an increased risk. In most cases of type 1 diabetes, people must inherit risk factors from both parents, and whites have the highest rate of this disease.[111] Yet genes do not tell the complete story. When one identical twin has type 1 diabetes, for example, the other twin gets the disease at most only half the time.[112] Possible environmental triggers include exposure to cold weather and certain viruses or other infectious agents that activate the immune system. Early diet also may play a role. For example, type 1 diabetes is less common in people who were breastfed and began eating solid food at older ages.[113]

A family history of type 2 diabetes is one of the strongest risk factors for getting the disease.[114] The ethnic groups at highest risk of type 2 diabetes are Native Americans, Hispanic Americans, and African Americans. An increased risk of type 2 diabetes seems to occur more frequently in people who follow a "Western" lifestyle characterized by too much fat; too few fruits, vegetables, and fiber; and not enough exercise.[115]

The risk of developing type 2 diabetes increases progressively as body fat increases, especially around the midsection. The dramatic surge in obe-

Table 15.8 Risk Factors for Type 1 and Type 2 Diabetes Mellitus

Risk factors for type 1 diabetes

- First-degree relative (parent, sibling) with type 1 diabetes

Risk factors for type 2 diabetes

- Age ≥ 45 years
- Overweight (BMI ≥ 25 kg/m^2)
- First-degree relative with diabetes
- Sedentary lifestyle
- Ethnicity: African American, Latino, Native American, Asian American, Pacific Islander
- Previously identified pre-diabetes
- History of gestational diabetes or delivery of a baby weighing more than 9 pounds
- Hypertension (≥ 140/90 mm Hg)
- HDL cholesterol level < 35 mg/dL and/or triglyceride level > 250 mg/dL
- Polycystic ovary syndrome
- History of vascular disease

Sources: American Diabetes Association. Position statement: prevention of type 1 diabetes. *Diabetes Care.* 2004;27(suppl 1):S133; and American Diabetes Association. Position statement: prevention or delay of type 2 diabetes. *Diabetes Care.* 2004;27(suppl 1):S47–S54.

Table 15.9 **Strength of Evidence Related to Lifestyle and Type 2 Diabetes Risk**

Evidence	Decreased Risk	Increased Risk
Convincing	Voluntary weight loss in overweight/obese people	Overweight and obesity
	Physical activity	Abdominal obesity Physical inactivity Maternal diabetes
Probable	Nonstarch polysaccharides	Saturated fats Intrauterine growth retardation

Source: *Diet, Nutrition and the Prevention of Chronic Diseases: A Report of a Joint WHO/FAO Expert Consultation.* Geneva, Switzerland: World Health Organization, 2003. WHO Technical Report Series 916.

sity rates in the United States is a major reason that the incidence of type 2 diabetes has tripled since 1970.[116] Compared with a normal-weight person, an obese person has a significantly increased risk of developing type 2 diabetes.[117] More than 80 percent of adults diagnosed with type 2 diabetes are overweight or obese at the time of their diagnosis.[118] Unfortunately, as more children and adolescents become overweight, type 2 diabetes is becoming more common in young people. Contrary to popular opinion, high sugar or high carbohydrate intake does not by itself cause diabetes as long as it does not contribute to excess energy intake and obesity.

Do other dietary factors make a difference? The Nurses' Health Study suggests that total, saturated, and monounsaturated fat intakes are not associated with risk of type 2 diabetes in women, but that trans fatty acids increase risk and polyunsaturated fatty acids reduce risk.[119] Eating a low-fat diet does not appear to be associated with any change in diabetes risk. Women instructed to follow a low-fat diet tended to be less likely to develop diabetes as compared with those following their usual diet; however, those women also lost more weight. Therefore, weight loss, not nutrient composition, may be the important factor in reducing risk of diabetes.[120] Numerous studies have shown a protective effect of increased consumption of nonstarch polysaccharides (fiber).[121] Drinking more sugar-sweetened beverages[122] or diet beverages[123] and eating fewer fruits and vegetables[124] have also been associated with an increased risk of type 2 diabetes. Table 15.9 summarizes the evidence linking lifestyle factors and type 2 diabetes risk.

Dietary and Lifestyle Factors for Reducing Diabetes Risk

Obesity is the single largest modifiable risk factor in the development of type 2 diabetes. Therefore, the best measures for preventing pre-diabetes and obesity-related type 2 diabetes are a healthful diet and regular exercise. Lack of exercise, a poor diet, smoking and abstinence from alcohol have all been associated with increased risk of diabetes in women.[125] Excess body fat has been found to be the single most important determinant of type 2 diabetes in adult women.[126] Reducing excess body fat will improve glucose tolerance and reduce related risk factors for heart disease. Regular exercise will improve carbohydrate and lipid metabolism and increase insulin sensitivity. (See **Figure 15.12**.) As previously mentioned, exercise improves blood flow to the extremities, bringing blood pressure down to normal levels and reduc-

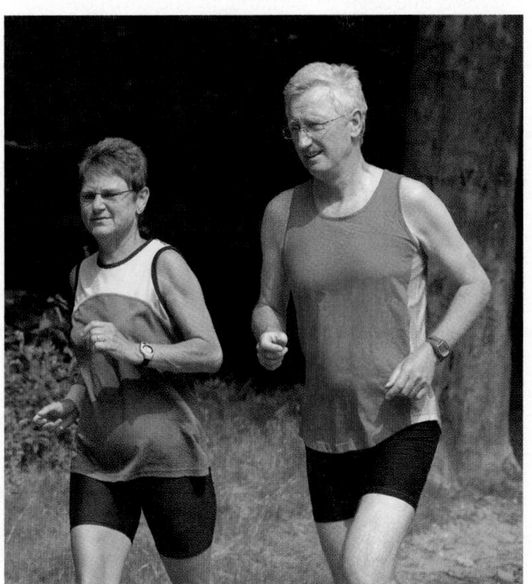

Figure 15.12 **Exercise and diabetes.** Regular physical activity improves glucose tolerance and helps reduce the risk of developing type 2 diabetes later in life.

ing risk of heart disease. In a study of 14,000 men, those who were most fit were 14 percent less likely to develop pre-diabetes and 52 percent less likely to get diabetes than the least fit of the group.[127]

The Diabetes Prevention Program, a study of more than 3,000 people, 45 percent of whom were minorities, found that people who received inten-

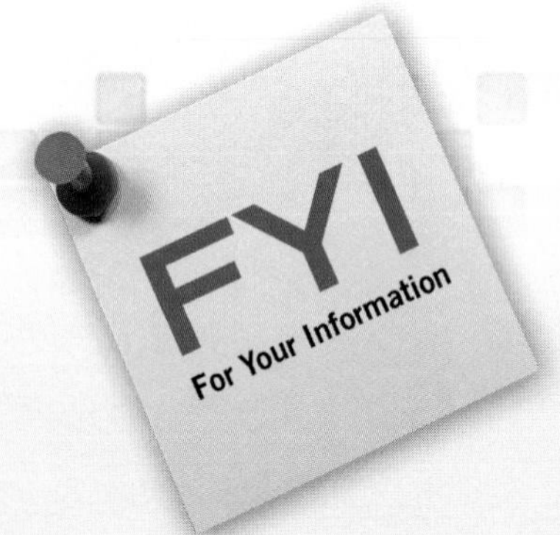

The Pima Indians

The Pima Indians of Arizona, along with teams of scientists and doctors from the National Institutes of Health, have been responsible for unraveling some of the complex interactions between genetics, lifestyle, and disease. Since 1965, Pima volunteers and scientists have been working together to try to understand why the Pimas have extremely high rates of obesity as well as the highest known rate of type 2 diabetes of any community in the world.[1] Half of all adult Pima Indians have diabetes, and 95 percent of those with diabetes are obese. Complications of diabetes such as kidney disease are extremely common in the Pima community.[2]

The ravages of diabetes were not always a problem for the Pimas. Hundreds of years ago they developed a sophisticated irrigation system that allowed them to cultivate such crops as wheat, beans, squash, and cotton. Hard physical work and a low-fat, high-fiber diet were the norm. Obesity and diabetes were essentially nonexistent. The Pimas lived this traditional lifestyle until the late nineteenth century, when American farmers living upstream diverted their water supply. Their way of life was seriously disrupted, resulting in poverty and severe malnutrition. The U.S. government gave the Pimas lard, sugar, and flour to help them survive. Although life improved for the Pimas as the economy rebounded after World War II, the increasing prosperity was accompanied by high-fat and sugary foods, more leisure time, and less physical work, resulting in an epidemic of obesity and diabetes. Although in the past 43 years the overall incidence has not changed, there has been nearly a sixfold increase in the prevalence of diabetes among youth under the age of 15, leading to an increase in midlife diabetic complications.[3]

Modern Pima Indians are not much different from most Americans in their diet and exercise habits, but they have much higher rates of obesity and diabetes. Scientists have postulated that they have inherited "thrifty genes" that allow them to retain fat more easily than most people. This genetic trait helped the ancestors of modern Pima Indians survive the hard times when food was not plentiful. During times of plenty, the "thrifty genes" allowed them to store extra fat so that they would not starve when famine struck. Unfortunately, the genetic traits that once helped them survive became a liability in modern times, when high-fat, high-calorie foods are readily available and the need for physical work is greatly diminished. In the 1890s, the traditional Pima Indian diet consisted of only about 15 percent fat; today, it is nearly 40 percent fat. Genetically, this is a recipe for disaster.

Although the specific genes for the inheritance of type 2 diabetes have not yet been located, several genes that play a role in insulin resistance (a major factor in the development of type 2 diabetes) have been found to be much more common in Pima Indians than in the general U.S. population. Pima Indians with diabetes develop kidney failure more often and at a younger age than non–Native Americans with diabetes. Ongoing research seeks to identify the genetic reasons for the high rate of kidney disease among American Indians and their families.[4]

Further evidence for the effects of diet and exercise on health is seen when the Arizona Pimas are compared with a genetically similar population in Mexico. The Pimas who currently live in Arizona migrated there from the Sierra Madre of Mexico hundreds of years ago. A Pima community still exists in a remote part of those mountains. These Mexican Pimas live much as their ancestors did, farming mostly by hand and eating a traditional diet that is very low in fat and high in fiber. Although the people in this region are genetically similar to the Arizona Pimas, obesity and diabetes are rarely seen among them.[5]

The challenge for the Arizona Pimas is to incorporate some healthy practices of their ancestors into their modern way of life. This is really the same challenge faced by most of us in the twenty-first century. Until the last 100 years, most humans had to engage in heavy physical work on a daily basis to survive. Our bodies simply were not designed to handle the amount of high-fat, high-calorie foods that most Americans eat, especially when sedentary pursuits occupy the bulk of our time.

1 Nelson RG, Pavkov ME, Hanson RL, Knowler WC. Changing course of diabetic nephropathy in the Pima Indians. *Diabetes Res Clin Pract.* 2008;82(suppl 1):S10–S14.

2 National Institute of Diabetes and Digestive and Kidney Diseases. The Pima Indians: pathfinders for health. http://www.niddk.nih.gov/health/diabetes/pima/obesity/obesity.htm. Accessed 9/1/09.

3 Nelson et al. Changing course of diabetic nephropathy in the Pima Indians.

4 National Institute of Diabetes and Digestive and Kidney Disease, National Diabetes Information Clearinghouse. *I Can Lower My Risk for Type 2 Diabetes: A Guide for American Indians.* http://www.diabetes.niddk.nih.gov/dm/pubs/amlatrisktype2AI/amerindrisk.pdf. Accessed 9/1/09.

5 National Institute of Diabetes and Digestive and Kidney Diseases. The Pima Indians.

sive lifestyle intervention were able to reduce their risk of developing type 2 diabetes by 58 percent. The lifestyle interventions included walking or other moderate physical exercise for about 30 minutes per day and weight reduction of 5 to 7 percent.[128]

Management of Diabetes

Before the discovery of insulin in 1921, everyone with type 1 diabetes died within a few years after diagnosis. Although insulin therapy is not a cure, its discovery represented the first major breakthrough in diabetes treatment.

Today, healthy eating, physical activity, and insulin delivery via injection (see **Figure 15.13**) or an insulin pump are the basic therapies for type 1 diabetes. The amount of insulin must be balanced with food intake and daily activities. Blood glucose concentrations must be closely monitored.

Healthy eating, physical activity, and blood glucose testing are the basic management tools for type 2 diabetes, and weight loss often restores normal glucose metabolism. Weight loss can decrease insulin resistance and improve blood glucose levels. Exercise increases the sensitivity of body cells to insulin, so the body needs less insulin to get glucose into cells. "Small Steps, Big Rewards Prevent Type 2 Diabetes" is a diabetes prevention campaign created by the National Diabetes Education Program based on the Diabetes Prevention Program.[129] Aimed at helping people lose a modest amount of weight, get 30 minutes of exercise five days a week, and make healthier food choices, the program enables people at risk to delay or prevent the onset of type 2 diabetes.

If diet and exercise fail to maintain blood glucose levels in the normal range, people with type 2 diabetes need medications to either increase insulin production or improve glucose uptake by cells. In some cases, insulin injections are needed to normalize blood glucose levels.

Nutrition

Although people with diabetes have the same nutritional needs as anyone else, good diabetes control requires that they monitor their food intake carefully.

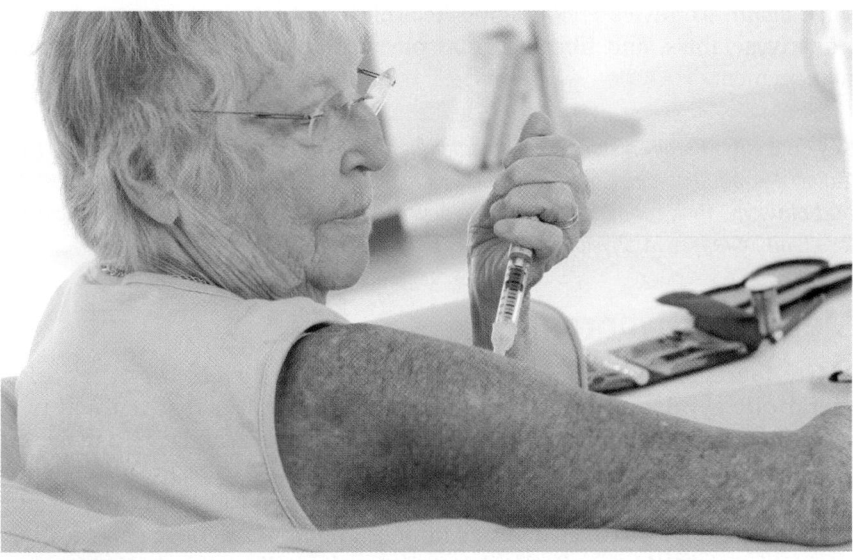

Figure 15.13 **Insulin injections.** In type 1 diabetes and some cases of type 2 diabetes, people need daily insulin injections to normalize blood glucose levels.

By eating well-balanced meals in the correct amounts, people can keep their blood glucose levels as close to normal (nondiabetes level) as possible. Choose Your Foods: Exchange Lists for Diabetes (see Appendix B) helps people with diabetes plan their diets. The American Diabetes Association also offers My Food Advisor, an online resource that helps with diabetes management and includes a database of foods, recipes, and nutrient information.[130]

Specific meal plans should be based on an individual's usual food intake. People with type 1 diabetes should eat at about the same time each day and should try to be consistent regarding the types of food they choose. Keeping calorie and carbohydrate intake consistent helps to prevent blood glucose levels from becoming too high or too low. People with type 2 diabetes should consume a diet that is well balanced, low in fat, especially saturated fat and trans fat, and promotes a healthy body weight. Dietary carbohydrates should come from fruits, vegetables, and whole grains.[131]

Having diabetes once meant a lifetime of meals that lacked one of the most pleasant aspect of taste: sweetness. Although in the past dietary treatment of diabetes eliminated simple sugars from the diet, current recommendations allow individuals with diabetes to include moderate amounts of simple sugars in their diet as long as sugar intake does not contribute to excess energy intake and obesity.[132]

Putting It All Together

Researchers continue to search for the cause or causes of diabetes and ways to prevent and cure it. Some genetic markers for type 1 diabetes have been identified, and it is now possible to screen relatives of people with type 1 diabetes to see whether they are at increased risk of developing the disease. In the future, it may be possible to administer insulin through inhalers, a pill, or a patch. Devices also are being developed that can monitor blood glucose levels without having to prick a finger to get a blood sample.

For now, the challenge is to slow the rate at which diabetes incidence is increasing. Healthy People 2010 objectives include a reduction in incidence of diabetes along with the economic burden it presents. Results from the Diabetes Prevention Program show that relatively modest changes in weight and exercise can be enough to reduce the incidence of diabetes. We turn, once again, to advice encouraging healthful eating (consumption of more fruits, vegetables, and fiber), regular physical activity, and lifelong weight management.

Key Concepts *Family history is a risk factor for both type 1 and type 2 diabetes. For type 2 diabetes, additional risk factors include increasing age, overweight, sedentary lifestyle, and ethnicity. Risk reduction can be achieved through healthy eating, modest weight loss, and increases in physical activity.*

Metabolic Syndrome

metabolic syndrome A cluster of at least three of the following risk factors for heart disease: hypertriglyceridemia (high blood triglycerides), low HDL cholesterol, hyperglycemia (high blood glucose), hypertension (high blood pressure), and excess abdominal fat.

Thirty four percent of adults in the United States meet the criteria for **metabolic syndrome**, a group of symptoms that occur together and promote the development of coronary artery disease, stroke, and type 2 diabetes. The prevalence will continue to grow because of the widespread tendency toward a sedentary lifestyle, according to the Centers for Disease Control and Prevention.[133] By 2010, as many as 50 to 75 million Americans may exhibit the syndrome.[134] Metabolic syndrome is usually indicated by a cluster of at least three of the following signs:[135]

- *Abdominal obesity:* For most men, a 40-inch waist or greater; for women, a waist of 35 inches or greater
- *High fasting blood glucose:* At least 100 mg/dL
- *High serum triglycerides:* At least 150 mg/dL
- *Low HDL cholesterol:* Less than 40 mg/dL for men; less than 50 mg/dL for women
- *Elevated blood pressure:* 130 mm Hg or above, systolic; or 85 mm Hg or above, diastolic

Taken individually, these risk factors may not look particularly serious. When you put them together, however, the problems rise substantially. Individuals with metabolic syndrome are at increased risk for both cardiovascular disease and type 2 diabetes.[136] More study is needed to understand the relationship between the risk factors embodied in metabolic syndrome, but researchers have identified people with metabolic syndrome as having the greatest risk of death from heart attack.

Although some scientists think that metabolic syndrome is genetically based, it is unlikely that metabolic syndrome results from a single cause. The primary underlying diabetic and cardiac risk factors appear to be insulin resistance and abdominal obesity. For many people, poor diet and lack of physical activity combined with a genetic predisposition lead to the development of the syndrome. The high prevalence of metabolic syndrome underscores an urgent need to develop comprehensive efforts directed at controlling the obesity epidemic and improving physical activity levels.

People with metabolic syndrome should work with their doctors to

- Monitor blood glucose, lipoproteins, and blood pressure
- Achieve and maintain a healthy body weight and increase physical activity—both are time-tested methods of improving insulin sensitivity, blood pressure, and lipoprotein levels
- Treat diabetes and hyperlipidemia according to established guidelines
- Choose drug therapy for hypertension with care—different medications have different effects on insulin sensitivity

Key Concepts *Metabolic syndrome, associated with an increased risk of death from heart attack, is a cluster including at least three of the following signs: abdominal fat, elevated blood glucose, elevated triglycerides and HDL cholesterol, and elevated blood pressure. A poor diet and sedentary lifestyle combined with a genetic predisposition are thought to be the underlying causes.*

Osteoporosis

Osteoporosis is a major public health problem, affecting more than 10 million Americans over the age of 50, with another 34 million people at risk.[137] Without a concerted effort to reduce risk, it is estimated that by the year 2020 half of all Americans over 50 will either have osteoporosis or be at high risk. Although 80 percent of those with osteoporosis are women, by age 75 one-third of all men have osteoporosis. However, women are most at risk for bone fractures related to osteoporosis. Experts estimate that 50 percent of U.S. white women aged 50 or older will break a bone due to osteoporosis.[138] Although we often associate osteoporosis with being elderly, the stage for its emergence is actually set much earlier in life, much like other chronic diseases. Fortunately, diet and lifestyle changes can help to delay the onset of osteoporosis and may prevent related fractures.

American College of Sports Medicine

Physical Activity and Bone Health

Maintaining a vigorous level of physical activity across the lifespan should be viewed as an essential component of the prescription for achieving and maintaining optimal bone health. The following exercise prescription is recommended to help preserve bone health during adulthood:

- Mode: weight-bearing endurance activities (tennis; stair climbing; jogging, at least intermittently during walking), activities that involve jumping (volleyball, basketball), and resistance exercise (weight lifting)
- Intensity: moderate to high, in terms of bone-loading forces
- Frequency: weight-bearing endurance activities 3–5 times per week; resistance exercise 2–3 times per week
- Duration: 30–60 minutes per day of a combination of weight-bearing endurance activities, activities that involve jumping, and resistance exercise that targets all major muscle groups

Source: Kohrt WM, Bloomfield SA, Little KD, et al. American College of Sports Medicine. Position stand. Physical activity and bone health. *Med Sci Sports Exerc.* 2004;36:1985–1996. Reprinted with permission from Wolters Kluwer Health.

What Is Osteoporosis?

Osteoporosis means "porous bone." It's a good description because bone mass or density declines and bone quality deteriorates, leaving the bones fragile and vulnerable to fracture. The hip, spine, and wrist bones are especially vulnerable. Often called a "silent disease," osteoporosis develops over several years without outward symptoms. Eventually bone loss makes bones so weak that they break with a mild strain, bump, or a fall. In fact, in some cases, the break may occur first and cause the fall!

Bone strength depends on two main features: bone density and bone quality. Bone density is determined by peak bone mass and amount of bone loss. Bone quality refers to architecture, turnover, damage accumulation (e.g., microfractures), and mineralization. Currently, no accurate measure of overall bone strength exists. Bone mineral density (BMD) is frequently used as a proxy measure and accounts for approximately 70 percent of bone strength.

Low bone mineral density is an important predictor of future bone fractures. Other predictors include a history of falls, low physical function such as slow gait speed and decreased leg muscle strength, impaired cognition, impaired vision, and the presence of environmental hazards (e.g., throw rugs). Some risks for fracture, such as age, low BMI, and low levels of physical activity, probably increase the rate of fractures through decreased bone density, increased propensity to fall, and inability to absorb impact.

Risk Factors for Osteoporosis

A common misperception is that osteoporosis always results from excessive bone loss. Bone loss commonly occurs as men and women age; however, a person who does not reach optimal (i.e., peak) bone mass during childhood and adolescence may develop osteoporosis without the occurrence of accelerated bone loss. Hence suboptimal bone growth in childhood and adolescence is as important as bone loss to the development of osteoporosis. Table 15.10 lists the risk factors for osteoporosis.

Bone mass typically peaks sometime around age 30. Starting in midlife, bone breakdown exceeds bone formation, and the progressive loss of bone

Table 15.10 Risk Factors for Osteoporosis

Advanced age
Female
Thin and/or small frame
Family history of osteoporosis
Early menopause, whether natural or surgically induced
Low testosterone levels in men
Abnormal absence of menstrual periods (amenorrhea)
Anorexia nervosa or bulimia nervosa
Medical conditions, such as thyroid disease, rheumatoid arthritis, and problems that block intestinal absorption of calcium
Use of certain medications, such as corticosteroids and anticonvulsants
Insufficient dietary calcium
Lack of weight-bearing exercise
Cigarette smoking
Excessive use of alcohol or caffeine

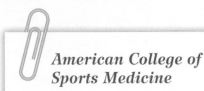

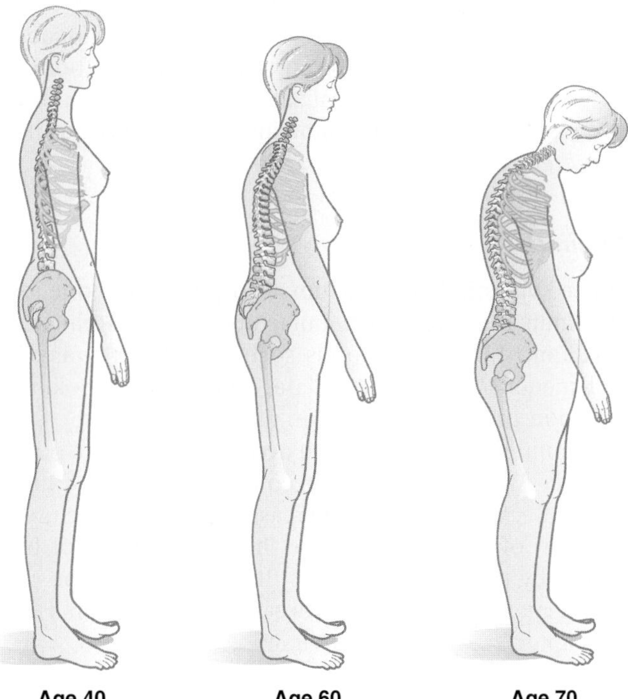

Figure 15.14 Progression of dowager's hump.

begins. If you got enough calcium and vitamin D earlier in life so that you maximized bone mass, then when bone loss begins you are likely to be a long way from low bone density and fractures.

Because declining estrogen levels accelerate bone loss, postmenopausal women have the highest risk of developing osteoporosis. By age 65, some women have lost half their skeletal mass, and they may show deformities of the upper spine, known as a "dowager's hump." (See **Figures 15.14** and **15.15**.) Women who reach menopause with low bone mass have a greatly increased risk of fractures.

Many medical disorders, such as genetic disorders, endocrine disorders, congestive heart failure, kidney disease, and alcoholism, as well as administration of certain drugs such as steroids, also may lead to osteoporosis and increased fracture risk.

Figure 15.15 **Dowager's hump.** In people with osteoporosis, the bones in the upper spine develop small compression fractures. These bones heal into wedge shapes, and the upper spine assumes a deformed, curved shape known as a "dowager's hump."

Dietary and Lifestyle Factors for Reducing Osteoporosis Risk

The main factor in reducing risk of osteoporosis and related fractures is maximum peak bone mass. Dietary components such as calcium and vitamin D help to achieve and maintain bone mass. Engaging in physical activity, especially weight-bearing exercise, helps to increase peak bone mass early in life and helps to maintain muscle strength and coordination that will reduce risk for falls later in life.

Calcium

Calcium is important for attaining peak bone mass and for preventing and treating osteoporosis. Adequate calcium intake throughout life helps prevent osteoporosis, and good calcium intake during childhood and adolescence helps maximize peak bone mass. Even in adulthood, adequate calcium slows bone loss, and it reduces fracture rates in postmenopausal women.

Calcium is clearly an important nutrient in bone health, but it's not the only one. Normal mineralization and maintenance of bone also require vitamins D, A, and K; the minerals phosphorus, fluoride, and magnesium; and protein.

Quick Bite

Lost in Space

Knowing that stress on bones maintains their strength, what would you guess happens in the gravity-free environment of outer space? Experience with prolonged space travel has made it clear that extensive bone and mineral loss are one health hazard of living without gravity's constant pull. Interestingly, changes in non-weight-bearing bones were not seen in studies of space travelers. As humans spend longer periods in space, scientists will be challenged to discover how to preserve bone strength without the constant stimulation of gravity on weight-bearing bones.

Vitamin D

You need vitamin D for calcium absorption and bone maintenance. Because aging limits the ability to manufacture active vitamin D, older people should use vitamin D–fortified foods such as milk or consider taking vitamin D supplements. Phytate and oxalate, caffeine, and smoking can reduce calcium absorption or increase excretion rates.

Vitamin D deficiency, which occurs more often in postmenopausal women and older Americans,[139] has been associated with a greater risk of hip fractures.[140] Because bone loss increases the risk of fractures, vitamin D supplementation of 400 IU daily may help reduce risk of hip and nonvertebral fractures by up to 20 percent.[141] It's important to be cautious with vitamin D supplements, because toxicity can quickly develop. For more on vitamin D, see Chapter 10, "Fat-Soluble Vitamins."

Vitamin A

Although vitamin A is essential for normal bone formation, animal, human, and laboratory research findings suggest an association between excessive vitamin A intake and weaker bones.[142] Researchers have also noticed that worldwide, the highest incidence of osteoporosis occurs in northern Europe, a population with a high intake of vitamin A.[143] However, this region has lower levels of sun exposure, which leads to decreased biosynthesis of vitamin D and may be at least partially responsible for these findings.

In the Nurses' Health Study, women who consumed the most vitamin A in foods and supplements (greater than or equal to 3,000 micrograms per day as retinol—more than triple the recommended intake) had a significantly increased risk of experiencing a hip fracture compared with those consuming the least amount (less than 1,250 micrograms per day of retinol).[144] This increased risk was attributed to retinol and not to vitamin A as beta-carotene.

On the other hand, the Centers for Disease Control and Prevention reviewed data from the Third National Health and Nutrition Examination survey (NHANES III), 1988–1994, and researchers did not identify any significant associations between bone mineral density and blood levels of retinyl esters, a form of vitamin A.[145]

No evidence indicates an association between beta-carotene intake and increased risk of osteoporosis. Instead, current evidence points to a possible association with vitamin A as retinol only. Because current studies yield conflicting results, additional research is needed to clarify the association between high levels of vitamin A intake and osteoporosis.[146]

Exercise

Regular weight-bearing and strength-training exercises enhance bone remodeling and strength. Exercise helps maximize bone mass when you're young and will slow bone loss during your later years. In addition to getting enough calcium and vitamin D to promote bone health and slow the development of osteoporosis, fitness experts make the following suggestions:

- Exercise should include weight-bearing and resistance training and should put stress on bones. Examples include walking and running.
- For continued improvement, exercise intensity should increase progressively.
- There is a maximum achievable bone density. As this point is approached, greater efforts are needed to achieve smaller gains.
- Discontinuing an exercise program reverses the benefits.
- Don't smoke, and drink alcoholic beverages only in moderation.

Putting It All Together

Osteoporosis is a debilitating degenerative disease that contributes to poor quality of life in older adults. Although bone loss with age is a major contributor to osteoporosis, maximizing peak bone mass early in life can go a long way toward preventing or at least delaying osteoporosis. Reducing the proportion of adults with osteoporosis is one of the Healthy People 2010 objectives.

Sodium is found naturally in many foods, but processed foods account for most of the salt and sodium Americans consume. Processed foods with high amounts of salt include regular canned vegetables and soups, frozen dinners, lunch meats, instant and ready-to-eat cereals, and salty chips and other snacks. You can use food labels to choose products lower in sodium.

Compare Labels

Which of these two items is lower in sodium? To tell, check the Percent Daily Value.

The frozen peas are lower in sodium, with just 5 percent of the DV per ½ cup serving. The canned peas have three times more sodium than the frozen peas: 16 percent of the DV in one serving.

Sodium also is found in many foods that may surprise you, such as baking soda, soy sauce, and monosodium glutamate (MSG), and sodium is found in some antacids—the range is wide. For more on the sodium content of foods, see Chapter 12, "Water and Major Minerals."

Before trying salt substitutes, check with your doctor, especially if you have high blood pressure. Many salt substitutes contain potassium chloride and may be harmful for individuals who have certain medical conditions or who take diuretic medications.

Nutrition Facts
Serving Size: 1/2 cup
Servings Per Container: about 3
Amount Per Serving
Calories: 60 **Calories from Fat:** 0

	% Daily Value*
Total Fat 0g	0%
Saturated Fat 0g	0%
Trans Fat 0g	
Cholesterol 0mg	0%
Sodium 380mg	16%
Total Carbohydrate 12g	4%
Dietary Fiber 3g	14%
Sugars 4g	
Protein 4g	

Vitamin A 6% Vitamin C 10%
Calcium 2% Iron 8%
*Percent Daily Values are based on a 2,000 calorie diet.

Canned Peas

Nutrition Facts
Serving Size: 1/2 cup
Servings Per Container: about 3
Amount Per Serving
Calories: 60 **Calories from Fat:** 0

	% Daily Value*
Total Fat 0g	0%
Saturated Fat 0g	0%
Trans Fat 0g	
Cholesterol 0mg	0%
Sodium 125mg	5%
Total Carbohydrate 11g	4%
Dietary Fiber 6g	22%
Sugars 5g	
Protein 5g	

Vitamin A 15% Vitamin C 30%
Calcium 0% Iron 6%
*Percent Daily Values are based on a 2,000 calorie diet.

Frozen Peas

To improve your bone health, the U.S. Surgeon General suggests the following: eat foods rich in calcium and vitamin D, be physically active every day, maintain a healthy body weight throughout your life, protect yourself from falls, avoid smoking and limit alcohol intake, and discuss increased risks with your doctor.[147] Postmenopausal women with low bone density may be advised to consider strength training to prevent or reduce bone loss.[148]

Key Concepts *Osteoporosis is the progressive loss of bone mass, resulting in fragile bones that break easily. Osteoporosis primarily affects postmenopausal women who have lower estrogen levels and accelerated rates of bone loss. Adequate calcium intake early in life helps maximize peak bone mass and reduces the risk of osteoporosis. Adequate amounts of vitamin D and regular exercise also are important for bone health.*

Learning Portfolio

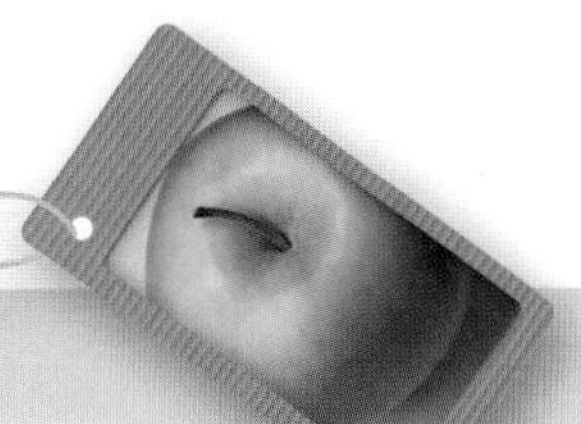

Key Terms

	page		page
aflatoxin	646	hypertension	636
atherosclerosis	627	insulin resistance	650
base pair	625	leukemia [loo-KEE-mee-a]	642
benign [beh-NINE]	642	lipoprotein a [Lp(a)]	628
blood pressure	636	lymph nodes [limf nodes]	643
C-reactive protein (CRP)	628	lymphoma [lim-FO-ma]	642
cancer	642	malignant [ma-LIG-nant]	642
carcinogens [kar-SIN-o-jins]	643	melanocytes [mel-AN-o-sites]	642
cardiovascular disease (CVD)	626	melanoma	642
complementary sequence	625	metabolic syndrome	656
coronary heart disease (CHD)	627	metastasis [meh-TAS-ta-sis]	642
DASH (Dietary Approaches to Stop Hypertension)	639	mutation	625
diastolic	636	nucleotides	625
endothelial cells	628	plaque	627
endothelium	628	platelets	628
essential hypertension	636	pre-diabetes	650
fasting hypoglycemia	651	reactive hypoglycemia	651
gene expression	626	risk factors	628
genes	624	secondary hypertension	636
genetic code	625	sphygmomanometer [sfig-mo-ma-NOM-eh-ter]	636
gestational diabetes	650	systolic	636
Human Genome Project	624	tissue	642
hypercholesterolemia	628	tumor	642
hyperglycemia [HIGH-per-gly-SEE-me-uh]	649	type 1 diabetes	650
hypoglycemia [HIGH-po-gly-SEE-me-uh]	651	type 2 diabetes	650

Study Points

- Genetics plays a part in nearly all human diseases.
- Much of the prevalence of cardiovascular disease and cancer can be attributed to smoking, consumption of a high-fat diet, and a sedentary lifestyle.
- LDL and HDL cholesterol levels predict heart disease risks more accurately than do total cholesterol levels. Infection and the inflammatory process may play a role in heart disease, and C-reactive protein may offer a new assessment of CVD risk.
- Ways to reduce risk for CVD include stopping smoking, exercising daily, managing weight, controlling blood pressure, and eating a healthful diet. Studies of groups with generous fish intakes show a low incidence of heart disease. Antioxidants and moderate alcohol consumption also may help protect against heart disease.
- Because hypertension usually has no specific symptoms or early warning signs, it is often called a "silent killer."
- Added weight places greater demands on the cardiovascular system, so people who are overweight are at higher risk for hypertension. Rates of hypertension are higher in countries with high sodium intakes.
- The three phases in the development of cancer are initiation, promotion, and progression.
- Evidence shows that generous intake of vegetables and fruits reduces risk of cancer.
- An estimated 23.6 million people—7.8 percent of the population—in the United States have diabetes mellitus, and one-third of these are unaware of their condition.
- Three major types of diabetes are type 1, type 2, and gestational diabetes.
- The dramatic surge in obesity rates in the United States is a major reason why the incidence of type 2 diabetes has tripled since 1970.
- Dietary recommendations for people with diabetes emphasize consuming diets rich in complex carbohydrates (including fiber) and low in fat.
- Often called a "silent disease," osteoporosis develops over several years without outward symptoms or diagnosis. Osteoporosis affects more than 25 million Americans, making it a major public health problem.
- To promote bone health and slow the development of osteoporosis, fitness experts suggest that exercise should be weight-bearing and should put stress on bones. Examples include walking and running.

Study Questions

1. In what ways do diet and exercise affect your health?
2. What is the major goal of the Human Genome Project?
3. What are the diet-related guidelines for reducing heart disease risk?

4. How do high levels of homocysteine contribute to heart disease?
5. What are the risk factors for hypertension?
6. How can people with hypertension lower their blood pressure?
7. What is the difference between cancer initiation and cancer promotion?
8. What are the major types of diabetes? Describe the differences between them.
9. What is metabolic syndrome?
10. What vitamin and mineral are most important for maximizing bone mass and reducing risk of osteoporosis?

Try This

Learn CPR!

The CPR (cardiopulmonary resuscitation) courses given by the American Red Cross, the American Heart Association, your local fire department, and other groups may help you save a life some day. Anyone can take these courses and become qualified to perform CPR. Investigate CPR courses in your community, and sign up to take one.

What's Your Family History?

Look into your family medical history. Is there cardiovascular disease in your family, as indicated by premature deaths from heart attack, stroke, or congestive heart failure? Are there any cases of cancer in your family, and has anyone died of cancer? How about diabetes, hypertension, or osteoporosis? Interview your parents and other relatives and develop a history of chronic disease in your family. These diseases may be risk factors for you. Keep that point in mind as you consider whether you need to make lifestyle changes to stay healthy and avoid chronic disease.

What About Bobbie?

Bobbie recently found out that her mother (age 50) has been diagnosed with hypertension. Her mother's parents both had hypertension, and both died in their early 60s from heart attacks. Bobbie is worried about her mom, but also about her own risk for hypertension and heart disease. After reading about the effectiveness of the DASH diet in lowering blood pressure, she decides to share what she has learned with her mom.

Let's take a look at Bobbie's diet and compare it to the DASH diet. You may want to review her one-day intake in Chapter 1. The National Heart, Lung and Blood Institute (NHLBI) has information on its Web site describing the DASH Eating Plan (http://www.nhlbi.nih.gov/health/public/heart/hbp/dash/new_dash.pdf).

A key part of the DASH diet is its emphasis on fruits and vegetables. With about 3 servings of vegetables, but only one serving of fruit, Bobbie is a long way from the DASH diet's 8 to 10 daily servings of fruits and vegetables! Eating more fruits and vegetables would boost Bobbie's potassium intake, which was low at 2,890 milligrams. Bobbie also is low in dairy products (and calcium). The DASH diet includes 2 to 3 servings of low-fat or fat-free dairy products, but again Bobbie falls short, with a splash of 2% milk in her coffee and cheese on her pizza. The DASH-Sodium study showed that reducing sodium intake, in conjunction with the DASH Eating Plan, reduced blood pressure even further. Bobbie's sodium intake, at 4,820 milligrams, is much higher than the Daily Value of 2,400 milligrams.

To reduce her hypertension risk, Bobbie could snack on fruits and vegetables instead of pizza and chips, include low-fat milk or yogurt on a regular basis, choose fewer canned or processed foods, and exercise regularly. Given her family history, it would be a good idea for Bobbie to have her blood pressure checked regularly.

References

1 World Health Organization. WHO definition of health. Preamble to the Constitution of the World Health Organization, 1948. http://www.who.int/about/definition/en/print.html. Accessed 8/7/06.

2 MedlinePlus Medical Dictionary. http://www.nlm.nih.gov/medlineplus/mplusdictionary.html. Accessed 8/27/09.

3 World Health Organization. *Diet, Nutrition and the Prevention of Chronic Diseases: A Report of a Joint WHO/FAO Expert Consultation*. Geneva, Switzerland: World Health Organization, 2003. WHO Technical Report Series 916.

4 US Department of Health and Human Services. *Healthy People 2010*. 2nd ed. With *Understanding and Improving Health and Objectives for Improving Health*. 2 vols. Washington, DC: US Government Printing Office, 2000.

5 US Department of Health and Human Services. *2008 Physical Activity Guidelines for Americans*. http://www.health.gov/Paguidelines/pdf/paguide.pdf. Accessed 8/27/09.

6 Centers for Disease Control and Prevention. Heart disease is the number one cause of death. February 2, 2009. http://www.cdc.gov/features/heartmonth/. Accessed 8/27/09.

7 Nicolopoulou-Stamati P, Hens H. *Cancer as an Environmental Disease*. Boston: Kluwer, 2004:21.

8 Collins FS, McKusick VA. Implications of the Human Genome Project for medical science. *JAMA*. 2001;285(5):540–544.

9 Klerk M, Verhoef P, Clarke R, et al. MTHFR 677C→T polymorphism and risk of coronary heart disease: a meta-analysis. *JAMA*. 2002;288(16):2023–2031.

10 Afman L, Müller M. Nutrigenomics: from molecular nutrition to prevention of disease. *J Am Diet Assoc*. 2006;106(4):569–576.

11 Khoury MJ, McCabe LL, McCabe ERB. Population screening in the age of genomic medicine. *N Engl J Med*. 2003;348(1):50–58.

12 Centers for Disease Control and Prevention. Heart disease is the number one cause of death.

13 Clinicians Group. *Clinician Reviews*. 2002;12(10):54–60; and Miniño AM, Heron MP, Smith BL. *Deaths: Preliminary Data for 2004*. Hyattsville, MD: National Center for Health Statistics, 2006. National Vital Statistics Reports, Vol. 54, No. 19. http://www.cdc.gov/nchs/data/nvsr/nvsr54/nvsr54_19.pdf. Accessed 8/27/09.

14 Epstein SE, Zhu J, Najafi AH, Burnett MS. Insights into the role of infection in atherogenesis and in plaque rupture. *Circulation*. 2009;119:3133–3141.

15 Tholstrup T, Samman S. Postprandial lipoprotein(a) is affected differently by specific individual dietary fatty acids in healthy young men. *J Nutr*. 2004;134:2550–2555.

16 American Heart Association. Cardiovascular disease statistics. http://www.americanheart.org/presenter.jhtml?identifier=4478. Accessed 8/31/09.

17 American Heart Association. *Heart Disease and Stroke Statistics—2009 Update: A Report from the American Heart Association Statistics Committee and Stroke Statistics Subcommittee*. http://www.americanheart.org/downloadable/heart/1240250946756LS-1982%20Heart%20and%20Stroke%20Update.042009.pdf. Accessed 8/27/09.

18 National Cholesterol Education Program, Expert Panel on Detection, Evaluation and Treatment of High Blood Cholesterol. *High Blood Cholesterol: What You Need to Know*. http://www.nhlbi.nih.gov/health/public/heart/chol/wyntk.htm#lifestyle. Accessed 8/27/09.

19 Rosamond WD, Chambless LE, Folsom AR, et al. Trends in the incidence of myocardial infarction and in mortality due to coronary heart disease, 1987 to 1994. *N Engl J Med*. 1998;339:861–867.

20 Athyros VG, Papageorgiou AA, Mercouris BR, et al. Treatment with atorvastatin to the National Cholesterol Educational Program goal versus "usual" care in secondary coronary heart disease prevention. The Greek Atorvastatin and Coronary-Heart-Disease Evaluation (GREACE) study. *Curr Med Res Opin*. 2002;18(4):220–228.

21 Steinhagen-Thiessen E, Bramlage P, Lösch C, et al. Dyslipidemia in primary care—prevalence, recognition, treatment and control: data from the German Metabolic and Cardiovascular Risk Project (GEMCAS). *Cardiovasc Diabetol*. 2008;15(7):31.

22 Hu FB. Diet and lifestyle influences on risk of coronary heart disease. *Curr Atheroscler Rep*. 2009;11(4):257–263.

23 American Heart Association. Inflammation, heart disease and stroke: the role of C-reactive protein. http://www.americanheart.org/presenter.jhtml?identifier=4648. Accessed 8/28/09.

24 Ridker PM, et al. C-reactive protein levels and outcomes after statin therapy. *N Engl J Med*. 2005;352:20–28.

25 American Heart Association. Inflammation, heart disease and stroke.

26 Ridker PM, Buring JE, Cook NR, Rifai N. C-reactive protein, the metabolic syndrome, and risk of incident cardiovascular events: an 8-year follow-up of 14,719 initially healthy American women. *Circulation*. 2003;107(3):391–397.

27 Lichtenstein AH, Appel LJ, Brands M, et al. Diet and lifestyle recommendations revision 2006: a scientific statement from the American Heart Association Nutrition Committee. *Circulation*. 2006;114:82–96.

28 Sivanandam S, Sinaiko AR, Jacobs DR Jr, et al. Relation of increase in adiposity to increase in left ventricular mass from childhood to young adulthood. *Am J Cardiol*. 2006;98(3):411–415; and Willett WC, Manson JE, Stampfer MJ, et al. Weight, weight change, and coronary heart disease in women. *JAMA*. 1995;273(6):461–465.

29 World Health Organization. *Diet, Nutrition and the Prevention of Chronic Diseases*.

30 Manson JE, Greenland P, LaCroix AZ, et al. Walking compared with vigorous exercise for the prevention of cardiovascular events in women. *N Engl J Med*. 2002;347(10):716–725.

31 Witzum JL. The oxidation hypothesis of atherosclerosis. *Lancet*. 1994;344:793–795.

32 Kris-Etherton PM, Lichtenstein AH, Howard BV, et al. for the Nutrition Committee of the American Heart Association Council on Nutrition, Physical Activity, and Metabolism. Antioxidant vitamin supplements and cardiovascular disease. *Circulation*. 2004;110:637–641; and Bjelakovic G, Nikolova D, Gluud LL, et al. Mortality in randomized trials of antioxidant supplements for primary and secondary prevention: systematic review and meta-analysis. *JAMA*. 2007;297:842–857.

33 Bjelakovic G, Nikolova D, Gluud LL, et al. Antioxidant supplements for prevention of mortality in healthy participants and patients with various diseases. *Cochrane Database Syst Rev*. 2008;(2):CD007176.

34 Hu FB. Plant-based foods and prevention of cardiovascular disease: an overview. *Am J Clin Nutr*. 2003;78(3):544S–551S.

35 Hung H-C, Joshipura KJ, Jiang R, et al. Fruit and vegetable intake and risk of major chronic disease. *J Natl Cancer Inst*. 2004;96:1577–1584.

36 Padayatty SJ, Levine M. Fruit and vegetables: think variety, go ahead, eat! *Am J Clin Nutr*. 2008;87(1):5–7.

37 Hu FB, Willett WC. Optimal diets for prevention of coronary heart disease. *JAMA*. 2002;288:2569–2578.

38 Wong J, de Souza R, Kendall C, et al. Colonic health: fermentation and short chain fatty acids. *J Clin Gastroenterol*. 2006;40(3):235–243.

39 Institute of Medicine, Food and Nutrition Board. *Dietary Reference Intakes for Energy, Carbohydrate, Fiber, Fat, Fatty Acids, Cholesterol, Protein, and Amino Acids*. Washington, DC: National Academies Press, 2005.

40 Mellen PB, Walsh TF, Herrington DM. Whole grain intake and cardiovascular disease: a meta-analysis. *Nutr Metab Cardiovasc Dis*. 2008;18(4):283–290.

41 Bang HO, Dyerberg J. The composition of food consumed by Greenlandic Eskimos. *Acta Med Scand*. 1973;200:69–73.

42 American Heart Association. Fish and omega-3 fatty acids: AHA recommendation. http://www.americanheart.org/presenter.jhtml?identifier=4632. Accessed 8/30/09.

43 Lavie CJ, Milani RV, Mehra MR, Ventura HO. Omega-3 polyunsaturated fatty acids and cardiovascular diseases. *J Am Coll Cardiol*. 2009;54:585–594.

44 Balk EM, Lichtenstein AH, Chung M, et al. Effects of omega-3 fatty acids on serum markers of cardiovascular disease risk: a systematic review. *Atherosclerosis*. 2006;189:19–30; and Harris WS, Isley WL. Clinical trial evidence for the cardioprotective effects of omega-3 fatty acids. *Curr Atheroscler Rep*. 2001;3:174–179.

45 Iso H, Rexrode KM, Stampfer MJ, et al. Intake of fish and omega-3 fatty acids and risk of stroke in women. *JAMA*. 2001;285:304–312.

46 National Institutes of Health, Office of Dietary Supplements. Omega-3 fatty acids and health. http://ods.od.nih.gov/FactSheets/Omega3FattyAcidsandHealth.asp. Accessed 8/30/09.

47 American Heart Association. Fish and omega-3 fatty acids.

48 Vitolins MZ, Anderson AM, Delahanty L, et al. Action for Health in Diabetes (Look AHEAD) trial: baseline evaluation of selected nutrients and food group intake. *J Am Diet Assoc*. 2009;109:1367–1375.

49 American Heart Association. Trans-fats. January 2009. http://www.americanheart.org/presenter.jhtml?identifier=3045792. Accessed 8/30/09.

50 Kris-Etherton PM, Pearson TA, Wan Y, et al. High-monounsaturated fatty acid diets lower both plasma cholesterol and triacylglycerol concentrations. *Am J Clin Nutr*. 1999;70:1009–1015.

51 Zazpe I, Sanchez-Tainta A, Estruch R, et al. A large randomized individual and group intervention conducted by registered dietitians increased adherence to Mediterranean-type diets: the PREDIMED study. *J Am Diet Assoc*. 2008;108(7):1134–1144; da Silva R, Bach-Faig A, Raidó Quintana B, et al.

Worldwide variation of adherence to the Mediterranean diet, in 1961–1965 and 2000–2003. *Public Health Nutr*. 2009;12(9A):1676–1684; and Piscopo S. The Mediterranean diet as a nutrition education, health promotion and disease prevention tool. *Public Health Nutr*. 2009;12(9A):1648–1655.

52 Appel LJ, Sacks FM, Carey VJ, et al. Effects of protein, monounsaturated fat, and carbohydrate intake on blood pressure and serum lipids: results of the OmniHeart randomized trial. *JAMA*. 2005;294:2455–2464.

53 Jakobsen MU, O'Reilly EJ, Heitmann BL, et al. Major types of dietary fat and risk of coronary heart disease: a pooled analysis of 11 cohort studies. *Am J Clin Nutr*. 2009;89(5):1425–1432.

54 Klatsky AL. Should patients with heart disease drink red wine? *JAMA*. 2001;285:2004–2006; and US Department of Health and Human Services and US Department of Agriculture. *Dietary Guidelines for Americans, 2010*. 7th ed. Washington DC: US Government Printing Office, December 2010.

55 Flesch M, Rosenkranz S, Erdmann E, Bohm M. Alcohol and the risk of myocardial infarction. *Basic Res Cardiol*. 2001;96:128–135.

56 Appel LJ, Miller ER III, Jee SH, et al. Effect of dietary patterns on serum homocysteine: results of a randomized, controlled feeding study. *Circulation*. 2000;102:852.

57 Sacks FM, Lichtenstein A, Van Horn L, et al. Soy protein, isoflavones, and cardiovascular health: an American Heart Association science advisory for professionals from the nutrition committee. *Circulation*. 2006;113:1034–1044.

58 Xiao CW. Health effects of soy protein and isoflavones in humans. *J Nutr*. 2008;138(6):1244S–1249S.

59 Ostchega Y, Yoon SS, Hughes J, Louis T. *Hypertension Awareness, Treatment, and Control-Continued Disparities in Adults: United States, 2005–2006*. January 2008. Available at http://www.cdc.gov/nchs/data/databriefs/db03.pdf. Accessed 8/30/09.

60 Chobanian AV, Bakris GL, Black HR, et al., and the National High Blood Pressure Education Program Coordinating Committee. The Seventh Report of the Joint National Committee on Prevention, Detection, Evaluation, and Treatment of High Blood Pressure: the JNC 7 Report. *JAMA*. 2003;289(19):2560–2572.

61 American Heart Association. A special high blood pressure message for African Americans. April 9, 2009. 4http://www.americanheart.org/presenter.jhtml?identifier=2150. Accessed 8/30/09.

62 Vasan RS, Beiser A, Seshadri S, et al. Residual life-time risk for developing hypertension in middle-aged women and men: the Framingham Heart Study. *JAMA*. 2002;287:1003–1010.

63 Chobanian AV, Bakris GL, Black HR, et al. The JNC 7 report.

64 Moran A, Diez Roux A, Jackson S, et al. Acculturation is associated with hypertension in a multiethnic sample. *Am J Hypertens*. 2007;20(4):354–363.

65 US Department of Health and Human Services, National Heart, Lung and Blood Institute. *Your Guide to Lowering Your Blood Pressure with DASH*. April 2006. NIH publication 06-4082. http://www.nhlbi.nih.gov/health/public/heart/hbp/dash/new_dash.pdf. Accessed 8/30/09.

66 Harsha DW, Lin PW, Obarzanek E, et al. Dietary Approaches to Stop Hypertension: a summary of study results. *J Am Diet Assoc*. 1999;99(8 suppl):S35–S39.

67 Vogt TM, Appel LJ, Obarzanek E, et al. Dietary approaches to stop hypertension: rationale, design, and methods. *J Am Diet Assoc*. 1999;99(8 suppl):S12–S18.

68 National Heart, Lung and Blood Institute. Healthy eating. http://www.nhlbi.nih.gov/hbp/prevent/h_eating/h_eating.htm. Accessed 8/30/09.

69 Sacks FM, Svetkey LP, Vollmer WM, et al. Effects on blood pressure of reduced dietary sodium and the Dietary Approaches to Stop Hypertension (DASH) diet. DASH-Sodium Collaborative Research Group. *N Engl J Med*. 2001;344(1):3–10.

70 Liese AD, Nichols M, Sun X, D'Agostino RB Jr, Haffner SM. Adherence to the DASH diet is inversely associated with incidence of type 2 diabetes: the insulin resistance atherosclerosis study. *Diabetes Care*. 2009;32(8):1434–1436.

71 Levitan EB, Wolk A, Mittleman MA. Consistency with the DASH diet and incidence of heart failure. *Arch Intern Med*. 2009;169(9):851–857.

72 Champagne CM. Dietary interventions on blood pressure: the Dietary Approaches to Stop Hypertension (DASH) trials. *Nutr Rev*. 2006;64(2 pt 2):S53–S56.

73 Svetkey LP, Harsha DW, Vollmer WM, et al. PREMIER: a clinical trial of comprehensive lifestyle modification for blood pressure control: rational, design and baseline characteristics. *Ann Epidemiol*. 2003;13(6):462–471.

74 PREMIER Collaborative Research Group. Effects of comprehensive lifestyle modification on blood pressure control: main results of the PREMIER clinical trial. *JAMA*. 2003;289(16):2083–2093.

75 Lin PH, Appel LJ, Funk K, et al. The PREMIER intervention helps participants follow the Dietary Approaches to Stop Hypertension dietary pattern and the current Dietary Reference Intakes recommendations. *J Am Diet Assoc*. 2007;107(9):1541–1551.

76 National Center for Health Statistics. Leading causes of deaths. http://www.cdc.gov/nchs/fastats/lcod.htm. Accessed 8/30/09.

77 Key TJ, Allen NE, Spencer EA, Travis RC. The effect of diet on risk of cancer. *Lancet*. 2002;360(9336):861–868.

78 National Cancer Institute. What causes cancer? http://www.cancer.gov/cancertopics/understandingcancer/cancer/Slide24. Accessed 8/30/09.

79 Lichtenstein P, Holm NV, Verkasalo PK, et al. Environmental and heritable factors in the causation of cancer. *N Engl J Med*. 2000;343(2):78–85.

80 Kushi LH, Byers T, Doyle C, et al., and the American Cancer Society 2006 Nutrition and Physical Activity Guidelines Advisory Committee. American Cancer Society guidelines on nutrition and physical activity for cancer prevention: reducing the risk of cancer with healthy food choices and physical activity. *CA Cancer J Clin*. 2006;56:254–281.

81 World Health Organization. *Diet, Nutrition and the Prevention of Chronic Diseases*.

82 Holmes MD, Hunter DJ, Colditz GA, et al. Association of dietary intake of fat and fatty acids with risk of breast cancer. *JAMA*. 1999;281:914–920.

83 Bingham SA, Luben R, Welch A, et al. Are imprecise methods obscuring a relation between fat and breast cancer? *Lancet*. 2003;362:212–214.

84 Sieri S, Krogh V, Ferrari P, et al. Dietary fat and breast cancer risk in the European Prospective Investigation into Cancer and Nutrition. *Am J Clin Nutr*. 2008;88(5):1304–1312.

85 Giovannucci E. Diet, body weight, and colorectal cancer: a summary of the epidemiologic evidence. *J Women's Health*. 2003;12(2):173–182; and Chao A, Thun MJ, Connell CJ, et al. Meat consumption and risk of colorectal cancer. *JAMA*. 2005;293:172–182.

86 Nelson WG, DeMarzo AM, Isaacs WB. Prostate cancer. *N Engl J Med*. 2003;394(4):366–381.

87 Katan MB, Grundy SM, Willett WC. Beyond low fat diets. *N Engl J Med*. 1997;337:563–566.

88 The Alpha-Tocopherol, Beta Carotene Cancer Prevention Study Group. The effect of vitamin E and beta carotene on the incidence of lung cancer and other cancers in male smokers. *N Engl J Med*. 1994;330:1029–1035; and Omenn G, Goodman G, Thornquist M, et al. Effects of a combination of beta carotene and vitamin A on lung cancer and cardiovascular disease. *N Engl J Med*. 1996;334:1150–1155.

89 Henneken SC, Buring J, Manson J, et al. Lack of effect of long term supplementation with beta-carotene on the incidence of malignant neoplasms and cardiovascular disease. *N Engl J Med*. 1996;334:1145–1149.

90 Centers for Disease Control and Prevention. Fruit and vegetable consumption among adults—United States, 2005. *MMWR*. 2007;56(10):214–217; and Centers for Disease Control and Prevention. Healthy Youth! Youth online: comprehensive results. United States 2007: percentage of students who ate fruits and vegetables (100% fruit juices, fruit, green salad, potatoes [excluding French fries, fried potatoes, or potato chips], carrots, or other vegetables) five or more times per day during the 7 days before the survey. http://apps.nccd

.cdc.gov/yrbss/QuestYearTable.asp?path=byHT&ByVar=CI&cat=5&quest=508&year=2007&loc=XX. Accessed 8/30/09.

91 Potter JD, Finnegan JR, Guinard J-X, et al. *5 A Day for Better Health Program Evaluation Report*. Bethesda, MD: National Institutes of Health, National Cancer Institute, 2000. NIH publication 01-4904; and US Department of Health and Human Services. Eat 5 to 9 a day for better health. http://www.5aday.gov/index.html. Accessed 8/28/06.

92 Fruit and Veggies—More Matters. http://www.fruitsandveggiesmorematters.org/ and http://www.fruitsandveggiesmatter.gov/. Accessed 8/30/09.

93 Slavin JL. Mechanisms for the impact of whole grain foods on cancer risk. *J Am Coll Nutr*. 2000;19:3002–3075.

94 Agurs-Collins T, Rosenberg L, Makambi K, et al. Dietary patterns and breast cancer risk in women participating in the Black Women's Health Study. *Am J Clin Nutr*. 2009;90(3):621–628.

95 Wu AH, Yu MC, Tseng C-C, et al. Dietary patterns and breast cancer risk in Asian American women. *Am J Clin Nutr*. 2009;89(4):1145–1154.

96 Schatzkin A, Lanza E, Corle D, et al. Lack of effect of a low-fat, high-fiber diet on the recurrence of colorectal adenomas. Polyp Prevention Trial Study Group. *N Engl J Med*. 2000;342:1149–1155; and Alberts DS, Martinez, ME, Roe DJ, et al. Lack of effect of a high-fiber cereal supplement on the recurrence of colorectal adenomas. Phoenix Colon Cancer Prevention Physicians' Network. *N Engl J Med*. 2000;342:1156–1162.

97 Yan L, Spitznagel EL. Soy consumption and prostate cancer risk in men: a revisit of a meta-analysis. *Am J Clin Nutr*. 2009;89(4):1155–1163; and Kolonel LN, Hankin JH, Whittemore AS, et al. Vegetables, fruits, legumes and prostate cancer: a multiethnic case-control study. *Cancer Epidemiol Biomarkers Prev*. 2000;9:795–804.

98 Messina M, Wu AH. Perspectives on the soy–breast cancer relation. *Am J Clin Nutr*. 2009;89:1673S–1679S.

99 Centers for Diseases Control and Prevention, National Center for Chronic Disease Prevention and Health Promotion. 2007 national diabetes fact sheet. July 2008. http://www.cdc.gov/diabetes/pubs/estimates07.htm. Accessed 8/31/09.

100 Ibid.

101 Gropper SS, Smith JL, Groff JL. *Advanced Nutrition and Human Metabolism*. 5th ed. Belmont, CA: Wadsworth, 2009.

102 National Institute of Diabetes and Digestive and Kidney Diseases (NIDDK). National diabetes statistics, 2007. http://diabetes.niddk.nih.gov/DM/PUBS/statistics/. Accessed 8/31/09.

103 Ibid.

104 American Diabetes Association. Type 2 diabetes complications. http://www.diabetes.org/type-1-diabetes/well-being/link-healthprof.jsp. Accessed 8/31/09.

105 Ibid.

106 NIDDK. National diabetes statistics, 2007.

107 Ibid.

108 Ibid.

109 American Diabetes Association. Diagnosis and classification of diabetes mellitus. *Diabetes Care*. 2007;30(suppl 1):S42–S47.

110 NIDDK. National diabetes statistics, 2007.

111 American Diabetes Association. Genetics of diabetes. http://www.diabetes.org/genetics.jsp. Accessed 8/31/09.

112 Ibid.

113 Ibid.

114 Ibid.

115 Ibid.

116 Diabetes Prevention Program Research Group. Reduction in the incidence of type 2 diabetes with lifestyle intervention or metformin. *N Engl J Med*. 2002;346:393–403.

117 Mokdad AH, Ford ES, Bowman BA, et al. Prevalence of obesity, diabetes, and obesity-related health risk factors, 2001. *JAMA*. 2003;289:76–79.

118 Pickup JC, Williams G, eds. *Textbook of Diabetes*. 2nd ed. Malden, MA: Blackwell Science, 1997.

119 Salmeron J, Hu FB, Manson JE, et al. Dietary fat intake and risk of type 2 diabetes in women. *Am J Clin Nutr*. 2001;73:1019–1026.

120 Tinker LF, Bonds DE, Margolis KL, et al. Low-fat dietary pattern and risk of treated diabetes mellitus in postmenopausal women. *Arch Intern Med*. 2008;168(14):1500–1511.

121 World Health Organization. *Diet, Nutrition and the Prevention of Chronic Diseases*.

122 Palmer JR, Boggs DA, Krishnan S, et al. Sugar-sweetened beverages and incidence of type 2 diabetes mellitus in African American women. *Arch Intern Med*. 2008;168(14):1487–1492.

123 Nettleton JA, Lutsey PL, Wang Y, et al. Diet soda intake and risk of incident metabolic syndrome and type 2 diabetes in the Multi-Ethnic Study of Atherosclerosis (MESA). Diabetes Care. 2009;32:688–694.

124 Harding A-H, Wareham NJ, Bingham SA, et al. Plasma vitamin C level, fruit and vegetable consumption, and the risk of new-onset type 2 diabetes mellitus. *Arch Intern Med*. 2008;168(14):1493–1499.

125 Hu FB, Manson JE, Stampfer MJ, et al. Diet, lifestyle, and the risk of type 2 diabetes mellitus in women. *N Engl J Med*. 2001;345:790–797.

126 Ibid.

127 Lee DC, Sui X, Church TS, et al. Associations of cardiorespiratory fitness and obesity with risks of impaired fasting glucose and type 2 diabetes in men. Diabetes Care. 2009;32:257–262.

128 Diabetes Prevention Program Research Group. Reduction in the incidence of type 2 diabetes with lifestyle intervention or metformin.

129 National Diabetes Education Program. Small Steps Big Rewards: prevent type 2 diabetes campaign. http://ndep.nih.gov/partners-community-organization/campaigns/SmallStepsBigRewards.aspx. Accessed 8/31/09.

130 American Diabetes Association. My food advisor. http://www.diabetes.org/food-nutrition-lifestyle/nutrition/my-food-advisor.jsp. Accessed 8/31/09.

131 American Diabetes Association. Nutrition recommendations and interventions for diabetes. A position statement of the American Diabetes Association. *Diabetes Care*. 2007;30(suppl 1):S48–S65.

132 Ibid.

133 Ervin RB. *Prevalence of Metabolic Syndrome Among Adults 20 Years of Age and Over, by Sex, Age, Race and Ethnicity, and Body Mass Index: United States, 2003–2006*. Hyattsville, MD: National Center for Health Statistics, 2009. National Health Statistics Reports No. 13.

134 Hansen BC. The metabolic syndrome X. *Ann N Y Acad Sci*. 1999;892:1–24.

135 Ervin. *Prevalence of Metabolic Syndrome Among Adults*.

136 Grundy SM, Cleeman JI, Daniels SR, et al. Diagnosis and management of the metabolic syndrome: an American Heart Association/National Heart, Lung, and Blood Institute scientific statement. *Circulation*. 2005;112:2735–2752.

137 US Department of Health and Human Services. *Bone Health and Osteoporosis: A Report of the Surgeon General*. Rockville, MD: US Department of Health and Human Services, Office of the Surgeon General, 2004.

138 National Osteoporosis Foundation. *Bone Tool Kit*. Washington, DC: National Osteoporosis Foundation, 2009.

139 Institute of Medicine, Food and Nutrition Board. *Dietary Reference Intakes: Calcium, Phosphorus, Magnesium, Vitamin D and Fluoride*. Washington, DC: National Academies Press, 1997.

140 Cauley JA, LaCroix AZ, Wu L, et al. Serum 25-hydroxyvitamin D concentrations and risk for hip fractures. *Ann Intern Med*. 2008;149(4):242–250.

141 Bischoff-Ferrari HA, Willett WC, Wong JB, et al. Prevention of nonvertebral fractures with oral vitamin D and dose dependency: a meta-analysis of randomized controlled trials. *Arch Intern Med*. 2009;169(6):551–561.

142 Binkley N, Krueger D. Hypervitaminosis A and bone. *Nutr Rev*. 2000;58:138–144.

143 Johansson S, Melhus H. Vitamin A antagonizes calcium response to vitamin D in man. *J Bone Miner Res*. 2001;16:1899–1905.

144 Feskanich D, Singh V, Willett WC, Colditz GA. Vitamin A intake and hip fractures among postmenopausal women. *JAMA*. 2002;287:47–54.

145 Ballew C, Galuska D, Gillespie C. High serum retinyl esters are not associated with reduced bone mineral density in the Third National Health and Nutrition Examination Survey, 1988–1994. *J Bone Miner Res*. 2001;16:2306–2312.

146 Institute of Medicine, Food and Nutrition Board. *Dietary Reference Intakes for Vitamin A, Vitamin K, Arsenic, Boron, Chromium, Copper, Iodine, Iron, Manganese, Molybdenum, Nickel, Silicon, Vanadium, and Zinc*. Washington, DC: National Academies Press, 2001.

147 US Department of Health and Human Services. *Bone Health and Osteoporosis*.

148 Bocalini DS, Serra AJ, dos Santos L, et al. Strength training preserves the bone mineral density of postmenopausal women without hormone replacement therapy. *J Aging Health*. 2009;21(3):519–527.

CHAPTER 16

Life Cycle

Maternal and Infant Nutrition

THINK About It

1 Saying she is eating for two, your pregnant friend can't stop eating. What do you think about this?

2 Your best friend tells you she is pregnant. You know that she enjoys wine with dinner. What do you say to her?

3 Were you breastfed? Do you know of any benefits?

4 At a fast food restaurant, you observe a man and woman giving a very young infant tiny pieces of french fries and a baby bottle filled with cola. Any thoughts?

Visit nutrition.jbpub.com

Academy of Nutrition and Dietetics

Nutrition and Lifestyle for a Healthy Pregnancy Outcome

It is the position of the Academy of Nutrition and Dietetics (AND) that women of childbearing age should maintain good nutritional status through a lifestyle that optimizes maternal health and reduces the risk of birth defects, suboptimal fetal development, and chronic health problems in their children. The key components of a health-promoting lifestyle during pregnancy include appropriate weight gain; appropriate physical activity; consumption of a variety of foods in accordance with the *Dietary Guidelines for Americans 2010*; appropriate and timely vitamin and mineral supplementation; avoidance of alcohol, tobacco, and other harmful substances; and safe food handling. Pregnant women with inappropriate weight gain, hyperemesis, poor dietary patterns, phenylketonuria, certain chronic health problems, or a history of substance abuse should be referred to a registered dietitian for medical nutrition therapy.

Source: Position of the American Dietetic Association: nutrition and lifestyle for a healthy pregnancy outcome. *J Am Diet Assoc.* 2008;108(3):553–561. Copyright © 2008. Reprinted with permission from Elsevier.

Imagine waking up tomorrow and finding a newborn baby in the house! Play along for a moment with the idea that it's your baby. Would your current eating habits have been sufficient to support the nutritional demands of pregnancy? If not, what changes should you have made and why? What about other aspects of your lifestyle that might need to be modified before pregnancy, such as smoking, alcohol use, exercise? How would you feed a new baby? Breastfeeding poses its own nutritional demands on the mother but has many benefits for the infant. If you've never shopped for infant formula or baby food before, you may be surprised at the variety of choices and confused as to which is best. So, while the likelihood of waking up tomorrow and finding a newborn in the house is remote, it's never too early to learn about the nutritional implications of pregnancy, breastfeeding, and infant feeding.

Pregnancy

In both mother and fetus, pregnancy is a time of tremendous physiological change that demands healthful dietary and lifestyle choices. Energy and nutrient needs both increase, but the need for calories increases by a smaller percentage than the need for most vitamins and minerals. As a result, food choices during pregnancy must be nutrient-dense.

What about tobacco and alcohol? Research clearly shows that both tobacco and alcohol have damaging effects on a developing fetus, and it's essential to abstain from both during pregnancy. Although research about the effects of caffeine is less conclusive, most health care professionals also recommend limiting caffeine intake during pregnancy.

Nutrition Before Conception

Everyone knows a woman needs to eat well once she becomes pregnant. But her nutritional status at the moment of conception is also important. Vitamin status at conception, for example, can mean the difference between a healthy baby and one with a devastating birth defect. In addition, a woman's weight at conception can influence her pregnancy and delivery and the baby's health.

For these reasons, it's important for a woman to get health care and guidance before she gets pregnant. Many experts recommend extending prenatal care—the routine health care that a woman receives during her pregnancy—to include the preconception period as well. (See **Figure 16.1**.) Although this is certainly a worthy goal, it is important to realize that about half the pregnancies in the United States are unplanned. Hence, good nutrition for all women of childbearing age is an important public health objective.

Preconception care can be defined as a set of interventions that identify and modify biomedical, behavioral, and social risks to a woman's health or pregnancy outcome through prevention and management.[1] The overall goal is to (1) screen for risks, (2) promote health and education, and (3) identify, prevent, and manage risks. Nutrition is an important aspect of all three goals. Risk screening includes an evaluation of a prospective mother's vitamin status and weight, as well as her health habits—including use of alcohol, tobacco, and other substances—and her overall medical condition. Health promotion and education means providing the would-be mother with information about the steps she can take to maximize her chances of a trouble-free pregnancy, an uneventful delivery, and a healthy, full-term baby. Intervention can be as simple as recommending a folic acid supplement or as complex as treating an eating disorder or a substance abuse problem. Before conception, the goal is to resolve the nutrition and health issues that could harm a mother

Figure 16.1 **Preconception care.** Planning and care before pregnancy are recommended for all prospective mothers.

Table 16.1 **Recommendations for Preconception Health**

Individual responsibility Each woman, man, and couple should be encouraged to have a reproductive life plan.

Consumer awareness Increase public awareness of appropriate preconception health behaviors.

Preventive visits Provide risk assessment and health promotion counseling to all women of childbearing age during primary care visits.

Interventions for identified risks Provide interventions to women following risk identification.

Interconception care Use the interconception period for intensive interventions.

Prepregnancy checkups Offer prepregnancy visits as a component of maternity care.

Health insurance coverage Increase coverage to ensure access for low-income women.

Public health programs Integrate preconception health into existing public health programs.

Research Increase the evidence base for methods to improve preconception health.

Monitoring Use public health surveillance mechanisms to monitor the effectiveness of preconception care.

Source: Centers for Disease Control and Prevention. Recommendations to improve preconception health and health care—United States. *MMWR Recomm Rep.* 2006;55(RR-06):1–23. http://www.cdc.gov/mmwr/preview/mmwrhtml/rr5506a1.htm. Accessed 8/21/09.

or her baby. Table 16.1 lists 10 recommendations for preconception health developed by the Centers for Disease Control and Prevention.

Dietary Guidelines for Americans, 2010
Key Recommendations

Balancing Calories to Manage Weight

- Maintain appropriate calorie balance during each stage of life—childhood, adolescence, adulthood, pregnancy and breastfeeding, and older age.

Recommendations for Specific Population Groups

Women capable of becoming pregnant

- Choose foods that supply heme iron, which is more readily absorbed by the body, additional iron sources, and enhancers of iron absorption such as vitamin C–rich foods.
- Consume 400 micrograms (mcg) per day of synthetic folic acid (from fortified foods and/or supplements) in addition to food forms of folate from a varied diet.

Women who are pregnant or breastfeeding

- Consume 8 to 12 ounces of seafood per week from a variety of seafood types.
- Due to their high methyl mercury content, limit white (albacore) tuna to 6 ounces per week and do not eat the following four types of fish: tilefish, shark, swordfish, and king mackerel.
- If pregnant, take an iron supplement, as recommended by an obstetrician or other health care provider.

Weight

Although everyone should be concerned about maintaining a healthful weight, a woman contemplating pregnancy needs to pay careful attention to weight. Maternal obesity can complicate pregnancy and delivery and may compromise a baby's health. Being too thin, meanwhile, carries its own risks.

Body mass index (BMI) is an indicator of a prospective mother's weight status. (See Chapter 9, "Energy Balance, Body Composition, and Weight Management," to review how to calculate BMI.) Lean women with a BMI less than 20 kg/m^2 have increased risks of **preterm delivery**.[2] At the other end of the spectrum, nearly two-thirds of U.S. women of childbearing age are overweight or obese, and one-fifth are obese at the start of pregnancy.[3] Overweight and obese women have increased risks of several problems, including preterm delivery and stillbirth.[4] In addition, obese women are at higher risk for the following:[5]

- High blood pressure
- Gestational diabetes—a form of diabetes that is associated with pregnancy; it often is controlled through diet alone (see Chapter 15, "Diet and Health")
- Preeclampsia—a condition marked by high blood pressure and protein in the urine

preterm delivery A delivery that occurs before the 37th week of gestation.

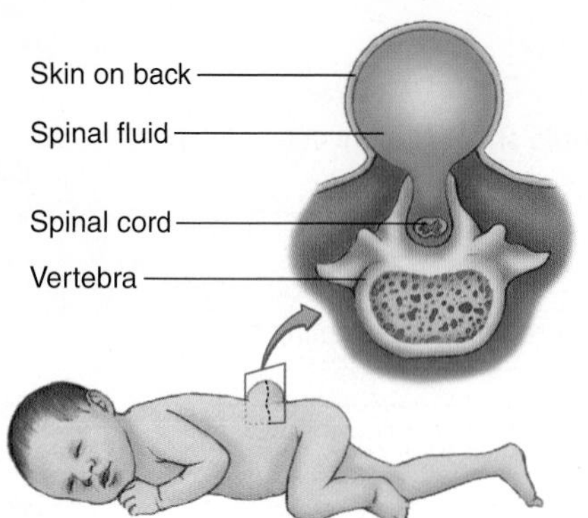

(a)

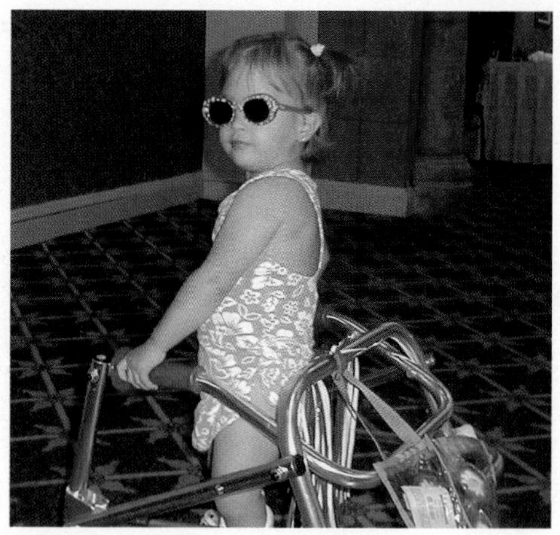

(b)

Figure 16.2 **Spina bifida: a neural tube defect.** Low folate status during the early stages of pregnancy can cause neural tube defects (a). Spina bifida causes varying degrees of limb paralysis. Some children will be able to walk using leg braces or crutches while others will require a wheelchair (b).

- Prolonged labor
- Unplanned cesarean section
- Difficulty initiating and continuing breastfeeding

Of course, the time to lose or gain weight is well before a pregnancy begins. It is not a good idea for pregnant women, even obese pregnant women, to diet. And a thin woman who finds it hard to put on weight under normal circumstances is unlikely to find it any easier when she's pregnant, especially if she experiences **morning sickness**.

Women with eating disorders have special pregnancy-related risks. Ideally, anorexia nervosa or bulimia nervosa is diagnosed and treated well before conception, to give the prospective mother's body plenty of time to recover and prepare for the demands of pregnancy, birth, and breastfeeding. A woman who begins her pregnancy with an active eating disorder may not gain enough weight—or may vomit too much—to sustain a growing fetus. Risks can include premature delivery, a **low-birth-weight infant**, and even fetal death.

morning sickness A persistent or recurring nausea that often occurs in the morning during early pregnancy.

low-birth-weight infant A newborn who weighs less than 2,500 grams (5.5 pounds) as a result of either premature birth or inadequate growth *in utero*.

Vitamins

A good diet goes a long way toward meeting the demands of pregnancy, but even a diet that includes all the food groups may not contain enough of certain nutrients. This is especially true for folic acid, a nutrient needed to prevent neural tube defects, which are birth defects that involve the spinal column.[6] One of the most common neural tube defects is spina bifida, a birth defect in which part of the spinal cord protrudes through the spinal column, causing varying degrees of paralysis and lack of bowel and bladder control. (See **Figure 16.2**.)

The U.S. Public Health Service and the Institute of Medicine of the National Academy of Sciences both recommend that to reduce the risk of having a pregnancy affected with a neural tube defect all women of childbearing age consume 400 micrograms of synthetic folic acid each day from fortified foods or supplements. This recommendation covers all women of childbearing age—not just pregnant women—because neural tube development occurs before the sixth week of fetal life. During this period, a woman may not know she is pregnant or may not have made appropriate dietary changes. This recommended intake of folic acid is in addition to folate (the natural form of the

Table 16.2 **Folate in Grain Products**

Foods	Folate (μg DFE)
Ready-to-eat cereals (25% DV), 1 C	170
Pasta, enriched, cooked, 1 C	140–160
Rice, enriched, cooked, 1 C	170
Tortilla, flour, enriched, 1 (10″ diameter)	140
Bagel, enriched, 2 oz. (3″ diameter)	70
Bread, white, enriched, 1 slice	25–40

Source: Data compiled from Suitor CW, Bailey LB. Dietary folate equivalents: interpretation and application. *J Am Diet Assoc.* 2000;100:88–94.

vitamin) consumed from other foods. Remember that folic acid is added to all enriched grain products and many ready-to-eat cereals. (See Chapter 11, "Water-Soluble Vitamins.") Table 16.2 presents the folate content of selected grain products.

The rate of neural tube defects has been declining in recent years, in part as a result of folic acid fortification. In 2006, spina bifida occurred at a rate of 17.99 cases per 1,000,000 live births in the United States. This rate is significantly less than in 1995, when the rate of spina bifida was 27.98 cases for every 1,000,000 live births.[7]

It is important to get enough folic acid, and it is also crucial to avoid getting too much vitamin A (retinol) during pregnancy. Some vitamin A is good for you; too much may be teratogenic. A teratogen is a substance that causes birth defects—literally, the term means "monster-producing." The Institute of Medicine considered this link between excessive retinol intake and birth defects in setting the Tolerable Upper Intake Level (UL) of retinol for women of childbearing age. The UL is 3,000 micrograms (10,000 IU) of retinol from food and supplements for women over the age of 18. For teens, the UL is 2,800 micrograms (9,300 IU).

Any woman who might become pregnant must avoid using drugs that contain vitamin A or vitamin A analogues; examples are the acne medications isotretinoin (Accutane) and tretinoin (Retin-A). Because these medications are potent teratogens, doctors prescribe such drugs to women of childbearing age only if tests show a woman is not pregnant, and she practices birth control.

Pregnant women can—and should—eat fruits and vegetables rich in beta-carotene and other carotenoids. These foods pose no risk of birth defects and offer many health benefits.

Figure 16.3 **Substance use.** Using tobacco, alcohol, or illicit drugs before and during pregnancy puts the baby at risk. If you use these substances, stop before becoming pregnant.

Substance Use

Many women plan to give up cigarettes, alcohol, or other drugs when they get pregnant. A better plan is to give up these substances well before becoming pregnant. (See **Figure 16.3**.) A woman who uses or abuses tobacco, alcohol, or illicit drugs during pregnancy is likely to have higher pregnancy-related complications and more infant health problems.

Key Concepts *Ideally, the time to prepare nutritionally for pregnancy is well before conception. A woman who has adequate nutrient stores, particularly of folic acid, and is at a healthy weight can reduce the risk for maternal and fetal complications during pregnancy. In addition to healthful diet selections, avoiding cigarettes, alcohol, and other drugs is important when contemplating pregnancy.*

Physiology of Pregnancy

Pregnancy is an awe-inspiring interactive process of growth and development for both mother and fetus. An understanding of the stages of growth and development of the fetus, along with the physiological changes that occur in the mother during pregnancy, will help to explain the nutrient needs of a pregnant woman.

Stages of Human Fetal Growth

How long does pregnancy last? Nine months, right? Well, it depends on when you start counting. When a health care provider gives an expectant mother a due date, it is typically calculated as 40 weeks from the date of the start of her last menstrual period, roughly 10 to 14 days before the actual date of conception. This 40-week period is often divided into three **trimesters** of 13

trimesters Three equal time periods of pregnancy, each lasting approximately 13 to 14 weeks, that do not coincide with specific stages in fetal development.

blastogenic stage The first stage of gestation, during which tissue proliferation by rapid cell division begins.

placenta The organ formed during pregnancy that produces hormones for the maintenance of pregnancy and across which oxygen and nutrients are transferred from mother to infant; it also allows waste materials to be transferred from infant to mother.

embryonic stage The developmental stage between the time of implantation (about two weeks after fertilization) through the seventh or eighth week; the stage of major organ system differentiation and development of main external features.

organogenesis The period when organ systems are developing in a growing fetus.

critical period of development Time during which the environment has the greatest impact on the developing embryo.

fetal stage The period of rapid growth from the end of the embryonic stage until birth.

or 14 weeks each; however, these time divisions do not coincide with specific stages in fetal development.

Figure 16.4 illustrates the early stages of pregnancy. Fertilization of the egg (ovum) sets off the **blastogenic stage**—a period of rapid cell division. As these cells divide, they begin to differentiate. The inner cells in this growing mass will form the fetus; the outer layer of cells will become the **placenta**. During this stage, which lasts about two weeks, the fertilized ovum implants itself in the wall of the mother's uterus.

The next period of pregnancy, the **embryonic stage**, extends from the end of the second week through the eighth week after conception. The placenta, a vital organ that serves as filter and conduit between mother and child, forms on the uterine wall during this stage. Attached to the placenta by the umbilical cord, the embryo now receives its nourishment from its mother; nearly everything the mother eats, drinks, or smokes reaches the embryo.

The embryonic stage also is a period of **organogenesis**. By the time the embryo is eight weeks old, all its main internal organs have formed, along with the major external body structures. (See **Figure 16.5**.) Because nutrient deficiencies or excesses and intake of harmful substances during this time can result in congenital abnormalities (birth defects) or spontaneous abortion (miscarriage), this stage is a **critical period of development**.

The longest period of pregnancy is the **fetal stage**, the period from the end of the embryonic period until the baby is born. During this time, the fetus is growing rapidly, with dramatic changes in body proportions. From the end of

Quick Bite

Would It Be Healthier to Menstruate *Less* Often?

Women in industrialized countries, who start menstruating at an average age of 12.5 years, will go through 350 to 400 menstrual cycles in their lifetimes. In populations where birth control is not used, however, women spend the majority of their fertile years either pregnant or lactating. Menarche in these populations occurs at an average age of 16. In addition, because menstrual cycles do not occur during pregnancy and may not occur during lactation, women in natural-fertility populations, such as the Dogon of West Africa, experience only about 110 menstrual cycles in a lifetime. Women who go through fewer menstrual cycles are exposed to less estrogen and other steroid hormones. Researchers hypothesize that this may partly explain why nonindustrialized societies have lower cancer rates than industrialized societies.

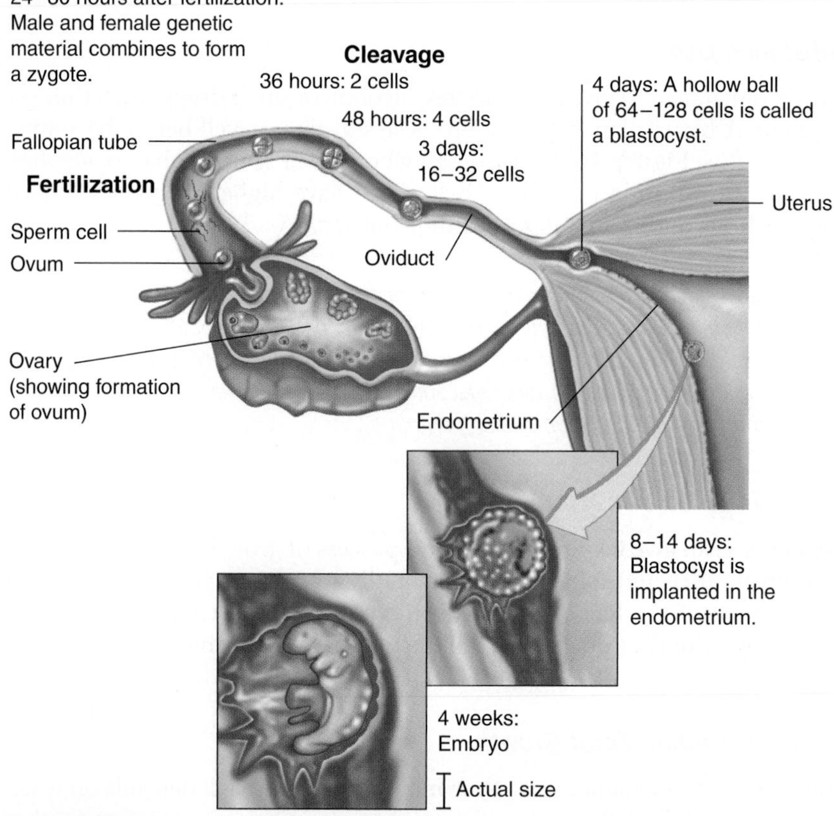

Figure 16.4 **Early stages of pregnancy.** The fertilized egg divides rapidly and begins to differentiate. The inner cells become the fetus, and the outer cells become the placenta.

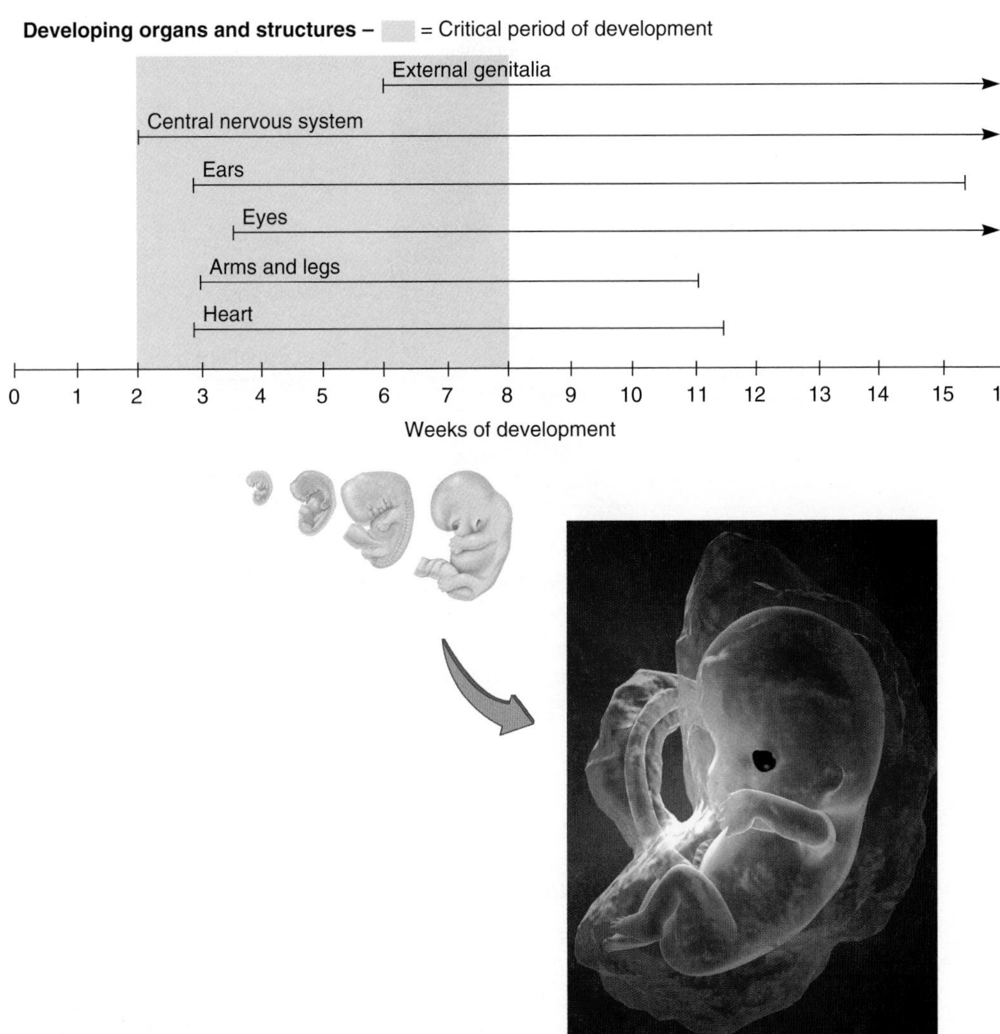

Figure 16.5 **Embryonic development.** During the embryonic stage—week 2 through week 8—all the major organ systems are forming. During this critical period of development, the embryo is highly vulnerable to nutrient deficiencies and toxicities as well as harmful substances, such as tobacco smoke.

the third month of pregnancy until delivery at full term, fetal weight increases nearly 500-fold. The typical newborn is about 20 inches (50 cm) long and weighs approximately 7 pounds 7 ounces (3.4 kg).

Key Concepts *From conception to full-term baby, the process of fetal development is typically divided into three stages. The blastogenic stage involves rapid cell division of the fertilized ovum and its implantation in the uterine wall. Cells differentiate and organ systems and body structures are formed during the embryonic stage. The fetal stage, the longest stage of pregnancy, is marked by growth in size and change in body proportions.*

Maternal Physiological Changes and Nutrition

While the fertilized ovum is developing from a mass of dividing cells to an embryo, and then into a fetus, changes are occurring in the mother's body as well. (See **Figure 16.6**.) These changes occur as the result of various hormones, secreted mainly by the placenta.

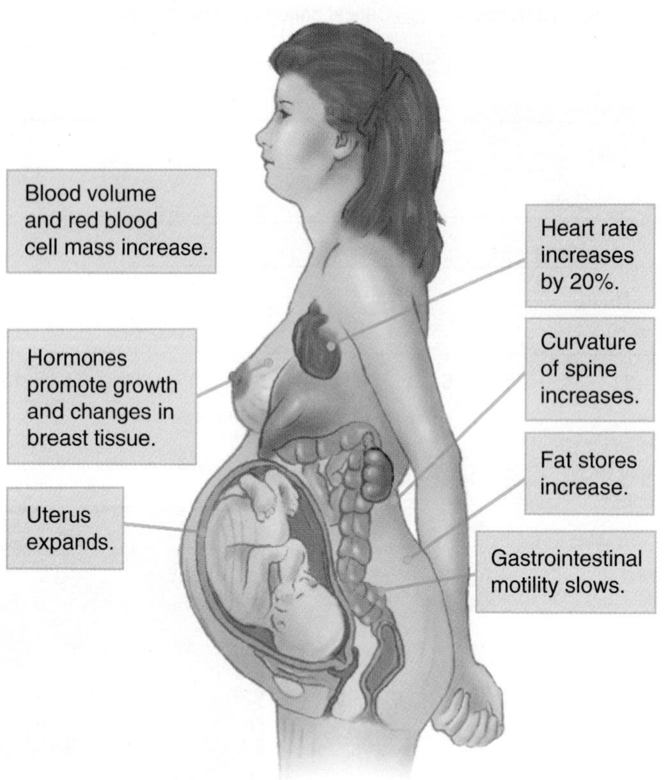
Blood volume and red blood cell mass increase.
Hormones promote growth and changes in breast tissue.
Uterus expands.
Heart rate increases by 20%.
Curvature of spine increases.
Fat stores increase.
Gastrointestinal motility slows.

Figure 16.6 **Maternal changes during pregnancy.** Hormones released throughout pregnancy influence the growth of the baby and alter the way the mother's organs function.

lactation The process of synthesizing and secreting breast milk.

Growth of Maternal Tissue

Maternal tissues, including the breasts, uterus, and adipose stores, increase in size during pregnancy. Hormones promote growth and changes in the breast tissue to prepare for **lactation**. Fat stores increase to provide energy for late pregnancy and for lactation and are a major component of maternal weight gain.

Maternal Blood Volume

During the course of pregnancy, maternal blood volume expands by nearly 50 percent. Production of red blood cells also increases. Iron, folate, and vitamin B_{12} are all key nutrients in red blood cell production. Hemoglobin and hematocrit values during pregnancy are lower than when a woman is not pregnant, but this is more often due to increased plasma volume diluting the blood cells than to nutrient deficiency.

Gastrointestinal Changes

During pregnancy, gastrointestinal motility slows, and food moves more slowly through the intestinal tract. Because nutrients spend more time in the small intestine, their slower transit permits greater nutrient absorption. On the other hand, slower motility can contribute to nausea, heartburn, constipation, and hemorrhoids.

Key Concepts *The mother's body is undergoing various changes during pregnancy, guided by changing levels of hormones. Uterine, breast, and adipose tissues grow; blood volume expands; and gastrointestinal motility slows. All these changes have nutritional and dietary implications for pregnant women.*

Table 16.3 **Guidelines for Weight Gain During Pregnancy**

Prepregnancy BMI (kg/m^2)	Weight Gain*	
	(lb)	*(kg)*
Underweight (<18.5)	28–40	12.5–18
Normal (18.5–24.9)	25–35	11.5–16
Overweight (25.0–29.9)	15–25	7.0–11.5
Obese (>30.0)	11–20	5–9

*Young adolescents should strive for gains at the upper end of the recommended range. Short women (<157 cm or 62 in.) should strive for gains at the lower end of the range.

Source: Rasmussen KM, Yaktine AL, eds. *Weight Gain During Pregnancy: Reexamining the Guidelines.* Washington, DC: Institute of Medicine, National Academies Press, 2009. Adapted from Table S-1, available at http://www.nap.edu/catalog .php?record_id=12584. Copyright © 2009 by the National Academy of Sciences, courtesy of the National Academies Press, Washington, DC. Reprinted with permission.

Maternal Weight Gain

How much weight should a woman gain during pregnancy? Doctors' recommendations have varied over the years from minimal weight gain to unlimited weight gain to recommendations based on prepregnancy BMI, as shown in Table 16.3. New pregnancy weight gain guidelines from the Institute of Medicine and the National Research Council consider that a woman's health and that of her infant are affected by the woman's weight at the start of pregnancy as well as how much she gains throughout the pregnancy.[8]

For underweight women with a BMI of less than 18.5 kg/m^2, the recommended weight gain is 28 to 40 pounds (12.5–18 kg). Normal-weight women with a starting BMI of 18.5 to 24.9 kg/m^2 should gain 25 to 35 pounds (11.5–16 kg). Women beginning pregnancy with an overweight BMI of 25.0 to 29.9 kg/m^2 are recommended to gain 15 to 25 pounds (7–11.5 kg). For the heaviest women—those with BMIs greater than 30.0 kg/m^2 at the start of pregnancy—a weight gain of 11 to 20 pounds (5–9 kg) is recommended.

When maternal weight gain is within these limits, infants are more likely to be born normal weight and at term. These guidelines reflect the greater number of overweight and obese women currently in the United States and advise women to choose a healthy diet and exercise to achieve a normal BMI prior to getting pregnant. Although weight gain varies widely among women who give birth to healthy, full-term infants, pregnancy weight gain guidelines aim to lower risks associated with pregnancy weight change.[9]

Twin births account for one of every 34 live births in the United States. Of course, women who carry two or more fetuses need to gain more weight than women who carry just one. For normal-weight women the recommended weight gain for carrying twins is 37 to 54 pounds (17–25 kg). Overweight women are recommended to gain 31 to 50 pounds (14–23 kg), and obese women should gain 25 to 42 pounds (11–19 kg).[10] There is currently not enough information to establish weight gain guidelines for underweight women with multiple fetuses. However, a higher weight gain is often recommended for women who were underweight prior to pregnancy.

The pattern of weight gain is also important to a healthy pregnancy outcome. During the first trimester, average weight gain is low, less than 5 pounds for most women. Over the second and third trimesters, the suggested weight gain for normal-weight women is a little less than 1 pound per week

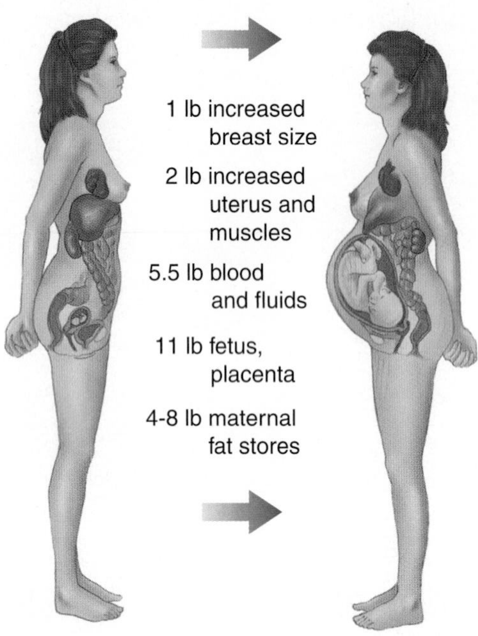

Figure 16.7 Components of maternal weight gain. During the first trimester, most women gain less than 5 pounds. Over the second and third trimesters, the suggested weight gain is a little less than 1 pound per week.

amniotic fluid The fluid that surrounds the fetus; contained in the amniotic sac inside the uterus.

(0.4 kg per week), with more gain suggested for underweight women and those carrying twins and a lower gain for women who are overweight and obese.[11] Monitoring the amount and rate of weight gain is an important component of prenatal care.

The weight gained during pregnancy is divided between (1) the fetus and associated tissues and fluids and (2) maternal tissue growth. In a typical final weight gain of 27.5 pounds (12.5 kg), the fetus, placenta, and **amniotic fluid** account for nearly 40 percent of that weight. Maternal tissues (i.e., adipose stores, breast and uterine growth, and expanded blood and extracellular fluid volumes) account for the remaining 60 percent. (See **Figure 16.7**.)

Key Concepts *Weight gained during pregnancy is a combination of increased weight in fetal and maternal tissues and fluids. Weight gain recommendations are based on BMI prior to pregnancy. Women of normal weight (BMI = 18.5–24.9 kg/m²) should gain 25 to 35 pounds over the course of pregnancy. Most of this weight gain occurs during the second and third trimesters.*

Energy and Nutrition During Pregnancy

A pregnant woman requires added calories to grow and maintain not just her developing fetus, but also its support system: placenta, increased breast tissue, and fat stores. Growth and development of the fetus also require protein, vitamins, and minerals.

Energy

Resting energy expenditure (REE) increases during pregnancy because of the energy requirements of the fetus and placenta and the increased workload on the heart and lungs.[12] Energy is also needed to support weight gain, primarily in the second and third trimesters. Using median energy expenditure as a guide, pregnant women need approximately 340 extra kilocalories per day during the second trimester and an extra 450 kilocalories per day during the third trimester.[13] Because actual energy expenditure varies widely, weight gain during pregnancy is probably the best indicator of adequate calorie intake.[14]

Nutrients to Support Pregnancy

Most healthy women who eat a well-balanced diet have no trouble meeting the majority of their nutrient requirements during pregnancy without vitamin and mineral supplements. However, despite even the best effort, many women have difficulty meeting increased recommendations during pregnancy for numerous nutrients, most often iron and folic acid. As a preventive measure, it is therefore recommended that all women planning to become pregnant take a multivitamin/mineral supplement containing folic acid.[15] (See the Nutrition Science in Action feature "Eating for Two.")

Essential nutrients can be divided into two broad categories: macronutrients (proteins, fats, and carbohydrates) and micronutrients (vitamins and minerals). Table 16.4 shows the nutrient recommendations for pregnant women compared with nonpregnant women. The USDA offers an interactive Web site that uses the MyPlate nutritional guidance system to help pregnant and nursing mothers meet their individual and unique nutritional requirements. At the time of this publication, The Pregnancy and Breastfeeding, Preschoolers, Kids, and Weight Loss sections of the Web site had not yet been updated to reflect the *2010 Dietary Guidelines for Americans*.[16]

Nutrition Science *in Action*

Eating for Two

Background: Most studies that have shown less than adequate dietary intakes for vitamins and minerals (especially iron) have focused on low-income (high-risk) pregnant women. Few studies have examined a low-risk population that would be more likely to consume an adequate diet before and during pregnancy. Estimated Average Requirement (EAR) values are the most appropriate comparison standards for assessing the nutrient intakes of groups.

Hypothesis: Diet records will show that study participants will fail to consume adequate amounts of iron from food to meet the EAR for iron during pregnancy.

Experimental Plan: Recruit healthy women in their first trimester, who have household incomes in the middle to upper range. Have subjects complete three-day diet records every month of their pregnancy. Analyze data and compare iron intakes to EAR values.

Results: The hypothesis is confirmed. The median iron intake of the 63 women who participated in the study was significantly less than the EAR.

Conclusion and Discussion: Pregnant women do not obtain adequate iron from diet alone, and the results of this study support the current recommendations for iron supplementation during pregnancy. For other nutrients, the mother's diet quality should be evaluated before recommending nutrient supplements. Most pregnant women probably need folic acid supplements to meet the increased requirements of pregnancy. Future studies might test the effects of peer support on healthful diet selection in pregnant women.

Source: Based on Turner RE, Langkamp-Henken B, Littell RC, et al. Comparing nutrient intake from food to the estimated average requirements shows middle- to upper-income pregnant women lack iron and possibly magnesium. *J Am Diet Assoc.* 2003;103(4):461–466.

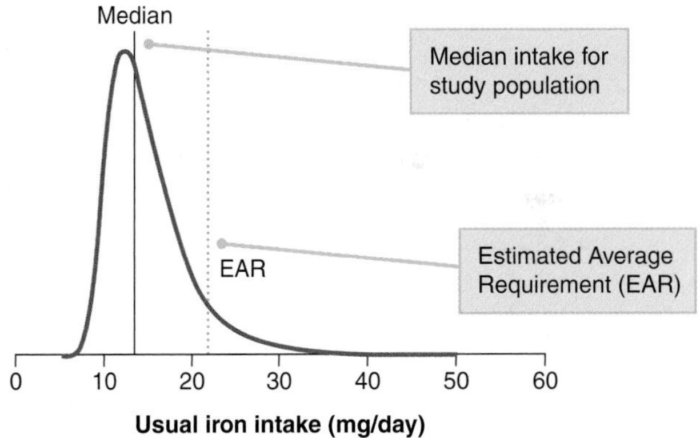

Table 16.4 **Nutritional Recommendations for Pregnancy**

	Nonpregnant	Pregnant	% Increase
Energy (kcal)	2,400	2,740/2,852	14–18
Protein (g)	46	71	54
Vitamin A (μg RAE)	700	770	10
Vitamin D (μg)	5	5	0
Vitamin E (mg)	15	15	0
Vitamin K (μg)	90	90	0
Thiamin (mg)	1.1	1.4	27
Riboflavin (mg)	1.1	1.4	27
Niacin (mg)	14	18	29
Vitamin B_6 (mg)	1.3	1.9	46
Folate (μg)	400	600	50
Vitamin B_{12} (μg)	2.4	2.6	8
Pantothenic acid (mg)	5	6	20
Biotin (μg)	30	30	0
Choline (mg)	425	450	6
Vitamin C (mg)	75	85	13
Calcium (mg)	1,000	1,000	0
Phosphorus (mg)	700	700	0
Magnesium (mg)	310	350	13
Iron (mg)	18	27	50
Zinc (mg)	8	11	38
Selenium (μg)	55	60	9
Iodine (μg)	150	220	47
Fluoride (mg)	3	3	0
Copper (μg)	900	1,000	11
Chromium (μg)	25	30	20
Manganese (mg)	1.8	2	11
Molybdenum (μg)	45	50	11
Sodium (mg)	1,500	1,500	0
Chloride (mg)	2,300	2,300	0
Potassium (mg)	4,700	4,700	0
Water (mL)	2,700	3,000	11

Needs for most nutrients increase during pregnancy. Generally, vitamin and mineral needs increase more than energy needs, which means that food choices should be nutrient-dense. Values for energy are based on Estimated Energy Requirements (EER) for a reference 19-year-old active woman. The first number for pregnancy represents the second trimester; the other number is for the third trimester. Values for protein, vitamins, minerals, and water are RDAs or AIs for ages 19 to 30.

Macronutrients

Macronutrients supply energy and provide the building blocks for protein synthesis. The recommended balance of energy sources does not change during pregnancy. A low-fat, moderate-protein, high-carbohydrate diet is still appropriate.

Protein Extra protein is needed during pregnancy for synthesizing new maternal, placental, and fetal tissues. A pregnant woman's RDA for protein is 1.1

grams per kilogram per day (an additional 25 grams per day over nonpregnant needs). This amount of protein is easily supplied in typical American diets consumed by nonpregnant women. Thus, many women need not increase their protein intake to reach the levels recommended for pregnancy. Pregnant women who are vegetarians, including vegans, also should be able to meet their protein needs from food sources alone—as long as they select a variety of protein sources and consume enough total calories. (See the FYI feature "Vegetarianism and Pregnancy.")

Fats Dietary fats provide vital fuel for the mother and for the development of placental tissues. Needs for essential fatty acids during pregnancy are slightly higher than those of nonpregnant women.[17] The pregnant woman's body also stores fats to support breastfeeding after childbirth. Very low fat diets (in which less than 10 percent of daily calories comes from dietary fats) are not recommended for pregnancy. Such diets are unlikely to supply sufficient amounts of essential fatty acids, fat-soluble vitamins, or calories.

Vegetarianism and Pregnancy

Can pregnant women meet all of their nutritional needs on a vegetarian diet? A fair question. Common vegetarian practices include the avoidance of meat, poultry, and fish (lacto-ovo-vegetarian and lactovegetarian) and the avoidance of all animal foods (vegan). These foods are important sources of iron, zinc, calcium, vitamin B_{12}, and other nutrients. Although vegetarian diets can provide reasonable quantities of trace elements, animal-derived foods frequently contribute larger amounts that the body absorbs more easily. To meet the demands of pregnancy, supplementation may be in order.

Supplemental iron is generally recommended for all pregnant women. Supplemental vitamin B_{12} (2.0 micrograms per day) is also recommended for vegan mothers. If their sun exposure is limited, they also may need daily supplementation of 10 micrograms of vitamin D.[1] Vegetarians with low calcium intake (<600 milligrams per day) should consume a supplement that provides at least 500 milligrams per day. Some vegan foods, such as fortified soy milks, may contain these important nutrients. It is important to check the label to be sure.

The overall nutrient content of a vegetarian diet depends on both the energy content and the variety of the foods consumed. The suggested dietary patterns in **Table 1** will meet the average energy levels recommended for pregnant women.

1 Institute of Medicine. *Dietary Reference Intakes for Calcium, Phosphorus, Magnesium, Vitamin D, and Fluoride*. Washington, DC: National Academies Press, 1997.

Table 1 Suggested Servings for Pregnant Vegans

Food Group	2,200 kcal	2,800 kcal
Bread, grains, cereals (50% whole-grain products)	10	12
Legumes, plant proteins	2	3
Vegetables	3	4
Dark-green leafy vegetables	2	2
Fruits	4	6
Nuts, seeds	1	1
Fortified soy drinks* and tofu	3	3
Added fats and oils	4	6
Approximate Composition		
Protein (g)	76	95
% kcal as fat	24	25
% kcal as carbohydrate	62	61

*Milk alternatives fortified with calcium, vitamin D, and vitamin B_{12}.

Source: Adapted from Haddad EH. Development of a vegetarian food guide. *Am J Clin Nutr.* 1994;59(suppl):1248S–1254S.

Carbohydrates Carbohydrates provide the main source of extra calories during pregnancy. Food choices should emphasize complex carbohydrates such as whole-grain breads, fortified cereals, rice, and pasta. In addition to supplying vitamins and minerals, these foods can increase fiber intake substantially. A fiber-rich diet is recommended during pregnancy to help prevent constipation and hemorrhoids. The AI for fiber increases from 25 to 28 grams per day during pregnancy.

Key Concepts *Most healthy women with well-balanced diets meet the majority of their nutrient requirements during pregnancy. The actual increase in energy needs varies substantially among women. The adequacy of energy intake can be measured by the amount of weight gained. Weight loss is not advised during pregnancy, even for obese women. As long as energy intake is adequate and a variety of foods are eaten, protein intake should be more than adequate to support prenatal growth and development.*

Micronutrients

A pregnant woman has an increased need for many vitamins and minerals that support fetal growth and development. In addition, her increased energy needs mean she requires higher amounts of nutrients such as the B vitamins thiamin, riboflavin, niacin, and pantothenic acid that are essential for energy metabolism.

Needs for the other B vitamins (except biotin) also increase. Folate and vitamin B_{12} are used to synthesize DNA and red blood cells, and vitamin B_6 is crucial for metabolizing amino acids. Of these vitamins, folate needs increase the most, from 400 micrograms per day to 600 micrograms per day during pregnancy. Vitamin C needs increase slightly during pregnancy, from 75 to 85 milligrams per day for women aged 19 to 50 years. For the fat-soluble vitamins, the RDA for vitamin A increases slightly during pregnancy, whereas recommended intake levels for vitamins D, E, and K are unchanged.

For most minerals, recommended intakes are higher during pregnancy—most dramatically for iron. The RDA for iron increases from 18 milligrams per day to 27 milligrams per day. Iron is necessary to make red blood cells and is important for normal growth and energy metabolism. Iron deficiency and its associated anemia is the most common nutrient deficiency in pregnancy. Table 16.5 lists the characteristics of women who are at particularly high risk for iron deficiency.

Because getting 27 milligrams of iron in the daily diet is not easy, experts recommend iron supplementation for the general population of pregnant women.[18] A woman can maximize absorption of an iron supplement by eating it on an empty stomach (between meals or at bedtime) and washing it down with liquids other than milk, tea, or coffee, which inhibit absorption.

Table 16.5 **Factors Associated with Increased Risk for Iron Deficiency During Pregnancy**

Young age (e.g., 15 to 19 years)
Multiple sequential pregnancies
Twin or triplet pregnancy
Diets low in meat
Diets high in coffee and tea
Low socioeconomic status
Low level of education
Black or Hispanic ethnicity
Previous diagnosis of iron deficiency or iron-deficiency anemia

Key Concepts *Needs for vitamins and minerals increase during pregnancy, some more than others. Extra vitamins and minerals are needed to support growth and development as well as increased energy use. Recommended intake levels increase most dramatically for folate and iron.*

Food Choices for Pregnant Women

You may be surprised to learn that the recommended diet for a pregnant woman is not much different from that for adults in the general population. Variety is the key to a well-balanced diet. The extra calories needed for pregnancy are easy to obtain from an additional serving from each of the following food groups: grains, vegetables, fruits, and low-fat milk. Because the increased need for energy is proportionately less than the increased need for most nutrients, nutrient-dense foods are important. There is little room in the diet plan for high-calorie, high-fat, low-nutrient "extras." In a study that assessed dietary intake of pregnant and nonpregnant women using the Healthy Eating Index (HEI), pregnant women generally consumed more servings of fruit and dairy products.[19] However, about 40 percent of the pregnant women did not meet the minimum recommended number of servings from all food groups.

Supplementation

Other than iron and folate, a pregnant woman can usually get all the nutrients she needs by making healthful choices, guided by the food intake patterns of MyPlate. Health care providers often evaluate the dietary intake of all prenatal patients and recommend dietary changes to improve nutrition where needed. However, to reduce preventable complications of nutrient deficiencies, pregnant women in the United States and Canada routinely receive prescriptions for prenatal vitamin/mineral supplements. The amount and balance of nutrients in prenatal formulations is appropriate for pregnancy. Because toxic levels can be reached quickly, especially for vitamins A and D, pregnant women should avoid high doses and multiple supplements. In addition, because most herbal preparations have not been evaluated for safety during pregnancy, they are not recommended.

Foods to Avoid

Alcohol is off limits to pregnant women. If a mother-to-be is experiencing problems with nausea and vomiting, she may want to abstain for a while from foods that aggravate these symptoms. Cultural traditions may dictate changes in diet during pregnancy, but these tend to reflect traditional beliefs and practices rather than health science.

The Food and Drug Administration (FDA) and the Environmental Protection Agency (EPA) advise women who may become pregnant, pregnant women, lactating mothers, and young children to avoid certain types of fish that are likely to contain significant amounts of mercury, enough to potentially harm a fetus or young child. The FDA and EPA recommend that women and young children

- Avoid eating shark, swordfish, king mackerel, or tilefish, because they contain high levels of mercury.
- Eat up to 12 ounces a week of a variety of fish and shellfish that are lower in mercury, such as shrimp, canned light tuna, salmon, pollock, and catfish.
- Check local advisories about the safety of fish caught by family and friends in local lakes, rivers, and coastal areas.[20]

The question of whether to reduce or eliminate caffeine intake during pregnancy continues to be debated. High caffeine intake has been linked to delayed conception, spontaneous miscarriage, and low birth weight.[21] The Academy of Nutrition and Dietetics recommends that pregnant women consume less than 300 milligrams of caffeine per day.[22] Table 16.6 shows the caffeine content of common beverages and foods.

Key Concepts *With the exception of iron and folate, a well-balanced, varied diet can often meet all of a pregnant woman's nutrient needs. Pregnant women should choose nutrient-dense and high-carbohydrate foods in the proportions found in MyPlate. Although vitamin/mineral supplementation is common during pregnancy, it probably is not needed other than for iron and folate. When supplements are used, they should be*

Table 16.6 Caffeine Content of Common Beverages and Foods

Food	Serving Size	Caffeine (mg)
Coffee, regular, brewed	8 fl. oz.	130
Coffee, Starbucks, brewed	8 fl. oz.	160
Espresso, regular	1 fl. oz.	40
Espresso, Starbucks	1 fl. oz.	75
Frappuccino beverage, Starbucks	9.5 fl. oz.	115
Tea, regular, brewed	8 fl. oz.	50
Tea, fruited, Snapple	8 fl. oz.	20
Tea, latte, Starbucks Tazo Chai	8 fl. oz.	50
Vault	12 fl. oz.	70
Mountain Dew	12 fl. oz.	55
Coca-Cola/Pepsi, regular, flavored, diet	12 fl. oz.	35–45
Sprite/7-Up	12 fl. oz.	0
Red Bull	8.3 fl. oz.	80
Ice cream, coffee	8 fl. oz.	50–80
Milk Chocolate, Hershey's	1.55 oz.	10
Dark Chocolate, Hershey's	1.45 oz.	20

Source: Adapted from Center for Science in the Public Interest. Caffeine content of food and drugs. http://www.cspinet.org/new/cafchart.htm. Accessed 8/21/09.

Figure 16.8 **Fetal alcohol syndrome.** The facial characteristics of a person with fetal alcohol syndrome include a short nose with a flattened bridge, eyelids with extra folds, and a thin upper lip with no groove below the nose.

designed for pregnant women. Pregnant women should avoid alcohol and moderate their intake of caffeine.

Substance Use and Pregnancy Outcome

What a pregnant woman eats, she eats for two. When she smokes, drinks, or uses drugs, she does so for two as well. The consequences of these behaviors may be felt for generations.

Tobacco and Alcohol

Smoking during pregnancy increases the risks of miscarrying, delivering a stillborn infant, giving birth prematurely, and delivering a low-birth-weight baby.[23] Women in lower socioeconomic groups have the highest rates of cigarette use before, during, and after pregnancy. Women in the highest socioeconomic groups, meanwhile, are the most likely to quit smoking during pregnancy, but are just as likely as other women to take up the habit again after giving birth.

Fetal alcohol syndrome (FAS) describes a consistent pattern of physical, cognitive, and behavioral problems in infants born to women who use alcohol heavily during pregnancy. Children severely afflicted by the syndrome show marked growth deficiencies before and after birth; physical anomalies such as a small head, certain characteristic facial deformities (see **Figure 16.8**), heart defects, and joint and limb irregularities; mental retardation; and central nervous system disorders. The greater a mother's alcohol use during pregnancy, the more severe the symptoms of FAS tend to be in the child. There is no known safe threshold for alcohol use in pregnancy. The only way to avoid alcohol-related risks to a fetus is to avoid all alcohol during pregnancy.

Drugs

Nearly 4 percent of pregnant women use illicit drugs such as marijuana, cocaine, and heroin.[24] Drug use is higher among younger women and African American women.

Marijuana use increases the risk for premature delivery and low birth weight. In addition, maternal marijuana use may result in some of the same physical abnormalities seen in infants with FAS. Effects on the fetus vary depending on the mother's diet, frequency of marijuana use, and the use of other drugs. Marijuana use also reduces fertility in both women and men.

Cocaine use increases risks of stroke, prematurity, fetal growth retardation, miscarriage, and certain birth defects. Some of these problems may stem from nutritional deficiencies in the mother both before and during pregnancy, as well as from concurrent tobacco and alcohol use, which is common among cocaine users. **Figure 16.9** illustrates the possible effects of a woman's use of drugs, alcohol, or tobacco while she is pregnant.

Key Concepts *Smoking, alcohol, and illicit drug use during pregnancy can all have devastating effects on fetal development. Low birth weight, preterm delivery, and birth defects are some of the consequences. Fetal alcohol syndrome is a specific set of physical, mental, and behavioral defects caused by maternal alcohol consumption during pregnancy. A pregnant woman should avoid all these substances.*

Special Situations During Pregnancy

Some women progress through pregnancy with no more than a mild period of morning sickness or problems with constipation or heartburn. However, even

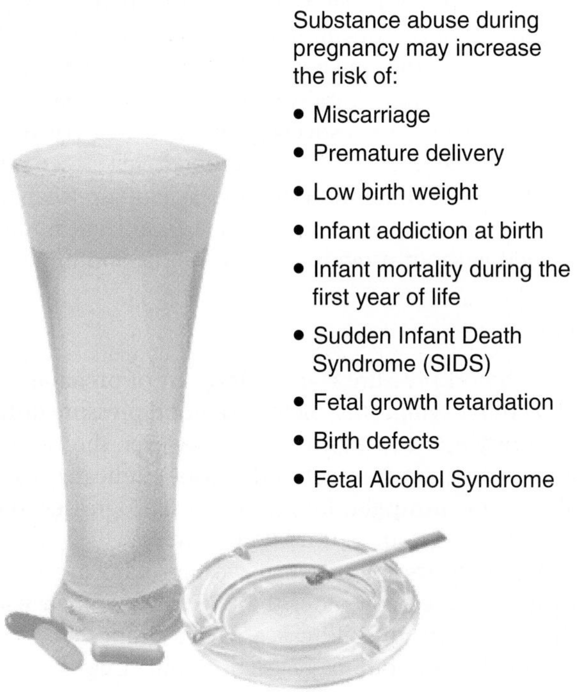

Substance abuse during pregnancy may increase the risk of:
• Miscarriage
• Premature delivery
• Low birth weight
• Infant addiction at birth
• Infant mortality during the first year of life
• Sudden Infant Death Syndrome (SIDS)
• Fetal growth retardation
• Birth defects
• Fetal Alcohol Syndrome

Figure 16.9 **Substance use can lead to birth defects.** When a pregnant woman smokes, drinks, or uses drugs, so does her growing baby. The consequences of these behaviors may be felt for generations.

these conditions, as well as complications such as abnormal glucose tolerance or elevated blood pressure, may affect dietary choices and nutritional status. In addition, some women have unique nutritional needs during pregnancy.

Gastrointestinal Distress

Morning sickness, or nausea associated with pregnancy, is most common early in pregnancy as the mother's body adjusts to changes in hormone levels. Many pregnant women find they experience less morning sickness if they eat dry cereal, toast, or crackers about half an hour before getting out of bed. (See **Figure 16.10**.) Keeping some food in the stomach throughout the day helps, too. This means eating smaller, more frequent meals, and drinking liquids between meals instead of with food. Avoiding food aromas that trigger nausea is another useful tactic.

Heartburn and constipation are the result of slowed GI movement. Remaining upright for at least an hour after eating and having smaller, more frequent meals may prevent heartburn. Getting plenty of fiber and fluids in the diet and getting regular mild to moderate exercise can limit constipation. Of course, a pregnant woman should always consult her health care provider before using a prescription drug, over-the-counter medicine, herbal supplement, or home remedy for nausea, vomiting, heartburn, or constipation.

Food Cravings and Aversions

Many pregnant women experience specific food cravings and/or aversions, and we often laugh at stories about unusual combinations such as pickles and ice cream. These changes in food preferences may be linked to taste and metabolic changes, but they rarely are based on a nutrient deficiency or other physiological conditions. Most cravings and aversions do not affect the quality of the diet unless food choices become very narrow.

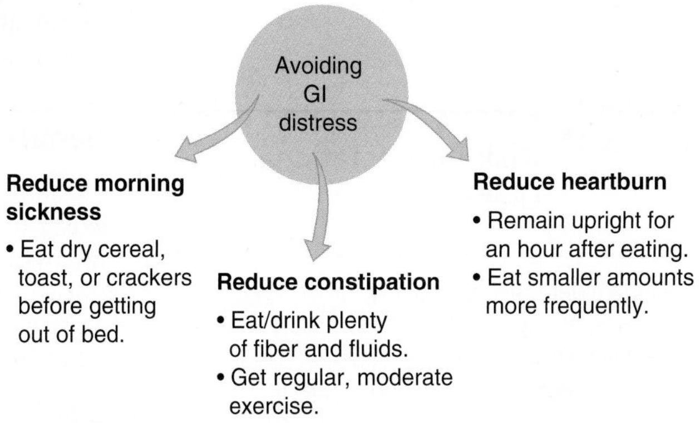

Figure 16.10 **Strategies for avoiding GI distress.** During pregnancy, most women experience GI distress as morning sickness, constipation, or heartburn.

preeclampsia A condition of late pregnancy characterized by hypertension, edema, and proteinuria.

eclampsia The occurrence of seizures in a pregnant woman that are unrelated to brain conditions.

Some pregnant women crave nonfood items such as starch or clay. The term *pica* describes routine consumption of nonfood items such as dirt, clay, laundry starch, ice, or burnt matches. Although this behavior may seem outlandish, in many cases it is a culturally accepted practice that affects significant numbers of pregnant women, especially in rural areas of the southeastern United States.[25] Pica can be harmful if nonfood items crowd nutritious foods out of the diet. In addition, nonfood items may contain toxins, bacteria, and parasites; and in the case of laundry starch, a significant number of calories may be consumed without providing any vitamins and minerals.

Hypertension

Measurement of blood pressure is a routine part of prenatal care. When not accompanied by other symptoms, increased blood pressure during pregnancy is usually temporary and carries little risk. However, the combination of hypertension and proteinuria (protein in the urine) indicates a serious medical condition called **preeclampsia**. If preeclampsia progresses to **eclampsia**, it can threaten the lives of both mother and baby.

Preeclampsia is more common in women who are pregnant for the first time, adolescents, women older than 35, and women with preexisting diabetes or hypertension. In mild cases, bed rest and close monitoring are the treatments of choice. Sodium restriction and drug therapy are not recommended. Severe cases may require more aggressive treatment. Calcium supplementation may be useful for prevention for women with low calcium intake; however, conclusive links between nutrient intake and development or prevention of preeclampsia have not been found.[26] Early identification of preeclampsia through routine prenatal care is important for good maternal and fetal outcomes.

Diabetes

A woman with diabetes faces special challenges in pregnancy. She has an increased risk of developing preeclampsia and a greater-than-average chance of problems that affect the fetus, including fetal death. However, with early prenatal intervention and careful control of blood glucose levels, these risks can be reduced to the same level as in nondiabetic pregnancies.[27]

Pregnancy may require frequent adjustments of both diet and insulin to keep blood glucose in check. Insulin requirements often decrease during the first half of pregnancy, but increase during the second half. Women who did not need insulin before they became pregnant and were able to control their blood glucose through diet alone may begin to need insulin during their pregnancy.

Table 16.7 Factors Associated with Risk for Gestational Diabetes

Being older than 25 years
Obesity, at any age
Family history of diabetes mellitus
Previous poor pregnancy outcome
History of abnormal glucose tolerance
Ethnicity associated with high incidence of diabetes

Gestational Diabetes

Gestational diabetes is a condition in which abnormal glucose tolerance exists only during pregnancy and resolves after delivery. The hormones of pregnancy tend to counteract insulin, and in about 4 percent of pregnancies, this results in a rise in blood glucose. Table 16.7 lists factors associated with an increased risk of gestational diabetes. Gestational diabetes often can be controlled through diet, although some cases require insulin therapy.

HIV/AIDS

Women infected with the human immunodeficiency virus (HIV) can potentially pass the virus to their children during pregnancy, delivery, or breastfeeding.

Medical treatments used routinely in the United States and other developed countries reduce the risk of transmission during pregnancy and delivery to less than 2 percent.[28] In developing countries, where treatments are not available, women with HIV or AIDS are likely to have multiple nutrition problems, including protein-energy malnutrition, vitamin and mineral deficiencies, and inadequate weight gain, all of which pose risks to the fetus.

Adolescence

Despite prevention efforts, adolescent pregnancy rates in the United States are among the highest in the developed world, the majority of which are unintended.[29] In 2007, teenage birthrates rose again for the second year in a row.[30] Pregnant adolescents are nutritionally at risk. Their own needs for growth and development are compromised by the extra demands posed by the growth and development of the fetus. Risks for preeclampsia, anemia, premature birth, low-birth-weight babies, infant mortality, and sexually transmitted diseases are all increased for pregnant adolescents under the age of 16.[31]

Even before becoming pregnant, many teenagers do not demonstrate healthful eating patterns. Their diets are likely to be inadequate in total calories, calcium, iron, zinc, riboflavin, folic acid, and vitamins A, D, and B_6. Poverty, smoking, and abuse of alcohol and other substances compound the negative effects of adolescent nutritional inadequacies.

Nutrition care for pregnant teens starts with determining daily energy needs. The Institute of Medicine recommends that pregnant adolescents be encouraged to strive for weight gains toward the upper end of the range recommended for adult mothers (see Table 16.3). The need for supplemental vitamins and minerals is also greater in this age group.

Key Concepts *Numerous factors affect the dietary needs and choices of pregnant women. Routine prenatal care is important to identify unhealthful eating behaviors and potential complications such as preeclampsia and gestational diabetes. Pregnant women with diabetes or HIV/AIDS need special dietary intervention. Pregnant teens have especially high nutrient needs to support not only fetal growth but also their own adolescent growth.*

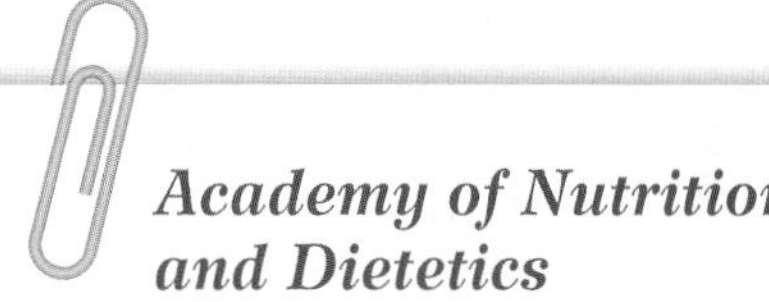

Academy of Nutrition and Dietetics

Promoting and Supporting Breastfeeding

It is the position of the Academy of Nutrition and Dietetics (AND) that exclusive breastfeeding provides optimal nutrition and health protection for the first 6 months of life, and breastfeeding with complementary foods for at least 12 months is the ideal feeding pattern for infants. Breastfeeding is also a public health strategy for improving infant and child health survival, improving maternal morbidity, controlling health care costs, and conserving natural resources.

Position of the American Dietetic Association: promoting and supporting breastfeeding. *J Am Diet Assoc.* 2005;105(5):810–818. Copyright © 2005. Reprinted with permission from Elsevier.

Lactation

During pregnancy, physiological changes in breast tissue and fat stores prepare the woman's body for the demands of lactation. Preparation for lactation also involves education. Although breastfeeding is a natural function of a woman's body, knowledge about lactation can make breastfeeding a success for both mother and infant.

Breastfeeding Trends

Public health goals since the late 1970s have sought to increase the percentage of infants who are breastfed. The goal of Healthy People 2010 is to increase the proportion of newborns who are initially breastfed to at least 75 percent. Efforts to promote breastfeeding have been successful; as of 2008, 62 percent of infants were breastfed initially,[32] up from a low of around 20 percent in the early 1970s.[33]

Less than 27 percent of infants are still being breastfed at 6 months of age,[34] a rate lower than the Healthy People 2010 goal of 50 percent. What are the reasons for this trend? Lack of knowledge about the benefits of breastfeeding for both mother and baby surely plays a role. Societal attitudes regarding the acceptability of breastfeeding also are influential and vary across cultural and demographic groups. Some states have actually had to pass laws stating that breastfeeding in public is not indecent exposure. In addition, the decline in breastfeeding through the 1950s and 1960s affected the attitudes and knowledge base of today's grandmothers.

Parents should make decisions about feeding their infants based on accurate information, so providing information about the mechanics of breastfeeding as well as the benefits for both mother and baby should be an integral part of prenatal care.

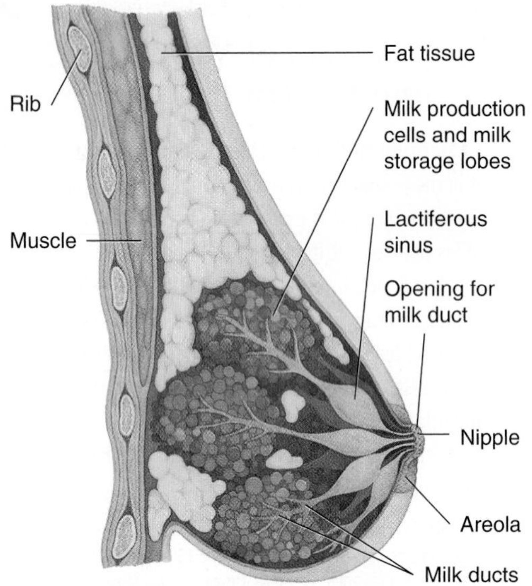

Figure 16.11 **Anatomy of the breast.** During pregnancy, breasts increase in size and undergo internal development. By the start of the third trimester, breasts are capable of producing milk.

colostrum A thick yellow fluid secreted by the breast during pregnancy and the first days after delivery.

prolactin A pituitary hormone that stimulates the production of milk in the breast tissue.

oxytocin A pituitary hormone that stimulates the release of milk from the breast.

Physiology of Lactation

Virtually every woman who wants to breastfeed her newborn can do so. The size or shape of the breast has no impact on the lactation process. **Figure 16.11** shows the anatomy of a normal breast.

Changes During Adolescence and Pregnancy

Although mammary tissue is present in newborns, that tissue does not grow and develop until the onset of puberty. Throughout adolescence, the amount of breast tissue grows and the mammary glands and ducts develop. An adolescent who becomes pregnant shortly after her first period or who has had only irregular periods prior to becoming pregnant may have underdeveloped mammary glands and insufficient breast tissue to support lactation. However, most teen mothers have no difficulty breastfeeding their babies.

During pregnancy, breast tissue changes so that milk production is possible. Not only does the breast change in size, but the structure of the glands and ducts also becomes more intricate, and secretory cells form. Mammary tissue is mature and capable of producing milk by the start of the third trimester.

After Delivery

Although birth triggers a rapid increase in a mother's milk production and secretion, full lactation does not begin as soon as the baby is born. An efficient way to establish lactation is to put the newborn to the breast as soon after delivery as possible. During the first two or three days after birth, a nursing infant receives **colostrum**, an immature milk that is quite high in protein and immunoglobulins (immunoprotective factors). If the newborn is fed regularly at the breast, lactation will be firmly established within two or three weeks after birth, and mature milk will be produced.

Hormonal Controls

Several hormones control the maturation of breast tissue and the production and release of breast milk. (See **Figure 16.12**.) During lactation, the pituitary gland produces two important hormones—**prolactin** and **oxytocin**. The infant suckling at the breast stimulates the release of prolactin from the pituitary gland. In turn, prolactin stimulates the production of milk in the breast tissue. Giving water or infant formula to the baby reduces the time spent nursing at the breast, and milk production declines.

The second hormone, oxytocin, allows milk to be released from the mammary glands to the nipple and therefore to the hungry infant. It would be inconvenient and messy if milk were released from the breast as soon as it was produced! So, the infant suckling at the breast signals the pituitary gland to release oxytocin, which in turn stimulates the release of milk. This process,

Quick Bite

Breastfeeding and Birth Control

Does breastfeeding prevent pregnancy? No. But under certain conditions, breastfeeding can dramatically reduce the chances of becoming pregnant. During the first six months after giving birth, a woman who has not yet had a period and fully breastfeeds her baby (no other liquids or solids) has less than a 2 percent chance of pregnancy. Still, it's important to use a reliable method of birth control while breastfeeding.

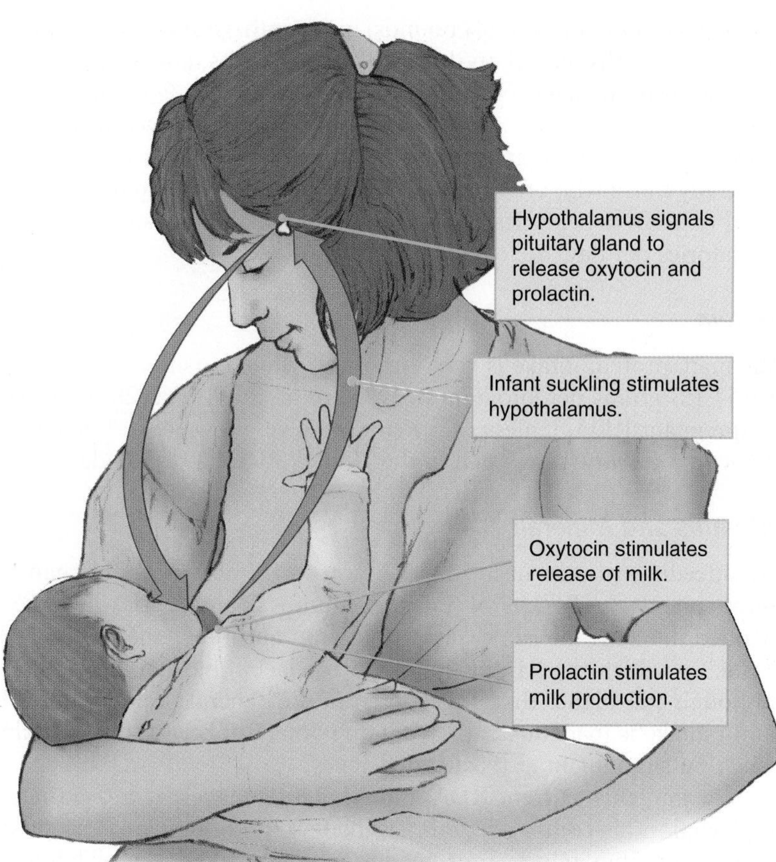
Hypothalamus signals pituitary gland to release oxytocin and prolactin.
Infant suckling stimulates hypothalamus.
Oxytocin stimulates release of milk.
Prolactin stimulates milk production.

Figure 16.12 **Hormonal control of lactation.** When an infant nurses, the infant's suckling stimulates the nipple, which sends nerve signals to the hypothalamus. In turn, the hypothalamus signals the pituitary gland to release hormones that stimulate milk production and release.

often called the **let-down reflex**, may be accompanied by a tingling or burning sensation in the breast that lets the mother know the infant is receiving milk. Let-down can be inhibited by anxiety, stress, and fatigue. It can also be stimulated by thoughts of the baby or hearing the baby cry.

let-down reflex The release of milk from the breast tissue in response to the stimulus of the hormone oxytocin. The major stimulus for oxytocin release is the infant suckling at the breast.

Key Concepts *Increasing the proportion of infants who are breastfed is an important public health goal. Prenatal care should include information about the physiology of lactation and its benefits for mother and baby. Changes in breast tissue that allow lactation culminate at delivery. Breast milk composition changes in the two or three weeks following the infant's birth. The first milk, colostrum, is high in protein and immune factors. Key hormones that regulate milk production and release are prolactin and oxytocin.*

Nutrition for Breastfeeding Women

To provide adequate nutrition for her baby while protecting her own nutritional status, a breastfeeding mother must choose a varied, healthful, nutrient-dense diet. Dietary inadequacies will lead to mobilization of stored maternal nutrients in effort to produce nutritionally complete breast milk. Her needs for energy and most nutrients are higher or the same as for pregnancy.

Energy

The energy needed to support milk production is obtained in part by mobilization of fat stores, with the remaining kilocalories provided by the diet. On average, well-nourished breastfeeding women lose weight slowly, about 0.8

kilograms (approximately 1¾ pounds) per month, with weight stabilizing after about six months. Based on this rate of weight loss, a breastfeeding woman needs an extra intake of 330 kilocalories per day during the first six months of lactation and 400 extra kilocalories daily during the second six months.[35] However, this may be an overestimation of actual needs for many women, especially those who are sedentary. To ensure adequate milk production and avoid nutrient deficiencies, a nursing mother should consume at least 1,800 kilocalories per day.

Protein

Adequate protein intake is very important while nursing. The RDA for protein is 1.3 grams per kilogram per day, or an additional 25 grams over the nonpregnant RDA. Unless calorie intake is very low, lack of dietary protein is uncommon among women in the United States and Canada.

Vitamins and Minerals

Breastfeeding women need higher amounts of most vitamins than they do during pregnancy. Exceptions include vitamins D and K, for which the recommended intake is the same during lactation and pregnancy, and niacin and folate, for which the RDA is lower during lactation than during pregnancy (although still higher than for women in the general population). When vitamin intake is inadequate, the vitamin content of breast milk can diminish, which puts the infant at risk for deficiency.

For minerals, current RDA and AI values suggest increased needs during lactation (as compared with pregnancy) for all minerals except sodium, chloride, calcium, phosphorus, magnesium, fluoride, and molybdenum. Iron needs decrease below nonpregnant values because iron losses from menstruation often do not occur during the early months of exclusive breastfeeding. Maternal intake of minerals has less influence on levels in breast milk than is true for vitamins.

Water

Breastfeeding women require plenty of fluids. A nursing mother should drink about 2 liters (≈8 cups) of water per day and at least 1 cup of water each time she breastfeeds her baby. The AI for total water (beverages plus foods) is 3.8 liters per day. Coffee and other caffeinated beverages are acceptable if limited to 1 or 2 cups per day—and if they do not replace other fluids. Because caffeine passes into the breast milk, caffeine can make some breastfed infants wakeful and jittery.

Key Concepts *Energy and nutrient needs are usually even higher during lactation than during pregnancy. Intake recommendations suggest an additional 330 to 400 kilocalories and 25 extra grams of protein each day above nonpregnant needs. Low vitamin intake affects the nutritional quality of breast milk. Recommended intake levels for minerals are generally higher during lactation than during pregnancy. Fluids are also important for adequate milk production.*

Food Choices

Choosing a variety of foods from the MyPlate Daily Food Plans for Pregnancy and Breastfeeding is the best way to meet the nutritional demands of lactation. Following the food intake patterns of the MyPlate Daily Food Plans for Pregnancy and Breastfeeding, diets of 2,000 to 2,800 kilocalories per day can easily meet most nutrient needs.

Nursing mothers should eat plenty of vegetables, the source of many essential micronutrients. Although vegetables in the cabbage family, including broccoli, cauliflower, kale, and Brussels sprouts, have long been considered causes of **colic** symptoms in breastfed infants, these vegetables may have an unwarranted bad reputation. Scientific evidence that these vegetables cause distress for infants remains weak. Removal of numerous foods from the diet should be done only under the supervision of a registered dietitian.

colic Periodic inconsolable crying in an otherwise healthy infant that appears to result from abdominal cramping and discomfort.

Supplementation

In general, breastfeeding women are recommended to continue their prenatal vitamin/mineral supplement to help meet the increased nutritional requirements of lactation. This advice especially applies to women who do not follow dietary guidelines and vegan women, who avoid all animal products. Vitamin B_{12} is likely to be too low in the milk of nursing vegans, and they should take a B_{12} supplement.[36] For breastfeeding women who do not get regular sun exposure and do not drink milk or other fortified products, a vitamin D supplement may be warranted.[37] For most nursing mothers, though, dietary counseling to improve food choices is the preferred way to address nutrient imbalances.

Practices to Avoid During Lactation

When a nursing mother smokes or uses alcohol or other drugs, these substances wind up in her breast milk. Women who smoke are encouraged to quit smoking. However, breast milk remains the ideal food for their infants.[38] It is a myth that drinking alcohol enhances the let-down reflex, making it easier to nurse. Rather, alcohol inhibits the milk-ejection reflex so that the baby gets less milk with a higher concentration of alcohol. An occasional drink may not be harmful, but breastfeeding should be avoided for two hours after alcohol consumption.[39] Illicit drugs also show up in breast milk and can be transferred to the infant. If a new mother cannot abstain from using these drugs, she should not breastfeed.

Key Concepts *Food choices during lactation should follow the MyPlate Daily Food Plans for Pregnancy and Breastfeeding and emphasize nutrient-dense foods. With good choices and adequate calories, a lactating woman may not need vitamin and mineral supplements. During pregnancy and lactation, a woman should avoid smoking, alcohol, and illicit drugs. She should consult a health care professional before taking medications or dietary supplements.*

Benefits of Breastfeeding

Breast milk is the optimal food for the health, growth, and development of infants.[40] Both mother and infant benefit from breastfeeding; in fact, the larger society benefits through reduced infant illness and health care costs.

Benefits for Infants

Human milk provides optimal nutrition for babies, as you will see in the section "Energy and Nutrient Needs of Infancy." Breast milk provides more than nutrients, however, and the health-promoting factors in breast milk are difficult, if not impossible, to replicate in infant formula.

Breast milk has been shown to reduce the incidence of respiratory, gastrointestinal, and ear infections; allergies; diarrhea; and bacterial meningitis. Evidence suggests that these effects occur in a dose-response relationship,

Quick Bite

Flavored Breast Milk

When lactating mothers exercise vigorously, the amount of lactic acid in breast milk can increase. Some babies dislike the taste and tend to nurse less. Alcohol can also cause a taste that babies dislike. What flavors do babies like? When mothers consume vanilla, mint, or garlic, some babies nurse more.

with the best outcomes for infants who are exclusively breastfed for at least six months.[41] Colostrum contains substantial amounts of antibodies, including immunoglobulin A (IgA), the first line of defense against most infectious agents.[42] Breastfeeding also appears to stimulate development of the infant's own immune system.[43]

Prolonged and exclusive breastfeeding improves children's cognitive development.[44] Breastfeeding promotes a close bond between mother and infant that may be important to normal psychological development. It is important for mothers (and fathers) who bottle-feed to promote the same type of closeness while feeding.

As long as mother and baby are in relatively close proximity, breast milk is always ready when the baby is ready to eat. There's nothing to prepare, mix, or heat; and for a hungry infant who doesn't want to wait, that's an important advantage! Breast milk is always the perfect temperature and is sterile. In addition, links between breastfeeding and reduced risk of disorders such as type 1 diabetes, cardiovascular diseases, childhood obesity, and Crohn's disease have been suggested, although these need further study. Table 16.8 lists some possible protective benefits of human milk.

Table 16.8 Suggested Protective Benefits of Human Milk

Breastfeeding may reduce a baby's risk of these disorders during infancy or later in life:

- Diarrhea and gastrointestinal illness
- Otitis media
- Bacterial meningitis
- Allergic diseases
- Childhood asthma
- Childhood leukemia
- Sudden infant death syndrome (SIDS)
- Type 1 diabetes mellitus
- Cardiovascular diseases

Source: Position of the American Dietetic Association: promoting and supporting breastfeeding. *J Am Diet Assoc.* 2005;105(5):810–818. Copyright 2005. Reprinted by permission of Elsevier.

Benefits for Mother

Following childbirth, breastfeeding stimulates uterine contractions, which help the uterus return to its normal size. If the baby is put to the breast immediately after delivery, these same contractions (an effect of oxytocin) also can help control blood loss. Although not an effective method of birth control, exclusive breastfeeding suppresses ovulation in many women.

Breastfeeding is as convenient for mother as it is for baby and is certainly less expensive than formula feeding. Although more comprehensive studies are needed, there is some evidence that breastfeeding will reduce a woman's risk of ovarian cancer, breast cancer, and osteoporosis.[45] If, as expected, a breastfed baby has fewer episodes of infectious illness, this saves health care costs and reduces employee absence and lost income for working mothers.

Contraindications to Breastfeeding

Nearly all women who want to breastfeed can do so successfully, and breastfeeding rates are steadily increasing.[46] There are times, however, when breastfeeding is inappropriate because of infant or maternal disease or drug use. Depending on the specifics of the operation, breast enlargement or reduction surgery may or may not preclude breastfeeding.[47] The main concern is whether milk ducts and major nerves were cut or damaged.

In the case of infectious or chronic diseases, individual situations should be discussed with the health care provider. For example, a woman with untreated tuberculosis should not breastfeed, because the illness may be transmitted to her child. In the United States and Canada, where safe feeding alternatives exist, women infected with HIV are advised not to breastfeed because HIV can be transmitted to the baby through breast milk.

Some medications pass directly into human milk, and some prescribed medications may preclude breastfeeding. If the mother is using an illegal drug such as cocaine, she should not breastfeed. Women taking prescription or over-the-counter medicines or herbal supplements should discuss the effects of these products on breast milk with their health care providers.

Quick Bite

Breastfeeding to Control Blood Pressure?

Oxytocin, the hormone produced while breastfeeding, can lower the blood pressure of nursing mothers. Research shows that breastfeeding mothers have lower blood pressures after nursing than do bottle-feeding mothers. When asked to discuss stressful events, nursing mothers show smaller increases in blood pressure than the bottle-feeders. Mothers often claim that they feel relaxed during breastfeeding, which may account for the difference in blood pressure.

Key Concepts *Health benefits and convenience are key advantages of breastfeeding. For the infant, breastfeeding has been linked to reduced incidence of many infectious* *diseases, as well as other conditions. For a mother, breastfeeding speeds recovery of normal uterine size and may reduce her disease risk. Although breastfeeding is the preferred method of infant feeding, there are times when breastfeeding is contraindicated. These situations should be identified and discussed as part of prenatal care.*

Resources for Pregnant and Lactating Women and Their Children

Many agencies support research and education programs that promote the health of pregnant and breastfeeding women and their children. You may be familiar with the March of Dimes and its efforts to reduce birth defects and prematurity through optimal nutrition during pregnancy. La Leche League is a voluntary health and education organization that offers programs and educational materials to help breastfeeding mothers learn about the benefits and practice of breastfeeding.

The **Special Supplemental Nutrition Program for Women, Infants, and Children (WIC)** is a much-acclaimed program of the Food and Nutrition Service of the U.S. Department of Agriculture. WIC provides food assistance, nutrition education, and referrals to health care services for low-income pregnant, postpartum, and breastfeeding women, as well as infants and children up to age 5. Compared with at-risk women and children who are eligible for WIC but who do not participate in the program, WIC participants have significantly fewer problems, such as being underweight.[48]

Although WIC services include breastfeeding education and support, WIC participants are less likely to breastfeed their infants.[49] Continued promotion of breastfeeding by WIC and other public health programs can have both health and economic benefits.[50] Periodically, WIC participants are required to bring their infants into the local WIC office. These visits give WIC staff an opportunity to evaluate the infant's growth and provide the caregiver with additional nutrition education.

Special Supplemental Nutrition Program for Women, Infants, and Children (WIC) A USDA program that provides federal grants to states for supplemental foods, health care referrals, and nutrition education for low-income pregnant, breastfeeding, and nonbreastfeeding postpartum women, and to infants and children at nutritional risk.

infancy The period between birth and 12 months of age.

prematurity Birth before 37 weeks of gestation.

full-term baby A baby delivered during the normal period of human gestation, between 38 and 41 weeks.

Infancy

Infancy is the period of a child's life between birth and 1 year. Because of the rapid growth that occurs during this time, nutritional needs are higher per unit of body weight than at any other time in the life cycle. Despite the critical importance of nutrition at this stage, feeding an infant is a fairly simple process. Human milk provides all the nutrients an infant needs and is the model for infant formulas. By 4 to 6 months, the infant's physical development and physiological maturation signal readiness for the addition of "solid" foods to the diet.

Human infants need love as much as they need food. Without love and nurturing, a baby can fail to thrive even if she is offered all the right nutrients. If an infant is not nourished emotionally, nutrition recommendations and requirements become meaningless.

Infant Growth and Development

Birth weight is the best predictor of a child's health in the first year of life; however, it is important to correlate weight with length of development. The risk profile of an infant who has a low birth weight because of **prematurity** differs from that of a **full-term baby** with a low birth weight.

Immediately after birth, an infant loses about 6 percent of his body weight. This is normal and expected. By 10 to 14 days, the infant should return to his birth weight. Over the next 12 months, the infant's growth will be phe-

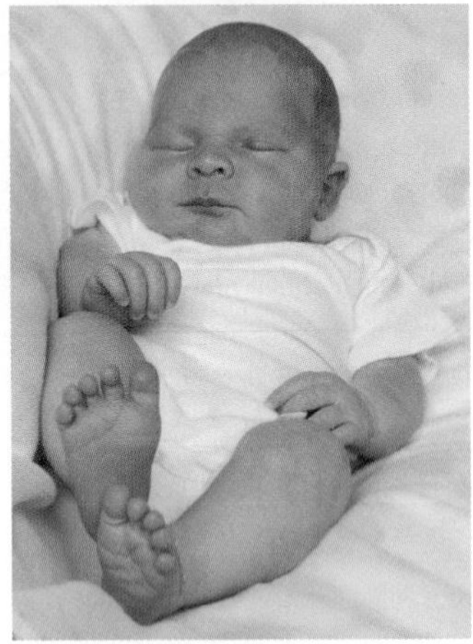

(a)

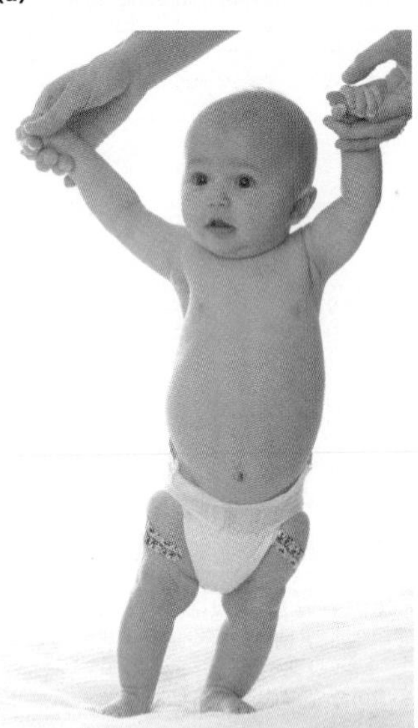

(b)

(c)

Figure 16.13 **Different stages of infancy.** (a) Newborn. (b) 4 to 6 months. (c) 12 months.

nomenal. By the age of 4 to 6 months, a healthy infant will have doubled his birth weight. By his first birthday, the infant will have tripled his birth weight and increased his length by about 50 percent. The infant's body proportions change, too, so that by age 1 he is looking less like a baby and more like a **toddler**. (See **Figure 16.13**.)

Length (used instead of height because infants can't stand) and **head circumference** are more sensitive measures than weight for assessing a baby's growth and nutritional status. Weight alone reflects just recent nutritional intake. Head circumference measures brain growth and development. Chronic malnutrition can limit this growth and is reflected in inadequate gains in head size. Regular measurements of head circumference, therefore, can verify desirable growth. Head circumference measurements are useful in infants and children up to age 2.

Growth Charts

During routine checkups throughout infancy (and during childhood and adolescence), health care practitioners measure weight, length or height, and head circumference and plot these values on **growth charts**. (See **Figure 16.14**.)

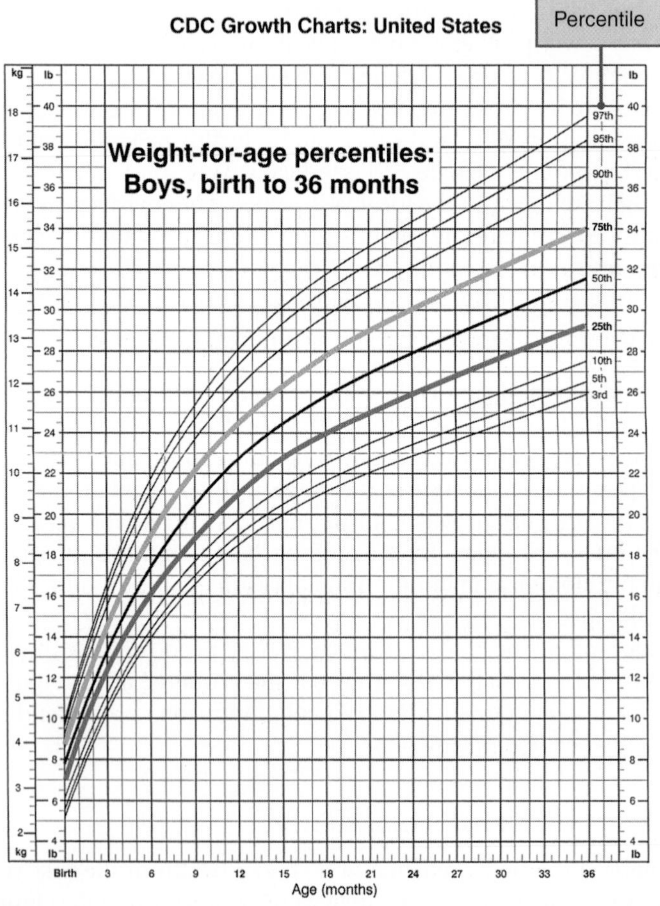

Figure 16.14 **Growth chart.** The Centers for Disease Control and Prevention (CDC) has complete sets of growth charts available on the Internet at www.cdc.gov/growthcharts. See Appendix H for full-scale samples of growth charts for boys and girls aged 2 to 20 years.

Source: Developed by the National Center for Health Statistics in collaboration with the National Center for Chronic Disease Prevention and Health Promotion (2000).

Charts for weight-for-age, length- (or height-) for-age, head circumference-for-age, weight-for-length, and BMI-for-age are available for boys and girls and for two age ranges: birth to 36 months and 2 to 20 years. (See Appendix H.) Health care practitioners use growth charts to show the growth of an individual child over time. These charts also allow comparison of one child's growth to that of children in the general population.

Key Concepts *A typical infant doubles her birth weight by age 4 to 6 months and triples it by 12 months. Infant length increases about 50 percent during the first year. Health care practitioners use growth charts to follow and assess an infant's growth in weight, length, and head circumference.*

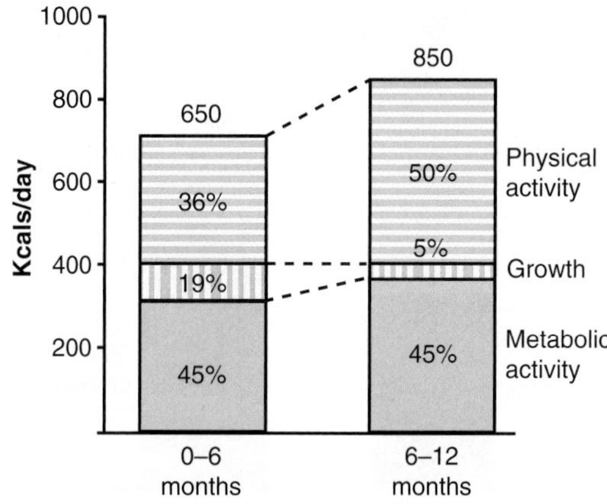

Figure 16.15 **Allocation of energy expenditure.** During the second six months, infants increase their energy expenditure for physical activity.

Source: Adapted from Foman SJ, Bell EF. Energy. In: Foman SJ, ed. *Nutrition of Normal Infants*. St. Louis: Mosby, 1993.

Energy and Nutrient Needs During Infancy

How do you suppose scientists determine the nutrient needs of newborns and young infants? Studies with babies as subjects are rare—the logistical and ethical questions are daunting! So how else can we know what babies need? It's simple; we just look at breast milk—the food designed especially for babies. The composition of human milk is the gold standard by which infant nutrient needs are determined. Babies who are not breastfed are given infant formula. In the United States, most infant formulas have a base of modified cow's milk or soy protein. To ensure that formula meets all of an infant's nutrient needs, federal regulations require that the formula's composition complies with nutritional standards.

toddler A child between 12 and 36 months of age.

head circumference Measurement of the largest part of the infant's head (just above the eyebrows and ears); used to determine brain growth.

growth charts Charts that plot the weight, length, and head circumference of infants and children as they grow.

Energy

An infant's energy need is the amount of energy she requires for basal functions, such as respiration and metabolism, in addition to growth and activity. An infant's basal energy needs, relative to her size, are about twice that of an adult. The amount of energy an infant needs for activity varies throughout the first year of life, increasing as the child becomes more mobile. (See **Figure 16.15**.) In general, a newborn requires about 100 kilocalories per kilogram of body weight.[51] Table 16.9 lists the specific equations for calculating infants' Estimated Energy Requirements (EER).

The appropriate balance of energy sources (carbohydrate, fat, and protein) for infants differs from that of adults. (See **Figure 16.16**.) The best diet for infants (as modeled by human milk) is high in fat and moderate in carbohydrate. Infants have high calorie needs but can consume only a small amount at any one time. An infant's stomach is quite small; a newborn can consume only about 1 to 2 ounces of liquid at a feeding. Because fat is the most concentrated source of calories, a high-fat diet supplies adequate calories in a smaller volume. A high-fat diet also is necessary for normal brain growth, which continues until about 18 to 24 months of age. **Figure 16.17** shows the primary functions of energy-yielding nutrients in infants, which are discussed in the next sections.

Table 16.9 **Estimated Energy Requirement RDA During Infancy**

Age (mo)	EER Equation
0–3	(89 × wt [kg] – 100) + 175 kcal/day
4–6	(89 × wt [kg] – 100) + 56 kcal/day
7–12	(89 × wt [kg] – 100) + 22 kcal/day

Source: Institute of Medicine, Food and Nutrition Board. *Dietary Reference Intakes for Energy, Carbohydrate, Fiber, Fat, Fatty Acids, Cholesterol, Protein, and Amino Acids (Macronutrients)*. Copyright © 2002 by the National Academy of Sciences, courtesy of the National Academies Press, Washington, DC. Reprinted with permission.

Protein

Protein needs during infancy are higher than at any other time in the life cycle. In fact, protein needs (measured in grams per kilogram of body weight) during the first six months of life are nearly twice as high as an adult's needs. Table 16.10 lists the protein recommendations for infants. Both human milk and infant formula provide complete protein with all the essential amino acids. Because of the types of proteins found in human milk (as compared with cow's milk), human milk protein is more easily digested and absorbed.

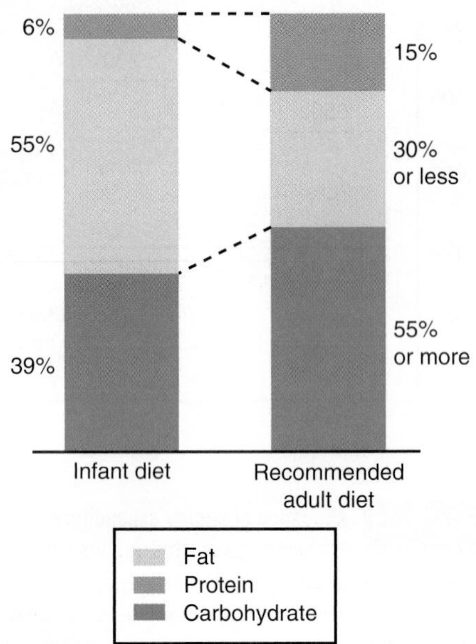

Figure 16.16 Percentages of energy-yielding nutrients in infant and adult diets. The best diets for infants are high in fat and moderate in carbohydrate. Infants need a high-fat diet for normal brain growth and to provide adequate calories in a smaller volume.

Protein
Growth

Carbohydrate (lactose)
Energy
Enhances absorption of calcium and phosphorus

Fat
Energy
Nervous system development
Accumulation of fat stores

Figure 16.17 Primary functions of energy-yielding nutrients for infants. To support growth, protein needs (per kg body weight) are higher in infancy than in any other life stage.

Table 16.10 Protein AI or RDA for Infants

Age (mo)	g/kg	g/d*
0–6	1.52	9
7–12	1.5	10

*The values for grams per day are based on reference weights of infants.

Source: Institute of Medicine, Food and Nutrition Board. *Dietary Reference Intakes for Energy, Carbohydrate, Fiber, Fat, Fatty Acids, Cholesterol, Protein, and Amino Acids (Macronutrients).* Copyright © 2002 by the National Academy of Sciences, courtesy of the National Academies Press, Washington, DC. Reprinted with permission.

Carbohydrate and Fat

Carbohydrates and triglycerides are the major energy sources for infants. This allows protein to be used primarily for growth and not as an energy source. Nearly all carbohydrate in human milk and in infant formulas made from cow's milk is lactose. Infants digest lactose easily and tolerate it well.

Triglycerides are the major energy source in human milk, providing about 50 to 55 percent of the calories. Fats in milk also enhance a baby's sense of fullness between feedings. Experts recommend that infants get at least 30 grams of fat per day.[52] Breast milk is rich in essential fatty acids: the omega-6 fatty acid arachidonic acid and two long-chain omega-3 fatty acids, eicosapentaenoic acid and docosahexaenoic acid. These fatty acids have roles in neurological development. The Food and Nutrition Board has set an AI for newborns (0 to 6 months of age) of 4.4 grams per day of linoleic acid and 0.5 gram per day of alpha-linolenic acid.[53] Infants also need cholesterol for brain development. Human milk is rich in cholesterol, containing about 20 to 30 milligrams per 100 milliliters.[54]

Water

Because water as a percentage of body weight is higher in babies than adults, infants need more fluids. The AI for water during infancy is 0.7 liter per day in the first six months (assumed to be from human milk) and 0.8 liter per day from 7 months to 1 year of age. Human milk fulfills not only the nutrient needs of the **neonate**, but also the fluid requirements. Properly prepared formula accomplishes the same task. During the first four to six months, supplemental water is not necessary for healthy infants who are exclusively breastfed or who receive properly mixed formula. This is true even in hot, humid weather.[55] Once solid foods are introduced, a baby's water needs change, and additional water may be required.

Vitamins and Minerals

Human milk provides the amounts of vitamins and minerals that human babies need. Therefore, the micronutrient composition of human milk is the reference point for designing infant formula. As long as an infant is receiving adequate calories from breast milk or infant formula, nearly all vitamin and mineral needs also are being met. Human milk is lower in a few nutrients (e.g., iron and vitamin D), but infants absorb these nutrients more efficiently from breast milk than from formula. This section focuses on a few vitamins and minerals that may be of concern for infants. (See **Figure 16.18**.)

Vitamin D Vitamin D is a key nutrient for absorbing calcium and mineralizing bone. Rickets is attributable to inadequate vitamin D intake and insufficient sunlight exposure in infants and children.[56] Recent evidence also suggests a role for vitamin D in maintaining innate immunity and preventing diseases such as cancer and diabetes.[57] Although human milk is low in vitamin D, infants absorb it well. Despite this, inadequate vitamin D levels are a concern for those infants who are exclusively breastfed, those not exposed to sunlight, and those with darkly pigmented skin who make less vitamin D from the same amount of sunlight exposure than do lighter-skinned infants. If a breastfed baby does not get adequate sunlight exposure and if the baby's mother is deficient in vitamin D, the infant's risk is especially high. In 2008 the American Academy of Pediatrics (AAP) increased its recommendation for daily vitamin D to 400 IU per day for all infants, children, and adolescents, beginning the first few days after birth.[58]

Vitamin K Vitamin K is necessary for the production of prothrombin, a substance needed for blood to clot. Although intestinal bacteria synthesize vitamin K, the gut is sterile at birth. Because babies are born with minimal stores of vitamin K, it is recommended that a single dose of vitamin K be given at birth. Both human milk and infant formula provide adequate vitamin K, and as feeding begins, helpful bacteria begin to flourish in the infant's intestinal tract.

Vitamin B_{12} Vitamin B_{12} is essential for cell division and normal folate metabolism. Mothers who include meat, fish, and dairy products in their diets produce milk that is adequate in vitamin B_{12}. This may not be true of strict vegetarians, whose diet—and therefore breast milk—may be deficient in vitamin B_{12}. Breastfed infants of vegan mothers may need a vitamin B_{12} supplement.

Iron Iron is essential for growth and development, and iron-deficiency anemia is the most common nutritional deficiency in the United States. Human milk is not a rich source of iron, but it does not need to be. Approximately 50 percent of the iron in breast milk is absorbed, compared with only 4 percent of the iron in infant formula. If the mother has consumed an iron-rich diet during pregnancy, the fetus builds up large enough iron stores during gestation to meet most of its iron needs for the first few months of life. These stores begin to diminish during the fourth month of life. By the age of 6 months, a breastfed infant needs an additional iron source. Iron-fortified infant cereals can meet this need. For formula-fed babies, iron supplementation is needed from birth. The AAP therefore recommends iron-fortified formula for all formula-fed babies.[59]

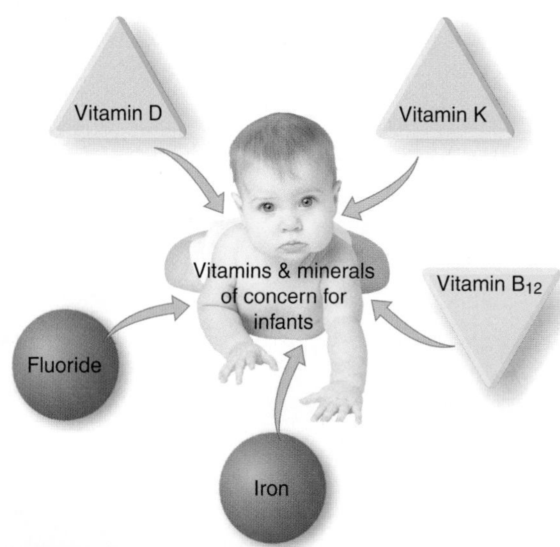

Figure 16.18 **Micronutrients of concern during infancy.** Infants who lack sun exposure can become deficient in vitamin D. A dose of vitamin K usually is given to babies at birth to ensure a sufficient supply. Because vegan mothers can have breast milk deficient in vitamin B_{12}, their babies may need a B_{12} supplement. By the age of 6 months, breastfed infants need additional iron. Formula-fed infants should consume iron-fortified formula. Human milk is low in fluoride.

Fluoride Human milk is low in fluoride, a mineral important for dental health. Current research has led the American Dental Association and the AAP to recommend fluoride supplements for breastfed infants after the age of 6 months.[60] If the local water supply has adequate fluoride and the formula is mixed with tap water, formula-fed infants do not need fluoride supplements. If the water used to mix formula has inadequate fluoride, fluoride supplements are indicated. Fluoridation policies and the fluoride content of tap water vary among municipalities.

neonate An infant from birth to 28 days.

lactation consultants Health professionals trained to specialize in education about and promotion of breastfeeding; may be certified as an International Board Certified Lactation Consultant (IBCLC).

Key Concepts *Energy and nutrient needs for infants are estimated based on the composition of human milk. Because of their rapid growth and development, infants have high energy and nutrient needs per kilogram of body weight. Caregivers must give special attention to vitamin D, iron, and fluoride to ensure that the infant obtains enough. If breast milk or formula (properly mixed) is meeting energy needs, the fluid needs of the infant also are being met.*

Newborn Breastfeeding

The AAP has identified breastfeeding as the ideal method of feeding to achieve optimal growth and development[61] and recommends that breastfeeding begin as soon after birth as possible and continue at least through the first 12 months of life.[62] Feedings should occur at least every 2 to 3 hours, for a total of 8 to 12 feedings per day. Duration of feedings is guided by the infant's behavior and may last from 10 to 15 minutes per breast. Hospitals should provide every opportunity for breastfeeding to begin before the baby goes home. Nurses or **lactation consultants** should be available to offer profes-

Quick Bite

What's a Biberon?

Many people consider Dr. Nils Rosen von Rosenstein to be the father of pediatrics. In his 1764 textbook, he describes a "biberon," a leather nipple used for artificial infant feeding. He also describes 14 types of infant diarrhea.

sional breastfeeding support to new mothers. The AAP recommends that no supplements of formula or water be given to breastfed neonates unless medically indicated.

Alternative Feeding: Infant Formula

Women may decide not to breastfeed or to breastfeed only briefly. Their infants need infant formulas designed to provide adequate nutrition.

Standard Infant Formulas

Standard infant formulas have cow's milk as a base. In making infant formula, manufacturers first remove the milk fat and replace it with vegetable oils. Infant formula is fortified with all the essential vitamins and minerals according to guidelines established by the AAP and enforced by the Food and Drug Administration. Infant formulas are available with or without added iron, but because of the decreased bioavailability of iron in infant formulas and the infant's high needs, the AAP recommends using only iron-fortified formulas.

Although formula manufacturers try to mimic the composition of human milk, formula remains an imperfect copy. Several brands of infant formula contain three fatty acids that are prevalent in human milk: arachidonic acid (ARA), eicosapentaenoic acid (EPA), and docosahexaenoic acid (DHA). Some studies show that supplemental ARA and EPA may benefit infants' visual function and cognitive development; however, a large review of studies found that most randomized controlled trials have not shown a beneficial effect of long-chain polyunsaturated fatty acid supplementation of formula milk on the neurodevelopmental, visual, and physical outcomes of full-term newborns.[63] Human milk also contains more cholesterol than infant formulas.

Soy-Based Formulas

Formula-fed infants who develop vomiting, diarrhea, constipation, abdominal pain, or colic are frequently switched to soy-based formulas. In these formulas, soy is the source of protein. To compensate for the inferior digestibility of soy protein, soy formulas contain more protein than formulas based on cow's milk. Soy formulas are lactose-free and iron-fortified. Corn syrup and sucrose are the carbohydrate sources.

Other Types of Formula

Choosing an infant formula can be confusing to parents and physicians because of the wide variety that is currently available. Formulas can be classified according to three basic criteria: caloric density, carbohydrate source, and protein composition.[64] Special formulas are available for infants who are allergic to both cow's milk and soy protein, those who are premature, and those who have rare defects in metabolic pathways. These special formulas often have their protein content modified in either its digestibility or its amino acid composition. Antireflux formulas are designed to decrease emesis and regurgitation. Many special formulas contain medium-chain triglycerides as the major fat source. This type of fat is very well digested and absorbed. These special formulas are expensive and often taste bad, but they are essential for many infants.

Formula Preparation

Formulas come in three forms: ready-to-feed, concentrate, and powdered. Although the ready-to-feed version is the most convenient, it is also the most expensive. As the name implies, the formula can be poured directly from the can into a bottle and fed to the baby. Liquid concentrate formula is mixed with an equal amount of water before feeding. Powdered formula also is mixed with water and is the least expensive.

When using infant formulas, principles of food safety must be observed. Infants have immature immune systems and may develop infections from improperly prepared or stored formula. Prepared formula should be refrigerated immediately and kept in the refrigerator until needed. If formula is not used within 48 hours, it should be discarded. For at least the first few months, the AAP recommends sterilizing all equipment used for feeding.

Going Green

How Safe Are Plastics?

Reduce, recycle, and reuse—even hard plastic water bottles? No, not those with the following symbol, say many health experts. They may actually leave a harmful substance behind in your body known as bisphenol A (BPA). Human exposure to BPA is widespread. According to scientists at the Centers for Disease Control and Prevention, 92 percent of Americans aged 6 and older have measurable levels of BPA in their bodies. Children had the highest levels, followed by teens, women, and then men.

Bisphenol A is a human-made industrial chemical used primarily in the production of plastics used in some food and drink packages, such as refillable water bottles, infant feeding bottles, reusable food storage containers, and some plastic eating utensils. BPA is also found in epoxy resins that coat water supply pipes as well as metal food cans and bottle tops.

BPA is classified as an "endocrine disruptor." This means that it alters the function of the endocrine system by mimicking the role of hormones that occur naturally in the body. BPA may be most harmful in the early stages of development. In animals, it has been shown to have hormonelike effects on the developing reproductive system, but whether the adverse effects observed in animals could also occur in people exposed to low environmental levels of these chemicals is still not clear. The National Toxicology Program (NTP), which is part of the National Institutes of Health, has concerns about the possibility that BPA could cause prostate and breast problems in adults and brain problems in infants and children.

BPA from food and beverage packages leaches into foods and then gets into the body through the diet. How much BPA enters the foods depends on such factors as food temperature and the age of the container. The temperature of the liquid may have the most impact. Researchers at the Harvard School of Public Health found that after just one week of drinking cold liquids from water bottles, urinary BPA levels increased by 69 percent. Once hard water bottles are exposed to boiling water, BPA is released into the water at faster and much higher levels. Bisphenol A is released from polycarbonate drinking bottles and mimics the neurotoxic actions of estrogen in developing cerebellar neurons. This would be of significant concern for infants, who may be particularly susceptible to BPAs, because formula is often warmed and served in the bottle.

In 2008, Canada banned the use of BPA in baby bottles. In addition, some plastic bottle manufacturers have voluntarily eliminated BPA from their products. What should you do if you are concerned about BPA? According to the NTP, since infants and children may be the most vulnerable to the effects of BPA, parents and caregivers can reduce exposures of their infants and children to BPA by opting for glass or porcelain containers for heating or serving hot foods and beverages, reducing the use of canned foods, and using baby bottles that are BPA-free.

Quick Bite

Ancient Baby Bottle

The earliest infant feeding vessel ever discovered is Egyptian and dates from 2000 B.C.E. Art found in the ruins of the palace of King Sardanapalus of Nineveh, who died in 888 B.C.E., depicts a mother holding a modern-looking baby bottle.

Improperly mixed formula is another danger, whether a result of ignorance in following instructions or of economics. Some caregivers on limited budgets might purposefully overdilute formula to make it last longer. This deprives the infant of necessary calories and protein and provides too much water. Other caregivers might overconcentrate the formula in the misguided belief that this might encourage faster growth. Overconcentrated formula provides too much protein and too little water and may cause problems with an infant's kidney function and hydration.

Breast Milk or Formula: How Much Is Enough?

It is fairly simple to use DRI values and breast milk or formula composition to estimate an infant's needs based on body weight. For example, a newborn who weighs 7 pounds, 11 ounces (3.5 kilograms) requires approximately 390 kilocalories and 5 grams of protein each day. This amount is provided by approximately 600 milliliters (≈20 fluid ounces) of breast milk or infant formula.

It's easy to keep track of how much formula an infant has consumed, but what about the breastfed baby? Although you can't see how much breast milk a nursing infant is consuming, there are other ways to tell that a baby is getting enough to eat. An adequately fed newborn will breastfeed 8 to 12 times, wet at least six diapers, and have at least three loose stools each day in the first week of life. The newborn will also regain his or her birth weight within the first two weeks. Normal growth, regular elimination patterns, and a satisfied demeanor are the best indicators that a baby is getting enough to eat.

Figure 16.19 **Breastfeeding.** Breastfeeding nurtures an infant emotionally as well as physically. This intensely rewarding time helps to bond a mother and her child.

Feeding Technique

Feeding should take place in a loving and affectionate environment. A breastfeeding mother holds her baby close, at a distance that encourages mother–baby eye contact. (See **Figure 16.19**.) During bottle-feeding, the caregiver should also hold the baby close and make eye contact. Propping the bottle against a pillow or other object, so that the baby can feed alone, should be avoided.

Babies swallow air while feeding, whether at the breast or with a bottle, and they need to be burped. Babies generally need to be burped after 15 minutes or 2 to 3 ounces of formula. Just as the infant sends signals of readiness for feeding, he also signals fullness. Fullness cues include fussiness, playfulness, sleep, or just turning away. Parents need to learn these cues and respond to them.

Key Concepts *Human milk provides all the necessary nutrients for growth and development and enhances the immune system of the maturing infant. Infants who are not breastfed receive infant formula, which should be fortified with iron. Careful preparation and storage of the formula ensures proper nutrient composition and food safety. Formula feedings should nourish the baby emotionally as well as nutritionally.*

Introduction of Solid Foods into the Infant's Diet

Based on an infant's physiological needs (e.g., depletion of iron stores) and physical development (e.g., the ability to sit up), solid foods, also called **complementary foods**, are introduced. To say that we are introducing solid foods is a bit of a misnomer: we are really referring to pureed and liquefied cereals, fruits, vegetables, and meats that are added to the infant's diet of breast milk or infant formula. According to the American Academy of Pediatrics, complementary foods are not needed in the diets of infants fed either breast milk or iron-fortified infant formula before the age of 6 months.[65]

Physiological Indicators of Infant Readiness for Solid Foods

Before a baby reaches 6 months of age, solid food is not necessary for nutrition; in fact, early introduction of supplemental foods can be detrimental. By the age of 4 to 6 months, however, an infant is physiologically ready to expand his diet. For example, at this age a baby has increased levels of digestive enzymes, so that foods other than human milk or formula can be digested with ease. In addition, the infant is better able to maintain adequate hydration by the age of 6 months. Before this age, adding cereals or other solid foods to the diet can negatively affect an infant's hydration. It is probably no coincidence that the iron stores acquired in the mother's womb become depleted at the same time the baby is physiologically ready to expand his or her diet. However, solid food is a supplement to, not a replacement for, human milk or formula at this time.

Developmental Readiness for Solid Foods

If you attempt to spoon-feed a very young infant, for example, at 3 weeks of age, the infant's tongue will push the spoon and food right back out. This **extrusion reflex** is a sign that the infant is not ready for solid foods. By 4 to 6 months of age, the infant will no longer push the food out and is capable of transferring food from the front of the mouth to the back, an ability necessary for swallowing solid foods. Also, the infant can purposefully bring her hand to her mouth, an ability necessary for self-feeding. In addition, if the baby is able to control her head and neck while sitting with minimal support, she is ready to be fed solids.

Start Healthy Feeding Guidelines

The *Start Healthy Feeding Guidelines for Infants and Toddlers* are science-based, practical guidelines for feeding healthy babies for the first two years.[66] The *Start Healthy Feeding Guidelines* were designed to answer parents' and caregivers' questions, such as "When is my baby ready for complementary foods? What foods should I feed my baby? How do I feed these foods?"[67] The appropriate age for introduction of complementary foods balances physiological and developmental readiness with nutritional requirements for growth and development. **Figure 16.20** summarizes the *Start Healthy Feeding Guidelines*.

Signs of readiness for the introduction of infant cereals and thin, pureed foods include the ability to sit with support and the ability to take food from a spoon and move it forward and backward in the mouth with the tongue. As the infant's body control improves and she can sit independently, she will also develop the ability to pick up and hold objects in her hand. She will be able to take in thicker pureed foods and soft mashed foods without lumps.

Babies who can crawl are also likely to be ready to self-feed finger foods such as baby biscuits or crackers. Babies at this stage can hold small foods between the thumb and first finger and also hold a cup (preferably one with a cap and spout) independently. A baby is able to participate in the feeding process, and as his dexterity improves, he will be able to pick up small pieces of food. It is important that caregivers monitor the child's eating to make sure the youngster does not choke on food or on nonfood items.

Quick Bite

Pumping Iron

The use of cow's milk for children younger than 1 year is a common cause of iron deficiency. Cow's milk is low in iron, and drinking it can cause intestinal bleeding in infants. The amount of iron in breast milk is low, but this iron is highly bioavailable. Breast milk also contains proteins that bind iron, thereby inhibiting the growth of diarrhea-causing bacteria that feed on iron. If formula is used, the AAP recommends that it be iron-fortified.

complementary foods Any foods or liquids other than breast milk or infant formula fed to an infant.

extrusion reflex A young infant's response when a spoon is put in its mouth; the tongue is thrust forward, indicating that the baby is not ready for spoon feeding.

Quick Bite

But the Breast Milk Looks Weak . . .

Mature breast milk looks similar to non-fat milk—thin, pale, and bluish. Not to worry! This appearance is normal, and breast milk always contains the right amount of nutrients for the baby. It is never too weak.

Development Stage	Newborn	Head Up	Supported Sitter	Independent Sitter	Crawler	Beginning to Walk	Independent Toddler
	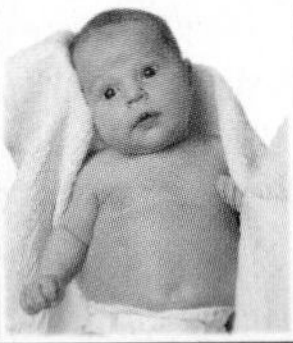	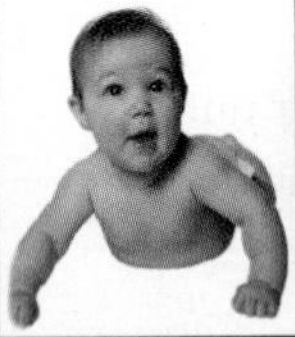	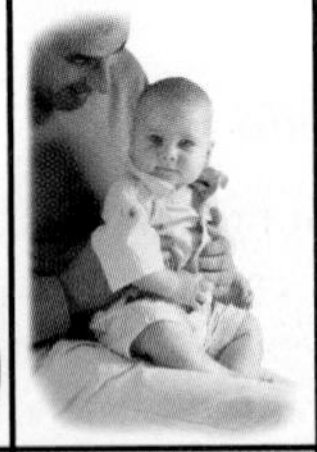	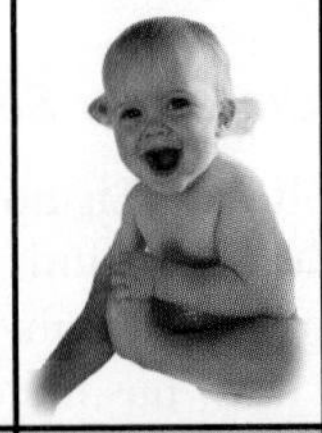	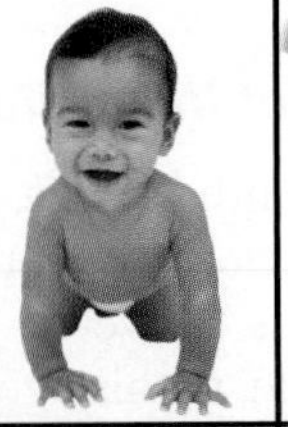	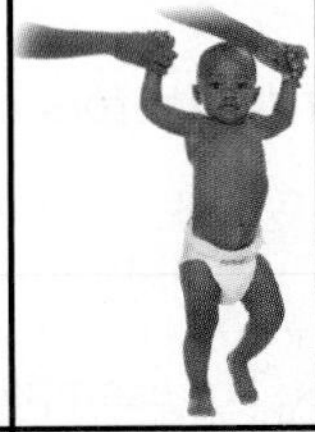	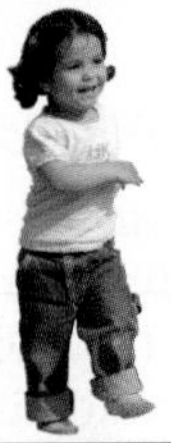
Physical Skills	• Needs head support	• More skillful head control with support emerging	• Sits with help or support • On tummy, pushes up on arms with straight elbows	• Sits independently • Can pick up and hold small object in hand • Leans toward food or spoon	• Learns to crawl • May pull self to stand	• Pulls self to stand • Stands alone • Takes early steps	• Walks well alone • Runs
Eating Skills	• Baby establishes a suck-swallow-breathe pattern during breast or bottle feeding	• Breastfeeds or bottle feeds • Tongue moves forward and back to suck	• May push food out of mouth with tongue, which gradually decreases with age • Moves pureed food forward and backward in mouth with tongue to swallow • Recognizes spoon and holds mouth open as spoon approaches	• Learns to keep thick purees in mouth • Pulls head downward and presses upper lip to draw food from spoon • Tries to rake foods toward self into fist • Can transfer food from one hand to the other • Can drink from a cup held by feeder	• Learns to move tongue from side to side to transfer food around mouth and push food to the side of the mouth so food can be mashed • Begins to use jaw and tongue to mash food • Plays with spoon at mealtime, may bring it to mouth, but does not use it for self-feeding yet • Can feed self finger foods • Holds cup independently • Holds small foods between thumb and first finger	• Feeds self easily with fingers • Can drink from a straw • Can hold cup with two hands and take swallows • More skillful at chewing • Dips spoon in food rather than scooping • Demands to spoon-feed self • Bites through a variety of textures	• Chews and swallows firmer foods skillfully • Learns to use a fork for spearing • Uses spoon with less spilling • Can hold cup in one hand and set it down skillfully
Baby's Hunger & Fullness Cues	• Cries or fusses to show hunger • Gazes at caregiver, opens mouth during feeding indicating desire to continue • Spits out nipple or falls asleep when full • Stops sucking when full	• Cries or fusses to show hunger • Smiles, gazes at caregiver, or coos during feeding to indicate desire to continue • Spits out nipple or falls asleep when full • Stops sucking when full	• Moves head forward to reach spoon when hungry • May swipe the food toward the mouth when hungry • Turns head away from spoon when full • May be distracted or notice surroundings more when full	• Reaches for spoon or food when hungry • Points to food when hungry • Slows down in eating when full • Clenches mouth shut or pushes food away when full	• Reaches for food when hungry • Points to food when hungry • Shows excitement when food is presented when hungry • Pushes food away when full • Slows down in eating when full	• Expresses desire for specific foods with words or sounds • Shakes head to say "no more" when full	• Combines phrases with gestures, such as "want that" and pointing • Can lead parent to refrigerator and point to a desired food or drink • Uses words like "all done" and "get down" • Plays with food or throws food when full
Appropriate Foods & Textures	• Breastmilk or infant formula	• Breastmilk or infant formula	• Breastmilk or infant formula • Infant cereals • Thin pureed foods	• Breastmilk or infant formula • Infant cereals • Thin pureed baby foods • Thicker pureed baby foods • Soft mashed foods without lumps • 100% Juice	• Breastmilk or infant formula • 100% Juice • Infant cereals • Pureed foods • Ground or soft mashed foods with tiny soft noticeable lumps • Foods with soft texture • Crunchy foods that dissolve (such as baby biscuits or crackers) • Increase variety of flavors offered	• Breastmilk or infant formula or whole milk • 100% Juice • Coarsely chopped foods, including foods with noticeable pieces • Foods with soft to moderate texture • Toddler foods • Bite sized pieces of food • Bites through a variety of texures	• Whole milk • 100% Juice • Coarsely chopped foods • Toddler foods • Bite-sized pieces of food • Becomes efficient at eating foods of varying textures and taking controlled bites of soft solids, hard solids, or crunchy foods by 2 years

Figure 16.20 The ***Start Healthy Feeding Guidelines.*** Summary of physical and eating skills, hunger and fullness cues, and appropriate food textures for children 0 to 24 months of age.

Source: Butte N, Cobb K, Dwyer J, et al. The *Start Healthy Feeding Guidelines for Infants and Toddlers. J Am Diet Assoc.* 2004;104(3):442–454.

At the end of the first year, when a baby is standing alone and beginning to walk, his diet can expand even further with bite-size pieces of table foods and a wider variety of textures. Self-feeding with his fingers is much easier, and he desires to self-feed with a spoon as well—a messy but developmentally appropriate thing to do. Most table foods are appropriate for the child at this stage.

There is no scientific evidence to support introduction of complementary foods in any particular order; cultural practices play a large role in determining which foods are introduced first. Introducing a source of iron, such as an iron-fortified infant cereal or pureed meats, is necessary because iron stores developed in pregnancy are declining. No matter what food is introduced first, new foods should be introduced one at a time, at intervals of about one week, to see how well the infant tolerates each food and to be on the lookout for allergic reactions. Throughout the first year, breast milk or infant formula still forms the major portion of the infant's diet. Ideally, however, the child will have been introduced to a variety of foods by his or her first birthday.

Parents and caregivers should take care that complementary foods be soft in texture to avoid the risk of choking. Delaying—until age 1—the introduction of common food allergens, particularly cow's milk, egg whites, and wheat, can prevent food allergies for many infants. In addition to its allergic potential, whole cow's milk provides too much protein and too little iron, is low in essential fatty acids, may impair kidney function and lead to dehydration, and has been linked to development of insulin-dependent diabetes mellitus.[68] In families with a strong history of allergies, introduction of eggs should be delayed until age 2, and peanuts, tree nuts, fish, and shellfish should not be introduced before age 3.

Along with observing the infant's developmental readiness for complementary foods, parents and caregivers need to be alert to an infant's hunger and satiety cues. The suggestions in Table 16.11 can help new parents establish a healthy feeding relationship with their child.

Various caregivers may be involved in a child's nutrition. In today's society, it is inappropriate to assume that the caregiver is solely the mother, father, grandparent, or even a relative of the child. Many children spend the majority of their feeding time in a child-care setting. Child-care staff can develop and implement strategies to overcome challenges and support healthy eating behaviors of children.[69]

Table 16.11 How to Feed Solid Foods

Do	Why
Wash the baby's hands before feeding.	To clean any dirt or germs off the hands to keep the baby's food clean.
Use a small spoon or let the baby use his or her fingers.	To help the baby learn proper eating habits.
Place food on the tip of the spoon and put food in the middle of the baby's tongue.	To make it easy for the baby to swallow.
Remove food from the jar before feeding. Do not feed the baby food from the jar.	To prevent the saliva from the baby's mouth from spoiling the remainder of the food in the jar.
Give only one new food at a time, and wait at least 1 week before giving another new food.	To give the baby time to get used to each new flavor and texture, and to see if the baby is allergic to the new food.

Source: US Department of Agriculture, Food and Nutrition Service. A Guide for Use in the Child Nutrition Programs. FNS-258. 2002. http://www.FNS.usda.gov/tn/resources/feeding_infants.html. Accessed 3/2/10.

Key Concepts *An infant's physiological needs and developmental readiness usually indicate the appropriate time to introduce solid foods. Semisolid and solid foods should be introduced slowly to check for infant food intolerances and allergic reactions. The caregiver should choose foods that meet the child's nutritional needs and suit his or her developmental capabilities.*

Feeding Problems During Infancy

Colic

The term *colic* refers to continuous crying and distress in a healthy infant—apparently due to abdominal cramping and discomfort. Infants with colic usually cry for hours, despite efforts to comfort them. In some cases, a change in formula or a change in the breastfeeding mother's diet provides some relief. However, diet (of either mother or infant) is not considered a cause of colic.[70] Most often, colic goes away on its own, usually by the age of 3 to 4 months.

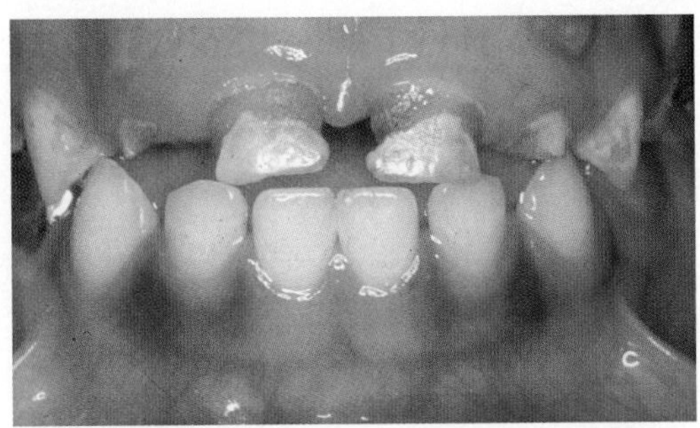

Figure 16.21 **Early childhood caries.** A baby routinely put to bed with a bottle can develop extensive tooth decay.

gastroesophageal reflux A backflow of stomach contents into the esophagus, accompanied by a burning pain because of the acidity of the gastric juices.

failure to thrive (FTT) Abnormally low gains in length (height) and weight during infancy and childhood; may result from physical problems or poor feeding, but many affected children have no apparent disease or defect.

Early Childhood Caries

Decay in the primary teeth, known as early childhood caries and sometimes called "baby bottle tooth decay" (see **Figure 16.21**), can result if baby teeth are bathed too long in milk, formula, or juice, which nourish decay-producing bacteria. Other factors, such as inadequate development of tooth enamel, also contribute.[71] The problem is often associated with routinely putting a baby to bed with a bottle so that the baby's teeth are awash in formula or juice for much or all of the night. Children with early childhood caries are more susceptible to caries in the permanent teeth and lifelong dental problems.[72]

Iron-Deficiency Anemia: Milk Anemia

Human milk and cow's milk both are low in iron. As discussed earlier, this is usually not a problem: the iron in breast milk is well absorbed, and regular cow's milk is not recommended for babies younger than 1 year. Iron deficiency may develop in older infants who do not eat enough iron-rich foods.

Gastroesophageal Reflux

Gastroesophageal reflux is the regurgitation of the stomach contents into the esophagus after a feeding. This type of spitting up occurs in 3 percent of newborns, usually males, and typically disappears within 12 to 18 months. Concern is warranted if reflux makes a child difficult to feed or results in coughing, choking, or frequent vomiting. Adding cereal to bottle feedings is not recommended for a baby who has reflux.

Diarrhea

Stool patterns vary from infant to infant, as well as in the same infant over time. Healthy, thriving breastfed infants may have up to 12 stools per day—or only 1 per week. Formula-fed infants usually have one to seven bowel movements per day. Diarrhea—the frequent passage of loose, watery stools—can rapidly dehydrate an infant. Infants with diarrhea require increased fluids, and caregivers should consult the child's pediatrician for specific advice about how to meet this need.

Failure to Thrive

Full-term infants who experience poor growth in the absence of disease or physical defect suffer from **failure to thrive (FTT)**. (See **Figure 16.22**.) Although this can occur at any age, in infancy it usually occurs in the second half of the first year. Common causes include poverty and a resulting shortage of food, inappropriate foods in an infant's diet, improper formula preparation, or excessive consumption of fruit juice or fruit drinks. (See the FYI feature "Fruit Juices and Drinks.") In addition, well-meaning parents may introduce low-fat or nonfat milk in an attempt to prevent obesity. Babies need a high-fat diet to support normal growth and brain development. As stated, regular cow's milk should not be introduced before age 1. Low-fat milks are inappropriate for children younger than 2 years.

Untreated, FTT can delay cognitive, motor, and language development. Studies indicate, however, that intensive intervention can correct FTT and allow resumption of a normal growth pattern. Such intervention includes nutrition education for caregivers, maintenance of food records by the caregiver, frequent weight checks of the infant, and perhaps social service intervention for the family.

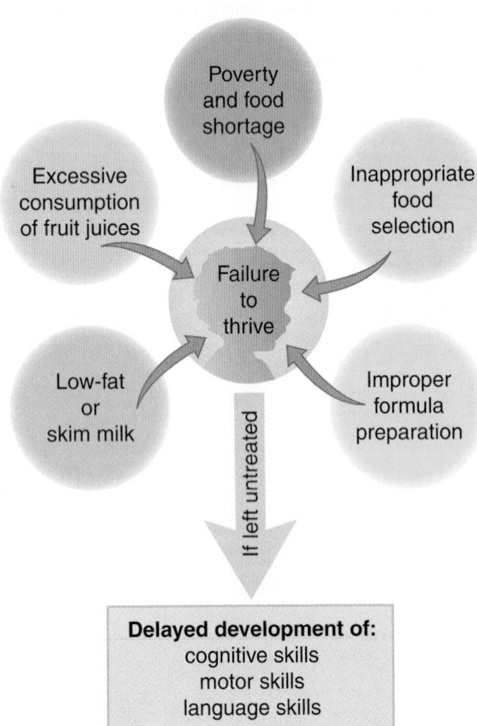

Figure 16.22 **Failure to thrive.** Failure to thrive can result from many different causes. If untreated, the effects are lifelong.

Although there is nothing complex about the nutrient needs and food choices appropriate for babies, it is important for caregivers to receive some education about proper feeding. Some practices that we learn from friends, parents, and other family members, or remember from our own childhood, are inappropriate for babies. Studies show that even people who receive nutrition education in the WIC program introduce solid foods much too early and feed infants sweetened tea, soft drinks, and other inappropriate foods.[73] Newborns don't come with instructions, but caregivers can always turn to a pediatrician or registered dietitian for answers to feeding questions.

Key Concepts *Feeding-related problems of infancy include colic, baby bottle tooth decay, iron-deficiency anemia, gastroesophageal reflux, diarrhea, and failure to thrive. Usually minor adjustments in food choices or feeding techniques solve these problems; however, caregivers may need the guidance of a pediatrician or registered dietitian.*

Fruit Juices and Drinks

Fruit juices are popular beverages for children aged 6 months to 5 years. Juices do have benefits to the diet. They are refreshing and sweet; accessible and affordable; more healthful than soft drinks; and provide energy, water, and selected minerals and vitamins. A glass of 100-percent fruit juice counts as one fruit serving. If juice is being used as a source of vitamin C, drinking just 3 to 6 fluid ounces per day meets vitamin C intake recommendations.

High fruit juice consumption among young children has been implicated as a contributing factor to both failure to thrive and obesity. Failure to thrive may result if fruit juices replace other food sources (particularly milk) or if sorbitol and fructose, found in higher amounts in apple and pear juice, cause diarrhea and malabsorption.[1] The link between excessive juice consumption and obesity has not been proven;[2] however, studies suggest that it is more likely to be a factor in those children who are at risk for overweight and obesity.[3]

The vast array of juice drinks and fruit beverages available in the marketplace can make it difficult for parents to find nutritious choices. At best, these beverages contain added vitamin C and, in some cases, vitamin A and calcium. However, beverages that are less than 100-percent fruit juice are more like soft drinks than fruits and, as such, should be severely limited in the diets of young children.

To keep intake of fruit juices to a healthy level, the American Academy of Pediatrics recommends the following practices:[4]

- Wait until at least 6 months of age before introducing juice.
- Avoid giving infants juice in bottles or other containers that allow easy consumption throughout the day. Avoid giving juice at bedtime.
- Limit consumption of fruit juice to 4 to 6 fluid ounces per day for children 1 to 6 years old.
- Encourage caregivers to offer fruit rather than fruit juice to children.
- Determine the amount of juice being consumed when evaluating children with malnutrition (overnutrition and undernutrition) and in children with dental caries.
- Educate parents about the differences between fruit juice and fruit drinks.

1 Nobugrot T, Chasalow F, Lifshitz F. Carbohydrate absorption from one serving of fruit juice in young children: age and carbohydrate composition effects. *J Am Coll Nutr.* 1997;16:152–158.

2 O'Connor TM, Yang S, Nicklas TA. Beverage intake among preschool children and its effect on weight status. *Pediatrics.* 2006;188:1010–1018.

3 Faith MS, Dennison B, Edmunds LS, Stratton HH. Fruit juice intake predicts increased adiposity gain in children from low-income families: weight status-by-environment interaction. *Pediatrics.* 2006;118:2066–2075; and Nelson JA, Carpenter K; Chiasson MA. Diet, activity, and overweight among preschool-age children enrolled in the Special Supplemental Nutrition Program for Women, Infants, and Children (WIC). *Prev Chronic Dis.* April 2006. http://www.cdc.gov/pcd/issues/2006/apr/05_0135.htm. Accessed 58/21/09.

4 American Academy of Pediatrics Committee on Nutrition. Policy statement. The use and misuse of fruit juice in pediatrics. *Pediatrics.* 2001;107:1210–1213. Statement reaffirmed October 2006. *Pediatrics.* 2007;119:405.

A pregnant woman requires more nutrients than usual. The RDA for both iron and folate increases by 50 percent during pregnancy. Iron, especially, is difficult to get in this quantity from the diet. Enriched grains and fortified foods, such as cereals, make it easier to obtain these essential nutrients. Let's take a look at the Nutrition Facts label from a popular breakfast cereal.

Take a look at how much folic acid a 1-cup serving of this breakfast cereal contains—50% DV (DV = 400 micrograms). The DV for folate is the same as the RDA for nonpregnant women; for pregnancy, the RDA increases to 600 micrograms. If orange juice accompanies the cereal, another 15% DV (60 mg) is added for a 1-cup serving. So, these two foods provide a substantial amount of the folate that a pregnant woman would need.

Iron also is extremely important for pregnancy because of its role in growth and its importance as blood volume increases during pregnancy. One serving of this breakfast cereal provides almost half of the DV of 18 milligrams (45 percent of 18 milligrams equals 8 milligrams). However, during pregnancy, the RDA for iron is 27 milligrams. So, one serving of this cereal provides nearly one-third of the iron needed each day—a good start. Having orange juice with the cereal will enhance iron absorption.

Nutrition Facts

Serving Size: 1 cup (30g)

Servings Per Container about 9

Amount Per Serving	Cheerios	with 1/2 cup skim milk
Calories	110	150
Calories from Fat	15	20
% Daily Value**		
Total Fat 2g*	3%	3%
Saturated Fat 0g	0%	3%
Trans Fat 0g		
Polyunsaturated Fat 0.5g		
Monounsaturated Fat 0.5g		
Cholesterol 0g	0%	1%
Sodium 280mg	12%	15%
Total Carbohydrate 22g	7%	9%
Dietary Fiber 0g	11%	11%
Sugars 1g		
Protein 3g		
Vitamin A	10%	15%
Vitamin C	10%	10%
Calcium	4%	20%
Iron	45%	45%
Vitamin D	10%	25%
Thiamin	25%	30%
Riboflavin	25%	35%
Niacin	25%	25%
Vitamin B_6	25%	25%
Folic Acid	50%	50%
Vitamin B_{12}	25%	35%
Phosphorus	10%	25%

Learning Portfolio

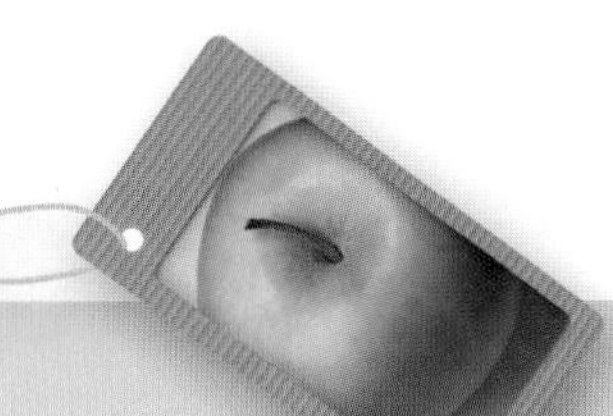

Key Terms

	page		page
amniotic fluid	678	let-down reflex	689
blastogenic stage	674	low-birth-weight infant	672
colic	691	morning sickness	672
colostrum	688	neonate	697
complementary foods	701	organogenesis	674
critical period of development	674	oxytocin	688
eclampsia	686	placenta	674
embryonic stage	674	preeclampsia	686
extrusion reflex	701	prematurity	693
failure to thrive (FTT)	704	preterm delivery	671
fetal stage	674	prolactin	688
full-term baby	693	Special Supplemental Nutrition Program for Women, Infants, and Children (WIC)	693
gastroesophageal reflux	704	toddler	695
growth charts	695	trimesters	673
head circumference	695		
infancy	693		
lactation	676		
lactation consultants	697		

Study Points

- Nutritional status before pregnancy is an important part of having a healthy baby. Moreover, it is an integral part of all aspects of preconception care: risk assessment, health promotion, and intervention. Being either overweight or underweight prior to pregnancy increases risk of complications.
- Folic acid supplementation before pregnancy has been shown to reduce the risk of neural tube defects such as spina bifida.
- Excessive intake of some vitamins (vitamin A, in particular) and use of tobacco, alcohol, and drugs increase the risk of poor pregnancy outcomes; women should discontinue these practices before they become pregnant.
- Pregnancy can be divided into three stages: blastogenic, embryonic, and fetal. In the blastogenic stage, the fertilized ovum begins rapid cell division and implants itself in the uterine wall. During the embryonic stage, organ systems and other body structures form. During the fetal stage, the longest period of pregnancy, the fetus grows in size and changes in proportions.
- Women who enter pregnancy at a normal BMI should gain 25 to 35 pounds during pregnancy. Underweight women should gain more weight, and overweight women less. Energy needs increase by 340 to 450 kilocalories per day for the second and third trimesters.
- By using the MyPlate Daily Food Plans for Pregnancy and Breastfeeding to plan food intake, pregnant women who consume enough energy should be able to meet all their nutrient needs with the exception of iron and folate. They should get needed extra calories mainly from grains, fruits, and vegetables.
- Limiting caffeine intake during pregnancy is recommended. Smoking during pregnancy increases the risk of preterm delivery and low birth weight. Alcohol and drug use can interfere with normal fetal development and should be avoided during pregnancy.
- Gastrointestinal distress such as morning sickness, heartburn, and constipation are common during pregnancy and result from the action of various hormones on the GI tract. Although most food cravings or aversions present no problems, excessive consumption of nonfood items, known as pica, interferes with adequate nutrition.
- During pregnancy, hormones control the development of breast tissue in preparation for milk production. Colostrum, the first milk, which is rich in protein and antibodies, is produced soon after delivery. By two to three weeks after delivery, lactation is well established, and mature milk is being produced.
- The pituitary hormone prolactin stimulates milk production. Oxytocin, another pituitary hormone, stimulates milk release, which is known as the let-down reflex.
- Unless they reduce their physical activity, breastfeeding women need 330 to 400 more kilocalories per day than they did when they were not pregnant. By obtaining adequate energy and using the MyPlate Daily Food Plans for Pregnancy and Breastfeeding to balance choices, most lactating women can obtain all the nutrients they need from their diet. Cigarettes, alcohol, and illicit drugs should not be used while breastfeeding.
- Mothers benefit from breastfeeding through enhanced physiologic recovery, convenience, and emotional bonding. Contraindications to breastfeeding include infection with HIV or active tuberculosis, and regular use of certain medications.

- Infants receive optimal nutrition from human milk. Breastfeeding can reduce the incidence of infectious diseases, allergies, and other problems during infancy.
- La Leche League, the March of Dimes, and the WIC program for low-income women are among the numerous resources for support and education of pregnant and breastfeeding women.
- Infancy is the fastest growth stage in the life cycle; infants double their birth weight in 4 to 6 months and triple it by 1 year of age. The nutritional status of infants is assessed primarily through measurements of growth.
- Infants' energy needs must be met through a high-fat diet, which provides the maximum calories in minimal volume. Infants' protein and fluid needs are also high.
- Human milk is low in vitamin D; breastfed babies need regular sun exposure or supplemental vitamin D. For breastfed infants, iron-fortified foods need to be introduced by 6 months of age. Formula-fed infants should be given iron-fortified formula.
- Infant formulas usually are based on either cow's milk or soy protein. Unmodified cow's milk is inappropriate for infants throughout the first year of life.
- The FDA regulates the vitamin and mineral composition of infant formulas to ensure adequate infant nutrition. Formula is available in ready-to-feed, liquid concentrate, and powdered forms.
- A nurturing environment is important to the feeding of infants, no matter what the milk source.
- Solid foods are introduced to the infant one at a time, usually beginning with iron-fortified infant cereal. Potential allergens, such as cow's milk, egg whites, and wheat, should be delayed until the baby is at least 12 months old. Developmental markers, such as head and body control and the absence of the extrusion reflex, show readiness for solid foods.
- Colic, although troublesome to infant and caregiver, is not caused by diet. Iron-deficiency anemia is common in infants who lack iron-rich foods. Infants are susceptible to dehydration, especially when diarrhea is prolonged. Failure to thrive describes an infant who is not growing well; intervention may be required to correct the feeding practices of caregivers.

Study Questions

1. Describe the three stages of fetal growth.
2. What are some of the physiological changes that occur in a woman during pregnancy?
3. How do the recommended intake values for calories, protein, folate, and iron change for pregnancy?
4. What contributes to morning sickness, and how can a woman minimize its effects?
5. What are some of the benefits of breastfeeding for the infant? For the mother?
6. Is it okay for an infant to experience weight loss immediately after birth? If an infant does lose weight, does it mean he or she is at nutritional risk?
7. How much water does a breastfed or formula-fed infant need each day?
8. Is it necessary to give breastfed infants supplements of vitamins and/or minerals? If so, which ones?
9. Describe the process for introducing solid foods into an infant's diet.
10. List the feeding problems that may occur during infancy.

Try This

For Just One Week, Can You Eat Like You're Expecting?

The purpose of this exercise is to see if you can follow the nutrition guidelines for pregnancy for just one week. Keep in mind that pregnant women attempt to do this for 38 to 40 weeks! Your goal is to reduce or eliminate caffeine, alcohol, and over-the-counter medications. Make an effort to eat according to MyPlate each day, selecting the most nutrient-dense choices from each group. You should also take a basic multivitamin/mineral tablet (in place of a woman's prenatal supplement) daily. This will ensure that you consume the amounts of vitamins and minerals recommended for pregnancy.

Costs of Infant Formula

The purpose of this exercise is to find out how much it might cost to feed an infant. An average 3-month-old baby weighs about 13 pounds (6 kilograms) and would need about 650 kilocalories per day. Using standard infant formula, this baby would need about 32 ounces of formula each day. Now, go to a grocery store and find the infant formulas. If you were to purchase ready-to-feed formula, how much would it cost to feed this baby for one day? What if you were to use concentrated liquid formula? Powdered formula?

What About Bobbie?

Let's pretend that Bobbie is pregnant and in her second trimester. She wants to know whether she's meeting her basic nutrient needs by following her usual diet. Refer to Chapter 1 to review her one-day intake. How do you think she's doing? Let's compare Bobbie's intake of nutrients to the recommendations for pregnant women.

Protein

If you remember reviewing Bobbie's diet after reading Chapter 6, "Proteins and Amino Acids," you may recall that it is quite high in protein. Her intake was 96 grams, and her nonpregnancy RDA (based on her weight) was 56 grams. During pregnancy, however, Bobbie needs extra protein to ensure her body can handle the demands of tissue growth. An extra 25 grams per day (for a total of 81 grams) is adequate to meet the needs of pregnancy. Bobbie's intake is higher than this and could be reduced.

Folate

Bobbie's intake of folate was 650 micrograms, which is consistent with her pregnancy RDA of 600 micrograms. Her intake is mainly from enriched grains. By adding other folate-rich foods to her diet, such as spinach, legumes, and orange juice, she would obtain other vital nutrients. If Bobbie is adhering to proper prenatal care, then she is consuming a prenatal supplement with folic acid as well.

Iron

Bobbie's intake of iron for one day was 20 milligrams. This is substantially lower than her pregnancy RDA of 27 milligrams. This places Bobbie at greater risk for iron-deficiency anemia, a common condition in pregnancy. In addition to taking a prenatal supplement that contains iron, Bobbie is advised to continue choosing iron-rich lean red meats, such as beef meatballs, for dinner. She would also benefit from adding more dark-green leafy vegetables to her diet, along with a squeeze of lemon (or other source of vitamin C) to increase the absorption of the nonheme iron. With these additions to her diet, Bobbie will lower her chances of having iron-deficiency anemia during her pregnancy.

References

1 Centers for Disease Control and Prevention. Recommendations to improve preconception health and health care—United States. *MMWR Recomm Rep*. 2006;55(RR-06):1–23. http://www.cdc.gov/mmwr/preview/mmwrhtml/rr5506a1.htm. Accessed 8/12/09.

2 Salihu HM, Mbah AK, Alio AP, et al. Low pre-pregnancy body mass index and risk of medically indicated versus spontaneous preterm singleton birth. *Eur J Obstet Gynecol Reprod Biol*. 2009;144(2):119–123.

3 Rasmussen KM, Yaktine AL, eds. *Weight Gain During Pregnancy: Reexamining the Guidelines*. Washington, DC: National Academies Press, 2009.

4 Ibid.

5 Ibid.

6 Institute of Medicine, Food and Nutrition Board. *Dietary Reference Intakes for Thiamin, Riboflavin, Niacin, Vitamin B_6, Folate, Vitamin B_{12}, Pantothenic Acid, Biotin, and Choline*. Washington, DC: National Academies Press, 1998.

7 Mathews TJ. *Trends in spina bifida and anencephalus in the United States, 1991–2006*. National Center for Health Statistics. http://www.cdc.gov/nchs/products/pubs/pubd/hestats/spine_anen.htm. Accessed 8/13/09.

8 Rasmussen, Yaktine. *Weight Gain During Pregnancy*.

9 Ibid.

10 Ibid.

11 Ibid.

12 Institute of Medicine, Food and Nutrition Board. *Dietary Reference Intakes for Energy, Carbohydrate, Fiber, Fat, Fatty Acids, Cholesterol, Protein, and Amino Acids*. Washington, DC: National Academies Press, 2002.

13 Ibid.

14 American Dietetic Association. Position of the American Dietetic Association: nutrition and lifestyle for a healthy pregnancy outcome. *J Am Diet Assoc*. 2008;108:553–561.

15 U.S. Preventive Services Task Force. Folic acid for the prevention of neural tube defects: U.S. Preventive Services Task Force recommendation statement. *Ann Intern Med*. 2009;150(9):626–631.

16 USDA Choose MyPlate.Gov Daily Food Plans for Pregnancy and Breastfeeding. June 4, 2011. http://www.choosemyplate.gov/mypyramidmoms/index.html. Accessed 10/9/11.

17 Institute of Medicine, Food and Nutrition Board. *Dietary Reference Intakes for Energy, Carbohydrate*.

18 American Dietetic Association. Nutrition and lifestyle for a healthy pregnancy.

19 Pick ME, Edwards M, Moreau D, Ryan EA. Assessment of diet quality in pregnant women using the Healthy Eating Index. *J Am Diet Assoc*. 2005;105:240–246.

20 US Department of Health and Human Services and US Environmental Protection Agency. What you need to know about mercury in fish and shellfish. March 2004. http://www.cfsan.fda.gov/~dms/admehg3.html. Accessed 8/16/09.

21 Higdon JV, Frei B. Coffee and health: a review of recent human research. *Crit Rev Food Sci Nutr*. 2006;46:101–123.

22 American Dietetic Association. Nutrition and lifestyle for a healthy pregnancy.

23 Raatikainen K, Huurinainen P, Heinonen S. Smoking in early gestation or through pregnancy: a decision crucial to pregnancy outcome. *Prev Med*. 2007;44:59–63.

24 March of Dimes. Illicit drug use during pregnancy. January 2008. http://www.marchofdimes.com/professionals/14332_1169.asp. Accessed 8/16/09.

25 Corbetet RW, Ryan C, Weinrich SP. Pica in pregnancy: does it affect pregnancy outcomes? *Am J Matern Child Nurs*. 2003;28:183–189.

26 Turner RE. Nutrition during pregnancy. In: Shils ME, Ross AC, Shike M, et al., eds. *Modern Nutrition in Health and Disease*. 10th ed. Baltimore, MD: Lippincott Williams & Wilkins, 2006; and Rumbold AR, Crowther CA, Haslam RR, et al. Vitamins C and E and the risks of preeclampsia and perinatal complications. *N Engl J Med*. 2006;354(17):1796–1806.

27 American Dietetic Association. Nutrition and lifestyle for a healthy pregnancy.

28 March of Dimes. HIV and AIDS in pregnancy. May 2009. http://www.marchofdimes.com/professionals/14332_1223.asp. Accessed 8/16/09.

29 Centers for Disease Control and Prevention. Adolescent reproductive health. July 2009. http://www.cdc.gov/Reproductivehealth/AdolescentReproHealth/index.htm. Accessed 8/16/09.

30 March of Dimes. Quick references fact sheet: teenage pregnancy. March 2009. http://www.marchofdimes.com/professionals/14332_1159.asp. Accessed 8/16/09.

31 Ibid.

32 Centers for Disease Control and Prevention. 2008 Pediatric Nutrition Surveillance: national summary of trends in breastfeeding children aged < 5 years. http://www.cdc.gov/pednss/pednss_tables/pdf/national_table13.pdf. Accessed 8/18/09.

33 Centers for Disease Control and Prevention. Breastfeeding practices: results from the National Immunization Survey. http://www.cdc.gov/breastfeeding/data/NIS_data/data_2004.htm. Accessed 8/17/09.

34 Centers for Disease Control and Prevention. 2008 Pediatric Nutrition Surveillance.

35 Ryan A, Wenjun Z, Acosta A. Breastfeeding continues to increase into the new millennium. *Pediatrics*. 2002;110:1103–1109.

36 US Department of Health and Human Services. Nutrition and fitness for Mom. February 2009. http://www.womenshealth.gov/breastfeeding/living/nutritionFitness.cfm. Accessed 8/17/09.

37 American Academy of Pediatrics. Policy statement. Breastfeeding and the use of human milk. *Pediatrics*. 2005;115:496–506.

38 US Department of Health and Human Services. When not to breastfeed. February 2009. http://www.womenshealth.gov/breastfeeding/notto/. Accessed 8/17/09.

39 American Academy of Pediatrics. Breastfeeding and the use of human milk.

40 Ibid.; and American Dietetic Association. Position of the American Dietetic Association: promoting and supporting breastfeeding. *J Am Diet Assoc*. 2005;105:810–843.

41 Ibid.

42 Niers L, Stasse-Wolthuis M, Rombouts FM, Rijkers GT. Nutritional support for the infant's immune system. *Nutr Rev*. 2007;65(8 pt 1):347–360.

43 Hanson LA, Korotkova M, Lundin S, et al. The transfer of immunity from mother to child. *Ann NY Acad Sci*. 2003;987:199–206.

44 Kramer MS, Aboud F, Mironova E, et al. Breastfeeding and child cognitive development: new evidence from a large randomized trial. *Arch Gen Psychiatry*. 2008;65(5):578–584.

45 American Academy of Pediatrics. Breastfeeding and the use of human milk.

46 Centers for Disease Control and Prevention. 2008 Pediatric Nutrition Surveillance.

47 Riordan J, Wambach K. *Breastfeeding and Human Lactation*. 4th ed. Sudbury, MA: Jones & Bartlett, 2010.

48 Black MM, Cutts DB, Frank DA, et al. Special Supplemental Nutrition Program of Women, Infants, and Children participation and infants' growth and health: a multisite surveillance study. *Pediatrics*. 2004;114:169–176.

49 Jacknowitz A, Novello D, Tiehen L. Special Supplemental Nutrition Program for Women, Infants, and Children and infant feeding practices. *Pediatrics*. 2007;119:281–289.

50 Montgomery DL, Splett PL. Economic benefits of breast-feeding infants enrolled in WIC. *J Am Diet Assoc*. 1997;97:379–386.

51 Institute of Medicine, Food and Nutrition Board. *Dietary Reference Intakes for Energy, Carbohydrate.*

52 Ibid.

53 Ibid.

54 Ibid.

55 Institute of Medicine, Food and Nutrition Board. *Dietary Reference Intakes for Water, Potassium, Sodium, Chloride, and Sulfate*. Washington, DC: National Academies Press, 2004.

56 Wagner CL, Greer FR, Section on Breastfeeding and Committee on Nutrition. Prevention of rickets and vitamin D deficiency in infants, children, and adolescents. *Pediatrics*. 2008;122(5):1142–1152.

57 Ibid.

58 Ibid.

59 Kleinman RE, ed. *Pediatric Nutrition Handbook*. 6th ed. Elk Grove Village, IL: American Academy of Pediatrics, 2008.

60 Ibid.

61 American Academy of Pediatrics. Breastfeeding and the use of human milk.

62 Kleinman. *Pediatric Nutrition Handbook*.

63 Simmer K, Patole SK, Rao SC. Longchain polyunsaturated fatty acid supplementation in infants born at term. *Cochrane Database Syst Rev*. 2008;(1):CD000376.

64 O'Connor NR. Infant formula. *Am Fam Physician*. 2009;79(7):565–570.

65 Auestad N, Scott DT, Janowsky JS, et al. Visual, cognitive, and language assessments at 39 months: a follow-up study of children fed formulas containing long-chain polyunsaturated fatty acids to 1 year of age. *Pediatrics*. 2003;112:177–183; and Thorpe M. Infant formula supplemented with DHA: are there benefits? *J Am Diet Assoc*. 2003;103:551–552.

66 Pac S, McMahon K, Ripple M, et al. Development of the *Start Healthy Feeding Guidelines for Infants and Toddlers*. *J Am Diet Assoc*. 2004;104:455–467.

67 Butte N, Cobb K, Dwyer J, et al. The *Start Healthy Feeding Guidelines for Infants and Toddlers*. *J Am Diet Assoc*. 2004;104:442–454.

68 Goldfarb MF. Relation of time of introduction of cow milk protein to an infant and risk of type-1 diabetes mellitus. *J Proteome Res*. 2008;7:2165–2167.

69 Needham L, Dwyer JJ, Randall-Simpson J, Heeney ES. Supporting healthy eating among preschoolers: challenges for child care staff. *Can J Diet Pract Res*. 2007;68(2):107–110.

70 Clifford TJ, Campbell K, Speechley KN, Gorodzinsky F. Infant colic: empirical evidence of the absence of an association with source of early infant nutrition. *Arch Pediatr Adolesc Med*. 2002;156:1123–1128.

71 American Academy of Pediatric Dentistry. Policy on early childhood caries (ECC): unique challenges and treatment options. Revised 2008. http://www.aapd.org/media/Policies_Guidelines/P_ECCUniqueChallenges.pdf. Accessed 8/20/09.

72 National Maternal and Child Oral Health Resource Center. Promoting awareness, preventing pain: facts on early childhood caries (ECC). 2004. http://www.mchoralhealth.org/PDFs/ECCFactSheet.pdf. Accessed 8/20/09.

73 Jacknowitz, Novello, Tiehen. Special Supplemental Nutrition Program for Women, Infants, and Children and infant feeding practices.

CHAPTER 17

Life Cycle

From Childhood Through Adulthood

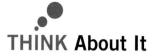

THINK About It

1 Were you a "picky" eater as a child? What about now?

2 What's your experience with acne and eating particular foods?

3 What behavior changes would you consider making now that would help you live longer?

4 Your grandfather lives by himself and relies on frozen foods for his nutritional needs. How do you feel about his diet?

Visit nutrition.jbpub.com

It's the year 2050. Who are you? Where do you live? What is your life like? How healthy are you? If projections made earlier in the century were accurate, you are part of the largest segment of the population—in 2050 between one-third and one-fourth of Americans are older than 65. Perhaps you have retired recently, or maybe you continue to work in your profession. Think about how technology has changed in your lifetime; new methods of communication have been developed that make e-mail and the Internet seem so old-fashioned, so late twentieth century!

Consider how much you have changed over the years. Throughout childhood and adolescence you were growing, sometimes quite rapidly! Whether you fueled that growth with burgers and fries, black beans and rice, chips and soft drinks, or yogurt and salads will have determined a lot about your health status in 2050. Did you continue the eating habits you had in college, and did these allow you to control your weight, blood cholesterol, and blood pressure? Or perhaps in the year 2050 these conditions are no longer of concern. Advances in genetics may have allowed gene therapy to replace diet therapy and medications for chronic diseases.

In the last chapter, we explored the nutritional needs of pregnant and breastfeeding women and their babies. Now we will look at how continued growth in childhood and adolescence affects nutritional needs. In addition, we'll see how nutritional needs change as we age, and we'll consider feeding practices, meal planning, and obstacles to healthful eating for each age group.

Childhood

childhood The period of life from age 1 to the onset of puberty.

adolescence The period between onset of puberty and adulthood.

Childhood is the term that refers to the years from age 1 through the beginning of **adolescence**. Growth in childhood, although continuous, occurs at a significantly slower rate than in infancy. During the childhood years, a typical child will gain about 5 pounds and grow 2 to 3 inches each year. Children can be divided into three groups based on their age and development: toddlers (ages 1–3), preschoolers (ages 4–5), and school-aged children (ages 6–10).

Energy and Nutrient Needs During Childhood

An average 1-year-old requires about 850 to 1,000 kilocalories per day.[1] This daily energy requirement gradually increases until it almost doubles by around age 10.

Estimated Energy Requirements (EER) for children can be calculated based on sex, age, height, weight, and activity level (see Table 17.1). In contrast to the 175 kilocalories per day needed during early infancy, the added energy cost for growth during childhood is only 20 kilocalories per day.

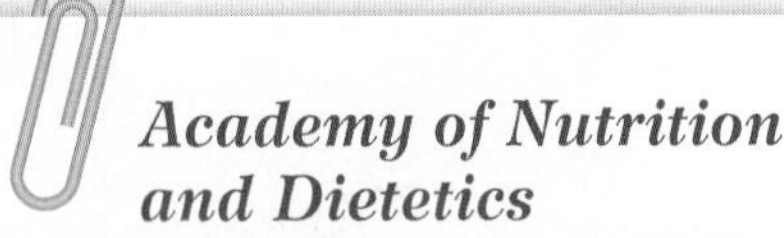

Academy of Nutrition and Dietetics

Dietary Guidance for Healthy Children Aged 2 to 11 Years

It is the position of the Academy of Nutrition and Dietetics that children ages 2 to 11 years should achieve optimal physical and cognitive development, attain a healthy weight, enjoy food, and reduce the risk of chronic disease through appropriate eating habits and participation in regular physical activity.

Source: Position of the American Dietetic Association: dietary guidelines for healthy children aged 2 to 11 years. *J Am Diet Assoc.* 2004;104(4):660–677. Copyright © 2004. Reprinted with permission from Elsevier.

Energy and Protein

Although total energy requirements increase, the kilocalories needed per kilogram of body weight slowly decrease as children move through childhood. The same is true for protein requirements (see Table 17.2).

Vitamins and Minerals

As long as a healthy child cooperates by eating a variety of healthful foods, a well-planned diet should provide most of the nutrients a child needs. One exception is iron. Children aged 4 to 8 years require 10 milligrams of iron per day, but may not get that amount without careful meal planning. High

Table 17.1 Estimated Energy Requirement Equations for Children (Ages 3 Through 8)

Males

EER = 88.5 – 61.9 × age [y] + PA × (26.7 × weight [kg] + 903 × height [m]) + 20 kcal/day

Physical activity (PA)

Sedentary = 1.00; Low active = 1.13;
Active = 1.26; Very active = 1.42

Females

EER = 135.3 – 30.8 × age [y] + PA × (10.0 × weight [kg] + 934 × height [m]) + 20 kcal/day

Physical activity (PA)

Sedentary = 1.0; Low active = 1.16;
Active = 1.31; Very active = 1.56

Source: Reproduced from Institute of Medicine, Food and Nutrition Board. *Dietary Reference Intakes for Energy, Carbohydrate, Fiber, Fat, Fatty Acids, Cholesterol, Protein, and Amino Acids (Macronutrients).* Copyright © 2005 by the National Academy of Sciences, courtesy of the National Academies Press, Washington, DC.

consumption of milk, a poor source of iron, can contribute to inadequate iron intake, and so milk intake during childhood should be limited to 3 to 4 cups per day. This allows room in the diet for high-iron food sources such as lean meats, legumes, fish, poultry, and iron-enriched breads and cereals. (See Table 17.3.) Iron deficiency not only affects growth, but also can impair the child's mood, attention span, focus, and ability to learn.[2]

Seventy percent of American children do not get enough vitamin D. Among U.S. children aged 1 to 21 in 2001 through 2004, 7.6 million, or 9 percent, were vitamin D deficient, and another 50.8 million, or 61 percent, had insufficient levels of vitamin D.[3] Traditionally rickets was the primary disease of concern with childhood vitamin D deficiency. New evidence links low levels of vitamin D to increased adverse cardiovascular risks, including high blood pressure and lower levels of high-density lipoprotein in children[4] and hypertension, hyperglycemia, and metabolic syndrome in adolescents regardless of body weight.[5] The American Academy of Pediatrics recommends that children and adolescents who do not obtain enough dietary vitamin D from fortified foods receive a supplement of 400 IU per day.[6]

A child's diet also may be low in other micronutrients, especially calcium, magnesium, potassium, and vitamin E.[7] (See **Figure 17.1**.) American children

Table 17.2 Protein RDAs for Childhood

Age (y)	Protein (g/kg)	Reference Weight* (kg)	Protein (g/d)
1–3	1.10	12	13
4–8	0.95	20	19

*Reference weights are based on median weights of children in that age group.

Source: Reproduced from Institute of Medicine, Food and Nutrition Board. *Dietary Reference Intakes for Energy, Carbohydrate, Fiber, Fat, Fatty Acids, Cholesterol, Protein, and Amino Acids.* Copyright © 2002 by the National Academy of Sciences, courtesy of National Academies Press, Washington, DC.

Table 17.3 Iron-Rich Foods and Snacks

Iron-Rich Foods

Ground beef
Poultry
Fish
Legumes
Dark-green vegetables
Enriched breads, cereals, rice, and pasta

Iron-Rich Snacks

Cream of Wheat
Cooked macaroni or pasta
Enriched cereals, either dry or with milk
Tortillas filled with refried beans
Dried apricots
Raisins (for older children)
Bean dip
Chili, mildly seasoned
Peanut butter on enriched bread or graham crackers
Sloppy Joe
Casseroles with meat (many children do not like plain meats)

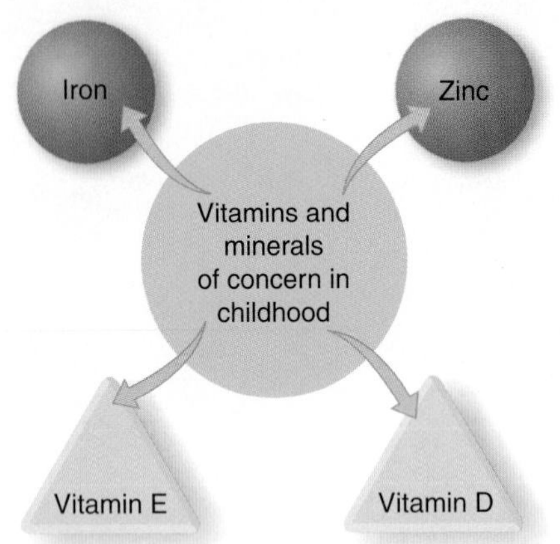

Figure 17.1 **Micronutrients of concern in childhood.** Milk is low in iron, and small children also may have low intakes of magnesium, potassium, calcium, and vitamin E.

do not consistently meet the recommendations of MyPlate for the fruit, grain, and dairy groups, which are important sources of these nutrients.

Vitamin and Mineral Supplements

Many caregivers would rather give a child a vitamin/mineral pill than plan and prepare the meals necessary to ensure an adequate diet. However, the balanced diet a child needs is not much different from the diet an adult needs. In fact, the old MyPyramid (see **Figure 17.2**) and the current MyPlate recommendations for children are the same balance of food groups as is recommended for adults. Caregivers who understand this may be less tempted to rely on supplements make the effort to achieve a balanced diet.

Some children should receive supplements. Among them are children whose diets are restricted for medical reasons, those with chronic diseases, those who are malnourished, and those with food allergies that require them to avoid multiple foods or food groups.[8] (For more on food allergies, see the FYI feature "Food Hypersensitivities and Allergies.") Caregivers need to be

(a)

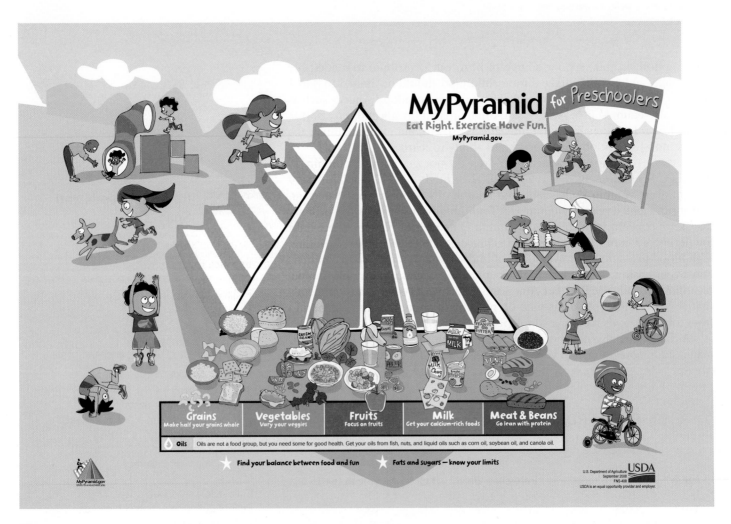

Figure 17.2 **(a) MyPyramid for Preschoolers and (b) MyPyramid for Kids.** Children's needs for a variety of foods and regular physical activity were reflected in pyramids designed just for them.

Source: US Department of Agriculture. www.MyPyramid.gov.

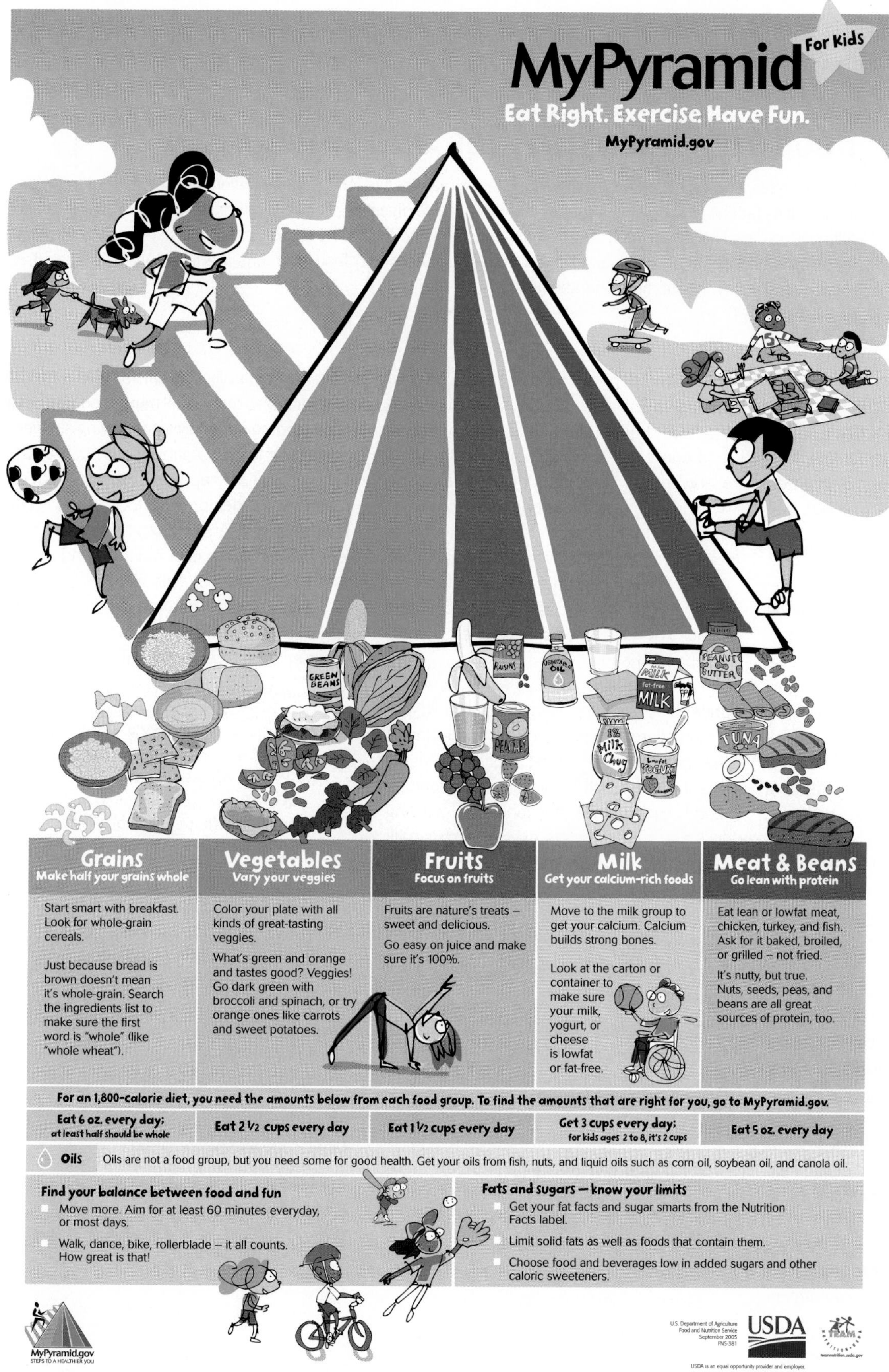
MyPyramid For Kids
Eat Right. Exercise. Have Fun.
MyPyramid.gov
GREEN BEANS
RAISINS
VEGETABLE OIL
fat-free MILK
PEANUT BUTTER
TUNA
PEACHES
1% Milk Chug
Lowfat YOGURT
Grains
Make half your grains whole
Start smart with breakfast. Look for whole-grain cereals.
Just because bread is brown doesn't mean it's whole-grain. Search the ingredients list to make sure the first word is "whole" (like "whole wheat").
Vegetables
Vary your veggies
Color your plate with all kinds of great-tasting veggies.
What's green and orange and tastes good? Veggies! Go dark green with broccoli and spinach, or try orange ones like carrots and sweet potatoes.
Fruits
Focus on fruits
Fruits are nature's treats – sweet and delicious.
Go easy on juice and make sure it's 100%.
Milk
Get your calcium-rich foods
Move to the milk group to get your calcium. Calcium builds strong bones.
Look at the carton or container to make sure your milk, yogurt, or cheese is lowfat or fat-free.
Meat & Beans
Go lean with protein
Eat lean or lowfat meat, chicken, turkey, and fish. Ask for it baked, broiled, or grilled – not fried.
It's nutty, but true. Nuts, seeds, peas, and beans are all great sources of protein, too.
For an 1,800-calorie diet, you need the amounts below from each food group. To find the amounts that are right for you, go to MyPyramid.gov.
Eat 6 oz. every day; at least half should be whole
Eat 2 1/2 cups every day
Eat 1 1/2 cups every day
Get 3 cups every day; for kids ages 2 to 8, it's 2 cups
Eat 5 oz. every day
Oils
Oils are not a food group, but you need some for good health. Get your oils from fish, nuts, and liquid oils such as corn oil, soybean oil, and canola oil.
Find your balance between food and fun
Move more. Aim for at least 60 minutes everyday, or most days.
Walk, dance, bike, rollerblade – it all counts. How great is that!
Fats and sugars – know your limits
Get your fat facts and sugar smarts from the Nutrition Facts label.
Limit solid fats as well as foods that contain them.
Choose food and beverages low in added sugars and other caloric sweeteners.
MyPyramid.gov
STEPS TO A HEALTHIER YOU
U.S. Department of Agriculture
Food and Nutrition Service
September 2005
FNS-381
USDA
USDA is an equal opportunity provider and employer.
TEAM

(b)

Food Hypersensitivities and Allergies

Food allergies, or food hypersensitivities, are allergic reactions to food proteins. Allergies are different from food intolerances (such as lactose intolerance) that may involve digestive problems rather than an immune response. Allergies are less likely than intolerances to be transient, and tend to have more serious consequences. Proteins that trigger allergies are known as allergens. The most common food allergens are found in milk, eggs, tree nuts, peanuts, soy, wheat, fish, and shellfish.

Food allergies occur when the immune system mounts a specific reaction to a food protein. About 25 percent of people in the general population think they suffer from food allergies. In 2007, 3.9 percent of children younger than 18 years—that's 3 million, or 4 of every 100 children—were reported to have food or digestive allergies, a figure 18 percent higher than in 1997.[1]

In a true allergic reaction, the immune system responds to an allergen with a cascade of chemical reactions that can cause wheezing, difficulty breathing, and hives, as well as a host of other symptoms. (See **Table 1**, "Symptoms of Food Allergies.") Food allergy symptoms often affect more than one body system and may change in severity from one reaction to the next.

Anaphylaxis, the most severe allergic reaction, usually takes place within the first hour after eating the offending food. Shock and respiratory failure can rapidly ensue. Anaphylaxis can be fatal, so immediate emergency care is essential.

Allergy symptoms that occur immediately after a food is eaten make detective work easier. If symptoms are slow to evolve, a child may suffer chronic diarrhea and even experience failure to thrive before the problem is identified.

When identification of the food culprit isn't so obvious, an elimination diet can help. All suspected foods are eliminated from the diet and slowly reintroduced, one by one, on a specific schedule. Both intake and reactions are carefully recorded. Prolonged or improper use of such a diet can have severe nutritional consequences. A registered dietitian can help with diet planning to ensure nutritional adequacy.

The double-blind, placebo-controlled food challenge is the gold standard of food allergy testing. Although definitive, it can be dangerous for people prone to anaphylactic reactions. In this test, increasing amounts of a suspected food are given to the child under the supervision of a physician, who looks for allergy symptoms and signs. This test must be done by trained personnel with emergency equipment handy.

The treatment for food allergy is avoidance of the offending allergen. Each child with a food allergy needs a nutrition assessment that pays attention to the specific nutrients missing as a result of avoiding the offending foods. For example, if a toddler is avoiding milk and milk products due to a cow's milk allergy, the nutrients most at risk would be protein, vitamin D, and calcium. As a child's diet includes more and more foods, careful label reading is the key to identifying allergen-containing foods. Organizations such as the Food Allergy & Anaphylaxis Network provide materials for deciphering food labels.[2] The Food Allergy & Anaphylaxis Network also offers tips for successful traveling and dining with a child who has food allergies.

Many children naturally outgrow food allergies by the time they are 3 years old. Once outgrown, the food allergy will not return.

1 Branum AM, Lukacs SL. *Food Allergy Among U.S. Children: Trends in Prevalence and Hospitalizations.* October 2008. NCHS Data Brief 10. http://www.cdc.gov/nchs/data/databriefs/db10.htm. Accessed 8/25/09.

2 The Food Allergy & Anaphylaxis Network. http://www.foodallergy.org. Accessed 8/25/09.

Table 1 Symptoms of Food Allergies

Gastrointestinal Tract	Respiratory Tract
Itching of the lips, mouth, and throat	Runny or stuffed-up nose, sneezing, and postnasal discharge
Swelling of the throat	Recurrent croup
Abdominal cramping and distention	Chronic pneumonia
Diarrhea	Middle-ear infections
Colic	**Systemic**
Gastrointestinal bleeding	Anaphylaxis
Protein-losing enteropathy	Heart rhythm irregularities
Skin	Low blood pressure
Hives	
Swelling	
Eczema, contact dermatitis	

reminded that vitamin and mineral supplements for children are dangerous in large doses. Vitamin and mineral preparations must be treated like all medicines and kept safely out of children's reach. Supplements containing iron in doses over 30 milligrams are especially dangerous to children. Accidental consumption of vitamin and mineral or iron supplements should be treated as a poisoning emergency.

Influences on Childhood Food Habits and Intake

Children develop food preferences at an early age. Toddlers start to exhibit unique feeding practices and styles. For some, this means that one food cannot touch another, or that foods cannot be green, or that all foods must be green. All of these "preferences" are merely the toddler's way of exhibiting control over his or her environment while experimenting and exploring. Although it may seem like an eternity to even the most patient caregiver, these food habits are usually temporary. The wise caregiver allows this process to occur naturally, rather than wage food battles that ultimately are always won by the child. Nutrition professionals advocate child-feeding practices in which caregivers are responsible for positive structure, age-appropriate support, and healthful food and beverage choices, and children are responsible for whether and how much to eat. This division of responsibility promotes self-regulation of energy intake.[9]

THINK About It 1

As a child's environment expands, more and more external factors influence the child's diet. It is estimated that children spend more time watching television than doing most other activities. Television advertising influences children's food preferences and purchasing requests.[10] Recognizing the influence that children have on household purchases, advertisers target commercials specifically at children during prime children's viewing hours. Cartoons, for example, feature countless ads for sweetened cereals, fast foods, candy, and other foods high in sugar or fat, none of which are necessary or desirable. Ninety-one percent of food ads during Saturday morning television programming push foods of poor nutritional quality.[11] Studies show an association among young children watching morning television and poor diet, including higher intakes of sugar-sweetened beverages, fast food, red and processed meat, and total energy intake and percent energy intake from trans fat, and lower intakes of fruit and vegetables, calcium, and dietary fiber.[12] When families make television watching a normal part of meal routines, children's diets have fewer fruits and vegetables and more pizzas, snack foods, and sodas than the diets of children in families that separate television viewing and eating.[13]

Social events and parties often promote unhealthful eating habits. No matter what the occasion, the menu for children's parties rarely varies. Popular snacks and beverages also tend to be too high in sugar and fat. Serving more healthful, but still child-friendly, snacks, such as those in Table 17.4, breaks this tradition.

Key Concepts *Children grow at a slower rate than they did as infants, but still gain 2 to 3 inches and about 5 pounds per year. They should be able to obtain adequate energy and nutrients from their meals and snacks. Iron-deficiency anemia is the most common nutritional deficiency among American children. Cow's milk is not an adequate source of iron and should be limited to 3 to 4 cups per day to allow for other, high-iron foods. Many children in the United States have low levels of vitamin D, placing them at risk for developing rickets and elevating their cardiac risk. Outside influences, such as television viewing, affect children's preferences for foods with low nutrient density.*

Quick Bite

Television Tubbies

The number of obese children in America has doubled in the past 20 years, and one in five American children is now overweight. Today's kids spend more time watching TV and playing video games than engaging in physical activity. Advertisers know it. When programs for children are broadcast, 91 percent of commercials advertise food, most of it high in sugar or fat.

Table 17.4 Healthy Snacks

Cereal and milk
Yogurt shake: plain yogurt, fresh fruit
Peanut butter on celery
Popcorn sprinkled with Parmesan cheese
Fresh vegetables and a yogurt dip
Pretzels
Bananas with peanut butter
Graham crackers and peanut butter
Sliced apples with cheese
Bagel and melted cheese
Bran muffins
Pumpkin, banana, or zucchini bread
Mini pizza on English muffin
Homemade pita pocket sandwiches
Yogurt and mini bagel
Vegetable soup
Fresh fruit
Hot chocolate (made with milk)

Nutritional Concerns of Childhood

The major challenges to promoting healthful childhood nutrition are combating malnutrition and hunger, chronic disease, overweight, lead toxicity, and nutrition concerns regarding vegetarian practices.

Malnutrition and Hunger in Childhood

Of all of the issues facing children with respect to growth and nutrition, none is so devastating as hunger and subsequent malnutrition. Throughout the world, over half of the deaths of young children can be attributed to undernutrition.[14] Deficiencies in vitamin A, zinc, iron, and protein also result in illness, stunted growth, limited development, and, in the case of vitamin A, possibly permanent blindness. Over 12 million children in the United States lived in food insecure households in 2007. The U.S. Department of Agriculture (USDA) has 15 nutrition assistance programs that address hunger, including the Supplemental Nutrition Assistance Program (SNAP)—formerly the Food Stamp Program—the National School Breakfast and Lunch Programs, and the Special Supplemental Nutrition Program for Women, Infants and Children (WIC). (See **Figure 17.3**.) See Chapter 19 for more information about these and other programs designed to reduce childhood hunger and malnutrition.

Food and Behavior

hyperactivity A maladaptive and abnormal increase in activity that is inconsistent with developmental levels. Includes frequent fidgeting, inappropriate running, excessive talking, and difficulty in engaging in quiet activities.

Many parents and caregivers mistakenly believe that consuming sugar-laden foods causes **hyperactivity** in children. The myth persists even though a number of carefully controlled studies have found no cause-and-effect relationship.[15] The term *hyperactivity* usually is defined as an abnormal increase in activity that is maladaptive and inconsistent with developmental level, but common usage has blurred its meaning. Parents often use this term to describe what they view as unruly behavior in children, particularly in social settings such as parties. Children typically react to situations surrounding parties (where high-sugar foods are often served) in excitable ways. This is not proof of a cause-and-effect relationship between those foods and those behaviors. Many people also believe that certain food additives, including preservatives and colorings, can cause or exacerbate behavioral disorders. Although the cause remains controversial, studies do suggest that certain food colorings and additives may enhance hyperactive behaviors in some children; further research is warranted.[16]

Caffeine products can make children jittery and interfere with their sleep. Because children have small body sizes, the effects of a caffeinated beverage are intensified. Many soft drinks are high in caffeine; examples include Mountain Dew (55 milligrams per 12-oz can), Surge (51 milligrams per 12-oz can), and Coca-Cola (37 milligrams per 12-oz can). Popular energy drinks can also be substantial sources of caffeine.

Figure 17.3 Federal safety net for children. Children are more vulnerable than adults to the effects of malnutrition. For many children, these federal programs provide the major—and, in some cases, the only—sources of calories and other nutrients.

Childhood Overweight

In the United States, overweight in childhood is increasing at an alarming rate. (See the FYI feature "Overweight in Children and Teens: Whose Problem Is It?") An overweight child is likely to reach maturity earlier than a child of normal weight, but perhaps at the expense of height. Some overweight children already deal with the cardiovascular consequences of obesity, such as lipid abnormalities and hypertension, and many overweight children develop type 2 diabetes prior to the teen years. Finally, overweight children are more likely to have academic difficulties[17] and experience the psychological trauma associated with obesity in our culture. Factors involved in the development of overweight in childhood include genetics, environment, behavior, and activity levels. (See **Figure 17.4**.)

Programs designed to treat childhood obesity generally provide behavior modification, exercise counseling, psychological support or therapy, family counseling, and family meal-planning advice. In many cases, the goal is not weight loss, but rather to allow the child's height to catch up with his or her weight. Instead of restricting caloric intake or food choices, the first strategy is usually to increase activity and improve food choices.

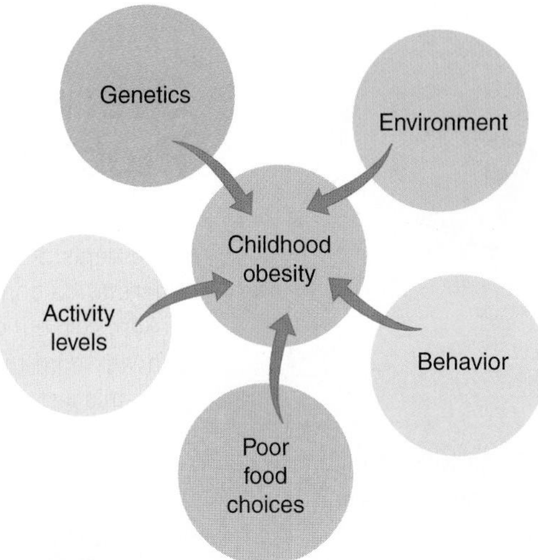

Figure 17.4 Factors that contribute to childhood obesity. Childhood obesity is on the rise and predisposes children to health problems when they become adults.

Nutrition and Chronic Disease in Childhood

When is it appropriate to adopt adult dietary guidelines for children? It is well documented that early signs of chronic disease can appear in childhood. Evidence of early plaque development has been seen in the coronary arteries of adolescents and is associated with adult cardiovascular diseases. However, the low-fat, high-fiber diet advocated for adults may jeopardize a very young child's growth. Infants and toddlers younger than 2 years old need fat in their diets for growth, organ protection, and central nervous system development. Dietary restrictions at this age are not appropriate.

For children older than 2 years, however, efforts to lower fat, saturated fat, and cholesterol intake may reduce risks of chronic disease. Dietary choices in line with the *Dietary Guidelines for Americans* are recommended. But it's important that parents and caregivers not misinterpret the recommendations and restrict children's energy intake. During the preschool and school years, gradual changes can bring food choices in line with the *Dietary Guidelines for Americans*. Caregivers should offer children healthful choices and, as they grow, educate them about proper nutrition.

Because of the rising rates of childhood obesity and incidence of chronic diseases related to weight, the American Academy of Pediatrics (AAP) now

Going Green

Farmers' Markets

Farmers' markets in the city serve up a fresh harvest for those of us who don't have gardens. Direct from the grower, the produce of farmers' markets supports healthy lifestyles by offering unique varieties of fresh, nutritious food at the peak of flavor. By increasing children's access to fresh fruits and vegetables, these markets promote child health and reduce childhood obesity.

Patrons can redeem Women, Infants, and Children (WIC) and Senior Farmers Market Nutrition (SFMNP) vouchers at participating markets, thus providing fresh fruits and vegetables to more than 2.3 million low-income families and more than 963,000 low-income seniors. Many farmers' markets also accept EBT cards that accompany the Supplemental Nutrition Assistance Food Program (formerly known as food stamps). They also donate hundreds of thousands of pounds of unsold, fresh produce to food banks, shelters, and other social service agencies.

Farmers' markets support small family farms and preserve America's rural landscapes. They maintain opportunities for farmers, promote diversity, preserve agricultural land from overdevelopment, and keep farmers farming. Farmers' markets strengthen communities and stimulate local economies by creating jobs, strengthening local economies, reducing the distance food travels, and making local food affordable.

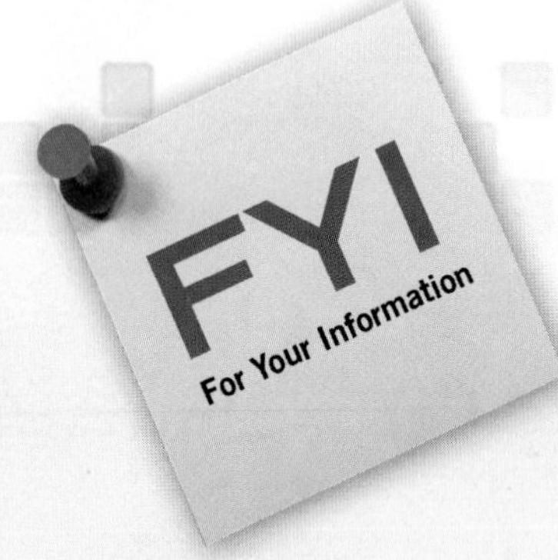

Overweight in Children and Teens: Whose Problem Is It?

The news, whether print or broadcast, is full of stories about the growing problem of overweight in children and adolescents. An epidemic, say some. A sign that all Americans will soon be overweight or obese, say others. What's to be done about it? Will lawsuits against fast food restaurants, snack-food companies, or soft-drink makers help our children's health? Will banning candy and sodas from schools assure healthful food choices? Can we afford to spend more school time on physical education when a school's success is measured by academic test scores?

As with so many public health issues, there are many questions but no easy answers. The prevalence of overweight and its attendant health problems is clearly on the rise among American children.[1] Currently, 11 percent of children aged 2 to 5 years and 15 percent of children aged 6 and older are overweight.[2] These values are more than double the rates of overweight in the early 1970s. This rise in prevalence of overweight is accompanied by increased rates of weight-related conditions, including type 2 diabetes. Once considered only an adult disease, rates of type 2 diabetes in children and adolescents have skyrocketed: in 1990, less than 4 percent of children diagnosed with diabetes had type 2; today, that rate is 30 to 50 percent.[3] In addition to posing health risks, overweight in children has many psychosocial and emotional effects, leading some to conclude that obesity is "one of the most stigmatizing and least socially acceptable conditions in childhood."[4]

What's to be done? Most health professionals agree that dieting and significant weight loss are inappropriate for children and teens who are still growing. The Society for Nutrition Education advocates for "health at any size"—an approach that is health centered instead of weight centered and that focuses on the whole person.[5] This approach promotes lifestyle behavior changes for living actively, eating healthfully, nurturing self-esteem, and respecting cultural and family traditions. This preventive (rather than treatment) approach is gaining acceptance along with the recognition that treatment can lead to other problems, such as eating disorders, nutrient deficiencies, size discrimination, and body hatred.

Promoting healthy lifestyles in children is something with which few can argue, but implementation of programs to promote behavior change can be complicated. Children and teens spend a significant portion of their days at school and with peers, yet they also are influenced by the behaviors and attitudes of parents and other family members. A poll by the Harvard Forums on Health found that 65 percent of those surveyed felt that schools should play a major role in helping to fight the obesity problem in the United States, and more than 90 percent supported healthier school lunches, inclusion of healthy eating and exercise topics in health classes, and more physical education in schools.[6] But where will such resources for schools come from? And if changes in schools do occur, how well will parents and the community at large support those programs? It does little good to encourage children to exercise if they lack safe places to play outside or if parents continue to model a couch-potato lifestyle.

Nevertheless, schools and communities are trying. At least 28 states have introduced legislation targeting sales of soft drinks and/or candy in schools, and many school districts have successfully replaced soft drinks with water, 100 percent fruit juice, and milk. Schools also are finding creative ways to promote exercise, turning tired old gymnasiums into fitness centers, using exercycles to power video games, and incorporating exercise principles into the science curriculum. Schools can't buck the overweight trend alone, however, which is why programs must integrate the family and community. For example, a handful of communities are trying out the "Walking School Bus," an effort to promote walking among children who live within a mile of their schools.[7] These community-based initiatives can encourage the small but sustainable lifestyle changes needed for long-term weight management and reduction of health risks in our nation's youth.

1 Daniels SR, Arnett DK, Eckel RH, et al. Overweight in children and adolescents: pathophysiology, consequences, prevention, and treatment. *Circulation.* 2005;111:1999–2012.

2 Ogden CL, Flegal KM, Carroll MD, Johnson CL. Prevalence and trends in overweight among US children and adolescents, 1999–2000. *JAMA.* 2002;288:1728–1732.

3 IFIC Foundation. The challenge of type 2 diabetes in children. *Food Insight.* January/February, 2003.

4 Schwimmer JB, Burwinkle TM, Varni JW. Health-related quality of life of severely obese children and adolescents. *JAMA.* 2003;289(14):1813–1819.

5 Society for Nutrition Education. Guidelines for childhood obesity prevention programs: promoting healthy weight in children. 2003. http://www.sne.org/Chi_Obesity.pdf. Accessed 8/25/09.

6 The Harvard Forums on Health. Obesity as a public health issue: a look at solutions. http://www.phsi.harvard.edu/health_reform/poll_results.pdf. Accessed 8/25/09.

7 Walking School Bus. http://www.walkingschoolbus.org. Accessed 8/25/09.

recommends screening children who have a positive family history of abnormal blood lipids or premature cardiovascular disease for blood lipid abnormalities.[18] For those children with high levels of LDL cholesterol, lifestyle interventions such as changes in diet and physical activity are recommended. In some circumstances, medication may be warranted.

Lead Toxicity

Reducing elevated blood lead levels among children is one of the 2010 U.S. national health objectives.[19] During the period from 1999 to 2004, 1.4 percent of children in the United States aged 1 to 5 years had elevated blood lead levels, compared with 8.6 percent of children during the period from 1988 to 1991.[20] Lead toxicity can result in slow growth and iron-deficiency anemia and can damage the brain and central nervous system, leading to a host of learning disabilities and behavior problems. Increased blood lead levels are associated with reduced IQ, even at levels less than the Centers for Disease Control and Prevention's "level of concern" of 10 micrograms per deciliter.[21] Evidence also suggests that lead exposure may delay **puberty** in girls.[22]

Lead is present in the plumbing of old homes; old paint; house dust in homes with cracked or peeling lead-based paint; and, in some areas, the soil. Children can ingest lead by drinking contaminated water, eating paint chips, or sucking their fingers after playing in or around lead-contaminated house dust or soil. Lead toxicity occurs more frequently in areas of poverty, where lead contamination is more common and where iron-deficiency anemia is present.

Low intakes of iron, calcium, and zinc tend to result in increased lead absorption. Children with an adequate intake of these micronutrients show less incidence of lead toxicity. Therefore, many of the programs established to reduce the incidence of lead toxicity in children also promote good nutrition, with an emphasis on adequate iron, calcium, and zinc consumption.

Vegetarianism in Childhood

Well-planned lacto-vegetarian, lacto-ovo-vegetarian, and vegan diets can satisfy the nutrient needs of children.[23] Vegetarian children have lower intakes of total fat, saturated fat, and cholesterol, and higher intakes of fruits, vegetables, and fiber. Sources of calcium, iron, zinc, vitamin B_{12}, and vitamin D need to be emphasized, especially for children following vegan diets. For a vegan child, legumes and nuts should be substituted for meats, and calcium- and vitamin B_{12}–fortified soy milk should be substituted for cow's milk. At least 15 minutes of direct sunlight exposure daily should provide enough vitamin D.[24] The AAP recommends that children who do not get regular sunlight exposure or drink at least 32 ounces of vitamin D–fortified milk each day should take supplemental vitamin D daily.[25]

Key Concepts *Hunger and malnutrition affect a significant number of our nation's children. To combat the growing number of hungry children, programs such as WIC, SNAP, and the National School Breakfast and Lunch Programs are vital. Other concerns common to childhood include overweight, lead toxicity, and chronic disease prevention. Infants and toddlers should not be given low-fat, high-fiber diets; when children reach the age of 2, caregivers should begin to adjust children's diets to follow appropriate dietary guidelines. For vegetarian children, dietary sources of calcium, iron, zinc, vitamin D, and vitamin B_{12} require special attention.*

American Heart Association

Overweight in Children

Overweight children are more likely to be overweight adults. Successfully preventing or treating overweight in childhood may reduce the risk of adult overweight. This may help reduce the risk of heart disease and other diseases.

Source: American Heart Association, Inc.

Quick Bite

Are Minority Children at High Risk for Cardiovascular Disease?

Early risk factors for cardiovascular disease are increasing in America. African American and Mexican American children are more likely to exhibit high blood pressure and high body mass index and to consume a higher percentage of calories from fat than are Caucasian children. The three ethnic groups have similar blood cholesterol levels, however, and Caucasian children are more likely to smoke.

puberty The period of life during which the secondary sex characteristics develop and the ability to reproduce is attained.

Quick Bite

Tragedy in Lead

Lead toxicity is defined as a blood level of 10 micrograms of lead per deciliter. When children are exposed to lead on a continuous or regular basis, brain function is affected.

> ***Dietary Guidelines for Americans, 2010***
> **Key Recommendations**
>
> **Balancing Calories to Manage Weight**
> - Maintain appropriate calorie balance during each stage of life—childhood, adolescence, adulthood, pregnancy and breastfeeding, and older age.

Adolescence

Adolescents seem to add inches overnight. Many caregivers complain that they cannot keep enough food in the house to satisfy an adolescent's appetite. Adolescence commonly is defined as the time between the onset of puberty and adulthood. This maturation process involves both physical growth and emotional maturation.

Physical Growth and Development

Hormones drive growth, which varies from child to child. In general, growth spurts begin between ages 10 and 12 for girls and between ages 12 and 14 for boys.[26] This spurt, or period of maximal growth, lasts about two years.

Height

The first phase of adolescent growth is linear. On average, boys grow 8 inches and girls grow 6 inches during puberty. This growth is uneven. The hands and feet enlarge first. The calves and forearms lengthen next, followed by expansion of the hips, chest, shoulders, and trunk. As a result, adolescents often appear awkward or clumsy. After the main growth spurt, growth continues for two to three years, but at a much slower rate.

For girls, peak growth occurs about one year before **menarche**, the onset of menstruation. A typical girl has achieved about 95 percent of her adult height by menarche and grows only 2 to 4 inches during the remainder of adolescence. Growth rates are closely related to sexual maturation, reflected in breast development (girls), change of voice (boys), development of sexual organs, and growth of pubic hair. When the growth plates at the ends of the long bones (**epiphyses**) close, skeletal growth is complete. This is a critical point in development. An adolescent who is malnourished and of small stature at the point of epiphyseal closure may not achieve his or her full potential height.

Weight

The second growth phase of adolescence involves lateral growth. Here, the adolescent "fills out," or gains weight. External factors such as diet and exercise affect weight gain more than linear growth, so weight gain can vary widely among adolescents. However, a typical healthy girl will gain 35 pounds during adolescence; a typical boy will gain 45 pounds. In our weight-sensitive society, adolescents should be prepared for this normal, expected weight gain. Although the bulk of an adolescent's lateral growth occurs after the linear growth spurt, a significant portion of the two growth stages overlap. For girls, for example, peak weight gain usually occurs around the time of menarche.

Body Composition

Before puberty, the body composition of boys and girls does not differ greatly. This changes dramatically during adolescence. Boys experience greater increases in lean body mass, resulting in more obvious muscle definition. Girls accumulate greater stores of body fat, specifically around the hips and buttocks, upper arms, breasts, and upper back. By adulthood, a typical woman's body composition is 23 percent fat; a typical man, in contrast, has 12 percent body fat.

> **menarche** First menstrual period.
>
> **epiphyses** The heads of the long bones that are separated from the shaft of the bone until the bone stops growing.

Emotional Maturity: Developmental Tasks

Adolescence is a time not only of great physical growth, but also of tremendous emotional growth. This psychological development affects food choices, eating habits, and body image. Many teens become more interested in the healthful aspects of nutrition. Others experiment with unhealthful food choices, as an exercise in independence or in an attempt to achieve an idealized body.

American Heart Association

Fiber and Children's Diets

Children older than 2 years should gradually adopt the American Heart Association Eating Plan. That means saturated fat intake should be 8–10 percent of total calories and dietary cholesterol should be limited to no more than 300 mg daily. Children should also get the majority of calories from complex carbohydrates high in fiber.

A fiber guideline of "age plus 5" has been proposed to set dietary fiber amounts for young children. This means, for example, a 5-year-old should consume 5 + 5 = 10 grams of fiber per day. Once a child's caloric intake approaches that of an adult (1,500 calories or more), 25 total grams should be well tolerated.

Source: American Heart Association, Inc.

Nutrient Needs of Adolescents

Although growth, not age, should be the ultimate indicator of nutrient needs, DRIs are established based on age. Separate recommendations for males and females reflect their differences in growth rates and body composition seen during adolescence.

Energy and Protein

Energy needs, as total kilocalories per day, are greater during adolescence than at any other time of life, with the exception of pregnancy and lactation. Equations used to calculate Estimated Energy Requirements (EER) are the same as for children, except for the added energy factor for growth, which is higher for adolescents. (See Table 17.5.) Recommended energy intakes are guidelines only; adjustments often are needed to meet individual requirements.

To support growth, an adolescent's protein needs per unit body weight are higher than an adult's but less than a rapidly growing infant's. (See Table 17.6.) By age 14 to 18, the protein RDA has declined nearly to adult levels (as g/kg body weight), reflecting the end of linear growth for most teens. American teens rarely have a problem with adequate protein intake, but teen girls risk a lack of protein if they cut calories too drastically in attempts to control weight.

Vitamins and Minerals

Along with increased needs for energy and protein, adolescents have higher vitamin and mineral needs compared with people at most other life stages.

Table 17.5 Estimated Energy Requirement Equations for Adolescence (Ages 9 Through 18)

Males

EER = 88.5 – 61.9 × age [y] + PA × (26.7 × weight [kg] + 903 × height [m]) + 25 kcal/day

Physical activity (PA)

Sedentary = 1.00; Low active = 1.13; Active = 1.26; Very active = 1.42

Females

EER = 135.3 – 30.8 × age [y] + PA × (10.0 × weight [kg] + 934 × height [m]) + 25 kcal/day

Physical activity (PA)

Sedentary = 1.0; Low active = 1.16; Active = 1.31; Very active = 1.56

Source: Reproduced from Institute of Medicine, Food and Nutrition Board. *Dietary Reference Intakes for Energy, Carbohydrate, Fiber, Fat, Fatty Acids, Cholesterol, Protein, and Amino Acids (Macronutrients).* Copyright © 2002 by the National Academy of Sciences, courtesy of the National Academies Press, Washington, DC.

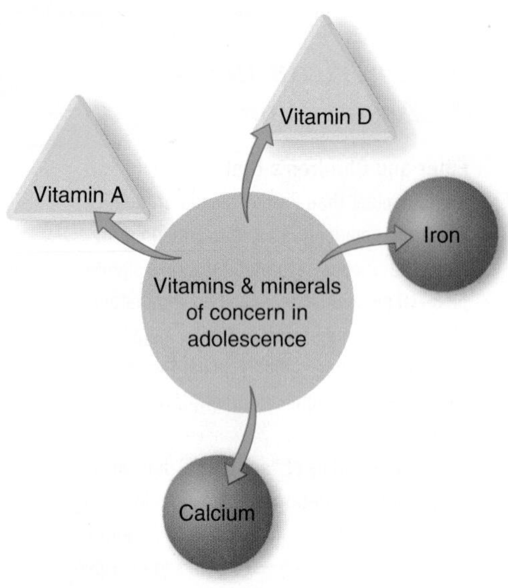

Figure 17.5 **Micronutrients of concern in adolescence.** Vitamin A is important for growth, and calcium and vitamin D are essential for building strong bones. Teen girls especially need adequate iron intake to replace iron lost due to menstruation.

Table 17.6 **Protein RDAs for Adolescence**

Age (y)	Protein (g/kg)	Reference Weight* (kg)	Protein (g/d)
9–13, female and male	0.95	36	34
14–18, female	0.85	54	46
14–18, male	0.85	61	52

*Reference weights are based on median weights for that sex and age group.

Source: Reproduced from Institute of Medicine, Food and Nutrition Board. *Dietary Reference Intakes for Energy, Carbohydrate, Fiber, Fat, Fatty Acids, Cholesterol, Protein, and Amino Acids (Macronutrients).* Copyright © 2002 by the National Academy of Sciences, courtesy of the National Academies Press, Washington, DC.

Nutrients of particular concern for adolescents are vitamin A, vitamin D, calcium, and iron. (See **Figure 17.5**.)

Teens can improve their vitamin A intake by including more fruits and vegetables in their diets. Adequate calcium and vitamin D are essential for bone formation, and maximal bone density can be hard to obtain if diets are deficient in these nutrients. Many teens, especially girls, actually reduce their calcium and vitamin D intake by replacing the milk in their diets with soft drinks. During puberty, adolescents gain 15 percent of their full adult height and accumulate half of their ultimate adult bone mass. Adolescents who do not achieve sufficient bone density have a greater risk of developing osteoporosis later in life. The AI for calcium in adolescence is 1,300 milligrams per day, and the DRI for vitamin D is 200 IU every day. Fortified milk and dairy products are rich in these nutrients and convenient to eat; without these or other fortified products, meeting the recommended intake is difficult to achieve.

Adolescent boys need added iron to support growth of muscle and lean body mass. Teenage girls need added iron to replace what is lost in blood during menstruation. The recommended iron intake for boys aged 14 to 18 is 11 milligrams per day; for teen girls, it is 15 milligrams per day. As long as they take in enough calories, both groups should be able to obtain this iron from nutrient-dense foods. During adolescence, however, food selection often is less than optimal. Careful meal planning is required to maximize teenagers' iron consumption.

Influences on Adolescent Food Intake

Teenagers want and need to make their own food choices and purchases and may want to take over preparation of their own food. While the parent can set a good example, parental influence is much weaker now. Factors that influence an adolescent's food selection and consumption include the desire to be healthy, fitness goals, amount of discretionary income, social practices, and peers. (See **Figure 17.6**.)

Teens have more access to foods than children do. They also usually have their own money and may have access to independent transportation. Along with this increased freedom comes greater spending power. Teens enjoy spending money on food and making their own selections. The food industry responds accordingly by marketing directly to teens. The message is enjoyment and pleasure, and advertised products may not be nutritionally adequate.

Teens perceive benefits to eating healthful foods, such as enhanced physical and mental performance, increased energy, and psychological well-being.

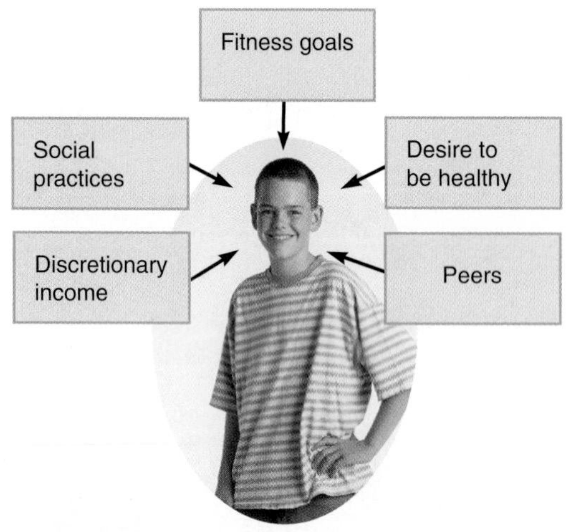

Figure 17.6 **Factors that influence adolescent food choices.** Social, cultural, and psychological factors, especially peer pressure, strongly influence adolescent food choices.

However, barriers to healthful eating include convenience and personal preference for fewer healthful alternatives along with lack of parental or school support and modeling.[27] Teens attending school are faced with more food choices than ever before. In addition to the standard school lunch or breakfast program outlined earlier, most middle schools and high schools have vending machines, snack carts, school stores, or even private vendors supplying foods such as pizza for cafeteria meals.[28] Vending and other food sales can be a major source of revenue for many schools, supporting athletic programs and other after-school activities.

Health professionals and others have expressed concern about the presence of low-nutrient-density "competitive" foods (e.g., snacks and soft drinks sold side by side with school lunches),[29] and many states have pursued legislation to either remove vending machines or change the products available during the school day. A study by the Arizona Department of Education found that replacing sodas, candy, and gum in schools with water, juice, low-fat milk, granola bars, pretzels, fruits, and vegetables resulted in equal or greater revenue for schools.[30]

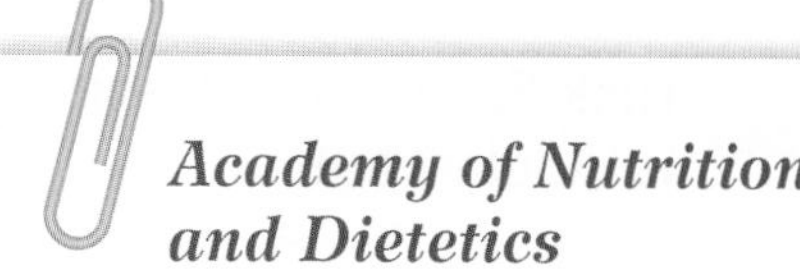

Academy of Nutrition and Dietetics

Child and Adolescent Food and Nutrition Programs

It is the position of the Academy of Nutrition and Dietetics that all children and adolescents, regardless of age; gender; socioeconomic status; racial, ethnic, or linguistic diversity; or health status, should have access to food and nutrition programs that ensure the availability of a safe and adequate food supply that promotes optimal physical, cognitive, social, and emotional growth and development. Appropriate food and nutrition programs include food assistance and meal programs, nutrition education initiatives, and nutrition screening and assessment followed by appropriate nutrition intervention and anticipatory guidance to promote optimal nutrition status.

Source: Position of the American Dietetic Association: child and adolescent food and nutrition programs. *J Am Diet Assoc.* 2006;106(9):1467–1475. Copyright © 2006. Reprinted with permission from Elsevier.

Key Concepts *Humans need more calories and nutrients during adolescence than at any other stage of life, with the exception of pregnancy and lactation. Boys grow about 8 inches, gain about 45 pounds, and increase their lean body mass. Girls grow about 6 inches, gain about 35 pounds, and increase their body fat. As at earlier ages, calcium, vitamin D, iron, and vitamin A are often lacking in adolescent diets. Factors that determine food selection and consumption include the desire to be healthy, fitness goals, amount of discretionary income, social practices, and peers.*

Nutrition-Related Concerns for Adolescents

Adolescents are often preoccupied with weight, appearance, and eating habits. They need to know whether and how their eating practices can affect body image and development, fitness, acne, and obesity.

Fitness and Sports

For many adolescents, an interest in fitness becomes the catalyst for learning about nutrition and improving dietary habits. Some teens, unfortunately, become obsessed with their athletic performance, food intake, and body appearance and go to extremes that can jeopardize not only their current athletic performance but also their long-term health. For more information about the nutritional needs of athletes, see Chapter 14, "Sports Nutrition."

Acne

Many teens blame certain foods for their **acne**. Myths surrounding acne and diet abound, but research has not found any correlation between acne and chocolate, greasy foods, soft drinks, nuts, or milk. Nevertheless, differences in acne incidence between Westernized and non-Westernized societies are striking, and researchers theorize a connection between acne and diets rich in refined carbohydrates.[31] Preliminary research suggests that a low-glycemic-load diet may be helpful, but further controlled testing is needed before specific recommendations can be made.[32] Effective treatments for acne include topical benzoyl peroxide, low-dose oral antibiotics, and two medications derived from vitamin A—Retin-A and Accutane. Although both of these medications are derivatives of vitamin A, there is no correlation between dietary vitamin A and acne.

THINK About It 2

acne An inflammatory skin eruption that usually occurs in or near the sebaceous glands of the face, neck, shoulders, and upper back.

Table 17.7 **Risk Factors for Obesity in Adolescents**

Genetics
Extent and duration of breastfeeding
Early menarche
Participation in high-risk behaviors such as smoking, alcohol use, and sexual experimentation
Family and parental dynamics
Food insecurity
Socioeconomic status
Lack of safe place for physical activity
Inconsistent access to healthful food choices
Low cognitive stimulation at home
Parental food choices
Parental food-related behaviors
Lack of regular family meals
Low level of physical activity—leisure time activities and activities of daily living, school physical activity programs
Television, computer, and video games

Source: Data from American Academy of Pediatrics. Prevention of pediatric overweight and obesity. *Pediatrics.* 2003;112(2):424–430.

Eating Disorders

Eating disorders, discussed more thoroughly in the "Spotlight on Eating Disorders," frequently begin during adolescence. Adolescents often become preoccupied with their weight, appearance, and eating habits. Although eating disorders still affect more girls than boys, the prevalence in males is increasing. Thus, eating disorders shouldn't be ignored or dismissed as only a "girl's problem."

Adolescent Obesity

As in childhood, obesity rates in adolescence are climbing. One contributing factor is a decline in physical activity by many teens.[33] Obese adolescents have an increased risk of developing high blood pressure, abnormal glucose tolerance, and metabolic syndrome.[34] They also suffer psychologically from teasing, being ostracized by peers, and from longing to be slimmer. In addition, adolescent obesity sets the stage for adult obesity, with all of its attendant health consequences.[35] (See Chapter 9, "Energy Balance, Body Composition, and Weight Management," for more on overweight and obesity.) Finally, overweight adolescents who use unhealthful weight-loss methods are also not engaging in other healthy weight-loss strategies such as healthier eating and increased physical activity.[36] Nutrition education may positively influence the knowledge, attitudes, and eating behaviors of high school students, leading to a healthier lifestyle and reducing their risk of becoming overweight.[37] See Table 17.7 for factors that put an adolescent at risk for obesity.

Tobacco, Alcohol, and Recreational Drugs

Developmentally, adolescence is a period of experimentation, and many adolescents experiment with smoking and/or prescription or illegal drugs. Although survey results from 2007 show a continuing gradual decline in tobacco and drug use, the nonmedical use of prescription medications continues at a high rate.[38] Nearly one-fourth of high school seniors graduate as smokers, and many young females smoke in an attempt to control appetite and weight. An adolescent who smokes tobacco often has a lower energy intake and subsequently decreased nutrient intake.

Marijuana has the opposite effect on hunger. Many teens who smoke marijuana will experience "the munchies," a desire to snack and munch—usually on snacks high in calories but with low nutrient density. Smoking marijuana carries the same risks as smoking tobacco. In addition, marijuana sometimes is laced with other drugs, including LSD and amphetamines.

Almost all the alcohol consumed by those under the age of 21 occurs during binge drinking—more than five drinks within two hours for men and four drinks within two hours for women. Binge drinkers are at greater risk of harming themselves or others through violence and accidental injury.[39] In addition, teens who drink are replacing needed nutrients with empty alcohol calories. Finally, alcohol can interfere with the absorption and metabolism of necessary nutrients. (For more information about nutrition and alcohol, see Chapter 8, especially the section "Alcoholics and Malnutrition.") Growing adolescents cannot afford to have nutrients replaced or poorly absorbed during growth.

Other drugs, such as cocaine, pose further risks. In using illegal drugs, the adolescent becomes preoccupied with both the acquisition and use of the drug; these activities take priority over food intake or selection. Teens who use drugs are usually underweight and report poor appetites.

Quick Bite

The Dangers of Teenage Smoking

The Centers for Disease Control and Prevention (CDC) estimate that nearly 4 million adolescents smoke regularly. Each day, about 6,000 young people try a cigarette, and more than 3,000 become regular smokers. The CDC predicts that of all young people currently under the age of 18, more than 5 million will die prematurely of a smoking-related disease. Research shows that the earlier a person begins to smoke, the greater the damage.

Key Concepts *Adolescence can be an uncomfortable time for the teen who is concerned with body image, body changes, or athletic activities. Although many teens blame certain foods for their acne, research has not found a definite correlation between acne and diet. Many adolescents are preoccupied with their weight, appearance, and eating habits. Adolescent obesity is on the rise, and eating disorders frequently begin during adolescence. Use of tobacco, alcohol, or recreational drugs can influence nutrient intake and interfere with good nutrition.*

Staying Young While Growing Older

Just when does old age begin? The answer is increasingly elusive, as more people remain healthy and active well into their seventies, eighties, and even nineties. Today, older adults represent the fastest-growing segment of the U.S. population, and the size of the older population (age 65 or older) is projected to double between 2000 and 2030. (See **Figure 17.7**.) The baby boomers turn 65 in 2011, and experts estimate that by 2030 nearly one in five Americans will be older than 65. The population aged 85 and older is projected to increase from 5.3 million in 2006 to nearly 21 million by 2050.[40]

Age-related changes in body composition, sensory abilities, organ systems, and immune function are normal. (See **Figure 17.8**.) We age at different rates, and many age-related declines will have little impact on our day-to-day lives. Other changes affect our nutrient needs and nutrient status (**Table 17.8**), so it becomes especially important to eat nutrient-dense food.

As we get older, many of us fear loss of mental function even more than loss of physical function. Yet, as the years advance, most people maintain cognitive function with only subtle changes. Staying physically and mentally active is a key factor in maintaining function.[41] In most cases, slight changes involving sensory acuity, secondary memory, and information-processing speed do not affect quality of life or lead to progressive or rapid declines in

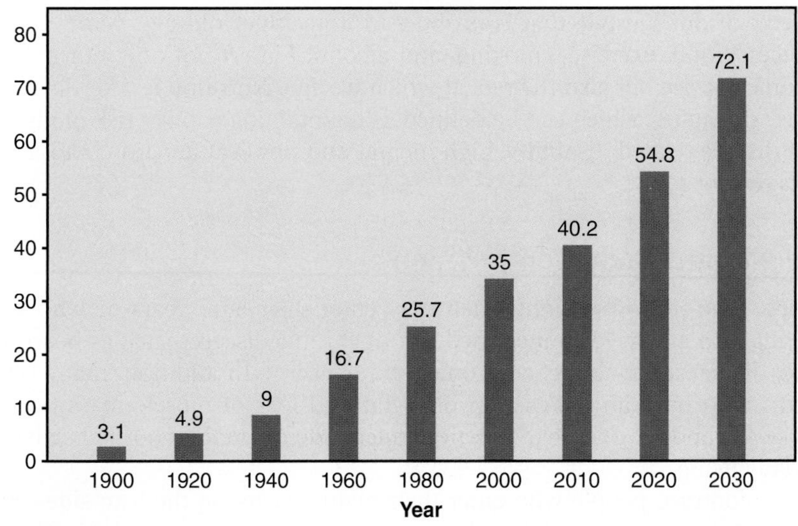

Figure 17.7 **The aging U.S. population.** The number of people over age 65 is growing rapidly.
Source: US Department of Health and Human Services. *A Profile of Older Americans 2008.* http://www.mowaa.org/Document.Doc?id=69. Accessed 09/29/09.

Saliva production
Digestive secretions
Lactase secretions
Gastrointestinal motility
Cardiac output
Blood volume
Kidney function
Liver function
Immune function
Vitamin absorption

Blood pressure
Body weight
Bone loss

Figure 17.8 **Age-related physiological changes.** As we age, most physiological changes emerge gradually.

Table 17.8 **Age-Related Changes and Nutrient Needs**

Change in Body Composition or Physiologic Function	Impact on Nutrient Requirement
Decreased muscle mass	Decreased need for energy
Decreased bone density	Increased need for calcium, vitamin D
Decreased immune function	Increased need for vitamin B_6, vitamin E, zinc
Increased gastric pH	Increased need for vitamin B_{12}, folic acid, calcium, iron, zinc
Decreased skin capacity for cholecalciferol synthesis	Increased need for vitamin D
Increased wintertime parathyroid hormone production	Increased need for vitamin D
Decreased calcium bioavailability	Increased need for calcium, vitamin D
Decreased hepatic uptake of retinol	Decreased need for vitamin A
Decreased efficiency in metabolic use of vitamin B_6	Increased need for vitamin B_6
Increased oxidative stress status	Increased need for beta-carotene, vitamin C, vitamin E
Increased levels of homocysteine	Increased need for folate, vitamin B_6, vitamin B_{12}

Source: Reproduced from Blumberg J. Nutritional needs of seniors. *J Am Coll Nutr.* 1997;16(6):517–523. Reprinted with permission.

mental function. However, when depression or dementia is suspected, professional evaluation becomes necessary. Overmedication or drug interactions, rather than disease, may be responsible for the changes in behavior.

Although it is not possible to stop the aging process, we can control aspects of our lifestyle that contribute to a healthier old age. Many of our choices—food, exercise, smoking, and alcohol—affect not only our risk for chronic disease but also the rate at which we age. Nutrition is a key factor in successful aging, which can be defined as maintaining a lower risk of disease and disease-related disability, high mental and physical function, and active engagement in life.[42]

Weight and Body Composition

People who are overweight when they enter their later years or who gain weight with age have an increased risk of chronic diseases such as heart disease, diabetes, metabolic syndrome, and cancer.[43] In addition, many older adults who have an increase in body fat and loss of muscle mass decline physically and are unable to function independently in their normal activities of daily living.

Longevity Champions
In the United States, women live an average of five years longer than men do.

In contrast, people who enter their mature years on the lean side—and who remain lean due to a healthy, active lifestyle—increase their chances of enjoying a healthy old age. But thinness alone is not always a health advantage. Obviously, older adults who lose weight due to illness enjoy no health benefits from losing these pounds. Weight loss puts them at increased risk for further illness, including cardiovascular disease and osteoporosis—especially if the

original illness also limits activity. And, of course, leanness due to tobacco use or alcoholism increases a person's vulnerability to a decline in health.

Physical Activity

Lean body mass (muscle mass) and strength are commonly observed to decline with age. However, this decline may not be a simple physiological consequence of aging. Decreases in physical activity that accompany age contribute to loss of lean mass and therefore strength.[44] Our posture begins deteriorating in our fifties—a result of bad habits, bone loss, and a decrease in muscle tone. Poor posture can affect lung and cardiovascular function, mobility, and balance. Diseases such as stroke, heart disease, arthritis, and diabetes become more common and may cause severe physical disability. These conditions, however, do not automatically preclude older adults from participating in physical activity with qualified supervision. In fact, they may instead provide additional justification for appropriate exercises for the older adult.[45] Medications and nutritional deficiencies may lead to impaired motor function; therefore, older adults should be evaluated by their physician prior to beginning a new exercise program.

Although physical activity cannot stop biological aging, regular exercise can help to minimize the physiological effects of a sedentary lifestyle and limit the progression of disabling conditions and chronic diseases.[46] The U.S. Department of Health and Human Services' 2008 *Physical Activity Guidelines for Americans* states that "regular physical activity is essential for healthy aging" and that all adults should avoid inactivity.[47] Canada also addresses this issue in its *Physical Activity Guide for Older Adults*. (See **Figure 17.9** and Appendix D.) The benefits of an individualized exercise prescription designed to increase physical activity that includes aerobic activities, flexibility exercises, and progressive resistance strength training may be most profound for those who are aging. Increased self-confidence, better balance and mobility, fewer falls and fractures, enhanced mental acuity, and improved appetite and nutrient intake are but a few of the physical and psychological benefits of exercise during our older years. (See **Figure 17.10**.)

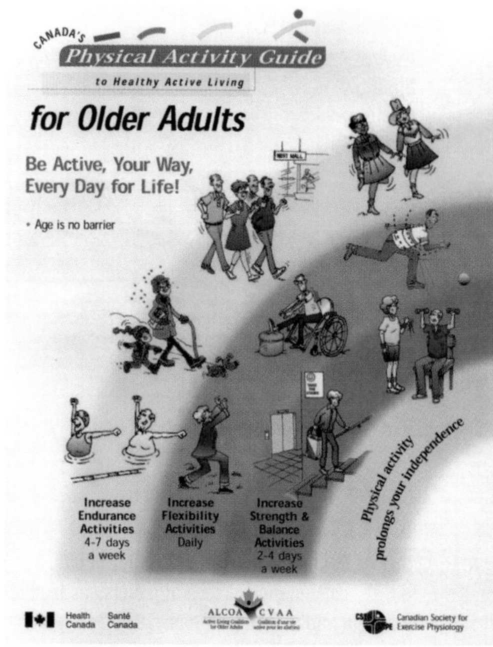

Figure 17.9 ***Canada's Physical Activity Guide for Older Adults*.** The guide explains why physical activity is important, offers tips for increasing physical activity, and recommends levels of activity necessary to good health and improved quality of living. See Appendix D for the complete guide.

Source: *Canada's Physical Activity Guide for Older Adults*. Reproduced with permission from Health Canada. © Minister of Public Works and Government Services Canada, 2010.

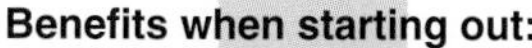

Benefits when starting out:
Meet new people
Feel more relaxed
Sleep better
Have more fun
Benefits from regular physical activity:
Continued independent living
Better physical and mental health
Improved quality of life
More energy
Move with fewer aches and pains
Better posture and balance
Improved self-esteem
Weight maintenance
Stronger muscles and bones
Relaxation and reduced stress
Scientists have proven that being active reduces the risk of:
Heart disease
Falls and injuries
Obesity
High blood pressure
Type 2 diabetes
Osteoporosis
Stroke
Depression
Colon cancer
Premature death

Figure 17.10 **Benefits from increased physical activity.** Physical activity helps adults maintain their health and independence as they age.

Source: *Eating Well with Canada's Food Guide*. 2007. Reproduced with permission from Health Canada. © Minister of Public Works and Government Services Canada, 2010.

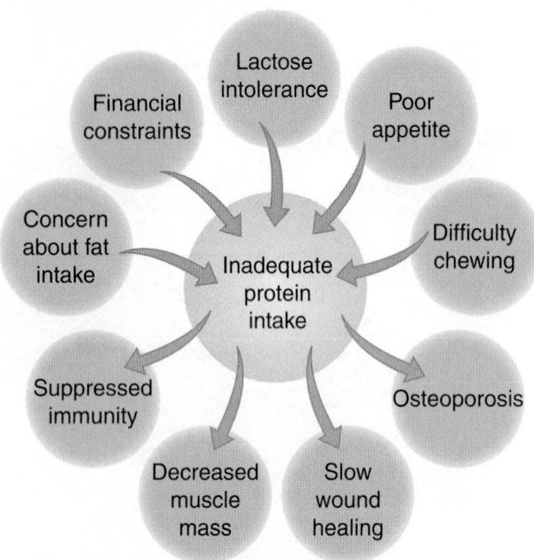

Figure 17.11 **Protein malnutrition in older adults.** A combination of several factors can lead to inadequate protein intake that compromises immunity and health.

Immunity

In the fifth decade of life, the body's defense mechanisms begin to weaken. The immune system loses some of its ability to fight viruses, bacteria, and other foreign bodies. Older adults are more vulnerable to upper respiratory tract infections such as influenza, pneumonia, urinary tract infections, pressure sores, and foodborne illnesses. Physical barriers to infectious agents, foreign bodies, and chemicals weaken as well. These barriers include the skin, the acid environment in the stomach, and the swallowing and coughing reflexes.

Inadequate consumption of protein and some antioxidant nutrients can compromise immunity and health in older adults. Because of poor appetite, difficulty chewing, financial constraints, concerns about fat intake, or lactose intolerance, older adults may reduce their intake of meat, dairy products, and fresh fruits and vegetables, making it difficult for them to get all the calories, protein, and other essential nutrients they need. (See **Figure 17.11**.) Poor dietary intake can lead to suppressed immunity, decreased muscle mass, slowed wound healing, and osteoporosis.

Key Concepts *Lifestyle choices, such as diet and exercise, affect how we age. Control of body weight can reduce our risk for many chronic diseases associated with aging. Adequate protein, vitamins, and minerals can protect our immune status. Regular exercise not only enhances our mobility but also reduces disease risk and improves mental health.*

Taste and Smell

taste threshold The minimum amount of flavor that must be present for a taste to be detected.

In older adults, the **taste threshold**—the minimum amount of a flavor that must be present to detect the taste—is more than double that of college-aged adults. Sensitivity to sweet and salty tastes goes first, so older adults often increase their intake of foods high in sugar and sodium—increasing health problems that stem from overconsumption of these nutrients. Along with taste, our sense of smell diminishes with age, especially in the seventh decade of life and beyond. Ideas that older adults should be served bland foods are misguided. When food has stronger flavors and odors, both healthy and ill older adults find it more palatable and eat more, thus increasing their nutrient intake.[48] (See **Figure 17.12**.)

Gastrointestinal Changes

Saliva production tends to decrease as we age, especially in people who take medications for conditions such as congestive heart failure. Lack of saliva affects the preparation of food for digestion and contributes to gum disease—a breach in one of the immune system's first lines of defense against infection.

With age, digestive secretions decline. Most significant are reductions in the stomach secretions of hydrochloric acid and pepsin. These reductions can allow the development of atrophic gastritis—a chronic inflammation of the stomach lining that is common among older adults. Atrophic gastritis can interfere with normal absorption of vitamin B_{12}, leading to a deficiency of this vitamin.[49] Although reduced lactase production also is associated with aging, a complete intolerance to milk and dairy products is less common than older adults often suspect. Most people with reduced lactase production can include some milk, cheese, and yogurt in their diets.

Constipation, gas, and bloating are common complaints of old age. These problems are due to a slowing of gastrointestinal motility with age, along with

Quick Bite

Losing Water

At birth, 75 percent of the body is composed of water. By the time a person reaches old age, that number has dwindled to 50 percent due to changes in body composition.

decreased physical activity, a diet low in fiber, and low fluid intake. Feelings of fullness may cause older adults to eat less. Reduced digestive secretions lower the amount of nutrients older adults absorb from the foods they do eat. Myths and misinformation about the GI effects of various foods, even among the medical community, may steer a person away from nutrient-dense foods such as dairy products, legumes, broccoli, cauliflower, tomatoes, and citrus products. Although many older adults mistakenly blame these foods for causing problems with gas, others may be sensitive to lactose in dairy products or may have had an adverse reaction to members of the cabbage family or "acid"-containing foods. GI distress also may be caused by factors totally unrelated to the food itself—inappropriate food preparation, lack of adequate fluid, and physical inactivity. Regardless of the cause, once people have an adverse reaction, they may associate it with a recently consumed food and become reluctant to try it again.

Key Concepts *The perception of taste declines with age. To detect flavors, older adults often need food with stronger flavors and odors. This loss of taste may contribute to loss of appetite and poor food intake. Age-related changes in the GI tract reduce nutrient absorption. Decreased motility contributes to constipation.*

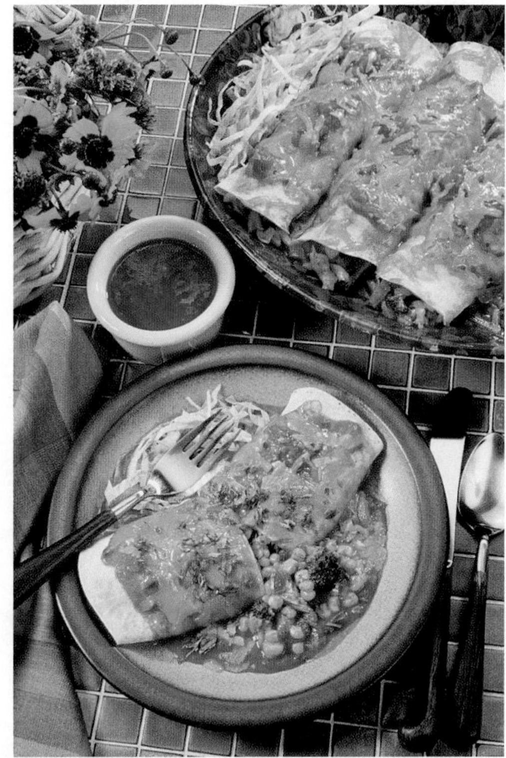

Figure 17.12 **Older adults need stronger flavors.** More highly spiced meals rather than bland ones may encourage an older adult to eat more.

Nutrient Needs of the Mature Adult

At any age, to live life to its fullest, you need good nutrition. A lifestyle that incorporates the *Dietary Guidelines for Americans* and MyPlate eating plan, together with regular physical activity, is essential to a long and productive life. **Figure 17.13** shows how dietary guidance has been adapted to illustrate the nutritional concerns of older adults.

Energy

Our energy requirements decline as we age, mainly because of reduced physical activity and loss of lean body mass. Physical activity can delay some of this loss, thus allowing us to eat more without gaining weight and increasing the likelihood that our diets will be adequate in essential nutrients.

The EER equations are the same for older adults as for younger adults. (See Chapter 9, "Energy Balance, Body Composition, and Weight Management.") The decline in total energy expenditure associated with aging is 10 kilocalories per year for men and 7 kilocalories per year for women. In other words, a 60-year-old man who maintains his weight while eating 2,300 kilocalories per day will need only 2,200 kilocalories at age 70. Individual energy needs depend on activity, lean body mass, and the presence of disease; a person who is bed- or chair-ridden, for example, usually requires fewer calories than a mobile person.

Protein

Protein needs (as grams per kilogram of body weight) may be somewhat harder for us to meet as our overall energy needs decrease and our tastes change. As our caloric needs decrease and our protein needs remain constant, an adequate diet must contain relatively more protein. For healthy older adults, the RDA for protein is 0.8 gram per kilogram of body weight, or on average 46 grams per day for women and 56 grams for men. To meet their protein needs and maximize muscle protein synthesis, older adults should

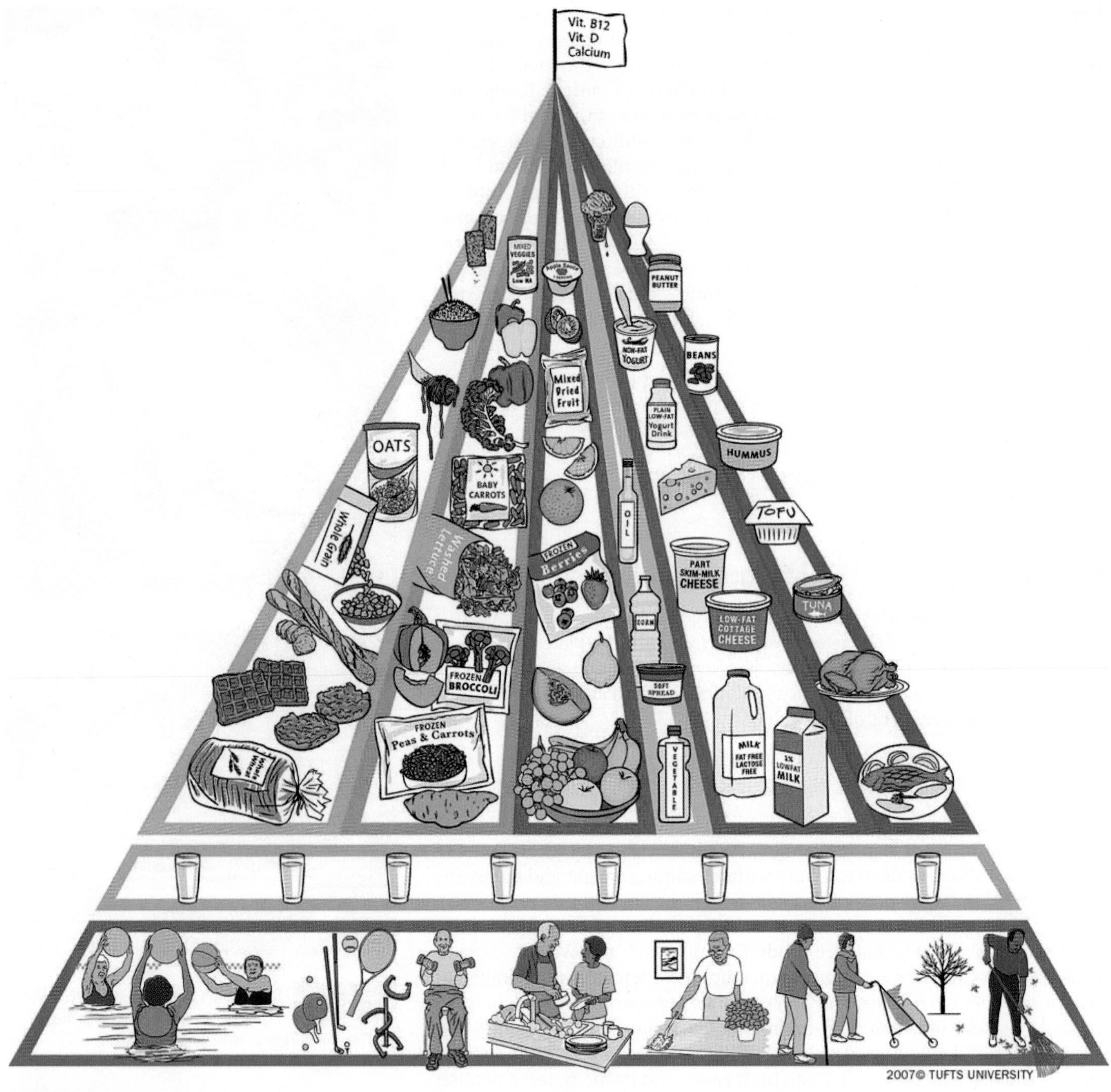

Figure 17.13 **Modified MyPyramid for older adults.**
Source: Lichtenstein AH, Rasmussen H, Yu WW, et al. Modified MyPyramid for older adults. *J Nutr.* 2008;138:78–82. http://nutrition.tufts.edu/1197972031385/Nutrition-Page-nl2w_1198058402614.html. Accessed 12/4/08. © 2007 Tufts University. Reprinted with permission.

include 25 to 30 grams of high-quality protein with each meal.[50] Chronically ill individuals may need more protein to maintain nitrogen balance. Trauma, stress, and infection also may increase protein needs. However, there are risks associated with high protein intake, including dehydration, nitrogen overload, and adverse effects on the kidneys.

Carbohydrate

After infancy, carbohydrates should make up 45 to 65 percent of the calories in the diet. Because foods with primarily simple carbohydrates provide little nutrient value, the best choices are foods with complex carbohydrates.

Fiber, a complex carbohydrate, has many potential benefits, including preventing constipation and diverticulosis, helping to promote a healthy body weight, and reducing risk for diabetes. (See Chapter 4, "Carbohydrates," for more information about fiber.) Because the AI for fiber is based on calorie intake (14 grams per 1,000 kcal per day), and energy needs decline with age, the AI for fiber is 30 grams per day for men over age 50 and 21 grams per day for women. Fiber also can help to reduce blood cholesterol, making these recommendations especially important for those who are at risk for heart disease. Five or more servings of fruits and vegetables daily, accompanied by whole-grain breads or cereals high in bran, will supply this amount easily. To avoid abdominal discomfort, increase dietary fiber intake gradually. When increasing dietary fiber intake, it is essential to consume adequate fluids—ideally water—to avoid dehydration and constipation.

Fat

Excess dietary fat can lead to obesity, which in turn increases the risk for diabetes, heart disease, and some types of cancer. Younger people should limit their dietary cholesterol and fat, but severe restrictions in older adults may be counterproductive. Extreme fat phobia may contribute to nutritional deficiencies among older adults who are afraid to drink milk, eat red meat, or even eat poultry or fish. Too few animal products in the diet may contribute to a lack of dietary protein; deficiency of minerals such as calcium, iron, and zinc; and poor vitamin D and vitamin B_{12} intake.

Healthy people who are at low risk for heart disease should obtain 20 to 35 percent of their daily calories from fat, with no more than 8 to 10 percent of the calories from saturated fat. They should limit their cholesterol intake to 300 milligrams per day. People at increased risk for heart disease should limit saturated fat and cholesterol even more, according to their physicians' advice.

Water

Nutritionists often call water the forgotten nutrient. Water is essential to all body functions; if intake is inadequate, cellular metabolism becomes difficult, if not impossible. In older adults, a decreased thirst response and a reduction in kidney function can increase the risk of dehydration.[51] Diuretic medications, alcohol, and caffeine all increase fluid excretion and can contribute to dehydration. Fluid recommendations for older adults are the same as for younger adults: 3,700 milliliters per day for men, and 2,700 milliliters per day for women.[52] These fluids should be obtained from both beverages and foods.

Key Concepts *Although caloric needs decline with loss of lean tissue and reduced physical activity, protein needs do not change for older adults. A high-carbohydrate, moderate-fat diet is still recommended. Water is important; because of their diminished thirst response, older adults may not drink enough.*

Vitamins and Minerals

As we age, our micronutrient status changes, especially our needs for vitamin D, vitamin B_{12}, and calcium. (See **Figure 17.14**.) In many cases, our

Quick Bite

Animal Lifetimes

In general, larger animals live longer than smaller animals, but there are many interesting exceptions. For instance, a mouse, a parakeet, and a bat are approximately the same size, but the mouse has a life span of 2 years, the parakeet 13 years, and the bat up to 50 years!

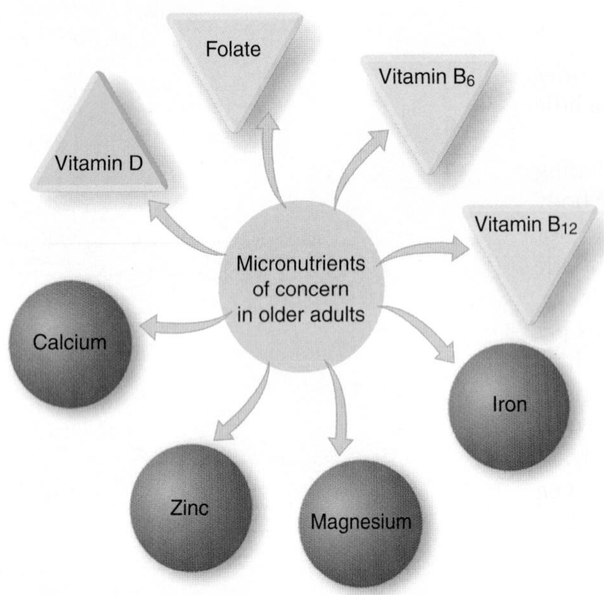

Figure 17.14 Micronutrients of particular concern for older adults. As we age, our energy needs decline, but our vitamin and mineral needs remain stable. This makes nutrient-dense foods especially important for older adults.

vitamin needs remain stable, while our energy needs decline. In other cases, age-related declines in absorption, use, or activation of nutrients lead to increased dietary vitamin and mineral needs. Therefore, it is especially important for older adults to eat nutrient-dense foods.

Vitamin D

Vitamin D promotes bone health; too little dietary vitamin D can lead to brittle and porous bones that are susceptible to fracture. In addition, individuals with low vitamin D levels have higher mortality rates from cardiovascular disease and other causes.[53] Older adults often have low vitamin D status.[54] Not only are aging tissues less able to take up vitamin D from the blood, but also aging skin also is less able to synthesize vitamin D when exposed to sunlight. In addition, many older adults spend more time indoors and have reduced exposure to sunlight. When they go outside, many avoid the sun and use sunscreens—a good strategy for skin cancer prevention but one that reduces vitamin D synthesis. Older adults with lactose intolerance often avoid dairy products, reducing their vitamin D intake and further compromising vitamin D status. The AI for vitamin D for adults aged 51 through 70 is 10 micrograms per day. For adults 70 and older, the AI is 15 micrograms per day. Younger adults only need 5 micrograms per day.

B Vitamins

The B vitamins deserve special consideration in adults and the aged. Extensive research links inadequate folate, vitamin B_6, and vitamin B_{12} to elevated levels of plasma homocysteine, which is associated with an increased risk for cardiovascular disease and mortality.[55] (See Chapter 11, "Water-Soluble Vitamins.") High homocysteine levels have also been found to be an independent risk factor for cognitive impairment and dementia.[56]

The prevalence of vitamin B_{12} deficiency increases with age. Six percent of adults aged 60 or older are vitamin B_{12} deficient, and close to 20 percent have marginal status.[57] Although most adults consume adequate amounts of dietary vitamin B_{12}, 10 to 30 percent of older adults lose their ability to absorb protein-bound vitamin B_{12} from foods. An intake of 2.4 micrograms per day of vitamin B_{12} is recommended for all adults older than 51 years. Because it is easier to absorb synthetic B_{12} than food-bound B_{12}, scientists suggest that adults older than 50 use fortified foods or B_{12}-containing supplements to meet their vitamin B_{12} requirements.

Key Concepts *Vitamin D, folate, vitamin B_6, and vitamin B_{12} are key nutrients for older adults. Vitamin D status can decline due to reduced intake, synthesis, and activation. Poor folate, vitamin B_6, and vitamin B_{12} status may result in high homocysteine levels, a risk factor for heart disease. Vitamin B_{12} absorption declines with age; vitamin B_{12} is more easily absorbed from fortified foods and supplements, so these become important sources for older adults.*

Dietary Guidelines for Americans, 2010
Key Recommendations

Balancing Calories to Manage Weight
- Maintain appropriate calorie balance during each stage of life—childhood, adolescence, adulthood, pregnancy and breastfeeding, and older age.

Recommendations for Specific Population Groups

Individuals Aged 50 years and Older
- Consume foods fortified with vitamin B_{12}, such as fortified cereals, or dietary supplements.

Calcium

Maintaining adequate calcium intake reduces the rate of age-related bone loss and the incidence of fractures, especially of the hip.[58] For all adults aged 51 and older, the AI for calcium is 1,200 milligrams per day, 200 milligrams per day higher than the AI for adults 31 to 50 years old.[59]

We are less able to absorb calcium as we age, partly because of a loss of vitamin D receptors in the gut. Stomach inflammation also reduces calcium absorption, as does an increase in the consumption of fiber—a practice that doctors recommend for its laxative effects. Because of real or perceived lactose intolerance, many older adults have a low intake of dairy foods and therefore of calcium.

Zinc

Although clinical zinc deficiencies are uncommon, older adults frequently have marginal zinc intakes. Stress, especially in hospitalized older adults, appears to increase the risk of zinc deficiency and suppress immune function. Studies show that zinc supplementation hastens wound healing, but only in those who are zinc deficient. Because excess zinc may interfere with immune function and the absorption of other minerals and may work to lower HDL cholesterol, people of all ages should avoid excessive and continuous zinc supplementation.

Magnesium

Magnesium plays an essential role in many cellular reactions. Magnesium deficiency has been observed in people with malabsorption syndromes, those with malnutrition or alcoholism, and in older adults. However, magnesium deficiency due to inadequate intake is rare. The potential role of increased dietary magnesium in the reduction of high blood pressure, cardiovascular disease, and diabetes is a top research priority.

Iron

Iron remains an important nutrient throughout the life cycle. Following menopause, the RDA for women drops to the same level as for men, 8 milligrams per day. Iron deficiency is a concern for older adults who have limited intake of iron from the best sources—red meats, fish, and poultry. Reduced meat consumption may result from taste changes, economics, poor dentition, or a combination of factors.

To Supplement or Not to Supplement

Increased use of dietary supplements, including vitamins, minerals, and herbal and botanical products, is widespread.[60] Although food is "the best medicine," some older adults may feel they need a supplement to meet their nutrient needs. Food is more than the sum of its known nutrients, however, and replacing food with supplements may be a poor trade-off. In addition, some nutrients in large amounts can be toxic; they also can affect the absorption of other nutrients or interfere with the absorption and metabolism of prescription medications.

Excessive use of vitamin supplements by older adults may result in **hypervitaminosis**. The need for vitamin A decreases with age, increasing the chances that supplementation may lead to liver dysfunction, bone and joint pain, headaches, and other problems. Also, taking large amounts of vitamin C can increase the likelihood of kidney stones and gastric bleeding. Because we know that many older adults use vitamin supplements and that megadoses may have negative effects on health, it is important to inform older adults of the ULs for micronutrients. The UL represents a level of intake from a combination of food and dietary supplements that should not be exceeded on a routine basis. (See Table 17.9.)

hypervitaminosis High levels of vitamins in the blood, usually a result of excess supplement intake.

Table 17.9 **The UL Values for Vitamins and Minerals for Adults**

Nutrient	UL	Unit
Vitamin A (as retinol)	3,000	μg/d
Vitamin C	2,000	mg/d
Vitamin D	50	μg/d
Vitamin E*	1,000	mg/d
Niacin*	35	mg/d
Vitamin B_6	100	mg/d
Folic acid*	1,000	μg/d
Choline	3,500	mg/d
Boron	20	mg/d
Calcium	2,500	mg/d
Chloride	3,600	mg/d
Copper	10,000	μg/d
Fluoride	10	mg/d
Iodine	1,100	μg/d
Iron	45	mg/d
Magnesium	350	mg/d
Manganese	11	mg/d
Molybdenum	2,000	μg/d
Nickel	1	mg/d
Phosphorus	4,000	mg/d
for > 70 yr	3,000	mg/d
Selenium	400	μg/d
Sodium	2,300	mg/d
Vanadium	1.8	mg/d
Zinc	40	mg/d

*From fortified foods and supplements only.

Key Concepts *Important minerals for older adults are calcium, zinc, magnesium, and iron. Calcium is important to reduce the risk for osteoporosis. Marginal zinc deficiency has been suspected in many older adults and may be the result of reduced intake of red meats. Iron needs decline for women as they go through menopause. Excessive supplementation with certain vitamins or minerals can lead to health problems.*

Nutrition-Related Concerns of Mature Adults

Many factors can interfere with intake or use of nutrients by older adults. Therefore, caretakers, health care practitioners, and seniors themselves must pay attention to nutritional status. To manage acute or chronic nutrition-related conditions, older adults may need to make specific dietary changes.

Drug–Drug and Drug–Nutrient Interactions

Drugs not only affect the way the body uses nutrients but also can alter the activities of other drugs. In turn, foods and nutrients can enhance or interfere with the effects of drugs. (See Table 17.10.) Some drugs interfere with appetite; others cause a dry mouth. Because many older adults take several medications or are on long-term drug therapy, they may find themselves at increased nutritional risk.

Table 17.10 Examples of Food–Drug Interactions

Drug	Food That Interacts	Effect of the Food	What to Do
Analgesic			
Acetaminophen (Tylenol)	Alcohol	Increases risk for liver toxicity	Avoid alcohol.
Antibiotic			
Tetracyclines	Dairy products; iron supplements	Decreases drug absorption	Do not take with milk. Take 1 hr before or 2 hr after food or milk.
Amoxicillin, penicillin	Food	Decreases drug absorption	Take 1 hr before or 2 hr after meals.
Azithromycin (Zithromax), erythromycin	Food	Decreases drug absorption	Take 1 hr before or 2 hr after meals.
Nitrofurantoin (Macrobid)	Food	Decreases GI distress, slows drug absorption	Take with food or milk.
Anticoagulant			
Warfarin (Coumadin)	Foods rich in vitamin K	Decreases drug effectiveness	Limit foods high in vitamin K: liver, broccoli, spinach, kale, cauliflower, and Brussels sprouts.
Antifungal			
Griseofulvin (Fulvicin)	High-fat meal	Increases drug absorption	Take with high-fat meal.
Antihistamine			
Diphenhydramine (Benadryl), chlorpheniramine (Chlor-Trimeton)	Alcohol	Increases drowsiness	Avoid alcohol.
Antihypertensive			
Felodipine (Plendil), nifedipine	Grapefruit juice	Increases drug absorption	Consult physician or pharmacist before changing diet.
Anti-inflammatory			
Naproxen (Aleve)	Food or milk	Decreases GI irritation	Take with food or milk.
Ibuprofen (Motrin)	Alcohol	Increases risk for liver damage or stomach bleeding	Avoid alcohol.
Diuretic			
Spironolactone (Aldactone)	Food	Decreases GI irritation	Take with food.
Psychotherapeutic (MAO inhibitors)			
Tranylcypromine (Parnate)	Foods high in tyramine: aged cheeses, Chianti wine, pickled herring, brewer's yeast, fava beans	Risk for hypertensive crisis	Avoid foods high in tyramine.

Note: Grapefruit juice contains a compound not found in other citrus juices. This compound increases the absorption of some drugs and can enhance their effects. Talk with your pharmacist or doctor to see if your medicine is affected by grapefruit juice before changing your routine.

Source: Bobroff LB, Lentz A, Turner RE. *Food/Drug and Drug/Nutrient Interactions: What You Should Know About Your Medications.* Gainesville, FL: University of Florida, 2009. Publication FCS 8092 in a series of the Department of Family, Youth and Community Sciences, Florida Cooperative Extension Service, Institute of Food and Agricultural Sciences. Retrieved from http://edis.ifas.ufl.edu. Reprinted by permission.

People should view herbal supplements and vitamins or minerals in high doses as drugs, particularly when taken in conjunction with prescription or over-the-counter medications. Although herbal products almost certainly interact with other medicines, many interactions are not well documented. In addition to the health and safety issues, supplement therapies can be costly. It is critical that older adults tell their health care providers all the drugs and supplements that they take on a regular basis so that possible interactions can be identified and avoided.

Depression

Many studies report high levels of well-being among older adults, especially those who remain independent. Although depression is one of the most common psychological effects of aging, it is most common among institutionalized and low-income people. Researchers believe that depression is related to the loss of receptors for the neurotransmitter serotonin. Loss of these receptors also may cause cognitive difficulties.

In older adults, life transitions and stressful events can become frequent companions that increase the likelihood and severity of depression. Among these stressors are the loss of loved ones, including spouse and friends; physical disability; perceived loss of physical attractiveness; inability to psychologically defend oneself from unpleasant events; inability to care for oneself, which forces one to depend upon caregivers and long-term care; social isolation; and, inevitably, the approach of death. In later life, depression often leads to malnutrition and may manifest itself as either anorexia (loss of appetite) or obesity. Anorectic older adults lose weight and muscle mass, putting them at risk for chronic conditions such as osteoporosis.

Alcoholism is prevalent among socially isolated or depressed older adults. People who consume excessive amounts of alcohol often have diets low in essential nutrients. Over time, excessive alcohol use can cause chronic liver disease, pancreatitis, secondary vitamin and mineral deficiencies, and protein-energy malnutrition.

Anorexia of Aging

Poor food intake that accompanies age can result from **anorexia of aging**. Reductions in appetite and food intake contribute to undernutrition in older adults.[61] Malnutrition, in turn, can contribute to numerous problems, including immune deficiencies, anemia, falls, and cognitive decline.

It can be difficult to pinpoint treatment strategies for anorexia in older adults. However, treating even one aspect of the problem can provide at least temporary improvement. Unfortunately, lifelong inappropriate food habits, social factors, living conditions, and fear of injury may interfere with a person's ability and desire to stay or become healthy.

Key Concepts *Among the problems older adults face are lack of appetite and the side effects and interactions of medications they use. Medicines have the potential to interact with food and nutrients in the diet, and a lack of knowledge of these possibilities increases the risk for harmful effects. Although many older adults have high levels of well-being, depression is common among institutionalized and low-income seniors.*

anorexia of aging Loss of appetite and wasting associated with old age.

Arthritis

Arthritis is a general term that describes more than 100 diseases that cause pain and swelling of joints and connective tissue. (See **Figure 17.15**.) Arthritis is a chronic, lifelong affliction that, at its worst, can make movement difficult or even impossible. Unfortunately, there is no proven cure for arthritis. At best, appropriate treatment programs reduce symptoms. In terms of nutrition, arthritis pain may impair appetite or make it hard to prepare meals, and some arthritis medications may interfere with nutrient absorption. These factors underscore the importance of a nutrient-dense diet for arthritis sufferers.

Weight management is important in treating arthritis. Excess weight puts undue pressure on the hips and knees. Weight loss by people who are overweight or obese may reduce the risk of developing osteoarthritis, particularly of the knee.[62]

People who have rheumatoid arthritis may benefit from adding foods that are high in unsaturated fatty acids, particularly the omega-3 fatty acids in flaxseed and cold-water fish. There is some evidence that these fatty acids may have beneficial effects on the immune system of people with rheumatoid arthritis, thus helping to reduce discomfort.[63]

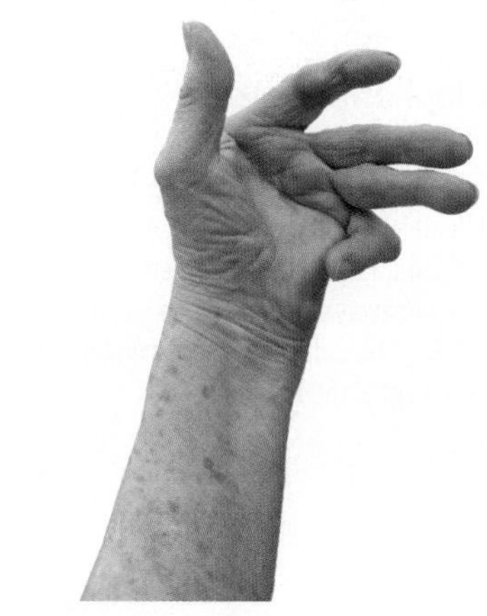

Figure 17.15 **Arthritis.** Degeneration of the finger joints can cause a debilitating lack of function.

Among the many kinds of arthritis, gout stands out because of the intensity of its pain. The classic attack occurs in someone who goes to bed feeling well and then awakens in the middle of the night with excruciating pain that has been likened to having someone walk on your eyeballs. This often leads to a visit to the emergency room.

Gout is directly linked to an excess of uric acid in the blood. Uric acid, a natural breakdown product of purines (organic compounds) found in all foods and body tissues, is normally dissolved in blood. But excess uric acid can accumulate as microscopic crystals in hand or foot joints, where it leads to painful inflammation, or gouty arthritis. Age-related degenerative osteoarthritis, particularly in the big toe, also enhances the risk of gout. Fructose consumption can also increase uric acid levels, and therefore high intake of sucrose- or fructose-sweetened beverages may also increase risk for gout.[64]

Certain medications, alcohol, overeating, and an unusual increase in exercise can trigger an attack of gout, but often it strikes without warning. After the attack passes, medications can help control uric acid levels. To reduce the risk of future attacks, people who are overweight should gradually lose weight, cut down on alcohol, and reduce their consumption of foods high in purines, such as organ meats, red meat, shellfish, and beans.

Bowel and Bladder Regulation

As a result of physiological and lifestyle changes, older adults are susceptible to problems with their bowels and bladder. Hospitalized or institutionalized elderly patients who require catheters to urinate run an increased risk of **urinary tract infection (UTI)**, both during and after the procedure.

Inadequate hydration not only affects the bladder but also makes constipation more likely. Age-related decreases in intestinal motility and transit time, accompanied by poor food intake, may exacerbate the problem. In addition, lack of physical activity contributes to loss of muscle tone needed for regular elimination.

Chronic constipation is one of the most common health complaints among older adults. If they do not have at least one bowel movement per day, many older adults wrongly consider themselves constipated and quickly self-prescribe laxatives. However, excessive use of laxatives may cause nutritional deficiencies by decreasing transit time and preventing adequate absorption of nutrients. Decreased transit time also reduces water reabsorption by the GI tract and contributes to dehydration.

Increasing dietary fiber and fluid is one of the most effective treatments for bowel and bladder problems. Older adults should gradually switch to—

urinary tract infection (UTI) An infection of one or more of the structures in the urinary tract; usually caused by bacteria.

and then maintain—a high-fiber diet. They also should be careful to maintain adequate fluid intake and get regular exercise. Supplementation with prebiotics, such as fructooligosaccharides, and probiotics, such as *Lactobacillus acidophilus*, may also improve their gastrointestinal health.[65]

Key Concepts *Arthritis and changes in bowel and bladder habits are common problems in older adults. Weight management is an important component of arthritis treatment. Because of an increased risk of dehydration and constipation, older adults should be encouraged to follow a high-fiber diet and consume plenty of fluids.*

Quick Bite

Why Elephants Don't Need Dentures

Elephants are the only mammals with a built-in tooth replacement system. As they age, elephants go through six sets of teeth, changing about every 10 years. When elephants are around 70 years old, about the maximum life span, the last set of molars wears out.

Dental Health

The mouth is the gateway to the rest of the gastrointestinal system. Poor oral health impairs the ability to eat and obtain adequate nutrition.[66] Missing teeth or poorly fitting dentures make some older adults self-conscious about eating, which leaves them unable to eat comfortably in public. Mouth pain and difficulty swallowing interfere with the process of eating, and tooth loss can alter choices and quality of food. Meats, fresh fruits, and fresh vegetables often are avoided. Oral infections affect the whole body and may increase the risk of other chronic diseases, including heart disease.

macular degeneration Progressive deterioration of the macula, an area in the center of the retina, that eventually leads to loss of central vision.

Vision Problems

Poor vision and blindness interfere with the ability to buy and prepare food; visually impaired people cannot read food labels, cookbooks, or the settings on stoves or microwave ovens. **Macular degeneration** is a common disease of the eye that gradually leads to loss of vision. It affects about 6 percent of people between the ages of 65 and 74, and about 20 percent of those aged 75 to 85. Research has found that people with a higher intake of green leafy vegetables are less likely to develop this sight-robbing disorder. Foods that contain the carotenoids lutein and zeaxanthin are most strongly associated with a reduced risk.[67] Greens, such as collards and spinach, show the most promise when consumed five or more times per week. By preventing free radical damage, antioxidants in these foods may protect the eye and the blood vessels that supply it. The National Eye Institute's Age-Related Eye Disease Study (AREDS) found that taking a specific high-dose formulation of antioxidants and zinc (beta-carotene; vitamins A, C, and E; copper; and zinc) significantly reduces the risk of advanced age-related macular degeneration and its associated vision loss. Slowing progression of the disease from the intermediate stage to the advanced stage will save the vision of many people.[68]

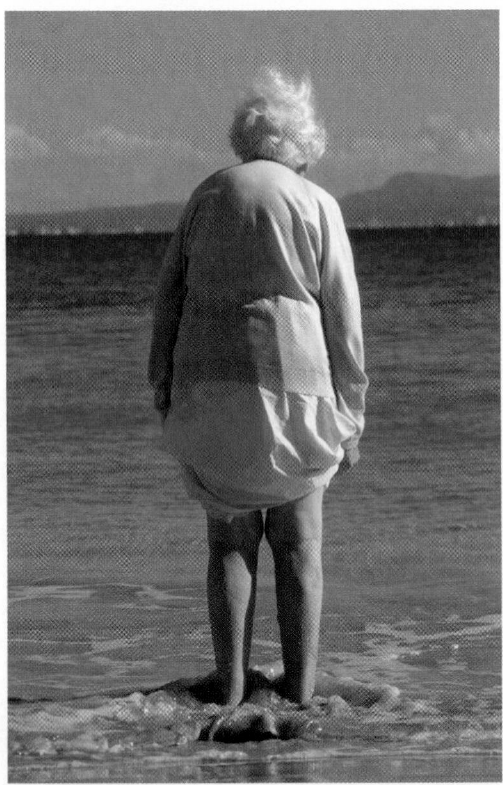

Figure 17.16 A hunched back (sometimes called a dowager's hump) due to collapsed vertebrae is a visible symptom of osteoporosis.

Osteoporosis

Although osteoporosis affects older adults of both genders, it is most common in postmenopausal women. Osteoporosis is the deterioration of bone structure (**Figure 17.16**) until, often without warning, the fragile bone breaks upon the slightest impact.

Nutritional factors, particularly early in life, are thought to play an important role in the development of osteoporosis. While regular weight-bearing exercise helps prevent osteoporosis, inactivity increases osteoporosis risk. Long periods of inactivity, such as may be imposed by complete bed rest or illnesses that limit mobility, can promote the disease. (See Chapter 12, "Water and Major Minerals," for more on osteoporosis, including risk factors.)

Although prevention is the best treatment for osteoporosis, many people enter later life with bad habits—poor nutrition and physical inactivity—that put them at risk. Adopting a diet that is rich in calcium and vitamin D and engaging in regular physical activity, particularly weight-bearing exercises, minimizes osteoporosis risks.

Academy of Nutrition and Dietetics

Nutrition Across the Spectrum of Aging
It is the position of the Academy of Nutrition and Dietetics that older Americans receive appropriate care; have broadened access to coordinated, comprehensive food and nutrition services; and receive the benefits of ongoing research to identify the most effective food and nutrition programs, interventions, and therapies across the spectrum of aging.

Source: Position of the American Dietetic Association: nutrition across the spectrum of aging. *J Am Diet Assoc.* 2005;105(4):616–633. Copyright © 2005. Reprinted with permission from Elsevier.

Alzheimer's Disease

Among its other ravages, **Alzheimer's disease (AD)** eventually destroys the ability to obtain, prepare, and consume an optimal diet. Although genetic factors can affect the risk for Alzheimer's disease, other risk factors include age, head trauma, and possibly exposure to environmental toxins. Although more research is needed, several antioxidants appear to offer some protection from the disease.[69]

Most cases of Alzheimer's disease begin after age 70, but it can strike genetically predisposed people at a younger age. During the first stage of the disease, the afflicted person can have difficulty recalling names, frequently lose possessions, and easily become lost. Sensory sensitivity, such as loss of the sense of smell, begins to change gradually and so may not be readily noticed.

As the disease progresses, the person becomes unable to complete simple tasks that require learned motor movement, such as using a can opener. There is an increase in behavior problems, including wandering, aggression, and sleep disorders. These behaviors, if they occur frequently, can affect the person's ability to maintain weight and nutritional status.

The late stages of the disease are marked by inability to communicate, and about one-third of those with AD develop overactivity that drains the nutritional reserve and increases calorie needs. Eventually, people with AD become unable to walk and are restricted to a chair or bed. At this time, the caregiver must carefully plan the person's diet to meet psychological and physical needs, paying particular attention to optimum nutrition without excess weight gain.

Key Concepts *Oral health, vision, and bone health all decline with aging. Tooth loss and oral pain can reduce food intake and nutrient quality. Loss of vision can make food shopping and preparation difficult. Osteoporosis, most common in postmenopausal women, can cause debilitating fractures. Alzheimer's disease eventually destroys the ability to obtain, prepare, and consume an optimal diet. Management of these conditions depends first on their identification by health care professionals.*

Meal Management for Mature Adults

Many older adults are at nutritional risk because of economics, social isolation, physical restrictions, inability to shop for or prepare food, and medical conditions. Fortunately, there are a number of ways that older adults can remain independent and have access to an adequate diet.

Managing Independently

Independent and assisted-living programs allow people to live relatively carefree yet independent lives. Senior citizen apartment buildings and retirement villages offer a variety of services, including balanced meals. Programs such as **Meals on Wheels** and the **Older Americans Act Nutrition Program** (formerly known as the Elderly Nutrition Program) provide meals to homebound people, as well as those in congregate (group) settings. Most programs provide meals at least five times per week. The Older Americans Act Nutrition Program is supported primarily with federal funds; volunteer time,

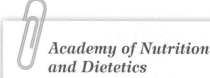

Alzheimer's disease (AD) A presenile dementia characterized by accumulation of plaques in certain regions of the brain and degeneration of a certain class of neurons.

Meals on Wheels A voluntary, not-for-profit organization established to provide nutritious meals to homebound people (regardless of age) so they may maintain their independence and quality of life.

Older Americans Act Nutrition Program A federally funded program (formerly known as the Elderly Nutrition Program) that provides older persons with nutritionally sound meals through home-delivered nutrition services, congregate nutrition services, and the nutrition services' incentive.

in-kind donations, and participant contributions make up the remainder. The **Supplemental Nutrition Assistance Program (SNAP)**, formerly the Food Stamp Program, is another option that provides low-income older adults with the means to purchase food. Unfortunately, because SNAP carries a "welfare" stigma, some older adults are reluctant to participate. In addition, many people who need some help buying food do not meet the eligibility requirements. An evaluation of the Older Americans Act Nutrition Program showed that program participants had higher nutrient intake levels than nonparticipants and had a higher number of regular social contacts—another important factor in eating well.[70] Also, researchers have found that participation in food assistance programs can reduce the incidence of depression and overweight associated with food insecurity.[71]

Quick Bite

Meno-What?

Most animal species do not go through menopause.

Wise Eating for One or Two

Preparing meals that are healthful and tasty is a challenge for those living alone or in small households. As discussed earlier in this chapter, our nutrition needs—with the exception of calories—do not decrease as we age, but our ability to meet them does. Reliance on convenience foods, fast foods, and eating out can adversely affect the nutritional status of older adults. Men who live alone are especially likely to eat out or skip meals rather than prepare food for themselves. For both men and women, physical disability or illness can diminish the desire to prepare and eat meals.

Supplemental Nutrition Assistance Program (SNAP) A USDA program that helps single people and families with little or no income to buy food. Formerly known as the Food Stamp Program.

Some simple changes in appliances and food-preparation techniques can help older adults overcome common obstacles to food preparation. Those who can't or won't cook can use microwave or toaster ovens and small appliances to prepare simple meals. A meal based on a lower-sodium, low-fat convenience entree can meet nutritional needs if accompanied by vegetables, whole-grain bread, milk, and fruit.

Table 17.11 Important Resources for Older Adults

Resource Directory for Older People

http://www.aoa.gov

The Resource Directory for Older People is a cooperative effort of the National Institute on Aging and the Administration on Aging. This directory provides resources for elders, their caregivers and family members, and those in the legal and health care professions. Available via the Internet, it provides telephone numbers (some toll free), names, addresses, and fax numbers for organizations that work with older adults.

The Eldercare Locator

http://www.eldercare.gov
(800) 677-1116 (toll free)

The National Association of Area Agencies on Aging and the National Association of State Units on Aging administer the Eldercare Locator, a public service of the Administration on Aging, U.S. Department of Health and Human Services. The Eldercare Locator is a nationwide directory-assistance service that helps older persons and their families identify resources for aging Americans.

Finding Community Resources

An older person's need for community support typically changes from decade to decade. Sometimes, identifying community resources can be challenging, and financial considerations may further limit access to resources that can assist older adults in their own homes. Within local communities, area agencies on aging, social and rehabilitation services, cooperative extension services, churches, and extended-care facilities may have lists of resources and educational programs for older adults. Table 17.11 lists important resources for older adults.

Key Concepts *Older adults who obtain adequate food and nutrient intake while living independently may require assistance from time to time. This assistance may take the form of help with food shopping or preparation or identification of community resources that can stretch the food dollar. Numerous resources exist to assist older adults in maintaining a productive, high-quality life.*

What is it about fruit snacks that attracts kids? The sweet flavors, bright colors, different shapes, or the logos of favorite movie or TV characters? Probably all of these. Parents may be attracted by claims for vitamins. So are these nutritious snacks or little more than candy? Let's have a look at the label.

Nutrition Facts
Serving Size: 1 pouch (26g/0.9 oz)
Servings Per Container 10
Amount Per Serving
Calories 80

	% Daily Value*
Total Fat 0g	
Sodium 15mg	**0%**
Total Carbohydrate 19g	**1%**
Sugars 14g	**6%**
Protein 1g	
Vitamin A 25% (100% as beta carotene)	
Vitamin C 25%	
Vitamin E 25%	

Not a significant source of calories from fat, saturated fat, trans fat, cholesterol, dietary fiber, calcium, or iron.

*Percent Daily Values are based on a 2,000 calorie diet. Your daily values may be higher or lower depending on your calorie needs:

	Calories:	2,000	2,500
Total Fat	Less Than	65g	80g
Sat Fat	Less Than	20g	25g
Cholesterol	Less Than	300mg	300mg
Sodium	Less Than	2,400mg	2,400mg
Total Carbohydrate		300g	375g
Dietary Fiber		25g	30g

Calories per gram:
Fat 9 • Carbohydrate 4 • Protein 4

On the positive side, this is a fat-free snack and contains little sodium. However, most of the calories—56 of 80—come from sugar (14 g × 4 kcal/g), and the remainder from starch and protein. The ingredient list shows that the first three ingredients are sugars: corn syrup, sucrose, and fruit juice from concentrate.

The vitamins added to fruit snacks are the only redeeming feature of the product, providing 25 percent of the DV for vitamins A, C, and E. But is there a better way to get these nutrients? One-half cup of orange juice provides two-thirds of the DV for vitamin C and significant amounts of thiamin, folate, and potassium as well. Just a handful of baby carrots provides more than 100 percent DV for vitamin A, along with some fiber. Vitamin E is widespread in the food supply—a small amount of salad dressing as a dip for the carrots would add vitamin E.

So, the fruit snacks are not as devoid of nutrients as candy, but are not as nutrient dense as fruits and vegetables. The fruit snacks may have some nutrient value, but they are high in sugar and, like all sugary snacks, should be used sparingly.

Learning Portfolio

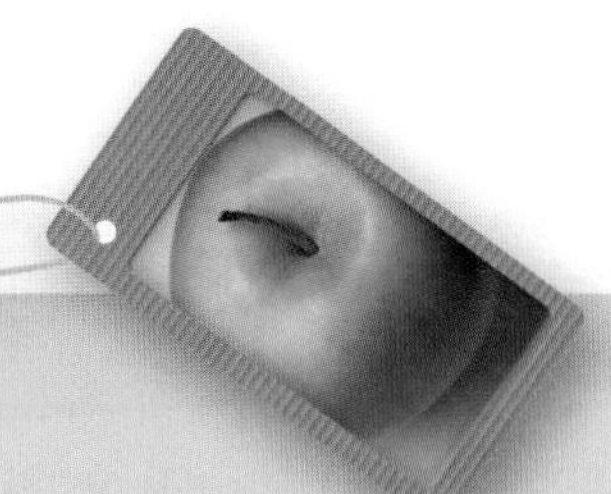

Key Terms

	page		page
acne	725	Meals on Wheels	741
adolescence	712	menarche	722
Alzheimer's disease (AD)	741	Older Americans Act Nutrition Program	741
anorexia of aging	738	puberty	721
childhood	712	Supplemental Nutrition Assistance Program (SNAP)	742
epiphyses	722	taste threshold	730
hyperactivity	718	urinary tract infection (UTI)	739
hypervitaminosis	735		
macular degeneration	740		

Study Points

- For children and adolescents, growth is the key determinant of nutrient needs. If diets are planned carefully, children do not need vitamin/mineral supplementation.
- Federally funded nutrition and feeding programs reduce malnutrition and hunger among American children.
- Adoption of adult-style diets to reduce risk of chronic disease should begin gradually after the age of 2.
- The prevalence of obesity and eating disorders is rising among American children and teens; treatment programs should address food choices and activity levels rather than impose strict calorie limits. Vegetarian diets for children need to be planned carefully to avoid nutrient deficiencies.
- The total energy and nutrient needs of adolescents are high to support growth and maturation. Girls need more iron than boys do to compensate for losses after the onset of menstruation. Active teens need more calories and nutrients than sedentary teens; fluid intake is also a priority.
- Nutrition and physical activity are two important, controllable components of a healthy life and healthful aging. Moreover, numerous physiological and psychological aspects of the aging process affect food intake and nutritional status.
- Energy needs decline with age, reflecting loss of lean body mass and reduced physical activity. The protein RDA and the recommended balance of carbohydrate and fat calories in the diet are similar for young and older adults. Fluid intake needs special attention due to the reduced thirst response that occurs with age.
- Because of reduced intake, synthesis, and activation, vitamin D status declines with age; recommended intake levels are therefore raised. Vitamin B_{12} status may be compromised due to inadequate absorption.
- Calcium and zinc intakes are likely to be marginal in the diets of older adults. Magnesium and iron remain important.
- Dietary supplements, both vitamin/mineral and herbal/botanical, should be used with caution, preferably with professional advice.
- Because many older adults take multiple medications, they are at risk for drug–nutrient, food–drug, and drug–drug interactions. Anorexia of aging is also a major public health problem.
- Arthritis is a prevalent chronic health problem in this age group. Weight management is a key element of arthritis treatment.
- Chronic constipation is a common complaint among older adults. Fluids, fiber, and regular exercise can reduce the likelihood of constipation.
- Both poor oral and visual health can compromise the ability of older adults to consume a nutritionally adequate diet.
- Osteoporosis is a major health problem that can be addressed through adequate calcium, vitamin D, regular weight-bearing exercise, and medication if needed.
- Adults can maintain independence while aging but may require special assistance to obtain and prepare food. Community resources can help respond to the needs of older adults and those of their caretakers and family.

Study Questions

1. Which vitamins and minerals are most likely to be deficient in a child's diet?
2. Identify several chronic nutrition problems that can affect children. How can these problems be avoided?
3. What are typical nutritional concerns for adolescents?

4. What are some of the consequences of decreased immunity among older adults?
5. Compared with a younger adult, does a person older than 65 need more, less, or about the same amount of protein?
6. Why are older adults at risk of vitamin D deficiency?
7. Discuss minerals that may need special attention in assessment of an older adult's nutrition status.
8. What problems might older adults encounter with dietary supplements?
9. What is the role of physical activity in osteoporosis prevention? What nutritional factors are important?

Try This

Eat Like a Kid

Children, especially toddlers, tend to be exploratory, and take in the sensory nature of food—the textures, smells, and tastes. In fact, you were probably once this way. The purpose of this exercise is to eat a meal like a kid and gain an appreciation of food's textures and taste. Make some mashed potatoes, macaroni and cheese, buttered peas, or spaghetti (favorite "kid food") and eat it with your fingers. Explore your food and play with it. Try mixing foods. How does this experience make you feel?

Aging Simulation

The purpose of this exercise is to simulate what it can be like to age and experience age-related declines in health. Have you ever thought of how difficult it is to be an older person with health problems and do routine tasks? Invite a few friends over and do the following:

- Put gloves on to simulate the difficulty of losing sensitivity in your hands.
- Use cotton balls in your ears to decrease your hearing ability.
- Apply some petroleum jelly to a pair of glasses or sunglasses to give yourself poor vision.

Now try a simple activity. Make a salad or put a CD in your CD player and listen to it. After completing the activity, switch disabilities with your friends so that everyone has experienced each of the limitations. What is it like to do these everyday activities with your impairment?

What About Bobbie?

Let's pretend that Bobbie is in her sixties and just read a newspaper article about how older adults may have low intakes of vitamins E and B_6, magnesium, calcium, and iron. How do you think her diet compares to the needs of a 65-year-old woman? You may want to review her one-day intake in Chapter 1. Although her calorie intake is probably much higher than that of most women in their sixties, let's look at her intake of these vitamins and minerals.

Bobbie was close to her RDA or AI for vitamin B_6, magnesium, and zinc, but her intake was lower for vitamin E and calcium. Since Bobbie's fat intake was ample, this low value for vitamin E probably reflects a lack of complete data for the vitamin E content of foods. As is true of many women in their sixties who don't have an adequate intake of calcium, this increases Bobbie's risk of osteoporosis.

Vitamin E	
RDA	15 mg
Bobbie's intake	9 mg
Vitamin B_6	
RDA	1.5 mg
Bobbie's intake	2.0 mg
Magnesium	
RDA	320 mg
Bobbie's intake	310 mg
Calcium	
AI	1,200 mg
Bobbie's intake	710 mg
Zinc	
RDA	8 mg
Bobbie's intake	12 mg

References

1 Institute of Medicine, Food and Nutrition Board. *Dietary Reference Intakes for Energy, Carbohydrate, Fiber, Fat, Fatty Acids, Cholesterol, Protein, and Amino Acids*. Washington, DC: National Academies Press, 2002.

2 Kleinman RE, ed. *Pediatric Nutrition Handbook*. 6th ed. Elk Grove Village, IL: American Academy of Pediatrics, 2008.

3 Kumar J, Muntner P, Kaskel FJ, et al. Prevalence and associations of 25-hydroxyvitamin D deficiency in U.S. children: NHANES 2001–2004. *Pediatrics*. Published online August 3, 2009. doi:10.1542/peds.2009-0051.

4 Ibid.

5 Reis JP, von Mühlen D, Miller ER III, et al. Vitamin D status and cardiometabolic risk factors in the United States adolescent population. *Pediatrics*. Published online August 3, 2009. doi:10.1542/peds.2009-0213.

6 Wagner CL, Greer FR, Section on Breastfeeding and Committee on Nutrition. Prevention of rickets and vitamin D deficiency in infants and children and adolescents. *Pediatrics*. 2008;122(5):1143–1152.

7 American Dietetic Association. Position of the American Dietetic Association: nutrition guidance for healthy children ages 2 to 11 years. *J Am Diet Assoc*. 2008;108:1038–1047.

8 Kleinman. *Pediatric Nutrition Handbook*.

9 American Dietetic Association. Nutrition guidance for healthy children ages 2 to 11 years.

10 McGinnis JM, Gootman JA, Kraak VI, eds. *Food Marketing to Children and Youth: Threat or Opportunity?* Washington, DC: National Academies Press, 2006.

11 Batada A, Seitz M, Wootan M. Nine out of 10 food advertisements shown during Saturday morning children's television programming are for foods high in fat, sodium, or added sugars, or low in nutrients. *J Am Diet Assoc*. 2008;108(4):673–678.

12 Miller SA, Taveras EM, Rifas-Shiman SL, Gillman MW. Association between television viewing and poor diet quality in young children. *Int J Pediatr Obes*. 2008;3(3):168–176.

13 Coon KA, Goldberg J, Rogers BL, Tucker KL. Relationship between use of television during meals and children's food consumption patterns. *Pediatrics*. 2001;107:E7.

14 Caulfield LE, de Onis M, Blossner M, Black RE. Undernutrition as an underlying cause of child deaths associated with diarrhea, pneumonia, malaria, and measles. *Am J Clin Nutr*. 2004;80:193–198.

15 Bellisle F. Effects of diet on behaviour and cognition in children. *Br J Nutr*. 2004;92(suppl 2):S227–S232; and Wolraich ML, Lindgren SD, Stumbo PJ, et al. Effects of diets high in sucrose or aspartame on the behavior and cognitive performance of children. *N Engl J Med*. 1994;330:301–307.

16 McCann D, Barrett A, Cooper A, et al. Food additives and hyperactive behaviour in 3-year-old and 8/9-year-old children in the community: a randomised, double-blinded, placebo-controlled trial. *Lancet*. 2007;370:1560–1567.

17 Gable S, Britt-Rankin J, Krull JL. *Ecological Predictors and Developmental Outcomes of Persistent Childhood Overweight*. Washington, DC: US Department of Agriculture, Economic Research Service, 2008. Contractor and Cooperator Report No. 42 (CCR-42). http://hdl.handle.net/10113/32852. Accessed 8/23/09.

18 Daniels SR, Greer FR, Committee on Nutrition. Lipid screening and cardiovascular health in childhood. *Pediatrics*. 2008;122:198–208.

19 US Department of Health and Human Services. *Healthy People 2010*. 2nd ed. Washington, DC: US Government Printing Office, 2000.

20 Wengrovitz AM, Brown MJ, Advisory Committee on Childhood Lead Poisoning. Recommendations for blood lead screening of Medicaid-eligible children aged 1–5 years: an updated approach to targeting a group at high risk. *MMWR*. 2009;58(RR09):1–11.

21 Centers for Disease Control and Prevention. Lead. http://www.cdc.gov/lead/. Accessed 8/22/09.

22 Selevan SG, Rice DC, Hogan KA, et al. Blood lead concentration and delayed puberty in girls. *N Engl J Med*. 2003;348:1527–1536.

23 Position of the American Dietetic Association and Dietitians of Canada: vegetarian diets. *J Am Diet Assoc*. 2003;103:748–765.

24 Wagner CL, Greer FR, Section on Breastfeeding and Committee on Nutrition. Prevention of rickets and vitamin D deficiency.

25 American Academy of Pediatrics. Vitamin D deficiency clinical report: patient FAQs. February 2009. http://www.aap.org/family/vitdpatients.htm. Accessed 8/22/09.

26 Kleinman. *Pediatric Nutrition Handbook*.

27 O'Dea JA. Why do kids eat healthful food? Perceived benefits of and barriers to healthful eating and physical activity among children and adolescents. *J Am Diet Assoc*. 2003;103:497–501.

28 Templeton SB, Marlette MA, Panemangalore M. Competitive foods increase the intake of energy and decrease the intake of certain nutrients by adolescents consuming school lunch. *J Am Diet Assoc*. 2005;105:215–220.

29 Kubik MY, Lytle LA, Story M. Soft drinks, candy, and fast food: what parents and teachers think about the middle school food environment. *J Am Diet Assoc*. 2005;105:233–239.

30 Department of Education, State of Arizona. *Arizona Healthy School Environment Model Policy: Implementation Pilot Study*. February 2005. http://www.cspinet.org/nutritionpolicy/AZPilot_RevenueReport.pdf. Accessed 8/23/09.

31 Cordain L, Lindeberg S, Hurtado M, et al. Acne vulgaris: a disease of Western civilization. *Arch Dermatol*. 2002;138:1591–1592.

32 Smith RN, Mann NJ, Braue A, et al. A low-glycemic-load diet improves symptoms in acne vulgaris patients: a randomized controlled trial. *Am J Clin Nutr*. 2007;86:107–115.

33 Nader PR, Bradley RH, Houts RM, et al. Moderate-to-vigorous physical activity from ages 9 to 15 years. *JAMA*. 2008;300:295–305.

34 Daniels SR, Arnett DK, Eckel RH, et al. Overweight in children and adolescents: pathophysiology, consequences, prevention, and treatment. *Circulation*. 2005;111:1999–2012.

35 Field AE, Cook NR, Gillman MW. Weight status in childhood as a predictor of becoming overweight or hypertensive in early adulthood. *Obes Res*. 2005;13:163–169.

36 Boutelle K, Neumark-Sztainer D, Story M, Resnick M. Weight control behaviors among obese, overweight, and nonoverweight adolescents. *J Pediatr Psychology*. 2002;27(6):531–540.

37 Watson LC, Kwon J, Nichols D, Rew M. Evaluation of the nutrition knowledge, attitudes, and food consumption behaviors of high school students before and after completion of a nutrition course. *Fam Consumer Sci Res J*. 2009;37(4):523–534.

38 Johnston LD, O'Malley PM, Bachman JG, Schulenberg JE. *Monitoring the Future: National Results on Adolescent Drug Use. Overview of Key Findings, 2007*. Bethesda, MD: National Institute on Drug Abuse, 2007. NIH publication 08-6418. http://monitoringthefuture.org/pubs/monographs/overview2007.pdf. Accessed 8/24/09.

39 Centers for Disease Control and Prevention. Alcohol quick stats: binge drinking. http://www.cdc.gov/alcohol/quickstats/binge_drinking.htm. Accessed 8/24/09.

40 Federal Interagency Forum on Aging-Related Statistics. *Older Americans 2008: Key Indicators of Well-Being*. Washington, DC: US Government Printing Office, 2008. http://www.agingstats.gov/agingstatsdotnet/Main_Site/Data/Data_2008.aspx. Accessed 08/25/09.

41 Verghese J, Lipton RB, Katz MJ, et al. Leisure activities and the risk of dementia in the elderly. *N Engl J Med*. 2003;348:2508–2516.

42 Position paper of the American Dietetic Association: nutrition across the spectrum of aging. *J Am Diet Assoc*. 2005;105:616–633.

43 Bernstein MA, Luggen AS, eds. *Nutrition for the Older Adult*. Sudbury, MA: Jones & Bartlett, 2010.

44 Fiatarone-Singh MA, Bernstein MA. Exercise for the older adult: nutritional implications. In: Bernstein MA, Luggen AS, eds. *Nutrition for the Older Adult*. Sudbury, MA: Jones & Bartlett, 2010.

45 Ibid.

46 Salem GJ, Skinner JS, Chodzko-Zajko WJ, et al. Exercise and physical activity for older adults. *Med Sci Sports Exer*. 2009;41(7):1510–1530.

47 US Department of Health and Human Services. Active older adults. In: *2008 Physical Activity Guidelines for Americans*. Rockville, MD: US Department of Health and Human Services, 2008.

48 Schiffman SS. Intensification of sensory properties of foods for the elderly. *J Nutr*. 2000;130(suppl):927S–930S; and Mathey MF, Siebelink E, de Graaf C, Van Staveren WA. Flavor enhancement of food improves dietary intake and nutritional status of elderly nursing home residents. *J Gerontol A Biol Sci Med Sci*. 2001;56:M200–M205.

49 Moskovitz DN, Saltzman J, Kim YI. The aging gut. In: Chernoff R, ed. *Geriatric Nutrition: The Health Professional's Handbook*. 3rd ed. Sudbury, MA: Jones & Bartlett, 2006.

50 Paddon-Jones D, Rasmussen BB. Dietary protein recommendations and the prevention of sarcopenia. *Curr Opin Clin Nutr Metab Care*. 2009;12(1):86–90.

51 Institute of Medicine, Food and Nutrition Board. *Dietary Reference Intakes for Water, Potassium, Sodium, Chloride, and Sulfate*. Washington, DC: National Academies Press, 2004.

52 Ibid.

53 Dobnig H, Pilz S, Scharnagl H, et al. Independent association of low serum 25-hydroxyvitamin D and 1,25-dihydroxyvitamin D levels with all-cause and cardiovascular mortality. *Arch Intern Med*. 2008;168:1340–1349.

54 Ibid; and Hanley DA, Davison KS. Vitamin D insufficiency in North America. *J Nutr*. 2005;135:332–387.

55 Dangour AD, Breeze E, Clarke R, et al. Plasma homocysteine, but not folate or vitamin B_{12}, predicts mortality in older adults in the United Kingdom. *J Nutr*. 2008;138:1121–1128; and Fairfield KM, Fletcher RH. Vitamins for chronic disease prevention in adults: scientific review. *JAMA*. 2002;287:3116–3126.

56 Haan MN, Miller JW, Aiello AE, et al. Homocysteine, B vitamins, and the incidence of dementia and cognitive impairment: results from the Sacramento Area Latino Study on Aging. *Am J Clin Nutr*. 2007;85(2):511–517.

57 Allen LH. How common is vitamin B-12 deficiency? *Am J Clin Nutr*. 2009;89(2):693S–696S.

58 US Department of Health and Human Services, Office of the Surgeon General. *Bone Health and Osteoporosis: A Report of the Surgeon General*. Rockville, MD: US Department of Health and Human Services, 2004. http://www.surgeongeneral.gov/library/bonehealth/content.html. Accessed 8/25/09.

59 Institute of Medicine, Food and Nutrition Board. *Dietary Reference Intakes for Calcium, Phosphorus, Magnesium, Vitamin D, and Fluoride*. Washington, DC: National Academies Press, 1997.

60 Wold RS, Lopez ST, Yau CL, et al. Increasing trends in elderly persons' use of nonvitamin, nonmineral dietary supplements and concurrent use of medications. *J Am Diet Assoc*. 2005;105:54–63.

61 Chapman IM. The anorexia of aging. *Clin Geriatr Med*. 2007;23(4):735–756.

62 National Institute of Arthritis and Musculoskeletal and Skin Diseases. Handout on health: osteoarthritis. Revised May 2006. http://www.niams.nih.gov/Health_Info/Osteoarthritis/default.asp. Accessed 8/25/09.

63 Sarubin Fragakis A, Thomson CA. *The Health Professional's Guide to Popular Dietary Supplements*. 3rd ed. Chicago: American Dietetic Association, 2006.

64 Choi HK, Curhan G. Soft drinks, fructose consumption, and the risk of gout in men: prospective cohort study. *BMJ*. 2008;336:309–312.

65 Sarubin Fragakis. *Health Professional's Guide to Popular Dietary Supplements*.

66 Sheiham A, Steele JG, Marcenes W, et al. The relationship among dental status, nutrient intake, and nutritional status in older adults. *J Dent Res*. 2001;80:408–413.

67 Stringham JM, Hammond BR Jr. Dietary lutein and zeaxanthin: possible effects on visual function. *Nutr Rev*. 2005;63:59–64.

68 National Eye Institute. The AREDS formulation and age-related macular degeneration. http://www.nei.nih.gov/amd/summary.asp. Accessed 8/25/09.

69 Frank B, Gupta S. A review of antioxidants and Alzheimer's disease. *Ann Clin Psychiatry*. 2005;17(4):269–286.

70 Millen BE, Ohls JC, Ponza M, McCool AC. The Elderly Nutrition Program: an effective national framework for preventive nutrition interventions. *J Am Diet Assoc*. 2002;102:234–240.

71 Kim K, Frongillo EA. Participation in food assistance programs modifies the relation of food insecurity with weight and depression in older adults. *J Nutr*. 2007;137:1005–1010.

CHAPTER 18

Food Safety and Technology

Microbial Threats and Genetic Engineering

THINK About It

1 Do you worry about getting sick from the food you eat?

2 To what extent do you rely on organically grown food to avoid pesticides?

3 What food safety measures, such as thawing meat in the refrigerator, do you practice at home?

4 Would genetically modified rice be welcome at your dinner table?

Visit nutrition.jbpub.com

Quick Bite

A Morbid Marginal Note
Every day more than 208,000 Americans get sick from something they ate. Fourteen of them die.

The newspaper headline screams, "POORLY COOKED HAMBURGER MEAT PROVES FATAL." You read further and discover that a child's death has been traced to bacteria thriving in undercooked hamburger meat. Additionally, several adults have become ill from the same source. This worries you. You hate well-done meat. You especially like your hamburgers blood red and your steaks rare. "Well," you ponder, "maybe I'll move my preferences up a notch to pink hamburgers and medium-rare steaks." Have you made the right choice? Or should you investigate this issue further?

Although once confined mainly to cookbooks and textbooks, today food safety advice shows up in many places—the popular press, the classroom, even the *Dietary Guidelines for Americans*. What has prompted such enthusiasm? Recent headlines tell part of the story. Microbial contamination of such foods as hamburger, apple juice, eggs, raw sprouts, peanuts, pistachios, melon, and both fresh and frozen berries has seriously sickened thousands and killed many, especially those most susceptible: young children, people with compromised immune systems, and seniors.

Consumers are voicing concerns about other food safety issues as well—including fears about excessive pesticide residues in plant foods, antibiotics and hormones in animals used for food, and hidden food allergens (e.g., nuts, milk, or eggs) in prepared foods. People often fail to recognize that a prepared food contains an ingredient to which they are allergic (e.g., caseinates as milk protein), and sometimes an allergen may be an unintentional food additive (e.g., peanut material found in a milk chocolate candy might be residue left on machinery from earlier processing of peanut butter cups). Other less frequently discussed food hazards include physical contamination with glass fragments and other sharp objects, heavy metals, and naturally occurring toxins in seafood and some agricultural products. (See **Figure 18.1**.)

Food Safety

This chapter reviews major food safety hazards and touches on controversial issues such as the merits of organic foods, the use of food irradiation, and the production of genetically modified foods.

Harmful Substances in Foods

In the United States and Canada most foodborne diseases are caused by microorganisms and can be prevented by cleaning hands and surfaces, cooking sufficiently, and refrigerating foods promptly.

Pathogens

In North America, most food safety experts agree that the chief cause of **foodborne illness** is pathogenic (disease-causing) microorganisms, including bacteria, viruses, and parasites. (See Table 18.1 for a list of common foodborne microbes and the serious illnesses they cause.) Researchers at the Centers for Disease Control and Prevention (CDC) estimate that foodborne microbes cause 76 million illnesses, 325,000 hospitalizations, and 5,000 deaths in the United States each year.[1] These figures take into account the estimated number of unrecognized and unreported food-caused illnesses. Illness can range from relatively mild stomach upset to severe symptoms that can be fatal.

THINK About It 1

Development of foodborne illness results from the interaction of three factors: the pathogen, the host, and the environment in which they exist and interact.[2] Foodborne illnesses can result directly from infection with a patho-

foodborne illness A sickness caused by food contaminated with microorganisms, chemicals, or other substances hazardous to human health.

botulism An often fatal type of food poisoning caused by a toxin released from *Clostridium botulinum*, a bacterium that can grow in improperly canned low-acid foods.

Salmonella Rod-shaped bacteria responsible for many foodborne illnesses.

gen or from toxins produced by a pathogenic microorganism. For example, the bacterium *Staphylococcus aureus* creates havoc with the gastrointestinal tract by producing a toxin. When food containing *S. aureus* stands unrefrigerated, the bacteria begin multiplying. After several hours the expanding bacterial population can produce enough of a nasty toxin to cause nausea, vomiting, and abdominal cramps. Staphylococcal food poisoning is extremely common, causing more than 1 million illnesses each year. Fortunately, the illness usually resolves after a day or so of vomiting and feeling miserable, with no further harmful effects. Another toxin-producing bacterium, *Clostridium botulinum*, causes the rare, but deadly, illness **botulism**. Improperly canned foods, as well as garlic-in-oil preparations, are sources of botulism. Honey can be contaminated with botulinum, but the acid in adult stomachs kills the bacteria. Infants produce insufficient amounts of stomach acid to kill botulinum, so even small amounts of contaminated honey can be fatal.

Salmonella bacteria are the most frequently reported cause of foodborne illness.[3] Each year, salmonellae cause an estimated 1.4 million cases of foodborne illness, and approximately 400 people die.[4] In 2009, eating peanut products contaminated with salmonellae sickened more than 700 people, many of whom were children.

Salmonella bacteria are prevalent on poultry and in eggs as well as in a wide variety of other foods. Choosing eggs cooked "over easy" is potentially

Quick Bite

Is It Stomach Flu or Food Poisoning?

Both can have similar symptoms—miserable vomiting, abdominal cramping, and diarrhea. Although we often do not know the exact cause, stomach flu tends to occur in the winter months and is preceded by other symptoms, such as sore throat. Food poisoning tends to occur in summer months, and symptoms usually appear suddenly without warning. Symptoms may not begin until 12 to 72 hours after eating tainted food. If many people who ate the same food get sick around the same time, it's probably food poisoning.

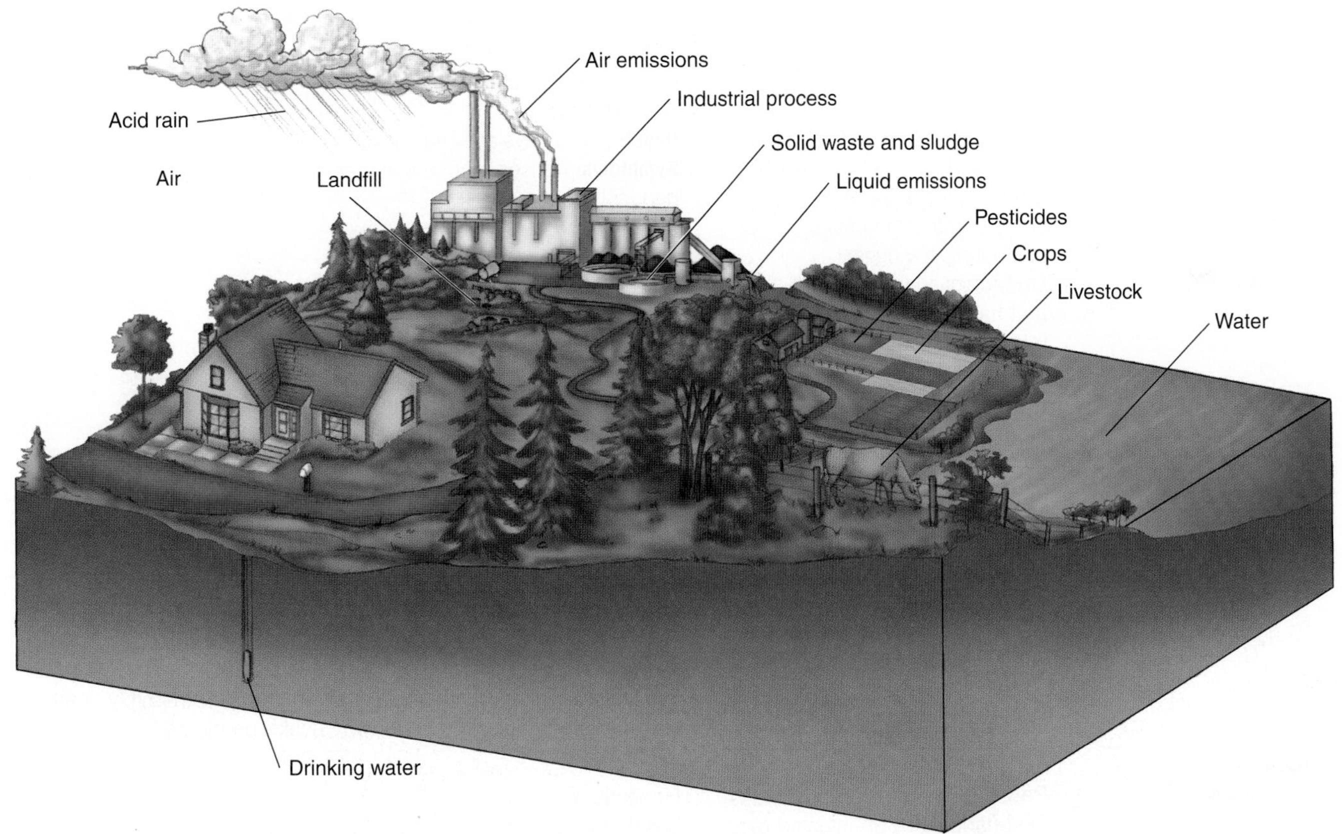

Figure 18.1 **Heavy metals and other contaminants can be found in foods.** Industrial plants and automobiles release heavy metals and other contaminants into the air. Rainfall carries these contaminants to the soil. Plants for food crops and animal feed absorb contaminants from the soil. Runoff can pick up contaminants from pesticides, fertilizers, and animal manure. This pollutes surface water (lakes and streams), groundwater, and coastal water. Polluted water contaminates seafood and other fish that people eat.

Table 18.1 Common Foodborne Pathogens and Illnesses

Organism	Sources	Diseases and Symptoms
Bacteria		
Campylobacter jejuni	Raw poultry and meat and unpasteurized milk	Campylobacteriosis **Onset:** usually 2 to 5 days after eating **Symptoms:** diarrhea, stomach cramps, fever, bloody stools; lasts 7 to 10 days
Clostridium botulinum—illness is caused by a toxin produced by this organism	Improperly canned foods, such as corn, green beans, soups, beets, asparagus, mushrooms, tuna, and liver pate; also, luncheon meats, ham, sausage, garlic in oil, lobster, and smoked and salted fish	Botulism **Onset:** 18 to 36 hours after eating **Symptoms:** nerve dysfunction, such as double vision, inability to swallow, speech difficulty, and progressive paralysis of respiratory system; can lead to death
Escherichia coli O157:H7	Raw or undercooked meat, raw vegetables, unpasteurized milk, minimally processed ciders and juices, contaminated water	*E. coli* infection **Onset:** 2 to 5 days after eating **Symptoms:** watery and bloody diarrhea, severe stomach cramps, dehydration, colitis, neurological symptoms, stroke, and hemolytic uremic syndrome (HUS), a particularly serious disease in young children that can cause kidney failure and death
Listeria monocytogenes	Soft cheeses, unpasteurized milk, hot dogs, luncheon meats, cold cuts, other deli-style meat and poultry **Note:** resists salt, heat, nitrites, and acidity better than most microorganisms	Listeriosis **Onset:** from 7 to 21 days after eating, but symptoms have been reported 9 to 48 hours after eating **Symptoms:** fever, headache, nausea, and vomiting; primarily affects pregnant women and their fetuses, newborns, older adults, and people with cancer and compromised immune systems; can cause death in fetuses and babies
Salmonella	Raw or undercooked meats, poultry, eggs; raw milk and other dairy products; seafood; fresh produce, including raw sprouts; coconut; pasta; chocolate; foods containing raw eggs	Salmonellosis **Onset:** 1 to 3 days after eating **Symptoms:** nausea, abdominal cramps, diarrhea, fever, and headache
Shigella	Undercooked liquid or moist food that has been handled by an infected person	Shigellosis (bacillary dysentery) **Onset:** 12 to 50 hours after eating **Symptoms:** stomach cramps; diarrhea; fever; sometimes vomiting; and blood, pus, and mucus in stools
Staphylococcus aureus—illness is caused by a toxin produced by this organism	Meat and poultry; egg products; tuna, potato, and macaroni salads; cream-filled pastries and other foods left unrefrigerated for long periods **Note:** *S. aureus* is frequently found in cuts on skin and in nasal passages	Staphylococcal food poisoning **Onset:** 1 to 6 hours after eating **Symptoms:** diarrhea, vomiting, nausea, stomach pain, and cramps; lasts 1 to 2 days
Vibrio vulnificus	Raw seafood, especially raw oysters	*Vibrio* infection **Onset:** 1 to 7 days **Symptoms:** chills, fever, nausea and vomiting, and possibly death, especially in people with underlying health problems
Viruses		
Hepatitis A	Raw shellfish from polluted water, food handled by an infected person	Hepatitis A **Onset:** average about 1 month after exposure **Symptoms:** at first, malaise, loss of appetite, nausea, vomiting, and fever; after 3 to 10 days, jaundice and darkened urine; severe cases can result in liver damage and death

Table 18.1 **Common Foodborne Pathogens and Illnesses (Continued)**

Organism	Sources	Diseases and Symptoms
Viruses		
Norwalk virus	Raw shellfish from polluted water; salads, sandwiches, and other ready-to-eat foods handled by an infected person	Gastroenteritis **Onset:** 1 to 3 days **Symptoms:** nausea, vomiting, diarrhea, stomach pain, headache, and low-grade fever
Protozoa		
Anisakis	Raw fish	Anisakiasis **Onset:** 12 to 24 hours **Symptoms:** abdominal pain, can be severe
Cryptosporidium	Food that comes in contact with sewage-contaminated water; foods handled by a person who did not wash hands after using the toilet	Cryptosporidiosis **Onset:** 1 to 12 days **Symptoms:** profuse watery stools, stomach pain, loss of appetite, vomiting, and low-grade fever
Giardia lamblia	Consumption of contaminated water, contamination of food by an infected person	Giardiasis **Onset:** 1 to 3 days **Symptoms:** diarrhea, abdominal cramps, nausea
Toxoplasma gondii	Raw or undercooked meat and, under certain conditions, unwashed fruits and vegetables; also, cats shed cysts in their feces during acute infection—organism may be transmitted to humans, if feces are handled	Toxoplasmosis **Onset:** 10 to 13 days **Symptoms:** fever, headache, rash, sore muscles, diarrhea; can kill a fetus or cause severe defects, such as mental retardation

disastrous because inadequate cooking can leave you vulnerable to the misery of salmonellosis. (See the FYI feature "Safe Food Practices" later in this chapter for more information on how to protect yourself from foodborne illness.)

***Escherichia coli* (*E. coli*)** are a diverse group of bacteria. Although most varieties are harmless, others can make you sick. Some types cause diarrhea, whereas others cause more serious illnesses, even death. Many foods, including eggs, dairy products, meat and poultry, seafood, fresh produce, unpasteurized juices, and cereal grains, can harbor these disease-causing bacteria.

Because bacteria and other infectious organisms are pervasive in the environment, the contamination of food can occur anywhere from the farm to your plate. Many organisms capable of causing foodborne illness in humans are naturally present in food-producing animals and their environment. For example, *Salmonella enteritidis* bacteria enter eggs directly from the egg-laying hen, and *E. coli* are normally present in the intestines of cattle. Microorganisms natural to the marine environment, but toxic to humans, can contaminate seafood. (See the FYI feature "Seafood Safety.")

Exposure to animal manure or sewage runoff can contaminate crops. Sewage runoff into rivers and streams also can contaminate fish that live there. In the food-processing stage, contamination can occur from dirty equipment, rodent droppings, improper food storage, and infectious employees who fail to wash their hands adequately or take proper precautions when handling food. Poor food safety practices in retail facilities and at home also can contaminate food.

Patterns of foodborne illness have changed dramatically over the last several decades as our food production has become more centralized. When

Quick Bite

Sticky *Salmonella*

One-quarter of Americans suffer a foodborne illness each year. In 2009, more than 700 people were reported sickened in 46 states and more than 3,200 products were recalled, costing industry over $1 billion. What made all these people sick? Not the most likely foods, such as undercooked chicken and hamburgers: it was *Salmonella*-contaminated peanut butter and foods with peanut products.

***Escherichia coli* (*E. coli*)** Bacteria that are the most common cause of urinary tract infections. Because they release toxins, some types of *E. coli* can rapidly cause shock and death.

bovine spongiform encephalopathy (BSE) A chronic degenerative disease, widely referred to as "mad cow disease," that affects the central nervous system of cattle.

mad cow disease See *bovine spongiform encephalopathy (BSE).*

prions Short for "proteinaceous infectious particle." Self-reproducing protein particles that can cause disease.

food animals and produce were grown, prepared, and eaten on the family farm, the consequences of errors in food handling were generally limited to a single family. Now, much of the food we eat is mass-produced at central locations and distributed widely to restaurant chains and supermarkets. Although most food poisoning cases arise from poor food handling in homes and restaurants, contamination at a processing plant can make hundreds or even thousands of people ill. This can have nationwide implications and therefore receives intense national media attention.

Prions and Mad Cow Disease

Bovine spongiform encephalopathy (BSE), known popularly as **mad cow disease**, is a chronic degenerative disease that affects the central nervous system of cattle. Once thought to infect only cows, scientists have found that BSE can cause a rare, but fatal, brain-wasting disease in humans.

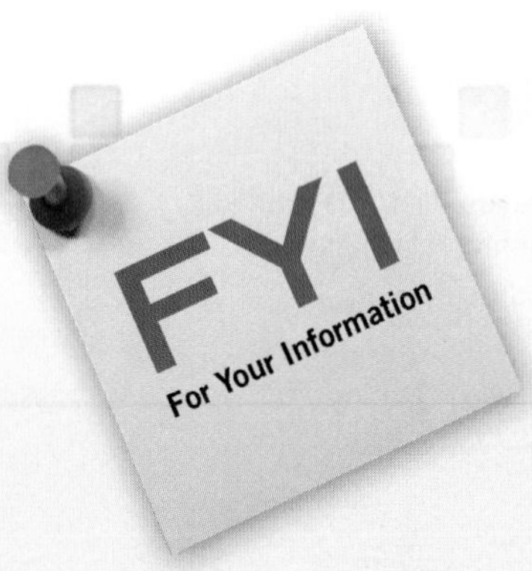

Seafood Safety

Seafood can be a delicious and heart-healthy part of our diets. However, as with all food, contamination can have serious consequences. Seafood is one of the most rapidly perishable foods, so proper refrigeration and rapid processing and transport to the consumer are essential. Although certain types of microbial contaminants and toxins are unique to seafood, properly handled and cooked seafood is as safe to eat as most other foods. To kill seafood parasites, cook the fish or freeze it for at least 72 hours.

Eating raw seafood is risky business. Despite the popularity of such dishes as sashimi, sushi, and raw oysters, uncooked fish, no matter how carefully prepared, poses a risk for infection. People with liver disease, diabetes, cancer, or other diseases that impair immune function should be especially careful to stay away from raw seafood. Pregnant women also should avoid uncooked seafood; some physicians recommend that pregnant women avoid seafood altogether. The rest of us should think twice before enjoying those raw oysters and sashimi and, at the very least, should make sure they are fresh and from a reliable source before letting those slippery delicacies pass our lips.

Seafood-related illness falls into several categories. Sources of infection include bacteria, viruses, and parasites. Toxins occur naturally in some fish, and human pollution may contaminate seafood. The following are several examples of seafood-caused illness:

- Raw or undercooked shellfish such as oysters, clams, and mussels may be contaminated with bacteria such as *Salmonella*, *Vibrio* species, and *Staphylococcus aureus*. Hepatitis A (caused by a virus) and gastroenteritis are other illnesses that can be contracted by eating uncooked shellfish from polluted waters.
- Fish such as mahi-mahi, tuna, and bluefish that have begun to spoil can cause scombroid poisoning. A toxin in these decomposing fish causes flushing, itching, and headache. Cooking does not destroy the toxin, so the best prevention is proper refrigeration and rapid use of fresh fish.
- Some tropical fish, such as red snapper and barracuda, may contain ciguatera toxin, which can cause gastrointestinal and neurological problems in humans. Larger warm-water fish are most often implicated in this illness. The toxin is actually produced by tiny plants that are eaten by small fish. When larger fish consume many small fish, the toxin can accumulate. The flesh of these large fish may contain enough of the toxin to make humans very ill. Heating or freezing does not destroy this toxin.
- *Anisakis* is a parasite found in raw fish. After a person eats an infected fish, the larvae of this roundworm can invade the human stomach, causing severe abdominal pain. Cooking or freezing the fish for at least 72 hours can kill this parasite.
- Red tide is a well-known phenomenon in which huge numbers of tiny toxic organisms called dinoflagellates infest seawater. Shellfish in the area become poisonous as a result. Respiratory paralysis and death are possible effects of eating shellfish from red tide areas.
- Human pollution is a serious problem, especially near population centers where industrial wastes and human sewage flow into the water. Heavy metals such as mercury can accumulate in

Researchers believe that **prions**—proteins found in the cells of humans and other mammals—are responsible. When mammals eat tissues contaminated with abnormal prions, they can develop BSE. Cooking and irradiation do not kill or deactivate abnormal prions.

The skull, brain, eyes, vertebral column, and spinal cord of cows at least 30 months of age are most likely to harbor abnormal prions. The tonsils and a portion of the small intestine of all cattle also may contain the agent. To protect the safety of meat, milk, and dairy products, Canadian and U.S. agencies prohibit these cow parts in the human food supply. Government agencies also regulate and provide guidance to manufacturers who produce cow-derived foods, such as gelatin and some dietary supplements.

Quick Bite

How Many *Salmonella* Does It Take?

In 1994, 224,000 people in 41 states came down with *Salmonella* food poisoning from eating contaminated ice cream. The amazing part? The ice cream contained only about six *Salmonella* bacteria per serving.

Key Concepts *Foodborne pathogens are a major cause of illness in the United States and Canada. Pathogenic (disease-causing) agents include bacteria, viruses, parasites, and prions. Contamination of food can occur at many points along the chain from farm to table.*

larger fish (e.g., sharks and swordfish) that have been exposed to mercury in their environment for long periods. Because commercially caught fish generally contain minimal amounts of mercury, even large fish are safe to eat, although pregnant women are advised to avoid eating shark or swordfish more than once a month.

- Dioxin and polychlorinated biphenols (PCBs) also can accumulate in fish living in polluted water. Commercial seafood companies tend to avoid contaminated areas, but local fishers who frequently catch and eat fish from these waters may be at some risk.

Table 1 **Understanding Seafood Safety**

Condition	Explanation
Scombroid poisoning	Scombroid poisoning is a type of food intoxication caused by the consumption of scombroid and scombroid-like marine fish species that have begun to spoil with the growth of particular types of food bacteria. Fish most commonly involved are members of the *Scombridae* family (tunas and mackerels) and a few nonscombroid relatives (bluefish, mahi-mahi, and amberjacks). The suspect toxin is an elevated level of histamine generated by bacterial degradation of substances in the muscle protein.
Anisakis	*Anisakis simplex* (herring worm) and *Pseudoterranova* (*Phocanema*, *Terranova*) decipiens (cod or seal worm) are anisakid nematodes (roundworms) that have been implicated in human infections caused by the consumption of raw or undercooked seafood. *Anisakiasis* is the term generally used to refer to the acute disease in humans.
Red tide	When temperature, salinity, and nutrients reach certain levels, algae grow very fast or "bloom" and accumulate into dense, visible patches near the surface of the water. *Red tide* is a common name for such a phenomenon where certain species of phytoplankton contain reddish pigments and "bloom" such that the water appears to be colored red. The term *red tide* is a misnomer because the reddish color is not associated with tides. A small number of species produce potent neurotoxins that can cause illness and even death.
Polychlorinated biphenols (PCBs)	A group of toxic, persistent chemicals used as insulation for electrical transformers and capacitors and as lubricants in gas pipeline systems. PCBs are a serious health problem because of their persistence in the environment, accumulation in the body, and potential for a long-term negative effect on health. In the United States, their manufacture was stopped in 1976.

organic foods Foods that originate from farms or handling operations that meet the standards set by the USDA National Organic Program.

pesticides Chemicals used to control insects, diseases, weeds, fungi, and other pests on plants, vegetables, fruits, and animals.

Chemical Contamination

To avoid foods exposed to chemicals, more and more people are turning to **organic foods**. (See the section "Organic Alternatives" later in this chapter.) Yet food safety experts consider contamination by pathogenic microorganisms to be a much greater risk to public health than contamination by chemicals. Chemical contaminants include pesticides, drugs, pollutants, and natural toxins.

Pesticides **Pesticides** play an important role in food production—controlling plant diseases, weeds, insects, and other pests. Pesticides protect crops and ensure a substantial yield, thus assuring consumers of a wide variety of foods at affordable prices. Without these chemicals, many argue that crop production would fall and prices for food would rise.

Every year, the U.S. Food and Drug Administration (FDA) collects thousands of domestic and imported food samples and analyzes them for pesticide residues.[5] During the period from 2004 to 2006, the FDA found no illegal residues in more than 98 percent of domestic and more than 94 percent of imported samples. When a violation occurred, it usually involved the use of a pesticide on crops for which it was not approved, rather than an excessive level. Results for the past 15 years have been fairly consistent.[6] Despite these reassuring results, concerns about pesticides in food persist.

The FDA also samples and analyzes domestic and imported animal feeds for pesticide residues. This monitoring focuses on feeds for livestock and poultry—animals that become or produce foods for human consumption. Processing methods can either reduce or concentrate pesticide residues in foods. (See **Figure 18.2**.) Infants and young children are particularly susceptible to the hazards of pesticides. Their small size and rapid growth make

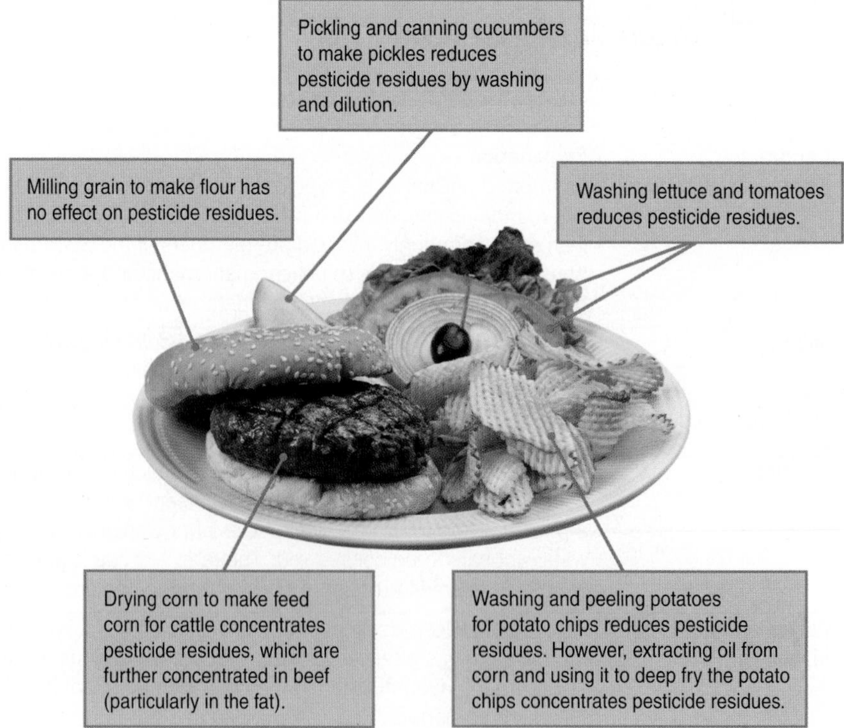

Pickling and canning cucumbers to make pickles reduces pesticide residues by washing and dilution.
Milling grain to make flour has no effect on pesticide residues.
Washing lettuce and tomatoes reduces pesticide residues.
Drying corn to make feed corn for cattle concentrates pesticide residues, which are further concentrated in beef (particularly in the fat).
Washing and peeling potatoes for potato chips reduces pesticide residues. However, extracting oil from corn and using it to deep fry the potato chips concentrates pesticide residues.

Figure 18.2 **Pesticide pathways to dinner.** Food processing and preparation methods can either reduce or concentrate pesticide residues in foods.

them especially vulnerable to pesticide residues, which can accumulate in their bodies over their lifetimes. Enacted in 1996, the Food Quality Protection Act includes landmark protections for the young. For the first time, manufacturers had to show that pesticide levels are safe for infants and children. In addition, when determining a safe level for a pesticide in a food, the Environmental Protection Agency (EPA) must account for the cumulative effect of exposures to similar pesticides and toxic chemicals.[7]

Excessive use of synthetic pesticides, herbicides, and fertilizers contributes substantially to the pollution of soil and water. Overuse can be particularly hazardous to farm workers, whose exposure to these chemicals typically is much higher than that of consumers. Overuse also threatens wildlife. Today, many farmers use **integrated pest management (IPM)** to reduce pesticide use. (See **Figure 18.3**.) IPM methods include crop rotation, use of natural rather than synthetic pesticides, and planting nonfood crops nearby that lure pests away from food crops. Releasing sterile fruit flies into orchards also allows reductions in pesticide use. Because fruit flies produce no offspring when they mate with sterile partners, the overall fruit fly population drops.

1. **Legal control**
   State and federal guidelines are designed to limit the spread of pests.
2. **Biological control**
   Beneficial organisms, such as predators, parasites, and viruses, are released into the environment to suppress pest organisms.
3. **Cultural control**
   Rotation, sanitation, and other good farming techniques are employed to help reduce pest populations.
4. **Physical control**
   Barriers, traps, and the location and timing of planting are all used to control pest infestations.
5. **Genetic control**
   Resistant plant strains are developed to reduce the impact of pests.
6. **Chemical control**
   Conventional pesticides, biopesticides, pheromones, and other chemicals are used to prevent or suppress pest outbreaks. The chemical controls are specific to a pest species and are ideally short-lived in the environment. In addition, the chemicals are used at their lowest effective rate and may be alternated to help prevent the development of pest resistance.

Figure 18.3 **Integrated pest management.** Integrated pest management is a sustainable approach that combines prevention, avoidance, monitoring, and suppression strategies in a way that minimizes economic, health, and environmental risks. It minimizes pesticide use and promotes economically sound practices.

Organic Alternatives Organic foods are grown or produced without synthetic pesticides and without synthetic fertilizers. Nearly 60 percent of U.S. households use organic products.[8] In 2005, sales of organic foods exceeded $14.6 billion annually, and sales continue to grow.[9] Growth of the industry reflects, in part, America's distrust of technology and a desire to return to a simpler, more "natural" way of food production.

The Organic Foods Production Act and the National Organic Program (NOP) are intended to assure U.S. consumers that the organic foods they purchase are produced, processed, and certified to consistent national standards. The labeling requirements of this program apply to raw meats, fresh produce, and processed foods that contain organic ingredients. Foods that are sold, labeled, or represented as organic must be produced and processed in accordance with the NOP standards.[10] Table 18.2 outlines the requirements for labeling a food product as being organic.

Under the NOP, farm and processing operations that grow and process organic foods must be certified by the USDA. The certification process includes an on-site inspection to verify that the applicant's operation complies with strict national organic standards. Certifying agents may collect and test soil, water, waste, plant and animal tissues, and processed products. A certified operation may label its products or ingredients as organic and may use the "USDA Organic" seal.

Although irradiation and genetic engineering have been approved for use in agriculture and may offer certain benefits for the environment and human health, consumers strongly oppose their use in organically grown foods. Because of consumer opposition, foods produced with these techniques are prohibited from carrying the organic label.[11]

Organic farming has its drawbacks. The use of manure as a natural fertilizer raises food safety concerns. The organic producer must manage animal and plant waste materials so they do not contribute to contamination of crops, soil, or water. Manure runoff can pollute nearby lakes and streams. Some critics charge that organic farming is "elitist" and that synthetic fertilizers and pesticides are necessary to meet the food needs of an expanding world population. They also point out that complete freedom from pesticides cannot be guaranteed, no matter how carefully a food is produced, because pesticide residues may still exist in soil, water, and air.

integrated pest management (IPM) Economically sound pest control techniques that minimize pesticide use, enhance environmental stewardship, and promote sustainable systems.

Table 18.2 **Labeling Requirements for Organic Food**

Labeling requirements are based on the percentage of a product's ingredients that are organic.

Foods labeled "100 percent organic" and "organic"

- Products labeled "100 percent organic" must contain only organically produced ingredients (excluding water and salt).
- Products labeled "organic" must consist of at least 95 percent organically produced ingredients (excluding water and salt). Any remaining ingredients must consist of nonagricultural substances approved on the National List maintained by the USDA National Organic Program or nonorganically produced agricultural products that are not commercially available in organic form.
- Products that meet the requirements may display these terms and the percentage of organic content on their principal display panel.
- The USDA seal and the seal or mark of certifying agents may appear on product packages and in advertisements.
- Foods labeled "100 percent organic" and "organic" cannot be produced using excluded methods, sewage sludge, or ionizing radiation.

Processed products labeled "made with organic (specified ingredients)"

- Products that contain at least 70 percent organic ingredients can use the phrase "made with organic ingredients" and list up to three of the organic ingredients or food groups on the principal display panel. For example, soup made with at least 70 percent organic ingredients and only organic vegetables may be labeled either "soup made with organic peas, potatoes, and carrots" or "soup made with organic vegetables."
- Foods labeled "made with organic ingredients" cannot be produced using excluded methods, sewage sludge, or ionizing radiation.
- The percentage of organic content and the certifying agent's seal or mark may be used on the package. However, the USDA seal cannot be used anywhere on the package.

Processed products that contain less than 70 percent organic ingredients

- These products cannot use the term *organic* anywhere on the primary display panel. However, they may identify the specific ingredients that are organically produced on the ingredients statement on the information panel.

Other labeling provisions

- Any product labeled as organic must identify each organically produced ingredient in the ingredient statement on the information panel.
- The name and address of the certifying agent of the final product must be displayed on the information panel.
- There are no restrictions on the use of other truthful labeling claims, such as "no drugs or growth hormones used," "free range," or "sustainably harvested."

Source: USDA Agricultural Marketing Service. *National Organic Program: Organic Labeling and Marketing Information.* Washington, DC: USDA, April 2008.

US Department of Agriculture

Organic foods are not pesticide-free foods. Organic farmers can use natural and approved synthetic pesticides to control weeds and insects.[12] Microbial contaminants that cause foodborne illness can be found in organic as well as conventional foods. Consumers must handle all food appropriately, whether organically or conventionally grown.

Animal Drugs Current agricultural practice depends heavily on the use of drugs in food animals and food-producing animals raised specifically to provide meat, milk, and eggs. Producers use drugs to maintain animal health and well-being, as well as to increase production. Keeping animals in good health reduces the chance that disease will spread from animals to humans, and healthy animals can use nutrients for growth and production rather than to fight infection. But there is a possibility that drugs used in animals could enter human food and possibly increase the risk of ill health in humans.

Many researchers fear that overuse of animal antibiotics will contribute to the emergence of antibiotic-resistant microorganisms that could threaten human health. Another potential problem, though with less widespread effects, is that humans with drug allergies could have reactions to drug residues in food-producing animals. Some people worry that the widespread use of hormones may impair animal health or the quality of the food obtained from treated animals.

There are five major classes of drugs used in animals raised for food:

1. Topical antiseptics, bactericides, and fungicides used to treat skin or hoof infections, cuts, and abrasions
2. Ionophores, which are feed additives that alter stomach microorganisms to more efficiently digest feeds and to help protect against some parasites
3. Hormone and hormonelike production enhancers (anabolic hormones for meat production and bovine somatotropin for increased milk production in dairy cows)
4. Antiparasitics
5. Antibiotics used to prevent infections, treat disease, and promote growth

The FDA is responsible for ensuring that drugs approved for use in animals are safe not only for the animals, but also for the humans who eat food produced from these animals. In addition, the FDA enforces regulations to ensure that drugs are used properly in cows, chickens, and seafood. However, FDA surveillance is not perfect; government investigations have revealed that a few U.S. veterinarians and farmers illegally use animal drugs that are known to be dangerous to humans.

Pollutants **Pollutants** from animal manure and other wastes, factories, human sewage, and other runoff can contaminate food-production areas. For example, some scientists theorize that dioxin contamination of foods may cause human cancer. **Dioxins** are chemical compounds created in the manufacturing, combustion, and chlorine bleaching of pulp and paper and in other industrial processes.[13] Dioxins can accumulate in the food chain and are potent animal carcinogens. Freshwater fish from inland waters highly contaminated with dioxin can contain significant amounts of dioxin, and regional advisories should be consulted.[14] The commercial fishing industry avoids areas of known dioxin pollution. Dioxins in tiny amounts are found in food packages, paper plates, and coffee filters made of bleached paper. Because the quantity of this toxic chemical is minimal, however, the FDA has concluded that use of these products poses no significant risk to human health.

Natural Toxins Other chemical contamination of food can occur from **natural toxins**. Examples include the following:

- **Aflatoxins**, found in contaminated food or animal feed. Aflatoxins are produced by certain strains of *Aspergillus* fungi under certain conditions of temperature and humidity. The most pronounced contamination has been found in tree nuts, peanuts, and other oilseeds, such as corn and cottonseed. Aflatoxins have been implicated as a factor in the development of liver cancer, particularly in parts of the world where food and water are frequently contaminated with this fungus.
- **Ciguatera** and other marine toxins. These toxins can accumulate in seafood (mainly in large tropical fish) and, when ingested, cause serious problems, including paralysis, amnesia, and nerve toxicity. Commercial fishers avoid waters known to harbor ciguatera toxin. Ciguatera poisoning sometimes occurs when these fish are caught as part of recreational fishing. Cooking does not destroy these toxins.
- **Methylmercury**. Mercury occurs naturally in the environment and is produced by human activities. It is soluble in water, where bacteria can cause chemical changes that transform

Quick Bite

Well-Traveled Dioxin

In Nunavut, a Canadian province, the breast milk of native Inuits has twice the average concentration of dioxin as does the milk of women in southern Quebec. Native Inuits primarily eat fatty animals high on the food chain. These animals accumulate dioxin, but where did the dioxin originate? Not Canada. Carried by the wind, most comes from industrial combustion in the eastern and midwestern United States, and some originates as far away as Mexico.

pollutants Gaseous, chemical, or organic waste that contaminates air, soil, or water.

dioxins Chemical compounds created in the manufacturing, combustion, and chlorine bleaching of pulp and paper and in other industrial processes.

natural toxins Poisons that are produced by or naturally occur in plants or microorganisms.

aflatoxins Carcinogenic and toxic factors produced by food molds.

ciguatera A toxin found in more than 300 species of Caribbean and South Pacific fish. It is a nonbacterial source of food poisoning.

methylmercury A toxic compound that results from the chemical transformation of mercury by bacteria. Mercury is water-soluble in trace amounts and contaminates many bodies of water.

poisonous mushrooms Mushrooms that contain toxins that can cause stomach upset, dizziness, hallucinations, and other neurological symptoms.

solanine A potentially toxic alkaloid that is present with chlorophyll in the green areas on potato skins.

mercury to methylmercury, a more toxic form. Fish absorb methylmercury from water passing over their gills and by eating other contaminated aquatic species. Because larger predatory fish can consume many contaminated smaller fish, they accumulate higher levels of methylmercury. (See **Figure 18.4**.) Because shark, swordfish, king mackerel, and tilefish contain high levels of mercury, the FDA and EPA recommend that women who may become pregnant, pregnant women, nursing mothers, and young children avoid eating these fish.[15]

- **Poisonous mushrooms**. These plants produce toxic substances that can cause stomach upset, dizziness, hallucinations, and other neurological symptoms. The more lethal mushroom species can cause liver and kidney failure, coma, and death.
- **Solanine**, a toxic substance in raw potato skins. Solanine develops in the greenish layer of improperly stored potatoes. It can be removed by thoroughly peeling the potato.

A variety of compounds in herbs and spices also can be toxic. However, foodborne illness caused by these and other natural toxins is relatively rare compared with illness from pathogenic microorganisms.

Going Green

Ocean Pollution and Mercury Poisoning

Humans suffer, of course, when ocean pollution reduces fish populations or stains the pristine nature of beach recreation. Industrial pollutants—especially toxic compounds like mercury or polychlorinated biphenyls (PCBs)—that end up in water bodies are absorbed by fish we eat, and eventually accumulate in our bodies. Mercury exposure is especially dangerous to the fetus, newborn infants, and young children during critical growth phases when the brain and other organs are rapidly developing. It leads to learning problems, reduced performance on intelligence tests, and other health problems later in life.

Source of Mercury Emissions

In May 2009, for the first time, researchers have tracked escalating mercury-laden air emissions that increasingly pollute the North Pacific Ocean and contaminate tuna, swordfish, and other popular seafood, to their source in coal-fired electrical power plants in Asia. The emissions transform into methylmercury, a potent neurotoxin, and enter long-range eastward transport by large ocean circulation currents. The study predicts a 50 percent spike in the Pacific's mercury level by the year 2050 if mercury emissions from power plants increase according to current projections.

EPA Declares "Major Health Threat"

The implications of the mercury cycle for human health are grave. According to the USGS, over 90 percent of human methylmercury exposure in the United States can be attributed to consumption of ocean fish and shellfish. Pacific tuna consumption accounts for 40 percent of Americans' exposure, and the EPA is suggesting new diplomatic efforts to persuade Asian nations "to significantly cut mercury pollution in the years ahead and protect the health of millions of people."

EPA's aggressive position on mercury contrasts sharply with that of the Food and Drug Administration (FDA), which has recently argued that the benefits of eating mercury-tainted seafood may outweigh the risks. FDA should elaborate on the guidance it and EPA issued in 2004 by adding more specific information about which low-mercury fish people can eat in place of species like tuna and swordfish, that tend to have elevated mercury levels.

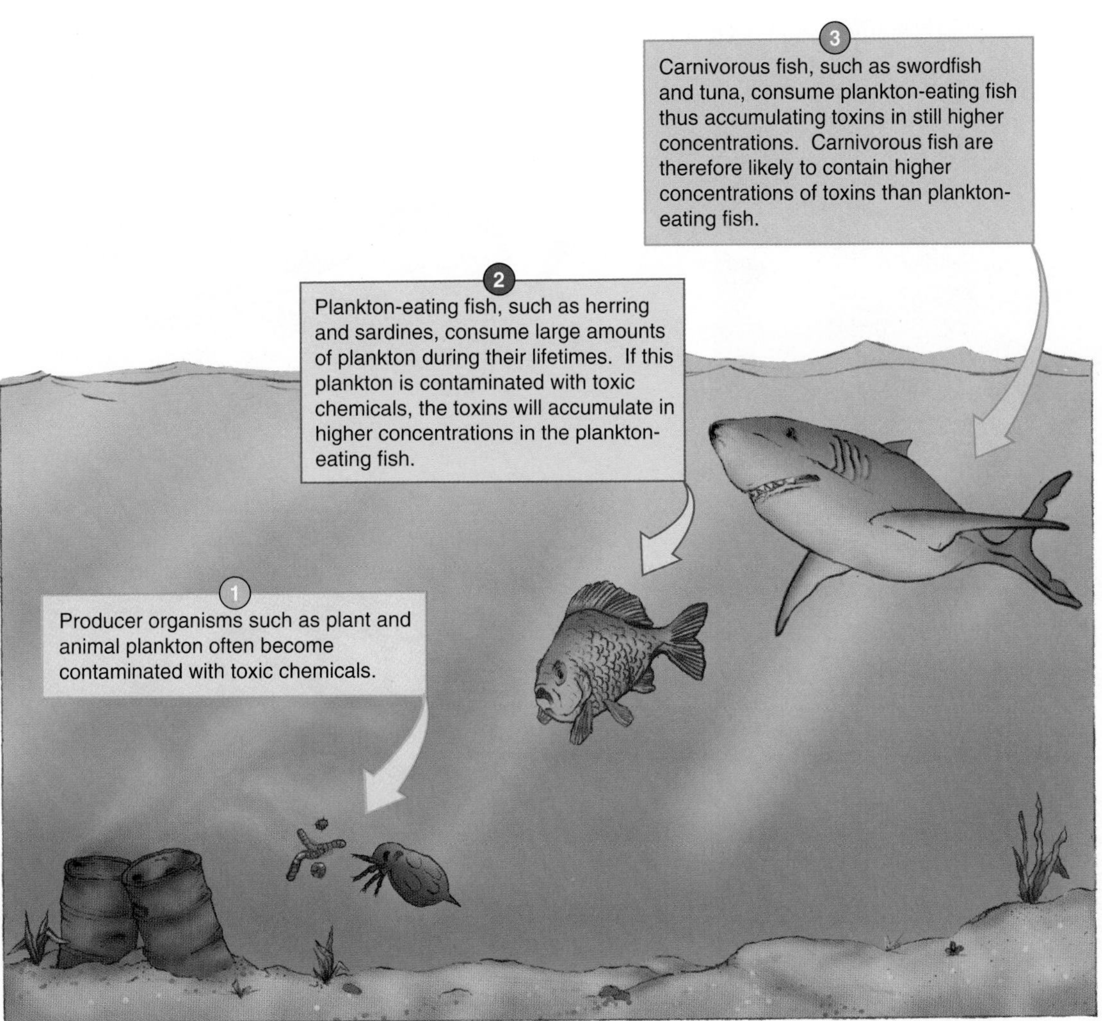

3
Carnivorous fish, such as swordfish and tuna, consume plankton-eating fish thus accumulating toxins in still higher concentrations. Carnivorous fish are therefore likely to contain higher concentrations of toxins than plankton-eating fish.
2
Plankton-eating fish, such as herring and sardines, consume large amounts of plankton during their lifetimes. If this plankton is contaminated with toxic chemicals, the toxins will accumulate in higher concentrations in the plankton-eating fish.
1
Producer organisms such as plant and animal plankton often become contaminated with toxic chemicals.

Figure 18.4 **Toxins in the food chain.** As toxins travel up the food chain, they become concentrated in larger fish.

Other Food Contaminants In the United States, about 2 percent of adults and 5 percent of infants and young children (nearly 11 million people) have food allergies. Eight major foods or food groups—milk, eggs, fish, shellfish, tree nuts, peanuts, wheat, and soybeans—account for 90 percent of allergic reactions. (See **Figure 18.5**.) Whenever these foods (or ingredients derived from them) are present in a food product, food labels must identify them.[16] In an allergic person, these foods can cause a variety of reactions, including gastrointestinal problems, skin irritation, breathing difficulty, shock, and even death.

Other contaminants, such as glass, metal, and other objects, may be introduced unintentionally during food production. Improper use of cleaning agents in food-contact areas can add these undesirable substances to food. Insects, dirt, and other undesirable items, although generally not a health hazard, also can find their way into food.

Key Concepts *Chemical contaminants in foods include pesticides, natural toxins, and contamination related to pollution. Although organic foods are grown without synthetic pesticides or fertilizers, they still can contain chemical contaminants. Other potential food hazards are allergens and nonfood contaminants.*

Quick Bite

Chill Out!

In 1939, Fred McKinley Jones, a prolific African American inventor, and Joe Numero received a patent for a vehicle refrigeration device for large trucks. Their invention eliminated the problem of food spoilage during long shipping times and permitted year-round delivery of fresh produce across the country. Refrigerated shipping launched international markets for food, helped create new industries such as frozen foods, fast foods, and container shipping, and forever altered consumers' eating habits.

Figure 18.5 **Foods that commonly cause allergic reactions.** In sensitive people, an allergic reaction to food can be life threatening.

Keeping Food Safe

Having safe foods to eat requires the efforts of a great many people along the way from the farm to your plate. Imagine yourself enjoying a piece of broiled chicken. Consider that harmful contamination of that chicken could have occurred at the farm, in the processing plant, or during transportation to the supermarket. Once at the supermarket, the chicken might have been under-refrigerated or kept too long before being sold. After buying the chicken, you might have left it in a warm car or kept it in a refrigerator that was not cold enough. Your kitchen hygiene might not have been the best; finally, you could have undercooked the chicken. Considering the many opportunities for contamination, it is truly amazing that most of the time our food does not make us sick.

Keeping foods free from contamination is a job that falls to many parties. It is the responsibility not only of government officials at the national, state, and local levels, but also of everyone who comes in contact with food—the producer, the manufacturer, the retailer, and ultimately the consumer.

Government Agencies

The basis of modern food law is the Federal Food, Drug, and Cosmetic (FD&C) Act of 1938, which gives the Food and Drug Administration authority over food and food ingredients and defines requirements for truthful labeling of ingredients. At the federal level, six agencies (**Figure 18.6**) share responsibility for food safety.

1. The Food and Drug Administration (FDA) enforces laws governing the safety of domestic and imported food, except meat and poultry.
2. The Centers for Disease Control and Prevention (CDC) monitor outbreaks of foodborne diseases, investigate their causes, and determine proper prevention.
3. The USDA Food Safety and Inspection Service (FSIS) enforces laws governing the safety of domestic and imported meat and poultry products.

Dietary Guidelines for Americans, 2010
Key Recommendations

Building Healthy Eating Patterns

- Follow food safety recommendations when preparing and eating foods to reduce the risk of foodborne illnesses.
- Four basic food safety principles work together to reduce the risk of foodborne illnesses:
  - **Clean** hands, food contact surfaces, and vegetables and fruits.
  - **Separate** raw, cooked, and ready-to-eat foods while shopping, storing, and preparing foods.
  - **Cook** foods to a safe temperature.
  - **Chill** (refrigerate) perishable foods promptly.

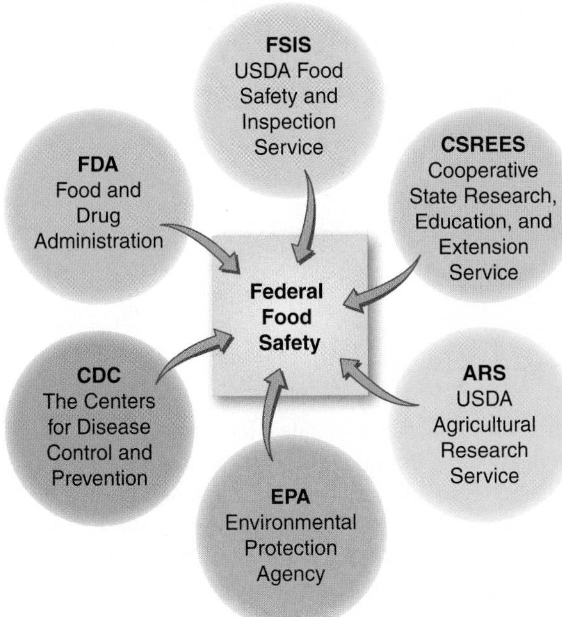

OTHER AGENCIES WITH FOOD SAFETY RESPONSIBILITIES

Federal Trade Commission (FTC)
- Regulates the advertising and marketing of food products.
- Has the authority to take legal action against unwarranted advertising claims.

Department of Justice
- Seizes products when federal food safety laws are violated.
- Prosecutes suspected violators of food safety laws.

Bureau of Alcohol, Tobacco and Firearms (BATF)
- Enforces laws that involve the production, distribution, and labeling of most alcoholic beverages.
- Sometimes shares responsibilities with FDA when alcoholic beverages are adulterated or contain food or color additives, pesticides, or contaminants.

National Marine Fisheries Service (NMFS)
- Responsible for seafood quality and identification, fisheries management and development, habitat conservation, and aquaculture production.

State and Local Governments
- Inspect restaurants, retail food outlets, dairies, grain mills, and other food establishments within their areas of jurisdiction.
- Embargo illegal food products in many situations.

Figure 18.6 **Government agencies that help protect our food supply.** Although the FDA has primary responsibility for the safety of much of our food supply, many government agencies provide oversight.

Safe Tables Our Priority (S.T.O.P.) A national organization devoted to preventing illness and death from foodborne illness by working with government agencies and industry to encourage practices and policies that promote safe food.

4. The USDA Cooperative State Research, Education, and Extension Service (CSREES) develops research and education programs on food safety for farmers and consumers.
5. The USDA Agricultural Research Service (ARS) conducts research to extend knowledge of various agricultural practices, including those involving animal and crop safety.
6. The Environmental Protection Agency (EPA) regulates public drinking water and approves pesticides and other chemicals used in the environment.

State and local health and agricultural departments oversee food safety in their jurisdictions, often in conjunction with federal agencies.

The public's heightened concern about food safety is evident in the creation of consumer advocacy groups such as **Safe Tables Our Priority (S.T.O.P.)**, a national organization that works with government agencies and industry to prevent foodborne illnesses and deaths. S.T.O.P. advocates regulatory reforms, builds awareness of foodborne diseases, and works to improve services for people made ill by food.

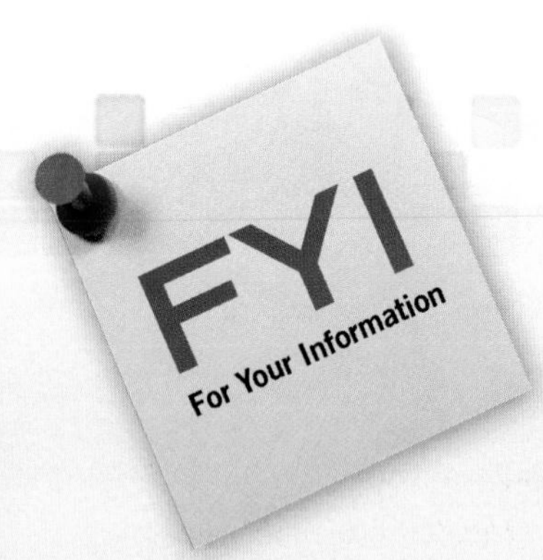

At War with Bioterrorism

Late one afternoon, restaurant owner Dave Lutgens first felt nauseated, then experienced mild stomach cramps. By evening he was dizzy and disoriented. Suffering from diarrhea, he had to crawl to reach the toilet. Weak and dehydrated, he was wracked with chills, fever, and vomiting. Two days later his wife became ill with the same symptoms. By the end of the week, 13 employees were sick as well as dozens of customers. The culprit was *Salmonella typhimurium*, a rod-shaped bacteria responsible for many foodborne illnesses. But this was not a simple case of food poisoning. Occurring in 1984, this was a criminal assault on the small Oregon town of Dalles. The Rajaneesh religious cult attempted to sway local election results by poisoning people to keep them away from the polls. The cult deliberately perpetrated this terrifying food experience by contaminating a number of self-service salad bars and coffee creamers with home-grown *Salmonella*. Ten restaurants were affected, and more than 700 people fell ill from the biological attack.

Biocriminals have also struck in Canada. In 1970, four students in Montreal, Quebec, were admitted to the hospital after eating eggs inoculated with a parasitic nematode, *Ascaris suum*. They had signs of a parasitic infection and suffered from asthma and other lung problems. In 2000, 27 people suffered food poisoning after drinking coffee from a single vending machine at Lavalle University in Quebec City. The coffee had been laced with arsenic. In 2003, arsenic-laced coffee also poisoned more than a dozen people after a church service in New Sweden, Maine. One person died.

Food and water poisonings can be divided into three categories:[1]

1. *Bioterrorism and biowarfare:* Terrorist acts by state-sponsored organizations or hate groups. Few such events have occurred to date.
2. *Biocrime:* Intent to harm for personal gain or revenge. A few dozen events have occurred during recent decades.
3. *Biomisfortune:* Naturally occurring foodborne disease. Virtually all foodborne disease falls into this category, which is a daily concern for public health agencies everywhere.

Bioterrorist attacks can range from making false statements or accusations to actively inflicting injury on people, animals, or crops. Threats can be as devastating as actual destruction. Just claiming that a product has been intentionally contaminated can be sufficient to trigger an expensive recall and harmful adverse publicity. Product tampering, whether a hoax or real, can provide notoriety to the perpetrator, who is attempting to terrorize people and businesses.

Our food supply is an obvious route for the delivery of certain chemical and biological agents. Food production and distribution is a complex system not protected easily from the deliberate introduction of toxic agents. The attacks on the World Trade Center and Pentagon and the anthrax assaults have increased the concern and vigilance of the

Hazard Analysis Critical Control Point

Hazard Analysis Critical Control Point (HACCP) is a food industry program that focuses on preventing contamination by identifying areas in food production and retail where contamination could occur. HACCP also is an important line of defense against intentional contamination by bioterrorists. (See the FYI feature "At War with Bioterrorism.") HACCP is intended to replace the traditional system of spot checks at manufacturing sites and random sampling of final products. That system uncovered problems only after they had occurred, whereas HACCP works by preventing contamination.

Companies and retailers analyze their food-production processes and determine **critical control points (CCPs)**—points at which hazards could occur. They then determine measures that they can institute at these points to prevent, control, or eliminate the hazards.[17] (See Table 18.3.) Critical control points can occur anywhere in a food's production—from its raw state through processing and shipping to purchase by the consumer. Preventive measures can include proper cooking, chilling, and sanitizing, as well as preventing cross-contamination and improving employee hygiene.

critical control points (CCPs) Operational steps or procedures in a process, production method, or recipe at which control can be applied to prevent, reduce, or eliminate a food safety hazard.

United States and Canadian governments, which are acutely aware that public food and water supplies are among the most vulnerable avenues for terrorist attacks.

At ports of entry, food inspection facilities, and research labs and buildings, government personnel are at a heightened state of alert. To prevent the entry of animal or plant pests and diseases, they are carrying out intensified product and cargo inspections of travelers and baggage. Food safety inspectors have been given a mandate to be alert to any irregularities at food-processing facilities. Within processing facilities, specific plans for security should be developed. Such plans can be based on HACCP principles.[2]

The FDA has adopted five broad strategies to counter bioterrorism:[3]

1. *Awareness:* Increasing awareness through collecting, analyzing, and spreading information and knowledge.
2. *Prevention:* Identifying specific threats or attacks that involve biological, chemical, radiological, or nuclear agents.
3. *Preparedness:* Developing and making available medical countermeasures, such as drugs, devices, and vaccines.
4. *Response:* Ensuring rapid and coordinated response to any terrorist attacks.
5. *Recovery:* Ensuring rapid and coordinated treatment for any illness that may result from a terrorist attack.

The Public Health Security and Bioterrorism Preparedness and Response Act of 2002 (called the Bioterrorism Act) mandated that the FDA take numerous steps to protect the safety and security of the food and drug supply. Since then, the FDA has developed additional food safety regulations, increased domestic and foreign surveillance, and continued to work toward reducing threats and vulnerabilities.[4]

What can consumers do to protect themselves from food contamination? We must be the final judges of the safety of the food we buy. At a minimum, we should:

1. Make sure the food package or can is intact before opening it. If it has been damaged or dented or opened prior to purchase, call it to the attention of the appropriate person.
2. Be alert to abnormal color, taste, and appearance of a food item. If you have any doubt, don't eat it.
3. If the food appears to be tampered with, report it immediately.
4. Follow safe food-handling practices. (See the FYI feature "Safe Food Practices.")

1 Sobel J. Epidemiologic preparedness and response to terrorist events involving the nation's food supply. Paper presented at: Centers for Disease Control Health Preparedness Conference; February 2005.

2 Bledsoe GE, Rasco BA. Addressing the risk of bioterrorism in food production. *Food Technol.* 2002;56(2):43–47.

3 Meadows M. The FDA and the fight against bioterrorism. *FDA Consumer.* 2004;38(1). http://www.fda.gov/fdac/features/2004/104_terror.html. Accessed 7/8/09.

4 US Food and Drug Administration. Building a stronger defense against bioterrorism. Updated June 18, 2009. http://www.fda.gov/ForConsumers/ConsumerUpdates/ucm048251.htm. Accessed 7/8/09.

Academy of Nutrition and Dietetics

Food and Water Safety

It is the position of the Academy of Nutrition and Dietetics that the public has the right to a safe food and water supply. The Association supports collaboration among dietetics professionals, academics, representatives of the agricultural and food industries, and appropriate government agencies to ensure the safety of the food and water supply by providing education to the public and industry, promoting technologic innovation and applications, and supporting further research.

Source: Position of the American Dietetic Association: food and water safety. *J Am Diet Assoc.* 2003;103(9):1203–1218. Copyright © 2003. Reprinted with permission from Elsevier.

Food Code A reference published periodically by the Food and Drug Administration for restaurants, grocery stores, institutional food services, vending operations, and other retailers on how to store, prepare, and serve food to prevent foodborne illness.

The USDA requires HACCP for the food products it regulates—meat and poultry. The FDA, which regulates all other foods, requires HACCP in the seafood and low-acid canned-food industries and the juice industry. Also, the FDA has incorporated HACCP principles in its **Food Code**, a reference for restaurants, grocery stores, institutional food services, vending operations, and other retailers on how to store, prepare, and serve food to prevent foodborne illness.[18] The FDA updates and publishes the *Food Code* periodically as a model for states to adopt and use to regulate retail food establishments in their jurisdictions.

Key Concepts *Food safety is the responsibility of many agencies at the federal and state levels. The use of the Hazard Analysis Critical Control Point system allows government and industry to identify possible sites of food contamination and correct problems before they occur.*

The Consumer's Role in Food Safety

Food safety advice to consumers used to consist of a simple message: "Keep hot foods hot and cold foods cold." (See **Figure 18.7**.) Now food safety experts urge consumers to follow the following four rules (see **Figure 18.8**):[19]

1. *Clean.* Wash hands and surfaces often. Clean fruits and vegetables. Meat and poultry should not be washed or rinsed.
2. *Separate.* Don't cross-contaminate. When shopping, preparing, or storing food, separate raw, cooked, and ready-to-eat foods.
3. *Cook.* Cook to proper temperatures. Avoid unpasteurized milk and juices, raw sprouts, raw or partially cooked eggs, and raw or undercooked meat and poultry.
4. *Chill.* Refrigerate promptly. Defrost foods properly and quickly refrigerate perishable foods.

Table 18.3 **HACCP: Hazard Analysis and Critical Control Point**

Step 1: Analyze hazards.	Identify the potential hazards associated with a food. The hazard could be biological (e.g., a microbe), chemical (e.g., mercury), or physical (e.g., ground glass or metal).
Step 2: Identify critical control points (CCPs).	Identify points in a food's production path—from its raw state through processing and shipping to consumption—where a potential hazard can be controlled or eliminated. Examples of CCPs are cooking, chilling, handling, cleaning, and storage.
Step 3: Establish preventive measures with critical limits for each control point.	An example is setting the minimum cooking temperature and time to ensure safety for a particular food (the temperature and time are critical limits).
Step 4: Establish procedures to monitor the control points.	Such procedures might include determining how and by whom cooking time and temperature should be monitored.
Step 5: Establish corrective actions to be taken when a critical limit has not been met.	For example, reprocessing or disposing of food if the minimum cooking temperature is not met.
Step 6: Establish effective record keeping to document the HACCP system.	For example, recording hazards and their control methods, the monitoring of safety requirements, and action taken to correct potential problems.
Step 7: Establish procedures to verify that the system is working consistently.	For example, testing time-recording and temperature-recording devised to verify that a cooking unit is working properly.

The HACCP method focuses on preventing hazards, relies heavily on scientific principles, permits efficient government oversight, and places greater responsibility on food operations to ensure food safety.

Source: HACCP: a state-of-the-art approach to food safety. *FDA Backgrounder.* October, 2001. http://www.foodsafety.gov/~lrd/bghaccp.html. Accessed 7/8/09.

THINK About It 3 Once a consumer takes possession of a food, food safety becomes his or her responsibility. Unfortunately, studies show that many consumers fail to follow safe food practices in the home. Current public health efforts focus on teaching consumers—from young children to older Americans—safe food practices in the home. (See the FYI feature "Safe Food Practices.")

Some food-handling practices are so important that the federal government requires specific instructions or warnings on labels of certain foods. Following outbreaks of illness from *E. coli* O157:H7 in contaminated hamburger in 1993, the USDA mandated instructions on labels of raw meat and poultry to encourage consumers to follow recommendations for safe handling and cooking of these products.

Labels of unpasteurized or otherwise untreated packaged juice products carry a warning statement about the product's possible danger to children, older adults, and people with weakened immune systems. The warning states that the product has not been pasteurized and therefore may contain harmful bacteria that can cause serious illness in these high-risk groups. This requirement was made after a number of people became seriously ill from drinking unpasteurized apple juice that was contaminated with *E. coli*.

Fresh eggs must be handled carefully, and even eggs with clean, uncracked shells may occasionally contain *Salmonella* that can cause an intestinal infection. The FDA requires the following safe handling statement on egg cartons:[20]

> *SAFE HANDLING INSTRUCTIONS: To prevent illness from bacteria: keep eggs refrigerated, cook eggs until yolks are firm, and cook foods containing eggs thoroughly.*

Food manufacturers may voluntarily place other safe handling instructions on the label, such as those for proper cooking and storage of the item. Consumers should always follow these instructions.

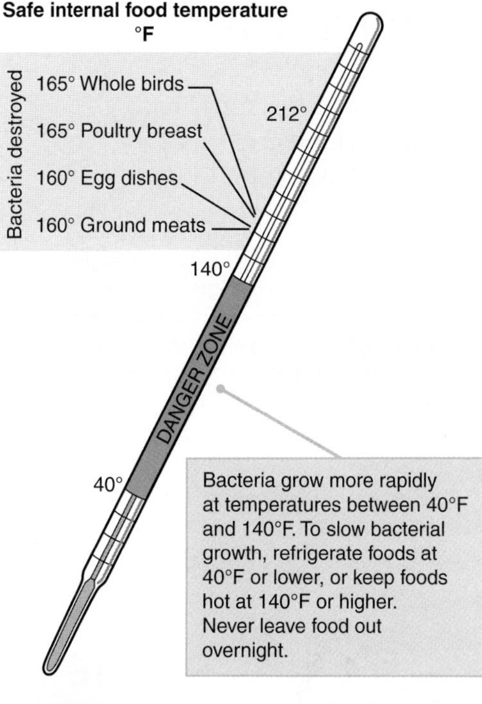
Safe internal food temperature
°F
Bacteria destroyed
165° Whole birds
165° Poultry breast
160° Egg dishes
160° Ground meats
212°
140°
DANGER ZONE
40°
Bacteria grow more rapidly at temperatures between 40°F and 140°F. To slow bacterial growth, refrigerate foods at 40°F or lower, or keep foods hot at 140°F or higher. Never leave food out overnight.

Figure 18.7 **Temperature guide.** To prevent bacterial growth, keep hot food hot and cold food cold.

Who's at Increased Risk for Foodborne Illness?

Although everyone should follow safe food practices, infants and young children, pregnant women, older adults, and those who are immunocompromised or have certain chronic conditions must be especially careful. In particular, they should not eat or drink raw (unpasteurized) milk or any products made from raw milk. They also should not eat raw or partially cooked eggs or foods containing raw eggs, raw or undercooked meat and poultry, raw or undercooked fish or shellfish, unpasteurized juices, and raw sprouts.

People who are at risk include individuals with the following conditions:

- Immune disorders, such as HIV infection
- Cancer
- Diabetes
- Long-term steroid use, such as for asthma or arthritis
- Liver disease
- Hemochromatosis, an iron storage disorder that affects the liver
- Stomach problems, including previous stomach surgery and low stomach acid (for example, from chronic antacid use)

Because these conditions are more common in older adults, seniors have an increased risk of foodborne illness. Young children do not have fully developed immune systems, so they are particularly vulnerable to serious illness from foodborne disease. Also, pregnant women and their fetuses are at special risk from the bacterium *Listeria monocytogenes* and the parasite

FIGHT BAC!
SEPARATE
Don't cross-contaminate.
CLEAN
Wash hands and surfaces often.
CHILL
Refrigerate promptly.
COOK
Cook to proper temperatures.
BAC
Keep Food Safe From Bacteria
TM

Clean: Wash hands and surfaces often
Separate: Don't cross-contaminate
Cook: Cook to safe temperature
Chill: Refrigerate properly

Figure 18.8 **Keeping harmful bacteria at bay.** Although our food supply generally is safe, home food safety practices are the weakest link in the food chain from farm to kitchen table. Be sure to follow the four basic practices: clean, separate, cook, and chill.

Source: Illustration courtesy of Partnership for Food Safety Education. www.fightbac.org.

Quick Bite

How Good Are Your Food Safety Habits?

Do Americans practice food safety in their own kitchens? Apparently not. A study conducted by the FDA and the Centers for Disease Control and Prevention showed that one-half of people surveyed ate undercooked eggs in the past year. Twenty percent of people ate undercooked hamburger, and 25 percent of men and 14 percent of women failed to wash their hands with soap after handling raw meat.

Toxoplasma gondii. Both of these microorganisms can harm—even kill—fetuses and young babies.

A Final Word on Food Safety

A totally risk-free system of food production is an unreasonable and unattainable goal. The United States and Canada enjoy a reputation as having food supplies that are among the safest in the world. We expect our food to be clean, fresh, and not contaminated with debris, chemicals, or organisms that cause sickness or discomfort. To make sure it stays that way, food safety experts are continually trying to ensure that every participant in the food production chain—from the farmer who produces the food to the manufacturer who processes it to the retailer who sells it and the consumer who buys it—undertakes measures to help reduce and perhaps even eliminate foodborne

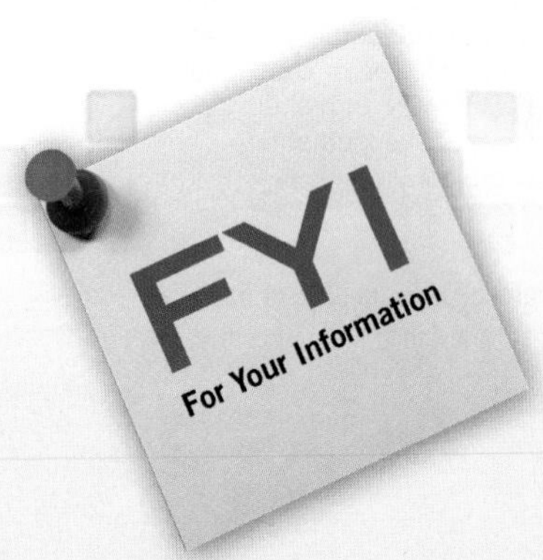

Safe Food Practices

Because bacteria grow rapidly between 40°F and 140°F (4–60°C), most food should be kept out of this temperature range, known as the Danger Zone. Cold temperatures keep bacteria from multiplying; the fewer bacteria, the less the risk of illness. Proper cooking (or other heat treatment, such as pasteurization) kills the bacteria. These principles serve as the basis for many of the following recommended food-handling practices.

Buying Food

- Buy from reputable dealers and grocers who keep their selling areas and facilities clean and sanitary and maintain food at the appropriate temperature—for example, holding dairy foods, eggs, meats, seafood, and certain produce such as cut melons and raw sprouts at refrigerator temperatures.
- Don't buy canned goods with dents or bulges. Avoid torn, crushed, or open food packages. Also, avoid buying packages that are above the frost line in the store's freezer. If the package cover is transparent, look for frost or ice crystals, signs that the product has been stored for a long time or thawed and refrozen.

Storing Food

- Separate raw, cooked, and ready-to-eat foods while shopping, preparing, or storing.
- Refrigerate perishable items as quickly as possible after purchase. The refrigerator temperature should be 40°F or colder. Check it periodically with a thermometer to make sure the correct temperature is being maintained.
- Keep eggs in their original carton and store them in the refrigerator itself, not the door, where the temperature is warmer.
- If raw meat, poultry products, or fresh seafood will be used within two days, store them in the coldest part of the refrigerator, usually under the freezer compartment or in a special "meat keeper." Store the packages loosely to allow air to circulate freely around each package, and be sure to wrap them tightly so that raw juices can't leak out and contaminate other foods.
- If raw meat, poultry, and seafood will not be used within two days, store them in the freezer, which should have a temperature of 0°F. Check this temperature periodically, too, and adjust as needed.
- Read label directions for storing other foods; for example, mayonnaise and ketchup need to be refrigerated after they have been opened.
- Store potatoes and onions in a cool dark place, but not under the sink because leakage from pipes can contaminate and damage them. Keep them away from household cleaning products and other chemicals as well.

Preparing Food

- Wash hands thoroughly with warm, soapy water for at least 20 seconds before beginning food preparation and every time you handle raw foods, including fresh produce.
- Defrost meat, poultry, and seafood products in the refrigerator, microwave oven, or in a watertight plastic bag submerged in cold water (the water must be changed every 30 minutes).

disease. That's one reason food safety advice today is turning up in so many places—to ensure that everyone gets the word on food safety.

Key Concepts *Consumers play a huge role in food safety. They can avoid foodborne illness by following a few simple food-handling and preparation rules: keep hands and food-preparation areas clean; avoid cross-contamination of foods; cook foods adequately; refrigerate foods promptly. People who have weak or less-developed immune systems are at higher risk for foodborne illnesses.*

Food Technology

Technology is having a larger and larger impact on the food we eat. Our use of preservatives, other preservation techniques, and genetic engineering

Never defrost at room temperature—an ideal temperature for bacteria to grow and multiply.

- Marinate foods in the refrigerator. Discard the marinade after use because it contains raw juices, which may harbor bacteria; make a separate batch for basting food while cooking.
- Always use a clean cutting board. Wash cutting boards with hot water, soap, and a scrub brush. Then sanitize them in an automatic dishwasher or by rinsing with a solution of 5 milliliters (1 teaspoon) chlorine bleach to about 1 liter (1 quart) of water. If possible, use one cutting board for fresh produce and a separate one for raw meat, poultry, and seafood. Once cutting boards become excessively worn or develop hard-to-clean grooves, you should replace them.
- Before opening canned foods, wash the top of the can to prevent dirt from coming in contact with the food.
- Wash fresh fruits and vegetables thoroughly with cold water. It is not necessary to wash or rinse meat or poultry.
- Avoid eating dough or batter containing raw eggs because of the risk of *Salmonella enteritidis*, a bacterium that can live in eggs.

Cooking Food

- Cook foods to the USDA Recommended Safe Minimum Internal Temperatures:

Steaks and roasts	145°F (63°C)
Fish	145°F (63°C)
Pork	160°F (71°C)
Ground beef	160°F (71°C)
Egg dishes	160°F (71°C)
Chicken breasts	165°F (74°C)
Whole poultry	165°F (74°C)

- The only safe way to know whether food is "done" is to use a food thermometer. Color is not a good guide. According to the USDA, one of every four hamburgers turns brown before reaching a safe internal temperature.
- Never place cooked food on a plate that previously held raw meat, poultry, or seafood.
- When microwaving foods, rotate the dish and stir its contents several times to ensure even cooking. Follow recommended standing times, then check meat, poultry, and seafood products with a thermometer to make sure they have reached the correct internal temperature.
- Cook eggs until the white is firm and the yolk is firm.

Serving Food

- Keep hot foods at 140°F (60°C) or higher and cold foods at 40°F (4°C) or lower.
- Refrigerate or freeze leftovers and perishables within two hours or sooner.
- Date leftovers so that they can be used within a safe time—generally, three to five days in the refrigerator.

has implications for our food supply in the years to come and has triggered debates about the risks and benefits of such practices.

Food Preservation

In our modern society, few people grow their own vegetables, fruits, and grains, or keep livestock as a source of meat and milk. Rather, we shop for our food, typically at a large, full-service supermarket. Because we don't consume our food at the point of harvest or slaughter, we use food preservation methods to help maintain the quality of the foods we purchase. Among food preservation methods are the addition of chemical preservatives, canning or freezing, **pasteurization**, and more recent methods, such as irradiation.

Preservatives

Preservatives are added to foods to prevent spoilage and increase shelf life. The most common antimicrobial agents are salt and sugar. Other preservatives, such as potassium sorbate and sodium propionate, extend the shelf life of baked goods and many other products. Antioxidants are a type of preservative that prevents the changes in color and flavor caused by exposure to air. Common antioxidants include vitamin C and vitamin E, sulfites, and BHA and BHT.

Preparation for Preservation

Some preservation techniques, such as salting and fermenting, date to ancient times and are still practiced along with their modern counterparts—freezing, canning, pasteurization, and the like. Salting, drying, or fermenting foods creates an environment in which bacteria cannot multiply and therefore cannot cause food spoilage. Canned foods are heated quickly to a temperature that kills microbes and then are sealed airtight to prevent both contamination and oxidative damage. Freezing temperatures not only keep bacteria from multiplying but also prevent normal enzymatic changes in food that would cause spoilage. Pasteurization of milk or other beverages uses a very high temperature for a very short time to kill bacteria, but minimizes changes that would result from longer heating. The food industry and the North American public readily accept these food preservation methods. One of the most modern preservation techniques—irradiation—is also the most controversial, in part because of our fear of anything that has to do with radiation.

Irradiation

Before it received official approval, food **irradiation** underwent more than 40 years of scientific research and testing—more than any other food technology.[21] During irradiation, foods are exposed to a measured dose of radiation to reduce or eliminate pathogenic bacteria, including *E. coli* O157:H7, *Salmonella*, and *Campylobacter*, the chief causes of foodborne illness today. Irradiation also can destroy insects and parasites, reduce spoilage, and inhibit sprouting and delay ripening of certain fruits and vegetables. Irradiated strawberries, for example, stay unspoiled for up to three weeks versus three to five days for untreated berries. Irradiation can reduce pathogens in raw poultry or meat by 99.9 percent.[22] Some people fear irradiation will make the food radioactive. This concern is unfounded. The energy used to irradiate foods passes through the food and leaves no residue—in the same way that microwaves pass through food. Despite its benefits, use of irradiation remains rare in North America.

Quick Bite

Wood vs. Plastic: The Cutting Controversy

Which type of cutting board is safer to use while cutting meat: wood or plastic? Both have drawbacks. A wood cutting board tends to absorb bacteria, sucking them down into the wood fibers. This may be safer than a plastic board, which keeps bacteria on the surface, in an easy position to rub off onto food and other objects. But with use, wooden cutting boards tend to keep more on the surface than new wooden boards, acting more like plastic boards. What's the solution? Keep cutting boards clean by heating wooden boards in the microwave or putting plastic boards in the dishwasher.

pasteurization A process for destroying pathogenic bacteria by heating liquid foods to a prescribed temperature for a specified time.

preservatives Chemicals or other agents that slow the decomposition of a food.

irradiation A food preservation technique in which foods are exposed to measured doses of radiation to reduce or eliminate pathogens and kill insects, reduce spoilage, and, in certain fruits and vegetables, inhibit sprouting and delay ripening.

Quick Bite

Where Do *E. coli* Hang Out?

Ground beef is the most common source of *E. coli* bacteria, but *E. coli* also have been found on apples and lettuce.

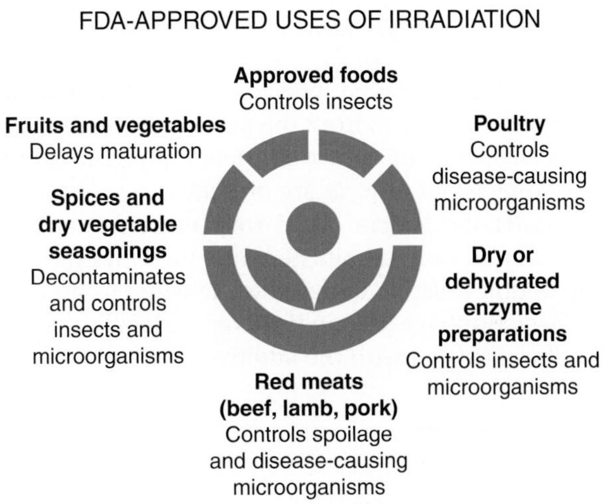

FDA-APPROVED USES OF IRRADIATION

Approved foods
Controls insects

Fruits and vegetables
Delays maturation

Poultry
Controls disease-causing microorganisms

Spices and dry vegetable seasonings
Decontaminates and controls insects and microorganisms

Dry or dehydrated enzyme preparations
Controls insects and microorganisms

Red meats (beef, lamb, pork)
Controls spoilage and disease-causing microorganisms

Figure 18.9 **Irradiation.** Irradiation can retard spoilage and reduce risk of foodborne illness.

Because food manufacturers fear consumer rejection, they have been reluctant to use irradiation on their products. Some consumers and advocacy groups protest its use because they are concerned that irradiation may compromise a food's nutritional value and change its texture, taste, or appearance. In fact, irradiation may cause less nutritive loss than conventional methods of food preservation.[23] At appropriate doses, irradiation of food does not significantly change its flavor, texture, or appearance.[24] Many organizations, including the Academy of Nutrition and Dietetics, the American Medical Association, and the World Health Organization, endorse irradiation as a means of providing the public with a safer food supply.

The FDA has approved irradiation for

- Spices and dry vegetable seasoning to decontaminate and control insects and microorganisms
- Dry or dehydrated enzyme preparations to control insects and microorganisms
- Fruits and vegetables to inhibit maturation
- Poultry and red meat to control spoilage and pathogenic microorganisms
- All the foods above, to control insects, mites, and other arthropod pests

The FDA requires labels of irradiated foods to state that the product was "treated with irradiation" or "treated by irradiation" and display the international symbol for irradiation, the radura. (See **Figure 18.9**.)

Some experts believe the time is right for food irradiation to become more widespread. News stories about deaths related to foodborne illness have made the public more aware of the need for protection against contamination of food. As more consumers become aware of the benefits of irradiation, the demand for irradiated foods is expected to increase.

Quick Bite

Bacteria at the Supermarket

Bacteria abound on the surface of supermarket meat. A piece of pork, on average, may harbor a few hundred bacteria per cubic centimeter, and a piece of chicken may have 10,000 in the same area.

Bacteriophages

The Food and Drug Administration has approved a mixture of viruses as a food additive to protect people from bacterial infections. The viruses used in the additive are called **bacteriophages** ("bacteria eaters"). A bacteriophage is any virus that infects bacteria.

Bacteriophages are common in soil, water, and our bodies. In the human gut and oral cavity, bacteriophages are normal and beneficial microbial in-

bacteriophages Viruses that infect bacteria.

habitants. Bacteriophages infect only bacteria and do not bother mammalian or plant cells.

The additive can be sprayed onto ready-to-eat meat and poultry products to protect consumers from the potentially life-threatening bacterium *Listeria monocytogenes*. The approved bacteriophage mixture targets *Listeria* and will thrive only when *Listeria* are present.

Under the Federal Meat Inspection Act and the Poultry Products Inspection Act, both administered by the USDA, the use of the bacteriophage preparation must be declared on labeling as an ingredient. Consumers will see "bacteriophage preparation" on the label of meat or poultry products that have been treated with the additive.[25]

Key Concepts *Various processing methods help protect us from contamination of food by pathogens. Drying, salting, canning, freezing, and pasteurizing are methods that consumers accept. Irradiation is a process in which foods are exposed to a measured dose of radiation to reduce or eliminate pathogenic bacteria. Although government and professional organizations deem irradiation a safe procedure, consumers are still wary. The FDA has also approved spraying ready-to-eat meats and poultry products with bacteriophages, viruses that infect bacteria.*

Quick Bite

Biotechnology in the 1930s

One of the first examples of genetic theory successfully applied to food production was hybrid corn. When first introduced, it seemed miraculous and convinced skeptical farmers of the potential benefits of this emerging agricultural science. To this day, tougher and healthier new hybrids continue to outyield their predecessors.

Genetically Modified Foods

Genetically modified (GM) foods have arrived, and most of us are already dining on them. When you prepare a dinner of broccoli and tofu, some of the soybeans used to make the tofu probably came from plants genetically modified to resist herbicide sprays or insect pests or both. And although your broccoli is currently "natural," you can be sure that in a lab somewhere genetically modified broccoli seeds are sprouting, perhaps with enhanced nutrient or other phytochemical levels. If you are eating tenderloin tonight, the steak probably came from a steer fed on genetically modified corn that had its DNA altered by the addition of foreign genes to allow the plant to resist insect pests and herbicides.

Should you be indignant that these new foods are showing up on your table without any indication on the label, or should you be grateful that these high-tech methods are keeping crop yields high and food costs low? An informed answer to this question requires some understanding of how genetic engineering works, how new crops and foods are regulated, and how gene modification of crops and animals differs from the classical methods of agricultural breeding that have been practiced for thousands of years.

A Short Course in Plant Genetics

How do GM food plants differ from those developed through traditional cross-pollination and hybridization? The answer, surprisingly, is that most crop modifications achieved by DNA manipulation and associated techniques of **biotechnology** could also be achieved with classical techniques, but the time scale and expense are very different. (See **Figure 18.10**.)

genetically modified (GM) foods Foods produced using plant or animal ingredients that have been modified using gene technology.

biotechnology The set of laboratory techniques and processes used to modify the genome of plants or animals and thus create desirable new characteristics. Genetic engineering in the broad sense.

The classical techniques for breeding a plant with new characteristics have been practiced for hundreds of years. They involve crossing two plants with different characteristics, then growing the resulting hybrid seeds and looking for plants with the desired combination of characteristics. Hybrid plants get half of their genes from one parent and half from the other. Though the hybrid may combine favorable qualities from both parents, a lot of undesirable genetic baggage must be sorted out after formation of such a hybrid. It usually takes dozens of additional crosses, and many years, to separate the desirable genes from the undesirable, and the process has a large element of chance. Due to human intervention, today millions of acres of genetically modified crops are planted in countries all over the world.

Genetic engineering, in contrast, allows scientists to transform a plant one gene at a time, using well-established methods for manipulating DNA sequences and integrating them into the plant **genome** (its set of genes). Because many plant genes have already been identified, and complete DNA sequences of plant genomes will be available soon, we can anticipate that the genetic engineering of plants will become increasingly powerful and precise. Designing a new GM plant should come to resemble a manufacturing process rather than the tedious guessing game of classical genetics. In some cases, a gene can be selected and introduced into plant cells, and new GM seeds can be prepared within a year or two. When we consider that it took centuries of selection and breeding to transform the weedy wild maize plant of pre-Columbian Mexico into our modern varieties of corn, the scale and speed of the gene revolution in agriculture are astounding.

genetic engineering Manipulation of the genome of an organism by artificial means for the purpose of modifying existing traits or adding new genetic traits.

genome The total genetic information of an organism, stored in the DNA of its chromosomes.

Genetically Modified Foods: An Unstoppable Experiment?

How extensive is the shift to gene-modified crops, and how many different crops are involved? In 2007, genetically altered crop planting increased nearly 12 percent from the previous year to cover 282.3 million acres. Twenty-three countries now plant GM crops, and an additional 29 allow imports for food or animal feed.[26]

The United States accounts for nearly two-thirds of all biotechnology crops planted globally. GM food crops grown by U.S. farmers include corn, cotton, soybeans, canola, squash, and papaya. About 85 percent of the U.S. soybean crop and over 75 percent of the cotton crop are genetically modified.[27] Other major producers of GM crops are Argentina, which plants primarily biotech soybeans; Canada, whose principal biotech crop is canola; Brazil, which recently approved the planting of GM soybeans; China, where the acreage of GM cotton continues to increase; and South Africa, where cotton is also the principle biotech crop. The increased yields and lower costs associated with GM crops make them attractive to farmers. There is now strong, perhaps unstoppable, momentum to continue and expand GM crop plantings.

European countries, however, have been slow to accept gene-modified crops. They are concerned about possible ecological damage from such crops and fear potential unintended consequences of genetic "tampering" with the food supply. Although some U.S. consumer groups voice similar concerns, agribusiness, the Academy of Nutrition and Dietetics, the American Medical Association, the National Academy of Science, and the Food and Agriculture Organization have been quite supportive of the trend toward GM foods.[28]

The GM crops mentioned earlier are just the tip of the genetic modification iceberg; hundreds more are under development in university laboratories and in the labs of giant agribusinesses such as Monsanto. Research in plant biotechnology has focused primarily on characteristics that improve resistance to pests, reduce the need for pesticides, and increase the ability of the plant to survive adverse growing conditions such as drought, soil salinity, and cold. Many of these goals would be achievable with classical selection techniques; but with genetic engineering, they move from laboratory to table in decades, rather than centuries.

Genetic engineering also has affected the food-processing industry. The cheese-making industry uses genetically modified bacteria to produce the

CROP DEVELOPMENT

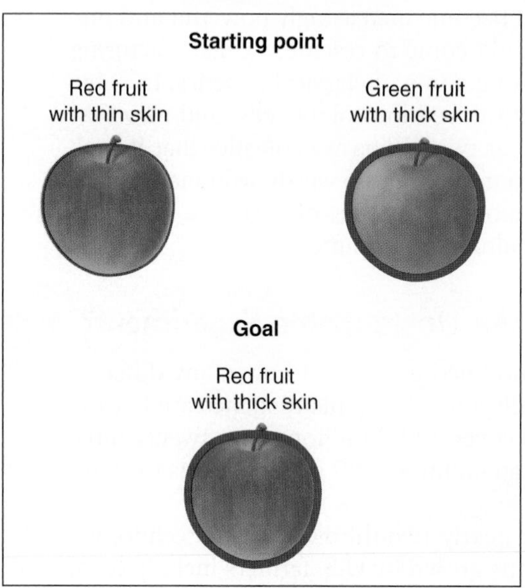

GENETIC ENGINEERING

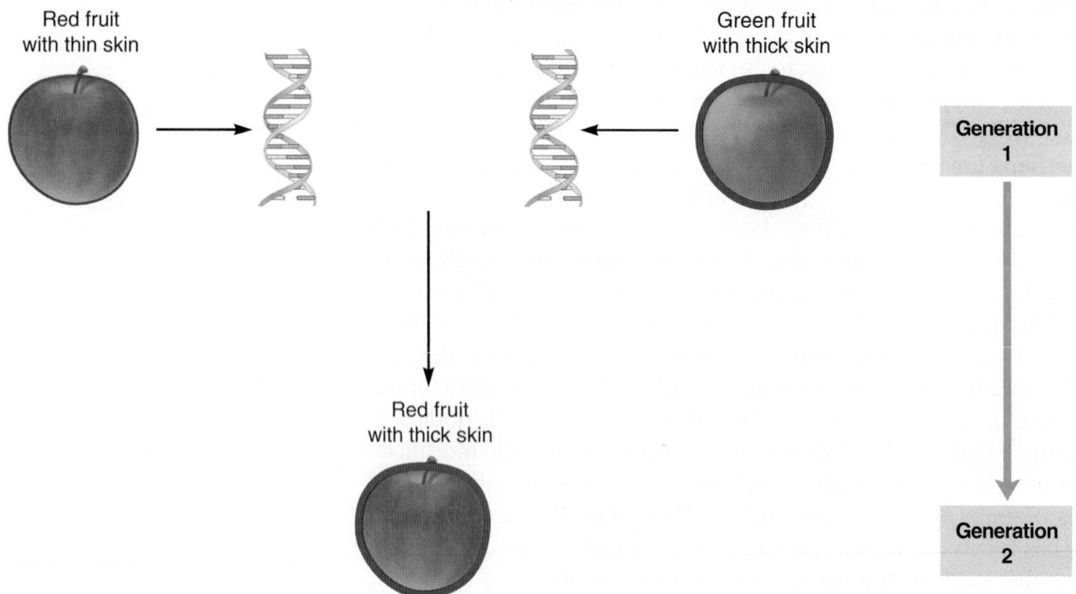

Scientists can use genetic engineering to combine certain traits in a single generation.

Figure 18.10 **Genetic engineering and traditional breeding.** Genetic engineering can fast-track crop development that can take years with traditional breeding practices.

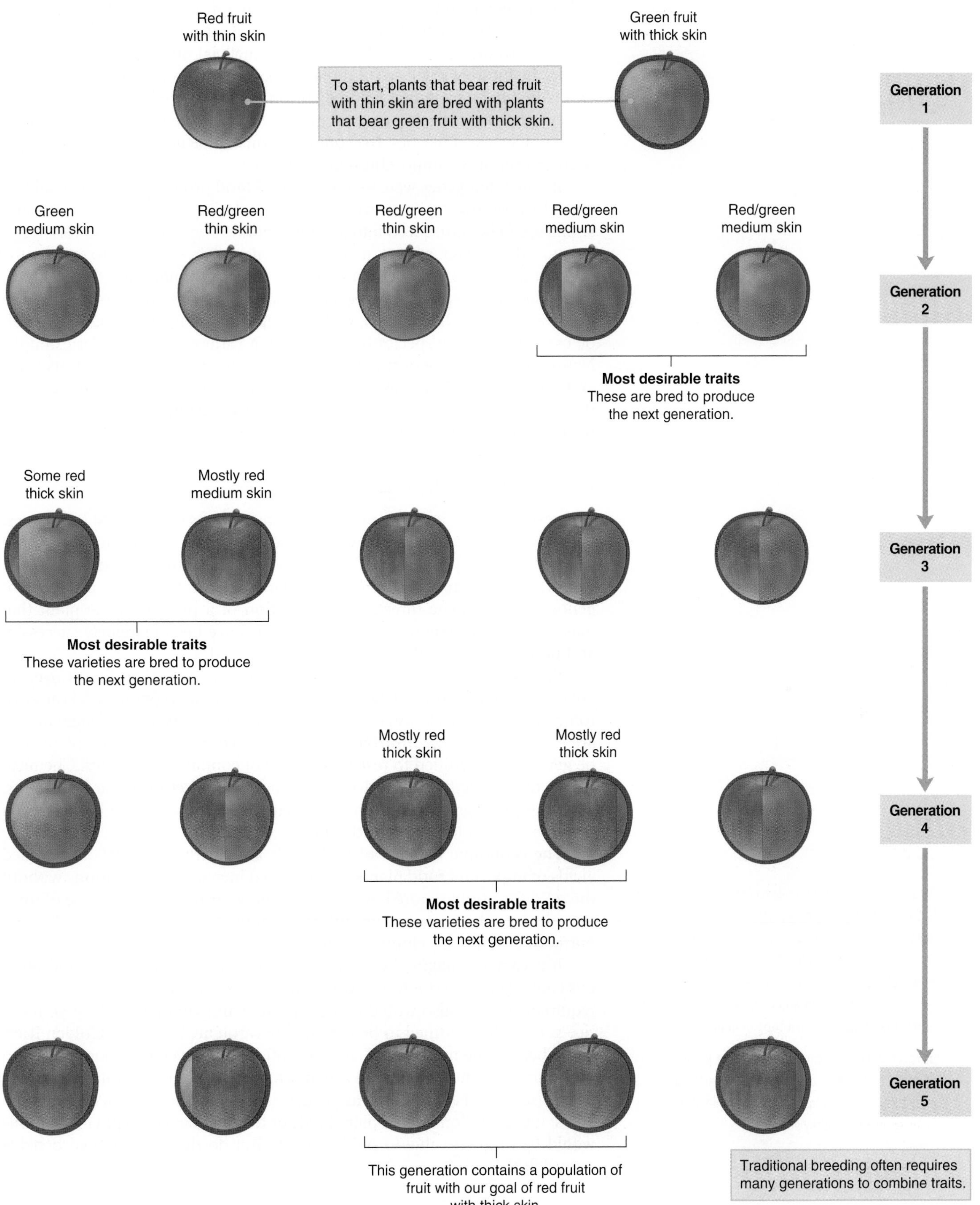
TRADITIONAL BREEDING
Red fruit with thin skin
Green fruit with thick skin
To start, plants that bear red fruit with thin skin are bred with plants that bear green fruit with thick skin.
Generation 1
Green medium skin
Red/green thin skin
Red/green thin skin
Red/green medium skin
Red/green medium skin
Generation 2
Most desirable traits
These are bred to produce the next generation.
Some red thick skin
Mostly red medium skin
Generation 3
Most desirable traits
These varieties are bred to produce the next generation.
Mostly red thick skin
Mostly red thick skin
Generation 4
Most desirable traits
These varieties are bred to produce the next generation.
Generation 5
This generation contains a population of fruit with our goal of red fruit with thick skin.
Traditional breeding often requires many generations to combine traits.

widely used enzyme chymosin. Chymosin has virtually replaced the natural milk-clotting enzyme rennet, which is extracted from the stomachs of calves. Animals may be genetically modified for several purposes, including increased resistance to disease and higher levels of beneficial nutrients.[29]

In the future we will see GM plants that have been modified to yield better textile fibers, including colored cotton, or specialized proteins for use in human pharmaceuticals—or even plants that produce the starting materials for manufacture of plastics. In economic terms, these nonfood GM crops may become even more important than GM foods.

If only plant genes were involved in GM food production, there would be much less controversy. However, any gene, including genes from bacteria and animals, can be introduced into a plant genome. Some people find this frightening, and an imaginative term, *Frankenfoods*, has been coined to express the "unnatural" nature of some GM products. But how unnatural is the exchange of DNA between species? It may be reassuring to realize that organisms have been swapping DNA for eons, with no help from humans. Foreign DNA can be carried from one species to another by a variety of viruses, for example. Nature has already performed millions of "gene modifications" on its own, and exchange of DNA is an established part of the evolutionary process. Now that we can do our own experiments with DNA manipulation, we hope the benefits will be increased.

Benefits of Genetic Engineering

Whatever the risks, no one can argue with the success of these GM techniques. For instance, a bacterial gene was used to create Monsanto's insect-resistant varieties of corn, potatoes, and soybeans. This gene, the **Bt gene**, was taken from the soil bacterium *Bacillus thuringiensis*. When inserted into a plant genome, the Bt gene directs the production of a protein in the plant that makes the plant toxic to insects. Such crops have been extremely successful and produce high yields without use of insecticides.

Bt-modified crops, which are now grown in the United States over an area larger than Rhode Island, are a boon to both the economy and the environment. Because chemical insecticides are not necessary, many benign insects are spared, and insect **biodiversity** is preserved. Similarly, other plants can be genetically modified to resist the effects of common herbicides. Chemical sprays that are lethal to most plant life have no effect on these GM plants. The crop plant grows larger in the absence of weeds, and the farmer gets a better yield with less effort and expense.

The economic benefits of GM foods are clearly substantial. Increased yields of important food plants can help feed increasing populations without the need for putting more land under the plow or increasing the use of toxic insecticides. This may be the difference between starvation and adequate nutrition in many developing countries.

It is easy to imagine how manipulation of plant amino acids and plant oils could yield superior foods, which not only would be able to satisfy calorie requirements, but also would address protein and vitamin needs. A strain of rice genetically modified to be rich in beta-carotene, known as Golden Rice, could benefit the more than 1 million children in developing countries who die or are weakened by vitamin A deficiency.[30] In developed countries, where heart disease and cancer loom as greater risks than malnutrition, the ability to adjust the saturation level of plant lipids or to boost beneficial phytochemicals would be of great value to public health. But do these undoubted benefits outweigh the risks?

Bt gene *Bacillus thuringiensis* (Bt) is a bacterium that produces a protein called the Bt toxin. One of the bacterium's genes, the Bt gene, carries the information for the Bt toxin. Inserting a copy of the Bt gene into plants enables them to produce Bt toxin protein and resist some insect pests. The Bt protein is not toxic to humans.

biodiversity The countless species of plants, animals, and insects that exist on the earth. An undisturbed tropical forest is an example of the biodiversity of a healthy ecosystem

Risks

What are the specific risks of GM foods? Many consumers are concerned about whether these new foods are safe to eat. The answer to this concern is a fairly unequivocal "yes." When a new protein or other substance is introduced into a food, the FDA requires substantial testing to demonstrate its safety. With GM foods, the potential risk appears to be the possibility of introducing a new allergen into a GM food.[31] To be cautious, the FDA has focused on allergy issues. Under the law and the FDA's biotech food policy, companies must tell consumers on the food label when a product includes a gene from a food that commonly causes an allergic reaction. The only exception is when the company can show that the protein produced by the added gene does not make the genetically modified food cause allergies.[32]

Of greater concern, and more difficult to predict, are environmental effects, although no ecological disasters have occurred thus far. What if the Bt-containing plants lead to the development of insects resistant to Bt-modified plants and to other insecticides? Would the appearance of Bt-resistant insects spell the doom of a large portion of our crops of soybeans or maize?

Farmers use different strains of Bt, each specific to a different insect. Because Bt is species specific, beneficial and nontarget insects are usually not harmed. Because Bt is a natural, nonpathogenic bacterium that is found naturally in the soil, Bt proteins are allowed in organic farming as an insecticide. For more than 50 years, organic farmers have used Bt proteins as a microbial pest control agent.

Another concern is the development of herbicide-resistant weeds, or "superweeds." When herbicide-resistant crops are planted in proximity to related wild plants, pollen may drift from food plant to weed, and the resistant genes might be passed to the weedy cousins of the GM plants. In the presence of herbicide, this might lead to the rapid selection of herbicide-resistant weeds. Although transfer of the herbicide-resistant gene to a related weed can occur, so far the effects have been minor, and the "superweeds" have rapidly lost the resistance gene once the herbicide was removed.

A final concern is that the herbicide-resistant food plants may become so successful that they are planted over a vast acreage in developing countries. In the worst scenario, this could lead to a loss of many species of unmodified plants as well as the insect and animal communities that depend on them. Many scientists feel that the loss of biodiversity is one of the greatest threats to the planet today. Because of the complexity and interdependence of the biosphere, this is perhaps the greatest unknown and the greatest danger of unmonitored use of GM crops. Table 18.4 summarizes benefits and current controversies.

Regulation

The FDA regulates foods and food safety, and it oversees genetically modified foods and animals as well as conventional foods. For foods derived from new varieties of plants, the FDA takes the position that whether modified by traditional breeding or genetic engineering, testing for safe human consumption is the legal responsibility of the producer or manufacturer of the foods. Crops such as Bt-modified soybeans do not require special testing, labeling, or FDA approval. Although the plant expresses the Bt protein, the beans do not contain it. Except for some foreign DNA sequences, the beans are identical to unmodified soybeans. However, when a new substance is added to a food, FDA review and approval are necessary. Thus, if a new substance is produced

Table 18.4 **GM Products: Benefits and Controversies**

Benefits
Crops
- Enhanced taste and quality
- Reduced maturation time
- Increased nutrients, yields, and stress tolerance
- Improved resistance to disease, pests, and herbicides
- New products and growing techniques

Animals
- Increased resistance, productivity, hardiness, and feed efficiency
- Better yields of meat, eggs, and milk
- Improved animal health and diagnostic methods

Environment
- "Friendly" bioherbicides and bioinsecticides
- Conservation of soil, water, and energy
- Bioprocessing for forestry products
- Better natural waste management
- More efficient processing

Society
- Increased food security for growing populations

Controversies
Safety
- Potential human health impacts, including allergens, transfer of antibiotic resistance markers, unknown effects
- Potential environmental impacts, including unintended transfer of transgenes through cross-pollination, unknown effects on other organisms (e.g., soil microbes), and loss of flora and fauna biodiversity

Access and intellectual property
- Domination of world food production by a few companies
- Increasing dependence on industrialized nations by developing countries
- Biopiracy, or foreign exploitation of natural resources

Ethics
- Violation of natural organisms' intrinsic values
- Tampering with nature by mixing genes among species
- Objections to consuming animal genes in plants and vice versa
- Stress for animals

Labeling
- Not mandatory in some countries (e.g., United States)
- Mixing GM crops with non-GM products confounds labeling attempts

Society
- New advances may be skewed to interests of rich countries

Source: US Department of Energy, Human Genome Project. Genetically modified foods and organisms. November 2008. http://www.ornl.gov/sci/techresources/Human_Genome/elsi/gmfood.shtml. Accessed 7/24/09.

or introduced into a food by genetic means, it must be tested as though it were a food additive. (See "Spotlight on Complementary and Alternative Nutrition: Functional Foods and Dietary Supplements.")

Some consumer groups are pushing for mandatory labeling of GM foods. They believe consumers have the right to know whether a food is bioengineered. Other groups desire labeling so they can adhere to cultural or religious beliefs that may ban certain animal foods. Because the FDA believes the way a food is developed or produced is irrelevant information, current FDA policy does not require labeling of GM foods.

The FDA does require that food labels disclose any significant difference between the bioengineered food and its conventional counterpart. Such differences would include changes in nutritional properties, the presence of an allergen that consumers would not expect in the food, or any property that would require special handling, storage, cooking, or preservation.

Similar to U.S regulations, Health Canada requires special labeling for genetically modified foods when there is a potential for allergic reactions, and a different name must be used for a GM food that is different in composition or nutritional value. Voluntary positive ("does contain") and voluntary negative ("does not contain") labeling is permitted, provided the statements are factual and not misleading or deceptive.[33]

Many groups (government agencies, such as the FDA; professional organizations, such as the ADA; and consumer advocacy groups) are monitoring developments in biotechnology. Web sites for these organizations can be a source of policy statements and breaking news in this area. Regardless of our views on genetic manipulation of food plants, research and development will continue.

Key Concepts *Genetic engineering allows scientists to transform a plant one gene at a time, using well-established methods for manipulating DNA sequences. The goals of genetic modification of foods are higher yields, lower costs, increased amounts of critical nutrients, and a healthier mix of plant oils. Because of the complexity and interdependence of the biosphere, loss of genetic biodiversity is perhaps the greatest unknown and the greatest danger of unmonitored GM crops.*

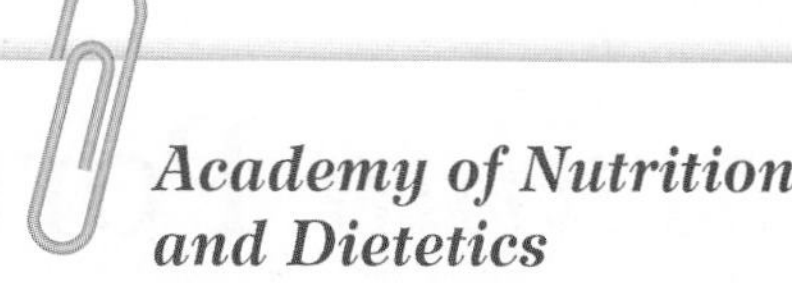

Academy of Nutrition and Dietetics

Agricultural and Food Biotechnology

It is the position of the Academy of Nutrition and Dietetics that agricultural and food biotechnology techniques can enhance the quality, safety, nutritional value, and variety of food available for human consumption and increase the efficiency of food production, food processing, food distribution, and environmental and waste management. The ADA encourages the government, food manufacturers, food commodity groups, and qualified food and nutrition professionals to work together to inform consumers about this new technology and encourage availability of these products in the marketplace.

Source: Position of the American Dietetic Association: agricultural and food biotechnology. *J Am Diet Assoc.* 2006;106(2):285–293. Copyright © 2006. Reprinted with permission from Elsevier.

Learning Portfolio

Key Terms

	page
aflatoxins	759
bacteriophages	771
biodiversity	776
biotechnology	772
botulism	750
bovine spongiform encephalopathy (BSE)	754
Bt gene	776
ciguatera	759
critical control points (CCPs)	765
dioxins	759
Escherichia coli (*E. coli*)	753
Food Code	766
foodborne illness	750
genetic engineering	773
genetically modified (GM) foods	772
genome	773
integrated pest management (IPM)	757
irradiation	770
mad cow disease	754
methylmercury	759
natural toxins	759
organic foods	756
pasteurization	770
pesticides	756
poisonous mushrooms	760
pollutants	759
preservatives	770
prions	754
Safe Tables Our Priority (S.T.O.P.)	764
Salmonella	750
solanine	760

Study Points

- Foodborne illness is extremely common; it affects millions of Americans each year. Estimates of the frequency of foodborne illness are difficult because the vast majority of foodborne illnesses go unreported.
- The incidence of foodborne illness may be on the rise in the United States and Canada. Many factors are responsible, including the increased centralization of food preparation, food imports, an increasing population of especially susceptible individuals (such as the elderly and those with weakened immune systems), and failure of consumers and retail establishments to follow appropriate food safety measures.
- Microorganisms cause most foodborne diseases in the United States and Canada. Most of these illnesses are preventable.
- *Staphylococcus aureus* is one of the most common causes of foodborne illness. Onset of illness is rapid, typically occurring between 30 minutes and a few hours after consuming the contaminated food.
- Common symptoms of foodborne illness are diarrhea, nausea, abdominal cramps, and sometimes fever. The severity of the illness depends on the type of organism and the amount of contaminant eaten.
- Ensuring a safe food supply is a farm-to-table continuum involving producers, manufacturers, retailers, and consumers.
- Pesticides, animal drugs, natural toxins, and pollutants are the major forms of chemical food contamination.
- The government monitors imported and domestic foods for pesticide residues by testing food samples for both amounts and types of pesticides. Efforts are under way to reduce the allowable amounts of certain pesticides to avoid harm to infants and children.
- The FDA evaluates drugs used in food-producing animals for safety in both animals and humans. Overuse of animal antibiotics could contribute to the emergence of antibiotic-resistant microorganisms that could threaten human health.
- The government and the food industry use the Hazard Analysis Critical Control Point system to prevent food contamination.
- Consumers must take responsibility for food safety in their homes. Cleaning hands and surfaces, avoiding cross-contamination, cooking adequately, and refrigerating foods promptly are important steps that prevent foodborne illness.
- Food preservation techniques inhibit growth of microorganisms. Canning, drying, freezing, fermentation, and pasteurization are common.
- Although the FDA has approved food irradiation for numerous uses, it is rarely used, mostly because of consumer fears. Food irradiation does not make foods radioactive. It can kill insects and most microorganisms. Appropriate doses of radiation extend the shelf life of many foods.
- Genetically modified (GM) foods are most likely already on your table. Soybeans, corn, and potatoes are some of the GM foods being commercially produced. Concerns about GM foods include worries about decreasing biodiversity and the development of herbicide-resistant weeds.

Study Questions

1. What are the two main ways that pathogenic bacteria can cause foodborne illness?
2. Why shouldn't your 97-year-old great-grandmother drink homemade eggnog made from raw eggs?
3. List four naturally occurring toxins.
4. What does "HACCP" stand for and what is its purpose?
5. What are some ways to keep food safe at home?
6. List the most common food preservation techniques.
7. What are scientists' two major concerns about genetically engineered crops?

Try This

Bacterial Detective

What sources of bacteria do you encounter in your everyday activities? Here's an experiment to find out.

First, you'll need . . .

Cotton swabs
Six or more Petri dishes with agar

If you are unable to obtain a set of agar-filled Petri dishes from your school or local health department, you can make your own culture medium. Here's how:

- Add 2 teaspoons of unflavored gelatin (1 packet) and 2 teaspoons of sugar to ⅔ cup of water.
- Bring the solution to a boil and stir for 1 minute until everything is dissolved. Pour ¼ inch of the solution into each Petri dish or other suitable container.

Then, using separate Petri dishes,

1. Pluck a hair and lay it in one Petri dish, labeled "Hair."
2. Sneeze or cough into another Petri dish, labeled "Cough."
3. Run a cotton swab around a nostril and carefully zigzag it across the agar in another Petri dish, labeled "Nose."
4. Run a cotton swab across a dampened kitchen sink sponge and carefully zigzag it across the agar in another Petri dish, labeled "Sponge."
5. Run a cotton swab around a clean kitchen countertop and carefully zigzag it across the agar in another Petri dish, labeled "Countertop."
6. Use the same procedure to collect additional samples from any other area in which bacteria may be present.
7. Store the Petri dishes in a warm environment, at a constant temperature around 80°F. Check your specimens periodically. Within a week, you should see something growing!

What do you observe? Which Petri dishes show the most growth? Which show the least? Does this change your ideas about cleaning habits?

Organic Foods

Organic foods are increasing in popularity. Are organic foods widely available in your neighborhood? What types of organic produce can you find? Go to either a natural food store or the local grocery store and look at the array of organic produce. Compare the prices of organic produce and nonorganic produce. Do you think the cost differences outweigh possible benefits? Compare the look of the organic and nonorganic produce. Do you see any differences? What other organic products can you find?

References

1 Centers for Disease Control and Prevention, National Center for Infectious Diseases. Food-related Diseases. October 2007. http://www.cdc.gov/ncidod/diseases/food/. Accessed 4/27/09.

2 Institute of Food Technologists. *IFT Expert Report on Emerging Microbiological Food Safety Issues: Implications for Control in the 21st Century*. Chicago, IL: Institute of Food Technologies, 2002. http://members.ift.org/IFT/Research/IFTExpertReports/microsfs_report.htm. Accessed 4/27/09.

3 Centers for Disease Control and Prevention, Division of Foodborne, Bacteria and Mycotic Diseases. Salmonellosis. May 21, 2008. http://www.cdc.gov/nczved/dfbmd/disease_listing/salmonellosis_gi.html. Accessed 4/30/09.

4 Ibid.; and Wright JG, Tengelsen LA, Smith KE, et al. Multidrug-resistant *Salmonella typhimurium* outbreak in four animal facilities. *Emerg Infect Dis*. [serial on the Internet]. August 2005. http://www.cdc.gov/ncidod/EID/vol11no08/05-0111.htm. Accessed 4/28/09.

5 US Food and Drug Administration. *Pesticide Program Residue Monitoring 2002*. Washington, DC: March 2004. http://www.cfsan.fda.gov/~dms/pes02rep.html. Accessed 6/8/08.

6 Ibid.

7 US Environmental Protection Agency. Assessing health risks from pesticides. April 5, 2007. http://www.epa.gov/pesticides/factsheets/riskassess.htm. Accessed 4/29/09.

8 Natural Marketing Institute. *The 2007 Organic Consumer Trends Report*. Harleysville, PA: Natural Marketing Institute, 2007.

9 Organic Trade Association. *U.S. Organic Sales Show Substantial Growth*. Greenfield, MA: Organic Trade Association. http://www.ota.com/pics/documents/short%20overview%20MMS.pdf. Accessed 4/29/09.

10 USDA Agricultural Marketing Service. National Organic Program: organic labeling and marketing information. Updated April 2008. http://www.ams.usda.gov/AMSv1.0/getfile?dDocName=STELDEV3004446&acct=nopgeninfo. Accessed 7/7/09.

11 US Department of Agriculture. *Organic Production and Handling Standards*. Washington, DC: USDA, 2008. http://www.ams.usda.gov/AMSv1.0/getfile?dDocName=STELDEV3004445. Accessed 7/22/09.

12 Ibid.; and USDA Agricultural Marketing Service. National Organic Program.

13 Food and Agriculture Organization. Dioxins in the food chain: prevention and control of contamination. April 2, 2008. http://www.fao.org/ag/AGN/agns/files/Dioxin_fact%20sheet.pdf. Accessed 7/7/09.

14 Mozaffarian D, Rimm EB. Fish intake, contaminants, and human health: evaluating the risks and the benefits. *JAMA*. 2006;296(15):1885–1899.

15 US Department of Health and Human Services and US Environmental Protection Agency. *What You Need to Know About Mercury in Fish and Shellfish*. March 2004. Publication EPA-823-R-04-005. http://www.cfsan.fda.gov/~dms/admehg3.html. Accessed 7/7/09.

16 US Food and Drug Administration. Food allergens: What you need to know. Updated June 2009. http://www.fda.gov/Food/ResourcesForYou/Consumers/ucm079311.htm. Accessed 7/7/09.

17 US Department of Health and Human Services and US Food and Drug Administration. *Hazard Analysis and Critical Control Point Principles and Application Guidelines*. Updated June 18, 2009. http://www.fda.gov/Food/FoodSafety/HazardAnalysisCriticalControlPointsHACCP/HACCPPrinciplesApplicationGuidelines/default.htm. Accessed 7/22/09.

18 US Department of Health and Human Services and US Food and Drug Administration. *Food Code 2005*. http://vm.cfsan.fda.gov/~dms/foodcode.html. Accessed 7/7/09.

19 Partnership for Food Safety Education. Fight bac! Four simple steps to food safety. http://www.fightbac.org. Accessed 7/7/09.

20 Food labeling, safe handling statements, labeling of shell eggs; refrigeration of shell eggs held for retail distribution, final rule. *Federal Register*. 2000;65:76091–76114.

21 US Environmental Protection Agency. Radiation protection: history of food irradiation. http://www.epa.gov/rpdweb00/sources/food_history.html. Accessed 7/7/09.

22 US Department of Agriculture, Food and Nutrition Service. Questions and answers on irradiated ground beef. May 29, 2003. http://www.fns.usda.gov/cga/PressReleases/2003/irradiation-qas.htm. Accessed 7/7/09.

23 Iowa State University, University Extension. Consumer questions about food irradiation. http://www.extension.iastate.edu/foodsafety/irradiation/index.cfm?articleID=25&parent=3. Accessed 7/7/09.

24 Ibid.

25 Bren L. Bacteria-eating virus approved as food additive. *FDA Consumer*. January–February 2007.

26 Analytica Research. Food crisis spurs calls for more research. Forbes.com. June 6, 2008. http://www.forbes.com/home/2008/06/05/food-genetics-agriculture-biz-cx_0606oxford.html. Accessed 7/7/09.

27 US Department of Agriculture. Biotechnology: frequently asked questions about biotechnology. Updated July 29, 2008. http://www.usda.gov/wps/portal/!ut/p/_s.7_0_A/7_0_1OB?contentidonly=true&navid=AGRICULTURE&contentid=BiotechnologyFAQs.xml. Accessed 7/7/09.

28 American Dietetic Association. Position of the American Dietetic Association: agricultural and food biotechnology. *J Am Diet Assoc*. 2006;106(2):285–293.

29 US Food and Drug Administration. FDA releases final guidance on genetically engineered animals. January 15, 2009. http://www.fda.gov/ForConsumers/ConsumerUpdates/ucm092738.htm. Accessed 7/8/09.

30 Tang G, Qin J, Dolnikowski GG, et al. Golden Rice is an effective source of vitamin A. *Am J Clin Nutr*. 2009;89(6):1776–1783.

31 Selgrade MK, Bowman CC, Ladics GS, et al. Safety assessment of biotechnology products for potential risk of food allergy: implications of new research. *Toxicol Sci*. 2009;110(1):31–39.

32 Thompson L. Are bioengineered foods safe? *FDA Consumer*. January–February 2000.

33 Health Canada. Novel foods (GMF). http://www.hc-sc.gc.ca/fn-an/gmf-agm/reg/question_answers-questions_reponses-eng.php. Accessed 7/8/09.

CHAPTER 19

World View of Nutrition

The Faces of Global Malnutrition

THINK About It

1 Have you ever experienced hunger without being able to satisfy it within a day?

2 Have you seen evidence of hunger or malnutrition in your community?

3 What can you do to help eliminate hunger in North America?

4 How do you feel about the United States sending food to impoverished nations?

Visit nutrition.jbpub.com

Each day on your way to class, you pass a soup kitchen. You look at the long line of men and women waiting to get their meals and wonder what brought them to this point. You wonder how many similar soup lines exist in your community and how many people need food assistance but can't get it. If **hunger** exists in our rich country, what about people living in poor countries?

Worldwide, more than 923 million people do not have enough to eat. This figure includes 91 million in industrialized countries, 25 million in countries in transition, and 820 million in the developing world.[1] More than half the deaths worldwide of children younger than 5 years are caused directly or indirectly by **malnutrition**, killing more than 10 million children per year.[2]

In this chapter, we look at hunger and malnutrition. By hunger we don't mean that mildly empty feeling one gets before mealtime. We mean the inability, day after day, to satisfy basic nutrition needs, the gnawing emptiness that creates a constant focus on eating and how to obtain food. In contrast to the hunger dieters feel from cutting calories, this deprivation is involuntary and unwanted.

Technically speaking, malnutrition can be any kind of unhealthy nutritional status, including the result of imbalance and excess—obesity or toxicity from oversupplementation, for example. And although we touch on obesity as an emerging issue, even in developing countries, by and large in this chapter *malnutrition* means undernutrition resulting from hunger.

Along the spectrum of malnutrition and hunger is the less extreme condition of **food insecurity**, the ongoing worry about having enough to eat. At the opposite end of the spectrum is **food security**, access to nutritionally adequate and safe food. Most people in the industrialized world are food-secure. Overabundance and obesity are the primary problems in these populations, but malnutrition is a serious problem among certain groups such as the homeless and urban poor.

hunger The internal, physiological drive to find and consume food. Unlike appetite, hunger is often experienced as a negative sensation, often manifesting as an uneasy or painful sensation; the recurrent and involuntary lack of access to food that may produce malnutrition over time.

malnutrition Failure to achieve nutrient requirements, which can impair physical and/or mental health. It may result from consuming too little food or a shortage or imbalance of key nutrients.

food insecurity (1) Limited or uncertain availability of nutritionally adequate and safe foods or (2) limited or uncertain ability to acquire acceptable foods in socially acceptable ways.

food security Access to enough food for an active, healthy life, including (1) the ready availability of nutritionally adequate and safe foods and (2) an assured ability to acquire acceptable foods in socially acceptable ways.

Malnutrition in the United States

Malnutrition and hunger are serious problems not only in developing countries, but also in the United States and other industrialized countries. Among those who suffer the worst malnutrition are the homeless, children, older adults, the working poor, and the rural poor.

The Face of American Malnutrition

In the food-rich United States, food insecurity remains a problem.[3] (See **Figure 19.1.**) It is characterized by anxiety about having enough to eat and about running out of food and having no money to purchase more. Some people actually go hungry in the United States: during 2007, 36.2 million people, including 12.4 million children, lived in one of the 13 million U.S. households experiencing food insecurity.[4]

Households that are struggling to meet basic food needs tend to follow a typical pattern as their plight worsens. First, adults worry about having enough food. Then, they stretch resources and juggle other necessities, with more of the budget going for fixed expenses than for food. The quality and variety of the diet decline. Next, the adults eat less and less often. And finally, as food becomes more limited, the children also eat less.

Surprisingly, obesity is more prevalent among low-income, food-insecure groups than among those with higher incomes. Households with little money often rely on cheaper, high-calorie foods to stave off hunger. Families try to maximize caloric intake for each dollar spent, which can lead to overconsump-

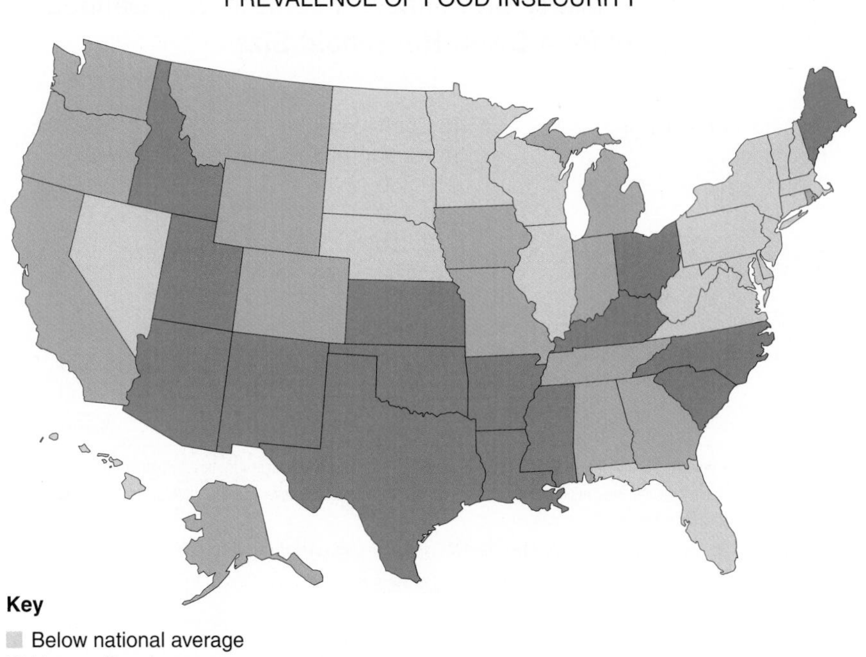

Figure 19.1 **Prevalence of food insecurity.** State-to-state differences in food insecurity reflect both differences in the makeup of state populations, such as the income, employment, age, education, and family structure of their residents, as well as differences in state characteristics, such as economic conditions, the accessibility and use of food assistance programs, and tax policies.

Source: Nord M, Andrews M, Carlsen S. *Household Food Security in the United States, 2006.* Washington, DC: USDA, 2007. Food Assistance and Nutrition Research Report 49. http://www.ers.usda.gov/publications/err49/. Accessed 4/21/09.

Quick Bite

Food Recovery and Gleaning

Each year more than 96 billion pounds of food produced in this country and half of the food produced worldwide is wasted. Programs throughout the country are rescuing much of this wholesome food and distributing it to people in need. *Gleaning* is harvesting excess food from farms, orchards, and packing houses. Perishable items are also salvaged from wholesale and retail markets; fresh foods that are wholesome but will spoil before they can be sold are given to local food pantries and meal providers. Canned goods and other staples are collected from groceries, distributors, food processors, and individual homes. Even surplus food from restaurants, caterers, and other food services is collected by some charities for local food programs.

tion of calories and a less healthful diet. Worsening food insecurity may be accompanied by progressively more disordered eating patterns, such as binge eating, which can contribute to obesity.[5]

Those who live in a state of food insecurity consume significantly fewer healthful foods and micronutrients. Although such suboptimal diets usually do not lead to overt deficiency diseases, more subtle effects are serious and costly, showing up years later as chronic illness or more immediately as reduced immune function. More illness, more medicines, more doctor visits and hospital stays, more missed days and poorer performance at school and work, poor pregnancy outcome, delayed growth and development—suboptimal nutrition contributes to them all.

Prevalence and Distribution

How much hunger and food insecurity exists in the United States? Until recently, it was difficult to measure. Estimates were based on the percentage of the population living in poverty, with the assumption that they were at risk of undernutrition. Such estimates are somewhat flawed because being at risk does not necessarily mean that people are poorly nourished. Many people with limited financial resources manage to eat well. However, under certain circumstances, such as loss of a job, people who live well above the poverty line (see Table 19.1) may be food-insecure.

The U.S. Department of Agriculture (USDA) tracks hunger with an annual **Food Security Supplement Survey**, which asks about food availability

Food Security Supplement Survey A federally funded survey that measures the prevalence and severity of food insecurity and hunger.

Table 19.1 **2009 Poverty Guidelines: Income Levels Defined as Poverty for a Given Household Size**

Persons in Family or Household	48 Contiguous States and D.C.	Alaska	Hawaii
1	$10,830	$13,530	$12,460
2	14,570	18,210	16,760
3	18,310	22,890	21,060
4	22,050	27,570	25,360
5	25,790	32,250	29,660
6	29,530	36,930	3,960
7	33,270	41,610	38,260
8	37,010	46,290	42,560
For each additional person, add	3,740	4,680	4,330

Note: Despite the limits to the use of household income as a proxy for estimating food insecurity, poverty remains an intuitively reasonable indicator. Keep in mind that, in addition to food, income must cover housing, clothing, transportation, medical care, and other essentials.

Source: Data from *Federal Register*. 2009;74(14):4199–4201. http://aspe.hhs.gov/poverty/09fedreg.shtml. Accessed 4/30/09.

and hunger in the household. (See Table 19.2.) Food insecurity is strongly associated with poverty and is interlinked with economic and social factors. Food insecurity and hunger were highest in households headed by single women with children and in Hispanic and African American households.[6] Geographically, food insecurity is more common in large cities and rural areas and, regionally, more prevalent in the South. (See **Figure 19.2.**) To combat food insecurity and hunger effectively, nutrition programs must be accompanied by social and economic efforts.

The Working Poor

Employment does not guarantee that families always have enough to eat. Often the pay is too little to lift households out of poverty, and work-related expenses, such as transportation or child care, further deplete family budgets. Food insecurity can be as common among the working poor as the unemployed. Low-paid workers may be unaware that they still qualify for food-assistance programs. However, their work hours may preclude program participation.

Migrant farm workers may have access to plenty of fresh produce but are poorly paid and may not have the money to buy other foods. Farm workers and undocumented workers (illegal aliens) may not qualify for government programs to help the poor or may not sign up for fear of deportation.

The Isolated

People in remote rural areas may live far from food resources and lack access to transportation. Other people become isolated despite living in populated cities. Even though they live in a crowded neighborhood or apartment building, they are alone and are physically or mentally unable to obtain adequate food.

Older Adults

The infirmities of age, along with feelings of vulnerability, keep some older people homebound and lonely, conditions hardly conducive to a healthy ap-

Table 19.2 **Sample Questions from the Food Security Questionnaire**

Light Food Insecurity

"We worried whether our food would run out before we got money to buy more."

Was that often, sometimes, or never true for you in the last 12 months?

"The food that we bought just didn't last and we didn't have money to get more."

Was that often, sometimes, or never true for you in the last 12 months?

Moderate Food Insecurity

In the last 12 months did you or other adults in the household ever cut the size of your meals or skip meals because there wasn't enough money for food?

In the last 12 months, were you ever hungry but didn't eat because you couldn't afford enough food?

Severe Food Insecurity

In the last 12 months did you or other adults in the household ever not eat for a whole day because there wasn't enough money for food?

(For households with children) In the last 12 months did any of the children ever not eat for a whole day because there wasn't enough money for food?

Source: Nord M, Andrews M, Carlson S. *Household Food Security in the United States, 2007*. November 2008. US Department of Agriculture Economic Research Service Report ERR-66. http://www.ers.usda.gov/Publications/ERR66/. Accessed 4/21/09.

Figure 19.2 **Americans at risk.** Americans most at risk for hunger include working poor, elders, homeless people, and children.

petite. Physical ailments may make cooking and eating difficult, while actually increasing nutrient needs. Older adults often have small incomes, with little prospect for improvement. Like others with limited resources, they cut food purchases to pay for other necessities. Although food assistance may be available, pride, shame, health conditions, or physical limitations may keep an older person from participating in such programs.

The Homeless or Inadequately Housed

The homeless rely on soup kitchens and other public programs for much of their food. Some resort to handouts and even forage through garbage. Many are mentally ill or substance abusers. The addict often has little interest in eating and may sell available food to buy more drugs. Many other people live in welfare hotels, single-room-occupancy facilities, or rooming houses without storage or cooking facilities. Budget-stretching strategies such as buying food in bulk and carefully using leftovers are out of the question for these people; as the monthly budget dwindles, they often rely on fast food meals and then soup kitchens.

Children

Perhaps no group is more vulnerable to hunger than the young. Growth and development are delayed in poorly nourished children. They get sick more often. It is harder for them to concentrate in school. Children are captives of their family circumstances; poverty and lack of nutritious food in the household are

Food Research and Action Center (FRAC) Founded in 1970 as a public interest law firm, FRAC is a nonprofit child advocacy group that works to improve public policies to eradicate hunger and undernutrition in the United States.

Electronic Benefits Transfer (EBT) Electronic delivery of government benefits by a single plastic card that allows access to food benefits at point-of-sale locations.

beyond a child's control. One-third to one-half of children and adolescents living in poverty reside in households that report inadequate access to food on one or more days per month. In the United States, roughly 14 million children and adolescents live in food-insecure households.[7]

Attacking Hunger in America

Government efforts to fight hunger began during the Great Depression of the 1930s. From that modest beginning, the USDA has grown to include 15 nutrition assistance programs that address hunger, including the Supplemental Nutrition Assistance Program (SNAP, formerly the Food Stamp Program), the School Meals Programs, and the Special Supplemental Nutrition Program for Women, Infants and Children (WIC). (See Table 19.3.) The School Lunch Program was created in 1946, after many young men had failed the physical requirements for military service in World War II because of poor nutrition.

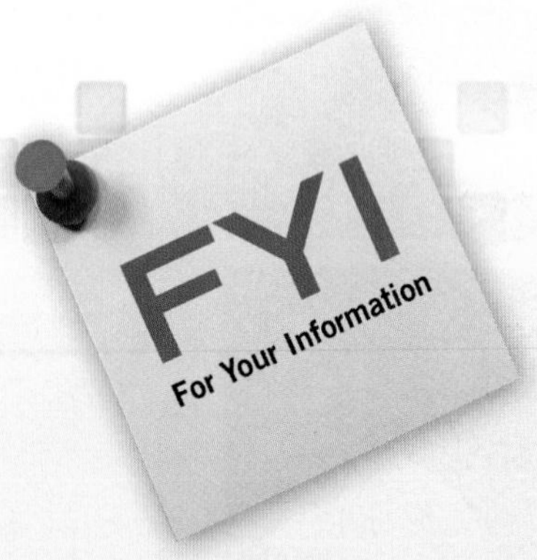

Hungry and Homeless

A shabbily dressed man slowly pushes a shopping cart along the sidewalk. It is laden with bottles and cans that he can redeem for cash. In front of a supermarket, a woman and child clutch a sign scrawled with the words "Hungry. Please help." On a street corner, a man confronts every passing car with a sign that says "Will work for food." When confronted by a homeless person, do you feel uncomfortable? Do you turn away? Or do you try to help?

Who are the homeless? Single men and families with children are the largest homeless groups. Households with children make up 23 percent of the persons using emergency shelters and transitional housing programs, whereas individuals make up 76 percent. Of the singles and unaccompanied youth, about 22 percent of the homeless are mentally ill, 37 percent are substance abusers, 13 percent are unemployed (17 percent for members of households with children), and 17 percent are veterans.[1]

Hunger in the homeless is caused by a number of interrelated factors, including low-paying jobs, unemployment and other employment-related problems, high housing costs, substance abuse, poverty or lack of income, and food stamp cuts. Family members—children and their parents—most frequently request emergency food assistance. For those in need of food assistance, 17 percent of all people and 15 percent of households with children are not receiving it.[2]

Complex challenges face the homeless, who may sleep in the streets or in emergency shelters. The homeless get food from many sources—shelters, drop-in centers, fast food restaurants, and garbage bins. Soup kitchens are a primary source of meals, yet navigating this system to obtain adequate food can be a formidable and time-consuming task. Also, although homeless people often are eligible for food stamps, they are extremely limited in their ability to store and prepare food, and few restaurants are authorized to accept food stamps.

A major public health concern for homeless people is not only whether they are getting enough to eat, but also the nutritional quality of their diet. This concern is complicated by the special needs of infants, children, and women, especially pregnant women. The diet of homeless people is often nutritionally inadequate, supplying less than half the RDA for many nutrients. Poor diets put the homeless at an increased risk for illness and chronic conditions. Pregnant women, children, and people with compromised health status are particularly vulnerable.

Homeless families and individuals rely on emergency food assistance facilities not only during emergencies, but also for extended periods. Unfortunately, these facilities are strained beyond their capacities—52 percent cannot provide an adequate quantity of food.[3] Some shelters have resorted to rationing to extend their food resources to a greater number of people. Because of a lack of resources, over half may be forced to turn people away. Addressing hunger is a top priority. Once access to food is secure, obtaining a nutritionally adequate diet and dealing with health issues become reasonable goals.

1 US Conference of Mayors. *A Status Report on Hunger and Homelessness in America's Cities: A 23-City Survey.* December 2007. http://www.usmayors.org/HHSurvey2007/hhsurvey07.pdf. Accessed 4/26/09.

2 Ibid.

3 Ibid.

The Food Stamp Program was greatly expanded in the early 1970s following an exposé of hunger in Appalachia and the Mississippi Delta and the television documentary "Hunger in America." The federal government initiated WIC in the 1970s as a response to concerns about maternal and child health. Other government programs have since been added to meet the special needs of the young, the elderly, the disadvantaged, and the disabled.

THINK About It 3

The **Food Research and Action Center (FRAC)** is a national nonprofit advocacy group that fights hunger and undernutrition at the national, state, and local levels. Nonprofit community agencies, charities, religious organizations, and similar groups create a large network of food pantries, soup kitchens, and services for home-delivered meals. Most of the federal government's programs for direct distribution of food or meals operate at the local level through these networks. Both laypeople and professionals, such as dietitians, work in these programs, either as volunteers or as staff, to fight hunger and malnutrition.

Food assistance programs have greatly reduced the prevalence of hunger, but not of food insecurity, which requires social and economic change. The following are among the federal government's most far-reaching programs against hunger.

The Supplemental Nutrition Assistance Program

On October 1, 2008, the Food Stamp Program was renamed the Supplemental Nutrition Assistance Program (SNAP). SNAP is our main food security program. Recipients can use benefits to purchase food, but not nonfood items such as paper goods, pet food, and alcohol. The benefit amount varies according to household size and income level.

Actually, the term *food stamp* is becoming a misnomer. Almost half of the people who receive benefits use **Electronic Benefits Transfer (EBT)** cards. (See **Figure 19.3**.) The card resembles and functions like a debit card. Each month the household's benefit amount is credited to the card, which is then used at participating retailers and farmers' markets.

Special Supplemental Nutrition Program for Women, Infants and Children

The WIC program provides food to pregnant and breastfeeding women, infants, and preschoolers. More than 8.2 million women and children received WIC benefits in 2008.[8] To be eligible for WIC services, the participant must be at nutritional risk, and household income must be less than the federal definition of poverty level. For a family of four in fiscal year 2008–2009, the eligibility cut-off point was an annual income of no more than $39,220.[9]

Nutrition assessment and nutrition education are important components of the WIC program. Participants receive vouchers, or "checks," for specific categories of healthful foods, and they "cash" them at participating grocery stores. Unlike food stamps, the amount of the WIC benefit varies with nutritional need, not income.

National School Lunch Program

The National School Lunch Program ensures that children in primary and secondary schools receive at least one healthful meal every school day (supplemented in many areas by the School Breakfast Program). For a family of four in the year 2008–2009, the child's meals were free if the household income was less than $27,560; the meals were reduced in price if household income was less than $39,220.[10] The lunch must provide one-third or more of dietary

Table 19.3 USDA Food and Nutrition Service Food Assistance Programs

Supplemental Nutrition Assistance Program (SNAP)
Women, Infants and Children (WIC) Program
Farmers' Market Nutrition Program
Senior Farmers' Market Nutrition Program
School meals
National School Lunch Program (NSLP)
School Breakfast Program (SBP)
Fresh Fruit and Vegetable Program
Special Milk Program
Team Nutrition
Summer Food Service Program (SFSP)
Child and Adult Food Care Program (CACFP)
Food assistance for disaster relief
Food distribution
Schools/Child Nutrition Commodity Program
Food Distribution on Indian Reservations (FDPIR)
Nutrition Services Incentive Program
The Emergency Food Assistance Program (TEFAP)

Source: Data from USDA Food and Nutrition Service. Food assistance programs. http://www.fns.usda.gov/fns/. Accessed 4/22/09.

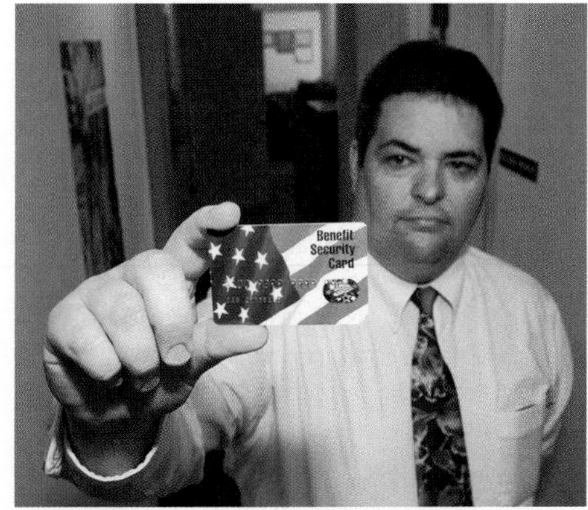

Figure 19.3 Electronic Benefits Transfer card. Electronic Benefits Transfer (EBT) is an electronic system that allows recipients to authorize transfer of their government benefits from a federal account to a retailer account to pay for products received.

Figure 19.4 National School Lunch Program.

requirements for key nutrients. The program operates in more than 101,000 public and nonprofit private schools and residential child-care institutions. It provides nutritionally balanced, low-cost or free lunches to more than 30.5 million children each school day.[11] (See **Figure 19.4**.)

Child and Adult Care Food Program

The **Child and Adult Care Food Program** provides funds for children's meals and snacks at nonprofit licensed child-care centers, day care homes, after-school programs, and similar settings. Nutritious meals for elderly or disabled people are also funded at nonprofit facilities such as adult day care centers and recreation centers.

Feeding America

Feeding America, formerly known as America's Second Harvest, is the largest charitable hunger-relief organization in the United States. This network of more than 200 member food banks and food-rescue organizations secures and distributes more than 2 billion pounds of donated food and groceries throughout the United States. Each year, Feeding America provides food assistance to more than 25 million hungry people, including 9 million children and nearly 3 million seniors.[12]

Feeding America focuses on nutritious products such as fresh produce, seafood, meat, cereal, rice, and pasta. The organization also works to effect changes in public attitudes and laws that assist Americans who are hungry or at risk of being hungry. Feeding America also works to educate the general public and keep them informed about hunger in America.

Child and Adult Care Food Program A federally funded program that reimburses approved family child-care providers for USDA-approved foods served to preschool children; it also provides funds for meals and snacks served at after-school programs for school-age children and to adult day care centers serving chronically impaired adults or people over age 60.

Feeding America The largest charitable hunger-relief organization in the United States. Its mission is to feed America's hungry through a nationwide network of member food banks and to engage the country in the fight to end hunger.

Key Concepts *Although overt malnutrition in the United States is uncommon, more than 13 million American households experience food insecurity at some time during the year. Food insecurity and hunger are interlinked with poverty. Groups at risk include the working poor, the isolated, the homeless, children, and elders. A large network of individual volunteers, nonprofit agencies, and charities, together with major government programs such as SNAP, WIC, and the School Lunch Program, have done much to reduce hunger. However, food insecurity, which continues among an unacceptably large number of people, must be overcome by social and economic improvements. Feeding America is the largest charitable hunger-relief organization in the United States.*

Malnutrition in the Developing World

"Proper nutrition and health are fundamental human rights," according to the **World Health Organization (WHO)**. "Nutrition is a cornerstone that affects and defines the health of all people, rich and poor. It paves the way for us to grow, develop, work, play, resist infection and aspire to realization of our fullest potential as individuals and societies. Conversely, malnutrition makes us all more vulnerable to disease and premature death."[13]

Hunger is a global problem. (See **Figure 19.5**.) "It is debilitating. Sometimes it is deadly. It blights the lives of all who are affected and undermines national economies and development processes where it is found on a large
THINK About It 4 scale," says the **Food and Agriculture Organization (FAO)** of the United Nations.[14]

"The world food system is in trouble and the hot spots of food risks will be where high food prices combine with shocks from weather or political crises. These are recipes for disaster," notes Joachim von Braun, the director general of the International Food Policy Research Institute.[15]

World Health Organization (WHO) A global organization that directs and coordinates international health work. Its goal is the attainment by all peoples of the highest possible level of health, defined as a state of complete physical, mental, and social well-being and not merely the absence of disease or infirmity.

Food and Agriculture Organization (FAO) The largest autonomous UN agency; the FAO works to alleviate poverty and hunger by promoting agricultural development, improved nutrition, and the pursuit of food security.

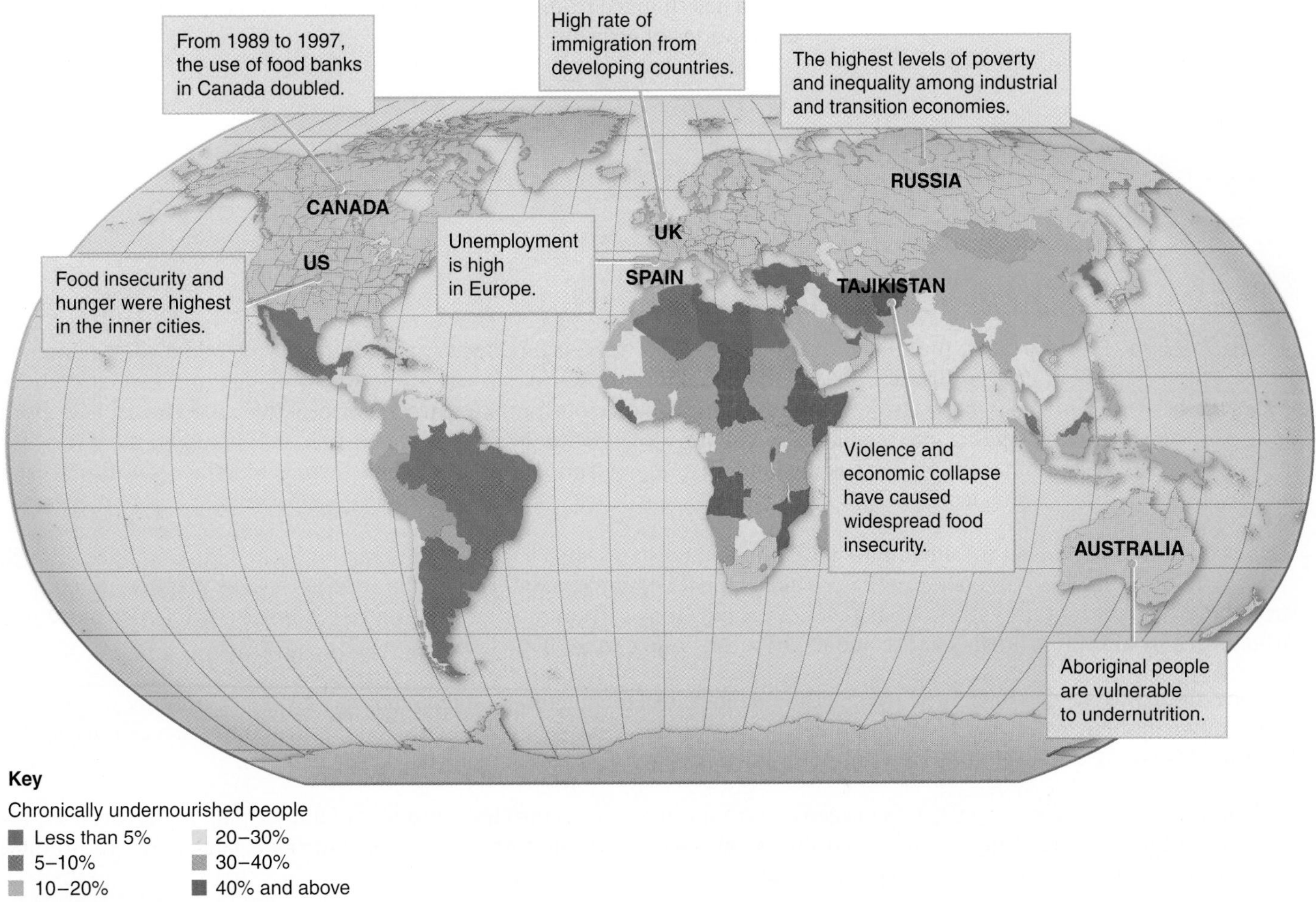

Figure 19.5 **Global hunger.** Although the proportion of the world's population that is chronically undernourished has been decreasing over the last few decades, undernutrition is still widespread, particularly in certain regions. Furthermore, projections suggest that there will be little change in the absolute number of chronically undernourished people.

Source: Food and Agriculture Organization. Hunger. http://www.fao.org/hunger/en.

The World Food Equation

Income growth, climate change, high energy prices, globalization, and urbanization are transforming food consumption. Soaring food prices are hitting the world's most vulnerable—those who must spend a substantial part of their income on food. Today, the world consumes more than it produces, and the cost of food has been rising steadily, reversing a downward trend of more than four decades. Food stocks are at a low, and the food supply is vulnerable to unpredictable factors, such as adverse weather. During a disaster, food prices rise rapidly while family incomes decline, thus producing an economic mismatch that is the root cause of most famines.[16]

Global Economic Boom

Some developing countries are undergoing rapid economic expansion. People in emerging economies, such as China, India, Brazil, and at least 10 African countries, have become more prosperous and are changing their diets. Since 1990, China has nearly doubled its consumption of meat, fish, and dairy products. Because it takes 7 pounds of grain to produce 1 pound of meat, this shift removes grain from the global marketplace. In just the past few years, China has changed from being one of the largest corn exporters to becoming an importer of corn.[17]

Going Green

Can Chocolate Help the Planet?

Cacao trees, the source of chocolate, used to be a thriving industry in the Mata Atlantica, a rainforest area of eastern Brazil. But now the shrinking price of chocolate in the world market and several decades of plant disease are working against chocolate production. The precious rainforest trees that produce cacao beans have been marked for destruction by logging interests. The short-sighted logging interests see more profit in cutting down these trees for wood, or burning them to make room for pasture land, than in cultivating the cacao. Thus, there is little incentive for farmers to cultivate cacao beans for chocolate.

But how does that affect the environment? Dario Anhert, a researcher at the University of Santa Cruz in eastern Brazil, suggests that the chocolate industry can help reduce global climate change. These rainforest trees store massive amounts of carbon and thus prevent the carbon from getting into the air as carbon dioxide. When a tree is burned it releases the stored carbon, thereby affecting climate change and contributing to a warmer planet.

One alternative to destroying the trees is cabruca farming: this method entails planting cacao trees among other trees, cutting down just a few of the tall rainforest trees, and planting the mid-height cacao trees underneath. Inside a cabruca forest, the ground is covered in a thick layer of composting leaves. It's moist, shady, and cool in the cabruca.

Planting inside the forest means fewer cacao trees to the acre, and in turn less production. But farming in the forest avoids drawbacks other farmers struggle with when they grow cacao trees on more open land. On open land they can produce greater volume, but have far more problems, including disease and more insects.

There's also an expanding market for environmentally friendly chocolate. Some forest farmers have been able to get a premium for their crop. Anhert hopes that cabruca can become part of the carbon credit market. Farmers would then get money for preserving forest trees, as well as for their chocolate. Anhert hopes to persuade farmers to preserve rainforest ecosystems and provide a viable, long-term economic opportunity with the chocolate option. A complicated process—but yes, producing chocolate in the rainforest can contribute to a better planet.

Oil Prices and Biofuels

Record oil prices have driven up costs along the entire food production chain—from fertilizer to diesel for tilling, planting, and harvesting to storage and shipping. High oil prices also make food stocks a more attractive alternative fuel. Production of biodiesel and other biofuels is pressuring the global markets for wheat, corn, sugar, oil-containing seeds, cassava, palm oil, and other crops.

Global Climate Change and Severe Weather Events

As a consequence of climate change, farmers will face growing unpredictability and variability in water supplies and increasing frequency of droughts and floods. However, these impacts will vary tremendously from place to place. Scientists expect that elevated temperatures will benefit agriculture in the northern latitudes, whereas large parts of the arid and semi-arid tropics will face declining rainfall and runoff—an ominous trend for the mostly food-insecure countries located there.[18]

Water is fundamental to the stability of global food production. Reliable access to water increases agricultural yields, and a lack of sustainable water management places global food security at risk. In developing countries, drought is the single most common natural cause of severe food shortages. Floods are another major cause of food emergencies. To the extent that climate change increases rainfall variability and the frequency of extreme weather events, it will threaten food security.

The Fight Against Global Hunger

International relief agencies and government programs help combat food shortages and hunger. Some U.S. agencies involved in the fight against global hunger are the USDA; the U.S. State Department, through its Agency for International Development; and the Centers for Disease Control and Prevention (CDC), through the Center for Communicable Diseases. These agencies offer both short-term emergency efforts and long-term programs for repair and rebuilding.

Long-term solutions to hunger are tremendously complex; they require economic, political, and social change, as well as improvements in nutrition, food production, and environmental safeguards. As you study the critical nutrient deficiencies in the developing world, you will see that poverty, infection, poor sanitation, and social upheaval interact with nutrient shortages to bring about these deficiencies.

Social and Economic Factors

Poverty, overpopulation, and migration to overcrowded cities are closely interrelated causes of hunger. (See **Figure 19.6**.) Each situation worsens the effects of the others as they steadily drive a population toward malnutrition.

Poverty

Poverty, hunger, and malnutrition stalk one another in a vicious circle, compromising health and wreaking havoc on the development of entire countries and regions. Nearly 30 percent of the global population—especially those in developing countries—bear this triple burden.[19]

Poverty is the most important underlying reason for chronic hunger. Obviously, it limits access to food. It limits purchase of farming supplies to

Academy of Nutrition and Dietetics

Addressing World Hunger, Malnutrition, and Food Insecurity

It is the position of the Academy of Nutrition and Dietetics that access to adequate amounts of safe, nutritious, and culturally appropriate food at all times is a fundamental human right. Hunger continues to be a worldwide problem of staggering proportions. The Association supports programs and encourages practices that combat hunger and malnutrition, produce food security, promote self-sufficiency, and are environmentally and economically sustainable.

Source: Position of the American Dietetic Association: addressing world hunger, malnutrition, and food insecurity. *J Am Diet Assoc.* 2003;103(8):1046–1057. Copyright © 2003. Reprinted with permission from Elsevier.

Quick Bite

Where Were You Born?

Your survival was greatly influenced by the location of your birth. Angola has the highest infant mortality rate (195 deaths per 1,000 live births), according to estimates for 2000. Other countries with high infant mortality rates include Sierra Leone (148 per 1,000), Afghanistan (149 per 1,000), and Liberia (134 per 1,000). At the other end of the spectrum is Finland (4 per 1,000). Canada (5 per 1,000) has a lower infant mortality rate than the United States (7 per 1,000).

Quick Bite

World Food Summit Goals: Can We Meet the Challenge?

The World Food Summit has pledged to halve the number of undernourished people by 2015. Although the proportion of malnourished people has declined, the number of hungry people has remained virtually unchanged since 1990–1992. To meet the summit's 2015 goal, the world must reduce the number of hungry people by 31 million annually—10 times the reduction achieved since 1990–1992.

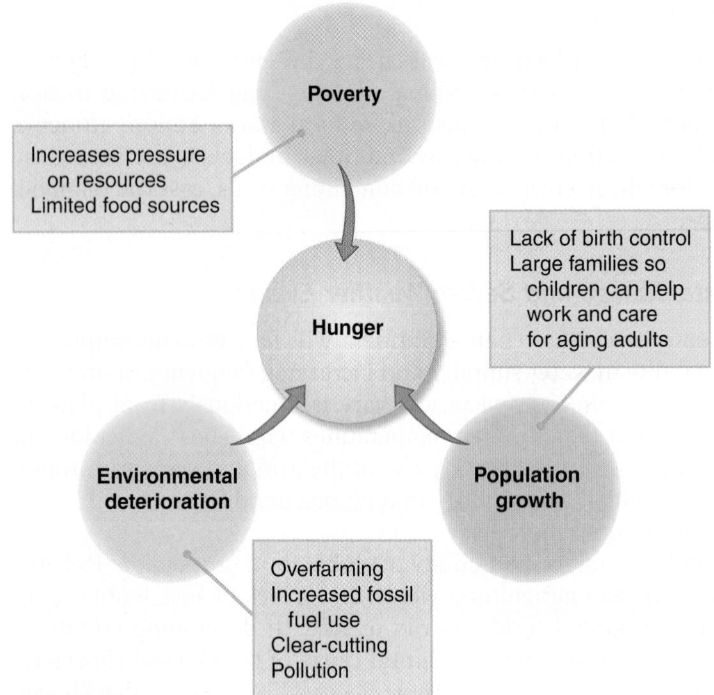

Figure 19.6 **Major problems causing hunger.** Poverty, population growth, and environmental degradation interact to make hunger worse.

grow food, boats and equipment to fish, and storage equipment to prevent spoilage. It limits access to medical care. It compromises sanitation efforts. It discourages education and the chance for personal advancement.

For nations, poverty means paralyzed economic development and too few jobs; inadequate investments in infrastructure and basic housing; and too few resources to train doctors, nutritionists, nurses, and other health care workers.

Quick Bite

Food Supply Versus Food Safety

Sometimes obtaining food is more important than safety. Food from street vendors is important in the diets of many urban populations, particularly the socially disadvantaged. Health authorities responsible for food safety should balance their risk management with issues of food availability and hunger. Rigorous application of codes and regulations suited to larger and permanent food service establishments may cause the disappearance of the street vendors, with consequent aggravation of hunger and malnutrition. WHO encourages the development of regulations that empower vendors to take greater responsibility for the preparation of safe food.

Population Growth

Population growth in many regions is outstripping gains in food production, education, employment, health care, and economic progress. The burgeoning numbers stress limited environmental resources, contributing to environmental degradation and pollution. In rural areas where farmland is limited, each small parcel of family land is subdivided with each generation, until there is too little land to support each family.

You might think that poverty would pressure parents to limit family size, but ironically, poverty and sickness do just the reverse. Where child mortality rates are high, having many babies is a guarantee some children will survive. In countries that have no economic safeguards for disability, unemployment, or old age, parents consider their children a source of security and support in times of need. Many other factors contribute to large families, from ignorance of birth control methods to the attitude that big families reflect the father's masculinity. Some political groups also encourage high birth rates and fast population growth as a way to achieve political or military dominance.

To slow population growth, socioeconomic and cultural changes that make smaller family size acceptable, even desirable, must accompany access to birth control.

Urbanization

Urbanization is a worldwide trend. As rural lands become too crowded or exhausted farmland no longer supports good crops, rural people migrate to the city in hopes of jobs and a better life. Unfortunately, in fast-growing cities, social disorder, sanitary conditions, and living standards may be much worse. Hunting, fishing, foraging, and gardening—sources of accessible food in the rural setting—are seldom an option in the city. Breastfeeding becomes impractical for many mothers who could nurse their babies while doing farm work, but cannot do so with jobs in the city.

Infection and Disease

Infection interacts with malnutrition, each making its victim more vulnerable to the other, each making the other worse, in a downward spiral. Nutrient deficiencies lower resistance to infections. In turn, the fever of infection speeds depletion of calories and nutrients. Other symptoms (e.g., loss of appetite, weakness, nausea, and mouth lesions) limit ability to eat. Infectious diarrhea is especially dangerous, quickly wasting what few nutrients are consumed; infants and young children can die quickly from loss of electrolytes. Programs that prevent or control infection (e.g., immunizations, improvements in hygiene and sanitation, safe water supplies, and access to medicine and medical care) all indirectly improve nutrition status.

Infection with the human immunodeficiency virus (HIV) provides a dramatic demonstration of the interaction between malnutrition and infection. Among those who are afflicted, the infection progresses fastest in people who are poorly nourished. Severe loss of weight and muscle is a hallmark of the advanced disease, acquired immune deficiency syndrome (AIDS). An estimated 33.2 million people are infected with HIV, and sub-Saharan Africa continues to be the region most affected by the AIDS pandemic. More than two of three adults and 90 percent of children infected with HIV live in this region.[20] Globally, about one-third of adults living with HIV are young people aged 15 to 24 years.

Political Disruptions

Social upheavals and natural disasters such as floods and drought can leave famine in their wake. The resulting displacement of populations and inequitable food distribution usually lead to hunger and malnutrition.

War

Whereas poverty is the underlying cause of chronic mild to moderate malnutrition, war and its aftermath cause severe malnutrition and famine. War diverts limited financial resources from development efforts to expenditures for fighting and destruction. Men and women no longer farm, fish, or bring home a paycheck—they are in the army. Households become fatherless and sometimes motherless, often permanently. Crops and croplands are destroyed, along with irrigation systems, food-processing facilities, and transportation infrastructure, which may have taken decades to develop.

Refugees

Masses of refugees—many very young, old, infirm, and already weakened by chronic hunger—find themselves without the basic elements of sustenance. The resulting famine has become an all too common sight on the evening news.

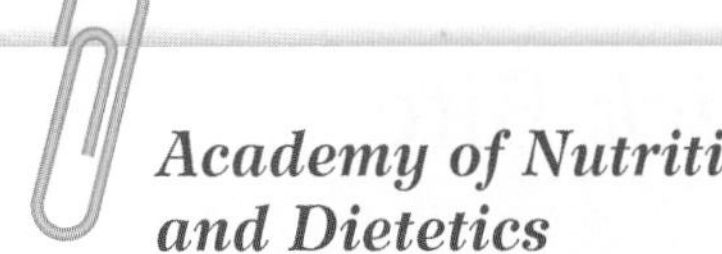

Academy of Nutrition and Dietetics

Nutrition Intervention in the Care of Persons with Human Immunodeficiency Virus Infection

It is the position of the Academy of Nutrition and Dietetics and Dietitians of Canada that efforts to optimize nutritional status, including medical nutrition therapy, assurance of food and nutrition security, and nutrition education, are essential components of the total health care available to people with human immunodeficiency virus infection throughout the continuum of care.

Source: Position of the American Dietetic Association and the Dietitians of Canada: nutrition intervention in the care of persons with human immunodeficiency virus infection. *J Am Diet Assoc.* 2004;104(9):1425–1441. Copyright © 2004. Reprinted with permission from Elsevier.

Quick Bite

Rehydration Therapy for Diarrhea

Simple and inexpensive packets of carbohydrate and salts diluted with sterile water replace lost fluids and electrolytes. These packets are saving thousands of people each year.

Quick Bite

Accidental Solution

Sometimes a solution to undernutrition is not planned. On October 9, 1998, the *Wall Street Journal* carried the headline "In Guatemala, Organic Farms Sprout on Civil War Turf." During the country's 35-year civil war, local farmers abandoned their land. As the farmlands reverted to jungle and pesticide levels diminished, wild spices thrived. With the trend for "organic" spices, coffee, and natural dyes, the premium prices commanded by these new crops could be significant for the farmers' incomes.

Quick Bite

Emergency Management
Imagine a civil war in a developing country that displaces tens of thousands of people. What are the most important measures for preventing sickness and death among these refugees? Protection from violence heads the list, closely followed by adequate food rations, clean water and sanitation, diarrheal disease control, measles immunization, and maternal and child health care.

International relief agencies have learned to respond to these emergencies quickly and with great determination, but logistic difficulties (e.g., mobilizing manpower, obtaining foods, transporting supplies, setting up feeding stations) may slow relief until it is too late for the sickest or weakest. Some refugee groups are inaccessible, hidden, or intentionally kept hungry as part of a political plan; emergency food may never reach many of them.

Sanctions

International sanctions and embargoes create food shortages, both directly and indirectly, by limiting access to agricultural supplies, fuel, and food-processing supplies. Some people argue that shortages created by embargoes hurt powerless people rather than government officials; others say that such actions are preferable to war.

Floods, Droughts, Mudslides, and Hurricanes

Many countries are not equipped to deal with food shortages, water and food sanitation concerns, and hunger caused by disruptions in food supply and distribution resulting from natural disasters. International relief agencies and other governments step in to help when possible. Emergency relief efforts in

AIDS and Malnutrition

Like other infections, HIV interacts with malnutrition in a vicious, devastating cycle. Left untreated, HIV infection progresses to acquired immunodeficiency syndrome (AIDS). The virus attacks by destroying its victim's immune system. When a person is unable to fight infections and malignancies, disease quickly depletes marginal nutrient stores, speeding the way to severe malnutrition and death. But malnutrition and HIV interact on several other levels, as well:

- Poor nutrition contributes to declining immune function, HIV progression, and further health deterioration.[1]
- HIV can be transmitted to infants in breast milk; but in impoverished regions, substitutions for breast milk can lead to increased infantile diarrhea, malnutrition, and death.
- AIDS leaves mothers too weak to feed and care for their children. Eventually AIDS turns children into orphans.
- AIDS disables parents so they cannot work to support and feed their families.
- Among those who are afflicted, the infection progresses faster in people who are poorly nourished.[2]
- Weight loss and muscle wasting in an infected person are associated with faster progression of HIV disease and AIDS.[3]
- Infections that accompany AIDS cause fever and diarrhea, making malnutrition worse. Nausea and loss of appetite also contribute to malnutrition.
- Severe protein-energy malnutrition (PEM) is characteristic of untreated AIDS and frequently the ultimate cause of death.

As of 2004, 39.4 million people were living with HIV. Sub-Saharan Africa had 25.4 million people infected with HIV. Southeast Asia had 8.2 million people infected with HIV, Latin America had 1.7 million, and Eastern Europe and Central Asia had 1.4 million.[4] Without treatment or a cure, these people are doomed to death, usually within 10 years of the initial infection. The fate of severe PEM in millions of people appears unavoidable. If we do not arrest the continued transmission of HIV, the number of PEM victims will climb even higher.

1 Semba RD, Miotti PG, Chiphangwi JD. Maternal vitamin A deficiency and mother-to-child transmission of HIV-1. *Lancet.* 1994;343:1593–1597.
2 UNAIDS. *Global Facts and Figures.* Geneva, Switzerland: UNAIDS, 2005.
3 Coodley GO, Loveless MO, Merrill TM. The HIV wasting syndrome: a review. *J Acq Immune Def Syndr.* 1994;7:681–694.
4 UNAIDS. *Global Facts and Figures.*

the United States that include food distribution have taken more of a prominent role in disaster preparedness. In the wake of terrorist attacks such as those on September 11, 2001, and natural disasters such as Hurricane Katrina, the U.S. military and both domestic and international relief agencies have reevaluated their level of preparedness to respond to these types of emergencies. Some U.S. agencies involved are the U.S. military, the USDA, the U.S. State Department through its Agency for International Development, the Federal Emergency Management Agency (FEMA), and the CDC through the Center for Communicable Diseases. These agencies offer both short-term emergency efforts and long-term programs for repair and rebuilding.

Quick Bite

Know Thine Enemy

Crops have a critical role in feeding the world's burgeoning population. "Responsible biotechnology is not the enemy; starvation is," says former President Jimmy Carter.

Agriculture and Environment: A Tricky Balance

Advances in agriculture increase food supplies and reduce food costs. Because the economies of most developing countries are based on agriculture, improvements boost rural incomes and buying power, increase demand for agricultural labor, stimulate commerce among small vendors and food processors, and ultimately help a nation's economy.

Dramatic gains in agricultural productivity took place in the 1960s and 1970s with the development of new seed varieties, especially rice and corn. The seeds greatly increased crop yields. Expectations were so strong that these seeds would finally solve the world's food shortage that their development and use was dubbed the "Green Revolution." Despite its successes, the Green Revolution had limitations. The seeds required irrigation and heavy use of pesticides and fertilizers, which poor farmers could not afford. The farming techniques were sometimes hard on the environment. Proponents of agricultural biotechnology see it as another step along the continuum of plant-breeding techniques and a promising tool to increase crop production. Some uses of biotechnology are well accepted—for example, diagnostic kits that identify plants and insects by DNA and tissue culture for plant reproduction, a technique already in widespread commercial use. More controversial is the modification of plant genetic material. The technology has the potential to improve plants' resistance to disease, tolerance to adverse conditions, yield, and nutritional quality. Chapter 18, "Food Safety and Technology," describes the techniques and controversies surrounding this application of biotechnology.

At the other end of the technology spectrum is a renewed appreciation and conservation of traditional seed varieties, those selected over the generations by local farmers because they do well in local conditions. In developing countries, farmers typically save some of these seeds at each harvest to use in the next planting season. The seeds grow well in the regions where they've evolved, whereas imported seeds, no matter how carefully bred, often fail.

In addition to seed selection, strategies to optimize agriculture include irrigation, soil preparation, improved planting and harvest methods, erosion prevention, fertilization, pest control, and flood control. The methods should be affordable, suitable for the level of local development, and protective of the environment. For example, where there is an abundant supply of willing farm laborers and gasoline is expensive, using heavy-duty farm machinery makes little sense. Other examples include mulching to conserve water and control weeds, and using manure (after composting to kill pathogens) to reduce the need for fertilizer.

Quick Bite

Vaccine Veggies

Genetic engineers are experimenting with inserting vaccine molecules into plants. William Landridge, a molecular biologist at the Loma Linda University School of Medicine in California, has successfully added anti–cholera toxin genes to the potato. Potatoes are a dietary staple in Peru, Bolivia, and India, where cholera causes dehydrating diarrhea and death. Every year, 2.2 million children die from dehydration due to diarrhea. Edible vaccines could overcome the problems of refrigeration and distribution that impede vaccination by injection. Next on the menu? Bananas and tomatoes may be even more effective vehicles than potatoes.

Environmental Degradation

Environmental degradation is a growing concern in both the developing and the industrialized world. In developing countries, there is pressure for more

Quick Bite

Who Produces the World's Soybeans?

Before 1900, the soybean was rarely grown in the United States. Today, it is the largest American crop. The United States produces 75 percent of the world's soybeans.

land to support rapidly expanding populations. In industrialized countries, there is pressure from the affluent for more land, more houses, larger properties, more recreation areas, and so on. Residents of the industrialized world consume vast amounts of resources (e.g., water, fuel, wood, paper, textiles, and food) without a thought and often without making the small effort to conserve or recycle. Residents of the developing world consume much less per person, but the impact of their numbers is greater.

Environmental degradation has nutritional consequences because it threatens food production. Urbanization and the expansion of cities reduce acreage available for farming. The pressure to supply food to growing populations leads to clear-cutting marginal land, eventually eroding hilly terrain or quickly exhausting fragile rainforest soils. Overdependence on irrigation can drain water, eventually creating deserts. The destruction of vast areas of natural ground cover can lead to global climate changes. Overuse of pesticides and fertilizers pollutes waterways, destroying fish and seafood.

Key Concepts *Despite gains in eradicating malnutrition, 30 percent of the people in the developing world continue to suffer from chronic hunger. Factors that allow hunger to continue include rising food prices, poverty, poor sanitation, urbanization, and inefficient food distribution. Infection, especially AIDS, rapid population growth, wars, and environmental degradation threaten to reverse hard-won gains.*

Malnutrition: Its Nature, Its Victims, and Its Eradication

Previous chapters discussed the diseases of nutritional deficiency. Most of these diseases exist throughout the developing world, but seldom in isolation. Typically, the malnourished person has two or more coexisting deficiencies, each increasing the severity of the other. Keep the potential for this deadly synergy in mind as we discuss some of the major categories of malnutrition.

Tough Choices

Imagine you live in a poor village of a developing country. How would you make these choices?

- You've learned you must boil your drinking water to prevent diarrhea. But that means cutting young trees for firewood. You recently planted those trees to stop erosion. What do you do?
- You've recently given birth to your fourth child. Your husband was injured in an accident and is unable to work. But you can work at a nearby factory and use your pay to buy food and clothes for the older children. How would you feed the new baby?
- Your small herd of goats provides milk for your young children. You like the goats because they can survive in the rough, hilly countryside. But the goats are overgrazing the grasses on the hillside. What can you do?
- Insects have destroyed your crop. In the past, you burned fields after harvest to control insects, but you've learned that "slash and burn" is bad for the land. You've thought about using a chemical pesticide, but it is too expensive. You could clear the jungle for another growing field. Do you have other choices? What should you do?
- You can grow either vegetables to feed your family or a "cash crop" to sell for export. The cash crop would help pay for medicine and other necessities. Which should you grow?

Protein-Energy Malnutrition

As you learned in Chapter 6, "Proteins and Amino Acids," lack of protein and also energy can have devastating consequences, especially on the young. In kwashiorkor, the body and face swell with excess fluid, the hair turns wispy and red, and a terrible rash develops; without treatment, the person dies. Marasmus paints an even more dramatic picture of sunken eyes, shriveled limbs, and a clearly visible outline of the skeleton; it is as deadly as kwashiorkor.

Protein-energy malnutrition (PEM) is by far the most lethal form of malnutrition, and children are its most visible victims.[21] Their rapid growth creates high nutrient demands, leaving them especially vulnerable to inappropriate food distribution in the family, inappropriate infant and child feeding practices, and interactions of infection with malnutrition. PEM typically develops after a child is weaned from the breast. Men in the household may have priority for nutritious food. In big families, the young child must also compete for food with many siblings.

In the developing world, breastfeeding is almost always essential to an infant's survival. Inappropriate bottle-feeding puts a baby at grave risk. Relative to income, formula is usually very expensive and is often diluted to make it "stretch." Contaminated water and lack of other hygienic requirements for bottle preparation cause diarrhea. The combination of diarrhea and nutritional deficiency from watered-down formula is often fatal.

A tremendous educational effort, including promotion of breastfeeding, has reduced the global prevalence and severity of infant and childhood PEM. Severe PEM typified by kwashiorkor or marasmus has become more sporadic, occurring mainly as a result of war or natural disaster. However, mild to moderate PEM continues to pose a grave problem in the developing world, putting children at risk of delayed growth, impaired psychological development, and the deadly interactions of disease and malnutrition.

Iodine Deficiency Disorders

Iodine deficiency is the world's most common cause of preventable brain damage and one of the main causes of impaired cognitive development in children.[22] Its impairment of intellectual ability and work performance is potentially so widespread that **iodine deficiency disorders (IDD)** can actually slow a nation's social and economic development.

Iodine deficiency is most devastating during pregnancy, causing spontaneous abortions, stillbirths, and birth defects, including cretinism, a disease of mental retardation that is often severe. Deafness and spastic paralysis are likely to accompany the retardation. In regions of Africa, dwarfism also occurs where diets rich in goitrogen-containing vegetables (e.g., cassava or cabbage) make the deficiency worse. Moreover, iodine deficiency is damaging at all ages, limiting mental development in infants and children and producing apathy and marginal mental function in adults.

Iodine deficiency disorders are endemic throughout much of the developing world where the soil is low in iodine. These areas typically are mountainous or far from the oceans. They often are isolated and impoverished. Although imported food is a potential source of iodine, it often is not consumed; according to WHO reports, 54 countries are still iodine-deficient.[23] The WHO estimates that 36.5 percent (285 million) of school-aged children have insufficient iodine intake. Extrapolating this to the general population, they estimate that nearly 2 billion people worldwide do not consume sufficient iodine for good health.[24] (See **Figure 19.7**.)

Disturbing though these figures may be, great strides have been made in IDD prevention, mainly through iodizing salt. More than two-thirds of

Quick Bite

Is Breastfeeding Always Best?

An HIV-positive mother can transmit the virus to her baby through breast milk. HIV-positive women whose infants were spared HIV transmission during pregnancy face the dilemma of how to feed those babies. In developing countries, the WHO is working to prevent HIV transmission through breastfeeding while continuing to protect, promote, and support breastfeeding as the best way to feed babies of women who are HIV negative and women who do not know their status. Unfortunately, alternatives such as formula feeding are expensive, carry the risk of food poisoning from contaminated water, and often carry a social stigma.

iodine deficiency disorders (IDD) A wide range of disorders due to iodine deficiency that affect growth and development.

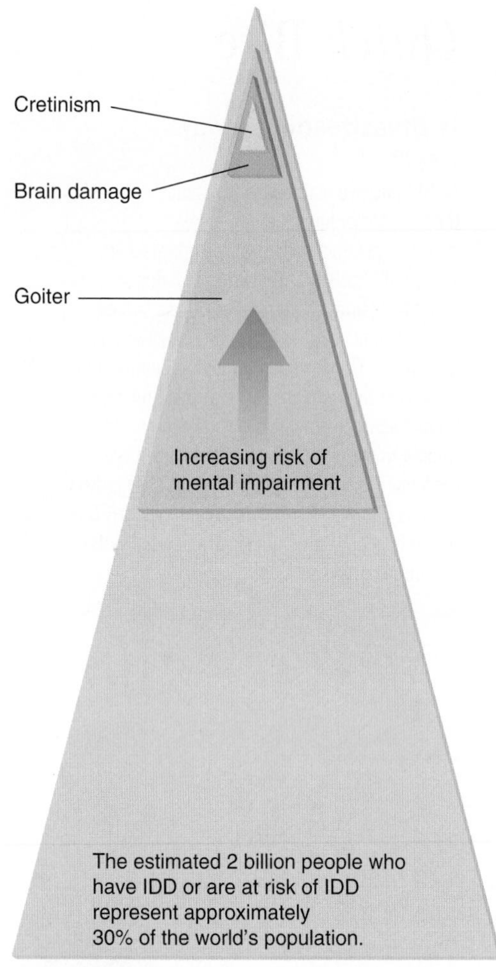
Cretinism
Brain damage
Goiter
Increasing risk of mental impairment
The estimated 2 billion people who have IDD or are at risk of IDD represent approximately 30% of the world's population.

Figure 19.7 **The toll of iodine deficiency.** Iodine deficiency remains the single greatest cause of preventable brain damage and mental retardation worldwide.

Source: Data compiled from Food and Agriculture Organization of the United Nations, Luxembourg Income Study; First World Hunger, USDA; Second Harvest. http://www.fao.org/es/ess/faostat/foodsecurity/FSMap/map14_en.htm.

households in IDD-affected countries now use iodized salt,[25] and in countries with salt iodization programs in place for five years or more, the improvement in iodine status has been dramatic. The cost is merely 5 cents per person per year.

Vitamin A Deficiency

Vitamin A deficiency is the leading cause of preventable blindness in children. It also increases the risk of disease and death from severe infections. In pregnant women, vitamin A deficiency causes night blindness and may increase the risk of maternal mortality.

Vitamin A deficiency is a public health problem in more than half of all countries, especially those in Africa and Southeast Asia, hitting young children and pregnant women in low-income countries hardest. The nutrient is crucial for maternal and child survival, and supplying adequate vitamin A in high-risk areas can significantly reduce mortality. Conversely, its absence causes a needlessly high risk of disease and death. An estimated 250 million preschool children are vitamin A–deficient, and it is likely that in vitamin A–deficient areas a substantial proportion of pregnant women are vitamin A–deficient.[26]

Vitamin A deficiency often coexists with marginal PEM. The vitamin deficiency predisposes infants and children to diarrheal diseases, which, in turn, worsen the child's nutritional status, leading to severe PEM. Common childhood infections, most notably measles, are much more serious in vitamin A–deficient children, with a much greater risk of death or permanent damage from complications.

In communities where vitamin A deficiency exists, pregnant and breastfeeding women often experience night blindness, an early symptom of deficiency. Maternal death, poor pregnancy outcome, and failure to lactate are all increased with vitamin A deficiency. Vitamin A levels in the breast milk of these women are likely to be low as well, putting their infants at risk of deficiency.

Many countries are taking a multipronged approach to vitamin A deficiency that includes promotion of breastfeeding, fortification of foods, supplementation, and nutrition education. Foods such as eggs, dairy foods, and liver are promoted as important for women and children; educational programs also encourage growing and eating fruits and vegetables high in beta-carotene. However, dietary change can be difficult and slow. The best sources of vitamin A are often the most expensive or inaccessible. For absorption and conversion to vitamin A, beta-carotene requires dietary fat—another expensive item in many areas. Meanwhile, periodic single, large-dose vitamin A supplements, often given in tandem with maternal–child immunizations, are proving an effective short-term measure.

Biotechnology may have a significant impact on vitamin A deficiency. As mentioned in Chapter 18, through genetic engineering, scientists have developed a strain of rice that is rich in beta-carotene. When these rice plants are crossed with locally grown strains of rice, they become suited to a particular region's climate and growing conditions. If local farmers and consumers accept such crops, bioengineered rice may play a critical role in feeding the world's burgeoning population and alleviating widespread vitamin A deficiency.[27]

Iron-Deficiency Anemia

Iron deficiency is the most common nutritional disorder in the world. The numbers are staggering: 2 billion people—over 30 percent of the world's population—are anemic, mainly due to iron deficiency. In resource-poor areas, the condition frequently is worsened by infectious diseases, including malaria, HIV/AIDS, and hookworm infestation.[28] Although iron deficiency occurs in all age groups, fast growth in young children and reproductive blood loss in women make them especially vulnerable to low-iron diets. Anemia impairs childhood development, work capacity, learning capacity, and resistance to disease.[29] Anemia during pregnancy increases illness and death rates for mother and baby. For all groups of people, anemia can cause profound fatigue, and severe anemia causes death.

The anemias of the developing world demonstrate the interaction of multiple nutrient deficiencies, which in turn interact with infection, sanitation, and poverty. Supplying iron alone is seldom enough to correct the problem.

Iron-deficient diets are typically high in starch and cereal grains. During digestion, cereals may bind with the very limited iron the diet provides, preventing its absorption. Other blood-building nutrients, such as vitamins B_6 and B_{12} and folate, are often in short supply as well.

Anemia-producing parasites are common in areas of iron deficiency, aggravating the effects of poor diet. Blood cells are destroyed by malarial infections. Intestinal malabsorption and intestinal bleeding are caused by hookworm, prevalent where human waste contaminates the fields where people walk barefoot, and by other parasites, acquired when human waste contaminates the water that people drink or in which people bathe.

People debilitated by anemia may be too weak to build outhouses, too poor to buy shoes or fuel to boil water, or too apathetic to clear standing water where malaria-carrying mosquitoes breed. Moreover, they often do not understand the connection between sanitation, infection, and malnutrition. Added to this mix are excessive blood loss from repeated pregnancies, inherited blood disorders such as sickle cell disease, and chronic bacterial or viral infections such as HIV.

Timely treatment can restore personal health and raise national productivity levels by as much as 20 percent.[30] The WHO has developed a comprehensive package of public health measures based on a three-pronged approach:

1. *Increase iron intake:* Dietary diversification, including iron-rich foods and enhancement of iron absorption, food fortification, and iron supplementation
2. *Control infection:* Immunization and control programs for malaria and parasitic worm diseases
3. *Improve nutritional status:* Prevention and control of other nutritional deficiencies, such as vitamin B_{12}, folate, and vitamin A

Deficiencies of Other Micronutrients

Deficiencies of zinc and calcium often coexist with other deficiencies, contributing to illness and death during periods of growth and threatening immune function and skeletal health in people who survive to old age.

Selenium deficiency, although limited to only a few countries, has serious consequences. It occurs where the soil is selenium-poor, in distinct regional patterns in China and Russia. In China, where the deficiency is most severe, it predisposes individuals to the fatal Keshan disease, in which heart muscle is destroyed. Keshan disease affects mainly women and children. The condition can be prevented by selenium supplementation or by fortification, as in programs undertaken in New Zealand, where soil is also low in selenium.

The classical deficiency diseases beriberi, pellagra, and scurvy still occur among the world's poorest and most underprivileged people. Most often, however, these diseases strike the victims of war and political strife—the

Quick Bite

The Importance of Rice

Rice is the principal food crop for one-half of the world's population.

refugees. Diets based on milled cereals and starchy roots, all poor thiamin sources, predispose refugee populations to beriberi. People who rely on corn-based diets low in niacin and tryptophan are susceptible to pellagra. The disruption of refugee life can easily tip the balance from marginal deficiency to overt deficiency disease.

Quick Bite

Undernutrition Cannot Be Blamed for Everything

In all populations in the developing world, low weight- and height-for-age affect 10 to 15 percent of preschool and school-aged children. Most experts attribute this shortfall to insufficiency of food. A study of African schoolchildren, however, found no significant difference between well-fed and underfed pupils on measures such as their class position, aptitude for games, and interest in education. Among children of school age, one must be careful not to overrate the effects of undernutrition nor the health disadvantages from mild to moderate malnutrition

Overweight and Obesity

Obesity has reached epidemic proportions globally, with more than 1 billion adults overweight—at least 300 million of them clinically obese. It is a major contributor to the global burden of chronic disease and disability.[31] In developed countries, obesity often exists right alongside undernutrition. Obesity is more likely in areas of economic advancement and in urban areas. Its prevalence is rising rapidly in Latin America and the Caribbean, but obesity still is relatively uncommon in Asia and Africa.

Societal changes and the worldwide nutrition transition are driving the obesity epidemic. Economic growth, modernization, urbanization, and globalization of food markets are just some of the forces thought to underlie the epidemic.

As incomes rise and populations become more urban, diets high in complex carbohydrates give way to more varied diets with a higher proportion of fats, saturated fats, and sugars. Calorie-dense foods that have few other nutrients are often cheap, satisfying, convenient, and heavily promoted; some are foreign brands that have become affordable status symbols. In poor communities, cultural attitudes toward overweight may be more accepting and even admiring.

Large shifts toward less physically demanding work have been observed worldwide. Moves toward less physical activity are also found in the increasing use of automated transport, technology in the home, and more passive leisure pursuits. The reductions in energy expenditure can be dramatic. If an individual is overweight, can we assume that the person is well nourished? Not necessarily. A new trend in developed countries is the presence of malnutrition with obesity. With too little physical activity, obese individuals may be eating too many calories of poor-nutrient foods and not enough nutritious foods including vegetables and fruit.

Key Concepts *The most critical nutritional deficiencies in today's developing world are deficiencies of protein, calories, iodine, vitamin A, and iron. There have been gains in reducing the severity and prevalence of protein-energy malnutrition through breastfeeding promotion, nutrition education, and improvements in food supplies. Fortification and supplementation programs are effectively attacking iodine and vitamin A deficiencies but have had less success overcoming iron deficiency. All of the underlying causes of malnutrition must be addressed to reduce and eliminate these and other deficiencies.*

Learning Portfolio

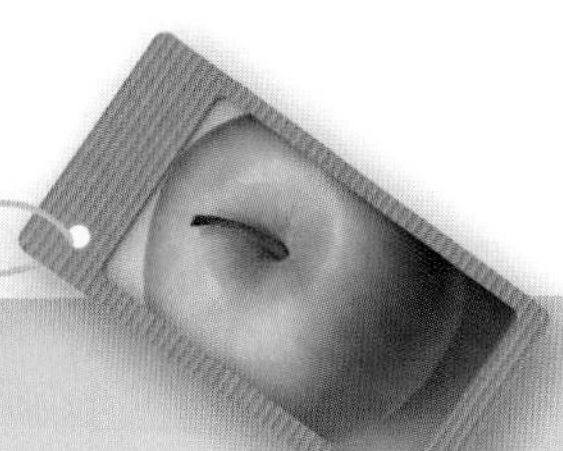

Key Terms

	page		page
Child and Adult Care Food Program	790	food security	784
Electronic Benefits Transfer (EBT)	788	Food Security Supplement Survey	785
Feeding America	790	hunger	784
Food and Agriculture Organization (FAO)	791	iodine deficiency disorders (IDD)	799
food insecurity	784	malnutrition	784
Food Research and Action Center (FRAC)	788	World Health Organization (WHO)	791

Study Points

- Hunger and malnutrition continue to be problems in both industrialized and developing countries.
- Although most people in the United States are food-secure, malnutrition is a serious problem among the working poor, the rural poor, the homeless, elders, and children.
- The Supplemental Nutrition Assistance Program (SNAP), the Special Supplemental Nutrition Program for Women, Infants and Children (WIC), the National School Lunch and Breakfast Programs, and the Child and Adult Care Food Program are among the many federal programs that address hunger in the United States. Feeding America is the largest charitable hunger-relief organization in the United States.
- Progress against global hunger and malnutrition is slow and uneven. It is estimated that more than 923 million people in the developing world do not have enough to eat.
- Social and economic factors, infection, disease, political disruptions, natural disasters, and inequitable food distribution all contribute to hunger in the developing world.
- Advances in agricultural practices have increased food supplies and reduced food costs in the developing world; however, the increase in production has led to environmental degradation as a result of urbanization, clear-cutting, overirrigation, and soil erosion.
- Protein-energy malnutrition (PEM) refers to conditions, such as kwashiorkor and marasmus, that result from not having enough to eat.
- Infants and children are most likely to suffer from PEM. However, nutrition education efforts, including promotion of breastfeeding, have reduced the severity and prevalence of PEM.
- Iodine deficiency is the largest cause of preventable brain damage and impaired psychomotor development in the developing world. It can cause damage to people of all ages.
- Great strides have been made in preventing iodine deficiency disorders (IDD) through salt iodization programs. More than two-thirds of households in IDD-affected countries now use iodized salt.
- Vitamin A deficiency is the leading cause of preventable childhood blindness. It also makes its victims more vulnerable to infection, diarrheal diseases, and PEM.
- Pregnant and breastfeeding women with vitamin A deficiency are at increased risk of death, poor pregnancy outcomes, and lactation failure.
- Many countries are taking a multipronged approach to vitamin A deficiency that includes promotion of breastfeeding, fortification of foods, supplementation, and nutrition education.
- The best sources of vitamin A often are expensive and inaccessible to people in developing countries. Scientists have developed bioengineered strains of rice that are rich in beta-carotene and that may play a critical role in alleviating widespread vitamin A deficiency.
- The anemias of the developing world demonstrate the interaction of multiple nutrient deficiencies, which in turn interact with infection, poor sanitation, and poverty.
- Food fortification and iron supplementation for women and children are the mainstays of anemia prevention and treatment, along with efforts to overcome poverty and improve sanitation.
- The classical deficiency diseases beriberi and pellagra still occur among the world's poorest and most underprivileged people.

- In some developed countries, obesity exists right alongside undernutrition.

Try This

Try Giving Up Your Stove and Refrigerator

A homeless person has no kitchen facilities to store or prepare food. For one day, eat a balanced diet without resorting to cooking or using your refrigerator. Some of the foods you could eat include the following:

Breads, bagels, tortillas, rolls
Cereals
Crackers
Milk—canned, evaporated, or aseptically packaged
Cheese—hard cheeses keep well
Pudding cups (single-serve, nonrefrigerated type)
Tuna, chicken—canned
Sardines, salmon—canned
Nuts, peanut butter
Beans—canned
Fruits and vegetables—fresh, canned, dried fruits

How satisfying did you find this eating pattern? What did you miss most? What would it be like to eat this way for an extended time?

Community Food Programs

The purpose of this exercise is to see how you can contribute to decreasing or eliminating food insecurity in your community. Look in the phone book or search the Web (under "Food Programs" and "Human Services") to see what programs are available. Consider volunteering at your local food bank or another community program to help feed people who do not have the means to feed themselves.

Study Questions

1. What is the difference between food insecurity and hunger?
2. What is food security?
3. What groups are most at risk for food insecurity in the United States?
4. List some of the organizations and programs fighting hunger and food insecurity in the United States.
5. List four causes of malnutrition worldwide.
6. List four common nutritional deficiencies worldwide and what is being done to combat the problem.
7. What populations are at increased risk of nutritional deficiencies, and why?

References

1 Food and Agriculture Organization. *The State of Food Insecurity in the World 2008: High Prices and Food Security—Threats and Opportunities*. Rome, Italy: Food and Agriculture Organization, 2008. http://www.fao.org/docrep/011/i0291e/i0291e00.htm. Accessed 4/21/09.

2 Bryce J, Boschi-Pinto C, Shibuya K, Black R. WHO estimates of the causes of death in children. *Lancet*. 2005;365(9465):1147–1152.

3 American Dietetic Association. Position of the American Dietetic Association: food insecurity and hunger in the United States. *J Am Diet Assoc*. 2006;106:446–458.

4 Nord M, Andrews M, Carlson S. *Household Food Security in the United States, 2007*. November 2008. US Department of Agriculture Economic Research Service Report ERR-66. http://www.ers.usda.gov/Publications/ERR66/. Accessed 4/21/09; and USDA Economic Research Service. Food security in the United States: key statistics and graphics. http://www.ers.usda.gov/Briefing/FoodSecurity/stats_graphs.htm#how_many. Accessed 4/22/09.

5 Scheier LM. What is the hunger-obesity paradox? *J Am Diet Assoc*. 2005;105:883–884, 886.

6 Nord, Andrews, Carlson. *Household Food Security in the United States, 2007*.

7 American Dietetic Association. Position of the American Dietetic Association: child and adolescent food and nutrition programs. *J Am Diet Assoc*. 2006;106:1467–1475.

8 USDA Food and Nutrition Service. Nutrition program facts: WIC. April 2009. http://www.fns.usda.gov/wic/WIC-Fact-Sheet.pdf. Accessed 4/23/09.

9 Ibid.

10 US Department of Agriculture. Child nutrition programs—income eligibility guidelines. *Federal Register*. 2008;23(69);19186–19187. http://www.fns.usda.gov/cnd/governance/notices/iegs/IEGs08-09.pdf. Accessed 4/23/09.

11 USDA Food and Nutrition Service. National School Lunch Program. July 2008. http://www.fns.usda.gov/cnd/lunch/AboutLunch/NSLPFactSheet.pdf. Accessed 4/23/09.

12 Feeding America. About us. http://feedingamerica.org/. Accessed 4/23/09.

13 Brundtland GH. *Nutrition, Health, and Human Rights*. Geneva, Switzerland: World Health Organization, 2003. http://www.who.int/director-general/speeches/1999/english/19990412_nutrition.html. Accessed 4/29/09.

14 Food and Agriculture Organization. *The State of Food Insecurity in the World 2008*.

15 von Braun J. *The World Food Situation: New Driving Forces and Required Actions*. Washington, DC: International Food Policy Research Institute, 2007. http://www.ifpri.org/pubs/fpr/pr18.asp. Accessed 4/23/09.

16 Sheeran J. The new face of hunger. Keynote address presented at: Center for Strategic and International Studies; April 18, 2008; Washington, DC.

17 Ibid.

18 Food and Agriculture Organization. Climate change, water, and food security. June 2008. ftp://ftp.fao.org/nr/HLCinfo/Water-Infosheet-En.pdf. Accessed 4/23/09.

19 Brundtland. *Nutrition, Health, and Human Rights.*

20 Joint United Nations Programme on HIV/AIDS and World Health Organization. *AIDS Epidemic Update*. December 2007. http://data.unaids.org/pub/EPISlides/2007/2007_epiupdate_en.pdf. Accessed 4/23/09.

21 World Health Organization. Protein-energy malnutrition. http://www.wpro.who.int/health_topics/protein_energy/. Accessed 4/23/09.

22 World Health Organization. Micronutrient deficiencies: iodine deficiency disorders. 2009. http://www.who.int/nutrition/topics/idd/en/. Accessed 4/24/09.

23 de Benoist B, Andersson M, Egli I, et al. *Iodine Status Worldwide*. Geneva: World Health Organization, 2004. http://whqlibdoc.who.int/publications/2004/9241592001.pdf. Accessed 4/24/09.

24 World Health Organization. Micronutrient deficiencies: iodine deficiency disorders.

25 Ibid.

26 World Health Organization. Micronutrient deficiencies: vitamin A deficiency. 2009. http://www.who.int/nutrition/topics/vad/en/index.html. Accessed 4/24/09.

27 United Nations Economic Commission for Africa. Realizing the promise of green biotechnology for the poor. In *Harnessing Technologies for Sustainable Development*. Addis Ababa, Ethiopia: UNECA, 2002:79–126. http://www.uneca.org/harnessing/chapter3.pdf. Accessed 4/24/09.

28 World Health Organization. Micronutrient deficiencies: iron deficiency anaemia. 2009. http://www.who.int/nutrition/topics/ida/en/index.html. Accessed 4/24/09.

29 Ibid.

30 Ibid.

31 World Health Organization. *Obesity and Overweight*. Geneva, Switzerland: World Health Organization. http://www.who.int/hpr/NPH/docs/gs_obesity.pdf. Accessed 4/24/09.

Appendix A *Food Composition Tables*

Baking/Cooking Ingredients: Retail, p. A-0; Bars, p. A-0; Beverages and Beverage Mixes, p. A-2; Condiments: Sauces, Relish, Dressings, Dips, Spreads, Spices, etc., p. A-6; Dairy Products and Non-Dairy Substitutes, p. A-10; Desserts, p. A-16; Fats, Oils, Margarines, Shortenings, and Substitutes, p. A-26; Food Additives and Industrial Ingredient Products, p. A-28; Food Service Products, p. A-28; Fruits, p. A-28; Grain Products: Unprepared and Prepared Baked Goods, p. A-32; Infant Foods, p. A-44; Meats and Meat Substitutes: BBQ, Breaded, Fried, Glazed, Grilled, Raw, etc., p. A-46; Prepared Foods: Shelf-Stable/Canned Dishes, p. A-56; Prepared Foods: Dry/Prepared from Dry Dishes, p. A-58; Prepared Foods: Frozen/Refrigerated Meals and Dishes, p. A-60; Prepared Homemade/Generic Dishes, p. A-62; Restaurants—Fast Food and Regular, p. A-66; Vegetables and Legumes, p. A-76

ESHA CODE	FOOD DESCRIPTION	AMT	UNIT	WT (g)	CAL (kcal)	KILO (kJ)	WTR (g)	PROT (g)	CARB (g)	FIBR (g)	FAT (g)	SATF (g)	MONO (g)	POLY (g)
BAKING/COOKING INGREDIENTS – RETAIL														
Baking Chips, Chocolates, Coatings, & Cocoas														
23010	Baking Chocolate-Square	1	ea	28.35	142	594	<1	4	8	5	15	9.2	4.6	0.4
23012	Chocolate Chips-Semisweet	1	cup	168	806	3372	1	7	107	10	50	29.8	16.7	1.6
28200	Cocoa Powder	1	Tbs	5.38	12	50	<1	1	3	2	1	0.4	0.2	<0.1
Baking/Cooking Ingredients														
53002	Soy Sauce	1	Tbs	16	8	33	11	1	1	<1	<1	<0.1	<0.1	<0.1
53267	Soy Sauce-Lite	1	Tbs	18	15	63		1	2	0	<1	0		
27205	Vinegar-Malt Ale	1	Tbs	16	0	0	3	0	0	0	0	0	0	0
53099	Worcestershire Sauce	1	Tbs	17	13	54	13	0	3	0	0	0	0	0
Leaveners & Yeast														
28003	Baking Soda	1	tsp	4.6	0	0	<1	0	0	0	0	0	0	0
28000	Yeast-Dry-Active-Baker's	1	tsp	4	13	54	<1	2	2	1	<1	<0.1	0.2	<0.1
Sugars, Sugar Substitutes, & Syrups														
63655	Agave Nectar	1	Tbs	21	60	251		0	16	0	0	0	0	0
25010	Corn Syrup-Dark	1	cup	328	938	3925	72	0	254	0	0	0	0	0
25000	Corn Syrup-Light	1	cup	328	928	3883	75	0	252	0	1	0	0	0
25001	Honey-Strained/Extracted	1	Tbs	21.2	64	268	4	<1	17	<1	0	0	0	0
25002	Maple Syrup	1	Tbs	20	52	218	6	0	13	0	<1	<0.1	<0.1	<0.1
23042	Pancake Syrup	1	Tbs	20	47	197	8	0	12	0	0	0	0	0
23090	Pancake Syrup+Butter	1	Tbs	19.69	58	243	5	<1	15	0	<1	0.2	0.1	<0.1
23172	Pancake Syrup-Reduced Cal	1	Tbs	15	25	105	8	0	7	0	0	0	0	0
25005	Sugar-Brown	1	tsp	4.6	17	71	<1	<1	5	0	0	0	0	0
63348	Sugar-Turbinado	1	tsp	4	15	63	0	0	4	0	0	0	0	0
25006	Sugar-White-Granulated	1	tsp	4.167	16	67	<1	0	4	0	0	0	0	0
25009	Sugar-White-Powdered	1	tsp	2.5	10	42	<1	0	2	0	0	0	0	0
BARS														
Cereal/Breakfast Bars														
53227	Cereal Bar-Nutrigrain-MixBerry	1	ea	37	137	573	5	2	27	1	3	0.6	1.8	0.4
Diet/Weight Loss Bars														
62640	SlimFast NutriBar-DutchChoc	1	ea	34	140	586		5	20	2	5	3		
62643	UltrSlmFstBar-ChwyCarmlCrnch	1	svg	28	120	502		2	18	1	4	3		
62641	UltrSlmFstBar-PntCarmlCrnch	1	svg	28	120	502		1	20	1	4	3		
Granola Bars														
23100	Granola Bar-Almond-Hard	1	ea	23.6	117	490	1	2	15	1	6	3	1.8	0.9
23105	Granola Bar-Choc Chip-Soft	1	ea	42.52	178	745	3	2	30	2	7	2.6	3	0.7
23108	Granola Bar-PeanutButter-Soft	1	ea	28.35	121	506	2	3	18	1	4	1	1.9	1.2

< = Trace amount present   Blank = Not available

ESHA, EatRight Analysis CD-ROM; **AMT**, amount; **WT**, weight; **CAL**, calories; **KILO**, KiloJoule; **WTR**, water; **PROT**, protein; **CARB**, carbohydrate; **FIBR**, fiber; **FAT**, fat; **SATF**, saturated fat; **MONO**, monounsaturated fat; **POLY**, polyunsaturated fat; **CHOL**, cholesterol; **V**, vitamin; **THI**, thiamin; **RIB**, riboflavin; **NIA**, niacin; **FOL**, folate; **CALC**, calcium; **PHOS**, phosphorus; **SOD**, sodium; **POT**, potassium; **MAG**, magnesium

CHOL (mg)	V-A (IU)	THI (mg)	RIB (mg)	NIA (mg)	V-B6 (mg)	FOL (μg)	V-B12 (μg)	V-C (mg)	V-E (mg)	CALC (mg)	PHOS (mg)	SOD (mg)	POT (mg)	MAG (mg)	IRON (mg)	ZINC (mg)
0	0	<0.1	<0.1	0.4	<0.1	8	0	0	0.1	29	113	7	235	93	4.9	2.7
0	0	0.1	0.2	0.7	0.1	22	0	0	0.4	54	222	18	613	193	5.3	2.7
0	0	<0.1	<0.1	0.1	<0.1	2	0	0	<0.1	7	39	1	82	27	0.7	0.4
0	0	<0.1	<0.1	0.4	<0.1	2	0	0	0	3	20	902	35	7	0.3	0.1
0	0							0		3		505			0.1	
0	0							0		0		0	5		0	
0	13	<0.1	<0.1	0.1	0	1	0	2.2	<0.1	18	10	167	136	2	0.9	<0.1
0	0	0	0	0	0	0	0	0	0	0	0	1259	0	0	0	0
0	0	0.4	0.2	1.6	0.1	94	<0.1	<1	0	1	25	2	38	2	0.1	0.3
0	0							0		0		0			0	
0	0	<0.1	<0.1	0.1	<0.1	0	0	0	0	59	36	508	144	26	1.2	0.1
0	0	0.2	0	0	0	0	0	0	0	43	0	203	3	3	0	1.4
0	0	0	<0.1	<0.1	<0.1	<1	0	0.1	0	1	1	1	11	<1	0.1	<0.1
0	0	<0.1	<0.1	<0.1	<0.1	0	0	0	0	13	<1	2	41	3	0.2	0.8
0	0	<0.1	<0.1	0	0	0	0	0	0	1	2	16	3	<1	<0.1	<0.1
1	12	<0.1	<0.1	<0.1	0	0	0	0		<1	2	19	1	<1	<0.1	<0.1
0	0	<0.1	<0.1	<0.1	<0.1	0	0	0	0	2	6	27	<1	<1	<0.1	<0.1
0	0	0	0	<0.1	<0.1	<1	0	0	0	4	<1	1	6	<1	<0.1	<0.1
0	0							0		0		0			0	
0	0	0	<0.1	0	0	0	0	0	0	<1	0	<1	<1	0	<0.1	<0.1
0	0	0	<0.1	0	0	0	0	0	0	<1	0	<1	<1	0	<0.1	<0.1
0	750	0.4	0.4	5	0.5	40	0	0		14	36	110	70	10	1.8	1.5
5	1250	0.4	0.4	5	0.4	40	1.5	15	3.4	100	100	85	150	16	4.5	3.8
5	750	0.2	0.3	3	0.3	60	0.9	9	2	250	100	50			2.7	
5	750	0.2	0.3	3	0.3	60	0.9	9	2	250	100	120			2.7	
0	9	0.1	<0.1	0.1	<0.1	3	0	0		8	54	60	64	19	0.6	0.4
0	0	0.1	<0.1	0.3	<0.1	7	0	0	0.1	17	75	76	101	27	0.9	0.6
<1	4	0.1	<0.1	0.9	<0.1	9	0.1	0		26	71	116	82	24	0.6	0.5

ESHA, EatRight Analysis CD-ROM; **AMT**, amount; **WT**, weight; **CAL**, calories; **KILO**, KiloJoule; **WTR**, water; **PROT**, protein; **CARB**, carbohydrate; **FIBR**, fiber; **FAT**, fat; **SATF**, saturated fat; **MONO**, monounsaturated fat; **POLY**, polyunsaturated fat; **CHOL**, cholesterol;

ESHA CODE	FOOD DESCRIPTION	AMT	UNIT	WT (g)	CAL (kcal)	KILO (kJ)	WTR (g)	PROT (g)	CARB (g)	FIBR (g)	FAT (g)	SATF (g)	MONO (g)	POLY (g)
BARS (CONTINUED)														
23059	Granola Bar-Plain-Hard	1	ea	24.5	115	481	1	2	16	1	5	0.6	1.1	3
23097	Granola Bar-Raisin-Soft	1	ea	42.52	190	795	3	3	28	2	8	4.1	1.2	1.4
23104	Granola Bar-Soft	1	ea	28.35	126	527	2	2	19	1	5	2.1	1.1	1.5
23065	Kudos Bar-Nutty Fudge	1	ea	28.35	120	502	1	1	20	1	4	2		
Sports/Energy Bars														
62205	Tiger Sport Bar	1	ea	35	140	586		6	18	1	5	1		
BEVERAGES & BEVERAGE MIXES														
Alcoholic Beverages & Mixes														
22500	Beer	12	floz	356.4	153	640	328	2	13	0	0	0	0	0
22512	Beer-Light	12	floz	354	103	431	336	1	6	0	0	0	0	0
20276	Beer-Non-Alcoholic	12	floz	340.5	56	234		<1	12		0	0	0	0
22519	Coffee Liqueur, 53 proof	1	floz	34.8	113	473	11	<1	16	0	<1	<0.1	<0.1	<0.1
22521	De Menthe Liqueur 72 proof	1	floz	33.6	125	523	10	0	14	0	<1	<0.1	<0.1	0.1
22543	Gin-Rum-Vodka-Whiskey, 100prf	1	floz	27.8	82	343	16	0	0	0	0	0	0	0
22514	Gin-Rum-Vodka-Whiskey, 80prf	1	floz	27.8	64	268	19	0	0	0	0	0	0	0
22516	Gin-Rum-Vodka-Whiskey, 86prf	1	floz	27.8	70	293	18	0	<1	0	0	0	0	0
22542	Gin-Rum-Vodka-Whiskey, 94prf	1	floz	27.8	76	318	17	0	0	0	0	0	0	0
22601	Sangria Wine Drink	6	floz	177	118	494	153	<1	16	<1	<1	<0.1	<0.1	<0.1
22518	Wine-Dessert, Dry	1	floz	29.5	45	188	21	<1	3	0	0	0	0	0
22507	Wine-Dessert, Sweet	1	floz	29.5	47	197	21	<1	4	0	0	0	0	0
20077	Wine-Light-Non Alcoholic	6	floz	174	10	42	171	1	2	0	0	0	0	0
20076	Wine-Non Alcoholic	6	floz	174	10	42	171	1	2	0	0	0	0	0
22501	Wine-Red	6	floz	177	150	628	153	<1	5	0	0	0	0	0
22862	Wine-Riesling	6	floz	177	142	594	153	<1	7		0	0	0	0
22638	Wine-Sherry-Spray Dried	1	g	1	4	17	<1	0	1	0	0	0	0	0
22504	Wine-White, Medium	6	floz	177	145	607	154	<1	5	0	0	0	0	0
Carbonated Drinks														
20006	Club Soda	1	cup	236.8	0	0	237	0	0	0	0	0	0	0
90615	Cola	1	cup	248	92	385	224	<1	24	0	<1	0	0	0
20054	Cola-Caffeine Free	1	cup	240	107	448	765	0	27	0	0	0	0	0
20056	Cola-Diet-Caffeine Free	1	cup	240	0	0		0	0	0	0	0	0	0
90617	Cola-Diet-w/asp	1	cup	236.8	5	21	236	<1	1	0	<1	0	0	0
20028	Cream Soda	1	cup	247.2	126	527	214	0	33	0	0	0	0	0
20189	Creme Soda, Diet	1	cup	240	0	0		0	0	0	0	0	0	0
20007	Diet Soda, Assorted Flavors	1	cup	236.8	0	0	236	0	<1	0	0	0	0	0
20027	Dr. Pepper Type Soda	1	cup	245.6	101	423	220	0	26	0	<1	0.2	0	0
20008	Ginger Ale	1	cup	244	83	347	223	0	21	0	0	0	0	0
20031	Grape Soda	1	cup	248	107	448	220	0	28	0	0	0	0	0
20032	Lemon-Lime Soda	1	cup	245.6	98	410	220	<1	25	0	<1	0	0	0
20029	Orange Soda	1	cup	248	119	498	217	0	31	0	0	0	0	0
20009	Root Beer	1	cup	246.4	101	423	220	0	26	0	0	0	0	0
20010	Tonic / Quinine Water	1	cup	244	83	347	222	0	21	0	0	0	0	0
4793	Tonic Water-Diet	1	cup	244	0	0	595	0	0	0	0	0	0	0
Coffees & Coffee Substitutes														
20093	Coffee+Chicory-Prep from Instant	1	cup	179	5	21	177	<1	1	0	0	<0.1	0	<0.1
20012	Coffee-Brewed	1	cup	237	2	8	236	<1	0	0	<1	<0.1	<0.1	<0.1

< = Trace amount present Blank = Not available

V, vitamin; **THI**, thiamin; **RIB**, riboflavin; **NIA**, niacin; **FOL**, folate; **CALC**, calcium; **PHOS**, phosphorus; **SOD**, sodium; **POT**, potassium; **MAG**, magnesium

CHOL (mg)	V-A (IU)	THI (mg)	RIB (mg)	NIA (mg)	V-B6 (mg)	FOL (μg)	V-B12 (μg)	V-C (mg)	V-E (mg)	CALC (mg)	PHOS (mg)	SOD (mg)	POT (mg)	MAG (mg)	IRON (mg)	ZINC (mg)
0	37	0.1	<0.1	0.4	<0.1	6	0	0.2		15	68	72	82	24	0.7	0.5
<1	0	0.1	0.1	0.5	<0.1	9	0.1	0		43	94	120	154	31	1	0.6
<1	0	0.1	<0.1	0.1	<0.1	7	0.1	0		30	65	79	92	21	0.7	0.4
0	100							1.2		200		75		8	0.4	
0	750	1.3	0.6	3	0.6		1.5	6		300	100	75		100	2.7	
0	0	<0.1	0.1	1.8	0.2	21	0.1	0	0	14	50	14	96	21	0.1	<0.1
0	0	<0.1	0.1	1.4	0.1	21	0.1	0	0	14	42	14	74	18	0.1	<0.1
0												3				
0	0	<0.1	<0.1	0.1	0	0	0	0	0	<1	2	3	10	1	<0.1	<0.1
0	0	0	0	<0.1	0	0	0	0	0	0	0	2	0	0	<0.1	<0.1
0	0	<0.1	<0.1	<0.1	<0.1	0	0	0		0	1	<1	1	0	<0.1	<0.1
0	0	<0.1	<0.1	<0.1	<0.1	0	0	0	0	0	1	<1	1	0	<0.1	<0.1
0	0	<0.1	<0.1	<0.1	<0.1	0	0	0	0	0	1	<1	1	0	<0.1	<0.1
0	0	<0.1	<0.1	<0.1	<0.1	0	0	0		0	1	<1	1	0	<0.1	<0.1
0	26	<0.1	<0.1	0.1	<0.1	5	<0.1	8.1	<0.1	8	8	12	63	6	0.2	0.1
0	0	<0.1	<0.1	0.1	0	0	0	0	0	2	3	3	27	3	0.1	<0.1
0	0	<0.1	<0.1	0.1	0	0	0	0	0	2	3	3	27	3	0.1	<0.1
0	0	0	<0.1	0.2	<0.1	2	0	0	0	16	26	12	153	17	0.7	0.1
0	0	0	<0.1	0.2	<0.1	2	0	0	0	16	26	12	153	17	0.7	0.1
0	4	<0.1	0.1	0.4	0.1	2	0	0	0	14	41	7	225	21	0.8	0.2
0	0						0	0		<1		<1			<0.1	
0	0	<0.1	<0.1	0.2	0.1	2	0	0	0	16	32	9	126	18	0.5	0.2
0	0	0	0	0	0	0	0	0	0	12	0	50	5	2	<0.1	0.2
0	0	0	0	0	0	0	0	0	0	5	25	10	5	0	0.3	<0.1
0							0				33	30	0			
0							0				33	37	36			
0	0	<0.1	0.1	0	0	0	0	0	0	7	21	19	19	2	0.3	<0.1
0	0	0	0	0	0	0	0	0	0	12	0	30	2	2	0.1	0.2
0							0				0	37	0			
0	0	0	0	0	0	0	0	0	0	9	26	38	9	2	<0.1	0.1
0	0	0	0	0	0	0	0	0		7	27	25	2	0	0.1	0.1
0	0	0	0	0	0	0	0	0	0	7	0	17	2	2	0.4	0.1
0	0	0	0	0	0	0	0	0		7	0	37	2	2	0.2	0.2
0	0	0	0	<0.1	0	0	0	0	0	5	0	22	2	2	0.3	0.1
0	0	0	0	0	0	0	0	0		12	2	30	5	2	0.1	0.2
0	0	0	0	0	0	0	0	0	0	12	0	32	2	2	0.1	0.2
0	0	0	0	0	0	0	0	0	0	2	0	29	0	0	<0.1	0.2
	0							0				35				
0	0	0	<0.1	0.4	0	0	0	0	0	7	5	13	63	5	0.1	<0.1
0	0	<0.1	0.2	0.5	<0.1	5	0	0	<0.1	5	7	5	116	7	<0.1	<0.1

ESHA, EatRight Analysis CD-ROM; **AMT**, amount; **WT**, weight; **CAL**, calories; **KILO**, KiloJoule; **WTR**, water; **PROT**, protein; **CARB**, carbohydrate; **FIBR**, fiber; **FAT**, fat; **SATF**, saturated fat; **MONO**, monounsaturated fat; **POLY**, polyunsaturated fat; **CHOL**, cholesterol;

ESHA CODE	FOOD DESCRIPTION	AMT	UNIT	WT (g)	CAL (kcal)	KILO (kJ)	WTR (g)	PROT (g)	CARB (g)	FIBR (g)	FAT (g)	SATF (g)	MONO (g)	POLY (g)
BEVERAGES & BEVERAGE MIXES (CONTINUED)														
20686	Coffee-Decaf	1	cup	236.8	0	0	235	<1	0	0	0	<0.1	0	<0.1
20091	Coffee-Decaf-Prep from Instant	1	cup	179	4	17	177	<1	1	0	0	<0.1	0	<0.1
20023	Coffee-Prep from Instant	1	cup	238.4	5	21	236	<1	1	0	0	<0.1	0	<0.1
20439	Espresso	1	cup	237	5	21	232	<1	0	0	<1	0.2	0	0.2
20972	Espresso-Decaf	1	cup	237	0	0	232	<1	0	0	<1	0.2	0	0.2
20048	Postum Coffee Substitute	1	cup	240	14	59	236	<1	3	1	<1	<0.1	<0.1	<0.1
Dairy Mixed Drinks & Mixes														
21	Cocoa, Prep w/Whole Milk	1	cup	250	192	803	206	9	27	2	6	3.6	1.6	0.2
46	Cocoa-SugarFree, Prep from Mix	1	cup	256	74	310	236	3	14	2	1	0.4	0.2	<0.1
48	Hot Cocoa-Prep w/water	1	cup	274.67	151	632	237	3	32	1	2	0.9	0.5	<0.1
27	Instant Breakfast+ Skim Milk	1	cup	282	216	904	635	16	36		1	0.7		
101	Instant Breakfast+1% Milk	1	cup	281	233	975	626	15	36	<1	3	1.8		
26	Instant Breakfast+2% Milk	1	cup	281	280	1172	611	15	36	<1	9	5.3		
25	Instant Breakfast+Whole Milk	1	cup	281	253	1059	619	15	36	<1	5	3.1		
41	Nestle's Quik-Strawberry+Milk	1	cup	266	234	979	215	8	33	0	8	5.1	2.4	0.3
38	Ovaltine Drink-Choc Flavor	1	cup	265	231	967	215	9	30	1	9	5	2.2	0.5
20925	Soy Eggnog, Silk, LowFat	0.5	cup	127	90	377		3	15	0	2	0		
Fruit Flavored Drinks														
3042	Cranberry Juice Cocktail	1	cup	252.8	137	573	218	0	34	0	<1	<0.1	<0.1	0.1
3276	CranberryJce Cocktail-LowCal	1	cup	236.8	45	188	225	<1	11	0	<1	0	0	0
20052	Five Alive Citrus Drink	1	cup	248	114	477	218	1	28	<1	<1	<0.1	<0.1	<0.1
20131	Fruit Punch-Prep w/Water	1	cup	262	97	406	237	0	25	0	<1	<0.1	<0.1	<0.1
20967	Fruit Drink-LowCal-Pwd	1	tsp	2	5	21	<1	<1	2	<1	<1	<0.1	<0.1	<0.1
20024	Fruit Punch Drink, Canned	1	cup	248	117	490	218	0	30	<1	0	0	<0.1	<0.1
20035	Fruit Punch Drink, Prep from Frzn	1	cup	247.2	114	477	218	<1	29	<1	0	<0.1	<0.1	<0.1
20101	Grape Drink-Canned	1	cup	250.4	153	640	211	0	39	0	0	0	0	0
3064	Grape Juice-FrznConc+Water	1	cup	250	128	536	217	<1	32	<1	<1	0.1	<0.1	0.1
20158	Hi-C Fruit Punch-Box	1	ea	250.1	120	502	544	0	32	0	0	0	0	0
20000	Lemonade, Prep from Frozen	1	cup	248	99	414	222	<1	26	0	<1	<0.1	<0.1	<0.1
20045	Lemonade, Prep from Mix	1	cup	266	72	301	247	0	18	0	<1	0	0	0
20047	Lemonade-LoCal, Prep from Mix	1	cup	236.8	7	29	235	<1	2	0	0	0	0	<0.1
20002	Limeade, Prep from Frozen	1	cup	247.2	129	540	213	0	34	0	0	0	0	0
20004	Orange Drink, Prep from Mix	1	cup	248	122	510	216	0	31	<1	0	0	0	0
20025	Pineapple Orange Drink, Canned	1	cup	250.4	125	523	218	3	30	<1	0	0	0	0
20117	Pink Lemonade, Prep from Frzn	1	cup	247.2	106	444	220	<1	27	<1	<1	<0.1	<0.1	<0.1
20070	Sunny Delight Orange Ade	1	cup	248	122	510	217	0	31	0	<1	<0.1	<0.1	<0.1
Juices – 100% Fruit, Vegetable, or Blended														
3008	Apple Juice-Canned/Bottled	1	cup	248	114	477	219	<1	28	<1	<1	0.1	<0.1	0.1
3010	Apple Juice-FrznConc+Water	1	cup	239	112	469	210	<1	28	<1	<1	<0.1	<0.1	0.1
3015	Apricot Nectar-Canned	1	cup	251	141	590	213	1	36	2	<1	<0.1	0.1	<0.1
5226	Carrot Juice-Canned	1	cup	236	94	393	210	2	22	2	<1	0.1	<0.1	0.2
3062	Grape Juice-Canned/Bottled	1	cup	253	152	636	214	1	37	1	<1	0.1	<0.1	0.1
3052	Grapefruit Juice-Canned	1	cup	247	94	393	223	1	22	<1	<1	<0.1	<0.1	0.1
3053	Grapefruit Juice-FrznConc+Water	1	cup	247	101	423	221	1	24	<1	<1	<0.1	<0.1	0.1
3304	Guava Nectar	1	cup	250	149	623	211	<1	38	2	<1	0.1	<0.1	0.1
3069	Lemon Juice-Bottled	1	Tbs	15.25	3	13	14	<1	1	<1	<1	<0.1	<0.1	<0.1

< = Trace amount present Blank = Not available

V, vitamin; **THI**, thiamin; **RIB**, riboflavin; **NIA**, niacin; **FOL**, folate; **CALC**, calcium; **PHOS**, phosphorus; **SOD**, sodium; **POT**, potassium; **MAG**, magnesium

CHOL (mg)	V-A (IU)	THI (mg)	RIB (mg)	NIA (mg)	V-B6 (mg)	FOL (μg)	V-B12 (μg)	V-C (mg)	V-E (mg)	CALC (mg)	PHOS (mg)	SOD (mg)	POT (mg)	MAG (mg)	IRON (mg)	ZINC (mg)
0	0	0	0	0.5	0	0	0	0	0	5	2	5	128	12	0.1	<0.1
0	0	0	<0.1	0.5	0	0	0	0	0	7	5	7	64	7	0.1	<0.1
0	0	0	<0.1	0.6	0	0	0	0	0	10	7	10	72	10	0.1	<0.1
0	0	<0.1	0.4	12.3	<0.1	2	0	0.5	<0.1	5	17	33	273	190	0.3	0.1
0	0	<0.1	0.4	12.3	<0.1	2	0	0.5	0	5	17	33	273	190	0.3	0.1
0	0	<0.1	<0.1	0.7	<0.1	2	0	0	<0.1	10	24	12	98	12	0.2	<0.1
20	438	0.1	0.5	0.3	0.1	12	1.2	0.5	0.1	285	262	110	492	58	1	1.6
0	3	0.1	0.3	0.2	0.1	3	0.2	0	0	123	179	184	540	44	1	0.7
0	3	<0.1	0.2	0.2	<0.1	3	0.1	0	0.1	58	118	201	272	33	0.5	0.6
9	2343	0.4	0.4	5.5	0.5	118	1.6	30.9	5.3	407	406	268	755	112	4.8	4.1
14	2345	0.4	0.5	5.5	0.5	118	1.5	30.9	5.4	406	392	267	731	119	4.9	4.1
38	2152	0.4	0.5	5.5	0.5	118	1.5	30.7	5.5	396	386	262	721	117	4.9	4.1
24	2345	0.4	0.5	5.5	0.5	118	1.5	30.9	5.5	403	390	264	726	119	4.9	4.1
32	309	0.1	0.4	0.2	0.1	13	0.9	2.4		293	229	128	370	32	0.2	0.9
26	3177	0.8	1.3	11	1	13	1.1	31.8	0.2	368	289	231	575	45	3.8	1.1
0	0							0		20		75			0.7	
0	20	0	0	0.1	0	0	0	106.9	0.6	8	3	5	35	3	0.3	0.1
0	5	0	<0.1	<0.1	<0.1	0	0	76.2	0.1	21	2	7	59	5	0.1	<0.1
0	92	<0.1	<0.1	0.2	<0.1	17	0	67.2	0.1	22	25	10	278	15	2.8	0.1
0	0	0	<0.1	<0.1	0	0	0	30.9	0	45	0	18	3	3	0.1	0.1
0	400	<0.1	0.1	1.6	0.2	<1	0	48	<0.1	16	10	<1	50	5	<0.1	<0.1
0	69	<0.1	0.1	0.1	<0.1	2	0	73.4	<0.1	20	7	94	77	7	0.2	<0.1
0	27	<0.1	<0.1	0.1	<0.1	2	0	108.3	0	10	2	12	32	5	0.2	<0.1
0	0	<0.1	<0.1	<0.1	<0.1	0	0	78.6	0	130	0	40	30	3	0.2	0.3
0	20	<0.1	0.1	0.3	0.1	2	0	59.7	0	10	10	5	52	10	0.3	0.1
	0							100				30				
0	2	<0.1	0.1	<0.1	<0.1	2	0	9.7	<0.1	10	5	10	37	5	0.4	<0.1
0	0	0	<0.1	0	0	0	0	7.7	0	11	19	35	8	35	<0.1	<0.1
0	0	0	0	0	0	0	0	7.6	0	66	31	9	2	2	0.1	<0.1
0	0	<0.1	<0.1	<0.1	<0.1	2	0	7.7	0	5	2	7	25	5	0	<0.1
0	635	0	0.2	2.5	0.3	0	0	73.2	0	129	47	12	62	2	0	<0.1
0	48	0.1	<0.1	0.5	0.1	23	0	56.3	0.1	13	10	8	115	15	0.7	0.2
0	0	<0.1	0	0.1	<0.1	5	0	7.7	<0.1	10	5	10	42	5	<0.1	<0.1
0	20	0	0	<0.1	0	5	0	142.1	<0.1	12	2	7	45	5	0.1	<0.1
0	2	0.1	<0.1	0.2	<0.1	0	0	2.2	<0.1	20	17	10	250	12	0.3	<0.1
0	0	<0.1	<0.1	0.1	0.1	0	0	1.4	<0.1	14	17	17	301	12	0.6	0.1
0	3303	<0.1	<0.1	0.7	0.1	3	0	1.5	0.8	18	23	8	286	13	1	0.2
0	45133	0.2	0.1	0.9	0.5	9	0	20.1	2.7	57	99	68	689	33	1.1	0.4
0	20	<0.1	<0.1	0.3	0.1	0	0	0.3	0	28	35	13	263	25	0.6	0.2
0	17	0.1	<0.1	0.6	<0.1	25	0	72.1	0.1	17	27	2	378	25	0.5	0.2
0	22	0.1	0.1	0.5	0.1	10	0	83.2	0.1	20	35	2	336	27	0.3	0.1
0	215	<0.1	<0.1	0.4	<0.1	3	0	46.5	0.4	11	10	7	93	5	0.1	0.1
0	2	<0.1	<0.1	<0.1	<0.1	2	0	3.8	<0.1	2	1	3	16	1	<0.1	<0.1

ESHA, EatRight Analysis CD-ROM; **AMT**, amount; **WT**, weight; **CAL**, calories; **KILO**, KiloJoule; **WTR**, water; **PROT**, protein; **CARB**, carbohydrate; **FIBR**, fiber; **FAT**, fat; **SATF**, saturated fat; **MONO**, monounsaturated fat; **POLY**, polyunsaturated fat; **CHOL**, cholesterol;

ESHA CODE	FOOD DESCRIPTION	AMT	UNIT	WT (g)	CAL (kcal)	KILO (kJ)	WTR (g)	PROT (g)	CARB (g)	FIBR (g)	FAT (g)	SATF (g)	MONO (g)	POLY (g)
BEVERAGES & BEVERAGE MIXES (CONTINUED)														
3073	Lime juice-bottled	1	Tbs	15.4	3	13	14	<1	1	<1	<1	<0.1	<0.1	<0.1
4949	Mango Nectar	1	cup	250	120	502		0	29	0	0	0	0	0
21113	Orange Juice +Calcium&Vit D	1	cup	249	117	490	217	2	28	1	<1	<0.1	0.1	0.1
3092	Orange Juice-Chilled	1	cup	249	122	510	217	2	29	1	<1	<0.1	0.1	0.1
3090	Orange Juice-Fresh	1	cup	248	112	469	219	2	26	<1	<1	0.1	0.1	0.1
3091	Orange Juice-FrznConc+Water	1	cup	249	112	469	219	2	27	<1	<1	<0.1	<0.1	<0.1
72123	Orange Strawberry Banana Juice	1	cup	234	117	490	203	1	29	<1	<1	0.1	<0.1	0.1
14460	Orange Tangerine Juice	1	cup	245	110	460		2	25	0	0	0	0	0
3095	Papaya Nectar-Canned	1	cup	250	142	594	213	<1	36	2	<1	0.1	0.1	0.1
3120	Pineapple Juice-Canned-Unswt	1	cup	250	132	552	216	1	32	1	<1	<0.1	<0.1	0.1
3128	Prune Juice-Bottled	1	cup	256	182	761	208	2	45	3	<1	<0.1	0.1	<0.1
5397	Tomato Juice-Canned-LowSod	1	cup	243	41	172	228	2	10	1	<1	<0.1	<0.1	0.1
5188	Tomato Juice-Canned-Regular	1	cup	243	41	172	228	2	10	1	<1	<0.1	<0.1	0.1
20080	V-8 Juice-LowSodium	1	cup	242	46	192	226	2	11	2	<1	<0.1	<0.1	0.1
Other Beverages														
20042	Clam and Tomato Juice	1	cup	241.6	116	485	211	1	26	1	<1	0	0	0
Sports/Energy Drinks														
20421	All Sport Drink, Fruit Punch	1	cup	240	53	222		0	15	0	0	0	0	0
63629	Gatorade-Orange-Powder	2	Tbs	25.875	100	418	1	0	24	0	<1			
Teas														
20118	Camomile Tea, Brewed	1	cup	236.8	2	8	236	0	<1	0	0	<0.1	<0.1	<0.1
20924	Chai Tea, Soy Milk-Silk	1	cup	248	140	586		6	19	0	4	0		
20036	Herbal Tea, Brewed	1	cup	236.8	2	8	236	0	<1	0	0	<0.1	<0.1	<0.1
20014	Tea-Brewed	1	cup	236.8	2	8	236	0	1	0	0	<0.1	<0.1	<0.1
20079	Tea-Decaf-LoCal-Prep from Frzn	1	cup	245	6	25	243	<1	2	0	<1	<0.1	<0.1	<0.1
20040	Tea-Lemon-LoCal-Prep from Inst	1	cup	236.8	5	21	235	<1	1	0	0	0	0	0
20020	Tea-Prep from Instant	1	cup	236.8	2	8	236	<1	<1	0	0	0	0	0
20022	Tea-Sweet-Prep from Instant	1	cup	259	91	381	236	<1	22	<1	<1	<0.1	<0.1	<0.1
Waters														
20050	Bottled Water-Perrier	1	cup	236.5	0	0	236	0	0	0	0	0	0	0
20051	Bottled Water-PolandSprings	1	cup	237	0	0	237	0	0	0	0	0	0	0
20041	Water	1	cup	236.5	0	0	236	0	0	0	0	0	0	0
Diet/Weight Loss Drinks														
62599	Diet Drink-Straw Supreme-PwdScp	1	ea	33	140	586		3	23	5	4	0.6	3.8	0
62652	UltraSlimFast Choc Pwdr Scoop	1	svg	33	127	531		3	23	5	4	0.6	2.5	0.6
CONDIMENTS – SAUCES, RELISH, DRESSINGS, DIPS, SPREADS, SPICES, ETC.														
Condiments – Mayonnaise, Mustards, Ketchups, Horseradish, etc.														
27000	Catsup/Ketchup	1	Tbs	15	15	63	10	<1	4	<1	<1	<0.1	<0.1	<0.1
27001	Catsup/Ketchup-Packet	1	ea	6	6	25	4	<1	2	<1	<1	<0.1	<0.1	<0.1
27004	Horseradish-Prepared	1	tsp	5	2	8	4	<1	1	<1	<1	<0.1	<0.1	<0.1
8046	Mayonnaise	1	Tbs	13.8	99	414	2	<1	<1	0	11	1.6	2.7	5.8
8069	Mayonnaise-FatFree	1	Tbs	16	11	46	13	<1	2	<1	<1	0.1		
8032	Mayonnaise-Imitation	1	Tbs	15	35	146	9	<1	2	0	3	0.5	0.7	1.6
44462	Mayonnaise-LowSod-LowCal	1	Tbs	14	32	134	9	<1	2	0	3	0.5	0.6	1.5
8021	Miracle Whip	1	Tbs	14.7	57	238	6	<1	4	0	5	0.7	1.3	2.6
8122	Miracle Whip-Light	1	Tbs	14	37	155	8	<1	3	0	3	0.4	0.6	1.5

< = Trace amount present Blank = Not available

V, vitamin; **THI**, thiamin; **RIB**, riboflavin; **NIA**, niacin; **FOL**, folate; **CALC**, calcium; **PHOS**, phosphorus; **SOD**, sodium; **POT**, potassium; **MAG**, magnesium

CHOL (mg)	V-A (IU)	THI (mg)	RIB (mg)	NIA (mg)	V-B6 (mg)	FOL (μg)	V-B12 (μg)	V-C (mg)	V-E (mg)	CALC (mg)	PHOS (mg)	SOD (mg)	POT (mg)	MAG (mg)	IRON (mg)	ZINC (mg)
0	2	<0.1	<0.1	<0.1	<0.1	1	0	1	<0.1	2	2	2	12	1	<0.1	<0.1
0	500							12		40		10	105		0.7	
0	105	0.1	0.1	0.7	0.2	47	0	83.7	0.5	500	117	5	443	27	0.3	0.2
0	105	0.1	0.1	0.7	0.2	47	0	83.7	0.5	27	42	5	443	27	0.3	0.2
0	496	0.2	0.1	1	0.1	74	0	124	0.1	27	42	2	496	27	0.5	0.1
0	266	0.2	<0.1	0.5	0.1	110	0	96.9	0.5	22	40	2	473	25	0.2	0.1
0	204	0.1	<0.1	0.4	<0.1	40	0	58.5	0.1	19	30	9	342	23	0.6	0.2
0	0	0.2	0.1	0.4	0.2	60		72		20		0	450	24	0	
0	902	<0.1	<0.1	0.4	<0.1	5	0	7.5	0.6	25	0	12	78	8	0.9	0.4
0	12	0.1	0.1	0.5	0.3	45	0	25	<0.1	32	20	5	325	30	0.8	0.3
0	8	<0.1	0.2	2	0.6	0	0	10.5	0.3	31	64	10	707	36	3	0.5
0	1094	0.1	0.1	1.6	0.3	49	0	44.5	0.8	24	44	24	556	27	1	0.4
0	1094	0.1	0.1	1.6	0.3	49	0	44.5	0.8	24	44	654	556	27	1	0.4
0	3770	0.1	0.1	1.8	0.3	51	0	67	0.8	27	41	653	467	27	1	0.5
0	360	0.1	<0.1	0.6	0.1	19	0.1	12.1	0.3	19	27	875	215	12	0.4	0.2
0	0						0	0		0	7	37	37		0	
0		<0.1	0.2	0.1	<0.1			0.1		10	31	16	8	<1	0.1	<0.1
0	47	<0.1	<0.1	0	0	2	0	0	0	5	0	2	21	2	0.2	0.1
0	300		0.3				0.9	0		300		50			1.1	0.9
0	0	<0.1	<0.1	0	0	2	0	0	0	5	0	2	21	2	0.2	0.1
0	0	0	<0.1	0	0	12	0	0	0	0	2	7	88	7	<0.1	<0.1
0	0	0	<0.1	0	0	13	0	0	0	<1	2	7	90	7	<0.1	<0.1
0	0	0	<0.1	<0.1	<0.1	0	0	0	0	7	2	14	33	5	0.1	<0.1
0	0	0	<0.1	0.1	<0.1	0	0	0	0	7	2	9	43	5	<0.1	<0.1
0	0	<0.1	0	<0.1	<0.1	0	0	0	0	5	0	5	39	3	0.1	<0.1
0	0	0	0	0	0	0	0	0		33	0	2	0	0	0	0
0	0	0	0	0	0	0	0	0		2	0	2	0	2	<0.1	0
0	0	0	0	0	0	0	0	0	0	7	0	7	2	2	0	0
0	952	0.5	0.2	12.7	0.8	127	2.7	34.3	17.3	254	127	165	203	127	8	5.7
0	952	0.5	0.2	12.7	0.8	127	2.7	34.3	17.3	254	127	152	330	127	6.9	5.7
0	140	<0.1	<0.1	0.2	<0.1	2	0	2.3	0.2	3	5	167	57	3	0.1	<0.1
0	56	<0.1	<0.1	0.1	<0.1	1	0	0.9	0.1	1	2	67	23	1	<0.1	<0.1
0	<1	<0.1	<0.1	<0.1	<0.1	3	0	1.2	<0.1	3	2	16	12	1	<0.1	<0.1
5	39	<0.1	<0.1	0	0.1	1	<0.1	0	0.7	1	3	78	2	<1	<0.1	<0.1
2	16							0		1	4	120	8		<0.1	
4	0	0	0	0	0	0	0	0	0.3	0	0	75	2	0	0	<0.1
3	0	0	<0.1	0	0	0	<0.1	0	0.9	0	0	15	1	0	0	<0.1
4	32	<0.1	<0.1	<0.1	<0.1	1	<0.1	0	0.3	2	4	105	1	<1	<0.1	<0.1
4	31	<0.1	<0.1	0	<0.1	1	<0.1	0	0.4	2	4	97	3	<1	<0.1	<0.1

ESHA, EatRight Analysis CD-ROM; **AMT**, amount; **WT**, weight; **CAL**, calories; **KILO**, KiloJoule; **WTR**, water; **PROT**, protein; **CARB**, carbohydrate; **FIBR**, fiber; **FAT**, fat; **SATF**, saturated fat; **MONO**, monounsaturated fat; **POLY**, polyunsaturated fat; **CHOL**, cholesterol;

ESHA CODE	FOOD DESCRIPTION	AMT	UNIT	WT (g)	CAL (kcal)	KILO (kJ)	WTR (g)	PROT (g)	CARB (g)	FIBR (g)	FAT (g)	SATF (g)	MONO (g)	POLY (g)
CONDIMENTS – SAUCES, RELISH, DRESSINGS, DIPS, SPREADS, SPICES, ETC. (CONTINUED)														
435	Mustard-Yellow-Prepared	1	tsp	5	3	13	4	<1	<1	<1	<1	<0.1	0.1	<0.1
Dips														
27135	French Onion Dip	2	Tbs	31	60	251		1	3	0	4	3		
Gravies														
53023	Beef Gravy-Canned	.5	cup	116.5	62	259	102	4	6	<1	3	1.3	1.1	0.1
53006	Beef Gravy-Homemade	0.5	cup	135	107	448	115	3	7	1	8	1.9	3.4	2
53022	Chicken Gravy-Canned	.5	cup	119	94	393	102	2	6	<1	7	1.7	3	1.8
53005	Chicken Gravy-Homemade	0.5	cup	130	97	406	110	6	6		5	1.4	2.2	1.3
53026	Mushroom Gravy-Canned	.5	cup	119	60	251	106	1	7	<1	3	0.5	1.4	1.2
53033	Turkey Gravy-Canned	.5	cup	119.2	61	255	106	3	6	<1	3	0.7	1.1	0.6
Jams, Jellies, & Glazes														
23000	Apple Butter	1	Tbs	18	31	130	10	<1	8	<1	<1	<0.1	<0.1	<0.1
23278	Fruit Spread-LowCal-Strawberry	1	Tbs	17	25	105		0	6	0	0	0	0	0
23054	Jam/Preserves	1	Tbs	20	56	234	6	<1	14	<1	<1	<0.1	<0.1	0
23003	Jelly	1	Tbs	19	51	213	6	<1	13	<1	<1	<0.1	<0.1	<0.1
23165	Jelly-Reduced Sugar	1	Tbs	18.8	34	142	10	<1	9	<1	<1	<0.1	<0.1	<0.1
23005	Marmalade-Orange	1	Tbs	20	49	205	7	<1	13	<1	0	0	0	0
Salad Dressings – Lower Calorie/Fat/Sodium/Cholest														
8023	1000 Island Dressing-LowCal	1	Tbs	15.3	30	126	9	<1	4	<1	2	0.1	1	0.4
8498	Catalina Dressing-FatFree	2	Tbs	33	35	146		0	8	1	0	0	0	0
44467	French Dressing-FatFree	1	Tbs	16	21	88	10	<1	5	<1	<1	<0.1	<0.1	<0.1
8014	French Dressing-LowCal	1	Tbs	16.3	36	151	9	<1	5	<1	2	0.1	0.7	0.6
8504	HoneyDijon Dressing-FatFree	2	Tbs	34	50	209		1	10	1	0	0	0	0
8491	Italian Dressing-FatFree	2	Tbs	33	20	84	27	<1	4	<1	<1	0.2		
8016	Italian Dressing-LowCal	1	Tbs	15	11	46	13	<1	1	0	1	0.1	0.3	0.3
8493	Ranch Dressing-FatFree	2	Tbs	35	48	201	22	<1	11	<1	<1	0.1		
Salad Dressings – Regular														
8024	1000 Island Dressing	1	Tbs	15.6	58	243	7	<1	2	<1	5	0.8	1.2	2.8
8013	Blue Cheese Dressing	2	Tbs	30.6	146	611	12	<1	1	<1	16	2.5	4.1	8.4
44705	Caesar Dressing	2	Tbs	29.4	159	665	10	1	1	<1	17	2.6	4	9.7
8015	French Dressing	1	Tbs	15.6	71	297	6	<1	2	0	7	0.9	1.3	3.3
8530	Honey Mustard Dressing	2	Tbs	30	140	586		0	6	0	13	2		
8020	Italian Dressing	1	Tbs	14.7	43	180	8	<1	2	0	4	0.7	0.9	1.9
8035	Oil & Vinegar Dressing	1	Tbs	15.6	70	293	7	0	<1	0	8	1.4	2.3	3.8
8555	Ranch Dressing	2	Tbs	29	148	619	11	<1	1	<1	16	2.4		
8022	Russian Dressing	1	Tbs	15.3	54	226	6	<1	5	<1	4	0.4	0.9	2.3
8123	Yogurt Dressing	1	Tbs	15.4	11	46	13	<1	1	<1	1	0.3	0.2	0.1
Salsas														
53466	Salsa Ready-to-Serve	.25	cup	64.8	17	71	58	1	4	1	<1	<0.1	<0.1	0.1
Sauces														
53388	Alfredo Sauce-DiGiorno	0.25	cup	62	180	753		3	3	0	18	7		
53000	Barbecue Sauce	.25	cup	62.5	94	393	38	0	23	<1	<1	0	<0.1	0.1
9570	Creamy Garlic Alfredo Sauce	0.25	cup	61	100	418		2	3	0	10	4		
53016	Curry Sauce	0.5	cup	115	74	310	182	3	3	<1	6	1		
53233	Enchilada Sauce-Mild Green Chili	0.25	cup	61	20	84		0	3	0	1	0		
53406	Horseradish Sauce	1	tsp	5	20	84		0	1	0	2	0		

< = Trace amount present Blank = Not available

V, vitamin; **THI**, thiamin; **RIB**, riboflavin; **NIA**, niacin; **FOL**, folate; **CALC**, calcium; **PHOS**, phosphorus; **SOD**, sodium; **POT**, potassium; **MAG**, magnesium

CHOL (mg)	V-A (IU)	THI (mg)	RIB (mg)	NIA (mg)	V-B6 (mg)	FOL (μg)	V-B12 (μg)	V-C (mg)	V-E (mg)	CALC (mg)	PHOS (mg)	SOD (mg)	POT (mg)	MAG (mg)	IRON (mg)	ZINC (mg)
0	4	<0.1	<0.1	<0.1	<0.1	<1	0	0.1	<0.1	3	5	57	7	2	0.1	<0.1
0	0							0		0		210			0	
3	3	<0.1	<0.1	0.8	<0.1	2	0.1	0	<0.1	7	35	652	94	2	0.8	1.2
3	498	<0.1	0.1	0.6	<0.1	3	0.1	0	0.2	27	39	779	147	3	0.6	1.1
2	4	<0.1	0.1	0.5	<0.1	2	0.1	0	0.2	24	35	687	130	2	0.6	1
55	1091	<0.1	0.2	1.6	0.1	49	2.3	0.6	0.3	16	62	683	151	5	1.5	1.5
0	0	<0.1	0.1	0.8	<0.1	14	0	0		8	18	678	126	2	0.8	0.8
2	0	<0.1	0.1	1.5	<0.1	2	0.1	0	0.1	5	35	688	130	2	0.8	1
0	4	<0.1	<0.1	<0.1	<0.1	<1	0	0.1	<0.1	3	1	3	16	1	0.1	<0.1
0	0							0		0		0			0	
0	0	<0.1	<0.1	<0.1	<0.1	2	0	1.8	<0.1	4	4	6	15	1	0.1	<0.1
0	1	<0.1	<0.1	<0.1	<0.1	<1	0	0.2	0	1	1	6	10	1	<0.1	<0.1
0	1	<0.1	<0.1	<0.1	<0.1	<1	0	0	0	1	1	<1	13	1	<0.1	<0.1
0	12	<0.1	<0.1	<0.1	<0.1	2	0	1	<0.1	8	1	11	7	<1	<0.1	<0.1
2	48	<0.1	<0.1	0.1	0	0	0	0.2	0.2	4	2	127	31	1	0.1	<0.1
0	0							0		0		320			0	
0	12	<0.1	<0.1	<0.1	0	2	0	0	<0.1	1	0	128	13	<1	0.1	<0.1
0	88	<0.1	<0.1	0.1	<0.1	<1	0	0.8	0.2	2	3	128	17	1	0.1	<0.1
0	0							0		0		340			0	
1	52							0.4		14	68	430	38		0.1	
1	2	0	<0.1	0	<0.1	0	0	0	<0.1	1	2	205	13	1	0.1	<0.1
<1	3							<1		9	28	354	31		<0.1	
4	33	0.2	<0.1	0.1	0	0	0	0	0.6	3	4	135	17	1	0.2	<0.1
9	22	<0.1	<0.1	<0.1	<0.1	2	<0.1	0.2	1.3	11	23	285	27	2	<0.1	0.1
11	10	<0.1	<0.1	<0.1	<0.1	1	<0.1	0.1	1.4	14	6	317	9	1	0.3	<0.1
0	72	<0.1	<0.1	<0.1	0	0	<0.1	0.6	0.8	4	3	130	10	1	0.1	<0.1
10	0							0		0		220			0	
0	5	<0.1	<0.1	0	<0.1	0	0	0	0.7	1	1	243	7	<1	0.1	<0.1
0	0	0	0	0	0	0	0	0	0.7	0	0	<1	1	0	0	0
8	11							0.1		8	26	287	14		0.1	
0	88	<0.1	<0.1	0.1	<0.1	1	0	0.9	0.5	2	3	152	26	2	0.1	<0.1
2	16	<0.1	<0.1	<0.1	<0.1	1	<0.1	0.4	<0.1	15	12	6	22	2	<0.1	0.1
0	189	<0.1	<0.1	<0.1	0.1	3	0	1.2	0.8	17	20	389	192	10	0.3	0.2
25	0							0		0		600			0	
0	147	<0.1	<0.1	0.3	<0.1	1	0	0.4	0.4	8	11	699	130	8	0.1	0.1
30	200							0		40		360			0	
0	221	<0.1	<0.1	1.6	<0.1	5	0.1	0.1	0.8	9	38	392	103	3	0.5	0.1
0	0							1.2		0		340			0	
5	0							0		0		35			0	

ESHA, EatRight Analysis CD-ROM; **AMT**, amount; **WT**, weight; **CAL**, calories; **KILO**, KiloJoule; **WTR**, water; **PROT**, protein; **CARB**, carbohydrate; **FIBR**, fiber; **FAT**, fat; **SATF**, saturated fat; **MONO**, monounsaturated fat; **POLY**, polyunsaturated fat; **CHOL**, cholesterol;

ESHA CODE	FOOD DESCRIPTION	AMT	UNIT	WT (g)	CAL (kcal)	KILO (kJ)	WTR (g)	PROT (g)	CARB (g)	FIBR (g)	FAT (g)	SATF (g)	MONO (g)	POLY (g)
CONDIMENTS – SAUCES, RELISH, DRESSINGS, DIPS, SPREADS, SPICES, ETC. (CONTINUED)														
53524	Marinara Sauce	0.5	cup	125	109	456	100	2	17	3	3	0.9	0.7	1.5
7563	Miso Sauce	1	cup	248	389	1628	141	13	73	6	7	1	1.5	3.8
53106	Pesto Sauce	2	Tbs	29	155	649	6	6	2	1	14	3.8	8.7	1
53718	Spaghetti Sauce w/Meat-Cnd	0.5	cup	125	60	251	131	3	14	3	1	0		
53010	Spaghetti Sauce w/Meat-Recipe	1	cup	248	287	1201	189	16	21		17	4.5	6.2	4.3
51018	Spaghetti Sauce w/Mushroom-Cnd	0.5	cup	125	60	251	132	2	14	2	1	0		
53471	Tabasco	1	tsp	4.7	1	4	4	<1	<1	<1	<1	<0.1	<0.1	<0.1
53415	Tartar Sauce-NonFat-Kraft	2	Tbs	32	25	105		0	5	0	0	0	0	0
53004	Teriyaki Sauce	1	Tbs	18	16	67	12	1	3	<1	<1	0	0	0
53468	White Sauce	1	cup	250	368	1540	187	10	23	1	27	7.1	11.1	7.2
Spices, Flavors, Seasonings, & Herbs														
26001	Basil-Dried	1	tsp	1.4	4	17	<1	<1	1	1	<1	<0.1	<0.1	<0.1
26040	Celery Seed	1	tsp	2	8	33	<1	<1	1	<1	1	<0.1	0.3	0.1
26002	Chili Powder	1	tsp	2.6	8	33	<1	<1	1	1	<1	0.1	0.1	0.2
26003	Cinnamon	1	tsp	2.3	6	25	<1	<1	2	1	<1	<0.1	<0.1	<0.1
26038	Coriander/Cilantro-Fresh	0.25	cup	4	1	4	4	<1	<1	<1	<1	<0.1	<0.1	<0.1
26004	Curry Powder	1	tsp	2	6	25	<1	<1	1	1	<1	<0.1	0.1	0.1
26021	Dill Weed-Dried	1	tsp	1	3	13	<1	<1	1	<1	<1	<0.1		
26007	Garlic Powder	1	tsp	2.8	9	38	<1	<1	2	<1	<1	<0.1	<0.1	<0.1
26023	Ginger-Ground	1	tsp	1.8	6	25	<1	<1	1	<1	<1	<0.1	<0.1	<0.1
7503	Miso (soybean)	1	cup	275	547	2289	118	32	73	15	17	3.1	3.4	8.8
26008	Onion Powder	1	tsp	2.1	7	29	<1	<1	2	<1	<1	<0.1	<0.1	<0.1
26009	Oregano-Ground	1	tsp	1.5	4	17	<1	<1	1	1	<1	<0.1	<0.1	<0.1
26010	Paprika	1	tsp	2.1	6	25	<1	<1	1	1	<1	<0.1	<0.1	0.2
26012	Parsley-Fresh-Chopped	0.5	cup	30	11	46	26	1	2	1	<1	<0.1	0.1	<0.1
26016	Pepper-Black	1	tsp	2.1	5	21	<1	<1	1	1	<1	<0.1	<0.1	<0.1
26037	Pepper-White	1	tsp	2.4	7	29	<1	<1	2	1	<1	<0.1	<0.1	<0.1
26031	Sage-Ground	1	tsp	0.7	2	8	<1	<1	<1	<1	<1	<0.1	<0.1	<0.1
26014	Salt	.25	tsp	1.5	0	0	<1	0	0	0	0	0	0	0
26091	Salt Substitute (Morton)	0.25	tsp	1.1	1	4	<1	<1	<1	0	<1			
26048	Salt-Light (Morton)	0.25	tsp	1.4	<1		<1	0	<1		<1			
Spreads & Pastes – Cracker or Sandwich														
13095	Chicken Lunchmeat Spread	1	oz	28.35	45	188	16	5	1	<1	5	0.9	1.4	0.7
13034	Ham Salad Spread	1	Tbs	15	32	134	9	1	2	0	2	0.8	1.1	0.4
7081	Hummous/Hummus	2	Tbs	30.75	54	226	20	1	6	1	3	0.4	1.5	0.6
56007	Tuna Salad	.5	cup	102.5	192	803	65	16	10	0	9	1.6	3	4.2
DAIRY PRODUCTS & NON-DAIRY SUBSTITUTES														
Cheese – Natural														
1003	Blue Cheese	.25	cup	33.75	119	498	14	7	1	0	10	6.3	2.6	0.3
1037	Brick Cheese-Shredded	.25	cup	28.25	105	439	12	7	1	0	8	5.3	2.4	0.2
1004	Brie Cheese-Sliced	.25	cup	36	120	502	17	7	<1	0	10	6.3	2.9	0.3
1006	Camembert Cheese	2	Tbs	30.75	92	385	16	6	<1	0	7	4.7	2.2	0.2
1423	Cheddar Cheese-LowFat	1	oz	28.35	70	293	4	8	1	0	4	3		
1448	Cheddar Cheese-LowFat-Shred	0.25	cup	28.25	49	205	18	7	1	0	2	1.2	0.6	0.1
1451	Cheddar Cheese-LowSod-Shred	0.25	cup	28.25	112	469	11	7	1	0	9	5.9	2.6	0.3
1008	Cheddar Cheese-Shredded	0.25	cup	28.25	114	477	10	7	<1	0	9	6	2.7	0.3

< = Trace amount present Blank = Not available

V, vitamin; **THI**, thiamin; **RIB**, riboflavin; **NIA**, niacin; **FOL**, folate; **CALC**, calcium; **PHOS**, phosphorus; **SOD**, sodium; **POT**, potassium; **MAG**, magnesium

CHOL (mg)	V-A (IU)	THI (mg)	RIB (mg)	NIA (mg)	V-B6 (mg)	FOL (μg)	V-B12 (μg)	V-C (mg)	V-E (mg)	CALC (mg)	PHOS (mg)	SOD (mg)	POT (mg)	MAG (mg)	IRON (mg)	ZINC (mg)
2	940	<0.1	0.1	4.9	0.2	16	0	2.5	3	28	45	512	395	26	0.9	0.7
0	97	0.1	0.3	1	0.2	37	0	0	<0.1	77	173	4062	208	53	3.2	3.7
10	290	<0.1	0.1	0.2	<0.1	7	0.2	2.3	1.4	220	113	238	91	16	1.1	0.5
0	750							9		40		720			1.4	
46	2434	0.2	0.3	6	0.5	30	1.4	37.4	5.3	59	173	868	1099	62	3.5	3.4
0	750							9		40		630			1.4	
0	77	<0.1	<0.1	<0.1	<0.1	<1	0	0.2	<0.1	1	1	30	6	1	0.1	<0.1
0	0							0		0		200			0	
0	0	<0.1	<0.1	0.2	<0.1	1	0	0	0	4	28	690	40	11	0.3	<0.1
18	942	0.2	0.5	1	0.1	20	0.7	2	0.7	295	245	885	390	35	0.8	1
0	131	<0.1	<0.1	0.1	<0.1	4	0	0.9	0.1	30	7	<1	48	6	0.6	0.1
0	1	<0.1	<0.1	0.1	<0.1	<1	0	0.3	<0.1	35	11	3	28	9	0.9	0.1
0	771	<0.1	<0.1	0.2	0.1	3	0	1.7	0.8	7	8	26	50	4	0.4	0.1
0	7	<0.1	<0.1	<0.1	<0.1	<1	0	0.1	0.1	23	1	<1	10	1	0.2	<0.1
0	270	<0.1	<0.1	<0.1	<0.1	2	0	1.1	0.1	3	2	2	21	1	0.1	<0.1
0	20	<0.1	<0.1	0.1	<0.1	3	0	0.2	0.4	10	7	1	31	5	0.6	0.1
0	58	<0.1	<0.1	<0.1	<0.1		0	0.5		18	5	2	33	5	0.5	<0.1
0	0	<0.1	<0.1	<0.1	<0.1	1	0	<1	<0.1	2	12	2	33	2	0.2	0.1
0	3	<0.1	<0.1	0.1	<0.1	1	0	0.1	0.3	2	3	1	24	3	0.2	0.1
0	239	0.3	0.6	2.5	0.5	52	0.2	0	<0.1	157	437	10252	578	132	6.8	7
0	0	<0.1	<0.1	<0.1	<0.1	1	0	0.5	<0.1	8	7	2	21	2	0.1	0.1
0	26	<0.1	<0.1	0.1	<0.1	4	0	<1	0.3	24	2	<1	19	4	0.6	<0.1
0	1107	<0.1	<0.1	0.3	0.1	2	0	1.5	0.6	4	7	1	49	4	0.5	0.1
0	2527	<0.1	<0.1	0.4	<0.1	46	0	39.9	0.2	41	17	17	166	15	1.9	0.3
0	6	<0.1	<0.1	<0.1	<0.1	<1	0	0.4	<0.1	9	4	1	26	4	0.6	<0.1
0	0	<0.1	<0.1	<0.1	<0.1	<1	0	0.5		6	4	<1	2	2	0.3	<0.1
0	41	<0.1	<0.1	<0.1	<0.1	2	0	0.2	0.1	12	1	<1	7	3	0.2	<0.1
0	0	0	0	0	0	0	0	0	0	<1	0	581	<1	<1	<0.1	<0.1
0							0					<1	476			
							0			1		276	354	1		
16	28	<0.1	<0.1	0.8	<0.1	1	<0.1	0		5	25	205	30	3	0.2	0.3
6	0	0.1	<0.1	0.3	<0.1	<1	0.1	0	0.3	1	18	137	22	2	0.1	0.2
0	2	<0.1	<0.1	0.1	0.1	18	0	2.4	0.2	15	34	74	53	9	0.5	0.3
13	99	<0.1	0.1	6.9	0.1	8	1.2	2.3		17	182	412	182	19	1	0.6
25	258	<0.1	0.1	0.3	0.1	12	0.4	0	0.1	178	131	471	86	8	0.1	0.9
27	305	<0.1	0.1	<0.1	<0.1	6	0.4	0	0.1	190	127	158	38	7	0.1	0.7
36	213	<0.1	0.2	0.1	0.1	23	0.6	0	0.1	66	68	226	55	7	0.2	0.9
22	252	<0.1	0.2	0.2	0.1	19	0.4	0	0.1	119	107	259	58	6	0.1	0.7
15	300							0		200		170			0	
6	58	<0.1	0.1	<0.1	<0.1	3	0.1	0	<0.1	117	137	173	19	5	0.1	0.5
28	281	<0.1	0.1	<0.1	<0.1	5	0.2	0	0.1	199	137	6	32	8	0.2	0.9
30	283	<0.1	0.1	<0.1	<0.1	5	0.2	0	0.1	204	145	175	28	8	0.2	0.9

ESHA, EatRight Analysis CD-ROM; **AMT**, amount; **WT**, weight; **CAL**, calories; **KILO**, KiloJoule; **WTR**, water; **PROT**, protein; **CARB**, carbohydrate; **FIBR**, fiber; **FAT**, fat; **SATF**, saturated fat; **MONO**, monounsaturated fat; **POLY**, polyunsaturated fat; **CHOL**, cholesterol;

ESHA CODE	FOOD DESCRIPTION	AMT	UNIT	WT (g)	CAL (kcal)	KILO (kJ)	WTR (g)	PROT (g)	CARB (g)	FIBR (g)	FAT (g)	SATF (g)	MONO (g)	POLY (g)
	DAIRY PRODUCTS & NON-DAIRY SUBSTITUTES (CONTINUED)													
1010	Colby Cheese-Shredded	0.25	cup	28.25	111	464	11	7	1	0	9	5.7	2.6	0.3
1047	Cottage Cheese-1% Lowfat	0.5	cup	113	81	339	93	14	3	0	1	0.7	0.3	<0.1
1014	Cottage Cheese-2% lowfat	0.5	cup	113	97	406	91	13	4	0	3	1.1	0.5	0.1
1013	CottageCheese-Crm-Lg Curd	0.5	cup	105	103	431	84	12	4	0	5	1.8	0.8	0.1
1012	CottageCheese-Crm-Sm Curd	0.5	cup	112.5	110	460	90	13	4	0	5	1.9	0.9	0.1
1015	Cream Cheese	1	Tbs	14.5	50	209	8	1	1	0	5	2.8	1.2	0.2
1115	Cream Cheese-FatFree	1	Tbs	16.5	15	63	4	2	<1	0	0	0	0	0
1098	Cream Cheese-LowFat	1	Tbs	15	30	126	10	1	1	0	2	1.4	0.6	0.1
1083	Cream Cheese-Soft	1	Tbs	15	44	184	3	1	1	0	4	2.4		
1050	Edam Cheese	1	oz	28.35	101	423	12	7	<1	0	8	5	2.3	0.2
1016	Feta Cheese-Shredded	0.25	cup	37.5	99	414	21	5	2	0	8	5.6	1.7	0.2
1052	Fontina Cheese-Shredded	0.25	cup	27	105	439	10	7	<1	0	8	5.2	2.3	0.4
1078	Goat cheese-hard	1	oz	28.35	128	536	8	9	1	0	10	7	2.3	0.2
1080	Goat cheese-soft type	1	oz	28.35	76	318	17	5	<1	0	6	4.1	1.4	0.1
1054	Gouda Cheese	1	oz	28.35	101	423	12	7	1	0	8	5	2.2	0.2
1074	Gruyere Cheese-Shredded	0.25	cup	27	112	469	9	8	<1	0	9	5.1	2.7	0.5
1017	Monterey Jack Cheese-Shredded	0.25	cup	28.25	105	439	12	7	<1	0	9	5.4	2.5	0.3
48289	Mozzarella Cheese-LowSod-1"Cube	1	ea	18	50	209	9	5	1	0	3	2	0.9	0.1
1056	Mozzarella Cheese-Whole-Shred	0.25	cup	28	84	351	14	6	1	0	6	3.7	1.8	0.2
1058	Mozzarella-PartSkim-Shredded	0.25	cup	28.25	72	301	15	7	1	0	4	2.9	1.3	0.1
13348	Mozzarella-String-Sticks	1	ea	28	50	209		8	1	0	2	1		
1021	Muenster Cheese-Shredded	0.25	cup	28.25	104	435	12	7	<1	0	8	5.4	2.5	0.2
1060	Neufchatel Cheese	1	oz	28.35	72	301	18	3	1	0	6	3.6	1.6	0.3
1075	Parmesan Cheese-Grated	1	Tbs	5	22	92	1	2	<1	0	1	0.9	0.4	0.1
1112	Parmesan Cheese-Shredded	1	Tbs	5	21	88	1	2	<1	0	1	0.9	0.4	<0.1
1062	Port du Salut Cheese-Shredded	0.25	cup	28.25	99	414	13	7	<1	0	8	4.7	2.6	0.2
1023	Provolone Cheese-Diced	0.25	cup	33	116	485	14	8	1	0	9	5.6	2.4	0.3
1024	Ricotta Cheese-Part Skim	0.5	cup	124	171	715	92	14	6	0	10	6.1	2.9	0.3
1064	Ricotta Cheese-Whole Milk	0.5	cup	124	216	904	89	14	4	0	16	10.3	4.5	0.5
1428	Swiss Cheese-LowFat	1	oz	28.35	90	377	4	8	1	0	6	4		
1027	Swiss Cheese-Shredded	0.25	cup	27	103	431	10	7	1	0	8	4.8	2	0.3
	Cheese – Processed													
1001	American Cheese Food	1	oz	28.35	94	393	12	6	2	0	7	4.4	2	0.2
47928	American Cheese Spread-Slice	1	ea	34	99	414	16	6	3	0	7	4.5	2.1	0.2
1287	American Cheese-Nonfat	1	pce	21.2625	31	130	12	5	2	<1	<1	0.1		
1000	American Processed Cheese	1	pce	21.26	80	335	8	5	<1	0	7	4.2	1.9	0.2
1002	Cheez Whiz/Cheese Spread	2	Tbs	30.5	88	368	15	5	3	0	6	4.1	1.9	0.2
1069	Pimento Proc Cheese-Shred	0.25	cup	28.25	106	444	11	6	<1	<1	9	5.6	2.5	0.3
1071	Swiss Cheese Food	1	oz	28.35	92	385	12	6	1	0	7	4.4	1.9	0.2
1272	Velveeta Cheese Spread	1	oz	28.35	86	360	13	5	3	0	6	4.1		
	Creams & Cream Substitutes													
501	Cream-Coffee/Table	2	Tbs	30	58	243	22	1	1	0	6	3.6	1.7	0.2
500	Cream-Half & Half	2	Tbs	30	39	163	24	1	1	0	3	2.1	1	0.1
502	Cream-Heavy Whipping-Liq	2	Tbs	29.75	103	431	17	1	1	0	11	6.9	3.2	0.4
503	Cream-Hvy Whipping-Whipped	2	Tbs	14.94	52	218	9	<1	<1	0	6	3.4	1.6	0.2
511	Cream-Light Whipping-Liq	2	Tbs	29.88	87	364	19	1	1	0	9	5.8	2.7	0.3

< = Trace amount present   Blank = Not available

V, vitamin; **THI**, thiamin; **RIB**, riboflavin; **NIA**, niacin; **FOL**, folate; **CALC**, calcium; **PHOS**, phosphorus; **SOD**, sodium; **POT**, potassium; **MAG**, magnesium

CHOL (mg)	V-A (IU)	THI (mg)	RIB (mg)	NIA (mg)	V-B6 (mg)	FOL (μg)	V-B12 (μg)	V-C (mg)	V-E (mg)	CALC (mg)	PHOS (mg)	SOD (mg)	POT (mg)	MAG (mg)	IRON (mg)	ZINC (mg)
27	281	<0.1	0.1	<0.1	<0.1	5	0.2	0	0.1	194	129	171	36	7	0.2	0.9
5	46	<0.1	0.2	0.1	0.1	14	0.7	0	<0.1	69	151	459	97	6	0.2	0.4
11	84	<0.1	0.2	0.1	<0.1	11	0.5	0	<0.1	103	184	373	95	8	0.2	0.5
18	147	<0.1	0.2	0.1	<0.1	13	0.5	0	0.1	87	167	382	109	8	0.1	0.4
19	158	<0.1	0.2	0.1	0.1	14	0.5	0	0.1	93	179	410	117	9	0.1	0.5
16	195	<0.1	<0.1	<0.1	<0.1	2	<0.1	0	<0.1	14	15	47	20	1	0.1	0.1
2	250							0		75		100			0	
8	83	<0.1	<0.1	<0.1	<0.1	3	0.1	0	<0.1	22	23	70	37	1	<0.1	0.1
17	145							0		10		63			0	
25	234	<0.1	0.1	<0.1	<0.1	5	0.4	0	0.1	207	152	274	53	9	0.1	1.1
33	158	0.1	0.3	0.4	0.2	12	0.6	0	0.1	185	126	418	23	7	0.2	1.1
31	247	<0.1	0.1	<0.1	<0.1	2	0.5	0	0.1	148	93	216	17	4	0.1	0.9
30	495	<0.1	0.3	0.7	<0.1	1	<0.1	0	0.1	254	207	98	14	15	0.5	0.5
13	293	<0.1	0.1	0.1	0.1	3	0.1	0	0.1	40	73	104	7	5	0.5	0.3
32	160	<0.1	0.1	<0.1	<0.1	6	0.4	0	0.1	198	155	232	34	8	0.1	1.1
30	256	<0.1	0.1	<0.1	<0.1	3	0.4	0	0.1	273	163	91	22	10	<0.1	1.1
25	217	<0.1	0.1	<0.1	<0.1	5	0.2	0	0.1	211	125	151	23	8	0.2	0.8
10	93	<0.1	0.1	<0.1	<0.1	2	0.2	0	<0.1	132	94	3	17	5	<0.1	0.6
22	189	<0.1	0.1	<0.1	<0.1	2	0.6	0	0.1	141	99	176	21	6	0.1	0.8
18	136	<0.1	0.1	<0.1	<0.1	3	0.2	0	<0.1	221	131	175	24	6	0.1	0.8
5	200							0		200		220			0	
27	286	<0.1	0.1	<0.1	<0.1	3	0.4	0	0.1	203	132	177	38	8	0.1	0.8
21	238	<0.1	<0.1	0.1	<0.1	4	0.1	0	0.1	33	39	95	43	3	<0.1	0.2
4	43	<0.1	<0.1	<0.1	<0.1	<1	0.1	0	<0.1	55	36	76	6	2	<0.1	0.2
4	43	<0.1	<0.1	<0.1	<0.1	<1	0.1	0	<0.1	63	37	85	5	3	<0.1	0.2
35	308	<0.1	0.1	<0.1	<0.1	5	0.4	0	0.1	184	102	151	38	7	0.1	0.7
23	290	<0.1	0.1	0.1	<0.1	3	0.5	0	0.1	249	164	289	46	9	0.2	1.1
38	476	<0.1	0.2	0.1	<0.1	16	0.4	0	0.1	337	227	155	155	19	0.5	1.7
63	552	<0.1	0.2	0.1	0.1	15	0.4	0	0.1	257	196	104	130	14	0.5	1.4
20	300							0		250		35			0	
25	224	<0.1	0.1	<0.1	<0.1	2	0.9	0	0.1	214	153	52	21	10	0.1	1.2
18	200	<0.1	0.1	<0.1	<0.1	1	0.4	0		141	113	274	103	9	0.2	0.9
19	222	<0.1	0.1	<0.1	<0.1	2	0.1	0	0.1	191	242	457	82	10	0.1	0.9
3	461		0.1					<1		151	196	276	50		<0.1	0.5
20	201	<0.1	0.1	<0.1	<0.1	2	0.1	0	0.1	117	109	317	36	6	<0.1	0.6
17	199	<0.1	0.1	<0.1	<0.1	2	0.1	0	0.1	171	217	410	74	9	0.1	0.8
27	291	<0.1	0.1	<0.1	<0.1	2	0.2	0.6	0.1	173	210	403	46	6	0.1	0.8
23	243	<0.1	0.1	<0.1	<0.1	2	0.7	0		205	149	440	81	8	0.2	1
23	314		0.1					0.1		132	245	425	95		0.1	0.5
20	197	<0.1	<0.1	<0.1	<0.1	1	0.1	0.2	0.2	29	24	12	37	3	<0.1	0.1
11	106	<0.1	<0.1	<0.1	<0.1	1	0.1	0.3	0.1	32	28	12	39	3	<0.1	0.2
41	437	<0.1	<0.1	<0.1	<0.1	1	0.1	0.2	0.3	19	18	11	22	2	<0.1	0.1
20	220	<0.1	<0.1	<0.1	<0.1	1	<0.1	0.1	0.2	10	9	6	11	1	<0.1	<0.1
33	303	<0.1	<0.1	<0.1	<0.1	1	0.1	0.2	0.3	21	18	10	29	2	<0.1	0.1

ESHA, EatRight Analysis CD-ROM; **AMT**, amount; **WT**, weight; **CAL**, calories; **KILO**, KiloJoule; **WTR**, water; **PROT**, protein; **CARB**, carbohydrate; **FIBR**, fiber; **FAT**, fat; **SATF**, saturated fat; **MONO**, monounsaturated fat; **POLY**, polyunsaturated fat; **CHOL**, cholesterol;

ESHA CODE	FOOD DESCRIPTION	AMT	UNIT	WT (g)	CAL (kcal)	KILO (kJ)	WTR (g)	PROT (g)	CARB (g)	FIBR (g)	FAT (g)	SATF (g)	MONO (g)	POLY (g)
DAIRY PRODUCTS & NON-DAIRY SUBSTITUTES (CONTINUED)														
540	Cremora NonDairy Creamer	1	tsp	2	10	42	0	0	1	0	1	1	0	0
517	Mocha Mix Creamer	1	Tbs	14.2	19	79	2	<1	1	0	2			
504	Sour Cream-Cultured	2	Tbs	28.75	55	230	21	1	1	0	6	3.3	1.5	0.2
505	Sour Cream-Imitation	2	Tbs	28.75	60	251	20	1	2	0	6	5.1	0.2	<0.1
515	Sour Cream-LowCal	2	Tbs	30	40	167	24	1	1	0	4	2.2	1	0.1
54316	Soy Creamer-French Vanilla	1	Tbs	16	21	88	12	0	3	0	1	0		
54317	Soy Creamer-Hazelnut	1	Tbs	16	21	88	12	0	3	0	1	0		
54315	Soy Creamer-Plain	1	Tbs	15.38	15	63	13	0	1	0	1	0		
Milks & Non-Dairy Milk Substitutes														
7	Buttermilk-Cultured-Skim	1	cup	245	98	410	221	8	12	0	2	1.3	0.6	0.1
21109	Chocolate Milk+Calc-LowFat	1	cup	250	195	816	205	7	30	2	5	2.9	1.1	0.2
19	Chocolate Milk-1% Fat	1	cup	250	158	661	206	8	26	1	2	1.5	0.8	0.1
18	Chocolate Milk-2% Fat	1	cup	250	190	795	205	7	30	2	5	2.9	1.1	0.2
20	Chocolate Milk-Whole	1	cup	250	208	870	206	8	26	2	8	5.3	2.5	0.3
72	Eggnog-Prep w/milk	1	cup	272	258	1079	215	8	39	0	8	4.6	2.1	0.5
17	Eggnog-Whole Milk	1	cup	254	224	937	210	12	20	0	11	6.6	3.3	0.5
10	Evaporated Milk-Skim	2	Tbs	32	25	105	25	2	4	0	<1	<0.1	<0.1	<0.1
23	Goat Milk	1	cup	244	168	703	212	9	11	0	10	6.5	2.7	0.4
54	Lactose Reduced Milk-1% Fat	1	cup	246	103	431	222	8	12	0	3	1.6	0.8	0.1
130	Milk Substitute	1	cup	244	149	623	215	4	15	0	8	7.4	0.4	<0.1
164	Milk, evaporated, low fat	2	Tbs	31.7	25	105		2	3	0	<1	0.5	0	0
21097	Milk, skim, lactose free w/ Vit A&D	1	cup	245	80	335	547	8	12	0	0	0	0	0
4	Milk-1% Fat	1	cup	244	102	427	219	8	12	0	2	1.5	0.7	0.1
2	Milk-2% Fat	1	cup	244	122	510	218	8	12	0	5	2.5	2.1	0.3
6	Milk-NonFat	1	cup	245	83	347	223	8	12	0	<1	0.1	0.1	<0.1
1	Milk-Whole, 3.25%	1	cup	244	149	623	215	8	12	0	8	4.6	2	0.5
57	Nonfat Dry Milk Powder+Water	1	cup	245	82	343	223	8	12	0	<1	0.1	<0.1	<0.1
20145	So Good Lite Soy Drink	1	cup	260	114	477	229	9	17	2	2	0.3	0.5	1
20144	So Good Soy Drink	1	cup	255	158	661	222	8	13	2	8	0.8	2	4.6
20033	Soy Milk	1	cup	245	132	552	216	8	15	1	4	0.5	1	2.4
7801	Soy Milk Bev-Carob (Eden)	1	cup	244	170	711		7	27	0	4	0.5	1	2
7775	Soy Milk Bev-Vanilla (VitaSoy)	1	cup	228.3	112	469	498	7	12	1	4	0.5		
20920	Soy Milk-Chocolate	1	cup	250	145	607	216	5	24	2	4	0.5		
20916	Soy Milk-Plain-organic	1	cup	245	100	418	224	7	8	1	4	0.5		
20918	Soy Milk-Van-organic	1	cup	246	101	423	225	6	10	1	4	0.5		
11	Sweetened Condensed Milk	2	Tbs	38.25	123	515	10	3	21	0	3	2.1	0.9	0.1
Yogurts & Non-Dairy Yogurt Substitutes														
11994	Soy Yogurt-Strawberry	1	ea	170.1	140	586		5	22	3	3	0		
7546	Tofu Yogurt	1	cup	262	246	1029	203	9	42	1	5	0.7	1	2.7
2001	Yogurt-LowFat-Fruit	1	cup	245	250	1046	182	11	47	0	3	1.7	0.7	0.1
2000	Yogurt-LowFat-Plain	1	cup	245	154	644	208	13	17	0	4	2.4	1	0.1
2012	Yogurt-NonFat-Plain	1	cup	245	137	573	209	14	19	0	<1	0.3	0.1	<0.1
11982	Yogurt-Nonfat-Vanilla	1	cup	226	220	920		12	40	0	0	0	0	0
72086	Yogurt-Nonfat-Vanilla+LoCalSwtnr	1	cup	225	97	406	197	9	17	0	<1	0.3	0.1	<0.1
2428	Yogurt-Strawberry-Light	1	cup	227	220	920	391	8	42	0	2	1.5		
2013	Yogurt-Whole Milk-Plain	1	cup	245	149	623	215	9	11	0	8	5.1	2.2	0.2

< = Trace amount present   Blank = Not available

V, vitamin; **THI**, thiamin; **RIB**, riboflavin; **NIA**, niacin; **FOL**, folate; **CALC**, calcium; **PHOS**, phosphorus; **SOD**, sodium; **POT**, potassium; **MAG**, magnesium

CHOL (mg)	V-A (IU)	THI (mg)	RIB (mg)	NIA (mg)	V-B6 (mg)	FOL (μg)	V-B12 (μg)	V-C (mg)	V-E (mg)	CALC (mg)	PHOS (mg)	SOD (mg)	POT (mg)	MAG (mg)	IRON (mg)	ZINC (mg)
0	0					0		0		0		10	15		0	
0											8		20	0		
15	179	<0.1	<0.1	<0.1	<0.1	2	0.1	0.3	0.1	32	33	23	41	3	<0.1	0.1
0	0	0	0	0	0	0	0	0	0.2	1	13	29	46	2	0.1	0.3
12	112	<0.1	<0.1	<0.1	<0.1	3	0.1	0.3	0.1	31	28	12	39	3	<0.1	0.2
0	0							0		0		11			0	
0	0							32		0		11			0	
0	0							0		0		10			0	
10	115	0.1	0.4	0.1	0.1	12	0.5	2.4	0.1	284	218	257	370	27	0.1	1
20	568	0.1	1.4	0.4	0.1	5	0.8	0	0.1	485	190	165	308	35	0.6	1
8	490	0.1	0.4	0.3	0.1	12	0.8	2.2	<0.1	290	258	152	425	32	0.7	1
20	568	0.1	0.5	0.4	0.1	5	0.8	0	0.1	272	255	165	422	35	0.6	1
30	245	0.1	0.4	0.3	0.1	12	0.8	2.2	0.2	280	252	150	418	32	0.6	1
30	256	0.1	0.5	0.3	0.1	14	1.1	0	0.2	250	209	150	329	27	0.3	1
150	523	0.1	0.5	0.3	0.1	3	1.1	3.8	0.5	330	277	137	419	48	0.5	1.2
1	126	<0.1	0.1	0.1	<0.1	3	0.1	0.4	0	93	62	37	106	9	0.1	0.3
27	483	0.1	0.3	0.7	0.1	2	0.2	3.2	0.2	327	271	122	498	34	0.1	0.7
10	504	0.1	0.4	0.2	0.1	13	0.9	2.4	0.1	303	237	124	384	34	0.1	1
0	0	<0.1	0.2	0	0	0	0	0		81	181	190	278	15	1	2.9
5	100		0.1					0		80	60	35	100		0	
5	500							0		500		125	460		0	
12	478	<0.1	0.5	0.2	0.1	12	1.1	0	<0.1	305	232	107	366	27	0.1	1
20	464	0.1	0.5	0.2	0.1	12	1.3	0.5	0.1	293	224	115	342	27	<0.1	1.2
5	500	0.1	0.4	0.2	0.1	12	1.2	0	<0.1	299	247	103	382	27	0.1	1
24	395	0.1	0.4	0.2	0.1	12	1.1	0	0.2	276	205	105	322	24	0.1	0.9
4	539	0.1	0.4	0.2	0.1	11	0.9	1.3	<0.1	285	224	132	388	29	0.1	1.1
0	1014	0.2	0.5		0.2	26	0.8	5.2		257		94	322		2.1	0.5
0	994	0.2	0.5		0.2	26	0.8	5.1		252		92	316		2	0.5
0	7	0.1	0.2	1.3	0.2	44	0	0	0.3	61	127	125	289	61	1.6	0.3
0	0	0.3	0.1	2	0.2	80		0		75	125	95	350	58	1.3	0.8
0	0							0		37		108	299		0.7	
0	515		0.5			25	3.1	0		308		102	360	40	1.5	0.6
0	505		0.5			24	3	0		301		120	301	39	1.1	0.6
0	507		0.5			25	3	0		303		96	303	39	1.1	0.6
13	102	<0.1	0.2	0.1	<0.1	4	0.2	1	0.1	109	97	49	142	10	0.1	0.4
0	0							96	23.2	150		20			1.1	
0	86	0.2	0.1	0.6	0.1	16	0	6.6	0.8	309	100	92	123	105	2.8	0.8
10	88	0.1	0.4	0.2	0.1	22	1.2	1.7	<0.1	372	292	142	478	37	0.2	1.8
15	125	0.1	0.5	0.3	0.1	27	1.4	2	0.1	448	353	172	573	42	0.2	2.2
5	17	0.1	0.6	0.3	0.1	29	1.5	2.2	0	488	385	189	625	47	0.2	2.4
5	500							3.6		450		180			0	
4	14	0.1	0.4	0.2	0.1	18	1	2.5	0	322	245	133	398	29	0.3	1.5
15	1000	0.1	0.2					0		250	200	130	390		0	
32	243	0.1	0.3	0.2	0.1	17	0.9	1.2	0.1	296	233	113	380	29	0.1	1.4

ESHA, EatRight Analysis CD-ROM; **AMT**, amount; **WT**, weight; **CAL**, calories; **KILO**, KiloJoule; **WTR**, water; **PROT**, protein; **CARB**, carbohydrate; **FIBR**, fiber; **FAT**, fat; **SATF**, saturated fat; **MONO**, monounsaturated fat; **POLY**, polyunsaturated fat; **CHOL**, cholesterol;

ESHA CODE	FOOD DESCRIPTION	AMT	UNIT	WT (g)	CAL (kcal)	KILO (kJ)	WTR (g)	PROT (g)	CARB (g)	FIBR (g)	FAT (g)	SATF (g)	MONO (g)	POLY (g)
DESSERTS														
Brownies & Dessert Squares														
47000	Brownie+Nuts+Icing-Commerc	1	ea	61	247	1033	8	3	39	1	10	2.6	5.5	1.4
47019	Brownie-FudgeNut-Recipe	1	ea	24	112	469	3	1	12		7	1.8	2.6	2.3
47078	Lemon Bar Cookie	1	ea	16	69	289	2	1	10	<1	3	0.6	1.4	0.8
44219	Rice Krispies Treats-Square	1	ea	22	91	381	1	1	18	<1	2	0.3	0.6	1.1
Cakes														
46004	Angelfood Cake-1/12	1	pce	28.35	73	305	9	2	16	<1	<1	<0.1	<0.1	0.1
46098	Applesauce Cake-No Icing	1	pce	87	313	1310	20	3	52	2	12	2.4	5	3.5
46103	Banana Cake-No Icing	1	pce	87	262	1096	29	3	46	1	8	1.6	3.6	2.1
49004	Cheesecake (pce=1/12)	1	pce	80	257	1075	36	4	20	<1	18	7.9	6.9	1.3
49001	Cheesecake-Mix-Prepared	1	pce	99	271	1134	44	5	35	2	13	6.6	4.5	0.8
46275	Choc Fudge Cake-Frzn	1	pce	69	250	1046		3	31	1	11	3		
71626	Choc Ganache Cheesecake-1/13	1	pce	153	580	2427		9	52		39	20		
46013	Chocolate Cake+Choc Icing	1	pce	64	235	983	15	3	35	2	10	3.1	5.6	1.2
46118	Chocolate Cake+Van Icing	1	pce	103	367	1536	48	3	53	1	17	4.3		
46093	CoffeeCake-Cinn+Crumb Top	1	pce	63	263	1100	14	4	29	1	15	3.7	8.2	2
46097	CoffeeCake-Fruit	1	pce	50	156	653	16	3	26	1	5	1.2	2.8	0.7
46106	Date Pudding Cake	1	pce	42	131	548	14	2	19	1	6	3	1.9	0.3
46000	Gingerbread Cake-Homemade	1	pce	74	263	1100	21	3	36		12	3.1	5.3	3.1
71650	Lemon Layer Cake-Frzn	1	pce	88	290	1213		2	43	0	12	3.5		
46070	Pineapple UpsideDown Cake-1/9	1	pce	115	367	1536	37	4	58	1	14	3.4	6	3.8
46107	Plum Pudding Cake	1	pce	42	131	548	14	2	19	1	6	3	1.9	0.3
46016	Pound Cake w/Butter	1	pce	28.35	110	460	7	2	14	<1	6	3.3	1.7	0.3
46011	Snack Cake/Choc+Filling	1	ea	50	200	837	9	2	30	2	8	2.4	4.3	0.9
46116	Spice Cake w/Icing	1	pce	109	368	1540	29	5	62	1	12	3.2	5.9	1.9
46078	Sponge Cake-Recipe	1	pce	63	187	782	19	5	36	1	3	0.8	1	0.4
46008	Twinkie Snack Cake	1	ea	42.5	159	665	8	1	27	<1	5	1.8	2.1	0.8
46007	White Cake+Choc Frosting	1	pce	100	428	1791	6	2	75	1	14	7.2		
46012	Yellow Cake w/Choc Icing	1	pce	64	243	1017	14	2	35	1	11	3	6.1	1.4
Candies, Confections, & Gums														
23136	100 Grand Candy Bar-Fun Size	1	ea	42.52	199	833	3	1	30	<1	8	5.1	2.6	0.6
23125	5th Avenue Candy Bar	1	ea	56.7	273	1142	1	5	36	2	14	3.8	6	1.9
23049	Almond Joy Candy Bar	1	ea	48.19	231	967	4	2	29	2	13	8.5	2.5	0.6
23110	Baby Ruth Candy Bar	1	ea	59.53	273	1142	4	3	39	1	13	7.2	3.3	1.6
4148	Bit-O-Honey Candy	1	ea	48.1	180	753	4	1	38	<1	4	2.6	0.5	0.2
23226	Breathsaver Mints-Spearmint	1	pce	2	10	42	0	0	2	0	0	0	0	0
23066	Butterfinger Candy Bar	1	ea	61.23	281	1176	1	3	45	1	12	5.8	3.1	1.9
23115	Butterscotch Candy	5	pce	30	117	490	2	<1	27	0	1	0.6	0.3	<0.1
92671	Cadbury Almond Candy Bar	10	pce	40	220	920	1	4	21	1	13	7		
23116	Caramello Candy Bar	1	ea	45.36	210	879	3	3	29	1	10	5.8	2.4	0.3
23015	Caramel-Plain/Chocolate	1	pce	10.1	39	163	1	<1	8	0	1	0.3	0.2	0.4
23082	Chewing Gum	1	pce	3	11	46	<1	0	3	<1	<1	<0.1	<0.1	<0.1
92196	Chewing Gum-NoSugar	1	pce	2	5	21	<1	0	2	<1	<1	<0.1	<0.1	<0.1
92197	Choc Candy-Dietetic	1	oz	28.35	168	703	1	3	11	1	12	6.2	3.1	1.2
90658	ChocCvrd Fondant Candy-Lrg	1	ea	43	157	657	3	1	35	1	4	2.3	1.3	0.1
23063	Chocolate Candy Kisses	6	pce	28.35	145	607	<1	2	17	1	9	5.2	2.8	0.3

< = Trace amount present Blank = Not available

V, vitamin; **THI**, thiamin; **RIB**, riboflavin; **NIA**, niacin; **FOL**, folate; **CALC**, calcium; **PHOS**, phosphorus; **SOD**, sodium; **POT**, potassium; **MAG**, magnesium

CHOL (mg)	V-A (IU)	THI (mg)	RIB (mg)	NIA (mg)	V-B6 (mg)	FOL (μg)	V-B12 (μg)	V-C (mg)	V-E (mg)	CALC (mg)	PHOS (mg)	SOD (mg)	POT (mg)	MAG (mg)	IRON (mg)	ZINC (mg)
10	42	0.2	0.1	1	<0.1	29	<0.1	0	0.1	18	62	190	91	19	1.4	0.4
18	198	<0.1	<0.1	0.2	<0.1	7	<0.1	0.1		14	32	82	42	13	0.4	0.2
12	137	<0.1	<0.1	0.2	<0.1	2	<0.1	0.6	0.4	7	12	42	11	1	0.2	0.1
0	238	0.3	0.3	3.6	0.2	24	0	0		1	9	77	9	3	0.3	0.1
0	0	<0.1	0.1	0.3	<0.1	10	<0.1	0		40	92	212	26	3	0.1	<0.1
22	38	0.1	0.1	1.1	0.1	6	<0.1	0.9	1.6	17	45	141	145	11	1.4	0.2
32	371	0.1	0.2	1.2	0.2	11	0.1	2.9	1.2	26	50	181	168	15	1.1	0.3
44	438	<0.1	0.2	0.2	<0.1	14	0.1	0.3	0.4	41	74	166	72	9	0.5	0.4
29	362	0.1	0.3	0.5	0.1	30	0.3	0.5		170	232	376	209	19	0.5	0.5
30	0							0		0		160			1.1	
135	150							0		60		330			0.4	
27	54	<0.1	0.1	0.4	<0.1	11	0.1	0.1		28	78	214	128	22	1.4	0.4
23	258	0.1	0.1	1	<0.1	33	0.1	0.2	0.9	23	47	232	61	11	1	0.3
20	70	0.1	0.1	1.1	<0.1	38	0.1	0.2		34	68	221	77	14	1.2	0.5
4	70	<0.1	0.1	1.3	<0.1	24	<0.1	0.4		22	59	192	45	8	1.2	0.3
15	34	0.1	0.1	0.5	0.1	3	0.1	0.4	0.2	46	36	66	199	23	1	0.2
24	36	0.1	0.1	1.3	0.1	24	<0.1	0.1		53	40	242	325	52	2.1	0.3
35												250				
25	291	0.2	0.2	1.4	<0.1	30	0.1	1.4		138	94	367	129	15	1.7	0.4
15	34	0.1	0.1	0.5	0.1	3	0.1	0.4	0.2	46	36	66	199	23	1	0.2
63	172	<0.1	0.1	0.4	<0.1	12	0.1	0		10	39	113	34	3	0.4	0.1
0	1	<0.1	<0.1	0.5	0.1	13	<0.1	0.9	0.5	58	44	194	88	18	1.8	0.5
50	145	0.1	0.2	1.1	<0.1	9	0.1	0.1	2.2	76	209	281	136	13	1.5	0.4
107	163	0.1	0.2	0.8	<0.1	25	0.2	0		26	63	144	89	6	1	0.4
17	7	0.1	0.1	0.7	0	16	0.1	<1	0.3	10	79	170	30	3	0.6	0.3
21	278	0.1	0.1	1.1	<0.1	30	<0.1	<1	0.5	43	148	356	80	19	0.9	0.3
35	70	0.1	0.1	0.8	<0.1	14	0.1	0		24	103	216	114	19	1.3	0.4
5	54	<0.1	0.1	0.1	<0.1	2	0.1	0.3	0.2	32	37	86	69	11	0.1	0.4
3	29	0.1	0.1	2.2	0.1	20	0.1	0.2	1.5	41	80	128	197	35	0.7	0.6
2	20							0.3		31	54	68	122		0.6	
0	0	<0.1	0.1	0.7	<0.1	7	<0.1	0	0.6	28	56	137	148	26	0.4	0.4
0	0	<0.1	<0.1	<0.1	<0.1	1	<0.1	0.4	0.1	17	13	142	21	3	0.1	0.2
0												0	0			
0	0	0.1	<0.1	1.6	<0.1	17	<0.1	0	1.1	22	59	141	135	29	0.5	0.6
3	30	<0.1	<0.1	<0.1	0	0	0	0	<0.1	1	<1	117	1	0	<0.1	<0.1
10	0							0		100		80			0.4	
12	137							0.8		97	68	55	155		0.5	
1	4	<0.1	<0.1	<0.1	<0.1	<1	<0.1	<1	<0.1	14	12	25	22	2	<0.1	<0.1
0	0	0	0	0	0	0	0	0	0	0	0	<1	<1	0	0	0
0	0	0	0	0	0	0	0	0	0	<1	0	<1	0	0	0	0
6	57	<0.1	0.1	0.4	<0.1	7	0.2	0.5	0.8	81	93	32	172	28	0.8	0.8
0	0	<0.1	<0.1	0.2	<0.1	1	0	0	0.1	7	41	11	72	27	0.7	0.2
6	52	<0.1	0.1	0.1	<0.1	2	0.1	0.1	0.4	54	61	23	109	17	0.4	0.4

ESHA, EatRight Analysis CD-ROM; **AMT**, amount; **WT**, weight; **CAL**, calories; **KILO**, KiloJoule; **WTR**, water; **PROT**, protein; **CARB**, carbohydrate; **FIBR**, fiber; **FAT**, fat; **SATF**, saturated fat; **MONO**, monounsaturated fat; **POLY**, polyunsaturated fat; **CHOL**, cholesterol;

ESHA CODE	FOOD DESCRIPTION	AMT	UNIT	WT (g)	CAL (kcal)	KILO (kJ)	WTR (g)	PROT (g)	CARB (g)	FIBR (g)	FAT (g)	SATF (g)	MONO (g)	POLY (g)
DESSERTS (CONTINUED)														
23021	Chocolate Coated Peanuts	1	cup	149	773	3234	3	20	74	7	50	21.8	19.3	6.5
23022	Chocolate Covered Raisins	1	cup	190	741	3100	21	8	130	6	28	19.5	6	1.1
23047	Chocolate Peanut Candy	0.25	cup	42.5	219	916	1	4	26	2	11	4.3	3.4	1.5
23074	Dietetic Hard Candy	1	pce	3	12	50	<1	0	3	0	0	0	0	0
93360	Divinity Candy	1	pce	11	40	167	1	<1	10	0	<1	0	0	0
23036	English Toffee Candy Bar	1	ea	39.69	212	887	1	1	24	1	13	7.5	3.7	0.5
23024	Fondant Candy	1	pce	16	60	251	1	0	15	0	<1	0	0	0
23025	Fudge-Chocolate	1	pce	17	70	293	2	<1	13	<1	2	1.1	0.5	0.1
23026	Fudge-Chocolate-Nuts	1	pce	19	88	368	1	1	13	<1	4	1.2	0.7	1.4
23129	Golden AlmondChoc Bar	1	ea	79.38	458	1916		10	37	3	31	13.2		
23130	Golden AlmondChoc Candies	1	ea	78	445	1862		9	37	3	29	11.9		
23132	Goobers Choc Peanut-Pce	10	pce	10	51	213	<1	1	5	1	3	1.2		
92647	Good & Plenty Candy-SnackSz	1	ea	17	60	251		0	14	0	0	0	0	0
23029	Gumdrops Candy-Small	10	pce	36	143	598	<1	0	36	<1	0	0	0	0
23030	Gummy Bears Candy	10	pce	22	87	364	<1	0	22	<1	0	0	0	0
23031	Hard Candy, all flavors	1	pce	6	24	100	<1	0	6	0	<1	0	0	0
23033	Jelly Beans Candy	10	pce	11	41	172	1	0	10	<1	<1	0	0	0
23060	Kit Kat candy bar	1	ea	42.52	220	920	1	3	27	<1	11	7.6	2.5	0.4
23061	Krackle candy bar	1	ea	42.52	218	912	<1	3	27	1	11	6.8	2.7	0.2
23047	M&M's Peanut Choc Candy-Pkg	1	cup	170	876	3665	4	16	103	6	44	17.3	13.7	5.9
23037	Mars Candy Bar-Fun Size	1	ea	50	234	979	2	4	31	1	12	3.6	5.3	2
23007	Marshmallows	1	ea	7.2	23	96	1	<1	6	<1	<1	<0.1	<0.1	<0.1
23018	Milk Choc Bar+Almonds	1	ea	41.10	216	904	1	4	22	3	14	7.3	4.9	1.2
23058	Milk Choc Bar+RiceCereal	1	ea	39.69	203	849	1	3	24	1	12	6.3	3.4	0.3
23045	Milk Chocolate Candy	0.25	cup	52	256	1071	1	2	37	1	11	6.8	2.7	0.5
23016	Milk Chocolate Candy Bar	1	ea	43.94	235	983	1	3	26	1	13	8.1	3.2	0.6
23016	Milk Chocolate Candy Bar	1	ea	44	235	983	1	3	26	1	13	8.1	3.2	0.6
23038	Milky Way Candy Bar	1	ea	59.53	271	1134	4	2	42	1	10	7.2	1.3	0.2
23035	Mounds Candy Bar	1	ea	53.86	262	1096	5	2	32	2	14	11.1	0.2	0.1
23062	Mr. Goodbar Candy Bar	1	ea	49.61	267	1117	<1	5	27	2	16	7	4.1	2.2
23135	Oh Henry! Candy Bar	1	ea	56.7	262	1096	1	4	37	1	13	5.4	3.1	1.5
23081	Peanut Brittle-Homemade	1.5	oz	42.53	207	866	<1	3	30	1	8	1.8	3.4	1.9
90803	Praline Candy-f/Recipe	1	pce	39.94	174	728	3	1	22	1	10	2.7		
23043	Reese's Peanut Butter Cup	1	ea	45.36	234	979	1	5	25	2	14	4.9	5.9	2.5
23140	Reese's Pieces Candy	10	pce	8	40	167	<1	1	5	<1	2	1.3	0.4	0.2
23141	Rolo Caramel Candy	1	pce	3	14	59	<1	<1	2	<1	1	0.4	0.1	<0.1
23142	Sesame Crunch Candy	20	pce	35	181	757	1	4	18	3	12	1.6	4.4	5.1
23431	Skittles Candy	1.5	oz	42.53	172	720	2	<1	39	0	2	1.8	0	0
23040	Snickers Candy Bar	1	ea	56.7	278	1163	3	4	35	1	14	5.1	4.5	1.7
23057	Special Dark Candy Bar	1	ea	41.10	229	958	<1	2	25	3	13		2.1	0.2
23144	Starburst Fruit Candy	1	pce	5	20	84	<1	<1	4	0	<1	0.4	0	0
91520	Sugar Coated Almonds	1	ea	3.5	17	71	<1	<1	2	<1	1	0.1	0.4	0.1
23146	Symphony Candy Bar	1	ea	42.52	226	946	<1	4	25	1	13	7.8	3.4	0.3
93430	Taffy Candy	1	pce	15	60	251	1	<1	14	0	<1	0.3	0.1	<0.1
23075	Three Musketeers Candy Bar	1	ea	60.38	263	1100	4	2	47	1	8	5.2	1.4	0.2
23076	Three Musketeer-Fun Size	1	ea	16.5	72	301	1	<1	13	<1	2	1.4	0.4	0.1

< = Trace amount present   Blank = Not available

V, vitamin; **THI**, thiamin; **RIB**, riboflavin; **NIA**, niacin; **FOL**, folate; **CALC**, calcium; **PHOS**, phosphorus; **SOD**, sodium; **POT**, potassium; **MAG**, magnesium

CHOL (mg)	V-A (IU)	THI (mg)	RIB (mg)	NIA (mg)	V-B6 (mg)	FOL (μg)	V-B12 (μg)	V-C (mg)	V-E (mg)	CALC (mg)	PHOS (mg)	SOD (mg)	POT (mg)	MAG (mg)	IRON (mg)	ZINC (mg)
13	195	0.2	0.3	6.3	0.1	76	0.8	0	3.6	155	316	61	748	143	2	3.9
6	173	0.2	0.3	0.8	0.1	15	0.7	0.4	0.6	163	272	68	977	86	3.2	2.4
3	31	<0.1	<0.1	1.4	<0.1	23	0.1	0	1.2	43	81	21	147	29	0.5	0.7
0	0	0	0	0	0	0	0	0	0	0	0	0	0	0	0	0
0	0	<0.1	<0.1	<0.1	<0.1	0	<0.1	0	0	1	<1	4	3	<1	<0.1	<0.1
21	285	<0.1	<0.1	0.1		1		0.2			24	126	61	4	0.2	0.1
0	0	<0.1	<0.1	0	0	0	0	0	0	<1	0	2	1	0	<0.1	<0.1
2	27	<0.1	<0.1	<0.1	<0.1	1	<0.1	0	<0.1	8	12	8	23	6	0.3	0.2
2	27	<0.1	<0.1	0.1	<0.1	3	<0.1	<1	<0.1	11	22	7	35	10	0.4	0.3
10								0		152		51			1.5	
10	0							0		158		41			2	
1	7							<1		9		4	50		0.1	
0	0							0		0		40			0.1	
0	0	<0.1	<0.1	<0.1	<0.1	0	0	0	0	1	<1	16	2	<1	0.1	0
0	0	<0.1	<0.1	<0.1	<0.1	0	0	0	0	1	<1	10	1	<1	0.1	0
0	0	<0.1	<0.1	<0.1	<0.1	0	0	0	0	<1	<1	2	<1	<1	<0.1	<0.1
0	0	<0.1	<0.1	<0.1	<0.1	0	0	0	0	<1	<1	6	4	<1	<0.1	<0.1
5	34	<0.1	0.1	0.2	<0.1	6	0.2	0	0.1	53	57	23	98	16	0.4	<0.1
5	43	<0.1	0.1	0.1	<0.1	3		0.3		67	52	83	138	6	0.5	0.2
14	126	0.1	0.2	5.7	0.2	94	0.5	0	4.8	173	323	85	590	117	2	3
8	26	<0.1	0.2	0.5	<0.1	4	0.2	0.3	3.9	84	117	85	162	36	0.6	0.6
0	0	<0.1	<0.1	<0.1	<0.1	<1	0	0	0	<1	1	6	<1	<1	<0.1	<0.1
8	72	<0.1	0.2	0.3	<0.1	6	0.3	0.1	1.3	92	109	30	182	37	0.7	0.6
9	86	0.1	0.1	0.3	<0.1	7	0.3	0.2	0.2	74	82	34	147	25	1.1	0.9
7	97	<0.1	0.1	0.1	<0.1	4	0.3	0.3	0.2	55	76	32	136	23	0.6	0.8
10	86	<0.1	0.1	0.2	<0.1	5	0.3	0	0.2	83	91	35	163	28	1	1
10	86	<0.1	0.1	0.2	<0.1	5	0.3	0	0.2	83	92	35	164	28	1	1
5	65	<0.1	0.1	0.1	<0.1	2	0.1	0.4	0.5	68	40	99	74	12	0.3	0.4
1	0	<0.1	<0.1	0.1	<0.1	3	0	0.2	0.1	11	49	78	173	30	1.1	0.6
5	62	0.1	0.1	1.7	<0.1	19	0.2	0.4	1.6	55	81	20	195	23	0.7	0.5
4	0	0.1	0.1	1.4	<0.1	25	0.1	0	1.3	39	79	109	147	29	0.3	0.7
5	60	0.1	<0.1	1.1	<0.1	20	<0.1	0	1.1	11	45	189	71	18	0.5	0.4
10	148	0.1	<0.1	0.1	<0.1	2	<0.1	0.2	0.4	20	33	40	67	13	0.3	0.4
3	25	0.1	<0.1	2	<0.1	23	0.1	0.1	0.1	35	73	142	156	28	0.5	0.6
0	0	<0.1	<0.1	0.5	<0.1	4	<0.1	0	0.1	6	17	16	29	7	<0.1	0.1
<1	4	<0.1	<0.1	<0.1	0	0	<0.1	<1	<0.1	4	2	6	6	0	<0.1	0
0	2	0.2	0.1	1.3	0.2	18	0	0	0.1	224	144	58	107	88	1.5	1.3
0	0	0	<0.1	<0.1	<0.1	0	0	28.4	0.1	0	<1	6	5	<1	0	<0.1
7	91	<0.1	0.1	2	0.1	15	0.1	0.3	0.9	53	108	139	183	41	0.4	1.4
2		0	<0.1	0	0	0		0		12	21	2	206	13	0.9	<0.1
0	<1	<0.1	<0.1	<0.1	0	<1	0	2.9	<0.1	0	<1	<1	<1	<1	<0.1	0
0	<1	<0.1	<0.1	<0.1	<0.1	1	0	0	0.4	4	6	<1	9	5	0.1	0.1
10	97							0.9		107	88	43	186		0.4	
1	15	<0.1	<0.1	<0.1	0	0	<0.1	0	<0.1	1	<1	8	<1	0	<0.1	<0.1
3	40	<0.1	<0.1	0.1	<0.1	2	0.1	0.1	0.6	33	42	117	80	18	0.4	0.3
1	11	<0.1	<0.1	<0.1	<0.1	1	<0.1	<1	0.2	9	11	32	22	5	0.1	0.1

ESHA, EatRight Analysis CD-ROM; **AMT**, amount; **WT**, weight; **CAL**, calories; **KILO**, KiloJoule; **WTR**, water; **PROT**, protein; **CARB**, carbohydrate; **FIBR**, fiber; **FAT**, fat; **SATF**, saturated fat; **MONO**, monounsaturated fat; **POLY**, polyunsaturated fat; **CHOL**, cholesterol;

ESHA CODE	FOOD DESCRIPTION	AMT	UNIT	WT (g)	CAL (kcal)	KILO (kJ)	WTR (g)	PROT (g)	CARB (g)	FIBR (g)	FAT (g)	SATF (g)	MONO (g)	POLY (g)
DESSERTS (CONTINUED)														
23117	Tootsie Roll Candy-BiteSz	7	ea	49	194	812	3	1	42	<1	2	0.5	1.9	0.1
23486	Turtles Candy	2	pce	40	160	669		2	16	1	11	3		
23154	Twizzlers-Small Pkg	1	ea	70.87	248	1038		2	57	0	2	0		
23151	Whatchamacallit Candy Bar	1	ea	48.2	238	996	1	4	30	1	11	8.2	1.8	0.4
23507	Yogurt Covered Raisins	35	pce	40	160	669	2	1	28	1	5	1		
23152	York Peppermint Patty-Lrg	1	ea	42	161	674	4	1	34	1	3	1.8	0.2	<0.1
Cookies														
91664	Almond Cookie	2	ea	29	170	711		2	19	0	10	3		
47005	Butter Cookie-Thin	5	ea	25	117	490	1	2	17	<1	5	2.8	1.4	0.2
47075	Butterscotch Brownie	1	ea	34	152	636	4	2	20	<1	8	1.4	3.3	2.5
47032	Choc Chip Cookie-Commerc	1	ea	10	45	188	<1	1	7	<1	2	0.4	0.6	0.5
47002	Choc Chip Cookie-Recipe-Marg	1	ea	16	78	326	1	1	9	<1	5	1.3	1.7	1.3
43728	Choc Mint Cake Cookie	1	ea	16	50	209		1	12	0	<1	0		
47041	Chocolate Wafer Cookie	2	ea	12	52	218	1	1	9	<1	2	0.5	0.6	0.5
47042	Coconut Macaroons-Recipe	1	ea	24	97	406	3	1	17	<1	3	2.7	0.1	<0.1
47012	Fig Bar Cookie	1	ea	16	56	234	3	1	11	1	1	0.2	0.5	0.4
47043	Fortune Cookie	1	ea	8	30	126	1	<1	7	<1	<1	0.1	0.1	<0.1
47376	Fruit Cookie-NoFat (Archway)	1	ea	28	90	377		2	21	0	0	0	0	0
47324	Fudge Brownie Cookie-SugFree	1	ea	24	90	377		1	17	0	4	1	1	0
47045	Gingersnap Cookie	1	ea	7	29	121	<1	<1	5	<1	1	0.2	0.4	0.1
47009	Lady Finger Cookie	4	ea	44	161	674	9	5	26	<1	4	1.4	1.7	0.6
47046	Marshmallow Cookie-ChocDip	1	ea	13	55	230	1	1	9	<1	2	0.6	1.2	0.3
47171	NillaWafer Cookie (Nabisco)	8	ea	32	140	586	1	1	24	1	5	1	1.5	0
47054	Oatmeal Cookie-Homemade	1	ea	15	67	280	1	1	10		3	0.5	1.2	0.8
47496	Oatmeal Raisin Cookie (Archway)	1	ea	26	106	444	3	1	18	1	3	0.7	1.3	0.3
47059	Peanut Butter Sandwich Cookie	1	ea	14	67	280	<1	1	9	<1	3	0.7	1.6	0.5
47010	PeanutButter Cookie-Homemade	1	ea	20	95	397	1	2	12		5	0.9	2.2	1.4
47062	Pecan Shortbread Cookie	1	ea	14	76	318	<1	1	8	<1	5	1.1	2.6	0.6
47038	Sandw Cookie-Choc-ChocDip	1	ea	17	82	343	<1	1	11	1	4	1.3	2.5	0.5
47006	Sandwich Cookie-all types	4	ea	40	188	787	1	2	28	1	8	2.6	3.4	1.4
47180	Sandwich Cookie-Oreo	3	ea	33	155	649	<1	1	23	1	7	1.5		
47059	Sandwich Cookie-Peanut Butter	1	ea	14	67	280	<1	1	9	<1	3	0.7	1.6	0.5
47071	Sandwich Cookie-Vanilla	1	ea	10	48	201	<1	<1	7	<1	2	0.3	0.8	0.8
47007	Shortbread Cookie	4	ea	32	161	674	1	2	21	1	8	2	4.3	1
47153	Snackwell DevFd Cookie-Svg	1	ea	16	49	205	3	1	12	<1	<1	0.1	<0.1	<0.1
47160	Snackwell VanSanCookie-Svg	2	ea	26	110	460		1	20	0	3	0.5		
47011	Snickerdoodle Cookie	1	ea	20	80	335	1	1	12	<1	3	2.1		
47064	Sugar Cookie	1	ea	15	72	301	1	1	10	<1	3	0.8	1.8	0.4
47065	Sugar Cookie, no sodium	1	ea	7	30	126	<1	<1	5	<1	1	0.1	0.4	0.3
47068	Sugar Cookie-Made w/Marg	1	ea	14	66	276	1	1	8	<1	3	0.7	1.4	1
47069	Sugar Wafers-CremeFilled	1	ea	9	46	192	<1	<1	6	<1	2	0.3	0.9	0.8
Doughnuts, Pastries, & Sweet Rolls														
45788	Apple Turnover	1	ea	89	284	1188	37	4	31	2	16	4		
45516	Baklava-2x2x2.5 in piece	1	pce	78	336	1406	19	5	29	2	23	9.3	8.1	4.2
45505	Cake Doughnut	1	ea	47	196	820	11	3	21	1	11	3.3	6	1.2
45524	Cake Doughnut-Choc Icing	1	ea	43	194	812	7	2	22	1	11	5.8	3.7	0.8

< = Trace amount present   Blank = Not available

V, vitamin; **THI**, thiamin; **RIB**, riboflavin; **NIA**, niacin; **FOL**, folate; **CALC**, calcium; **PHOS**, phosphorus; **SOD**, sodium; **POT**, potassium; **MAG**, magnesium

CHOL (mg)	V-A (IU)	THI (mg)	RIB (mg)	NIA (mg)	V-B6 (mg)	FOL (μg)	V-B12 (μg)	V-C (mg)	V-E (mg)	CALC (mg)	PHOS (mg)	SOD (mg)	POT (mg)	MAG (mg)	IRON (mg)	ZINC (mg)
1	0	<0.1	<0.1	0.1	<0.1	4	0	0	0.3	18	28	22	57	11	0.4	0.2
7	98							0		43		29			0	
0	0							0		0		203			0.4	
6	65	0.1	0.1	1.2	<0.1	9	0.2	0.4	0.6	57	67	144	146	13	0.5	0.2
0	4							1		30		10			0	
<1	3							0		5	0	12	47		0.4	
0	0							0		0		75			0	
29	150	0.1	0.1	0.8	<0.1	19	0.1	0	0.1	7	26	88	28	3	0.6	0.1
21	292	0.1	0.1	0.5	<0.1	5	<0.1	0.1	1	24	31	90	72	10	0.8	0.2
0	<1	<0.1	<0.1	0.3	<0.1	7	0	0		2	8	38	12	3	0.3	0.1
5	109	<0.1	<0.1	0.2	<0.1	5	<0.1	<1		6	16	58	36	9	0.4	0.1
0	0							0		0		40			0.4	
<1	1	<0.1	<0.1	0.3	<0.1	7	<0.1	0	0.1	4	16	70	25	6	0.5	0.1
0	0	<0.1	<0.1	<0.1	<0.1	1	<0.1	0	<0.1	2	10	59	37	5	0.2	0.2
0	5	<0.1	<0.1	0.3	<0.1	6	<0.1	<1	0.1	10	10	56	33	4	0.5	0.1
<1	<1	<0.1	<0.1	0.1	<0.1	5	<0.1	0	<0.1	1	3	22	3	1	0.1	<0.1
0	0							0	<0.1	0		95			0.4	
0	0							0		0		130			1.1	
0	<1	<0.1	<0.1	0.2	<0.1	6	0	0	0.1	5	6	46	24	3	0.4	<0.1
97	22	0.1	0.2	0.9	0.1	26	0.3	1.6	0.3	21	76	65	50	5	1.6	0.5
0	1	<0.1	<0.1	0.1	<0.1	3	<0.1	<1	<0.1	6	13	22	24	5	0.3	0.1
5										20		100	30		1.1	
5	114	<0.1	<0.1	0.2	<0.1	5	<0.1	<1		16	25	90	27	6	0.4	0.1
2	4	0.1	<0.1	0.4		12		0		10		88	74		0.6	
0	1	<0.1	<0.1	0.5	<0.1	9	<0.1	<1	0.3	7	26	52	27	7	0.4	0.1
6	129	<0.1	<0.1	0.7	<0.1	11	<0.1	<1		8	23	104	46	8	0.4	0.2
5	<1	<0.1	<0.1	0.3	<0.1	9	<0.1	0		4	12	39	10	3	0.3	0.1
0	1	<0.1	<0.1	0.2	<0.1	3	<0.1	0	<0.1	6	15	55	41	7	0.5	0.1
0	1	0.1	<0.1	0.9	0	28	0	0	1	9	40	201	86	20	3.5	0.4
0	0							0		0		175			1.4	
0	1	<0.1	<0.1	0.5	<0.1	9	<0.1	<1	0.3	7	26	52	27	7	0.4	0.1
0	0	<0.1	<0.1	0.3	<0.1	5	0	0	0.2	3	8	35	9	1	0.2	<0.1
6	28	0.1	0.1	1.1	<0.1	22	<0.1	0	0.1	11	35	146	32	5	0.9	0.2
0	<1	<0.1	<0.1	0.2	<0.1	3	<0.1	<1		5	11	28	18	4	0.4	0.1
0	0							0		0		130			0.4	
9	127	0.1	<0.1	0.4	<0.1	14	<0.1	0.1	0.1	8	10	75	23	2	0.5	0.1
8	14	<0.1	<0.1	0.4	<0.1	8	<0.1	<1	<0.1	3	12	54	9	2	0.3	0.1
0	0	<0.1	<0.1	0.3	<0.1	5	0	0	0.1	2	5	<1	7	1	0.3	<0.1
4	144	<0.1	<0.1	0.3	<0.1	9	<0.1	<1	0.4	10	13	69	11	2	0.3	0.1
0	0	<0.1	<0.1	0.2	<0.1	5	0	0	0.2	2	5	13	5	1	0.2	<0.1
												176			1.2	
36	512	0.2	0.2	1.4	<0.1	11	<0.1	1.4	2	33	93	293	144	35	1.7	0.5
4	5	0.1	0.1	0.9	<0.1	38	<0.1	0.6	0.9	12	123	262	53	8	1.4	0.3
8	7	0.1	0.1	0.7	<0.1	28	<0.1	0.6	0.9	10	90	178	86	13	1.7	0.4

ESHA, EatRight Analysis CD-ROM; **AMT**, amount; **WT**, weight; **CAL**, calories; **KILO**, KiloJoule; **WTR**, water; **PROT**, protein; **CARB**, carbohydrate; **FIBR**, fiber; **FAT**, fat; **SATF**, saturated fat; **MONO**, monounsaturated fat; **POLY**, polyunsaturated fat; **CHOL**, cholesterol;

ESHA CODE	FOOD DESCRIPTION	AMT	UNIT	WT (g)	CAL (kcal)	KILO (kJ)	WTR (g)	PROT (g)	CARB (g)	FIBR (g)	FAT (g)	SATF (g)	MONO (g)	POLY (g)
DESSERTS (CONTINUED)														
45523	Cheese Croissant	1	ea	57	236	987	12	5	27	1	12	6.1	3.7	1.4
42164	Cheese Sweet Roll	1	ea	66	238	996	19	5	29	1	12	4	6	1.3
45557	Chinese Pastry	2	oz	56.7	136	569	26	1	26	1	3	0.5	0.9	1.7
45508	Chocolate Eclair+Custard	1	ea	100	262	1096	52	6	24	1	16	4.1	6.5	3.9
42166	Cinnamon Roll-Bkd-Frosted	1	ea	30	109	456	7	2	17		4	1	2.2	0.5
45509	Cream Puff + Custard	1	ea	130	335	1402	70	9	30	1	20	4.8	8.5	5.4
45563	Crm Filled Yeast Doughnut	1	ea	85	307	1284	32	5	26	1	21	4.6	10.3	2.6
14118	French Cruller Doughnut	1	ea	49	150	628		2	17	1	8	2		
45527	French Cruller Doughnut	1	ea	41	169	707	7	1	24	<1	8	1.9	4.3	0.9
45562	Funnel Cake-6 inch diam	1	pce	90	278	1163	38	7	29	1	14	2.7	4.4	6.3
45555	Guava Turnover	1	ea	78	234	979	34	2	28	3	13	2.5	5.5	3.9
45507	Jelly Filled Doughnut	1	ea	85	289	1209	30	5	33	1	16	4.1	8.7	2
45560	Oriental Doughnut/Okinawan	1	ea	18	76	318	3	1	10	<1	4	0.9	2	0.5
42094	Pan Dulce w/Topping	1	ea	79	291	1218	17	5	48	1	9	1.8	4	2.5
45504	Poptart-Fruit Filled	1	ea	52	203	849	8	2	36	1	5	1.4	3.3	0.6
45604	Poptart-Fruit Filled-Frosted	1	ea	52	205	858	6	2	37	1	6	1	3.2	1.3
45506	Yeast Doughnut-Plain	1	ea	60	239	1000	14	4	30	1	11	3.3	6	1.7
Frozen Desserts														
2070	Banana Split w/WhipCream	1	ea	425	1089	4556	217	15	124	1	65	37.5	18.7	5.3
72207	Caramel Crunch Ice Cream Bar	1	ea	93	270	1130		3	26	0	17	13		
72208	Choc Choc Ice Cream Bar	1	ea	91	280	1172		3	23	1	19	14		
71819	Choc Frozen Yogurt-Nonfat	1	cup	186	199	833	137	8	37	4	1	0.9	0.4	0.1
46110	Choc Ice Cream Cake Roll	1	pce	34	101	423	13	1	14	<1	5	2.1	1.8	0.8
72330	Cookies & Cream Ice Cream Bar	1	ea	60	190	795		2	21	1	12	6		
72191	Creamsicle Ice Cream Bar	1	ea	65	100	418		1	18	0	2	1.5		
72255	Creamsicle Ice Cream Bar-Rasp	1	ea	65	100	418		1	18	0	2	1.5		
90723	Frozen Dessert Pop	1	ea	59.43	47	197	48	0	11	0	<1	<0.1	<0.1	<0.1
72190	Frozen Dessert Pop-No Sugar Added	1	ea	44	25	105	36	1	6	<1	<1	0.2		
23174	Frozen Fruit Juice Bar	1	ea	77	67	280	60	1	16	1	<1	0	0	<0.1
72124	Frozen Yogurt (duplicate)	0.5	cup	87	110	460	62	3	19	0	3	2	0.9	0.1
2043	Frozen Yogurt Bar-Choc Coat	1	ea	41	109	456	21	1	12	<1	7	5.3	0.8	0.2
2035	Frozen Yogurt-Choc-Soft	0.5	cup	72	115	481	46	3	18	2	4	2.6	1.3	0.2
2064	Frozen Yogurt-Vanilla	0.5	cup	72	114	477	47	3	17	0	4	2.5	1.1	0.2
72188	Fudgsicle Ice Cream Bar	1	ea	61	90	377	24	3	16	1	2	1		
2216	Ice Cream-ChChipCookDo-Rich	0.5	cup	105	273	1142		4	32	0	15	10.1		
2105	Ice Cream-Cookies&Crm-LowFat	0.5	cup	71	120	502		3	21	1	2	1	1	0
2050	Ice Cream-Hard-Choc	0.5	cup	66	143	598	37	3	19	1	7	4.5	2.1	0.3
71809	Ice Cream-Orange Float Sherbet	0.5	cup	65	120	502		2	21	0	4	2.5		
2008	Ice Cream-Soft-French Vanilla	0.5	cup	86	191	799	51	4	19	1	11	6.4	3	0.4
2063	Ice Cream-Strawberry	0.5	cup	66	127	531	40	2	18	1	6	3.4		
2004	Ice Cream-Vanilla	0.5	cup	66	137	573	40	2	16	<1	7	4.5	2	0.3
2006	Ice Cream-Vanilla-Rich	0.5	cup	74	184	770	42	3	16	0	12	7.6	3.3	0.5
2057	Ice Milk-Chocolate	0.5	cup	65.5	95	397	43	3	17	<1	2	1.3	0.6	0.1
2009	Ice Milk-Hard-Vanilla	0.5	cup	66	119	498	40	3	19	<1	3	1.9	0.8	0.1
23051	Ice Slushy	1	cup	193	247	1033	129	1	63	0	0	0	0	0
49198	Lemon Sorbet	0.5	cup	70	90	377		0	22	0	0	0	0	0

< = Trace amount present Blank = Not available

V, vitamin; **THI**, thiamin; **RIB**, riboflavin; **NIA**, niacin; **FOL**, folate; **CALC**, calcium; **PHOS**, phosphorus; **SOD**, sodium; **POT**, potassium; **MAG**, magnesium

CHOL (mg)	V-A (IU)	THI (mg)	RIB (mg)	NIA (mg)	V-B6 (mg)	FOL (μg)	V-B12 (μg)	V-C (mg)	V-E (mg)	CALC (mg)	PHOS (mg)	SOD (mg)	POT (mg)	MAG (mg)	IRON (mg)	ZINC (mg)
32	459	0.3	0.2	1.2	<0.1	42	0.2	0.1	0.8	30	74	316	75	14	1.2	0.5
50	168	0.1	0.1	0.5	<0.1	28	0.2	0.1		78	65	236	90	13	0.5	0.4
0	1	<0.1	<0.1	0.5	0.1	2	0	0	0.5	12	31	5	51	15	0.4	0.3
127	828	0.1	0.3	0.8	0.1	43	0.3	0.3	2	63	107	337	117	15	1.2	0.6
0	1	0.1	0.1	1.1	<0.1	16	<0.1	0.1		10	104	250	19	4	0.8	0.1
174	768	0.2	0.4	1.1	0.1	48	0.5	0.4	1.9	86	142	443	150	16	1.5	0.8
20	34	0.3	0.1	1.9	0.1	60	0.1	0	0.2	21	65	263	68	17	1.6	0.7
20	0							0		0		105			0	
5	3	0.1	0.1	0.9	<0.1	17	<0.1	0	0.1	11	50	141	32	5	1	0.1
63	202	0.2	0.3	1.9	0.1	14	0.2	0.4	2.4	128	137	117	155	18	1.9	0.6
<1	264	0.1	0.1	1.5	0.1	6	<0.1	48	2	13	33	13	120	9	1.1	0.2
22	60	0.3	0.1	1.8	0.1	58	0.2	0	0.4	21	72	249	67	17	1.5	0.6
13	23	<0.1	0.1	0.4	<0.1	2	<0.1	<1	0.5	24	22	38	15	2	0.4	0.1
26	287	0.2	0.2	2	<0.1	19	0.1	0.1	1.2	13	56	75	57	9	1.8	0.4
0	535	0.2	0.3	2.7	0.2	27	0	0	0.4	6	37	174	39	6	2	0.2
0	500	0.2	0.2	2	0.2	52	0	0		11	46	211	44	8	1.8	0.6
18	14	0.2	0.1	1.6	<0.1	65	0.1	0.7	0.9	28	83	232	60	11	2.2	0.8
204	1946	0.1	0.9	0.5	0.2	19	1.4	2.4	0.5	466	485	360	783	92	1.6	2.7
25	200							0		100		80			0	
20	200							0		80		55			1.1	
7	13	0.1	0.3	0.4	0.1	22	0.9	1.3	0.1	296	240	151	631	74	0.1	0.9
15	79	<0.1	0.1	0.3	<0.1	2	0.1	0.1	0.3	42	40	45	57	9	0.5	0.2
10	100							0		60		120			0.4	
5	0							0		40		30			0	
5	0							0		40		30			0	
0	0	0	0	0	0	0	0	0.4	0	0	0	4	9	1	0.3	0.1
1	10							0.2		60		18			0.1	
0	14	<0.1	<0.1	0.1	<0.1	5	0	7.3	0	4	5	3	41	3	0.1	<0.1
11	153	<0.1	0.2	0.1	<0.1	3	0.1	0.6	0.1	87	77	55	136	9	0.4	0.2
1	68	<0.1	0.1	0.1	<0.1	2	0.1	0.3	<0.1	46	43	28	74	6	0.1	0.2
4	115	<0.1	0.2	0.2	0.1	8	0.2	0.2		106	100	71	188	19	0.9	0.4
1	153	<0.1	0.2	0.2	0.1	4	0.2	0.6	0.1	103	93	63	152	10	0.2	0.3
5	0							0		80		65			0.4	
66	505							0		151		91			0.7	
5	200	<0.1	0.2					0		100	141	90	254			
22	275	<0.1	0.1	0.1	<0.1	11	0.2	0.5	0.2	72	71	50	164	19	0.6	0.4
15	100							1.2		60		40			0	
78	507	<0.1	0.2	0.1	<0.1	8	0.4	0.7	0.5	113	100	52	152	10	0.2	0.4
19	211	<0.1	0.2	0.1	<0.1	8	0.2	5.1		79	66	40	124	9	0.1	0.2
29	278	<0.1	0.2	0.1	<0.1	3	0.3	0.4	0.2	84	69	53	131	9	0.1	0.5
68	483	<0.1	0.1	0.1	<0.1	6	0.3	0	0.4	87	78	45	116	8	0.3	0.3
6	72	<0.1	0.1	0.1	<0.1	4	0.3	0.5	0.1	94	78	41	155	13	0.2	0.4
18	296	<0.1	0.2	0.1	<0.1	4	0.3	0.8	0.1	106	68	49	137	9	0.1	0.5
0	0	<0.1	0	<0.1	<0.1	0	0	1.9	0	4	2	42	6	2	0.3	<0.1
0												33	3			

ESHA, EatRight Analysis CD-ROM; **AMT**, amount; **WT**, weight; **CAL**, calories; **KILO**, KiloJoule; **WTR**, water; **PROT**, protein; **CARB**, carbohydrate; **FIBR**, fiber; **FAT**, fat; **SATF**, saturated fat; **MONO**, monounsaturated fat; **POLY**, polyunsaturated fat; **CHOL**, cholesterol;

ESHA CODE	FOOD DESCRIPTION	AMT	UNIT	WT (g)	CAL (kcal)	KILO (kJ)	WTR (g)	PROT (g)	CARB (g)	FIBR (g)	FAT (g)	SATF (g)	MONO (g)	POLY (g)
DESSERTS (CONTINUED)														
2011	Orange Sherbet	0.5	cup	74	107	448	49	1	22	1	1	0.9	0.4	0.1
49197	Strawberry Sorbet	0.5	cup	70	80	335		0	19	0	0	0	0	0
2592	Vanilla Rasp Frzn Yogurt-LowFat	0.5	cup	108	170	711		4	32	0	2	1.5		
Fruit Desserts														
49015	Apple Strudel	1	pce	71	195	816	31	2	29	2	8	1.5	2.3	3.8
49018	Fruit Filled Blintz	1	ea	70	124	519	44	4	17	<1	4	1.3	1.8	0.9
49063	Peach Cobbler-Ckd f/Frzn	0.25	ea	120.5	360	1506		3	47	0	18	6		
Gelatin Desserts														
23052	Gelatin/Jello-Prepared	0.5	cup	135	84	351	114	2	19	0	0	0	0	0
23093	Gelatin/Jello-SugFree-Prepared	0.5	cup	117	23	96	111	1	5	0	0	0	0	0
Pies & Tarts														
70536	Apple Pie-1/10	1	pce	130	300	1255	95	2	39	2	15	3		
48022	Apple Pie-Homemade	1	ea	1240	3286	13749	587	30	460		155	37.8	66.9	41.4
49071	Blueberry Tart-LowFat	1	ea	40	130	544	3	2	28	1	2	0		
70557	Boston Cream Pie-1/10	1	pce	78	220	920		2	32	0	9	2.5		
70538	Cherry Pie-1/10	1	pce	130	330	1381	82	3	48	1	15	3		
70554	Chocolate Cream Pie-1/10	1	pce	130	370	1548	79	3	44	1	21	13		
70562	Lemon Meringue Pie-1/9	1	pce	120	250	1046		2	46	0	6	1.5		
70559	Pecan Pie-1/8	1	pce	128	550	2301	24	7	75	2	26	6		
70561	Pumpkin Pie-1/10th	1	pce	125	310	1297		5	47	2	12	3		
Puddings, Custards, & Pie Fillings														
57915	Bread Pudding-f/Recipe	1	svg	270.9	475	1987	459	15	66	2	17	8		
2613	Egg Custard-Mix+Whl Milk	0.5	cup	133	162	678	98	5	23	0	5	2.7	1.5	0.4
2625	Flan CarmCustardMix+WhMlk	0.5	cup	133	150	628	99	4	25	0	4	2.4	1.1	0.1
2628	Pudding-Instant+2%Milk	0.5	cup	147	154	644	110	4	29	0	2	1.4	0.7	0.2
58203	Pudding-Inst-LowCal	1	svg	8	28	117	1	<1	7	<1	<1	<0.1	<0.1	<0.1
2636	Pudding-RegMix+2% Milk	0.5	cup	142	158	661	105	5	28	1	3	1.8	0.8	0.1
2604	Pudding-RegMix+Whole Milk	0.5	cup	142	170	711	104	4	28	1	4	2.6	1.2	0.3
48044	Pumpkin Pie Mix-Canned	0.5	cup	135	140	586	97	1	36	11	<1	0.1	<0.1	<0.1
2653	TapiocaPudding + 2% Milk	0.5	cup	141	148	619	106	4	28	0	2	1.4	0.6	0.1
Scones														
42071	Scone	1	ea	42	150	628	12	4	19	1	6	2	2.6	1.3
42072	Scone-Whole Wheat	1	ea	42	144	602	11	5	18	3	7	2.1	2.6	1.4
46077	Shortcake Biscuit-Recipe	2	oz	56.7	196	820	16	3	27	1	8	2.1	3.4	2.1
Toppings														
23069	Butterscotch Topping	2	Tbs	41	103	431	13	1	27	<1	<1	<0.1	<0.1	0
23070	Caramel Topping	2	Tbs	41	103	431	13	1	27	<1	<1	<0.1	<0.1	0
23013	Chocolate syrup-Thin	2	Tbs	37.5	105	439	12	1	24	1	<1	0.2	0.1	<0.1
509	Dessert Topping/DreamWhip	2	Tbs	10	19	79	7	<1	2	0	1	1.1	0.1	<0.1
569	Dream Whip Topping-Dry Mix	1	svg	2	10	42	0	0	2		0	0	0	0
508	FrznDessertTopping/Cool Whip	2	Tbs	9.375	30	126	5	<1	2	0	2	2	0.2	<0.1
23014	HotFudge ChocolateTopping	2	Tbs	38	133	556	8	2	24	1	3	1.5	1.5	0.1
23064	Marshmallow Creme	2	Tbs	12	40	167	<1	0	10	0	0	0	0	0
23071	Marshmallow Creme Topping	1	oz	28.35	91	381	6	<1	22	<1	<1	<0.1	<0.1	<0.1
23162	Nuts in Syrup Topping	2	Tbs	41	184	770	6	2	24	1	9	0.8	2	5.6
510	Whipped Cream-Pressurized	2	Tbs	7.5	19	79	5	<1	1	0	2	1	0.5	0.1

< = Trace amount present   Blank = Not available

V, vitamin; **THI**, thiamin; **RIB**, riboflavin; **NIA**, niacin; **FOL**, folate; **CALC**, calcium; **PHOS**, phosphorus; **SOD**, sodium; **POT**, potassium; **MAG**, magnesium

CHOL (mg)	V-A (IU)	THI (mg)	RIB (mg)	NIA (mg)	V-B6 (mg)	FOL (μg)	V-B12 (μg)	V-C (mg)	V-E (mg)	CALC (mg)	PHOS (mg)	SOD (mg)	POT (mg)	MAG (mg)	IRON (mg)	ZINC (mg)
1	34	<0.1	0.1	<0.1	<0.1	3	0.1	1.7	<0.1	40	30	34	71	6	0.1	0.4
0												1	34			
25	0							1.2		100		35			0	
4	21	<0.1	<0.1	0.2	<0.1	20	0.2	1.2	1	11	23	191	106	6	0.3	0.1
53	376	0.1	0.1	0.4	<0.1	8	0.2	0.5	0.5	35	59	93	78	7	0.8	0.3
0	0							3.6		0		240			1.1	
0	0	0	<0.1	<0.1	0	1	0	0	0	4	30	101	1	1	<0.1	<0.1
0	0	0	0	0	0	0	0	0	0	4	80	56	1	1	<0.1	0
0	0	<0.1	<0.1	0.4	0.1			0		0		390	96		0.4	
0	719	1.8	1.3	15.3	0.4	298	0	21.1		87	347	2616	980	87	13.9	2.4
0	100	0.2	0.2	2	0.2	40	0.6	1.2		250		80			0.7	
30	0	<0.1	0.1	0.2	<0.1			0		20		170	77		0.4	
0	400	<0.1	<0.1	0.2	0.1			0		80		360	112		0.4	
20	99	<0.1	0.1	1.4	<0.1			0		35		359	176		0.9	
0	0							0		0		290	23		0	
85	200							0		0		510	90		0.7	
45	3500	0.1	0.2	0.5				0		80		390	193		1.4	
243	855	0.3	0.6	2.2	0.2	78	1	1.7	1	241	267	666	406	39	2.7	1.4
68	242	0.1	0.3	0.2	0.1	12	0.7	0.1	0.1	185	173	112	275	21	0.5	0.7
16	150	<0.1	0.2	0.1	<0.1	5	0.3	0.9		148	112	149	213	16	0.1	0.5
9	250	<0.1	0.2	0.1	0.1	6	0.4	1.2		150	318	435	193	18	0.1	0.5
0	0	<0.1	<0.1	<0.1	<0.1	<1	<0.1	0	<0.1	11	189	340	2	<1	<0.1	<0.1
10	231	<0.1	0.2	0.2	<0.1	6	0.5	0.1	<0.1	159	133	145	222	30	0.5	0.8
13	197	0.1	0.2	0.2	<0.1	6	0.4	0	0.1	151	124	139	213	28	0.5	0.7
0	11202	<0.1	0.2	0.5	0.2	47	0	4.7		50	61	281	186	22	1.4	0.4
8	226	<0.1	0.2	0.1	<0.1	6	0.4	1		148	116	171	188	17	0.1	0.5
49	273	0.1	0.2	1.2	<0.1	8	0.1	0.1	0.7	80	74	171	49	7	1.3	0.3
50	278	0.1	0.1	1.3	0.1	11	0.1	0.1	0.9	86	126	175	114	33	1.1	0.8
2	41	0.2	0.2	1.5	<0.1	30	<0.1	0.1		116	81	287	60	9	1.4	0.3
<1	37	<0.1	<0.1	<0.1	<0.1	1	<0.1	0.1		22	19	143	34	3	0.1	0.1
<1	37	<0.1	<0.1	<0.1	<0.1	1	<0.1	0.1		22	19	143	34	3	0.1	0.1
0	0	<0.1	<0.1	0.1	<0.1	1	0	0.1	<0.1	5	48	27	84	24	0.8	0.3
1	12	<0.1	<0.1	<0.1	<0.1	<1	<0.1	0.1	<0.1	9	9	7	15	1	<0.1	<0.1
0	0							0		0		0			0	
0	13	0	0	0	0	0	0	0	0.1	1	1	2	2	<1	<0.1	<0.1
<1	1	<0.1	<0.1	0.1	<0.1	2	<0.1	0.1	1	19	37	131	108	18	0.5	0.3
0	0							0		0		10			0	
0	<1	<0.1	<0.1	<0.1	<0.1	<1	0	0	0	1	2	23	1	1	0.1	<0.1
0	3	0.1	<0.1	0.2	0.1	11	0	0.1	0.1	14	48	17	62	22	0.4	0.4
6	51	<0.1	<0.1	<0.1	<0.1	<1	<0.1	0	<0.1	8	7	10	11	1	<0.1	<0.1

ESHA, EatRight Analysis CD-ROM; **AMT**, amount; **WT**, weight; **CAL**, calories; **KILO**, KiloJoule; **WTR**, water; **PROT**, protein; **CARB**, carbohydrate; **FIBR**, fiber; **FAT**, fat; **SATF**, saturated fat; **MONO**, monounsaturated fat; **POLY**, polyunsaturated fat; **CHOL**, cholesterol;

ESHA CODE	FOOD DESCRIPTION	AMT	UNIT	WT (g)	CAL (kcal)	KILO (kJ)	WTR (g)	PROT (g)	CARB (g)	FIBR (g)	FAT (g)	SATF (g)	MONO (g)	POLY (g)
EGGS & EGG SUBSTITUTES														
19581	Egg Beaters-Egg Substitute	0.25	cup	61	30	126		6	1	0	0	0	0	0
19522	Egg White-Cooked	1	ea	33.4	17	71	29	4	<1	0	0	0	0	0
19507	Egg White-Raw-Fresh	0.25	cup	60.75	29	121	53	7	<1	0	<1	0	0	0
19506	Egg White-Raw-Fresh-Large	1	ea	33.4	16	67	29	4	<1	0	<1	0	0	0
19523	Egg Yolk-Cooked	1	ea	16.6	59	247	8	3	<1	0	5	1.6	1.9	0.7
19508	Egg Yolk-Raw-Fresh-Large	1	ea	16.6	53	222	9	3	1	0	4	1.6	1.9	0.7
19511	Egg-Hard Boiled-Chopped	0.33	cup	45.33	70	293	34	6	1	0	5	1.5	1.8	0.6
19510	Egg-Hard Cooked/Boiled	1	ea	50	78	326	37	6	1	0	5	1.6	2	0.7
19509	Egg-Large-Fried in Marg	1	ea	46	90	377	32	6	<1	0	7	2	2.9	1.2
19517	Egg-Poached-Large	1	ea	50	71	297	38	6	<1	0	5	1.5	1.9	0.7
19500	Egg-Whole-Raw-Fresh-Large	0.25	cup	60.75	87	364	46	8	<1	0	6	1.9	2.3	0.8
FATS, OILS, MARGARINES, SHORTENINGS, & SUBSTITUTES														
Fat Substitutes														
44466	Butter Substitute-LowFat-Pwd	1	Tbs	5	19	79	<1	<1	4	0	<1	<0.1	<0.1	<0.1
Fats & Oils – Animal														
8004	Beef Fat/Tallow-Drippings	1	Tbs	12	108	452	0	0	0	0	12	6	5	0.5
8031	Butter Oil/Ghee	1	Tbs	12.8	112	469	<1	<1	0	0	13	7.9	3.7	0.5
8005	Chicken Fat	1	Tbs	12.8	115	481	<1	0	0	0	13	3.8	5.7	2.7
8067	Cod Liver Oil (Fish Oil)	1	Tbs	13.6	123	515	0	0	0	0	14	3.1	6.4	3.1
Fats & Oils – Vegetable														
8084	Canola Oil	1	Tbs	14	124	519	0	0	0	0	14	1	8.9	3.9
8037	Coconut Oil	1	Tbs	13.6	117	490	0	0	0	0	14	11.8	0.8	0.2
8009	Corn Oil	1	Tbs	13.6	120	502	0	0	0	0	14	1.8	3.8	7.4
8081	Cottonseed Oil	1	Tbs	13.6	120	502	0	0	0	0	14	3.5	2.4	7.1
8012	Crisco/Wesson Oil	1	Tbs	13.6	120	502	0	0	0	0	14	2.1	3.1	7.9
8008	Olive Oil	1	Tbs	13.5	119	498	0	0	0	0	14	1.9	9.8	1.4
8083	Palm Kernel Oil	1	Tbs	13.6	117	490	0	0	0	0	14	11.1	1.6	0.2
8082	Palm Oil	1	Tbs	13.6	120	502	0	0	0	0	14	6.7	5	1.3
8002	Pam CkingSpray-BtrFlav-1/3sec	1	ea	0.266	2	8	0	0	0	0	<1			
8026	Peanut Oil	1	Tbs	13.5	119	498	0	0	0	0	14	2.3	6.2	4.3
8010	Safflower Oil	1	Tbs	13.6	120	502	0	0	0	0	14	0.8	2	10.1
8027	Sesame Oil	1	Tbs	13.6	120	502	0	0	0	0	14	1.9	5.4	5.7
8028	Soybean + Cottonseed Oil	1	Tbs	13.6	120	502	0	0	0	0	14	2.4	4	6.5
8085	Walnut Oil	1	Tbs	13.6	120	502	0	0	0	0	14	1.2	3.1	8.6
8011	Wesson Sunlite/Sunflower Oil	1	Tbs	13.6	120	502	0	0	0	0	14	1.4	2.7	8.9
8038	Wheat Germ Oil-Tablespoon	1	Tbs	13.6	120	502	0	0	0	0	14	2.6	2.1	8.4
Butters, Margarines, & Spreads														
250	Benecol Spread	1	Tbs	14	70	293	1	0	0	0	8	1	4.5	2
8825	Benecol Spread-Light	1	Tbs	14	50	209	8	0	1		5	0.7	2.7	1.7
8001	Butter-Pat	1	ea	5	36	151	1	<1	<1	0	4	2.6	1.1	0.2
8000	Butter-Regular-Salted	1	Tbs	14	100	418	2	<1	<1	0	11	7.2	2.9	0.4
8025	Butter-Unsalted	1	Tbs	14	100	418	3	<1	<1	0	11	7.2	2.9	0.4
8142	Butter-Whipped	1	Tbs	9.44	68	285	1	<1	<1	0	8	4.8	2.2	0.3
8698	I Can't Believe It's Not Butter	1	Tbs	14	90	377	1	0	0	0	10	2		
90219	Margarine-Hard	1	Tbs	14.1	101	423	2	<1	<1	0	11	2.4	5.5	2.9
8485	Margarine-Hard-Unsalted	1	Tbs	14	100	418	<1	0	0	0	11	1.5	8	1.5

< = Trace amount present Blank = Not available

V, vitamin; **THI**, thiamin; **RIB**, riboflavin; **NIA**, niacin; **FOL**, folate; **CALC**, calcium; **PHOS**, phosphorus; **SOD**, sodium; **POT**, potassium; **MAG**, magnesium

CHOL (mg)	V-A (IU)	THI (mg)	RIB (mg)	NIA (mg)	V-B6 (mg)	FOL (μg)	V-B12 (μg)	V-C (mg)	V-E (mg)	CALC (mg)	PHOS (mg)	SOD (mg)	POT (mg)	MAG (mg)	IRON (mg)	ZINC (mg)
0	300		0.9		0.1	32	0.6	0	0.8	20		125	85		1.1	0.6
0	0	<0.1	0.1	<0.1	<0.1	1	0.1	0	0	2	4	55	48	4	<0.1	<0.1
0	0	<0.1	0.3	0.1	<0.1	2	0.1	0	0	4	9	101	99	7	<0.1	<0.1
0	0	<0.1	0.1	<0.1	<0.1	1	<0.1	0	0	2	5	55	54	4	<0.1	<0.1
213	323	<0.1	0.1	<0.1	0.1	18	0.4	0	0.5	23	81	7	16	1	0.6	0.5
205	239	<0.1	0.1	<0.1	0.1	24	0.3	0	0.4	21	65	8	18	1	0.5	0.4
192	236	<0.1	0.2	<0.1	0.1	20	0.5	0	0.5	23	78	56	57	5	0.5	0.5
212	260	<0.1	0.3	<0.1	0.1	22	0.6	0	0.5	25	86	62	63	5	0.6	0.5
210	335	<0.1	0.2	<0.1	0.1	23	0.6	0	0.6	27	96	94	68	6	0.9	0.6
211	242	<0.1	0.2	<0.1	0.1	18	0.6	0	0.5	26	95	147	66	6	0.9	0.6
257	296	<0.1	0.3	<0.1	0.1	29	0.8	0	0.6	32	116	85	81	7	1.1	0.7
<1	0	0	0	0	0	0	0	0	0	1	<1	60	<1	0	0.1	0
13	0	0	0	0	0	0	0	0	0.3	0	0	0	0	0	0	0
33	393	<0.1	<0.1	<0.1	<0.1	0	<0.1	0	0.4	1	<1	<1	1	0	0	<0.1
11	0	0	0	0	0	0	0	0	0.3	0	0	0	0	0	0	0
78	13600		0	0	0	0	0	0		0	0	0	0	0	0	0
0	0	0	0	0	0	0	0	0	2.4	0	0	0	0	0	0	0
0	0	0	0	0	0	0	0	0	<0.1	0	0	0	0	0	<0.1	0
0	0	0	0	0	0	0	0	0	1.9	0	0	0	0	0	0	0
0	0	0	0	0	0	0	0	0	4.8	0	0	0	0	0	0	0
0	0	0	0	0	0	0	0	0	1.1	0	0	0	0	0	<0.1	<0.1
0	0	0	0	0	0	0	0	0	1.9	<1	0	<1	<1	0	0.1	0
0	0	0	0	0	0	0	0	0	0.5	0	0	0	0	0	0	0
0	0	0	0	0	0	0	0	0	2.2	0	0	0	0	0	<0.1	0
0	0							0		0		0			0	
0	0	0	0	0	0	0	0	0	2.1	0	0	0	0	0	<0.1	<0.1
0	0	0	0	0	0	0	0	0	4.6	0	0	0	0	0	0	0
0	0	0	0	0	0	0	0	0	0.2	0	0	0	0	0	0	0
0	0	0	0	0	0	0	0	0	1.6	0	0	0	0	0	0	0
0	0	0	0	0	0	0	0	0	0.1	0	0	0	0	0	0	0
0	0	0	0	0	0	0	0	0	5.6	0	0	0	0	0	0	0
0	0	0	0	0	0	0	0	0	20.3	0	0	0	0	0	0	0
0	500							0	2.7	0		110			0	
	639	<0.1	0	0	0				5.2	1	1	94	1	<1	0	0
11	125	<0.1	<0.1	<0.1	<0.1	<1	<0.1	0	0.1	1	1	29	1	<1	<0.1	<0.1
30	350	<0.1	<0.1	<0.1	<0.1	<1	<0.1	0	0.3	3	3	81	3	<1	<0.1	<0.1
30	350	<0.1	<0.1	<0.1	<0.1	<1	<0.1	0	0.3	3	3	2	3	<1	<0.1	<0.1
21	236	<0.1	<0.1	<0.1	<0.1	<1	<0.1	0	0.2	2	2	78	2	<1	<0.1	<0.1
0	500							0		0		90			0	
0	504	<0.1	<0.1	<0.1	<0.1	<1	<0.1	<1	0.4	4	3	133	6	<1	0	0
	500							0		0		0			0	

ESHA, EatRight Analysis CD-ROM; **AMT**, amount; **WT**, weight; **CAL**, calories; **KILO**, KiloJoule; **WTR**, water; **PROT**, protein; **CARB**, carbohydrate; **FIBR**, fiber; **FAT**, fat; **SATF**, saturated fat; **MONO**, monounsaturated fat; **POLY**, polyunsaturated fat; **CHOL**, cholesterol;

ESHA CODE	FOOD DESCRIPTION	AMT	UNIT	WT (g)	CAL (kcal)	KILO (kJ)	WTR (g)	PROT (g)	CARB (g)	FIBR (g)	FAT (g)	SATF (g)	MONO (g)	POLY (g)
FATS, OILS, MARGARINES, SHORTENINGS, & SUBSTITUTES (CONTINUED)														
8790	Margarine-Soft	1	Tbs	14	100	418	<1	0	0	0	11	2		
8176	Shedd's Spread	1	Tbs	14.5	62	259		0	0	0	7	1.6		
Shortenings														
8007	Shortening (Crisco)	1	Tbs	12.8	113	473	0	0	0	0	13	3.2	5.7	3.3
FOOD ADDITIVES & INDUSTRIAL INGREDIENT PRODUCTS														
Ingredient: Thickeners – Gums, Fibers, Starches, Pectins, Alginates, & Emulsifiers														
30000	Cornstarch	1	Tbs	8	30	126	1	<1	7	<1	<1	<0.1	<0.1	<0.1
Ingredient: Butters, Fats, Margarines, Shortenings, Oils, & Substitutes														
44784	Margarine-Liquid	1	Tbs	14	100	418	2	<1	0	0	11	2.9	6.5	1.3
Ingredient: Sweeteners														
31183	Blackstrap Molasses	1	Tbs	20.5	53	222	5	1	13	1	<1	<0.1	<0.1	<0.1
FOOD SERVICE PRODUCTS														
Food Service: Beverages														
20931	French Vanilla Cappuccino, dry mix	1	pkt	28	120	502		2	22		3	1		
Food Service: Prepared Breads/Grain Products														
42717	Cornbread-Dry Mix	1	pce	52	199	833	5	4	36	1	5	1		
Food Service: Condiments, Sauces, Gravies, Dips, Dressings, Spreads, etc.														
9054	Enchilada Sauce	0.25	cup	61	20	84	34	0	3	0	1	0		
Food Service: Prepared Dishes														
57428	Beef Cannelloni	2	ea	170.1	391	1636		20	28	1	22	7.8		
57416	Beef Ravioli	1	cup	214	450	1883		22	48	3	19	9		
57411	Beef Ravioli	9	pce	146.3	300	1255		14	40	1	8	3.8		
57400	Beef Ravioli-Breaded	1	cup	120	270	1130		11	43	2	6	2		
57407	Beef Tortellini	1	cup	128	250	1046		11	38	2	6	3.5		
57420	Chicken Ravioli	1	cup	214	450	1883		21	52	2	17	10		
8954	Chicken Ravioli, jalapeno filled	6	pce	137.4	316	1322		15	49	2	7	2.7		
52035	Cucumber Salad	0.5	cup	100	50	209		1	13		0	0	0	0
52066	Egg Salad	0.5	cup	100	230	962		9	8	0	18	4		
40067	Salisbury Stk-Flame Brld	1	ea	72.3	162	678		16	2		10	3.9		
52065	Seafood Salad	0.5	cup	100	230	962		6	14	8	17	2.5		
52064	Shrimp Salad	0.5	cup	100	170	711		7	5	3	14	2		
57408	Spinach & Cheese Tortellini-PreCkd	1	cup	128	280	1172		13	40	2	8	5		
91464	Tamale-Beef-w/Sauce	2	ea	190	310	1297		6	26	4	23	10		
FRUITS														
Candied, Concentrates, Pastes, Dehydrated, & Dried Fruits														
3005	Apple Rings-Dried	10	ea	64	156	653	20	1	42	6	<1	<0.1	<0.1	0.1
3013	Apricot Halves-Dried-Each	1	ea	3.5	8	33	1	<1	2	<1	<1	<0.1	<0.1	<0.1
3307	Banana Chips	1	oz	28.35	147	615	1	1	17	2	10	8.2	0.6	0.2
3043	Dates-Chopped	1	cup	178	502	2100	37	4	134	14	1	0.1	0.1	<0.1
3044	Dates-Whole-Each	10	ea	83	234	979	17	2	62	7	<1	<0.1	<0.1	<0.1
3162	Dried Figs	1	ea	19	47	197	6	1	12	2	<1	<0.1	<0.1	0.1
3126	Prunes-Dried	10	ea	84	202	845	26	2	54	6	<1	0.1	<0.1	0.1
3129	Raisins-Seedless-Packed	1	cup	165	493	2063	25	5	131	6	1	0.1	0.1	0.1
3130	Raisins-Seedless-Unpacked	1	cup	145	434	1816	22	4	115	5	1	0.1	0.1	0.1
61372	Strawberry Fruit Leather	1	ea	14	45	188	<1	0	11	1	0	0	0	0

< = Trace amount present   Blank = Not available

V, vitamin; **THI**, thiamin; **RIB**, riboflavin; **NIA**, niacin; **FOL**, folate; **CALC**, calcium; **PHOS**, phosphorus; **SOD**, sodium; **POT**, potassium; **MAG**, magnesium

CHOL (mg)	V-A (IU)	THI (mg)	RIB (mg)	NIA (mg)	V-B6 (mg)	FOL (μg)	V-B12 (μg)	V-C (mg)	V-E (mg)	CALC (mg)	PHOS (mg)	SOD (mg)	POT (mg)	MAG (mg)	IRON (mg)	ZINC (mg)
0	500							0		0		95			0	
0	518							0				114			0	
0	0	0	0	0	0	0	0	0	0.1	0	0	0	0	0	0	0
0	0	0	0	0	0	0	0	0	0	<1	1	1	<1	<1	<0.1	<0.1
0	600	<0.1	<0.1	<0.1	<0.1	<1	<0.1	0.1	0.6	9	7	123	13	1	0	0
<1	2	<0.1	<0.1	0.5				0.4		213		70	431		3.2	
0	0							0		40		70			0	
4	5					42		<1		129		792			1.8	
0	750							1.2		0		380			0	
137										149		672			2.1	
135	100							0		100		930			3.6	
77										119		400			2.1	
25	0							1.2		60		660			2.7	
40	100							1.2		60		490			1.8	
115	300							0		200		420			2.7	
48										83		841			3	
0												580				
240	0							0		40		570			1.4	
	91							1.5		29		503			2	
20	0							0		20		770			0.4	
85	0							0		4		620			0.7	
30	600							0		150		320			1.8	
20	1000							1.8		40		870			1.1	
0	0	0	0.1	0.6	0.1	0	0	2.5	0.3	9	24	56	288	10	0.9	0.1
0	126	<0.1	<0.1	0.1	<0.1	<1	0	<1	0.2	2	2	<1	41	1	0.1	<0.1
0	24	<0.1	<0.1	0.2	0.1	4	0	1.8	0.1	5	16	2	152	22	0.4	0.2
0	18	0.1	0.1	2.3	0.3	34	0	0.7	0.1	69	110	4	1168	77	1.8	0.5
0	8	<0.1	0.1	1.1	0.1	16	0	0.3	<0.1	32	51	2	544	36	0.8	0.2
0	2	<0.1	<0.1	0.1	<0.1	2	0	0.2	0.1	31	13	2	129	13	0.4	0.1
0	656	<0.1	0.2	1.6	0.2	3	0	0.5	0.4	36	58	2	615	34	0.8	0.4
0	0	0.2	0.2	1.3	0.3	8	0	3.8	0.2	82	167	18	1236	53	3.1	0.4
0	0	0.2	0.2	1.1	0.3	7	0	3.3	0.2	72	146	16	1086	46	2.7	0.3
0	0							0		0		0	110		0	

ESHA, EatRight Analysis CD-ROM; **AMT**, amount; **WT**, weight; **CAL**, calories; **KILO**, KiloJoule; **WTR**, water; **PROT**, protein; **CARB**, carbohydrate; **FIBR**, fiber; **FAT**, fat; **SATF**, saturated fat; **MONO**, monounsaturated fat; **POLY**, polyunsaturated fat; **CHOL**, cholesterol;

ESHA CODE	FOOD DESCRIPTION	AMT	UNIT	WT (g)	CAL (kcal)	KILO (kJ)	WTR (g)	PROT (g)	CARB (g)	FIBR (g)	FAT (g)	SATF (g)	MONO (g)	POLY (g)
Canned & Pickled Fruits														
3147	Applesauce-Canned-Sweet	1	cup	255	173	724	209	<1	45	3	<1	0.1	<0.1	0.1
3006	Applesauce-Canned-Unsweet	1	cup	244	102	427	215	<1	27	3	<1	<0.1	<0.1	<0.1
3152	Apricot Halves+Juice-Canned	0.5	cup	122	59	247	106	1	15	2	<1	<0.1	<0.1	<0.1
3040	Cranberry Sauce-Strained	1	cup	277	418	1749	168	1	108	3	<1	<0.1	0.1	0.2
3045	Fruit Cocktail+HeavySyrup	1	cup	248	181	757	199	1	47	2	<1	<0.1	<0.1	0.1
3163	Fruit Cocktail+LiteSyrup	1	cup	242	138	577	204	1	36	2	<1	<0.1	<0.1	0.1
3164	Fruit Cocktail-Juice Pack	1	cup	237	109	456	207	1	28	2	<1	<0.1	<0.1	<0.1
3313	Fruit Cocktail-Water Pack	1	cup	237	76	318	215	1	20	2	<1	<0.1	<0.1	<0.1
27009	Olives-Large-Ripe-Pitted	10	ea	44	51	213	35	<1	3	1	5	0.6	3.5	0.4
3089	Oranges-Mandarin-Canned	1	cup	249	92	385	223	2	24	2	<1	<0.1	<0.1	<0.1
3174	Peach Halves+LtSyrup-Canned	0.5	cup	125.5	68	285	106	1	18	2	<1	<0.1	<0.1	<0.1
3098	Peaches-Canned+Heavy Syrup	1	cup	262	194	812	208	1	52	3	<1	<0.1	0.1	0.1
3107	Pears-Canned+Heavy Syrup	1	cup	266	197	824	214	1	51	4	<1	<0.1	0.1	0.1
3179	Pears-Canned+Juice	1	cup	248	124	519	214	1	32	4	<1	<0.1	<0.1	<0.1
3177	Pears-Canned+Light Syrup	1	cup	251	143	598	212	<1	38	4	<1	<0.1	<0.1	<0.1
3115	Pineapple-Canned+HeavySyrup	1	cup	254	198	828	201	1	51	2	<1	<0.1	<0.1	0.1
3183	Pineapple-Canned+Juice	1	cup	249	149	623	208	1	39	2	<1	<0.1	<0.1	0.1
3181	Pineapple-Canned+Light Syrup	1	cup	252	131	548	216	1	34	2	<1	<0.1	<0.1	0.1
Cooked Fruits														
3388	Apple Slices-Peeled-Cooked	0.5	cup	85.5	45	188	73	<1	12	2	<1	<0.1	<0.1	0.1
5632	Plantain-Fried-Ripe	1	cup	169	425	1778	81	2	61	4	22	3	6.8	11.5
3133	Rhubarb-Fzn-Cooked+Sugar	1	cup	240	278	1163	163	1	75	5	<1	<0.1	<0.1	0.1
Fresh Fruits														
3000	Apple+Peel-Medium	1	ea	138	72	301	118	<1	19	3	<1	<0.1	<0.1	0.1
3003	Apple-Peeled-Medium	1	ea	128	61	255	111	<1	16	2	<1	<0.1	<0.1	<0.1
3157	Apricots-Fresh-Pitted	1	ea	35	17	71	30	<1	4	1	<1	<0.1	0.1	<0.1
3016	Avocado-Fresh	1	ea	201	322	1347	147	4	17	13	29	4.3	19.7	3.7
3020	Banana-Fresh	1	ea	118	105	439	88	1	27	3	<1	0.1	<0.1	0.1
3024	Blackberries-Fresh	1	cup	144	62	259	127	2	14	7	1	<0.1	0.1	0.4
3029	Blueberries-Fresh	1	cup	145	83	347	122	1	21	3	<1	<0.1	0.1	0.2
3663	Breadfruit-Fresh	0.25	ea	96	99	414	68	1	26	5	<1	<0.1	<0.1	0.1
3076	Cantaloupe Melon	1	ea	552	188	787	498	5	45	5	1	0.3	<0.1	0.4
3075	Cantaloupe Melon-Cubes	1	cup	160	54	226	144	1	13	1	<1	0.1	<0.1	0.1
3240	Carambola/Starfruit-Fresh	1	ea	127	39	163	116	1	9	4	<1	<0.1	<0.1	0.2
3079	Casaba/Crenshaw Melon	1	ea	1640	459	1920	1506	18	108	15	2	0.4	<0.1	0.6
3078	Casaba/Crenshaw Melon-Cubes	1	cup	170	48	201	156	2	11	2	<1	<0.1	<0.1	0.1
3036	Cherries-Fresh	0.5	cup	72.5	46	192	60	1	12	2	<1	<0.1	<0.1	<0.1
71089	Concord Grapes	10	ea	24	16	67	20	<1	4	<1	<1	<0.1	<0.1	<0.1
3039	Cranberries-Fresh	1	cup	95	44	184	83	<1	12	4	<1	<0.1	<0.1	0.1
3271	Feijoa Fruit-Raw	1	ea	50	24	100	43	1	5	2	<1			
3160	Figs-Medium-Fresh	1	ea	50	37	155	40	<1	10	1	<1	<0.1	<0.1	0.1
3048	Grapefruit-Fresh-Pieces	1	cup	230	74	310	209	1	19	3	<1	<0.1	<0.1	0.1
3047	Grapefruit-Fresh-White	0.5	ea	118	39	163	107	1	10	1	<1	<0.1	<0.1	<0.1
3207	Guava-Fresh	1	ea	90	61	255	73	2	13	5	1	0.2	0.1	0.4
3081	Honeydew Melon (1/10th)	1	pce	160	58	243	144	1	15	1	<1	0.1	<0.1	0.1
3080	Honeydew Melon-Cubes	1	cup	170	61	255	153	1	15	1	<1	0.1	<0.1	0.1

< = Trace amount present   Blank = Not available

V, vitamin; **THI**, thiamin; **RIB**, riboflavin; **NIA**, niacin; **FOL**, folate; **CALC**, calcium; **PHOS**, phosphorus; **SOD**, sodium; **POT**, potassium; **MAG**, magnesium

CHOL (mg)	V-A (IU)	THI (mg)	RIB (mg)	NIA (mg)	V-B6 (mg)	FOL (μg)	V-B12 (μg)	V-C (mg)	V-E (mg)	CALC (mg)	PHOS (mg)	SOD (mg)	POT (mg)	MAG (mg)	IRON (mg)	ZINC (mg)
0	15	<0.1	0.1	0.2	0.1	3	0	4.3	0.5	8	15	5	191	8	0.3	0.1
0	71	0.1	0.1	0.2	0.1	7	0	2.4	0.4	10	12	5	181	7	0.6	0.1
0	2063	<0.1	<0.1	0.4	0.1	2	0	6	0.7	15	24	5	201	12	0.4	0.1
0	116	<0.1	0.1	0.3	<0.1	3	0	5.5	2.3	11	17	80	72	8	0.6	0.1
0	508	<0.1	<0.1	0.9	0.1	7	0	4.7	1	15	27	15	218	12	0.7	0.2
0	503	<0.1	<0.1	0.9	0.1	7	0	4.6	1.2	15	27	15	215	12	0.7	0.2
0	723	<0.1	<0.1	1	0.1	7	0	6.4	0.9	19	33	9	225	17	0.5	0.2
0	592	<0.1	<0.1	0.9	0.1	7	0	5	0.9	12	26	9	223	17	0.6	0.2
0	177	<0.1	0	<0.1	<0.1	0	0	0.4	0.7	39	1	384	4	2	1.5	0.1
0	2121	0.2	0.1	1.1	0.1	12	0	85.2	0.2	27	25	12	331	27	0.7	1.3
0	444	<0.1	<0.1	0.7	<0.1	4	0	3	0.6	4	14	6	122	6	0.5	0.1
0	870	<0.1	0.1	1.6	<0.1	8	0	7.3	1.3	8	29	16	241	13	0.7	0.2
0	0	<0.1	0.1	0.6	<0.1	3	0	2.9	0.2	13	19	13	173	11	0.6	0.2
0	15	<0.1	<0.1	0.5	<0.1	2	0	4	0.2	22	30	10	238	17	0.7	0.2
0	0	<0.1	<0.1	0.4	<0.1	3	0	1.8	0.2	13	18	13	166	10	0.7	0.2
0	36	0.2	0.1	0.7	0.2	13	0	18.8	<0.1	36	18	3	264	41	1	0.3
0	95	0.2	<0.1	0.7	0.2	12	0	23.7	<0.1	35	15	2	304	35	0.7	0.2
0	96	0.2	0.1	0.7	0.2	13	0	18.9	<0.1	35	18	3	265	40	1	0.3
0	38	<0.1	<0.1	0.1	<0.1	1	0	0.2	<0.1	4	7	1	75	3	0.2	<0.1
0	1616	0.1	0.1	1.2	0.5	21	0	24.6	4.7	5	65	8	858	71	1.1	0.3
0	175	<0.1	0.1	0.5	<0.1	12	0	7.9	0.5	348	19	2	230	29	0.5	0.2
0	75	<0.1	<0.1	0.1	0.1	4	0	6.3	0.2	8	15	1	148	7	0.2	0.1
0	49	<0.1	<0.1	0.1	<0.1	0	0	5.1	0.1	6	14	0	115	5	0.1	0.1
0	674	<0.1	<0.1	0.2	<0.1	3	0	3.5	0.3	5	8	<1	91	4	0.1	0.1
0	293	0.1	0.3	3.5	0.5	163	0	20.1	4.2	24	105	14	975	58	1.1	1.3
0	76	<0.1	0.1	0.8	0.4	24	0	10.3	0.1	6	26	1	422	32	0.3	0.2
0	308	<0.1	<0.1	0.9	<0.1	36	0	30.2	1.7	42	32	1	233	29	0.9	0.8
0	78	0.1	0.1	0.6	0.1	9	0	14.1	0.8	9	17	1	112	9	0.4	0.2
0	0	0.1	<0.1	0.9	0.1	13	0	27.8	0.1	16	29	2	470	24	0.5	0.1
0	18669	0.2	0.1	4.1	0.4	116	0	202.6	0.3	50	83	88	1474	66	1.2	1
0	5411	0.1	<0.1	1.2	0.1	34	0	58.7	0.1	14	24	26	427	19	0.3	0.3
0	77	<0.1	<0.1	0.5	<0.1	15	0	43.7	0.2	4	15	3	169	13	0.1	0.2
0	0	0.2	0.5	3.8	2.7	131	0	357.5	0.8	180	82	148	2985	180	5.6	1.1
0	0	<0.1	0.1	0.4	0.3	14	0	37.1	0.1	19	8	15	309	19	0.6	0.1
0	46	<0.1	<0.1	0.1	<0.1	3	0	5.1	0.1	9	15	0	161	8	0.3	0.1
0	24	<0.1	<0.1	0.1	<0.1	1	0	1	<0.1	3	2	<1	46	1	0.1	<0.1
0	57	<0.1	<0.1	0.1	0.1	1	0	12.6	1.1	8	12	2	81	6	0.2	0.1
0	0	<0.1	<0.1	0.1	<0.1	19	0	10.1		8	10	2	78	4	<0.1	<0.1
0	71	<0.1	<0.1	0.2	0.1	3	0	1	0.1	18	7	<1	116	8	0.2	0.1
0	2132	0.1	<0.1	0.6	0.1	23	0	79.1	0.3	28	18	0	320	18	0.2	0.2
0	39	<0.1	<0.1	0.3	0.1	12	0	39.3	0.2	14	9	0	175	11	0.1	0.1
0	562	0.1	<0.1	1	0.1	44	0	205.5	0.7	16	36	2	375	20	0.2	0.2
0	80	0.1	<0.1	0.7	0.1	30	0	28.8	<0.1	10	18	29	365	16	0.3	0.1
0	85	0.1	<0.1	0.7	0.1	32	0	30.6	<0.1	10	19	31	388	17	0.3	0.2

ESHA, EatRight Analysis CD-ROM; **AMT**, amount; **WT**, weight; **CAL**, calories; **KILO**, KiloJoule; **WTR**, water; **PROT**, protein; **CARB**, carbohydrate; **FIBR**, fiber; **FAT**, fat; **SATF**, saturated fat; **MONO**, monounsaturated fat; **POLY**, polyunsaturated fat; **CHOL**, cholesterol;

ESHA CODE	FOOD DESCRIPTION	AMT	UNIT	WT (g)	CAL (kcal)	KILO (kJ)	WTR (g)	PROT (g)	CARB (g)	FIBR (g)	FAT (g)	SATF (g)	MONO (g)	POLY (g)
FRUITS (CONTINUED)														
3065	Kiwifruit	1	ea	76	46	192	63	1	11	2	<1	<0.1	<0.1	0.2
3066	Lemon-Fresh-Peeled	1	ea	58	17	71	52	1	5	2	<1	<0.1	<0.1	0.1
3071	Lime-Fresh-Peeled	1	ea	67	20	84	59	<1	7	2	<1	<0.1	<0.1	<0.1
3257	Lychees	1	ea	9.6	6	25	8	<1	2	<1	<1	<0.1	<0.1	<0.1
3221	Mango-Fresh-Whole	1	ea	207	135	565	169	1	35	4	1	0.1	0.2	0.1
3215	Nectarine-Fresh	1	ea	136	60	251	119	1	14	2	<1	<0.1	0.1	0.2
3082	Orange-Fresh-Medium	1	ea	131	62	259	114	1	15	3	<1	<0.1	<0.1	<0.1
3083	Orange-Fresh-Sections-Cup	1	cup	180	85	356	156	2	21	4	<1	<0.1	<0.1	<0.1
3171	Papaya-Fresh	1	ea	304	119	498	270	2	30	5	<1	0.1	0.1	0.1
3096	Peach-Fresh-Medium	1	ea	98	38	159	87	1	9	1	<1	<0.1	0.1	0.1
3103	Pears-Bartlett-Fresh-Med	1	ea	166	96	402	139	1	26	5	<1	<0.1	<0.1	<0.1
3113	Pineapple-Fresh-Slices	1	pce	84	42	176	72	<1	11	1	<1	<0.1	<0.1	<0.1
3121	Plum-Medium-Fresh	1	ea	66	30	126	58	<1	8	1	<1	<0.1	0.1	<0.1
3648	Raspberries-Fresh	10	ea	19	10	42	16	<1	2	1	<1	<0.1	<0.1	0.1
3056	Red Grapes	10	ea	50	34	142	40	<1	9	<1	<1	<0.1	<0.1	<0.1
3209	Rhubarb-raw-diced	1	cup	122	26	109	114	1	6	2	<1	0.1	<0.1	0.1
3664	Starfruit-Raw-Cube-Cup	1	cup	137	42	176	125	1	9	4	<1	<0.1	<0.1	0.3
3136	Strawberries-Medium Size	1	ea	12	4	17	11	<1	1	<1	<1	<0.1	<0.1	<0.1
3135	Strawberries-Sliced-Cup	1	cup	166	53	222	151	1	13	3	<1	<0.1	0.1	0.3
71991	Tangelo-Fresh-Medium	1	ea	109	50	209	100	1	15	3	<1	0		
3138	Tangerine-Fresh	1	ea	84	45	188	72	1	11	2	<1	<0.1	0.1	0.1
3055	Thompson Seedless Grapes	10	ea	50	34	142	40	<1	9	<1	<1	<0.1	<0.1	<0.1
3142	Watermelon-Fresh Pieces	1	cup	152	46	192	139	1	11	1	<1	<0.1	0.1	0.1
Frozen Fruits														
3028	Blackberries-Frozen	1	cup	151	97	406	124	2	24	8	1	<0.1	0.1	0.4
3031	Blueberries-Frozen	1	cup	155	79	331	134	1	19	4	1	0.1	0.1	0.4
3232	Blueberries-Swtnd-Frzn	0.5	cup	115	93	389	89	<1	25	3	<1	<0.1	<0.1	0.1
71120	Raspberries-Swtnd-Frzn	0.5	cup	125	129	540	91	1	33	6	<1	<0.1	<0.1	0.1
3236	Strawberries-Frzn/Sweet/Thaw	1	cup	255	245	1025	187	1	66	5	<1	<0.1	<0.1	0.2
3158	Sweet Cherries-frozen	1	cup	259	231	967	196	3	58	5	<1	0.1	0.1	0.1
GRAIN PRODUCTS – UNPREPARED & PREPARED BAKED GOODS														
Bagels														
42100	Bagel-Cinnamon Raisin	1	ea	71	194	812	23	7	39	2	1	0.2	0.1	0.5
42041	Bagel-Egg-3.5 inch diam	1	ea	71	197	824	23	8	38	2	1	0.3	0.3	0.5
42103	Bagel-Oat Bran	1	ea	71	181	757	23	8	38	3	1	0.1	0.2	0.3
42000	Bagel-Plain-3.5in diam	1	ea	71	182	761	26	7	36	2	1	0.3	0.4	0.5
72307	Bagel-Whole Wheat	1	ea	95	260	1088	27	11	52	9	2	0.5		
Biscuits														
42206	Biscuit-Cheese-2" diam	1	ea	30	113	473	8	3	13	<1	6	1.7	2.3	1.4
42110	Biscuit-LowFat Dough-Baked	1	ea	21	63	264	6	2	12	<1	1	0.3	0.6	0.2
42002	Biscuit-Prep f/Dry	1	oz	28.35	95	397	8	2	14	1	3	0.8	1.2	1.2
42001	Biscuit-Prep f/Recipe	1	ea	60	212	887	17	4	27	1	10	2.6	4.2	2.5
42205	Biscuit-Whole Wheat-3inch	1	ea	63	199	833	18	6	30	5	7	1.7	3	2.2
42325	Crumpet-Whole Wheat	1	oz	28.35	48	201	15	2	10	1	<1			
Bread Crumbs, Breading Mixes, Batters, & Croutons														
42004	Bread Crumbs-Dry-Grated	1	cup	108	427	1787	7	14	78	5	6	1.3	1.1	2.2

< = Trace amount present   Blank = Not available

V, vitamin; **THI**, thiamin; **RIB**, riboflavin; **NIA**, niacin; **FOL**, folate; **CALC**, calcium; **PHOS**, phosphorus; **SOD**, sodium; **POT**, potassium; **MAG**, magnesium

CHOL (mg)	V-A (IU)	THI (mg)	RIB (mg)	NIA (mg)	V-B6 (mg)	FOL (μg)	V-B12 (μg)	V-C (mg)	V-E (mg)	CALC (mg)	PHOS (mg)	SOD (mg)	POT (mg)	MAG (mg)	IRON (mg)	ZINC (mg)
0	66	<0.1	<0.1	0.3	<0.1	19	0	70.5	1.1	26	26	2	237	13	0.2	0.1
0	13	<0.1	<0.1	0.1	<0.1	6	0	30.7	0.1	15	9	1	80	5	0.3	<0.1
0	34	<0.1	<0.1	0.1	<0.1	5	0	19.5	0.1	22	12	1	68	4	0.4	0.1
0	0	<0.1	<0.1	0.1	<0.1	1	0	6.9	<0.1	<1	3	<1	16	1	<0.1	<0.1
0	1584	0.1	0.1	1.2	0.3	29	0	57.3	2.3	21	23	4	323	19	0.3	0.1
0	452	<0.1	<0.1	1.5	<0.1	7	0	7.3	1	8	35	0	273	12	0.4	0.2
0	295	0.1	0.1	0.4	0.1	39	0	69.7	0.2	52	18	0	237	13	0.1	0.1
0	405	0.2	0.1	0.5	0.1	54	0	95.8	0.3	72	25	0	326	18	0.2	0.1
0	3326	0.1	0.1	1	0.1	116	0	187.9	2.2	73	15	9	781	30	0.3	0.2
0	319	<0.1	<0.1	0.8	<0.1	4	0	6.5	0.7	6	20	0	186	9	0.2	0.2
0	38	<0.1	<0.1	0.3	<0.1	12	0	7	0.2	15	18	2	198	12	0.3	0.2
0	49	0.1	<0.1	0.4	0.1	15	0	40.2	<0.1	11	7	1	92	10	0.2	0.1
0	228	<0.1	<0.1	0.3	<0.1	3	0	6.3	0.2	4	11	0	104	5	0.1	0.1
0	6	<0.1	<0.1	0.1	<0.1	4	0	5	0.2	5	6	<1	29	4	0.1	0.1
0	33	<0.1	<0.1	0.1	<0.1	1	0	5.4	0.1	5	10	1	96	4	0.2	<0.1
0	124	<0.1	<0.1	0.4	<0.1	9	0	9.8	0.3	105	17	5	351	15	0.3	0.1
0	84	<0.1	<0.1	0.5	<0.1	16	0	47.1	0.2	4	16	3	182	14	0.1	0.2
0	1	<0.1	<0.1	<0.1	<0.1	3	0	7.1	<0.1	2	3	<1	18	2	<0.1	<0.1
0	20	<0.1	<0.1	0.6	0.1	40	0	97.6	0.5	27	40	2	254	22	0.7	0.2
0	0						0	30		40		0			0	
0	572	<0.1	<0.1	0.3	0.1	13	0	22.4	0.2	31	17	2	139	10	0.1	0.1
0	33	<0.1	<0.1	0.1	<0.1	1	0	5.4	0.1	5	10	1	96	4	0.2	<0.1
0	865	0.1	<0.1	0.3	0.1	5	0	12.3	0.1	11	17	2	170	15	0.4	0.2
0	172	<0.1	0.1	1.8	0.1	51	0	4.7	1.8	44	45	2	211	33	1.2	0.4
0	71	<0.1	0.1	0.8	0.1	11	0	3.9	0.7	12	17	2	84	8	0.3	0.1
0	56	<0.1	0.1	0.3	0.1	8	0	1.2	0.6	7	8	1	69	2	0.4	0.1
0	75	<0.1	0.1	0.3	<0.1	32	0	20.6	0.9	19	21	1	142	16	0.8	0.2
0	61	<0.1	0.1	1	0.1	38	0	105.6	0.6	28	33	8	250	18	1.5	0.2
0	490	0.1	0.1	0.5	0.1	10	0	2.6	0.2	31	41	3	515	26	0.9	0.1
0	52	0.3	0.2	2.2	<0.1	79	0	0.5	0.2	13	71	229	105	20	2.7	0.8
17	77	0.4	0.2	2.4	0.1	62	0.1	0.4		9	60	359	48	18	2.8	0.5
0	3	0.2	0.2	2.1	<0.1	70	0	0.1	0.2	9	78	360	82	22	2.2	0.6
0	0	0.4	0.2	2.8	<0.1	103	0	0.7	0.1	63	62	318	53	16	4.3	1.3
0	0	0.2	0.1	4		32		0		100		450			2.7	
4	63	0.1	0.1	0.8	<0.1	3	0.1	0.1	0.6	91	68	150	46	6	0.8	0.3
0	0	0.1	<0.1	0.7	<0.1	17	0	0	<0.1	4	98	305	39	4	0.6	0.1
1	27	0.1	0.1	0.9	<0.1	15	0.1	0.1		52	133	271	53	7	0.6	0.2
2	49	0.2	0.2	1.8	<0.1	37	<0.1	0.1		141	98	348	73	11	1.7	0.3
2	51	0.1	0.1	2.2	0.1	13	0.1	0.2	1.3	155	199	210	200	57	1.7	1.2
	0	<0.1	0	0.4				0		21		245	32	8	0.5	0.1
0	0	1	0.4	7.2	0.1	116	0.4	0	0.1	198	178	791	212	46	5.2	1.6

ESHA, EatRight Analysis CD-ROM; **AMT**, amount; **WT**, weight; **CAL**, calories; **KILO**, KiloJoule; **WTR**, water; **PROT**, protein; **CARB**, carbohydrate; **FIBR**, fiber; **FAT**, fat; **SATF**, saturated fat; **MONO**, monounsaturated fat; **POLY**, polyunsaturated fat; **CHOL**, cholesterol;

ESHA CODE	FOOD DESCRIPTION	AMT	UNIT	WT (g)	CAL (kcal)	KILO (kJ)	WTR (g)	PROT (g)	CARB (g)	FIBR (g)	FAT (g)	SATF (g)	MONO (g)	POLY (g)
GRAIN PRODUCTS – UNPREPARED & PREPARED BAKED GOODS (CONTINUED)														
42144	Bread Crumbs-Seasoned-Dry	1	cup	120	460	1925	8	17	82	6	7	1.7	1.4	2.8
42016	Croutons	1	cup	30	122	510	2	4	22	2	2	0.5	0.9	0.4
42148	Croutons-Seasoned	1	cup	40	186	778	1	4	25	2	7	2.1	3.8	0.9
Breads & Rolls														
42039	Banana Bread-Recipe w/Marg	1	pce	60	196	820	18	3	33	1	6	1.3	2.7	1.9
42052	Boston Brown Bread-Canned	1	pce	45	88	368	21	2	19	2	1	0.1	0.1	0.3
42090	Challah/Egg Bread	1	pce	40	113	473	14	4	19	1	2	0.6	0.9	0.4
42115	Cornbread-Dry Mix-Prep	1	ea	60	188	787	19	4	29	1	6	1.6	3.1	0.7
42116	Cornbread-Recipe w/2%Milk	1	ea	65	173	724	25	4	28	2	5	1	1.2	2.1
42042	Cracked Wheat Bread-Slice	1	pce	25	65	272	9	2	12	1	1	0.2	0.5	0.2
42015	Croissant-4.5x4x2	1	ea	57	231	967	13	5	26	1	12	6.6	3.1	0.6
42173	Cuban/Spanish/Portug Bread	1	pce	20	55	230	7	2	10	1	1	0.1	0.2	0.1
42157	Dinner Roll/Bun	1	ea	28	87	364	8	3	15	1	2	0.4	0.5	0.7
42160	Dinner Roll/Bun-Wheat	1	ea	28.35	77	322	10	2	13	1	2	0.4	0.9	0.3
42070	Dinner Roll-Oat Bran	1	ea	33	78	326	15	3	13	1	2	0.2	0.5	0.5
42091	Egg Bread/Challah-Toasted	1	pce	37	117	490	10	4	19	1	2	0.6	1.1	0.4
42043	French/Vienna Bread	1	pce	32	92	385	9	4	18	1	1	0.2	0.1	0.3
42184	Garlic Roll	1	ea	35	105	439	11	3	18	1	3	0.6	1.3	0.4
42020	Hamburger Bun	1	ea	43	120	502	15	4	21	1	2	0.5	0.5	0.8
42022	Hard Roll-White	1	ea	57	167	699	18	6	30	1	2	0.3	0.6	1
42381	Hoagie Roll	1	ea	69	200	837		7	33	2	5	1.5		
42021	Hotdog/Frankfurter Bun	1	ea	43	120	502	15	4	21	1	2	0.5	0.5	0.8
49012	Hush Puppies-Recipe	1	ea	22	74	310	6	2	10	1	3	0.5	0.7	1.6
72411	Indian Fry Bread	2	oz	56.7	187	782	18	4	27		7	2.6	2.5	0.6
42046	Italian Bread	1	pce	30	81	339	11	3	15	1	1	0.3	0.2	0.4
42185	Mexican Bolillo Roll	1	ea	117	307	1284	43	10	61	2	2	0.5	0.2	0.6
42047	Mixed Grain Bread-Slice	1	pce	26	69	289	10	3	11	2	1	0.2	0.2	0.5
62746	Multigrain Bread-Low Fat	1	pce	31	60	251		3	14	5	1	0		
42190	Pannetone-Italian Sweetbread	1	pce	27	87	364	8	2	15	1	2	1.2	0.7	0.2
71227	Pita Bread-4"	1	ea	28	77	322	9	3	16	1	<1	<0.1	<0.1	0.1
42007	Pita Pocket Bread-White	1	ea	60	165	690	19	5	33	1	1	0.1	0.1	0.3
42080	Pita Pocket Bread-Whole Wheat	1	ea	64	170	711	20	6	35	5	2	0.3	0.2	0.7
42006	Pumpernickel Bread-Slice	1	pce	26	65	272	10	2	12	2	1	0.1	0.2	0.3
42051	Raisin Bread	1	pce	26	71	297	9	2	14	1	1	0.3	0.6	0.2
42005	Rye Bread	1	pce	32	83	347	12	3	15	2	1	0.2	0.4	0.3
42045	Sourdough Bread-Med Slice	1	pce	32	92	385	9	4	18	1	1	0.2	0.1	0.3
12485	Sprouted Multigrain Bread	2	oz	56.7	130	544	13	6	26	4	0	0	0	0
42012	Wheat Berry Bread	1	pce	25	66	276	9	3	12	1	1	0.2	0.2	0.4
42136	Wheat Bran Bread	1	pce	36	89	372	14	3	17	1	1	0.3	0.6	0.2
42012	Wheat Bread	1	pce	25	66	276	9	3	12	1	1	0.2	0.2	0.4
42095	Wheat Bread-LowCal	1	pce	23	46	192	10	2	10	3	1	0.1	0.1	0.2
42216	White Bread	1	pce	30	80	335	11	2	15	1	1	0.2	0.2	0.4
42084	White Bread-LowCal	1	pce	23	48	201	10	2	10	2	1	0.1	0.2	0.1
42014	Whole Wheat Bread	1	pce	28	69	289	11	4	12	2	1	0.2	0.4	0.2
42057	Whole Wheat Roll	1	ea	28.35	75	314	9	2	14	2	1	0.2	0.3	0.6
Cereals – Hot														

< = Trace amount present Blank = Not available

V, vitamin; **THI**, thiamin; **RIB**, riboflavin; **NIA**, niacin; **FOL**, folate; **CALC**, calcium; **PHOS**, phosphorus; **SOD**, sodium; **POT**, potassium; **MAG**, magnesium

CHOL (mg)	V-A (IU)	THI (mg)	RIB (mg)	NIA (mg)	V-B6 (mg)	FOL (μg)	V-B12 (μg)	V-C (mg)	V-E (mg)	CALC (mg)	PHOS (mg)	SOD (mg)	POT (mg)	MAG (mg)	IRON (mg)	ZINC (mg)
1	232	1.2	0.5	7.4	0.2	143		3.2	0.3	218	212	2111	277	55	5.9	1.7
0	0	0.2	0.1	1.6	<0.1	40	0	0		23	34	209	37	9	1.2	0.3
3	13	0.2	0.2	1.9	<0.1	42	0.1	0	0.2	38	56	495	72	17	1.1	0.4
26	296	0.1	0.1	0.9	0.1	20	0.1	1		13	35	181	80	8	0.8	0.2
<1	39	<0.1	0.1	0.5	<0.1	5	<0.1	0	0.1	32	50	284	143	28	0.9	0.2
20	84	0.2	0.2	1.9	<0.1	42	<0.1	0	0.1	37	42	197	46	8	1.2	0.3
37	123	0.1	0.2	1.2	0.1	33	0.1	0.1		44	226	467	77	12	1.1	0.4
26	180	0.2	0.2	1.5	0.1	50	0.1	0.2		162	110	428	96	16	1.6	0.4
0	0	0.1	0.1	0.9	0.1	15	<0.1	0		11	38	134	44	13	0.7	0.3
38	424	0.2	0.1	1.2	<0.1	50	0.1	0.1	0.5	21	60	424	67	9	1.2	0.4
0	0	0.1	0.1	0.9	<0.1	6	0	0	<0.1	9	21	122	23	5	0.5	0.2
1	1	0.1	0.1	1.5	<0.1	28	<0.1	0.1	0.1	50	34	150	39	7	1	0.3
0	0	0.1	0.1	1.2	<0.1	17	0	0	0.1	50	29	96	33	10	1	0.3
0	0	0.1	0.1	1.6	<0.1	31	0	0	0.2	28	38	136	40	11	1.4	0.3
21	85	0.1	0.2	1.8	<0.1	36	<0.1	0	0.1	38	43	200	47	8	1.2	0.3
0	0	0.1	0.1	1.5	<0.1	47	0	0.1	0.1	14	36	208	41	9	1.2	0.3
<1	0	0.2	0.1	1.4	<0.1	10	<0.1	0.1	0.3	42	41	181	47	8	1.1	0.3
0	0	0.2	0.1	1.8	<0.1	48	0.1	0	<0.1	59	27	206	40	9	1.4	0.3
0	0	0.3	0.2	2.4	<0.1	54	0	0	0.2	54	57	310	62	15	1.9	0.5
0	0	0.2	0.1	2		40		0		80		320			1.4	
0	0	0.2	0.1	1.8	<0.1	48	0.1	0	<0.1	59	27	206	40	9	1.4	0.3
10	41	0.1	0.1	0.6	<0.1	20	<0.1	<1	0.3	61	42	147	32	5	0.7	0.1
4		0.2	0.1	2.6	<0.1	69	0		0	32	70	187	44	10	2.3	0.2
0	0	0.1	0.1	1.3	<0.1	57	0	0	0.1	23	31	175	33	8	0.9	0.3
1	15	0.7	0.5	6.6	<0.1	41	<0.1	<1	0.1	14	90	7	98	22	3.8	0.8
0	0	0.1	<0.1	1.1	0.1	20	0	<1	0.1	27	59	109	60	20	0.6	0.4
0	0	0.2	0.2	2	0.2	40	0.9	0		60		90		40	1.1	2.2
19	88	0.1	0.1	1	<0.1	19	0.1	0.3	0.1	16	40	28	54	5	0.8	0.2
0	0	0.2	0.1	1.3	<0.1	30	0	0	0.1	24	27	150	34	7	0.7	0.2
0	0	0.4	0.2	2.8	<0.1	64	0	0	0.2	52	58	322	72	16	1.6	0.5
0	0	0.2	0.1	1.8	0.2	22	0	0	0.4	10	115	340	109	44	2	1
0	0	0.1	0.1	0.8	<0.1	24	0	0	0.1	18	46	174	54	14	0.7	0.4
0	0	0.1	0.1	0.9	<0.1	28	0	<1	0.1	17	28	101	59	7	0.8	0.2
0	2	0.1	0.1	1.2	<0.1	35	0	0.1	0.1	23	40	211	53	13	0.9	0.4
0	0	0.1	0.1	1.5	<0.1	47	0	0.1	0.1	14	36	208	41	9	1.2	0.3
0	0							0		20		3			1.8	
0	0	0.1	0.1	1.3	<0.1	21	0	0.1	<0.1	36	39	130	46	12	0.9	0.3
0	0	0.1	0.1	1.6	0.1	38	0	0	0.1	27	67	175	82	29	1.1	0.5
0	0	0.1	0.1	1.3	<0.1	21	0	0.1	<0.1	36	39	130	46	12	0.9	0.3
0	0	0.1	0.1	0.9	<0.1	21	0	<1	0.1	18	23	118	28	9	0.7	0.3
0	0	0.1	0.1	1.3	<0.1	33	0	0	0.1	45	30	204	30	7	1.1	0.2
0	1	0.1	0.1	0.8	<0.1	22	0.1	0.1	<0.1	22	28	104	17	5	0.7	0.3
0	1	0.1	0.1	1.3	0.1	14	0	0	0.2	30	57	132	69	23	0.7	0.5
0	0	0.1	<0.1	1	0.1	9	0	0	0.3	30	64	136	77	24	0.7	0.6

ESHA, EatRight Analysis CD-ROM; **AMT**, amount; **WT**, weight; **CAL**, calories; **KILO**, KiloJoule; **WTR**, water; **PROT**, protein; **CARB**, carbohydrate; **FIBR**, fiber; **FAT**, fat; **SATF**, saturated fat; **MONO**, monounsaturated fat; **POLY**, polyunsaturated fat; **CHOL**, cholesterol;

ESHA CODE	FOOD DESCRIPTION	AMT	UNIT	WT (g)	CAL (kcal)	KILO (kJ)	WTR (g)	PROT (g)	CARB (g)	FIBR (g)	FAT (g)	SATF (g)	MONO (g)	POLY (g)
GRAIN PRODUCTS – UNPREPARED & PREPARED BAKED GOODS (CONTINUED)														
40178	Corn Grits-Unenrich-Ckd	1	cup	242	143	598	207	3	31	1	<1	0.1	0.1	0.2
40094	Corn Grits-White, cooked	1	cup	242	143	598	207	3	31	1	<1	0.1	0.1	0.2
40093	Corn Grits-White-Enr, cooked	1	cup	242	172	720	201	4	36	2	1	0.2	0.2	0.4
40078	Cream of Rice Cereal, cooked	1	cup	244	127	531	214	2	28	<1	<1	0.1	0.1	0.1
40006	Farina Cereal-Enrich-Cooked	1	cup	233	123	515	202	4	25	2	1	0.2	0.1	0.3
40239	Maypo Cereal-Ckd w/Salt	1	cup	240	170	711	198	6	32	5	2	0.4	0.6	0.5
40015	Maypo Cereal-Cooked	0.75	cup	180	128	536	149	4	24	4	2	0.3	0.5	0.7
40083	Multigrain Cereal-Dry	0.33	cup	31	100	418	3	4	22	6	1	0.1	0.1	0.3
40431	Oat Bran Cereal-Hot-Dry	0.5	cup	40	146	611	4	7	25	6	3	0.6	1	1.2
40000	Oatmeal-Cooked-No Salt	1	cup	234	166	695	196	6	28	4	4	0.7	1	1.3
40072	Oatmeal-Instant-Pkt-Prepared	1	cup	234	159	665	197	6	27	4	3	0.6	0.9	1
40075	Oatmeal-Inst-Flavored-Pkt-Prep	1	ea	155	157	657	116	4	31	3	2	0.3	0.7	0.6
40088	Ralston Cereal-Cooked	1	cup	253	134	561	218	6	28	6	1	0.1	0.1	0.4
38008	Rolled Oats-Dry	1	cup	81	307	1284	9	11	55	8	5	0.9	1.6	1.9
40002	Rolled wheat-cooked	1	cup	242	150	628	202	5	33	4	1	0.1	0.1	0.5
40016	Roman Meal Cereal-Cooked	0.75	cup	181	110	460	150	5	25	6	1	0.1		
40191	Wheatena Cereal-Ckd w/Salt	1	cup	243	143	598	208	5	29	5	1	0.2	0.2	0.6
40080	Wheatena Cereal-Cooked	1	cup	243	136	569	208	5	29	7	1	0.2	0.2	0.6
Cereals – Ready to Eat														
40063	100% Natural Cereal	0.5	cup	48	206	862	1	5	35	3	6	3.8	1.3	0.8
61644	7 Whole Grain Flakes Cereal	1	cup	50	175	732	2	6	41	6	1	0.2	0.2	0.6
60959	7 Whole Grain Puffs Cereal	1	cup	25	98	410	1	3	20	2	1	0.2	0.2	0.3
61198	Alpha-Bits Cereal-frosted	1	cup	32	130	544	<1	3	27	1	1	0.3	0.4	0.5
40123	Amaranth Flakes Cereal	1	cup	38	134	561	1	6	27	4	3	0.5	0.8	1
61702	Apple Zings Cereal	1	cup	33	130	544	1	2	29	1	1	0.1	0.4	0.3
61388	Autumn Wheat Cereal	1	cup	54	191	799	2	5	45	6	1	0.1	0.1	0.3
40029	Bran Buds Cereal	0.33	cup	30	75	314	1	2	24	13	1	0.1	0.1	0.4
14903	Bran Flakes Cereal	0.75	cup	29	90	377	1	3	23	5	1	0.1	0.1	0.4
40032	Cap'n Crunch Cereal	0.75	cup	27	109	456	1	1	23	1	2	1.1	0.2	0.2
40033	Cap'N Crunch Cereal-Crunchberries	0.75	cup	26	105	439	1	1	22	1	1	1	0.2	0.2
40034	Cap'n Crunch, Peanut Butter	0.75	cup	27	112	469	1	2	21	1	2	1.1	0.7	0.6
40033	Cap'n Crunchberries	0.75	cup	26	105	439	1	1	22	1	1	1	0.2	0.2
40335	Chex Wheat Cereal	1	cup	30	108	452	1	3	24	3	1	0.1	0.1	0.2
61645	Cinnamon Harvest Cereal	1	cup	54	184	770	3	4	44	6	1	0.2	0.2	0.6
60927	Cinnamon Oat Crunch Cereal	1	cup	60	228	954	2	6	48	5	3	0.5	0.9	0.8
60929	Cocoa Bumpers Cereal	1	cup	33	124	519	1	2	29	1	1	0.1	0.1	0.2
12440	Corn Flakes Cereal-Honey'd	0.75	cup	30	120	502	<1	2	26	2	<1	0		
40205	Cracklin' Oat Bran Cereal	0.75	cup	49	197	824	1	4	35	6	7	3	2.3	1.5
61393	Cranberry Sunshine Cereal	1	cup	29	116	485	1	2	26	3	1	0.1	0.2	0.5
40040	Crispy Wheat`n Raisins Cereal	1	cup	55	183	766	4	4	45	5	1	0.2	0.1	0.4
40217	Frosted Flakes Cereal	0.75	cup	31	114	477	1	1	28	1	<1	<0.1	<0.1	<0.1
40043	Frosted Mini Wheats Cereal	1	cup	51	175	732	3	5	42	5	1	0.2	0.1	0.5
61261	Frosted Oat Cereal w/Marshmallows	1	cup	28	109	456	1	2	24	1	1	0.2	0.3	0.4
61546	Fruit & Bran Cereal	1	cup	55	200	837		4	42	6	3	0		
61204	Fruity Pebbles Cereal	0.75	cup	30	120	502	1	1	26	<1	1	0.3	0.5	0.4
61213	Golden Crisp Cereal	0.75	cup	27	107	448	1	1	25	0	<1	0.1	0.1	0.1

< = Trace amount present Blank = Not available

V, vitamin; **THI**, thiamin; **RIB**, riboflavin; **NIA**, niacin; **FOL**, folate; **CALC**, calcium; **PHOS**, phosphorus; **SOD**, sodium; **POT**, potassium; **MAG**, magnesium

CHOL (mg)	V-A (IU)	THI (mg)	RIB (mg)	NIA (mg)	V-B6 (mg)	FOL (μg)	V-B12 (μg)	V-C (mg)	V-E (mg)	CALC (mg)	PHOS (mg)	SOD (mg)	POT (mg)	MAG (mg)	IRON (mg)	ZINC (mg)
0	75	<0.1	<0.1	0.4	0.1	2	0	0	<0.1	7	27	540	51	12	0.4	0.2
0	2	<0.1	<0.1	0.4	0.1	2	0	0	<0.1	7	27	5	51	12	0.4	0.2
0	0	0.2	0.1	1.9	0.1	68	0	0	0.1	2	48	5	65	17	1.4	0.4
0	0	0	0	1	0.1	7	0	0	<0.1	7	41	2	49	7	0.5	0.4
0	0	0.3	0.2	3.5	0.2	179	0	0	0.1	226	86	42	54	16	12.4	0.5
0	2335	0.7	0.8	9.4	0.9	12	2.8	28.3	0.2	130	247	259	211	53	8.4	1.5
0	1753	0.5	0.5	7	0.7	7	2.2	21.6	0.1	94	185	7	158	38	6.3	1.1
0	0	0.2	0.1	2.1	0.1	22	0	0		20	146	2	205	73	1.4	1.2
0	40	0.4	0.1	0.3	<0.1	15	0	0		32	278	2	232	96	3.2	1.7
0	0	0.2	<0.1	0.5	<0.1	14	0	0	0.2	21	180	9	164	63	2.1	2.3
0	1453	0.6	0.5	7.1	0.7	103	0	0	0.2	187	180	115	143	61	13.9	1.5
0	1056	0.3	0.3	4	0.4	85	0	0	0.2	108	129	253	107	39	3.8	0.9
0	0	0.2	0.2	2	0.1	18	0.1	0		13	147	5	154	58	1.6	1.4
0	0	0.4	0.1	0.9	0.1	26	0	0	0.3	42	332	5	293	112	3.4	2.9
0	0	0.2	0.1	2.2	0.2	34	0	0	0.6	17	167	0	172	53	1.5	1.2
0	0	0.2	0.1	2.3	0.1	18	0	0		22	161	2	226	81	1.6	1.3
0	7	<0.1	0.1	1.3	<0.1	22	0	0	1.3	15	146	578	187	51	1.4	1.7
0	0	<0.1	<0.1	1.3	<0.1	17	0	0		10	146	5	187	49	1.4	1.7
<1	3	0.2	0.1	1	0.1	17	0.1	0.1	0.8	56	176	24	222	54	1.3	1.3
0	0							0		15	142	152	160	50	1.5	1.2
0	2	<0.1	<0.1	0.8	0.1	8	0	0	0.2	10	60	2	83	38	0.7	0.8
0	750	0.4	0.4	5	0.5	100	1.5	0	<0.1	10	67	212	62	25	2.7	1.5
0	0	<0.1	<0.1	1	<0.1	4	0	1	0.5	6	126	13	134	10	0.7	0.1
<1	921	0.4	0.7	6.6	0.9	116	2.1	19.7	0.1	142	41	170	46	12	5.6	4.8
0	0	0.2	<0.1	2.3	0.1	16	0	0	0.4	0	122	0	180	44	1.6	0.8
0	510	0.4	0.4	5.1	2	404	6	6	0.5	19	150	203	300	62	4.5	1.5
	514	1.4	2.1	26.3	2			69.5	23.3	13	155	236	183	55	19.6	18.7
0	40	0.4	0.5	5.7	0.6	420	0	0	0.2	3	45	202	50	15	5.2	4.3
0	37	0.4	0.5	5.5	0.6	400	<0.1	<1	0.2	4	43	182	49	14	5	4.2
0	41	0.4	0.5	5.5	0.6	420	0	0	0.2	2	53	200	64	19	5	4.1
0	37	0.4	0.5	5.5	0.6	400	<0.1	<1	0.2	4	43	182	49	14	5	4.2
0	300	0.2	0.3	3	0.3	240	0.9	3.6	0.2	60	90	252	114	24	8.6	2.2
0	0							0		0		5	169		1.5	
0	5	0.2	0.2	1.4	0.1	22	0	0.1		44	215	251	322	64	2.2	1.5
0	54	<0.1	0.2	0.4	<0.1	4	0	0		46	55	180	260	20	1.7	0.4
0	100							0		0		170			0.4	
0	750	0.4	0.4	5	0.5	100	1.5	15.2	0.3	29	195	151	220	76	1.8	1.5
0												21	83		0.4	
0	500	0.7	0.9	10	1	200	3	0	0.3	0	140	251	227	42	7.5	7.5
0	608	0.6	0.6	8.3	0.9	118	2.5	8.3	<0.1	1	13	143	23	2	7.3	<0.1
0	0	0.5	0.5	5.1	0.5	103	1.5	0	0.3	17	153	5	180	47	16.3	1.5
0	1235	0.4	0.4	4.9	0.5	99	1.5	14.8	0.2	20	39	158	58	8	4.4	2.2
0	750							0		20		260			5.4	
0	750	0.4	0.4	5	0.6	100	1.7	0	0.4	2	17	175	33	6	1.8	1.7
0	750	0.4	0.4	5	0.5	100	1.5	0	0.1	4	37	40	34	16	1.8	1.5

ESHA, EatRight Analysis CD-ROM; **AMT**, amount; **WT**, weight; **CAL**, calories; **KILO**, KiloJoule; **WTR**, water; **PROT**, protein; **CARB**, carbohydrate; **FIBR**, fiber; **FAT**, fat; **SATF**, saturated fat; **MONO**, monounsaturated fat; **POLY**, polyunsaturated fat; **CHOL**, cholesterol;

ESHA CODE	FOOD DESCRIPTION	AMT	UNIT	WT (g)	CAL (kcal)	KILO (kJ)	WTR (g)	PROT (g)	CARB (g)	FIBR (g)	FAT (g)	SATF (g)	MONO (g)	POLY (g)
GRAIN PRODUCTS – UNPREPARED & PREPARED BAKED GOODS (CONTINUED)														
38361	Granola Cereal-Low Fat	0.5	cup	55	213	891	2	4	45	3	3	0.7	1.2	0.9
40197	Granola-LowFat w/Raisins (duplicate)	0.66	cup	60	230	962	2	5	49	4	3	0.8	1.2	1
40265	GrapeNut Flakes Cereal	0.75	cup	29	106	444	1	3	24	3	1	0.2		
60928	Groovy Grahams Cereal	0.75	cup	28	104	435	1	2	24	1	<1	0.1	0.1	0.2
40051	Honey Nut Cheerios Cereal	1	cup	30	118	494	1	3	23	2	2	0	0.5	0.5
61526	Honey Nut O's Cereal	1	cup	30	120	502	<1	3	24	2	2	0	0.5	0.5
60965	Honey Roundups Cereal	0.75	cup	28	107	448	1	2	25	1	1	0.1	0.2	0.2
61340	Just Flakes Cereal	0.75	cup	28	100	418		4	19	3	2	0		
40108	Just Right Cereal	1	cup	55	204	854	2	4	46	3	1	0.1	0.3	1
40055	Kashi Breakfast Pilaf Cereal	0.5	cup	140	170	711		6	30	6	3	0		
60961	Kashi Good Friends Cereal	0.75	cup	30	95	397	1	3	25	7	1	0.1	0.3	0.5
60960	Kashi Honey Puffed Cereal	1	cup	30	114	477	1	3	25	2	1	0.1	0.2	0.3
40054	King Vitamin Cereal	1.5	cup	31	120	502	1	2	26	1	1	0.5	0.2	0.4
40010	Kix Cereal	1.33	cup	30	110	460	1	2	25	3	1	0.2	0.3	0.4
40011	Life Cereal	0.75	cup	32	119	498	1	3	25	2	1	0.3	0.5	0.5
40451	Maple Buckwheat Flakes Cereal	1	cup	43	170	711		4	35	1	1	0	0.5	0.5
40046	Marshmallow Safari Cereal	0.75	cup	30	119	498	1	2	25	1	2	0.4	0.8	0.4
40418	Mueslix Cereal	0.66	cup	55	196	820	5	5	40	4	3	0.4	1.6	1
61168	Oat Bran Flakes Cereal	1	cup	47	166	695	2	5	37	6	1	0.1	0.2	0.2
61168	Oat Bran Flakes Cereal	1	cup	47	166	695	2	5	37	6	1	0.1	0.2	0.2
61310	Oat Bran Granola Cereal	0.5	cup	50	210	879		6	31	5	8	1		
40018	Puffed Rice Cereal	1	cup	14	54	226	1	1	12	<1	<1	<0.1	<0.1	<0.1
60951	Puffed Wheat Cereal	.75	cup	9	29	121	<1	1	7	1	<1	<0.1	0.1	0.1
40023	Puffed Wheat Cereal	1.25	cup	15	55	230	1	2	11	1	<1	0.1	<0.1	0.2
40066	Quisp Cereal	1	cup	27	109	456	1	1	23	1	2	1.2	0.2	0.2
61212	Raisin Bran Cereal	1	cup	59	187	782	5	6	45	7	1	0.2	0.3	0.6
61689	Raisin Bran Cereal	1	cup	59	213	891	5	5	45	8	1	0.3	0.2	0.6
40393	Raisin Nut Bran Cereal	1	cup	55	200	837	4	4	42	5	3	0.5	1.5	0.5
61681	Rice Crisps Cereal	1.25	cup	33	126	527	1	2	28	<1	<1	0.1	0.1	0.1
40017	Rice Krispies Cereal	1	cup	28	102	427	1	2	24	<1	<1	0.1	0.1	0.1
61558	Shredded Wheat Cereal-Biscuits	2	ea	47	160	669	2	5	37	6	1	0		
61218	Shredded Wheat Cereal-Spoon Size	1	cup	49	167	699	2	5	41	6	1	0.1	0.1	0.2
40062	Shredded Wheat-Lg Biscuit	2	ea	47.2	159	665	3	5	37	6	1	0.2	0.2	0.6
40068	Sugar Smacks Cereal	0.75	cup	27	104	435	1	2	24	1	<1	0.1	0.2	0.2
40047	Sweet Puffs Cereal	1	cup	34	133	556	1	2	30	1	1	0.1	0.1	0.3
12430	Synergy 8 Grain Cereal	0.75	cup	30	100	418		3	24	5	1	0		
40070	Tasteeos Cereal	1	cup	24	96	402	1	3	18	3	1	0.2	0.4	0.4
60926	Toasted Oat Bran Cereal+BrwnSug	0.75	cup	32	119	498	1	4	24	3	2	0.3	0.5	0.6
40413	Toasty O's Cereal	1	cup	30	121	506	1	4	22	3	2	0.4	0.6	0.7
40021	Total Wheat Cereal	0.75	cup	30	100	418	1	2	23	3	1	0.1	0.1	0.2
40128	Uncle Sam's Fiber Cereal	1	cup	55	237	992	2	9	36	11	6	0.7	1.1	4.6
38026	Wheat Germ-Toasted	1	cup	113	432	1807	6	33	56	17	12	2.1	1.7	7.5
Crackers														
139	Butter Crackers (Club)	2	ea	8	40	167	<1	1	5	<1	2	0.4	0.5	1

< = Trace amount present   Blank = Not available

V, vitamin; **THI**, thiamin; **RIB**, riboflavin; **NIA**, niacin; **FOL**, folate; **CALC**, calcium; **PHOS**, phosphorus; **SOD**, sodium; **POT**, potassium; **MAG**, magnesium

CHOL (mg)	V-A (IU)	THI (mg)	RIB (mg)	NIA (mg)	V-B6 (mg)	FOL (µg)	V-B12 (µg)	V-C (mg)	V-E (mg)	CALC (mg)	PHOS (mg)	SOD (mg)	POT (mg)	MAG (mg)	IRON (mg)	ZINC (mg)
0	842	0.4	0.5	5.6	2.3	449	6.7	1.1	1.3	21	132	120	137	42	2	4.2
0	750	0.4	0.4	5	2	400	6	1.2	1.4	23	140	148	184	44	1.8	3.8
0	750	0.4	0.4	5	0.5	100	1.5	0		11	88	140	99	30	8.1	1.2
0	41	<0.1	0.2	0.4	<0.1	4	0	0		39	45	243	211	16	1.4	0.3
0	536	0.4	0.5	5.4	0.5	214	1.6	6.4	0.3	107	107	204	123	34	4.8	4
0	500	0.4		5	0.5	100		6		100	80	250	70	24	4.5	3.8
0	39	0.1	<0.1	0.3	<0.1	5	0	0		6	55	164	66	18	0.5	0.4
0	0							0		20		190	80		1.1	
0	1250	0.4	0.4	5	0.5	102	1.5	0	1.5	14	106	338	121	34	16.2	0.9
0	0							0		20		15			1.4	
0	36	0.1	<0.1	1.2	0.1	13	0	0	0.3	10	71	73	148	34	0.9	0.8
0	1	<0.1	<0.1	0.8	0.1	8	0	0	0.3	9	79	6	79	34	0.7	0.8
0	1039	0.4	0.4	5.2	0.5	414	1.6	12.4	1.4	3	79	259	85	26	9	3.9
0	904	0.6	0.6	7.3	0.7	236	1.7	7.6	0.1	171	57	199	56	15	9.6	5.2
0	13	0.4	0.5	5.6	0.6	268	0	0	0.2	112	132	164	91	30	9	4.1
0	0	0.2	<0.1	1.6				6		20		190	100		0.7	
0	1000	0.4	0.4	5	0.5	100	0	12	0.1	26	58	192	42	17	4.5	3.8
0	300	0.4	0.4	5.5	2	406	6	0.2	4	32	100	170	240	49	4.5	3.7
0	4	0.2	0.2	3.2	0.1	22	0	0.2	0.2	18	238	17	151	79	2.4	1.2
0	4	0.2	0.2	3.2	0.1	22	0	0.2	0.2	18	238	17	151	79	2.4	1.2
0	100							1.2		20		0			1.4	
0	0	0.1	<0.1	0.5	0	22	0	0	<0.1	1	17	1	16	4	0.4	0.2
0	0						0	0		4	38	<1	43		0	
0	0	0.1	0.1	0.8	<0.1	23	0	0	0	4	50	1	55	20	0.7	0.5
0	40	0.4	0.5	5.5	0.6	420	0	0	<0.1	2	45	200	50	15	5	4.1
0	750	1	1	7.7	1.1	201	3.2	4.7	0.5	32	232	289	362	93	14.2	4.6
1	743	0.6	0.8	13.9	0.9	200	1.9	7.7	0.4	27	239	392	341	84	5.8	6.5
0	4	0.4	0.4	5	0.5	100	1.5	0	0.9	20	150	250	200	40	4.5	3.8
	669	0.7	0.8	8.7	0.9			15.2	<0.1	2	32	280	36	8	3.5	0.4
0	657	0.6	0.8	8.1	0.5	170	1.5	18.1	<0.1	1	27	214	31	6	9.2	0.4
0	0							0		20		0			1.1	
0	0	0.1	0.1	2.7	0.2	21	0	0	0	21	175	3	203	57	1.6	1.3
0	0	0.1	0.1	2.5	0.5	20	0	4.8	0	24	175	3	177	63	1.4	1.4
0	509	0.4	0.4	5	0.5	101	1.5	6.1	0.1	6	46	50	41	16	0.4	0.4
0	1	<0.1	<0.1	1.5	<0.1	6	0.1	0	0.4	3	48	80	50	19	0.6	0.4
0	0							0		20		0			2.7	
0	411	0.4	0.5	5.8	0.5	160	1.3	3.6	0.1	86	126	205	74	30	7.2	3.4
	23	0.1	0.1	0.6	<0.1	13	0	0		21	147	202	157	46	1.3	1
<1	218	0.5	0.6	5.7	0.7	156	1.8	6.2	0.2	122	112	269	95	36	9.8	4.4
0	500	1.5	1.7	20	2	400	6	60	13.5	1000	80	190	90	24	18	15
0	0	1.2	1.5	9	0.5	29	0	33.8	0.4	52	206	113	245	113	2.2	2.1
0	116	1.9	0.9	6.3	1.1	398	0	6.8	18.1	51	1295	5	1070	362	10.3	18.8
0	0	<0.1	<0.1	0.3	<0.1	9	0	0	0.3	8	21	69	9	1	0.3	<0.1

ESHA, EatRight Analysis CD-ROM; **AMT**, amount; **WT**, weight; **CAL**, calories; **KILO**, KiloJoule; **WTR**, water; **PROT**, protein; **CARB**, carbohydrate; **FIBR**, fiber; **FAT**, fat; **SATF**, saturated fat; **MONO**, monounsaturated fat; **POLY**, polyunsaturated fat; **CHOL**, cholesterol;

ESHA CODE	FOOD DESCRIPTION	AMT	UNIT	WT (g)	CAL (kcal)	KILO (kJ)	WTR (g)	PROT (g)	CARB (g)	FIBR (g)	FAT (g)	SATF (g)	MONO (g)	POLY (g)
GRAIN PRODUCTS – UNPREPARED & PREPARED BAKED GOODS (CONTINUED)														
43771	Cheese Crackers	22	ea	30	150	628	<1	3	18	1	8	2		
43500	Cheese Crackers-Cheez-its	10	ea	10	50	209	<1	1	6	<1	3	0.9	1.2	0.2
43501	CheeseCrackers-PnutButter Filled	6	ea	42	208	870	1	5	24	1	11	1.9	5.5	2.1
11759	Crackers-Cheese-Hot & Spicy	25	ea	30	150	628	<1	2	18	1	8	2		
43527	Graham Cracker-Chocolate	1	ea	14	68	285	<1	1	9	<1	3	1.9	1.1	0.1
43502	Graham Cracker-Plain	2	ea	14	59	247	1	1	11	<1	1	0.2	0.6	0.5
43534	Matzoh Crackers-Plain	1	ea	28.35	112	469	1	3	24	1	<1	0.1	<0.1	0.2
43509	Melba Toast-Plain	1	pce	5	20	84	<1	1	4	<1	<1	<0.1	<0.1	0.1
43507	Oyster Crackers	1	cup	45	189	791	2	4	33	1	4	0.9	1	1.8
43505	Oyster crackers-crushed	1	cup	70	295	1234	3	7	52	2	6	1.4	1.6	2.8
43543	Round Crackers (Ritz)	10	ea	30	151	632	1	2	18	1	8	1.6	2	3.8
43541	Rye Crackers-Cheese Filled	6	ea	42	202	845	2	4	26	2	9	2.5	5.1	1.2
43532	Rye Crispbread	1	ea	10	37	155	1	1	8	2	<1	<0.1	<0.1	0.1
43506	Saltine Crackers	4	ea	12	51	213	<1	1	9	<1	1	0.2	0.3	0.5
43586	Saltine Crackers-UnsaltedTops	2	ea	6	28	117	<1	<1	4	0	1	0		
72335	Stoned Wheat Crackers-LowFat	5	ea	14	60	251	<1	2	10	1	1	0		
43508	Triscuits WhlWheatCracker	2	ea	8	34	142	<1	1	6	1	1	0.2	0.3	0.6
12683	Wheat Crackers	5	ea	16	80	335	<1	1	10	<1	4	1	2	1
43547	Wheat Crackers	5	ea	10	46	192	<1	1	7	<1	2	0.3	0.4	0.9
43548	Wheat Crackers-Cheese Filled	6	ea	42	209	874	1	4	24	1	10	1.7	4.3	3.8
43747	Wheat Thins Crackers-LowSod	16	ea	31	150	628	<1	3	21	1	6	1		
43549	WheatCrackers-PnutBtr Filled	1	ea	7	35	146	<1	1	4	<1	2	0.3	0.8	0.6
43818	Whole Wheat Saltine Crackers	5	ea	15	60	251		1	11	<1	2	0.5	0.5	0
Muffins														
44520	Blueberry Muffin-made w/2% Milk	1	ea	57	162	678	23	4	23	1	6	1.2	1.5	3.1
11785	Chocolate Chocolate Chip Muffin-DryMix	0.25	cup	33	150	628		2	23	2	5	2		
44524	Corn Muffin-made w/2%Milk	1	ea	57	180	753	19	4	25	2	7	1.3	1.7	3.5
42059	English Muffin	1	ea	57	129	540	25	5	25	2	1	0.4	0.2	0.3
42082	English Muffin-100% Wheat	1	ea	66	134	561	30	6	27	4	1	0.2	0.3	0.6
42214	English Muffin-Cheese	1	ea	63	153	640	26	5	28	2	2	0.8	0.5	0.6
42060	English Muffin-Sourdough	1	ea	57	129	540	25	5	25	2	1	0.4	0.2	0.3
44515	Muffin-Plain-Made w/2% Milk	1	ea	57	169	707	21	4	24	2	6	1.2	1.6	3.3
44514	Oat Bran Muffin	1	ea	57	154	644	20	4	28	3	4	0.6	1	2.4
44522	Toasted Muffin-Corn	1	ea	33	114	477	8	2	19	1	4	0.6	0.9	2.1
44518	Toaster Muffin-Blueberry	1	ea	33	103	431	10	2	18	1	3	0.5	0.7	1.8
18098	Whole Grain Muffin w/Fruit&Nuts	1	ea	65	170	711		3	34	7	4	1		
44536	Zucchini Muffin w/Nuts	1	ea	58	219	916	16	3	27	1	11	1.5	3.4	5.3
Pancakes, French Toast, & Waffles														
45194	Crepe	1	ea	12.8	30	126		1	5	0	<1	0		
42156	French Toast-Rec w/2%Milk	1	pce	65	149	623	36	5	16		7	1.8	2.9	1.7
45023	Pancake-Blueberry-Recipe	1	ea	38	84	351	20	2	11	<1	3	0.8	0.9	1.6
45025	Pancake-Buttermilk-Recipe	1	ea	38	86	360	20	3	11	<1	4	0.7	0.9	1.7
45044	Pancake-Chinese	1	ea	28	58	243	14	1	13	<1	<1	<0.1	<0.1	<0.1
45067	Pancake-Frozen-Heated-6in	1	ea	73	164	686	35	4	29	2	4	0.6	1.4	0.8
45002	Pancake-Mix-Prepared	1	ea	38	74	310	20	2	14	<1	1	0.2	0.3	0.3

< = Trace amount present   Blank = Not available

V, vitamin; **THI**, thiamin; **RIB**, riboflavin; **NIA**, niacin; **FOL**, folate; **CALC**, calcium; **PHOS**, phosphorus; **SOD**, sodium; **POT**, potassium; **MAG**, magnesium

CHOL (mg)	V-A (IU)	THI (mg)	RIB (mg)	NIA (mg)	V-B6 (mg)	FOL (μg)	V-B12 (μg)	V-C (mg)	V-E (mg)	CALC (mg)	PHOS (mg)	SOD (mg)	POT (mg)	MAG (mg)	IRON (mg)	ZINC (mg)
3	0							0		20		360			1.1	
1	11	0.1	<0.1	0.5	0.1	15	<0.1	0	<0.1	15	22	100	14	4	0.5	0.1
0	1	0.2	0.1	2.4	0.1	39	0.1	0	1	21	113	298	92	24	1.1	0.4
0	100							0		0		280			1.4	
0	2	<0.1	<0.1	0.3	<0.1	3	0	0	<0.1	8	19	41	29	8	0.5	0.1
0	<1	<0.1	<0.1	0.6	<0.1	6	0	0	<0.1	3	15	85	19	4	0.5	0.1
0	0	0.1	0.1	1.1	<0.1	5	0	0	<0.1	4	25	1	32	7	0.9	0.2
0	0	<0.1	<0.1	0.2	<0.1	6	0	0	<0.1	5	10	41	10	3	0.2	0.1
0	<1	0.3	0.1	2.4	<0.1	63	<0.1	0	0.5	9	50	502	72	11	2.3	0.4
0	1	0.4	0.2	3.7	<0.1	98	0.1	0	0.8	15	78	781	111	18	3.6	0.6
0	0	0.1	0.1	1.3	<0.1	35	0	0	1.1	28	77	260	33	5	1.1	0.2
4	140	0.3	0.2	1.5	<0.1	34	0.1	0.2		93	142	438	144	16	1	0.3
0	0	<0.1	<0.1	0.1	<0.1	5	0	0	0.1	3	27	26	32	8	0.2	0.2
0	<1	0.1	<0.1	0.6	<0.1	17	<0.1	0	0.1	3	13	134	19	3	0.6	0.1
0	0							0		0		46			0.3	
0	0							0		20		140			0.4	
0	0	<0.1	<0.1	0.4	<0.1	2	0	0	0.1	3	26	48	28	9	0.3	0.2
0	0							0		0		140			0.4	
0	0	0.1	<0.1	0.5	<0.1	12	<0.1	0	0.1	8	26	92	21	5	0.5	0.2
3	30	0.2	0.2	1.3	0.1	27	0.1	0.6		86	160	383	129	23	1.1	0.4
0	0							0		0		80			1.1	
0	0	<0.1	<0.1	0.4	<0.1	5	0	0		12	24	56	21	3	0.2	0.1
0	0							0		0		230			0.4	
21	80	0.2	0.2	1.3	<0.1	27	0.1	0.9		108	83	251	70	9	1.3	0.3
0	0							0		20		200			1.4	
24	137	0.2	0.2	1.4	0.1	43	0.1	0.2		148	101	333	83	13	1.5	0.3
0	0	0.3	0.1	2.3	<0.1	54	<0.1	1	0.2	93	52	242	62	14	2.3	0.6
0	3	0.2	0.1	2.3	0.1	32	0	0	0.3	175	186	312	139	47	1.6	1.1
3	33	0.3	0.2	2.3	<0.1	23	<0.1	0.1	0.1	127	96	297	82	13	1.5	0.5
0	0	0.3	0.1	2.3	<0.1	54	<0.1	1	0.2	93	52	242	62	14	2.3	0.6
22	80	0.2	0.2	1.3	<0.1	29	0.1	0.2		114	87	266	69	10	1.4	0.3
0	0	0.1	0.1	0.2	0.1	51	<0.1	0	0.4	36	214	224	289	89	2.4	1
4	32	0.1	0.1	0.8	<0.1	19	<0.1	0		6	50	142	30	5	0.5	0.1
2	105	0.1	0.1	0.7	<0.1	21	<0.1	0	0.3	4	19	158	27	4	0.2	0.1
30	0							1.2		20		190			1.1	
38	102	0.1	0.1	1	<0.1	9	0.1	1	2	39	48	113	66	8	1.2	0.3
5	0							0		0		50			0	
75	327	0.1	0.2	1.1	<0.1	28	0.2	0.2		65	76	311	87	11	1.1	0.4
21	76	0.1	0.1	0.6	<0.1	14	0.1	0.8		78	57	157	52	6	0.7	0.2
22	40	0.1	0.1	0.6	<0.1	14	0.1	0.2		60	53	198	55	6	0.6	0.2
0	0	<0.1	<0.1	0.3	<0.1	1	0	0	<0.1	5	18	1	18	4	0.1	0.2
13	158	0.3	0.4	2.1	0.1	52	0.1	0.2	0.2	52	214	369	91	10	1.6	0.3
5	12	0.1	0.1	0.7	<0.1	14	0.1	0.1		48	127	239	66	8	0.6	0.1

ESHA, EatRight Analysis CD-ROM; **AMT**, amount; **WT**, weight; **CAL**, calories; **KILO**, KiloJoule; **WTR**, water; **PROT**, protein; **CARB**, carbohydrate; **FIBR**, fiber; **FAT**, fat; **SATF**, saturated fat; **MONO**, monounsaturated fat; **POLY**, polyunsaturated fat; **CHOL**, cholesterol;

ESHA CODE	FOOD DESCRIPTION	AMT	UNIT	WT (g)	CAL (kcal)	KILO (kJ)	WTR (g)	PROT (g)	CARB (g)	FIBR (g)	FAT (g)	SATF (g)	MONO (g)	POLY (g)
GRAIN PRODUCTS – UNPREPARED & PREPARED BAKED GOODS (CONTINUED)														
45001	Pancake-Plain-Recipe	1	ea	38	86	360	20	2	11	<1	4	0.8	0.9	1.7
45008	Pancake-Whole Wheat	1	ea	44	92	385	23	4	13	1	3	0.8	0.8	1.1
45036	Rye Pancakes-4 inch	1	ea	21	63	264	7	1	10	1	2	0.5	0.9	0.6
45035	Sourdough Pancakes-4 inch	1	ea	21	46	192	11	1	7	<1	1	0.3	0.4	0.6
45094	Waffle-Blueberry-Frzn	2	ea	70	190	795	20	4	30	1	6	1.5		
45093	Waffle-Buttermilk-Eggo	2	ea	70	180	753	22	5	26	1	6	1.5		
45005	Waffle-Frozen-Toasted	1	ea	33	103	431	10	2	16	1	3	0.5	1.6	0.7
45003	Waffles-From Recipe	1	ea	75	218	912	32	6	25	1	11	2.1	2.6	5.1
45083	Waffles-Whole Grain-Frzn	2	ea	71	154	644	21	6	29	3	3	0.9	1.1	0.6
Pastas														
38048	Chow Mein Noodles-dry	1	cup	45	237	992	<1	4	26	2	14	2	3.5	7.8
38076	Couscous-Cooked	1	cup	157	176	736	114	6	36	2	<1	<0.1	<0.1	0.1
38260	Egg Noodles-Cooked	1	cup	160	221	925	108	7	40	2	3	0.7	0.9	0.9
38047	Egg Noodles-Enr-Cooked	1	cup	160	221	925	108	7	40	2	3	0.7	0.9	0.9
38102	Macaroni-Enriched-Cooked	1	cup	140	221	925	87	8	43	3	1	0.2	0.2	0.4
38092	Pasta/Noodles-Fresh-Cooked	3	oz	85.05	111	464	58	4	21	1	1	0.1	0.1	0.4
38067	Ramen Noodles-Cooked	1	cup	227	154	644	195	3	20	1	7	1.7	1.2	3.3
38163	Rice & Pasta-Cooked	1	cup	202	246	1029	145	5	43	5	6	1.1	2.3	1.9
38551	Rice Noodles-Cooked	0.5	cup	88	96	402	65	1	22	1	<1	<0.1	<0.1	<0.1
38105	Shells Pasta-Small-Cooked	1	cup	115	182	761	71	7	35	2	1	0.2	0.2	0.4
38118	Spaghetti Noodles-Enr-Cooked	1	cup	140	221	925	87	8	43	3	1	0.2	0.2	0.4
38121	SpagNoodles-Enr-Ckd+Salt	1	cup	140	220	920	87	8	43	3	1	0.2	0.2	0.4
38066	SpagNoodles-Spinach-Cooked	1	cup	140	182	761	95	6	37	6	1	0.1	0.1	0.4
38060	SpagNoodles-WhlWheat-Cooked	1	cup	140	174	728	94	7	37	6	1	0.1	0.1	0.3
Pastry/Pie/Dessert Crusts & Cones														
49013	Ice Cream Cone-Cake/Wafer	1	ea	4	17	71	<1	<1	3	<1	<1	<0.1	0.1	0.1
49014	Ice Cream Cone-Sugar/Rolled	1	ea	10	40	167	<1	1	8	<1	<1	0.1	0.1	0.1
Snack Foods – Chips, Pretzels, Popcorn, etc.														
44039	BBQ Flavor Pork Skin	1	oz	28.35	153	640	1	16	<1		9	3.3	4.3	1
44029	Bugles Corn Chips-Plain	1	oz	28.35	145	607	1	2	18	<1	8	6.4	0.5	0.2
44032	Chex Party Mix	1	cup	42.5	180	753	1	4	32	2	4	0.6	1.2	1.9
44033	Combos Pretzels w/Cheese	10	pce	30	139	582	1	3	20		5	3		
44031	Cornnuts-Toasted Corn Nuggets	1	oz	28.35	126	527	<1	2	20	2	4	0.7	2.7	0.9
44037	Cracker Jacks Snack	1	cup	42.5	170	711	1	3	34	2	3	0.4	1.2	1.4
44012	Popcorn-Air Popped-Plain	1	cup	8	31	130	<1	1	6	1	<1	<0.1	0.1	0.2
44014	Popcorn-Caramel Corn	1	oz	28.35	122	510	1	1	22	1	4	1	0.8	1.3
44038	Popcorn-Cheese	1	cup	11	58	243	<1	1	6	1	4	0.7	1.1	1.7
44013	Popcorn-Cooked in Oil+Salt	1	cup	11	64	268	<1	1	5	1	5	0.8	1.1	2.6
44006	Potato Chips	1	oz	28.35	154	644	1	2	14	1	10	1.1	4.5	4.5
44043	Potato Chips-Light	1	oz	28.35	134	561	<1	2	19	2	6	1.2	1.4	3.1
44015	Pretzels-Dutch Twist	10	pce	60	228	954	2	6	48	2	2	0.3	0.7	0.6
44312	Rice Cake-CaramelCorn-Mini	7	ea	15	60	251		1	13	0	0	0	0	0
44028	Rice Cake-Plain	1	ea	9	35	146		1	7	0	0	0	0	0
44016	Rice Cake-Plain-Regular Size	1	ea	9	35	146	<1	1	7	<1	<1	0.1	0.1	0.1
61056	Sweet Potato Chips-Spiced	1	oz	28.35	140	586		1	16	3	7	1		
44266	Tortilla Chips-Low Fat	13	pce	28	110	460		3	24	2	1	0		

< = Trace amount present   Blank = Not available

V, vitamin; **THI**, thiamin; **RIB**, riboflavin; **NIA**, niacin; **FOL**, folate; **CALC**, calcium; **PHOS**, phosphorus; **SOD**, sodium; **POT**, potassium; **MAG**, magnesium

CHOL (mg)	V-A (IU)	THI (mg)	RIB (mg)	NIA (mg)	V-B6 (mg)	FOL (μg)	V-B12 (μg)	V-C (mg)	V-E (mg)	CALC (mg)	PHOS (mg)	SOD (mg)	POT (mg)	MAG (mg)	IRON (mg)	ZINC (mg)
22	74	0.1	0.1	0.6	<0.1	14	0.1	0.1		83	60	167	50	6	0.7	0.2
27	99	0.1	0.2	1	<0.1	13	0.1	0.2		110	164	252	123	20	1.4	0.5
8	14	<0.1	<0.1	0.3	<0.1	2	<0.1	0.1	0.3	22	25	58	97	15	0.5	0.2
8	12	0.1	0.1	0.6	<0.1	7	<0.1	<1	0.3	3	16	53	17	3	0.5	0.1
15	1000	0.3	0.3	4	0.4	40	1.2	0		100	200	370	55		3.6	
15	1000	0.3	0.3	4	0.4	40	1.2	0		100	200	420	60		3.6	
5	439	0.2	0.2	2.9	0.3	25	1	0	0.3	101	142	241	48	8	2.3	0.2
52	171	0.2	0.3	1.6	<0.1	34	0.2	0.3		191	142	383	119	14	1.7	0.5
5	0							0		221	406	676	176	34	5.8	0.6
0	<1	0.3	0.2	2.7	<0.1	40	0	0	1.6	9	72	198	54	23	2.1	0.6
0	0	0.1	<0.1	1.5	0.1	24	0	0	0.2	13	35	8	91	13	0.6	0.4
46	34	<0.1	<0.1	0.6	0.1	11	0.1	0	0.3	19	122	8	61	34	1	1
46	34	0.5	0.2	3.3	0.1	134	0.1	0	0.3	19	122	8	61	34	2.4	1
0	0	0.4	0.2	2.4	0.1	102	0	0	0.1	10	81	1	62	25	1.8	0.7
28	17	0.2	0.1	0.8	<0.1	54	0.1	0		5	54	5	20	15	1	0.5
<1	8	<0.1	<0.1	0.3	<0.1	3	<0.1	<1	2.3	13	24	802	49	10	0.4	0.2
2	0	0.2	0.2	3.6	0.2	89	0.1	0.4		16	75	1147	85	24	1.9	0.6
0	0	<0.1	<0.1	0.1	<0.1	3	0	0		4	18	17	4	3	0.1	0.2
0	0	0.3	0.2	1.9	0.1	84	0	0	0.1	8	67	1	51	21	1.5	0.6
0	0	0.4	0.2	2.4	0.1	102	0	0	0.1	10	81	1	62	25	1.8	0.7
0	0	0.4	0.2	2.4	0.1	102	0	0	0.1	10	81	183	62	25	1.8	0.7
0	213	0.1	0.1	2.1	0.1	17	0	0		42	151	20	81	87	1.5	1.5
0	4	0.2	0.1	1	0.1	7	0	0	0.4	21	125	4	62	42	1.5	1.1
0	0	<0.1	<0.1	0.2	<0.1	7	0	0	<0.1	1	4	6	4	1	0.1	<0.1
0	0	0.1	<0.1	0.5	<0.1	14	0	0	<0.1	4	10	32	14	3	0.4	0.1
33	189	<0.1	0.1	1	<0.1	9	<0.1	0.4		12	62	756	51	0	0.3	0.2
0	90	0.1	0.1	0.4	<0.1	1	0	0		1	12	290	23	3	0.7	0.1
	0	0.1	0.1	1.8	<0.1	21				14	65	511	83	17	1.3	0.5
<1	20	0.1	0.2	1	<0.1	2	<0.1	0.1		54	43	466	39	7	0.3	0.2
0	0	<0.1	<0.1	0.5	0.1	0	0	0	0.6	3	78	156	79	32	0.5	0.5
0	33	<0.1	0.1	0.8	0.1	7	0	0	0.4	28	54	125	151	34	1.7	0.5
0	16	<0.1	<0.1	0.2	<0.1	2	0	0	<0.1	1	29	1	26	12	0.3	0.2
1	2	<0.1	<0.1	0.6	<0.1	1	<0.1	0	0.3	12	24	58	31	10	0.5	0.2
1	27	<0.1	<0.1	0.2	<0.1	1	0.1	0.1		12	40	98	29	10	0.2	0.2
0	17	<0.1	<0.1	0.1	<0.1	3	0	<1	0.3	<1	22	116	20	9	0.2	0.3
0	0	<0.1	0.1	1.2	0.2	21	0	5.3	1.9	7	44	149	466	20	0.5	0.7
0	0	0.1	0.1	2	0.2	8	0	7.3	1.6	6	55	139	494	25	0.4	<0.1
0	0	0.3	0.2	3.1	<0.1	112	0	0	0.2	11	68	814	82	17	3.1	0.9
0	0							0		0		150			0	
0	0							0		0		0			0	
0	0	<0.1	<0.1	0.6	0.1	2	0	0	<0.1	1	33	14	25	14	0.1	2
0	4000							4.8		60		105			1.1	
0	0	0.1			0.1			0		40	60	200			0.4	

ESHA, EatRight Analysis CD-ROM; **AMT**, amount; **WT**, weight; **CAL**, calories; **KILO**, KiloJoule; **WTR**, water; **PROT**, protein; **CARB**, carbohydrate; **FIBR**, fiber; **FAT**, fat; **SATF**, saturated fat; **MONO**, monounsaturated fat; **POLY**, polyunsaturated fat; **CHOL**, cholesterol;

ESHA CODE	FOOD DESCRIPTION	AMT	UNIT	WT (g)	CAL (kcal)	KILO (kJ)	WTR (g)	PROT (g)	CARB (g)	FIBR (g)	FAT (g)	SATF (g)	MONO (g)	POLY (g)
GRAIN PRODUCTS – UNPREPARED & PREPARED BAKED GOODS (CONTINUED)														
61250	Tortilla Chips-Lowfat-Baked	1	svg	28	116	485	<1	3	22	1	2	0.2	0.5	0.8
44054	Tortilla Chips-Nacho-LowFat	1	oz	28.35	126	527	<1	2	20	1	4	0.8	2.5	0.6
44058	Trail Mix-Regular	1	cup	150	693	2900	14	21	67		44	8.3	18.8	14.5
44085	Trail Mix-Regular-Unsalted	1	cup	150	693	2900	14	21	67		44	8.3	18.8	14.5
44060	Trail Mix-Tropical	1	cup	140	570	2385	13	9	92		24	11.9	3.5	7.2
Stuffings														
42037	Stuffing Mix-Bread-Prep	0.5	cup	100	177	741	65	3	22	3	9	1.7	3.8	2.6
42147	Stuffing Mix-Cornbread-Prep	0.5	cup	100	179	749	65	3	22	3	9	1.8	3.9	2.7
Tortillas & Taco/Tostada Shells														
42168	Taco Shell-Bkd	1	ea	13.3	62	259	1	1	8	1	3	0.8	0.9	1
42023	Tortilla-Corn-Enr-Reg-6in	1	ea	26	57	238	12	1	12	2	1	0.1	0.2	0.4
42025	Tortilla-Flour-8 inch	1	ea	72	225	941	22	6	37	2	6	1.4	2.8	1.1
71938	Tortilla-Whole Wheat	1	ea	47	140	586		4	22	2	3	0		
GRAINS, FLOURS, & FRACTIONS														
38030	AllPurpose WhiteFlour-Enrich	1	cup	125	455	1904	15	13	95	3	1	0.2	0.1	0.5
38003	Barley-Pearled-Cooked	1	cup	157	193	808	108	4	44	6	1	0.1	0.1	0.3
38001	Barley-Whole-Cooked	1	cup	200	270	1130	130	7	59	14	2	0.4	0.3	1.2
38010	Brown Rice-LongGrain-Cooked	1	cup	195	216	904	143	5	45	4	2	0.4	0.6	0.6
38082	Brown Rice-MedGrain-Cooked	0.5	cup	97.5	109	456	71	2	23	2	1	0.2	0.3	0.3
38028	Bulgar Wheat-Cooked	1	cup	182	151	632	142	6	34	8	<1	0.1	0.1	0.2
38039	Cake Flour-Baked Value	1	cup	109	395	1653	14	9	85	2	1	0.1	0.1	0.4
38041	Cornmeal-Enrich-BakedValu	1	cup	138	505	2113	16	12	107	10	2	0.3	0.6	1
38083	Glutinous Sticky Rice-Ckd	1	cup	174	169	707	133	4	37	2	<1	0.1	0.1	0.1
38044	Light RyeFlour-BakedValue	1	cup	102	374	1565	9	9	82	15	1	0.1	0.2	0.6
38052	Millet-Cooked	1	cup	174	207	866	124	6	41	2	2	0.3	0.3	0.9
38078	Oat Bran-Cooked	1	cup	219	88	368	184	7	25	6	2	0.4	0.6	0.7
38064	Oat Bran-Dry	1	cup	94	231	967	6	16	62	14	7	1.2	2.2	2.6
38043	Rolled Oats-Baked Value	1	cup	80	307	1284	7	13	54	8	5	0.9	1.6	1.8
38438	Unbleach Enrich White Flour	0.25	cup	34	120	502	1	5	26	1	<1	0		
38024	Wheat Bran-Crude	0.5	cup	29	63	264	3	5	19	12	1	0.2	0.2	0.6
38055	Wheat Germ-HoneyCrunch	1.66	Tbs	14	52	218	<1	4	8	1	1	0.2	0.1	0.7
38037	White Flour-Enr-Baked	1	cup	125	455	1904	15	13	95	3	1	0.2	0.1	0.5
38013	White Rice-LongGrain-Cooked	1	cup	158	205	858	108	4	45	1	<1	0.1	0.1	0.1
38019	White Rice-LongGrain-Inst-Ckd	1	cup	165	193	808	119	4	41	1	1	<0.1	0.1	<0.1
38097	White Rice-MedGrain-Cooked	1	cup	186	242	1013	128	4	53	1	<1	0.1	0.1	0.1
38032	Whole Wheat Flour	1	cup	120	407	1703	12	16	87	15	2	0.4	0.3	0.9
38040	Whole Wheat Flour-Baked	1	cup	120	407	1703	12	16	87	15	2	0.4	0.3	0.9
38021	Wild Rice-Cooked	1	cup	164	166	695	121	7	35	3	1	0.1	0.1	0.3
INFANT FOODS														
60616	BabyFd Cereal-Rice+MixFruit	1	Tbs	15	12	50	12	<1	3	<1	<1	<0.1	<0.1	<0.1
60491	BabyFd Beef Stew-Toddler	1	Tbs	16	8	33	14	1	1	<1	<1	0.1	0.1	<0.1
62893	BabyFd Veg Beef Dinner-Jr	1	Tbs	16	12	50	14	<1	1	<1	1	0.2	0.2	<0.1
60638	BabyFd Turkey Meat Sticks	1	ea	10	18	75	7	1	<1	<1	1	0.4	0.5	0.4
60500	BabyFd Carrots	1	Tbs	14	4	17	13	<1	1	<1	<1	<0.1	<0.1	<0.1
60632	BabyFd Sweet Potatoes	1	Tbs	14	8	33	12	<1	2	<1	<1	<0.1	<0.1	<0.1

< = Trace amount present   Blank = Not available

V, vitamin; **THI**, thiamin; **RIB**, riboflavin; **NIA**, niacin; **FOL**, folate; **CALC**, calcium; **PHOS**, phosphorus; **SOD**, sodium; **POT**, potassium; **MAG**, magnesium

CHOL (mg)	V-A (IU)	THI (mg)	RIB (mg)	NIA (mg)	V-B6 (mg)	FOL (μg)	V-B12 (μg)	V-C (mg)	V-E (mg)	CALC (mg)	PHOS (mg)	SOD (mg)	POT (mg)	MAG (mg)	IRON (mg)	ZINC (mg)
0	29	0.1	0.1	0.1	0.1	4	0	0.1	0.2	45	89	117	76	27	0.4	0.3
1	108	0.1	0.1	0.1	0.1	7	0	0.1		45	90	284	77	27	0.5	
0	27	0.7	0.3	7.1	0.4	106	0	2.1		117	518	344	1028	237	4.6	4.8
0	27	0.7	0.3	7.1	0.4	106	0	2.1		117	518	15	1028	237	4.6	4.8
0	69	0.6	0.2	2.1	0.5	59	0	10.6		80	260	14	993	134	3.7	1.6
0	313	0.1	0.1	1.5	<0.1	39	<0.1	0	1.4	32	42	543	74	12	1.1	0.3
0	340	0.1	0.1	1.2	<0.1	97	<0.1	0.8	0.9	26	34	455	62	13	0.9	0.2
0	2	<0.1	<0.1	0.2	<0.1	9	0	0	0.1	13	30	52	30	11	0.2	0.2
0	1	<0.1	<0.1	0.4	0.1	1	0	0	0.1	21	82	12	48	19	0.3	0.3
0	0	0.4	0.2	2.6	<0.1	75	0	0	0.1	93	89	458	112	16	2.4	0.4
0	0							0		0		170			1.1	
0	0	1	0.6	7.4	0.1	229	0	0	0.1	19	135	2	134	28	5.8	0.9
0	11	0.1	0.1	3.2	0.2	25	0	0	<0.1	17	85	5	146	35	2.1	1.3
0	0	0.2	0.1	2.8	0.2	16	0	0	1.2	26	230	1	230	44	2.1	1.6
0	0	0.2	<0.1	3	0.3	8	0	0	0.1	20	162	10	84	84	0.8	1.2
0	0	0.1	<0.1	1.3	0.1	4	0	0		10	75	1	77	43	0.5	0.6
0	4	0.1	0.1	1.8	0.2	33	0	0	<0.1	18	73	9	124	58	1.7	1
0	0	0.7	0.4	7	<0.1	84	0	0	0.1	15	93	2	114	17	8	0.7
0	570	0.7	0.5	6.6	0.3	52	0	0	0.5	7	116	4	224	55	5.7	1
0	0	<0.1	<0.1	0.5	<0.1	2	0	0	0.1	3	14	9	17	9	0.2	0.7
0	0	0.3	0.1	0.8	0.2	11	0	0	0.6	21	198	2	238	71	1.8	1.8
0	5	0.2	0.1	2.3	0.2	33	0	0	<0.1	5	174	3	108	77	1.1	1.6
0	0	0.4	0.1	0.3	0.1	13	0	0		22	261	2	201	88	1.9	1.2
0	0	1.1	0.2	0.9	0.2	49	0	0	0.9	55	690	4	532	221	5.1	2.9
0	81	0.4	0.1	0.6	0.1	13	0	0	0.6	42	379	3	280	118	3.4	2.5
0	0	0.1	0.1	1.2				0		0		0	35		1.1	
0	3	0.2	0.2	3.9	0.4	23	0	0	0.4	21	294	1	343	177	3.1	2.1
0	0	0.2	0.1	0.7	0.1	85	0	0	2.8	7	142	2	135	38	1.1	1.9
0	0	0.7	0.5	7	<0.1	96	0	0	0.1	19	135	2	134	28	5.8	0.9
0	0	0.3	<0.1	2.3	0.1	92	0	0	0.1	16	68	2	55	19	1.9	0.8
0	0	0.1	<0.1	2.9	0.1	116	0	0	<0.1	13	61	7	15	8	2.9	0.8
0	0	0.3	<0.1	3.4	0.1	108	0	0		6	69	0	54	24	2.8	0.8
0	11	0.5	0.3	7.6	0.4	53	0	0	1	41	415	6	486	166	4.7	3.5
0	0	0.4	0.2	7.3	0.3	26	0	0	1.5	41	415	6	486	166	4.7	3.5
0	5	0.1	0.1	2.1	0.2	43	0	0	0.4	5	134	5	166	52	1	2.2
0	2	<0.1	<0.1	0.3	<0.1	<1	<0.1	1.4	<0.1	2	3	2	8	1	0.4	<0.1
2	264	<0.1	<0.1	0.2	<0.1	1	0.1	0.5	0.1	1	7	55	23	2	0.1	0.1
1	788	<0.1	<0.1	0.1	<0.1	1	0.1	<1	0.1	3	5	3	23	2	0.1	0.1
6	2	<0.1	<0.1	0.2	<0.1	1	0.1	0.2	<0.1	7	10	48	9	2	0.1	0.2
0	1653	<0.1	<0.1	0.1	<0.1	2	0	0.8	0.1	3	3	7	28	2	0.1	<0.1
0	929	<0.1	<0.1	0.1	<0.1	1	0	1.3	0.1	2	3	3	34	2	0.1	<0.1

ESHA, EatRight Analysis CD-ROM; **AMT**, amount; **WT**, weight; **CAL**, calories; **KILO**, KiloJoule; **WTR**, water; **PROT**, protein; **CARB**, carbohydrate; **FIBR**, fiber; **FAT**, fat; **SATF**, saturated fat; **MONO**, monounsaturated fat; **POLY**, polyunsaturated fat; **CHOL**, cholesterol;

ESHA CODE	FOOD DESCRIPTION	AMT	UNIT	WT (g)	CAL (kcal)	KILO (kJ)	WTR (g)	PROT (g)	CARB (g)	FIBR (g)	FAT (g)	SATF (g)	MONO (g)	POLY (g)
MEATS & MEAT SUBSTITUTES – BBQ, BREADED, FRIED, GLAZED, GRILLED, RAW, ETC.														
Beef														
10051	Beef Jerky-Large Piece	1	ea	19.8	81	339	5	7	2	<1	5	2.1	2.2	0.2
11237	Beef Roast-Brsd	3	oz	85.05	190	795	49	29	0	0	8	2.7	3.2	0.3
11280	Beef-Filet Mignon-Brld	3	oz	85.05	164	686	54	24	0	0	7	2.5	2.7	0.2
10020	Beef-Flank Steak-Brld	3	oz	85.05	165	690	54	24	0	0	7	2.9	2.8	0.3
10268	Beef-Lean-Ckd	3	oz	85.05	179	749	50	25	0	0	8	3	3.3	0.3
10706	Beef-Rib Eye Steak-Lean-Brld	3	oz	85.05	174	728	52	25	0	0	8	2.9	3.1	0.3
58327	Beef-Sirloin Steak-Lean-Brld	3	oz	85.05	159	665	54	25	0	0	6	2.2	2.3	0.2
11286	Beef-Strip Steak-Brld	3	oz	85.05	155	649	55	25	0	0	5	2.1	2.2	0.2
11162	Beef-Top Round Steak-Fried	3	oz	85.05	236	987	44	28	0	0	13	4.5	5	1.5
11170	Beef-TopRoundSteak-Lean-Fried	3	oz	85.05	193	808	47	30	0	0	7	2.1	2.4	1.4
10008	Corned Beef-Canned	3	oz	85.05	213	891	49	23	0	0	13	5.3	5.1	0.5
58117	Grnd Beef Patty-15%Fat-Brld	1	ea	77	192	803	45	20	0	0	12	4.5	5.1	0.4
58122	Grnd Beef Patty-20% fat-Brld	1	ea	77	209	874	43	20	0	0	14	5.2	6.1	0.4
58107	Grnd Beef Patty-5%Fat-Brld	1	ea	82	140	586	54	22	0	0	5	2.4	2.2	0.3
10028	Porterhouse Steak-Broiled-Ln	1	ea	170	366	1531	102	44	0	0	20	6.7	9.6	0.6
10624	ShortRibs-Braised	3	oz	85.05	401	1678	30	18	0	0	36	15.1	16.1	1.3
10035	Sizzlean Formed Bacon-Cooked	3	ea	34	153	640	9	11	<1	0	12	4.9	5.7	0.5
10007	TBoneSteak-Broiled-Lean	3	oz	85.05	174	728	52	23	0	0	9	3.1	4.2	0.3
Chickens														
15050	Chicken Back-Meat-Fried	1	ea	116	334	1397	56	35	7	0	18	4.8	6.6	4.2
15001	Chicken Breast+Skin-Roastd	1	ea	98	193	808	61	29	0	0	8	2.1	3	1.6
15057	Chicken Breast-NoSkin-Fried	1	ea	86	161	674	52	29	<1	0	4	1.1	1.5	0.9
15004	Chicken Breast-NoSkin-Roasted	1	ea	86	142	594	56	27	0	0	3	0.9	1.1	0.7
15042	Chicken Drumstick-Fried	1	ea	42	82	343	26	12	0	0	3	0.9	1.2	0.8
15035	Chicken Drumstick-NoSkin-Roast	1	ea	44	76	318	29	12	0	0	2	0.7	0.8	0.6
15008	Chicken Drumstick-Roasted	1	ea	52	112	469	33	14	0	0	6	1.6	2.2	1.3
15028	Chicken Meat-All-Fried	1	cup	140	307	1284	81	43	2	<1	13	3.4	4.7	3
15000	Chicken Meat-All-Roasted	1	cup	140	266	1113	89	41	0	0	10	2.9	3.7	2.4
15006	Chicken Meat-All-Stewed	1	cup	140	248	1038	94	38	0	0	9	2.6	3.3	2.2
15010	Chicken Thigh+Skin-Roasted	1	ea	62	153	640	37	16	0	0	10	2.7	3.8	2.1
15011	Chicken Thigh-NoSkin-Fried	1	ea	52	113	473	31	15	1	0	5	1.4	2	1.3
15012	Chicken Thigh-NoSkin-Roast	1	ea	52	109	456	33	13	0	0	6	1.6	2.2	1.3
15002	Chicken Wing+Skin-Roasted	1	ea	34	99	414	19	9	0	0	7	1.9	2.6	1.4
15016	Chicken+Broth-Can	1	ea	142	234	979	97	31	0	0	11	3.1	4.5	2.5
15027	Chicken-Dark Meat-Roasted	1	cup	140	287	1201	88	38	0	0	14	3.7	5	3.2
15032	Chicken-Light Meat-Roasted	1	cup	140	242	1013	91	43	0	0	6	1.8	2.2	1.4
Ducks, Emus, Ostriches, & Other Poultry														
15240	Cornish Game Hen+Skin-Rstd	3	oz	85.05	220	920	50	19	0	0	15	4.3	6.8	3.1
16295	Duck+Skin-Rstd	3	oz	85.05	287	1201	44	16	0	0	24	8.2	11	3.1
14000	Duck-Meat Only-Roasted	3	oz	85.05	171	715	55	20	0	0	10	3.4	3.3	1.3
81166	Emu-Top Loin-Brld	3	oz	85.05	129	540	57	25	0	0	3	0.7	1.1	0.4
14002	Goose Meat-NoSkin-Roasted	3	oz	85.05	202	845	49	25	0	0	11	3.9	3.7	1.3
14003	Goose+Skin-Domestic-Roast	3	oz	85.05	259	1084	44	21	0	0	19	5.8	8.7	2.1
81180	Ostrich-Tenderloin-Raw	4	oz	113.4	139	582	84	25	0	0	4	1.3	1.4	0.9
Fish, Seafood, & Shellfish														

< = Trace amount present   Blank = Not available

V, vitamin; **THI**, thiamin; **RIB**, riboflavin; **NIA**, niacin; **FOL**, folate; **CALC**, calcium; **PHOS**, phosphorus; **SOD**, sodium; **POT**, potassium; **MAG**, magnesium

CHOL (mg)	V-A (IU)	THI (mg)	RIB (mg)	NIA (mg)	V-B6 (mg)	FOL (μg)	V-B12 (μg)	V-C (mg)	V-E (mg)	CALC (mg)	PHOS (mg)	SOD (mg)	POT (mg)	MAG (mg)	IRON (mg)	ZINC (mg)
10	0	<0.1	<0.1	0.3	<0.1	27	0.2	0	0.1	4	81	438	118	10	1.1	1.6
84	0	0.1	0.2	5	0.4	9	1.6	0	0.4	7	177	37	230	19	2.3	4.8
67	0	0.1	0.1	6.9	0.5	9	1.4	0	0.3	15	191	50	308	20	1.5	4.5
47	0	0.1	0.1	7	0.5	8	1.5	0	0.3	13	179	48	287	20	1.6	4.3
73	0	0.1	0.2	3.4	0.3	7	2.2	0	0.1	7	196	56	302	22	2.5	5.8
77	0	0.1	0.1	7.2	0.5	9	1.5	0	0.3	14	193	51	309	21	1.7	4.7
54	0	0.1	0.1	6.6	0.5	8	1.4	0	0.3	14	196	52	314	21	1.7	4.7
54	0	0.1	0.1	7.1	0.5	9	1.4	0	0.3	16	195	51	315	21	1.6	4.6
82	0	0.1	0.2	4.3	0.5	10	2.7	0	0.2	5	228	58	400	27	2.5	3.6
82	0	0.1	0.2	4.7	0.5	11	2.9	0	0.1	4	248	60	436	30	2.7	3.9
73	0	<0.1	0.1	2.1	0.1	8	1.4	0	0.1	10	94	856	116	12	1.8	3
69	0	<0.1	0.1	4.1	0.3	7	2	0	0.3	14	152	55	245	16	2	4.9
70	0	<0.1	0.1	3.9	0.3	8	2.1	0	0.4	18	149	58	234	15	1.9	4.8
62	0	<0.1	0.1	4.9	0.3	6	2	0	0.3	6	169	53	285	18	2.3	5.3
117	0	0.2	0.4	7.9	0.7	14	3.9	0	0.2	10	359	117	512	42	5.5	8.6
80	0	<0.1	0.1	2.1	0.2	4	2.2	0	0.2	10	138	43	191	13	2	4.2
40	0	<0.1	0.1	2.2	0.1	3	1.2	0	0.1	3	80	766	140	9	1.1	2.2
50	0	0.1	0.2	3.9	0.3	7	1.9	0	0.1	5	183	65	278	22	3.1	4.3
108	114	0.1	0.3	8.9	0.4	10	0.4	0		30	204	115	291	29	1.9	3.2
82	91	0.1	0.1	12.5	0.5	4	0.3	0	0.3	14	210	70	240	26	1	1
78	20	0.1	0.1	12.7	0.6	3	0.3	0	0.4	14	212	68	237	27	1	0.9
73	18	0.1	0.1	11.8	0.5	3	0.3	0	0.2	13	196	64	220	25	0.9	0.9
39	26	<0.1	0.1	2.6	0.2	4	0.1	0		5	78	40	105	10	0.6	1.4
41	26	<0.1	0.1	2.7	0.2	4	0.1	0	0.1	5	81	42	108	11	0.6	1.4
47	52	<0.1	0.1	3.1	0.2	4	0.2	0	0.1	6	91	47	119	12	0.7	1.5
132	83	0.1	0.3	13.5	0.7	10	0.5	0	0.6	24	287	127	360	38	1.9	3.1
125	74	0.1	0.2	12.8	0.7	8	0.5	0	0.4	21	273	120	340	35	1.7	2.9
116	70	0.1	0.2	8.6	0.4	8	0.3	0	0.4	20	210	98	252	29	1.6	2.8
58	102	<0.1	0.1	3.9	0.2	4	0.2	0	0.2	7	108	52	138	14	0.8	1.5
53	36	<0.1	0.1	3.7	0.2	5	0.2	0		7	103	49	135	14	0.8	1.5
49	34	<0.1	0.1	3.4	0.2	4	0.2	0	0.1	6	95	46	124	12	0.7	1.3
29	54	<0.1	<0.1	2.3	0.1	1	0.1	0	0.1	5	51	28	63	6	0.4	0.6
88	166	<0.1	0.2	9	0.5	6	0.4	2.8	0.4	20	158	714	196	17	2.2	2
130	101	0.1	0.3	9.2	0.5	11	0.4	0	0.4	21	251	130	336	32	1.9	3.9
119	41	0.1	0.2	17.4	0.8	6	0.5	0	0.4	21	302	108	346	38	1.5	1.7
111	90	0.1	0.2	5	0.3	2	0.2	0.4	0.3	11	124	54	208	15	0.8	1.3
71	179	0.1	0.2	4.1	0.2	5	0.3	0	0.6	9	133	50	174	14	2.3	1.6
76	65	0.2	0.4	4.3	0.2	9	0.3	0	0.6	10	173	55	214	17	2.3	2.2
75	0	0.3	0.5	7.8	0.7	8	7.4	0	0.2	8	233	49	318	26	4.3	2.9
82	34	0.1	0.3	3.5	0.4	10	0.4	0		12	263	65	330	21	2.4	2.7
77	60	0.1	0.3	3.5	0.3	2	0.3	0	1.5	11	230	60	280	19	2.4	2.2
91	0	0.2	0.3	5.4	0.6	9	5.7	0	0.2	7	249	98	363	25	5.5	4.4

ESHA, EatRight Analysis CD-ROM; **AMT**, amount; **WT**, weight; **CAL**, calories; **KILO**, KiloJoule; **WTR**, water; **PROT**, protein; **CARB**, carbohydrate; **FIBR**, fiber; **FAT**, fat; **SATF**, saturated fat; **MONO**, monounsaturated fat; **POLY**, polyunsaturated fat; **CHOL**, cholesterol;

ESHA CODE	FOOD DESCRIPTION	AMT	UNIT	WT (g)	CAL (kcal)	KILO (kJ)	WTR (g)	PROT (g)	CARB (g)	FIBR (g)	FAT (g)	SATF (g)	MONO (g)	POLY (g)
MEATS & MEAT SUBSTITUTES – BBQ, BREADED, FRIED, GLAZED, GRILLED, RAW, ETC. (CONTINUED)														
19086	Abalone-Cooked	1	cup	150	315	1318	74	51	18	0	2	0.4	0.3	0.3
17124	Anchovies+Oil-Canned	5	ea	20	42	176	10	6	0	0	2	0.4	0.8	0.5
17106	Butterfish Fillet-Baked/Broiled	1	ea	25	47	197	17	6	0	0	3			
17179	Catfish-Brld	3	oz	85.05	129	540	61	16	0	0	7	1.5	3.5	1.2
17034	Caviar-Granular-Black/Red	1	Tbs	16	40	167	8	4	1	0	3	0.6	0.7	1.2
19002	Clams-Canned-Drained	1	cup	160	237	992	102	41	8	0	3	0.3	0.3	0.9
19036	Crab Leg-Alaska King-Boiled	1	ea	134	130	544	104	26	0	0	2	0.2	0.2	0.7
19038	Crayfish/Crawdads-Steam/Boiled	3	oz	85.05	70	293	68	14	0	0	1	0.2	0.2	0.3
19022	Crayfish/Crawfish-raw	8	ea	27	21	88	22	4	0	0	<1	<0.1	<0.1	0.1
19004	Dungeness Crab-Stmd	3	oz	85.05	94	393	62	19	1	0	1	0.1	0.2	0.3
17071	Grouper Fillet-Bkd/Brld	1	ea	202	238	996	148	50	0	0	3	0.6	0.5	0.8
17090	Haddock Fillet-Bkd/Brld	1	ea	150	168	703	111	36	0	0	1	0.3	0.2	0.5
17047	Herring Fillet-Baked/Broiled	1	ea	143	290	1213	92	33	0	0	17	3.7	6.8	3.9
17012	Herring-Pickled	1	pce	20	52	218	11	3	2	0	4	0.5	2.4	0.3
19006	Lobster-Northern-Stmd	3	oz	85.05	83	347	65	17	1	0	1	0.1	0.1	0.1
19044	Mussels-Steamed/Boiled	3	oz	85.05	146	611	52	20	6	0	4	0.7	0.9	1
19048	Octopus-Cooked-Moist	3	oz	85.05	139	582	51	25	4	0	2	0.4	0.3	0.4
19025	Octopus-Raw	4	oz	113.4	93	389	91	17	2	0	1	0.3	0.2	0.3
17121	Orange Roughy-Baked/Broiled	3	oz	85.05	89	372	57	19	0	0	1	<0.1	0.4	0.2
19027	Oysters-Eastern-Boiled/Steamed	6	ea	42	58	243	30	6	3	0	2	0.6	0.3	0.8
19026	Oysters-Eastern-Raw	1	cup	248	169	707	211	17	10	0	6	1.9	0.8	2.4
17107	Pacific Cod Fish-Fillet-Bkd/Brld	3	oz	85.05	89	372	65	20	0	0	1	0.1	0.1	0.3
19012	Prawns/Lrg Shrimp-Steamed	4	ea	22	22	92	17	5	0	0	<1	0.1	<0.1	0.1
17123	Salmon Fillet-Baked/Broiled	0.5	ea	154	280	1172	92	39	0	0	13	1.9	4.2	5
17060	Sardines+Oil-Cnd-Drained	1	ea	12	25	105	7	3	0	0	1	0.2	0.5	0.6
19011	Scallops-Stmd	3	oz	85.05	95	397	62	20	0	0	1	0.1	0.1	0.4
17086	Sea Bass Fillet-Baked/Broiled	1	ea	101	125	523	73	24	0	0	3	0.7	0.5	1
19000	Small Clams-Steamed/Boiled	20	ea	190	281	1176	121	49	10	0	4	0.4	0.3	1
17022	Snapper Fillet-Baked/Broiled	1	ea	170	218	912	120	45	0	0	3	0.6	0.5	1
17068	Sole/Flounder-Fillet-Broiled	1	ea	127	149	623	93	31	0	0	2	0.5	0.4	0.8
19068	Squid/Calamari-Baked	1	cup	140	194	812	99	26	5	0	7	1.4	2.2	2.1
17104	Striped Bass-Baked/Broiled	1	ea	124	154	644	91	28	0	0	4	0.8	1	1.2
17072	Striped Mullet Fillet- Baked	1	ea	93	140	586	66	23	0	0	5	1.3	1.3	0.9
17080	Surimi	3	oz	85.05	84	351	65	13	6	0	1	0.2	0.1	0.4
17066	Swordfish Broiled/Baked	1	ea	106	164	686	73	27	0	0	5	1.5	2.1	1.3
17024	Tuna Fish+Oil-Canned	0.5	cup	73	145	607	44	21	0	0	6	1.1	2.2	2.1
17026	Tuna Fish+Wtr-Canned	0.5	cup	77	89	372	57	20	0	0	1	0.2	0.1	0.3
17101	Tuna-Bluefin-Baked/Broiled	3	oz	85.05	156	653	50	25	0	0	5	1.4	1.7	1.6
19040	Whelk-Steamed/Boiled	3	oz	85.05	234	979	27	41	13	0	1	0.1	<0.1	<0.1
Game Meats														
14008	Beefalo Meat-Roasted	3	oz	85.05	160	669	52	26	0	0	5	2.3	2.3	0.2
14009	Bison/Buffalo Meat-Roasted	3	oz	85.05	122	510	57	24	0	0	2	0.8	0.8	0.2
14013	Deer/Venison-Roasted	3	oz	85.05	134	561	55	26	0	0	3	1.1	0.7	0.5
40570	Deer-Round Steak-Lean-Brld	3	oz	85.05	129	540	56	27	0	0	2	0.9	0.4	0.1
14014	Elk Meat-Roasted	3	oz	85.05	124	519	56	26	0	0	2	0.6	0.4	0.3
14029	Frog Legs-Steamed	2	ea	100	106	444	74	24	0	0	<1	0.1	0.1	0.1

< = Trace amount present   Blank = Not available

V, vitamin; **THI**, thiamin; **RIB**, riboflavin; **NIA**, niacin; **FOL**, folate; **CALC**, calcium; **PHOS**, phosphorus; **SOD**, sodium; **POT**, potassium; **MAG**, magnesium

CHOL (mg)	V-A (IU)	THI (mg)	RIB (mg)	NIA (mg)	V-B6 (mg)	FOL (μg)	V-B12 (μg)	V-C (mg)	V-E (mg)	CALC (mg)	PHOS (mg)	SOD (mg)	POT (mg)	MAG (mg)	IRON (mg)	ZINC (mg)
255	14	0.5	0.2	3.4	0.4	11	1.3	4.5	12	88	399	768	525	122	8.6	2.5
17	8	<0.1	0.1	4	<0.1	3	0.2	0	0.7	46	50	734	109	14	0.9	0.5
21	27	<0.1	<0.1	1.4	0.1	4	0.5	0		7	77	28	120	8	0.2	0.2
54	43	0.4	0.1	2.1	0.1	6	2.4	0.7		8	208	68	273	22	0.7	0.9
94	145	<0.1	0.1	<0.1	0.1	8	3.2	0	0.3	44	57	240	29	48	1.9	0.2
107	965	0.2	0.7	5.4	0.2	46	158.2	35.4	1	147	541	179	1005	29	44.7	4.4
71	39	0.1	0.1	1.8	0.2	68	15.4	10.2		79	375	1436	351	84	1	10.2
113	43	<0.1	0.1	1.9	0.1	37	1.8	0.8	1.3	51	230	80	252	28	0.7	1.5
31	14	<0.1	<0.1	0.6	<0.1	10	0.5	0.3	0.8	7	69	16	82	7	0.2	0.4
65	88	<0.1	0.2	3.1	0.1	36	8.8	3.1		50	149	321	347	49	0.4	4.7
95	333	0.2	<0.1	0.8	0.7	20	1.4	0		42	289	107	960	75	2.3	1
111	94	0.1	0.1	6.9	0.5	20	2.1	0		63	362	130	598	75	2	0.7
110	172	0.2	0.4	5.9	0.5	17	18.8	1	2	106	433	164	599	59	2	1.8
3	172	<0.1	<0.1	0.7	<0.1	<1	0.9	0	0.3	15	18	174	14	2	0.2	0.1
61	74	<0.1	0.1	0.9	0.1	9	2.6	0	0.9	52	157	323	299	30	0.3	2.5
48	259	0.3	0.4	2.6	0.1	65	20.4	11.6		28	242	314	228	31	5.7	2.3
82	255	<0.1	0.1	3.2	0.6	20	30.6	6.8	1	90	237	391	536	51	8.1	2.9
54	170	<0.1	<0.1	2.4	0.4	18	22.7	5.7	1.4	60	211	261	397	34	6	1.9
68	68	<0.1	0.1	1.5	0.1	4	0.4	0	1.6	9	87	59	154	15	1	0.3
44	76	0.1	0.1	1	<0.1	6	14.7	2.5		38	85	177	118	40	5	76.3
131	248	0.2	0.2	3.4	0.2	25	48.3	9.2	2.1	112	335	523	387	117	16.5	225.2
40	27	<0.1	<0.1	2.1	0.4	7	0.9	2.6		8	190	77	440	26	0.3	0.4
43	50	<0.1	<0.1	0.6	<0.1	1	0.3	0.5	0.3	9	30	49	40	7	0.7	0.3
109	68	0.4	0.7	15.5	1.5	45	4.7	0		23	394	86	967	57	1.6	1.3
17	13	<0.1	<0.1	0.6	<0.1	1	1.1	0	0.2	46	59	61	48	5	0.4	0.2
45	85	0.1	0.1	1.1	0.1	10	1.1	0	1.3	98	287	225	405	47	2.6	2.6
54	215	0.1	0.2	1.9	0.5	6	0.3	0		13	250	88	331	54	0.4	0.5
127	1083	0.3	0.8	6.4	0.2	55	187.9	42		175	642	213	1193	34	53.1	5.2
80	196	0.1	<0.1	0.6	0.8	10	6	2.7		68	342	97	887	63	0.4	0.7
86	55	0.1	0.1	2.8	0.3	11	3.2	0	0.8	23	367	133	437	74	0.4	0.8
395	236	<0.1	0.6	3.5	0.1	8	2.1	7.6	2.7	56	376	124	420	56	1.2	2.6
128	129	0.1	<0.1	3.2	0.4	12	5.5	0		24	315	109	407	63	1.3	0.6
59	131	0.1	0.1	5.9	0.5	9	0.2	1.1		29	227	66	426	31	1.3	0.8
26	57	<0.1	<0.1	0.2	<0.1	2	1.4	0	0.5	8	240	122	95	37	0.2	0.3
53	145	<0.1	0.1	12.5	0.4	2	2.1	1.2		6	357	122	391	36	1.1	1.6
13	56	<0.1	0.1	9.1	0.1	4	1.6	0	0.6	9	227	258	151	23	1	0.7
23	44	<0.1	0.1	10.2	0.3	3	2.3	0	0.3	8	126	260	182	21	1.2	0.6
42	2143	0.2	0.3	9	0.4	2	9.3	0		9	277	43	275	54	1.1	0.7
111	138	<0.1	0.2	1.7	0.6	9	15.4	5.8		96	240	350	590	146	8.6	2.8
49	0	<0.1	0.1	4.2		15	2.2	7.7		20	213	70	390		2.6	5.4
70	0	0.1	0.2	3.2	0.3	7	2.4	0	0.3	7	178	48	307	22	2.9	3.1
95	0	0.2	0.5	5.7				0		6	192	46	285	20	3.8	2.3
72	0	0.2	0.4	7.1	0.6	9	1.9	0	0.5	3	231	38	321	26	3.6	3.1
62	0					8		0		4	153	52	279	20	3.1	2.7
72	65	0.2	0.3	1.6	0.2	16	0.5	0	1.4	26	160	84	372	29	2	1.4

ESHA, EatRight Analysis CD-ROM; **AMT**, amount; **WT**, weight; **CAL**, calories; **KILO**, KiloJoule; **WTR**, water; **PROT**, protein; **CARB**, carbohydrate; **FIBR**, fiber; **FAT**, fat; **SATF**, saturated fat; **MONO**, monounsaturated fat; **POLY**, polyunsaturated fat; **CHOL**, cholesterol;

ESHA CODE	FOOD DESCRIPTION	AMT	UNIT	WT (g)	CAL (kcal)	KILO (kJ)	WTR (g)	PROT (g)	CARB (g)	FIBR (g)	FAT (g)	SATF (g)	MONO (g)	POLY (g)
MEATS & MEAT SUBSTITUTES – BBQ, BREADED, FRIED, GLAZED, GRILLED, RAW, ETC. (CONTINUED)														
14004	Rabbit-Roasted	3	oz	85.05	168	703	52	25	0	0	7	2	1.8	1.3
14030	Turtle Meat-Cooked	1	cup	140	220	920	96	33	<1	0	9	1.8	4.1	2.6
Goats														
13623	Goat-Rstd	3	oz	85.05	122	510	58	23	0	0	3	0.8	1.2	0.2
Lambs														
13524	Ground Lamb-Broiled	3	oz	85.05	241	1008	47	21	0	0	17	6.9	7.1	1.2
13522	Lamb Kabob Meat-Broiled-Lean	3	oz	85.05	158	661	54	24	0	0	6	2.2	2.5	0.6
13513	Lamb Loin Chop Broiled-Lean	1	ea	46	99	414	28	14	0	0	4	1.6	2	0.3
13523	Lamb Stew Meat-Braised-Lean	3	oz	85.05	190	795	48	29	0	0	7	2.7	3	0.7
13501	Leg of Lamb-Roasted-Lean	3	oz	85.05	162	678	54	24	0	0	7	2.3	2.9	0.4
Lunchmeats – Processed/Pressed/Formed (Sausages, Hotdogs, Deli Turkey, etc.)														
13000	Beef lunchmeat-thin slice	5	pce	21	25	105	15	4	1	0	1	0.2	0.3	<0.1
13010	Beef+Pork Hotdog	1	ea	45	137	573	25	5	1	0	12	4.8	6.2	1.2
13006	Bologna-Beef & Pork	1	pce	28.35	87	364	15	4	2	0	7	2.6	3	0.3
13007	Bologna-Turkey	2	pce	56.7	119	498	37	6	3	<1	9	2.5	3.9	2.2
13079	Bratwurst Sausage Link-Cooked	1	ea	85	283	1184	44	12	2	0	25	8.5	12.5	2.2
13066	Braunschweiger Sausage	1	pce	18	59	247	9	3	1	0	5	1.7	2.3	0.6
13070	Chorizo Sausage-Link	1	ea	60	273	1142	19	14	1	0	23	8.6	11	2.1
57966	Hot Dog-Beef-Fat Free	1	ea	49	45	188	18	6	3	0	2	1		
13008	Hotdog-Beef-2oz	1	ea	57	188	787	30	6	2	0	17	6.7	8.2	0.7
13012	Hotdog-Turkey	1	ea	45	100	418	28	6	2	0	8	1.8	2.6	1.8
13015	Italian Pork Sausage Link-Ckd	1	ea	67	230	962	32	13	3	<1	18	6.5	8.6	2.3
13043	Kielbasa Sausage	1	pce	26	80	335	14	3	1	0	7	2.4	3.1	1
13019	Liverwurst-Pork	1	pce	18	59	247	9	3	<1	0	5	1.9	2.4	0.5
13020	Pastrami-Turkey	2	pce	56.7	75	314	41	9	1	<1	4	1	1.2	0.9
13021	Pepperoni Sausage	1	pce	5.5	27	113	2	1	0	0	2	0.8	0.9	0.2
13051	Pickle & Pimento Loaf	2	pce	56.7	128	536	34	6	5	1	9	3	4	1.6
13022	Polish Sausage-Pork	1	ea	227	740	3096	121	32	4	0	65	23.4	30.7	7
13267	Pork Sausage	2	oz	56.7	192	803	28	11	0	0	16	5.2	7	2.1
13023	Salami-Beef-Cooked	1	pce	23	60	251	14	3	<1	0	5	2.3	2.4	0.2
13026	Salami-Dry-Beef & Pork	2	pce	20	77	322	7	5	1	0	6	2.1	3	0.6
11913	Spam	2	oz	56.7	176	736	30	8	2	0	15	5.6	7.8	1.7
13114	Turkey Lunchmeat-Fat Free	1	oz	28.35	24	100	22	4	1	0	<1	0.1	0.1	<0.1
58007	Turkey Sausage-Link	2	ea	56.7	133	556	36	9	1	0	10	2.2	2.9	2.6
13112	TurkeyBreast-Smkd-FatFree	1	pce	28	30	126	6	5	1		<1	0		
Meat Substitutes – Soy, Tofu, & Vegetable														
7726	BlackBean Burger	1	ea	78	133	556	44	13	15	5	4	0.6	1.2	2.6
7752	Breakfast Strip-Frozen	2	ea	16	55	230	7	2	2	1	4	0.7	1	2.6
7724	Deli Franks	1	ea	45	56	234	29	7	6	1	1	0.1	0.1	0.4
7518	Firm Tofu-Raw	0.5	cup	126	88	368	107	10	2	1	5	1.1	1.5	2.3
7674	HarvestBurger-Original-Frozen	1	ea	90	138	577	58	18	7	6	4	1	2.1	0.3
7718	Soy Burger-BlackBean&Salsa	1	ea	142	200	837		19	20	3	4	1.5		
7564	Tempeh	.5	cup	83	160	669	50	15	8		9	1.8	2.5	3.2
8835	Tofu Franks/Wiener-Each	1	ea	38	45	188		9	2	0	<1	0		
7520	Tofu-Fried	1	pce	13	35	146	7	2	1	1	3	0.4	0.6	1.5
7500	Tofu-Regular	1	cup	248	151	632	216	16	4	<1	9	1.3	2	5.2

< = Trace amount present   Blank = Not available

V, vitamin; **THI**, thiamin; **RIB**, riboflavin; **NIA**, niacin; **FOL**, folate; **CALC**, calcium; **PHOS**, phosphorus; **SOD**, sodium; **POT**, potassium; **MAG**, magnesium

CHOL (mg)	V-A (IU)	THI (mg)	RIB (mg)	NIA (mg)	V-B6 (mg)	FOL (μg)	V-B12 (μg)	V-C (mg)	V-E (mg)	CALC (mg)	PHOS (mg)	SOD (mg)	POT (mg)	MAG (mg)	IRON (mg)	ZINC (mg)
70	0	0.1	0.2	7.2	0.4	9	7.1	0		16	224	40	326	18	1.9	1.9
82	514	0.2	0.3	1.7	0.2	21	1.5	<1	2.1	197	299	209	383	33	2.3	1.6
64	0	0.1	0.5	3.4	0	4	1	0	0.3	14	171	73	344	0	3.2	4.5
82	0	0.1	0.2	5.7	0.1	16	2.2	0	0.1	19	171	69	288	20	1.5	4
77	0	0.1	0.3	5.6	0.1	20	2.6	0	0.2	11	191	65	285	26	2	4.9
44	0	0.1	0.1	3.2	0.1	11	1.2	0	0.1	9	104	39	173	13	0.9	1.9
92	0	0.1	0.2	5.1	0.1	18	2.3	0	0.2	13	174	60	221	24	2.4	5.6
76	0	0.1	0.2	5.4	0.1	20	2.2	0	0.2	7	175	58	287	22	1.8	4.2
10	0	<0.1	0.1	1	0.1	1	0.4	0	<0.1	1	53	235	65	4	0.4	0.7
22	26	0.1	0.1	1.2	0.1	2	0.6	0	0.1	5	39	504	75	4	0.5	0.8
17	24	0.1	0.1	0.7	0.1	2	0.5	0.2	0	24	46	209	89	5	0.3	0.7
43	18	<0.1	0.1	1.5	0.1	5	0.1	7.5	0.3	70	65	710	77	9	1.7	0.7
63	5	0.4	0.3	4.1	0.3	3	0.6	0	0.2	24	177	719	296	18	0.5	2.8
32	2529	<0.1	0.3	1.5	0.1	8	3.6	0	0.1	2	30	209	36	2	2	0.5
53	0	0.4	0.2	3.1	0.3	1	1.2	0	0.1	5	90	741	239	11	1	2
15	0							0		0		400			1.1	
30	0	<0.1	0.1	1.4	0.1	3	1	0	0.1	8	91	650	89	8	0.9	1.4
35	0	<0.1	0.1	1.7	0.1	4	0.4	0	0.3	67	77	485	176	6	0.7	0.8
38	11	0.4	0.2	2.8	0.2	3	0.9	0.1	0.2	14	114	809	204	12	1	1.6
17	0	0.1	0.1	0.9	<0.1	<1	0.2	0	0.1	4	44	235	78	3	0.2	0.4
28	4980	<0.1	0.2	0.8	<0.1	5	2.4	0		5	41	155	31	2	1.2	0.4
39	7	<0.1	0.1	2	0.2	3	0.1	4.6	0.1	6	113	556	196	8	2.4	1.2
6	0	<0.1	<0.1	0.3	<0.1	<1	0.1	<1	0	1	10	91	15	1	0.1	0.1
33	147	0.2	0.1	1.4	0.2	21	0.3	4.4	0.2	62	87	739	210	19	0.8	1
159	0	1.1	0.3	7.8	0.4	5	2.2	2.3		27	309	1989	538	32	3.3	4.4
48	23	0.2	0.1	3.5	0.2	2	0.7	0.4	0.3	7	92	425	167	10	0.8	1.2
16	0	<0.1	<0.1	0.7	<0.1	<1	0.7	0	<0.1	1	47	262	43	3	0.5	0.4
20	0	0.1	0.1	1	0.1	<1	0.4	0	0.1	2	28	402	76	3	0.3	0.6
40	0					2		0.5		8		776	130	8	0.5	1
9	0							0		3	66	338	58	8	0.3	0.2
91	0	<0.1	0.1	2.1	0.1	2	0.4	0.3	0.1	18	88	332	130	9	0.6	1.7
10	0							0		0		260			0	
1	78	10.6	0.2	1.4	0.1	38	0	0.8		80	147	406	296	40	1.7	0.8
<1	0	1.6	0.1	1.4	0.1		0.5	0		7	46	234	16		0.6	0.1
0	31	0.1	0.1	10.8	<0.1	1	0	0		22	58	464	45		0.4	0.4
0	0	0.1	0.1	0.1	0.1	24	0	0.3	<0.1	253	152	15	186	47	2	1
0	0	0.3	0.2	6.3	0.4	22	0	0		102	225	411	432	70	3.9	8.1
0												660				
0	0	0.1	0.3	2.2	0.2	20	0.1	0		92	221	7	342	67	2.2	0.9
0	0	0.2					0.6	0		20		240	90	8	2.2	0.6
0	4	<0.1	<0.1	<0.1	<0.1	4	0	0	<0.1	48	37	2	19	8	0.6	0.3
0	17	0.1	0.1	1.3	0.1	109	0	0.5	<0.1	275	228	20	298	67	2.8	1.6

ESHA, EatRight Analysis CD-ROM; **AMT**, amount; **WT**, weight; **CAL**, calories; **KILO**, KiloJoule; **WTR**, water; **PROT**, protein; **CARB**, carbohydrate; **FIBR**, fiber; **FAT**, fat; **SATF**, saturated fat; **MONO**, monounsaturated fat; **POLY**, polyunsaturated fat; **CHOL**, cholesterol;

ESHA CODE	FOOD DESCRIPTION	AMT	UNIT	WT (g)	CAL (kcal)	KILO (kJ)	WTR (g)	PROT (g)	CARB (g)	FIBR (g)	FAT (g)	SATF (g)	MONO (g)	POLY (g)
MEATS & MEAT SUBSTITUTES – BBQ, BREADED, FRIED, GLAZED, GRILLED, RAW, ETC. (CONTINUED)														
91489	Vegan Burger	1	ea	71	70	293		13	6	4	1			
7665	Vege Chicken Patties-Frozen	1	ea	71	84	351	50	9	7	4	3	0.4	0.7	2.3
7727	Vege ChickenNugget Frozen	5	pce	85	250	1046		13	14	2	15	2	4.5	8
7722	Vege Patties	1	ea	67	118	494	40	12	9	3	4	0.5	1	2.1
8169	Veget Baloney-Pce LLF	1	pce	14.33	20	84	4	3	1	0	1	0.3		
8127	Veget Frank/Wiener-Jumbo	1	ea	76	80	335	42	16	4	1	0	0	0	0
8166	Veget Sausage-Lean-Breakfast	1	ea	35	60	251	8	4	4	0	3	1		
92033	Vegetarian Beef-Herb Crusted	1	ea	71	142	594	40	9	13	3	7	0.6	4.3	1.8
7511	Vegetarian BreakfastLinks	1	ea	25	64	268	13	5	2	1	5	0.7	1.1	2.3
7512	Vegetarian BreakfastPatty	1	ea	38	98	410	19	7	4	1	7	1.1	1.7	3.5
7732	Vegetarian Burger	0.25	cup	55	68	285	39	10	3	1	2	0.3	0.3	0.9
91060	Vegetarian Burger	1	ea	67	120	502		12	9	3	4	0.5	1	2.5
7548	Vegetarian Chicken-BreadFried	1	pce	57	133	556	32	12	5	2	7	0.6	1.8	2.6
7636	Vegetarian Chicken-Frozen	2	pce	57	88	368	39	9	2	1	5	0.7	1	2.6
7610	Vegetarian Choplets-Canned	2	pce	92	95	397	68	18	4	3	1	0.1	0.1	0.5
7642	Vegetarian Fillets-Frozen	2	pce	85	180	753		16	8	4	9	1	3.5	4.5
7549	Vegetarian Fish Sticks	2	ea	57	165	690	26	13	5	3	10	1.6	2.5	5.3
7746	Vegetarian Grillers	1	ea	64	136	569	36	15	5	3	6	1.1	1.7	3.2
91501	Vegetarian Ground Beef	0.5	cup	57	60	251		13	6	3	<1			
8173	Vegetarian Ham-Country-Piece	1	pce	14.33	17	71		3	1	0	0	0	0	0
92148	Vegetarian Hot Dog	1	ea	70	163	682	41	14	5	3	10	1.4	2.7	5.5
8159	Vegetarian Italian Sausage-Lean	1	ea	40	60	251	11	5	5	0	2	1		
7734	Vegetarian Leanies-Frozen	1	ea	40	100	418	22	8	2	2	7	1.1	2.5	2.9
7551	Vegetarian Luncheon Meat	1	pce	67	127	531	44	12	3	0	7	0.9	1.4	2.9
7561	Vegetarian Meat Patties	1	ea	71	140	586	41	15	6	3	6	1	1.6	3.3
7552	Vegetarian Meatballs	7	ea	70	138	577	41	15	6	3	6	1	1.5	3.3
91059	Vegetarian Pizza Burger	1	ea	67	121	506	42	10	7	2	6	1.5	1.4	2.6
7618	Vegetarian Salami-Frozen	3	pce	57	120	502		12	3	2	7	1	1	5
7555	Vegetarian Sandwich Spread	1	Tbs	15	22	92	10	1	1	<1	1	0.2	0.3	0.7
7624	Vegetarian Tuno-Frozen	0.5	cup	55	90	377		7	3	2	6	1	2	3
Pork & Ham														
12000	Bacon-Regular-Cooked	3	pce	19	103	431	2	7	<1	0	8	2.6	3.5	0.9
12002	Canadian Bacon-Grilled	2	pce	46.5	86	360	29	11	1	0	4	1.3	1.9	0.4
12175	Cured Ham-Rstd	3	oz	85.05	145	607	54	21	0	0	6	2	2.7	0.7
12225	Ham-Canned-Unheated-XLean	1	cup	140	202	845	100	25	0	0	10	3.4	5	1.1
12006	Ham-Whole-Rstd-Lean Only	1	cup	140	220	920	92	35	0	0	8	2.6	3.5	0.9
12236	Pork Country Rib-Lean-Rstd	3	oz	85.05	210	879	49	23	0	0	13	4.5	5.5	0.9
12035	Pork Loin Chop-Broiled-Lean	1	ea	79	166	695	48	23	0	0	8	2.9	3.5	0.6
12031	Pork Loin-Roasted Slice	1	pce	89	221	925	51	24	0	0	13	4.8	5.8	1.1
12098	Spareribs-Braised-Lean	3	oz	85.05	210	879	48	24	0	0	12	4.3	5.3	1.4
Turkeys														
16040	Tom Turkey-NoSkin-Roasted	1	cup	140	235	983	91	41	0	0	7	2.2	1.4	1.9
16003	Turkey-Ground Patty-Cooked	1	ea	82	193	808	49	22	0	0	11	2.8	4	2.6
16000	Turkey Meat-All-Roasted	1	cup	140	238	996	91	41	0	0	7	2	1.6	2.1
51101	Turkey-Dark Meat-Rstd	3	oz	85.05	160	669	54	24	<1	0	6	1.9	1.5	2
51152	Turkey-Light+Water-Canned	2	oz	56.7	80	335		16	0	0	1	0.5		

< = Trace amount present   Blank = Not available

V, vitamin; **THI**, thiamin; **RIB**, riboflavin; **NIA**, niacin; **FOL**, folate; **CALC**, calcium; **PHOS**, phosphorus; **SOD**, sodium; **POT**, potassium; **MAG**, magnesium

CHOL (mg)	V-A (IU)	THI (mg)	RIB (mg)	NIA (mg)	V-B6 (mg)	FOL (μg)	V-B12 (μg)	V-C (mg)	V-E (mg)	CALC (mg)	PHOS (mg)	SOD (mg)	POT (mg)	MAG (mg)	IRON (mg)	ZINC (mg)
0	0							0		60		330			1.8	
0	8	<0.1	<0.1	0	0	4	0	0		38	89	593	278		1.8	0.4
0	0	0.4	0.2	6	0.8		3	0		20		490	210		1.4	
1	250	7.5	0.2	0.9	0.6			0.7		40	110	352	141		1.5	0.7
0	0							0.8		7		80			0.2	
0	0							1.2		40		590			0.7	
0	0							2.4		20		130			0.9	
0	65	0.1	0.1	1.7	0.1		0.7	0		45	112	413	186	3	1.4	2.4
0	0	0.6	0.1	2.8	0.2	6	0	0	0.5	16	56	222	58	9	0.9	0.4
0	0	0.9	0.2	4.3	0.3	10	0	0	0.8	24	86	337	88	14	1.4	0.6
0	0	0.1	0.1	1.6	0.2		2.4	0		4	54	248	24		1.4	0.7
0	0							0		20		470	250		1.4	
0	0	0.7	0.2	7.3	0.5	32	2.9	0	1.1	24	140	228	171	7	2.2	0.4
1	0	0.4	0.1	4.3	0.3		2.1	0		155	139	258	235		2.2	0.4
0	0	0	0					0		7	69	420	35		1.4	0.9
0	0	0.4	0.1	0.8	0.4		2.7	0		20		650	130		1.8	
0	0	0.6	0.5	6.8	0.9	58	2.4	0	2.3	54	256	279	342	13	1.1	0.8
2	0	1.8	0.2	4.1	0.4		2.9	0		39	118	270	116		2.7	0.8
0	0							0		60		270			1.8	
0	0							0.4		0		100			1.8	
0	0	0.3	0.6	2.2	0.1	55	1.6	0	1.3	23	241	330	69	13	1	0.8
0	0							2.4		20		160			1.1	
1	0	0.2	0.1	0.8	0.2		0.9	0		29	82	431	41		0.7	0.3
0	0	2.7	0.2	7.4	0.6	67	2.7	0	2	27	296	476	134	15	1.2	1.1
0	0	0.6	0.4	7.1	0.9	55	1.7	0	1.2	21	244	390	128	13	1.5	1.3
0	0	0.7	0.1	1.8	0.1	55	1	0	1.2	18	241	385	126	13	1.5	1.3
7	285	0.1	0.2					14.7		32	93	261	159		1.2	
0	0	0.8	0.2	4	0.2		0.6	0		0		800	95		1.1	
0	2	0.1	0.1	2	0.2	15	0.5	0	0.3	7	33	94	51	19	0.2	0.2
0	0	0.2	<0.1	4	0.3		2.1	0		20		300	45		1.8	
21	7	0.1	0.1	2.1	0.1	<1	0.2	0	0.1	2	101	439	107	6	0.3	0.7
27	0	0.4	0.1	3.2	0.2	2	0.4	0	0.2	5	138	719	181	10	0.4	0.8
41	0	0.6	0.2	4.1	0.3	3	0.9	0	0.2	9	207	1047	248	14	0.9	2.5
53	0	1.2	0.3	6.4	0.6	8	1.1	0	0.3	8	290	1786	468	22	1.3	2.6
77	0	1	0.4	7	0.7	6	1	0	0.4	10	318	1858	442	31	1.3	3.6
79	7	0.5	0.3	4	0.4	4	0.7	0.3		25	188	25	297	20	1.1	3.2
62	6	0.7	0.3	4.1	0.4	5	0.6	0.6	0.2	13	200	51	346	23	0.7	2
73	8	0.9	0.3	5	0.5	5	0.6	0.5	0.2	17	215	53	363	23	0.9	2.1
89	0	0.4	0.3	4.9	0.4	0	0.8	0	0.1	28	177	51	253	20	1.2	3.8
108	0	0.1	0.3	7.4	0.7	11	0.5	0		35	300	104	421	36	2.5	4.4
84	0	<0.1	0.1	4	0.3	6	0.3	0	0.3	20	161	88	221	20	1.6	2.3
106	0	0.1	0.3	7.6	0.6	10	0.5	0	0.5	35	298	98	417	36	2.5	4.3
72	0	0.1	0.2	3.1	0.3	8	0.3	0	0.5	27	174	67	247	20	2	3.8
55	0							0		0		150			0	

ESHA, EatRight Analysis CD-ROM; **AMT**, amount; **WT**, weight; **CAL**, calories; **KILO**, KiloJoule; **WTR**, water; **PROT**, protein; **CARB**, carbohydrate; **FIBR**, fiber; **FAT**, fat; **SATF**, saturated fat; **MONO**, monounsaturated fat; **POLY**, polyunsaturated fat; **CHOL**, cholesterol;

ESHA CODE	FOOD DESCRIPTION	AMT	UNIT	WT (g)	CAL (kcal)	KILO (kJ)	WTR (g)	PROT (g)	CARB (g)	FIBR (g)	FAT (g)	SATF (g)	MONO (g)	POLY (g)
MEATS & MEAT SUBSTITUTES – BBQ, BREADED, FRIED, GLAZED, GRILLED, RAW, ETC. (CONTINUED)														
16001	Turkey-White Meat-Roasted	1	cup	140	196	820	96	42	0	0	2	0.5	0.3	0.4
Variety Meats & By-Products														
10015	Beef Heart-Simmered	3	oz	85.05	140	586	56	24	<1	0	4	1.2	0.9	0.8
10010	Beef Liver-fried	3	oz	85.05	149	623	53	23	4	0	4	1.3	0.6	0.5
10089	Beef Tripe-Cooked	1	cup	140	132	552	114	16	3	0	6	1.9	2.2	0.3
15025	Chicken Gizzards-Simmered	1	cup	145	223	933	98	44	0	0	4	1	0.8	0.5
16048	Goose Liver Pate-Cnd	1	Tbs	13	60	251	5	1	1	0	6	1.9	3.3	0.1
Veal														
11530	Veal- Ground-Broiled	3	oz	85.05	146	611	57	21	0	0	6	2.6	2.4	0.5
11517	Veal Loin Cutlet-Brsd-Lean+Fat	1	ea	80	227	950	42	24	0	0	14	5.4	5.4	0.9
11519	Veal Rib-Roasted-Lean+Fat	3	oz	85.05	194	812	51	20	0	0	12	4.6	4.6	0.8
11527	Veal Sirloin-Roasted	3	oz	85.05	172	720	53	21	0	0	9	3.8	3.5	0.6
NUTS, SEEDS, & PRODUCTS														
4534	Almond Butter-Plain	1	Tbs	16	101	423	<1	2	3	1	9	0.9	6.1	2
4572	Almond Butter-Salted	1	Tbs	16	101	423	<1	2	3	1	9	0.9	6.1	2
4503	Almonds-Slivered/Pkd Measure	1	cup	108	621	2598	5	23	23	13	53	4	33.4	13
4525	Black Walnuts-Chopped	1	cup	125	772	3230	6	30	12	9	74	4.2	18.8	43.8
4519	Cashews-Dry Roasted+Salt	1	cup	137	786	3289	2	21	45	4	63	12.5	37.4	10.7
4621	Cashews-Dry Roast-No Salt	1	cup	137	786	3289	2	21	45	4	63	12.5	37.4	10.7
4596	Cashews-Oil Roasted	1	cup	130	755	3159	3	22	39	4	62	11	33.7	11.1
4622	Cashews-Oil Roast-No Salt	1	cup	130	754	3155	5	22	39	4	62	11	33.7	11.1
4538	Chestnuts-Roasted	1	cup	143	350	1464	58	5	76	7	3	0.6	1.1	1.2
4649	Coconut Cream-Canned	1	cup	296	1057	4422	86	3	158	1	48	45.8	2	0.5
4528	Coconut Milk-Raw	1	cup	240	552	2310	162	5	13	5	57	50.7	2.4	0.6
4511	Coconut-Dried-Sweet-Shred	1	cup	93	466	1950	12	3	44	4	33	29.3	1.4	0.4
4510	Coconut-Dried-Unsweet	2	Tbs	9.25	61	255	<1	1	2	2	6	5.3	0.3	0.1
4508	Coconut-Raw Piece-2.5x2in	1	pce	45	159	665	21	1	7	4	15	13.4	0.6	0.2
4556	English Walnuts-Chopped	1	cup	120	785	3284	5	18	16	8	78	7.4	10.7	56.6
4557	English Walnuts-Halves	1	cup	100	654	2736	4	15	14	7	65	6.1	8.9	47.2
4514	Filberts/Hazelnuts-Chopped	1	cup	115	722	3021	6	17	19	11	70	5.1	52.5	9.1
4513	Filberts/Hazelnuts-Whole	1	cup	135	848	3548	7	20	23	13	82	6	61.6	10.7
4533	Mixed Nuts+Pnuts-Oil Roast	1	cup	142	876	3665	3	24	30	14	80	12.4	45	18.9
4594	MixedNuts-NoPnts-Oil Roast	1	cup	144	886	3707	5	22	32	8	81	13.1	47.7	16.5
4576	Peanut Butter-Chunky-NoSalt	2	Tbs	32	188	787	<1	8	7	3	16	2.6	7.9	4.7
4626	Peanut Butter-Smooth-Salted	2	Tbs	32	188	787	<1	8	7	3	16	2.6	7.9	4.7
4542	Peanuts-Oil Roasted-Unsalted	1	cup	133	773	3234	3	35	25	9	66	9.1	32.5	20.7
4578	Pecans-Dried Halves	1	cup	108	746	3121	4	10	15	10	78	6.7	44.1	23.3
4577	Pecans-Dried-Chopped	1	cup	119	822	3439	4	11	16	11	86	7.4	48.6	25.7
4554	Pine Nuts/Pinon-Dried	10	ea	1	6	25	<1	<1	<1	<1	1	0.1	0.2	0.3
4521	Pistachios	47	ea	28.35	159	665	1	6	8	3	13	1.6	6.8	3.9
4564	PumpkinSeeds-Roasted+Salt	1	cup	64	285	1192	3	12	34	12	12	2.3	3.9	5.7
4523	Sesame Seeds-Whole-Dried	1	cup	144	825	3452	7	26	34	17	72	10	27	31.4
4545	Sunflower Seeds-Dry	1	cup	144	841	3519	7	30	29	12	74	6.4	26.7	33.3
4552	SunflowerSeeds-Oil Roasted	1	cup	135	799	3343	2	27	31	14	69	9.5	10.9	46.3
4532	Tahini (Sesame Butter)	1	Tbs	14	85	356	<1	3	3	1	8	1.1	3	3.5

< = Trace amount present Blank = Not available

V, vitamin; **THI**, thiamin; **RIB**, riboflavin; **NIA**, niacin; **FOL**, folate; **CALC**, calcium; **PHOS**, phosphorus; **SOD**, sodium; **POT**, potassium; **MAG**, magnesium

CHOL (mg)	V-A (IU)	THI (mg)	RIB (mg)	NIA (mg)	V-B6 (mg)	FOL (μg)	V-B12 (μg)	V-C (mg)	V-E (mg)	CALC (mg)	PHOS (mg)	SOD (mg)	POT (mg)	MAG (mg)	IRON (mg)	ZINC (mg)
120	0	0.1	0.2	9.7	0.8	8	0.5	0		21	302	78	388	39	2.2	2.9
180	0	0.1	1	5.7	0.2	4	9.2	0	0.2	4	216	50	186	18	5.4	2.4
324	22188	0.2	2.9	14.9	0.9	221	70.7	0.6	0.4	5	412	65	299	19	5.2	4.4
220	0	0	<0.1	0.6	0	4	1	0	0.2	113	92	95	59	21	0.9	2.4
536	0	<0.1	0.3	4.5	0.1	7	1.5	0	0.3	25	274	81	260	4	4.6	6.4
20	433	<0.1	<0.1	0.3	<0.1	8	1.2	0.3		9	26	91	18	2	0.7	0.1
88	0	0.1	0.2	6.8	0.3	9	1.1	0	0.1	14	185	71	287	20	0.8	3.3
94	0	<0.1	0.2	7.2	0.2	11	1	0	0.3	22	176	64	224	19	0.9	2.9
94	0	<0.1	0.2	5.9	0.2	11	1.2	0	0.3	9	168	78	251	19	0.8	3.5
87	0	0.1	0.3	7.5	0.3	13	1.2	0	0.4	11	190	71	299	22	0.8	2.8
0	0	<0.1	0.1	0.5	<0.1	10	0	0.1		43	84	2	121	48	0.6	0.5
0	<1	<0.1	0.1	0.5	<0.1	10	0	0.1	4.2	43	84	72	121	48	0.6	0.5
0	1	0.2	1.1	3.7	0.2	54	0	0	28.3	285	523	1	761	289	4	3.3
0	50	0.1	0.2	0.6	0.7	39	0	2.1	2.2	76	641	2	654	251	3.9	4.2
0	0	0.3	0.3	1.9	0.4	95	0	0	1.3	62	671	877	774	356	8.2	7.7
0	0	0.3	0.3	1.9	0.4	95	0	0	1.3	62	671	22	774	356	8.2	7.7
0	0	0.5	0.3	2.3	0.4	32	0	0.4	1.2	56	690	400	822	355	7.9	7
0	0	0.5	0.3	2.3	0.4	32	0	0.4	1.2	56	690	17	822	355	7.9	7
0	34	0.3	0.3	1.9	0.7	100	0	37.2	0.7	41	153	3	847	47	1.3	0.8
0	0	0.1	0.1	0.1	0.1	41	0	0	0.4	12	65	107	299	50	0.4	1.8
0	0	0.1	0	1.8	0.1	38	0	6.7	0.4	38	240	36	631	89	3.9	1.6
0	0	<0.1	<0.1	0.4	0.3	7	0	0.7	0.4	14	100	244	313	46	1.8	1.7
0	0	<0.1	<0.1	0.1	<0.1	1	0	0.1	<0.1	2	19	3	50	8	0.3	0.2
0	0	<0.1	<0.1	0.2	<0.1	12	0	1.5	0.1	6	51	9	160	14	1.1	0.5
0	24	0.4	0.2	1.4	0.6	118	0	1.6	0.8	118	415	2	529	190	3.5	3.7
0	20	0.3	0.2	1.1	0.5	98	0	1.3	0.7	98	346	2	441	158	2.9	3.1
0	23	0.7	0.1	2.1	0.6	130	0	7.2	17.3	131	334	0	782	187	5.4	2.8
0	27	0.9	0.2	2.4	0.8	153	0	8.5	20.3	154	392	0	918	220	6.3	3.3
0	27	0.7	0.3	7.2	0.3	118	0	0.7		153	659	16	825	334	4.6	7.2
0	29	0.7	0.7	2.8	0.3	81	0	0.7		153	647	16	783	361	3.7	6.7
0	0	<0.1	<0.1	4.4	0.1	29	0	0	2	14	102	5	238	51	0.6	0.9
0	0	<0.1	<0.1	4.4	0.1	29	0	0	2	14	102	156	238	51	0.6	0.9
0	0	0.3	0.1	19	0.3	168	0	0	9.2	117	688	8	907	246	2.4	8.8
0	60	0.7	0.1	1.3	0.2	24	0	1.2	1.5	76	299	0	443	131	2.7	4.9
0	67	0.8	0.2	1.4	0.2	26	0	1.3	1.7	83	330	0	488	144	3	5.4
0	<1	<0.1	<0.1	<0.1	<0.1	1	0	<1		<1	<1	1	6	2	<0.1	<0.1
0	118	0.2	<0.1	0.4	0.5	14	0	1.6	0.7	30	139	<1	291	34	1.1	0.6
0	40	<0.1	<0.1	0.2	<0.1	6	0	0.2		35	59	1626	588	168	2.1	6.6
0	13	1.1	0.4	6.5	1.1	140	0	0	0.4	1404	906	16	674	505	21	11.2
0	72	2.1	0.5	12	1.9	327	0	2	50.6	112	950	13	929	468	7.6	7.2
0	12	0.4	0.4	5.6	1.1	316	0	1.5	49	117	1538	554	652	171	5.8	7
0	9	0.2	<0.1	0.8	<0.1	14	0	0		20	111	<1	64	49	0.9	1.5

ESHA, EatRight Analysis CD-ROM; **AMT**, amount; **WT**, weight; **CAL**, calories; **KILO**, KiloJoule; **WTR**, water; **PROT**, protein; **CARB**, carbohydrate; **FIBR**, fiber; **FAT**, fat; **SATF**, saturated fat; **MONO**, monounsaturated fat; **POLY**, polyunsaturated fat; **CHOL**, cholesterol;

ESHA CODE	FOOD DESCRIPTION	AMT	UNIT	WT (g)	CAL (kcal)	KILO (kJ)	WTR (g)	PROT (g)	CARB (g)	FIBR (g)	FAT (g)	SATF (g)	MONO (g)	POLY (g)
PREPARED FOODS														
Shelf-Stable/Canned Dishes														
7040	Baked Beans w/Pork-Canned	1	cup	253	268	1121	181	13	51	14	4	1.5	1.7	0.5
7038	BakedBeans-Vegetarian-Cnd	0.5	cup	127	119	498	91	6	27	5	<1	0.1	0.1	0.2
5068	Creamed Corn-Canned	0.5	cup	128	92	385	101	2	23	2	1	0.1	0.2	0.3
7023	Pork & Beans, Sweet Sauce	1	cup	253	283	1184	179	13	53	11	4	1.2	1.3	1
7004	Pork & Beans, Tomato Sauce	1	cup	253	238	996	186	13	47	10	2	0.7	0.7	0.4
7024	RefriedBeans/Frijoles-Canned	1	cup	252.8	230	962	193	14	39	13	3	1	1	0.8
5552	Sweet Potatoes+Syrup-Canned	1	cup	228	203	849	176	2	48	6	<1	0.1	<0.1	0.2
Shelf-Stable/Canned Soups, Stews, & Chilis														
50000	Bean+Bacon Soup w/Water	1	cup	253	159	665	216	7	21	7	5	1.4	2	1.7
20057	Beef Broth+TomatoJce-Cnd	1	tsp	30.5	11	46	27	<1	3	<1	<1	<0.1	<0.1	<0.1
50183	Beef Broth-Canned-LowSodium	1	cup	240	38	159	230	5	1	0	1	0.4	0.7	0.3
50198	Beef MushroomSoup+Wat-Can	1	cup	244	73	305	226	6	6	<1	3	1.5	1.2	0.1
50003	Beef Noodle Soup + Water	1	cup	244	83	347	225	5	9	1	3	1.1	1.2	0.5
50066	Beef Soup-Chunky-Prepared	1	cup	240	158	661	200	10	24	1	3	1.3	1.1	0.1
57659	Beef Stew-Canned	1	svg	232	230	962	187	10	18	2	13	5.1	5.9	0.6
50060	Black Bean Soup + Water	1	cup	247	114	477	216	6	19	8	2	0.4	0.6	0.5
50204	Bouillabaise Soup/Chowder	1	cup	227	241	1008	177	34	5	1	9	2	3.9	1.5
50071	Cheese Soup + Milk	1	cup	251	231	967	207	9	16	1	15	9.1	4.1	0.5
50004	Chicken Broth-Can + Water	1	cup	244	39	163	234	5	1	0	1	0.4	0.6	0.3
50005	Chicken Noodle Soup+Water	1	cup	241	60	251	226	3	7	<1	2	0.6	1	0.6
50020	Chicken Rice Soup+Water	1	cup	241	58	243	226	3	7	1	2	0.4	0.9	0.4
50091	Chicken Veget Soup+Water	1	cup	241	75	314	223	4	9	1	3	0.8	1.3	0.6
50074	ChickenDumplingSoup+Water	1	cup	241	96	402	221	6	6	<1	6	1.3	2.5	1.3
56001	Chili + Beans-Canned	1	cup	256	287	1201	193	15	30	11	14	6	6	0.9
50007	Chili Beef Soup + Water	1	cup	250	142	594	214	6	23	3	3	1.5	1.2	0.1
50145	Chunky Vegetable Soup	1	cup	240	122	510	210	4	19	1	4	0.6	1.6	1.4
50008	Clam Chowder-NewEng+Milk	1	cup	248	151	632	212	8	19	1	5	2.7	0.7	1.3
50093	ClamChowder-Manhattan-Prep	1	cup	240	134	561	206	7	19	3	3	2.1	1	0.1
50098	Consomme+Gelatin+Water	1	cup	241	29	121	232	5	2	0	0	0	0	0
50011	Cream Mushroom Soup+Milk	1	cup	248	166	695	215	6	14	0	10	3.3	2	1.8
50049	Cream Mushroom Soup+Water	1	cup	244	102	427	225	2	8	0	7	1.6	1.3	1.7
40675	Cream of Broccoli Soup	1	svg	305	143	598	275	3	17	7	7	2		
50006	Cream of ChickenSoup+Milk	1	cup	248	191	799	210	7	15	<1	11	4.6	4.5	1.6
50018	Cream of ChickenSoup+Water	1	cup	244	117	490	221	3	9	<1	7	2.1	3.3	1.5
50026	Cream Potato Soup + Milk	1	cup	248	149	623	215	6	17	<1	6	3.8	1.7	0.6
50103	Gazpacho Soup-Prepared	1	cup	244	46	192	229	7	4	<1	<1	<0.1	<0.1	0.1
50105	Lentil & Ham Soup-Prepared	1	cup	248	139	582	213	9	20		3	1.1	1.3	0.3
28181	Lobster Bisque Soup-Semi Cond	0.67	cup	152.5	160	669		4	12	1	11	5		
50009	Minestrone Soup + Water	1	cup	241	82	343	220	4	11	1	3	0.6	0.7	1.1
50024	Oyster Stew + Milk	1	cup	245	135	565	218	6	10	0	8	5	2.1	0.3
50025	Split Pea+Ham Soup+Water	1	cup	253	190	795	207	10	28	2	4	1.8	1.8	0.6
50135	Tomato Bisque Soup-Prep f/Cnd	1	cup	247	124	519	215	2	24	<1	3	0.5	0.7	1.1
50012	Tomato Soup + Milk	1	cup	248	136	569	213	6	22	1	3	1.7	0.8	0.3
50028	Tomato Soup + Water	1	cup	244	73	305	223	2	16	1	1	0.2	0.2	0.2
91659	Vegetarian Chili-Pkg	1	ea	300	230	962		21	37	14	1	0		

< = Trace amount present   Blank = Not available

V, vitamin; **THI**, thiamin; **RIB**, riboflavin; **NIA**, niacin; **FOL**, folate; **CALC**, calcium; **PHOS**, phosphorus; **SOD**, sodium; **POT**, potassium; **MAG**, magnesium

CHOL (mg)	V-A (IU)	THI (mg)	RIB (mg)	NIA (mg)	V-B6 (mg)	FOL (μg)	V-B12 (μg)	V-C (mg)	V-E (mg)	CALC (mg)	PHOS (mg)	SOD (mg)	POT (mg)	MAG (mg)	IRON (mg)	ZINC (mg)
18	0	0.1	0.1	1.1	0.2	91	0	5.1		134	273	1047	782	86	4.3	3.7
0	137	0.1	<0.1	0.5	0.1	15	0	0	0.2	43	94	436	284	34	1.5	2.9
0	95	<0.1	0.1	1.2	0.1	58	0	5.9	0.1	4	65	365	172	22	0.5	0.7
18	20	0.1	0.1	0.9	0.1	20	0	7.1	0.1	149	258	845	653	83	4.2	3.5
18	213	0.1	0.1	1.2	0.2	38	0	7.6	0.3	142	293	1106	746	86	8.2	13.9
0	0	0.1	<0.1	1.1	0.3	28	0	15.2	0.1	83	281	1135	849	96	4.2	1.6
0	17168	0.1	0.1	1	0.1	16	0	23.9	2.1	34	62	100	422	30	1.8	0.4
3	820	0.1	<0.1	0.5	<0.1	30	<0.1	1.5	1.1	78	121	883	372	43	1.9	1
0	39	<0.1	<0.1	0.1	<0.1	1	<0.1	0.3		3	4	40	29	1	0.2	<0.1
0	0	0	0.1	3.3	<0.1	5	0.2	0	<0.1	10	72	72	206	2	0.5	0.2
7	0	<0.1	0.1	1	<0.1	10	0.2	4.6		5	34	942	154	10	0.9	1.5
5	246	0.1	0.1	1	<0.1	20	0.2	0.5	1.2	20	46	930	98	7	1.1	1.5
14	2611	0.1	0.2	2.7	0.1	14	0.6	7	0.7	31	120	862	336	5	2.3	2.6
30	517	0.2	0.1	2.5	0.2	32	1.2	1.6	0.6	28	97	900	378	19	5.8	2.3
0	548	0.1	<0.1	0.5	0.1	82	0	0.2	0.4	47	94	1203	309	42	1.9	1.4
90	481	0.2	0.2	5	0.4	28	10.4	12	2	83	340	416	733	74	3.9	1.9
48	1242	0.1	0.3	0.5	0.1	10	0.4	1.3		289	251	1019	341	20	0.8	0.7
0	0	<0.1	0.1	3.3	<0.1	5	0.2	0	<0.1	10	73	776	210	2	0.5	0.2
12	484	0.1	0.1	1.3	<0.1	19	<0.1	0	0.1	14	41	639	53	10	1.6	0.4
7	422	<0.1	<0.1	1.1	<0.1	0	0.2	0.2	0.1	22	22	805	99	0	0.7	0.3
10	1851	<0.1	0.1	1.2	<0.1	5	0.1	1	0.4	17	41	945	154	7	0.9	0.4
34	525	<0.1	0.1	1.8	<0.1	2	0.2	0	0.6	14	60	860	116	5	0.6	0.4
44	863	0.1	0.3	0.9	0.3	59	0	4.4	1.3	120	394	1336	934	115	8.8	5.1
12	1408	0.1	0.1	1	0.1	10	0.4	3.8	1.3	45	138	970	490	25	2	1.9
0	5878	0.1	0.1	1.2	0.2	17	0	6	1.3	55	72	862	396	7	1.6	3.1
17	315	0.2	0.4	2	0.2	22	12	5.2	0.5	174	429	895	444	30	3	1.1
14	3216	0.1	0.1	1.8	0.3	10	7.9	12.2	1.6	67	84	1001	384	19	2.6	1.7
0	0	<0.1	<0.1	0.7	<0.1	2	0	1		10	31	636	154	0	0.5	0.4
10	278	0.1	0.3	0.6	<0.1	7	0.6	0.2	1	164	154	823	268	20	1.4	0.8
0	34	0.1	0.1	0.5	0	2	0	0	1	17	32	776	73	5	1.3	0.2
6	101							0		21		891			0.7	
27	714	0.1	0.3	0.9	0.1	7	0.5	1.2		181	151	1047	273	17	0.7	0.7
10	561	<0.1	0.1	0.8	<0.1	2	0.1	0.2		34	37	986	88	2	0.6	0.6
22	444	0.1	0.2	0.6	0.1	10	0.5	1.2		166	161	1061	322	17	0.5	0.7
0	298	<0.1	<0.1	0.9	0.1	20	0	7.1	0.4	24	37	739	224	7	1	0.2
7	360	0.2	0.1	1.4	0.2	50	0.3	4.2		42	184	1319	357	22	2.7	0.7
40	200							0		40		1090			0.7	
2	2338	0.1	<0.1	0.9	0.1	36	0	1.2		34	55	911	313	7	0.9	0.7
32	225	0.1	0.2	0.3	0.1	10	2.6	4.4		167	162	1041	235	20	1.1	10.3
8	445	0.1	0.1	1.5	0.1	3	0.3	1.5		23	213	1007	400	48	2.3	1.3
5	721	0.1	0.1	1.1	0.1	15	0	5.9		40	59	1047	417	10	0.8	0.6
10	712	0.1	0.3	1.4	0.2	5	0.7	15.6	0.4	171	154	719	454	30	1.4	0.9
0	468	<0.1	0.1	1.2	0.1	0	0	15.4	0.4	20	34	664	273	17	1.3	0.3
0	1600							30		150		850	1010		7.2	

ESHA, EatRight Analysis CD-ROM; **AMT**, amount; **WT**, weight; **CAL**, calories; **KILO**, KiloJoule; **WTR**, water; **PROT**, protein; **CARB**, carbohydrate; **FIBR**, fiber; **FAT**, fat; **SATF**, saturated fat; **MONO**, monounsaturated fat; **POLY**, polyunsaturated fat; **CHOL**, cholesterol;

ESHA CODE	FOOD DESCRIPTION	AMT	UNIT	WT (g)	CAL (kcal)	KILO (kJ)	WTR (g)	PROT (g)	CARB (g)	FIBR (g)	FAT (g)	SATF (g)	MONO (g)	POLY (g)
PREPARED FOODS														
50013	Vegetarian Vege Soup+Water	1	cup	241	67	280	223	2	12	1	2	0.3	0.8	0.7
50027	Vichyssoise Soup	1	cup	248	149	623	215	6	17	<1	6	3.8	1.7	0.6
50181	Wonton Soup	1	cup	241	182	761	203	14	14	1	7	2.3	3	1
50999	Zesty Gumbo Soup-Cnd	1	cup	244	100	418	527	6	15	3	2	1		
DRY/PREPARED FROM DRY DISHES														
Dry/Prepared from Dry Dishes – Main														
90738	Cheeseburger Macaroni-DryMix	1	svg	42.53	168	703	3	5	27		4	1.2		
38613	Herb & Butter Rice-Dry Mix	1	oz	28.35	97	406		2	21	<1	1	0.2		
38619	Red Beans & Rice-Dry Mix	1	oz	28.35	97	406		3	21	2	1	0		
57534	Stroganoff-Prep f/Dry	1	cup	124	448	1874		14	90	3	3	0		
Dry/Prepared from Dry Dishes – Vegetarian Main														
52166	Fried Rice-Dry	1	svg	56.7	190	795		4	43	1	<1	0		
57323	Pasta&Sc-CreamBrocc (Lipton)	0.66	cup	69	270	1130		8	47	1	5	3.5		
5276	Potatoes-Au Gratin from Mix	1	svg	137	127	531	108	3	18	1	6	3.5	1.6	0.2
5464	Potatoes-Mashed-Flakes-Prep	0.5	cup	105	102	427	85	2	11	1	5	3.4	1.4	0.2
5271	Potatoes-Scalloped from Mix	1	svg	137	127	531	108	3	17	2	6	3.6	1.7	0.3
57331	Rice Pilaf-Dry Mix	0.5	cup	61	220	920		6	46	1	1	0		
57333	Spanish Rice-Dry Mix	0.5	cup	67	240	1004		6	51	2	1	0		
Dry/Prepared from Dry Soups, Stews, & Chilis														
50033	Beef Broth-Cube + Water	1	cup	241	7	29	238	1	1	0	<1	0.1	0.1	<0.1
50035	Chicken Broth-Cube + Water	1	cup	243	12	50	237	1	2	0	<1	0.1	0.1	0.1
50193	Chicken Broth-Dry Cube	1	ea	4.8	10	42	<1	1	1	0	<1	0.1	0.1	0.1
50037	Chicken Noodle Soup-Dry+Water	1	cup	252.3	58	243	238	2	9	<1	1	0.3	0.5	0.4
50038	ChickenVegSoup-dry+water	1	cup	250.7	50	209	237	3	8		1	0.2	0.3	0.2
50040	Onion Soup-Dry Mix+Water	1	cup	246	30	126	236	1	7	1	<1	<0.1	<0.1	<0.1
FROZEN/REFRIGERATED MEALS & DISHES														
Frozen/Refrigerated Meals – Lunch/Dinners														
11118	BeefPotRoast Din-HealthyChoice	1	ea	312	300	1255		20	41	8	6	2		
16194	Chicken Enchilada w/Rice	1	svg	255	268	1121	191	11	47	3	4	1.6	1.2	1
15967	Chicken Parmesan-LeanCuisine	1	svg	308	310	1297	729	21	39	5	8	2	2	3
82034	ChickenEnchiladaDin-HlthyChce	1	svg	320	352	1473	239	12	58	5	8	3.3	2.3	2.1
70379	Fish & Chips-Batter Fried	1	svg	284	490	2050		19	59	5	20	4		
70954	Herb Bkd Fish Dinner-Frzn	1	ea	309	340	1423		16	54	5	7	1.5		
18825	Lemon Pepper Fish-HealthyChc	1	ea	303	320	1339		14	50	5	7	2		
11093	Meatloaf-LeanCuisine	1	svg	265.8	260	1088		21	25	3	8	3	2.5	2.5
70767	MexicanStyleDinner-HungryMan	1	ea	567	690	2887	2382	26	87	13	27	9		
11063	Salisbury Steak Dinner-Swansons	1	ea	312	340	1423		16	35	6	15	6		
56738	Stuffed Cabbage-LeanCuisine	1	svg	269	196	820	224	11	24	4	6	1.7	3	0.9
Frozen/Refrigerated Dishes														
57544	BBQ Beef Hot Pocket-Frzn	1	ea	128	312	1305		11	42	1	10	3.4	3.4	3.4
70688	Beef Chow Mein-Frzn	1	cup	247	105	439		9	15	3	2	0.8		
16234	Beef Pot Pie-Banquet	1	ea	198.5	400	1674		9	38	1	23	11		
70893	Beef Pot Pie-Frzn	1	ea	198	436	1824	115	14	44	2	23	8.2	10.5	2.9
70734	Beef Pot Pie-Swansons	1	ea	198	415	1736	239	11	41	2	23	9		
11050	Beef Stroganoff-Frzn	1	svg	276.4	380	1590	552	22	34	2	17	5		
18139	Chicken & Dumplings	1	svg	340.2	370	1548	884	23	41	5	13	3.5		

< = Trace amount present   Blank = Not available

V, vitamin; **THI**, thiamin; **RIB**, riboflavin; **NIA**, niacin; **FOL**, folate; **CALC**, calcium; **PHOS**, phosphorus; **SOD**, sodium; **POT**, potassium; **MAG**, magnesium

CHOL (mg)	V-A (IU)	THI (mg)	RIB (mg)	NIA (mg)	V-B6 (mg)	FOL (μg)	V-B12 (μg)	V-C (mg)	V-E (mg)	CALC (mg)	PHOS (mg)	SOD (mg)	POT (mg)	MAG (mg)	IRON (mg)	ZINC (mg)
0	3425	0.1	<0.1	0.9	0.1	10	0	1.4	1.4	24	34	815	207	7	1.1	0.5
22	444	0.1	0.2	0.6	0.1	10	0.5	1.2		166	161	1061	322	17	0.5	0.7
53	896	0.4	0.3	4.6	0.2	19	0.4	3.4	0.4	31	153	543	316	21	1.8	1.1
10	200							3.6		40		480			0.7	
4												863				
0	40	0.1	<0.1	0.8		40		0.5		8		433			0.7	
0	81	0.1	<0.1	0.6		57		6.1		24		450			0.7	
0	0	0.5	0.3	5.5		138		0		69		2687	413		2.5	
0										35		560			1.8	
10	0	0.5	0.2	4		120		0		40		740	0		1.8	
21	292	<0.1	0.1	1.3	0.1	10	0	4.2		114	130	601	300	21	0.4	0.3
15	181	0.1	0.1	0.8	0.1	7	0.1	10.2	0.1	34	41	172	172	12	0.2	0.2
15	203	<0.1	0.1	1.4	0.1	14	0	4.5		49	77	467	278	19	0.5	0.3
0	0	0.4	0.1	4		100		0		20		880	0		1.8	
0	200	0.4	0.1	4		100		4.8		20		880	0		2.7	
0	0	<0.1	<0.1	0.1	<0.1	0	<0.1	0	<0.1	10	7	627	14	5	<0.1	<0.1
0	17	<0.1	<0.1	0.3	0	2	<0.1	0		12	12	792	24	2	0.1	<0.1
1	<1	<0.1	<0.1	0.2	<0.1	2	<0.1	<1	<0.1	9	9	1152	18	3	0.1	<0.1
10	28	0.2	0.1	1.1	<0.1	18	0.1	0	0.1	5	30	578	33	8	0.5	0.2
3	15	0.1	<0.1	0.7	0.1	3	0.1	1.3		15	33	807	68	23	0.6	0.2
0	2	<0.1	<0.1	0.2	0.1	0	0	0.2	<0.1	22	22	851	76	10	0.1	0.1
40	1250							18		20		600			1.8	
20	258	0.2	0.2	1.7				2.8		158		507	349		1	
35	499							18		150		659	819			
35	406									58		573			1	
45	100							2.4		60		1030			1.4	
35	3000							0		40		480			0.7	
30	500							30		20		480			1.1	
35	0							0		80		610	880			
35	1500							36		300		2170			3.6	
30	5000							6		80		920			2.7	
13	113	0.2	0.1	2.6				0.5		89		710	732		1.5	
25	101	0.3	0.2	3		60	0.6			101	101	806			2.7	
12	58							11.1		30		756			0.6	
30	750							0		20		1000			1.1	
42		0.4	0.2	3.2	0.3	36	0.6	0.6	0.5	28	133	723	228	26	2.5	2.2
25	750							0		20		740			1.8	
70	200							0		80		990			2.7	
60	4500							2.4		80		1120			1.4	

ESHA, EatRight Analysis CD-ROM; **AMT**, amount; **WT**, weight; **CAL**, calories; **KILO**, KiloJoule; **WTR**, water; **PROT**, protein; **CARB**, carbohydrate; **FIBR**, fiber; **FAT**, fat; **SATF**, saturated fat; **MONO**, monounsaturated fat; **POLY**, polyunsaturated fat; **CHOL**, cholesterol;

ESHA CODE	FOOD DESCRIPTION	AMT	UNIT	WT (g)	CAL (kcal)	KILO (kJ)	WTR (g)	PROT (g)	CARB (g)	FIBR (g)	FAT (g)	SATF (g)	MONO (g)	POLY (g)
FROZEN/REFRIGERATED MEALS & DISHES (CONTINUED)														
4104	Chicken & Noodles- Escalloped	1	svg	226.8	330	1381	372	14	28	2	18	4		
15964	Chicken Chow Mein+Rice-LnCuis	1	svg	255	260	1088	495	14	41	3	4	1	1.5	1.5
70692	Chicken Chow Mein-Frzn	1	svg	250	91	381		5	11	2	4	0.9		
82030	Chicken Enchilada Suiza	1	svg	284	280	1172		14	43	5	6	3		
15978	Chicken Enchilada Suiza	1	svg	255	311	1301	185	14	45	3	8	3.6	2.3	1.3
17880	Chicken Oriental w/Rice	1	svg	255	230	962		12	39	2	2	0.5	0.5	1
16200	Chicken Parmigiana-Frzn	1	svg	340.2	410	1715	858	23	47	4	14	3.5		
81223	Chicken Patty-Ckd f/Frzn	1	ea	90	210	879		13	10	0	13	3		
83170	Chicken Teriyaki w/Vegetables	1	svg	212	150	628		17	15	4	2	0.5		
18229	Chicken Tuscan w/linguine	1	svg	340.2	280	1172	933	22	34	5	6	2	2	1.5
16260	ChickenBroc Alfredo-HealthyChce	1	svg	326	300	1255		25	34	2	7	3		
16252	ChickenFettucAlfred-HealthyChce	1	svg	241	280	1172		25	30	4	7	2.5		
92888	ChickTomaSpinach Pizza-DiGiorno	1	pce	133	260	1088		16	33	2	8	3.5		
83000	Egg Roll-Chicken-ChunKing	6	pce	205.5	210	879		6	25	2	9	2.5		
83009	Egg Roll-Pork	1	ea	170.1	220	920		5	24	2	11	2.5		
56704	Egg Roll-Pork&Shrimp-ChunKing	6	pce	205.5	210	879		6	27	2	9	2.5		
83001	Egg Roll-Shrimp-ChunKing	6	pce	205.5	190	795		5	28	2	6	1.5		
70259	Fish Fillet-Battered-Frzn	1	ea	75	180	753	31	8	12	0	11			
17002	Fish Sticks	1	ea	28	70	293	15	3	6	<1	4	0.8	1.2	1.6
17002	Fish Sticks-Frozen-Heated	1	ea	28	70	293	15	3	6	<1	4	0.8	1.2	1.6
56736	FrBread Deluxe Pizza-LnCuisine	1	ea	174	341	1427		16	46	4	10	3.5	2.5	1.5
56735	FrBread PepperoniPizza-LnCuisn	1	ea	149	330	1381		17	46	4	9	2.5	2.5	3
5791	French Fries-Cottage Cut-Frzn	10	pce	65	99	414	43	2	16	2	4	1.8	1.5	0.3
5139	French Fries-Frozen-Heated	10	pce	50	166	695	18	2	20	2	9	3	5.7	0.7
17040	Fried Fish Cakes-Frzn-Heated	1	ea	85	231	967	44	8	15		15	6	3.4	3.4
70697	Fried Rice	1	svg	139	236	987		5	53	2	1	0.2		
42368	Garlic Bread-Frozen PPF	1	pce	47	160	669	7	5	20	1	8	1.9		
56740	Lasagna w/Meat Sauce-LnCuisne	1	svg	298	320	1339		20	43	4	7	3.5	2	1
81080	Manicotti-3 Cheese HealthyChce	1	svg	312	300	1255		15	40	5	9	3		
14072	Meatloaf-Beef+Pork	3	oz	85.05	169	707	55	15	5	<1	9	3.3	4.1	0.6
70696	Oriental Beef Pepper-Frzn	1	cup	246	104	435		10	12	4	2	0.6		
56997	Pizza Bagel-Cheese Sausage Pepperoni	4	ea	88	210	879	36	8	30	2	7	3		
70693	Pork Chow Mein-Frzn	1	svg	250	89	372		6	11	3	3	1.2		
70916	Pot Pie-Chicken	1	ea	198	380	1590	127	11	36	3	21	8.3	9.2	3.7
70700	Shrimp Chow Mein-Frzn	1	svg	141.75	35	146		2	6	2	1	0		
56732	Spaghetti w/Meatballs-LnCuisine	1	svg	269	250	1046	210	18	33	4	5	2	1.9	0.8
56076	Spinach Souffle	1	cup	136	234	979	96	11	8	1	18	8.3	4.1	0.8
4110	Stuffed Bell Pepper-Frzn	1	svg	226.8	210	879	418	11	20	3	9	3		
977	Teriyaki Beef Dish+Rice-Frzn	1	svg	340.2	317	1326		17	50	6	5	2		
17927	Thai Peanut Chicken+Noodles	1	svg	255	260	1088		14	43	2	4	0.5	1.5	1
57140	Three Cheese Tortellini-DiGiorno	1	svg	81	250	1046	20	11	37	2	7	3.5		
18820	Tuna Noodle Casserole	1	svg	283.5	375	1569	696	18	37	2	17	5		
16928	Turkey Pot Pie-Banquet	1	ea	198	370	1548	252	10	38	3	20	8		
70698	Vegetable Chop Suey-Frzn	1	cup	85	11	46		1	2	1	<1	0		

< = Trace amount present   Blank = Not available

V, vitamin; **THI**, thiamin; **RIB**, riboflavin; **NIA**, niacin; **FOL**, folate; **CALC**, calcium; **PHOS**, phosphorus; **SOD**, sodium; **POT**, potassium; **MAG**, magnesium

CHOL (mg)	V-A (IU)	THI (mg)	RIB (mg)	NIA (mg)	V-B6 (mg)	FOL (μg)	V-B12 (μg)	V-C (mg)	V-E (mg)	CALC (mg)	PHOS (mg)	SOD (mg)	POT (mg)	MAG (mg)	IRON (mg)	ZINC (mg)
35	400							0		100		910			0.7	
25	2249							3.6		60		550	380			
9	25							4.1		43		865			0.7	
40	300							2.4		150		440			1.1	
33	469							3.8		189		727			0.8	
35	1000							1.2		40		640			0.4	
40	500							0		150		900			1.8	
45	0							0		0		400			0.7	
25	1750							12		20		990			0.4	
40	750							4.8		60		780	640			
50	100							12		100		530			1.8	
35	0							2.4		100		600			1.1	
25	500							1.2		200		550			1.4	
15	100	0.2	0.1	1.4				0		20	174	650	233		1.1	
10	300							0		20		390			1.1	
15	100	0.4	0.2	1.4				0		20	136	540	252		1.1	
10	500	0.2	0.1	0.8				0		20	97	730	155		1.1	
20											200		190			
9	31	<0.1	<0.1	0.4	<0.1	9	0.4	0	0.3	7	51	118	60	8	0.3	0.1
9	31	<0.1	<0.1	0.4	<0.1	9	0.4	0	0.3	7	51	118	60	8	0.3	0.1
20	401							12		150		762	331			
15	300							6		200		691	290			
0	0	0.1	<0.1	1.2	0.1	10	0	5.5		5	30	21	220	10	0.7	0.2
0	0	<0.1	<0.1	1.3	0.1	11	0	3.1		6	48	306	270	12	0.8	0.2
22		<0.1	0.1	1.4	<0.1	11	0.9	0	0.5	9	143		298	15	0.3	0.3
0	0							0		2		1024			4.6	
6	188							3.4		38		291			1	
30	501							3.6		200		591	711			
35	750							0		250		550			1.8	
69	55	0.1	0.2	3.2	0.1	9	1.1	0.6	0.1	35	138	101	250	18	1.4	2.5
12	435							7.3		24		969			0.5	
14	200							0		80		410	280		0.7	
10	42							4.2		3		1242			8.1	
30	1370									30		842			1	
18	52							13.2		2		547			2.4	
24	256	0.2	0.2	4.3				3		100		568	511		2.2	
160	3932	0.1	0.4	0.7	0.1	99	0.5	9.9	1.3	224	189	770	314	41	1.6	1.2
20	100							6		60		1180			1.4	
26	3064							2.5		41		1420			1.5	
25	2500							1.2		40		570			0.7	
35	0							0		0		300			0	
58	167							1		167		825			0.9	
45	750							0		40		850			1.1	
0	0							3.2		15		439			0.1	

ESHA, EatRight Analysis CD-ROM; **AMT**, amount; **WT**, weight; **CAL**, calories; **KILO**, KiloJoule; **WTR**, water; **PROT**, protein; **CARB**, carbohydrate; **FIBR**, fiber; **FAT**, fat; **SATF**, saturated fat; **MONO**, monounsaturated fat; **POLY**, polyunsaturated fat; **CHOL**, cholesterol;

ESHA CODE	FOOD DESCRIPTION	AMT	UNIT	WT (g)	CAL (kcal)	KILO (kJ)	WTR (g)	PROT (g)	CARB (g)	FIBR (g)	FAT (g)	SATF (g)	MONO (g)	POLY (g)
FROZEN/REFRIGERATED MEALS & DISHES (CONTINUED)														
Frozen/Refrigerated Meals/Dishes – Vegetarian														
56737	Cheese Cannelloni-LeanCuisine	1	svg	258.7	240	1004		17	30	3	6	3	1.5	1
56901	Cheese Ravioli-LeanCuisine	1	svg	241	240	1004		11	38	3	6	3.5	1	0.5
56733	FrBread Cheese Pizza-LnCuisine	1	ea	145	290	1213		14	45	4	6	2.6	1.3	0.9
7758	Lentil Rice Loaf	1	pce	90	160	669		8	16	4	7	1	1.5	4.5
66047	Macaroni & Cheese-HealthyChce	1	svg	255	240	1004		12	36	3	5	2.5		
7669	Nine Bean Loaf	1	ea	91	150	628		8	15	4	7	1.5	2	3.5
5190	Onion Rings-Frozen-Heated	10	ea	71	289	1209	20	4	27	1	19	6.1	7.7	3.6
5265	Potato Puffs-Heated f/Frzn	1	cup	128	243	1017	76	3	36	3	11	2.3	7.7	0.6
5269	Potatoes-O'brien-Frozen-Cooked	0.5	cup	97	198	828	60	2	21	2	13	3.2	5.6	3.4
56868	Ravioli-Cheese+Tomato Sauce	1	svg	301.2	336	1406	774	17	42	4	12	7.1		
5154	Succotash-Frozen-Boiled	0.5	cup	85	79	331	63	4	17	3	1	0.1	0.1	0.4
PREPARED HOMEMADE/GENERIC DISHES														
Dishes – Breakfast														
19516	Egg-Scrambled+Milk+Marg	1	ea	61	102	427	45	7	1	0	7	2.2	2.9	1.3
19543	Omelette-1Egg+Mushroom	1	ea	69	88	368	54	6	2	<1	6	1.8	2.4	1
19534	Omelette-Plain (1 Lrg Egg)	1	ea	61	96	402	46	6	<1	0	7	2	3	1.4
Dishes – Main & Side														
15907	Almond Chicken	1	cup	242	280	1172	186	22	16	3	15	1.9	6.1	5.6
7037	Baked Beans-Homemade	1	cup	253	392	1640	165	14	55	14	13	4.9	5.4	1.9
10081	Beef Cube Steak-FlourFried	1	ea	165	460	1925	79	44	18	1	22	6.2	8.2	5.8
15930	Cashew Chicken	1	cup	162	431	1803	88	29	11	2	31	5.2	13.9	9.7
15003	Chicken Breast+Skin-FlourFried	1	ea	98	218	912	55	31	2	<1	9	2.4	3.4	1.9
15915	Chicken Teriyaki-Breast	1	ea	128	178	745	86	27	7	<1	4	0.9	1.1	0.9
15916	Chicken Teriyaki-Drumstick	1	ea	68	94	393	45	14	4	<1	2	0.5	0.6	0.5
15009	Chicken Thigh+Skin-FlourFried	1	ea	62	162	678	34	17	2	<1	9	2.5	3.6	2.1
15029	Chicken Wing-Flour Fried	1	ea	32	103	431	16	8	1	<1	7	1.9	2.8	1.6
56112	Chiles Rellenos	1	ea	143	365	1527	84	17	8	1	30	12.5	9	6.7
57618	Chow Mein, pork, w/ndles	1	cup	220	448	1874	136	22	31	4	27	4.8	7.7	12.8
19080	Clams-Breaded-Fried-Sml	3	oz	85.05	172	720	52	12	9	0	9	2.3	3.9	2.4
18805	Codfish Ball	1	ea	63	125	523	39	9	8	1	7	1.4	2.8	1.9
18806	Codfish Cake	1	ea	120	237	992	75	16	15	1	13	2.7	5.3	3.7
19420	Crab Cakes-Blue Crab	1	ea	60	93	389	43	12	<1	0	5	0.9	1.7	1.4
56132	Egg Foo Yung Patty	1	ea	86	113	473	67	6	3	1	8	2	3.4	2.1
56119	Flauta-Beef	1	ea	113	354	1481	57	14	13	2	28	4.8	11.8	9.4
56120	Flauta-Chicken	1	ea	113	330	1381	62	13	12	2	26	4.2	10.7	9.3
17103	Gefiltefish-Sweet-Commercial	1	pce	42	35	146	34	4	3	0	1	0.2	0.3	0.1
56242	Gumbo w/Rice	1	cup	244	193	808	203	14	17	2	8	1.6	2.6	2.7
56150	Hash-Roast Beef	1	cup	190	312	1305	131	21	21	2	16	4.9	5.7	3.3
56239	Jambalaya-Shrimp	1	cup	243	310	1297	176	27	28	1	9	1.8	3.8	2.8
56296	Knish-Meat	1	ea	50	175	732	19	7	13	1	11	2.6	4.9	2.3
56294	Knish-Potato	1	ea	61	215	900	22	5	21	1	12	2.6	5.8	3.3
13900	Lamb Curry	1	cup	236	256	1071	189	28	3	1	14	3.9	4.9	3.4
56108	Lasagna w/Meat-Recipe	1	pce	245	392	1640	164	23	40		16	8	5.2	0.8
18800	Lobster Newburg	1	cup	244	611	2556	150	30	11	<1	50	29.6	14.7	2.3
56250	Moo Goo Gai Pan	1	cup	216	272	1138	168	15	12	3	19	3.8	6.7	7

< = Trace amount present Blank = Not available

V, vitamin; **THI**, thiamin; **RIB**, riboflavin; **NIA**, niacin; **FOL**, folate; **CALC**, calcium; **PHOS**, phosphorus; **SOD**, sodium; **POT**, potassium; **MAG**, magnesium

CHOL (mg)	V-A (IU)	THI (mg)	RIB (mg)	NIA (mg)	V-B6 (mg)	FOL (μg)	V-B12 (μg)	V-C (mg)	V-E (mg)	CALC (mg)	PHOS (mg)	SOD (mg)	POT (mg)	MAG (mg)	IRON (mg)	ZINC (mg)
20	400							2.4		250		690	480			
40	400							1.2		150		600	540			
13	341							4.1		298		580	264			
0	500							0		20		350	150		1.1	
20	0							0		200		600			1.1	
5	500							1.2		40		320	200		0.7	
0	160	0.2	0.1	2.6	0.1	47	0	1		22	58	266	92	13	1.2	0.3
0	6	0.2	<0.1	1.9	0.2	18	0	8.1	0.3	18	132	614	399	22	0.8	0.4
0	182	0.1	0.1	1.4	0.4	12	0	10.1		19	90	42	459	33	0.9	0.5
71	885							8		266		885			1.6	
0	165	0.1	0.1	1.1	0.1	28	0	5	0.2	13	60	38	225	20	0.8	0.4
215	329	<0.1	0.3	<0.1	0.1	18	0.5	0.1	0.7	43	104	171	84	7	0.7	0.6
177	361	<0.1	0.2	0.3	0.1	17	0.4	0.1	0.7	43	100	147	97	9	0.7	0.6
217	349	<0.1	0.2	<0.1	0.1	24	0.7	0	0.7	28	98	98	69	6	0.9	0.6
40	351	0.1	0.2	9.5	0.4	26	0.3	6.9	3.8	69	252	526	549	60	2	1.6
13	0	0.3	0.1	1	0.2	121	0	2.8		154	276	1068	906	109	5	1.8
125	16	0.3	0.5	7	0.7	17	4.7	0.1	1.7	80	380	316	653	54	6.4	8.4
64	553	0.2	0.1	13.2	0.6	43	0.3	7.5	3.9	49	263	907	428	63	2	1.5
87	49	0.1	0.1	13.5	0.6	6	0.3	0		16	228	74	254	29	1.2	1.1
82	64	0.1	0.2	8.8	0.5	12	0.3	3.2	0.4	27	199	1683	309	35	1.7	2
44	34	<0.1	0.1	4.7	0.2	6	0.2	1.7	0.2	14	105	894	164	19	0.9	1
60	61	0.1	0.2	4.3	0.2	7	0.2	0		9	116	55	147	16	0.9	1.6
26	40	<0.1	<0.1	2.1	0.1	2	0.1	0		5	48	25	57	6	0.4	0.6
168	1348	0.1	0.4	0.9	0.3	29	0.5	112.9	4.7	1	307	522	386	36	1.7	2.1
48	183	0.8	0.4	6.2	0.4	42	0.4	20.2	2.7	45	249	848	489	53	3.3	2.6
52	257	0.1	0.2	1.8	0.1	31	34.2	8.5		54	160	310	277	12	11.8	1.2
35	44	0.1	0.1	1.3	0.2	7	0.3	2.4	0.9	18	108	175	275	20	0.4	0.3
67	84	0.1	0.1	2.5	0.3	13	0.6	4.5	1.6	34	206	334	523	38	0.8	0.7
90	151	0.1	<0.1	1.7	0.1	32	3.6	1.7		63	128	198	194	20	0.6	2.5
185	307	<0.1	0.3	0.4	0.1	30	0.4	4.8	1.2	31	93	317	117	12	1	0.7
37	212	0.1	0.1	1.9	0.2	10	1.2	19.3	4.7	51	179	68	313	28	1.9	3.4
35	217	0.1	0.1	3.1	0.2	8	0.1	17.8	4.4	50	140	71	269	27	1	1.1
13	37	<0.1	<0.1	0.4	<0.1	1	0.4	0.3		10	31	220	38	4	1	0.3
40	533	0.2	0.2	4.5	0.2	46	2.4	13.5	1.4	71	152	542	446	40	2.6	15.2
57	<1	0.2	0.2	3.7	0.5	16	1.8	7.1	1.2	19	204	470	587	36	2.5	5
181	823	0.3	0.1	4.8	0.2	12	1.2	16.9	2.3	104	300	370	439	64	4.4	1.7
52	379	0.1	0.2	1.5	<0.1	8	0.3	0.4	1.2	12	61	107	88	8	1.2	1
59	548	0.2	0.2	1.5	0.1	10	0.1	0.9	1.7	16	60	140	96	10	1.3	0.4
89	18	0.1	0.3	8.1	0.2	28	2.9	1.3	1.2	36	284	323	496	40	3	6.6
58	1005	0.2	0.3	4.2	0.2	20	1	14.5	1.2	270	299	391	460	50	3.1	3.3
369	1886	0.1	0.4	1.6	0.2	32	4	0.8	2	241	398	647	607	55	1.2	4.1
35	1386	0.2	0.3	4.4	0.3	42	0.3	34.3	3.7	131	199	304	488	34	1.7	1.6

ESHA, EatRight Analysis CD-ROM; **AMT**, amount; **WT**, weight; **CAL**, calories; **KILO**, KiloJoule; **WTR**, water; **PROT**, protein; **CARB**, carbohydrate; **FIBR**, fiber; **FAT**, fat; **SATF**, saturated fat; **MONO**, monounsaturated fat; **POLY**, polyunsaturated fat; **CHOL**, cholesterol;

ESHA CODE	FOOD DESCRIPTION	AMT	UNIT	WT (g)	CAL (kcal)	KILO (kJ)	WTR (g)	PROT (g)	CARB (g)	FIBR (g)	FAT (g)	SATF (g)	MONO (g)	POLY (g)
PREPARED HOMEMADE/GENERIC DISHES (CONTINUED)														
56080	Moussaka-Lamb/Eggplant	1	cup	250	238	996	937	17	13	4	13	4.6		
19403	Oysters Rockefeller	1	cup	224	301	1259	165	16	21	3	17	7.7	5.7	2.4
19009	Oysters-BreadFried-East	6	ea	88	173	724	57	8	10	0	11	2.8	4.1	2.9
56234	Pork Chop Suey+Noodles	1	cup	220	448	1874	136	22	31	4	27	4.8	7.7	12.8
12082	Pork Chop-Breaded-Baked	1	ea	80	184	770	44	21	5	<1	8	2.9	3.7	0.9
56292	Pork Dumpling-Fried	1	ea	100	341	1427	41	13	25	1	21	4.8	9.1	5.7
56288	Pork Egg Foo Yung-Patty	1	ea	86	124	519	65	8	4	1	8	2.1	3	2.3
56098	Quiche Lorraine-1/8 Pie	1	pce	176	526	2201	93	15	25	1	41	18.9	14.3	5.2
56303	Ravioli-Meat w/Tomato Sauce	2	ea	70	110	460	48	6	10	1	5	1.7	2.1	0.5
18807	Salmon Croquette	1	ea	63	137	573	38	9	7	1	8	1.9	3.4	2.4
56239	Shrimp Jambalaya w/Rice	1	cup	243	310	1297	176	27	28	1	9	1.8	3.8	2.8
56236	Stuffed Grape Leaves-Lamb	1	ea	21	56	234	12	2	2	1	4	1.1	2.5	0.5
56244	Sukiyaki	1	cup	162	172	720	126	19	7	1	8	2.9	3.1	0.7
91818	Sushi-California Roll	1	ea	198	292	1222		8	49	3	3	1		
91912	Sushi-Crab Salad Roll	1	ea	198	306	1280		8	49	3	5	1		
91816	Sushi-Tuna Roll	6	pce	105	150	628		8	30	1	0	0	0	0
15921	SweetSour Chicken Breast	1	ea	131	118	494	103	8	15	1	3	0.5	0.9	1.4
56061	Taco-Chicken	1	ea	77.3	175	732	34	15	9	1	9	2.8		
56062	Tostada-Bean+Chicken	1	ea	156.2	242	1013	168	19	16	3	11	4.5		
11902	Veal Scallopini	1	pce	96	238	996	57	18	1	<1	17	4.8	7.4	3.2
11583	Veal Steak-Breaded-Fried	3	oz	85.05	202	845	44	23	8	<1	8	2.6	2.9	1.3
Salads														
56005	Potato Salad+Mayo + Eggs	1	cup	250	358	1498	190	7	28	3	20	3.6	6.2	9.3
5537	Spinach Salad-No Dressing	1	cup	74	108	452	51	5	11	2	5	1.4	2.2	0.7
56917	Tabouli Salad	1	cup	160	589	2464	15	17	122	13	4	0.8	0.6	2.1
56006	Waldorf salad	1	cup	137	411	1720	113	4	12	3	41	4.3		
Sandwiches														
56009	BLT Sandwich	1	ea	123.8	318	1331	86	10	29	2	18	4.1		
56281	Bologna Sandwich	1	ea	83	256	1071	34	7	26	1	13	4.1	6.3	2.1
13093	Chicken Hotdog on Bun	1	ea	85	235	983	38	9	24	1	11	3	5	2.2
56020	Corned Beef+Swiss on Rye	1	ea	156	427	1787	111	28	22	6	26	9.5		
56013	Grilled Cheese Sandwich	1	ea	119	399	1669	54	17	30	1	23	11.9		
56033	Ham & Swiss on Rye Sandwich	1	ea	149.5	385	1611	118	22	30	4	19	6.5		
56066	Ham Salad Sandwich on Wheat	1	ea	130.6	357	1494	75	11	33	2	20	4.7		
56031	Ham Sandwich on Wheat	1	ea	156.3	356	1490	125	25	26	2	17	3.6		
56267	Pastrami Sandwich	1	ea	134	331	1385	71	14	27	2	18	6.2	8.7	1
56038	Patty Melt Sandwich on Rye	1	ea	181.9	561	2347	143	37	22	6	37	12.7		
56040	PeanutButter&Jelly on White	1	ea	101	348	1456	29	11	47	3	14	2.7		
56046	Roast Beef Sandwich on Wheat	1	ea	155.8	397	1661	109	30	30	2	17	3.2		
56048	Tuna Salad Sandwich	1	ea	121.8	326	1364	68	13	35	1	14	1.9		
56053	Turkey Sandwich-Whole Wheat	1	ea	168.8	360	1506	142	27	29	4	16	2.3		
56103	TurkeyHam Sandwich on Rye	1	ea	149.5	279	1167	131	21	20	6	13	2.5		
56059	TurkeyHam+Cheese on Wheat	1	ea	156.3	396	1657	122	23	28		22	8.2		
Soups, Stews, & Chilis														
50190	Egg Drop Soup	1	cup	244	73	305	229	8	1	0	4	1.1	1.5	0.6
50211	Fish Chowder	1	cup	244	194	812	201	24	12	1	5	2.4	1.9	0.6

< = Trace amount present   Blank = Not available

V, vitamin; **THI**, thiamin; **RIB**, riboflavin; **NIA**, niacin; **FOL**, folate; **CALC**, calcium; **PHOS**, phosphorus; **SOD**, sodium; **POT**, potassium; **MAG**, magnesium

CHOL (mg)	V-A (IU)	THI (mg)	RIB (mg)	NIA (mg)	V-B6 (mg)	FOL (μg)	V-B12 (μg)	V-C (mg)	V-E (mg)	CALC (mg)	PHOS (mg)	SOD (mg)	POT (mg)	MAG (mg)	IRON (mg)	ZINC (mg)
97	543	0.2	0.3	4.1	0.2	46	1.5	5.9	1	75	185	460	565	40	1.7	2.6
87	7430	0.4	0.4	4	0.3	122	21	26.8	2.2	195	254	708	583	115	10.3	97.9
71	266	0.1	0.2	1.5	0.1	27	13.8	3.3		55	140	367	215	51	6.1	76.7
48	183	0.8	0.4	6.2	0.4	42	0.4	20.2	2.7	45	249	848	489	53	3.3	2.6
57	5	0.7	0.3	3.9	0.4	5	0.5	0.5	0.4	17	197	333	331	22	0.8	1.8
27	106	0.5	0.3	3.6	0.2	9	0.3	0.3	2.3	33	131	86	198	18	1.8	1.1
167	299	0.1	0.2	0.8	0.1	22	0.4	3.2	1.1	27	105	131	157	12	0.8	0.9
221	962	0.3	0.5	2	0.1	19	0.6	0.6	2	231	261	221	239	24	1.9	1.5
48	327	0.1	0.1	1.7	0.1	8	0.5	2	0.7	20	62	50	148	11	1.2	1
30	47	<0.1	0.1	2.9	0.2	10	1.2	2.1	1.3	95	145	266	203	17	0.5	0.5
181	823	0.3	0.1	4.8	0.2	12	1.2	16.9	2.3	104	300	370	439	64	4.4	1.7
5	1450	<0.1	<0.1	0.6	<0.1	6	0.1	1.5	0.5	22	19	14	41	8	0.4	0.3
148	2220	0.1	0.4	3.1	0.4	61	1.5	4.5	0.7	62	204	675	463	47	3.2	3.6
3	450							4.8		20		952			1.1	
6	450							4.8		20		968			1.1	
5	500							1.2		0		120			0.7	
23	194	0.1	0.1	3.1	0.2	6	0.1	12.1	0.7	15	75	506	185	21	0.8	0.7
45	192	0.1	0.1	4.1	0.3	13	0.2	0.6	0.6	82	156	132	157	28	1	1.3
55	316	0.1	0.1	4.3	0.3	25	0.3	5.1	0.7	146	220	387	263	41	1.6	1.9
65	451	<0.1	0.2	5.1	0.2	12	0.9	0.7	1.7	54	172	278	253	19	1	2.8
95	29	0.1	0.3	8.8	0.3	23	1.1	0	0.5	33	213	386	316	26	1.4	2.3
170	392	0.2	0.1	2.2	0.4	18	0	25		48	130	1322	635	38	1.6	0.8
77	1551	0.1	0.3	1.7	0.1	60	0.2	6.7	0.9	46	83	227	242	27	1.5	0.6
	1267							6.2		105		54			4.9	
21	182	0.1	0.1	0.5	0.4	34	0.1	5.4	8.6	44	89	235	258	37	1	0.7
20	247	0.4	0.3	3.7	0.2	66	0.3	6	2.3	68	123	631	239	22	2.2	1
16	164	0.3	0.2	2.7	0.1	19	0.4	<1	0.8	60	74	598	112	15	2	0.9
45	58	0.2	0.1	2.7	0.2	17	0.1	0	0.1	83	82	819	76	13	2	0.8
83	290	0.2	0.3	2.8	0.2	32	1.7	0.2	2.6	267	269	1470	232	28	3	3.6
53	837	0.3	0.4	2.4	0.1	60	0.4	<1	1	407	470	1155	162	26	2	2
56	256	0.6	0.4	5	0.3	55	1	0.4	2.5	240	345	1392	369	42	2.7	3
30	28	0.5	0.2	3.6	0.2	44	0.5	0	3.7	65	164	947	212	32	2.3	1.3
56	34	0.9	0.4	6.9	0.4	44	0.6	0.2	2.7	68	307	1254	439	43	3.1	2.9
51	29	0.3	0.3	4.8	0.1	21	1	2	0.3	68	135	1335	243	23	2.6	2.7
113	477	0.2	0.5	6.1	0.4	37	2.4	0.2	3.5	221	324	714	391	39	4.2	7
1	2	0.3	0.2	5.4	0.1	79	<0.1	1.7	2.6	76	143	429	240	52	2.3	1.1
45	40	0.3	0.3	6.9	0.4	51	2.3	0	3.6	67	232	1640	492	41	4.2	4.1
13	76	0.3	0.2	5.9	0.1	63	0.7	1.1	2.8	76	152	588	168	25	2.4	0.7
47	42	0.3	0.2	10.1	0.5	35	1.9	0	3.9	53	356	1734	417	71	2.5	2.2
55	35	0.2	0.3	4.3	0.3	29	0.3	0.3	2.9	51	211	1175	342	26	4	2.9
64	369	0.3	0.4	4.4	0.3	30	0.4	0	3.2	246	411	1389	354	44	3.7	3.2
103	137	<0.1	0.2	3	0.1	15	0.5	0	0.3	21	108	729	220	5	0.8	0.5
56	224	0.2	0.3	2.9	0.4	16	1.3	7.3	0.4	148	298	180	711	49	0.7	1.1

ESHA, EatRight Analysis CD-ROM; **AMT**, amount; **WT**, weight; **CAL**, calories; **KILO**, KiloJoule; **WTR**, water; **PROT**, protein; **CARB**, carbohydrate; **FIBR**, fiber; **FAT**, fat; **SATF**, saturated fat; **MONO**, monounsaturated fat; **POLY**, polyunsaturated fat; **CHOL**, cholesterol;

ESHA CODE	FOOD DESCRIPTION	AMT	UNIT	WT (g)	CAL (kcal)	KILO (kJ)	WTR (g)	PROT (g)	CARB (g)	FIBR (g)	FAT (g)	SATF (g)	MONO (g)	POLY (g)
PREPARED HOMEMADE/GENERIC DISHES (CONTINUED)														
50182	Hot & Sour Soup	1	cup	244	162	678	211	15	5	1	8	2.7	3.4	1.2
50207	Pork Rice Vegetable Soup	1	cup	244	124	519	219	12	8	1	4	1.5	2.1	0.4
50209	Sweet & Sour Soup	1	cup	244	72	301	222	3	14	2	1	0.3	0.3	0.1
50186	Vege Soup-LowSod+Water	1	cup	241	80	335	220	3	15	3	1	0.2	0.2	0.5
7559	Vegetarian Stew	1	cup	247	304	1272	173	42	17	3	7	1.2	1.8	3.8
Dishes – Vegetarian Main & Side														
7084	Bean Cake	1	ea	32	130	544	7	2	16	1	7	1	2.9	2.6
56075	Cheese Souffle-Recipe	1	cup	112	192	803	93	11	6	<1	14	5.1		
19539	Deviled Egg-1/2+Filling	1	ea	31	63	264	22	4	<1	0	5	1.2	1.7	1.5
5621	Hawaiian Vegetables-Pickled	0.5	cup	75	19	79	68	1	4	2	<1	0.1	<0.1	0.1
7086	Lentil Loaf-3/4 in slice	1	pce	47	83	347	29	4	10	3	4	0.4	0.9	2.1
5514	Mushroom-Batter Fried	5	ea	70	156	653	44	2	11	1	12	1.5	3.6	6
5644	Okra-Batter Fried	1	cup	92	175	732	62	2	14	2	13	1.7	3.1	7.1
27042	Olives-Green-Stuffed	10	ea	40	41	172	32	1	1	<1	4	0.6	3.2	0.4
5569	Potatoes-Mashed w/Milk+Butter	0.5	cup	105	119	498	79	2	18	2	4	2.7	1.1	0.2
5270	Scalloped potatoes-recipe	0.5	cup	122.5	108	452	99	4	13	2	5	1.7	1.7	0.9
2995	Spring Roll-Thai Veg-f/Recipe	1	pce	63.22	158	661	40	4	20	1	7	0.9		
91814	Sushi-Cucumber Roll	6	pce	85	120	502		3	25	2	1	0		
92384	Sushi-Vegetarian Roll	4.5	pce	110	140	586		4	27	1	2	0		
5166	Sweet Potatoes-Candied	1	pce	105	151	632	70	1	29	3	3	1.4	0.7	0.2
RESTAURANTS – FAST FOOD & REGULAR														
Arby's														
6432	Arby's Curly Fries	1	svg	99.22	316	1322		4	37	4	19	3.4		
81476	Arby's Melt Sandwich	1	ea	147	303	1268		15	36	1	12	4.5		
53256	Arby's Sauce	1	svg	14	15	63		0	4	0	<1	0		
69056	Beef'nCheddar Sandwich	1	ea	198	454	1900		22	45	2	21	6.5		
48162	Cherry Turnover-Iced	1	ea	128	377	1577		4	64	2	15	4.6		
69048	Italian Sub Sandwich	1	ea	312	699	2925		26	55	2	37	7.9		
69055	Phily Beef'nSwiss Sandwich	1	ea	311	678	2837		35	47	4	36	10.9		
81477	Roast Beef Gyro Sandwich	1	ea	240	541	2264		23	48	2	29	7.6		
56336	Roast Beef Sandwich-Reg	1	ea	157	326	1364		20	35	1	14	5.5		
56337	Roast Beef Sandwich-Jr	1	ea	129	280	1172		15	35	1	10	4		
69049	Roast Beef Sub Sandwich	1	ea	334	807	3376		38	53	3	47	12.6		
69044	Turkey Sub Sandwich	1	ea	306	681	2849		38	52	2	32	6.1		
Auntie Anne's														
42454	Pretzel-Soft	1	ea	138	391	1636		12	83	3	1	0		
42456	Pretzel-Soft-Whole Wheat	1	ea	140	408	1707		13	84	8	2	0		
Boston Market														
81411	Meatloaf-Angus+Sauce	1	svg	156	310	1297		22	16	1	19	8		
Burger King														
57002	BK Broiler Chicken Sandwich	1	ea	258	550	2301		30	52	3	25	5		
56360	Chicken Sandwich-Burger King	1	ea	224	660	2761		25	53	3	39	8		
57001	Double Cheeseburger	1	ea	197	570	2385		35	32	2	34	17		
56362	Ocean Catch Fish Filet	1	ea	263	710	2971		24	67	4	38	14		
56363	Onion Rings-Serving	1	svg	91	320	1339		4	40	3	16	4		
56999	Whopper Jr Sandwich	1	ea	167	410	1715	153	18	32	2	23	7		

< = Trace amount present Blank = Not available

V, vitamin; **THI**, thiamin; **RIB**, riboflavin; **NIA**, niacin; **FOL**, folate; **CALC**, calcium; **PHOS**, phosphorus; **SOD**, sodium; **POT**, potassium; **MAG**, magnesium

CHOL (mg)	V-A (IU)	THI (mg)	RIB (mg)	NIA (mg)	V-B6 (mg)	FOL (μg)	V-B12 (μg)	V-C (mg)	V-E (mg)	CALC (mg)	PHOS (mg)	SOD (mg)	POT (mg)	MAG (mg)	IRON (mg)	ZINC (mg)
34	15	0.3	0.3	5	0.2	13	0.4	0.7	0.1	29	188	1011	384	29	1.9	1.5
41	2946	0.3	0.1	2.5	0.2	6	0.3	1.1	0.2	16	96	55	206	15	1.1	2
5	315	0.1	0.1	0.9	0.1	16	<0.1	16.7	0.5	27	43	1292	227	15	0.6	0.3
0	2073	0.1	0.1	1.9	0.2	14	0	1	1.7	29	55	468	523	31	0.8	0.5
0	2317	1.7	1.5	29.6	2.7	254	5.4	0	1.2	77	543	988	296	314	3.2	2.7
0	0	0.1	<0.1	0.5	<0.1	9	0	0	1.2	3	21	1	58	6	0.7	0.2
195	590	0.1	0.4	0.3	0.1	27	0.8	0.5	1.3	191	191	274	146	16	0.8	1
122	166	<0.1	0.1	<0.1	<0.1	13	0.3	0	0.6	15	50	50	37	3	0.4	0.3
0	255	<0.1	<0.1	0.4	0.1	25	0	0	<0.1	30	17	795	148	7	0.4	0.2
0	4	0.1	<0.1	0.7	0.1	61	<0.1	0.8	2.2	18	88	44	156	27	1.5	0.6
2	22	0.1	0.3	2.3	<0.1	8	<0.1	1.2	2.3	15	119	112	154	7	1.2	0.4
2	344	0.2	0.1	1.4	0.1	38	<0.1	10.3	3	61	122	122	190	36	1.3	0.5
0	252	<0.1	<0.1	<0.1	<0.1	1	0	4.8	1.1	21	7	826	28	8	0.6	0.1
12	145	0.1	<0.1	1.1	0.2	8	0.1	6.3	0.1	25	47	333	298	19	0.3	0.3
7	184	0.1	0.1	1.3	0.2	13	0	13		70	77	410	463	23	0.7	0.5
3	698	0.2	0.1	1.9	<0.1	32	<0.1	0.9	1.3	58	42	263	75	12	1.8	0.4
0	250							0		0		90			0.4	
0	1000							2.4		0		105			0.7	
8	0	<0.1	<0.1	0.4	<0.1	12	0	7		27	27	74	198	12	1.2	0.2
0	326							4.8		40		740			1.6	
30	100							0		60		921			2.9	
0	0							1.2		0		177			0	
52	153							1.2		82		1301			4	
0	50							1.8		10		201			1.3	
57	619							14.2		304		2237			3.4	
91	253							9.1		314		1968			4.6	
59	500							10.8		100		1504			5.4	
45	0							0		61		972			3.7	
30	0							0		61		758			3.1	
98	447							7.4		302		2470			5.4	
81	431							5.8		302		2186			3.7	
0	0							0		34		1035			2.7	
0	0							0		35		1283			2.3	
75												650				
105	300							6		60		1110			3.6	
70	100							0		80		1330			2.7	
110	500							0		250		1020			4.5	
50	100							0		80		1200			3.6	
0	0						0	0		100		460			0	
50	200							4.8		80		520			3.6	

ESHA, EatRight Analysis CD-ROM; **AMT**, amount; **WT**, weight; **CAL**, calories; **KILO**, KiloJoule; **WTR**, water; **PROT**, protein; **CARB**, carbohydrate; **FIBR**, fiber; **FAT**, fat; **SATF**, saturated fat; **MONO**, monounsaturated fat; **POLY**, polyunsaturated fat; **CHOL**, cholesterol;

ESHA CODE	FOOD DESCRIPTION	AMT	UNIT	WT (g)	CAL (kcal)	KILO (kJ)	WTR (g)	PROT (g)	CARB (g)	FIBR (g)	FAT (g)	SATF (g)	MONO (g)	POLY (g)
RESTAURANTS – FAST FOOD & REGULAR (CONTINUED)														
57000	Whopper Jr Sandwich+Cheese	1	ea	180	460	1925		21	33	2	27	10		
56354	Whopper Sandwich	1	ea	278	648	2711	157	30	52	5	36	11.8	13	9.4
56355	Whopper Sandwich+Cheese	1	ea	303	758	3171	166	34	51	3	46	17.5	15.3	11.5
Carl's Junior														
91408	Chicken Sandwich-Charbroiled Club	1	ea	239	460	1925		32	33	2	22	7		
91410	Chicken Sandwich-Crispy Ranch	1	ea	266	730	3054		29	77	4	34	7.1		
91413	Fish Sandwich-Carl's Catch	1	ea	201	510	2134	207	18	50	1	27	7		
Chick-fil-A														
69154	Chicken Club Sandwich-Chargrld	1	ea	202	360	1506		30	31	2	13	5		
Chili's														
4826	Chicken Salad+Dressing	1	svg	445	272	1138		29	27	6	5	1		
Dairy Queen														
2131	Banana Split	1	ea	369	510	2134		8	96	3	12	8		
72141	Banana Split Blizzard	1	ea	382	580	2427		12	97	1	17	11		
2133	Buster Bar	1	ea	149	450	1883		10	41	2	28	12		
69069	Chili Cheese Hot Dog	1	ea	262	710	2971		27	42	3	47	18		
2222	Cone-Chocolate-Reg	1	ea	198	340	1423		8	53	0	11	7		
2135	Dilly Bar	1	ea	85	210	879	40	3	21	0	13	7		
2136	Dipped Cone-Regular	1	ea	220	490	2050		8	59	1	24	13		
69027	Double Bacon Cheeseburger	1	ea	269	670	2803		40	29	2	43	19		
13236	Hot Dog-Super-1/4lb	1	ea	198	580	2427		20	39	2	37	13		
56374	Hotdog	1	ea	99	240	1004	54	9	19	1	14	5		
2134	Ice Cream Sandwich	1	ea	85	200	837		4	31	1	6	3		
2348	Ice Cream-Soft Serve-Choc	0.5	cup	94	150	628		4	22	0	5	3.5		
2368	Oreo Blizzard	1	ea	326	640	2678		12	97	1	23	11		
2151	Peanut Buster Parfait	1	ea	305	730	3054		16	99	2	31	17		
2224	Shake-Chocolate-Reg	1	ea	539	770	3222		17	130	0	20	13		
56371	Single Cheeseburger	1	ea	152	340	1423	126	20	29	2	17	8		
56368	Single Hamburger	1	ea	138	290	1213	107	17	29	2	12	5		
2154	Sundae-Chocolate-Regular	1	ea	234	400	1674		8	71	0	10	6		
Denny's														
2117	Milkshake-Chocolate Malt	1	ea	284	487	2038		10	68	1	22	13.4		
19548	Omelette-Ham & Cheddar	1	ea	397	833	3485		57	7	0	66	22.4		
56612	Omelette-Veggie Cheese	1	ea	454	659	2757		40	15	3	52	16		
Domino's Pizza														
91370	Chicken Buffalo Wings-Hot	1	ea	24.9	45	188		5	1	<1	2	0.6		
Dunkin' Donuts														
42636	Apple Fritter	1	ea	95	174	728		2	24	1	8	1.7		
Hardee's														
56411	Biscuit 'n Gravy	1	ea	221	530	2218	272	10	56		30	9		
2247	Cool Twist Cone-Van/Choc	1	ea	118	180	753		4	34		2	1		
69061	Frisco Hamburger	1	ea	219	717	3000		33	37	2	49	13.9		
56420	Hot Ham 'n Cheese Sandwich	1	ea	201	421	1761		23	43	3	17	9.6		
56418	RoastBeef Sandwich-Regular	1	ea	123	310	1297		17	26	2	16	6		
Jack in the Box														
69032	Bacon Cheeseburger	1	ea	274	783	3276		32	48	2	52	17.7		

< = Trace amount present   Blank = Not available

V, vitamin; **THI**, thiamin; **RIB**, riboflavin; **NIA**, niacin; **FOL**, folate; **CALC**, calcium; **PHOS**, phosphorus; **SOD**, sodium; **POT**, potassium; **MAG**, magnesium

CHOL (mg)	V-A (IU)	THI (mg)	RIB (mg)	NIA (mg)	V-B6 (mg)	FOL (μg)	V-B12 (μg)	V-C (mg)	V-E (mg)	CALC (mg)	PHOS (mg)	SOD (mg)	POT (mg)	MAG (mg)	IRON (mg)	ZINC (mg)
60	400							4.8		150		740			3.6	
83		0.6	0.5	8	0.3	131		0.6	0.4	108	250	870	470	50	12.1	7.9
109		0.6	0.6	7.8	0.2	155		0.6	0.2	248	342	1373	512	55	6.1	4.8
90	400							6		200		1110			2.7	
59	353							5.6		177		1436			4.2	
80	300							2.4		150		1030			1.8	
80	200							3.6		150		1370			2.7	
47	2082							16		36		1475			4	
30	1000							15		250		180			1.8	
50	1250							9		400		260			1.8	
15	400							0		150		280			1.1	
105	750							2.4		250		2270			4.5	
30	750							1.2		250		160			1.8	
10	300							0		100		75			0.4	
30	750							2.4		250		190			1.8	
135	750							9		250		1210			4.5	
75	0							0		250		1710			4.5	
25	100							3.6		60		730			1.8	
10	200							0		80		140			1.1	
15	500							0		100		75			0.7	
45	1250							1.2		400		500			2.7	
35	750							1.2		300		400			1.8	
70	2000							2.4		600		420			2.7	
55	500							3.6		150		850			3.6	
45	200							3.6		60		630			2.7	
30	750							0		250		210			1.4	
83												232				
1096												1680				
997												960				
26	136							1.1		5		354			0.3	
0	0							0		0		209			0.6	
15												1550				
10												120				
100												1079				
78												1831				
43												804				
89												1500	391			

ESHA, EatRight Analysis CD-ROM; **AMT**, amount; **WT**, weight; **CAL**, calories; **KILO**, KiloJoule; **WTR**, water; **PROT**, protein; **CARB**, carbohydrate; **FIBR**, fiber; **FAT**, fat; **SATF**, saturated fat; **MONO**, monounsaturated fat; **POLY**, polyunsaturated fat; **CHOL**, cholesterol;

ESHA CODE	FOOD DESCRIPTION	AMT	UNIT	WT (g)	CAL (kcal)	KILO (kJ)	WTR (g)	PROT (g)	CARB (g)	FIBR (g)	FAT (g)	SATF (g)	MONO (g)	POLY (g)
RESTAURANTS – FAST FOOD & REGULAR (CONTINUED)														
56430	Breakfast Jack Sandwich	1	ea	126	292	1222		17	29	1	12	4.5		
56441	Chicken Fajita Pita	1	ea	230	317	1326		24	33	3	11	4.7		
69035	Chicken Sandwich-Jack in the Box	1	ea	164	452	1891		17	43	2	24	5.1		
69033	Grilled Sourdough Burger	1	ea	233	675	2824		26	34	3	49	17.1		
56436	Jumbo Jack Burger	1	ea	271	623	2607		22	53	3	36	12.5		
56437	Jumbo Jack Burger+Cheese	1	ea	296	714	2987		26	56	3	43	16.6		
69040	Sourdough Breakfast Sandwich	1	ea	162	436	1824		21	32	2	25	8.3		
11919	Southwest Pita Sandwich	1	ea	179	260	1088		20	35	4	4	1		
Kentucky Fried Chicken														
15169	Chicken Breast-ExtraCrispy	1	ea	168	450	1883	86	36	14		28	5.9	9.1	10.5
15163	Chicken Breast-Original	1	ea	153	338	1414	88	34	8		18	4.2	6.5	5.8
81293	Chicken Drumstick	1	ea	59	141	590	33	13	3		8	1.9	3	2.5
81291	Chicken Drumstick-Extra Crispy	1	ea	60	164	686	31	12	5		11	2.3	3.6	3.8
15177	Hot Wings-Pieces	6	pce	135	453	1895		24	23	1	29	6		
15184	Hot&Spicy Chicken Drumstick	1	ea	64	160	669	21	14	4	0	10	2.7		
15187	Hot&Spicy Chicken Wing	1	ea	55	180	753	13	11	9	0	11	3		
Long John Silver's														
91388	Cheese Sticks-Fried	3	ea	45	140	586	9	4	12	1	8	2		
56457	Chicken Strips-Breaded&Fried	1	pce	52.5	140	586	14	8	9	0	8	2.5		
91383	Clam Strips-Breaded&Fried	1	svg	85	240	1004	32	8	22	1	13	2		
69030	Fish Sandwich Batter Dip	1	ea	174.3	434	1816	153	17	46	3	21	4.9		
56461	Fish-Batter Fried	1	pce	92.14	230	962	46	11	16	0	13	4		
McDonald's														
69010	Big Mac Sandwich	1	ea	216	555	2322	111	26	43	3	32	8.2	7.5	0.7
42332	Biscuit+BiscuitSpread	1	ea	69	240	1004	16	4	30	1	11	2.5		
56675	Breakfast Burrito	1	ea	113	296	1238	56	13	24	1	17	6.1	6.5	2.4
69009	Cheeseburger	1	ea	121	318	1331	54	16	34	1	14	5.4	4.4	0.4
15174	Chicken McNuggets	4	pce	72	210	879	34	11	12	1	13	2.3	5.9	4.2
42335	Danish-Apple	1	ea	105	340	1423		5	47	2	15	3		
69005	Egg McMuffin	1	ea	136	292	1222	75	17	28	1	12	4.4	3.7	2.5
69013	Filet-O-Fish Sandwich	1	ea	156	429	1795	72	17	43	2	21	4.1	6	8.8
2166	FrozenYogurt Cone-Vanilla	1	ea	90	146	611	57	4	24	<1	4	2.2	1.1	0.3
4732	Grill Chick Dlxe Sand w/oMayo	1	ea	215	340	1423		26	45	2	7	1.5		
69008	Hamburger	1	ea	107	270	1130	49	13	33	1	10	3.1	3.4	0.2
6155	Hashbrown Potatoes	1	svg	53	139	582	28	1	14	1	9	1.2	4.5	2.6
45069	Hotcakes+Marg+Syrup	1	svg	228	600	2510		9	104	0	17	3		
47147	McDonaldland Cookies	1	ea	57	255	1067	2	4	41	1	9	1.8	4.6	1.2
69011	Quarter Pounder	1	ea	172	420	1757	87	24	38	3	20	6.9	7.2	0.5
69012	Quarter Pounder+Cheese	1	ea	200	516	2159	98	29	40	3	28	11.3	9.2	0.9
69006	Sausage McMuffin	1	ea	112	373	1561	44	14	27	2	24	8.1	8.7	3.6
19579	Scrambled Eggs	1	svg	102	197	824	68	15	2		15	4.1	5.3	2.2
2167	Shake-LowFat-Choc	1	ea	294.6	480	2008	186	11	82	1	13	6.8	3.3	0.6
2168	Shake-LowFat-Strawberrry	1	ea	294	465	1946	189	10	79	0	13	6.6	3.2	0.6
2169	Shake-LowFat-Vanilla	1	ea	293.4	458	1916	190	10	78	0	13	6.6	3.2	0.6
Pizza Hut														
56481	Cheese Pizza-Pan Style	1	pce	110	308	1289	48	13	33	2	14	5.7	3.5	3

< = Trace amount present Blank = Not available

V, vitamin; **THI**, thiamin; **RIB**, riboflavin; **NIA**, niacin; **FOL**, folate; **CALC**, calcium; **PHOS**, phosphorus; **SOD**, sodium; **POT**, potassium; **MAG**, magnesium

CHOL (mg)	V-A (IU)	THI (mg)	RIB (mg)	NIA (mg)	V-B6 (mg)	FOL (μg)	V-B12 (μg)	V-C (mg)	V-E (mg)	CALC (mg)	PHOS (mg)	SOD (mg)	POT (mg)	MAG (mg)	IRON (mg)	ZINC (mg)
222												766	212			
69												928	475			
40												826	271			
71												1170	409			
47												976	395			
72												1356	424			
239												1018	239			
40												880	450			
128		0.1	0.2	13.7	0.5		0.5			45	361	1020	433	40	1	1.3
125		0.1	0.2	13.6	0.5		0.5			47	349	901	416	40	0.9	1.3
69		<0.1	0.1	2.9	0.1		0.3			17	124	369	148	14	0.6	1.2
65		<0.1	0.1	2.8	0.1		0.3			15	119	379	142	13	0.5	1.1
146	302							3.6		81		1128			1.8	
69	0							0		0		405			0.8	
60	0							0		0		420			0.7	
10	200	<0.1	<0.1	0.3	<0.1	6	0.3	0	0.5	100	74	320	27	6	0.7	0.4
20	0	0.1	0.1	3.4	0.1	18	0.1	2.4	0.5	0	59	400	66	8	0.4	0.3
10	0	0.1	0.1	1	<0.1	13	19.8	0	1.1	20	96	1110	155	9	1.1	0.7
39	296	0.3	0.2	2.9	0.1	66	1.8	8.9	1.8	59	263	1105	221	46	3.6	0.6
30	0	0.1	0.1	1.5	0.1	26	1.6	4.8	1.4	20	207	701	170	34	1.8	0.4
78	406	0.4	0.5	7.3		99	1.9	0.9		251	264	994	391	43	4.3	4.1
0	10			2		4		0	0.7	40	321	640	95	8	1.8	0.3
173	382	0.2	0.3	1.9	0.4	70	0.6	0.9	0.2	203	247	763	155	19	1.8	1.3
42	294	0.3	0.3	4.9		71	1	0.7		202	169	757	242	24	2.8	2.3
32	0	0.1	0.1	5.3	0.3	20	0.2	0.9		10	239	455	181	16	0.7	0.4
20	500	0.3	0.2	2				15		60	0	340	113		1.4	
224	540	0.4	0.5	4.2	0.2	107	0.9	1.6	0.8	269	264	842	214	26	2.9	1.6
44	137	0.4	0.3	3.7		76	1.2	0.2		179	184	757	273	31	2.3	0.8
14	289	<0.1	0.2	0.4	<0.1	8	0.5		<0.1	116	100	60	174	12	0.3	0.4
50	200							6		200		890			2.7	
29	59	0.3	0.3	4.9		68	0.9	0.6		129	114	542	217	21	2.8	2
0	0	0.1	<0.1	1.2	0.1	20		0.9		7	57	290	207	11	0.3	0.2
20	400					<1		<1	1.2	100	516	770	292	28	4.5	0.5
	0	0.2	0.2	2.1	0.1	58			1.1	10	63	275	56	10	1.9	0.3
67	96	0.3	0.6	7.7		96	2.2	1.5		144	213	734	390	38	4.1	4.6
94	560	0.3	0.7	7.7		102	2.5	1.6		288	322	1158	438	44	4.2	5.3
44	291	0.4	0.3	4.7	0.2	77	0.5	0	0.3	251	183	776	211	24	2.3	1.4
436	618	0.1	0.6	0.1	0.2	71	1.1		1.5	67	266	196	142	12	2.1	1.5
41	890	0.1	0.6	0.4	0.1	3	1.6		0	359	309	209	666	47	1.6	1.5
41	894	0.1	0.6	0.4	0.1	9	1.6	1.2	0	359	294	144	541	35	0.3	1.3
41	892	0.1	0.6	0.3	0.1	0	1.6		0	355	293	156	516	35	0.2	1.3
23	286	0.3	0.3	4.3	0.1		0.7	0	1.2	229	265	686	185	23	2	1.8

ESHA, EatRight Analysis CD-ROM; **AMT**, amount; **WT**, weight; **CAL**, calories; **KILO**, KiloJoule; **WTR**, water; **PROT**, protein; **CARB**, carbohydrate; **FIBR**, fiber; **FAT**, fat; **SATF**, saturated fat; **MONO**, monounsaturated fat; **POLY**, polyunsaturated fat; **CHOL**, cholesterol;

ESHA CODE	FOOD DESCRIPTION	AMT	UNIT	WT (g)	CAL (kcal)	KILO (kJ)	WTR (g)	PROT (g)	CARB (g)	FIBR (g)	FAT (g)	SATF (g)	MONO (g)	POLY (g)
RESTAURANTS – FAST FOOD & REGULAR (CONTINUED)														
56490	Pepperoni Pizza-HandTossed	1	pce	116	325	1360	48	15	37	2	13	6	4.7	2.4
56482	Pepperoni Pizza-Pan Style	1	pce	106	316	1322	43	13	32	2	15	5.6	4.7	3.7
56493	Pepperoni Pizza-Pers Pan	1	ea	257	716	2996		29	76	4	34	12.6		
56486	Pepperoni Pizza-Thin/Crispy	1	pce	81	221	925	28	11	22	1	11	4.7		
56483	Supreme Pizza-Pan Style	1	pce	133	335	1402		14	31	2	17	6.3		
56487	Supreme Pizza-Thin/Crispy	1	pce	117	265	1109		12	24	2	12	5.5		
Starbucks														
20592	Cappuccino, LowFat Milk-Tall	1.5	cup	244	110	460		8	11	0	4	2.5		
20639	Cappuccino, Whole Milk-Tall	1.5	cup	244	140	586		7	11	0	7	4.5		
20659	Coffee Latte, Iced, LowFat Milk-Tall	1.5	cup	392	90	377		7	10	0	3	2		
20662	Coffee Latte, Iced, Whole Milk-Tall	1.5	cup	392	120	502		6	10	0	6	4		
20668	Coffee Latte, LowFat Milk-Tall	1.5	cup	366	170	711		12	17	0	6	4		
20671	Coffee Latte, Whole Milk-Tall	1.5	cup	366	210	879		11	17	0	11	7		
20677	Coffee Mocha, LowFat Milk-Tall	1.5	cup	392	300	1255		12	33	1	15	9		
20680	Coffee Mocha, Whole Milk-Tall	1.5	cup	392	340	1423		12	33	1	20	12		
Subway														
69117	Club Sandwich (6-inch)	1	ea	255	320	1339		24	46	4	6	2		
52120	Cold Cut Salad	1	svg	316	230	962		14	11	3	15	6		
69129	Meatball Sandwich (6-inch)	1	ea	287	530	2218		24	53	6	26	10		
52116	Seafood/Crab Salad	1	svg	314	200	837		9	17	4	11	3.5		
52118	Tuna Salad	1	svg	314	240	1004		13	10	3	16	4		
69107	Tuna Sandwich (6-inch)	1	ea	168	330	1381		13	36	3	16	4.5		
52113	Veggie Delite Salad	1	ea	233	50	209		2	9	3	1	0		
69109	Veggie Sandwich (6-inch)	1	ea	166	230	962		9	44	4	3	1		
Taco Bell														
56691	7 Layer Burrito	1	ea	283	530	2218		18	67	10	22	8		
56522	Burrito-Beef Supreme	1	ea	248	469	1962	150	20	52	8	20	7.6	8.1	2
56688	Chicken Burrito	1	ea	171	306	1280	104	17	35	4	11	4	4.4	1.4
56689	Chicken Soft Taco	1	ea	121	244	1021	68	17	24	2	9	3.2	3.4	1.3
45585	Cinnamon Twists	1	svg	28	128	536		1	22	0	4	0.8		
56531	Mexican Pizza	1	ea	220	560	2343		21	47	7	32	11.2		
56534	Nachos Bellgrande	1	svg	312	790	3305		20	81	12	44	13.2		
56684	Nachos Supreme	1	svg	198	487	2038	106	15	46	8	27	7.9	13.9	2.8
56536	Pintos+Cheese+Red Sauce	1	svg	120	169	707	106	9	19	6	7	3.3		
56526	Soft Taco Supreme	1	ea	142	276	1155		12	23	3	15	7.4		
56693	Steak Soft Taco	1	ea	128	288	1205	73	15	22	2	15	4.3	5	4.5
56524	Taco	1	ea	78	184	770	44	8	14	3	11	3.6	4.2	1.6
56692	Taco Supreme	1	ea	113	220	920		9	14	3	14	7		
56525	Taco-Beef-Soft	1	ea	99	217	908	55	12	20	3	10	4.2	4.3	1
21037	Tea-Lemon-Btl/Cnd	1	cup	245	86	360	223	0	22	0	0	0	0	0
Taco Time														
12418	Cheddar Tator Tots	1	svg	198.45	519	2171		12	40		35			
7273	Chicken Taco Salad	1	ea	255.15	370	1548		19	27	3	21	7		
56540	Crispy Bean Burrito	1	ea	164.2	471	1971		17	58	10	20	5.5		
56541	Crispy Meat Burrito	1	ea	162.8	604	2527		37	43	8	33	10.9		
56553	Mexi-Fries	1	svg	114.2	268	1121		3	27		17			

< = Trace amount present   Blank = Not available

V, vitamin; **THI**, thiamin; **RIB**, riboflavin; **NIA**, niacin; **FOL**, folate; **CALC**, calcium; **PHOS**, phosphorus; **SOD**, sodium; **POT**, potassium; **MAG**, magnesium

CHOL (mg)	V-A (IU)	THI (mg)	RIB (mg)	NIA (mg)	V-B6 (mg)	FOL (μg)	V-B12 (μg)	V-C (mg)	V-E (mg)	CALC (mg)	PHOS (mg)	SOD (mg)	POT (mg)	MAG (mg)	IRON (mg)	ZINC (mg)
30	237	0.4	0.3	4.7	0.2		0.8	0	0.9	180	253	929	240	27	2.5	1.9
26	181	0.3	0.3	4.1	0.1		0.7	0	0.8	155	217	734	211	23	2.3	1.6
63	843							5.1		337		1432			6.1	
26	316							2.5		158		579			1.5	
26	314							6.3		157		681			2.8	
28	331							9.9		166		706			2	
15	400							2.4		250		110			0	
30	300							2.4		250		105			0	
15	300							1.2		250		100			0	
25	200							1.2		250		95			0	
25	500							3.6		400		170			0	
45	400							3.6		400		170			0	
55	750							2.4		400		160			2.7	
70	750							2.4		400		150			2.7	
35	300							21		60		1300			5.4	
55	1000							30		150		1370			1.8	
55	750							27		150		1360			5.4	
25	1000							30		100		970			1.1	
40	1000							30		100		880			1.1	
25	400							12		150		830			3.6	
0	750							30		40		310			1.1	
0	300							21		60		510			3.6	
25	500							4.8		300		1360			3.6	
40	203	0.4	0.4	4.3	0.3	112	1.2		1.1	231	337	1424	608	62	5.6	2.6
36	140	0.3	0.3	6.7	0.2	82	0.6		0.7	161	279	964	451	48	2.7	1.1
45	30	0.3	0.2	7.7	0.2	58	0.4		0.4	127	271	733	287	27	2.1	1
0	0							0		0		120			0.3	
46	764							6.1		356		1049			3.7	
35	506							6.1		203		1317			2.7	
38	139	0.2	0.3	1.9	0.3	57	0.8		1.4	145	390	851	479	91	4.2	2.7
14	469							3.4		141		656			1	
42	530							5.1		159		668			1.9	
40	29	0.4	0.2	3.8	0.1	47	1.2		0.6	150	198	705	234	27	2.8	2.8
24	60	0.1	0.1	1.5	0.1	15	0.7		0.5	62	139	349	168	26	1.5	1.7
40	500							4.8		80		360			1.4	
28	78	0.2	0.2	2.6	0.1	51	0.8		0.4	115	161	626	179	20	2.4	1.6
0										2	64	51	47	0	0	<0.1
												1372				
48												861				
13												500				
63												1094				
												805				

ESHA, EatRight Analysis CD-ROM; **AMT**, amount; **WT**, weight; **CAL**, calories; **KILO**, KiloJoule; **WTR**, water; **PROT**, protein; **CARB**, carbohydrate; **FIBR**, fiber; **FAT**, fat; **SATF**, saturated fat; **MONO**, monounsaturated fat; **POLY**, polyunsaturated fat; **CHOL**, cholesterol;

ESHA CODE	FOOD DESCRIPTION	AMT	UNIT	WT (g)	CAL (kcal)	KILO (kJ)	WTR (g)	PROT (g)	CARB (g)	FIBR (g)	FAT (g)	SATF (g)	MONO (g)	POLY (g)
RESTAURANTS – FAST FOOD & REGULAR (CONTINUED)														
50979	Quesadilla-Cheddar Melt	1	ea	92.14	205	858		11	17	1	11	6		
56544	Soft Combo Burrito	1	ea	272	623	2607		39	67	18	23	10.1		
Wendy's														
56571	Bacon Cheeseburger	1	ea	165	380	1590		20	34	2	19	7		
56574	Big Classic Burger+Cheese	1	ea	282	570	2385		34	46	3	29	12		
2177	Frosty Dairy Dessert-Med	1	ea	298	393	1644	206	10	70	10	8	4.9	2.1	0.3
69059	Grilled Chicken Sandwich	1	ea	188	300	1255		24	36	2	7	1.5		
69058	Junior Cheeseburger Deluxe	1	ea	179	350	1464		17	37	2	15	6		
69057	Junior Hamburger	1	ea	117	284	1188	56	15	33	2	10	4.1	4.1	1.3
56566	Single Burger-Deluxe	1	ea	218	464	1941	127	28	37	3	23	8	8.9	3.4
71596	Spring Mix Salad-No Dressing	1	ea	315	180	753		11	12	5	11	6		
81443	Ultimate Grill Chicken Sandwich	1	ea	225	403	1686	134	33	42	2	11	2.3	3.3	4.1
USDA/GENERIC FAST FOODS														
66025	Burrito-Bean	1	ea	108.5	224	937	57	7	36		7	3.4	2.4	0.6
56629	Burrito-Bean+Cheese	1	ea	93	189	791	50	8	27		6	3.4	1.2	0.9
66024	Burrito-Beef	1	ea	110	262	1096	55	13	29		10	5.2	3.7	0.4
66021	Cheese enchilada	1	ea	163	319	1335	103	10	29		19	10.6	6.3	0.8
56628	Chef Style Salad	1.5	cup	326	267	1117	269	26	5		16	8.2	5.2	1.4
56656	Chicken Fillet Sandwich+Cheese	1	ea	228	632	2644	105	29	42		39	12.4	13.7	9.9
56634	Chimichanga-Beef	1	ea	174	425	1778	88	20	43		20	8.5	8.1	1.1
56634	Chimichanga-Beef	1	ea	174	425	1778	88	20	43		20	8.5	8.1	1.1
56668	Corndog (hotdog+coating)	1	ea	175	460	1925	82	17	56		19	5.2	9.1	3.5
56606	Croissant + Egg & Cheese	1	ea	127	368	1540	58	13	24		25	14.1	7.5	1.4
66020	Enchirito-Bean+Beef+Cheez	1	ea	193	344	1439	121	18	34		16	7.9	6.5	0.3
42064	English Muffin+Butter	1	ea	63	189	791	21	5	30	2	6	2.4	1.5	1.3
17187	Fish Fillet-Batter Fried	3	oz	85.05	197	824	46	12	14	<1	10	2.4	2.2	5.3
66011	FishSandwich+Cheese+TartarSc	1	ea	183	523	2188	83	21	48		29	8.1	8.9	9.4
5460	French Fries-Veg Oil-Serving	1	svg	169	539	2255	67	6	63	6	29	6.7	16.7	5.1
56638	Frijoles + Cheese	1	cup	167	225	941	115	11	29		8	4.1	2.6	0.7
5463	Hashbrown Potatoes-Svg	0.5	cup	72	235	983	30	2	23	2	16	3.6	8.3	2.7
2032	Hot Fudge Sundae	1	ea	158	284	1188	94	6	48	0	9	5	2.3	0.8
56667	Hotdog + Chili	1	ea	114	296	1238	54	14	31		13	4.9	6.6	1.2
66004	Hotdog/Frankfurter & Bun	1	ea	98	242	1013	53	10	18		15	5.1	6.9	1.7
2020	Milkshake-Chocolate	1	cup	166.4	211	883	119	6	34	3	6	3.8	1.8	0.2
47109	Molasses Cookie	1	ea	15	64	268	1	1	11	<1	2	0.5	1.1	0.3
56639	Nachos-Chips + Cheese	7	pce	113	346	1448	46	9	36		19	7.8	8	2.2
6176	Onion Rings-Serving	8.5	pce	83	276	1155	31	4	31		16	7	6.7	0.7
56672	Roast Beef Submarine Sandwich	1	ea	216	410	1715	127	29	44		13	7.1	1.8	2.6
19114	Scallops-Bread-Fried	3	oz	85.05	228	954	41	9	23		11	2.9	7.4	0.4
56670	Steak Sandwich	1	ea	204	459	1920	104	30	52		14	3.8	5.3	3.3
2022	Strawberry Milkshake	1	cup	283	320	1339	210	10	53	1	8	4.9		
2033	Strawberry sundae	1	ea	153	268	1121	93	6	45	0	8	3.7	2.7	1
56671	Submarine Sandwich w/Coldcuts	1	ea	228	456	1908	132	22	51		19	6.8	8.2	2.3
56643	Taco Salad	1.5	cup	198	279	1167	143	13	24		15	6.8	5.2	1.7
56645	Tostada-Beef+Cheese	1	ea	163	315	1318	101	19	23		16	10.4	3.3	1
56623	Vegetable Salad-No Dressing	1.5	cup	207	33	138	198	3	7		<1	<0.1	<0.1	0.1

< = Trace amount present   Blank = Not available

V, vitamin; **THI**, thiamin; **RIB**, riboflavin; **NIA**, niacin; **FOL**, folate; **CALC**, calcium; **PHOS**, phosphorus; **SOD**, sodium; **POT**, potassium; **MAG**, magnesium

CHOL (mg)	V-A (IU)	THI (mg)	RIB (mg)	NIA (mg)	V-B6 (mg)	FOL (μg)	V-B12 (μg)	V-C (mg)	V-E (mg)	CALC (mg)	PHOS (mg)	SOD (mg)	POT (mg)	MAG (mg)	IRON (mg)	ZINC (mg)
30												255				
64												1356				
55	400							9		150		890	320		3.6	
100	750							15		200		1460	580		5.4	
48		0.2	2.1	1	0		1.8	0		381	334	292	551	60	3.1	1.3
55	200							9		80		740	430		2.7	
45	500							9		150		890	320		3.6	
32		0.5	0.3	4.5	0.1		1.5	0.6		53	125	631	205	25	3.9	2.5
76		0.6	0.4	7	0.2		3.2	1.1		74	225	861	425	39	6	5.4
30	8500							30		300		230	620		1.8	
90		0.9	0.6	9.4	0.3		0.7	2.5		56	378	961	497	54	3.5	1.3
2	166	0.3	0.3	2	0.2	43	0.5	1		56	49	493	327	43	2.3	0.8
14	625	0.1	0.4	1.8	0.1	37	0.4	0.8		107	90	583	248	40	1.1	0.8
32	139	0.1	0.5	3.2	0.2	65	1	0.6		42	87	746	370	41	3	2.4
44	1161	0.1	0.4	1.9	0.4	65	0.7	1		324	134	784	240	51	1.3	2.5
140	1053	0.4	0.4	6	0.4	101	0.8	16.3		235	401	743	401	49	2	3.1
78	620	0.4	0.5	9.1	0.4	109	0.5	3		258	406	1238	333	43	3.6	2.9
9	146	0.5	0.6	5.8	0.3	84	1.5	4.7		63	124	910	586	63	4.5	5
9	146	0.5	0.6	5.8	0.3	84	1.5	4.7		63	124	910	586	63	4.5	5
79	206	0.3	0.7	4.2	0.1	103	0.4	0		102	166	973	262	18	6.2	1.3
216	1001	0.2	0.4	1.5	0.1	47	0.8	0.1		244	348	551	174	22	2.2	1.8
50	1015	0.2	0.7	3	0.2	95	1.6	4.6		218	224	1251	560	71	2.4	2.8
13	136	0.3	0.3	2.6	<0.1	57	<0.1	0.8	0.1	103	85	386	69	13	1.6	0.4
29	32	0.1	0.1	1.8	0.1	14	0.9	0		15	145	452	272	20	1.8	0.4
68	432	0.5	0.4	4.2	0.1	92	1.1	2.7	1.8	185	311	939	353	37	3.5	1.2
0	0	0.3	0.1	4.2	0.6	51	0	4.6	1.3	22	233	328	930	57	2.3	1.2
37	456	0.1	0.3	1.5	0.2	112	0.7	1.5		189	175	882	605	85	2.2	1.7
0	0	0.1	0.1	1.2	0.2	14	0	2.1	0.7	12	79	373	256	14	0.5	0.2
21	221	0.1	0.3	1.1	0.1	9	0.6	2.4	0.7	207	228	182	395	33	0.6	0.9
51	58	0.2	0.4	3.7	<0.1	73	0.3	2.7		19	192	480	166	10	3.3	0.8
44	0	0.2	0.3	3.6	<0.1	48	0.5	0.1		24	97	670	143	13	2.3	2
22	155	0.1	0.4	0.3	0.1	8	0.6	0.7	0.2	188	170	161	333	28	0.5	0.7
0	0	0.1	<0.1	0.5	<0.1	13	0	0	<0.1	11	14	69	52	8	1	0.1
18	559	0.2	0.4	1.5	0.2	10	0.8	1.2		272	276	816	172	55	1.3	1.8
14	8	0.1	0.1	0.9	0.1	55	0.1	0.6	0.3	73	86	430	129	16	0.8	0.3
73	413	0.4	0.4	6	0.3	71	1.8	5.6		41	192	845	330	67	2.8	4.4
64	82	0.1	0.5	0	<0.1	31	0.3	0		11	173	543	174	19	1.2	0.6
73	367	0.4	0.4	7.3	0.4	90	1.6	5.5		92	298	798	524	49	5.2	4.5
31	340	0.1	0.6	0.5	0.1	8	0.9	2.3		320	283	235	515	37	0.3	1
21	222	0.1	0.3	0.9	0.1	18	0.6	2	0.8	161	155	92	271	24	0.3	0.7
36	424	1	0.8	5.5	0.1	87	1.1	12.3		189	287	1651	394	68	2.5	2.6
44	588	0.1	0.4	2.5	0.2	83	0.6	3.6		192	143	762	416	51	2.3	2.7
41	712	0.1	0.6	3.1	0.2	75	1.2	2.6		217	179	896	572	64	2.9	3.7
0	2352	0.1	0.1	1.1	0.2	77	0	48		27	81	54	356	23	1.3	0.4

ESHA, EatRight Analysis CD-ROM; **AMT**, amount; **WT**, weight; **CAL**, calories; **KILO**, KiloJoule; **WTR**, water; **PROT**, protein; **CARB**, carbohydrate; **FIBR**, fiber; **FAT**, fat; **SATF**, saturated fat; **MONO**, monounsaturated fat; **POLY**, polyunsaturated fat; **CHOL**, cholesterol;

ESHA CODE	FOOD DESCRIPTION	AMT	UNIT	WT (g)	CAL (kcal)	KILO (kJ)	WTR (g)	PROT (g)	CARB (g)	FIBR (g)	FAT (g)	SATF (g)	MONO (g)	POLY (g)
VEGETABLES & LEGUMES														
Canned/Pickled Vegetables & Legumes														
5191	Artichoke Hearts-Marinated-Cnd	0.5	cup	65	58	243	14	2	7	2	3	0		
5842	Asparagus-Canned+Liq-LowSod	0.5	cup	122	18	75	115	2	3	1	<1	0.1	<0.1	0.1
5007	Asparagus-Spears-Canned	1	pce	18	3	13	17	<1	<1	<1	<1	<0.1	<0.1	0.1
5401	Bamboo Shoots-Canned Slices	1	cup	131	25	105	124	2	4	2	1	0.1	<0.1	0.2
5231	Beans-Green-Cannd+Liq-LowSod	1	cup	240	36	151	227	2	8	4	<1	0.1	<0.1	0.1
7087	Beans-Kidney-Canned+Liquid	0.5	cup	128	108	452	100	7	19	7	1	0.1	0.4	0.3
7051	Beans-Pinto-Canned+Liquid	0.5	cup	120	103	431	93	6	18	6	1	0.2	0.2	0.3
7135	Beans-Red Kidney-Canned-Drain	1	cup	256	302	1264	176	19	55	23	1			
5310	Beets-Pickled-Slices	1	cup	227	148	619	186	2	37	6	<1	<0.1	<0.1	0.1
5515	Corn w/Red Pepper-Mexican	1	cup	227	170	711	176	5	41	5	1	0.2	0.4	0.6
5201	Corn-Canned + Liquid	0.5	cup	128	82	343	104	2	20	2	1	0.1	0.2	0.3
5066	Corn-Canned-Drained	0.5	cup	82	66	276	63	2	15	2	1	0.1	0.2	0.4
5562	Corn-White-Canned+Liquid	0.5	cup	128	82	343	104	2	20	1	1	0.1	0.2	0.3
5563	Corn-White-Canned-Drained	0.5	cup	82	66	276	63	2	15	2	1	0.1	0.2	0.4
90580	Dill Pickle-Large	1	ea	135	16	67	127	1	3	1	<1	<0.1	<0.1	0.1
27013	Dill Pickle-Slices	10	ea	70	8	33	66	<1	2	1	<1	<0.1	<0.1	<0.1
7055	Fava/Broadbeans-Canned+Liq	0.5	cup	128	91	381	103	7	16	5	<1	<0.1	0.1	0.1
7088	GarbanzoBeans/Chickpeas+Liq	0.5	cup	120	143	598	84	6	27	5	1	0.1	0.3	0.6
6751	Green Beans-Canned	0.5	cup	67.5	16	67	63	1	3	2	<1	<0.1	<0.1	<0.1
38077	Hominy-White-Canned	1	cup	165	119	498	136	2	24	4	1	0.2	0.4	0.7
5470	Hominy-Yellow-Canned	1	cup	160	115	481	132	2	23	4	1	0.2	0.4	0.6
5293	Jalapeno Peppers-Chop-Can	0.5	cup	68	18	75	60	1	3	2	1	0.1	<0.1	0.3
5305	Mixed Vegetable-Canned-Drain	1	cup	163	80	335	142	4	15	5	<1	0.1	<0.1	0.2
5197	Mung Bean Sprouts-Canned	1	cup	125	15	63	120	2	3	1	<1	<0.1	<0.1	<0.1
5094	Mushroom Pieces-Canned	0.5	cup	78	20	84	71	1	4	2	<1	<0.1	<0.1	0.1
5281	Peas+Carrots-Canned+Liquid	1	cup	255	97	406	225	6	22	5	1	0.1	0.1	0.3
7016	Peas-Cowpea/Blackeye-Canned	1	cup	240	185	774	191	11	33	8	1	0.3	0.1	0.6
5214	Peas-Green-Canned+Liquid	0.5	cup	124	66	276	107	4	12	4	<1	0.1	<0.1	0.2
5267	Peas-Green-LowSod-Cnd+Liq	0.5	cup	85	45	188	73	3	8	3	<1	<0.1	<0.1	0.1
27016	Pickle-Sweet-Medium	1	ea	35	32	134	27	<1	7	<1	<1	<0.1	<0.1	<0.1
5227	Pimento-Canned	1	Tbs	12	3	13	11	<1	1	<1	<1	<0.1	<0.1	<0.1
5228	Pimiento Slices-Canned	20	pce	20	5	21	19	<1	1	<1	<1	<0.1	<0.1	<0.1
5352	Potato Pieces-Canned	0.5	cup	90	54	226	76	1	12	2	<1	<0.1	<0.1	0.1
5145	Sauerkraut-Canned+Liquid	0.5	cup	118	22	92	109	1	5	3	<1	<0.1	<0.1	0.1
5531	Sauerkraut-Canned-LowSod	0.5	cup	71	16	67	66	1	3	2	<1	<0.1	<0.1	<0.1
5601	Succotash-Whole Corn-Canned	0.5	cup	127.5	80	335	104	3	18	3	1	0.1	0.1	0.3
6255	Three Bean Salad	0.5	cup	121	80	335		3	18	3	0	0	0	0
5476	Tomato Puree-Canned	1	cup	250	95	397	220	4	22	5	1	0.1	0.1	0.2
5179	Tomatoes-Canned	0.5	cup	120	20	84	113	1	5	1	<1	<0.1	<0.1	0.1
5474	Tomatoes-Stewed-Cnd-LowSod	0.5	cup	127.5	33	138	117	1	8	1	<1	<0.1	<0.1	0.1
9522	Vegetables-Unsalt-Canned	0.5	cup	96	36	151	87	1	7	3	<1	<0.1	<0.1	0.1
5387	WaterChestnuts-Canned-Slices	0.5	cup	70	35	146	60	1	9	2	<1	<0.1	<0.1	<0.1
Cooked Vegetables & Legumes														
5314	Acorn Squash-Baked	0.5	cup	102.5	57	238	85	1	15	5	<1	<0.1	<0.1	0.1
5000	Artichoke-Globe-Cooked	1	ea	120	64	268	101	3	14	10	<1	0.1	<0.1	0.2

< = Trace amount present   Blank = Not available

V, vitamin; **THI**, thiamin; **RIB**, riboflavin; **NIA**, niacin; **FOL**, folate; **CALC**, calcium; **PHOS**, phosphorus; **SOD**, sodium; **POT**, potassium; **MAG**, magnesium

CHOL (mg)	V-A (IU)	THI (mg)	RIB (mg)	NIA (mg)	V-B6 (mg)	FOL (μg)	V-B12 (μg)	V-C (mg)	V-E (mg)	CALC (mg)	PHOS (mg)	SOD (mg)	POT (mg)	MAG (mg)	IRON (mg)	ZINC (mg)
0	0							13.9		0		244			0	
0	947	0.1	0.1	1	0.1	104	0	20.1	0.4	18	46	32	210	11	0.7	0.6
0	148	<0.1	<0.1	0.2	<0.1	17	0	3.3	0.2	3	8	52	31	2	0.3	0.1
0	17	<0.1	<0.1	0.2	0.2	4	0	1.4	0.8	10	33	9	105	5	0.4	0.9
0	770	0.1	0.1	0.5	0.1	43	0	8.2	0.3	58	46	34	221	31	2.2	0.5
0	0	0.1	0.1	0.5	0.1	46	0	1.5	<0.1	44	115	379	303	35	1.5	0.6
0	0	0.1	0.1	0.4	0.1	72	0	1.1	0.7	52	110	353	292	32	1.8	0.8
0	6	0.4	0.3	1.6	0.1	179	0				333			99		2
0	111	<0.1	0.1	0.6	0.1	61	0	5.2	0.1	25	39	599	336	34	0.9	0.6
0	527	<0.1	0.2	2.2	0.2	77	0	20		11	141	788	347	57	1.8	0.8
0	83	<0.1	0.1	1.2	<0.1	49	0	7	<0.1	5	65	273	210	20	0.5	0.5
0	37	<0.1	<0.1	0.3	0.1	35	0	0.6	0.1	4	39	244	111	12	0.6	0.3
0	1	<0.1	0.1	1.2	<0.1	49	0	7		5	65	15	210	20	0.5	0.5
0	1	<0.1	0.1	1	<0.1	40	0	7	0.1	4	53	265	160	16	0.7	0.3
0	247	<0.1	<0.1	0.1	<0.1	1	0	1.1	0.1	57	16	1181	124	9	0.5	0.1
0	128	<0.1	<0.1	0.1	<0.1	1	0	0.6	0.1	29	8	612	64	5	0.3	0.1
0	13	<0.1	0.1	1.2	0.1	42	0	2.3		33	101	580	310	41	1.3	0.8
0	25	<0.1	<0.1	0.2	0.6	80	0	4.6		38	108	359	206	35	1.6	1.3
0	238	<0.1	<0.1	0.1	<0.1	22	0	2.9	<0.1	19	14	177	75	9	0.6	0.2
0	2	<0.1	<0.1	0.1	<0.1	2	0	0	0.1	16	58	346	15	26	1	1.7
0	176	<0.1	<0.1	0.1	<0.1	2	0	0		16	56	336	14	26	1	1.7
0	1156	<0.1	<0.1	0.3	0.1	10	0	6.8	0.5	16	12	1136	131	10	1.3	0.2
0	18991	0.1	0.1	0.9	0.1	39	0	8.2	0.5	44	68	243	474	26	1.7	0.7
0	10	<0.1	0.1	0.3	<0.1	12	0	0.4	<0.1	18	40	175	34	11	0.5	0.4
0	0	0.1	<0.1	1.2	<0.1	9	0	0	<0.1	9	51	332	101	12	0.6	0.6
0	14714	0.2	0.1	1.5	0.2	46	0	16.8		59	117	663	255	36	1.9	1.5
0	31	0.2	0.2	0.8	0.1	122	0	6.5		48	168	718	413	67	2.3	1.7
0	1791	0.1	0.1	1	0.1	36	0	12.2	<0.1	22	66	310	124	21	1.3	0.9
0	1227	0.1	0.1	0.7	0.1	25	0	8.3	<0.1	15	45	8	85	14	0.9	0.6
0	267	<0.1	<0.1	<0.1	<0.1	<1	0	0.2	0.1	21	6	160	35	2	0.1	<0.1
0	319	<0.1	<0.1	0.1	<0.1	1	0	10.2	0.1	1	2	2	19	1	0.2	<0.1
0	531	<0.1	<0.1	0.1	<0.1	1	0	17	0.1	1	3	3	32	1	0.3	<0.1
0	0	0.1	<0.1	0.8	0.2	5	0	4.6		4	25	197	206	13	1.1	0.3
0	21	<0.1	<0.1	0.2	0.2	28	0	17.3	0.2	35	24	780	201	15	1.7	0.2
0	13	<0.1	<0.1	0.1	0.1	17	0	10.4	0.1	21	14	219	121	9	1	0.1
0	186	<0.1	0.1	0.8	0.1	41	0	5.9		14	70	282	208	24	0.7	0.6
0	200							0		20		470			1.1	
0	1275	0.1	0.2	3.7	0.3	28	0	26.5	4.9	45	100	998	1098	58	4.4	0.9
0	140	0.1	0.1	0.9	0.1	10	0	11.2	0.8	37	23	172	226	13	1.2	0.2
0	219	0.1	<0.1	0.9	<0.1	6	0	10.1	1.1	43	26	282	264	15	1.7	0.2
0	11185	<0.1	<0.1	0.5	0.1	17	0	3.6	0.3	20	36	25	132	14	0.6	0.5
0	0	<0.1	<0.1	0.3	0.1	4	0	0.9	0.4	3	13	6	83	4	0.6	0.3
0	439	0.2	<0.1	0.9	0.2	19	0	11.1		45	46	4	448	44	1	0.2
0	16	0.1	0.1	1.3	0.1	107	0	8.9	0.2	25	88	72	343	50	0.7	0.5

ESHA, EatRight Analysis CD-ROM; **AMT**, amount; **WT**, weight; **CAL**, calories; **KILO**, KiloJoule; **WTR**, water; **PROT**, protein; **CARB**, carbohydrate; **FIBR**, fiber; **FAT**, fat; **SATF**, saturated fat; **MONO**, monounsaturated fat; **POLY**, polyunsaturated fat; **CHOL**, cholesterol;

ESHA CODE	FOOD DESCRIPTION	AMT	UNIT	WT (g)	CAL (kcal)	KILO (kJ)	WTR (g)	PROT (g)	CARB (g)	FIBR (g)	FAT (g)	SATF (g)	MONO (g)	POLY (g)
VEGETABLES & LEGUMES (CONTINUED)														
5004	Asparagus-Spears-Cooked	4	pce	60	13	54	56	1	2	1	<1	<0.1	0	0.1
5249	Bamboo Shoots-Cooked Slices	1	cup	120	14	59	115	2	2	1	<1	0.1	<0.1	0.1
5250	Bamboo Shoots-Whole-Boiled	1	ea	144	17	71	138	2	3	1	<1	0.1	<0.1	0.1
5319	Beans-Baby Limas-Boiled	0.5	cup	85	105	439	57	6	20	5	<1	0.1	<0.1	0.1
7058	Beans-Baby Limas-Dry-Boiled	0.5	cup	91	115	481	61	7	21	7	<1	0.1	<0.1	0.2
7012	Beans-Black-Dry-Ckd	1	cup	172	227	950	113	15	41	15	1	0.2	0.1	0.4
7021	Beans-Great Northern-Boiled	1	cup	177	209	874	122	15	37	12	1	0.2	<0.1	0.3
5011	Beans-Green-Fresh-Boiled	0.5	cup	62.5	22	92	56	1	5	2	<1	<0.1	<0.1	0.1
5013	Beans-Green-Frozen-Boiled	1	cup	135	38	159	123	2	9	4	<1	0.1	<0.1	0.1
7022	Beans-Navy-Dry-Cooked	1	cup	182	255	1067	116	15	47	19	1	0.2	0.2	0.8
7013	Beans-Pinto-Dry-Cooked	1	cup	171	245	1025	108	15	45	15	1	0.2	0.2	0.4
7047	Beans-Red Kidney-Boiled	1	cup	177	225	941	118	15	40	13	1	0.1	0.1	0.5
5022	Beets-Fresh-Diced-Cooked	0.5	cup	85	37	155	74	1	8	2	<1	<0.1	<0.1	0.1
5679	Broccoflower-Cooked	1	cup	156	50	209	140	5	10	5	<1	0.1	<0.1	0.2
5653	Broccoli Pieces-Steamed	1	cup	156	44	184	141	5	8	5	1	0.1	<0.1	0.3
5029	Broccoli Spear-Cooked	1	ea	180	63	264	161	4	13	6	1	0.1	0.1	0.3
5028	Broccoli-Pieces-Boiled	0.5	cup	78	27	113	70	2	6	3	<1	0.1	<0.1	0.1
5030	Broccoli-Pieces-Frozen-Cooked	1	cup	184	52	218	167	6	10	6	<1	<0.1	<0.1	0.1
5033	Brussels Sprouts-Cooked	1	cup	156	56	234	139	4	11	4	1	0.2	0.1	0.4
5035	Brussels Sprouts-Frozen-Cooked	1	cup	155	65	272	134	6	13	6	1	0.1	<0.1	0.3
5237	Cabbage-Bok Choy-Boiled	1	cup	170	20	84	162	3	3	2	<1	<0.1	<0.1	0.1
5671	Cabbage-Chinese-Steamed	0.5	cup	85	11	46	81	1	2	1	<1	<0.1	<0.1	0.1
5038	Cabbage-Cooked	1	cup	150	34	142	139	2	8	3	<1	0	<0.1	<0.1
5235	Cabbage-Pe-Tsai-Boiled	1	cup	119	17	71	113	2	3	2	<1	<0.1	<0.1	0.1
5047	Carrots-Cooked	0.5	cup	78	27	113	70	1	6	2	<1	<0.1	<0.1	0.1
5358	Carrots-Frozen-Cooked	0.5	cup	73	27	113	66	<1	6	2	<1	0.1	<0.1	0.2
5625	Cassava/Yuca Blanca-Cooked	1	cup	137	221	925	81	2	53	2	<1	0.1	0.1	0.1
5052	Cauliflower Flowerets-Boiled	3	ea	54	12	50	50	1	2	1	<1	<0.1	<0.1	0.1
5053	Cauliflower-Frozen-Cooked	1	cup	180	34	142	169	3	7	5	<1	0.1	<0.1	0.2
5061	Collard Greens-Boiled	1	cup	190	49	205	175	4	9	5	1	0.1	<0.1	0.3
5062	Collard Greens-Frozen-Boiled	1	cup	170	61	255	150	5	12	5	1	0.1	<0.1	0.4
5364	CornOnCob-Small-Frozen-Ckd	1	ea	63	59	247	46	2	14	2	<1	0.1	0.1	0.2
5560	CornOnCob-White-Boiled	1	ea	77	75	314	56	3	17	2	1	0.2	0.3	0.5
5380	CornOnCob-Yellow-Med-Boiled	1	ea	77	74	310	57	3	16	2	1	0.2	0.3	0.5
5393	Corn-White-Frozen-Cooked	0.5	cup	82	66	276	63	2	16	2	<1	0.1	0.1	0.2
5379	Corn-Yellow-Boiled	0.5	cup	82	79	331	60	3	17	2	1	0.2	0.3	0.5
5065	Corn-Yellow-Frozen-Boiled	0.5	cup	82	66	276	63	2	16	2	1	0.1	0.2	0.3
5673	Eggplant Pieces-Steamed	1	cup	96	25	105	88	1	6	2	<1	<0.1	<0.1	0.1
5674	Eggplant Pieces-Stir Fried	1	cup	96	25	105	88	1	6	2	<1	<0.1	<0.1	0.1
7027	Fava/Broadbeans-Dry-Cooked	1	cup	170	187	782	122	13	33	9	1	0.1	0.1	0.3
5536	Fried Green Tomatoes	1	ea	144	284	1188	97	5	19	1	22	4.6	9.4	6.4
7001	GarbanzoBeans/Chickpeas-Ckd	1	cup	164	269	1125	99	15	45	12	4	0.4	1	1.9
5140	HashBrownPotatoes-Frzn-Ckd	1	cup	78	170	711	44	2	22	2	9	3.5	4	1
5141	HashBrowns-Frozen-FriedPatty	1	ea	29	63	264	16	1	8	1	3	1.3	1.5	0.4
5640	Hominy-Cooked	1	cup	165	119	498	136	2	24	4	1	0.2	0.4	0.7

< = Trace amount present Blank = Not available

V, vitamin; **THI**, thiamin; **RIB**, riboflavin; **NIA**, niacin; **FOL**, folate; **CALC**, calcium; **PHOS**, phosphorus; **SOD**, sodium; **POT**, potassium; **MAG**, magnesium

CHOL (mg)	V-A (IU)	THI (mg)	RIB (mg)	NIA (mg)	V-B6 (mg)	FOL (μg)	V-B12 (μg)	V-C (mg)	V-E (mg)	CALC (mg)	PHOS (mg)	SOD (mg)	POT (mg)	MAG (mg)	IRON (mg)	ZINC (mg)
0	604	0.1	0.1	0.7	<0.1	89	0	4.6	0.9	14	32	8	134	8	0.5	0.4
0	0	<0.1	0.1	0.4	0.1	2	0	0		14	24	5	640	4	0.3	0.6
0	0	<0.1	0.1	0.4	0.1	3	0	0		17	29	6	768	4	0.3	0.7
0	258	0.1	0.1	0.9	0.2	22	0	8.6	0.1	27	110	14	484	63	2.1	0.7
0	0	0.1	0.1	0.6	0.1	136	0	0		26	116	3	365	48	2.2	0.9
0	10	0.4	0.1	0.9	0.1	256	0	0		46	241	2	611	120	3.6	1.9
0	2	0.3	0.1	1.2	0.2	181	0	2.3		120	292	4	692	88	3.8	1.6
0	438	<0.1	0.1	0.4	<0.1	21	0	6.1	0.3	28	18	1	91	11	0.4	0.2
0	752	<0.1	0.1	0.5	0.1	31	0	5.5	0.1	57	39	1	215	26	0.9	0.3
	0	0.4	0.1	1.2	0.3	255	0	1.6	<0.1	126	262	0	708	96	4.3	1.9
0	0	0.3	0.1	0.5	0.4	294	0	1.4	1.6	79	251	2	746	86	3.6	1.7
0	0	0.3	0.1	1	0.2	230	0	2.1	0.1	50	251	4	713	80	5.2	1.9
0	30	<0.1	<0.1	0.3	0.1	68	0	3.1	<0.1	14	32	65	259	20	0.7	0.3
0	105	0.1	0.1	1.2	0.3	76	0	98.1	0.5	50	100	36	502	31	1.1	0.8
0	2281	0.1	0.2	0.9	0.2	94	0	123.4	0.7	75	103	42	505	39	1.4	0.6
0	2786	0.1	0.2	1	0.4	194	0	116.8	2.6	72	121	74	527	38	1.2	0.8
0	1207	<0.1	0.1	0.4	0.2	84	0	50.6	1.1	31	52	32	229	16	0.5	0.4
0	1860	0.1	0.1	0.8	0.2	103	0	73.8	2.4	61	90	20	261	24	1.1	0.5
0	1209	0.2	0.1	0.9	0.3	94	0	96.7	0.7	56	87	33	495	31	1.9	0.5
0	1435	0.2	0.2	0.8	0.4	157	0	70.8	0.8	40	87	23	450	28	0.7	0.4
0	7223	0.1	0.1	0.7	0.3	70	0	44.2	0.2	158	49	58	631	19	1.8	0.3
0	2422	<0.1	0.1	0.4	0.1	47	0	32.5	0.1	89	31	55	214	16	0.7	0.2
0	120	0.1	0.1	0.4	0.2	45	0	56.2	0.2	72	50	12	294	22	0.3	0.3
0	1151	0.1	0.1	0.6	0.2	63	0	18.8		38	46	11	268	12	0.4	0.2
0	13286	0.1	<0.1	0.5	0.1	11	0	2.8	0.8	23	23	45	183	8	0.3	0.2
0	12357	<0.1	<0.1	0.3	0.1	8	0	1.7	0.7	26	23	43	140	8	0.4	0.3
0	31	0.1	0.1	1.1	0.1	24	0	18.5	0.3	21	34	18	338	28	0.4	0.4
0	6	<0.1	<0.1	0.2	0.1	24	0	23.9	<0.1	9	17	8	77	5	0.2	0.1
0	18	0.1	0.1	0.6	0.2	74	0	56.3	0.1	31	43	32	250	16	0.7	0.2
0	15417	0.1	0.2	1.1	0.2	177	0	34.6	1.7	266	57	30	220	38	2.2	0.4
0	19538	0.1	0.2	1.1	0.2	129	0	44.9	2.1	357	46	85	427	51	1.9	0.5
0	146	0.1	<0.1	1	0.1	20	0	3	0.1	2	47	3	158	18	0.4	0.4
0	2	0.1	<0.1	1.3	0.1	15	0	4.8	0.1	2	71	2	194	24	0.4	0.4
0	203	0.1	<0.1	1.3	0.1	18	0	4.2	0.1	2	59	1	168	20	0.3	0.5
0	2	0.1	0.1	1.1	0.1	25	0	2.5	0.1	3	47	4	121	16	0.3	0.3
0	216	0.1	<0.1	1.4	0.1	19	0	4.5	0.1	2	63	1	179	21	0.4	0.5
0	163	<0.1	0.1	1.1	0.1	29	0	2.9	0.1	2	65	1	191	23	0.4	0.5
0	77	<0.1	<0.1	0.5	0.1	16	0	1.4	<0.1	7	21	3	208	13	0.3	0.1
0	73	<0.1	<0.1	0.5	0.1	15	0	1.4	<0.1	7	21	3	208	13	0.3	0.1
0	26	0.2	0.2	1.2	0.1	177	0	0.5	<0.1	61	212	8	456	73	2.6	1.7
41	635	0.2	0.2	1.4	0.1	13	0.1	20.9	3	101	102	134	254	17	1.5	0.4
0	44	0.2	0.1	0.9	0.2	282	0	2.1	0.6	80	276	11	477	79	4.7	2.5
0	0	0.1	<0.1	1.9	0.1	5	0	4.9	0.1	12	56	27	340	13	1.2	0.2
0	0	<0.1	<0.1	0.7	<0.1	2	0	1.8	0.1	4	21	10	126	5	0.4	0.1
0	0	<0.1	<0.1	0.1	<0.1	2	0	0	0.1	16	58	346	15	26	1	1.7

ESHA, EatRight Analysis CD-ROM; **AMT**, amount; **WT**, weight; **CAL**, calories; **KILO**, KiloJoule; **WTR**, water; **PROT**, protein; **CARB**, carbohydrate; **FIBR**, fiber; **FAT**, fat; **SATF**, saturated fat; **MONO**, monounsaturated fat; **POLY**, polyunsaturated fat; **CHOL**, cholesterol;

ESHA CODE	FOOD DESCRIPTION	AMT	UNIT	WT (g)	CAL (kcal)	KILO (kJ)	WTR (g)	PROT (g)	CARB (g)	FIBR (g)	FAT (g)	SATF (g)	MONO (g)	POLY (g)
VEGETABLES & LEGUMES (CONTINUED)														
5075	Kale-Cooked	1	cup	130	36	151	119	2	7	3	1	0.1	<0.1	0.3
7006	Lentils-Cooked	1	cup	198	230	962	138	18	40	16	1	0.1	0.1	0.3
5187	Mixed Vegetables-Frzn-Cooked	1	cup	182	118	494	151	5	24	8	<1	0.1	<0.1	0.1
5021	Mung Bean Sprouts-Boiled	1	cup	124	26	109	116	3	5	1	<1	<0.1	<0.1	<0.1
5092	Mushroom Pieces-Boiled	0.5	cup	78	22	92	71	2	4	2	<1	<0.1	<0.1	0.1
5096	Mustard Greens-Boiled	1	cup	140	21	88	132	3	3	3	<1	<0.1	0.2	0.1
7508	Natto-Soybean-Fermented	1	cup	175	371	1552	96	31	25	9	19	2.8	4.3	10.9
5098	Okra Pods-Boiled	8	ea	85	19	79	79	2	4	2	<1	<0.1	<0.1	<0.1
6832	Okra Pods-Frozen-Boiled	0.5	cup	92	26	109	84	2	5	3	<1	0.1	<0.1	0.1
5099	Okra Slices-Boiled	0.5	cup	80	18	75	74	1	4	2	<1	<0.1	<0.1	<0.1
5108	Onions-Boiled	0.5	cup	105	46	192	92	1	11	1	<1	<0.1	<0.1	0.1
5212	Parsnips-Boiled	1	cup	156	111	464	125	2	27	6	<1	0.1	0.2	0.1
5123	Peas+Carrots-Frozen-Boiled	0.5	cup	80	38	159	69	2	8	2	<1	0.1	<0.1	0.2
7018	Peas-Cowpea/Blackeye-Dry-Boil	1	cup	172	200	837	120	13	36	11	1	0.2	0.1	0.4
5117	Peas-Green-Boiled	0.5	cup	80	67	280	62	4	13	4	<1	<0.1	<0.1	0.1
5118	Peas-Greens-Frozen-Boiled	0.5	cup	80	62	259	64	4	11	4	<1	<0.1	<0.1	0.1
5126	Pepper-Sweet Green-Cooked	0.5	cup	68	19	79	62	1	5	1	<1	<0.1	<0.1	0.1
5339	Potato Skin-Oven Baked	1	ea	58	115	481	27	2	27	5	<1	<0.1	<0.1	<0.1
5130	Potato-Baked-Flesh-Medium	0.5	cup	61	57	238	46	1	13	1	<1	<0.1	<0.1	<0.1
5947	Potato-Baked-Salted w/Skin	1	ea	202	188	787	151	5	43	4	<1	0.1	<0.1	0.1
5136	Potato-Peeled-Boiled-Pieces	0.5	cup	78	67	280	60	1	16	1	<1	<0.1	<0.1	<0.1
5238	Red Cabbage-Boiled	0.5	cup	75	22	92	68	1	5	2	<1	<0.1	<0.1	<0.1
5969	Rutabaga-Mashed-w/Salt	0.5	cup	120	47	197	107	2	10	2	<1	<0.1	<0.1	0.1
5385	Shiitake Mushroom-Boiled Piece	1	cup	145	81	339	121	2	21	3	<1	0.1	0.1	<0.1
5122	Snow Pea Pods-Boiled	1	cup	160	67	280	142	5	11	4	<1	0.1	<0.1	0.2
5296	Snow Pea Pods-Frozen-Boiled	0.5	cup	80	42	176	69	3	7	2	<1	0.1	<0.1	0.1
7015	Soybeans-Dry-Cooked	1.25	cup	215	372	1556	134	36	21	13	19	2.8	4.3	10.9
5147	Spinach-Boiled	0.5	cup	90	21	88	82	3	3	2	<1	<0.1	<0.1	0.1
7020	Split Peas-Cooked	1	cup	196	231	967	136	16	41	16	1	0.1	0.2	0.3
5317	Squash-Butternut-Baked	0.5	cup	102.5	41	172	90	1	11	3	<1	<0.1	<0.1	<0.1
5453	Squash-Hubbard-Baked	0.5	cup	120	60	251	102	3	13	2	1	0.2	0.1	0.3
5455	Squash-Spaghetti-Boiled	0.5	cup	77.5	21	88	72	1	5	1	<1	<0.1	<0.1	0.1
5152	Squash-Summer-Boiled	0.5	cup	90	18	75	84	1	4	1	<1	0.1	<0.1	0.1
5303	Squash-Winter-Baked	0.5	cup	102.5	38	159	91	1	9	3	<1	0.1	<0.1	0.2
5251	Succotash-Boiled	0.5	cup	96	110	460	66	5	23	4	1	0.1	0.1	0.4
5155	Sweet Potato-Baked+Skin	1	ea	114	103	431	86	2	24	4	<1	<0.1	<0.1	0.1
5059	Swiss Chard-Boiled	0.5	cup	87.5	18	75	81	2	4	2	<1	<0.1	<0.1	<0.1
5302	Taro Slices-Cooked	0.5	cup	66	94	393	42	<1	23	3	<1	<0.1	<0.1	<0.1
5178	Tomatoes-Cooked	0.5	cup	120	22	92	113	1	5	1	<1	<0.1	<0.1	0.1
5183	Turnip Cubes-Boiled	0.5	cup	78	17	71	73	1	4	2	<1	<0.1	<0.1	<0.1
5185	Turnip Greens-Boiled	0.5	cup	72	14	59	67	1	3	3	<1	<0.1	<0.1	0.1
5186	Turnip Greens-Frozen-Boiled	0.5	cup	82	24	100	74	3	4	3	<1	0.1	<0.1	0.1
7490	Wasabi Radish-Cooked	0.5	cup	73.5	12	50	70	<1	3	1	<1	0.1	<0.1	0.1
7053	White Beans-Boiled	1	cup	179	249	1042	113	17	45	11	1	0.2	0.1	0.3
5160	Yams-Orange-Peeled-Boiled	1	cup	328	249	1042	263	4	58	8	<1	0.1	0	0.2

< = Trace amount present   Blank = Not available

V, vitamin; **THI**, thiamin; **RIB**, riboflavin; **NIA**, niacin; **FOL**, folate; **CALC**, calcium; **PHOS**, phosphorus; **SOD**, sodium; **POT**, potassium; **MAG**, magnesium

CHOL (mg)	V-A (IU)	THI (mg)	RIB (mg)	NIA (mg)	V-B6 (mg)	FOL (μg)	V-B12 (μg)	V-C (mg)	V-E (mg)	CALC (mg)	PHOS (mg)	SOD (mg)	POT (mg)	MAG (mg)	IRON (mg)	ZINC (mg)
0	17707	0.1	0.1	0.6	0.2	17	0	53.3	1.1	94	36	30	296	23	1.2	0.3
0	16	0.3	0.1	2.1	0.4	358	0	3	0.2	38	356	4	731	71	6.6	2.5
0	7784	0.1	0.2	1.5	0.1	35	0	5.8	0.7	46	93	64	308	40	1.5	0.9
0	16	0.1	0.1	1	0.1	36	0	14.1	0.1	15	35	12	125	17	0.8	0.6
0	0	0.1	0.2	3.5	0.1	14	0	3.1	<0.1	5	68	2	278	9	1.4	0.7
0	8852	0.1	0.1	0.6	0.1	102	0	35.4	1.7	104	57	22	283	21	1	0.2
0	0	0.3	0.3	0	0.2	14	0	22.8	<0.1	380	304	12	1276	201	15.1	5.3
0	241	0.1	<0.1	0.7	0.2	39	0	13.9	0.2	65	27	5	115	31	0.2	0.4
0	312	0.1	0.1	0.7	<0.1	134	0	11.2	0.3	88	42	3	215	47	0.6	0.6
0	226	0.1	<0.1	0.7	0.1	37	0	13	0.2	62	26	5	108	29	0.2	0.3
0	2	<0.1	<0.1	0.2	0.1	16	0	5.5	<0.1	23	37	3	174	12	0.3	0.2
0	0	0.1	0.1	1.1	0.1	90	0	20.3	1.6	58	108	16	573	45	0.9	0.4
0	7611	0.2	0.1	0.9	0.1	21	0	6.5	0.4	18	39	54	126	13	0.8	0.4
0	26	0.3	0.1	0.9	0.2	358	0	0.7	0.5	41	268	7	478	91	4.3	2.2
0	641	0.2	0.1	1.6	0.2	50	0	11.4	0.1	22	94	2	217	31	1.2	1
0	1680	0.2	0.1	1.2	0.1	47	0	7.9	<0.1	19	62	58	88	18	1.2	0.5
0	318	<0.1	<0.1	0.3	0.2	11	0	50.6	0.3	6	12	1	113	7	0.3	0.1
0	6	0.1	0.1	1.8	0.4	13	0	7.8	<0.1	20	59	12	332	25	4.1	0.3
0	0	0.1	<0.1	0.9	0.2	5	0	7.8	<0.1	3	30	3	239	15	0.2	0.2
0	20	0.1	0.1	2.8	0.6	57	0	19.4	0.1	30	141	493	1081	57	2.2	0.7
0	2	0.1	<0.1	1	0.2	7	0	5.8	<0.1	6	31	4	256	16	0.2	0.2
0	25	0.1	<0.1	0.3	0.2	18	0	25.8	0.1	32	25	21	196	13	0.5	0.2
0	2	0.1	<0.1	0.9	0.1	18	0	22.6	0.4	58	67	305	391	28	0.6	0.4
0	0	0.1	0.2	2.2	0.2	30	0	0.4	0	4	42	6	170	20	0.6	1.9
0	1648	0.2	0.1	0.9	0.2	46	0	76.6	0.6	67	88	6	384	42	3.2	0.6
0	1049	0.1	0.1	0.5	0.1	28	0	17.6	0.4	47	46	4	174	22	1.9	0.4
0	19	0.3	0.6	0.9	0.5	116	0	3.7	0.8	219	527	2	1107	185	11.1	2.5
0	9433	0.1	0.2	0.4	0.2	131	0	8.8	1.9	122	50	63	419	78	3.2	0.7
0	14	0.4	0.1	1.7	0.1	127	0	0.8	0.1	27	194	4	710	71	2.5	2
0	11434	0.1	<0.1	1	0.1	19	0	15.5	1.3	42	28	4	291	30	0.6	0.1
0	7242	0.1	0.1	0.7	0.2	19	0	11.4		20	28	10	430	26	0.6	0.2
0	85	<0.1	<0.1	0.6	0.1	6	0	2.7	0.1	16	11	14	91	9	0.3	0.2
0	191	<0.1	<0.1	0.5	0.1	18	0	5	0.1	24	35	1	173	22	0.3	0.4
0	5354	<0.1	0.1	0.5	0.2	20	0	9.8	0.1	23	19	1	247	13	0.5	0.2
0	282	0.2	0.1	1.3	0.1	32	0	7.9		16	112	16	394	51	1.5	0.6
0	21909	0.1	0.1	1.7	0.3	7	0	22.3	0.8	43	62	41	542	31	0.8	0.4
0	5358	<0.1	0.1	0.3	0.1	8	0	15.8	1.7	51	29	157	480	75	2	0.3
0	55	0.1	<0.1	0.3	0.2	13	0	3.3	1.9	12	50	10	319	20	0.5	0.2
0	587	<0.1	<0.1	0.6	0.1	16	0	27.4	0.7	13	34	13	262	11	0.8	0.2
0	0	<0.1	<0.1	0.2	0.1	7	0	9	<0.1	26	20	12	138	7	0.1	0.1
0	5490	<0.1	0.1	0.3	0.1	85	0	19.7	1.4	99	21	21	146	16	0.6	0.1
0	8827	<0.1	0.1	0.4	0.1	32	0	17.9	2.2	125	28	12	184	21	1.6	0.3
0	0	0	<0.1	0.1	<0.1	12	0	11.1	0	12	18	10	209	7	0.1	0.1
0	0	0.2	0.1	0.3	0.2	145	0	0	1.7	161	202	11	1004	113	6.6	2.5
0	51627	0.2	0.2	1.8	0.5	20	0	42	3.1	89	105	89	754	59	2.4	0.7

ESHA, EatRight Analysis CD-ROM; **AMT**, amount; **WT**, weight; **CAL**, calories; **KILO**, KiloJoule; **WTR**, water; **PROT**, protein; **CARB**, carbohydrate; **FIBR**, fiber; **FAT**, fat; **SATF**, saturated fat; **MONO**, monounsaturated fat; **POLY**, polyunsaturated fat; **CHOL**, cholesterol;

ESHA CODE	FOOD DESCRIPTION	AMT	UNIT	WT (g)	CAL (kcal)	KILO (kJ)	WTR (g)	PROT (g)	CARB (g)	FIBR (g)	FAT (g)	SATF (g)	MONO (g)	POLY (g)
VEGETABLES & LEGUMES (CONTINUED)														
5667	Zucchini Slices-Steamed	0.5	cup	90	13	54	86	1	3	1	<1	<0.1	<0.1	0.1
5327	Zucchini Squash-Boiled	0.5	cup	90	14	59	86	1	2	1	<1	0.1	<0.1	0.1
Dehydrated, Dried, & Condensed Vegetables & Legumes														
5446	Tomatoes-Sun Dried	0.5	cup	27	70	293	4	4	15	3	1	0.1	0.1	0.3
Fresh Vegetables & Legumes														
5010	Alfalfa Sprouts	0.5	cup	16.5	4	17	15	1	<1	<1	<1	<0.1	<0.1	0.1
6033	Arugula-Chopped-Raw	0.5	cup	10	2	8	9	<1	<1	<1	<1	<0.1	<0.1	<0.1
5678	Broccoflower-Raw	1	cup	100	32	134	90	3	6	3	<1	<0.1	<0.1	0.1
5041	Cabbage-Bok Choy-Raw	1	cup	70	9	38	67	1	2	1	<1	<0.1	<0.1	0.1
5040	Cabbage-Pe Tsai-Raw-Pieces	1	cup	76	12	50	72	1	2	1	<1	<0.1	<0.1	0.1
5036	Cabbage-Raw-Shredded	1	cup	70	18	75	65	1	4	2	<1	<0.1	<0.1	<0.1
5042	Cabbage-Red-Raw	1	cup	70	22	92	63	1	5	1	<1	<0.1	<0.1	0.1
5046	Carrot-Raw-Grated	0.5	cup	55	23	96	49	1	5	2	<1	<0.1	<0.1	0.1
90423	Carrot-Raw-Whole	1	ea	72	30	126	64	1	7	2	<1	<0.1	<0.1	0.1
5439	Carrots-Baby-Raw-2.75inch	1	ea	10	4	17	9	<1	1	<1	<1	<0.1	<0.1	<0.1
5049	Cauliflower-Raw-Cup	0.5	cup	50	12	50	46	1	2	1	<1	<0.1	<0.1	<0.1
5054	Celery-Raw-Chopped	0.5	cup	60	10	42	57	<1	2	1	<1	<0.1	<0.1	<0.1
5055	Celery-Raw-Large Outer Stalk	1	ea	40	6	25	38	<1	1	1	<1	<0.1	<0.1	<0.1
5399	Chili Peppers-Hot Green-Raw	0.5	cup	75	30	126	66	2	7	1	<1	<0.1	<0.1	0.1
5288	Chili Peppers-Red-Raw Pieces	0.5	cup	75	30	126	66	1	7	1	<1	<0.1	<0.1	0.2
6811	Cornsalad-Fresh	0.5	cup	28	6	25	26	1	1		<1			
5071	Cucumber-Raw-Pieces w/Peel	0.5	cup	52	8	33	50	<1	2	<1	<1	<0.1	<0.1	<0.1
5070	Cucumber-Whole-8 inch	1	ea	301	45	188	287	2	11	2	<1	0.1	<0.1	0.1
5202	Escarole/Curly Endive	1	cup	50	8	33	47	1	2	2	<1	<0.1	<0.1	<0.1
26005	Garlic Cloves-Fresh	1	ea	3	4	17	2	<1	1	<1	<1	<0.1	<0.1	<0.1
9181	Jicama-Fresh	0.5	cup	65	25	105	59	<1	6	3	<1	<0.1	<0.1	<0.1
5206	Leeks-Raw	1	ea	89	54	226	74	1	13	2	<1	<0.1	<0.1	0.1
5080	Lettuce-Butterhead-Chopped	1	cup	55	7	29	53	1	1	1	<1	<0.1	<0.1	0.1
5083	Lettuce-Iceberg-Chopped	1	cup	55	8	33	53	<1	2	1	<1	<0.1	<0.1	<0.1
5084	Lettuce-Iceberg-Leaf	1	pce	15	2	8	14	<1	<1	<1	<1	<0.1	<0.1	<0.1
5086	Lettuce-Looseleaf-Chopped	1	cup	56	8	33	53	1	2	1	<1	<0.1	<0.1	<0.1
5087	Lettuce-Looseleaf-Leaf	1	pce	10	2	8	10	<1	<1	<1	<1	<0.1	<0.1	<0.1
5090	Mushroom Slices-Raw	0.5	cup	35	8	33	32	1	1	<1	<1	<0.1	0	0.1
5091	Mushroom-Raw-Whole	1	ea	23	5	21	21	1	1	<1	<1	<0.1	0	<0.1
5106	Onion Slices-Raw	1	pce	38	15	63	34	<1	4	1	<1	<0.1	<0.1	<0.1
5104	Onion-Raw-Medium-Whole	1	ea	110	44	184	98	1	10	2	<1	<0.1	<0.1	<0.1
5101	Onions-Chopped-Raw	1	cup	160	64	268	143	2	15	3	<1	0.1	<0.1	<0.1
5124	Pepper-Sweet Green-Fresh	0.5	cup	74.5	15	63	70	1	3	1	<1	<0.1	<0.1	<0.1
5125	Pepper-Sweet Green-Whole	1	ea	74	15	63	69	1	3	1	<1	<0.1	<0.1	<0.1
5128	Pepper-Sweet Red- Raw-Chpd	0.5	cup	74.5	23	96	69	1	4	1	<1	<0.1	<0.1	0.1
5441	Pepper-Sweet Yellow-Large	1	ea	186	50	209	171	2	12	2	<1	0.1		
5451	Radicchio-Raw-Shredded	1	cup	40	9	38	37	1	2	<1	<1	<0.1	<0.1	<0.1
5144	Radish-Red-Slices	0.5	cup	58	9	38	55	<1	2	1	<1	<0.1	<0.1	<0.1
5143	Radish-Red-Whole	10	ea	45	7	29	43	<1	2	1	<1	<0.1	<0.1	<0.1
5088	Romaine Lettuce-Chopped	1	cup	56	10	42	53	1	2	1	<1	<0.1	<0.1	0.1
5427	Shallots-Raw-Chopped	1	Tbs	10	7	29	8	<1	2	0	<1	<0.1	<0.1	<0.1

< = Trace amount present Blank = Not available

V, vitamin; **THI**, thiamin; **RIB**, riboflavin; **NIA**, niacin; **FOL**, folate; **CALC**, calcium; **PHOS**, phosphorus; **SOD**, sodium; **POT**, potassium; **MAG**, magnesium

CHOL (mg)	V-A (IU)	THI (mg)	RIB (mg)	NIA (mg)	V-B6 (mg)	FOL (μg)	V-B12 (μg)	V-C (mg)	V-E (mg)	CALC (mg)	PHOS (mg)	SOD (mg)	POT (mg)	MAG (mg)	IRON (mg)	ZINC (mg)
0	292	0.1	<0.1	0.3	0.1	17	0	6.9	0.1	14	29	3	223	20	0.4	0.2
0	1005	<0.1	<0.1	0.5	0.1	25	0	11.6	0.1	16	33	3	238	17	0.3	0.3
0	236	0.1	0.1	2.4	0.1	18	0	10.6	<0.1	30	96	566	925	52	2.5	0.5
0	26	<0.1	<0.1	0.1	<0.1	6	0	1.4	<0.1	5	12	1	13	4	0.2	0.2
0	237	<0.1	<0.1	<0.1	<0.1	10	0	1.5	<0.1	16	5	3	37	5	0.1	<0.1
0	71	0.1	0.1	0.8	0.2	57	0	74	0.3	32	64	23	322	20	0.1	0.5
0	3128	<0.1	<0.1	0.4	0.1	46	0	31.5	0.1	74	26	46	176	13	0.6	0.1
0	242	<0.1	<0.1	0.3	0.2	60	0	20.5	0.1	59	22	7	181	10	0.2	0.2
0	69	<0.1	<0.1	0.2	0.1	30	0	25.6	0.1	28	18	13	119	8	0.3	0.1
0	781	<0.1	<0.1	0.3	0.1	13	0	39.9	0.1	32	21	19	170	11	0.6	0.2
0	9188	<0.1	<0.1	0.5	0.1	10	0	3.2	0.4	18	19	38	176	7	0.2	0.1
0	12028	<0.1	<0.1	0.7	0.1	14	0	4.2	0.5	24	25	50	230	9	0.2	0.2
0	1379	<0.1	<0.1	0.1	<0.1	3	0	0.3		3	3	8	24	1	0.1	<0.1
0	0	<0.1	<0.1	0.3	0.1	28	0	24.1	<0.1	11	22	15	150	8	0.2	0.1
0	269	<0.1	<0.1	0.2	<0.1	22	0	1.9	0.2	24	14	48	156	7	0.1	0.1
0	180	<0.1	<0.1	0.1	<0.1	14	0	1.2	0.1	16	10	32	104	4	0.1	0.1
0	884	0.1	0.1	0.7	0.2	17	0	181.9	0.5	14	34	5	255	19	0.9	0.2
0	714	0.1	0.1	0.9	0.4	17	0	107.8	0.5	10	32	7	242	17	0.8	0.2
0	1986	<0.1	<0.1	0.1	0.1	4	0	10.7		11	15	1	129	4	0.6	0.2
0	55	<0.1	<0.1	0.1	<0.1	4	0	1.5	<0.1	8	12	1	76	7	0.1	0.1
0	316	0.1	0.1	0.3	0.1	21	0	8.4	0.1	48	72	6	442	39	0.8	0.6
0	1084	<0.1	<0.1	0.2	<0.1	71	0	3.2	0.2	26	14	11	157	8	0.4	0.4
0	<1	<0.1	<0.1	<0.1	<0.1	<1	0	0.9	<0.1	5	5	1	12	1	0.1	<0.1
0	14	<0.1	<0.1	0.1	<0.1	8	0	13.1	0.3	8	12	3	98	8	0.4	0.1
0	1484	0.1	<0.1	0.4	0.2	57	0	10.7	0.8	53	31	18	160	25	1.9	0.1
0	1822	<0.1	<0.1	0.2	<0.1	40	0	2	0.1	19	18	3	131	7	0.7	0.1
0	276	<0.1	<0.1	0.1	<0.1	16	0	1.5	0.1	10	11	6	78	4	0.2	0.1
0	75	<0.1	<0.1	<0.1	<0.1	4	0	0.4	<0.1	3	3	2	21	1	0.1	<0.1
0	4147	<0.1	<0.1	0.2	0.1	21	0	10.1	0.2	20	16	16	109	7	0.5	0.1
0	740	<0.1	<0.1	<0.1	<0.1	4	0	1.8	<0.1	4	3	3	19	1	0.1	<0.1
0	0	<0.1	0.1	1.3	<0.1	6	<0.1	0.7	<0.1	1	30	2	111	3	0.2	0.2
0	0	<0.1	0.1	0.8	<0.1	4	<0.1	0.5	<0.1	1	20	1	73	2	0.1	0.1
0	1	<0.1	<0.1	<0.1	<0.1	7	0	2.8	<0.1	9	11	2	55	4	0.1	0.1
0	2	0.1	<0.1	0.1	0.1	21	0	8.1	<0.1	25	32	4	161	11	0.2	0.2
0	3	0.1	<0.1	0.2	0.2	30	0	11.8	<0.1	37	46	6	234	16	0.3	0.3
0	276	<0.1	<0.1	0.4	0.2	7	0	59.9	0.3	7	15	2	130	7	0.3	0.1
0	274	<0.1	<0.1	0.4	0.2	7	0	59.5	0.3	7	15	2	130	7	0.3	0.1
0	2333	<0.1	0.1	0.7	0.2	34	0	95.1	1.2	5	19	3	157	9	0.3	0.2
0	372	0.1	<0.1	1.7	0.3	48	0	341.3		20	45	4	394	22	0.9	0.3
0	11	<0.1	<0.1	0.1	<0.1	24	0	3.2	0.9	8	16	9	121	5	0.2	0.2
0	4	<0.1	<0.1	0.1	<0.1	14	0	8.6	0	14	12	23	135	6	0.2	0.2
0	3	<0.1	<0.1	0.1	<0.1	11	0	6.7	0	11	9	18	105	4	0.2	0.1
0	4878	<0.1	<0.1	0.2	<0.1	76	0	13.4	0.1	18	17	4	138	8	0.5	0.1
0	119	<0.1	<0.1	<0.1	<0.1	3		0.8		4	6	1	33	2	0.1	<0.1

ESHA, EatRight Analysis CD-ROM; **AMT**, amount; **WT**, weight; **CAL**, calories; **KILO**, KiloJoule; **WTR**, water; **PROT**, protein; **CARB**, carbohydrate; **FIBR**, fiber; **FAT**, fat; **SATF**, saturated fat; **MONO**, monounsaturated fat; **POLY**, polyunsaturated fat; **CHOL**, cholesterol;

ESHA CODE	FOOD DESCRIPTION	AMT	UNIT	WT (g)	CAL (kcal)	KILO (kJ)	WTR (g)	PROT (g)	CARB (g)	FIBR (g)	FAT (g)	SATF (g)	MONO (g)	POLY (g)
VEGETABLES & LEGUMES (CONTINUED)														
5146	Spinach-Raw-Chopped	1	cup	30	7	29	27	1	1	1	<1	<0.1	<0.1	<0.1
5114	Spring/Green Onion-Pieces	0.5	cup	50	16	67	45	1	4	1	<1	<0.1	<0.1	<0.1
5170	Tomatoes-Fresh-Chopped	0.5	cup	90	16	67	85	1	4	1	<1	<0.1	<0.1	0.1
90530	Tomatoes-Red Cherry-Fresh	1	ea	17	3	13	16	<1	1	<1	<1	<0.1	<0.1	<0.1
5169	Tomato-Fresh-Medium	0.5	ea	74.5	13	54	70	1	3	1	<1	<0.1	<0.1	0.1
5173	Tomato-Fresh-Slices	2	pce	40	7	29	38	<1	2	<1	<1	<0.1	<0.1	<0.1
5174	Tomato-Fresh-Wedge	1	pce	31	6	25	29	<1	1	<1	<1	<0.1	<0.1	<0.1
5172	Tomato-Italian/Plum-Fresh	1	ea	62	11	46	59	1	2	1	<1	<0.1	<0.1	0.1
5223	Watercress Sprigs-Fresh	10	ea	25	3	13	24	1	<1	<1	<1	<0.1	<0.1	<0.1
5222	Watercress-Fresh	1	cup	34	4	17	32	1	<1	<1	<1	<0.1	<0.1	<0.1
5326	Zucchini Squash-Raw	0.5	cup	62	11	46	59	1	2	1	<1	0.1	<0.1	0.1
Frozen Vegetables & Legumes														
9667	Chinese Stir Fry Vegetables-Frzn	1	cup	85	25	105		2	6	2	0	0	0	0

< = Trace amount present   Blank = Not available

V, vitamin; **THI**, thiamin; **RIB**, riboflavin; **NIA**, niacin; **FOL**, folate; **CALC**, calcium; **PHOS**, phosphorus; **SOD**, sodium; **POT**, potassium; **MAG**, magnesium

CHOL (mg)	V-A (IU)	THI (mg)	RIB (mg)	NIA (mg)	V-B6 (mg)	FOL (μg)	V-B12 (μg)	V-C (mg)	V-E (mg)	CALC (mg)	PHOS (mg)	SOD (mg)	POT (mg)	MAG (mg)	IRON (mg)	ZINC (mg)
0	2813	<0.1	0.1	0.2	0.1	58	0	8.4	0.6	30	15	24	167	24	0.8	0.2
0	498	<0.1	<0.1	0.3	<0.1	32	0	9.4	0.3	36	18	8	138	10	0.7	0.2
0	750	<0.1	<0.1	0.5	0.1	14	0	11.4	0.5	9	22	4	213	10	0.2	0.2
0	142	<0.1	<0.1	0.1	<0.1	3	0	2.2	0.1	2	4	1	40	2	<0.1	<0.1
0	621	<0.1	<0.1	0.4	0.1	11	0	9.5	0.4	7	18	4	177	8	0.2	0.1
0	333	<0.1	<0.1	0.2	<0.1	6	0	5.1	0.2	4	10	2	95	4	0.1	0.1
0	258	<0.1	<0.1	0.2	<0.1	5	0	3.9	0.2	3	7	2	73	3	0.1	0.1
0	516	<0.1	<0.1	0.4	<0.1	9	0	7.9	0.3	6	15	3	147	7	0.2	0.1
0	798	<0.1	<0.1	0.1	<0.1	2	0	10.8	0.2	30	15	10	82	5	0.1	<0.1
0	1085	<0.1	<0.1	0.1	<0.1	3	0	14.6	0.3	41	20	14	112	7	0.1	<0.1
0	124	<0.1	0.1	0.3	0.1	15	0	11.1	0.1	10	24	5	162	11	0.2	0.2
0	3500							18		20		15	160		0.4	

Appendix B *Exchange Lists for Diabetes*

The following chart shows the amount of nutrients in one serving from each list.

Food List	Carbohydrate (g)	Protein (g)	Fat (g)	Calories
Carbohydrates				
Starch: breads, cereals and grains, starchy vegetables, crackers, snacks, and beans, peas, and lentils	15	0–3	0–1	80
Fruits	15	—	—	60
Milk				
Fat-free, low-fat, 1%	12	8	0–3	100
Reduced-fat, 2%	12	8	5	120
Whole	12	8	8	160
Sweets, Desserts, and Other Carbohydrates	15	Varies	Varies	Varies
Nonstarchy Vegetables	5	2	—	—
Meat and Meat Substitutes				
Lean	—	7	0–3	45
Medium-fat	—	7	4–7	75
High-fat	—	7	8+	100
Plant-based proteins	Varies	7	Varies	Varies
Fats	—	—	5	45
Alcohol	Varies	—	—	100

Starch List

Cereals, grains, pasta, breads, crackers, snacks, starchy vegetables, and cooked beans, peas, and lentils are starches. In general, one starch choice is:

- ½ cup of cooked cereal, grain, or starchy vegetable
- ⅓ cup of cooked rice or pasta
- 1 ounce of a bread product, such as 1 slice of bread
- ¾ to 1 ounce of most snack foods (some snack foods may also have extra fat)

Bread

	Food	Serving Size
	Bagel, large	¼ (1 oz)
!	Biscuit, 2½ in. across	1
☺	Bread, reduced-calorie	2 slices (1½ oz)
	Bread, white, whole-grain, pumpernickel, rye, unfrosted raisin	1 slice (1 oz)
	Chapati, small, 6 in. across	1
!	Cornbread, 1¾ in. cube	1 (1½ oz)
	English muffin	½
	Hot dog or hamburger bun	½ (1 oz)
	Naan, 8 in. × 2 in.	¼
	Pancake, 4 in. across, ¼ in. thick	1
	Pita, 6 in. across	½
	Roll, plain, small	1 (1 oz)
!	Stuffing, bread	⅓ cup
!	Taco shell, 5 in. across	2
	Tortilla, corn, 6 in. across	1
	Tortilla, flour, 6 in. across	1
	Tortilla, flour, 10 in. across	⅓
!	Waffle, 4 in. square or 4 in. across	1

Cereals and Grains

	Food	Serving Size
	Barley, cooked	⅓ cup
	Bran, dry	
	☺ oat	¼ cup
	☺ wheat	½ cup
☺	Bulgur	½ cup
	Cereals	
	☺ bran	½ cup
	cooked (oats, oatmeal)	½ cup
	puffed	1½ cups
	shredded wheat, plain	½ cup
	sugar-coated	½ cup
	unsweetened, ready-to-eat	¾ cup
	Couscous	⅓ cup
	Granola	
	low-fat	¼ cup
	! regular	¼ cup
	Grits, cooked	½ cup
	Kasha	½ cup
	Millet, cooked	⅓ cup
	Muesli	¼ cup
	Pasta, cooked	⅓ cup
	Polenta, cooked	⅓ cup
	Quinoa, cooked	⅓ cup
	Rice, white or brown, cooked	⅓ cup
	Tabbouleh (tabouli), prepared	½ cup
	Wheat germ, dry	3 Tbsp
	Wild rice, cooked	½ cup

Starchy Vegetables

	Food	Serving Size
	Cassava	⅓ cup
	Corn	½ cup
	on cob, large	½ cob (5 oz)
☺	Hominy, canned	¾ cup
☺	Mixed vegetables with corn, peas, or pasta	1 cup
☺	Parsnips	½ cup
☺	Peas, green	½ cup
	Plantain, ripe	⅓ cup
	Potato	
	baked with skin	¼ large (3 oz)
	boiled, all kinds	½ cup or ½ medium (3 oz)
	! mashed, with milk and fat	½ cup
	French fried (oven-baked)	1 cup (2 oz)
☺	Pumpkin, canned, no sugar added	1 cup
	Spaghetti/pasta sauce	½ cup
☺	Squash, winter (acorn, butternut)	1 cup
☺	Succotash	½ cup
	Yam, sweet potato, plain	½ cup

Crackers and Snacks

Food	Serving Size
Animal crackers	8
Crackers	
! round-butter type	6
saltine-type	6
! sandwich-style, cheese or peanut butter filling	3
! whole-wheat regular	2–5 (¾ oz)
☺ whole-wheat lower fat or crispbreads	2–5 (¾ oz)
Graham cracker, 2½ in. square	3
Matzoh	¾ oz
Melba toast, about 2 in. × 4 in. piece	4 pieces
Oyster crackers	20
Popcorn	3 cups
! ☺ with butter	3 cups
☺ no fat added	3 cups
☺ lower fat	3 cups
Pretzels	¾ oz
Rice cakes, 4 in. across	2
Snack chips	
fat-free or baked (tortilla, potato)	15–20 (¾ oz)
! regular (tortilla, potato)	9–13 (¾ oz)

Beans, Peas, and Lentils

(Count as 1 starch plus 1 lean meat.)

	Food	Serving Size
☺	Baked beans	⅓ cup
☺	Beans, cooked (black, garbanzo, kidney, lima, navy, pinto, white)	½ cup
☺	Lentils, cooked (brown, green, yellow)	½ cup
☺	Peas, cooked (black-eyed, split)	½ cup
Δ☺	Refried beans, canned	½ cup

Fruits List

Fresh, frozen, canned, and dried fruits and fruit juices are on this list. In general, one fruit choice is:

- 1 small fresh fruit (4 oz)
- ½ cup of canned or fresh fruit or unsweetened fruit juice
- 2 tablespoons of dried fruit

Fruit

The weight listed includes skin, core, seeds, and rind.

	Food	Serving Size
	Apple, unpeeled, small	1 (4 oz)
	Apples, dried	4 rings
	Applesauce, unsweetened	½ cup
	Apricots	
	canned	½ cup
	dried	8 halves
	☺ fresh	4 whole (5½ oz)
	Banana, extra small	1 (4 oz)
☺	Blackberries	¾ cup
	Blueberries	¾ cup
	Cantaloupe, small	⅓ melon or 1 cup cubed (11 oz)
	Cherries, sweet	
	canned	½ cup
	fresh	12 (3 oz)
	Dates	3
	Dried fruits (blueberries, cherries, cranberries, mixed fruit, raisins)	2 Tbsp
	Figs	
	dried	1½
	☺ fresh	1½ large or 2 medium (3½ oz)
	Fruit cocktail	½ cup
	Grapefruit	
	large	½ (11 oz)
	sections, canned	¾ cup
	Grapes, small	17 (3 oz)
	Honeydew melon	1 slice or 1 cup cubed (10 oz)
☺	Kiwi	1 (3½ oz)
	Mandarin oranges, canned	¾ cup
	Mango, small	½ fruit (5½ oz) or ½ cup
	Nectarine, small	1 (5 oz)
☺	Orange, small	1 (6½ oz)
	Papaya	½ fruit or 1 cup cubed (8 oz)
	Peaches	
	canned	½ cup
	fresh, medium	1 (6 oz)

Food	Serving Size
Pears	
canned	½ cup
fresh, large	½ (4 oz)
Pineapple	
canned	½ cup
fresh	¾ cup
Plums	
canned	½ cup
dried (prunes)	3
small	2 (5 oz)
☺ Raspberries	1 cup
☺ Strawberries	1¼ cup whole berries
☺ Tangerines, small	2 (8 oz)
Watermelon	1 slice or 1¼ cups cubed (13½ oz)

Fruit Juice

Food	Serving Size
Apple juice/cider	½ cup
Fruit juice blends, 100% juice	⅓ cup
Grape juice	⅓ cup
Grapefruit juice	½ cup
Orange juice	½ cup
Pineapple juice	½ cup
Prune juice	⅓ cup

Milk List

Different types of milk and milk products are on this list. However, two types of milk products are found on other lists:

- Cheeses are on the Meat and Meat Substitutes list (because they are rich in protein)
- Cream and other dairy fats are on the Fats list.

Milks and yogurts are grouped in three categories (fat-free/low-fat, reduced-fat, or whole) based on the amount of fat they have.

Fat-Free and Low-Fat Milk (1%; count as 1 fat-free milk)

Food	Serving Size
Milk, buttermilk, acidophilus milk, Lactaid	1 cup
Evaporated milk	½ cup
Yogurt, plain or flavored with an artificial sweetener	⅔ cup (6 oz)

Reduced-Fat Milk (2%; count as 1 reduced-fat milk)

Food	Serving Size
Milk, acidophilus milk, kefir, Lactaid	1 cup
Yogurt, plain	⅔ cup (6 oz)

Whole Milk (count as 1 whole milk)

Food	Serving Size
Milk, buttermilk, goat's milk	1 cup
Evaporated milk	½ cup
Yogurt, plain	8 oz

Dairy-Like Foods

Food	Serving Size	Count as
Chocolate milk		
fat-free	1 cup	1 fat-free milk + 1 carbohydrate
whole	1 cup	1 whole milk + 1 carbohydrate
Eggnog, whole milk	½ cup	1 carbohydrate + 2 fats
Rice drink		
flavored, low-fat	1 cup	2 carbohydrates
plain, fat-free	1 cup	1 carbohydrate
Smoothies, flavored, regular	10 oz	1 fat-free milk + 2½ carbohydrates
Soy milk		
light	1 cup	1 carbohydrate + ½ fat
regular, plain	1 cup	1 carbohydrate + 1 fat
Yogurt		
and juice blends	1 cup	1 fat-free milk + 1 carbohydrate
low carbohydrate	⅔ cup (6 oz)	½ fat-free milk
with fruit, low-fat	⅔ cup (6 oz)	1 fat-free milk + 1 carbohydrate

Sweets, Desserts, and Other Carbohydrates

Substitute food choices from this list for other carbohydrate-containing foods (such as those found on the Starch, Fruit or Milk lists) in your meal plan, even though these foods have added sugars and fat.

Beverages, Soda, and Energy/Sports Drinks

Food	Serving Size	Count as
Cranberry juice cocktail	½ cup	1 carbohydrate
Energy drink	1 can (8.3 oz)	2 carbohydrates
Fruit drink or lemonade	1 cup (8 oz)	2 carbohydrates
Hot chocolate		
regular	1 envelope added to 8 oz water	1 carbohydrate + 1 fat
sugar-free or light	1 envelope added to 8 oz water	1 carbohydrate
Soft drink (soda), regular	1 can (12 oz)	2½ carbohydrates
Sports drink	1 cup (8 oz)	1 carbohydrate

Brownies, Cake, Cookies, Gelatin, Pie, and Pudding

Food	Serving Size	Count as
Brownie, small, unfrosted	1¼ in. square (about 1 oz)	1 carbohydrate + 1 fat
Cake		
angel food, unfrosted	1⁄12 of cake (about 2 oz)	2 carbohydrates
frosted	2 in. square (about 2 oz)	2 carbohydrates + 1 fat
unfrosted	2 in. square (about 2 oz)	1 carbohydrate + 1 fat
Cookies		
chocolate chip	2 cookies (2¼ in. across)	1 carbohydrate + 2 fats
gingersnap	3 cookies	1 carbohydrate
sandwich, with crème filling	2 small (about ⅔ oz)	1 carbohydrate + 1 fat
sugar-free	3 small or 1 large (¾–1 oz)	1 carbohydrate + 1–2 fats
vanilla wafer	5 cookies	1 carbohydrate + 1 fat
Cupcake, frosted	1 small (about 1¾ oz)	2 carbohydrates + 1–1½ fats
Fruit cobbler	½ cup (3½ oz)	3 carbohydrates + 1 fat
Gelatin, regular	½ cup	1 carbohydrate
Pie		
commercially prepared fruit, 2 crusts	⅙ of 8-in. pie	3 carbohydrates + 2 fats
pumpkin or custard	⅛ of 8 in. pie	1½ carbohydrates + 1½ fats
Pudding		
regular (made with reduced-fat milk)	½ cup	2 carbohydrates
sugar-free or sugar- and fat-free (made with fat-free milk)	½ cup	1 carbohydrate

Candy, Spreads, Sweets, Sweeteners, Syrups, and Toppings

Food	Serving Size	Count as
Candy bar, chocolate/peanut	2 "fun size" bars (1 oz)	1½ carbohydrates + 1½ fats
Candy, hard	3 pieces	1 carbohydrate
Chocolate "kisses"	5 pieces	1 carbohydrate + 1 fat
Coffee creamer		
dry, flavored	4 tsp	½ carbohydrate + ½ fat
liquid, flavored	2 Tbsp	1 carbohydrate
Fruit snacks, chewy (pureed fruit concentrate)	1 roll (¾ oz)	1 carbohydrate
Fruit spreads, 100% fruit	1½ Tbsp	1 carbohydrate
Honey	1 Tbsp	1 carbohydrate
Jam or jelly, regular	1 Tbsp	1 carbohydrate

Food	Serving Size	Count as
Sugar	1 Tbsp	1 carbohydrate
Syrup		
chocolate	2 Tbsp	2 carbohydrates
light (pancake type)	2 Tbsp	1 carbohydrate
regular (pancake type)	1 Tbsp	1 carbohydrate

Condiments and Sauces

Food	Serving Size	Count as
Barbeque sauce	3 Tbsp	1 carbohydrate
Cranberry sauce, jellied	1/4 cup	1 1/2 carbohydrates
Δ Gravy, canned or bottled	1/2 cup	1/2 carbohydrate + 1/2 fat
Salad dressing, fat-free, low-fat, cream-based	3 Tbsp	1 carbohydrate
Sweet and sour sauce	3 Tbsp	1 carbohydrate

Doughnuts, Muffins, Pastries, and Sweet Breads

Food	Serving Size	Count as
Banana nut bread	1-in. slice (1 oz)	2 carbohydrates + 1 fat
Doughnut		
cake, plain	1 medium (1 1/2 oz)	1 1/2 carbohydrates + 2 fats
yeast type, glazed	3 3/4 in. across	2 carbohydrates + 2 fats
Muffin (4 oz)	1/4 muffin (1 oz)	1 carbohydrate + 1/2 fat
Sweet roll or Danish	1 (2 1/2 oz)	2 1/2 carbohydrates + 2 fats

Frozen Bars, Frozen Desserts, Frozen Yogurt, and Ice Cream

Food	Serving Size	Count as
Frozen pops	1	1/2 carbohydrate
Fruit juice bars, frozen, 100% juice	1 bar (3 oz)	1 carbohydrate
Ice cream		
fat-free	1/3 cup	1 1/2 carbohydrates
light	1/2 cup	1 carbohydrate + 1 fat
no sugar added	1/2 cup	1 carbohydrate + 1 fat
regular	1/2 cup	1 carbohydrate + 2 fats
Sherbet, sorbet	1/2 cup	2 carbohydrates
Yogurt, frozen		
fat-free	1/3 cup	1 carbohydrate
regular	1/2 cup	1 carbohydrate + 0–1 fat

Granola Bars, Meal Replacement Bars/Shakes, and Trail Mix

Food	Serving Size	Count as
Granola or snack bar, regular or low-fat	1 bar (1 oz)	1 1/2 carbohydrates
Meal replacement bar	1 bar (1 1/3 oz)	1 1/2 carbohydrates + 0–1 fat
Meal replacement bar	1 bar (2 oz)	2 carbohydrates + 1 fat
Meal replacement shake, reduced calorie	1 can (10–11 oz)	1 1/2 carbohydrates + 0–1 fat
Trail mix		
candy/nut-based	1 oz	1 carbohydrate + 2 fats
dried fruit-based	1 oz	1 carbohydrate + 1 fat

Nonstarchy Vegetable List

Vegetables that contain small amounts of carbohydrates and calories are on this list. In general, one nonstarchy vegetable choice is:

- ½ cup of cooked vegetables or vegetable juice
- 1 cup of raw vegetables

If you eat 3 cups or more of raw vegetables or 1½ cups of cooked vegetables at one meal, count them as 1 carbohydrate choice.

Amaranth or Chinese spinach
Artichoke
Artichoke hearts
Asparagus
Baby corn
Bamboo shoots
Beans (green, wax, Italian)
Bean sprouts
Beets
Δ Borscht
Broccoli
☺ Brussels sprouts
Cabbage (green, bok choy, Chinese)
☺ Carrots
Cauliflower
Celery
☺ Chayote
Coleslaw, packaged, no dressing
Cucumber
Eggplant
Gourds (bitter, bottle, luffa, bitter melon)
Green onions or scallions
Greens (collard, kale, mustard, turnip)
Hearts of palm
Jicama
Kohlrabi
Leeks
Mixed vegetables (without corn, peas, or pasta)
Mung bean sprouts
Mushrooms, all kinds, fresh
Okra
Onions
Oriental radish or daikon
Pea pods
☺ Peppers (all varieties)
Radishes
Rutabaga
Δ Sauerkraut
Soybean spouts
Spinach
Squash (summer, crookneck, zucchini)
Sugar pea snaps
☺ Swiss chard
Tomato
Tomatoes, canned
Δ Tomato sauce
Δ Tomato/vegetable juice
Turnips
Water chestnuts
Yard-long beans

Meat and Meat Substitutes

Meat and meat substitutes are rich in protein. Foods from this list are divided into 4 groups based on the amount of fat they contain.

Lean Meats and Meat Substitutes

	Food	Amount
	Beef: Select or Choice grades trimmed of fat: ground round, roast (chuck, rib, rump), round, sirloin, steak (cubed, flank, porterhouse, T-bone), tenderloin	1 oz
Δ	Beef jerky	1 oz
	Cheeses with 3 grams of fat or less per oz	1 oz
	Cottage cheese	¼ cup
	Egg substitutes, plain	¼ cup
	Egg whites	2
	Fish, fresh or frozen, plain: catfish, cod, flounder, haddock, halibut, orange roughy, salmon, tilapia, trout, tuna	1 oz
Δ	Fish, smoked: herring or salmon (lox)	1 oz
	Game: buffalo, ostrich, rabbit, venison	1 oz
Δ	Hot dog with 3 grams of fat or less per oz (8 hot dogs per 14 oz package) *Note: may be high in carbohydrate.*	1
	Lamb: chop, leg, or roast	1 oz
	Organ meats: heart, kidney, liver *Note: may be high in cholesterol.*	
	Oysters, fresh or frozen	6 medium
	Pork	
	Δ Canadian bacon	1 oz
	rib or loin chop/roast, ham, tenderloin	1 oz
	Poultry, without skin: Cornish hen, chicken, domestic duck or goose (well drained of fat), turkey	1 oz
	Processed sandwich meats with 3 grams or less fat per oz: chipped beef, deli thin-sliced meats, turkey ham, turkey kielbasa, turkey pastrami	1 oz
	Salmon, canned	1 oz
	Sardines, canned	2 medium
Δ	Sausage with 3 grams of fat or less per oz	1 oz
	Shellfish: clams, crab, imitation shellfish, lobster, scallops, shrimp	1 oz
	Tuna, canned in water or oil, drained	1 oz
	Veal: lean chop, roast	1 oz

Medium-Fat Meat and Meat Substitutes

	Food	Amount
	Beef: corned beef, ground beef, meatloaf, Prime grades trimmed of fat (prime rib), short ribs, tongue	1 oz
	Cheeses with 4–7 grams of fat per oz: feta, mozzarella, pasteurized processed cheese spread, reduced-fat cheeses, string	1 oz
	Egg	1
	Note: high in cholesterol, limit to 3 per week.	
	Fish: any fried product	1 oz
	Lamb: ground, rib roast	1 oz
	Pork: cutlet, shoulder roast	1 oz
	Poultry: chicken with skin, dove, pheasant, wild duck or goose, fried chicken, ground turkey	1 oz
	Ricotta cheese	2 oz or 1/4 cup
Δ	Sausage with 4–7 grams of fat per oz	1 oz
	Veal, cutlet (no breading)	1 oz

High-Fat Meat and Meat Substitutes

These foods are high in saturated fat, cholesterol, and calories and may raise blood cholesterol levels if eaten on a regular basis. Try to eat 3 or fewer servings from this group per week.

	Food	Amount
	Bacon	
	Δ pork	2 slices (16 slices/lb or 1 oz each before cooking)
	Δ turkey	3 slices (1/2 oz each before cooking)
	Cheese, regular: American, bleu, brie, cheddar, hard goat, Monterey Jack, queso, and Swiss	1 oz
Δ !	Hot dog: beef, pork, or combination (10/lb)	1
Δ	Hot dog: turkey or chicken (10/lb)	1
	Pork: ground, sausage, spareribs	1 oz
	Processed sandwich meats with 8 grams of fat or more per oz: bologna, pastrami, hard salami	1 oz
Δ	Sausage with 8 grams of fat or more per oz: bratwurst, chorizo, Italian, knockwurst, Polish, smoked, summer	1 oz

Plant-Based Proteins

Because carbohydrate content varies among plant-based proteins, you should read the food label.

	Food	Amount	Count as
	"Bacon" strips, soy-based	3 strips	1 medium-fat meat
☺	Baked beans	1/3 cup	1 starch + 1 lean meat
☺	Beans, cooked: black, garbanzo, kidney, lima, navy, pinto, white	1/2 cup	1 starch + 1 lean meat
☺	"Beef" or "sausage" crumbles, soy-based	2 oz	1/2 carbohydrate + 1 lean meat
	"Chicken" nuggets, soy-based	2 nuggets (1 1/2 oz)	1/2 carbohydrate + 1 medium-fat meat
☺	Edamame	1/2 cup	1/2 carbohydrate + 1 lean meat
	Falafel (spiced chickpea and wheat patties)	3 patties (about 2 in. across)	1 carbohydrate + 1 high-fat meat
	Hot dog, soy-based	1 (1 1/2 oz)	1/2 carbohydrate + 1 lean meat
☺	Hummus	1/3 cup	1 carbohydrate + 1 high-fat meat
☺	Lentils, brown, green, or yellow	1/2 cup	1 carbohydrate + 1 lean meat
☺	Meatless burger, soy-based	3 oz	1/2 carbohydrate + 2 lean meats
☺	Meatless burger, vegetable- and starch-based	1 patty (about 2 1/2 oz)	1 carbohydrate + 2 lean meats
	Nut spread: almond butter, cashew butter, peanut butter, soy nut butter	1 Tbsp	1 high-fat meat
☺	Peas, cooked: black-eyed and split peas	1/2 cup	1 starch + 1 lean meat
Δ ☺	Refried beans, canned	1/2 cup	1 starch + 1 lean meat
	"Sausage" patties, soy-based	1 (1 1/2 oz)	1 medium-fat meat
	Soy nuts, unsalted	3/4 oz	1/2 carbohydrate + 1 medium-fat meat
	Tempeh	1/4 cup	1 medium-fat meat
	Tofu	4 oz (1/2 cup)	1 medium-fat meat
	Tofu, light	4 oz (1/2 cup)	1 lean meat

Fats

Fats are divided into three groups, based on the main type of fat they contain: unsaturated fats (omega-3, monounsaturated, and polyunsaturated) are primarily vegetable and are liquid at room temperature. These fats have good health benefits. Saturated fats have been linked with heart disease. Saturated fats are solid at room temperature. Trans fats are made in a process that changes vegetable oils into semi-solid fats. These fats can raise blood cholesterol and should be eaten in small amounts. Trans fats are found in the following types of food: solid vegetable shortening, stick margarines, and some tub margarines; crackers, candies, cookies, snack foods, fried foods, baked goods; and other food items made with partially hydrogenated vegetable oils.

Unsaturated Fats/Monounsaturated Fats

Food	Serving Size
Avocado, medium	2 Tbsp (1 oz)
Nut butters (trans fat-free): almond butter, cashew butter, peanut butter (smooth or crunchy)	1½ tsp
Nuts	
almonds	6
Brazil	2
cashews	6
filberts	5
macadamia	3
mixed (50% peanuts)	6
peanuts	10
pecans	4 halves
pistachios	16
Oil: canola, olive, peanut	1 tsp
Olives:	
black (ripe)	8 large
green, stuffed	10 large

Polyunsaturated Fats

Food	Serving Size
Margarine: lower-fat spread (30 to 50% vegetable oil, trans fat-free)	1 Tbsp
Margarine: stick, tub (trans fat-free), or squeeze (trans fat-free)	1 tsp
Mayonnaise	
reduced-fat	1 Tbsp
regular	1 tsp
Mayonnaise-type salad dressing	
reduced-fat	1 Tbsp
regular	2 tsp
Nuts	
Pignolia (pine)	1 Tbsp
walnuts, English	4 halves
Oil: corn, cottonseed, flaxseed, grape seed, safflower, soybean, sunflower	1 tsp
Oil: made from soybean and canola oil—Enova	1 tsp
Plant stanol esters	
light	1 Tbsp
regular	2 tsp
Salad dressing	
Δ reduced-fat	2 Tbsp
Note: may be high in carbohydrate.	
Δ regular	1 Tbsp
Seeds	
flaxseed, whole	1 Tbsp
pumpkin, sunflower	1 Tbsp
sesame seeds	1 Tbsp
Tahini or sesame paste	2 tsp

Saturated Fats

Food	Serving Size
Bacon, cooked, regular or turkey	1 slice
Butter	
reduced-fat	1 Tbsp
stick	1 tsp
Butter blends made with oil	
reduced-fat or light	1 Tbsp
regular	1½ tsp
Chitterlings, boiled	2 Tbsp (½ oz)
Coconut, sweetened, shredded	2 Tbsp
Coconut milk	
light	⅓ cup
regular	1½ Tbsp
Cream	
half and half	2 Tbsp
heavy	1 Tbsp
light	1½ Tbsp
whipped	2 Tbsp
whipped, pressurized	¼ cup
Cream cheese	
reduced-fat	1½ Tbsp (¾ oz)
regular	1 Tbsp (½ oz)
Lard	1 tsp
Oil: coconut, palm, palm kernel	1 tsp
Salt pork	¼ oz
Shortening, solid	1 tsp
Sour cream	
reduced-fat	3 Tbsp
regular	2 Tbsp

Free Foods

A "free" food is any food or drink choice that contains less than 20 calories and 5 or fewer grams of carbohydrate per serving. Most foods on this list should be limited to three servings per day. Foods listed without a serving size can be eaten as often as you like.

Low Carbohydrate Foods

Food	Serving Size
Cabbage, raw	½ cup
Candy, hard (regular or sugar-free)	1 piece
Carrots, cauliflower, or green beans, cooked	¼ cup
Cranberries, sweetened with sugar substitute	½ cup
Cucumber, sliced	½ cup
Gelatin	
dessert, sugar-free	
unflavored	
Gum	
Jam or jelly, light or no sugar added	2 tsp
Rhubarb, sweetened with sugar substitute	½ cup
Salad greens	
Sugar substitutes (artificial sweeteners)[†]	
Syrup, sugar-free	2 Tbsp

[†]Sugar substitutes, alternatives, or replacements that are approved by the Food and Drug Administration (FDA) are safe to use. Common brand names include:

Equal and Nutrasweet (aspartame)
Splenda (sucralose)
Sugar Twin, Sweet-10, Sweet'N Low, and Sprinkle Sweet® (saccharin)
Sweet One (acesulfame K)
Sweet-10® (saccharin)

Although each sweetener is tested for safety before it can be marketed and sold, use a variety of sweeteners and in moderate amounts.

Modified Fat Foods with Carbohydrate

Food	Serving Size
Cream cheese, fat-free	1 Tbsp (½ oz)
Creamers	
nondairy, liquid	1 Tbsp
nondairy, powdered	2 tsp
Margarine spread	
fat-free	1 Tbsp
reduced-fat	1 tsp
Mayonnaise	
fat-free	1 Tbsp
reduced-fat	1 tsp
Mayonnaise-style salad dressing	
fat-free	1 Tbsp
reduced-fat	1 tsp
Salad dressing	
fat-free or low-fat	1 Tbsp
fat-free, Italian	2 Tbsp
Sour cream, fat-free or reduced-fat	1 Tbsp
Whipped topping, light or fat-free	2 Tbsp
regular	1 Tbsp

Condiments

Food	Serving Size
Barbeque sauce	2 tsp
Catsup (ketchup)	1 Tbsp
Honey mustard	1 Tbsp
Horseradish	
Lemon juice	
Miso	1½ tsp
Mustard	
Parmesan cheese, freshly grated	1 Tbsp
Pickle relish	1 Tbsp
Pickles	
Δ dill	1½ medium
sweet, bread and butter	2 slices
sweet, gherkin	¾ oz
Salsa	¼ cup
Δ Soy sauce, light or regular	1 Tbsp
Sweet and sour sauce	2 tsp
Sweet chili sauce	2 tsp
Taco sauce	1 Tbsp
Vinegar	
Yogurt, any type	2 Tbsp

Drinks/Mixes

Any food on this list—without a serving size listed—can be consumed in any moderate amount

Δ Bouillon, broth, consommé
Δ Bouillon or broth, low-sodium
Carbonated or mineral water
Club soda
Cocoa powder, unsweetened (1 Tbsp)
Coffee, unsweetened or with sugar substitute
Diet soft drinks, sugar-free
Drink mixes, sugar-free
Tea, unsweetened or with sugar substitute
Tonic water, diet
Water
Water, flavored, carbohydrate-free

Seasonings

Any food on this list can be consumed in any moderate amount.

Flavoring extracts (for example, vanilla, almond, peppermint)
Garlic
Herbs, fresh or dried
Hot pepper sauce
Nonstick cooking spray
Pimento
Spices
Wine, used in cooking
Worcestershire sauce

Δ *Be careful with seasonings that contain sodium or are salts, such as garlic or celery salt, and lemon pepper.*

Combination Foods

Many of the foods we eat are mixed together in various combinations, such as casseroles. These "combination" foods do not fit into any one choice list. This is a list of choices for some typical combination foods.

Entrees

Food	Serving Size	Count as
Δ Casserole-type (tuna noodle, lasagna, spaghetti with meatballs, chili with beans, macaroni and cheese)	1 cup (8 oz)	2 carbohydrates + 2 medium-fat meats
Δ Stews (beef/other meats and vegetables)	1 cup (8 oz)	1 carbohydrate + 1 medium-fat meats + 0–3 fats
Tuna salad or chicken salad	½ cup (3½ oz)	½ carbohydrate + 2 lean meats + 1 fat

Frozen Entrées and Meals

Food	Serving Size	Count as
Δ ☺ Burrito (beef and bean)	1 (5 oz)	3 carbohydrates + 1 lean meat + 2 fats
Δ Dinner-type meal,	generally 14–17 oz	3 carbohydrates + 3 medium-fat meats + 3 fats
Δ Entrée or meal with fewer than 340 calories	about 8–11 oz	2–3 carbohydrates + 1–2 lean meats
Pizza		
Δ cheese/vegetarian, thin crust	¼ of 12 in. (4½–5 oz)	2 carbohydrates + 2 medium-fat meats
Δ meat topping, thin crust	¼ of 12 in. (5 oz)	2 carbohydrates + 2 medium-fat meats + 1½ fats
Δ Pocket sandwich	1 (4½ oz)	3 carbohydrates + 1 lean meat + 1–2 fats
Δ Pot pie	1 (7 oz)	2½ carbohydrates + 1 medium-fat meat + 3 fats

Salads (Deli-Style)

Food	Serving Size	Count as
Coleslaw	½ cup	1 carbohydrate + 1½ fats
Macaroni/pasta salad	½ cup	2 carbohydrates + 3 fats
Δ Potato salad	½ cup	1½–2 carbohydrates + 1–2 fats

Soups

Food	Serving Size	Count as
Δ Bean, lentil or split pea	1 cup	1 carbohydrate + 1 lean meat
Δ Chowder (made with milk)	1 cup (8 oz)	1 carbohydrate + 1 lean meat + 1½ fats
Δ Cream (made with water)	1 cup (8 oz)	1 carbohydrate + 1 fat
Δ Instant	6 oz prepared	1 carbohydrate
Δ with beans/lentils	8 oz prepared	2½ carbohydrates + 1 lean meat
Δ Miso soup	1 cup	½ carbohydrate + 1 fat
Δ Oriental noodle	1 cup	2 carbohydrates + 2 fats
Rice (congee)	1 cup	1 carbohydrate
Δ Tomato (made with water)	1 cup (8 oz)	1 carbohydrate
Δ Vegetable beef, chicken noodle, or other broth-type	1 cup (8 oz)	1 carbohydrate

Fast Foods

The choices in the Fast Foods list are not specific fast food meals or items, but are estimates based on popular foods. Ask at the restaurant or check its Web site for nutrition information about your favorite fast foods.

Breakfast Sandwiches

	Food	Serving Size	Count as
Δ	Egg, cheese, meat, English muffin	1 sandwich	2 carbohydrates + 2 medium-fat meats
Δ	Sausage biscuit sandwich	1 sandwich	2 carbohydrates + 2 high-fat meats + 3½ fats

Main Dishes/Entrées

	Food	Serving Size	Count as
Δ ☺	Burrito (beef and beans)	1 (about 8 oz)	3 carbohydrates + 3 medium-fat meats + 3 fats
Δ	Chicken breast, breaded and fried	1 (about 5 oz)	1 carbohydrate + 4 medium-fat meats
	Chicken drumstick, breaded and fried	1 (about 2 oz)	2 medium-fat meats
Δ	Chicken nuggets	6 (about 3½ oz)	1 carbohydrate + 2 medium-fat meats + 1 fat
Δ	Chicken thigh, breaded and fried	1 (about 4 oz)	½ carbohydrate + 3 medium-fat meats + 1½ fats
Δ	Chicken wings, hot	6 (5 oz)	5 medium-fat meats + 1½ fats

Oriental

	Food	Serving Size	Count as
Δ	Beef/chicken/shrimp with vegetables in sauce	1 cup (about 5 oz)	1 carbohydrate + 1 lean meat + 1 fat
Δ	Egg roll, meat	1 (about 3 oz)	1 carbohydrate + 1 lean meat + 1 fat
	Fried rice, meatless	½ cup	1½ carbohydrates + 1½ fats
Δ	Meat and sweet sauce (orange chicken)	1 cup	3 carbohydrates + 3 medium-fat meats + 2 fats
Δ ☺	Noodles and vegetables in sauce (chow mein, lo mein)	1 cup	2 carbohydrates + 1 fat

Pizza

	Food	Serving Size	Count as
	Pizza		
Δ	cheese, pepperoni, regular crust	⅛ of 14 in. (about 4 oz)	2½ carbohydrates + 1 medium-fat meat + 1½ fats
Δ	cheese/vegetarian, thin crust	¼ of 12 in. (about 6 oz)	2½ carbohydrates + 2 medium-fat meats + 1½ fats

Sandwiches

	Food	Serving Size	Count as
Δ	Chicken sandwich, grilled	1	3 carbohydrates + 4 lean meats
Δ	Chicken sandwich, crispy	1	3½ carbohydrates + 3 medium-fat meats + 1 fat
	Fish sandwich with tartar sauce	1	2½ carbohydrates + 2 medium-fat meat + 2 fats
	Hamburger		
Δ	large with cheese	1	2½ carbohydrates + 4 medium-fat meats + 1 fat
	regular	1	2 carbohydrates + 1 medium-fat meat + 1 fat
Δ	Hot dog with bun	1	1 carbohydrate + 1 high-fat meat + 1 fat
	Submarine sandwich		
Δ	fewer than 6 grams fat	6-in. sub	3 carbohydrates + 2 lean meats
Δ	regular	6-in. sub	3½ carbohydrates + 2 medium-fat meats + 1 fat
	Taco, hard or soft shell (meat and cheese)	1 small	1 carbohydrate + 1 medium-fat meat + 1½ fats

Salads

	Food	Serving Size	Count as
Δ☺	Salad, main dish (grilled chicken type, no dressing or croutons)	salad	1 carbohydrate + 4 lean meats
	Salad, side, no dressing or cheese	small (about 5 oz)	1 vegetable

Sides/Appetizers

	Food	Serving Size	Count as
!	French fries, restaurant style	small	3 carbohydrates + 3 fats
		medium	4 carbohydrates + 4 fats
		large	5 carbohydrates + 6 fats
Δ	Nachos with cheese	small (about 4½ oz)	2½ carbohydrates + 4 fats
Δ	Onion rings	1 serving (about 3 oz)	2½ carbohydrates + 3 fats

Desserts

Food	Serving Size	Count as
Milkshake, any flavor	12 oz	6 carbohydrates + 2 fats
Soft-serve ice cream cone	1 small	2½ carbohydrates + 1 fat

Alcohol

In general, 1 alcohol choice (½ oz absolute alcohol) has about 100 calories.

Alcoholic Beverages	Serving Size	Count as
Beer		
light (4.2%)	12 fl oz.	1 alcohol equivalent + ½ carbohydrate
regular (4.9%)	12 fl oz.	1 alcohol equivalent + 1 carbohydrate
Distilled spirits: vodka, rum, gin, whiskey (80 or 86 proof)	1½ fl oz.	1 alcohol equivalent
Liqueur, coffee (53 proof)	1 fl oz.	1 alcohol equivalent + 1 carbohydrate
Sake	1 fl oz.	½ alcohol equivalent
Wine		
dessert (sherry)	3½ fl oz.	1 alcohol equivalent + 1 carbohydrate
dry, red or white (10%)	5 fl oz.	1 alcohol equivalent

Source: Choose Your Foods: Exchange Lists for Diabetes. The American Diabetes Association, Alexandria, VA, and The American Dietetic Association, Chicago, IL.

☺ = More than 3 g of dietary fiber per serving ! = Extra fat or prepared with added fat Δ = 480 mg of sodium per serving; 600 mg of sodium per serving (for combination or fast food main dishes/meals)

Appendix C *USDA Food Intake Patterns*

The suggested amounts of food to consume from the basic food groups, subgroups, and oils to meet recommended nutrient intakes at 12 different calorie levels. Nutrient and energy contributions from each group are calculated according to the nutrient-dense forms of foods in each group (e.g., lean meats and fat-free milk). The table also shows the empty calories that can be accommodated within each calorie level, in addition to the suggested amounts of nutrient-dense forms of foods in each group.

Daily Amount of Food from Each Group

Calorie Level[1]	1,000	1,200	1,400	1,600	1,800	2,000	2,200	2,400	2,600	2,800	3,000	3,200
Fruits[2]	1 cup	1 cup	1.5 cups	1.5 cups	1.5 cups	2 cups	2 cups	2 cups	2 cups	2.5 cups	2.5 cups	2.5 cups
Vegetables[3]	1 cup	1.5 cups	1.5 cups	2 cups	2.5 cups	2.5 cups	3 cups	3 cups	3.5 cups	3.5 cups	4 cups	4 cups
Grains[4]	3 oz-eq	4 oz-eq	5 oz-eq	5 oz-eq	6 oz-eq	6 oz-eq	7 oz-eq	8 oz-eq	9 oz-eq	10 oz-eq	10 oz-eq	10 oz-eq
Protein Foods[5]	2 oz-eq	3 oz-eq	4 oz-eq	5 oz-eq	5 oz-eq	5.5 oz-eq	6 oz-eq	6.5 oz-eq	6.5 oz-eq	7 oz-eq	7 oz-eq	7 oz-eq
Dairy[6]	2 cups	2.5 cups	2.5 cups	3 cups	3 cups	3 cups	3 cups	3 cups	3 cups	3 cups	3 cups	3 cups
Oils[7]	15 g	17 g	17 g	22 g	24 g	27 g	29 g	31 g	34 g	36 g	44 g	51 g
SoFAs limit[8]	137	121	121	121	161	258	266	330	362	395	459	596

[1] **Calorie Levels** are set across a wide range to accommodate the needs of different individuals. The following table "USDA Food Intake Pattern Calorie Levels," can be used to help assign individuals to the food intake pattern at a particular calorie level.

[2] **Fruit Group** includes all fresh, frozen, canned, and dried fruits and fruit juices. In general, 1 cup of fruit or 100% fruit juice, or 1/2 cup of dried fruit can be considered as 1 cup from the fruit group.

[3] **Vegetable Group** includes all fresh, frozen, canned, and dried vegetables and vegetable juices. In general, 1 cup of raw or cooked vegetables or vegetable juice, or 2 cups of raw leafy greens can be considered as 1 cup from the vegetable group.

Vegetable Subgroup Amounts Are per Week

Calorie Level	1,000	1,200	1,400	1,600	1,800	2,000	2,200	2,400	2,600	2,800	3,000	3,200
Dark green veg.	0.5 c/wk	1 c/wk	1 c/wk	1.5 c/wk	1.5 c/wk	1.5 c/wk	2 c/wk	2 c/wk	2.5 c/wk	2.5 c/wk	2.5 c/wk	2.5 c/wk
Red and orange veg.	2.5 c/wk	3 c/wk	3 c/wk	4 c/wk	5.5 c/wk	5.5 c/wk	6 c/wk	6 c/wk	7 c/wk	7 c/wk	7.5 c/wk	7.5 c/wk
Beans and peas (legumes)	0.5 c/wk	0.5 c/wk	0.5 c/wk	1 c/wk	1.5 c/wk	1.5 c/wk	2 c/wk	2 c/wk	2.5 c/wk	2.5 c/wk	3 c/wk	3 c/wk
Starchy veg.	2 c/wk	3.5 c/wk	3.5 c/wk	4 c/wk	5 c/wk	5 c/wk	6 c/wk	6 c/wk	7 c/wk	7 c/wk	8 c/wk	8 c/wk
Other veg.	1.5 c/wk	2.5 c/wk	2.5 c/wk	3.5 c/wk	4 c/wk	4 c/wk	5 c/wk	5 c/wk	5.5 c/wk	5.5 c/wk	7 c/wk	7 c/wk

[4] **Grains Group** includes all foods made from wheat, rice, oats, cornmeal, and barley, such as bread, pasta, oatmeal, breakfast cereals, tortillas, and grits. In general, 1 slice of bread, 1 cup of ready-to-eat cereal, or 1/2 cup of cooked rice, pasta, or cooked cereal can be considered as 1 ounce equivalent from the grains group. *At least half of all grains consumed should be whole grains.*

[5] **Protein Foods Group** in general, 1 ounce of lean meat, poultry, or fish, 1 egg, 1 Tbsp. peanut butter, 1/4 cup cooked dry beans, or 1/2 ounce of nuts or seeds can be considered as 1 ounce equivalent from the protein foods group.

[6] **Dairy Group** includes all fluid milk products and foods made from milk that retain their calcium content, such as yogurt and cheese. Foods made from milk that have little to no calcium, such as cream cheese, cream, and butter, are not part of the group. Most milk group choices should be fat-free or low-fat. In general, 1 cup of milk or yogurt, 1 1/2 ounces of natural cheese, or 2 ounces of processed cheese can be considered as 1 cup from the dairy group.

[7] **Oils** include fats from many different plants and from fish that are liquid at room temperature, such as canola, corn, olive, soybean, and sunflower oil. Some foods are naturally high in oils, like nuts, olives, some fish, and avocados. Foods that are mainly oil include mayonnaise, certain salad dressings, and soft margarine.

[8] **SoFAs** are calories from solid fats and added sugars. The limit for SoFAs is the remaining amount of calories in each food pattern after selecting the specified amounts in each food group in nutrient-dense forms (forms that are fat-free or low-fat and with no added sugars). The number of SoFAs is lower in the 1,200-, 1,400-, and 1,600-calorie patterns than in the 1,000-calorie pattern. The nutrient goals for the 1,200- to 1,600-calorie patterns are higher and require that more calories be used for nutrient-dense foods from the food groups.

Source: Reproduced from *Dietary Guidelines for Americans 2010*, 7th ed., US Government Printing Office, 2010. Courtesy of US Department of Agriculture and US Department of Health and Human Services.

USDA Food Intake Pattern Calorie Levels

USDA food patterns assign individuals to a calorie level based on their sex, age, and activity level. The chart below identifies the calorie levels for males and females by age and activity level. Calorie levels are provided for each year of childhood, from 2–18 years, and for adults in five-year increments. The estimates are rounded to the nearest 200 calories. An individual's calorie needs may be higher or lower than these average estimates.

	Males				Females		
Activity level	**Sedentary***	**Mod. active***	**Active***	**Activity level**	**Sedentary***	**Mod. active***	**Active***
Age				**Age**			
2	1,000	1,000	1,000	2	1,000	1,000	1,000
3	1,000	1,400	1,400	3	1,000	1,200	1,400
4	1,200	1,400	1,600	4	1,200	1,400	1,400
5	1,200	1,400	1,600	5	1,200	1,400	1,600
6	1,400	1,600	1,800	6	1,200	1,400	1,600
7	1,400	1,600	1,800	7	1,200	1,600	1,800
8	1,400	1,600	2,000	8	1,400	1,600	1,800
9	1,600	1,800	2,000	9	1,400	1,600	1,800
10	1,600	1,800	2,200	10	1,400	1,800	2,000
11	1,800	2,000	2,200	11	1,600	1,800	2,000
12	1,800	2,200	2,400	12	1,600	2,000	2,200
13	2,000	2,200	2,600	13	1,600	2,000	2,200
14	2,000	2,400	2,800	14	1,800	2,000	2,400
15	2,200	2,600	3,000	15	1,800	2,000	2,400
16	2,400	2,800	3,200	16	1,800	2,000	2,400
17	2,400	2,800	3,200	17	1,800	2,000	2,400
18	2,400	2,800	3,200	18	1,800	2,000	2,400
19–20	2,600	2,800	3,000	19–20	2,000	2,200	2,400
21–25	2,400	2,800	3,000	21–25	2,000	2,200	2,400
26–30	2,400	2,600	3,000	26–30	1,800	2,000	2,400
31–35	2,400	2,600	3,000	31–35	1,800	2,000	2,200
36–40	2,400	2,600	2,800	36–40	1,800	2,000	2,200
41–45	2,200	2,600	2,800	41–45	1,800	2,000	2,200
46–50	2,200	2,400	2,800	46–50	1,800	2,000	2,200
51–55	2,200	2,400	2,800	51–55	1,600	1,800	2,200
56–60	2,200	2,400	2,600	56–60	1,600	1,800	2,200
61–65	2,000	2,400	2,600	61–65	1,600	1,800	2,000
66–70	2,000	2,200	2,600	66–70	1,600	1,800	2,000
71–75	2,000	2,200	2,600	71–75	1,600	1,800	2,000
76 and up	2,000	2,200	2,400	76 and up	1,600	1,800	2,000

*Calorie levels are based on the Estimated Energy Requirements (EER) and activity levels from the Institute of Medicine Dietary Reference Intakes Macronutrients Report, 2002. *Sedentary* means a lifestyle that includes only the light physical activity associated with typical day-to-day life. *Moderately active* means a lifestyle that includes physical activity equivalent to walking about 1.5 to 3 miles per day at 3 to 4 miles per hour, in addition to the light physical activity associated with typical day-to-day life. *Active* means a lifestyle that includes physical activity equivalent to walking more than 3 miles per day at 3 to 4 miles per hour, in addition to the light physical activity associated with typical day-to-day life.

Source: Reproduced from *Dietary Guidelines for Americans 2010*, 7th ed., US Government Printing Office, 2010. Courtesy of US Department of Agriculture and US Department of Health and Human Services.

Appendix D *Nutrition and Health for Canadians*

- **Canadian Guidelines for Nutrition**
- **Nutrient Intake Recommendations for Canadians**
- ***Canada's Food Guide to Healthy Eating***
- ***Canada's Food Guide***
- ***Canada's Physical Activity Guide to Healthy Active Living***
- **Nutrition Labeling for Canadians**
- **Canadian Diabetes Association's Meal Planning Guide**

Canadian Guidelines for Nutrition

For more than 60 years, the Canadian government has worked to promote healthy and nutritious eating habits. In 1987, Health and Welfare Canada began a major review of the system for guiding Canadians on their food choices. To perform the review, the government appointed two advisory committees—the Scientific Review Committee and the Communications and Implementation Committee.

After examining research evidence available on nutrition and public health, the Scientific Review Committee issued a report in 1990 called *Nutrition Recommendations.* The report included both updated Recommended Nutrient Intakes (RNI) and a scientific description of a healthy dietary pattern that would deliver adequate nutrients for health and reduce the risk of nutrition-related chronic diseases.

Meanwhile, the Communications and Implementation Committee translated these scientific findings into understandable guidelines and outlined implementation strategies in a report called *Action Towards Healthy Eating: Technical Report* (1990). This report suggested that Canada develop a "total diet approach" towards healthy eating. A total diet approach would give consumers a better idea of eating patterns associated with reducing the risk of developing chronic diseases.

In 1990, the government issued *Nutrition Recommendations: A Call for Action*, a summary report produced jointly by the Scientific Review Committee and the Communications and Implementation Committee.

A Revised Food Guide

In accordance with the recommendations of its two advisory groups, the Health Department undertook to revise *Canada's Food Guide*. In 1992, the agency launched *Canada's Food Guide to Healthy Eating* and an explanatory document called *Using the Food Guide.* It promoted dietary diversity, a reduction in total fat intake, and an active lifestyle and offered consumers a pattern for establishing healthy eating habits in their daily selection of foods.

Moreover, the guide introduced a number of new concepts. A range of servings from the four food groups accommodated the wide range of energy needs for different ages, body sizes, activity levels, genders, and conditions such as pregnancy and nursing. The wide range of servings in grain products, vegetables, and fruits was designed to give consumers a better idea of the type of diet that would help reduce the risk of developing nutrition-related chronic diseases.

The guide also introduced a category of "other" foods such as sweets, fats such as butter, and drinks like coffee, that, though part of the diets of many Canadians, would traditionally not have been mentioned in a food guide. The guide recommended moderation in the consumption of these foods and acknowledged their role, along with the wide range of servings in grains, vegetables, and fruits, as a "total diet approach" to healthy eating.

A Work in Progress

Some groups and organizations challenged specific aspects of the government's *Nutrition Recommendations.* In a typically Canadian twist, the government responded to challengers by including them in the development process. When the Canadian Pediatric Society, for example, queried the dietary recommendations on fat consumption in children, the Society was invited to join Health Canada in researching the issue. The result was *Nutrition Recommendations Update: Dietary Fat and Children* (1993), which adjusted the recommendation of appropriate levels of dietary fat for growing children. In 1995, Health Canada issued *Canada's Food Guide to Healthy Eating: Focus on Preschoolers* as a background paper for educators and communicators.

A thorough review of the 1992 *Food Guide* began in 2002. Many strengths as well as some challenges in understanding and using the information from the 1992 *Food Guide* were identified. An assessment of the nutritional adequacy of the 1992 *Food Guide* using Dietary Reference Intakes was undertaken. The assessment also sought to address changes in the food supply and patterns of food use. Extensive stakeholder consultation was also carried out. Health Canada worked with three advisory groups, an external *Food Guide* Advisory Committee, an Interdepartmental Working Group, and the Expert Advisory Committee on Dietary Reference Intakes throughout the revision process. In 2007, Health Canada released *Eating Well with Canada's Food Guide*, which is available in 10 languages. In addition, *A Food Guide for First Nations, Inuit, and Métis,* which recognizes the cultural, spiritual, and physical importance of traditional aboriginal foods, was also released in 2007.

Health Canada has positioned nutrition in a broader health context, which includes physical activity and a positive outlook on life. One result of this comprehensive approach was the Vitality Leaders Kit (1994), intended to help community leaders promote healthy eating, active living, and positive self-image and body image in an integrated way. *Canada's Physical Activity Guide* was released in 1998, followed by the *Guide for Older Adults* and the *Guides for Children and Youth*.

Looking Ahead

The job of keeping Canada's nutrition policy and consumer guidelines up-to-date is an ongoing task. New scientific research on nutrition and health continually uncovers new relationships and connections between them. Consumer tastes in foods vary in response to prevailing fashions and shifting demographics. Global trade also influences the food choices that appear on the Canadian dinner table.

The science underlying nutrition recommendations knows no borders. An increasingly complex knowledge base on nutrients, food and health, global trade, and international agreements requires international efforts. Scientists from Canada and the United States worked with the National Academy of Sciences to develop the Dietary Reference Intakes (DRIs), recommended nutrient intake levels for healthy people in the U.S. and Canada.

To keep abreast of the latest developments in Canada's nutrition policies, visit the Food and Nutrition area of the Health Canada Web site at: http://www.hc-sc.gc.ca.

Nutrient Intake Recommendations for Canadians

Health Canada has reviewed and made recommendations on nutrient requirements on a periodic basis since 1938. Known as the Recommended Nutrient Intakes, or RNI, these values were last published in 1990 as part of *Nutrition Recommendations: The Report of the Scientific Review Committee.* Since that time, there have been advances in science and by 1994, it was clear that it was time to initiate another review of the scientific data.

At the same time, the Food and Nutrition Board of the National Academy of Sciences was beginning a consultation process on the review of the Recommended Dietary Allowances, the nutrient recommendations used in the United States. Health Canada considered that participating in the U.S. review would offer several advantages to Canada. These were as follows:

- The science underlying nutrient requirements knows no borders and scientists everywhere are utilizing the same knowledge produced from studies conducted all over the world.
- The knowledge base on nutrients, foods, and health is increasing rapidly in scope and complexity. This increases the need for specialized expertise. Participating in the U.S. review permits Canada to expand the base of scientific expertise that could be utilized.
- International trade considerations, including NAFTA, suggest that the harmonization of the science base underlying nutrition policy will facilitate harmonization of such trade-related matters as nutrition labeling and food composition.

Canadian and American scientists establish Dietary Reference Intakes (DRIs) through a review process overseen by the Food and Nutrition Board of the Institute of Medicine, National Academy of Sciences. DRIs have replaced the RNIs and are found printed inside the covers of this text.

The National Academy of Sciences is an American private nonprofit society of distinguished scholars engaged in scientific and engineering research, dedicated to the advancement of science and technology and to their use for the general welfare. The Academy has a mandate that requires it to advise the U.S. federal government on scientific and technical matters.

The Food and Nutrition Board (FNB) is a unit of the Institute of Medicine, part of the National Academy of Sciences. The Board is a multidisciplinary group of biomedical scientists with expertise in various aspects of nutrition, food sciences, biochemistry, medicine, public health, epidemiology, food toxicology, and food safety. The major focus of the FNB is to evaluate emerging knowledge of nutrient requirements and relationships between diet and the reduction of risk of common chronic diseases and to relate this knowledge to strategies for promoting health and preventing disease.

Canada's Food Guide

Scientists have known for some time that adequate nutrition is essential for proper growth and development. More recently, healthy eating has been accepted as a significant factor in reducing the risk of developing nutrition-related problems, including heart disease, cancer, obesity, hypertension (high blood pressure), osteoporosis, anemia, dental decay, and some bowel disorders.

What "Reducing Risk" Means

Reducing risk means lowering the chances of developing a disease. It does not guarantee the prevention of a disease. Since the development of disease involves several factors, risk reduction usually involves several different strategies or approaches. Healthy eating is just one positive action that may help to avoid a potential problem.

Healthy Eating with *Canada's Food Guide*

The revised *Food Guide* was designed to meet the body's needs for vitamins, minerals, and other nutrients; to reduce the risk of obesity, type 2 diabetes, heart disease, and certain types of cancer and osteoporosis; and to enhance the overall health and vitality of Canadians over the age of 2. The *Food Guide* outlines the recommended number of servings from the different food groups based on age and gender. **Figure D.1** shows the current *Food Guide*.

Canada's Physical Activity Guide to Healthy Active Living

High levels of physical inactivity are a serious threat to public health in Canada. Nearly two-thirds of Canadians are not active enough to achieve optimal health benefits. These Canadians are at risk for heart disease, obesity, high blood pressure, adult-onset diabetes, osteoporosis, stroke, depression, and colon cancer. Although physical activity levels increased during the 1980s and early 1990s, the progress has stalled. Health Canada estimates that physical inactivity results in at least 21,000 premature deaths annually.

Canada's Physical Activity Guide to Healthy Active Living, produced by a joint effort of Health Canada and the Canadian Society for Exercise Physiology, provides the first set of Canadian guidelines for physical activity. It provides information to help Canadians understand how to achieve health benefits by being physically active. The guide complements the popular *Canada's Food Guide to Healthy Eating* and provides concrete examples of how to incorporate physical activity into daily life.

Designed for adults, the guide recommends 60 minutes of physical activity every day to stay healthy or improve your health. As a person progresses to more intense activity, he or she can cut down to 30 minutes, four days a week. The guide also suggests Canadians can add up their activities in periods of at least 10 minutes each, starting slowly and building up. **Figure D.2** shows the *Physical Activity Guide*.

Federal, provincial, and territorial governments are working to reduce the number of inactive Canadians. *Canada's Physical Activity Guide to Healthy Active Living* is a major step toward building the knowledge and awareness necessary for all Canadians to become more active. The healthy active living series now also includes *Physical Activity Guide to Healthy Active Living for Older Adults, Physical Activity Guide for Youth, Physical Activity Guide for Children*, and *Active Living at Work*.

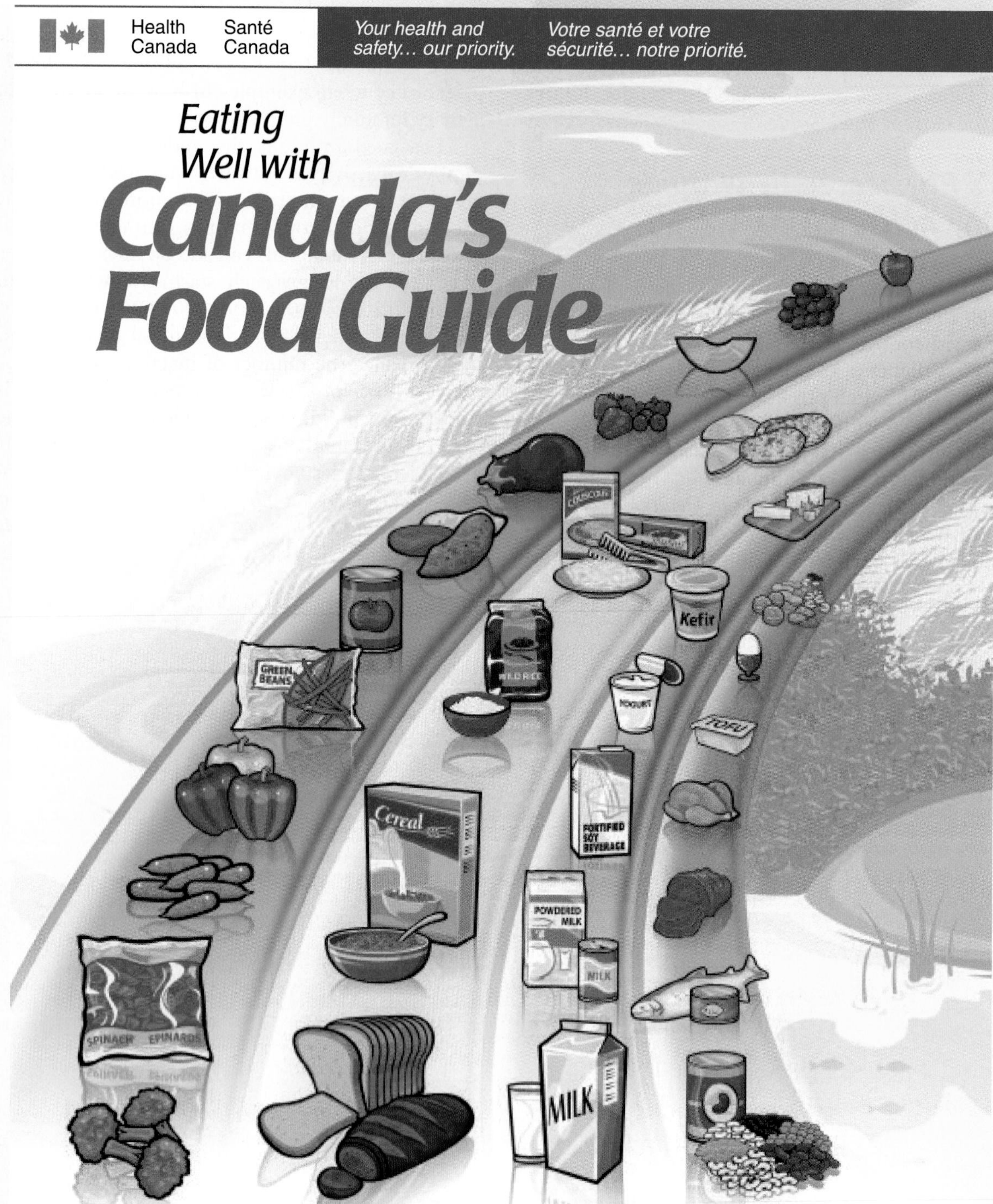

Figure D.1 ***Eating Well with Canada's Food Guide. Source:*** Health Canada, 2007. Reprinted with the permission of the Minister of Public Works and Government Services Canada, 2010.

Recommended Number of Food Guide Servings per Day

	Children			Teens		Adults			
Age in Years	2-3	4-8	9-13	14-18		19-50		51+	
Sex	Girls and Boys			Females	Males	Females	Males	Females	Males
Vegetables and Fruit	4	5	6	7	8	7-8	8-10	7	7
Grain Products	3	4	6	6	7	6-7	8	6	7
Milk and Alternatives	2	2	3-4	3-4	3-4	2	2	3	3
Meat and Alternatives	1	1	1-2	2	3	2	3	2	3

The chart above shows how many Food Guide Servings you need from each of the four food groups every day.

Having the amount and type of food recommended and following the tips in *Canada's Food Guide* will help:

- Meet your needs for vitamins, minerals and other nutrients.
- Reduce your risk of obesity, type 2 diabetes, heart disease, certain types of cancer and osteoporosis.
- Contribute to your overall health and vitality.

What is One Food Guide Serving?
Look at the examples below.

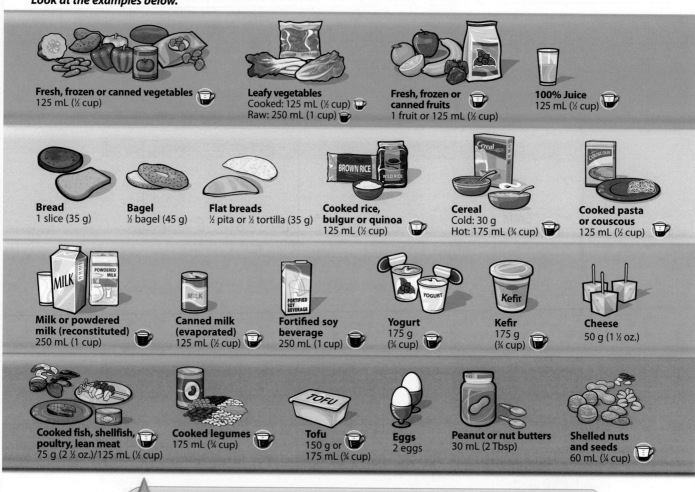

Fresh, frozen or canned vegetables
125 mL (½ cup)

Leafy vegetables
Cooked: 125 mL (½ cup)
Raw: 250 mL (1 cup)

Fresh, frozen or canned fruits
1 fruit or 125 mL (½ cup)

100% Juice
125 mL (½ cup)

Bread
1 slice (35 g)

Bagel
½ bagel (45 g)

Flat breads
½ pita or ½ tortilla (35 g)

Cooked rice, bulgur or quinoa
125 mL (½ cup)

Cereal
Cold: 30 g
Hot: 175 mL (¾ cup)

Cooked pasta or couscous
125 mL (½ cup)

Milk or powdered milk (reconstituted)
250 mL (1 cup)

Canned milk (evaporated)
125 mL (½ cup)

Fortified soy beverage
250 mL (1 cup)

Yogurt
175 g (¾ cup)

Kefir
175 g (¾ cup)

Cheese
50 g (1 ½ oz.)

Cooked fish, shellfish, poultry, lean meat
75 g (2 ½ oz.)/125 mL (½ cup)

Cooked legumes
175 mL (¾ cup)

Tofu
150 g or 175 mL (¾ cup)

Eggs
2 eggs

Peanut or nut butters
30 mL (2 Tbsp)

Shelled nuts and seeds
60 mL (¼ cup)

Oils and Fats

- Include a small amount – 30 to 45 mL (2 to 3 Tbsp) – of unsaturated fat each day. This includes oil used for cooking, salad dressings, margarine and mayonnaise.
- Use vegetable oils such as canola, olive and soybean.
- Choose soft margarines that are low in saturated and trans fats.
- Limit butter, hard margarine, lard and shortening.

Make each Food Guide Serving count…
wherever you are – at home, at school, at work or when eating out!

- **Eat at least one dark green and one orange vegetable each day.**
  - Go for dark green vegetables such as broccoli, romaine lettuce and spinach.
  - Go for orange vegetables such as carrots, sweet potatoes and winter squash.
- **Choose vegetables and fruit prepared with little or no added fat, sugar or salt.**
  - Enjoy vegetables steamed, baked or stir-fried instead of deep-fried.
- **Have vegetables and fruit more often than juice.**

- **Make at least half of your grain products whole grain each day.**
  - Eat a variety of whole grains such as barley, brown rice, oats, quinoa and wild rice.
  - Enjoy whole grain breads, oatmeal or whole wheat pasta.
- **Choose grain products that are lower in fat, sugar or salt.**
  - Compare the Nutrition Facts table on labels to make wise choices.
  - Enjoy the true taste of grain products. When adding sauces or spreads, use small amounts.

- **Drink skim, 1%, or 2% milk each day.**
  - Have 500 mL (2 cups) of milk every day for adequate vitamin D.
  - Drink fortified soy beverages if you do not drink milk.
- **Select lower fat milk alternatives.**
  - Compare the Nutrition Facts table on yogurts or cheeses to make wise choices.

- **Have meat alternatives such as beans, lentils and tofu often.**
- **Eat at least two Food Guide Servings of fish each week.***
  - Choose fish such as char, herring, mackerel, salmon, sardines and trout.
- **Select lean meat and alternatives prepared with little or no added fat or salt.**
  - Trim the visible fat from meats. Remove the skin on poultry.
  - Use cooking methods such as roasting, baking or poaching that require little or no added fat.
  - If you eat luncheon meats, sausages or prepackaged meats, choose those lower in salt (sodium) and fat.

Enjoy a variety of foods from the four food groups.

Satisfy your thirst with water!

Drink water regularly. It's a calorie-free way to quench your thirst. Drink more water in hot weather or when you are very active.

* Health Canada provides advice for limiting exposure to mercury from certain types of fish. Refer to www.healthcanada.gc.ca for the latest information.

Advice for different ages and stages...

Children

Following *Canada's Food Guide* helps children grow and thrive.

Young children have small appetites and need calories for growth and development.

- Serve small nutritious meals and snacks each day.
- Do not restrict nutritious foods because of their fat content. Offer a variety of foods from the four food groups.
- Most of all... be a good role model.

Women of childbearing age

All women who could become pregnant and those who are pregnant or breastfeeding need a multivitamin containing **folic acid** every day. Pregnant women need to ensure that their multivitamin also contains **iron**. A health care professional can help you find the multivitamin that's right for you.

Pregnant and breastfeeding women need more calories. Include an extra 2 to 3 Food Guide Servings each day.

Here are two examples:

- Have fruit and yogurt for a snack, or
- Have an extra slice of toast at breakfast and an extra glass of milk at supper.

Men and women over 50

The need for **vitamin D** increases after the age of 50.

In addition to following *Canada's Food Guide*, everyone over the age of 50 should take a daily vitamin D supplement of 10 μg (400 IU).

How do I count Food Guide Servings in a meal?

Here is an example:

Vegetable and beef stir-fry with rice, a glass of milk and an apple for dessert		
250 mL (1 cup) mixed broccoli, carrot and sweet red pepper	=	2 **Vegetables and Fruit** Food Guide Servings
75 g (2 ½ oz.) lean beef	=	1 **Meat and Alternatives** Food Guide Serving
250 mL (1 cup) brown rice	=	2 **Grain Products** Food Guide Servings
5 mL (1 tsp) canola oil	=	part of your **Oils and Fats** intake for the day
250 mL (1 cup) 1% milk	=	1 **Milk and Alternatives** Food Guide Serving
1 apple	=	1 **Vegetables and Fruit** Food Guide Serving

Eat well and be active today and every day!

The benefits of eating well and being active include:

- Better overall health.
- Lower risk of disease.
- A healthy body weight.
- Feeling and looking better.
- More energy.
- Stronger muscles and bones.

Be active

To be active every day is a step towards better health and a healthy body weight.

Canada's Physical Activity Guide recommends building 30 to 60 minutes of moderate physical activity into daily life for adults and at least 90 minutes a day for children and youth. You don't have to do it all at once. Add it up in periods of at least 10 minutes at a time for adults and five minutes at a time for children and youth.

Start slowly and build up.

Eat well

Another important step towards better health and a healthy body weight is to follow *Canada's Food Guide* by:

- Eating the recommended amount and type of food each day.
- Limiting foods and beverages high in calories, fat, sugar or salt (sodium) such as cakes and pastries, chocolate and candies, cookies and granola bars, doughnuts and muffins, ice cream and frozen desserts, french fries, potato chips, nachos and other salty snacks, alcohol, fruit flavoured drinks, soft drinks, sports and energy drinks, and sweetened hot or cold drinks.

Read the label

- Compare the Nutrition Facts table on food labels to choose products that contain less fat, saturated fat, trans fat, sugar and sodium.
- Keep in mind that the calories and nutrients listed are for the amount of food found at the top of the Nutrition Facts table.

Nutrition Facts
Per 0 mL (0 g)

Amount	% Daily Value
Calories 0	
Fat 0 g	0 %
Saturates 0 g	0 %
+ Trans 0 g	
Cholesterol 0 mg	
Sodium 0 mg	0 %
Carbohydrate 0 g	0 %
Fibre 0 g	0 %
Sugars 0 g	
Protein 0 g	

Vitamin A	0 %	Vitamin C	0 %
Calcium	0 %	Iron	0 %

Limit trans fat

When a Nutrition Facts table is not available, ask for nutrition information to choose foods lower in trans and saturated fats.

Take a step today...

- ✓ Have breakfast every day. It may help control your hunger later in the day.
- ✓ Walk wherever you can – get off the bus early, use the stairs.
- ✓ Benefit from eating vegetables and fruit at all meals and as snacks.
- ✓ Spend less time being inactive such as watching TV or playing computer games.
- ✓ Request nutrition information about menu items when eating out to help you make healthier choices.
- ✓ Enjoy eating with family and friends!
- ✓ Take time to eat and savour every bite!

For more information, interactive tools, or additional copies visit Canada's Food Guide on-line at:
www.healthcanada.gc.ca/foodguide

or contact:

Publications
Health Canada
Ottawa, Ontario K1A 0K9
E-Mail: publications@hc-sc.gc.ca
Tel.: 1-866-225-0709
Fax: (613) 941-5366
TTY: 1-800-267-1245

Également disponible en français sous le titre : Bien manger avec le Guide alimentaire canadien

This publication can be made available on request on diskette, large print, audio-cassette and braille.

HC Pub.: 4651 Cat.: H164-38/1-2007E ISBN: 0-662-44467-1

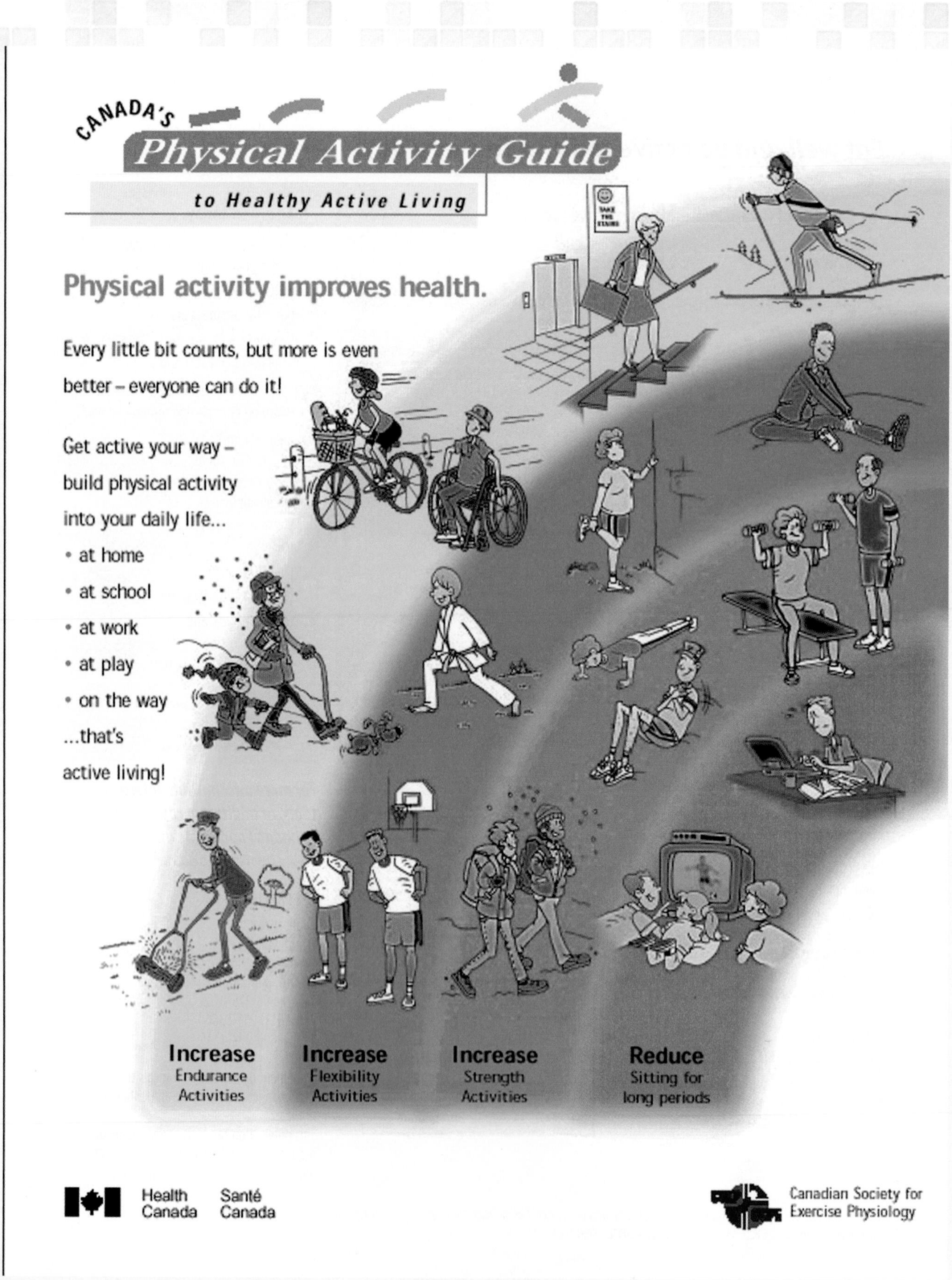

CANADA'S
Physical Activity Guide
to Healthy Active Living

Physical activity improves health.

Every little bit counts, but more is even better – everyone can do it!

Get active your way – build physical activity into your daily life...

- at home
- at school
- at work
- at play
- on the way

...that's active living!

Increase Endurance Activities

Increase Flexibility Activities

Increase Strength Activities

Reduce Sitting for long periods

Health Canada Santé Canada

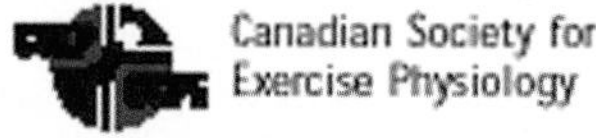

Figure D.2 *Canada's Physical Activity Guide to Healthy Active Living.* **Source:** Health Canada. Reprinted with the permission of the Minister of Public Works and Government Services Canada, 2010.

Choose a variety of activities from these three groups:

Endurance

4-7 days a week
Continuous activities for your heart, lungs and circulatory system.

Flexibility

4-7 days a week
Gentle reaching, bending and stretching activities to keep your muscles relaxed and joints mobile.

Strength

2-4 days a week
Activities against resistance to strengthen muscles and bones and improve posture.

Starting slowly is very safe for most people. Not sure? Consult your health professional.

For a copy of the *Guide Handbook* and more information: **1-888-334-9769**, or **www.paguide.com**

Eating well is also important. Follow *Canada's Food Guide to Healthy Eating* to make wise food choices.

Get Active Your Way, Every Day–For Life!

Scientists say accumulate 60 minutes of physical activity every day to stay healthy or improve your health. As you progress to moderate activities you can cut down to 30 minutes, 4 days a week. Add-up your activities in periods of at least 10 minutes each. Start slowly... and build up.

Time needed depends on effort

Very Light Effort	Light Effort *60 minutes*	Moderate Effort *30-60 minutes*	Vigorous Effort *20-30 minutes*	Maximum Effort
• Strolling • Dusting	• Light walking • Volleyball • Easy gardening • Stretching	• Brisk walking • Biking • Raking leaves • Swimming • Dancing • Water aerobics	• Aerobics • Jogging • Hockey • Basketball • Fast swimming • Fast dancing	• Sprinting • Racing
	Range needed to stay healthy			

You Can Do It – Getting started is easier than you think

Physical activity doesn't have to be very hard. Build physical activities into your daily routine.

- Walk whenever you can – get off the bus early, use the stairs instead of the elevator.
- Reduce inactivity for long periods, like watching TV.
- Get up from the couch and stretch and bend for a few minutes every hour.
- Play actively with your kids.
- Choose to walk, wheel or cycle for short trips.
- Start with a 10 minute walk – gradually increase the time.
- Find out about walking and cycling paths nearby and use them.
- Observe a physical activity class to see if you want to try it.
- Try one class to start – you don't have to make a long-term commitment.
- Do the activities you are doing now, more often.

Benefits of regular activity:	Health risks of inactivity:
• better health • improved fitness • better posture and balance • better self-esteem • weight control • stronger muscles and bones • feeling more energetic • relaxation and reduced stress • continued independent living in later life	• premature death • heart disease • obesity • high blood pressure • adult-onset diabetes • osteoporosis • stroke • depression • colon cancer

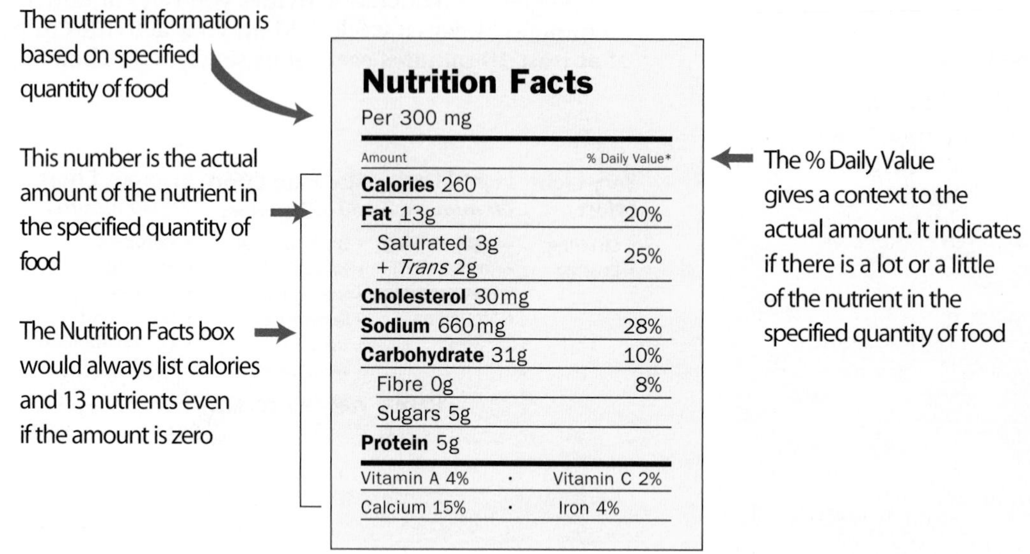
The Nutrition Facts Box
The Nutrition Facts box allows consumers to make informed choices.
The nutrient information is based on specified quantity of food
This number is the actual amount of the nutrient in the specified quantity of food
The Nutrition Facts box would always list calories and 13 nutrients even if the amount is zero
The % Daily Value gives a context to the actual amount. It indicates if there is a lot or a little of the nutrient in the specified quantity of food
Nutrition Facts
Per 300 mg
Amount
% Daily Value*
Calories 260
Fat 13g 20%
Saturated 3g + Trans 2g 25%
Cholesterol 30mg
Sodium 660mg 28%
Carbohydrate 31g 10%
Fibre 0g 8%
Sugars 5g
Protein 5g
Vitamin A 4% · Vitamin C 2%
Calcium 15% · Iron 4%

Figure D.3 How to read a food label.

Nutrition Labeling for Canadians

The nutrition label is one of the most useful tools in selecting foods for healthy eating (**Figure D.3**). The *Food Guide* outlines a pattern of healthy eating; the nutrition label supports the *Food Guide* by helping consumers to choose foods according to healthy eating messages.

Consumers can use labels to compare products and make choices on the basis of nutrient content. For example, consumers can choose a lower-fat product based on the fat content given on the labels.

Consumers also can use label information to evaluate products in relation to healthy eating. For instance, the *Nutrition Recommendations* advise Canadians to get 30 percent or less of their day's energy (kilocalories/kilojoules) from fat. This translates into a range of fat, in grams, that can be used as a benchmark against which individual foods and meals can be evaluated. The *Food Guide* covers a range of energy needs from 1,800 to 3,200 kilocalories (7,500 to 13,400 kilojoules) per day. A fat intake of 30 percent or less of a day's calories means a fat intake between 60 and 105 grams of fat.

Label Claims

A claim on a food label highlights a nutritional feature of a product. It is known to influence consumers' buying habits. Manufacturers often position label claims in a bold, banner-format on the front panel of a package or on the side panel along with the nutrition label. Because a label claim must be backed up by detailed facts relating to the claim, the consumer should look for the nutrition label for more information.

Nutrient Content Claims

A nutrient content claim describes the amount of a nutrient in a food. A food whose label carries the claim *high fibre* must contain 4 grams or more of fiber per reference amount and serving of stated size. A "sodium-free" food must contain less than 5 mg of sodium per reference amount and serving of stated size.

Diet-Related Health Claims

Optional health claims highlight the characteristics of a diet that reduces the chance of developing a disease such as cancer or heart disease. They also tell how the food fits into the diet.

Characteristic of the Diet:	Reduced Risk of:
Low in sodium and high in potassium	High blood pressure
Adequate in calcium and vitamin D	Osteoporosis
Low in saturates and trans fats	Heart disease
Rich in fruits and vegetables	Some types of cancer

For the latest information, visit the Nutrition Labeling area of the Health Canada Web site at: http://www.hc-sc.gc.ca/.

Canadian Diabetes Association's Meal Planning Guide

The Canadian Diabetes Association (CDA) works to promote the health of Canadians through diabetes research, education, service, and advocacy. In response to the introduction of new medications and new methods for the management of diabetes, the CDA has revised its meal planning guide. Like the Exchange Lists, the CDA meal planning guide was designed to make it easier for people with diabetes to eat the right amount of food for their insulin supply. The system is based on two concepts: Most foods are eaten by people with diabetes in measured amounts, and foods within each of the system's eight food groups can be interchanged.

The new guide, *Beyond the Basics: Meal Planning for Diabetes Prevention and Management,* has several features. First, food items have been modified to reflect current thinking on heart health, glycemic index, and carbohydrate counting. A wider range of multicultural foods have also been added. Portion sizes have been adjusted to be more similar to *Canada's Food Guide,* and to the Quebec and U.S. meal planning systems. The guide also used color coding to help consumers: green for "choose more often" or "everyday" foods and amber for "choose less often" or "special occasion foods." The listed portions of all carbohydrate-rich foods now contain 15 grams of available carbohydrate (total carbohydrate minus fiber and half of any sugar alcohols).

Beyond the Basics classifies foods into eight food groups:

- Grains & Starches
- Fruits
- Milk & Alternatives
- Other Choices
- Vegetables
- Meat & Alternatives
- Fats
- Extras

Within each group, food items are listed along with portions to show how much of one food is interchangeable with another food in the same group. In the past, symbols for the meal planning guide food groups were used on food labels, but this has been phased out with the new food labeling regulations. However, the CDA partnered with Dietitians of Canada to develop *Healthy Eating Is in Store for You*™, a nutrition labeling education program. For more information visit the CDA Web site: http://www.healthyeatingisinstore.ca.

Appendix E *The Gastrointestinal Tract*

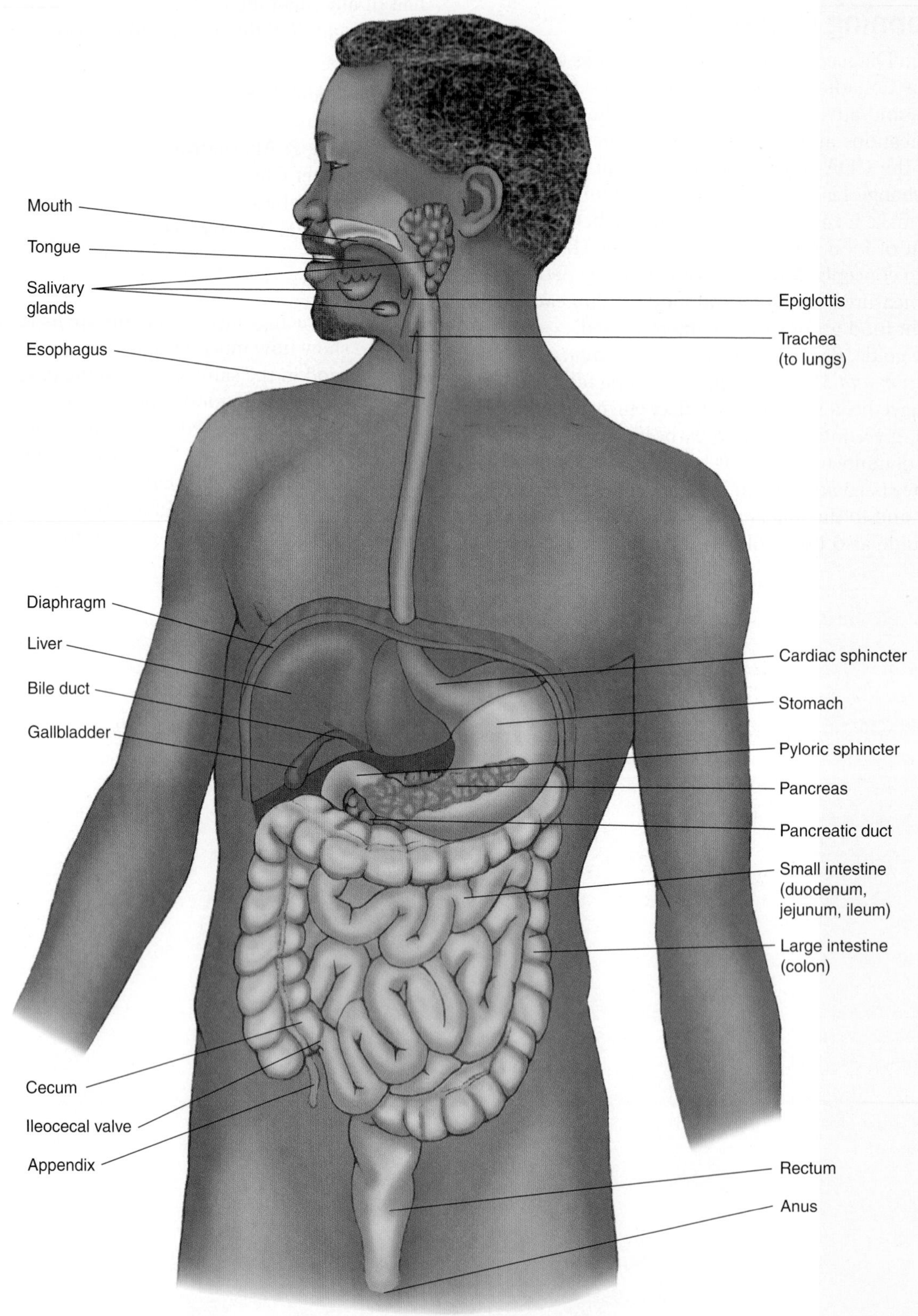

Mouth

- In the mouth, food is broken up by chewing with the teeth and tongue. Saliva lubricates food and makes swallowing easier. Salivary amylase begins the digestion of starch. The mouth warms or cools the food so that it is closer to body temperature. When the food bolus (a fairly liquid ball of food) is ready, swallowing is consciously initiated.

Tongue

- The tongue is a mobile mass of muscle that helps teeth tear food into pieces by forcing it against the bony palate. The tongue contains receptors for sweet, salty, sour, and bitter tastes. Umami, a fifth taste elicited by mono sodium glutamate, is a meaty, savory sensation. Flavor is a complex combination of taste, smells (the nose has about 6 million olfactory receptor cells), physical sensations (e.g., spicy foods), and food texture.

Salivary glands

- The three pairs of salivary glands produce saliva. The water in saliva helps dissolve food particles, facilitating taste sensations. The mucus in saliva lubricates food for swallowing and transport. Digestive enzymes begin breaking down foodstuffs. Salivary amylase begins the chemical breakdown of starches into simple sugars. Lingual lipase initiates the breakdown of fat. The mineral sodium and the enzyme lysozyme in the saliva act as disinfectants, destroying bacteria and other microorganisms in food.

Epiglottis

- The epiglottis is a flap of tissue that acts as a valve during swallowing. It closes the entrance to the larynx and prevents food from entering the respiratory passages.

Trachea

- These tubes allow air to pass to and from the lungs.

Esophagus

- The esophagus is the tube that connects the mouth to the stomach. Wavelike muscle action (peristalsis) moves food through the esophagus to the stomach. The upper one-third of the muscles of the esophagus are under voluntary control, the middle third are a mixture of voluntarily controlled muscle and automatically controlled smooth muscle, while the lower third is smooth muscle alone.

Cardiac sphincter

- The cardiac sphincter is a muscular valve at the lower end of the esophagus. This control valve relaxes to allow food to pass into the stomach. When contracted, it prevents backflow (reflux) of stomach contents into the esophagus. Named for its proximity to the heart, a malfunction can cause painful esophageal reflux (heartburn) which can be so severe that it is mistaken for a heart attack.

Stomach

- The upper bag like portion of the stomach acts as a hopper to receive and hold the food prior to delivery to the lower two-thirds. Three layers of smooth muscle surround this lower portion of the stomach. Muscular contractions churn the food, so the solids can ferment and mix with acids, fluid and protein-splitting enzymes. The result is a sticky semiliquid, called chyme, that is gradually released into the duodenum (the first part of the small intestine). Stomach acid halts the digestion of starch, but the stomach also produces gastric lipase, an enzyme that acts on fat.

Pyloric sphincter

- The pyloric sphincter is a muscular valve that controls passage of chyme from the stomach to the small intestine. When contracted, it prevents backflow from the small intestine into the stomach.

Liver

- The liver is the body's chemical factory and detoxification center. It has many functions in controlling metabolism and deactivating hormones, drugs, and toxins. It also produces bile—a mixture of bile salts, phospholipids, cholesterol, pigments, proteins, and inorganic ions such as sodium. The detergent-like action of bile emulsifies fat, facilitating fat digestion.

Gallbladder

- The gallbladder stores and concentrates bile. The arrival of fatty food in the duodenum stimulates the release of the duodenal hormone CCK which signals the gallbladder to contract. The bile is then released into the duodenum, where it aids fat digestion.

Bile duct

- The bile duct carries bile from the gallbladder to the duodenum.

Pancreas

- The pancreas is a complex gland that produces a pancreatic juice rich in bicarbonate and enzymes. The pancreatic juice is released into the duodenum where it does its work. Pancreatic amylase breaks down starch into maltose. Lipase splits fats into monoglycerides, fatty acids, and glycerol. The pancreatic proenzyme trypsinogen is converted to the enzyme trypsin. Trypsin splits polypeptides and proteins into amino acids. Bicarbonate produced by the pancreas neutralizes the acid chyme that enters the small intestine. In addition, the pancreas produces insulin and glucagon—hormones that have important roles in regulating carbohydrate metabolism and blood sugar.

Pancreatic duct

- The pancreatic duct carries pancreatic juice from the pancreas to the duodenum.

Small intestine

- The small intestine is a tube approximately 10 feet long that is divided into three parts: the duodenum (the first 10 to 12 inches), the jejunum (about 4 feet), and the ileum (about 5 feet). Whereas the duodenum is mainly responsible for breaking down food, the jejunum and ileum primarily deal with the absorption of food. The duodenum secretes mucus, enzymes, and hormones to aid digestion. Most digestion and absorption occur in the small intestine. Intestinal cells secrete disaccharidases and peptidases to help complete carbohydrate and protein digestion. The intestinal lining is highly folded to increase its surface area and is richly supplied with circulatory vessels, which carry away absorbed nutrients in the blood and lymph. Undigested material is passed on to the large intestine.

Ileocecal valve (sphincter)

- The ileocecal valve is the sphincter at the lower end of the small intestine. When open, it permits food residue to move from the small intestine to the large intestine. When closed, it prevents backflow from the large intestine.

Large intestine

- The large intestine is made up of the appendix, cecum, colon, rectum, and anus. The colon is about 2.5 inches in diameter and about 4 feet long. In the large intestine, bacteria break down dietary fiber and other undigested carbohydrates, releasing acids and gas. The large intestine absorbs water and minerals while dehydrating and processing the remaining undigested material into solid feces. The colon walls secrete a viscous mucus to help lubricate and mold the feces. This mucus also helps protect the colon wall from mechanical damage.

Appendix

- The appendix is a fingerlike appendage attached to the cecum, the first part of the colon. The appendix has no known function.

Cecum

- The cecum is the pouchlike beginning of the large intestine. The small intestine's ileum empties into the cecum.

Rectum

- The rectum stores waste prior to elimination.

Anus

- The anal sphincter holds the rectum closed. Either voluntary or involuntary control may open it to allow elimination.

Appendix F *Biochemical Structures*

- ▶ Nomenclature
- ▶ ATP and Derivatives
- ▶ Carbohydrates
- ▶ Amino Acids
- ▶ Fatty Acids
- ▶ Fat-Soluble Vitamins
- ▶ Water-Soluble Vitamins and Coenzymes
- ▶ B Vitamins in Major Metabolic Pathways

Nomenclature

Prefixes

mono-	Means one subunit. For instance *mono*saccharide means a one-unit saccharide.
bi-, di-, and tri-	Mean two and three subunits bonded together to form a larger molecule.
poly-	Means many or a lot. A *poly*saccharide has many linked monosaccharide subunits.
oligo-	Means a structure with typically 3 to 10 subunits, but smaller than a polymer.

Suffixes

-ose	Sugars are named with *-ose* as a suffix. They are subclassified with regard to the number of carbons, i.e., 3 = triose, 4 = tetrose, 5 = pentose, 6 = hexose, 7 = heptose. The suffix *-ose* refers to monosaccharides and disaccharides: sugars like gluc*ose*, fruct*ose*, sucr*ose*, etc.
-ase	Many enzymes are named by attaching the suffix *-ase* to the substrate of the enzyme (the compound altered by enzymatic action). For instance, a lipase cleaves a lipid substrate, a disaccharidase cleaves a disaccharide, and a peptidase breaks the peptide bond between two amino acids.
-ol	Suffix for naming alcohols and phenols (e.g., ethan*ol*, glycer*ol*).
-ic, -ate, -oic, -oate	Suffixes for naming acids and acid salts.

Although the terms *lactic acid* and *lactate* often are used interchangeably, they are not identical chemical compounds. Lactic acid ($C_3H_6O_3$), as its name implies, is an acid. Lactate is any salt of lactic acid, for instance sodium lactate. When anaerobic glycolysis forms lactic acid, the acid quickly dissociates, releasing hydrogen (H^+) into solution. The lactate ion then immediately associates with sodium (Na^+) or potassium (K^+) to form a salt–sodium or potassium lactate. In substances such as pyruvate and lactate, the carboxyl group is COO^- (one oxygen has an available bond). In acids such as pyruvic acid and lactic acid, the carboxyl group is COOH (the available bond is filled with hydrogen). The suffixes -ic and -ate are used for the acid and salt forms of most carboxyl groups. For reasons of pronunciation, some carboxyl groups require the *-oic* or *-oate* suffixes, for instance butan*oic* acid, and its salt form butan*oate*.

-peptide — The suffix *peptide* refers to a molecule composed of 2 or more amino acids joined by peptide bonds. A di*peptide* is composed of 2 amino acids, a tri*peptide* of three, etc. A short string of amino acids is called a poly*peptide* and a long string is a protein.

-saccharide — The suffix *saccharide* refers to sugar. A poly*saccharide*, for example, is a large molecule composed of many sugar subunits. A polysaccharide may be composed of only one type of sugar (starch is made up of many glucose units) or of many different sugars. A lipopoly*saccharide*, for instance, is made up of a variety of sugars bonded to a lipid.

hydrogen ion — Also known as a proton, this lone hydrogen has a positive charge (H^+). It has lost its electron and associates readily with negatively charged ions, like the hydroxyl ion (OH^-).

atomic hydrogen — A hydrogen atom with a single electron. This proton-electron combination is unstable and is a short-lived intermediate in some enzymatically catalyzed reactions. During oxidation-reduction reactions it is atomic hydrogen (hydrogen 1 electron), not hydrogen ions (H^+), that is transferred.

Acids are substances that form hydrogen ions in solution. An acid dissociates to form a cation (H^+) and an anion (e.g., SO_4^-).

When the anion ends with the suffix *-ate* its acid name is simply the anion with suffix *-ic*, followed by the word *acid*. Here are some examples:

- H_2SO_4 - hydrogen sulf*ate* becomes sulfur*ic acid*
- H_3PO_4 - hydrogen phosph*ate* becomes phosphor*ic acid*
- $HClO_3$ - hydrogen chlor*ate* becomes hydrochlor*ic acid*

Functional Group	Structural Formula	Models
Hydroxyl	-OH	O–H
Carbonyl	-C(=O)-	C, O
Carboxyl	-C(=O)OH	C, O, O–H
Amino	-N(H)H	N, H, H
Sulfhydryl	-SH	S–H
Phosphate	-O-P(=O)(OH)-OH	O–P–O–H, O, O–H

Functional groups
These six functional groups are commonly involved in covalent and non-covalent bonding to form molecules such as proteins and DNA.

ATP and Derivatives

ATP, ADP, and AMP

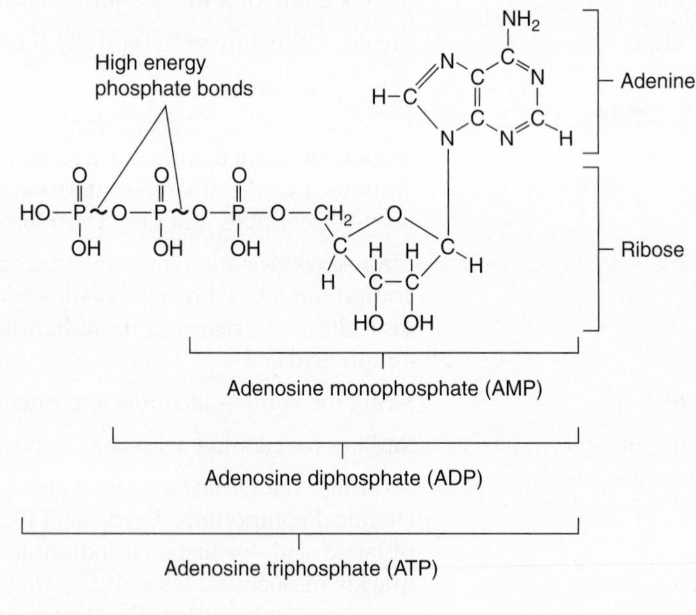

Carbohydrates

Monosaccharides

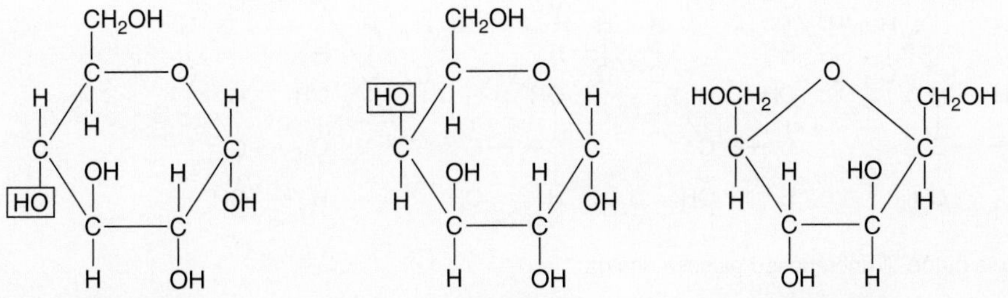

Glucose **Galactose** **Fructose**

The structures of glucose and galactose differ only by the location of the OH on carbon number 4.

Disaccharides

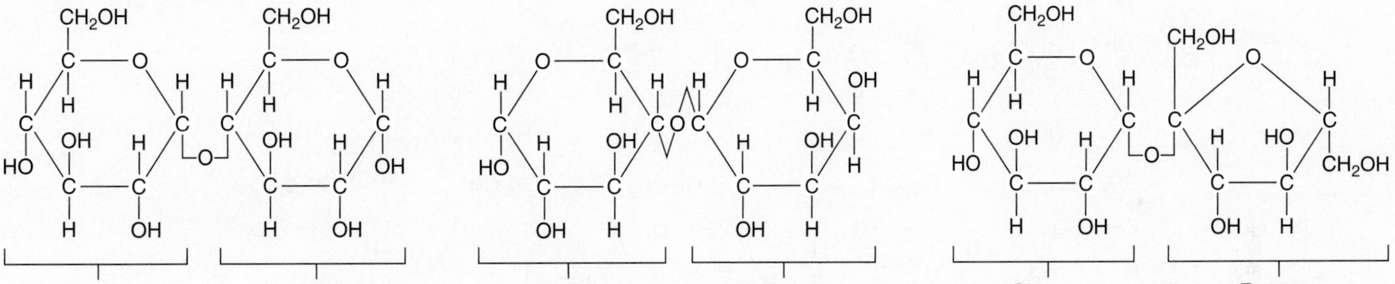

Glucose Glucose

Maltose

Glucose Galactose

Lactose

Glucose Fructose

Sucrose

In maltose and sucrose, the monosaccharides are linked by alpha bonds. In lactose, a beta bond links galactose and glucose. The human digestive enzyme lactase can hydrolyze the beta bond in lactose.

Polysaccharides

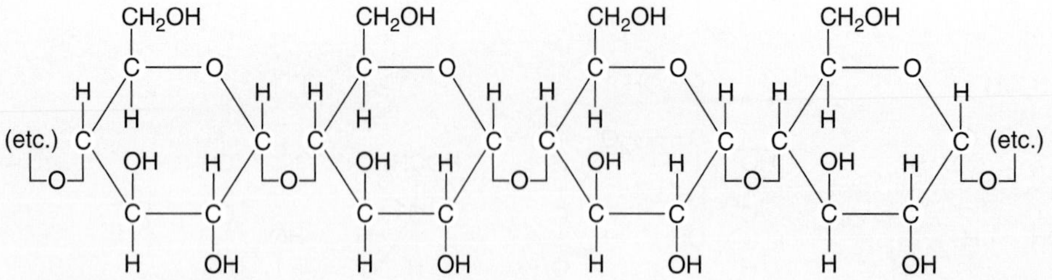

Amylose

Starch molecule made of unbranched glucose chains.

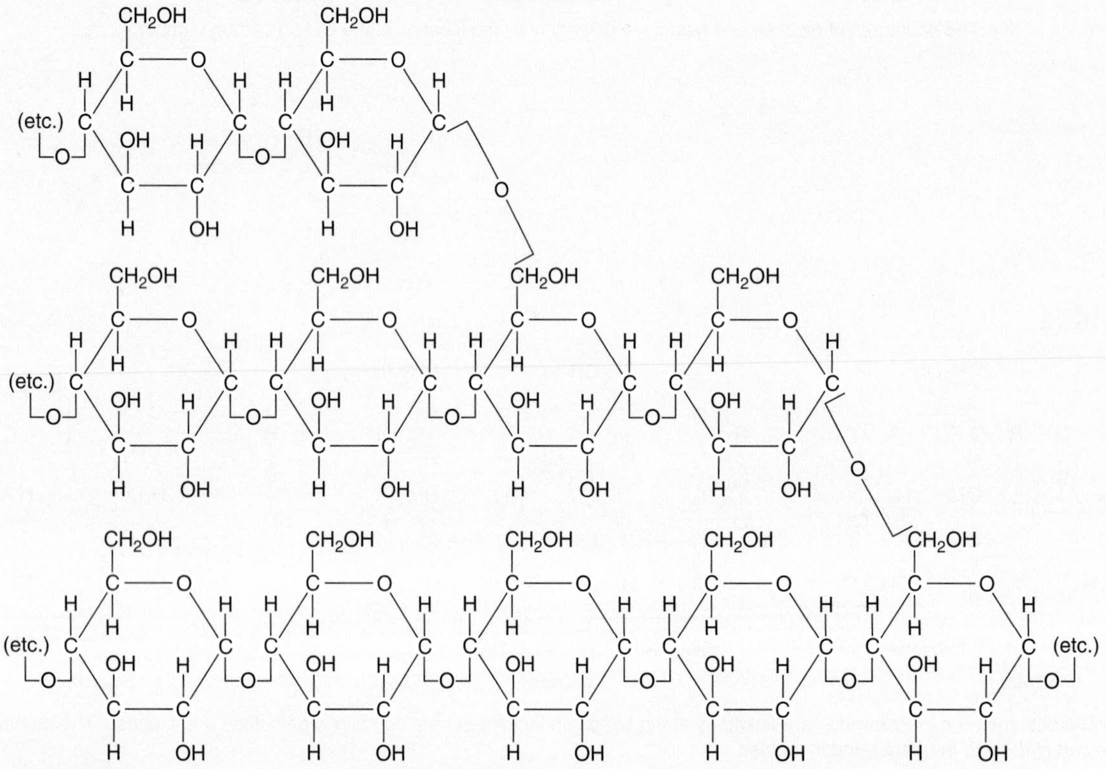

Amylopectin

Starch molecule made of branched glucose chains. In amylopectin, the chain branches every thirty glucose units. Glycogen is similar, but more highly branched (every ten glucose units).

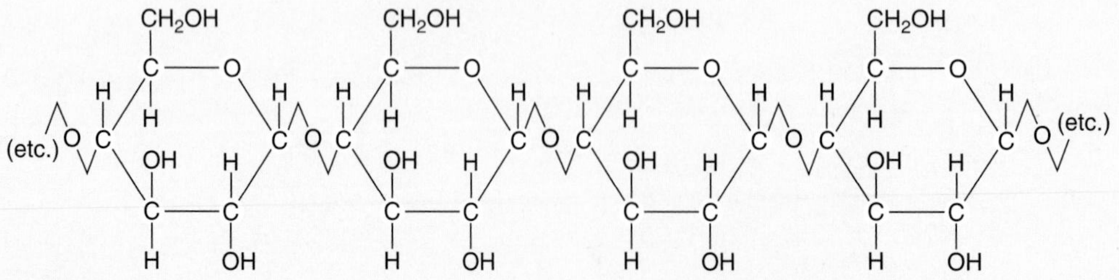

Cellulose

Cellulose is a nearly straight chain of glucose units where the glucose molecules are linked by beta bonds. Humans do not have the enzymes necessary to break the beta linkages in cellulose.

Amino Acids

Indispensable amino acids

Amino acids consist of a central carbon atom bonded to a carboxyl group, an amino group, a hydrogen, and a side group. The shaded areas show the structure common to all amino acids.

Valine (Val)

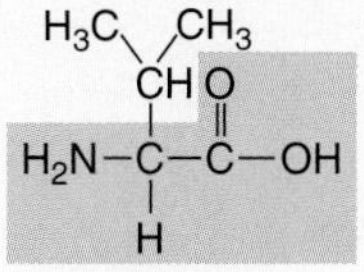

Leucine (Leu)

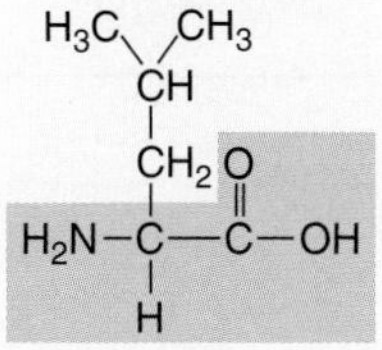

Isoleucine (Ile)

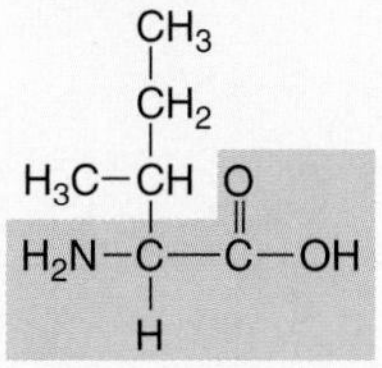

Threonine (Thr)

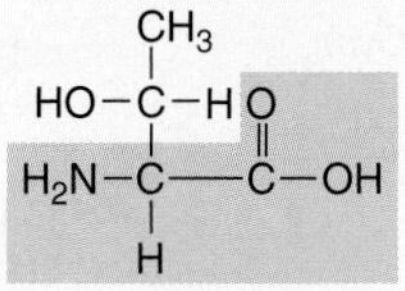

Lysine (Lys)

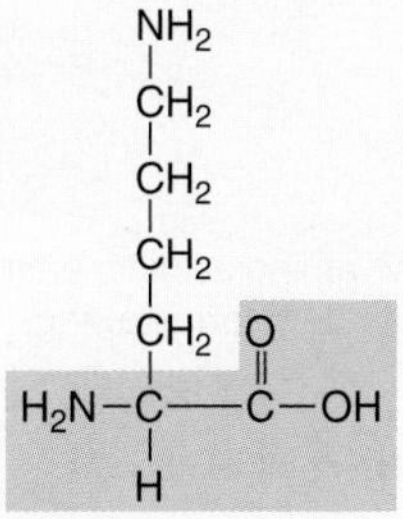

Histidine (His)

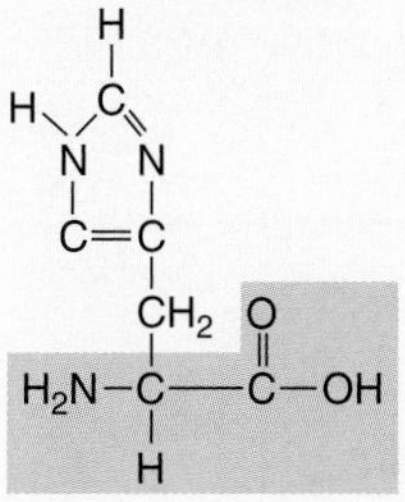

Phenylalanine (Phe)

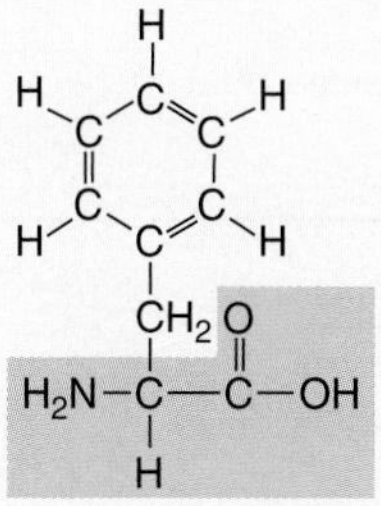

Tryptophan (Trp)

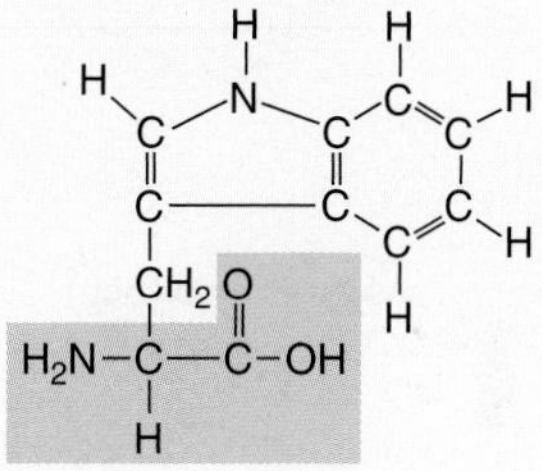

Methionine (Met)

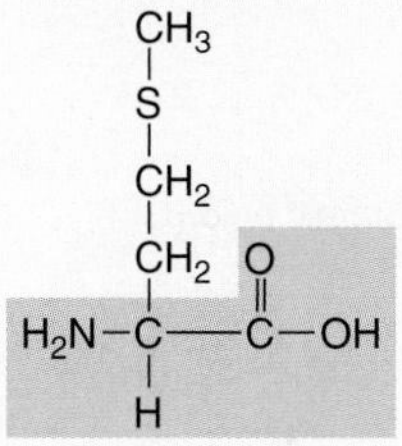

Dispensable amino acids

Glycine (Gly)

Alanine (Ala)

Serine (Ser)

Aspartic acid (Asp)

Glutamic acid (Glu)

Asparagine (Asn)

Glutamine (Gln)

Arginine (Arg)

Tyrosine (Tyr)

Cysteine (Cys)

Proline (Pro)

Proline is an amino acid. Its amino group has only one hydrogen and forms a ring.

Fatty Acids

Table F.1 Saturated Fatty Acids Found in Food

Saturated Fatty Acid	Chemical Formula	Number of Carbons	Major Food Sources
Butyric	$CH_3(CH_2)_2COOH$	4	Small amounts in butterfat
Caproic	$CH_3(CH_2)_4COOH$	6	Small amounts in butterfat
Caprylic	$CH_3(CH_2)_6COOH$	8	Small amounts in many fats, including butterfat. Especially found in oils of plant origin.
Capric	$CH_3(CH_2)_8COOH$	10	Small amounts in many fats, including butterfat. Especially found in oils of plant origin.
Lauric	$CH_3(CH_2)_{10}COOH$	12	Cinnamon, palm kernel, coconut oil, butter
Myristic	$CH_3(CH_2)_{12}COOH$	14	Nutmeg, palm kernel, coconut oil, butter
Palmitic	$CH_3(CH_2)_{14}COOH$	16	Common in all animal and plant fats
Stearic	$CH_3(CH_2)_{16}COOH$	18	Common in all animal and plant fats
Arachidic	$CH_3(CH_2)_{18}COOH$	20	Peanut oil
Behenic	$CH_3(CH_2)_{20}COOH$	22	Seeds
Lignoceric	$CH_3(CH_2)_{22}COOH$	24	Peanut oil

Table F.2 Unsaturated Fatty Acids Found in Food

Unsaturated Fatty Acid	Chemical Formula	Number of Carbons	Number of Double Bonds	Omega Notation*	Major Food Sources
Palmitoleic	$CH_3(CH_2)_5CH = CH(CH_2)_7COOH$	16	1	16:1ω7	Nearly all fats
Oleic	$CH_3(CH_2)_7CH = CH(CH_2)_7COOH$	18	1	18:1ω9	Perhaps the most common fatty acid in food
Linoleic	$CH_3(CH_2)_4(CH = CHCH_2)_2(CH_2)_6COOH$	18	2	18:2ω6	Corn, peanut, cottonseed, soybean, and several oils from other plants
Linolenic	$CH_3CH_2(CH = CHCH_2)_3(CH_2)_6COOH$	18	3	18:3ω3	Often in foods with linoleic acid, but particularly found in linseed oil
Arachidonic	$CH_3(CH_2)_4(CH = CHCH_2)_4(CH_2)_2COOH$	20	4	20:4ω6	Animal fats and peanut oil
Eicosapentanoic	$CH_3(CH_2)_3(CH = CHCH_2)_4(CH_2)_3COOH$	20	5	20:5ω3	Fish oils such as cod liver, mackerel, and salmon
Docosahexanoic	$CH_3(CH_2)_2(CH = CHCH_2)_6COOH$	22	6	22:6ω3	Fish oils such as cod liver, mackerel, and salmon

*Omega Notation = number of carbons: number of double bonds, the number following the omega symbol (ω) represents the location of the first double bond counting from the methyl (CH_3) end.

Fat-Soluble Vitamins

Vitamin A and Beta-carotene

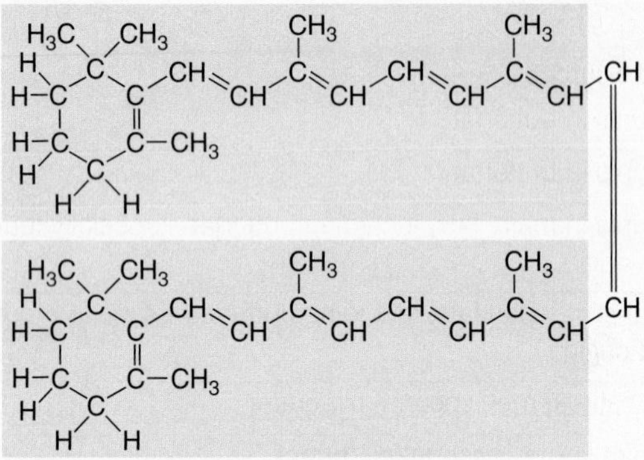

Vitamin A precursor: beta-carotene

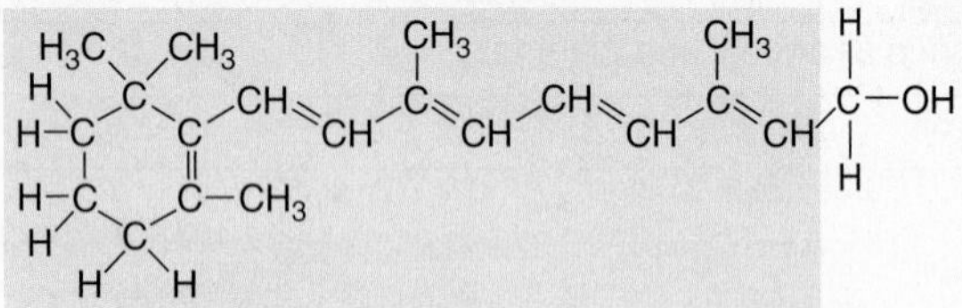

Vitamin A: retinol

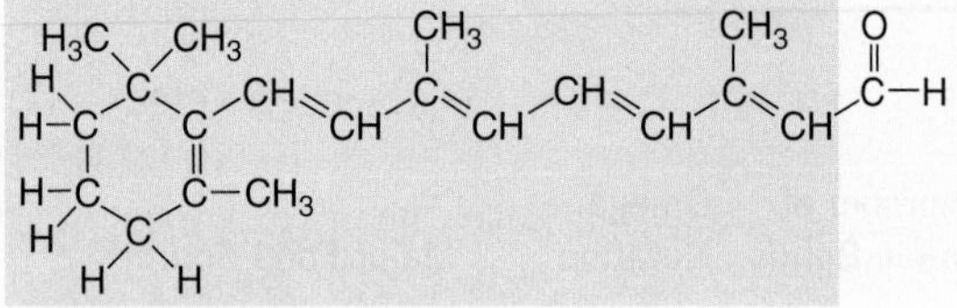

Vitamin A: retinal

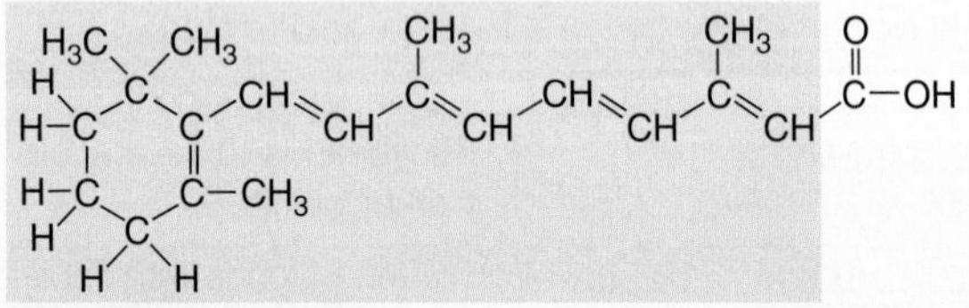

Vitamin A: retinoic acid

The shaded area highlights the structure common to all four molecules.

Vitamin D

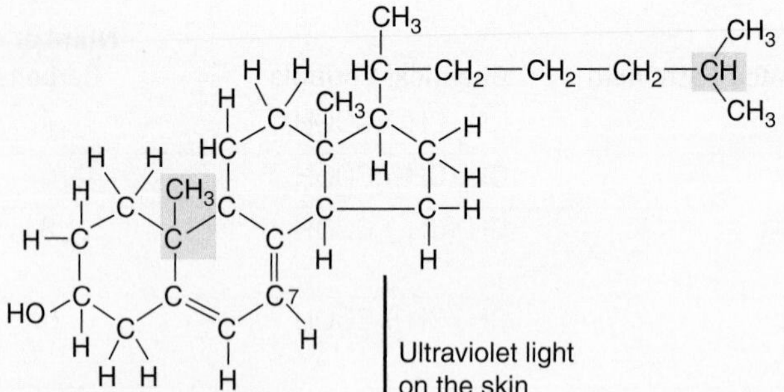

7–Dehydrocholesterol

Ultraviolet light on the skin

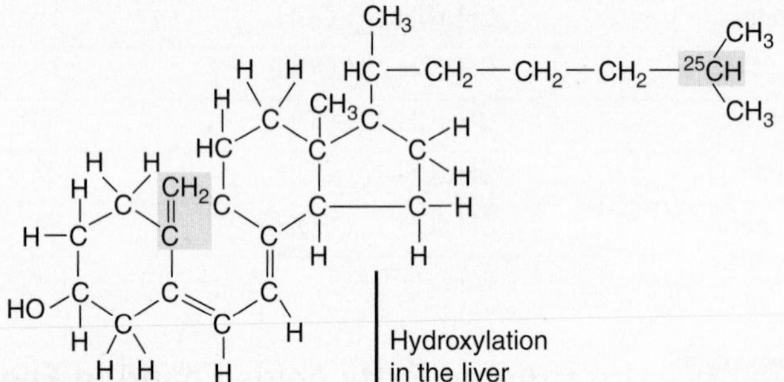

Cholecalciferol
(vitamin D_3)

Hydroxylation in the liver

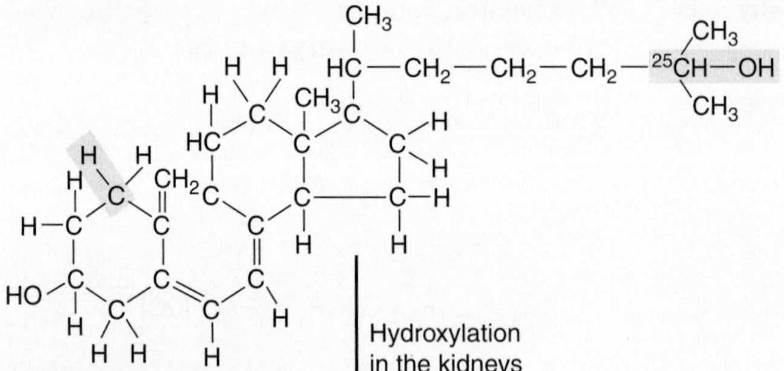

25–Hydroxycholecalciferol
(25–hydroxyvitamin D_3)

Hydroxylation in the kidneys

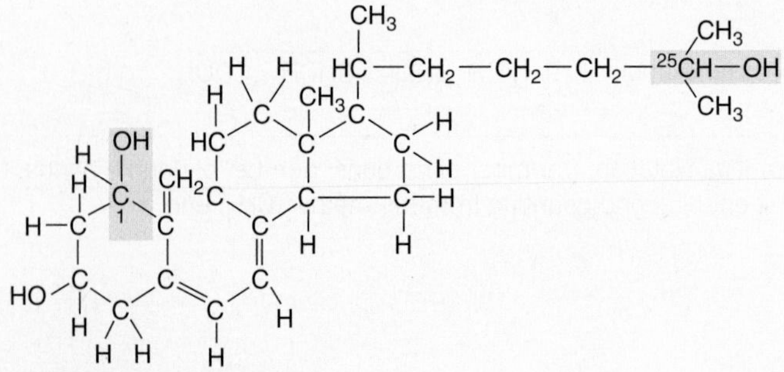

1, 25–Dihydroxycholecalciferol
(1, 25–dihydroxyvitamin D_3)
(calcitriol)

The shaded areas highlight the portion of the molecule that changes from stage to stage.

Vitamin E

R_1 (CH_3), R_2 (H_3C); HO, H, H, H, H, CH_3, CH_3, O

$-CH_2-CH_2-CH_2-CH(CH_3)-CH_2-CH_2-CH_2-CH(CH_3)-CH_2-CH_2-CH_2-CH(CH_3)-CH_3$

Vitamin E (alpha-tocopherol)
4 isomers α, β, γ, δ

R_1 (CH_3), R_2 (H_3C); HO, H, H, H, H, CH_3, CH_3, O

$-CH_2-CH_2-CH_2{=}C(CH_3)-CH_2-CH_2-CH_2{=}C(CH_3)-CH_2-CH_2-CH_2{=}C(CH_3)-CH_3$

Vitamin E (alpha-tocotrienol)
4 isomers α, β, γ, δ

Isomers for tocopherols and tocotrienols

For α,	$R_1 = CH_3$	$R_2 = CH_3$
For β,	$R_1 = CH_3$	$R_2 = H$
For γ,	$R_1 = H$	$R_2 = CH_3$
For δ,	$R_1 = H$	$R_2 = H$

Vitamin E occurs in 8 forms but vitamin E activity is based on alpha-tocopherol. Humans do not convert β-, γ-, δ-tocopherols or the tocotrienols to alpha-tocopherol, so these forms do not contribute toward meeting the vitamin E requirement. The shading highlights the differences between tocopherols and tocotrienols.

Vitamin K

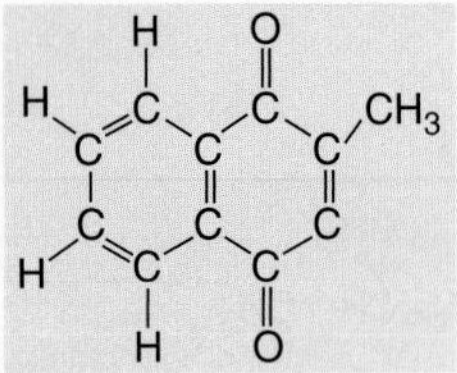

Menadione (vitamin K_3)
Synthetic form of Vitamin K

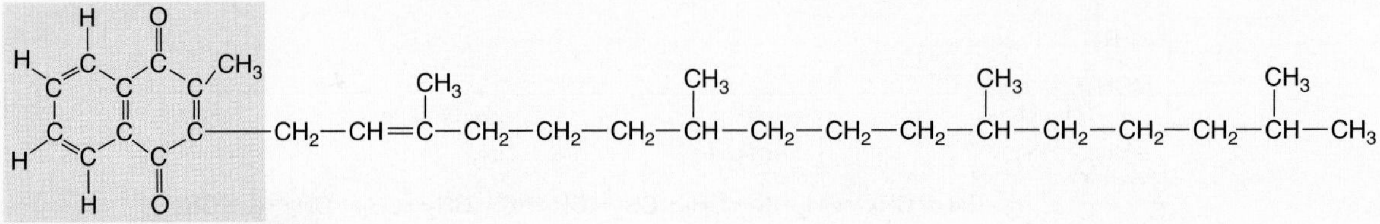

Phylloquinone (vitamin K_1)
Vitamin K naturally occurring in food

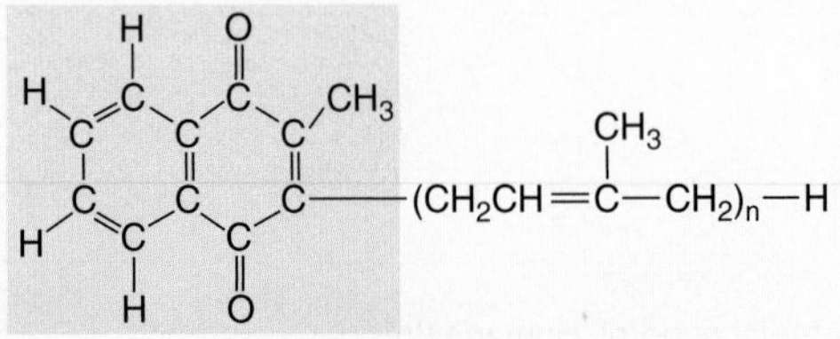

Menaquinone-n (vitamin K_2; n = 6, 7, or 9)
Vitamin K formed by bacteria in the large intestine

The shaded areas highlight the structure common to all three forms.

Water-Soluble Vitamins and Coenzymes

Thiamin and Coenzyme

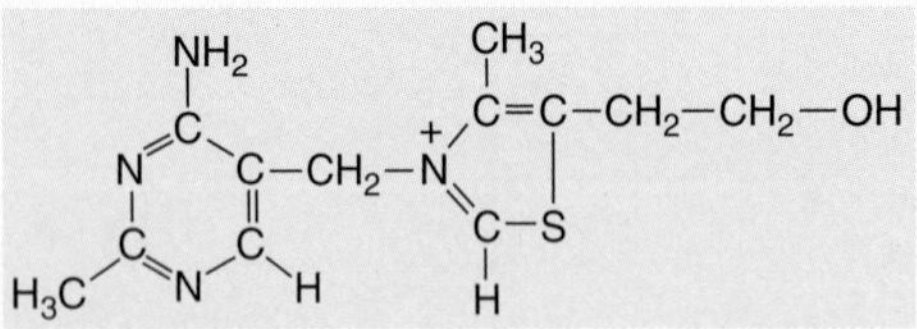

Thiamin

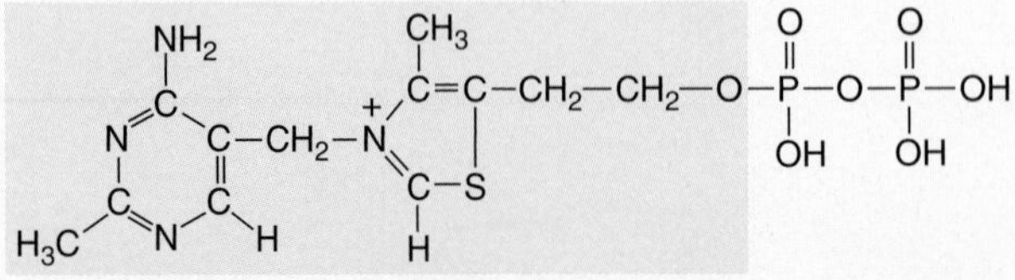

Thiamin pyrophosphate (TPP)

Thiamin is part of the active coenzyme TPP. The shaded areas highlight the structure common to both molecules.

Water-Soluble Vitamins and Coenzymes (cont.)

Riboflavin and Coenzymes

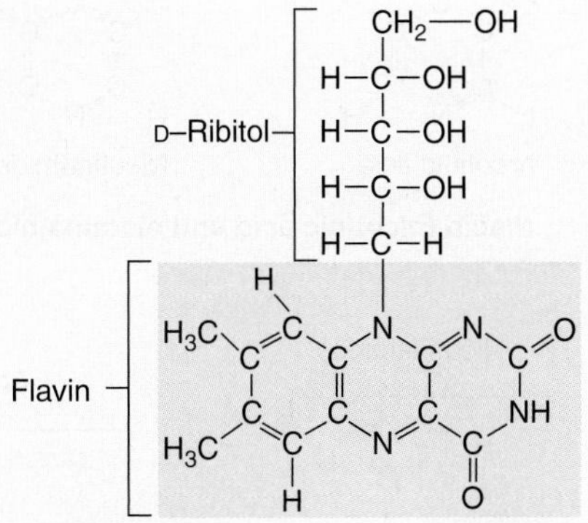

Riboflavin

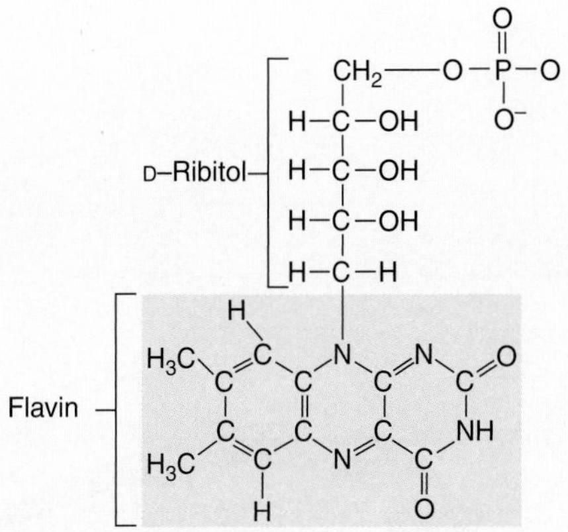

Flavin mononucleotide (FMN)

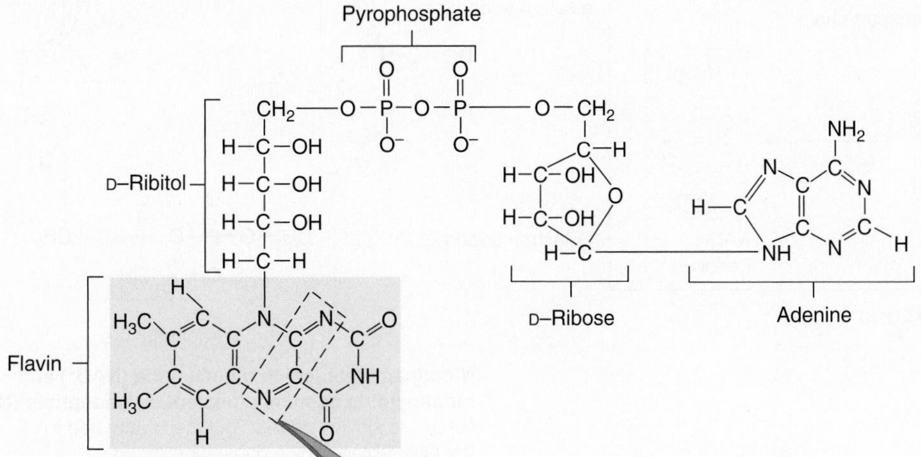

Flavin dinucleotide (FAD)

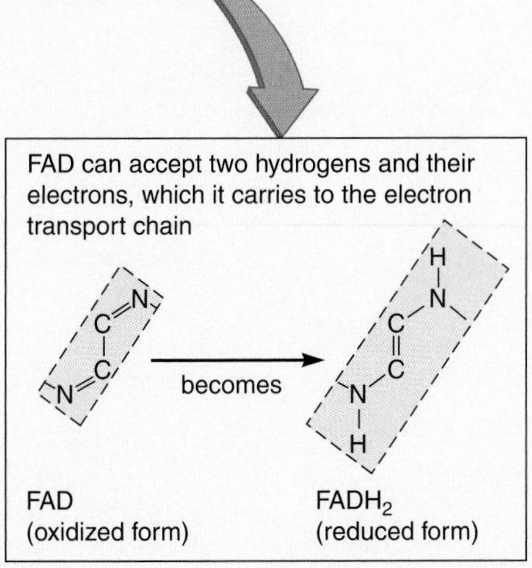

FAD can accept two hydrogens and their electrons, which it carries to the electron transport chain

FAD and $FADH_2$

The flavin portion of these molecules is highlighted.

Niacin and Coenzymes

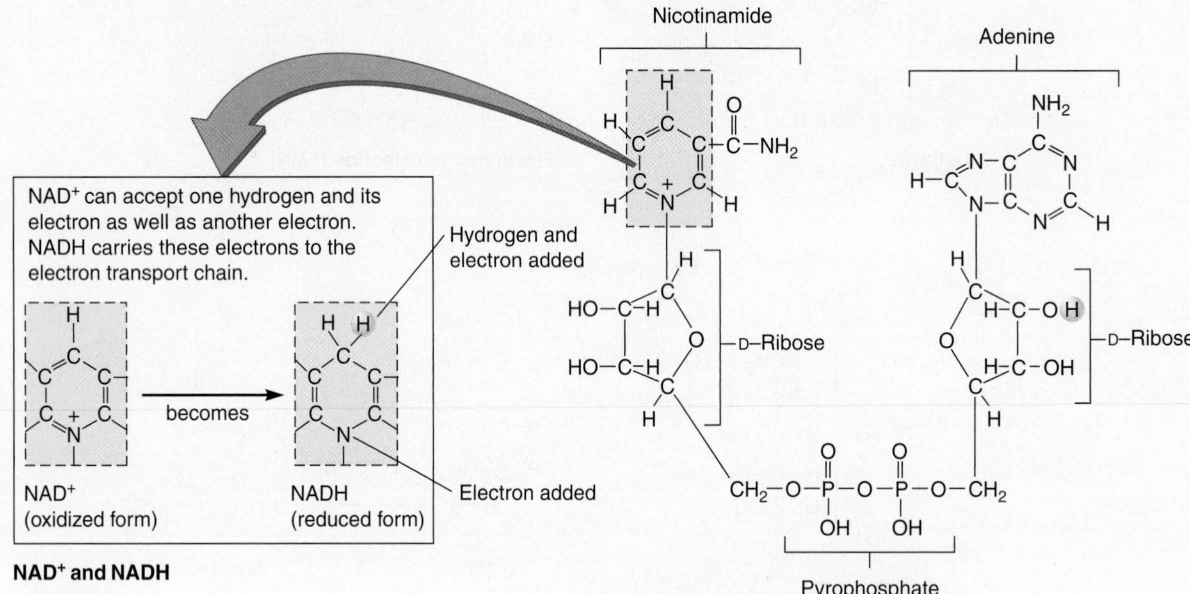

Niacin (nicotinic acid and nicotinamide)

NAD⁺ and NADH

Nicotinamide adenine dinucleotide (NAD⁺) and nicotinamide adenine dinucleotide phosphate (NADP⁺)
NADP⁺ is similar to NAD⁺ but the H attached to the O is replaced by a phosphate group.

Pantothenic Acid and Coenzyme A

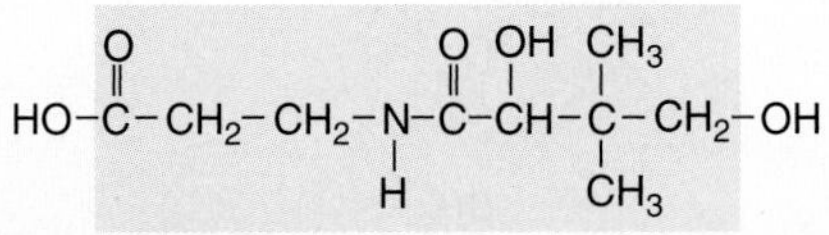

$HO{-}C({=}O){-}CH_2{-}CH_2{-}N(H){-}C({=}O){-}CH(OH){-}C(CH_3)_2{-}CH_2{-}OH$

Pantothenic acid

Thioethanolamine

Pyrophosphate

Adenine

Ribose 3–phosphate

$HS{-}CH_2{-}CH_2{-}N(H){-}C({=}O){-}CH_2{-}CH_2{-}N(H){-}C({=}O){-}CH(OH){-}C(CH_3)_2{-}CH_2{-}O{-}P({=}O)(OH){-}O{-}P({=}O)(OH){-}O{-}CH_2{-}$

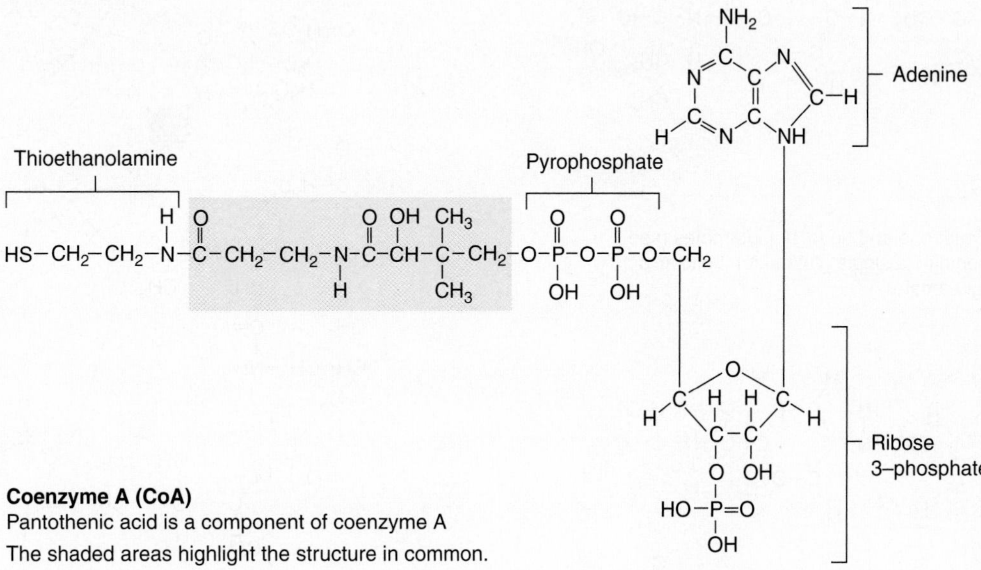

Coenzyme A (CoA)

Pantothenic acid is a component of coenzyme A

The shaded areas highlight the structure in common.

Biotin

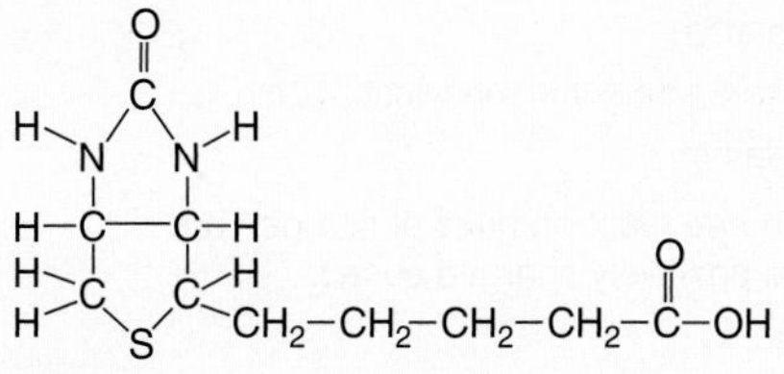

$H{-}C{-}S{-}C{-}CH_2{-}CH_2{-}CH_2{-}CH_2{-}C({=}O){-}OH$

Biotin

Vitamin B_6 and Coenzymes

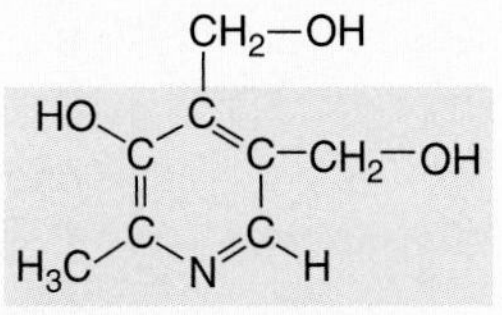

$CH_2{-}OH$ $C{=}O$ $CH_2{-}NH_2$

HO, $C{-}CH_2{-}OH$, H_3C, N, H

Pyridoxine

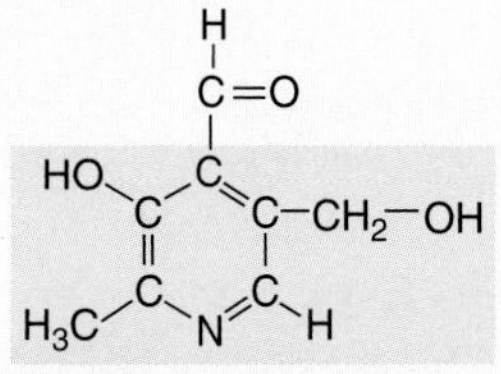

Pyridoxal

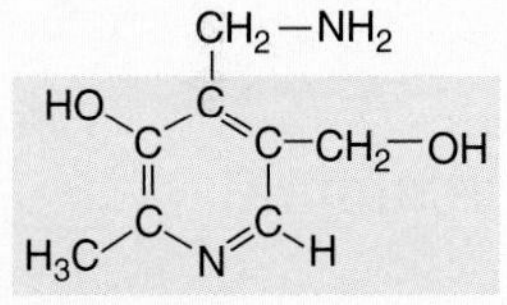

Pyridoxamine

Vitamin B_6 (pyridoxine, pyridoxal, and pyridoxamine)

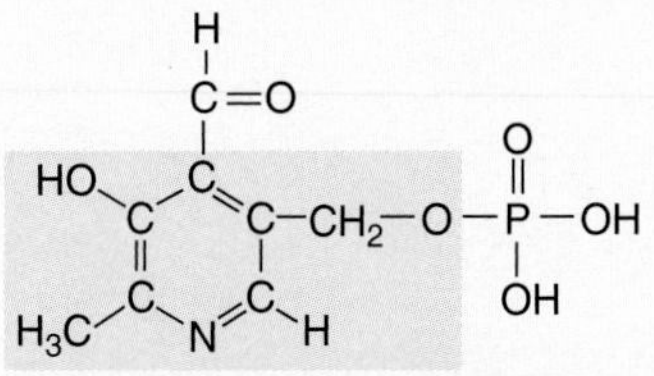

$C{-}CH_2{-}O{-}P({=}O)(OH){-}OH$

Pyridoxal phosphate (PLP)

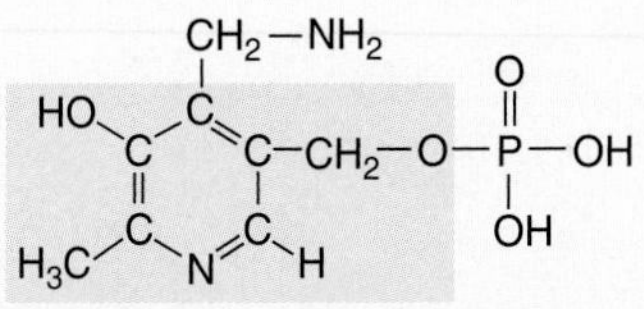

Pyridoxamine phosphate (PMP)

Pyridoxal phosphate (PLP) and pyridoxamine phosphate (PMP) are the two active coenzyme forms of vitamin B_6

The shaded areas highlight the structures in common.

Folate and Coenzyme

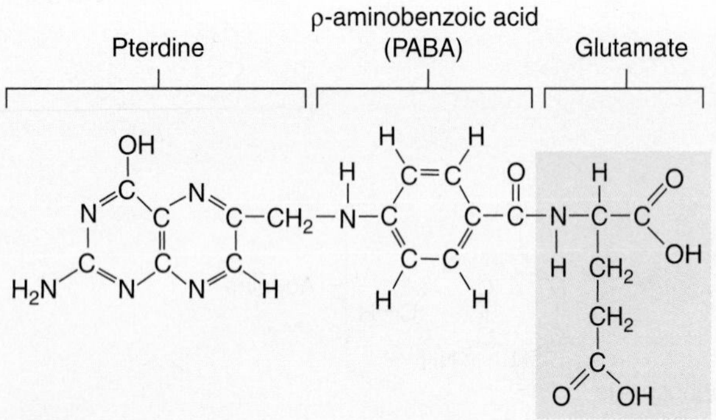

Pterdine | ρ-aminobenzoic acid (PABA) | Glutamate

Folate
Folate contains at least one and up to 11 glutamates (see shaded area that contains a single glutamate). Folic acid contains only one glutamate.

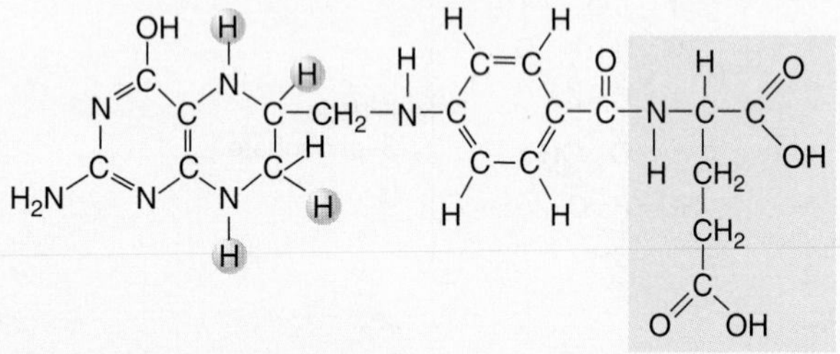

Tetrahydrofolic acid (THFA)
Adding 4 hydrogens to folate produces THFA, the active coenzyme form.

Vitamin C

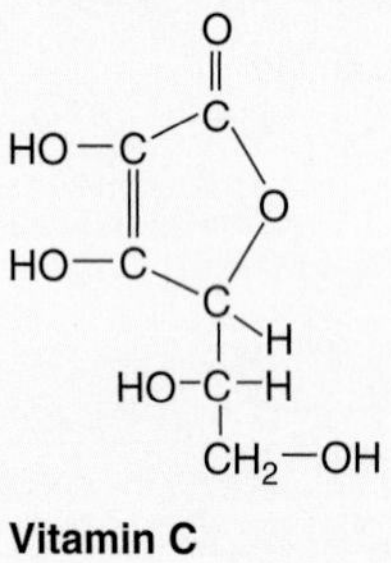

Vitamin C
(Ascorbic acid)

Vitamin B_{12}

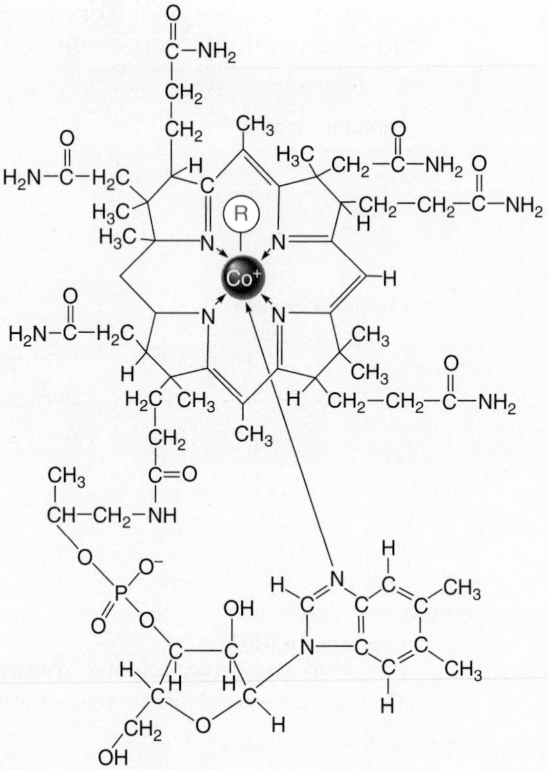

Vitamin B_{12} (cobalamin)

R = CN in cyanocobalamin
R = OH in hydroxocobalamin
R = 5′–deoxyadenosyl in 5′–deoxyadenosylcobalamin
R = CH_3 in methylcobalamin

Arrows indicate that the free electron pairs of nitrogen are in close proximity to the positively charged cobalt.

B Vitamins in Major Metabolic Pathways

Thiamin	Pyruvate to acetyl CoA (TPP) Citric acid cycle (TPP)
Riboflavin	Pyruvate to acetyl CoA (FAD) Citric acid cycle (FAD) Electron transport chain (FAD, FMN) Beta-oxidation (fatty acids to acetyl CoA) (FAD) Amino acid breakdown (FAD)
Niacin	Glycolysis (NAD^+) Pyruvate to acetyl CoA (NAD^+) Citric acid cycle (NAD^+) Electron transport chain (NAD^+) Beta-oxidation (fatty acids to acetyl CoA) (NAD^+) Fatty acid synthesis (acetyl CoA to fatty acids) (NADPH) Amino acid breakdown (NAD^+) Amino acid synthesis (NAD^+, NADPH) Gluconeogenesis (NAD^+)
Pantothenic acid	Pyruvate to acetyl CoA (coenzyme A) Citric acid cycle (coenzyme A) Beta-oxidation (fatty acids to acetyl CoA) (coenzyme A) Fatty acid synthesis (acetyl CoA to fatty acids) (coenzyme A)
Biotin	Fatty acid synthesis (acetyl CoA to fatty acids) (biotin-enzyme) Gluconeogenesis (biotin-enzyme)
Vitamin B_6	Glycogen to glucose (PLP) Amino acid breakdown (PLP) Amino acid synthesis (PLP)
Folate	Amino acid synthesis (THFA) Synthesis of some components of DNA and RNA (THFA)
Vitamin B_{12}	Amino acid breakdown (B_{12}) Synthesis of some components of DNA and RNA (B_{12})

Appendix G *Major Metabolic Pathways*

- Glycolysis
- Citric Acid Cycle
- Electron Transport Chain
- Urea Cycle

Glycolysis

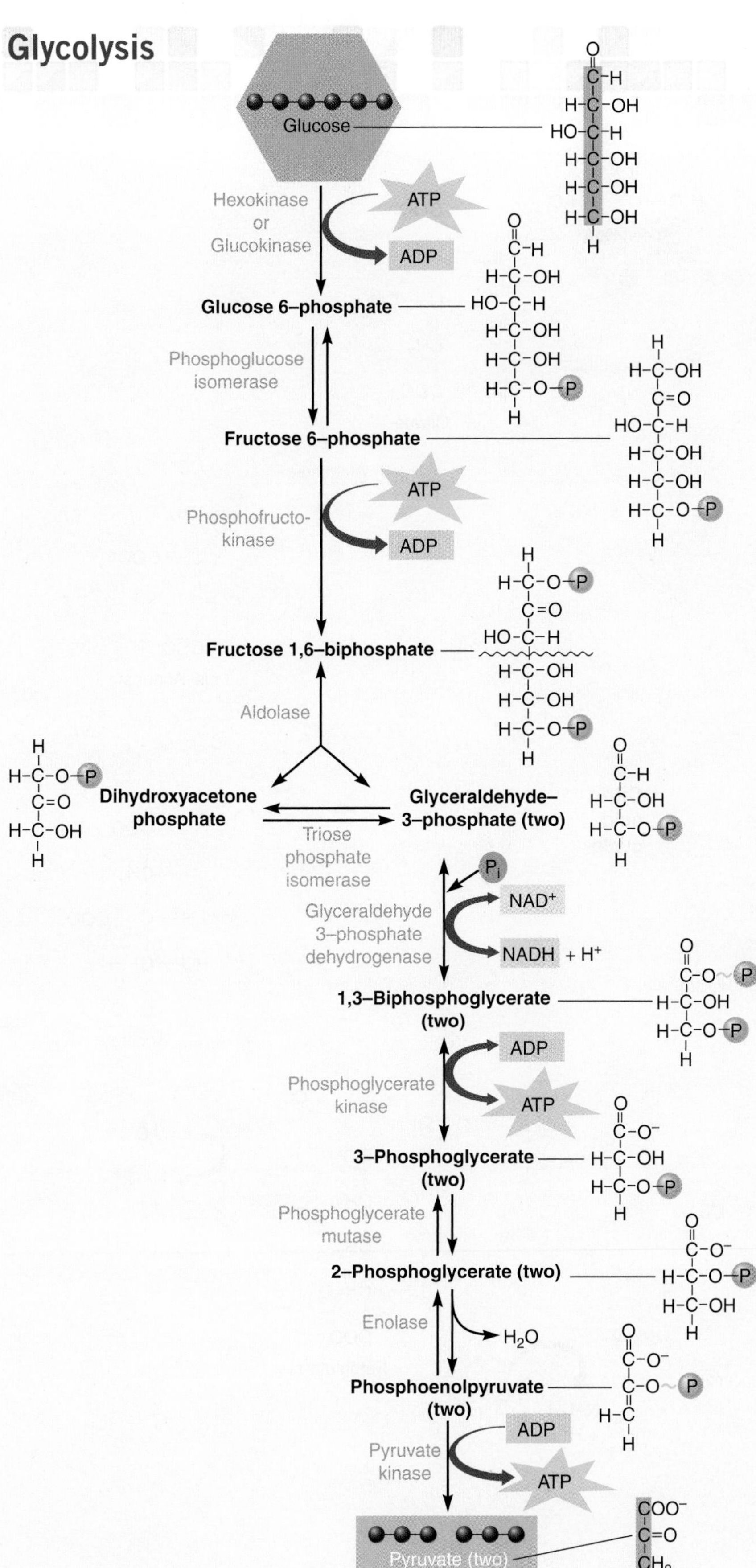

Glycolysis is the first step in metabolizing glucose and other monosaccharides for energy. Unlike the reaction that converts blood glucose to glucose 6-phosphate, the reaction that converts glucose from glycogen to glucose 6-phosphate does not require ATP. Thus the glycolysis of glucose from glycogen directly yields 3 ATP as compared to the 2 ATP from blood glucose. Additional ATP is produced from glycolytic NADH in the electron transport chain.

The reactions that convert fructose to fructose 6-phosphate require ATP so fructose produces the same amount of ATP as blood glucose. The same is true for galactose, which enters at glucose 6-phosphate.

Citric Acid Cycle

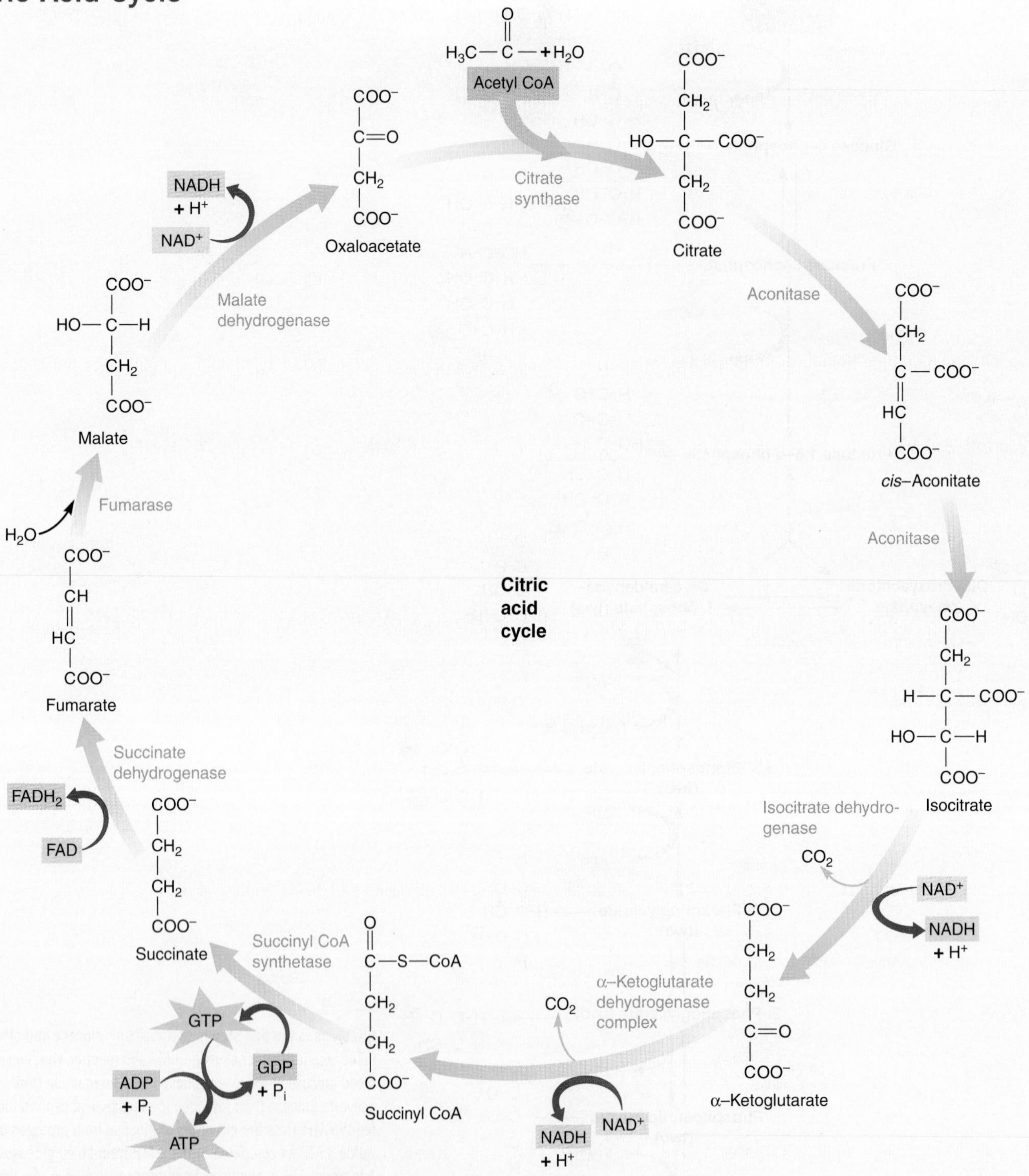

Acetyl CoA (H_3C-CO) + H_2O

Citrate synthase

Citrate

Aconitase

cis–Aconitate

Aconitase

Isocitrate

Isocitrate dehydrogenase

CO_2

NAD^+ → NADH + H^+

α–Ketoglutarate

α–Ketoglutarate dehydrogenase complex

CO_2

NAD^+ → NADH + H^+

Succinyl CoA

Succinyl CoA synthetase

GDP + P_i → GTP

ADP + P_i → ATP

Succinate

Succinate dehydrogenase

FAD → $FADH_2$

Fumarate

Fumarase

H_2O

Malate

Malate dehydrogenase

NAD^+ → NADH + H^+

Oxaloacetate

Citric acid cycle

Electron Transport Chain

(site of oxidative phosphorylation)

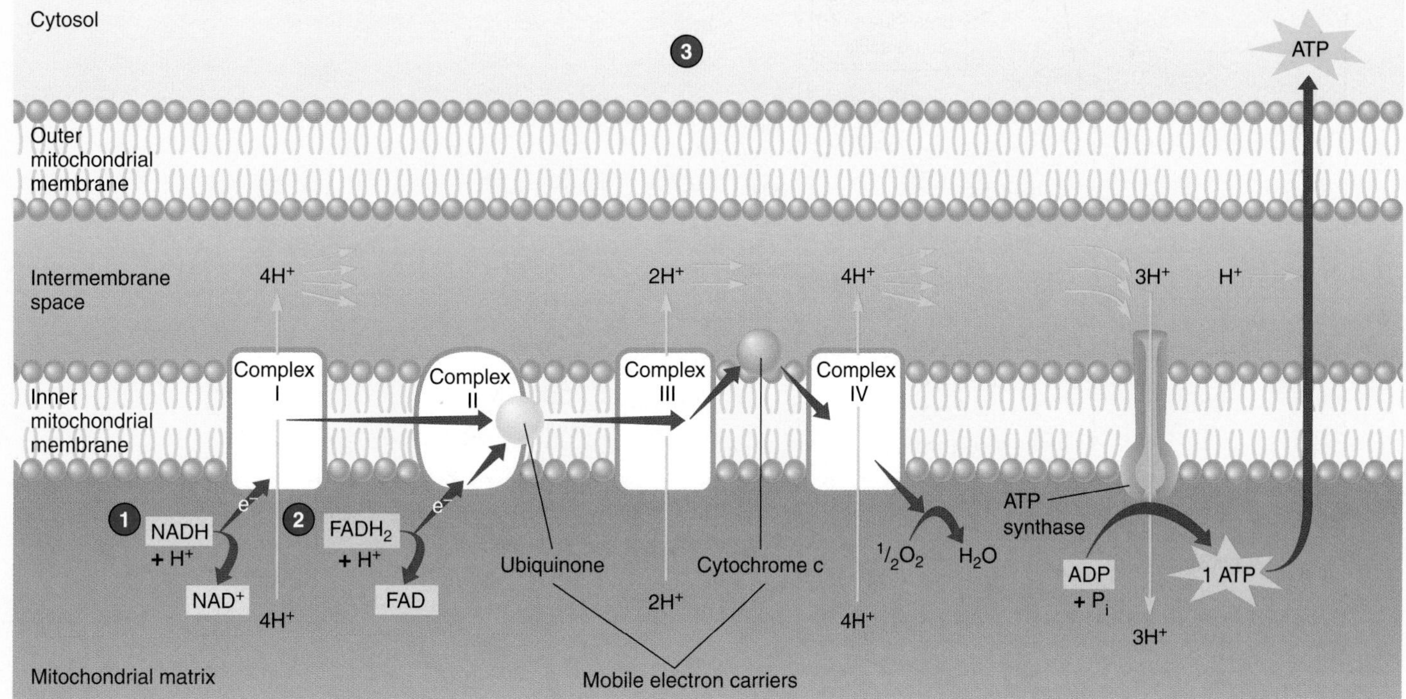

Complex I	NADH–Q reductase
Complex II	Succinate–Q reductase
Complex III	Cytochrome reductase
Complex IV	Cytochrome oxidase

Complexes I, III, and IV are proton (H^+) pumps. Complex II does not pump protons.
The three proton pumps are linked by the mobile electron carriers ubiquinone and cytochrome c.

NADH

1 A pair of electrons from NADH enters the chain at complex I (NADH-Q reductase). The flow of electrons from NADH to ubiquinone leads to the pumping of 4 H^+ from the matrix to the intermembrane space. The flow of electrons from ubiquinone to cytochrome c through complex III (cytochrome reductase) pumps another 2 H^+ into the intermembrane space. As complex IV (cytochrome oxidase) catalyzes the transfer of electrons from cytochrome c to O_2, it pumps another 4 H^+. (Complex IV actually uses 4 electrons to produce 2 H_2O from a single O_2.) The transit of the NADH electron pair through the electron transport chain pumps a total of 10 H^+ into the intermembrane space. Each 3 H^+ returning to the matrix through the ATP synthase produces 1 ATP. Another H^+ is consumed in transporting ATP from the matrix to the cytosol. Thus the two electrons from NADH produce about 2.5 ATP (10 pumped $\div$ 4 = 2.5).

$FADH_2$

2 A pair of electrons from $FADH_2$ enter the chain at complex II (succinate-Q), which is the non-pumping complex. The flow of electrons from $FADH_2$ to ubiquinone does not pump any protons to the intermembrane space. The flow of electrons through complexes III and IV is the same as for NADH. Thus the transit of the two $FADH_2$ electrons through the electron transport chain pumps a total of 6 H^+ into the intermembrane space and produces about 1.5 ATP (6 $\div$ 4 = 1.5).

Cytosolic NADH

3 Glycolysis forms NADH in the cytosol, but the outer mitochondrial membrane is impervious to NADH. How can NADH deliver its electrons to the electron transport chain? NADH transfers its pair of electrons to special carriers that can cross the mitochondrial membrane. One carrier, glycerol 3-phosphate, shuttles the electrons to the matrix and delivers them to FAD, thereby forming $FADH_2$. This $FADH_2$ delivers the electrons to the chain where they form 1.5 ATP. In the heart and liver, malate shuttles the electrons from cytosolic NADH to the matrix. Malate crosses the mitochondrial membrane and delivers the electrons to NAD^+, thereby forming NADH inside the mitochondrion. This NADH delivers the electron pair to the chain where they form 2.5 ATP. Depending on the carrier, cytosolic NADH may produce 1.5 or 2.5 ATP.

Urea Cycle

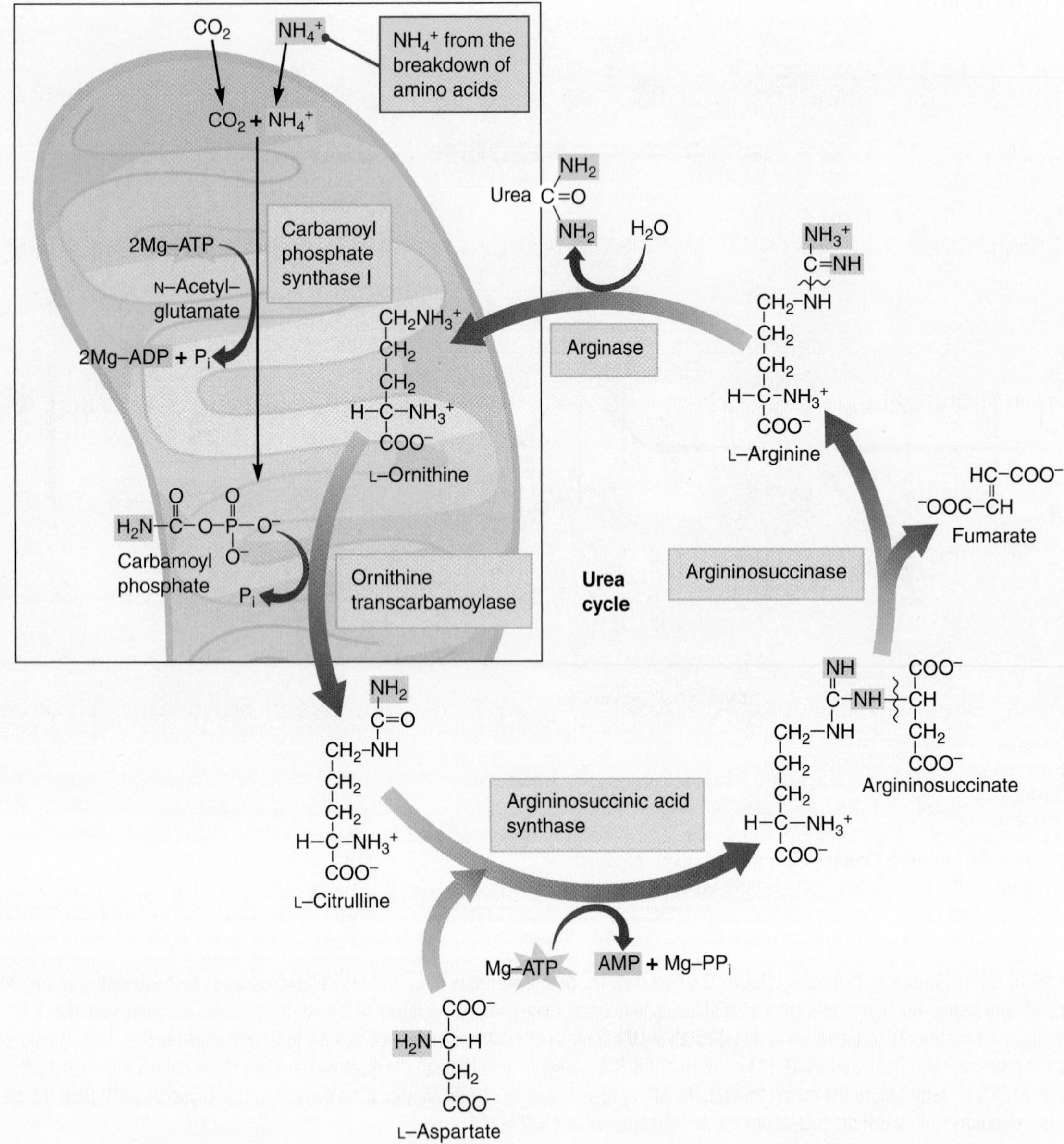

Some NH_4^+ from the breakdown of amino acids is used for biosynthesis of nitrogen compounds. Excess NH_4^+ is converted to urea and excreted.

Appendix H *Calculations and Conversions*

- Energy from Food
- Recommended Protein Intake for Adults
- Niacin Equivalents (NE)
- Dietary Folate Equivalents (DFE)
- Retinol Activity Equivalents (RAE)
- Vitamin D
- Vitamin E
- Estimating Energy Expenditure
- Body Mass Index (BMI)
- Metric Prefixes
- Length: Metric and U.S. Equivalents
- Capacities or Volumes
- Food Measurement Equivalents
- Food Measurement Conversions: U.S. to Metric
- Food Measurement Conversions: Metric to U.S.
- Conversion Factors
- Fahrenheit and Celsius (Centigrade) Scales
- Do You Speak Metric?

Energy from Food

grams carbohydrate × 4 kcal/g
grams protein × 4 kcal/g
grams fat × 9 kcal/g
grams alcohol × 7 kcal/g

total = energy from food

Example:			
	Carbohydrate	275 g × 4 kcal/g =	1,100 kcal
	Protein	64 g × 4 kcal/g =	256 kcal
	Fat	60 g × 9 kcal/g =	540 kcal
	Alcohol	15 g × 7 kcal/g =	105 kcal
		TOTAL ENERGY	2,001 kcal

Calculating the percentage of calories for each:

Carbohydrate	(1,100 kcal ÷ 2,001 kcal) × 100 = 54.97% (55%)
Protein	(256 kcal ÷ 2,001 kcal) × 100 = 12.79% (13%)
Fat	(540 kcal ÷ 2,001 kcal) × 100 = 26.99% (27%)
Alcohol	(105 kcal ÷ 2,001 kcal) × 100 = 5.25% (5%)

1 kilocalorie = 4.184 kilojoules
1 kilojoule = 0.239 kilocalories

Recommended Protein Intake for Adults

grams of recommended protein = weight in kilograms × 0.8 g/kg
Example:

A 70-kg (154-lb) person
grams of recommended protein = 70 kg × 0.8 g/kg = 56 grams protein, or
grams of recommended protein = (154 lb ÷ 2.2) × 0.8 g/kg = 56 grams protein

Note: Endurance athletes involved in heavy training may require 1.2 to 1.4 grams of protein per kilogram of body weight per day.

Niacin Equivalents (NE)

Determining the amount of niacin from tryptophan:

NE = milligrams niacin
NE from tryptophan = grams excess protein ÷ 6
NE from tryptophan = (grams dietary protein – protein RDA) ÷ 6

Example: **Assume dietary protein = 86 g and protein RDA = 56 g**
NE from tryptophan = (86 g – 56 g) ÷ 6
NE from tryptophan = 5

Dietary Folate Equivalents (DFE)

Dietary folate equivalents account for differences in the absorption of food folate, synthetic folic acid in dietary supplements, and folic acid added to fortified foods. Food in the stomach also affects bioavailability. Folic acid taken as a supplement when fasting is two times more bioavailable than food folate. Folic acid taken with food and folic acid in fortified foods are 1.7 times more bioavailable than food folate.

1 µg DFE = 1 microgram of food folate
= 0.5 µg of folic acid supplement taken on an empty stomach
= 0.6 µg of folic acid supplement consumed with meals
= 0.6 µg of folic acid in fortified foods

1 µg folic acid as a fortificant = 1.7 µg DFE
1 µg folic acid as a supplement, fasting = 2.0 µg DFE

Example:

Food folate in cooked spinach	100 µg = 100 µg DFE
Ready-to-eat cereal fortified with folic acid	100 µg = 170 µg DFE
Supplemental folic acid taken without food	100 µg = 200 µg DFE

Estimating DFE from Daily Value:

DFE = %DV × DV × bioavailability factor

Example:
Assume that a serving of fortified breakfast cereal contains 10% of the Daily Value for folate
Daily Value = 400 µg folic acid

DFE = %DV × DV × bioavailability factor
DFE = 0.10 × 400 µg × 1.7
DFE = 68 µg, which can be rounded to 70 µg DFE

Retinol Activity Equivalents (RAE)

Retinol activity equivalents are a standardized measure of vitamin A activity that account for differences in the bioavailability of different sources of vitamin A. Of the provitamin A carotenoids, beta-carotene produces the most vitamin A.

1 µg RAE = 1 µg retinol
= 12 µg beta-carotene
= 24 µg of other vitamin A precursors

Although outdated, many vitamin supplements still report vitamin A content as International Units (IU).

1 µg RAE = 3.33 IU from retinol
= 10 IU from beta-carotene in supplements
= 20 IU from beta-carotene in foods

Vitamin D

Although outdated, many vitamin supplements still report vitamin D content as International Units (IU).

1 IU = 0.025 µg cholecalciferol

µg cholecalciferol = IU ÷ 40

Example:

A vitamin supplement contains 100 IU vitamin D
µg cholecalciferol = 100 ÷ 40 = 2.5

Vitamin E

Although outdated, many vitamin supplements still report vitamin E content as International Units (IU) rather than as milligrams of α-tocopherol. Two conversion factors are used to convert IU to milligrams of α-tocopherol. If the form of the supplement is "natural" or RRR-α-tocopherol (historically labeled as *d*-alpha-tocopherol), the conversion factor is 0.67 mg/IU. If the form of the supplement is *all rac*-α-tocopherol (historically labeled *dl*-α-tocopherol), the conversion factor is 0.45 mg/IU.

Examples:

A multivitamin supplement contains 30 IU of *d*-α-tocopherol
30 IU × 0.67 = 20 mg α-tocopherol
A multivitamin supplement contains 30 IU of *dl*-α-tocopherol
30 IU × 0.45 = 13.5 mg α-tocopherol

Estimating Energy Expenditure

The Estimated Energy Requirement (EER) is defined as the dietary energy intake (in kilocalories per day) that is predicted to maintain energy balance in a healthy adult of a defined age, gender, weight, height, and level of physical activity consistent with good health.* The EER equations predict Total Energy Expenditure (TEE).

Adult men (age 19 and older):

EER = 662 – 9.53 × Age [yr] + PA × (15.91 × Weight [kg] + 539.6 × Height [m])

PA is the Physical Activity coefficient that represents physical activity level

Sedentary	**PA = 1.0**
Low active	**PA = 1.11**
Active	**PA = 1.25**
Very active	**PA = 1.48**

Adult women (age 19 and older):

EER = 354 – 6.91 × Age [yr] + PA × (9.36 × Weight [kg] + 726 × Height [m])

PA is the Physical Activity coefficient that represents physical activity level

Sedentary	**PA = 1.0**
Low active	**PA = 1.12**
Active	**PA = 1.27**
Very active	**PA = 1.45**

Example: **A 21-year-old woman, 5'4" (1.6 m) tall, who weighs 120 pounds (54.5 kilograms) and is active.**

Example: **= 354 – 6.91 × 21 yr + 1.27 × (9.36 × 54.5 kg + 726 × 1.6 m)**
= 354 – 145.11 + 1.27 × (510.12 + 1,161.6)
= 354 – 145.11 + 1.27 × 1,671.72
= 354 – 145.11 + 2,123.08
= 2,331.97
= 2,332 kcal/day

***Source:** Institute of Medicine, Food and Nutrition Board. *Dietary Reference Intakes for Energy, Carbohydrate, Fiber, Fat, Fatty Acids, Cholesterol, Protein, and Amino Acids.* Washington, DC: National Academy Press; 2005.

Total energy expenditure can also be estimated by first estimating resting energy expenditure (REE) and then adding additional energy to account for physical activity and the thermic effect of food.

Resting Energy Expenditure (REE)

Harris-Benedict Equations

Adult men **REE = 66 + 13.7*W* + 5.0*H* – 6.8*A***
Adult women **REE = 655 + 9.6*W* + 1.8*H* – 4.7*A***

(*W* = weight in kilograms, *H* = height in centimeters, *A* = age)

Note: Harris-Benedict equations may overestimate resting energy expenditure, especially for obese people.

Quick Estimate

Adult men **REE – weight (kg) × 1.0 kcal/kg × 24 hours**
REE = weight (kg) × 1.0 × 24
Adult women **REE = weight (kg) × 0.9 kcal/kg × 24 hours**
REE = weight (kg) × 0.9 × 24

Physical Activity (PA)

Physical activity can be estimated as a percentage of the resting energy expenditure (REE) based on the frequency and intensity of physical activity.

Percentage of REE	Activity Level	Descriptor
20–30%	Sedentary	Mostly resting, with little or no activity
30–45%	Light	Occasional unplanned activity (e.g., going for a stroll)
45–65%	Moderate	Daily planned activity, such as brisk walks
65–90%	Heavy	Daily workout routine requiring several hours of continuous exercise
90–120%	Exceptional	Daily vigorous workouts for extended hours; training for competition

Thermic Effect of Food (TEF)

The thermic effect of food can be estimated as 10% of the sum of REE + physical activity

Total energy expenditure (TEE) = REE + PA + TEF

Example using quick estimate of REE:

A 175-pound (79.5 kg), 30-year-old man engages in moderate activity (60% of REE).

REE = 79.5 kg × 1.0 kcal/kg/hr × 24 hr/day
= 1,908 kcal/day

PA = 60% of REE
= 0.60 × 1908 kcal/day
= 1144.8 kcal/day

TEF = 10% of REE + PA
= 0.10 × (1908 + 1144.8 kcal/day)
= 0.10 × 3052.8 kcal/day
= 305.3 kcal/day

TEE = REE + PA + TEF
= 1908 + 1144.8 + 305.3 kcal/day
= 3358 kcal/day

Body Mass Index (BMI)

U.S. Formula

BMI = [weight in pounds ÷ (height in inches)^2] × 703

Example: **A 154-pound man is 5 ft 8 inches (68 inches) tall**
BMI = [154 ÷ (68 in × 68 in)] × 703
BMI = (154 ÷ 4,624) × 703
BMI = 23.41

Metric Formula

BMI = weight in kilograms ÷ [height in meters]^2
or
BMI = [weight in kilograms ÷ (height in cm)^2] × 10,000

Example: **A 70-kg man is 1.75 meters tall**
BMI = 70 kg ÷ (1.75 m × 1.75 m)
BMI = 70 ÷ 3.0625
BMI = 22.86

Metric Prefixes

giga-	G	1,000,000,000
mega-	M	1,000,000
kilo-	k	1,000
hecto-	h	100
deka-	da	10
deci-	d	0.1
centi-	c	0.01
milli-	m	0.001
micro-	µ	0.000001
nano-	n	0.000000001

Length: Metric and U.S. Equivalents

1 centimeter	0.3937 inch
1 decimeter	3.937 inches
1 foot	0.3048 meter
1 inch	2.54 centimeters
1 meter	39.37 inches
	1.094 yards
1 micron	0.001 millimeter
	0.00003937 inch
1 millimeter	0.03937 inch
1 yard	0.9144 meter

Capacities or Volumes

1 cup, measuring	8 fluid ounces
	1/2 liquid pint
1 gallon (U.S.)	231 cubic inches
	3.785 liters
	0.833 British gallon
	128 U.S. fluid ounces
1 gallon (British Imperial)	277.42 cubic inches
	1.201 U.S. gallons
	4.546 liters
	160 British fluid ounces
1 liter	1.057 liquid quarts
	0.908 dry quart
	61.024 cubic inches
1 milliliter	0.061 cubic inches
1 ounce, fluid or liquid (U.S.)	1.805 cubic inches
	29.574 milliliters
	1.041 British fluid ounces

1 pint, dry . . . . . 33.600 cubic inches
. . . . . 0.551 liter
1 pint, liquid . . . . . 28.875 cubic inches
. . . . . 0.473 liter
1 quart, dry (U.S.) . . . . . 67.201 cubic inches
. . . . . 1.101 liters
. . . . . 0.969 British quart
1 quart, liquid (U.S.) . . . . . 57.75 cubic inches
. . . . . 0.946 liter
. . . . . 0.833 British quart
1 quart (British) . . . . . 69.354 cubic inches
. . . . . 1.032 U.S. dry quarts
. . . . . 1.201 U.S. liquid quarts
1 tablespoon, measuring . . . . . 3 teaspoons
. . . . . 1/2 fluid ounce
1 teaspoon, measuring . . . . . 1/3 tablespoon
. . . . . 1/6 fluid ounce
1 kilogram . . . . . 2.205 pounds
1 microgram (μg) . . . . . 0.000001 gram

Food Measurement Equivalents

16 tablespoons = 1 cup
12 tablespoons = 3/4 cup
10 tablespoons + 2 teaspoons = 2/3 cup
8 tablespoons = 1/2 cup
6 tablespoons = 3/8 cup
5 tablespoons + 1 teaspoon = 1/3 cup
4 tablespoons = 1/4 cup
2 tablespoons = 1/8 cup
2 tablespoons + 2 teaspoons = 1/6 cup
1 tablespoon = 1/16 cup
2 cups = 1 pint
2 pints = 1 quart
3 teaspoons = 1 tablespoon
48 teaspoons = 1 cup

Food Measurement Conversions: U.S. to Metric

Capacity

1/5 teaspoon . . . . 1 milliliter
1 teaspoon . . . . . . 5 milliliters
1 tablespoon . . . . 15 milliliters
1 fluid ounce . . . . 30 milliliters
1/5 cup . . . . 47 milliliters
1 cup . . . . 237 milliliters
2 cups (1 pint) . . . 473 milliliters
4 cups (1 quart) . . 0.95 liter
4 quarts (1 gal.) . . 3.8 liters

Weight

1 ounce . . . . 28 grams
1 pound . . . . 454 grams

Food Measurement Conversions: Metric to U.S.

Capacity

1 milliliter . . . . 1/5 teaspoon
5 milliliters . . . . . . 1 teaspoon
15 milliliters . . . . . 1 tablespoon
100 milliliters . . . . 3.4 fluid oz
240 milliliters . . . . 1 cup
1 liter . . . . 34 fluid oz
. . . . 4.2 cups
. . . . 2.1 pints
. . . . 1.06 quarts
. . . . 0.26 gallon

Weight

1 gram . . . . 0.035 ounce
100 grams . . . . 3.5 ounces
500 grams . . . . 1.10 pounds
1 kilogram . . . . . . 2.205 pounds
. . . . 35 ounces

Conversion Factors

To change	To	Multiply by
centimeters	inches	0.3937
centimeters	feet	0.03281
cubic feet	cubic meters	0.0283
cubic meters	cubic feet	35.3145
cubic meters	cubic yards	1.3079
cubic yards	cubic meters	0.7646
feet	meters	0.3048
gallons (U.S.)	liters	3.7853
grams	ounces avdp	0.0353
grams	pounds	0.002205
inches	millimeters	25.4000
inches	centimeters	2.5400
inches	meters	0.0254
kilograms	pounds	2.2046
liters	gallons (U.S.)	0.2642
liters	pints (dry)	1.8162
liters	pints (liquid)	2.1134
liters	quarts (dry)	0.9081
liters	quarts (liquid)	1.0567
meters	feet	3.2808
meters	yards	1.0936
millimeters	inches	0.0394
ounces avdp	grams	28.3495
ounces	pounds	0.0625
pints (dry)	liters	0.5506
pints (liquid)	liters	0.4732
pounds	kilograms	0.4536
pounds	ounces	16
quarts (dry)	liters	1.1012
quarts (liquid)	liters	0.9463

Fahrenheit and Celsius (Centigrade) Scales

°Celsius	°Fahrenheit
–273.15	–459.67
–250	–418
–200	–328
–150	–238
–100	–148
–50	–58
–40	–40
–30	–22
–20	–4
–10	14
0	32
5	41
10	50
15	59
20	68
25	77
30	86
35	95
40	104
45	113
50	122
55	131
60	140
65	149
70	158
75	167
80	176
85	185
90	194
95	203
100	212

Zero on the Fahrenheit scale represents the temperature produced by the mixing of equal weights of snow and common salt.

	°Fahrenheit	°Celsius
Boiling point of water	212°	100°
Freezing point of water	32°	0°
Normal body temperature	98.6°	37°
Comfortable room temperature	68–77°	20–25°
Absolute zero	–459.6°	–273.1°

Absolute zero is theoretically the lowest possible temperature, the point at which all molecular motion would cease.

To Convert Temperature Scales

To convert Fahrenheit to Celsius (Centigrade), subtract 32 and multiply by $5/9$.

$$°C = 5/9(°F - 32)$$

To convert Celsius (Centigrade) to Fahrenheit, multiply by $9/5$ and add 32.

$$°F = (9/5 \times °C) + 32$$

Do You Speak Metric?

Although the metric system isn't really a language like English or Spanish, in some sense it is the language of science. Nutritionists must be fluent in metrics. Pick up any nutrition journal and you will find units of measurement expressed in terms like kilograms and liters.

The metric system is a decimal-based system of measurement units. Like our monetary system, units are related by factors of 10. There are 10 pennies in a dime, and 10 dimes equal 1 dollar. Calculations involve the simple process of moving the decimal point to the right or to the left.

There are only seven basic units in the metric system. The most common units are the meter (m) to measure length, the gram (g) for mass, the liter (L) for volume, and degree Celsius (°C) for temperature. The metric system avoids the confusing dual use of terms, such as the current use of ounces to measure both weight and volume.

One strategy for learning metric is to find common or familiar associations. For example, when using degrees Celsius you should equate 22 degrees Celsius (22°C) with room temperature, 37 degrees Celsius (37°C) with body temperature, and 0 and 100 degrees Celsius with the freezing and boiling points of water, respectively. A millimeter (1 mm) is about the thickness of a dime, and 2 centimeters (2 cm) is about the diameter of a nickel. When you pick up a 2-pound box of sugar, you are holding about 900 grams.

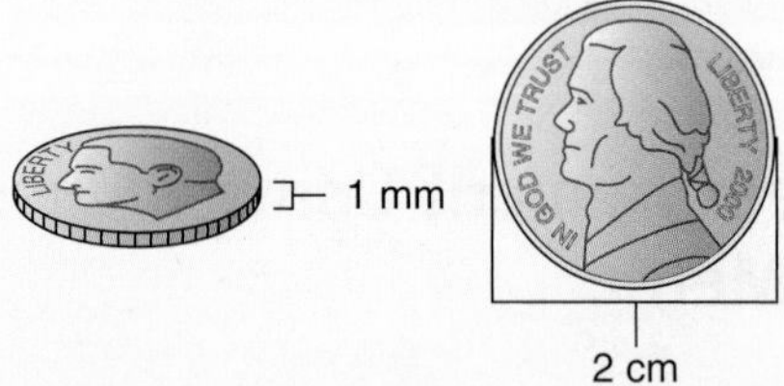

A fluid ounce can be tricky because it's a measure of liquid volume, not weight. Most people already recognize 1-liter and 2-liter soft-drink bottles. A 1-liter bottle equals 33.8 fluid ounces.

The United States is the only industrialized country in the world not officially using the metric system. Because of its many advantages (e.g., easy conversion between units of the same quantity), the metric system has become the internationally accepted system of measurement.

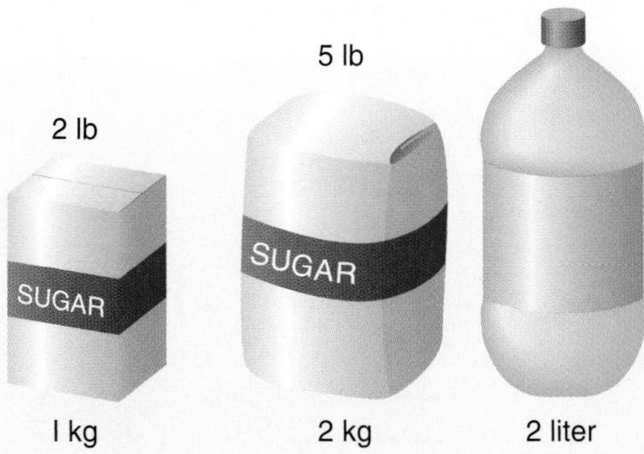

Many members of the international scientific community use the International System of Units (SI). The SI is the modern metric system and has adopted the joule rather than the calorie to measure food energy. Although we think of the calorie as a measure of energy, it is more accurately a measure of heat. Joules are a measure of work, not heat, and the amount of energy potential in foods is expressed best in kilojoules (kjoules). Each kilocalorie is equivalent to approximately 4.2 (4.184) kilojoules. For example, a 100-kilocalorie glass of juice provides about 420 kilojoules.

The Celsius (C) temperature scale should be used instead of the Fahrenheit (F) scale. The following are familiar points:

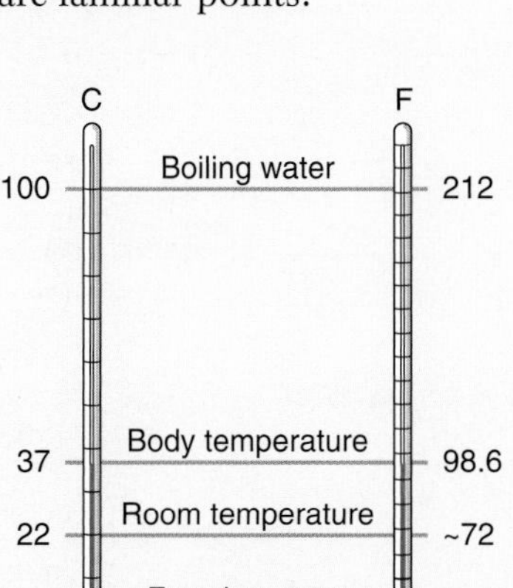

Table H.1 Measures Commonly Used in Nutrition

	Metric	English
Length	1 meter (m)	39.4 inches (in)
	1 centimeter (cm)	0.394 inch (in)
	2.54 centimeters (cm)	1 inch (in)
Weight (mass)	1 kilogram (kg)	2.2 pounds (lb)
	454 grams (g)	1 pound (lb)
	5 grams (g) of salt	about 1 teaspoon (tsp)
Volume	1 liter (L)	1.057 quarts (about 4 cups)
	236 milliliters (mL)	about 1 cup (c)
	15 milliliters (mL)	about 1 tablespoon (Tbsp)
	5 milliliters (mL)	about 1 teaspoon (tsp)

Note:
1 gram = 1,000 milligrams
1 milligram = 1,000 micrograms (µg or mcg)

Appendix I *Growth Charts*

A complete set of growth charts is available on the Internet at www.cdc.gov/growthcharts. There are three sets, each with a different set of percentiles. Each set includes the following charts for girls and boys:

Weight-for-age percentiles: birth to 36 months

Length-for-age percentiles: birth to 36 months

Weight-for-length percentiles: birth to 36 months

Head circumference-for-age percentiles: birth to 36 months

Weight-for-age percentiles: 2 to 20 years

Stature-for-age percentiles: 2 to 20 years

Weight-for-stature percentiles

Body mass index-for-age percentiles: 2 to 20 years

2 to 20 years: Girls
Stature-for-Age and Weight-for-Age Percentiles

NAME ______________________

RECORD # ______________

Mother's Stature ____________ Father's Stature ____________

Date	Age	Weight	Stature	BMI*

***To Calculate BMI**: Weight (kg) ÷ Stature (cm) ÷ Stature (cm) x 10,000
or Weight (lb) ÷ Stature (in) ÷ Stature (in) x 703

AGE (YEARS)

12 13 14 15 16 17 18 19 20

STATURE

STATURE

WEIGHT

WEIGHT

Percentiles: 97, 90, 75, 50, 25, 10, 3

AGE (YEARS)

2 3 4 5 6 7 8 9 10 11 12 13 14 15 16 17 18 19 20

SOURCE: Developed by the National Center for Health Statistics in collaboration with
the National Center for Chronic Disease Prevention and Health Promotion (2000).
http://www.cdc.gov/growthcharts

2 to 20 years: Boys
Stature-for-Age and Weight-for-Age Percentiles

NAME ____________________

RECORD # ____________

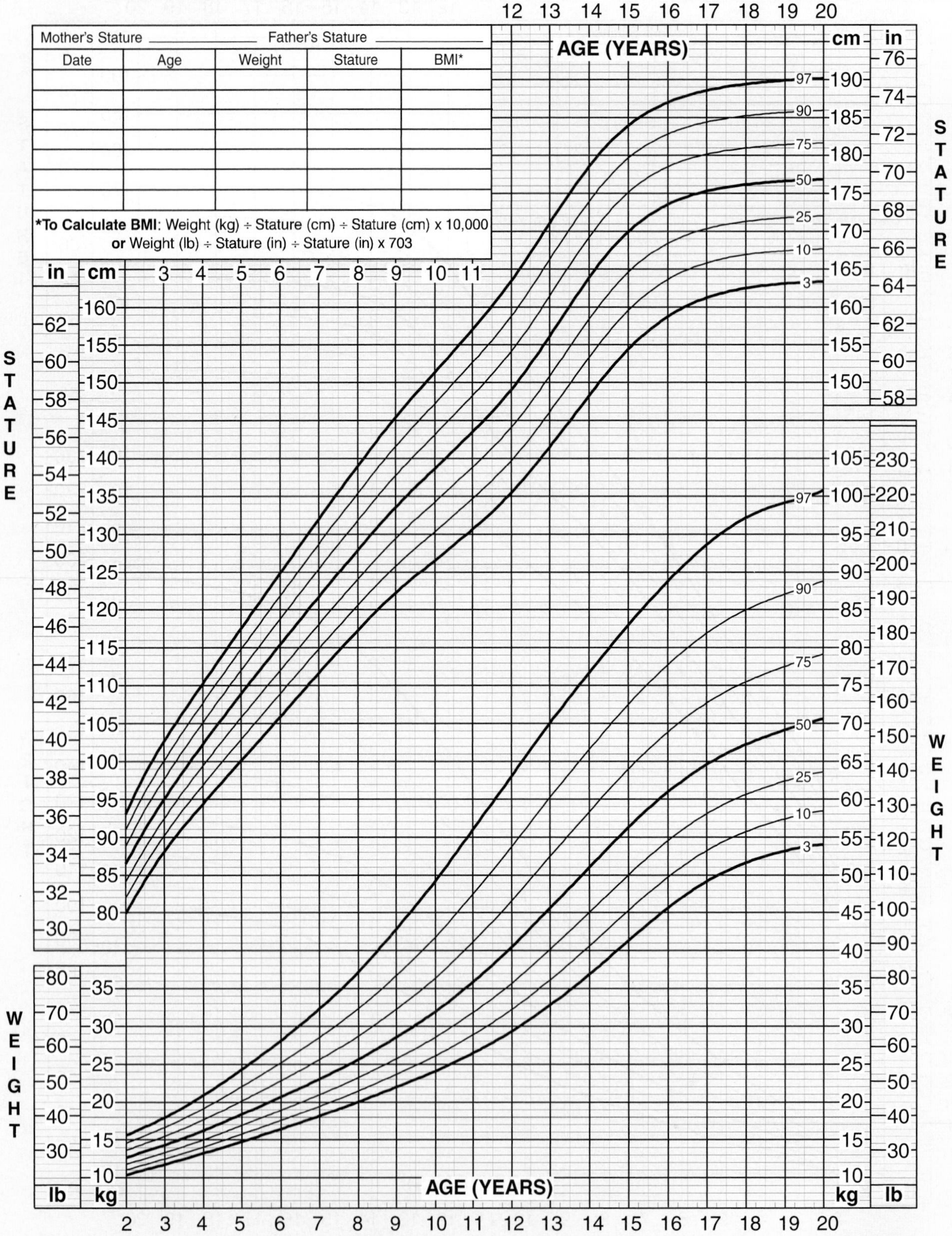

Mother's Stature ____________ Father's Stature ____________

Date	Age	Weight	Stature	BMI*

***To Calculate BMI**: Weight (kg) ÷ Stature (cm) ÷ Stature (cm) x 10,000
or Weight (lb) ÷ Stature (in) ÷ Stature (in) x 703

AGE (YEARS)

STATURE

WEIGHT

SOURCE: Developed by the National Center for Health Statistics in collaboration with the National Center for Chronic Disease Prevention and Health Promotion (2000).
http://www.cdc.gov/growthcharts

Glossary

ABC model of behavior A behavioral model that includes the external and internal events that precede and follow the behavior. The "A" stands for antecedents, the events that precede the behavior ("B"), which is followed by consequences ("C") that positively or negatively reinforce the behavior.

ABCDs of nutrition assessment Nutrition assessment components: anthropometric measurements, biochemical tests, clinical observations, and dietary intake.

absorption The movement of substances into or across tissues; in particular, the passage of nutrients and other substances into the walls of the gastrointestinal tract and then into the bloodstream.

Acceptable Macronutrient Distribution Ranges (AMDRs) Range of intakes for a particular energy source that are associated with reduced risk of chronic disease while providing adequate intakes of essential nutrients.

acculturation The process of adopting the cultural traits and social behaviors of another group.

acesulfame K [ay-SUL-fame] An artificial sweetener that is 200 times sweeter than common table sugar (sucrose). Because it is not digested and absorbed by the body, acesulfame contributes no calories to the diet and yields no energy when consumed.

acetaldehyde A toxic intermediate compound formed by the action of the alcohol dehydrogenase enzyme during the metabolism of alcohol.

acetyl CoA A key intermediate in the metabolic breakdown of carbohydrates, fatty acids, and amino acids. It consists of a two-carbon acetate group linked to coenzyme A, which is derived from pantothenic acid.

acidosis An abnormally low blood pH (below about 7.35) due to increased acidity.

acne An inflammatory skin eruption that usually occurs in or near the sebaceous glands of the face, neck, shoulders, and upper back.

acrolein A pungent decomposition product of fats, generated from dehydrating the glycerol components of fats; responsible for the coughing attacks caused by the fumes released by burning fat. This toxic water-soluble liquid vaporizes easily and is highly flammable.

active transport The movement of substances into or out of cells against a concentration gradient. Active transport requires energy (ATP) and involves carrier (transport) proteins in the cell membrane.

additives Substances added to food to perform various functions, such as adding color or flavor, replacing sugar or fat, improving nutritional content, or improving texture or shelf life.

adenosine diphosphate (ADP) The compound produced upon hydrolysis of ATP, and used to synthesize ATP. Composed of adenosine and two phosphate groups.

adenosine monophosphate (AMP) Hydrolysis product of ADP and of nucleic acids. Composed of adenosine and one phosphate group.

adenosine triphosphate (ATP) [ah-DEN-oh-seen try-FOS-fate] A high-energy compound that is the main direct fuel that cells use to synthesize molecules, contract muscles, transport substances, and perform other tasks.

Adequate Intake (AI) The nutrient intake that appears to sustain a defined nutritional state or some other indicator of health (e.g., growth rate or normal circulating nutrient values) in a specific population or subgroup. AI is used when there is insufficient scientific evidence to establish an EAR.

adipocytes Fat cells.

adipose tissue Body fat tissue.

adolescence The period between onset of puberty and adulthood.

aerobic [air-ROW-bic] Referring to the presence of or need for oxygen. The complete breakdown of glucose, fatty acids, and amino acids to carbon dioxide and water occurs only via aerobic metabolism. The citric acid cycle and electron transport chain are aerobic pathways.

aerobic endurance The ability of skeletal muscle to obtain a sufficient supply of oxygen from the heart and lungs to maintain muscular activity for a prolonged time.

aflatoxin A toxin produced by a mold that grows on crops, such as peanuts, tree nuts, corn, wheat, and oil seeds (like cottonseed).

albumin A protein that circulates in the blood and functions in the transport of many minerals and some drugs.

alcohol Common name for ethanol or ethyl alcohol. As a general term, it refers to any organic compound with one or more hydroxyl (–OH) groups.

alcohol dehydrogenase (ADH) The enzyme that catalyzes the oxidation of ethanol and other alcohols.

alcohol poisoning An overdose of alcohol. The body is overwhelmed by the amount of alcohol in the system and cannot metabolize it fast enough.

aldehyde dehydrogenase (ALDH) The enzyme that catalyzes the conversion of acetaldehyde to acetate, which forms acetyl CoA.

aldosterone [al-DOS-ter-own] A steroid hormone secreted from the adrenal glands that acts on the kidneys to regulate electrolyte and water balance. It raises blood pressure by promoting retention of sodium (and thus water) and excretion of potassium.

alkalosis An abnormally high blood pH (above about 7.45) due to increased alkalinity.

alpha (α) bonds Chemical bonds linking two monosaccharides (glycosidic bonds) that can be broken by human intestinal enzymes, releasing the individual monosaccharides. Maltose and sucrose contain alpha bonds.

alpha-linolenic acid [al-fah lin-oh-LEN-ik] An essential omega-3 fatty acid that contains 18 carbon atoms and three carbon–carbon double bonds (18:3).

Alzheimer's disease (AD) A presenile dementia characterized by accumulation of plaques in certain regions of the brain and degeneration of a certain class of neurons.

amenorrhea [A-men-or-Ee-a] Absence or abnormal stoppage of menses in a female; commonly indicated by the absence of three to six consecutive menstrual cycles.

amino acid pool The amino acids in body tissues and fluids that are available for new protein synthesis.

amino acid scoring A method to determine the protein quality of a food by comparing its amino acid composition with that of a reference protein. Also called chemical scoring.

amino acids Organic compounds that function as the building blocks of protein.

amniotic fluid The fluid that surrounds the fetus; contained in the amniotic sac inside the uterus.

amylase [AM-ih-lace] A salivary enzyme that catalyzes the hydrolysis of amylose, a starch. Also called ptyalin.

amylopectin [am-ih-low-PEK-tin] A branched-chain polysaccharide composed of glucose units.

amylose [AM-ih-los] A straight-chain polysaccharide composed of glucose units.

anabolism [an-A-bol-iz-um] Any metabolic process whereby cells convert simple substances into more complex ones.

anaerobic [AN-ah-ROW-bic] Referring to the absence of oxygen or the ability of a process to occur in the absence of oxygen.

android obesity [AN-droyd] Excess storage of fat located primarily in the abdominal area.

anemia Abnormally low concentration of hemoglobin in the bloodstream; can be caused by impaired synthesis of red blood cells, increased destruction of red cells, or significant loss of blood.

anencephaly A type of neural tube birth defect in which part or all of the brain is missing.

angiotensin I [an-jee-oh-TEN-sin one] A 10-amino-acid peptide that is a precursor of angiotensin II.

angiotensin II In the lungs, the eight-amino-acid peptide angiotensin II is formed from angiotensin I. Angiotensin II is a powerful vasoconstrictor that rapidly raises blood pressure.

angiotensinogen A circulating protein produced by the liver from which angiotensin I is cleaved by the action of renin.

angular stomatitis Inflammation and cracking of the skin at the corners of the mouth; a symptom of riboflavin deficiency.

anions Ions that carry a negative charge.

anorexia of aging Loss of appetite and wasting associated with old age.

anorexia athletica Eating disorder associated with competitive participation in athletic activity.

anorexia nervosa [an-or-EX-ee-uh ner-VOH-sah] An eating disorder marked by prolonged decrease of appetite and refusal to eat, leading to self-starvation and excessive weight loss. It results in part from a distorted body image and intense fear of becoming fat, often linked to social pressures.

anthropometric measurements Measurements of the physical characteristics of the body, such as height, weight, head circumference, girth, and skinfold measurements. Anthropometric measurements are particularly useful in evaluating the growth of infants, children, and adolescents and in determining body composition.

antibodies [AN-tih-bod-ees] Large blood proteins produced by B lymphocytes in response to exposure to particular antigens (e.g., a protein on the surface of a virus or bacterium). Each type of antibody specifically binds to and helps eliminate its matching antigen from the body. Once formed, antibodies circulate in the blood and help protect the body against subsequent infection.

antidiuretic hormone (ADH) A peptide hormone secreted by the pituitary gland. It increases blood pressure and prevents fluid excretion by the kidneys. Also called vasopressin.

antioxidant A substance that combines with or otherwise neutralizes a free radical, thus preventing oxidative damage to cells and tissues.

antirachitic Pertaining to activities of an agent used to treat rickets.

appetite A psychological desire to eat that is related to the pleasant sensations often associated with food.

ariboflavinosis Riboflavin deficiency.

aspartame [AH-spar-tame] An artificial sweetener composed of two amino acids and methanol. It is 200 times sweeter than sucrose. Its trade name is NutraSweet.

atherosclerosis A type of "hardening of the arteries" in which cholesterol and other substances in the blood build up in the walls of arteries. As the process continues, the arteries to the heart may narrow, cutting down the flow of oxygen-rich blood and nutrients to the heart.

ATP–CP energy system A simple and immediate anaerobic energy system that maintains ATP levels. Creatine phosphate is broken down, releasing energy and a phosphate group, which is used to form ATP.

atrophic gastritis An age-related condition in which the stomach loses its ability to secrete acid. In severe cases, ability to make intrinsic factor is also impaired.

autonomic nervous system The part of the central nervous system that regulates the automatic responses of the body; consists of the sympathetic and para-sympathetic systems.

avidin A protein in raw egg whites that binds biotin, preventing its absorption. Avidin is destroyed by heat.

bacteriophages Viruses that infect bacteria.

baryophobia [barry-oh-FO-bee-ah] An uncommon eating disorder that stunts growth in children and young adults as a result of underfeeding.

basal energy expenditure (BEE) The basal metabolic rate (BMR) extrapolated to 24 hours. Often used interchangeably with REE.

basal metabolic rate (BMR) A clinical measure of resting energy expenditure performed upon awakening, 10 to 12 hours after eating, and 12 to 18 hours after significant physical activity. Often used interchangeably with RMR.

base pair Two nitrogenous bases (adenine and thymine or guanine and cytosine), held together by weak bonds, that form a "rung" of the "DNA ladder." The bonds between base pairs hold the DNA molecule together in the shape of a double helix.

benign [beh-NINE] Not cancerous; does not invade nearby tissue or spread to other parts of the body.

beriberi Thiamin-deficiency disease. Symptoms include muscle weakness, loss of appetite, nerve degeneration, and edema in some cases.

beta (β) bonds Chemical bonds linking two monosaccharides (glycosidic bonds) that cannot be broken by human intestinal enzymes. Cellulose contains beta bonds.

β-glucans Functional fiber, consisting of branched polysaccharide chains of glucose, that helps lower blood cholesterol levels. Found in barley and oats.

beta-oxidation The breakdown of a fatty acid into numerous molecules of the two-carbon compound acetyl coenzyme A (acetyl CoA).

bile An alkaline, yellow-green fluid that is produced in the liver and stored in the gallbladder. The primary constituents of bile are bile salts, bile acids, phospholipids, cholesterol, and bicarbonate. Bile emulsifies dietary fats, aiding fat digestion and absorption.

binge Consumption of a very large amount of food in a brief time (e.g., two hours) accompanied by a loss of control over how much and what is eaten.

binge drinking Consuming excessive amounts of alcohol in short periods of time.

binge eaters Individuals who routinely consume a very large amount of food in a brief period of time (e.g., two hours) and lose control over how much and what is eaten.

binge-eating disorder An eating disorder marked by repeated episodes of binge eating and a feeling of loss of control. The diagnosis is based on a person's having an average of at least two binge-eating episodes per week for six months.

bioavailability A measure of the extent to which a nutrient becomes available to the body after ingestion and thus is available to the tissues.

biochemical assessment Assessment by measuring a nutrient or its metabolite in one or more body fluids, such as blood and urine, or in feces. Also called laboratory assessment.

biocytin A biotin–lysine complex released from digested protein.

biodiversity The countless species of plants, animals, and insects that exist on the earth. An undisturbed tropical forest is an example of the biodiversity of a healthy ecosystem.

bioelectrical impedance analysis (BIA) Technique to estimate amounts of total body water, lean tissue mass, and total body fat. It uses the resistance of tissue to the flow of an alternating electric current.

bioflavonoids Naturally occurring plant chemicals, especially from citrus fruits, that reduce the permeability and fragility of capillaries.

biological value (BV) The extent to which protein in a food can be incorporated into body proteins. BV is expressed as the percentage of the absorbed dietary nitrogen retained by the body.

biosynthesis Chemical reactions that form simple molecules into complex biomolecules, especially carbohydrate, lipids, protein, nucleotides, and nucleic acids.

biotechnology The set of laboratory techniques and processes used to modify the genome of plants or animals and thus create desirable new characteristics. Genetic engineering in the broad sense.

biotinidase An enzyme in the small intestine that releases biotin from biocytin.

blastogenic stage The first stage of gestation, during which tissue proliferation by rapid cell division begins.

bleaching process A complex light-stimulated reaction in which rod cells lose color as rhodopsin is split into retinal and opsin.

blood glucose levels The amount of glucose in the blood at any given time. Also known as blood sugar levels.

blood pressure The pressure of blood against the walls of a blood vessel or heart chamber. Unless there is reference to another location, such as the pulmonary artery or one of the heart chambers, this term refers to the pressure in the systemic arteries, as measured, for example, in the forearm.

BodPod A device used to measure the density of the body based on the volume of air displaced as a person sits in a sealed chamber of known volume.

body composition The chemical or anatomical composition of the body. Commonly defined as the proportions of fat, muscle, bone, and other tissues in the body.

body dysmorphic disorder (BDD) An eating disorder in which a distressing and impairing preoccupation with an imagined or slight defect in appearance is the primary symptom.

body fat distribution The pattern of fat distribution on the body.

body image A person's mental concept of his or her physical appearance, constructed from many different influences.

body mass index (BMI) Body weight (in kilograms) divided by the square of height (in meters), expressed in units of kg/m^2. Also called Quetelet index.

bolus [BOH-lus] A chewed, moistened lump of food that is ready to be swallowed.

bomb calorimeter A device that uses the heat of combustion to measure the energy content of a food.

botulism An often fatal type of food poisoning caused by a toxin released from *Clostridium botulinum*, a bacterium that can grow in improperly canned low-acid foods.

bovine spongiform encephalopathy (BSE) A chronic degenerative disease, widely referred to as "mad cow disease," that affects the central nervous system of cattle.

bran The layers of protective coating around the grain kernel that are rich in dietary fiber and nutrients.

Bt gene *Bacillus thuringiensis* (Bt) is a bacterium that produces a protein called the Bt toxin. One of the bacterium's genes, the Bt gene, carries the information for the Bt toxin. Inserting a copy of the Bt gene into plants enables them to produce Bt toxin protein and resist some insect pests. The Bt protein is not toxic to humans.

buffers Compounds or mixtures of compounds that can take up and release hydrogen ions to keep the pH of a solution constant. The buffering action of proteins and bicarbonate in the bloodstream plays a major role in maintaining the blood pH at 7.35 to 7.45.

built environment Any human-formed, developed, or structured areas, including the urban environment that consists of buildings, roads, fixtures, parks, and all other human developments that form its physical character.

bulimia nervosa [bull-EEM-ee-uh] An eating disorder marked by consumption of large amounts of food at one time (binge eating) followed by a behavior such as self-induced vomiting, use of laxatives, excessive exercise, fasting, or other practices to avoid weight gain.

calcitonin A hormone secreted by the thyroid gland in response to elevated blood calcium. It stimulates calcium deposition in bone and calcium excretion by the kidneys, thus reducing blood calcium.

calcitriol See *1,25-dihydroxyvitamin D_3*.

calmodulin A calcium-binding protein that regulates a variety of cellular activities, such as cell division and proliferation.

calorie The general term for energy in food, used synonymously with the term *energy*. Often used instead of *kilocalorie* on food labels, in diet books, and in other sources of nutrition information.

calorimeter A device used to measure quantities of heat generated by various processes.

calorimetry [kal-oh-RIM-eh-tree] The measurement of the amount of heat given off by an organism. It is used to determine total energy expenditure.

Canada's Guidelines for Healthy Eating Key messages that are based on the 1990 *Nutrition Recommendations for Canadians* and provide positive, action-oriented, scientifically accurate eating advice to Canadians.

cancer A term for diseases in which abnormal cells divide without control. Cancer cells can invade nearby tissues and can spread through the bloodstream and lymphatic system to other parts of the body.

carbohydrate loading Changes in dietary carbohydrate intake and exercise regimen before competition to maximize glycogen stores in the muscles. It is appropriate for endurance events lasting 60 to 90 consecutive minutes or longer. Also known as glycogen loading.

carbohydrates Compounds, including sugars, starches, and dietary fibers, that usually have the general chemical formula $(CH_2O)n$, where *n* represents the number of CH_2O units in the molecule. Carbohydrates are a major source of energy for body functions.

carboxylation A reaction that adds a carboxyl group (–COOH) to a substrate, replacing a hydrogen atom.

carcinogens [kar-SIN-o-jins] Any substances that cause cancer.

cardiac output The amount of blood expelled by the heart.

cardiovascular disease (CVD) Any abnormal condition characterized by dysfunction of the heart and blood vessels. CVD includes atherosclerosis (especially coronary heart disease, which can lead to heart attacks), cerebrovascular disease (e.g., stroke), and hypertension (high blood pressure).

carnitine [CAR-nih-teen] A compound that transports fatty acids from the cytosol into the mitochondria, where they undergo beta-oxidation.

carotenodermia A harmless yellow-orange cast to the skin due to high levels of carotenoids in the bloodstream resulting from consumption of extremely large amounts of carotenoid-rich foods, such as carrot juice.

carotenoids A group of yellow, orange, and red pigments in plants, including foods. Many of these compounds are precursors of vitamin A.

case control studies An investigation that uses a group of people with a particular condition, rather than a randomly selected population. These cases are compared with a control group of people who do not have the condition.

catabolism [ca-TA-bol-iz-um] Any metabolic process whereby cells break down complex substances into simpler, smaller ones.

catalyze To speed up a chemical reaction.

cations Ions that carry a positive charge.

cecum The blind pouch at the beginning of the large intestine into which the ileum opens from one side and which is continuous with the colon.

celiac disease [SEA-lee-ak] A disease that involves an inability to digest gluten, a protein found in wheat, rye, oats, and barley. If untreated, it causes flattening of the villi in the intestine, leading to severe malabsorption of nutrients. Symptoms include diarrhea, fatty stools, swollen belly, and extreme fatigue.

cells The basic structural units of all living tissues, which have two major parts: the nucleus and the cytoplasm.

cellulose [SELL-you-los] A straight-chain polysaccharide composed of hundreds of glucose units linked by beta bonds. It is nondigestible by humans and a component of dietary fiber.

central nervous system (CNS) The brain and the spinal cord. The central nervous system transmits signals that control muscular actions and glandular secretions along the entire GI tract.

cephalic phase responses The responses of the parasympathetic nervous system to the sight, smell, thought, and sound of food. Also called preabsorptive phase responses.

ceruloplasmin A copper-dependent enzyme responsible for the oxidation of ferrous ion (Fe^{2+}) to ferric ion (Fe^{3+}), enabling iron to bind to transferrin. Also known as ferroxidase I.

chain length The number of carbons that a fatty acid contains. Foods contain fatty acids with chain lengths of 4 to 24 carbons, and most have an even number of carbons.

cheilosis Inflammation and cracking of the lips; a symptom of riboflavin deficiency.

chelation therapy Use of a chelator (e.g., EDTA) to bind metal ions to remove them from the body.

chemical energy Energy contained in the bonds between atoms of a molecule.

chemical scoring A method to determine the protein quality of a food by comparing its amino acid composition with that of a reference protein. Also called amino acid scoring.

chemosenses [key-mo-SEN-sez] The chemical sensing system in the body, including taste and smell. Sensory cells in the nose, mouth, or throat transmit messages through nerves to the brain, where smells and tastes are identified.

Child and Adult Care Food Program A federally funded program that reimburses approved family child-care providers for USDA-approved foods served to preschool children; it also provides funds for meals and snacks served at after-school programs for school-age children and to adult day care centers serving chronically impaired adults or people over age 60.

childhood The period of life from age 1 to the onset of puberty.

chitin A long-chain structural polysaccharide of slightly modified glucose. Found in the hard exterior skeletons of insects, crustaceans, and other invertebrates; also occurs in the cell walls of fungi.

chitosan Polysaccharide derived from chitin.

chloride shift The movement of chloride ions in and out of red blood cells to maintain a lower level of chloride in red blood cells in the arteries than in the veins.

cholecystokinin (CCK) [ko-la-sis-toe-KY-nin] A hormone produced by cells in the small intestine that stimulates the release of digestive enzymes from the pancreas and bile from the gallbladder.

cholesterol [ko-LES-te-rol] A waxy lipid (sterol) whose chemical structure contains multiple hydrocarbon rings.

choline A nitrogen-containing compound that is part of phosphatidylcholine, a phospholipid. Choline is also part of the neurotransmitter acetylcholine. The body synthesizes choline from the amino acid methionine.

chylomicron [kye-lo-MY-kron] A large lipoprotein particle formed in intestinal cells following the absorption of dietary fats. A chylomicron has a central core of triglycerides and cholesterol surrounded by phospholipids and proteins.

chyme [KIME] A mass of partially digested food and digestive juices moving from the stomach into the duodenum.

chymotrypsinogen/chymotrypsin A protease produced by the pancreas that is converted from the inactive proenzyme form (chymotrypsinogen) to the active form (chymotrypsin) in the small intestine.

ciguatera A toxin found in more than 300 species of Caribbean and South Pacific fish. It is a nonbacterial source of food poisoning.

ciliary action Wavelike motion of small hairlike projections on some cells.

circular muscle Layers of smooth muscle that surround organs, including the stomach and the small intestine.

circulation Movement of substances through the vessels of the cardiovascular or lymphatic system.

cis fatty acid Unsaturated fatty acid in which the hydrogens surrounding a double bond are both on the same side of the carbon chain, causing a bend in the chain. Most naturally occurring unsaturated fatty acids are cis fatty acids.

citric acid cycle The metabolic pathway occurring in mitochondria in which the acetyl portion (CH_3COO–) of acetyl CoA is oxidized to yield two molecules of carbon dioxide and one molecule each of NADH, $FADH_2$, and GTP. Also known as the Krebs cycle and the tricarboxylic acid cycle.

clinical observations Assessment by evaluating the characteristics of well-being that can be seen in a physical exam. Nonspecific, clinical observations can provide clues to nutrient deficiency or excess that can be confirmed or ruled out by biochemical testing.

clinical trials Studies that collect large amounts of data to evaluate the effectiveness of a treatment.

coenzyme A Coenzyme A is a cofactor derived from the vitamin pantothenic acid.

coenzymes Organic compounds, often B vitamin derivatives, that combine with an inactive enzyme to form an active enzyme. Coenzymes associate closely with these enzymes, allowing them to catalyze certain metabolic reactions in a cell.

cofactors Compounds required for an enzyme to be active. Cofactors include coenzymes and metal ions such as iron (Fe^{2+}), copper (Cu^{2+}), and magnesium (Mg^{2+}).

colic Periodic inconsolable crying in an otherwise healthy infant that appears to result from abdominal cramping and discomfort.

collagen The most abundant fibrous protein in the body. Collagen is the major constituent of connective tissue, forms the foundation for bones and teeth, and helps maintain the structure of blood vessels and other tissues.

colon The portion of the large intestine extending from the cecum to the rectum. It is made up of four parts—the ascending, transverse, descending, and sigmoid colons. Although often used interchangeably with the term *large intestine,* these terms are not synonymous.

color additive Any dye, pigment, or other substance that can impart color when added or applied to a food, drug, or cosmetic or to the human body.

colostrum A thick yellow fluid secreted by the breast during pregnancy and the first days after delivery.

common chemical sense A chemosensory mechanism that contributes to our senses of smell and taste. It comprises thousands of nerve endings, especially on the moist surfaces of the eyes, nose, mouth, and throat.

complementary and alternative medicine (CAM) A broad range of healing philosophies, approaches, and therapies that include treatments and health care practices not taught widely in medical schools, not generally used in hospitals, and not usually reimbursed by medical insurance companies.

complementary foods Any foods or liquids other than breast milk or infant formula fed to an infant.

complementary protein An incomplete food protein whose assortment of amino acids makes up for, or complements, another food protein's lack of specific indispensable amino acids so that the combination of the two proteins provides sufficient amounts of all the indispensable amino acids.

complementary sequence Nucleic acid base sequence that can form a double-stranded structure with another DNA fragment by following base-pairing rules (A pairs with T, and C pairs with G). The complementary sequence to GTAC, for example, is CATG.

complete (high-quality) proteins Proteins that supply all of the indispensable amino acids in the proportions the body needs.

complex carbohydrates Chains of more than two monosaccharides. May be oligosaccharides or polysaccharides.

compulsive overeating See *binge-eating disorder.*

computed tomography (CT) The gathering of anatomical information from cross-sectional images generated by a computer synthesis of x-ray data.

concentration gradients Differences between the solute concentrations of two substances.

condensation In chemistry, a reaction in which a covalent bond is formed between two molecules by removal of a water molecule.

conditionally indispensable amino acids Amino acids that are normally made in the body (dispensable) but become indispensable under certain circumstances, such as during critical illness.

cones Light-sensitive cells in the retina that are sensitive to bright light and translate it into color images.

congeners Biologically active compounds in alcoholic beverages that include nonalcoholic ingredients as well as other alcohols such as methanol. Congeners contribute to the distinctive taste and smell of the beverage and may increase intoxicating effects and subsequent hangover.

conjugated linoleic acid A polyunsaturated fatty acid in which the position of the double bonds has moved, so that a single bond alternates with two double bonds.

connective tissues Tissues composed primarily of fibrous proteins such as collagen, and which contain few cells. Their primary function is to bind together and support various body structures.

constipation Infrequent and difficult bowel movements, followed by a sensation of incomplete evacuation.

control group A set of people used as a standard of comparison to the experimental group. The people in the control group have characteristics similar to those in the experimental group and are selected at random.

Cori cycle The circular path that regenerates NAD^+ and glucose when oxygen is low and lactate and NADH build up in excess in muscle tissue.

cornea The transparent outer surface of the eye.

coronary heart disease (CHD) A type of heart disease caused by narrowing of the coronary arteries that feed the heart, which needs a constant supply of oxygen and nutrients carried by the blood in the coronary arteries. When the coronary arteries become narrowed or clogged by fat and cholesterol deposits and cannot supply enough blood to the heart, CHD results.

correlations Connections, co-occurring more frequently than can be explained by chance or coincidence, but without a proven cause.

C-reactive protein (CRP) A protein released by the body in response to acute injury, infection, or other inflammatory stimuli. CRP is associated with future cardiovascular events.

creatine An important nitrogenous compound found in meats and fish, and synthesized in the body from amino acids (glycine, arginine, and methionine).

creatine phosphate An energy-rich compound that supplies energy and a phosphate group for the formation of ATP. Also called phosphocreatine.

cretinism A congenital condition often caused by severe iodine deficiency during gestation, which is characterized by arrested physical and mental development.

critical control points (CCPs) Operational steps or procedures in a process, production method, or recipe at which control can be applied to prevent, reduce, or eliminate a food safety hazard.

critical period of development Time during which the environment has the greatest impact on the developing embryo.

Crohn's disease A disease that causes inflammation and ulceration along sections of the intestinal tract.

cystic fibrosis An inherited disorder that causes widespread dysfunction of the exocrine glands, resulting in chronic lung disease, abnormally high levels of electrolytes (e.g., sodium, potassium, chloride) in sweat, and deficiency of pancreatic enzymes needed for digestion.

cytochromes Heme proteins that transfer electrons in the electron transport chain through the alternate oxidation and reduction of iron.

cytoplasm The material of the cell, excluding the cell nucleus and cell membranes. The cytoplasm includes the semifluid cytosol, the organelles, and other particles.

cytosol The semifluid inside the cell membrane, excluding organelles. The cytosol is the site of glycolysis and fatty acid synthesis.

Daily Values (DVs) A single set of nutrient intake standards developed by the Food and Drug Administration to represent the needs of the "typical" consumer; used as standards for expressing nutrient content on food labels.

dark adaptation The process that increases the rhodopsin concentration in your eyes, allowing them to detect images in the dark better.

DASH (Dietary Approaches to Stop Hypertension) An eating plan low in total fat, saturated fat, and cholesterol and rich in fruits, vegetables, and low-fat dairy products that has been shown to reduce elevated blood pressure.

deamination The removal of the amino group ($-NH_2$) from an amino acid.

decarboxylation Removal of a carboxyl group (–COOH) from a molecule. The carboxyl group is then released as carbon dioxide (CO_2).

Delaney Clause The part of the 1960 Color Additives Amendment to the Federal Food, Drug, and Cosmetic Act that bars the FDA from approving any additives shown in laboratory tests to cause cancer.

denaturation An alteration in the three-dimensional structure of a protein resulting in an unfolded polypeptide chain that usually lacks biological activity.

densitometry A method for estimating body composition from measurement of total body density.

dental caries [KARE-ees] Destruction of the enamel surface of teeth caused by acids resulting from bacterial breakdown of sugars in the mouth.

desaturation Insertion of double bonds into fatty acids to change them into new fatty acids.

diabetes mellitus A chronic disease in which uptake of blood glucose by body cells is impaired, resulting in high glucose levels in the blood and urine. Type 1 is caused by decreased pancreatic release of insulin. In type 2, target cells (e.g., fat and muscle cells) lose the ability to respond normally to insulin.

diabulimia The deliberate injection by those with type 1 diabetes of less insulin than prescribed for the purpose of losing weight.

diarrhea Watery stools due to reduced absorption of water.

diastolic Pertaining to the time between heart contractions, a period known as diastole. Diastolic blood pressure is measured at the point of maximum cardiac relaxation.

diet history Record of food intake and eating behaviors that includes recent and long-term habits of food consumption. Done by a skilled interviewer, the diet history is the most comprehensive form of dietary intake data collection.

dietary fiber Carbohydrates and lignins that are naturally in plants and are nondigestible; that is, they are not digested and absorbed in the human small intestine.

dietary folate equivalents (DFE) A measure of folate intake used to account for the high bioavailability of folic acid taken as a supplement compared with the lower bioavailability of the folate found in foods.

Dietary Guidelines for Americans The *Dietary Guidelines for Americans* are the foundation of federal nutrition policy and are developed by the U.S. Department of Agriculture (USDA) and the Department of Health and Human Services (DHHS). These science-based guidelines are intended to reduce the number of Americans who develop chronic diseases such as hypertension, diabetes, cardiovascular disease, obesity, and alcoholism.

Dietary Reference Intakes (DRIs) A framework of dietary standards that includes Estimated Average Requirement (EAR), Recommended Dietary Allowance (RDA), Adequate Intake (AI), and Tolerable Upper Intake Level (UL).

dietary standards Set of values for recommended intake of nutrients.

Dietary Supplement Health and Education Act (DSHEA) Legislation that regulates dietary supplements.

dietary supplements Products taken by mouth in tablet, capsule, powder, gelcap, or other nonfood form that contain one or more of the following: vitamins, minerals, amino acids, herbs, enzymes, metabolites, or concentrates.

digestion The process of transforming the foods we eat into units for absorption.

digestive secretions Substances released at different places in the GI tract to speed the breakdown of ingested carbohydrates, fats, and proteins into smaller compounds that can be absorbed by the body.

diglycerides Molecules composed of glycerol combined with two fatty acids.

dihydrochalcones (DHCs) Nonnutritive sweeteners derived from bioflavonoids of citrus fruits. Approximately 300 to 2,000 times sweeter than sucrose and have a licorice aftertaste.

dioxins Chemical compounds created in the manufacturing, combustion, and chlorine bleaching of pulp and paper and in other industrial processes.

dipeptide Two amino acids joined by a peptide bond.

direct additives Substances added to foods for a specific purpose.

direct calorimetry Determination of energy use by the body by measuring the heat released from an organism enclosed in a small insulated chamber surrounded by water. The rise in the temperature of the water is directly related to the energy used by the organism.

disaccharides [dye-SACK-uh-rides] Carbohydrates composed of two monosaccharide units linked by a glycosidic bond. They include sucrose (common table sugar), lactose (milk sugar), and maltose.

disordered eating An abnormal change in eating pattern related to an illness, a stressful event, or a desire to improve one's health or appearance. If it persists it may lead to an eating disorder.

dispensable amino acids Amino acids that the body can make if supplied with adequate nitrogen. Dispensable amino acids do not need to be supplied in the diet.

disulfide bridge A bond between the sulfur components of two sulfur-containing amino acids that helps stabilize the structure of protein.

diuresis The formation and secretion of urine.

diuretics [dye-u-RET-iks] Drugs or other substances that promote the formation and release of urine. Diuretics are given to reduce body fluid volume in treating such disorders as high blood pressure, congestive heart disease, and edema. Both alcohol and caffeine act as diuretics.

DNA (deoxyribonucleic acid) The carrier of genetic information. Specific regions of each DNA molecule, called genes, act as blueprints for the synthesis of proteins.

double-blind study A research study set up so that neither the subjects nor the investigators know which study group is receiving the placebo and which is receiving the active substance.

doubly labeled water A method for measuring daily energy expenditure over extended time periods, typically 7 to 14 days, while subjects are living in their usual environments. Small amounts of water that is isotopically labeled with deuterium and oxygen-18 (^2H_2O and $H_2{}^{18}O$) are ingested. Energy expenditure can be calculated from the difference between the rates at which the body loses each isotope.

dual-energy x-ray absorptiometry (DEXA) A body composition measurement technique originally developed to measure bone density.

duodenum [doo-oh-DEE-num, or doo-AH-den-um] The portion of the small intestine closest to the stomach. The duodenum is 10 to 12 inches long and wider than the remainder of the small intestine.

eating disorders A spectrum of abnormal eating patterns that eventually may endanger a person's health or increase the risk for other diseases. Generally, psychological factors play a key role.

Eating Well with Canada's Food Guide Recommendations to help Canadians select foods to meet energy and nutrient needs while reducing the risk of chronic disease. The *Food Guide* is based on the *Nutrition Recommendations for Canadians* and Canada's Guidelines for Healthy Eating and is a key nutrition education tool for Canadians aged 4 years and older.

eclampsia The occurrence of seizures in a pregnant woman that are unrelated to brain conditions.

edema Swelling caused by the buildup of fluid between cells.

eicosanoids A class of hormonelike substances formed in the body from long-chain fatty acids.

electrolytes [ih-LEK-tro-lites] Substances that dissociate into charged particles (ions) when dissolved in water or other solvents and thus become capable of conducting an electrical current. The terms *electrolyte* and *ion* often are used interchangeably.

electron transport chain An organized series of carrier molecules—including flavin mononucleotide (FMN), coenzyme Q, and several cytochromes—that are located in mitochondrial membranes and shuttle electrons from NADH and $FADH_2$ to oxygen, yielding water and ATP.

Electronic Benefits Transfer (EBT) Electronic delivery of government benefits by a single plastic card that allows access to food benefits at point-of-sale locations.

elongation Addition of carbon atoms to fatty acids to lengthen them into new fatty acids.

embryonic stage The developmental stage between the time of implantation (about two weeks after fertilization) through the seventh or eighth week; the stage of major organ system differentiation and development of main external features.

emetics Agents that induce vomiting.

emulsifiers Agents that blend fatty and watery liquids by promoting the breakup of fat into small particles and stabilizing their suspension in aqueous solution.

endocytosis The uptake of material by a cell by the indentation and pinching off of its membrane to form a vesicle that carries material into the cell.

endosperm The largest, middle portion of a grain kernel. The endosperm is high in starch to provide food for the growing plant embryo.

endothelial cells Thin, flattened cells that line internal body cavities in a single layer.

endothelium See *endothelial cells*.

enemas Infusions of fluid into the rectum, usually for cleansing or other therapeutic purposes.

energy The capacity to do work. The energy in food is chemical energy, which the body converts to mechanical, electrical, or heat energy.

energy balance The balance in the body between amounts of energy consumed and expended.

energy equilibrium A balance of energy intake and output that results in little or no change in weight over time.

energy intake The caloric or energy content of food provided by the sources of dietary energy: carbohydrate (4 kcal/g), protein (4 kcal/g), fat (9 kcal/g), and alcohol (7 kcal/g).

energy output The use of calories or energy for basic body functions, physical activity, and processing of consumed foods.

enrich To add vitamins and minerals lost or diminished during food processing, particularly the addition of thiamin, riboflavin, niacin, folic acid, and iron to grain products.

enteric nervous system A network of nerves located in the gastrointestinal wall.

enterocytes Intestinal cells.

enterohepatic circulation [EN-ter-oh-heh-PAT-ik] Recycling of certain compounds between the small intestine and the liver. For example, bile acids move from the liver to the gallbladder, and then into the small intestine, from whence they are absorbed into the portal vein and transported back to the liver.

enzymes [EN-zimes] Large proteins in the body that accelerate the rate of chemical reactions but are not altered in the process.

epidemiology The science of determining the incidence and distribution of diseases in different populations.

epinephrine A hormone released in response to stress or sudden danger, epinephrine raises blood glucose levels to ready the body for "fight or flight." Also called adrenaline.

epiphyses The heads of the long bones that are separated from the shaft of the bone until the bone stops growing.

epithelial cells The millions of cells that line and protect the external and internal surfaces of the body. Epithelial cells form epithelial tissues such as skin and mucous membranes.

epithelial tissues Closely packed layers of epithelial cells that cover the body and line its cavities.

ergogenic aids Substances that can enhance athletic performance.

***Escherichia coli* (*E. coli*)** Bacteria that are the most common cause of urinary tract infections. Because they release toxins, some types of *E. coli* can rapidly cause shock and death.

esophageal sphincter The opening between the esophagus and the stomach that relaxes and opens to allow the bolus to travel into the stomach, and then closes behind it. Also acts as a barrier to prevent the reflux of gastric contents. Commonly called the cardiac sphincter.

esophagitis Inflammation of the esophagus.

esophagus [ee-SOFF-uh-gus] The food pipe that extends from the pharynx to the stomach, about 25 centimeters long.

essential fatty acids The fatty acids that the body needs but cannot synthesize, and which must be obtained from diet.

essential hypertension Hypertension for which no specific cause can be identified. Ninety to 95 percent of people with hypertension have essential hypertension.

essential nutrients Substances that must be obtained in the diet because the body either cannot make them or cannot make adequate amounts of them.

ester A chemical combination of an organic acid (e.g., fatty acid) and an alcohol. When hydrogen from the alcohol combines with the acid's hydrogen and oxygen, water is released and an ester linkage is formed. A triglyceride is an ester of three fatty acids and glycerol.

esterification [e-ster-ih-fih-KAY-shun] A condensation reaction in which an organic acid (e.g., fatty acid) combines with an alcohol with the loss of water, creating an ester.

Estimated Average Requirement (EAR) The intake value that meets the estimated nutrient needs of 50 percent of individuals in a specific life-stage and gender group.

Estimated Energy Requirement (EER) Dietary energy intake that is predicted to maintain energy balance in a healthy adult of a defined age, gender, weight, height, and level of physical activity consistent with good health.

ethanol Chemical name for drinking alcohol. Also known as ethyl alcohol.

ethyl alcohol See *ethanol*.

Exchange Lists Lists of foods that in specified portions provide equivalent amounts of carbohydrate, fat, protein, and energy. Any food in an Exchange List can be substituted for any other without markedly affecting macronutrient intake.

experimental group A set of people being studied to evaluate the effect of an event, substance, or technique.

experiments Tests to examine the validity of a hypothesis.

extracellular fluid The fluid located outside of cells. It is composed largely of the liquid portion of the blood (plasma) and the fluid between cells in tissues (interstitial fluid), with fluid in the GI tract, eyes, joints, and spinal cord contributing a small amount. It constitutes about one-third of body water.

extreme obesity Obesity characterized by body weight exceeding 100 percent of normal; a condition so severe it often requires surgery.

extrusion reflex A young infant's response when a spoon is put in its mouth; the tongue is thrust forward, indicating that the baby is not ready for spoon feeding.

facilitated diffusion A process by which carrier (transport) proteins in the cell membrane transport substances into or out of cells down a concentration gradient.

$FADH_2$ The reduced form of flavin adenine dinucleotide (FAD). This coenzyme, which is derived from the B vitamin riboflavin, acts as an electron carrier in cells and undergoes reversible oxidation and reduction.

failure to thrive (FTT) Abnormally low gains in length (height) and weight during infancy and childhood; may result from physical problems or poor feeding, but many affected children have no apparent disease or defect.

fasting hypoglycemia A type of hypoglycemia that occurs because the body produces too much insulin even when no food is eaten.

fast-twitch (FT) fibers Muscle fibers that can develop high tension rapidly. These fibers can fatigue quickly, but are well suited to explosive movements in sprinting, jumping, and weight lifting.

fat replacers Compounds that imitate the functional and sensory properties of fats, but contain less available energy than fats.

fatty acids Compounds containing a long hydrocarbon chain with a carboxyl group (COOH) at one end and a methyl group (CH_3) at the other end.

fatty liver Accumulation of fat in the liver, a sign of increased fatty acid synthesis.

Feeding America The largest charitable hunger-relief organization in the United States. Its mission is to feed America's hungry through a nationwide network of member food banks and to engage the country in the fight to end hunger.

female athlete triad A syndrome in young female athletes that involves disordered eating, amenorrhea, and lowered bone density.

fermentation The anaerobic conversion of various carbohydrates to carbon dioxide and an alcohol or organic acid.

ferric iron (Fe^{3+}) The oxidized form of iron able to be bound to transferrin for transport.

ferritin A complex of iron and apoferritin that is a major storage form of iron.

ferrous iron (Fe^{2+}) The reduced form of iron most commonly found in food.

fetal alcohol syndrome A set of physical and mental abnormalities observed in infants born to women who abuse alcohol during pregnancy. Affected infants exhibit poor growth, characteristic abnormal facial features, limited hand–eye coordination, and mental retardation.

fetal stage The period of rapid growth from the end of the embryonic stage until birth.

fibrin A stringy, insoluble protein that is the final product of the blood-clotting process.

flatus Lower intestinal gas that is expelled through the rectum.

flavin adenine dinucleotide (FAD) A coenzyme synthesized in the body from riboflavin. It undergoes reversible oxidation and reduction and thus acts as an electron carrier in cells. FAD is the oxidized form; $FADH_2$ is the reduced form.

flavor The collective experience that describes both taste and smell.

fluorosis Mottled discoloration and pitting of tooth enamel caused by prolonged ingestion of excessive fluoride.

Food and Agriculture Organization (FAO) The largest autonomous UN agency; the FAO works to alleviate poverty and hunger by promoting agricultural development, improved nutrition, and the pursuit of food security.

Food Code A reference published periodically by the Food and Drug Administration for restaurants, grocery stores, institutional food services, vending operations, and other retailers on how to store, prepare, and serve food to prevent foodborne illness.

Food and Drug Administration (FDA) The federal agency responsible for ensuring that foods sold in the United States (except for eggs, poultry, and meat, which are monitored by the USDA) are safe, wholesome, and labeled properly. The FDA sets standards for the composition of some foods, inspects food plants, and monitors imported foods. The FDA is an agency of the Department of Health and Human Services (DHHS).

food frequency questionnaire (FFQ) A questionnaire for nutrition assessment that asks how often the subject consumes specific foods or groups of foods, rather than what specific foods the subject consumes daily. Also called food frequency checklist.

food groups Categories of similar foods, such as fruits or vegetables.

Food Guide Pyramid A graphic representation of U.S. dietary guidelines; now replaced by the MyPlate icon, a graphic respresentation of the USDA's food groups.

food insecurity (1) Limited or uncertain availability of nutritionally adequate and safe foods or (2) limited or uncertain ability to acquire acceptable foods in socially acceptable ways.

food label Labels required by law on virtually all packaged foods and having five requirements: (1) a statement of identity; (2) the net contents (by weight, volume, or measure) of the package; (3) the name and address of the manufacturer, packer, or distributor; (4) a list of ingredients; and (5) nutrition information.

Food and Nutrition Board A board within the Institute of Medicine of the National Academy of Sciences. It is responsible for assembling the group of nutrition scientists who review available scientific data to determine appropriate intake levels of the known essential nutrients.

food records Detailed information about day-to-day eating habits; typically includes all foods and beverages consumed for a defined period, usually three to seven consecutive days.

Food Research and Action Center (FRAC) Founded in 1970 as a public interest law firm, FRAC is a nonprofit child advocacy group that works to improve public policies to eradicate hunger and undernutrition in the United States.

food security Access to enough food for an active, healthy life, including (1) the ready availability of nutritionally adequate and safe foods and (2) an assured ability to acquire acceptable foods in socially acceptable ways.

Food Security Supplement Survey A federally funded survey that measures the prevalence and severity of food insecurity and hunger.

foodborne illness A sickness caused by food contaminated with microorganisms, chemicals, or other substances hazardous to human health.

fortify Refers to the addition of vitamins or minerals that were not originally present in a food.

free radicals Short-lived, highly reactive chemicals often derived from oxygen-containing compounds, which can have detrimental effects on cells, especially DNA and cell membranes.

French paradox A phenomenon observed in the French, who have a lower incidence of heart disease than people whose diets contain comparable amounts of fat. Part of the difference has been attributed to the regular and moderate drinking of red wine.

fructose [FROOK-tose] A common monosaccharide containing six carbons that is naturally present in honey and many fruits; often added to foods in the form of high-fructose corn syrup. Also called levulose or fruit sugar.

full-term baby A baby delivered during the normal period of human gestation, between 38 and 41 weeks.

functional dyspepsia Chronic pain in the upper abdomen not due to any obvious physical cause.

functional fiber Isolated nondigestible carbohydrates, including some manufactured carbohydrates, that have beneficial effects in humans.

functional food A food that may provide a health benefit beyond basic nutrition.

galactose [gah-LAK-tose] A monosaccharide containing six carbons that can be converted into glucose in the body. In foods and living systems, galactose usually is joined with other monosaccharides.

gallbladder A pear-shaped sac that stores and concentrates bile from the liver.

galvanized Iron or steel with a thin layer of zinc plated onto it to protect against corrosion.

gastric inhibitory peptide (GIP) [GAS-trik in-HIB-ihtor-ee PEP-tide] A hormone released from the walls of the duodenum that slows the release of the stomach contents into the small intestine and also stimulates release of insulin from the pancreas.

gastric lipase An enzyme in the stomach that hydrolyzes certain triglycerides into fatty acids and glycerol.

gastrin [GAS-trin] A polypeptide hormone released from the walls of the stomach mucosa and duodenum that stimulates gastric secretions and motility.

gastritis Inflammation of the stomach.

gastroesophageal reflux A backflow of stomach contents into the esophagus, accompanied by a burning pain because of the acidity of the gastric juices.

gastroesophageal reflux disease (GERD) A condition in which gastric contents move backward (reflux) into the esophagus, causing pain and tissue damage.

gastrointestinal (GI) tract [GAS-troh-in-TES-tin-al] The connected series of organs and structures used for digestion of food and absorption of nutrients; also called the alimentary canal or the digestive tract. The GI tract contains the mouth, esophagus, stomach, small intestine, large intestine (colon), rectum, and anus.

gene expression The process by which proteins are made from the instructions encoded in DNA.

Generally Recognized as Safe (GRAS) Refers to substances that are "generally recognized as safe" for consumption and can be added to foods by manufacturers without establishing their safety by rigorous experimental studies. Congress established the GRAS list in 1958.

genes Sections of DNA that contain hereditary information. Most genes contain information for making proteins.

genetic code The instructions in a gene that tell the cell how to make a specific protein. A, T, G, and C are the "letters" of the DNA code; they stand for the chemicals adenine, thymine, guanine, and cytosine, respectively, which make up the nucleotide bases of DNA. Each gene's code combines the four chemicals in various ways to spell out three-letter "words" that specify which amino acid is needed at every step in making a protein.

genetic engineering Manipulation of the genome of an organism by artificial means for the purpose of modifying existing traits or adding new genetic traits.

genetically modified (GM) foods Foods produced using plant or animal ingredients that have been modified using gene technology.

genome The total genetic information of an organism, stored in the DNA of its chromosomes.

geophagia Ingestion of clay or dirt.

germ The innermost part of a grain, located at the base of the kernel, that can grow into a new plant. The germ is rich in protein, oils, vitamins, and minerals.

gestational diabetes A condition that results in high blood glucose levels during pregnancy.

ghrelin A peptide hormone produced by the stomach that stimulates feeding; sometimes called the "hunger hormone."

glossitis Inflammation of the tongue; a symptom of riboflavin deficiency.

glucagon [GLOO-kuh-gon] Produced by alpha cells in the pancreas, this polypeptide hormone promotes the breakdown of liver glycogen to glucose, thereby increasing blood glucose. Glucagon secretion is stimulated by low blood glucose levels and by growth hormone.

glucogenic In the metabolism of amino acids, a term describing an amino acid broken down into pyruvate or an intermediate of the citric acid cycle; that is, any compound that can be used in gluconeogenesis to form glucose.

gluconeogenesis [gloo-ko-nee-oh-JEN-uh-sis] Synthesis of glucose within the body from noncarbohydrate precursors such as amino acids, lactate, and glycerol. Fatty acids cannot be converted to glucose.

glucose [GLOO-kose] A common monosaccharide containing six carbons that is present in the blood; also known as dextrose and blood sugar. It is a component of the disaccharides sucrose, lactose, and maltose and various complex carbohydrates.

glutathione A tripeptide of glycine, cysteine, and glutamic acid that is involved in protection of cells from oxidative damage.

glutathione peroxidase A selenium-containing enzyme that promotes the breakdown of fatty acids that have undergone peroxidation.

glycemic index A measure of the effect of food on blood glucose levels. It is the ratio of the blood glucose value after eating a particular food to the value after eating the same amount of white bread or glucose.

glycerol [GLISS-er-ol] An alcohol that contains three carbon atoms, each of which has an attached hydroxyl group (–OH). It forms the backbone of mono-, di-, and triglycerides.

glycogen [GLY-ko-jen] A very large, highly branched polysaccharide composed of multiple glucose units. Sometimes called animal starch, glycogen is the primary storage form of glucose in animals.

glycogen loading See *carbohydrate loading*.

glycogenesis The formation of glycogen from glucose.

glycogenolysis The breakdown of glycogen to glucose.

glycolysis [gligh-COLL-ih-sis] The anaerobic metabolic pathway that breaks a glucose molecule into two molecules of pyruvate and yields two molecules of ATP and two molecules of NADH. Glycolysis occurs in the cytosol of a cell.

glycyrrhizin Nonnutritive sweetener derived from licorice root. Has a licorice flavor and is 50 to 100 times sweeter than sucrose.

goblet cells One of the many types of specialized cells that produce and secrete mucus. These cells are found in the stomach, intestines, and portions of the respiratory tract.

goiter A chronic enlargement of the thyroid gland, visible as a swelling at the front of the neck; usually associated with iodine deficiency.

goitrogens Compounds that can induce goiter.

gout An intensely painful form of inflammatory arthritis that results from deposits of needlelike crystals of uric acid in connective tissue and/or the joint space between bones.

growth charts Charts that plot the weight, length, and head circumference of infants and children as they grow.

guanosine triphosphate (GTP) A high-energy compound, similar to ATP, but with three phosphate groups linked to guanosine.

gums Dietary fibers, which contain galactose and other monosaccharides, found between plant cell walls.

gustatory cells Surface cells in the throat and on the taste buds in the mouth that transmit taste information. Also called taste cells.

gynoid obesity Excess storage of fat located primarily in the buttocks and thighs. Also called gynecoid obesity.

hangover The collection of symptoms experienced by someone who has consumed a large quantity of alcohol. Symptoms can include pounding headache, fatigue, muscle aches, nausea, stomach pain, heightened sensitivity to light and sound, dizziness, and possibly depression, anxiety, and irritability.

head circumference Measurement of the largest part of the infant's head (just above the eyebrows and ears); used to determine brain growth.

health claim Any statement that associates a food or a substance in a food with a disease or health-related condition. The FDA authorizes health claims.

heat capacity The amount of energy required to raise the temperature of a substance 1°C.

hematocrit Percentage volume occupied by packed red blood cells in a centrifuged sample of whole blood.

heme A chemical complex with a central iron atom (ferric iron Fe^{3+}) that forms the oxygen-binding part of hemoglobin and myoglobin.

heme iron The iron found in the hemoglobin and myoglobin of animal foods.

hemicelluloses [hem-ih-SELL-you-los-es] A group of large polysaccharides in dietary fiber that are fermented more easily than cellulose.

hemochromatosis A metabolic disorder that results in excess iron deposits in the body.

hemoglobin [HEEM-oh-glow-bin] The oxygen-carrying protein in red blood cells that consists of four heme groups and four globin polypeptide chains. The presence of hemoglobin gives blood its red color.

hemolysis The breakdown of red blood cells that usually occurs at the end of a red blood cell's normal life span. This process releases hemoglobin.

hemosiderin An insoluble form of storage iron.

herbal therapy (phytotherapy) The therapeutic use of herbs and other plants to promote health and treat disease.

high-density lipoproteins (HDL) The blood lipoproteins that contain high levels of protein and low levels of triglycerides. Synthesized primarily in the liver and small intestine, HDL picks up cholesterol released from dying cells and other sources and transfers it to other lipoproteins.

homocysteine An amino acid precursor of cysteine and a risk factor for heart disease.

hormones Chemical messengers that are secreted into the blood by one tissue and act on cells in another part of the body.

Human Genome Project An effort coordinated by the Department of Energy and the National Institutes of Health to map the genes in human DNA.

hunger The internal, physiological drive to find and consume food. Unlike appetite, hunger is usually experienced as a negative sensation, often manifesting as an uneasy or painful sensation; the recurrent and involuntary lack of access to food that may produce malnutrition over time.

husk The inedible covering of a grain kernel. Also known as the chaff.

hydrochloric acid An acid of chloride and hydrogen atoms made by the gastric glands and secreted into the stomach. Also called gastric acid.

hydrogen bonds Noncovalent bonds between hydrogen and an atom, usually oxygen, in another molecule.

hydrogen ions Also called protons. A lone hydrogen ion has a positive charge (H^+). It does not have its own electron, but it can share one with another atom.

hydrogenation [high-dro-jen-AY-shun] A chemical reaction in which hydrogen atoms are added to carbon–carbon double bonds, converting them to single bonds. Hydrogenation of monounsaturated and polyunsaturated fatty acids reduces the number of double bonds they contain, thereby making them more saturated.

hydrolysis A reaction that breaks apart a compound through the addition of water.

hydrophilic [high-dro-FILL-ik] Readily interacting with water (literally, "water-loving"). Hydrophilic compounds are polar and soluble in water.

hydrophilic amino acids Amino acids that are attracted to water (water-loving).

hydrophobic Insoluble in water.

hydrophobic amino acids Amino acids that are repelled by water (water-fearing).

hydrostatic weighing See *underwater weighing*.

hydroxyapatite A crystalline mineral compound of calcium and phosphorus that makes up bone.

hyperactivity A maladaptive and abnormal increase in activity that is inconsistent with developmental levels. Includes frequent fidgeting, inappropriate running, excessive talking, and difficulty in engaging in quiet activities.

hypercalcemia Abnormally high concentrations of calcium in the blood.

hypercellular obesity Obesity due to an above-average number of fat cells.

hypercholesterolemia The presence of greater than normal amounts of cholesterol in the blood.

hyperglycemia [HIGH-per-gly-SEE-me-uh] Abnormally high concentration of glucose in the blood.

hyperkalemia Abnormally high potassium concentrations in the blood.

hyperkeratosis Excessive accumulation of the protein keratin that produces rough and bumpy skin, most commonly affecting the palms and soles, as well as flexure areas (elbows, knees, wrists, ankles). It can affect moist epithelial tissues and impair their ability to secrete mucus. Also called hyperkeratinization.

hypermagnesemia An abnormally high concentration of magnesium in the blood.

hypernatremia Abnormally high sodium concentrations in the blood due to increased kidney retention of sodium or rapid ingestion of large amounts of salt.

hyperparathyroidism Excessive secretion of parathyroid hormone, which alters calcium metabolism.

hyperphosphatemia Abnormally high phosphate concentration in the blood.

hyperplastic obesity (hyperplasia) Obesity due to an increase in both the size and number of fat cells.

hypertension When resting blood pressure persistently exceeds 140 mm Hg systolic or 90 mm Hg diastolic.

hyperthermia A much higher than normal body temperature.

hypertrophic obesity Obesity due to an increase in the size of fat cells.

hypervitaminosis High levels of vitamins in the blood, usually a result of excess supplement intake.

hypervolemia An abnormal increase in the circulating blood volume.

hypocalcemia A deficiency of calcium in the blood.

hypoglycemia [HIGH-po-gly-SEE-mee-uh] Abnormally low concentration of glucose in the blood; any blood glucose value below 40 to 50 mg/dL of blood.

hypogonadism Decreased functional activity of the gonads (ovaries or testes) with retardation of growth and sexual development.

hypokalemia Inadequate levels of potassium in the blood.

hypomagnesemia An abnormally low concentration of magnesium in the blood.

hyponatremia Abnormally low sodium concentrations in the blood due to excessive excretion of sodium (by the kidney), prolonged vomiting, or diarrhea.

hypophosphatemia Abnormally low phosphate concentration in the blood.

hypothalamus [high-po-THAL-ah-mus] A region of the brain involved in regulating hunger and satiety, respiration, body temperature, water balance, and other body functions.

hypotheses Scientists' "educated guesses" to explain phenomena.

hypothyroidism The result of a lowered level of circulating thyroid hormone, with slowing of mental and physical functions.

ileocecal valve The sphincter at the junction of the small and large intestines.

ileum [ILL-ee-um] The terminal segment (about 5 feet) of the small intestine, which opens into the large intestine.

immune response A coordinated set of steps, including production of antibodies, that the immune system takes in response to an antigen.

incomplete (low-quality) proteins Proteins that lack one or more amino acids.

indirect additives Substances that become part of the food in trace amounts due to its packaging, storage, or other handling.

indirect calorimetry Determination of energy use by the body without directly measuring the production of heat. Methods include gas exchange, the measurement of oxygen uptake and/or carbon dioxide output, and the doubly labeled water method.

indispensable amino acids Amino acids that the body cannot make at all or cannot make enough of to meet physiological needs. Indispensable amino acids must be supplied in the diet.

infancy The period between birth and 12 months of age.

infantile anorexia Severe feeding difficulties that begin with the introduction of solid foods to infants. Symptoms include persistent food refusal for more than one month, malnutrition, parental concern about the child's poor food intake, and significant caregiver–infant conflict during feeding.

inorganic Any substance that does not contain carbon, excepting certain simple carbon compounds such as carbon dioxide and monoxide. Common examples include table salt (sodium chloride) and baking soda (sodium bicarbonate).

insensible water loss The continual loss of body water by evaporation from the respiratory tract and diffusion through the skin.

insulin [IN-suh-lin] Produced by beta cells in the pancreas, this polypeptide hormone stimulates the uptake of blood glucose into muscle and adipose cells, the synthesis of glycogen in the liver, and various other processes.

insulin resistance Reduction in the ability of cells to respond to the action of insulin and take up glucose.

integrated pest management (IPM) Economically sound pest control techniques that minimize pesticide use, enhance environmental stewardship, and promote sustainable systems.

intermediate-density lipoproteins (IDL) The lipoproteins formed when lipoprotein lipase strips some of the triglycerides from VLDL. Containing about 40 percent triglycerides, this type of lipoprotein is more dense than VLDL and less dense than LDL. Also called a VLDL remnant.

international units (IU) An outdated system to measure vitamin activity. This measurement does not consider differences in bioavailability.

interstitial fluid [in-ter-STISH-ul] The fluid between cells in tissues. Also called intercellular fluid.

intracellular fluid The fluid in the body's cells. It usually is high in potassium and phosphate and low in sodium and chloride. It constitutes about two-thirds of total body water.

intravascular fluid The fluid portion of the blood (plasma) contained in arteries, veins, and capillaries. It accounts for about 15 percent of the extracellular fluid.

intrinsic factor A glycoprotein released from parietal cells in the stomach wall that binds to and aids in absorption of vitamin B_{12}.

iodine-deficiency disorders (IDD) A wide range of disorders due to iodine deficiency that affect growth and development.

iodopsin Color-sensitive pigment molecules in cone cells that consist of opsinlike proteins combined with retinal.

ions Atoms or groups of atoms with an electrical charge resulting from the loss or gain of one or more electrons.

iron overload Toxicity from excess iron.

irradiation A food preservation technique in which foods are exposed to measured doses of radiation to reduce or eliminate pathogens and kill insects, reduce spoilage, and, in certain fruits and vegetables, inhibit sprouting and delay ripening.

irritable bowel syndrome (IBS) A disruptive state of intestinal motility with no known cause. Symptoms include constipation, abdominal pain, and episodic diarrhea.

isoflavones Plant chemicals that include genistein and daidzein and may have positive effects against cancer and heart disease. Also called phytoestrogens.

isotopes [EYE-so-towps] Forms of an element in which the atoms have the same number of protons but different numbers of neutrons.

jejunum [je-JOON-um] The middle section (about 4 feet) of the small intestine, lying between the duodenum and ileum.

keratin A water-insoluble fibrous protein that is the primary constituent of hair, nails, and the outer layer of the skin.

Keshan disease Selenium-deficiency disease that impairs the structure and function of the heart.

ketoacidosis Acidification of the blood caused by a buildup of ketone bodies. It is primarily a consequence of uncontrolled type 1 diabetes mellitus and can be life threatening.

ketogenesis The process in which excess acetyl CoA from fatty acid oxidation is converted into the ketone bodies acetoacetate, beta-hydroxybutyrate, and acetone.

ketogenic In the metabolism of amino acids, a term describing an amino acid broken down into acetyl CoA (which can be converted into ketone bodies).

ketone bodies Molecules formed when insufficient carbohydrate is available to completely metabolize fat. Formation of ketone bodies is promoted by a low glucose level and high acetyl CoA level within cells. Acetone, acetoacetate, and beta-hydroxybutyrate are ketone bodies. Beta-hydroxybutyrate is sometimes improperly called a ketone.

ketones [KEE-tones] Organic compounds that contain a chemical group consisting of C=O (a carbon–oxygen double bond) bound to two hydrocarbons. Pyruvate and fructose are examples of ketones. Acetone and acetoacetate are both ketones and ketone bodies. Although beta-hydroxybutyrate is not a ketone, it is a ketone body.

ketosis [kee-TOE-sis] Abnormally high concentration of ketone bodies in body tissues and fluids.

kilocalories (kcal) [KILL-oh-kal-oh-rees] Units used to measure energy. Food energy is measured in kilocalories (1,000 calories = 1 kilocalorie).

Krebs cycle See *citric acid cycle.*

kwashiorkor A type of malnutrition that occurs primarily in young children who have an infectious disease and whose diets supply marginal amounts of energy and very little protein. Common symptoms include poor growth, edema, apathy, weakness, and susceptibility to infections.

lactate The ionized form of lactic acid, a three-carbon acid. It is produced when insufficient oxygen is present in cells to oxidize pyruvate.

lactation The process of synthesizing and secreting breast milk.

lactation consultants Health professionals trained to specialize in education about and promotion of breastfeeding; may be certified as an International Board Certified Lactation Consultant (IBCLC).

lacteal A small lymphatic vessel in the interior of each intestinal villus that picks up chylomicrons and fat-soluble vitamins from intestinal cells.

lactic acid energy system Anaerobic energy system; using glycolysis, it rapidly produces energy (ATP) and lactate. Also called anaerobic glycolysis.

lactose [LAK-tose] A disaccharide composed of glucose and galactose; also called milk sugar because it is the major sugar in milk and dairy products.

lanugo [lah-NEW-go] Soft, downy hair that covers a normal fetus from the fifth month but is shed almost entirely by the time of birth. It also appears on semistarved individuals who have lost much of their body fat, serving as insulation normally provided by body fat.

large intestine The tube (about 5 feet) extending from the ileum of the small intestine to the anus. The large intestine includes the appendix, cecum, colon, rectum, and anal canal.

laxatives Substances that promote evacuation of the bowel by increasing the bulk of the feces, lubricating the intestinal wall, or softening the stool.

lean body mass The portion of the body exclusive of stored fat, including muscle, bone, connective tissue, organs, and water.

lecithin In the body, a phospholipid with the nitrogenous component choline. In foods, lecithin is a blend of phospholipids with different nitrogenous components.

legumes A family of plants with edible seed pods, such as peas, beans, lentils and soybeans; also called pulses.

leptin A hormone produced by adipose cells that signals the amount of body fat content and influences food intake; sometimes called the "satiety hormone."

let-down reflex The release of milk from the breast tissue in response to the stimulus of the hormone oxytocin. The major stimulus for oxytocin release is the infant suckling at the breast.

leukemia [loo-KEE-mee-a] Cancer of blood-forming tissue.

lignins [LIG-nins] Insoluble fibers composed of multi-ring alcohol units that constitute the only noncarbohydrate component of dietary fiber.

limiting amino acid The amino acid in shortest supply during protein synthesis. Also the amino acid in the lowest quantity when evaluating protein quality.

linear growth Increase in body length/height.

lingual lipase A fat-splitting enzyme secreted by cells at the base of the tongue.

linoleic acid [lin-oh-LAY-ik] An essential omega-6 fatty acid that contains 18 carbon atoms and two carbon–carbon double bonds (18:2).

lipid peroxidation Production of unstable, highly reactive lipid molecules that contain excess amounts of oxygen.

lipids A group of fat-soluble compounds that includes triglycerides, sterols, and phospholipids.

lipogenesis [lye-poh-JEN-eh-sis] Synthesis of fatty acids, primarily in liver cells, from acetyl CoA derived from the metabolism of alcohol and some amino acids.

lipophilic Attracted to fat and fat solvents; fat-soluble.

lipophobic Adverse to fat solvents; insoluble in fat and fat solvents.

lipoprotein Complexes that transport lipids in the lymph and blood. They consist of a central core of triglycerides and cholesterol surrounded by a shell composed of proteins and phospholipids. The various types of lipoproteins differ in size, composition, and density.

lipoprotein a [Lp(a)] A substance that consists of an LDL "bad cholesterol" part plus a protein (apoprotein a), whose exact function is currently unknown.

lipoprotein lipase The major enzyme responsible for the hydrolysis of plasma triglycerides.

liver The largest glandular organ in the body, it produces and secretes bile, detoxifies harmful substances, and helps metabolize carbohydrates, lipids, proteins, and micronutrients.

longitudinal muscle Muscle fibers aligned lengthwise.

low-birth-weight infant A newborn who weighs less than 2,500 grams (5.5 pounds) as a result of either premature birth or inadequate growth *in utero*.

low-density lipoproteins (LDL) The cholesterol-rich lipoproteins that result from the breakdown and removal of triglycerides from intermediate-density lipoprotein in the blood.

lumen Cavity or hollow channel in any organ or structure of the body.

lycopene One of a family of plant chemicals, the carotenoids. Others in this big family are alpha-carotene and beta-carotene.

lymph Fluid that travels through the lymphatic system, made up of fluid drained from between cells and large fat particles.

lymph nodes [limf nodes] Rounded masses of lymphatic tissue that are surrounded by a capsule of connective tissue. Lymph nodes filter lymph (lymphatic fluid), and they store lymphocytes (white blood cells). They are located along lymphatic vessels. Also called lymph glands.

lymphatic system A system of small vessels, ducts, valves, and organized tissue (e.g., lymph nodes) through which lymph moves from its origin in the tissues toward the heart.

lymphoma [lim-FO-ma] Cancer that arises in cells of the lymphatic system.

macrobiotic diet A highly restrictive dietary approach applied as a therapy for risk factors or chronic disease in general.

macrocytes Abnormally large red blood cells with short life spans.

macrominerals Major minerals required in the diet and present in the body in large amounts compared with trace minerals.

macronutrients Nutrients, such as carbohydrate, fat, or protein, that are needed in relatively large amounts in the diet.

macular degeneration Progressive deterioration of the macula, an area in the center of the retina, that eventually leads to loss of central vision.

mad cow disease See *bovine spongiform encephalopathy (BSE).*

magnetic resonance imaging (MRI) Medical imaging technique that uses a magnetic field and radio-frequency radiation to generate anatomical information.

major mineral A major mineral is required in the diet and present in the body in large amounts compared with trace minerals.

malabsorption syndromes Conditions that result in imperfect, inadequate, or otherwise disordered gastrointestinal absorption.

malignant [ma-LIG-nant] Cancerous; a growth with a tendency to invade and destroy nearby tissue and spread to other parts of the body.

malnutrition Failure to achieve nutrient requirements, which can impair physical and/or mental health. It may result from consuming too little food or a shortage or imbalance of key nutrients.

maltose [MALL-tose] A disaccharide composed of two glucose molecules; sometimes called malt sugar. Maltose seldom occurs naturally in foods but is formed whenever long molecules of starch break down.

marasmus A type of malnutrition resulting from chronic inadequate consumption of protein and energy that is characterized by wasting of muscle, fat, and other body tissue.

Meals on Wheels A voluntary, not-for-profit organization established to provide nutritious meals to homebound people (regardless of age) so they may maintain their independence and quality of life.

megadoses Doses of a nutrient that are 10 or more times the recommended amount.

megaloblastic anemia Excess amounts of megaloblasts in the blood caused by deficiency of folate or vitamin B_{12}.

megaloblasts Large, immature red blood cells produced when precursor cells fail to divide normally due to impaired DNA synthesis.

melanocytes [mel-AN-o-sites] Cells in the skin that produce and contain the pigment called melanin.

melanoma A form of skin cancer that arises in melanocytes, the cells that produce pigment. Melanoma usually begins in a mole.

menadione A medicinal form of vitamin K that can be toxic to infants. Also known as vitamin K_3.

menaquinones Forms of vitamin K that come from animal sources. Also produced by intestinal bacteria, they are collectively known as vitamin K_2.

menarche First menstrual period.

Menkes' syndrome A genetic disorder that results in copper deficiency.

messenger RNA (mRNA) Long, linear, single-stranded molecules of ribonucleic acids formed from DNA templates that carry the amino acid sequence of one or more proteins from the cell nucleus to the cytoplasm, where the ribosomes translate mRNA into proteins.

metabolic alkalosis An abnormal pH of body fluids, usually caused by significant loss of acid from the body or increased levels of bicarbonate.

metabolic fitness The absence of all metabolic and biochemical risk factors associated with obesity.

metabolic pathway A series of chemical reactions that either break down a large compound into smaller units (catabolism) or synthesize more complex molecules from smaller ones (anabolism).

metabolic syndrome A cluster of at least three of the following risk factors for heart disease: hypertriglyceridemia (high blood triglycerides), low HDL cholesterol, hyperglycemia (high blood glucose), hypertension (high blood pressure), and excess abdominal fat.

metabolism All chemical reactions within organisms that enable them to maintain life. The two main categories of metabolism are catabolism and anabolism.

metabolites Any substances produced during metabolism.

metalloproteins Proteins with a mineral element as an essential part of their structure.

metallothionein An abundant, nonenzymatic, zinc-containing protein.

metastasis [meh-TAS-ta-sis] The spread of cancer from one part of the body to another. Tumors formed from cells that have spread are called "secondary tumors" and contain cells that are like those in the original (primary) tumor. The plural is *metastases.*

methanol The simplest alcohol. Also known as methyl alcohol and wood alcohol.

methyl alcohol See *methanol.*

methylmercury A toxic compound that results from the chemical transformation of mercury by bacteria. Mercury is water-soluble in trace amounts and contaminates many bodies of water.

micelles Tiny emulsified fat packets that can enter enterocytes. The complexes are composed of emulsifier molecules oriented with their hydrophobic part facing inward and their hydrophilic part facing outward toward the surrounding aqueous environment.

microcytic hypochromic anemia Anemia characterized by small, pale red blood cells that lack adequate hemoglobin to carry oxygen; can be caused by deficiency of iron or vitamin B_6.

microminerals See *trace minerals.*

micronutrients Nutrients, such as vitamins and minerals, that are needed in relatively small amounts in the diet.

microsomal ethanol-oxidizing system (MEOS) An energy-requiring enzyme system in the liver that normally metabolizes drugs and other foreign substances. When the blood alcohol level is high, alcohol dehydrogenase cannot metabolize it fast enough, and the excess alcohol is metabolized by MEOS.

microvilli Minute, hairlike projections that extend from the surface of absorptive cells facing the intestinal lumen. Singular is *microvillus.*

mineralization The addition of minerals, such as calcium and phosphorus, to bones and teeth.

minerals Inorganic compounds needed for growth and for regulation of body processes.

mitochondria (mitochondrion) The sites of aerobic production of ATP, where most of the energy from carbohydrate, protein, and fat is captured. Called the "power plants" of the cell, the mitochondria contain two highly specialized membranes, an outer membrane and a highly folded inner membrane, that separate two compartments, the internal matrix space and the narrow intermembrane space. A human cell contains about 2,000 mitochondria.

mitochondrial membrane The mitochondria are enclosed by a double shell separated by an intermembrane space. The outer membrane acts as a barrier and gatekeeper, selectively allowing some molecules to pass through while blocking others. The inner membrane is where the electron transport chains are located.

monoglycerides Molecules composed of glycerol combined with one fatty acid.

monosaccharides Any sugars that are not broken down during digestion and have the general formula $C_nH_{2n}O_n$, where $n = 3$ to 7. The common monosaccharides glucose, fructose, and galactose all have six carbon atoms ($n = 6$).

monounsaturated fatty acid A fatty acid in which the carbon chain contains one double bond.

morbid obesity See *extreme obesity.*

morning sickness A persistent or recurring nausea that often occurs in the morning during early pregnancy.

motor proteins Proteins that use energy and convert it into some form of mechanical work. Motor proteins are active in processes such as dividing cells, contracting muscle, and swimming sperm.

mucilages Gelatinous soluble fibers containing galactose, mannose, and other monosaccharides; found in seaweed.

mucosa [myu-KO-sa] The innermost layer of a cavity. The inner layer of the gastrointestinal tract, also called the intestinal wall. It is composed of epithelial cells and glands.

mucus A slippery substance secreted in the GI tract (and other body linings) that protects cells from irritants such as digestive juices.

multilevel marketing A system of selling in which each salesperson recruits assistants, who then recruit others to help them. The person at each level collects a commission on sales made by the later recruits.

muscle fibers Individual muscle cells.

mutation A permanent structural alteration in DNA. In most cases, DNA changes either have no effect or cause harm. Occasionally, a mutation can improve an organism's chance of surviving and passing the beneficial change on to its descendants. Certain mutations may lead to cancer or other diseases.

myelin sheath The protective coating that surrounds nerve fibers.

myelinization Development of the myelin sheath, a substance that surrounds nerve fibers.

myoglobin The oxygen-transporting protein of muscle that resembles blood hemoglobin in function.

MyPlate An educational tool that translates the principles of the *Dietary Guidelines for Americans* and other nutritional standards to help consumers in making healthier food and physical activity choices.

NADH The reduced form of nicotinamide adenine dinucleotide (NAD^+). This coenzyme, derived from the B vitamin niacin, acts as an electron carrier in cells, and undergoes reversible oxidation and reduction.

NADPH The reduced form of nicotinamide adenine dinucleotide phosphate. This coenzyme, which is derived from the B vitamin niacin, acts as an electron carrier in cells, undergoing reversible oxidation and reduction. The oxidized form is $NADP^+$.

National Center for Complementary and Alternative Medicine (NCCAM) An NIH organization established to stimulate, develop, and support objective scientific research on complementary and alternative medicine for the benefit of the public.

natural toxins Poisons that are produced by or naturally occur in plants or microorganisms.

near-infrared interactance The measurement of body composition using infrared radiation. It is based on the principle that substances of different densities absorb, reflect, or transmit infrared light at different rates.

negative energy balance Energy intake is lower than energy expenditure, resulting in a depletion of body energy stores and weight loss.

negative nitrogen balance Nitrogen intake is less than the sum of all sources of nitrogen excretion.

negative self-talk Mental or verbal statements made to one's self that reinforce negative or destructive self-perceptions.

neonate An infant from birth to 28 days.

neophobia A dislike for anything new or unfamiliar.

neotame An artificial sweetener similar to aspartame, but one that is sweeter and does not require a warning label for phenylketonurics.

net protein utilization (NPU) Percentage of ingested protein nitrogen retained by the body. It measures the amount of dietary protein the body uses.

neural tube defect (NTD) A birth defect resulting from failure of the neural tube to develop properly during early fetal development.

neuropeptide Y (NPY) A neurotransmitter widely distributed throughout the brain and peripheral nervous tissue. NPY activity has been linked to eating behavior, depression, anxiety, and cardiovascular function.

neurotransmitters Substances released at the end of a stimulated nerve cell that diffuse across a small gap and bind to another nerve cell or muscle cell, stimulating or inhibiting it.

niacin equivalents (NE) A measure that includes preformed dietary niacin as well as niacin derived from tryptophan; 60 milligrams of tryptophan yields about 1 milligram of niacin.

nicotinamide adenine dinucleotide (NAD^+) The oxidized form of nicotinamide adenine dinucleotide. This coenzyme, which is derived from the B vitamin niacin, acts as an electron carrier in cells, undergoing reversible oxidation and reduction. The reduced form is NADH.

night blindness The inability of the eyes to adjust to dim light or to regain vision quickly after exposure to a flash of bright light.

night-eating syndrome (NES) An eating disorder in which a habitual pattern of interrupting sleep to eat is the primary symptom.

nitrogen balance Nitrogen intake minus the sum of all sources of nitrogen excretion.

nitrogen equilibrium Nitrogen intake equals the sum of all sources of nitrogen excretion; nitrogen balance equals zero.

nonessential fatty acids The fatty acids that your body can make when they are needed. It is not necessary to consume them in the diet.

nonexercise activity thermogenesis (NEAT) The output of energy associated with fidgeting, maintenance of posture, and other minimal physical exertions.

nonheme iron The iron in plants and the iron in animal foods that is not part of hemoglobin or myoglobin.

nonnutritive sweeteners Substances that impart sweetness to foods but supply little or no energy to the body; also called artificial or alternative sweeteners. They include acesulfame, aspartame, saccharin, and sucralose.

nucleic acids A family of more than 25,000 molecules found in chromosomes, nucleoli, mitochondria, and the cytoplasm of cells.

nucleotides Subunits of DNA or RNA consisting of a nitrogenous base (adenine, guanine, thymine, or cytosine in DNA; adenine, guanine, uracil, or cytosine in RNA), a phosphate molecule, and a sugar molecule (deoxyribose in DNA and ribose in RNA). Thousands of nucleotides are linked to form a DNA or RNA molecule.

nucleus The primary site of genetic information in the cell, enclosed in a double-layered membrane. The nucleus contains the chromosomes and is the site of messenger RNA (mRNA) and ribosomal RNA (rRNA) synthesis, the "machinery" for protein synthesis in the cytosol.

nutrient content claims These claims describe the level of a nutrient or dietary substance in the product, using terms such as *good source, high*, or *free*.

nutrient density A description of the healthfulness of foods. Foods high in nutrient density are those that provide substantial amounts of vitamins and minerals and relatively few calories; foods low in nutrient density are those that supply calories but relatively small amounts of vitamins and minerals (or none at all).

nutrients Any substances in food that the body can use to obtain energy, synthesize tissues, or regulate functions.

nutrigenomics The study of how nutrition interacts with specific genes to influence a person's health.

nutrition The science of foods and their components (nutrients and other substances), including the relationships to health and disease (actions, interactions, and balances); processes within the body (ingestion, digestion, absorption, transport, functions, and disposal of end products); and the social, economic, cultural, and psychological implications of eating.

nutrition assessment Measurement of the nutritional health of the body. It can include anthropometric measurements, biochemical tests, clinical observations, and dietary intake, as well as medical histories and socioeconomic factors.

Nutrition Facts A portion of the food label that states the content of selected nutrients in a food in a standard way prescribed by the Food and Drug Administration. By law, Nutrition Facts must appear on nearly all processed food products in the United States.

Nutrition Labeling and Education Act (NLEA) An amendment to the Food, Drug, and Cosmetic Act of 1938. The NLEA made major changes to the content and scope of the nutrition label and to other elements of food labels. Final regulations were published in 1993 and went into effect in 1994.

Nutrition Recommendations for Canadians A set of scientific statements that provide guidance to Canadians for a dietary pattern that will supply recommended amounts of all essential nutrients while reducing the risk of chronic disease.

nutritive sweeteners Substances that impart sweetness to foods and that can be absorbed and yield energy in the body. Simple sugars, sugar alcohols, and high-fructose corn syrup are the most common nutritive sweeteners used in food products.

obesity BMI at or above 30 kg/m^2.

obsessive-compulsive disorder A disorder in which a person attempts to relieve anxiety by ritualistic behavior and continuous repetition of certain acts.

Older Americans Act Nutrition Program A federally funded program (formerly known as the Elderly Nutrition Program) that provides older persons with nutritionally sound meals through home-delivered nutrition services, congregate nutrition services, and the nutrition services incentive program.

olestra A fat replacer that can withstand heat and is stable at frying temperatures. Olestra, whose trade name is Olean, is a sucrose polyester: Sucrose (instead of glycerol) is the "backbone" molecule, with six to eight fatty acids attached (instead of triglyceride's three). The fatty acid arrangement prevents hydrolysis by digestive lipases, so the fatty acids are not absorbed.

olfactory cells Nerve cells in a small patch of tissue high in the nose connected directly to the brain to transmit messages about specific smells. Also called smell cells.

oligopeptide Four to 10 amino acids joined by peptide bonds.

oligosaccharides Short carbohydrate chains composed of 3 to 10 sugar molecules.

omega-3 fatty acids Any polyunsaturated fatty acid in which the first double bond starting from the methyl (CH_3) end of the molecule lies between the third and fourth carbon atoms.

omega-6 fatty acid Any polyunsaturated fatty acid in which the first double bond starting from the methyl (CH_3) end of the molecule lies between the sixth and seventh carbon atoms.

omega-9 fatty acid Any polyunsaturated fatty acid in which the first double bond starting from the methyl (CH_3) end of the molecule lies between the ninth and tenth carbon atoms.

1,25-dihydroxyvitamin D_3 [1,25$(OH)_2D_3$] The active form of vitamin D. It is an important regulator of blood calcium levels.

opsin A protein that combines with retinal to form rhodopsin in rod cells.

orexin A type of hormone in the brain that might affect food consumption.

organelles Various membrane-bound structures that form part of the cytoplasm. Organelles, including mitochondria and lysosomes, perform specialized metabolic functions.

organic In chemistry, any compound that contains carbon, except carbon oxides (e.g., carbon dioxide) and sulfides and metal carbonates (e.g., potassium carbonate). The term *organic* also is used to denote crops that are grown without synthetic fertilizers or chemicals.

organic foods Foods that originate from farms or handling operations that meet the standards set by the USDA National Organic Program.

organogenesis The period when organ systems are developing in a growing fetus.

orthomolecular medicine The preventive or therapeutic use of high-dose vitamins to treat disease.

osmolarity The concentration of dissolved particles (e.g., electrolytes) in a solution expressed per unit of volume.

osmoreceptors Neurons in the hypothalamus that detect changes in the fluid concentration in blood and regulate the release of antidiuretic hormone.

osmosis The movement of a solvent, such as water, through a semipermeable membrane from the low-solute to the high-solute solution until the concentrations on both sides of the membrane are equal.

osmotic pressure The pressure exerted on a semipermeable membrane by a solvent, usually water, moving from the side of low-solute to the side of high-solute concentration.

osteoblasts Bone cells that promote bone deposition and growth.

osteoclasts Bone cells that promote bone resorption and calcium mobilization.

osteomalacia A disease in adults that results from vitamin D deficiency; it is marked by softening of the bones, leading to bending of the spine, bowing of the legs, and increased risk for fractures.

osteoporosis A bone disease characterized by a decrease in bone mineral density and the appearance of small holes in bones due to loss of minerals.

overnutrition The long-term consumption of an excess of nutrients. The most common type of overnutrition in the United States is due to the regular consumption of excess calories, fats, saturated fats, and cholesterol.

overweight BMI at or above 25 kg/m^2 and less than 30 kg/m^2.

oxalate (oxalic acid) An organic acid in some leafy green vegetables, such as spinach, that binds to calcium to form calcium oxalate, an insoluble compound the body cannot absorb.

oxaloacetate A four-carbon intermediate compound in the citric acid cycle. Acetyl CoA combines with free oxaloacetate in the mitochondria, forming citrate and beginning the cycle.

oxidation Oxygen attaches to the double bonds of unsaturated fatty acids. Rancid fats are oxidized fats.

oxidative phosphorylation Formation of ATP from ADP and P_i coupled to the flow of electrons along the electron transport chain.

oxygen energy system A complex energy system that requires oxygen. To release ATP, it completes the breakdown of carbohydrate and fatty acids via the citric acid cycle and electron transport chain.

oxytocin A pituitary hormone that stimulates the release of milk from the breast.

palatable Pleasant tasting.

pancreas An organ that secretes enzymes that affect the digestion and absorption of nutrients and that releases hormones, such as insulin, that regulate metabolism as well as the disposition of the end products of food in the body.

pancreatic amylase Starch-digesting enzyme secreted by the pancreas.

parathyroid hormone A hormone secreted by the parathyroid glands in response to low blood calcium. It stimulates calcium release from bone and calcium absorption by the intestines, while decreasing calcium excretion by the kidneys. It acts in conjunction with $1,25(OH)_2D_3$ to raise blood calcium. Also called parathormone.

passive diffusion The movement of substances into or out of cells without the expenditure of energy or the involvement of transport proteins in the cell membrane. Also called simple diffusion.

pasteurization A process for destroying pathogenic bacteria by heating liquid foods to a prescribed temperature for a specified time.

pathogenic Capable of causing disease.

pectins A type of dietary fiber found in fruits.

peer review An appraisal of research against accepted standards by professionals in the field.

pentoses Sugar molecules containing five carbon atoms.

pepsin A protein-digesting enzyme produced by the stomach.

pepsinogen The inactive form of the enzyme pepsin.

peptidases Enzymes that act on small peptide units by breaking peptide bonds.

peptide bond The bond between two amino acids formed when a carboxyl (–COOH) group of one amino acid joins an amino ($–NH_2$) group of another amino acid, releasing water in the process.

perceived exertion The subjective experience of how difficult an effort is.

peristalsis [per-ih-STAHL-sis] The wavelike, rhythmic muscular contractions of the GI tract that propel its contents down the tract.

pernicious anemia A form of anemia that results from an autoimmune disorder that damages cells lining the stomach and inhibits vitamin B_{12} absorption, leading to vitamin B_{12} deficiency.

pesticides Chemicals used to control insects, diseases, weeds, fungi, and other pests on plants, vegetables, fruits, and animals.

pH A measurement of the hydrogen ion concentration, or acidity, of a solution. It is equal to the negative logarithm of the hydrogen ion (H^+) concentration expressed in moles per liter.

phagocytosis The process by which cells engulf large particles and small microorganisms. Receptors on the surface of cells bind these particles and organisms to bring them into large vesicles in the cytoplasm. From *phago*, "eating," and *cyto*, "cell."

phenylketonuria (PKU) An inherited disorder caused by a lack or deficiency of the enzyme that converts phenylalanine to tyrosine.

phosphate group A chemical group ($–PO_4$) on a larger molecule, where the phosphorus is single-bonded to each of the four oxygens, and the other bond of one of the oxygens is attached to the rest of the molecule. Often hydrogen atoms are attached to the oxygens. Sometimes there are double bonds between the phosphorus and an oxygen.

phosphocreatine See *creatine phosphate.*

phospholipids Compounds that consist of a glycerol molecule bonded to two fatty acid molecules and to a phosphate group with a nitrogen-containing component. Phospholipids have both hydrophilic and hydrophobic regions that make them good emulsifiers.

phosphorylation The addition of phosphate to an organic (carbon-containing) compound. Oxidative phosphorylation is the formation of high-energy phosphate bonds (ADP + Pi $\rightarrow$ ATP) from the energy released by oxidation of energy-yielding nutrients.

photosynthesis The process by which green plants use radiant energy from the sun to produce carbohydrates (hexoses) from carbon dioxide and water.

phylloquinone The form of vitamin K that comes from plant sources. Also known as vitamin K_1.

phytate (phytic acid) A phosphorus-containing compound in the outer husks of cereal grains that binds with minerals and inhibits their absorption.

phytochemicals Substances in plants that may possess health-protective effects, even though they are not essential for life.

phytoestrogens Plant compounds that have weak estrogen activity in the body.

phytosterols Sterols found in plants. Phytosterols are poorly absorbed by humans and reduce intestinal absorption of cholesterol. They have been used as a cholesterol-lowering food ingredient.

pica The craving for and consumption of nonfood items such as dirt, clay, or laundry starch.

pinocytosis The process by which cells internalize fluids and macromolecules. To do so, the cell membrane invaginates and forms a pocket around the substance. From *pino,* "drinking," and *cyto,* "cell."

placebo An inactive substance that is outwardly indistinguishable from the active substance whose effects are being studied.

placebo effect A physical or emotional change that is not due to properties of an administered substance. The change reflects participants' expectations.

placenta The organ formed during pregnancy that produces hormones for the maintenance of pregnancy and across which oxygen and nutrients are transferred from mother to infant; it also allows waste materials to be transferred from infant to mother.

plaque A buildup of substances that circulate in the blood (e.g., calcium, fat, cholesterol, cellular waste, and fibrin) on a blood vessel wall, making it vulnerable to blockage from blood clots

plasma The fluid portion of the blood that contains blood cells and other components.

platelets Tiny disk-shaped components of blood that are essential for blood clotting.

poisonous mushrooms Mushrooms that contain toxins that can cause stomach upset, dizziness, hallucinations, and other neurological symptoms.

pollutants Gaseous, chemical, or organic waste that contaminates air, soil, or water.

polyols See *sugar alcohols.*

polypeptide More than 10 amino acids joined by peptide bonds.

polyphenols Organic compounds that include an unsaturated ring containing more than one –OH group as part of their chemical structures; may produce bitterness in coffee and tea.

polysaccharides Long carbohydrate chains composed of more than 10 sugar molecules. Polysaccharides can be straight or branched.

polyunsaturated fatty acid A fatty acid in which the carbon chain contains two or more double bonds.

positive energy balance Energy intake exceeds energy expenditure, resulting in an increase in body energy stores and weight gain.

positive nitrogen balance Nitrogen intake exceeds the sum of all sources of nitrogen excretion.

positive self-talk Constructive mental or verbal statements made to one's self to change a belief or behavior.

post-traumatic stress disorder (PTSD) An anxiety disorder characterized by an emotional response to a traumatic event or situation involving severe external stress.

precursor A substance that is converted into another active substance. Enzyme precursors are also called proenzymes.

pre-diabetes A condition in which blood glucose levels are higher than normal but not high enough to warrant a diagnosis of diabetes.

preeclampsia A condition of late pregnancy characterized by hypertension, edema, and proteinuria.

preformed vitamin A Retinyl esters, the main storage form of vitamin A. About 90 percent of dietary retinol is in the form of esters, mostly found in foods from animal sources.

prematurity Birth before 37 weeks of gestation.

preservatives Chemicals or other agents that slow the decomposition of a food.

preterm delivery A delivery that occurs before the 37th week of gestation.

prions Short for "proteinaceous infectious particle." Self-reproducing protein particles that can cause disease.

prior-sanctioned substance All substances that the FDA or the U.S. Department of Agriculture (USDA) had determined were safe for use in specific foods before passage of the 1958 Food Additives amendment are designated as prior-sanctioned substances. These substances are exempt from the food additive regulation process.

proenzymes Inactive precursors of enzymes.

prolactin A pituitary hormone that stimulates the production of milk in the breast tissue.

proteases [PRO-tea-ace-ez] Enzymes that break down protein into peptides and amino acids.

protein digestibility corrected amino acid score (PDCAAS) A measure of protein quality that takes into account the amino acid composition of the food and the digestibility of the protein. It is calculated by multiplying the amino acid score by the percentage of the digestible food protein.

protein efficiency ratio (PER) Protein quality calculated by comparing the weight gain of growing animals fed a test protein with growing animals fed a high-quality reference protein. It depends on both the digestibility and the amino acid composition of a protein.

protein hydrolysates Proteins that have been treated with acid or enzymes to break them down into amino acids and polypeptides.

protein turnover The constant synthesis and breakdown of proteins in the body.

protein-energy malnutrition (PEM) A condition resulting from long-term inadequate intakes of energy and protein that can lead to wasting of body tissues and increased susceptibility to infection.

proteins Large, complex compounds consisting of many amino acids connected in varying sequences and forming unique shapes.

protoporphyrin A chemical complex that combines with iron to form heme.

provitamin A Carotenoid precursors of vitamin A in foods of plant origin, primarily deeply colored fruits and vegetables.

provitamins Inactive forms of vitamins that the body can convert into active usable forms. Also referred to as vitamin precursors.

psyllium The dried husk of the psyllium seed.

puberty The period of life during which the secondary sex characteristics develop and the ability to reproduce is attained.

purge Emptying of the GI tract by self-induced vomiting and/or misuse of laxatives, diuretics, or enemas.

pyloric sphincter [pie-LORE-ic] A circular muscle that forms the opening between the stomach and the duodenum. It regulates the passage of food into the small intestine.

pyrophosphate (P_i) Inorganic phosphate. This high-energy phosphate group is an important component of ATP, ADP, and AMP.

pyruvate The three-carbon compound that results from glycolytic breakdown of glucose. Pyruvate, the salt form of pyruvic acid, also can be derived from glycerol and some amino acids.

reactive hypoglycemia A type of hypoglycemia that occurs about one hour after eating carbohydrate-rich food. The body overreacts and produces too much insulin in response to food, rapidly decreasing blood glucose.

Recommended Dietary Allowances (RDAs) The nutrient intake levels that meet the nutrient needs of almost all (97 to 98 percent) individuals in a life-stage and gender group.

Recommended Nutrient Intakes (RNIs) Canadian dietary standards that have been replaced by Dietary Reference Intakes.

rectum The muscular final segment of the intestine, extending from the sigmoid colon to the anus.

reducing agent A compound that donates electrons or hydrogen atoms to another compound.

refined sweeteners Composed of monosaccharides and disaccharides that have been extracted and processed from other foods.

renin An enzyme, produced by the kidney, that affects blood pressure by catalyzing the conversion of angiotensinogen to angiotensin I.

requirement The lowest continuing intake level of a nutrient that prevents deficiency in an individual.

resistant starch A starch that is not digested.

resting energy expenditure (REE) The minimum energy needed to maintain basic physiological functions (e.g., heart beat, muscle function, respiration). The resting metabolic rate (RMR) extrapolated to 24 hours. Often used interchangeably with BEE.

resting metabolic rate (RMR) A clinical measure of resting energy expenditure performed three to four hours after eating or performing significant physical activity. Often used interchangeably with BMR.

restrained eaters Individuals who routinely avoid food as long as possible, and then gorge on food.

retina A paper-thin tissue that lines the back of the eye and contains cells called rods and cones.

retinal The aldehyde form of vitamin A; one of the retinoids; the active form of vitamin A in the photoreceptors of the retina; interconvertible with retinol.

retinoic acid The acid form of vitamin A; one of the retinoids; formed from retinal but not interconvertible; helps growth, cell differentiation, and the immune system; does not have a role in vision or reproduction.

retinoids Compounds in foods that have chemical structures similar to vitamin A. Retinoids include the active forms of vitamin A (retinol, retinal, and retinoic acid) and the main storage forms of retinol (retinyl esters).

retinol The alcohol form of vitamin A; one of the retinoids; thought to be the main physiologically active form of vitamin A; interconvertible with retinal.

retinol activity equivalents (RAE) A unit of measurement of the vitamin A content of a food. One RAE equals 1 μg of retinol.

retinol-binding protein (RBP) A carrier protein that binds to retinol and transports it in the bloodstream from the liver to destination cells.

retinyl esters The main storage form of vitamin A; one of the retinoids. Retinyl esters are retinol combined with fatty acids, usually palmitic acid. Also known as preformed vitamin A.

rhodopsin Found in rod cells, a light-sensitive pigment molecule that consists of a protein called opsin combined with retinal.

ribosomal RNA (rRNA) A type of ribonucleic acid that is a major component of ribosomes. It provides a structural framework for protein synthesis and orchestrates the process.

ribosomes Cell components composed of protein located in the cytoplasm that translate messenger RNA into protein sequences.

rickets A bone disease in children that results from vitamin D deficiency.

risk factors Anything that increases a person's chance of developing a disease, including substances, agents, genetic alterations, traits, habits, or conditions.

rods Light-sensitive cells in the retina that react to dim light and transmit black-and-white images.

R-protein A protein produced by the salivary glands that may protect vitamin B_{12} as it travels through the stomach and into the small intestine.

saccharin [SAK-ah-ren] An artificial sweetener that tastes about 300 to 700 times sweeter than sucrose.

Safe Tables Our Priority (S.T.O.P.) A national organization devoted to preventing illness and death from foodborne illness by working with government agencies and industry to encourage practices and policies that promote safe food.

salivary glands Glands in the mouth that release saliva.

Salmonella Rod-shaped bacteria responsible for many foodborne illnesses.

salts Compounds that result from the replacement of the hydrogen of an acid with a metal or a group that acts like a metal.

satiation Feeling of satisfaction and fullness that terminates a meal.

satiety The effects of a food or meal that delay subsequent intake. A feeling of satisfaction and fullness following eating that quells the desire for food.

saturated fatty acid A fatty acid completely filled by hydrogen with all carbons in the chain linked by single bonds.

seborrheic dermatitis Disease of the oil-producing glands of the skin; a symptom of riboflavin deficiency.

secondary hypertension Hypertension caused by an underlying condition such as a kidney disorder. Once the underlying condition is treated, the blood pressure usually returns to normal.

secretin [see-CREET-in] An intestinal hormone released during digestion that stimulates the pancreas to release water and bicarbonate.

segmentation Periodic muscle contractions at intervals along the GI tract that alternate forward and backward movement of the contents, thereby breaking apart chunks of the food mass and mixing in digestive juices.

selenocysteine A selenium-containing amino acid that is the biologically active form of selenium.

selenomethionine A selenium-containing amino acid derived from methionine that is the storage form of selenium.

semipermeable membrane Membrane that allows passage of some substances but blocks others.

serosa A smooth membrane composed of a mesothelial layer and connective tissue. The intestines are covered in serosa.

silicosis A disease that results from excess silicon exposure.

simple carbohydrates Sugars composed of a single sugar molecule (a monosaccharide) or two joined sugar molecules (a disaccharide).

skeletal muscles Muscles composed of bundles of parallel, striated muscle fibers under voluntary control. Also called voluntary muscle or striated muscle.

skinfold measurements A method to estimate body fat by measuring with calipers the thickness of a fold of skin and subcutaneous fat.

sleep apnea Periods of absence of breathing during sleep.

slow-twitch (ST) fibers Muscle fibers that develop tension more slowly and to a lesser extent than fast-twitch muscle fibers. ST fibers have high oxidative capacities and are slower to fatigue than fast-twitch fibers.

small intestine The tube (approximately 10 feet long) where the digestion of protein, fat, and carbohydrate is completed, and where the majority of nutrients are absorbed. The small intestine is divided into three parts: the duodenum, the jejunum, and the ileum.

social facilitation Encouragement of the interactions between people.

soda loading Consumption of bicarbonate (baking soda) to raise blood pH. The intent is to increase the capacity to buffer acids, thus delaying fatigue. Also known as bicarbonate loading.

sodium–potassium pumps Mechanisms that pump sodium ions out of a cell, allowing potassium ions to enter the cell.

solanine A potentially toxic alkaloid that is present with chlorophyll in the green areas on potato skins.

solutes Substances that are dissolved in a solvent.

Special Supplemental Nutrition Program for Women, Infants, and Children (WIC) A USDA program that provides federal grants to states for supplemental foods, health care referrals, and nutrition education for low-income pregnant, breastfeeding, and nonbreastfeeding postpartum women, and to infants and children at nutritional risk.

sphincters [SFINGK-ters] Circular bands of muscle fibers that surround the entrance or exit of a hollow body structure (e.g., the stomach) and act as valves to control the flow of material.

sphygmomanometer [sfig-mo-ma-NOM-eh-ter] An instrument for measuring blood pressure and especially arterial blood pressure.

spina bifida A type of neural tube birth defect.

sports anemia A lowered concentration of hemoglobin in the blood due to dilution. The increased plasma volume that dilutes the hemoglobin is a normal consequence of aerobic training.

squalene A cholesterol precursor found in whale liver and plants.

standard drink One serving of alcohol (about 15 grams), defined as 12 ounces of beer, 4 to 5 ounces of wine, or 1.5 ounces of liquor.

starch The major storage form of carbohydrate in plants; starch is composed of long chains of glucose molecules in a straight (amylose) or branching (amylopectin) arrangement.

statement of identity A mandate that commercial food products prominently display the common or usual name of the product or identify the food with an "appropriately descriptive term."

steatorrhea Production of stools with an abnormally high amount of fat.

stem cells A formative cell whose daughter cells may differentiate into other cell types.

sterols A category of lipids that includes cholesterol. Sterols are hydrocarbons with several rings in their structures.

stevia See *stevioside*.

stevioside A dietary supplement, not approved for use as a sweetener, that is extracted and refined from *Stevia rebaudiana* leaves.

stomach The enlarged, muscular, saclike portion of the digestive tract between the esophagus and the small intestine, with a capacity of about 1 quart.

structure/function claims These statements may claim a benefit related to a nutrient-deficiency disease (e.g., *vitamin C prevents scurvy*) or describe the role of a nutrient or dietary ingredient intended to affect a structure or function in humans (e.g., *calcium helps build strong bones*).

subcutaneous fat Fat stores under the skin.

submucosa The layer of loose, fibrous connective tissue under the mucous membrane.

sucralose An artificial sweetener made from sucrose; it was approved for use in the United States in 1998, and has been used in Canada since 1992. Sucralose is nonnutritive and about 600 times sweeter than sugar.

sucrose [SOO-crose] A disaccharide composed of one molecule of glucose and one molecule of fructose joined together. Also known as table sugar.

sugar alcohols Compounds formed from monosaccharides by replacing a hydrogen atom with a hydroxyl group (–OH); commonly used as nutritive sweeteners. Also called polyols.

Supplement Facts Content label that must appear on all dietary supplements.

Supplemental Nutrition Assistance Program (SNAP) A USDA program that helps single people and families with little or no income to buy food. Formerly known as the Food Stamp Program.

systolic Pertaining to a heart contraction. Systolic blood pressure is measured during a heart contraction, a time period known as systole.

D-tagatose An artificial sweetener derived from lactose that has the same sweetness as sucrose with only half the calories.

taste threshold The minimum amount of flavor that must be present for a taste to be detected.

teratogen Any substance that causes birth defects.

thaumatin Mixture of sweet-tasting proteins from a West African fruit. Approximately 2,000 times sweeter than sucrose and has a licorice aftertaste. Breaks down when heated to cooking temperatures.

thermic effect of food (TEF) The energy used to digest, absorb, and metabolize energy-yielding foodstuffs. It constitutes about 10 percent of total energy expenditure but is influenced by various factors.

thiamin pyrophosphate (TPP) A coenzyme of which the vitamin thiamin is a part. It plays a key role in decarboxylation and helps drive the reaction that forms acetyl CoA from pyruvate during metabolism.

thyroglobulin The storage form of thyroid hormone in the thyroid gland.

thyroid-stimulating hormone (TSH) Secreted from the pituitary gland at the base of the brain, a hormone that regulates synthesis of thyroid hormones.

thyroxine (T4) An iodine-containing hormone secreted by the thyroid gland to regulate the rate of cell metabolism; known chemically as tetraiodothyronine.

tissue [TISH-yoo] A group or layer of cells that are alike and that work together to perform a specific function.

tocopherol The chemical name for vitamin E. There are four tocopherols (alpha, beta, gamma, delta), but only alpha-tocopherol is active in the body.

tocotrienols Four compounds (alpha, beta, gamma, delta) chemically related to tocopherols. The tocotrienols and tocopherols are collectively known as vitamin E.

toddler A child between 12 and 36 months of age.

Tolerable Upper Intake Levels (ULs) The maximum levels of daily nutrient intakes that are unlikely to pose health risks to almost all of the individuals in the group for whom they are designed.

total body water All of the water in the body, including intracellular and extracellular water, and water in the urinary and GI tracts.

total energy expenditure (TEE) The total of the resting energy expenditure (REE), energy used in physical activity, and energy used in processing food (TEF); usually expressed in kilocalories per day.

total fiber The sum of dietary fiber and functional fiber.

total parenteral nutrition (TPN) Feeding a person by giving all essential nutrients intravenously.

trace minerals Trace minerals are present in the body and required in the diet in relatively small amounts compared with major minerals. Also known as microminerals.

trans fatty acids Unsaturated fatty acids in which the hydrogens surrounding a double bond are on opposite sides of the carbon chain. This straightens the chain, and the fatty acid becomes more solid.

transamination [TRANS-am-ih-NAY-shun] The transfer of an amino group from an amino acid to a carbon skeleton to form a different amino acid.

transfer RNA (tRNA) A type of ribonucleic acid that is composed of a complementary RNA sequence and an amino acid specific to that sequence. It inserts the appropriate amino acid when the messenger RNA sequence and the ribosome call for it.

transferrin A protein synthesized in the liver that transports iron in the blood to the erythroblasts for use in heme synthesis.

transferrin receptors Specialized receptors on the cell membrane that bind transferrin.

transferrin saturation The extent to which transferrin has vacant iron-binding sites (e.g., low transferrin saturation indicates a high proportion of vacant iron-binding sites).

trehalose A disaccharide of two glucose molecules, but with a linkage different from maltose. Used as a food additive and sweetener.

tricarboxylic acid (TCA) cycle See *citric acid cycle*.

triglycerides Fats composed of three fatty acid chains linked to a glycerol molecule.

triiodothyronine (T3) An iodine-containing thyroid hormone with several times the biologic activity of thyroxine (T4).

trimesters Three equal time periods of pregnancy, each lasting approximately 13 to 14 weeks, that do not coincide with specific stages in fetal development.

tripeptide Three amino acids joined by peptide bonds.

trypsinogen/trypsin A protease produced by the pancreas that is converted from the inactive proenzyme form (trypsinogen) to the active form (trypsin) in the small intestine.

tryptophan An amino acid that serves as a niacin precursor in the body. In the body, 60 milligrams of tryptophan yields about 1 milligram of niacin, or 1 niacin equivalent (NE).

tumor [TOO-mer] An abnormal mass of tissue that results from excessive cell division. Tumors perform no useful body function. They may be benign (not cancerous) or malignant (cancerous).

24-hour dietary recall A form of dietary intake data collection. The interviewer takes the client through a recent 24-hour period (usually midnight to midnight) to determine what foods and beverages the client consumed.

type 1 diabetes Diabetes that occurs when the body's immune system attacks the pancreas, causing its cells to lose the ability to make insulin.

type 2 diabetes Diabetes that occurs when target cells (e.g., fat and muscle cells) lose the ability to respond normally to insulin.

ulcer A craterlike lesion that occurs in the lining of the stomach or duodenum; also called a peptic ulcer to distinguish it from a skin ulcer.

umami [ooh-MA-mee] A Japanese term that describes a delicious meaty or savory sensation. Chemically, this taste detects the presence of glutamate.

undernutrition Poor health resulting from depletion of nutrients due to inadequate nutrient intake over time. It is now most often associated with poverty, alcoholism, and some types of eating disorders.

underwater weighing Determining body density by measuring the volume of water displaced when the body is fully submerged in a specialized water tank. Also called hydrostatic weighing.

underweight BMI less than 18.5 kg/m^2.

unsaturated fatty acid A fatty acid in which the carbon chain contains one or more double bonds.

urea The main nitrogen-containing waste product in mammals. Formed in liver cells from ammonia and carbon dioxide, urea is carried via the bloodstream to the kidneys, where it is excreted in the urine.

urinary tract infection (UTI) An infection of one or more of the structures in the urinary tract; usually caused by bacteria.

U.S. Department of Agriculture (USDA) The government agency that monitors the production of eggs, poultry, and meat for adherence to standards of quality and wholesomeness. The USDA also provides public nutrition education, performs nutrition research, and administers the WIC program.

U.S. Department of Health and Human Services (DHHS) The principal federal agency responsible for protecting the health of all Americans and providing essential human services. The agency is especially concerned with those Americans who are least able to help themselves.

U.S. Pharmacopeia (USP) Established in 1820, the USP is a voluntary, nonprofit health care organization that sets quality standards for a range of health care products.

vascular system A network of veins and arteries through which the blood carries nutrients. Also called the circulatory system.

vasoconstrictor A substance that causes blood vessels to constrict.

vasopressin See *antidiuretic hormone*.

very low calorie diets (VLCD) Diets supplying 400 to 800 kilocalories per day, which include adequate high-quality protein, little or no fat, and little carbohydrate.

very low density lipoproteins (VLDL) The triglyceride-rich lipoproteins formed in the liver. VLDL enters the bloodstream and is gradually acted upon by lipoprotein lipase, releasing triglyceride to body cells.

villi Small, fingerlike projections that blanket the folds in the lining of the small intestine. Singular is *villus*.

visceral fat Fat stores that cushion body organs.

vitamin precursors See *provitamins*.

vitamins Organic compounds necessary for reproduction, growth, and maintenance of the body. Vitamins are required in miniscule amounts.

waist circumference The waist measurement, as a marker of abdominal fat content; can be used to indicate health risks.

wasting The breakdown of body tissue such as muscle and organ for use as a protein source when the diet lacks protein.

weighed food records Detailed food records obtained by weighing foods before eating and then weighing leftovers to determine the exact amount consumed.

weight cycling Repeated periods of gaining and losing weight. Also called yo-yo dieting.

weight management The adoption of healthful and sustainable eating and exercise behaviors that reduce disease risk and improve well-being.

Wilson's disease Genetic disorder of increased copper absorption, which leads to toxic levels in the liver and heart.

wood alcohol Common name for methanol.

World Health Organization (WHO) A global organization that directs and coordinates international health work. Its goal is the attainment by all peoples of the highest possible level of health, defined as a state of complete physical, mental, and social well-being and not merely the absence of disease or infirmity.

xerophthalmia A condition caused by vitamin A deficiency that dries the cornea and mucous membranes of the eye.

Index

ABCDs of nutrition assessment, 65
ABC model of behavior, 370, 371–372
Absorption
of alcohol, 314
of amino acids, 239–240
bacterial influences on, 131
of calcium, 493–495
of carbohydrates, 157
of carotenoids, 402, 404
chemical influences on, 131
of chromium, 539–540
of copper, 533
defined, 106
of fluoride, 538
hormonal system regulation of, 126–127, 129
how digestion works together with, 112, 114–126
of iodine, 531
of iron, 457, 511–514
of lipids, 205–207
of manganese, 536
of molybdenum, 541–542
nervous system regulation of, 126
organs for, 115–117
overview of, 112, 114–115
of peptides, 240–241
pizza example, 140
of proteins, 239–240
psychological influences on, 130–131
of sterols, 208
of triglycerides, 205–207
of vitamin B12, 453
of vitamins, 389
of water, 471
of zinc, 521–522
Academy of Nutrition and Dietetics (AND)
adolescents and, 723, 725
agricultural and food biotechnology and, 779
breastfeeding and, 687
children and, 712, 723, 725
dietary fiber and, 174
dietary supplements and, 85, 579–580
eating disorders, nutrition intervention and, 604
elderly and, 734, 741
fat replacers and, 214
fats and, 36, 210–212
fluoride and, 538
food and nutrition misinformation and, 23, 24
food biotechnology and, 779
food insecurity and hunger and, 793
food irradiation and, 771
food safety and, 763
functional foods and, 78
infants and, 712
nutrition and athletic performance, 554, 579–580
nutrition intervention and AIDS and, 795
physical activity and, 552
pregnancy and, 670, 671
role of dietetics professionals in health promotion and disease prevention and, 621
sodium and, 482
sweeteners and, 171
total diet approach, 35
vegetarian diets and, 256
water safety and, 766
weight management and, 35, 362, 364, 366
world hunger, malnutrition, and food insecurity and, 793
Acceptable Macronutrient Distribution Ranges (AMDRs)
for adults, 56
carbohydrate and, 164, 244
defined, 56
fat and, 211, 244
proteins and, 244
Acculturation, 485
Acesulfame K, 171
Acetaldehyde, 314
Acetyl CoA
conversion of pyruvate to, 275–277, 281
defined, 275
Acid–base balance, 235–236
Acidosis, 236
Acne
defined, 725
treatment and vitamin A, 400–401
Acrodermatitis enteropathica, 526
Acrolein, 131
Active transport, 114, 115, 236, 239, 240
Additives
color, 80
defined, 78
Delaney Clause and, 81–82
direct, 79
FDA regulation of, 78, 79–82
in functional foods, 78, 79–82
indirect, 79
sweeteners, 171–172
Adenosine diphosphate. *See* ADP
Adenosine monophosphate. *See* AMP
Adenosine triphosphate. *See* ATP
Adequate Intake (AI)
comparing dietary intake data to, 69
defined, 55
Adipocytes, 191
Adipose tissue
defined, 191
metabolic profile of, 299
Adolescence, 712
Adolescents
acne, 725
alcohol and, 726
drugs and, 726
eating disorders and, 726
energy needs, 723
food preferences and, 2
influences on food intake, 724–725
minerals and, 723–724
nutritional concerns, 725–726
nutritional needs, 723–724
obesity/overweight and, 161, 623, 720, 726
physical activity and, 552, 725
physical growth and development, 722
pregnancy and, 687
proteins and, 245, 723, 724
smoking and, 726
type 2 diabetes in, 161
vitamins and, 723–724
ADP (adenosine diphosphate), 272, 273
Adrenaline. *See* Epinephrine
Adults, protein requirements for, 245
Advertising
of dietary supplements, 92–93
influence of, 5–6
Aerobic
defined, 275
endurance, 558, 559
Aflatoxins, 646, 759
African Americans
diabetes and, 651, 652
hypertension and, 638
lactose intolerance in, 122–123
obesity/overweight and, 357
Age
See also Adolescents; Children; Elderly
aging process, 727–728
body composition and, 728–729
diabetes and, 652
disease and, 729
food preferences and, 2
gastrointestinal tract and, 730–731
hypertension and, 638
immune system and, 730
longevity, 728
mobility and, 729
nutritional needs and, 728, 731–736
obesity/overweight and, 356, 728
physical activity and, 576, 577, 729
taste and smell and, 730
weight, 728–729
Agricultural Research Service (ARS), 764
Agriculture and environment, balancing, 797–798

AIDS
  malnutrition and, 795, 796
  pregnancy and, 686–687
Albumin, 540
Alcohol
  absorption of, 314
  adolescents and, 726
  anemia and, 330
  aversion therapy, 314
  benefits of, 328–332
  binge drinking, 312, 313, 322
  blood alcohol concentration (BAC), 316–317
  brain and nervous system, effects on, 319–324, 330
  breastfeeding and, 320, 691
  calories in, 313, 331
  cancer and, 312, 330
  chemistry and character of, 311–312
  college drinking, 322–323
  consumption, how much is too much, 329
  defined, 310, 311
  diet and, 326
  Dietary Guidelines for Americans recommendations, 37, 310, 327
  elderly and, 318
  fermentation, 310, 311–312
  fetal alcohol syndrome, 325
  fluid balance and, 476
  formation and production of, 311–312
  gastrointestinal system, effects on, 324, 330
  gender differences and, 318–319
  hangover, 316, 317–318
  harmful effects of, 330
  heart disease and, 329–330, 634–635
  hypertension and, 638
  historical use of, 310
  impairment chart, 321
  liver, effects on, 314, 315, 324–325, 330
  macronutrients and, 327
  malnutrition and alcoholics, 326–328
  metabolism, 314–319
  mineral deficiencies and, 327
  moderate drinking, defined, 313
  myths about, 320
  nutritional value of, 311, 312, 331
  osteoporosis and, 330
  pancreatitis, 330
  poisoning, 316, 317
  pregnancy and, 325, 673, 683, 684
  smoking, 324
  sources, 311–312
  thiamin deficiency and, 434
  vitamin B6 and, 445
  vitamin deficiencies and, 326–327
  weight and, 328
  who should not drink any, 327, 332
  women and, 318–319
Alcohol dehydrogenase (ADH), 314
Aldehyde dehydrogenase (ALDH), 314, 315
Aldosterone, 474
Alimentary canal. *See* Gastrointestinal tract
Alkalosis, 236
Allergens, 761
Allergies, children and food, 716
Aloe, 90
Alpha (α) bonds, 155, 156
Alpha-linolenic acid
  defined, 187, 189
  sources of, 194
Alzheimer's disease
  defined, 741
  ginkgo biloba and, 89
  vitamin E and, 416
Amenorrhea, 588
American Cancer Society, 644–646
American College of Nutrition (CAN), 24
American College of Sports Medicine (ACSM)
  bone health and exercise, advice on, 658
  exercise for health distinguished from exercise for fitness, 552
  fluid replacement, advice on, 576
  hypertension and exercise, advice on, 639
American diet, 10
American Heart Association (AHA)
  alcohol and, 330
  calcium and, 489
  cardiovascular disease, advice on preventing, 630–636
  children and, 721
  chloride and, 488
  dietary guidelines, 210–211
  dietary supplements and, 86
  fiber and, 722
  fish and, 188, 195, 212–213
  high-protein diets and, 256
  lipids and, 210–211
  omega-3 fatty acids and, 188, 195
  physical activity and, 553
  weight management and, 367
American Medical Association, 552, 771
American Journal of Clinical Nutrition, 22
American Society for Nutrition (ASN), 24
American Society for Parenteral and Enteral Nutrition (ASPEN), 24
Amino acid pool, 242
Amino acids
  absorption of, 239–240
  conditionally indispensable, 227
  defined, 13
  dispensable, 227
  end products of catabolism, 285
  how the body makes, 293–294
  hydrophilic, 229–230
  hydrophobic, 230
  indispensable, 226
  proteins and, 226–228, 242
  sequences, 228–229
  structure of, 227–228
  supplements, 246, 251, 580–581
  synthesis of nonprotein molecules, 242–243
Amino acid scoring, 249, 250
Amniotic fluid, 678
AMP (adenosine monophosphate), 272, 273
Amylase
  defined, 117
  pancreatic, 155
Amylopectin, 152
Amylose, 152
Anabolic steroids, 577, 585
Anabolism, 270
Android obesity, 354, 355
Anaerobic, 275
Androgens, 202
Anemia
  alcohol and, 330
  defined, 445
  folate and, 450–451
  hemolytic, 418, 424
  infants and, 704
  iron-deficiency, 511, 516–518, 704, 800–801
  megaloblastic, 450–451
  microcytic hypochromic, 444, 445, 518
  pernicious, 455
  sports, 571
  vitamin B12 and, 86, 454–455
Anencephaly, 451, 452
Angiotensin I, 474
Angiotensin II, 474
Angiotensinogen, 474
Angular stomatitis, 436
Animal drugs, 758–759
Animal starch. *See* Glycogen
Animal studies, 18
Anions, 470, 471
Anisakis, 754, 755
Anorexia athletic, 610, 611
Anorexia nervosa
  causes of, 600–601
  defined, 596, 599–600
  diagnostic criteria for, 597
  side effects of, 603
  treatment of, 601–603
  warning signs of, 601
Anorexia of aging, 738
Anthropometric measurements, 65–66
Antibiotics, diarrhea from, 131
Antibodies, 235
Antidiuretic hormone (ADH), 472, 473, 474
Antioxidants
  carotenoids as, 401
  defined, 11
  supplements, 582
  vitamin C and, 457
Antirachitic, 407
Appetite, 338
Apples, 154
Arginase, 535

Ariboflavinosis, 436–437
Arsenic, 542–543
Artesian water, 479
Arthritis
  defined, 738–739
  obesity/overweight and, 622, 739
Artichoke, Jerusalem, 175
Artificial sweeteners. *See* Nonnutritive sweeteners
Asians, lactose intolerance in, 122–123
Aspartame
  defined, 170
  phenylketonuria and, 170
Assize of Bread, 79
Atherosclerosis
  cholesterol and, 628–629
  defined, 202, 627–628
  dietary and lifestyle factors for reducing risk of, 630–636
  inflammation and, 629
  risk factors for, 625, 629–630
Athletes
  See also Physical performance
  amino acids and, 580–582
  anorexia athletic, 610, 611
  antioxidants and, 582
  caffeine and, 582–583
  calcium and, 571
  carbohydrates and, 153, 563–565, 567
  chromium and, 539, 584
  creatine and, 581–582
  dehydration, 475–476
  diet, training, 561–562, 572
  dietary fat, 567
  endurance training, 557–558
  energy intake and, 562–563
  energy systems and, 555–557
  ephedrine and, 583
  fat intake and, 567
  female athlete triad, 587–589, 611–612
  fluid needs, 572–576
  glycogen depletion, 567
  iron and, 584
  lactate and, 560–561
  meals before events, timing of, 565
  minerals and, 570–572
  muscles and muscle fibers and, 559–560
  muscle soreness and, 584, 588
  needs of young, 577
  nutrition and, 552–555, 561–562
  proteins and, 569–570
  sodium bicarbonate and, 583–584
  sports drinks, 471, 574–576, 589
  supplements and ergogenic aids, 577–580
  training, importance of, 568
  vitamin B and, 571
  vitamins and, 570–572
  water and, 475–476, 572–576
  weight and body composition and, 584–589
Atkins Diet, 368, 369, 373
ATP (adenosine triphosphate), 272–273, 279–280
ATP-CP energy system, 555–556
Atrophic gastritis, 452, 453
Autonomic nervous system, 126
Avidin, 442, 443

Bacteria, 130
  See also under type of
  colonic, 443
  digestion and absorption, bacterial influences on, 131
  food safety and, 752, 766–767
  health effects of intestinal, 134
  supermarket statistics, 771
  ulcers and, 138–139
Bacteriophages, 771–772
Balance
  in eating, 31
  water, 472–476
Bananas, 486
Baryophobia, 612–613
Basal energy expenditure (BEE), 341
Basal metabolic rate (BMR), 342
Base pair, 625
Basic Four, 40
Beef fat, color of, 216
Beer, 310
  calories in, 313, 331
  nutrients in, 312, 331
Behavior
  See also Eating behavior
  ABC model of, 370, 371–372
  obesity/overweight and, 16–17, 357–358
  sugar, affects of, 172
  tools for changing, 372
  weight management, 374
Benecol, 82, 83
Benign, 642
Beriberi, 18, 431, 434–435, 801
Beta (β) bonds, 155, 156
Beta-carotene, 75, 84, 388, 390
β-glucans, 154
Beta-oxidation, 282–283
Beverly Hills Diet, 372
Biberon, 697
Bile, 116, 204
Binge, 605
Binge drinking, 312, 313, 322
Binge eaters, 358, 360
Binge-eating disorder
  causes of, 607–608
  defined, 596, 597
  diagnostic criteria for, 597
  treatment of, 608
  warning signs of, 607
Bioavailability, 193
  of calcium, 495
  defined, 97
  of major minerals, 481
Biochemical assessment, 67
Biochemical structures, F-0 to F-15
Biocytin, 442
Biodiversity, 776
Bioelectrical impedance analysis (BIA), 353–354
Bioflavonoids, 92
Biofuel versus fossil fuel, 284
Biological value (BV), 249–250
Bioremediation, 234
Biosynthesis, 272, 273, 274, 285–294
Biotechnology, 772
Bioterrorism, 764–765
Biotin, 14
  deficiency, 443
  dietary recommendations for, 443
  functions of, 442–443
  history of, 442
  sources of, 443
  toxicity, 443
Biotinidase, 442, 443
Birth control, breastfeeding and, 688
Bisphenol A (BPA), 699
Bladder cancer, 81, 170
Blastogenic stage, 674
Bleaching process, 392
Blood alcohol concentration (BAC), 316–317
Blood calcium levels, regulation of, 407, 409, 490–492
  hypercalcemia, 413
Blood cell synthesis, vitamin B6 and, 444
Blood clotting
  calcium and, 490
  vitamin E and, 418–419
  vitamin K and, 419, 420, 423
Blood glucose levels
  defined, 160
  low, 651
  regulating, 160–161
Blood pressure
  See also Hypertension
  breastfeeding and, 692
  classifications, 638
  defined, 636, 637
  reading, 637
  regulation of, 474, 475
Blood sugar. *See* Blood glucose levels
BodPod, 352, 353
Body composition
  adolescents and, 722
  age and, 728–729
  athletes and, 584–587
  body fatness, assessing, 352–354
  Body Size Acceptance campaign, 615
  body weight, assessing, 350–351
  chromium, physical activity, and, 541
  defined, 350
  gender differences and, 318, 354, 355
  water and, 468, 469, 730
Body dysmorphic disorder (BDD), 608–609

Body fat distribution, 354–355
Body fatness, assessing, 352–354
Body fluids, water as a component of, 469
Body image, 596
Body mass index (BMI)
  chart for calculating, 351
  defined, 350
  mortality and, 350, 351
Bolus, 117
Bomb calorimeter, 336
Bone health
  See also Osteoporosis
  calcium and, 489–490
  fluoride and, 537, 538
  gravity and, 660
  physical activity and, 658, 659–660
  vitamin A and, 396
  vitamin D and, 405
  vitamin K and, 419, 421
Books and manuals, diet self-help, 373
Borage seed oil, 196
Boron, 543
Bottled water, 478–479
Botulism, 750, 751
Bovine spongiform encephalopathy (BSE), 754
Bowel and bladder regulation, elderly and, 739–740
Brain
  alcohol consumption and effects on, 319–324, 330
  freeze, 4
  iron and, 511
  metabolic profile of, 298
Bran, 165
Branched-chain amino acids (BCAAs), 580–581
Bread, adulteration of, 79
Breast cancer
  carotenoids and, 402
  diet and, 646
  folate and, 449
  mammograms and, 647
  soy and, 17–18, 77, 254
Breastfeeding
  alcohol and, 320, 691
  benefits of, 691–692
  birth control and, 688
  blood pressure and, 692
  contraindications to, 692
  dietary supplements and, 85, 691
  drugs and, 691, 692
  HIV and, 691, 692, 799
  how much to feed, 700
  nutrition for women who are, 689
  physical activity and, 552
  physiology of lactation, 688–689
  protein requirements and, 245, 690
  resources for women who are, 693
  smoking and, 691
  technique, 697–698, 700
  thiamin and, 432
  trends in, 687–688
  vitamins and minerals and, 690
  water and, 690
Breast milk
  appearance of, 701
  benefits of, 691–692
  digestibility of, 246
  flavored, 690
  oligosaccharides in, 151
  protein in, 245, 690
  vitamin D in, 409–410
Breathing problems, obesity/overweight and, 622
Bt gene (*Bacillus thuringiensis*), 776
Buffers, 235–236
Bugs, proteins and, 226, 259
Built environment, 357
Bulimia nervosa
  binge-and-purge cycle, 605–606
  causes of, 604–605
  defined, 597, 603–604
  diagnostic criteria for, 597
  side effects of, 606
  treatment of, 606–607
  warning signs of, 604
Butter, margarine versus, 198–199
Butyric acid, 183

Caffeine
  athletes and, 582–583
  children and, 718
  fluid balance and, 476
  pregnancy and, 683
Calcitonin, 407, 492
Calcitriol. *See* Dihydroxyvitamin D3
Calcium
  absorption of, 493–495
  athletes and, 571
  bioavailability of, 495
  children and, 492
  deficiency, 495, 801
  dietary recommendations for, 492
  elderly and, 492, 734–735
  functions of, 489–490
  megadoses of, 88
  Nutrition Facts label for finding, 501
  osteoporosis and, 492, 495–496, 634, 659–660
  regulation of blood, 490–492
  sources of, 492–493, 494
  supplements, 494
  toxicity, 495
  vitamin D and, 491
  women and, 489, 492, 495–496
Calculations and conversions, H-0 to H-7
Calmodulin, 490
Calorie
  calculating percentages of, 16
  control, 31
  defined, 15
Calorimeter, 346
Calorimetry, 346–347
Campylobacter jejuni, 752
Canada
  dietary supplements, 89, 90–91, 96
  Eating Well with Canada's Food Guide, 42, 44
  Food Guide, 42, 44
  guidelines for healthy eating, 42–43, 44–45
  guidelines, D-0 to D-13
  Official Food Rules, 43, 44
Canada's Guidelines for Healthy Eating, 42
Canada's Physical Activity Guide, 43
Canada's Physical Activity Guide for Older Adults, 729
Cancer
  alcohol and, 312, 330
  beta-carotene and, 75, 84
  bladder, 81, 170
  breast, 17–18, 254, 402, 449
  carotenoids and, 402
  colon, 408, 449, 462
  colorectal, 137–138
  conjugated linoleic acid and, 197
  defined, 642–643
  Delaney Clause and, 81–82
  development of, 642–643
  diet and link to, 644
  dietary and lifestyle factors for reducing risk of, 644–648
  esophageal, 135
  fats and, 218, 646
  fiber and, 75, 136
  folate and, 449, 451
  fruits and vegetables and, 646–647
  legumes and, 647
  liver, 324, 330
  lung, 78, 402
  obesity/overweight and, 360, 361, 622, 644
  physical activity and, 644
  phytochemicals and, 74, 77
  prostate, 89, 93, 254, 402, 404
  proteins and, 261
  risk factors for, 624, 643–644
  saccharin and, 81, 170
  saw palmetto and, 89
  smoking and, 324, 330
  soy and, 17–18, 74 , 77, 254
  vitamin C and, 457, 459
  vitamin D and, 405, 408
  vitamin E and, 415, 416
  whole grains and, 647
Cantaloupe, 401
Carbohydrate loading, 563–564
Carbohydrates
  absorption of, 157
  Acceptable Macronutrient Distribution Range for, 164, 244
  athletes and, 153, 563–565, 567
  in the body, 157–161
  choosing wisely, 165–166

complex, 150–155, 167
current consumption, 164–165
defined, 13, 146–147
in the diet, 161, 164–173, 367
Dietary Guidelines for Americans recommendations, 164
digestion of, 155–157
elderly and, 733
energy and, 157, 275–278, 283, 286–288
excess of, turning into fat, 291
from fat, 291
foods high in, 167
gas and, 138
health and, 173–176
high-protein, low-carbohydrate diet, 368–369
infants and, 696
metabolism and vitamin B6, 444
Nutrition Facts label for finding, 175
physical activity and, 563–565, 567
pregnancy and, 682
recommended intake, 164, 244
simple, 147–150, 167
sources of, 13, 146
Carbon skeletons, 385, 293
Carboxylation, 442–443
Carcinogens, 643
Cardiac output, 586
Cardiovascular disease (CVD)
See also under type of
cardiovascular system and, 626–627
children and, 721
defined, 626
fiber and, 174
phytochemicals and, 77
preventing, 630–636
Carnitine, 281, 457, 460
Carotenodermia, 388
Carotenoids
absorption and storage of, 402, 404
as antioxidants, 401
benefits of, 75
cancer and, 402, 404
defined, 391
functions of, 401
immune system and, 402
sources of, 75, 403, 404
supplementation, 404–405
vision and, 402
Carrots, 388
Cascara, 90
Case control studies, 18
Cast-iron pots and pans, to avoid iron deficiency, 516
Catabolism
defined, 270
end products of amino acid, 285
end products of glucose, 280
Catalyze, 111
Cataracts
carotenoids and, 402
vitamin C and, 457, 459
vitamin E and, 416
Cations, 468, 469–470
Cecum, 124
Celiac disease, 239
Cell differentiation, vitamin A and, 395–396
Cells
culture studies, 18
defined, 270
membranes, 200, 271
metabolism and role of, 270–272
nucleus, 270, 271
structure of, 271
vitamin C and synthesis of vital cell compounds, 457
zinc and death of, 521
Cellular metabolism, calcium and, 490
Cellulose, 154
Centers for Disease Control and Prevention (CDC), 763
Central nervous system (CNS), 126
Cephalic phase responses, 107
Ceruloplasmin, 533
Chain length, 183–184
Chamomile, 90, 91
Chaparral, 90, 91
Cheilosis, 436
Chelation therapy, 535
Chemical contamination, 756–761
Chemical energy, 268, 269
Chemical influences, on digestion and absorption, 131
Chemical scoring, 249, 250
Chemosenses, 106–107
Chewing of food, repeated, 369
Child and Adult Care Food Program, 790
Childhood, 712
Children
behavior and food, 718
caffeine and, 718
calcium and, 492
chronic disease and, 719, 721
dietary supplements and, 85, 714, 717
eating disorders and, 612–613
energy needs, 712, 713
fiber and, 719, 722
fluoride and, 539
food allergies and, 716
food preferences and, 2
food safety and, 756–757, 760, 761, 763, 767
influences on food habits and intake, 717
iron and, 516, 518–519, 713
lead toxicity, 721
malnutrition and, 257–258, 718, 787–788
minerals and, 712–717
MyPlate and, 714, 715
nutritional concerns, 718–721
nutritional needs, 712–717
obesity/overweight and, 363, 623, 717, 718–719, 720
physical activity and, 552
proteins and, 245, 713
sugar and, 169
vegetarian diet and, 721
vitamin D and, 405, 405, 407, 409–410, 411, 713
vitamins and, 712–717
Chili peppers, benefits of eating, 456
Chitin, 154
Chitosan, 154
Chloride, 487
deficiency, 488–489
dietary recommendations for, 488
functions of, 488
shift, 488
sources of, 488
Chlorophyll, cooking and, 499
Chocolate, 792
Cholecystokinin (CCK), 116, 127, 204
Cholesterol
alcohol and, 327, 328
atherosclerosis and, 628–629
defined, 202
diabetes and, 652
-free foods, 202
functions of, 202
garlic and, 84, 90
heart disease and, 202, 216, 217
how the body makes, 292
levels, 630
-lowering margarines, 199
-lowering medications, how they work, 629
niacin and, 395, 440
sources of, 202–203
synthesis of, 202
Choline, 200, 459–460
Chromium
absorption, transport, and excretion of, 539–540
athletes and, 539, 584
body composition, physical activity, and 541
deficiency, 540
dietary recommendations for, 540
functions of, 539
history of, 539
picolinate, 84
sources of, 540
toxicity, 540–541
Chylomicrons, 207, 208–209
Chyme, 110
Chymotrypsin/chymotrypsinogen, 239
Ciguatera, 759
Ciliary action, 490
Circular muscle, 108
Circulation
defined, 13
of nutrients, 129–130
Cis fatty acid, 186
Citric acid cycle, 277–278, 281, 283, G-2

Clay, eating of, 5
Clinical observations, 67
Clinical trials, 18
Clostridium botulinum, 751
Cobalamin. *See* Vitamin B12
Cod liver oil, 405
Coenzyme A, 276
Coenzyme Q10 (CoQ10), 84
Coenzymes, 272
Cofactors, 272
Cognitive influences, food preferences and, 3–6
Colds
  vitamin C and, 457, 459
  zinc and, 525
Colic, 691, 703
Collagen
  defined, 230–231
  vitamin C and synthesis of, 456–457
College drinking, 322–323
Colon
  defined, 124
  folate and cancer of the, 408, 449, 462
  gum chewing following surgery, 128
  importance of, 126
  vitamin D and cancer of the, 408
Color additive, 80
Colorectal cancer, 137–138, 646
Colostrum, 688
Comfort foods, 4–5
Comfrey, 90, 91
Common chemical sense, 106
Complementary and alternative medicine (CAM)
  defined, 74
  nutrition and, 99–100
Complementary foods, 701
Complementary proteins, 247, 248
Complementary sequence, 625
Complete (high-quality) proteins, 247
Complex carbohydrates
  defined, 150
  description of, 150–155
  foods high in, 167
Composting, 113
Compulsive overeating. *See* Binge-eating disorder
Computed tomography (CT), 354, 355
Concentration gradients, 112
Condensation, 150
Conditionally indispensable amino acids, 227
Cones, 392
Congeners, 312
Conjugated linoleic acid (CLA)
  cancer and, 197
  defined, 186
Connective tissues, 456–457
Constipation, 133, 682
Consumer Health Information for Better Nutrition, 61
Control group, 18
Cooking utensils
  cast-iron, 516
  copper, 534
Cooling, water and, 469
Cooperative State Research, Education, and Extension Service (CSREES), 764
Copper
  absorption, use, and metabolism of, 533
  cooking utensils, 535
  deficiency, 534–535
  dietary recommendations for, 533–534
  functions of, 533
  history of, 533
  infants and, 534–535
  megadoses of, 88
  pregnancy and, 534–535
  sources of, 533–534
  toxicity, 535
Cori cycle, 288, 560, 561
Cornea, 392
Corn sweeteners, 167
Coronary heart disease (CHD)
  defined, 627
  fruits and vegetables and, 632
  vitamin E and, 86, 99
Correlations, 18
Cost, food preferences and, 2, 7
Counselors, weight management and, 375–376
Cranberry juice, 84, 90
Crash diets, 366
Cravings, 5, 519
  pregnancy and, 5, 660
C-reactive protein (CRP), 628, 629
Creatine
  athletes and, 581–582
  benefits of, 84
  defined, 581
  phosphate, 555–556
Cretinism, 528, 530
Critical control points (CCPs), 765–766
Critical period of development, 674
Crohn's disease, 524
Cryptosporidium, 753
Cultural influences, food preferences and, 8–10
Currant seed oil, black, 196
Current good manufacturing practices (cGMPs), FDA, 92, 97
Cutting boards, wood versus plastic, 770
Cyclamates, 170
Cystic fibrosis, 239, 418
Cytochromes, 510, 511
Cytoplasm, 270, 271
Cytosol, 270, 271

Daily Values (DVs), 60
Dam, Henrik, 419
Dark adaptation, 394
DASH (Dietary Approaches to Stop Hypertension), 639–641
Deamination, 237, 285
Death, overweight/obesity and premature, 622
Decarboxylation, 432
Dehydration, 475–478
  signs of, 477, 573
Dehydroepiandrosterone (DHEA), 96, 197, 202
Delaney Clause, 81–82
Denaturation, 230
Densitometry, 352, 353
Dental caries
  defined, 173
  fluoride and, 536–537
  infants and, 704
  sugar alcohols and, 170
  sugar and, 173–174
Dental health
  elderly and, 740
  risk factors for dental/oral diseases, 624
Deoxyribonucleic acid. *See* DNA
Depression
  elderly and, 738
  St. John's wort and, 84, 89
Desaturation, 187
Developing world, malnutrition in the
  agriculture and environment, balancing, 797–798
  causes of, 792–795
  FAO conclusions, 791
  food safety and, 794
  inequitable food distribution, 794
  infection and disease, 795
  iodine deficiency disorders and, 799–800
  iron-deficiency anemia and, 800–801
  overweight and obesity and, 802
  political disruptions and natural disasters, 795–797
  protein-energy malnutrition and, 799
  social and economic factors, 793–795
  vitamin A deficiency and, 800
Dexedrine, 376
Dexfenfluramine, 376
Dextrose. *See* Glucose
DHA. *See* Docosahexaenoic acid
DHEA. *See* Dehydroepiandrosterone
Diabetes mellitus
  age and, 652
  cholesterol and, 652
  chromium picolinate and, 84
  defined, 161, 649–650
  diagnosis of, 303, 649–650
  dietary and lifestyle factors for reducing risk of, 653–655
  ephedra and, 84
  ethnicity and, 652
  exchange lists for B-1 to B-11
  fiber and, 174
  heredity and, 652
  hypertension and, 652
  management of, 655–656
  Native Americans and, 651, 652, 654
  niacin and, 440

obesity/overweight and, 303, 360, 361, 622, 623, 648, 652–653
pre-, 651
pregnancy (gestational) and, 650, 651, 686
race and, 651, 652
risk factors for, 624, 652–653
sedentary lifestyle and, 652
statistics, 648
sweet urine and diagnosis of, 303
type 1, 650
type 2, 161, 174, 650–651
vitamin E and, 86
Diabetes Prevention Program, 161
Diabulimia, 612
Diarrhea, 132
antibiotics and, 131
defined, 134
how to reduce symptoms, 135
infants and, 704
rehydration therapy for, 795
sugar alcohols and, 170
Diastolic, 636, 637
Diet(s)
alcohol and, 326
American, 10
Atkins, 368, 369, 373
Beverly Hills, 372
cancer and link with, 644
carbohydrates in the, 161, 164–173, 367
composition, 338–339
crash, 366
DASH, 639–641
dining out, tips for, 218, 635
global warming and, 32
high-protein, low-carbohydrate, 368–369
history, 67
lipids in the, 210–216, 366–367
macrobiotic, 100
proteins in the, 244–247, 256–261, 367
training, 561–562, 572
vegetarian, 99–100, 251–253, 256, 681, 721
very low calorie (VLCD), 375
weight management and, 366–367, 368–369
Diet, Nutrition and the Prevention of Chronic Diseases, 646
Dietary fiber, 174
benefits of, 75
defined, 153
sources of, 75, 152–153, 155
Dietary folate equivalents (DFE), 448
Dietary guidelines
See also Dietary Guidelines for Americans
Canadian, 42–43, 44, 47
Korean, 33
Dietary Guidelines for Americans
alcoholic beverages, 37, 310, 327
carbohydrates, 164, 173
comparing dietary intake data to, 69
defined, 34
dietary supplements and, 85
fats, 36, 210–212
food groups, 43
Food Guide Pyramid and, 44
food safety, 40–41
functional foods and, 78
lipids, 210–212
MyPlate and, 44, 46–48
physical activity, 36
potassium, 37
sodium, 37, 482
using the, 34–42
weight management, 36, 362, 364
Dietary intake data
collecting, 67–69
evaluating, 68
Dietary Reference Intakes (DRIs)
defined, 53
elements of, 53–56
for energy, 348–349
use of, 56–57
Dietary standards
comparing dietary intake data to, 69
defined, 53
history of, 53
role of, 53
use of, 56–57
Dietary Supplement Health and Education Act (DSHEA), 92, 93, 579
Dietary supplements
advertising of, 92–93
amino acids, 246, 251, 580–581
athletes and, 577–580
bioflavonoids, 92
breastfeeding and, 85, 691
calcium, 494
Canadian regulations regarding, 91, 96
carotenoid, 404–405
children and, 85, 714, 717
choosing, 96–98
defined, 74
elderly and, 85, 735–736
FDA and, 90, 91–92, 93, 579
fraudulent products, 98–99
infants and, 85
iron, 584
labels for, 94–95
megadoses of, 86–88, 481
minerals, 83–88, 714, 717, 735–736
moderate use of, 85–86
natural health products, 88–92
pregnancy and, 85, 91, 683
protein, 246, 251, 570
shopping for, 87
vitamins, 83–88, 430, 714, 717, 735–736
weight management and, 85, 377
Digestion
bacterial influences on, 131
of carbohydrates, 155–157
chemical breakdown of food, 111
chemical influences on, 131
defined, 106
gastrointestinal tract, role of, 107–110
hormonal system regulation of, 126–127, 129
how absorption works together with, 112, 114–126
of lipids, 204–205
nervous system regulation of, 126
of phospholipids, 204–205
physical movement and breaking up of food, 110–111
pizza example, 140
of proteins, 237–239
psychological influences on, 130–131
of sterols, 208
of triglycerides, 204–205
Digestive secretions, 119
Diglycerides, 190
Dihydrochalcones (DHCs), 173
Dihydroxyvitamin D3, 407
Dining out, dietary tips for, 218, 635
Dioxins, 759
Dipeptide, 228
Direct additives, 79
Direct calorimetry, 346
Disaccharides, 147, 149–150
Discoloration of food, 488
Discomfort foods, 4–5
Disease
See also under type of
age and, 729
children and chronic, 719, 721
defined, 620
genetics and, 624–626
infection and malnutrition and, 795
nutrition and, 620–623
obesity and, 621–623
physical inactivity and, 622–623
risk factors for, 624
Disordered eating, 587–588, 596
Dispensable amino acids, 227
Disulfide bridge, 230
Diuresis, 570
Diuretics, 600, 601
Diverticulitis, 135
Diverticulosis, 132, 135
risk factors for, 624
DNA (deoxyribonucleic acid), 241, 625–626
Docosahexaenoic acid (DHA), 188, 189, 190, 212, 213
sources of, 194, 195, 196
Double-blind study, 21
Doubly labeled water, 347–348
Dowager's hump, 659, 740
Drugs
adolescents and, 726
animal, 758–759
breastfeeding and, 691, 692

Drugs *(Cont.)*
- elderly and interactions with, 736–738
- fluid balance and, 476
- interactions, 90, 736–738
- over-the-counter, weight management and, 377
- pregnancy and, 673, 684, 685
- prescription, weight management and, 376–377

D-tagatose, 171
Dual energy x-ray absorptiometry (DEXA), 353, 353
Duodenum, 119
Dyslipidemia, 210

Eating behavior
- *See also* Food preferences
- emotional influences, 340, 358, 360
- environmental and social influences, 340
- gastrointestinal sensations, 340
- neurological and hormonal influences, 340–341
- weight management and, 366–368

Eating disorders
- *See also under type of*
- adolescents and, 726
- categories of, 596–597
- causes of, 598–599
- children and, 612–613
- defined, 596
- diagnostic criteria for, 597
- *Diary of an Eating Disorder* excerpt, 605
- dietary supplements and, 85
- elderly and, 738
- female athlete triad, 587–589, 611–612
- history of, 597–598
- infants and, 613
- males and, 610–611
- pregnancy and, 672
- preventing, 613–615
- signs of, 611
- smoking and, 612
- statistics, 613
- vegetarian diets and, 612

Eating Well with Canada's Food Guide, 42, 44
Echinacea, 84, 91
Eclampsia, 686
Edema, 230, 435
Egg(s)
- copper bowls and, 534
- protein denaturation, 230
- whites, beating, 231
- yolk, 201

Eicosanoids, 188–189
Eicosapentaenoic acid (EPA), 188, 189, 212, 213
- sources of, 194, 195, 196

Elderly
- *See also* Age; Osteoporosis
- alcohol and, 318
- Alzheimer's disease, 86, 92, 741
- anorexia of aging, 738
- arthritis, 738–739
- bowel and bladder regulation and, 739–740
- calcium and, 734–735
- carbohydrates and, 733
- community resources for, 742, 743
- dehydration and, 476
- dental health and, 740
- depression and, 738
- dietary supplements and, 85, 735–736
- drug interactions and, 736–738
- energy needs, 731
- fats and, 733
- fiber and, 733
- gout and, 739
- iron and, 512, 735
- magnesium and, 735
- malnutrition and, 786–787
- meal management, 741–742
- minerals and, 733–736
- MyPlate and, 732
- nutritional concerns, 736–741
- nutritional needs, 728, 731–736
- obesity/overweight and, 739
- physical activity and, 552, 738–739
- proteins and, 245, 730, 731–732
- vision and, 740
- vitamin B6 and, 734
- vitamin B12 and, 734
- vitamin D and, 405, 412, 734
- vitamins and, 733–736
- water and, 476, 733
- zinc and, 735

Electrolytes, 468, 469–470
Electronic Benefits Transfer (EBT), 788, 789
Electron transport chain, 278–280, 281, 283, G-3
Elongation, 187
Embryonic stage, 674
Emetics, 600, 601
Emotions
- adolescents and, 723
- eating behavior and, 340, 358, 360, 718
- weight management and, 370–372

Emulsifiers
- defined, 115
- phospholipids as, 200–201

Endocytosis, 114, 115
Endoplasmic reticulum (ER), 271, 290
Endosperm, 165
Endothelial cells, 628
Endothelium. *See* Endothelial cells
Endurance
- aerobic, 558, 559
- training, 557

Enemas, 600, 601
Energy
- adolescents and, 723, 724
- breakdown and release of, 275–285
- carbohydrates and, 157, 275–278, 283, 286–288
- chemical, 268
- children and, 712, 713
- conservation of, 268
- defined, 14
- elderly and, 731
- equilibrium, 336
- extraction of, 268–270
- fat and, 190–191, 192, 281–283
- in foods, calculating, 15–16
- glucose for, 157
- infant requirements, 695
- key players, 272–274
- measures of, 15
- metabolism and, 268–285
- nutrients and, 14–15
- output, 336
- proteins and, 237, 285
- transferring food energy to cellular energy, 268–270
- triglycerides and, 190–191
- yield and interconversions, 290

Energy balance
- defined, 336, 337
- first experiments in, 336
- negative, 336
- positive, 336

Energy expenditure
- components of, 342
- estimating total, 348–349
- infants and, 695
- measurement of, 346–348
- physical activity and, 343, 344, 345
- weather, effect of, 343

Energy intake
- athletes and, 562–563
- defined, 336
- food, regulation of, 337–341

Energy systems
- ATP-CP, 555–556
- lactic acid, 556
- oxygen, 556, 557
- teamwork in, 556–557

Enrich, 59
Enteric nervous system, 126
Enterocytes, 205
Enterohepatic circulation, 116
Environment
- balancing agriculture and, 797–798
- eating behavior and, 340
- food preferences and, 7–8
- obesity/overweight and, 16–17, 357

Environmental Protection Agency (EPA), 760, 764
Enzymes
- co-, 272
- defined, 111
- iron and, 510
- as proteins, 233
- zinc and, 520

EPA. *See* Eicosapentaenoic acid; Environmental Protection Agency
Ephedra (ma huang), 84, 90, 91, 377

Ephedrine, athletes and, 583
Epidemiological studies, 17–18
Epidemiology, 17
Epinephrine, 161
Epiphyses, 722
Epithelial cells, 396
Epithelial tissues, 396
Ergogenic aids, 577–580
Escherichia coli (E. coli), 753, 770
Esophageal cancer, 135
Esophageal sphincter, 117
Esophagitis, 324
Esophagus, 117
Essential fatty acids
  defined, 187
  dietary requirements, 212
  sources of, 213
Essential hypertension, 636, 637
Essential nutrients, 10–11
Ester, 190
Esterification, 190
Estimated Average Requirement (EAR), 54–55
Estimated Energy Requirement (EER), 56
Estrogens, 202
Ethanol, 310, 311
Ethnic differences
  diabetes and, 652
  obesity/overweight and, 357
Ethyl alcohol. *See* Ethanol
European Nicotinamide Diabetes Intervention Trial (ENDIT), 440
Evening primrose seed oil, 196
Exchange Lists
  defined, 48
  diet planning and using, 49
Excretion, 108
  of chromium, 539–540
  of fluoride, 538
  of proteins and nitrogen, 243
  of water, 471–472
  of zinc, 522–523
Exercise. *See* Physical activity; Physical performance
Exercise is Medicine program, 552
Experimental group, 18
Experiments, 18
Extracellular fluid, 235, 470, 474, 481–482
Extreme obesity, 377
Extrusion reflex, 701

Facilitated diffusion, 114, 115
FAD (flavin adenine dinucleotide), 274, 435–436
FAD^+ (flavin adenine dinucleotide oxidized), 272
FADH2 (flavin adenine dinucleotide reduced), 272, 274
Failure to thrive (FTT), 704–705
Farmers' markets, 719
Fasting (starvation), 297–302
Fasting hypoglycemia, 651
Fast-twitch (FT) fibers, 558, 559
Fat(s)
  See also Lipids
  Acceptable Macronutrient Distribution Range for, 244
  athletes and intake of, 567
  cancer and, 218, 645
  carbohydrates from, 291
  commercial processing of, 194–197
  Dietary Guidelines for Americans recommendations, 36, 210–212
  elderly and, 733
  energy and, 190–191, 192, 281–283
  excess of carbohydrates turning into, 291
  heart disease and, 216, 217, 218, 633–634
  how the body makes, 288–290
  infants and, 696
  Nutrition Facts label for finding, 215, 219, 379
  obesity/overweight and, 216
  pregnancy and, 681
  sources of, 210–213
  storage efficiency of, 192
  subcutaneous, 192
  taste and, 183, 193
  use of term, 183
  visceral, 192
"Fat burning," physical activity and, 585
Fat cell development, 356
Fat replacers
  composition of, 213–214
  defined, 213
  do they work, 215, 216
  safety issues, 214–216
Fatty acids
  benefits of, 75
  chain length of, 183–184
  cis, 186
  defined, 183
  eicosanoids, 188–190
  geometric and positional isomers of, 186
  how the body makes, 288–290
  monounsaturated, 184–185, 194, 213
  nonessential versus essential, 187
  omega-3, 186–187, 188, 189–190, 194, 212–213
  omega-6, 186–187, 188, 194, 212–213
  omega-9, 186–187
  polyunsaturated, 184–185, 194, 213
  saturation of, 184–185, 194, 213
  sources of, 75
  trans, 186, 213
Fatty liver, 314, 315, 324, 361
FDA. *See* Food and Drug Administration
Feasting, 296–297
Federal Meat Inspection Act, 772
Federal Trade Commission (FTC), 92–93, 763
Feeding America, 790
Female athlete triad
  amenorrhea, 588
  defined, 587, 611–612
  disordered eating, 587–588
  premature osteoporosis, 588
  preventing, 588–589
Fenfluramine, 376
Fermentation, 310, 311–312
Ferric iron (Fe^{3+}), 510, 511
Ferritin, 511
Ferrous iron (Fe^{2+}), 510, 511
Fetal alcohol syndrome, 325, 684
Fetal growth, stages of, 673–675
Fetal stage, 674–675
Feverfew, 84, 90
Fiber
  benefits of, 135
  cancer and, 75, 136
  cardiovascular disease and, 174, 631, 633
  children and, 719, 722
  content in foods, 133
  diabetes and, 174
  dietary, 75, 153–154, 174
  foods rich in, 155
  functional, 153, 154
  gastrointestinal disorders and, 175
  heart disease and, 135, 174
  increasing your intake of, 165–167
  negative effects of excess, 175–176
  Nutrition Facts label for finding, 136–137
  obesity and, 174
  total, 153
Fibrin, 490
Filtered water, 478–479
Finnish Diabetes Prevention Study, 161
Fish
  heart disease and, 188, 195, 633
  muscle tissue of, 561
  omega-3 fatty acids and, 188, 195
  pregnancy and avoiding, 683
  puffer, 8
  seafood safety issues, 754–755, 760
Fitness. *See* Physical fitness
Flatulence, 138, 175
Flatus, 138
Flavin adenine dinucleotide. *See* FAD
Flavin adenine dinucleotide reduced. *See* FADH2
Flavin mononucleotide (FMN), 435–436
Flavonoids, 75
Flavor, 3
Flaxseed oil, 196
Fletcherism (dietary craze), 369
Fluid balance, proteins and, 235
Fluid intake, recommended amounts
  athletes and, 572–576
  breastfeeding and, 690
Fluoride
  absorption and excretion of, 538
  children and, 539
  deficiency, 539
  dietary recommendations for, 538
  functions of, 537–538
  history of, 536–537

Fluoride *(Cont.)*
infants and, 539, 697
sources of, 538
toxicity, 539
Fluorosis, 538, 539
Folate, 14
anemia and, 450–451
cancer and, 449, 451
deficiency, 449–450
dietary recommendations for, 448
functions of, 447–448
heart disease and, 86, 444–445, 450
megadoses of, 86
neural tube defects and, 448, 449, 451, 672
Nutrition Facts label for finding, 462, 706
pregnancy and, 447–448, 449, 672–673, 706
sources of, 448–449
toxicity, 451
Food(s)
additives, 78, 79–82
allergies, 716
behavior and children, 718
composition tables, A-0 to A-85
cravings, 5, 660, 685–686
-drug interactions, 736–738
eating habits and children, 717
gleaning, 785
insecure households, 718
linking nutrients, health, and, 30–34
records, 68
recovery, 785
regulation of, 337–341
Food, Drug, and Cosmetic Act (1938), 80, 81, 93, 762–763
Food Allergy & Anaphylaxis Network, 716
Food and Agriculture Organization (FAO), 791
Food and Drug Administration (FDA)
anti-obesity drugs and, 376, 377
aspartame and, 170, 171
creatine and, 582
current good manufacturing practices (cGMPs), 92, 97
defined, 57
dietary supplements and, 90, 91–92, 93, 377, 579, 583
fat replacers and, 214–215
food additives and, 78, 79–82, 771
food irradiation and, 771
food labels and, 57, 60–62
food safety and, 763
fraudulent products and, 98–99
functional foods and, 78, 79–82
genetically modified foods and, 773, 777–779
health claims and, 62–63
olestra and, 214–215
pesticides and, 756–757
saccharin and, 170
sweeteners and, 170, 171
Food and Nutrition Board, 53
Food and Nutrition Science Alliance (FANSA), 24
Foodborne illness
defined, 750
risk factors for, 767–768
symptoms of, 751
Food Code, 766
Food frequency questionnaire (FFQ), 68
Food groups
defined, 39–40
Dietary Guidelines for Americans recommendations, 36
plans, history of, 40
Food Guide Pyramid, 40
Food insecure households, 718
Food insecurity
See also Malnutrition
defined, 784
Food labels
See also Nutrition Facts panel
Daily Values, 60
defined, 57
health claims, 62–63
ingredients and other basic information, 57–58
nutrient content claims, 60–62
Nutrition Facts panel, 58–59
structure/function claims, 63
using them to make healthful food choices, 63–64
Food Marketing Institute, 58
Food measurement conversions, H-5
Food poisoning. *See* Foodborne illness
Food preferences
See also Eating behavior
age and, 2
cognitive influences, 3–6
cultural influences, 8–10
environmental influences, 7–8
factors that affect, 3
sensory influences, 3, 339
Food processing, sodium and potassium content and, 486
Food Quality Protection Act (1996), 757
Food Research and Action Center (FRAC), 788, 789
Food safety
additives and, 79–82
airline drinking water and, 476
bioterrorism, 764–765
consumer's role in, 766–767
cutting boards, wood versus plastic, 770
Dietary Guidelines for Americans recommendations, 41, 763
foodborne illness, 767–768
food supply versus, 794
genetically modified foods, 772–779
government agencies, 762–766
harmful substances in foods, 750–762
how to keep food safe, 762–767
malnutrition in the developing world and, 794
plastic water bottles, 699
practices, 768–769
preparation, 768–769
preservation, 770–772
seafood, 754–755, 760
technology, 769–770
Food Safety and Inspection Service (FSIS), 763
Food security, 784
Food Security Supplement Survey
defined, 785–786
sample questions from, 787
Food Stamp Program. *See* Supplemental Nutrition Assistance Program (SNAP)
Food supply, food safety versus, 794
Fortify, 59
Fossil fuel, biofuel versus, 284
Fraudulent products, 98–99
Free radicals
defined, 77
selenium and, 527, 528
vitamin E and, 414, 416
French paradox, 330
Fructose, 148
Fruit juices/drinks, infants and, 705
Fruits
cancer and, 646–647
cardiovascular disease and, 631
hypertension and, 639, 640
snacks, 743
versus vegetables, naming of, 430
Full-term baby, 693
Functional dyspepsia, 132, 139
Functional fiber, 153, 154
Functional foods
additives in, 78, 79–82
defined, 74
examples of, 75–76
foods enhanced with, 78
health claims for, 82–83
phytochemicals and, 74, 76–78
regulatory issues for, 78, 79–82
strategies for using, 83
structure/function claims for, 83

Galactose, 148
Galen, 30
Gallbladder
defined, 116
function of, 116
obesity/overweight and disease of, 360, 361
Galvanized, 520
Gamma-linolenic acid (GLA), 188, 196
Garlic, 84, 90
Gas, 132, 138
Gastric banding and bypass, 377–378
Gastric inhibitory peptide (GIP), 127
Gastric juice, 118
Gastric lipase, 118, 119
Gastrin, 118, 119, 127
Gastritis, 324, 330
Gastroenteritis, 753, 754

Gastroesophageal reflux, 704
Gastroesophageal reflux disease (GERD), 132, 135–136
Gastrointestinal disorders
fiber and, 175
food safety and, 751, 753, 754
pregnancy and, 685
Gastrointestinal (GI) tract, E-0 to E-2
age and, 730–731
alcohol consumption and effects on, 324
average daily fluids in, 112
chemical breakdown of food, 111
defined, 108
description of, 107–110
disorders, 131–140
eating behavior influenced by sensations from, 340
fiber and, 175
functions of, 108
hormonal system regulation of, 126–127, 129
iron absorption and, 512
nervous system regulation of, 126
physical movement and breaking up of food, 110–111
reabsorption of water in, 476
regulation of activity in, 126–127, 129
Gelatin, nails and, 98
Gender differences
alcohol consumption and, 318–319
body composition and, 318, 354, 355
calcium intake and, 489, 492, 495–496
fat storage and, 192
longevity and, 728
muscle and, 559
obesity and, 356–357
physical activity and, 562
resting metabolic rate and, 342–343
vitamin supplements and, 430
Gene expression, 626
Generally Recognized as Safe (GRAS), 80
Genes
defined, 624
DNA and, 625–626
unique combination of, 626
zinc and the regulation of, 521
Genetically modified (GM) foods
benefits of, 776, 778
defined, 772
extent of the shift to 773, 776
plant genetics, short course in, 772–773
regulation of, 777–779
risks of, 777
Genetic code, 625
Genetic engineering
See also Genetically modified (GM) foods
defined, 773
vaccines and, 797
Genetics
disease and, 624–626
food preferences and, 3
obesity and, 16, 356
Genome, 773
Geophagia, 520
Germ, 165
Gestational diabetes, 650, 651, 686
Ghrelin, 341
Giardia lamblia, 753
Ginger, 90
Ginkgo biloba, 84, 89, 90, 91
Ginseng
adverse effects of, 91
benefits of, 84
Glossitis, 436
Glucagon, 160–161
Glucocorticoids, 202
Glucogenic, 288
Gluconeogenesis, 288, 289
Glucosamine, 84
Glucose
defined, 148
end products of catabolism, 280
for energy, 157
how the body makes, 286–288
metabolism, 275–281
normal use of, 157–160
proteins and, 237
regulating blood glucose levels, 160–161
storing, as glycogen, 158, 288
structure of, 148
tolerance test, 649
Glutamate, 3, 227
Glutamine, athletes and, 581
Glutathione, 414
Glutathione peroxidase, 436
Glycemic index, 564
debate over usefulness of, 162–163
defined, 161
Glycemic index *(Cont)*
food values, list of, 162
substitutions, 163
Glycerol, 190, 311
Glycocidic bonds. *See* Alpha (α) bonds; Beta (β) bonds
Glycogen
defined, 152
depletion, 557
proteins and, 158
starch and, 152
storing glucose as, 158, 288
structure of, 152–153
Glycogenesis, 288
Glycogen loading. *See* Carbohydrate loading
Glycogenolysis, 288
Glycolysis, 275, 276, 281, G-1
Glycyrrhizin, 172–173
Goblet cells, 396
Going Green
biofuel versus fossil fuel, 284
bioremediation, 234
chocolate and climate change, 792
composting, 113
depletion of water resources and effects on salmon, 477
diet and global warming, 32
examples of, 7
farmers' markets, 719
fish, benefits of, 195
iron and global warming, 519
physical activity at high altitudes, 562
pollution and mercury poisoning, 760
resisting oxidative stress, 405
safety of plastic water bottles, 699
salads, value of, 365
skin color and vitamin D, 452
smokers, litter from, 645
whole grains, benefits of, 166
Goiter, 530, 531, 532
Goitrogens, 532
Golgi apparatus, 271
Gout
defined, 261
elderly and, 739
obesity/overweight and, 364
proteins and, 260, 261
Grapes, heart disease and, 77
Gravity, bone health and, 660
Green revolution. *See* Going Green
Ground water, 479
Growth
charts, 694–695, I-0 to I-23
plates, 722
vitamin A and, 391, 392
zinc and, 520
GTP (guanosine triphosphate), 273
Guarana, 90
Gum chewing, following surgery, 128
Gums, 154
Gustatory cells, 106
Gynoid obesity, 354, 355

Habits, eating, 4
Hair analysis, 509
Hangover, 316, 317–318
Hawthorn, 90
Hazard Analysis Critical Control Point (HACCP), 765–766
Headache(s)
ice cream, 4
migraine, 84
Head circumference, 694, 695
Health
carbohydrates and, 173–176
laws of, 30
linking nutrients, foods, and, 30–34
lipids and, 216, 218
vegetarian diets and, 253
Health beliefs, nutrition and, 6

Health Canada, 42, 53, 90, 552
  Health Products and Food Branch, 54
  Natural Health Products Directorate, 96
Health claims
  defined, 62
  FDA-approved list of, 62–63
  functional foods and, 82
  qualified, 63
Health Management Resources (HMR), 375
Health on the Net Foundation, 24
Healthy People 2010, 620–621
Heart
  hardiness of, 626, 731
  major arteries of, 627
  metabolic profile of, 299
Heartburn, 132, 135–136
Heart disease
  See also under type of
  alcohol and, 329–330
  beta-carotene and, 84
  cholesterol and, 202, 216
  coenzyme Q10 and, 84
  ephedra and, 84
  fats and, 216, 217, 218, 633–634
  fiber and, 135, 174, 631, 633
  fish and, 188, 195, 633
  folate and, 444–445, 450
  grapes and, 77
  obesity/overweight and, 360, 361, 622, 623
  omega-3 fatty acids and, 188
  phytochemicals and, 74, 77
  proteins and, 261
  red wine and, 77, 329–330
  soy and, 74, 76, 636
  sugar and, 172, 634
  vitamin B and, 635–636
  vitamin B6 and, 444–445
  vitamin B12 and, 444–445
  vitamin C and, 457, 459
  vitamin E and, 86, 416, 418
  whole grains and, 60, 164
Heat capacity, 468, 469
Height
  for adolescents, 722
  growth charts, 694–695, I-0 to I-2
  nutrition assessment and, 65–66
Helicobacter pylori, 139
Hematocrit, 518
Heme, 510, 511
Heme iron, 512
Hemicelluloses, 154
Hemochromatosis
  defined, 459
  hereditary, 519
Hemodialysis, 539
Hemoglobin
  defined, 229
  zinc and, 520
Hemolysis, 418
Hemosiderin, 514
Hepatitis A, 752, 754
Herbal therapy, 89
Herbs
  adverse effects of, 91
  benefits of, 89, 90
  culinary, 89
  drug interactions, 90
  helpful versus harmful, 89–92
Heredity
  diabetes and, 652
  hemochromatosis, 519
  hypertension and, 638
  obesity and, 16, 356
High-density lipoproteins (HDL), 210
Hippocrates, 82, 395, 614
Hispanics
  diabetes and, 651, 652
  obesity/overweight and, 357
HIV (human immunodeficiency virus)
  breastfeeding and, 691, 692, 799
  pregnancy and, 686–687
HMB (hydroxymethylbutyrate), 581
Homeless people, malnutrition and, 787, 788
Homocysteine, 444–445
Honey, infants and, 168
Hormones
  defined, 13
  eating behavior influenced by, 340–341
  formation of, 233–234
  gastrointestinal activity regulation by, 126–127, 129
  of metabolism, 295–296
  zinc and, 521
Horse chestnut, 90
Human Genome Project. 624
Human studies, 18–21
Hunger, 337, 784
  See also Malnutrition
Husk, 165
Hydration, 574–575
Hydrochloric acid, 118
Hydrogenation, 186, 196–197
Hydrogen bonds, 468
Hydrogen ions, 274
Hydrolysis, 111, 195
Hydrophilic, 182
Hydrophilic amino acids, 229–230
Hydrophobic, 182
Hydrophobic amino acids, 230
Hydrostatic weighting. *See* Underwater weighing
Hydroxyapatite, 489
Hyperactivity, 718
Hypercalcemia, 413, 495
Hypercellular obesity, 356, 357
Hypercholesterolemia, 210, 628
Hyperglycemia, 163, 649
Hyperkalemia, 487
Hyperkeratosis, 399
Hyperlipidemia, 210
Hypermagnesemia, 500–501
Hypernatremia, 483
Hyperparathyroidism, 498
Hyperphosphatemia, 498
Hyperplastic obesity (hyperplasia), 356, 357
Hypertension
  age and, 638
  alcohol and, 638
  blood pressure defined, 637
  DASH diet and, 639–641
  defined, 636–637
  diabetes and, 652
  dietary and lifestyle factors for reducing risk of, 638–642
  ephedra and, 84
  essential, 636, 637
  fruits and vegetables and, 639, 640
  heredity and, 638
  obesity/overweight and, 360, 361, 638
  physical activity and, 484, 638, 639
  potassium and, 485, 641, 642
  pregnancy and, 686
  race and, 638
  renin and, 637–638
  risk factors for, 624, 638
  secondary, 636, 637
  sodium and, 483–485, 639
  stress and, 638
Hyperthermia, 586–587
Hypertriglyceridemia, 210
Hypertrophic obesity, 356, 357
Hypervitaminosis, 735
Hypervolemia, 483
Hypocalcemia, 495
Hypochloremia, 488–489
Hypoglycemia, 651
Hypogonadism, 520
Hypokalemia, 487
Hypomagnesemia, 500
Hyponatremia, 483
Hypophosphatemia, 498
Hypothalamus, 340
Hypotheses, 17
Hypothyroidism, 527–528

Ice cream headache, 4
Ileocecal valve, 124
Ileum, 119
Immune response, 235
Immune system
  age and, 730
  carotenoids and, 402
  iron and, 510
  proteins and, 234–235
  vitamin A and, 396, 400
  vitamin C and, 457, 459
  zinc and, 520
Inborn errors of metabolism, 460

Incomplete (low-quality) proteins, 247
Indirect additives, 79
Indirect calorimetry, 346–347
Indispensable amino acids, 226
Infancy, 693
Infant formula
  feeding technique, 700
  how much to feed, 700
  other types of, 698
  preparation of, 699–700
  soy-based, 698
  standard, 698
Infantile anorexia, 613
Infants
  See also Breastfeeding
  anemia and, 704
  carbohydrates and, 696
  colic, 703
  copper and, 534–535
  cow's milk inappropriate for, 701, 704
  dehydration and, 476
  dental caries and, 704
  diarrhea and, 704
  dietary supplements and, 85
  eating disorders and, 613
  energy needs, 695
  fats and, 696
  feeding amounts, how to determine, 700, J-0 to J-3
  feeding problems, 703–705
  feeding technique, 700, 703
  fetal alcohol syndrome, 325, 684
  fluoride and, 697
  food safety and, 756–757, 760, 761, 763
  formula for feeding, 698–700
  fruit juices/drinks and, 705
  growth and development, 693–695
  honey and, 168
  iron and, 516, 697, 701, 704
  malnutrition and, 257–258
  mortality rates, world, 793
  nutritional needs, 695–697
  proteins and, 245, 695
  solid foods, introducing, 700–703
  Start Healthy Feeding Guidelines for Infants and Toddlers, 701–703
  vitamin A and, 398–399
  vitamin B12 and, 697
  vitamin D and, 409, 696
  vitamin E and, 418
  vitamin K and, 423, 424, 697
  vitamins and minerals and, 696–697
  water and, 476, 696
Infection, disease and malnutrition and, 795
Inflammation, atherosclerosis and, 629
Information resources, K-0 toKL-8
Ingredients, listing of on food labels, 58–59
Inorganic substances, 12
Inositol, 460–461
Insensible water loss, 472
Insomnia, 90
Institute of Food Technologists (IFT), 24
Insulin, 160
Insulin resistance, 650
Integrated pest management (IPM), 757
Intermediate-density lipoproteins (IDL), 209
International units (IU), 397
Internet, evaluating information on the, 24
Interstitial fluid, 235
Intracellular fluid, 235, 468, 470, 481, 482, 485
Intravascular fluid, 235
Intrinsic factor, 118, 119
Inuits, 452, 633, 759
Iodide, 532
Iodine
  absorption and metabolism of, 531
  deficiency, 528, 532
  dietary recommendations for, 531
  functions of, 531
  history of, 530
  sources of, 531–532
  toxicity, 532
Iodine deficiency disorders (IDD), 799–800
Iodopsin, 395
Iron
  absorption of, 457, 511–514
  athletes and, 571
  cast-iron pots and pans to avoid deficiency, 516
  children and, 516, 518–519, 713
  deficiency, 5, 516–518, 697, 800–801
  dietary recommendations for, 515–516
  elderly and, 512, 735
  enzymes and, 510
  functions of, 510–511
  global warming and, 519
  infants and, 516, 697, 701, 704
  megadoses of, 88
  menstruation and, 85, 514, 519
  Nutrition Facts label for finding, 706
  overload, 519
  pregnancy and, 512, 515–516, 679, 681
  regulation of, in the body, 511–515
  sources of, 516, 517
  supplements, 584
  toxicity, 518–519
  transport and storage of, 514
  vitamin C and absorption of, 457
Irradiation
  defined, 770–771
  FDA and, 771
Irritable bowel syndrome (IBS), 132, 136–137
Isoflavones, 74, 76
Isolated people, malnutrition and, 786
Isopropanol, 311
Isothiocyanates, 75
Isotope dilution, 352–353
Isotopes, 347
Japan
  functional foods in, 74
  puffer fish consumption in, 8
Jejunum, 119
Jell-o, nails and, 98
Journal of the Academy of Nutrition and Dietetics, 22
"Junk science," 24

Kava, 84, 90, 91
Keratin, 230, 231, 399
Keshan disease, 527, 529, 530, 801
Ketoacidosis, 292–293
Ketogenesis, 292
Ketogenic, 288
Ketone bodies
  defined, 159
  how the body makes, 291–293
Ketones, 291
Ketosis, 158–160
Kidneys
  metabolic profile of, 299
  proteins and function of, 258–259
  water and function of, 468–469
Kilocalories (kcal), 15
Korean Dietary Guidelines, 33
Krebs cycle. *See* Citric acid cycle
Kwashiorkor, 257–258

Labels
  See also Food labels; Nutrition Facts panel
  for dietary supplements, 94–95
Lactate, 288
  athletes and, 560–561
  defined, 276–277
Lactation
  See also Breastfeeding
  consultants, 697–698
  defined, 676
Lacteal, 124
Lactic acid energy system, 556
Lactose
  deficiency, 132
  defined, 149, 150
  intolerance, 122–123
Lanugo, 192
Large intestine
  absorption in, 125–126
  defined, 124
  digestion in, 124–125
Lavoisier, Antoine, 346
Laxatives, 600, 601
Lead toxicity, 721
Lean body mass, 342
Lecithin
  defined, 200
  as emulsifiers, 200–201
  oil or granules, 197
Legumes
  cancer and, 647

Legumes *(Cont.)*
defined, 13
Lemon, 90
Lentils, 254
Leptin, 234, 341, 376–377
Let-down reflex, 689
Leukemia, 642
Levulose. *See* Fructose
Licorice, 90, 91, 172–173
Lifestyle
food preferences and, 8
weight management and, 364–365
Lignins, 154
Lima beans, 9
Limiting amino acid, 249, 250
Lind, James, 18–19, 395, 456
Linear growth, 489
Lingual lipase, 117
Linoleic acid
alpha-, 187, 189, 194
conjugated, 186, 197
defined, 188
gamma-, 188, 196
Lipid peroxidation, 414
Lipids
absorption of, 205–208
in the body, 208–210
defined, 13, 182–183
in the diet, 210–216, 366–367
digestion of, 204–205, 208
fatty acids, 183–190, 212
health and, 216, 218
phospholipids, 198–201, 204–207
sources of, 13
sterols, 201–203, 208
transport, 200
triglycerides, 190–197, 204–207
Lipogenesis, 290
Lipoic acid, 461
Lipophilic, 182
Lipophobic, 182
Lipoprotein a [Lp(a)], 628
Lipoprotein lipase, 208
Lipoproteins
defined, 207
high-density (HDL), 210
intermediate-density (IDL), 209
low-density (LDL), 209–210
very low density (VLDL), 209
Liposuction, 378
Listeria monocytogenes, 752, 767, 772
Liver
alcohol consumption and effects on, 314, 315, 324–325, 330
cancer, 324, 330
defined, 116
fatty, 314, 315, 324, 361
metabolic profile of, 299
milk thistle and disease of the, 89
role of, 116
toxicity of polar bear, 400
Longevity, 728
world infant mortality rates, 793
Longitudinal muscle, 108
Low-birth-weight infant, 672
Low-density lipoproteins (LDL), 209–210
Lumen, 112
Lung cancer, 78, 402
Lutein, 75, 77
Lycopene, 74, 75, 193, 401, 402, 403, 404
Lymph, 124
Lymphatic system, 129, 130
Lymph nodes, 643
Lymphoma, 642
Lysosome, 271

Macrobiotic diet, 100
Macrocytes, 451
Macrominerals
See also Major minerals
defined, 14
Macronutrients
alcohol and, 327
defined, 11
pregnancy and, 680–682
Macular degeneration, 86, 416, 740
Mad cow disease. *See* Bovine spongiform encephalopathy (BSE)
Magnesium
deficiency, 500–510
dietary recommendations for, 499
elderly and, 735
functions of, 499
sources of, 499–500
toxicity, 500–501
Magnetic resonance imaging (MRI), 354, 355
Ma huang (ephedra), 84, 90, 91, 377
Major minerals
bioavailability of, 481
calcium, 489–496, 501
chloride, 487–489
defined, 480
magnesium, 499–501
phosphorus, 496–498
potassium, 485–487
sodium, 481–485
sulfur, 502
water, 468–480
Malabsorption syndromes, 86
Males, eating disorders and, 610–611
Malignant, 642
Malnutrition
agriculture and environment, balancing, 797–798
AIDS and, 795, 796
alcoholics and, 325–328
children and, 257–258, 787–788
defined, 784
in the developing world, 791–802
elderly and, 786–787
homeless people and, 787, 788
inequitable food distribution and, 785
infants and, 257–258
infection and disease and, 795
iodine deficiency disorders and, 799–800
iron-deficiency anemia and, 800–801
isolated people and, 786
overweight and obesity and, 802
political disruptions and natural disasters and, 795–797
prevalence of, 785–786
programs that address, 789–790
protein-energy, 257–258, 799
in the United States, 784–791
vitamin A deficiency and, 800
working poor and, 786–788
Maltose, 149, 150
Mammograms, breast cancer and, 647
Manganese
absorption, use, and homeostasis of, 536
deficiency, 536
dietary recommendations for, 536
functions of, 535
sources of, 536, 537
toxicity, 536
Marasmus, 257, 258
Margarine
butter versus, 198–199
cholesterol-lowering, 199
Mayonnaise, 99
Meal replacements, 375
Meals on Wheels, 741
Meat
analogues, 255
consumption, past versus present, 248
softening tough, 239
Media, use of research by, 22–23
Medications. *See* Drugs
Medium-chain triglycerides (MCTs), 196–197, 205
MedWatch, 98–99
Megadoses
in conventional medical management, 86
defined, 85
drawbacks of, 88
effects of, 481
moderate supplementation, 85–86
in orthomolecular nutrition, 86–88
Megaloblastic anemia, 450–451
Megaloblasts, 450–451
Melanocytes, 642
Melanoma, 642
Melatonin, 84
Menadione, 419
Menaquinones, 419
Menarche, 722
Menkes' syndrome, 533, 535
Menopause, 735, 736, 742
Menstruation

health affected by, 674
iron and, 85, 514, 519
Mental illness, dietary supplements and, 86
Mercury, 754–755, 759–760
Meridia, 376
Messenger RNA (mRNA), 241
Metabolic alkalosis, 488
Metabolic fitness, 364
Metabolic pathway
defined, 270
major, G0 to G4
Metabolic syndrome, 656–657
Metabolism
alcohol, 314–319
biosynthesis and storage, 285–294
carbohydrate, 444
cells, role of, 270–272
cellular, 490
copper, 533
defined, 268, 269, 270
energy and, 268–285
hormones of, 295–296
of important body parts, 298–299
iodine, 531
molybdenum, 541
physical activity and, 303, 304
protein, 444
regulation of, 294–296
special states of, 296–303
water and, 469
zinc and, 520
Metabolites, 269
Metalloproteins, 520
Metallothionein, 522–523
Metastasis, 642
Methanol, 310, 311
Methyl alcohol. *See* Methanol
Methylmercury, 759–760
Micelles, 204
Microcytic hypochromic anemia, 444, 445, 518
Microminerals. *See* Trace minerals
Micronutrients
defined, 11
pregnancy and, 682
Microsomal ethanol-oxidizing system (MEOS), 315
Microvilli, 124
Migraine headaches, 84
Milk, cow
infants, inappropriate for, 701, 704
Nutrition Facts label for, 424
vitamin A in, 424
vitamin D in, 409–410
vitamin K in, 424
Milk, human. *See* Breast milk
Milk, soy, 255
Milk sugar. *See* Lactose
Milk thistle, 84, 89
Mineralization, 537
Mineralocorticoids, 202
Minerals
See also Major minerals; Trace minerals
adolescents and, 723–724
alcohol and deficiencies of, 327
amount in the body, 480
athletes and, 570–572
breastfeeding and, 690
children and, 712–717
defined, 14
dietary supplements, 83–88, 430, 714, 717, 735–736
elderly and, 733–736
infants and, 696–697
macro-, 14
micro-, 14
proteins and loss of, 259
sources of, 14
trace, 14
ultratrace, 542–544
Mineral water, 479
Mint, 90
Mitochondria (mitochondrion), 270, 271
Mitochondrial membrane, 279
Mn-superoxide dismutase, 535
Mobility, age and, 729
Moderation, in eating, 33
Molybdenum
absorption, use, and metabolism of, 541–542
deficiency, 542
dietary recommendations for, 542
sources of, 542
toxicity, 542
Monoglycerides, 190
Monolaurin capsules, 197
Monosaccharides, 147–149
Monosodium glutamate (MSG), 3, 486
Monounsaturated fatty acid
defined, 184–185
sources of, 194, 213
Morbid obesity. *See* Extreme obesity
Morning sickness, 672, 684, 685
Motor proteins, 230, 231
Mouth, digestion and, 117
Mucilages, 154
Mucosa, 108
Mucous membranes, vitamin A and, 396
Mucus, 118
Mulder, Gerardus, 226
Multilevel marketing, 97
Multiple sclerosis, 407, 412, 461
Muscle(s)
athletes and, 559–560
contraction, calcium and, 490
energy systems, physical performance, and, 555–558
fibers, 558, 559
gender differences and, 559
metabolic profile of, 298
skeletal, 558, 559
soreness, 584, 588
structure of, 559
Mushrooms, poisonous, 760
Mutation, 625
Myelinization, 511
Myelin sheath, 452, 453
Myoglobin, 510, 511
MyPlate
basic concepts, 44
children and, 714, 715
comparing dietary intake data to, 69
defined, 44
development of, 44
diet planning, 46–48
elderly and, 732
food intake patterns, C-0 to C-1
foods, serving sizes, and tips, 47, 50–51
portion sizes, 46–48
proportionality and, 21

NAD^+ (nicotinamide adenine dinucleotide oxidized), 272, 274
NADH (nicotinamide adenine dinucleotide reduced), 272, 274
$NADP^+$ (nicotinamide adenine dinucloetide phosphate oxidized, 272
NADPH (nicotinamide adenine dinucleotide phosphate reduced), 272, 274
Nails
gelatin/jell-o and, 98
nutrition and, 65
National Academy of Sciences, 2002 dietary report, 211
National Center for Complementary and Alternative Medicine (NCCAM), 89, 90
National Cholesterol Education Program (NCEP), 210
tips for healthful eating out, 218, 635
National Collegiate Athletic Association (NCAA), 583
National Health and Nutrition Examination Survey (NHANES), 16, 63
National High Blood Pressure Education Program (NHBPEP), 638–639
National Institutes of Health (NIH), 210, 354, 552
National Nutritional Monitoring and Related Research Act (1990), 31
National Organic Program (NOP), 757
National School Lunch Program, 718, 788, 789–790
Native Americans
diabetes and, 651, 652, 654
lactose intolerance in, 122–123
obesity/overweight and, 357
Natural disasters, malnutrition and, 796–797
Natural toxins, 759–761
NCAA. *See* National Collegiate Athletic Association
Near-infrared interactance, 354, 355
Negative energy balance, 336
Negative nitrogen balance, 243
Negative self-talk, 370
Neonate, 696, 697

Neophobia, 2
Neotame, 171
Nerve function, calcium and, 490
Nervous system
  alcohol consumption and effects on, 319–324, 330
  regulation of gastrointestinal activity by, 126
Net protein utilization (NPU), 249, 250
Neural tube defect (NTD)
  defined, 451
  folate and, 448, 449, 451, 672
Neurological influences, eating behavior and, 340–341
Neuropeptide Y (NPY), 341
Neurotransmitters
  defined, 243
  vitamin B6 and synthesis of, 444
Niacin (vitamin B3), 14
  cholesterol and, 395, 440
  deficiency, 440
  diabetes and, 440
  dietary recommendations for, 438
  functions of, 438
  history of, 437–438
  megadoses of, 86
  sources of, 438–439
  toxicity and medicinal uses of, 440
Niacin equivalents (NE), 438, 439
Nickel, 543–544
Nicotinamide adenine dinucleotide (oxidized). *See* NAD^+
Nicotinamide adenine dinucleotide (reduced). *See* NADH
Nicotinamide adenine dinucleotide phosphate (oxidized). *See* $NADP^+$
Nicotinamide adenine dinucleotide phosphate (reduced). *See* NADPH
Night blindness, 394, 399, 521
Night-eating syndrome (NES), 609–610
Nitrites, 485
Nitrogen
  balance, 243
  equilibrium, 243
  excretion, 243
Nonessential fatty acids, 187
Nonexercise activity thermogenesis (NEAT), 343, 345, 346
Nonheme iron, 512
Nonnutritive sweeteners, 170–171
Nucleic acids
  defined, 86
  zinc and the metabolism of, 520
Nucleotides. 625
Nucleus, 270, 271
NutraSweet, 170–171
Nutrients
  alcohol and, 311, 312, 331
  carbohydrates, 13
  circulation of, 129–130
  classes of, 11
  conditional, 460–461
  content claims, 57–58, 59
  defined, 10, 11–12
  density, 31–33
  Dietary Guidelines for Americans recommendations, 35–37
  energy and, 14–15
  essential, 10–11
  functions of, 11, 12
  linking foods, health, and, 30–34
  lipids, 13
  minerals, 14
  proteins, 13
  vitamins, 13–14
  water, 14
Nutrigenomics, 18, 19
Nutrition
  adolescents and, 723–724
  age and, 728
  applying scientific process to, 17–21
  before conception, 670–673
  breastfeeding and, 689–690
  children and, 712–717
  defined, 2
  disease and, 620–623
  elderly and, 728, 731–736
  health beliefs and, 6
  how much do doctors and dentists know about, 31
  infants and, 695–697
  physical performance and, 552–555, 561–562
  pregnancy and, 670–673, 678–682
  in school cafeterias, 36
Nutrition and Physical Activity Guidelines for Cancer Prevention, 644–646
Nutrition assessment
  defined, 64
  of individuals, 65
  methods, 65–69
  outcomes of, 69
  of populations, 65
  purpose of, 64
  status, 64
Nutrition Facts panel
  calcium, finding amount of, 501
  carbohydrate, finding amount of, 175
  description of, 58–59
  fat, finding amount of, 215, 219, 379
  fiber, finding amount of, 136–137
  folate, finding amount of, 462, 706
  fruit snacks and, 743
  iron, finding amount of, 706
  protein, finding amount of, 262
  sodium, finding amount of, 661
  sports drinks and, 589
  trace minerals, finding amount of, 545
  vitamins, finding amount of, 424, 462
Nutrition Labeling and Education Act (NLEA), 57, 60
Nutrition Recommendations for Canadians, 42
Nutritive sweeteners, 168

Obesity
  See also Overweight; Weight management
  adolescents and, 623, 720, 726
  age and, 356, 728
  android, 354, 355
  breathing problems and, 622
  cancer and, 360, 361, 622, 644
  children and, 363, 623, 717, 718–719, 720
  death, increased risk of premature, 622
  defined, 350, 353
  diabetes and, 161, 303, 360, 361, 622, 623, 648, 652–653
  disease and, 621–623
  drugs for, 376–377
  environment and, 16–17, 357
  ethnic differences, 357
  extreme/morbid, 377
  factors contributing to, 355–360, 363
  fats and, 216
  fiber and, 174
  gallbladder disease and, 360, 361, 623
  gender differences and, 354–355, 356–357
  genetics and heredity and, 16, 356
  gynoid, 354, 355
  health risks of, 360–362, 622–623
  heart disease and, 360, 361, 622, 623
  hypercellular, 356, 357
  hyperplastic, 356, 357
  hypertension and, 360, 361, 638
  hypertrophic, 356, 357
  malnutrition and, 802
  physical activity and, 357–358
  portion sizes and, 52
  pregnancy and, 622–623, 671–672
  prevalence of, 16–17, 48, 355, 363
  proteins and, 259
  psychological factors, 358, 360
  racial differences, 357
  reproductive complications and, 622–623
  risk factors for, 364, 624
  social influences and, 357, 358
  socioeconomic status and, 357
  stroke and, 360, 361
  sugar and, 172
  surgery and, 377–378
  U.S. state trends, 359
Obsessive-compulsive disorder, 598, 599
Office of Dietary Supplements (ODS), 92
Oils. *See* Lipids
Older Americans Act Nutrition Program, 741–742
Olestra, 214–216
Olfactory cells, 106
Oligopeptide, 229
Oligosaccharides, 150–151
Omega-3 fatty acid
  alpha-linolenic acid, 189–190

amounts of, balancing, 212–213
defined, 186–187
sources of, 188, 194, 195, 213
Omega-6 fatty acid
amounts of, balancing, 212–213
defined, 186–187
linoleic acid, 188
sources of, 194, 213
Omega-9 fatty acid, 186–187
Onions, crying from, 500
Opsin, 392
Optifast, 375
Orexin, 599
Organelles, 270, 271
Organic foods
debate over, 757
defined, 756
labeling requirements for, 758
Organic Foods Production Act, 757
Organic substances, 12
Organogenesis, 674
Orthomolecular medicine, 86–88
Orthorexia, 612
Osmolarity, 474
Osmoreceptors, 472
Osmosis, 470, 471
Osmotic pressure, 470, 471
Osteoarthritis, 361
Osteoblasts, 409, 489
Osteoclasts, 407, 489
Osteomalacia, 412
Osteoporosis
alcohol and, 330
calcium and, 495–496, 513, 659–660
defined, 412, 658
description of, 740–741
dietary and lifestyle factors for reducing risk of, 659–661
fluoride and, 539
physical activity and, 658, 660–661
premature, 588
risk factors for, 624, 658–659
soy proteins and, 254
statistics, 657
vitamin A and, 396, 660
vitamin D and, 405, 412, 660
Overhydration, 480
Overnutrition, 64
Overweight
See also Obesity; Weight management
adolescents and, 623, 720
arthritis and, 361, 622, 739
behavior and, 16–17, 357–358
breathing problems and, 622
children and, 363, 623, 718–719, 720
defined, 350, 353
disease and, 621–623
elderly and, 739
fats and, 216
fatty liver disease and, 361
fiber and, 174
gender differences and, 354–355
health risks of, 360–362, 622–623
malnutrition and, 802
physical activity and, 357–358
portion sizes and, 422
pregnancy and, 622–623, 671–672
prevalence of, 355
as a public health crisis, 16–17
sleep apnea and, 361–362
sugar and, 172
Oxalate (oxalic acid), 481
Oxaloacetate, 277
Oxidation, 195–196
Oxidative phosphorylation, 279
Oxidative stress, 405
Oxygen energy system, 556, 557
Oxygen transport, iron and, 510
Oxytocin, 688

Palatable, 575
Pancreas
alcohol consumption and effects on, 330
defined, 117
role of, 117
Pancreatic amylase, 155
Pantothenic acid, 14
deficiency, 441–442
dietary recommendations for, 441
functions of, 441
history of, 441
sources of, 441, 442
toxicity, 442
Parathyroid hormone, 407, 409, 491–492
Passive diffusion, 112, 114
Pasteurization, 770
Pathogenic, 586
Pathogens, in food, 750–754
Pau d'Arco, 90, 91
Pauling, Linus, 86–87
PCBs (polychlorinated biphenols), 755
Pectins, 154
Peer review, 22
Pellagra, 440, 801
Pennyroyal, 91
Pentoses, 148–149
Pepsin, 118
Pepsinogen, 118
Peptidases, 239
Peptide bond, 228
Peptides, absorption of, 239–240
Perceived exertion, 573
Peristalsis, 110, 111
Pernicious anemia, 455
Pesticides, 756–757
pH
balance, and role of water, 469
defined, 118
proteins and, 235–236
scale, 118
Phagocytosis, 115
Phenolic acids, 75
Phenylketonuria (PKU), 227
aspartame and, 171
defined, 171
Phosphate group, 198
Phosphocreatine. *See* Creatine phosphate
Phospholipids
defined, 182
digestion of, 204–205
as emulsifiers, 200–201
functions of, 199–200
sources of, 201
structure of, 198–199
Phosphorus
deficiency, 498
dietary recommendations for, 496
functions of, 496
sources of, 496–498
toxicity, 498
Phosphorylation, 496
Photosynthesis, 268, 269
Phylloquinone, 419
Physical activity
See also Athletes; Physical performance
adolescents and, 552, 725
age and, 576, 577, 729
bone health and, 658, 659–660
breastfeeding and, 552
cancer and, 644
children and, 552
chromium, body composition, and, 541
diabetes and, lack of, 653–654
Dietary Guidelines for Americans recommendations, 36, 552
disease and lack of, 622–623
elderly and, 552, 738–739
energy expenditure and, 343, 344, 345, 348
"fat burning," 585
fuels needed for, 303, 304
gender differences and, 562
guidelines for, 554
high altitudes and, 562
hypertension and, 483, 638, 639
obesity/overweight and, 357–358
osteoporosis and, 658, 660–661, 738–739
pregnancy and, 552
sodium and, 483
variety of, 554
weight management and, 369–370
Physical fitness
components of, 552–553
defined, 552
Physical performance
amino acids, 580–582
antioxidants, 582
caffeine, 582–583

Physical performance *(Cont.)*
  carbohydrates and, 563–565, 567
  chromium, 584
  dietary fat, 567
  endurance training, 557–558
  energy intake, 562–563
  energy systems, 555–557
  ephedrine, 583
  fluid needs, 572–576
  glycogen depletion, 567
  iron, 584
  muscles and muscle fibers, 559–560
  nutrition and, 552–555, 561–562
  protein, 569–570
  sodium bicarbonate, 583–584
  supplements, 577–580
  vitamins and minerals, 570–572
  weight and body composition, 584–589
Phytate (phytic acid), 481
Phytochemicals
  benefits of, 77
  cancer and, 74, 77
  cardiovascular disease and, 74, 77
  defined, 11
  functional foods and, 74, 76–78
  heart disease and, 74, 77
Phytoestrogens, 76, 77
Phytosterols, 203
Phytotherapy. *See* Herbal therapy
Pica, 5, 519
Pima Indians, 654
Pinocytosis, 115
Pizza, 404
  digestion and absorption of, 140
Placebo, 21
Placebo effect, 21, 577
Placenta, 674
Plaque, 627
Plasma, 470, 471
Platelets, 628
Poisoning
  See also Foodborne illness
  alcohol, 316, 317
  iron, 518–519
Poisonous mushrooms, 760
Poisons
  mercury, 759–760
  from puffer fish, 8
Political disruptions, malnutrition and, 795–796
Pollutants, 759
Polyols. *See* Sugar alcohols
Polypeptide, 229
Polyphenols, 512, 513
Polysaccharides, 151–154
Polyunsaturated fatty acid
  defined, 184–185
  sources of, 194, 213
Population growth, malnutrition and, 794
Portion sizes
  MyPlate, 46–48
  role of, 52, 339–340
  "supersize," 340
Positive energy balance, 336
Positive nitrogen balance, 243
Positive self-talk, 370
Post-traumatic stress disorder (PTSD), 598–599
Potassium
  deficiency, 487
  Dietary Guidelines for Americans recommendations, 37
  dietary recommendations for, 485–486
  food processing, effects of, 486
  functions of, 485
  hypertension and, 485, 641, 642
  -sodium pumps, 470, 471
  sources of, 486–487
  stroke and, 485
  toxicity, 487
Poultry Products Inspection Act, 772
Poverty
  guidelines for defining, 786
  malnutrition and, 786–788, 793–794
Prebiotics, 76, 134
Precursor, 237–238
Pre-diabetes, 650
Preeclampsia, 671, 686
Preformed vitamin A, 397
Pregnancy
  adolescence and, 687
  alcohol and, 325, 673, 683, 684
  caffeine and, 683
  carbohydrates and, 682
  copper and, 534–535
  diabetes and, 650, 651, 686
  dietary supplements and, 85, 91, 683
  drugs and, 673, 684, 685
  fats and, 681
  fetal alcohol syndrome, 325, 684
  folate and, 447–448, 449, 672–673, 706
  food choices during, 682–683
  food cravings and aversions during, 5, 660, 685–686
  food safety and, 752, 754, 755, 760, 763, 767
  gastrointestinal disorders and, 685
  HIV/AIDS and, 686–687
  hypertension and, 686
  iron and, 512, 514–515, 679, 681, 706
  macronutrients and, 680–681
  micronutrients and, 682
  neural tube defects and, 448, 449, 451, 672
  nutrition before conception, 670–673
  nutrition during, 678–682
  obesity/overweight and, 622–623, 671–672
  physical activity and, 552
  physiology of, 673–676
  protein requirements and, 245, 680–681
  resources for women who are pregnant, 693
  smoking and, 673, 684
  thiamin and, 432
  vegetarian diet and, 681
  vitamin A and, 396, 400, 673
  vitamins, 672–673
  weight management and, 671–672, 677–678
  zinc and, 524
Pregorexia, 613
Prematurity, 693
Premenstrual syndrome (PMS), vitamin B6 and, 446–447
PREMIER clinical trial, 641
Preservation, food, 770–772
Preservatives, 770
Preterm delivery, 671
Prions, 755
Prior-sanctioned substance, 80–81
Probiotics, 76, 134
Proenzymes, 237, 239
Progesterones, 202
Programs, weight-management, 367, 375
Prolactin, 688
Prostate cancer, 93
  carotenoids and, 402, 404
  saw palmetto and, 89
  soy and, 254
Proteases, 238–239
Protein digestibility corrected amino acid score (PDCAAS), 250
Protein efficiency ratio (PER), 249, 250
Protein-energy malnutrition (PEM), 257–258, 799
Protein hydrolysates, 251
Proteins
  absorption of, 239–240
  Acceptable Macronutrient Distribution Range for, 244
  acid–base balance and, 235–236
  adolescents and, 245, 723, 724
  adults and, 245
  amino acids and, 226–228, 242
  athletes and, 246, 569–570
  in the body, 241–243
  breastfeeding requirements, 246, 690
  cancer and, 259, 261
  children and, 245, 713
  complementary, 247, 248
  complete (high-quality), 247
  dangers of high intake, 570
  defined, 13
  denaturation of, 230
  in the diet, 244–247, 256–261, 367
  dietary recommendations for, 244–246, 569, 695
  digestion of, 237–239
  elderly and, 245, 730, 731–732
  energy and, 237, 285
  enzymes, 233
  estimating your intake of, 250–251
  excess, 258–261
  excretion of, 243

fluid balance and, 235
functions of, 230–237
glucose and, 158, 237
glycogen and, 158
gout and, 260, 261
health effects of too little or too much, 256–257
heart disease and, 259, 261
high-protein, low-carbohydrate diet, 368–369
hormones, 233–234
how the body makes, 293–294
in human milk, 246, 695
immune system and, 234–235
importance of, 226
incomplete (low-quality), 247
infants and, 245, 695
metabolism and vitamin B6, 444
metallo-, 520
motor, 230, 231
nitrogen balance and, 243
Nutrition Facts label for finding, 262
obesity and, 259
plant sources of, 226, 254–255
pregnancy and, 245, 680–681
quality of, 247–250
R-protein, 452, 453
shapes of, 229–230
sources of, 13, 226, 248, 254–255
soy and, 254, 255
structural and mechanical functions, 230–231
structure of, 228–230
supplements, 246, 251, 570
synthesis of, 241–242
transport functions and, 236, 237, 239–240
turnover, 242
Protoporphyrin, 518
Provitamin A, 391
Provitamins, 390
Psychological influences
on digestion and absorption, 130–131
on overweight and obesity, 358, 360
Psychological stress, 302–303
Psyllium, 154
Puberty, 721
Public Health Security and Bioterrorism Preparedness and Response Act (2002), 765
Puffer fish, 8
Purge, 605
Purified water, 479
Pyloric sphincter, 118, 119
Pyridoxine. *See* Vitamin B6
Pyrophosphate, 272, 273
Pyruvate
athletes and, 560, 561
conversion of, 275–277, 281
defined, 275
importance of, 294–295
Pyruvate carboxylase, 535

Quinones, 416

Racial differences
cardiovascular disease in children and, 721
diabetes and, 651, 652
hypertension and, 638
obesity/overweight and, 357
Raffinose, 151
Reabsorption, of water, 476
Reactive hypoglycemia, 651
Recommended Dietary Allowances (RDAs)
biotin and, 443
calcium and, 492
chloride and, 488
chromium and, 540
comparing dietary intake data to, 69
copper and, 533
defined, 53, 55
fluoride and, 538
folate and, 448
iodine and, 531
iron and, 515–516
lipids and, 210–212
magnesium and, 499
manganese and, 536
molybdenum and, 542
niacin and, 438
pantothenic acid and, 441
phosphorus and, 496
potassium and, 485–486
proteins and, 244–246, 569, 695
riboflavin and, 436
selenium and, 529
sodium and, 482
thiamin and, 432
vitamin A and, 396–397
vitamin B6 and, 445
vitamin B12 and, 454
vitamin C and, 457
vitamin D and, 409
vitamin E and, 416–417
vitamin K and, 421
water and, 470–471
zinc and, 523
Recommended Nutrient Intakes (RNIs), 53
Rectum, 126
Red blood cells, metabolic profile of, 299
Red tide, 754, 755
Reducing agent, 456
Redux, 376
Refined sweeteners, 168, 170
Refrigerated shipping of food, 761
Refugees, malnutrition and, 795–796
Rehydration therapy, for diarrhea, 795
Religion, food preferences and, 9
vegetarian diets, 252
Renin
defined, 474
hypertension and, 637–638

Reproduction
obesity/overweight and complications with, 622–623
vitamin A and, 396
zinc and, 524
Requirement, 54
Research
animal studies, 18
cell culture studies, 18
double-blind study, 21
epidemiological studies, 17–18
human studies, 18–19, 21
Internet, evaluating information on the, 24
media use of, 22–23
peer review, 22
placebo effect, 21
Resistant starch, 152
Resting energy expenditure (REE), 341
Resting metabolic rate (RMR), 342
Restrained eaters, 358, 360
Retina, 392
Retinal, 391, 392
Retinoic acid, 391, 392
Retinoids, 390, 391
See also Vitamin A
Retinol, 390, 391, 392
Retinol activity equivalents (RAE), 391, 397
Retinol-binding protein (RBP), 392
Retinyl esters, 392
Rhodopsin, 392
Rhubarb, 90
Riboflavin (vitamin B2), 14
deficiency, 436–437
dietary recommendations for, 436
functions of, 435–436
history of, 435
sources of, 436, 437
toxicity, 437
Ribosomal RNA (rRNA), 241–242
Ribosomes, 241, 271
Rice
gas and, 132, 138
importance of, 801
Rickets, 405, 405, 407, 411–412
Risk factors
for atherosclerosis, 624, 629–630
for cancer, 624, 643–644
defined, 628, 629
for dental/oral diseases, 624
for diabetes, 624, 652–653
for diverticulosis, 624
for hypertension, 624
for obesity/overweight, 624
for osteoporosis, 624
for stroke, 624
Rimonabant, 376
Rods, 392
R-protein, 452, 453
Russell, Gerald, 603

Saccharin
  cancer and, 81, 170
  defined, 170
  discovery of, 170
Safe Tables Our Priority (S.T.O.P.), 764
Safety issues. *See* Food safety
St. John's wort, 84, 89, 90, 91
Salads, value of, 365
Salmon, 477
Salisbury steak, 257
Salivary glands
  amylase and, 117, 155
  defined, 115
  role of, 115
Salmonella, 750, 751, 753, 755, 764
Salt
  See also Sodium
  daily requirements, 37
  dissolving in water, 469, 470
  sacred, 483
  sweetness and, 3
Saltpeter, 485
Salts, 468, 469
Saltwater, 472
Sanctions, malnutrition and, 796
Satiation, 337
Satiety, 337
Saturated fatty acid, 633–634
  defined, 184–185
  sources of, 194, 213
Saw palmetto, 84, 89–90
School Breakfast Program, 718, 789
School cafeterias, nutrition in, 36
School Lunch Program, 788, 789–790
Scientific process, applying to nutrition, 17–21
Scombroid poisoning, 755
Scurvy, 801
  vitamin C and, 17, 19, 21, 395, 456, 459
Seafood safety, 754–755, 760
Seborrheic dermatitis, 436, 437
Secondary hypertension, 636, 637
Secretin, 119–120, 127
Segmentation, 110, 111
Selenium, 512
  deficiency, 530, 801
  dietary recommendations for, 529
  functions of, 527–528
  history of, 527
  regulation of, in the body, 528–529
  sources of, 529, 530
  toxicity, 530
Selenocysteine, 527
Selenomethionine, 527
Self-help books and manuals, weight management, 373
Self-help groups, weight-management, 375
Semipermeable membrane, 470, 471
Senna, 90, 91
Sensory influences, food preferences and, 3, 339
Serosa, 108
Shark cartilage, 96–97
Shark liver oil, 197
Shigella, 752
Shopping for Health survey, 56
Short bowel syndrome, 129
Sialic acid, 151
Silicon, 544
Silicosis, 544
Simple carbohydrates
  defined, 147–150
  foods high in, 167
Size acceptance, basic tenets of, 373
Skeletal muscles, 558, 559
Skin, vitamin A and, 399
Skin color, vitamin D and, 452
Skinfold measurements, 66, 353
Sleep apnea, 361–362
Slow-twitch (ST) fibers, 558, 559
Small intestine
  absorption in, 124
  absorptive structures of, 121, 124
  defined, 119
  digestion in, 119–121
  digestion of proteins in, 238–239
Smell
  age and, 730
  food preferences and, 3
  organs for, 106–107
Smokers, diet and litter issues, 645
Smoking
  adolescents and, 726
  alcohol and, 324
  breastfeeding and, 691
  cancer and, 324, 330
  eating disorders and, 612
  pregnancy and, 673, 684, 685
Snacks
  fruit, 743
  healthy, 718
Social facilitation, 6
Social influences
  eating behavior and, 340
  food preferences and, 6
  obesity/overweight and, 357, 358
Society for Nutrition Education (SNE), 24
Soda loading, 583–584
Sodium
  content of various foods, 482
  daily requirements, 37
  deficiency, 483–485
  Dietary Guidelines for Americans and, 37, 482
  dietary recommendations for, 482
  food processing, effects of, 482–483
  functions of, 481–482
  hypertension and, 483–485, 639
  Nutrition Facts label for finding, 661
  physical activity and, 484
  sources of, 482–483
  thirst and, 475
Sodium bicarbonate, athletes and, 583–584
Sodium-potassium pumps, 470, 471
Soft drinks, 718
Solanine, 760
Solutes, 470, 471
Sorbitol, 149
Soy
  -based infant formula, 698
  cancer and, 17–18, 74, 77, 254
  food products and uses, 255
  heart disease and, 74, 76, 636
  protein, 254
Soybean statistics, 798
Special Supplemental Food Program for Women, Infants, and Children (WIC), 54
Special Supplemental Nutrition Program for Women, Infants, and Children (WIC), 693, 718, 788, 789
Sphincters, 108, 110
Sphygmomanometer, 636, 637
Spina bifida, 451, 452, 672
Splenda, 171
Sports anemia, 571
Sports drinks, 471, 575–576
  Nutrition Facts label and, 589
Sports nutrition. *See* Athletes
Sports trainers, 569
Spring water, 479
Squalene
  capsules, 197
  defined, 203
Stachyose, 151
Standard drink, 312, 313
Stanols, 76
Staphylococcus aureus, 751
Starch
  animal (glycogen), 152
  defined, 151
  forms of, 152
  resistant, 152
  sources of, 151–152
Start Healthy Feeding Guidelines for Infants and Toddlers, 701–703
Starvation (fasting), 297–302
Statement of identity, 57
Steatorrhea, 204
Stem cells, 396
Sterols
  absorption of, 208
  benefits of, 76
  cholesterol functions, 202
  cholesterol synthesis, 202
  defined, 182
  digestion of, 208

sources of, 76, 202–203
structure of, 201
Stevia. *See* Stevioside
Stevioside, 171–172
Stomach
absorption in, 118
defined, 117
digestion in, 118, 119
digestion of proteins in, 237–238
Stress
hypertension and, 638
protein needs and physical, 245–246
psychological, 302–303
weight management and, 371–372
Stroke
mayonnaise and, 99
obesity and, 360, 361
potassium and, 485
risk factors for, 624
Structure/function claims
defined, 63
for functional foods, 83
Subcutaneous fat, 192
Submucosa, 108
Sucralose, 171, 488
Sucrose, 149, 150
Sugar(s)
See also Sweeteners
children and, 169
consumption statistics, 167, 168
dental caries and, 173–174
forms of, 167
heart disease and, 172, 634
joining and cleaving molecules, 150
moderating your intake of, 167–168
obesity/overweight and, 172
simple, 147–150
unfounded claims against, 172
Sugar alcohols
benefits of, 76
defined, 148, 149
dental caries and, 170
diarrhea and, 170
sources of, 76
Sulfides, 76
Sulfur, 502
Summer Food Service Program, 718, 789
Sunette, 171
Supplemental Nutrition Assistance Program (SNAP), 718, 742, 788, 789
Supplement Facts, 94–95
Supplements. *See* Dietary supplements
Surgery
gum chewing following, 128
obesity and, 377–378
Swallowing, process of, 117
Sweating, 572, 573
Sweeteners
additives, 171–172
comparison of, 170
consumption statistics, 167, 168
natural, 168
nonnutritive, 170–171
nutritive, 168
refined, 168, 170
sugar alcohols, 76, 148–149, 170
Sweetness, salt and, 3
Systolic, 636, 637

Table sugar. *See* Sucrose
Tagatose, 171
Take Control, 82, 83
Tap water, 478–479
Taste
age and, 730
buds, 106, 542, 802
fat and, 183, 193
food preferences and, 3
organs for, 106–107
threshold, 730
zinc and, 524, 525
Taurine, 461
Technology, food, 769–770
Teenagers. *See* Adolescents
Teeth, fluoride and, 536–537
Tempeh, 255
Teratogen, 400
Testosterone, 202
Tetrahydrofolic acid (THFA), 448, 452–453
Texture, food preferences and, 3
Thaumatin, 173
Thermic effect of food (TEF), 346
Thiamin (vitamin B1), 14
breastfeeding and, 432
deficiency, 431, 434–435
dietary recommendations for, 432
functions of, 432
history of, 431–432
pregnancy and, 432
sources of, 432, 434
structure of, 432
toxicity, 435
Thiamin pyrophosphate (TPP), 432, 433
Thiols, 76
Thirst, 474–476
Thyroglobulin, 531
Thyroid-stimulating hormone (TSH), 233–234, 531
Thyroxine (T4), 234, 531
Tissue, 642
Tocopherol, 414
Tocotrienols, 414
Toddlers, 694, 695
feeding amounts, how to determine, J-3
Tofu, 82, 255
Tolerable Upper Intake Levels (ULs), 56
Tomato juice, 404
Tooth decay. *See* Dental caries
Total body water, 352–353
Total energy expenditure (TEE), 341
Total fiber, 153
Total parenteral nutrition (TPN), 530, 531
Toxins, natural, 759–761
Toxoplasma gondii, 753, 768
Trace minerals
arsenic, 542–543
athletes and, 571–572
boron, 543
characteristics of, 509
chromium, 539–541
copper, 533–535
defined, 14, 508
fluoride, 536–539
importance of, 508–509
iodine, 530–532
iron, 510–519
manganese, 535–536
molybdenum, 541–542
nickel, 543–544
Nutrition Facts label for finding, 545
periodic table, 509
selenium, 527–530
silicon, 544
vanadium, 544
zinc, 520–527
Transamination, 293
Trans fatty acids, 633–634
defined, 186
sources of, 194, 213
Transferrin, 511, 514
Transferrin receptors, 514
Transferrin saturation, 518
Transfer RNA (tRNA), 241
Transport functions, proteins and, 236, 237
Trehalose, 171
Tricarboxylic acid (TCA) cycle. *See* Citric acid cycle
Triglycerides
absorption of, 205–207
defined, 13
digestion of, 204–205, 206
functions of, 190–193
levels, 630
medium-chain, 196–197, 205
sources of, 193–194
stored, 290
structure of, 190
Triiodothyronine (T3), 531
Trimesters, 673–674
Tripeptide, 228–229
Trypsin/trypsinogen, 239
Tryptophan, 438, 439
Tumor, 642
Tuna, 754
24-hour dietary recall, 68
Type 1 diabetes, 650

Type 2 diabetes, 161, 650–651
  fiber and, 174
Tyrosine, 227

Ulcers
  bacteria and, 139
  defined, 132, 138
Ultratrace minerals, 542–544
Umami, 3
Undernutrition, 64, 802
Underwater weighing, 352, 353
Underweight
  causes and assessment of, 378–380
  defined, 350, 378
  weight-gain strategies, 380
United Nations, Food and Agriculture Organization (FAO) of, 791
U.S. Department of Agriculture (USDA)
  Agricultural Research Service (ARS), 764
  Cooperative State Research, Education, and Extension Service (CSREES), 764
  defined, 34
  food assistance programs, 789
  Food Safety and Inspection Service (FSIS), 763
U.S. Department of Health and Human Services (DHHS), 34
U.S. Pharmacopoeia (USP), 97
Unsaturated fatty acid, 184
Urbanization, malnutrition and, 795
Urea, 242, 243, 472, G-4
Urinary tract infection (UTI), 89–90, 739
Urine, diabetes diagnosis and sweet, 303

Vaccines, genetically engineered, 797
Valerian, 84, 90, 91
Vanadium, 544
Variety, in eating, 33–34
Vascular system, 129, 130
Vasoconstrictor, 474
Vasopressin. *See* Antidiuretic hormone
Vegetables
  America's favorite, 10
  cancer and, 646–647
  cardiovascular disease and, 631
  hypertension and, 639, 640
  versus fruits, naming of, 430
Vegetarian diets, 99–100
  benefits of, 253
  children and, 721
  eating disorders and, 612
  high-protein plant foods, 254–255
  iron absorption and, 513
  pregnancy and, 681
  religion and, 252
  risks of, 253
Vegetarians
  dietary recommendations for, 253, 256
  reasons for becoming, 251–252
  types of, 252–253
Very low calorie diets (VLCD), 375
Very low density lipoproteins (VLDL), 209
Vibrio species, 752, 754
Villi, 124
Viruses, 752–753
Visceral fat, 192
Vision
  carotenoids and, 402
  cataracts, 402, 416, 457, 459
  color, 395
  elderly and, 740
  macular degeneration, 416, 740
  night blindness, 394, 399, 521
  vitamin A and, 392, 394–395, 399
  vitamin C and, 457, 459
  vitamin E and, 416
  xerophthalmia, 399
  zinc and, 521
Vitamin A, 13
  acne treatment, 400–401
  bone health and, 396
  cell differentiation, 395–396
  deficiency, 398–400, 800
  dietary recommendations for, 396–397
  forms of, 391
  functions of, 392–396
  history of, 395
  immune function and, 396, 400
  infants and, 398–399
  megadoses of, 88, 400
  osteoporosis and, 396, 660
  preformed, 397
  pregnancy and, 396, 400, 673
  reproduction and, 396
  skin and, 399
  sources of, 393, 397–398
  storage and transport of, 392
  toxicity, 400–401
  vision and, 392, 394–395, 399
Vitamin Bs
  See also under name of
  athletes and, 571
  categories of, 430–431
  elderly and, 734
  functions of, 431
  heart disease and, 635–636
Vitamin B1. *See* Thiamin
Vitamin B2. *See* Riboflavin
Vitamin B3. *See* Niacin
Vitamin B6 (pyridoxine), 14
  compounds, 443
  deficiency, 445
  dietary recommendations for, 445
  elderly and, 734
  functions of, 444–445
  heart disease and, 444–445
  megadoses of, 86 , 88, 446–447
  sources of, 445, 446
  toxicity and medicinal uses of, 446–447
Vitamin B12 (cobalamin), 14
  absorption of, 453
  anemia and, 86, 454–455
  deficiency, 454–455
  dietary recommendations for, 454
  elderly and, 734
  functions of, 452–453
  heart disease and, 444–445
  history of, 352
  infants and, 697
  megadoses of, 86
  sources of, 454, 455
  toxicity, 456
Vitamin C, 13–14
  cancer and, 457, 459
  cataracts and, 457, 459
  colds and, 457, 459
  deficiency, 17, 459
  dietary recommendations for, 457
  functions of, 456–457
  heart disease and, 457, 459
  history of, 395, 456
  megadoses of, 88, 459
  scurvy and, 17, 19, 21, 395, 456, 459
  sources of, 457–458
  toxicity, 459
Vitamin D, 13
  bone health and, 405
  calcium and, 491
  cancer and, 405, 408
  children and, 405, 407, 409–410, 411, 713
  deficiency, 411–413
  dietary recommendations for, 409
  elderly and, 405, 412, 734
  forms and formation of, 407
  functions of, 407, 409–410
  infants and, 409, 696
  megadoses of, 88, 413
  osteoporosis and, 405, 412, 660
  skin color and, 452
  sources of, 406, 410–411
  toxicity, 413
Vitamin E, 13
  cancer and, 415, 416
  deficiency, 418
  diabetes and, 86
  dietary recommendations for, 416–417
  forms of, 413–414
  functions of, 414, 416
  heart disease and, 86, 416, 419
  megadoses of, 86, 88, 418–419
  oxidation and, 196, 416
  sources of, 415, 417–418
  storage and processing losses, 417, 418
  toxicity, 418–419
  vision and, 416
Vitamin K, 13
  blood clotting and, 419, 420, 423
  deficiency, 421, 423

dietary recommendations for, 421
functions of, 419–420
infants and, 423, 424, 697
megadoses of, 88
sources of, 421, 422, 423
toxicity, 424
Vitamin precursors. *See* Provitamins
Vitamins
See also under name of
absorption of, 389
adolescents and, 723–724
alcohol and deficiencies of, 326–327
athletes and, 570–572
bogus, 461
breastfeeding and, 690
children and, 712–717
cooking and, 430
defined, 13
dietary supplements, 83–88, 430, 714, 717, 735–736
elderly and, 733–736
fat-soluble, 13, 387–424
functions for, 13
history of, 395
infants and, 696–697
like compounds, 459–460
Nutrition Facts label for finding, 424, 462
pro-, 390
roles of, 388
selecting and preparing foods to maximize content of, 433
sources of, 314, 388, 391
storage and toxicity of, 390
water-soluble, 13–14, 389–390, 429–462
Vitamin supplements, harmful effects, 14

Waist circumference, 354–355
War, malnutrition and, 795
Wasting, 226
Water
absorption of, 471
athletes and, 475–476, 572–576
balance, 472–476
body composition and, 468, 469, 730
breastfeeding and, 690
content of various foods, 472
dehydration, 475–478
doubly labeled, 347–348
elderly and, 476, 733
electrolytes and, 469–470
excretion of, 471–472
fluoridation of, 539
functions of, 14, 468–469
importance of, 14, 468
infants and, 476, 696
intake recommendations, 470–471
intoxication, 479–480
reabsorption of, 476
safety, 476, 766
tap, filtered, or bottled, 478–479
thirst, 474–476
Water bottles, safety of plastic, 699
Watermelon, 402
Weather
eating behavior, effect on, 340
energy expenditure, effect on, 343
Weighed food records, 68
Weight
See also Obesity; Overweight; Underweight; Weight management
for adolescents, 722
alcohol and, 328
assessing body, 350–351
athletes and, 584–587
nutrition assessment and, 65–66
Weight cycling, 362
Weight-gain strategies, 380, 585
Weight-gain powders, 580
Weight management
See also Obesity; Overweight; Underweight
approaches to, 373–378
athletes and, 584–587
benefits of weight loss, 623
books and manuals, 373, 375
components of, 365
counselors, 375–376
defined, 362
diet and, 366–367, 368–369
Dietary Guidelines for Americans recommendations, 36, 362
dietary supplements and, 85, 377
eating behavior and, 367–368
emotions and, 370–372
goals for, 364
lifestyle and, 364–365
loss, pros and cons, 585–587
meal replacements, 375
over-the-counter drugs and, 377
perception of weight, 362–364
physical activity and, 369–370
pregnancy and, 671–672, 677–678
prescription drugs and, 376–377
programs, 367, 375
self-help groups, 375
size acceptance, basic tenets of, 373
stress and, 371–372
surgery, 377–378
Weight training, 246, 570, 581
Well water, 479
Wernicke-Korsakoff syndrome, 435
What We Eat in America report, 63
Whole grains
benefits of, 166
cancer and, 647
cardiovascular disease and foods high in, 631, 633
heart disease and, 60, 164
Wilson's disease, 527, 533, 535
Wine, 310
calories in, 313
heart disease and red, 77, 329–330
Women
See also Breastfeeding; Gender differences; Pregnancy
alcohol consumption and, 318–319
calcium and, 489, 492, 495–496
Women's Health Initiative (WHI), 217
Wood alcohol, 310
Working poor, malnutrition and, 786
World Anti-Doping Agency (WADA), 583
World Health Organization (WHO), 646, 771, 791
World hunger. *See* Developing world, malnutrition in the
Wrestlers, Sumo, 371

Xenical, 376
Xerophthalmia, 399

Yin and yang, 100
Yohimbe, 90

Zeaxanthin, 75, 77
Zinc
absorption of, 521–522
colds and, 525
deficiency, 524, 526, 801
dietary recommendations for, 523
elderly and, 735
enzymes and, 520
excretion of, 522–523
functions of, 520–521
history of, 520
homeostasis, 522–523
megadoses of, 86 , 88
pregnancy and, 524
regulation of, in the body, 521–522
sources of, 523–524
toxicity, 525–527
transport and distribution of, 522

Photo Credits

Chapter 1

1, © Elena Elisseeva/Dreamstime.com; 3, © Photodisc; 4, (left) © Mary Kate Denny/PhotoEdit; 4, (middle) © Suza Scalora/Photodisc; 4, (right) © Jules Frazier/Photodisc; 6, (top) Courtesy of the Idaho Potato Commission; 6, (bottom) © SuperStock/age fotostock; 7, © Photowitch/Dreamstime.com; 8, © 2005 Peter Menzel/menzelphoto.com; 11, 13–15 © Photodisc; 24, Courtesy of the Food and Drug Administration; 25, © Martin Trebbin/Dreamstime.com

Chapter 2

25, © Martin Trebbin/Dreamstime.com; 29, © CreativEye99/ShutterStock, Inc.; 43, (top, bottom) © Photodisc; 48, (top) © Matthew Benoit/ShutterStock, Inc.; 48, (bottom) © Layland Masuda/ShutterStock, Inc.; 51, © Hisham F. Ibrahim/Photodisc; 52, © Photodisc; 68, © Martin Trebbin/Dreamstime.com

Spotlight on Complementary and Alternative Nutrition

73, © Michael Pettigrew/ShutterStock, Inc.; 74, 77, 80, © Photodisc; 102, © Martin Trebbin/Dreamstime.com

Chapter 3

105, © Suto Norbert Zsolt/ShutterStock, Inc.; 131, (top, left) © EyeWire; 131, (top, right) © Chris Shorten/Cole Group/Photodisc; 131, (bottom, left) © PhotoLink/Photodisc; 131, (bottom, right) Courtesy of Dr. Wood/USDA; 138, © Dr. E. Walker/Photo Researchers, Inc; 139, © A.B. Dowsett/SPL/Photo Researchers, Inc.; 140, © Photodisc; 141, © Martin Trebbin/Dreamstime.com

Chapter 4

145, © Gregory Gerber/ShutterStock, Inc.; 146, (top, left) © Cn Boon/Alamy Imaages; 146, (top, right) Courtesy of David Nance/ARS Photo Library/USDA; 146, (bottom, left) Courtesy of ARS Photo Library/USDA; 146, (bottom, right) Courtesy of the USDA; 151, © Gary Gaugler/Visuals Unlimited; 153, © J.D. Litvay/Visuals Unlimited; 163, (top) © Digital Vision; 163, (bottom) © Photodisc; 164, © Photodisc; 169, © Eric Gevaert/ShutterStock, Inc.; 177, © Martin Trebbin/Dreamstime.com

Chapter 5

181, © Danny E. Hooks/ShutterStock, Inc.; 191, © Hannamariah/ShutterStock, Inc.; 192, © Veronica Burmeister/Visuals Unlimited; 193, © Photodisc; 210, © W. Ober/Visuals Unlimited; 213, © Photodisc; 220, © Martin Trebbin/Dreamstime.com

Chapter 6

225, © Diana Lundin/ShutterStock, Inc.; 244, (left) © EyeWire; 244, (middle) © Keith Brofsky/Photodisc/Getty Images; 244, (right) © EyeWire; 245, (top) © Boris Ryzhkov/Dreamstime.com; 245, (middle) © Jules Frazier/PhotoDisc; 245, (bottom) © msheldrake/ShutterStock, Inc.; 246, © Photodisc; 258, (top) © CDC/ Dr. Lyle Conrad; 258, (bottom) © CDC/Dr. Edward Brink; 260, (left) © David Hernandez/ShutterStock, Inc.; 260, (middle) © Stephen Walls/ShutterStock, Inc.; 260, (right) © Photodisc; 263, © Martin Trebbin/Dreamstime.com

Chapter 7

267, © Mikael Damkier/ShutterStock, Inc.; 297, © Monkey Business Images/ShutterStock, Inc.; 304, © Losevsky Pavel/ShutterStock, Inc.; 305, © Martin Trebbin/Dreamstime.com

Chapter 8

309, © Roman Sigaev/ShutterStock, Inc.; 311, (top, left) © Jack Star/Photodisc; 311, (top, right) 311, © Mitch Hrdlicka/Photodisc; 311, (middle, right) © Photodisc; 313, (top) © David M. Phillips/Visuals Unlimited; 313 (bottom), 317, 318, © Photodisc; 324, © The University of Alabama at Birmingham Department of Pathology PEIR Digital Library (http://peir.net); 333, © Martin Trebbin/Dreamstime.com

Chapter 9

336, © Celso Diniz/ShutterStock, Inc.; 339, © Photodisc; 352, Courtesy of Life Measurement, Inc.; 353, © Photodisc; 354, © Bill Bachmann/The Medical File/Peter Arnold, Inc.; 356, © Dr. Dennis Kunkel/Visuals Unlimited; 363, (left) © ImageState/Alamy Images; 363, © (middle) Visual Arts Library (London)/Alamy Images; 363, (right) © Yui Mok/PA Wire/AP Photos; 370, © Comstock Images/Alamy Images; 381, © Martin Trebbin/Dreamstime.com

Chapter 10

387, © Wong Hock Weng/ShutterStock, Inc.; 395, Courtesy of Joe Valbuena/USDA; 408, © Digital Stock; 411, © Photodisc; 412, © Dr. Michael Klein/Peter Arnold, Inc.; 417, 423, © Photodisc; 425, © Martin Trebbin/Dreamstime.com

Chapter 11

429, © wael hamdan/ShutterStock, Inc.; 434, © Photodisc; 435, Courtesy of Scott Landis, Bryan College; 439, © Photodisc; 440, © Tina Manley/Alamy Images; 449, © Photos.com; 455, © Photodisc; 463, © Martin Trebbin/Dreamstime.com

Chapter 12

467, © Yellowj/ShutterStock, Inc.; 469, © Juha Sompinmäki/ShutterStock, Inc.; 484, © Jack Star/PhotoLink/Photodisc/Getty Images; 493, © Graca Victoria/ShutterStock, Inc.; 500, © Photodisc; 503, © Martin Trebbin/Dreamstime.com

Chapter 13

507, © Ewa Brozek/ShutterStock, Inc.; 508, © Scott Bauer/ARS Photo Library/USDA; 517, 524, 529, 534, 537, © Photodisc; 539, © NIH/Custom Medical Stock Photo; 546, © Martin Trebbin/Dreamstime.com

Chapter 14

551, © Vasyl Helevachuk/ShutterStock, Inc.; 555, 556, 557 © Photodisc; 566, © Shawn Pecor/ShutterStock, Inc.; 569, © Marc Pagani Photography/ShutterStock, Inc.; 578, © Photodisc; 587, © Kamran Jebrili/AP Photo; 590, © Martin Trebbin/Dreamstime.com

Spotlight on Eating Disorders

595, © Marcel Nijhuis/ShutterStock, Inc.; 596, © Photodisc; 598, © Trinity Morror/Mirrorpix/Alamy Images; 604, © Andrew Gentry/ShutterStock, Inc.; 606, © Jack Star/PhotoLink/Photodisc; 608, © Bill Aron\PhotoEdit, Inc.; 611, © AP Photo/AP World Wide; 613, © VStock LLC/age fotostock; 616, © Martin Trebbin/Dreamstime.com

Chapter 15

619, © Jacek Chabraszewski/ShutterStock, Inc.; 621, © Photodisc; 632, © Photodisc/Getty Images; 637, © Paul Maguire/ShutterStock, Inc.; 647, © Keith Brofsky/Photodisc; 653, © M.G. Mooij/ShutterStock, Inc.; 655, © CHASSENET/age fotostock; 659, © Bengt-Goran Carlsson/age fotostock; 663, © Martin Trebbin/Dreamstime.com

Chapter 16

669, © Ximagination/ShutterStock, Inc.; 670, © iofoto/ShutterStock, Inc.; 672, Courtesy of Spina Bifida Association of America; 673, © Photodisc; 675, © MedicalRF.com/Alamy Images; 679, © Jose Luis Pelaez, Inc./Blend Images/age fotostock; 684, © Richard Pipes, Albuquerque Journal/AP Photos; 694, (top) © Johanna Goodyear/ShutterStock, Inc.; 694, (middle) © Andrew Taylor/ShutterStock, Inc., 694, (bottom) © Laura Dwight/Peter Arnold, Inc.; 697, 700, 702 (left), © Photodisc; 702, (second from left) © Barbara Penoyar/Photodisc/Getty Images; 702, (middle, left) © Stuart Pearce/age fotostock; 702, (middle) © Maureen Lawrence/StockImage/age fotostock; 702, (middle, right) © Picture Partners/age fotostock; 702, (second from right) © Tom Grill/age fotostock; 702, (right) © Picture Partners/age fotostock; 704, © Gill/Custom Medical Stock Photo; 707, © Martin Trebbin/Dreamstime.com

Chapter 17

711, © clarence s. lewis/ShutterStock, Inc.; 724, © Photodisc; 731, (top, bottom) © PhotoLink/Photodisc; 739, © Peterfactors/Dreamstime.com; 740, © TravelStockCollection-Homer Sykes/Alamy Images; 744, © Martin Trebbin/Dreamstime.com

Chapter 18

749, © Martin Kubát/ShutterStock, Inc.; 756, © Photodisc; 757, © Ivaschenko Roman/ShutterStock, Inc.; 762, (top, left) © Photodisc; 762, (top, right) © PhotoLink/Photodisc; 762, (bottom, right) © C Squared Studios/Photodisc; 762, (bottom, right) © Photodisc; 780, © Martin Trebbin/Dreamstime.com

Chapter 19

783, © Alnoor/ShutterStock, Inc.; 787, (top, second from top) © Photodisc; 787, (second from bottom) © Jack Star/PhotoLink/Photodisc; 787, (bottom) © Jaimie Duplass/ShutterStock, Inc.; 789, © Danny Johnston/AP Photo; 790, Courtesy of Ken Hammond/USDA; 803, © Martin Trebbin/Dreamstime.com